SUPRE

SUPREME VISION.

PILKINGTON
OPTRONICS

Pilkington P.E. Limited
Glascoed Road, St. Asaph, Clwyd LL17 0LL. U.K.
Telephone (0745) 588000
Telex: 61430 Pilks G. Fax: (0745) 584258
Barr & Stroud Limited
Caxton Street, Anniesland, Glasgow G13 1HZ. U.K.
Telephone: 041-954 9601
Telex: 778114 Fax: 041-954 2380

Dawn. A pilot approaches the confines of one of the world's most sophisticated combat aircraft. He is ready to resume his role in the front line of his country's defence.

He is the watchful eyes of a nation.

A supreme responsibility that demands the supreme vision of Pilkington Optronics – manufacturers of the most advanced head-up display optics, forward looking infra-red and thermal imaging systems for helicopters and fixed wing aircraft.

The far-seeing air forces of tomorrow.

AERMACCHI

THE PRESTIGE OF EXPERIENCE

- **10,000 pilots trained worldwide**
- **7,000 aircraft built**
- **present in 15 Countries**

PUBBLIAERMACCHI 90

Aermacchi represents the result of high technology finalized to the best combination of performance, safety, versatility and cost-effectiveness: a synthesis of technology and style, closely linked to the Italian cultural heritage. Aermacchi's 77 years of history have been rich in innovative aeronautical achievements, forerunners in advanced technology, always in line with the principles of quality which identify Aermacchi's products all over the world.

JANE'S ALL THE WORLD'S AIRCRAFT

EIGHTY-FIRST EDITION

EDITOR IN CHIEF: Mark Lambert
DEPUTY EDITOR: Kenneth Munson
ASSISTANT EDITOR: Michael J H Taylor

EDITOR EMERITUS: John W R Taylor

1990-91

ISBN 0 7106 0908 6
JANE'S DEFENCE DATA
"Jane's" is a registered trade mark

In the USA and its dependencies
Jane's Information Group Inc, 1340 Braddock Place, Suite 300, Alexandria, Virginia 22314-1651, USA

Printed in the United Kingdom

GRIFO: airborne multimode radar

The GRIFO Multimode Pulse Doppler Radar is the key element for enhancing the effectiveness of proven aircraft (such as the Mirage, MIG, A-4, F-5) in today's tactical scenarios.

The comprehensive set of Air-to-Air and Air-to-Surface Search and Track modes, the effective all-altitude, all-aspect, look up-look down target detectability, the low weight coupled with high degree of modularity and low maintenance costs make the GRIFO an attractive choice for new aircraft or for weapon system upgrading.

The GRIFO, FIAR's latest achievement in 30-years of experience in the airborne radars field, is available now for the needs of the 1990's

For further information please contact:
Electronic Systems Group Marketing manager
Phone + 39.2.35790537
Telefax + 39.2.3567325
Telex 331265 FIARGR I

HIGHWAY
TO TECHNOLOGY

CONTENTS

This Edition has been compiled by:

Kenneth Munson   AIRCRAFT SECTION: ARGENTINA TO FINLAND, GREECE TO ISRAEL, JAPAN TO TURKEY; LIGHTER THAN AIR

Paul Jackson   AIRCRAFT SECTION: FRANCE, UNITED KINGDOM, UNITED STATES OF AMERICA (MILITARY AIRCRAFT), YUGOSLAVIA

Mike Jerram   AIRCRAFT SECTION: FRANCE, UNITED KINGDOM, UNITED STATES OF AMERICA (CIVIL AIRCRAFT)

John Taylor   AIRCRAFT SECTION: UNION OF SOVIET SOCIALIST REPUBLICS

Michael Taylor   AIRCRAFT SECTION: WEST GERMANY, ITALY; SPORT AIRCRAFT; MICROLIGHTS; SAILPLANES; HANG GLIDERS; METRIC CONVERSIONS

Bill Gunston   GLOSSARY; AERO ENGINES

Alphabetical List of Advertisers

[4]

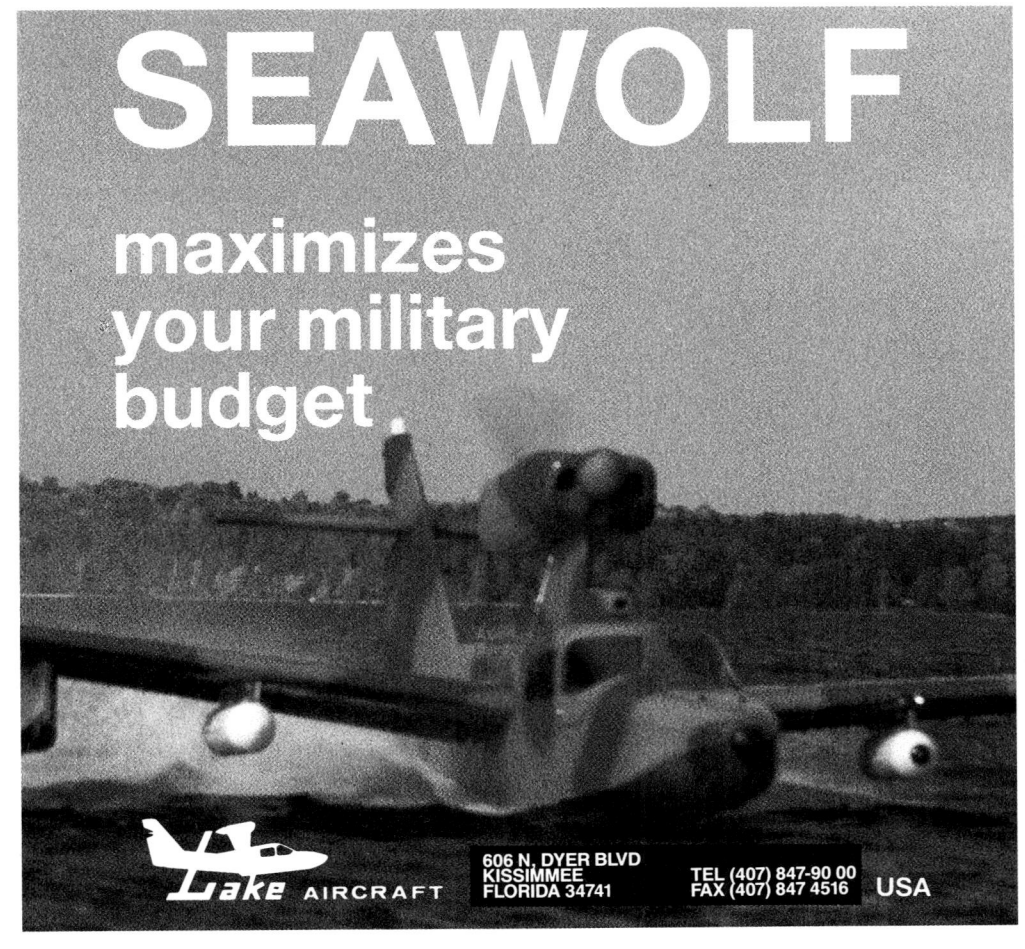

Classified List of Advertisers

The companies listed advertising in this publication have informed us that they are involved in the fields of manufacture indicated below:

AC motors
Lucas Aerospace

Accelerometers and gyroscopes
Air Precision

Actuators, electric
Carleton Technologies
Dassault Aviation
Lucas Aerospace

Actuators, hydraulic
DAF Special Products
Flight Refuelling

Advisory and consultants service
FR Aviation

Aero engine controls and accessories
Flight Refuelling
Hymatic Engineering

Aero-engine test plant
Central Engineering

Aero-engines
FIAT Aviazione

Air compressors (cabin and engine starting)
Lucas Aerospace

Air compressors for engine starting
Lucas Aerospace

Air conditioning equipment
Carleton Technologies
Hymatic Engineering

Air conditioning equipment – airborne
Flight Refuelling

Air conditioning and pressurising equipment – airborne
Hymatic Engineering

Air traffic control services
FR Aviation

Aircraft, ambulance
Pilatus
Lake Aircraft

Aircraft, amphibian
Lake Aircraft

Aircraft, combat
Embraer/Aeritalia (AMX)
Kaman Aerospace

Aircraft, commercial
Aermacchi
Lake Aircraft
SHORT Brothers

Aircraft, commercial trainers
Lake Aircraft

Aircraft, construction
Dassault Aviation
Lake Aircraft
Pilatus

Aircraft, executive
Dassault Aviation
FR Aviation

Aircraft, military
Aermacchi
Dassault Aviation
Embraer/Aeritalia (AMX)
Kaman Aerospace
Lake Aircraft
Pilatus
SHORT Brothers

Aircraft, naval
Dassault Aviation
Lake Aircraft
Kaman Aerospace

Aircraft, private
Dassault Aviation
Lake Aircraft

Aircraft, radio controlled
Flight Refuelling
Kaman Aerospace

Aircraft, supersonic
Dassault Aviation

Aircraft, training
Aermacchi
Dassault Aviation
Lake Aircraft
Omnipol
Pilatus
SHORT Brothers

Aircraft, transport
Lake Aircraft
Kaman Aerospace
SHORT Brothers

Aircraft, v/stol
Lake Aircraft
Pilatus

Aircraft canopies
Dassault Aviation
Lucas Aerospace

Aircraft developments
Dassault Aviation
Kaman Aerospace

Aircraft field operations and support
Dassault Aviation
Lake Aircraft
Kaman Aerospace

Aircraft freight handling equipment
SHORT Brothers

Aircraft integrated data systems
Dassault Aviation

Aircraft modifications
Dassault Aviation
Kaman Aerospace

Aircraft product support
Aermacchi
Dassault Aviation
Kaman Aerospace

Airframes
FR Aviation

Airport ground handling equipment
Aermacchi
Alan Cobham Engineering
Stanley Aviation

Air traffic control equipment
FIAR

Alternators
Lucas Aerospace

Antennas, aircraft
Elettronica

ASW
Dassault Aviation

Automatic checkout systems
Dassault Aviation

Automatic digital data equipment
Central Engineering
Dassault Aviation

Automatic voltage and current regulators
Lucas Aerospace

Auxiliary power plants
FIAT Aviazione
Lucas Aerospace

Avionic systems
FIAR

Bomb racks
Dassault Aviation

Brake lining
Goodyear Tyre and Rubber

Brakes for aircraft
Goodyear Tyre and Rubber

Cables, electric
Flight Refuelling

ONLY GOODYEAR HAS THREE FLIGHTS THAT COVER THE WORLD.

FLIGHT CUSTOM II
General Aviation

FLIGHT EAGLE
Business Jet

FLIGHT LEADER
Commercial Aviation

It makes no difference whether it's North or South America, Europe, Africa, Asia, or Australia. Because anywhere in the world that you'll find aircraft, you'll find Goodyear Aircraft tyres.

Only Goodyear produces aircraft tyres and retreads at 20 plants worldwide. And when you add worldwide availability to Goodyear's outstanding record of prompt supply and service, that's good news. Whether you manufacture airplanes, fly for fun, or fly for a living.

Flight Custom II for general aviation. Flight Eagle for business jets. Flight Leader for commercial aviation. Goodyear's three Flights that cover the world.

And whatever your aircraft, wherever your destination, they're ready whenever you need them.

For more information, please contact: The Goodyear Tyre and Rubber Company (Great Britain) Ltd., Aviation Products, Viscount Way, Heathrow Airport–London, Hounslow, Middlesex TW6 2JN. Tel: 01-759 1922.

GOOD**YEAR**
AVIATION PRODUCTS

Carbon fibre components
SHORT Brothers

Coating, erosion resistant
Goodyear Tyre and Rubber

Cockpit windows — heated and unheated
Lucas Aerospace

Combustion systems (gas turbine)
Lucas Aerospace

Components
Flight Refuelling
Kaman Aerospace

Composite, carbon fibre, plastic materials
Wes Plastics

Composite structures
Dassault Aviation
Kaman Aerospace
Lucas Aerospace
SHORT Brothers

Computers
Dassault Aviation

Computers, aerodynamic analogue and digital
Dassault Aviation

Constant speed drive test benches
Lucas Aerospace

Control equipment for aircraft
Dassault Aviation

Controls, main engine fuel
Lucas Aerospace

Conversions, aircraft and equipment
FR Aviation

Cooling engines
Lucas Aerospace

Couplings
Flight Refuelling
Stanley Aviation

Couplings, self-sealing
Kaman Aerospace

Cryogenic equipment
Carleton Technologies
Hymatic Engineering

Data links
Airdata

Data processing equipment
Airdata

DC generators
Lucas Aerospace

DC motors
Lucas Aerospace

Defence contractors
Flight Refuelling
FR Aviation
Hymatic Engineering
Kaman Aerospace
SHORT Brothers
Wes Plastics

De-icing equipment
Flight Refuelling
Lucas Aerospace

Desktop aluminium model planes
FOM Aeromodelli

Design services
FR Aviation

Display systems
Dassault Aviation
FIAR

Displays, in cockpit
FIAR

Drones
Kaman Aerospace

Electrical equipment
Airdata
Lucas Aerospace

Electrical equipment and components
Air Precision
Hymatic Engineering

Electrical solenoids and relays
Hymatic Engineering

Electrical wiring assemblies
Kaman Aerospace

Electro-hydraulic power packs
Lucas Aerospace

Electro-optical systems
Carleton Technologies
Eurofirst Consortium

Electronic countermeasures (ECM)
Elettronica
FR Aviation

Electronic equipment
FR Aviation
Hymatic Engineering
Lucas Aerospace

Electronic equipment displays
Air Precision

Electronic flight controls
Dassault Aviation
Lucas Aerospace

Electronic fuel control systems
Lucas Aerospace

Electronic support measures (ESM)
Elettronica
FR Aviation

Engine parts fabrication
FIAT Aviazione

Engine run-up facilities — mobile
Central Engineering

Engine starting equipment
FIAT Aviazione
Lucas Aerospace

Engine testing equipment
Central Engineering

Engines, aircraft
Omnipol

Engines, auxiliary
Lucas Aerospace

Environmental control systems
Dassault Aviation

EW systems
Elettronica

Fibre optics
Dassault Aviation

Filters, air/liquid
Hymatic Engineering

Filters — fuel and oil
FR Group

Flight instrument test sets
Dassault Aviation

Fuel flow proportioners
FR Group
Lucas Aerospace

Fuel pipes
Stanley Aerospace

Fuel pumps
Lucas Aerospace

Fuel sprayers
Lucas Aerospace

Fuel systems
Alan Cobham Engineering

Fuel systems and refuelling equipment
Hymatic Engineering

Fuelling equipment — airborne
Flight Refuelling

Fuelling equipment — ground
Flight Refuelling

Galley equipment
Flight Refuelling

Gamah systems
Stanley Aviation

[9]

Gas turbine starting systems
Lucas Aerospace

Gas turbines
FIAT Aviazione
Lucas Aerospace

Gauges
Alan Cobham Engineering

Generators
Aermacchi
Lucas Aerospace

Ground support equipment
Aermacchi
Alan Cobham Engineering
Kaman Aerospace
Stanley Aviation

Guided missiles
SHORT Brothers

Guided weapon control and equipment
Carleton Technologies

Heated windows
Lucas Aerospace

Heated windscreen controllers
Lucas Aerospace

Helicopter gun turrets
Lucas Aerospace

Helicopter parts and components
FIAT Aviazione
Flight Refuelling
Kaman Aerospace

Helicopter stabilisation
Kaman Aerospace

Helicopter surface-to-air refuelling equipment
Flight Refuelling

Helicopter support
Kaman Aerospace
The Clivedon Collection

Helicopter training and support
Kaman Aerospace

Helicopter winches
Kaman Aerospace

High pressure couplings
Kaman Aerospace

Hydraulic actuation systems
Dassault Aviation
Lucas Aerospace

Hydraulic control/systems
Dassault Aviation

Hydraulic equipment
Flight Refuelling

Hydraulic equipment and components
Hymatic Engineering

Hydraulic pressure pumps
Lucas Aerospace

Hydromechanical engine controls
Lucas Aerospace

Ignition exciters
Lucas Aerospace

Infra-red
Carleton Technologies

Infra-red detectors
Elettronica

Infra-red equipment
Flight Refuelling
Hymatic Engineering

Infra-red materials
Barr & Stroud
Hymatic Engineering

Infra-red systems
Barr & Stroud
Dassault Aviation
Elettronica
FIAR

Installation services
FR Aviation

Instruments, accessories
Air Precision

Instruments, aircraft
Air Precision

Instruments – test equipment
Dassault Aviation

Integrated total pneumatic systems
Lucas Aerospace

Jacks-hydraulic
Flight Refuelling

Jet engine parts
FIAT Aviazione
SHORT Brothers

Jet engine test parts
Central Engineering

Jet fuel starters
Lucas Aerospace

Jet trainer, military
Aermacchi

Joining compound
Goodyear Tyre & Rubber

Lamps, cockpit
Lucas Aerospace

Landing gear
SHORT Brothers

Lasers
FIAR
Kaman Aerospace

Laser rangefinders
Barr & Stroud
FIAR

Life support systems
Carleton Technologies

Linear actuators
Lucas Aerospace

Linings-brakes
Goodyear Tyre & Rubber

Low altitude airfield attack
Dassault Aviation

Low light level TV systems
FIAR

Machines for paper and card production
Markhorst

Maintenance and overhaul – airframe
FR Aviation

Maintenance and overhaul – avionics
Air Precision
FR Aviation

Maintenance and overhaul – electrical equipment
Air Precision
FR Aviation

Maintenance and overhaul – mechanical and hydraulic equipment
Air Precision
FR Aviation

Management systems, aircraft
Airdata

Manufacturing services
Stanley Aviation

Materials technology
Kaman Aerospace

Micro-thermal imaging and remote radiometrics
Barr & Stroud

Military and civilian jets
Dassault Aviation

Military aircraft training
Dassault Aviation
SHORT Brothers

Missile optics
FIAR

Missiles, guided
SHORT Brothers

Model Aircraft
FOM Aeromodelli
The Clivedon Collection

Model planes in aluminium
FOM Aeromodelli
The Clivedon Collection

Modernisation and conversion, aircraft and equipment modifications
FR Aviation

Motor generators
Lucas Aerospace

Motors, electric
Lucas Aerospace

Night vision equipment
Barr & Stroud
Carleton Technologies
Flight Refuelling
Hymatic Engineering

Optical infra-red detectors
Barr & Stroud
Dassault Aviation

Optical equipment
Barr & Stroud

Overhaul and modification kits
Kaman Aerospace

Oxygen apparatus
Carleton Technologies
Hymatic Engineering

Oxygen breathing apparatus
Carleton Technologies

Packaging materials
Wes Plastics

Parts for US built aircraft
Kaman Aerospace

Passenger cabin windows
Lucas Aerospace

Patrol aircraft, maritime
Dassault Aviation
Lake Aircraft
SHORT Brothers

Plastic fabrications (reinforced with fibreglass)
Lucas Aerospace

Pneumatic actuation systems
Hymatic Engineering
Lucas Aerospace

Pneumatic controls
Hymatic Engineering
Lucas Aerospace

Pneumatic equipment
Carleton Technologies
Hymatic Engineering

Powered flying controls
Lucas Aerospace

Precision gears
FIAT Aviazione
Kaman Aerospace

Pressure regulation valves, fluids and gases
Lucas Aerospace

Pressure vessels
Carleton Technologies
Hymatic Engineering

Private planes, civil and military
Lake Aircraft

Project management
FR Aviation

Provisioning parts breakdown lists
Kaman Aerospace

Pumps, fuel and oil
Lucas Aerospace

Pumps, hydraulic
Lucas Aerospace

Radar processing
FIAR

Radar test sets
FIAR

Radar warning receivers
Elettronica

Ramjet fuel/air radio controls
Lucas Aerospace

Reconnaissance equipment
Dassault Aviation
Flight Refuelling

Reconnaissance, airborne
Dassault Aviation
Flight Refuelling
Lake Aircraft

Refrigeration
Hymatic Engineering

Repair and maintenance of aircraft
Aermacchi
FR Aviation
Kaman Aerospace

Repair and overhaul of aero-engines
FR Aviation

Repair of aircraft instruments
Air Precision

Rotary actuators
Lucas Aerospace

RPV electronics
Flight Refuelling

RPVs
Flight Refuelling
Kaman Aerospace

Safety and life saving equipment – airborne
Carleton Technologies
Chelton (Electrostatic)

Satellite navigation
FIAR

Servo actuators
Dassault Aviation
Lucas Aerospace

Sheet metal components
Wes Plastics

Sheet metal containers
Markhorst

Sheet metal work
Markhorst
Lucas Aerospace

Simulators
Dassault Aviation
FR Aviation

Simulators, combat
Dassault Aviation

Sonar
FIAR

Space systems
Dassault Aviation

Spacecraft
Dassault Aviation

Spare parts for US built aircraft
Kaman Aerospace

Starting systems, airborne
Lucas Aerospace

Static inverters
Lucas Aerospace

Storage equipment
Wes Plastics

Support operations
The Clivedon Collection

Surveillance systems
Barr & Stroud
Dassault Aviation
Flight Refuelling
Lake Aircraft

Switchgear
Lucas Aerospace

Targets, aerial
Flight Refuelling
Kaman Aerospace
SHORT Brothers

It takes leading-edge innovation to fly.

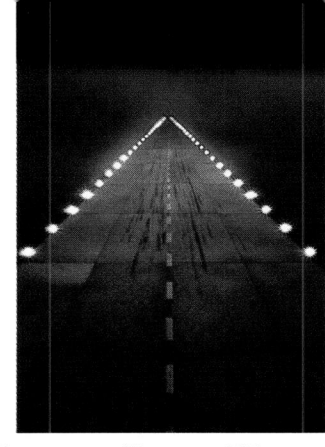

FiatAvio means aeronautic, marine and space propulsion, and energy production. The most important international aerospace programmes use FiatAvio at every turn – from research to service.

In the defence sector, FiatAvio designs, develops and manufactures mechanical engine components for the latest military aircraft and helicopters. It designs and manufactures auxiliary power units, helicopter transmissions and turbines for marine propulsion which are used by navies throughout the world.

In civil aviation, FiatAvio participates in international programmes to design, develop and manufacture engines for a wide range of commercial aircraft and transmissions for helicopters.

In space propulsion, FiatAvio is designing and manufacturing the turbine-driven liquid oxygen pump that will be used on the Ariane 5 European rocket. It conducts ongoing research on the most sophisticated aspects of the cryogenic and airbreathing engines for the suborbital aircraft of the future.

In energy generators, FiatAvio manufactures gas turbines with outputs ranging from 18 to 130 MW for power generation and other industrial applications, and supplies complete power plants worldwide.

Once its products have been installed, Fiat-Avio offers the most comprehensive and competitively priced service, from overhauling to technical assistance and logistic support.

FiatAvio S.p.A. - Via Nizza 312 - 10127 Turin
Tel. 011/6931.1 - Fax 011/636385-6931291

FiatAvio. Out of the blue.

FiatAvio

Target towing winches
FR Aviation

Technical publications
Dassault Aviation
Kaman Aerospace

Technical publications, special studies
Kaman Aerospace

Telemetry equipment
Dassault Aviation

Temperature control equipment
Lucas Aerospace

Test equipment
Aermacchi
Central Engineering
Dassault Aviation
FIAR
Kaman Aerospace

Test equipment, aero-engines
Air Precision

Test equipment, radar, air data computer, fire control systems, avionics etc
Dassault Aviation
Kaman Aerospace

Test equipment airborne radio
Dassault Aviation

Test facilities
Central Engineering
Dassault Aviation

Thermal imaging systems
Barr & Stroud
FIAR

Thrust reversers
Lucas Aerospace

Training and simulation
Dassault Aviation
FR Aviation
SHORT Brothers

Training devices
Aermacchi
Dassault Aviation
Kaman Aerospace
SHORT Brothers

Transfer of technology
Dassault Aviation

Transformer rectifier units
Lucas Aerospace

Troop transport
SHORT Brothers

Turboprop
SHORT Brothers

Unmanned Aircraft
Meteor

Valves
FR Group
Lucas Aerospace

Voltage and current regulators
Lucas Aerospace

Weapons equipment
Dassault Aviation

Weapon subsystems
Hymatic Engineering

Wheels for aircraft
Goodyear Tyre & Rubber

(Upper) **Northrop B-2A refuelling from McDonnell Douglas KC-10A Extender.** *(Lower)* **Sukhoi Su-27 makes a low, slow approach at Paris Le Bourget** *(Brian M. Service)*

JANE'S
ALL THE WORLD'S AIRCRAFT
1990-91

Jane's Information Group Limited, Sentinel House, 163 Brighton Road, Coulsdon, Surrey CR5 2NH, UK
Jane's Information Group Inc, 1340 Braddock Place, Suite 300, Alexandria, Virginia 22314-1651, USA

RETROFIT AND READY FOR ACTION

Smiths Industries' retrofit service offers military aircraft a new lease of life with State-of-the-Art Nav/Attack systems.

A whole squadron of current inventory aircraft can now have an enhanced weapon delivery performance for less than the cost of a single new aircraft.

Smiths Industries' retrofit capability goes far beyond simply providing the hardware. By co-ordinating a team of systems engineers, installation specialists, flight test managers and a recertification authority, Smiths Industries provides a complete turnkey service.

Current contracts include up-grades of the F-5E, F-4E and A-4, improving target acquisition, weapon delivery and navigation accuracy, threat warning and survivability, and reconnaissance facilities.

Smiths Industries have earned a reputation for innovation and leadership in many of the World's major advances in systems development. The retrofit service now provides the opportunity to give a new operational life to the aircraft of today with the technology for tomorrow.

Smiths Industries – together we move towards a bigger and better future in Aerospace.

SMITHS INDUSTRIES
Aerospace & Defence Systems

CHELTENHAM, ENGLAND. TEL: 024 267 3333.

GRAND RAPIDS, U.S.A. TEL: (616) 241 7000.

THE LOGICAL CHOICE

In the earliest days of konversiya, the USSR was displaying its new airliners, like this Il-96-300, in the West. What will Soviet objectives now be in aviation dealings with the rest of the world?
(Brian M. Service)

FOREWORD: The year of reorientation

The past year has seen an almost unimaginable change in the so-called communist bloc and its relations with the West. From dictatorship or one-party rule to democracy; from warlike to peaceable outlooks; but also from oppression to freedom in penury; from inefficient central direction to chaotic and faltering market-driven economy.

Since aerospace is, and will continue to be, an integral part of society and international affairs, it has been directly affected by all these changes. With it, the contents of this book have changed. In these columns of last year's 1989-90 edition, referring to the first manifestations of those changes, my predecessor John Taylor wrote "There has never been an edition like this in the book's eighty years. As Ronald Reagan might say, 'You ain't seen nothin' yet!'"

It was at this moment that I came on the scene. Nine months ago, fate chose to place me, on my return to England from Switzerland and *Interavia Aerospace Review*, in the editorial chair of *Jane's All the World's Aircraft* in succession to John. It was he who nurtured and shaped this world-renowned book for more than 30 years and maintained it as the world standard aircraft and engine reference work. During all my years in aviation journalism, I reached for *Jane's* thousands of times and the hardest lesson I have had to learn is that, now, I have to shape this reference work so that others can consult it.

With characteristic skill, John gathered about him and, in the jargon, orchestrated the efforts of Deputy Editor Kenneth Munson, Assistant Editor Michael Taylor, and compilers Bill Gunston, Mike Jerram and Paul Jackson, not forgetting Dennis Punnett of Pilot Press and Mike Keep, who produce the hundreds of three-view drawings and Maurice Allward, who compiles the ten-year index.

There are no better, and the work of this team continues to find its justification and fulfilment every time our customers reach out to open the book and, as I used to, 'look it up in *Jane's*'.

Let me hasten to add that John Taylor is with us still. He continues as Editor Emeritus and he also continues as our authority on the Soviet Union and compiler of that section of the book.

Our worldwide list of contributors includes Delden Badcock in Australia, Neil A. Macdougall and David Godfrey in Canada, Wolfgang Wagner in Germany, Roland Eichenberger in Switzerland, Nelson Fuller and Jay Miller in the USA, Dipl Ing Andrzej Glass and Dipl Ing Jerzy Grzegorzewski in Poland, William Green and Gordon Swanborough of *Air International*, Brian Walters of *Airnews*, James Gilbert of *Pilot*, Arnold Nayler of *Airship*, the editorial staffs of *Air Force Magazine* (USA), *Flight International* (UK), *Aviation Magazine International* (France), *FLYGvapenNYTT* (Sweden), *Australian Aviation* and *Aircraft* (Australia), *Canadian Aviation* (Canada), and *Letectvi + Kosmonautika* (Czechoslovakia). The many photographers who provide often exclusive pictures are credited in the captions.

My respect for John as a craftsman and friend is unlimited. I must strive to carry on his tradition and maintain the pace of progress. And even as I came to the conclusion that one of the driving influences on *Jane's* from now on would be electronic publishing methods, Jane's Information Group in the USA developed the technique of putting the whole book, including its thousands of photographs and three-view drawings, on CD-ROM digital compact disc in time for it to go on sale this year alongside the hard-cover book. We are in fact offering both the 1989-90 and 1990-91 editions in the new electronic form.

This hard-cover book, of course, continues, sold in the same way and through the same channels as before. But those who want to consult it on a screen beside their desk will now be able to call up any item of information in the 800 pages with a single-word, ultra-fast search facility that will put the data or picture on screen in a second or so. This is no ordinary data base, with its hierarchy of access channels and complex codes. Just a few instinctive keystrokes will lead directly to the desired fact.

As for the contents of the book itself, the year has brought unusually extensive changes. The continuing copious flow of new data from the Soviet Union and China has allowed us to rewrite most of those sections. Those parts of the Engines section, particularly, are almost completely new, not only because of the additional information that has emerged, but also because the Soviets have extensively reorganised their aero engine design bureaux and industry.

The traditional names, like Lyulka or Isotov, have changed. In their place, Saturn, Leningrad and several others. The Klimov name has been resurrected many years after the death of Klimov himself. The reader may have to search under the new bureau names for the old engines.

In the same way, this book's picture of the Chinese aircraft industry has become more detailed, especially in the new background information on many of the established programmes that are still current today.

In search of a relationship with the USSR

How should the western aircraft industry now regard its Soviet opposite number? It used to be the enemy to beat. Suddenly, the Soviet aircraft industry and the country's market are both apparently accessible to the West. Soviet manufacturers have been given authority by central government to strike virtually whatever commercial deals they wish with the West. The first agreements, notably on the supersonic business and Kamov Ka-226, and a few sales have already been concluded.

In numerous contacts and public displays, the Soviets have presented fine credentials to prove their capability in every field but one, small engines. They are offering modern production facilities and low labour costs as a powerful inducement to include them in co-operative production programmes. They are offering full shared development, manufacturing and marketing, often with alternative engines for western and eastern markets. But their industry leaders, who have shown themselves to be intelligent innovators and sound engineers much like our own, are accustomed to being directed by the ministries.

In power plants, the Soviet manufacturers know their weakness and are making efforts to remedy it. Already, the Soviet Ministry of Aviation Industry has signed an initial agreement with US and Canadian Pratt & Whitney and Germany's MTU.

There are weaknesses which the Soviets have yet to understand. They have little experience of identifying an exploitable market in a pluralist world. They are not accustomed to working with the pricing structure of a demand-regulated economy. They are not used to managing real costs. Many details, such as contracts, patents and support procedures will also have to be harmonised. This will complicate the conclusion of down-to-earth Soviet-western commercial business for some time.

It is important to raise the issue of certification standards. There is no reason to suppose that the Soviet industry cannot meet western airworthiness standards, but it will take some time before all the procedures have been completed and their manufacturing centres as well as their design standards have actually been approved. This will not be the Soviets' fault. Western certification can be a byzantine procedure.

As time goes on, aviation trade will become possible. But a central question remains unanswered; what will the Soviet objectives be? For example, China has not, in 20 years, turned out to be the vast new market for western aircraft that many manufacturers foresaw. Quite the reverse; China has become an international supplier of military aircraft and even a purveyor of space launches.

The Chinese authorities struck a balance between acquiring technology and exporting. They bought token quantities of many different types of foreign aircraft. Some of them they put into small-scale production under licence. They set up an assembly line for the McDonnell Douglas MD-82 and have recently authorised a second batch of 20 to be built, but they are negotiating for a more

It takes the right props to train an RAF pilot. Shorts Tucano

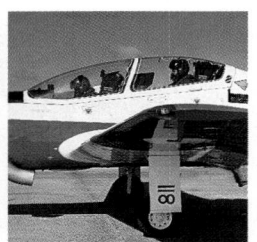

If it can win over the Royal Air Force, the Shorts Tucano turbo-prop has got to be a cut above the rest.

Tucano's outstanding achievements in rigorous open international competition ensured its selection by the RAF to replace the Jet Provost basic trainer.

In virtually every respect, Tucano, with its turbo-prop economy, has out-performed its jet-powered predecessor and has established itself as the most advanced trainer in its class. And not just the RAF has taken notice. The Shorts Tucano is now also in production for overseas forces.

But the Tucano is only one of the ways in which Shorts is making its mark in the military contracts field. Shorts manufactures the C-23 Sherpa freighter aircraft in use with the United States forces, and is also an acknowledged pioneer and leader in close-air defence systems. On the civilian side, Shorts is a major force in the commuter aircraft industry and a key supplier of aerostructures for the world's largest aircraft manufacturers.

Now, with the high-performance Tucano, Shorts is helping a new generation of the world's most skilled jet pilots get off the ground.

While keeping the cost down to earth.

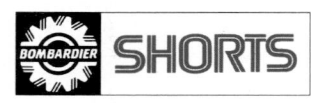

PIONEERS OF THE SKIES

SHORT BROTHERS PLC PO Box 241, Airport Road, Belfast, BT3 9DZ substantial share in the manufacturing process. They allowed foreign companies to produce upgrade kits for Chinese fighters and an airliner.

A large block order did eventually materialise in early June this year, 17 years after trade contacts began, when CAAC arranged to buy 72 assorted Boeings, with engines from all three major manufacturers, on behalf of Air China, China Southwest Airlines and Guangzhou CAAC.

The Soviet industry has been serving several distinct internal markets, one of which is aerial work operations. I was particularly impressed by the remark of Kamov Design Bureau leader Sergei Mikheyev that every Spring, 10,000 helicopters move north into the taiga and tundra of the Soviet Union to continue the exploitation of natural resources. Current efforts to use gas, which is plentiful in the north, as helicopter fuel (as well as for Tupolev airliners, as reported in the Addenda) stems from the difficulty of keeping this fleet supplied with conventional fuel from the south.

In aviation centres such as Omsk and Irkutsk, I have stood and watched scores of An-2s departing or returning, on wheels or skis, at the start and end of the working day. In the USSR, local air transport is an indispensable commodity.

It will take the USSR years to create an effective road and rail infrastructure to get internal trade moving. In much of the far north, surface communications will never be possible. This explains the production of some highly specialised aircraft, such as the Mi-26 'Halo' and the An-72/74 'Coaler', a breed that would not be considered justified or affordable in the West. These aircraft and the An-124 Ruslan and Myasishchev VM-T Atlant super-carriers are already being offered on charter to the West.

Meanwhile, the range of new helicopters, particularly the Mi-38, but also the Ka-126/226, Ka-118 and V-62, are under development with western airworthiness standards in mind. The manufacturers realise that commercial success is within reach and might depend on the not impossible task of completing development ahead of the competing new western designs.

The situation is not as clear in airliners, but Tupolev, Antonov and Ilyushin designs are advancing as fast as the engine technology allows. In the short term, western imports have already begun and will probably increase as new independent airlines are formed. But this is an interim measure and self-sufficiency will not be far behind.

So we ask ourselves, will the Soviets have enough hard currency to play their part and will they be willing to do so? Or will they guard their market and their balance of trade? Will they open their traditional markets to western manufacturers through joint products? Will they have any firm plan in which western manufacturers can play a profitable part?

In fact, we must know what importance the new Soviet market economy will give to its aircraft industry. We are told that development of the immediate future generation of Soviet military aircraft has virtually ceased and this could reduce the national status of the industry.

As the decline in military output forces the pace towards *konversiya*, will the West be willing or able to help use freed Soviet factory floorspace and the trained workforce, as the Soviets would like, or could that capacity be turned over to roughly equivalent, but investment-intensive non-aviation activities, such as car manufacture?

It would be logical for Soviet manufacturers and authorities to want to keep their big home market as a Soviet preserve. The present willingness to work together with the West in any way possible is simply a first reaction to the drive for *konversiya*. A more measured reaction will emerge and the most instinctive one is protectionism. This, however, would lead to self-defeating isolation.

The alternative of cut-throat competition might be unwinnable. The way to live together ultimately lies in co-operation. But how and with which bloc: Europe, USA or the developing industries? We have not yet seen any Soviet policy statement about this situation and, without a policy, no-one can decide how to act.

The strange fact is that the Soviet aviation community is totally separated from the rest of the USSR, not only industrially, but economically and even socially, and has been so since long before *glasnost*. As a new member of the worldwide aircraft production community, this 'inner society' may find it difficult to adapt or to expand or contract in response to outside influences. Nothing is so inflexible as an elite.

Changing status of the USA

Throughout the 1980s, two trends have been apparent in the USA. First, the aerospace industry has been struggling to reconcile the need for rationalisation with the demand for competition. Secondly, the technological leadership that the whole nation had assumed to be its birthright has been seeping away to smaller countries for the past ten years or more. Both trends have caused just as much pain in the USA as they did in Europe in their time.

In the first case, the US industry is going through the same process as the European one has been doing since the 1960s. The major programmes have become too expensive for a single company or too few to satisfy all the companies, with the result that groupings have had to be formed. In Europe, these took the form of

Special conditions in the USSR have produced unique utility aircraft like the Mi-26 Halo, shown here, and the An-124 Ruslan. Both are now offered for special charter in the West

Top Guns.

It's a shoot-out for share on the regional frontiers. You need a tough, savvy team to fight and win.

Start with the EMB-120 Brasilia for proven reliability. Fast as hell. Works hard without breaking your pocketbook. Slim and trim and gets along good with the folks.

Put the CBA-123 on the flanks and show the raiders some new tricks. Faster, quieter and smooth as silk.

Up front you'll want the EMB-145 where size, speed and high class service count most.

A family team from an outfit with 15 years experience in helping regional airlines to survive and prosper.

EMB-145: 45 Pax, 430 Kt • EMB-120: 30 Pax, 310 Kt • CBA-123: 19 Pax, 350 Kt. For more information call (305) 359-9416 (USA) or (123) 25-1478 (Brazil).

The first substantive US/Soviet programme is the Gulfstream/Sukhoi Supersonic Business Jet, to be powered by Rolls-Royce/Lyulka variable-cycle engines. Several hundred might be sold

government-inspired mergers. In the USA, programme-orientated, multi-company teams have proliferated. This has now reached the sublime level where companies are competing in one programme and co-operating in another, as has happened with the Advanced Tactical Fighter, V-22, LH and Advanced Tactical Aircraft.

Superimposed on this has been the obsessive pursuit by the government customer of competition, as an article of faith and as an indispensable method of restraining cost. Also, fixed-price contracts have been used for large and high-risk development programmes that force the manufacturers to spend their own money and, in effect, to finance the government.

In the comparative plenty of the Reagan years this could still work, but the judgement day faced by Europe so many years ago may soon be facing the USA. Now that world events are causing a scaling down of defence development and production, a company shake-out of some kind is inevitable. Already three airframe companies, Rockwell, LTV and Grumman, have virtually retired as prime airframe developers. If the B-2A is drastically cut and the rival Lockheed/Boeing/General Dynamics team wins ATF, Northrop could follow suit. One or other of the big four helicopter makers might once again be at risk after downselection in the LH programme. Each major cut grinds a little more off the sharp edge of technology. Each teaming weakens the drive to innovate.

While we have been almost mesmerised by stealth technology and the bizarre aircraft it has produced, stealth is only an adjunct and will be a routine component of all new combat aircraft. The real new departure of recent years has been the tilt-rotor, and that is the baby that looks like being thrown away with the bath water.

Technology payoff

The new area in which technology is saving money is the flight and weapon control avionics of new military aircraft and the built-in test and fault

survival equipment that the new systems contain. And for the first time, this astonishing new technology is being incorporated at the same time into a fighter and a helicopter, namely, ATF and LH.

An essential feature of these new systems is that they make the highly capable and complex aircraft cheaper to operate and maintain than their slightly less complex predecessors. It has taken years for these techniques to pay off and only one of the new wave of aircraft, the F/A-18, has yet gone into service. The V-22A Osprey could be the next, and a major point in the battle for its survival is to convince the government that this feature will make the V-22A cheaper in the long term, as well as operationally more effective, than the UH-60/ CH-53E combination now being proposed as an alternative.

The message has not yet been fully appreciated. ATF, ATA and LH are all designed on the same principles. First cost will continue to be high, but lifetime cost will not reach the ultimate, unsustainable ceiling towards which earlier aircraft were remorselessly heading.

The key factor in that is not the traditional crafts and sciences of the aircraft maker, but digital electronics. They are making aerodynamics predictable for both airframes and engines, blending design and manufacture into a single process and making the aeroplane into a true companion of the human brain and hand.

There is only one way to keep technology moving forward, and that is by new programmes and these will be mostly, but not invariably, military. If there are not enough military programmes, the technology for civil programmes withers. The eventual outcome is government subsidy for civil development, which Europe was forced to adopt and the American system still claims to abhor.

Europe takes the initiative

The USA seems to be trying to avoid going through the same kind of process that the United Kingdom and then Europe as a whole had to go through in the late 1950s and 60s, that is, the

consolidation of each nation's aerospace industry into one or two major groups and the adoption of international co-operation as the principal method of tackling big new programmes.

West Germany, having consolidated its aircraft and space sectors into two main companies, has just combined those with avionics and engine companies in the multi-discipline Deutsche Aerospace, or DASA. This is part of a new round of mergers and associations in which competition between several cross-frontier groups will supersede competition between countries.

The consequent process of launching aircraft, missile and space programmes as international ventures is now firmly established, to the extent that Aeritalia, a substantial and internationally respected company, has hardly a single development programme under its own name, as its entry in this edition shows. All its main efforts are co-operative and accordingly are listed elsewhere in the International section of this book, which is growing year by year.

Now, there is a tendency for the national companies to merge their identities in programme companies called 'Eurothis' and 'Eurothat'. Airbus groups Europe's medium and big airliner activities and now Eurocopter is going to merge the helicopter activities of Aerospatiale and MBB. The process has produced stronger companies and better products and these have turned US/ Europe military trade into a balanced two-way street.

The bigger the new European programmes, the more the USA is shut out of the European market. Europe has even been accused of becoming protectionist in certain military programmes, such as the radar for the European Fighter Aircraft and the engine for the Tiger helicopter.

The USA has learned another European experience. Co-operation often means setting up a new competitor in a former export market so that subsequent sales become more difficult. Setting up Japan to develop the F-16 as its FS-X has been a recent portentous experience. Everyone has had

The high promise of the big Chinese aviation market has not blossomed in 20 years, although batches of Aerospatiale Dauphins have been produced under licence as the Z-9A, shown here, and a limited number of McDonnell Douglas MD-80s is being assembled under licence

THE COLOR OF PROGRESS.

LUCAS GREEN. UNIQUE.

SYSTEMS AT THE HEART OF THE WORLD'S

GREAT AIRCRAFT.

IN POWER GENERATION, FLIGHT

CONTROL AND ENGINE MANAGEMENT,

LUCAS' COMMITMENT TO ITS PARTNERS

IS TOTAL.

OUR COLOR FLIES WITH THE LATEST

BOEING, THE OSPREY, THE AIRBUS, THE

C-17, THE TORNADO, THE EH101 AND

MANY LEADING AEROSPACE PROJECTS

THROUGHOUT THE WORLD.

TO THOSE WHO PURSUE EXCELLENCE,

THERE IS ONE COLOR. LUCAS GREEN.

THE ART OF AEROSPACE, THE WORLD OVER.

HEAD OFFICES IN **Lucas Aerospace**

BRITAIN 021 704 5171, USA 703 264 1704,

FRANCE 1 45 61 95 25.

to digest the problem of offsets as more and more countries have started up aircraft industries and demanded more and more exorbitant proportions of offset.

Meanwhile, as Europe consolidates and prepares for the future, the fortunes of the US aerospace industry are being guided by relatively short-term considerations of frugality and good housekeeping. So defence programmes are becoming less profitable and less numerous.

As the government applies money-saving measures, the industry is left to take its own corrective measures, selling off defence businesses and cutting defence capacity. The reversal of fortunes between the civil and military parts of McDonnell Douglas is a remarkable example of the trend. It is already worrying the US Office of Technology Assessment that shrinkage that is not achieved as part of a coherent policy may go too far and leave the US short of defence capacity at some future date. Single-minded management for economy is not a long-term policy. Mergers among the big US aerospace companies are hardly conceivable, but we will probably see equivalents to 'Eurothis' and 'Eurothat'. Already we have First Team and Superteam in the LH programme.

European military outlook

Proposals to cancel the European Fighter Aircraft must not go unchallenged. As usual, there were plausible reasons for cancelling it from the moment it was conceived but, if the partner countries have any defence at all, for any purpose, then they will need a fighter and, to match even the smaller air forces, it simply has to be agile and equipped with the most up-to-date controls and weapon-aiming systems. At this moment, the RAF has none, the German Luftwaffe has none and the Italian Air Force has none. On the other hand, Spain has F/A-18s and Belgium, the Netherlands, Denmark and Norway have F-16s, though they are assigned as bombers rather than fighters.

EFA should be cheaper to buy than Tornado and a cheaper aircraft to support and maintain. It is not simply the most expensive item anyone can imagine. It is also nonsense to say that Tornado, fine as it is for its present roles, can in any conceivable form fulfil the function of EFA. EFA must be seen as part of a simple fleet replacement process. One day, we will need to replace what we have unless we really mean to renounce air defence altogether. Industrially, one cannot afford to skip a generation, as the UK tried to do by cancelling TSR.2 in 1965. France has maintained its resolve and its initiative, but can only just sustain the Rafale programme. The EFA consortium has

Under the pressure of konversiya, Soviet manufacturers are proposing a broad range of new civil projects that overlap types existing elsewhere. The Il-114 shown here represents the first wave of these

learned how to co-operate and make the most of its combined technology and resources, but is in danger of losing its resolve. Sadly, neither group will learn from the other.

The hard road to co-operation

The multiple reshuffle of companies in Europe in preparation for the single market of 1992 and the tense run-up to the production launch of the EFA programme are greatly changing the outlook for European co-operation. How the governments and armed forces are facing the new situation was admirably illustrated by a conference in London in February organised by Barclays de Zoete Wedd bank under the deliberately provocative title 'EFA: the last transnational project?'

The conference was the more interesting for being overshadowed by the political changes in Europe and the expected rundown in defence spending. But it had also barely been beaten to the post as the first opportunity for public inspection of EFA by a tardy press presentation of EFA by British Aerospace just a week earlier.

Introducing the conference, Barclay Group's chairman Sir John Quinton noted that, although Europe's defence industry is moving towards a kind of 'defence 1992', the implementation of such a single market is a positively Herculean task. The growing cost of defence projects is rising to the point where the increases have exceeded growth in gross domestic product and defence budgets.

Current political changes are adding to these pressures. Western Europe is faced with conflicting signals. East European changes are creating instability. The survival of President Gorbachev is unpredictable. Soviet armed forces are being re

duced in size, but their capability is being improved. Yet concessions are being made at disarmament talks. Demosthenes' advice was "What sane man would allow a person's words and not his deeds to persuade him who is at peace and who is at war?"

Pressures on collaboration

The UK Chief of Defence Procurement, Sir Peter Levene, is driving strongly for better collaborative arrangements. In the face of rising costs, he says, collaboration may be the only viable alternative to off-the-shelf procurement from outside Europe. The advantages are well known, but they are only potential. Difficulties with requirements, management and worksharers can cause slippages and uncompetitive procurement. Collaboration must be a method and not an end in itself. The disadvantages should not be accepted as inevitable.

The EFA programme incorporates the lessons learned with Tornado. The NATO management agency NEFMA acts for the governments. It will place contracts with the jointly owned Eurofighter and Eurojet companies. Work is allocated in proportion to each country's participation, and a tight maximum-price contract has been drawn up with payment against agreed milestones. Eurofighter and Eurojet select the subcontractors. Now, an incentive is being negotiated to improve the reliability targets.

The new prospective reductions in armaments will shorten national production runs and increase the need for collaboration. But the demonstration of better value for money will require greater competition among companies and a departure from agreements about worksharers. Sir Peter wants to move away from joint management companies to individual prime contractors offering competition at the top and clear responsibility. This means a more commercial relationship between government and industry in collaborative programmes.

The new cross-frontier alliances between European companies will give governments a chance to emphasise competition more than national considerations in collaborative programmes. Another form of collaboration is reciprocal purchasing, as agreed between the UK and France some years ago, under which all competitions within stated value bands are open to suppliers from either country without requirement for equal shares or offsets.

It will take time for it to be accepted, but it is an example which can be followed by the similar initiative now being pursued by the NATO Independent European Programme Group (IEPG), whose effort to establish an open European defence

The Bell Boeing V-22 Osprey is the technological baby that is being washed away by the budgetary bathwater. In our view, it is a more significant technological development than stealth

ITALTEL'S EXPERIENCE AT THE SERVICE OF DEFENSE

To detect to identify, to identify to prevent: all this is of main importance today, both in game and in reality. From Italtel, the range of high technology IFF systems: fixed and mobile surface interrogators, airborne interrogators and transponders. Developed and manufactured in Italtel's facilities, they are tailored to the specific national requirements and they can all operate in crypto modes. For any information please write to Italtel – Defense Telecommunications Division – Via Due Macelli 66 – 00187 Roma.

IRI-STET GROUP

equipment market is well on the way to implementation. The UK, France, West Germany, Italy, the Netherlands, Belgium, Norway, Turkey and Denmark, now all publish contracts bulletins.

Meanwhile, the notion of *juste retour* must be only transitional and there must be a 'level playing field' for all bidders. Excess defence industry capacity, arms cuts and purchasing outside the user nation will favour further cross-frontier mergers, with North America as well as within Europe.

Procurements will be collaborative by virtue of the fact that the suppliers are international. The countries may thereby be encouraged to reduce political constraints and to co-ordinate their requirements. But monolithic companies must not dominate entire market sectors.

In future, collaboration will be more varied. Very big programmes may still use the Tornado/ EFA-type organisation, but cross-frontier companies could automatically ensure collaboration. Industry must offer governments the best value for money on each occasion.

Mobility, flexibility and reach

Looking at the politico-military situation, Gp Capt David Bolton, director of studies at the Royal United Services Institute, pointed out some of the stresses of the new world situation. The Baltic states and other republics of the Soviet Union, Romania, Albania and many other countries are in turmoil. Not one of the East European countries is ethnically homogeneous. Three million soldiers are stationed outside their own country. Poland's frontiers may not be assured. The various national elections could still produce governments that are too weak or too authoritarian. Soviet troops may be needed to guarantee the Polish frontier and to prevent German revanchism. The Warsaw Pact has virtually ceased to function. NATO has the advantage of containing a political as well as a military command.

Thus, the western armed forces are changing. There will be a minimum of nuclear arms. Military units will be small, highly lethal, mobile and flexible. There will be fewer tanks. Artillery will be more mobile, highly accurate and will scatter submunitions. The helicopter will continue to be attractive, as will close air support. Aircraft will be very advanced.

Collective military formations will have priority, with brigades and squadrons being the largest single-nation units. Interoperability will be more important. A defence community, possibly an EEC-wide NATO, will continue to be important in order to contain instability, adventurism and any resurgence of Soviet militarism.

Surveillance, reconnaissance and C³I will be emphasised and weapons will have to have mobility, flexibility and reach. These are just the qualities that distinguish the European Fighter Aircraft.

The West is bemused and bewildered

Western defence ministries and armed forces are in a state of shock; they are bemused and bewildered, announced David Greenwood, director of the Centre for Defence Studies at the University of Aberdeen. The monolithic eastern bloc of the Brezhnev doctrine has changed in 15 months into the 'Sinatra doctrine' in which the eastern countries all 'do it their way'.

As the armed forces try to plan a future for NATO, the outlook for defence-related industry is clouded. In NATO countries, formerly rising spending has levelled off and stable spending is declining. Defence spending is publicly unpopular and also under pressure from the disarmament talks. Individual states will have to observe their own agreed disarmament limits. But smaller quantities of arms also means the best and both the armed forces and industry think that modernisation or replacement plans should not be greatly affected. At the same time, finance ministries are tending to put new programmes on hold, so that it is hard to identify the winners, or rather the survivors.

In the meantime, the single market of 1992 and the seven-nation IEPG plans for the defence market are developing and moving into action. The 1987 Single European Act opens the way for the previously segregated national defence industry to be included in EEC industry as a whole, on the model of such initiatives as BRITE/EURAM, in which the EEC is financing aerospace research covering dual-use technologies.

The manufacturers are setting up their cross-frontier alliances and deciding which lines of business to follow. More manufacturers are going to move away from defence, as some have already done. More of the big defence contracts will be competed for by the national and international defence consortia already formed.

There will be fewer large contracts, but some sectors will still expand, such as European military computers. This does not include embedded systems and strategic intelligence applications, which already account for $1 billion plus. But demand will shift from special-to-purpose systems to commercial off-the-shelf systems and software and services will produce more business than hardware and maintenance.

But what of CFE-capped items such as tanks, combat aircraft and helicopters? All big programmes will be re-examined but, while new single-nation battle tanks might not survive, EFA probably will, because NATO will want to have just such an aircraft in its 'residual mix' of thinned-out forces.

The strange story of the military ultralights

Military aviation has never finally answered the question of how small and simple an aeroplane can effectively be used for close air support. Count von Rosen's men used MFI Juniors in the Biafran war. The Soviets dropped small bombs from Po-2s over the Russian front at night during the Second World War. But countless special designs for light fighters have come to nothing. Sadly, it hardly seems possible that Rutan's ingenious asymmetric ARES could find a buyer, any more than the much more powerfully supported British Aerospace Small Agile Battlefield Aircraft (SABA) did back in the mid-1980s.

In the 1950s, NATO specified a light fighter that weighed half as much as the existing front-line subsonic jets. Lockheed won the huge German F-104G order with a 'light' fighter that delivered twice the performance without weighing any more. Light is relative, but the relativity is virtually impossible to specify.

Now, the powered hang glider has gone to war. Throughout the 1980s, the techniques and specialist units have been developing, a large proportion of them operated by the Palestinian terrorist organisations supported by Syria, Libya and Iran. They have been used as vehicles for single soldiers making raids, as weapon platforms and as manned or unmanned flying bombs. Zenith in France demonstrated the firing of unguided rockets from a three-axis microlight aircraft. The photograph overleaf shows the wing fabric flapping under the blast of a single departing rocket.

The first and one of the very few actual attacks carried out using microlights came from Lebanon in 1981, but both pilots, who were trying to attack the Haifa oil refineries, lost their way in the dark and were captured. In November, four pilots

The US Army's LH helicopter (the Boeing Sikorsky proposal is shown here) will have avionic controls and displays of the same generation and architecture as those of the US Air Force's Advanced Tactical Fighter

AIRBORNE SELF PROTECTION EW

Success in airborne operations largely depends on the ability to overcome the adversary's offensive capability.
This is why self protection, based on threat warning receivers and deception jammers - internally installed or pod contained - constitute the cost effective ingredient of mission success. ELETTRONICA, with thirty years' experience in airborne EW, produces a full range of Self Protection EW suites meeting present and future operational requirements.

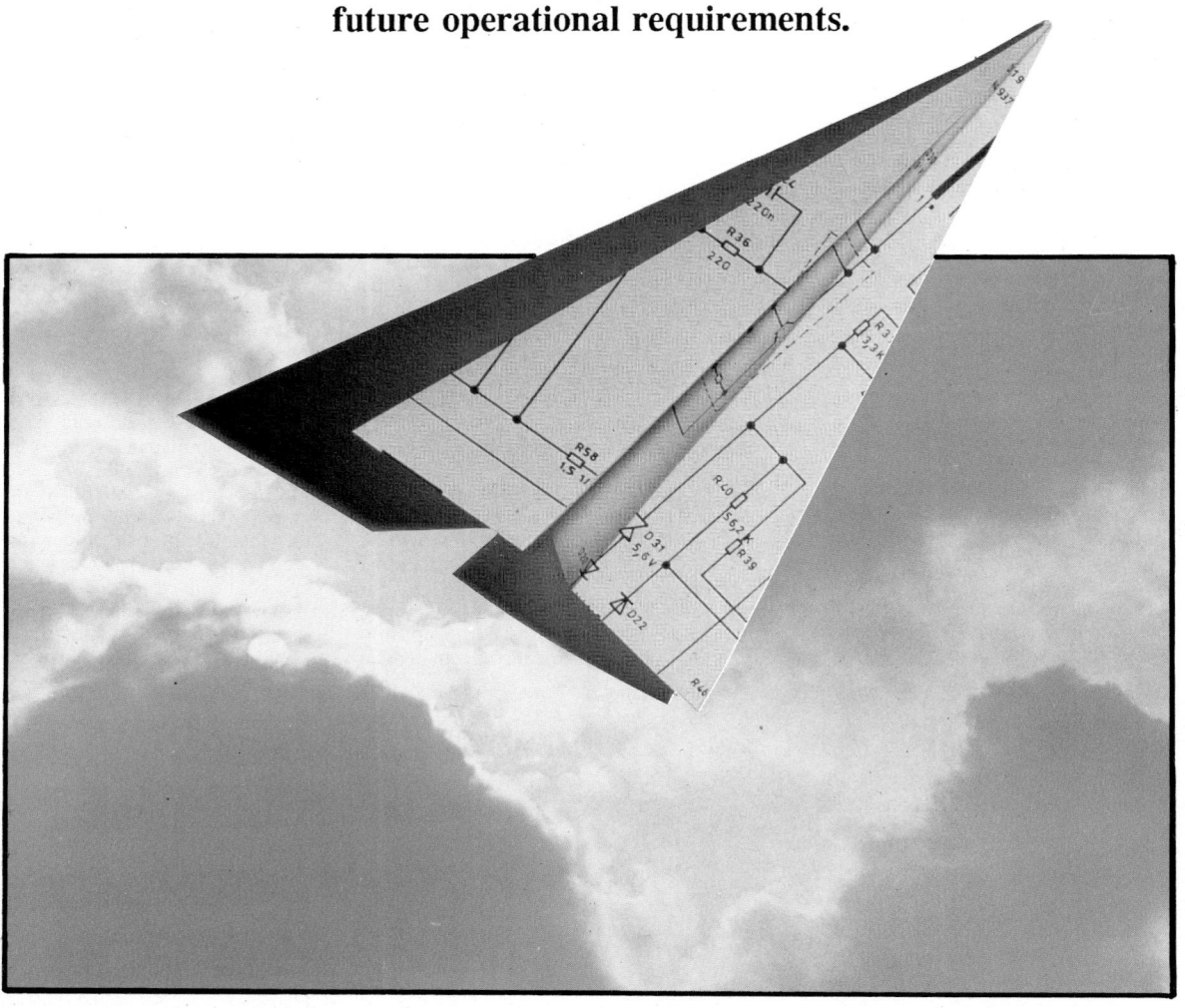

ELETTRONICA - THE EW PEOPLE

ELETTRONICA S.p.A. Via Tiburtina Km 13.700 ROME - ITALY

departed from Lebanon to attack an Israeli army camp. One turned back with mechanical trouble. Two more crashed en route, but the fourth reached the camp and killed six soldiers and wounded 10 before being shot.

Earlier that same year, the Soviet army paper *Krasnaya Svezda* had written about 'mosquito aviation' and the use of hang gliders for penetration, attack of special targets behind the lines, reconnaissance and so on. The techniques were investigated or adopted by the Soviet GRU, the VDV Airborne Forces, the VVS Interior Troops and, in order to generate a pool of pilots, by the DOSAAF civil air sporting organisation.

There is even a report that a ram-air parachute with a powered trike has been launched out of a C-130 Hercules.

The Indian armed forces adopted the technique, obtaining both Soviet and UK equipment. Manufacturers in the UK and France know that their hang gliders and microlights have found their way through middlemen to the Middle East and Libya.

When will aerospace have to change?

One unavoidable consideration must now accompany all thoughts about the distant future of aviation. We are bound to ask ourselves where the forecasts of doubled world air travel and even a reduced level of armaments production will lead us. When will the foreseeable effects of consumption and pollution begin to change the face of aviation?

The 'swords into ploughshares' arguments are, of course, as implausible now as they ever have been. It is as absurd to think that it is possible to abandon defence and switch the money and resources immediately into 'green' products as it was some years ago to try to spend it immediately on cancer research. At least the environment might be better able than cancer research to absorb such an onrush of funds.

It would take years to convert the R&D and output of defence-orientated companies to equipment that could help preserve the environment, just as it did for the mighty tobacco empires to change their businesses and for the governments to find replacement sources of tax revenue.

It is in any case much too early to consider that defence is a thing of the past. The world is far from being out of that wood. As I write, India and Pakistan look like being on the brink of the first non-superpower war in which both sides are thought to possess and are talking about using nuclear weapons.

It sometimes seems that the world is looking for a new enemy and, sadly, religion looks like an all-too-likely focus.

By the same token, the revolutions in the communist countries were fuelled to a great extent by the expectation of a higher standard of living. That will include, at the earliest possible moment, the right and the facilities to travel. That right and those facilities are endemic to the developed western countries. Newly prosperous populations will not deny themselves that same wave of experience, so that travel will greatly expand before it can be damped down again. The volume of air travel will probably be restrained by airspace and airport capacity before the question of resources becomes dominant. Is it reasonable to think that advanced ships may once again rival the airliner?

At all events, terminal disaster is unlikely. The world has always shown that it can pull back from the brink. It has managed to do so in nuclear warfare so far and it will undoubtedly cope with the demands of the threatened environment.

But we in the aerospace world still have to ask ourselves at what time and in what way the demands of world survival will impose change on the traditions and expectations of our aerospace business.

Too often, aviation forecasters have not seen the downturns coming and, even today, the signals are still set at full ahead. Will aerospace industry and operators take the lead in adapting to change, or will they be driven and lose the initiative?

Coulsdon, June 1990   Mark Lambert

Unlike many small air forces that are already flying modern Soviet fighters, the British, German and Italian air forces do not possess a modern agile fighter like the European Fighter Aircraft, but the governments are nevertheless considering cancelling the programme

The microlight at war: 89 mm unguided rockets were successfully fired from the French Zenith-Aviation Baroudeur microlight several years ago and such aircraft are now increasingly being adopted by armed forces for patrol and insurgency

AMX-T
THE TWO-SEATER
IS NOW READY
FOR ACTION

AMX
INTERNATIONAL
AERITALIA AERMACCHI EMBRAER

[30]

First Flights

Some of the first flights made during the period 1 April 1989 to 16 June 1990

APRIL 1989

3 Grumman A-6E Intruder, first flight with Boeing all-composites wings (USA)
6 Aerospatiale AS 365N$_1$ Dauphin, first flight with fly by wire flight control system (F-WZJJ) (France)
7 BAe Hawk Mk 66, first for Swiss Air Force (U-1251) (UK)
13 McDonnell Douglas MD-80 UHB testbed, first flight with PW-Allison 578-DX engines (USA)
25 Beechcraft Starship 1, first production (c/n NC-4, N2000S) (USA)
26 EHI EH 101, second Italian and first naval pre-production aircraft (PP6) (International)
27 MBB/Kawasaki BK 117, testbed with all-composites airframe (D-HBMT) (International)
27 Glaser-Dirks DG-500 Elan Trainer sailplane (D-5007) (West Germany)
30 Socata Oméga (F-WOMG) (France)

MAY 1989

4 General Dynamics FB-111A (68-0254), first flight after digital flight control system retrofit (USA)
10 McDonnell Douglas F-15S/MTD (71-290), first flight with two-dimensional vectoring nozzles (USA)
13 PZL I-22 Iryd, third prototype (second to fly) (SP-PWB) (Poland)
13 Antonov An-225 Mriya (SSSR-480182), first flight carrying *Buran* orbiter (USSR)
23 Boeing Model 767, first flight with RB211 engines (USA)
23 Grumman X-29A, second aircraft (82-0049) (USA)
28 AIDC Ching-Kuo (77-8001) (Taiwan)
29 Swearingen SA-32T Turbo Trainer (N6Y) (USA)

JUNE 1989

8 Canadair CL-215T (C-FASE) (Canada)
8 Glaser-Dirks DG-500/22 Elan sailplane (West Germany)
9 McDonnell Douglas/BAe Harrier GR. Mk 5 (ZD402), first flight with Pegasus 11-61 engine (International)
13 General Avia F.22 Pinguino (I-GEAD) (Italy)
15 EHI EH 101, fourth pre-production aircraft (fifth to fly) (PP4/ZF644) (International)
24 Spacial MLA-32-B Toluca airship (Mexico)
30 Boeing Model 737-500 (N5048W) (USA)

JULY 1989

8 Celair GA-1 Celstar sailplane (ZS-GSS) (South Africa)
17 BAC One-Eleven (N162W), Westinghouse testbed for Northrop/McDonnell Douglas YF-23A avionics (USA)
17 Northrop B-2A (82-1066) (USA)
31 Sadler A-22 (N22AB) (USA)

AUGUST 1989

2 TBM 700, second prototype (F-WKPG) (International)
12 AMX, first Brazilian Air Force production A-1 (5500) (International)
31 Boeing Model 767-300R, first flight with R-R Trent engines (USA)
31 Boeing/Grumman E-8A, second J-STARS testbed (N8411) (USA)

SEPTEMBER 1989

9 Bell/Boeing V-22 Osprey, second prototype (163912) (USA)
14 Bell/Boeing V-22 Osprey (163911), first transition to wingborne flight (USA)
15 BAe 125 Series 600B (XW930), first flight with B model Blue Vixen radar for Sea Harrier FRS. Mk 2 (UK)
20 Canadair CL-215T, second prototype (C-FAWO) (Canada)
22 Beechcraft Beechjet 400A (N1556W) (USA)
25 IAI TD (third Lavi prototype) (Israel)
25 Fairchild SA 227-DC Metro 25 (N2671V) (USA)

OCTOBER 1989

1 Aero L-39 MS, first production (Czechoslovakia)
7 Enstrom Model 480 (N8631E) (USA)
11 TBM 700, third prototype (F-WKDL) (International)
11 Shorts S312 Tucano (ZH203), first Mk 51 for Kenya (UK)
16 Boeing Chinook HC. Mk 1 (ZA718), first flight with full authority digital engine control (USA/UK)
22 PZL I-22 Iryd, fourth prototype (third to fly) (Poland)
24 EHI EH 101, pre-production aircraft for Royal Navy Merlin (PP5/ZF649) (International)
26 Panavia Tornado, first production ECR (46 + 23) (International)
28 Aircorp Bushmaster B2N (VH-BOI) (Australia)
29 Grumman EA-6B Prowler (156482), first in ADVCAP configuration (USA)

17 July 1989: the Northrop B-2A stealth bomber lifts off from Palmdale

EUROFIRST 1.

INFRA RED SEARCH AND TRACK

PIRATE (Passive Infra Red Airborne
Tracking Equipment)
for the European Fighter Aircraft
EFA.

PIRATE is the all European
collaborative solution being offered
by EUROFIRST for the European
Fighter Aircraft Infra Red Search and
Track System (IRST).
The EUROFIRST consortium led by Fiar
comprises Eltro of Germany,
Fiar of Italy, Eurotronica of Spain and
Thorn Emi Electronics of the United Kingdom.

 Eltro   **FIAR))** **E₀** Eurotrónica **THORN EMI Electronics**

NOVEMBER 1989

9   Airbus A320, first flight with 'riblet' skin covering (International)
11   Glaser-Dirks DG-600M motor glider (D-KMDG) (West Germany)
16   Westland Super Lynx (ZH219/90-0701), first Mk 99 for South Korea (UK)
24   Dassault Mirage 2000, first flight with operational standard Rubis FLIR pod (France)
28   Ilyushin Il-96-300, second prototype (USSR)
28   Croplease Fieldmaster (G-NACL), first flight in Firemaster 65 configuration (UK)
29   McDonnell Douglas/BAe Harrier GR. Mk 7 (ZD318, converted GR. Mk 5) (International)
29   Westland Lynx AH. Mk 9/Battlefield Lynx, prototype conversion (XZ170) (UK)
29   LTV YA-7F Corsair II (71-344, converted A-7D) (USA)

DECEMBER 1989

7   Westland Sea King HAS. Mk 6, first production (ZG816) (UK)
8   Cardoen 206L-III (converted Bell 206L-1, N38958) (Chile)
10   California Polytechnic University Da Vinci 3 human powered helicopter (USA)
18   EHI EH 101, seventh pre-production aircraft (first in Utility configuration) (PP7) (International)
19   PZL Warszawa-Okecie PZL-105 Flaming (SP-PRC) (Poland)
20   Dassault Atlantique 2, second production (France)
21   Bell/Boeing V-22 Osprey, fourth prototype (third to fly) (163914) (USA)
26   NAMC N-5A (China, People's Republic)
28   Kaman YSH-2G (161653), first flight in full operational SH-2G Super Seasprite configuration (USA)
29   McDonnell Douglas MD 530N (N530NT) (USA)

JANUARY 1990

5   Boeing E-3D Sentry, first fully equipped AEW. Mk 1 for Royal Air Force (ZH101) (USA)
10   McDonnell Douglas MD-11 (N111MD) (USA)
12   Bell Model 222 Twin Two-Twelve (N5008Q), first Heli-Air conversion to Allison 250-C30G engines (USA)
26   Boeing VC-25A (Presidential Model 747-200B) (82-8000) (USA)

FEBRUARY 1990

11   Atlas XH-2 Rooivalk (South Africa)
19   Scaled Composites Model 151 ARES (N151SC) (USA)
23   Taylorcraft Model AA-23 STOL 180 (USA)
27   Dassault Rafale A, first flight with one F404 engine replaced by Snecma M88-2 (France)

MARCH 1990

1   Beechcraft Model 1900D (N5584B) (USA)
1   McDonnell Douglas MD-11 (MD-11F), second aircraft (N211MD) (USA)
14   AMX-T, first two-seater (International)
29   Ilyushin Il-114 (SSSR-54000) (USSR)

APRIL 1990

3   LTV YA-7F Corsair II, second prototype (70-1039, converted A-7D) (USA)
4   Celair Eagle 300 (ZS-WLD) (South Africa)
6   MBB/Kawasaki BK 117, first flight with Arriel 1E engines (F-WMBB) (International)
20   PZL Warszawa-Okecie PZL-126 Mrówka (SP-PMA) (Poland)
24   EHI EH 101, pre-production aircraft for Heliliner version (PP8/G-0101) (International)
26   McDonnell Douglas MD-11, third aircraft (first with PW engines) (USA)
27   Aero Mercantil EL1 Gavilán (HK-3500-1) (Colombia)
30   Cessna Citation 500, FJ44 engine testbed for Model 525 CitationJet (N501CC) (USA)

MAY 1990

2   McDonnell Douglas F-15E, first flight with two F100-PW-229 engines (USA)
4   Saab JAS 39 Gripen, second prototype (52) (Sweden)
9   Bell/Boeing V-22 Osprey, third prototype (fourth to fly) (163913) (USA)
24   BAe Sea Harrier FRS. Mk 2 (XZ439), first flight with B model Blue Vixen radar (UK)
30   Piaggio P.180 Avanti, first production (NC 1004) (Italy)

JUNE 1990

early   Sikorsky H-76 (N3124G), testbed for Boeing/Sikorsky LH Fantail ('fan-in-fin') tail rotor (USA)
1   Boeing MH-47E Chinook (88-0267) (USA)
5   McDonnell Douglas MD-11, fourth aircraft (USA)
16   BAe 1000 (G-EXLR) (UK)

4 May 1990: Flight testing of the Saab JAS 39 Gripen restarts with the first flight of the second prototype

26 April 1990: the third McDonnell Douglas MD-11 departs Long Beach for the flight test base at Yuma, Arizona

14 March 1990: the two-seat AMX-T makes its first landing, escorted by a single-seat AMX

Programme milestones of the 1990s

Events as forecast by manufacturers and recorded in this edition

1990

September	Boeing VC-25A 'Air Force One'	First of two delivered
September	Lockheed F-117A	Last of 59 delivered
October	McDonnell Douglas MD-11	Certificated
November	Embraer/FAMA CBA-123	Third prototype flies in Argentina
Second half	Bell/Boeing V-22 Nos. 5 and 6	Fly
Second half	General Dynamics FB-111A/F-111G	Transferred from SAC to TAC
Second half	Ilyushin Il-86	Flies with PS-90As
Second half	Kamov Ka-226	Flies
Second half	Lockheed/Boeing/General Dynamics YF-22A ATF	Flies
Second half	Northrop/McDonnell Douglas YF-23A ATF	Flies
Second half	Robinson R44	Flies
Late	Dornier Seastar	Delivered
Late	EH Industries EH 101	PP9 flies
Late	Enstrom Model 480 (TH-28)	Certificated
Late	FFT Eurotrainer	Flies
Late	International X-31A	Flies
Late	International AMX-T	No. 2 with radar flies
Late	Hindustan ALH	Flies (or early 1991)
Late	Schweizer Model 330	Certificated
End	Piaggio P.180 Avanti	Delivered
End	Beechcraft Beechjet 400A	Delivered

1991

	BAe Hawk 200 No. 3	Flies
	Beechcraft Starship	First European delivery
	Boeing/Grumman E-8A J-STARS	Decision on acquisition of 22
	Eurofighter EFA	Flies (or Summer 1992)
	Panavia Tornado ECR	Delivered to Luftwaffe
	Valmet Redigo	Delivered
Early	MBB BO 108V2	Flies
Early	McDonnell Douglas MD 520N/530N	Delivered
Early	Soko G-4M Super Galeb	Flies
Early	Tupolev Tu-204	Full certification
January	Boeing E-3D Sentry AEW. Mk 1	Delivered
January	US Army AH-66 LH	Down-select and start FSD
February	Dassault Rafale ACT-C01	Flies
Spring	Cessna 525 CitationJet	Flies
May	Cessna Citation VI	Delivered
May	Eurocopter Tiger	Flies
May	US Air Force YF-22A/YF-23A (ATF)	Winner selected
June	Boeing VC-25A 'Air Force One'	Second aircraft delivered
June	McDonnell Douglas C-17	Flies
July	Dornier 328	Flies
Mid	BAe 1000	Delivered
Mid	Dassault Rafale ACM-01	Flies
Summer	BAe Jetstream 41	Flies
September	Lockheed P-3	Last aircraft delivered as Canadian CP-140A Arcturus
September	Lockheed P-7A	Rolled out
October	Beechcraft T-1A Jayhawk	First USAF delivery
November	McDonnell Douglas Longbow Apache	Flies
December	Bell Model 230	Certificated
December	Lockheed P-7A	Flies
December	Tridair Gemini st Twin LongRanger	Certificated
Late	Airbus A340-200 and -300	Fly
Late	Embraer EMB-145	Flies
Late	Embraer/FAMA CBA-123	Certificated

Advanced integrated avionics and stealth will come to the helicopter world for the first time in the US Army LH. This is the Boeing/Sikorsky First Team proposal

Late	Eurofighter EFA	Flies
Late	IAv Bucuresti One-Eleven (Tay)	Might fly
Late	Kaman SH-2G Super Seasprite	Production starts
Late	Panavia Tornado GR. Mk 4	Flies

1992

	Aero L-270	Possible first flight
	Boeing 727-100 (Tay 650)	Delivered
	Dassault Falcon 2000	Flies
	Dassault Rafale ACT-B01	Flies
	Hindustan Light Attack Helicopter	Flies
	Ilyushin Il-114	Delivered
	Mil Mi-38	Possible first flight
	Northrop B-2	Delivered
	Soko G-4M Super Galeb	Delivered
	Sukhoi S-80	Flies
January	Bell Model 230	Delivered
January	Cessna Citation VII	Delivered
Early	Fairchild Metro 25	Certificated
Early	FFT Eurotrainer	Delivered
Early	BAe VC10 C. Mk 1(K)	Redelivered
Mid	Saab 2000	Flies

Launched in June 1987, concurrently with the A330, the A340 in both its -200 and -300 versions is due to fly in late 1991

The McDonnell Douglas C-17 military transport, under threat of budget reductions, emerged from its 'automated join tool' in July 1990 and is due to fly in June 1991

The Northrop/McDonnell Douglas YF-23A Advanced Tactical Fighter prototype was expected to fly during July 1990, to be followed by the Lockheed/Boeing/General Dynamics YF-22A a few weeks later

Mid	Tupolev Tu-334	Flies
Summer	Eurofighter EFA	Delayed flight date
July	International A 139	Flies
July	McDonnell Douglas MDX	Flies
September	Boeing MH-47E	Delivery of first 17 completed
October	Cessna 525 CitationJet	Certificated
Autumn	BAe Jetstream 41	Delivered
Late	Airbus A330	Flies
Late	Airbus A340-200 and -300	JAR certification
Late	Airbus A340-200 and -300	Delivered
Late	Dornier 328	JAR certification

1993

	Boeing/Grumman E-8A J-STARS	In service
	Eurofighter EFA P.05	Flies with ECR-90 radar
	Ilyushin Il-96-350	Flies
	Sukhoi/Gulfstream S-21/G VI	Might fly
	McDonnell Douglas MD-90	Flies
	NASA X-30 Aero-Space Plane	Programme go-ahead
	Saab JAS 39 Gripen	Delivered
Early	Airbus A321	Flies
Early	Dassault Rafale ACM	Flies with RBE2 radar
Early	International P 120L	Flies
Mid	Embraer EMB-145	Delivered
Mid	International NH 90	Flies
Mid	Ishida TW-68	Flies
Mid	LTV F-8E(FN) upgrades	First 6 delivered
June	McDonnell Douglas F-15E Eagle	Production ends
August	Boeing 747-400F	Delivered
August	General Dynamics F-111D/F Pacer Strike update	Kits delivered
August	US Army AH-66 LH	Flies
September	McDonnell Douglas C-17	Initial operational capability
October	Boeing CH-47D Chinook	Production of 472 complete
October	International A 139	Delivered
October	McDonnell Douglas MDX	Certificated
Second half	Saab 2000	Delivered
Late	Airbus A321	JAR certification
Late	Airbus A330	JAR certification
Late	Airbus A330	Delivered
Late	Boeing Canada Dash 8-400	Flies

1994

	CASA AX	Pre-feasibility study ends
	Dassault Falcon 2000	Certificated
	Italian Navy EHI EH 101	Delivered
	Fokker 50-200	Possible delivery
	Gulfstream/Sukhoi SSBJ	Flies
	International Eurofar	Flies
	Lockheed P-7A	Delivery
	McDonnell Douglas MD-12X	Possible first flight
	McDonnell Douglas Longbow Apache	Conversions begin
Early	Airbus A321	Delivered
May	General Electric GE90	Certificated
October	International MPC-75-100	Flies
Fourth quarter	McDonnell Douglas MD90-30	Delivered
Late	Boeing Canada Dash 8-400	Delivered

1995

Early	General Dynamics/McDonnell Douglas A-12A (ATA)	Flies
Early	IPTN N-250	Flies
Early	LTV F-8E(FN) upgrades	Last 10 delivered
First quarter	McDonnell Douglas MD90-10	Certificated
First half	Boeing 777	Delivered
Mid	McDonnell Douglas MD-12X	Possible delivery
December	International MPC-75-100	Certificated

1996

	Aerospatiale AS 532 U2 Orchidée	Delivered
	Royal Navy EHI EH 101	Delivered
	Eurofighter EFA	In RAF service
	International Euroflag	Full scale development starts
	International MPC-75	Production starts
	US Air Force YF-22A or YF-23A ATF	Delivered
	Yugoslav Novi Avion	Might fly
July	Dassault Rafale ACM	Deliveries start
November	US Army AH-66 LH	In service

1997

	Eurocopter HAP Tigre	Delivered to France
	Eurofighter EFA	In Luftwaffe service
	International NH 90	Delivered
	Yakovlev Yak-46	Delivered

1998

	Eurocopter PAH-2 Tiger	Delivered to Germany
November	International MPC-75-200	Certificated
Late	Dassault Rafale ACM	First 15 delivered

1999

Early	International MPC-75-200	Delivered

2000

	International Euroflag	Flies

Retractable weapon pylons and undercarriage are features of both LH proposals. While the Bell/McDonnell Douglas Super Team has chosen the Notar rotorless anti-torque system, the Boeing/Sikorsky First Team has opted for the tilted Fantail arrangement shown above

1993 will see the start of flight testing of the McDonnell Douglas MD-90 powered by IAE V2500 turbofans. The manufacturer now says that the hyphen in MD-90 is only omitted when a sub-type designation is added, as in MD90-200

Glossary of aerospace terms in this book

AAM Air-to-air missile.
AATH Automatic approach to hover.
AC Alternating current.
ACLS (1) Automatic carrier landing system; (2) Air cushion landing system.
ACMI Air combat manoeuvring instrumentation.
ACN Aircraft classification number (ICAO system for aircraft pavements).
ADAC Avion de décollage et attérrissage court (STOL).
ADAV Avion de décollage et attérrissage vertical (VTOL).
ADC (1) US Air Force Aerospace Defense Command (no longer active); (2) air data computer.
ADF Medium frequency automatic direction finding (equipment).
ADG Accessory-drive generator.
ADI Attitude/director indicator.
aeroplane (N America, airplane) Heavier-than-air aircraft with propulsion and a wing that does not rotate in order to generate lift.
AEW Airborne early warning.
AFB Air Force Base (USA).
AFCS Automatic flight control system.
AFRP Aramid fibre reinforced plastics.
afterburning Temporarily augmenting the thrust of a turbofan or turbojet by burning additional fuel in the jetpipe.
AGREE Advisory Group on Reliability in Electronic Equipment.
Ah Ampère-hours.
AHRS Attitude/heading reference system.
AIDS Airborne integrated data system.
aircraft All man-made vehicles for off-surface navigation within the atmosphere, including helicopters and balloons.
airstair Retractable stairway built into aircraft.
AIS Advanced instrumentation subsystem.
ALCM Air-launched cruise missile.
AM Amplitude modulation.
AMAD Airframe mounted accessory drive.
anhedral Downward slope of wing seen from front, in direction from root to tip.
ANVIS Aviator's night vision system.
AP Ammonium perchlorate.
APFD Autopilot flight director.
approach noise Measured 1 nm from downwind end of runway with aircraft passing overhead at 113 m (370 ft).
APS Aircraft prepared for service; a fully equipped and crewed aircraft without usable fuel and payload.
APU Auxiliary power unit (part of aircraft).
ARINC Aeronautical Radio Inc, US company whose electronic box sizes (racking sizes) are the international standard.
ASE (1) Automatic stabilisation equipment; (2) Aircraft survivability equipment.
ASI Airspeed indicator.
ASIR Airspeed indicator reading.
ASM Air-to-surface missile.
aspect ratio Measure of wing (or other aerofoil) slenderness seen in plan view, usually defined as the square of the span divided by gross area.
ASPJ Advanced self-protection jammer.
AST Air Staff Target (UK).
ASV (1) Air-to-surface vessel; (2) Anti-surface vessel.
ASW Anti-submarine warfare.
ATA Air Transport Association of America.
ATC Air traffic control.
ATDS Airborne tactical data system.
ATHS Airborne target handover (US, handoff) system.
ATR Airline transport radio, series of ARINC standard box sizes.
attack, angle of (alpha) Angle at which airstream meets aerofoil (angle between mean chord and free-stream direction). Not to be confused with angle of incidence (which see).
augmented Boosted by afterburning.
autogyro Rotary-wing aircraft propelled by a propeller (or other thrusting device) and lifted by a freely running autorotating rotor.
AUW All-up weight (term meaning total weight of aircraft under defined conditions, or at a specific time during flight). Not to be confused with MTOGW (which see).
avionics Aviation electronics, such as communications radio, radars, navigation systems and computers.
AVLF Airborne very low frequency.
AWACS Airborne warning and control system (aircraft).

bar Non-SI unit of pressure adopted by this yearbook pending wider acceptance of Pa. 1 bar = 10^5 Pa, and ISA pressure at S/L is 1,013.2 mb. or just over 1 bar.
bare weight Undefined term meaning unequipped empty weight.
basic operating weight MTOGW minus payload (thus, including crew, fuel and oil, bar stocks, cutlery etc).

BCAR British Civil Airworthiness Requirements.
bearingless rotor Rotor in which flapping, lead/lag and pitch change movements are provided by the flexibility of the structural material and not by bearings. No rotor is rigid.
Beta mode Propeller or rotor operating regime in which pilot has direct control of pitch.
BFO Beat-frequency oscillator.
BITE Built-in test equipment.
bladder tank Fuel (or other fluid) tank of flexible material.
bleed air Hot high-pressure air extracted from gas turbine engine compressor or combustor and taken through valves and pipes to perform useful work such as pressurisation, driving machinery or anti-icing by heating surfaces.
blisk Blade plus disc (of turbine engine) fabricated in one piece.
blown flap Flap across which bleed air is discharged at high (often supersonic) speed to prevent flow breakaway.
BOW Basic operating weight (which see).
BPR Bypass ratio.
BRW Brake release weight, maximum permitted weight at start of T-O run.
BTU Non-SI unit of energy (British Thermal Unit) = 0.9478 J.
bulk cargo All cargo not packed in containers or on pallets.
bus Busbar, main terminal in electrical system to which battery or generator power is supplied.
BVR Beyond visual range.
bypass ratio Airflow through fan duct (not passing through core) divided by airflow through core.

CAA Civil Aviation Authority (UK).
cabin altitude Height above S/L at which ambient pressure is same as inside cabin.
CAD/CAM Computer-assisted design/computer-assisted manufacture.
CAM Cockpit-angle measure (crew field of view).
canards Foreplanes, fixed or controllable aerodynamic surfaces ahead of CG.
CAN 5 Committee on Aircraft Noise (ICAO) rules for new designs of aircraft.
CAR Civil Airworthiness Regulations.
CAS (1) Calibrated airspeed, ASI calibrated to allow for air compressibility according to ISA S/L; (2) close air support; (3) Chief of the Air Staff (also several other aerospace meanings).
CBR California bearing ratio, measure of ability of airfield surface (paved or not) to support aircraft.
CBU Cluster bomb unit.
CCV Control configured vehicle.
CEAM Centre d'Expériences Aériennes Militaires.
CEAT Centre d'Essais Aéronautiques de Toulouse.
CEP Circular error probability (50/50 chance of hit being inside or outside) in bombing, missile attack or gunnery.
CEV Centre d'Essais en Vol.
CFRP Carbonfibre-reinforced plastics.
CG Centre of gravity.
chaff Thin slivers of radar-reflective material cut to length appropriate to wavelengths of hostile radars and scattered in clouds to protect friendly aircraft.
chord Distance from leading-edge to trailing-edge measured parallel to longitudinal axis.
CKD Component knocked down, for assembly elsewhere.
clean (1) In flight configuration with landing gear, flaps, slats etc retracted; (2) Without any optional external stores.
c/n Construction (or constructor's) number.
COINS Computer operated instrument system.
combi Civil aircraft carrying both freight and passengers on main deck.
comint communications intelligence.
composite material Made of two constituents, such as filaments or short whiskers plus adhesive.
CONUS Continental USA (ie, excluding Hawaii, etc).
convertible Transport aircraft able to be equipped to carry passengers or cargo.
core Gas generator portion of turbofan comprising compressor(s), combustion chamber and turbine(s).
C/R Counter-rotating (propellers).
CRT Cathode-ray tube.
CSAS Command and stability augmentation system (part of AFCS).
CSD Constant-speed drive (output shaft speed held steady, no matter how input may vary).
CSRL Common strategic rotary launcher (for ALCMs or SRAMs).

DADC Digital air data computer.
DADS Digital air data system.
daN Decanewtons (Newtons force × 10).
DARPA Defense Advanced Research Projects Agency.

databus Electronic highway for passing digital data between aircraft sensors and system processors, usually MIL-STD-1553B or ARINC 419.
dB Decibel.
DC Direct current.
DECU Digital engine control unit.
derated Engine restricted to power less than potential maximum (usually such engine is flat rated).
design weight Different authorities have different definitions; weight chosen as typical of mission but usually much less than MTOGW.
DF Direction finder, or direction finding.
DGAC Direction Générale à l'Aviation Civile.
dibber bomb Designed to cause maximum damage to concrete runways.
dihedral Upward slope of wing seen from front, in direction from root to tip.
DINS Digital inertial navigation system.
disposable load Sum of masses that can be loaded or unloaded, including payload, crew, usable fuel etc; MTOGW minus OWE.
DLC Direct lift control.
DME UHF distance-measuring equipment; gives slant distance to a beacon; DME element of Tacan.
dog-tooth A step in the leading-edge of a plane resulting from an increase in chord. (See also saw-tooth).
Doppler Short for Doppler radar — radar using fact that received frequency is a function of relative velocity between transmitter or reflecting surface and receiver; used for measuring speed over ground or for detecting aircraft or moving vehicles against static ground or sea.
double-slotted flap One having an auxiliary aerofoil ahead of main surface to increase maximum lift.
dP Maximum design differential pressure between pressurised cabin and ambient (outside atmosphere).
drone Pilotless aircraft, usually winged, following preset programme of manoeuvres.
DS Directionally solidified.

EAA Experimental Aircraft Association (divided into local branches called Chapters).
EAS Equivalent airspeed, RAS minus correction for compressibility.
ECCM Electronic counter-countermeasures.
ECM Electronic countermeasures.
EFIS Electronic flight instrument(ation) system, in which large multifunction CRT displays replace traditional instruments.
EGT Exhaust gas temperature.
ehp Equivalent horsepower, measure of propulsive power of turboprop made up of shp plus addition due to residual thrust from jet.
EICAS Engine indication (and) crew alerting system.
EIS Entry into service.
ekW Equivalent kilowatts, SI measure of propulsive power of turboprop (see ehp).
elevon wing trailing-edge control surface combining functions of aileron and elevator.
ELF Extreme low frequency.
elint electronics intelligence.
ELT Emergency locator transmitter, to help rescuers home on to a disabled or crashed aircraft.
EMP Electro-magnetic pulse of nuclear or electronic origin.
EO Electro-optical.
EPA Environmental Protection Agency.
EPNdB Effective perceived noise decibel, SI unit of EPNL.
EPNL Effective perceived noise level, measure of noise effect on humans which takes account of sound intensity, frequency, character and duration, and response of human ear.
EPU Emergency power unit (part of aircraft, not used for propulsion).
EROPS Alternative abbreviation (favoured by airlines) for ETOPS.
ERP Effective radiated power.
ESA European Space Agency.
ESM (1) Electronic surveillance (or support) measures; (2) Electronic signal monitoring.
ETOPS Extended-range twin (engine) operations, routing not more than a given flight time (120 min or 180 min) from a usable alternative airfield.
EVA Extra-vehicular activity, ie outside spacecraft.
EW Electronic warfare.
EWSM Early-warning support measures.

FAA Federal Aviation Administration.
factored Multiplied by an agreed number to take account of extreme adverse conditions, errors, design deficiencies or other inaccuracies.
FADEC Full authority digital engine (or electronic) control.
FAI Fédération Aéronautique Internationale.

fail-operational System which continues to function after any single fault has occurred.

fail-safe Structure or system which survives failure (in case of system, may no longer function normally).

FAR Federal Aviation Regulations.

FAR Pt 23 Defines the airworthiness of private and air taxi aeroplanes of 5,670 kg (12,500 lb) MTOGW and below.

FAR Pt 25 Defines the airworthiness of public transport aeroplanes exceeding 5,670 kg (12,500 lb) MTOGW.

FBW Fly by wire (which see).

FDS Flight director system.

feathering Setting propeller or similar blades at pitch aligned with slipstream to give resultant torque (not tending to turn shaft) and thus minimum drag.

FEBA Forward edge of battle area.

FEL Fibre elastomeric rotor head.

fence A chordwise projection on the surface of a wing, used to modify the distribution of pressure.

fenestron Helicopter tail rotor with many slender blades rotating in short duct.

ferry range Extreme safe range with zero payload.

FFAR Folding-fin (or free-flight) aircraft rocket.

FFVV Fédération Française de Vol à Voile (French gliding authority).

field length Measure of distance needed to land and/or take off; many different measures for particular purposes, each precisely defined.

flaperon Wing trailing-edge surface combining functions of flap and aileron.

flat-four Engine having four horizontally opposed cylinders; thus, flat-twin, flat-six etc.

flat rated Propulsion engine capable of giving full thrust or power for take-off to high airfield height and/or high ambient temperature (thus, probably derated at S/L).

FLIR Forward-looking infra-red.

FLOT Forward line of own troops.

fly by light Flight control system in which signals pass between computers and actuators along fibre optic leads.

fly by wire Flight control system with electrical signalling (ie, without mechanical interconnection between cockpit flying controls and control surfaces).

FM Frequency modulation.

FMCS Flight management computer system.

FMS Foreign military sales (US DoD).

FOL Forward operating location.

footprint (1) A precisely delineated boundary on the surface, inside which the perceived noise of an aircraft exceeds a specified level during take-off and/or landing; (2) Dispersion of weapon or submunition impact points.

Fowler flap Moves initially aft to increase wing area and then also deflects down to increase drag.

free turbine Turbine mechanically independent of engine upstream, other than being connected by rotating bearings and the gas stream, and thus able to run at its own speed.

frequency agile (frequency hopping) Making a transmission harder to detect by switching automatically to a succession of frequencies.

FSD Full scale development.

FSW Forward-swept wing.

FY Fiscal year (1 July to 30 June in US government affairs).

g Acceleration due to mean Earth gravity, ie of a body in free fall; or acceleration due to rapid change of direction of flight path.

gallons Non-SI measure; 1 Imp gallon (UK) = 4.546 litres, 1 US gallon = 3.785 litres.

GCI Ground-controlled interception.

GfK Glassfibre-reinforced plastics (German).

GFRP Glassfibre reinforced plastics.

glide ratio Of a sailplane, distance travelled along track divided by height lost in still air.

glove (1) Fixed portion of wing inboard of variable sweep wing; (2) additional aerofoil profile added around normal wing for test purposes.

GPS Global Positioning System, US military/civil satellite-based precision navaid.

GPU Ground power unit (not part of aircraft).

GPWS Ground-proximity warning system.

green aircraft Aircraft flyable but unpainted, unfurnished and basically equipped.

gross wing area See wing area.

GS Glideslope, of ILS.

GSE Ground support equipment (such as special test gear, steps and servicing platforms).

GTS Gas turbine starter (ie starter is miniature gas turbine).

gunship Helicopter designed for battlefield attack, normally with slim body carrying pilot and weapon operator only.

h Hour(s).

hardened Protected as far as possible against nuclear explosion.

hardpoint Reinforced part of aircraft to which external load can be attached, eg weapon or tank pylon.

helicopter Rotary-wing aircraft both lifted and propelled by one or more power-driven rotors turning about substantially vertical axes.

HF High frequency.

HMD Helmet mounted display.

hot and high Adverse combination of airfield height and high ambient temperature, which lengthens required TOD.

hovering ceiling Ceiling of helicopter (corresponding to air density at which maximum rate of climb is zero), either IGE or OGE.

HP High pressure (HPC, compressor; HPT, turbine).

hp Horsepower.

HSI Horizontal situation indicator.

HUD Head-up display (bright numbers and symbols projected on pilot's windscreen and focused on infinity so that pilot can simultaneously read display and look ahead).

HVAR High-velocity aircraft rocket.

Hz Hertz, cycles per second.

IAS Indicated airspeed, ASIR corrected for instrument error.

IATA International Air Transport Association.

ICAO International Civil Aviation Organisation.

ICNIA Integrated communications, navigation and identification avionics.

IFF Identification friend or foe.

IFR Instrument flight rules (ie, not VFR).

IGE In ground effect: helicopter performance with theoretical flat horizontal surface just below it.

ILS Instrument landing system.

IMC Instrument meteorological conditions, basically IFR.

IMK Increased manoeuvrability kit.

Imperial gallon 1.20095 US gallons; 4.546 litres.

IMS Integrated multiplex system.

INAS Integrated nav/attack system.

incidence Strictly, the angle at which the wing is set in relation to the fore/aft axis. Wrongly used to mean angle of attack (which see).

inertial navigation Measuring all accelerations imparted to a vehicle and, by integrating these with respect to time, calculating speed at every instant (in all three planes) and by integrating a second time calculating total change of position in relation to starting point.

INEWS Integrated electronic warfare system.

INS Inertial navigation system.

integral construction Machined from solid instead of assembled from separate parts.

integral tank Fuel (or other liquid) tank formed by sealing part of structure.

intercom Wired telephone system for communication within aircraft.

inverter Electric or electronic device for inverting (reversing polarity of) alternate waves in AC power to produce DC.

IOC Initial operational capability.

IP Intermediate pressure.

IR Infra-red.

IRAN Inspect and repair as necessary.

IRLS Infra-red linescan (builds TV-type picture showing cool regions as dark and hot regions as light).

IRS Inertial reference system.

IRST Infra-red search and track.

ISA International Standard Atmosphere.

ISIS (1 Boeing Vertol) Integral spar inspection system; (2 Ferranti) integrated strike and interception sight.

ITE Involute throat and exit (rocket nozzle).

IVSI Instantaneous VSI.

J Joules, SI unit of energy.

JAR Joint Airworthiness Requirements, agreed by all major EC countries (JAR.25 equivalent to FAR.25).

JASDF Japan Air Self-Defence Force.

JATO Jet-assisted take-off (actually means rocket-assisted).

JCAB Japan Civil Airworthiness Board.

JDA Japan Defence Agency.

JGSDF Japan Ground Self-Defence Force.

JMSDF Japan Maritime Self-Defence Force.

joined wing Tandem wing layout in which forward and aft wings are swept so that the outer sections meet.

J-STARS US Air Force/Navy Joint Surveillance Target Attack Radar System in Boeing E-8A.

JTIDS Joint Tactical Information Distribution System.

K One thousand bits of memory.

Kevlar Aramid fibre used as basis of high-strength composite material.

km/h Kilometres per hour.

kN Kilonewtons (the Newton is the SI unit of force; 1 lbf = 4.448 N).

knot 1 nm per hour.

Krueger flap Hinges down and then forward from below the leading-edge.

kVA Kilovolt-ampères.

kW Kilowatt, SI measure of all forms of power (not just electrical).

LABS Low-altitude bombing system designed to throw the bomb up and forward (toss bombing).

LANTIRN Low-altitude navigation and targeting infra-red, night.

LARC Low-altitude ride control.

LBA Luftfahrtbundesamt (West German civil aviation authority).

lbf Pounds of thrust.

LCD Liquid crystal display, used for showing instrument information.

LCN Load classification number, measure of 'flotation' of aircraft landing gear linking aircraft weight, weight distribution, tyre numbers, pressures and disposition.

LDNS Laser Doppler navigation system.

LED Light-emitting diode.

LGSC Linear glideslope capture.

Lidar Light detection and ranging (laser counterpart of radar).

LITVC Liquid-injection thrust vector control.

LLTV Low-light TV (thus, LLLTV, low-light-level).

load factor (1) percentage of max payload; (2) stress limit.

LOC Localiser (which see).

localiser Element giving steering guidance in ILS.

loiter Flight for maximum endurance, such as supersonic fighter on patrol.

longerons Principal fore-and-aft structural members (eg in fuselage).

Loran Long range navigation; family of hyperbolic navaids based on ground radio emissions, now mainly Loran C.

LOROP Long-range oblique photography.

low observables Materials and structures designed to reduce aircraft signatures of all kinds.

lox Liquid oxygen.

LP Low pressure (LPC, compressor; LPT, turbine).

LRMTS Laser ranger and marked-target seeker.

LRU Line-replaceable unit.

m Metre(s), SI unit of length.

M or Mach number The ratio of the speed of a body to the speed of sound (1,116 ft; 340 m/sec in air at 15°C) under the same ambient conditions.

MAC (1) US Air Force Military Airlift Command; (2) mean aerodynamic chord.

MAD Magnetic anomaly detector.

Madar Maintenance analysis, detection and recording.

Madge Microwave aircraft digital guidance equipment.

marker, marker beacon Ground beacon giving position guidance in ILS.

mb Millibars, bar $\times$ 10⁻³.

MBR Marker beacon receiver.

MEPU Monofuel emergency power unit.

METO Maximum except take-off.

MF Medium frequency.

MFD Multi function (electronic) display.

mg Milligrammes, grammes $\times$ 10⁻³.

MLS Microwave landing system.

MLW Maximum landing weight.

mm Millimetres, metres $\times$ 10⁻³.

MMH Monomethyl hydrazine.

Mмo Maximum permitted operating Mach number.

MMS Mast mounted sight.

MNPS Minimum navigation performance specification.

monocoque Structure with strength in outer shell, devoid of internal bracing.

MoU Memorandum of understanding.

MPA Man-powered aircraft.

mph Miles per hour.

MRW Maximum ramp weight.

MSIP US armed forces multi-staged improvement programme.

MTBF Mean time between failures.

MTBR Meantime between removals.

MTI Moving-target indication (radar).

MTOGW Maximum take-off gross weight (MRW minus taxi/run-up fuel).

MTTR Mean time to repair.

MZFW Maximum zero-fuel weight.

NACA US National Advisory Committee for Aeronautics (now NASA).

Nadge NATO air defence ground environment.

NAS US Naval Air Station.

NASA National Aeronautics and Space Administration.

NASC US Naval Air Systems Command (also several other aerospace meanings).

NATC US Naval Air Training Command or Test Center (also several other aerospace meanings).

NBAA US National Business Aircraft Association.

NDB Non-directional beacon.

NDT Non-destructive testing.

NGV Nozzle guide vane.

NH₄ClO₄ Ammonium perchlorate.

nm nautical mile, 1.8532 km, 1.15152 miles.

NOAA US National Oceanic and Atmospheric Administration.

NOE Nap-of-the-Earth (low flying in military aircraft, using natural cover of hills, trees etc).

NOGS Night observation gunship.
NOS Night observation surveillance.
Ns Newton-second (1 N thrust applied for 1 second.)
NVG Night vision goggles.

OAT Outside air temperature.
OBOGS On-board oxygen generating system.
OCU Operational Conversion Unit.
OEI One engine inoperative.
offset Workshare granted to a customer nation to offset the cost of an imported system.
OGE Out of ground effect; helicopter hovering, far above nearest surface.
Omega Long-range hyperbolic radio navaid.
OMI Omni-bearing magnetic indicator.
omni Generalised word meaning equal in all directions (as in omni-range, omni-flash beacon).
on condition maintenance According to condition rather than at fixed intervals.
OSTIV Organisation Scientifique et Technique Internationale du Vol à voile (international gliding authority).
OTH Over the horizon.
OTPI On-top position indicator (indicates overhead of submarine in ASW).
OWE Operating weight empty. MTOGW minus payload, usable fuel and oil and other consumables.

PA system Public or passenger address.
pallet (1) for freight, rigid platform for handling by forklift or conveyor; (2) for missile, mounting and electronics box outside aircraft.
payload Disposable load generating revenue (passengers, cargo, mail and other paid items), in military aircraft loosely used to mean total load carried of weapons, cargo or other mission equipment.
PD radar Pulse-Doppler.
penaids Penetration aids, such as jammers, chaff or decoys to help aircraft fly safely through hostile airspace.
PFA Popular Flying Association (UK).
phased array Radar in which the screen is swept electronically in one or both axes without moving the antenna.
PHI Position and heading (or homing) indicator.
plane A lifting surface (eg wing, tailplane).
plug door Door larger than its frame in pressurised fuselage, either opening inwards or arranged to retract parts prior to opening outwards.
plume The region of hot air and gas emitted by a helicopter jetpipe.
pneumatic de-icing Covered with flexible surfaces alternately pumped up and deflated to throw off ice.
port Left side, looking forward.
power loading Aircraft weight (usually MTOGW) divided by total propulsive power or thrust at T-O.
prepreg Glassfibre cloth or rovings pre-impregnated with resin to simplify layup.
pressure fuelling Fuelling via a leakproof connection through which fuel passes at high rate under pressure.
pressure ratio In gas turbine engine, compressor delivery pressure divided by ambient pressure (in supersonic aircraft, divided by ram pressure downstream of inlet).
primary flight controls Those used to control trajectory of aircraft (thus, not trimmers, tabs, flaps, slats, airbrakes or lift dumpers etc).
primary flight display Single screen bearing all data for aircraft flight path control.
propfan A family of new technology propellers characterised by multiple scimitar-shaped blades with thin sharp-edged profile. Single and contra-rotating examples promise to extend propeller efficiency up to about Mach 0.8. See also UDF.
pulse-Doppler Radar sending out pulses and measuring frequency-shift to detect returns only from moving target(s) in background clutter.
pylon Structure linking aircraft to external load (engine nacelle, drop tank, bomb etc). Also used in conventional sense in pylon racing.

radius In terms of performance, the distance an aircraft can fly from base and return without intermediate landing.
RAE Royal Aerospace Establishment.
RAI Registro Aeronautico Italiano.
RAM Radar absorbent material.
ram pressure Increased pressure in forward-facing aircraft inlet, generated by converting (relative) kinetic energy to pressure.
ramp weight Maximum weight at start of flight (MTOGW plus taxi/run-up fuel).
range Too many definitions to list, but essentially the distance an aircraft can fly (or is permitted to fly) with specified load and usually whilst making allowance for specified additional manoeuvres (diversions, stand-off, go-around etc).
RANSAC Range surveillance aircraft.
RAS Rectified airspeed, IAS corrected for position error.
raster Generation of large-area display, eg TV screen, by close-spaced horizontal lines scanned either alternately or in sequence.

RAT Ram air turbine.
redundant Provided with spare capacity or data channels and thus made to survive failures.
refanned Gas turbine engine fitted with new fan of higher BPR.
RFP Request(s) for proposals.
rigid rotor (see bearingless rotor).
RLD Rijksluchtvaartdienst. Netherlands civil aviation department.
RMI Radio magnetic indicator; combines compass and navaid bearings.
R/Nav Calculates position, distance and time from groups of airways beacons.
rotor-kite Rotary-wing aircraft with no internal power, lifted by a freely running autorotating rotor and towed by an external vehicle.
roving Multiple strands of fibre, as in a rope (but usually not twisted).
RPV Remotely piloted vehicle (pilot in other aircraft or on ground).
RSA Réseau du Sport de l'Air.
ruddervators Flying control surfaces, usually a V tail, that control both yaw and pitch attitude.
RVR Runway visual range.

s Second(s)
SAC US Air Force Strategic Air Command.
safe-life A term denoting that a component has proved by testing that it can be expected to continue to function safely for a precisely defined period before replacement.
salmon (French saumon) Streamlined fairings, usually at wingtip of sailplane, serving same function as endplate and acting also as tip-skid.
SAR (1) Search and rescue; (2) synthetic aperture radar.
SAS Stability augmentation system.
SATS (1) Small airfield for tactical support; (2) Small Arms Target System.
saw-tooth Same as dog-tooth.
SCAS Stability and control augmentation system.
second-source Production of identical item by second factory or company.
semi-active Homing on to radiation reflected from target illuminated by radar or laser energy beamed from elsewhere.
service ceiling Usually height equivalent to air density at which maximum attainable rate of climb is 100ft/min.
servo A device which acts as a relay, usually augmenting the pilot's efforts to move a control surface or the like.
SFAR Special Federal Aviation Regulation(s).
sfc Specific fuel consumption.
SGAC Secrétariat Général à l'Aviation Civile (now DGAC).
shaft Connection between gas turbine and compressor or other driven unit. Two-shaft engine has second shaft, rotating at different speed, surrounding the first (thus, HP surrounds inner LP or fan shaft).
Shoran Short range navigation (radio).
shp Shaft horsepower, measure of power transmitted via rotating shaft.
sideline noise EPNdB measure of aircraft landing and taking off, at point 0.25 nm (2- or 3-engined) or 0.35 nm (4-engined) from runway centreline.
sidestick Control column in the form of a short hand-grip beside the pilot.
SIF Selective identification facility.
sigint Signals intelligence.
signature Characteristic 'fingerprint' of all electro-magnetic radiation (radar, IR etc).
single-shaft Gas turbine in which all compressors and turbines are on common shaft rotating together.
S/L Sea level.
SLAR Side-looking airborne radar.
snap-down Air-to-air interception of low-flying aircraft by AAM fired from fighter at a higher altitude.
soft target Not armoured or hardened.
specific fuel consumption Rate at which fuel is consumed divided by power or thrust developed, and thus a measure of engine efficiency. For jet engines (air-breathing, ie not rockets) unit is mg/Ns, milligrams per Newton-second; for shaft engines unit is μg/J, micrograms (millionths of a gram) per Joule (SI unit of work or energy).
specific impulse Measure of rocket engine efficiency; thrust divided by rate of fuel/oxidant consumption per second, the units for mass and force being the same so that the answer is expressed in seconds.
SPILS Stall protection and incidence-limiting system.
spool One complete axial compressor rotor; thus a two-shaft engine may have a fan plus an LP spool.
SSB Single-sideband (radio).
SSR Secondary surveillance radar.
SST Supersonic transport.
st Static thrust.
stabiliser Fin (thus, horizontal stabiliser = tailplane).
stall strips Sharp-edged strips on wing leading-edge to induce stall at that point.
stalling speed Airspeed at which aircraft stalls at 1g, ie wing lift suddenly collapses.
standard day ISA temperature and pressure.
starboard Right side, looking forward.

static inverter Solid-state inverter of alternating waveform (ie, not rotary machine) to produce DC from AC.
stick-pusher Stall-protection device that forces pilot's control column forward as stalling angle of attack is neared.
stick-shaker Stall-warning device that noisily shakes pilot's control column as stalling angle of attack is neared.
STOL Short take-off and landing. (Several definitions, stipulating allowable horizontal distance to clear screen height of 35 or 50 ft or various SI measures).
store Object carried as part of payload on external attachment (eg bomb, drop tank).
strobe light High-intensity flashing beacon.
substrate The underlying layer on which something (such as a solar cell or integrated circuit) is built up.
supercritical wing Wing of relatively deep, flat-topped profile generating lift right across upper surface instead of concentrated close behind leading edge.
sweepback Backwards inclination of wing or other aerofoil, seen from above, measured relative to fuselage or other reference axis, usually measured at quarter-chord (25%) or at leading-edge.
synchronous satellite Geostationary.

t Tonne, 1 Megagram, 1,000 kg.
tabbed flap Fitted with narrow-chord tab along entire trailing-edge which deflects to greater angle than main surface.
tabs Small auxiliary surfaces hinged to trailing-edge of control surfaces for purposes of trimming, reducing hinge moment (force needed to operate main surface) or in other way assisting pilot.
TAC US Air Force Tactical Air Command.
Tacan Tactical air navigation UHF military navaid giving bearing and distance to spaced beacons.
taileron Left and right tailplanes used as primary control surfaces in both pitch and roll.
tailplane Main horizontal tail surface, originally fixed and carrying hinged elevator(s) but today often a single 'slab' serving as control surface.
TANS Tactical air navigation system; Decca Navigator or Doppler-based computer, control and display unit.
TAS True airspeed, EAS corrected for density (often very large factor) appropriate to aircraft height.
TBO Time between overhauls.
t/c ratio Ratio of the thickness (aerodynamic depth) of a wing or other surface to its chord, both measured at the same place parallel to the fore-and-aft axis.
TET Turbine entry temperature (of the gas); also turbine inlet temperature (TIT), inter-turbine temperature (ITT) and turbine gas temperature (TGT).
TFR Terrain-following radar (for low-level attack).
thickness Depth of wing or other aerofoil; maximum perpendicular distance between upper and lower surfaces.
tilt-rotor Aircraft with fixed wing and rotors that tilt up for hovering and forward for fast flight.
T-O Take-off.
T-O noise EPNdB measure of aircraft taking off, at point directly under flight path 3.5 nm from brakes-release (regardless of elevation).
TOD Take-off distance.
TOGW Take-off gross weight (not necessarily MTOGW).
ton Imperial (long) ton = 1.016t(Mg) or 2,240 lb, US (short) ton = 0.9072 t or 2,000 lb.
track Distance between centres of contact areas of main landing wheels measured left/right across aircraft (with bogies, distance between centres of contact areas of each bogie).
transceiver Radio transmitter/receiver.
transponder Radio transmitter triggered automatically by a particular received signal as in civil secondary surveillance radar (SSR).
TRU Transformer/rectifier unit.
TSFC Thrust specific fuel consumption of jet engine (turbojet, turbofan, ducted propfan or ramjet).
TSO Technical Standard Order (FAA).
turbofan Gas-turbine jet engine generating most thrust by a large-diameter cowled fan, with small part added by jet from core.
turbojet Simplest form of gas turbine comprising compressor, combustion chamber, turbine and propulsive nozzle.
turboprop Gas turbine in which as much energy as possible is taken from gas jet and used to drive reduction gearbox and propeller.
turboshaft Gas turbine in which as much energy as possible is taken from gas jet and used to drive high-speed shaft (which in turn drives external load such as helicopter gearbox).
TVC Thrust vector control (rocket).
TWT Travelling-wave tube.
tyre sizes In simplest form, first figure is rim diameter (in or mm) and second is rim width (in or mm). In more correct three-unit form, first figure is outside diameter, second is max width and third is wheel diameter.

UAV Unmanned air vehicle.
UBE, Ubee Ultra bypass engine, alternative terminology (Boeing) for UDF.

UDF Unducted fan, one form of advanced propulsion system in which gas turbine blading directly drives large fan (propfan) blades mounted around the outside of the engine pod. (GE registered abbreviation).

UHF Ultra-high frequency.

unfactored Performance level expected of average pilot, in average aircraft, without additional safety factors.

upper surface blowing Turbofan exhaust vented over upper surface of wing to increase lift.

usable fuel Total mass of fuel consumable in flight, usually 95-98 per cent of system capacity.

useful load Usable fuel plus payload.

US gallon 0.83267 Imperial gallon; 3.785 litres.

variable geometry Capable of grossly changing shape in flight, especially by varying sweep of wings.

V$_D$ Maximum permitted diving speed.

VDU Video (or visual) display unit.

vernier Small thruster, usually a rocket, for final precise adjustment of a vehicle's trajectory and velocity.

VFR Visual flight rules.

VHF Very high frequency.

VLF Very low frequency (area-coverage navaid).

V$_{MO}$ Maximum permitted operating flight speed (IAS, EAS or CAS must be specified).

V$_{NE}$ Never-exceed speed (aerodynamic or structural limit).

VOR VHF omni-directional range (VHF radio beacons providing bearing to or from beacon).

vortex generators Small blades attached to wing and tail surfaces to energise local airflow and improve control.

VSI Vertical speed (climb/descent) indicator.

VTOL Vertical take-off and landing.

washout Inbuilt wing twist reducing angle of incidence towards the tip.

wheelbase Minimum distance from nosewheel or tailwheel (centre of contact area) to line joining mainwheels (centres of contact areas).

wing area Total projected area of clean wing (no flaps, slats etc) including all control surfaces and area of fuselage bounded by leading- and trailing-edges projected to centreline (inapplicable to slender-delta aircraft with extremely large leading-edge sweep angle). Described in *Jane's* as gross wing area; net area excludes projected areas of fuselage, nacelles, etc.

wing loading Aircraft weight (usually MTOGW) divided by wing area.

winglet Small auxiliary aerofoil, usually sharply up-turned and often sweptback, at tip of wing.

wire guidance Guidance of missile on UAV by signals transmitted through fine wire(s) linking it with operator.

zero-fuel weight MTOGW minus usable fuel and other consumables, in most aircraft imposing severest stress on wing.

zero/zero seat Ejection seat designed for use even at zero speed on ground.

ZFW Zero-fuel weight.

µg Microgrammes, grammes × 10^6.

AIRCRAFT

ARGENTINA

AERO BOERO
AERO BOERO SA
Brasil y Alem, 2421 Morteros, Córdoba
Telephone: 54 (562) 2121 and 2690
PRESIDENT: Hector A. Boero
OTHER WORKS: Av 9 de Julio 1101, 2400 San Francisco,
Córdoba
Telephone: 54 (562) 22972 and 24118

Aero Boero has so far produced more than 300 aircraft of various models, including 40 for export to Brazil. A total of 450 AB 115 civil trainers and over 70 AB 180 RVRs have been ordered, and in 1989 an agreement was signed with Indaer-Peru (which see) for the manufacture of both types in that country.

AERO BOERO 115 TRAINER
The original AB 115 was developed from the AB 95 (1969-70 *Jane's*). Thirty had been built by January 1983, including examples of the AB 115 BS ambulance version and the 112 kW (150 hp) AB 115/150, descriptions of which can be found in the 1983-84 edition.

An order for 100 AB 115 Trainers was received from the Brazilian government in 1988, followed by an order for 350 more in the Summer of 1989. Deliveries are due to be completed in mid-1993.

TYPE: Two/three-seat light aircraft.
AIRFRAME: As described for AB 180, but with Dacron fabric covering and no rudder tab.
POWER PLANT: One 86 kW (115 hp) Textron Lycoming O-235-C2A flat-four engine, driving a Sensenich 72-CK-0-50 two-blade fixed-pitch propeller with spinner. Two aluminium fuel tanks in wings, combined capacity 128 litres (33.9 US gallons; 28.2 Imp gallons). Gravity refuelling point in top of each tank.
ACCOMMODATION: Pilot and one or two passengers in fully enclosed, heated and ventilated cabin.
ELECTRICAL SYSTEM: 40A alternator and 12V battery.
AVIONICS AND EQUIPMENT: Com/nav equipment, blind-flying instrumentation and landing lights optional.
DIMENSIONS, EXTERNAL, AND AREAS: As for AB 180 (which see), plus:
Propeller diameter   1.93 m (6 ft 4 in)
WEIGHTS AND LOADINGS:
Weight empty   556 kg (1,226 lb)
Max T-O weight   802 kg (1,768 lb)
Max wing loading   45.7 kg/m² (9.36 lb/sq ft)
Max power loading   9.33 kg/kW (15.37 lb/hp)
PERFORMANCE (at max T-O weight):
Never-exceed speed   118 knots (220 km/h; 136 mph)
Max cruising speed   91 knots (169 km/h; 105 mph)
Stalling speed, power off:
flaps up   41 knots (75 km/h; 47 mph)
flaps down   35 knots (64 km/h; 40 mph)
Max rate of climb at S/L   204 m (669 ft)/min
T-O run   100 m (330 ft)
T-O to, and landing from, 15 m (50 ft)   250 m (820 ft)
Landing run   80 m (265 ft)
Range with max fuel   664 nm (1,230 km; 765 miles)

Aero Boero 180 RVR glider towing aircraft

Aero Boero 115 Trainer two/three-seat training and touring aircraft *(Kenneth Munson)*

AERO BOERO 180 RVR
The Aero Boero 180 is a higher-powered variant of the AB 150 (see 1983-84 *Jane's*). It has been built in four versions, of which the 180 RV, 180 Ag and 180 SP have been described in earlier editions. Production is continuing of the glider towing AB 180 RVR, for customers in Brazil (seven ordered in 1987, followed by 70 more in 1989, for delivery by mid-1993) and Argentina. This version has a cabin rear window and a towing hook.
TYPE: Single/three-seat light aircraft.
WINGS: Strut braced high-wing monoplane. Streamline section V bracing strut each side. Wing section NACA 23012 (modified). Dihedral 1° 45'. Incidence 3° at root, 1° at tip. Light alloy structure, including skins. Aluminium alloy flaps and ailerons. No tabs.
FUSELAGE: Welded steel tube structure (SAE 4130), covered with Ceconite.
TAIL UNIT: Wire braced welded steel tube structure, covered with Ceconite. Sweptback fin and rudder; non-swept fixed incidence tailplane with elevators. Ground adjustable tab on rudder; trim tab in port elevator.
LANDING GEAR: Non-retractable tailwheel type, with shock absorption by helicoidal springs inside fuselage. Mainwheels carried on faired-in V struts and half-axles. Mainwheels and tyres size 6.00-6; tailwheel tyre size 2.80-2.50. Hydraulic disc brakes on main units; tailwheel steerable and fully castoring.

POWER PLANT: One 134 kW (180 hp) Textron Lycoming O-360-A1A flat-four engine, driving a Sensenich 76-EM8 fixed-pitch or Hartzell HC-92ZK-8D constant-speed two-blade propeller with spinner. Fuel capacity (two aluminium wing tanks) 200 litres (53 US gallons; 44 Imp gallons); oil capacity 8 litres (2.1 US gallons; 1.75 Imp gallons).
ACCOMMODATION: Pilot and two passengers in fully enclosed, heated and ventilated cabin. Cockpit rear window.
DIMENSIONS, EXTERNAL:
Wing span   10.90 m (35 ft 9 in)
Wing chord, constant   1.61 m (5 ft 3½ in)
Wing aspect ratio   6.8
Length overall   7.08 m (23 ft 2¾ in)
Height overall   2.10 m (6 ft 10½ in)
Wheel track   2.05 m (6 ft 8¾ in)
Wheelbase   5.10 m (16 ft 8¾ in)
AREAS:
Wings, gross   17.55 m² (188.9 sq ft)
Ailerons (total)   1.84 m² (19.81 sq ft)
Trailing-edge flaps (total) 1.94 m² (20.88 sq ft)
Fin   0.93 m² (10.01 sq ft)
Rudder   0.41 m² (4.41 sq ft)
Tailplane   1.40 m² (15.07 sq ft)
Elevators (total, incl tab) 0.97 m² (10.44 sq ft)
WEIGHTS AND LOADINGS:
Weight empty   602 kg (1,327 lb)
Max T-O weight   890 kg (1,962 lb)
Max wing loading   50.7 kg/m² (10.38 lb/sq ft)
Max power loading   6.64 kg/kW (10.90 lb/hp)
PERFORMANCE (at max T-O weight except where indicated):
Never-exceed speed   132 knots (245 km/h; 152 mph)
Max level speed at S/L   122 knots (225 km/h; 140 mph)
Max cruising speed at S/L
                      108 knots (201 km/h; 125 mph)
Stalling speed, flaps down   40 knots (73 km/h; 45 mph)
Max rate of climb at S/L   312 m (1,025 ft)/min
Rate of climb: with single-seat sailplane
                        more than 180 m (590 ft)/min
with two-seat sailplane   120 m (394 ft)/min
Time to 600 m (1,970 ft), 75% power, with Blanik
two-seat sailplane   3 min 10 s
Service ceiling   more than 7,000 m (22,965 ft)
T-O run   100 m (330 ft)
T-O to 15 m (50 ft), two persons   188 m (615 ft)
Landing from 15 m (50 ft)   160 m (525 ft)
Landing run   60 m (195 ft)
Range with max fuel   636 nm (1,180 km; 733 miles)

CHINCUL
CHINCUL S.A.C.A.I.F.I.
25 de Mayo 489, 6° Piso, 1339 Buenos Aires
Telephone: 54 (1) 312 5671/5
Telex: 22706 MACUB AR
Fax: 54 (1) 111 1828
WORKS: Calle Mendoza entre 6 y 7, 5400 San Juan, Pcia de San Juan; and at Avenida Diaz Velez 1034, 1702 Ciudadela, Buenos Aires
PRESIDENT: José Maria Beraza
SALES DIRECTOR: Juan Pablo Beraza
EXPORT MANAGER: Oscar A. Prieto

This company, a wholly owned subsidiary of La Macarena SA, Piper's Argentine distributor, was formed in 1972 to assemble a range of Piper aircraft in Argentina with a gradually increasing degree of local manufacture. Some Chincul products have incorporated more than 60 per cent local manufacture. The factory at San Juan has a covered area of 16,500 m² (177,600 sq ft) and a workforce of about 300 people, and had delivered approximately 900 aircraft by January 1990. The Ciudadela plant produces jigs, dies and aircraft parts for production and as spares. All Piper kits delivered to Chincul have for several years been for Phase 3 completion, involving the assembly and riveting of wings

and control surfaces, manufacture of interiors, electrical harness, and other systems installation. Items of Argentine manufacture include batteries, upholstery, fabrics, tyres, engine instruments, fire extinguishers, and glassfibre components. Chincul also assembles a range of Bendix/King avionics for its Piper product line.

Under an agreement signed on 17 May 1989, Chincul and Embraer of Brazil rationalised their licence production and marketing of Piper aircraft and the EMB-201A Ipanema agricultural aircraft to avoid duplication of types. Following this agreement, Chincul no longer produces the Saratoga or Seneca III.

Piper-designed aircraft currently produced by Chincul are the PA-18-115 and PA-18-150 Super Cub, PA-25-235 and PA-25-260 Pawnee, PA-28-161 Warrior II, PA-28-181 Archer II, PA-28-236 Dakota, PA-28RT-201 Arrow IV, PA-28RT-201T Turbo Arrow IV, PA-31-350 Navajo Chieftain, PA-31T Cheyenne I and II, PA-36-375 Pawnee Brave, and PA-42 Cheyenne III and 400. The company has developed its own tandem two-seat conversion of the Pawnee D agricultural aircraft, and a two-seat aerobatic military trainer based on the Cherokee Arrow, as described in the 1983-84 and earlier editions of *Jane's*.

Chincul built example of the Piper PA-25-235/-260 Pawnee

ENET 1
ESCUELA NACIONAL DE EDUCACIÓN TECNICA No. 1
Fuerza Aérea Argentina, Aerodromo Militar, 1684 El Palomar, Buenos Aires

The ENETs are a series of aeronautical technical schools, administered by the Argentine Air Force. Students at ENET No. 1, after building a Pazmany PL-4A very quickly in 1986, followed this in 1987 by completing a two-seat PL-2 in about eight months. In 1988 they began preparing for type certification and series production of a modernised version of the PL-2 known as the **PL-3 Guri**. A description of this aircraft appeared in the Addenda to the 1989-90 *Jane's*, but by the beginning of 1990 the project had been suspended due to Argentina's prevailing economic situation.

FMA
FÁBRICA MILITAR DE AVIONES
Avenida Fuerza Aérea Argentina Km 5½, 5103 Guarnición Aérea Córdoba
Telephone: 54 (51) 690364
Telex: 51965 AMCOR AR
Fax: 54 (51) 111 1774
MANAGING DIRECTOR:
Brigadier Alberto H. Lindow
COMMERCIAL DEPARTMENT: Eng Enrique Corti

The original Fábrica Militar de Aviones (Military Aircraft Factory) came into operation on 10 October 1927 as a central organisation for aeronautical research and production in Argentina. After several changes of name (see 1987-88 and earlier *Jane's*), it reverted to its original title in 1968 as a component of the Area de Material Córdoba (AMC) division of the Argentine Air Force. FMA is currently owned 46 per cent by the Argentine Air Force, 22 per cent each by Aeritalia and Agusta (see Italian section) and 10 per cent by the national industrial company Techint.

FMA comprises two large divisions. The Instituto de Investigaciónes Aeronáuticas y Espacial (IIAE) is responsible for the design of aircraft, and the design, manufacture and testing of rockets, sounding equipment and other equipment. FMA itself controls the aircraft manufacturing facilities (Grupo Fabricación) situated in Córdoba, as well as the Centro de Ensayos en Vuelo (Flight Test Centre), to which all aircraft produced in Argentina are sent for certification tests. The laboratories, factories and other aeronautical division buildings occupy a total covered area of approx 253,000 m² (2,723,265 sq ft); the Area de Material Córdoba employs more than 3,500 persons, of whom about 2,000 are in the Grupo Fabricación.

Major current product is the nationally designed IA 63 Pampa basic and advanced jet trainer. Upgrading of the IA 58 Pucará close support aircraft continues. The development of the airframe of the Agusta A 129 Utility and its marketing in Latin America has been assigned to a consortium of TEA, Techint and Agusta. Some 200 are expected to be sold in 15 years.

CBA-123
This twin-turboprop regional transport aircraft is described under the Embraer/FAMA heading in the International section.

FMA IA 58A PUCARÁ
Four versions of this twin-turboprop light attack aircraft were built, of which the IA 58B and IA 66 did not go beyond the prototype stage and the single-seat IA 58C (1989-90 and earlier *Jane's*) has been suspended. Major version was the two-seat IA 58A. A total of 108 was ordered for the Fuerza Aérea Argentina (FAA). Deliveries began in the Spring of 1976, and the last example was completed in 1986. Some early production aircraft were converted to single-seat configuration, with an extra fuselage fuel tank in place of the rear seat; none of these is currently operational, and no further conversions are planned. Six IA 58As were delivered to the Fuerza Aérea Uruguaya, and a further 40 were made available for export in 1986. No details of further sales have been received, but five Pucarás were loaned to the Colombian government in late 1989 for anti-drug traffic operations.

The IA 58A currently equips the III Brigada Aérea, 3rd Attack Group, of the FAA at Reconquista, Santa Fe; others serve with the IX Brigada's 9th Transport Group at

Standard two-seat IA 58A Pucarás of the Argentine Air Force

Comodoro Rivadavia in Chubut Province. Aircraft still in service are currently receiving a new, autonomous navigation and weapon delivery system known as SINT (Sistema Integrado de Navegación y de Tiro), developed by the FAA at its Rio Cuarto base.

A full description of the IA 58A in its final production form can be found in the 1987-88 edition. The following is a shortened version of that description:

TYPE: Twin-turboprop close support, reconnaissance and counter-insurgency aircraft.

AIRFRAME: See 1987-88 *Jane's*.

POWER PLANT: Two 729 kW (978 shp) Turbomeca Astazou XVIG turboprops, each driving a Ratier-Forest 23LF-379 three-blade variable-pitch fully-feathering metal propeller with spinner. Fuel in two AMC (Area de Material Córdoba) fuselage tanks (combined capacity 772 litres; 204 US gallons; 170 Imp gallons) and one AMC self-sealing tank in each wing (combined capacity 508 litres; 134 US gallons; 111 Imp gallons). Overall usable internal capacity 1,280 litres (338 US gallons; 281 Imp gallons). Gravity refuelling point for all tanks on top of fuselage aft of cockpit. Fuel system includes two accumulator tanks, permitting up to 30 s of inverted flight. A long-range auxiliary tank, usable capacity 318 or 1,100 litres (84 or 290 US gallons; 70 or 242 Imp gallons) can be attached to the fuselage centreline pylon, and a 318 litre (84 US gallon; 70 Imp gallon) auxiliary tank on each underwing pylon. Possible external fuel loads are therefore 318, 636, 954, 1,100 or 1,736 litres (84, 168, 252, 290 or 458 US gallons; 70, 140, 210, 242 or 382 Imp gallons); max internal and external usable fuel capacity is 3,016 litres (796 US gallons; 663 Imp gallons).

ACCOMMODATION: Pilot and co-pilot in tandem on Martin-Baker AP06A zero/zero ejection seats beneath single AMC moulded Plexiglas canopy which is hinged at rear and opens upward. Rear (co-pilot) seat elevated 25 cm (10 in) above front seat. Rearview mirror for each crew member. Teleflex heated and bulletproof windscreen, with wiper. Armour plating in cockpit floor, resistant to 7.62 mm ground fire from 150 m (500 ft). Dual controls and blind-flying instrumentation standard. Cockpits heated and ventilated by mixture of engine bleed and external air.

SYSTEMS, AVIONICS AND EQUIPMENT: As detailed in 1987-88 *Jane's*.

ARMAMENT: Two 20 mm Hispano DCA-804 cannon, each with 270 rds, in underside of forward fuselage; and four 7.62 mm FN-Browning M2-30 machine-guns, each with 900 rds, in sides of fuselage abreast of cockpit. Alkan 115E ejector pylon on centreline beneath fuselage, capacity 1,000 kg (2,205 lb); Alkan 105E pylon, capacity 500 kg (1,102 lb), beneath each wing outboard of engine nacelle. Max external stores load with full internal fuel is 1,500 kg (3,307 lb), including gun and rocket pods, bombs, cluster bombs, incendiaries, mines, torpedoes, air-to-surface missiles, camera pod(s), a Bigua 2 reconnaissance RPV or auxiliary fuel tank(s). Max external weapons load when carrying drop tanks on the fuselage or wing stations is 1,000 kg (2,205 lb). Typical loads can include twelve 125 kg bombs; seven launchers each with nineteen 2.75 in rockets; a 12.7, 20 or 30 mm gun pod and two 318 litre drop tanks; six 125 kg bombs and sixteen 5 in rockets; six launchers each with forty 74 mm cartridges, plus onboard ECM; twelve 250 lb napalm bombs; three 500 kg delayed action bombs; or two twin-7.62 mm machine-gun pods, plus three launchers each containing nineteen 2.75 in rockets. SFOM 83A3 reflector sight permits weapon release at any desired firing angle; optional Bendix AWE-1 programmer allows release in step or ripple modes of single weapons, pairs or salvos.

DIMENSIONS, EXTERNAL:

Wing span	14.50 m (47 ft 6⅞ in)
Length overall	14.253 m (46 ft 9⅛ in)
Height overall	5.362 m (17 ft 7⅛ in)
Wheel track (c/l of shock absorbers)	
	4.20 m (13 ft 9¼ in)
Wheelbase	3.885 m (12 ft 9 in)

AREA:

Wings, gross	30.30 m² (326.1 sq ft)

WEIGHTS AND LOADINGS:

Weight empty, equipped	4,020 kg (8,862 lb)
Max fuel load: internal	1,000 kg (2,205 lb)
external	1,359 kg (2,997 lb)
Max external stores load with full internal fuel	
	1,500 kg (3,307 lb)
Max T-O weight	6,800 kg (14,991 lb)

Max zero-fuel weight	4,546 kg (10,022 lb)
Max landing weight	5,600 kg (12,345 lb)
Max wing loading	224.4 kg/m² (45.97 lb/sq ft)
Max power loading	4.66 kg/kW (7.66 lb/shp)

PERFORMANCE (at AUW of 5,500 kg; 12,125 lb except where indicated):

Max critical Mach number at max T-O weight	0.77
Never-exceed speed at max T-O weight	
	Mach 0.63 (405 knots; 750 km/h; 466 mph)
Max level speed at 3,000 m (9,840 ft)	
	270 knots (500 km/h; 310 mph)
Max cruising speed at 6,000 m (19,680 ft)	
	259 knots (480 km/h; 298 mph)
Econ cruising speed	232 knots (430 km/h; 267 mph)
Stalling speed, flaps and landing gear down, AUW of	
4,790 kg (10,560 lb)	78 knots (143 km/h; 89 mph)
Max rate of climb at S/L	1,080 m (3,543 ft)/min
Service ceiling	10,000 m (32,800 ft)
Service ceiling, one engine out	6,000 m (19,680 ft)
T-O run	300 m (985 ft)
T-O to 15 m (50 ft)	705 m (2,313 ft)
Landing from 15 m (50 ft), landing weight of 5,100 kg	
(11,243 lb)	603 m (1,978 ft)
Landing run, landing weight as above	200 m (656 ft)

Attack radius at T-O weight of 6,500 kg (14,330 lb), 10% reserves of initial fuel:

with 1,500 kg (3,307 lb) of external weapons:	
lo-lo-lo	121 nm (225 km; 140 miles)
lo-lo-hi	175 nm (325 km; 202 miles)
hi-lo-hi	189 nm (350 km; 217 miles)
with 1,200 kg (2,645 lb) of external weapons:	
lo-lo-lo	216 nm (400 km; 248 miles)
lo-lo-hi	310 nm (575 km; 357 miles)
hi-lo-hi	350 nm (650 km; 404 miles)
with 800 kg (1,764 lb) of ordnance and 450 litres (119	
US gallons; 99 Imp gallons) of external fuel:	
lo-lo-lo	310 nm (575 km; 357 miles)
lo-lo-hi	445 nm (825 km; 512 miles)
hi-lo-hi	526 nm (975 km; 606 miles)
Ferry range at 5,485 m (18,000 ft) with max internal and	
external fuel	2,002 nm (3,710 km; 2,305 miles)
g limits	+6/−3

FMA IA 63 PAMPA

The Fuerza Aérea Argentina (FAA) initiated the IA 63 programme in 1979, and the eventual configuration, powered by a single Garrett TFE731 turbofan, was selected from seven possible designs in early 1980. Dornier GmbH of West Germany provided technical assistance during development, including manufacture of the wings and tailplanes for the prototypes and ground test airframes, and is continuing to assist in developing additional versions.

Two IA 63 airframes were allocated for static and fatigue testing. The first of three flying prototypes (EX-01) flew on 6 October 1984, and the first production aircraft was completed in October 1987. A version for the Argentine Navy is under development, as is a new autonomous navigation/weapon aiming system.

Firm orders have been placed for 100 Pampas, of which the first three were delivered to the IV Brigada Aérea at Mendoza in April 1988. Twelve were in service with this Brigada's Escuadrón 2 at El Plumerillo Air Base by the end of 1989, at which time the Pampa production rate was one per month. Two prototypes were reported in early 1990 to have been upgraded to ground attack configuration, with a HUD and other new avionics, prior to this becoming a standard installation for existing and future production Pampas.

The following description applies to the production trainer version, except where indicated:

TYPE: Single-engined basic and advanced jet trainer.

AIRFRAME: Incorporates integrated structures for high-load components such as wing spar box and main frames;

IA 63 Pampa tandem-seat jet trainer in Argentine Air Force camouflage

numerically controlled, mechanically and chemically milled components; and the use of fibre composites.

WINGS: Cantilever shoulder-wing monoplane. Non-swept tapered wings are of Dornier DoA-7 advanced transonic section, with thickness/chord ratios of 14.5 per cent at root, 12.5 per cent at tip. Dihedral 3°. Two-spar wing box forms integral fuel tank. Hydraulically actuated two-segment single-slotted Fowler trailing-edge flaps inboard of ailerons. Redundant primary controls, actuated hydraulically with assistance by Liebherr servo actuators. Stick forces simulated by artificial feel. Three-axis trim is operated electro-mechanically.

FUSELAGE: Conventional semi-monocoque structure. Hydraulically actuated door type airbrake on each side of upper rear fuselage.

TAIL UNIT: Sweptback fin and rudder; non-swept all-moving anhedral tailplane. Control surface actuation as for ailerons.

LANDING GEAR: SHL (Israel) retractable tricycle type, with hydraulic extension/retraction and emergency free-fall extension. Oleo-pneumatic shock absorbers. Single wheel and low-pressure tyre on each unit. Tyre sizes 6.50-10 (10 ply rating) on mainwheels, 380 × 150 mm (4-6 ply rating) on nosewheel. Nosewheel retracts rearward, mainwheels inward into underside of engine air intake trunks. Braking system incorporates an anti-skid device; nosewheel steering is optional. Gear designed for operation from unprepared surfaces.

POWER PLANT: One 15.57 kN (3,500 lb st) Garrett TFE731-2-2N turbofan installed in rear fuselage, with twin lateral air intakes. Standard internal fuel capacity of 968 litres (255 US gallons; 213 Imp gallons) in integral wing tank of 550 litres (145 US gallons; 121 Imp gallons) and 418 litre (110 US gallon; 92 Imp gallon) flexible fuselage tank with a negative g chamber. Additional 415 litres (109 US gallons; 91 Imp gallons) can be carried in auxiliary tanks inside outer wing panels, to give a max internal capacity of 1,383 litres (364 US gallons; 304 Imp gallons). Single-point pressure refuelling, plus gravity point in upper surface of each wing. Engine air intakes anti-iced by engine bleed air.

ACCOMMODATION: Instructor and pupil in tandem (instructor at rear, on elevated seat), on UPC (Stencel) S-III-S3IA63 zero/zero ejection seats. Ejection procedure can be pre-selected for separate single ejections, or for both seats to be fired from front or rear cockpit. Dual controls standard. One-piece wraparound windscreen. One-piece canopy, with internal screen, is hinged at rear and opens upward. Entire accommodation pressurised and air-conditioned.

SYSTEMS: AiResearch air-conditioning system, supplied by high or low pressure engine bleed air, also provides ram air for negative g system and canopy seal. Oxygen system supplied by lox converter. Two independent hydraulic systems, each at pressure of 207 bars (3,000 lb/sq in), supplied by engine driven pumps. Each system incorporates a bootstrap reservoir pressurised at 4 bars (58 lb/sq in). No. 1 system, with flow rate of 16 litres (4.2 US gallons; 3.5 Imp gallons)/min, actuates primary flight controls, airbrakes, landing gear and wheel brakes; No. 2 system, with flow rate of 8 litres (2.1 US gallons; 1.75 Imp gallons)/min, actuates primary flight controls, wing flaps, emergency and parking brakes, and (if fitted) nosewheel steering. A ram air turbine provides emergency hydraulic power for No. 2 system if pressure in this system drops below minimum. Electrical system (28V DC) supplied by 11.5kW engine driven starter/generator; secondary supply (115/26V AC power at 400Hz) from two 450VA static inverters and two 27Ah nickel-cadmium batteries.

AVIONICS: Standard avionics package comprises two redundant VHF com transceivers, intercom system, VOR/ILS with marker beacon receiver, DME, and ADF radio compass. Navigation system allows complete navigation/ landing training under IFR conditions. Attitude and heading information provided by a three-gyro platform, with magnetic flux valve compass for additional heading reference.

ARMAMENT: No built-in weapons. Five attachments for external stores, with max pylon load of 400 kg (882 lb) on each inboard underwing station, 250 kg (551 lb) each on fuselage centreline and outboard underwing pair. With a 30 mm gun pod containing 145 rds on the fuselage station, typical underwing loads can include six Mk 81 bombs, two each Mk 81 and Mk 82 bombs, or one 7.62 mm twin-gun pod and one practice bomb/rocket training container. Gyro-stabilised sighting system in front cockpit (optional in rear cockpit), with recorder in front sight. Weapon management system adequate for several different tactical configurations.

DIMENSIONS, EXTERNAL:

Wing span	9.686 m (31 ft 9¼ in)
Wing aspect ratio	6.0
Length overall (excl pitot probe)	10.90 m (35 ft 9¼ in)
Height overall	4.29 m (14 ft 1 in)
Tailplane span	4.58 m (15 ft 0⅓ in)
Wheel track	2.66 m (8 ft 8¾ in)
Wheelbase	4.42 m (14 ft 6 in)

AREAS:

Wings, gross reference	15.63 m² (168.2 sq ft)
Vertical tail surfaces (total)	2.52 m² (27.13 sq ft)
Horizontal tail surfaces (total)	4.35 m² (46.82 sq ft)

WEIGHTS AND LOADINGS:

Weight empty	2,821 kg (6,219 lb)
Fuel load:	
wings (incl auxiliary tanks)	780 kg (1,719 lb)
fuselage	338 kg (745 lb)
Max underwing load with normal internal fuel	
	1,160 kg (2,557 lb)
Design gross weight	3,500 kg (7,716 lb)

FMA IA 63 Pampa two-seat basic and advanced jet trainer (*Pilot Press*)

T-O weight, clean configuration:
968 litres internal fuel   3,700 kg (8,157 lb)
1,383 litres internal fuel   3,800 kg (8,377 lb)
Max T-O weight with external stores
                                                  5,000 kg (11,023 lb)
Typical landing weight   3,500 kg (7,716 lb)
Wing loading:
at clean T-O weight:
968 litres internal fuel
                                      236.72 kg/m² (48.51 lb/sq ft)
1,383 litres internal fuel
                                      243.12 kg/m² (49.82 lb/sq ft)
at max T-O weight with external stores
                                      319.90 kg/m² (65.55 lb/sq ft)
Power loading:
at clean T-O weight:
968 litres internal fuel   237.8 kg/kN (2.33 lb/lb st)
1,383 litres internal fuel
                              244.2 kg/kN (2.39 lb/lb st)
at max T-O weight with external stores
                              321.4 kg/kN (3.15 lb/lb st)

PERFORMANCE (ISA, at design gross weight with 50% normal fuel, except where indicated):
Max limiting Mach number at 9,500 m (31,170 ft)   0.81
Max level speed:
at S/L   Mach 0.62 (407 knots; 755 km/h; 469 mph)
at 7,000 m (22,965 ft)
                                442 knots (819 km/h; 509 mph)
Max cruising speed at 4,000 m (13,125 ft)
                                403 knots (747 km/h; 464 mph)
Max rate of climb at S/L   1,813 m (5,950 ft)/min
Time to 11,000 m (36,000 ft)   10 min 54 s
Turn rate (max sustained) at 4,000 m (13,125 ft)   12.9°/s
Service ceiling   12,900 m (42,325 ft)
T-O run at T-O weight of 3,700 kg (8,157 lb)
                                                450 m (1,477 ft)
T-O to 15 m (50 ft) at S/L, T-O weight of 3,700 kg (8,157 lb)   700 m (2,297 ft)
Landing from 15 m (50 ft), landing weight of 3,500 kg (7,716 lb)   850 m (2,789 ft)
Landing run at landing weight of 3,500 kg (7,716 lb)   430 m (1,411 ft)

Typical mission radius with 30 min reserves:
air-to-air gunnery (hi-hi), T-O weight of 3,950 kg (8,708 lb) with 250 kg (551 lb) external load, 5 min allowance for dogfight   237 nm (440 km; 273 miles)
air-to-ground (hi-lo-hi), T-O weight of 4,860 kg (10,714 lb) with 1,000 kg (2,205 lb) external load, 5 min allowance for weapon delivery   194 nm (360 km; 223 miles)
Range at 300 knots (556 km/h; 345 mph) at 4,000 m (13,125 ft):
968 litres internal fuel   540 nm (1,000 km; 621 miles)
1,383 litres internal fuel
                             809 nm (1,500 km; 932 miles)
Max endurance at 300 knots (556 km/h; 345 mph) at 4,000 m (13,125 ft), 1,383 litres internal fuel   3 h 48 min
g limit   +4.5 max sustained

AUSTRALIA

AIRCORP
AIRCORP PTY LTD
Brisbane, Queensland

AIRCORP BUSHMASTER B2N
Four years in design and development, the Bushmaster B2N is a two- to four-seat aerobatic light aircraft intended for club training, private flying and rural support. Designed by Mr C. W. Whitney of Seabird Aviation (which see), it conforms to FAR Pt 23 standards and flew for the first time, at the latter company's airfield, on 28 October 1989. Structural testing has been completed, and it was hoped to obtain Australian type certification by the beginning of 1990. An initial production batch of five Bushmasters was expected to become available from Spring 1990.
TYPE: Two- to four-seat light aircraft.
WINGS: High-wing monoplane, with V strut bracing each side. All-metal constant chord wings, with rounded tips. Three-stage flaps on production version. (Prototype has no flaps.)

FUSELAGE: Welded steel tube structure, with light alloy skin. Prototype has fabric covered rear fuselage.
TAIL UNIT: Conventional structure, with wire braced horizontal surfaces.
LANDING GEAR: Non-retractable tailwheel type. Main units have faired-in side Vs, half-axles, and speed fairings on wheels.
POWER PLANT: One 67.1 kW (90 hp) Norton Aerotor 90 two-chamber rotary engine in prototype. Production aircraft to offer choice between this and an 85.75 kW (115 hp) Textron Lycoming O-235-N2C flat-four. Three-blade spinnered propeller. Fuel capacity 100 litres (26.4 US gallons; 22 Imp gallons) standard.
ACCOMMODATION: To be offered with choice of two, '2 + 2', three or four seats, in fully enclosed cabin with forward opening door on each side. Space for 55 kg (121 lb) of baggage aft of seats.
DIMENSIONS, EXTERNAL:
Wing span   10.00 m (32 ft 9¾ in)
Length overall   6.40 m (21 ft 0 in)

Wheel track   2.14 m (7 ft 0¼ in)
Wheelbase   4.00 m (13 ft 1½ in)
DIMENSIONS, INTERNAL:
Cabin: Length   2.20 m (7 ft 2½ in)
Max width   1.10 m (3 ft 7¼ in)
Max height   1.10 m (3 ft 7¼ in)
AREA:
Wings, gross   14.00 m² (150.7 sq ft)
WEIGHTS:
Weight empty: Norton   350 kg (772 lb)
Lycoming   370 kg (816 lb)
Max T-O weight: Utility category   700 kg (1,543 lb)
Normal category   811 kg (1,788 lb)
PERFORMANCE:
Max cruising speed
                      more than 100 knots (185 km/h; 115 mph)
Stalling speed   35 knots (65 km/h; 41 mph)
g limits (Utility category)   +4.4/–2.2

ASTA
AEROSPACE TECHNOLOGIES OF AUSTRALIA PTY LTD
226 Lorimer Street, Fishermen's Bend, Port Melbourne, Victoria 3207
Telephone: 61 (3) 647 3111
Telex: AA 34851 ASTAML
Fax: 61 (3) 646 4381
MANAGING DIRECTOR: George W. Stuart
MANAGER, CORPORATE AFFAIRS: Andre R. van der Zwan
BUSINESS UNITS:

ASTA Aircraft Services Pty Ltd, Pousties Road, Lara, Victoria 3212
Telephone: 61 (52) 821188
Fax: 61 (52) 823505
GENERAL MANAGER: Graeme Reed

ASTA Military Aircraft Services, Beach Road, Lara, Victoria 3212
Telephone: 61 (52) 822988
Fax: 61 (52) 823345
GENERAL MANAGER: John Jansen

ASTA Systems, 226 Lorimer Street, Fishermen's Bend, Port Melbourne, Victoria 3207
Telephone: 61 (3) 647 3111
Telex: AA 34851 ASTAML
Fax: 61 (3) 646 4381
GENERAL MANAGER: George Watts
ASST GENERAL MANAGER, AND MANAGER UAVs: Les Jones
MANAGER, DEFENCE ELECTRONICS AND SOFTWARE: David Prowse
ASTA Engineering, 226 Lorimer Street, Fishermen's Bend, Port Melbourne, Victoria 3207
Telephone: 61 (3) 647 3111
Telex: AA 34851 ASTAML
Fax: 61 (3) 646 4381
MANAGER, PROJECTS AND BUSINESS DEVELOPMENTS: Noel Jenkinson
AeroSpace Technologies of Australia was established in 1986 as a private enterprise organisation, to succeed the former Government Aircraft Factories (GAF: see earlier editions of *Jane's*). The ASTA group specialises in the design, development, manufacture, assembly, maintenance and modification of aircraft, target drones and guided weapons. The early 1990 workforce totalled about 1,900,

located at Fishermen's Bend and Avalon. At Avalon airfield, subassembly of components, final assembly, modification, repair and test flying of jet and other aircraft are undertaken.
ASTA's current aircraft activity includes component manufacture (trailing-edge flaps, flap shrouds, windscreens, canopies and radomes), forward fuselage fitting out, final assembly and flight test of AF/ATF-18A Hornets for the RAAF, and 40 per cent of the Australian production work on the RAAF Pilatus PC-9/A programme. ASTA also produces Krueger flaps for the Boeing 747, in-spar wing ribs and rudders for the 757, rotor blade components for the Sikorsky Black Hawk and Seahawk, fixed shrouds for the Airbus A320, and components for the McDonnell Douglas MD-80 series. In addition, ASTA is contracted by Rohr Industries to manufacture CFM56 nacelle components for the McDonnell Douglas MD-11, and is co-operating as a risk-sharing contractor to Aerospatiale to design, develop and manufacture carbonfibre main and central landing gear doors and floor support panels for the Airbus A330 and A340. ASTA Military Aircraft Services (AMAS) assembles and flight tests the Seahawk helicopter.

AUSTRALIAN AUTOGYRO
THE AUSTRALIAN AUTOGYRO CO
29 Benning Avenue, Turramurra, Sydney, NSW 2074
Telephone: 61 (2) 449 9816
PROPRIETOR: E. R. Minty

AUSTRALIAN AUTOGYRO SKYHOOK
Development history of Mr Ted Minty's Skyhook 'mini-chopper' was recorded in the 1982-83 and earlier editions of *Jane's*. Other specific design features were summarised in the 1989-90 and previous editions. A basic 'open frame' model with 1,835 cc Volkswagen engine is designated **Mk I**; also available are a **Mk II** (unpainted, with enclosed body) and a fully customised **Mk III**. Sales by 1 February 1990 included 24 Mk Is and two Mk IIIs, as well as numerous kits and components.
At that time Mr Minty had decided to suspend production of the Skyhook pending availability, later in 1990, of the latest dual-ignition Rotax engines in Australia, after which these will supersede the earlier VW engine as standard power plant. Mr Minty has meanwhile completed

one development aircraft powered by a 38.8 kW (52 hp) Rotax 503, using a Mk I Skyhook airframe. He also hoped to complete during 1990 an improved glassfibre body shell for the enclosed version.
The following description applies to the original Volkswagen powered version of the Skyhook:
TYPE: Single-seat lightweight autogyro.
ROTOR SYSTEM: Two-blade rotor, with aluminium alloy Rotordyne blades attached directly to a fully adjustable hub bar. Joystick control actuates two nylon encased 6.35 mm (¼ in) stainless steel push/pull cables to operate rotor head and blades.
FUSELAGE: Single keel to which are attached the landing gear, fuselage structure, seat, engine mounting frame, rotor mast and tail unit. Keel and rotor mast are of 5.1 cm (2 in) square section 6061-T6 aluminium alloy with radiused corners. The majority of structural attachments are clamped, rather than bolted or riveted, to reduce to a minimum the number of potential fracture locations in the airframe. Glassfibre fuselage shell on Mks II and III.
TAIL UNIT: Twin rudders, united by a dihedral tailplane

attached to the keel. The upper ends of the rudders are braced by double V triangular frames of light alloy and chrome molybdenum steel tube. Rudders manufactured from marine quality aluminium, tailplane from 2024 aluminium sheet. Entire tail assembly operates as a single unit which swivels from side to side to provide directional stability and power-off manoeuvrability.
LANDING GEAR: Non-retractable type with small sprung tailwheel at rear end of keel. Fully sprung steerable nosewheel, linked to rudders. Mainwheels are ultra-lightweight 5 in nylon go-kart rims, each with a 4.00-5 tyre and tube. Disc brakes optional.
POWER PLANT: One 1.42 kN (320 lb st) 1,835 cc VW engine, mounted on chrome molybdenum brackets attached to mast and keel, and driving a Skyhook two-blade fixed-pitch pusher propeller of Queensland maple. VW engine installed with computer designed camshaft for extra torque; Rotax engine with three-blade propeller to be offered later. Fuel contained in pilot's hollow seat, capacity 43 litres (11.4 US gallons; 9.5 Imp gallons) plus a reserve of 7 litres (1.8 US gallons; 1.5 Imp gallons).

ACCOMMODATION: Pilot only, in enclosed cockpit, on rotationally moulded super-strength cross-linked polyethylene seat/fuel tank located just forward of mast/keel junction, close to CG. Aircraft can be flown without fuselage shell and Plexiglas windscreen enclosure if desired. Adjustable vents in fuselage nose provide ventilation when the aircraft is flown with the cockpit enclosed.

EQUIPMENT: Standard equipment includes cylinder head high temperature and low fuel warning lights.

DIMENSIONS, EXTERNAL:

Rotor diameter	7.01 m (23 ft 0 in)
Length overall	3.35 m (11 ft 0 in)
Height: to top of rotor head	2.06 m (6 ft 9 in)
to top of cockpit canopy	1.42 m (4 ft 8 in)
Tailplane span (incl rudders)	0.86 m (2 ft 10 in)
Wheel track	1.68 m (5 ft 6 in)
Propeller diameter: VW	1.35 m (4 ft 5 in)
Rotax 503	1.37 m (4 ft 6 in)

AREA:

Rotor disc	38.6 m² (415.5 sq ft)

WEIGHTS:
Weight empty, excl rotor blades:

Mk I	121 kg (267 lb)
Mk III	147 kg (325 lb)
Max T-O weight	271 kg (597 lb)

PERFORMANCE:

Max level speed	more than 87 knots (161 km/h; 100 mph)
Max rate of climb at S/L	305 m (1,000 ft)/min
T-O run (depending on headwind)	approx 122 m (400 ft)
Landing run (with disc brakes)	approx 5 m (15 ft)
Range with 43 litres (11.4 US gallons; 9.5 Imp gallons) fuel at constant 61 knots (113 km/h; 70 mph)	243 nm (450 km; 280 miles)

Australian Autogyro Co (Minty) Skyhook single-seat autogyro in Mk III production form

EAA
EAGLE AIRCRAFT AUSTRALIA LTD
Clarence Industrial Area, Cockburn Road, Henderson, WA 6166
Telephone: 61 (9) 410 1077
Fax: 61 (9) 410 2430
MARKETING DIRECTOR: Deryck F. Graham Jr

EAA EAGLE X
The Eagle X is an all-composites light aircraft intended primarily for farming operations, to perform safely in hazardous low-level conditions such as those encountered in aerial cattle mustering. The prototype is built mainly of glassfibre, but production Eagles will utilise Kevlar, carbonfibre, Nomex honeycomb and advanced resins. The design has a 'three flying surface' configuration, with a high-mounted main wing, a low-mounted foreplane and a tailplane, conceived by US engineer Mr John Roncz, who was chief aerodynamics designer for the round-the-world Voyager aircraft. It is said to be difficult to stall, virtually impossible to spin, and to have good handling characteristics at the point of stall. The production Eagle X is designed to conform to ANO 101-55, similar to that of the European JAR 22.

The XTS (for two-seat) prototype, which conforms to current Australian experimental category regulations (ANO 101-25), first flew in the Spring of 1988, and by October of that year had completed a rigorous 200 hour test programme in which all original design criteria were met. During flight trials, the original 58 kW (78 hp) Aeropower engine was replaced by a 75 kW (100 hp) Continental O-100. The intended production Eagle will have a 67 kW (90 hp) Norton GR-36 rotary engine.

Series production was due to begin in 1989, but the absence of promised loan guarantees by the state government has led EAA to seek an overseas joint venture partner, with whom negotiations were in progress in early 1990. Production has been delayed as a result, but certification and production are due within 12 months of

Eagle XTS two-seat prototype (75 kW; 100 hp Continental O-200 engine)

resuming operations; it was hoped that this could occur in mid-1991. Meanwhile, EAA has completed its 6,500 m² (69,965 sq ft) facility, and some 85 per cent of production tooling has been completed.

DIMENSION, EXTERNAL:

Main wing span	6.40 m (21 ft 0 in)

WEIGHTS:

Max T-O weight: prototype	659 kg (1,453 lb)
production	450 kg (992 lb)

PERFORMANCE (A: prototype with O-100 engine, B: estimated for production aircraft with Norton engine):

Max cruising speed: A		121 knots (224 km/h; 139 mph)
B		130 knots (241 km/h; 149 mph)
Normal cruising speed: A		115 knots (213 km/h; 132 mph)
B		120 knots (222 km/h; 138 mph)
Min flying speed (no stall, flaps down):		
A		44 knots (82 km/h; 51 mph)
B		40 knots (74 km/h; 46 mph)
Max rate of climb at S/L: A		244 m (800 ft)/min
B		366 m (1,200 ft)/min
Endurance, with reserves: B		4 h

HDH
HAWKER DE HAVILLAND LTD (Member company of the Hawker Siddeley Group)
PO Box 30 (361 Milperra Road), Bankstown, NSW 2200
Telephone: 61 (2) 772 8111
Telex: AA20719
Fax: 61 (2) 771 2632
MANAGING DIRECTOR: J. B. Hattersley
TECHNICAL DIRECTOR: R. H. Jeal
COMMERCIAL DIRECTOR: P. A. Smith

Hawker de Havilland is primarily an aerospace and defence company engaged in design, production and support activities for civil and military customers in Australia, the USA, UK and more than 20 nations in Asia, the Pacific and the Middle East. Employment in early 1990 was about 3,000, at 16 locations in Australia, Singapore and the USA.

International airframe subcontracting is the largest single element of HDH's production activity, with sole source contracts for a variety of major subassemblies on Airbus

A300, A310, A320 and A330/A340, Boeing 737, 747 and 757, and McDonnell Douglas MD-11 and MD-80 airliners.

HDH is prime contractor to the RAAF for production of PC-9/A turboprop trainers. Earlier, it was a major participant in the RAAF's Hornet programme, part producing and assembling the aircraft's F404 engines, landing gear, weapons/fuel pylons, engine access doors, rear fuselage fairings, electro-hydraulic actuators and accessory drive gearbox. Production of complete F404 engines for the RAAF was completed in mid-1989; F404 upgrade, and manufacture of selected engine items, is continuing for General Electric.

Engine component production is a major activity at Hawker de Havilland Victoria, Australia's only aero-engine manufacturer. Through its Space Office, HDH is involved in a variety of space related activities, including the production of hardware for Hughes Aussat B satellites.

HDH operates airframe and engine overhaul facilities around Australia, including Bankstown, NSW; Fishermen's Bend and Laverton, Victoria; Perth, WA; and Townsville,

Queensland. Customers include the Australian Defence Forces and regional civil and military operators of small/medium-sized fixed-wing aircraft and helicopters. A new systems integration hangar on Tullamarine International Airport, Victoria, is fitting in-flight refuelling equipment to RAAF Boeing 707 transports.

HDH's Systems Division at the Defence Research Centre, South Australia, is involved in airborne weapons system development. Its ASTER (advanced staggered triple ejector rack) bomb rack was test flown on an RAAF AF-18 in late 1988. A Harpoon CCWS (captive carriage weapon simulator) is in production for the RAAF.

Under contract to Sikorsky Aircraft, HDH is carrying out at Bankstown structural modification, assembly, systems integration and testing of RAAF/Army Black Hawk helicopters. The Australian Black Hawks incorporate a variety of Australian role-specific modifications including a Seahawk AFCS.

Twenty Black Hawks had been delivered by early 1990, with a one per month rate established. HDH is producing 37 of the 39 Black Hawks currently on order by the Australian Government.

Under a risk sharing agreement signed on 21 February 1989, HDH will be responsible for final design and production of the airframe for the McDonnell Douglas MDX light helicopter (see United States section), shipping the airframes to the US manufacturer for final assembly installation, including the engine, transmission and other systems.

HDH (PILATUS) PC-9/A

The version of the PC-9 ordered for the RAAF is designated PC-9/A, differing from the standard Swiss built PC-9 (see Pilatus entry) in having Bendix EFIS instrumentation, and PC-7 low pressure tyres with bulged mainwheel doors. Under a joint marketing arrangement with Pilatus, HDH is offering the PC-9/A to potential regional customers.

The first of two Swiss built PC-9/As (A23-001) was delivered to the RAAF in the Summer of 1987, a further 17 were completed from kits supplied by Pilatus, and HDH is now producing the remaining 48 of the total Australian order for 67. The first three HDH assembled PC-9/As were handed over to the RAAF on 19 December 1987, and 25 had been delivered by early 1990, with deliveries then scheduled to increase to two per month.

MAC

MELBOURNE AIRCRAFT CORPORATION PTY LTD
(trading as International Aircraft Corporation Pty Ltd)

Hangar 102, Essendon Airport, Essendon, Victoria 3041
Telephone: 61 (3) 379 7855
Telex: 31473 MELAIR AA
Fax: 61 (3) 379 4555
MANAGING DIRECTOR: Jess Smith
MARKETING MANAGER: Roger James

MAC MAMBA

After two years in conception and design, the prototype of this new light aircraft (VH-JSA) flew for the first time on 25 January 1989. It is a strut braced, all-metal high-wing monoplane, with non-retractable tricycle landing gear and an extensively glazed cabin seating two persons in tandem. The prototype's 86.5 kW (116 hp) Textron Lycoming O-235 flat-four engine is now replaced by the O-320-D1A or IO-320-D1G giving 119 kW (160 hp); fuel capacity is 327 litres (86 US gallons; 72 Imp gallons).

A pre-production Mamba first flew in December 1989. Certification to Australian ANO 101-22/FAR 23 was expected in June 1990. Guns and rockets can be carried under the wings.

The following details apply to the pre-production aircraft, a more detailed airframe description of which can be found in the Addenda.

Prototype MAC Mamba two-seat light aircraft

DIMENSIONS, EXTERNAL:

Wing span	8.74 m (28 ft 8 in)
Wing chord, constant	1.12 m (3 ft 8 in)
Wing aspect ratio	7.9
Length overall	6.63 m (21 ft 9 in)
Height overall	2.67 m (8 ft 9 in)
Propeller diameter	1.83 m (6 ft 0 in)
Propeller ground clearance	0.20 m (8 in)

AREA:

Wings, gross	9.66 m² (104.0 sq ft)

WEIGHTS AND LOADINGS:

Weight empty	567 kg (1,250 lb)
Max T-O and landing weight	839 kg (1,850 lb)
Max wing loading	86.81 kg/m² (17.79 lb/sq ft)
Max power loading	7.04 kg/kW (11.56 lb/hp)

PERFORMANCE:

Max level speed at S/L, ISA	152 knots (281 km/h; 175 mph)
Max cruising speed at S/L, ISA	136 knots (252 km/h; 156 mph)
Econ cruising speed at S/L, ISA	128 knots (237 km/h; 147 mph)
Stalling speed, flaps down, power off	53 knots (99 km/h; 61 mph) EAS
Max rate of climb at S/L	464 m (1,524 ft)/min
Service ceiling	4,875 m (16,000 ft)
T-O run	152 m (500 ft)
T-O to 15 m (50 ft)	305 m (1,000 ft)
Range: at 75% power	620 nm (1,149 km; 714 miles)
at 60% power	680 nm (1,260 km; 783 miles)

SADLEIR

VTOL INDUSTRIES AUSTRALIA LTD

8th Floor, 160 St George's Terrace, Perth, WA 6000
Telephone: 61 (9) 481 0524
Telex: ATEPS AA 94635
Fax: 61 (9) 481 0287
MANAGING DIRECTOR: Kim V. Sadleir

SADLEIR AIR BEARING FAN

The principle of this new approach to VTOL technology design was described and illustrated in the 1989-90 *Jane's*. No recent news of the ABF programme had been received at the time of going to press.

SEABIRD

SEABIRD AVIATION AUSTRALIA PTY LTD

Hervey Bay Airport, PO Box 618, Pialba, Queensland 4655
Telephone: 61 (71) 253144
Fax: 61 (71) 253123
MANAGING DIRECTOR: Donald C. Adams
CHIEF DESIGN ENGINEER: C. W. Whitney

SEABIRD SB-4 SENTINEL

Unlike Seabird's other aircraft (see Sport Aircraft section of the 1986-87 *Jane's*), the Sentinel was designed to achieve full certification under FAR Pt 23. It first flew in October 1989. Its primary application is for observation and reconnaissance, for which it offers a helicopter-like view

from the cockpit and very good low-speed handling characteristics. A secondary role as a training or agricultural aircraft is also foreseen.

By January 1990 the first prototype (VH-SBI), which is powered by a Norton NR 642 rotary engine, had flown a total of 60 hours, and a second Sentinel had completed structural testing up to Utility and Normal category gross weights of 650 kg (1,433 lb) and 750 kg (1,653 lb) respectively. Sentinel 003, which has an Emdair geared engine and fuel injection, was expected to fly in April 1990, and planning for the first 10 production aircraft was well advanced.

TYPE: Two-seat observation and training light aircraft.
WINGS: Strut braced high-wing monoplane, with NACA 63₂-215 aerofoil section and constant chord except at tips. Dihedral 2° 30′ from roots. Incidence 4°. No sweepback. Aluminium alloy structure, with slotted ailerons and trailing-edge slotted flaps. Single bracing strut, with jury strut, each side. Full-chord fence on top of each wing at mid-span.
FUSELAGE: Pod and boom structure, mainly of 4130 chrome molybdenum steel tube with a Kevlar non-load-bearing skin. Aluminium alloy semi-monocoque tailboom.
TAIL UNIT: Swept fin (with dorsal fin) and horn balanced rudder; non-swept fixed incidence cantilever tailplane with one-piece horn balanced elevator. Construction similar to that of wings. Elevator trim tab.
LANDING GEAR: Fixed, with Cleveland 5.00-5 mainwheels (6.00-6 optional) on cantilever spring steel legs plus a Maule solid-tyred tailwheel. Mainwheel tyre pressure 1.38 bars (20 lb/sq in); Cleveland disc brakes. Alternative float gear to be developed.
POWER PLANT: One 67 kW (90 hp) Norton NR 642 rotary (first prototype) or 65 kW (87 hp) Emdair 112B four-stroke engine (second flying prototype), pod mounted above and behind cabin and driving a Hoffmann or MT two-blade fixed-pitch pusher propeller (wood and composite blades) via a 3:1 reduction gear. Fuel in two wing tanks, combined usable capacity 114 litres (30 US gallons; 25 Imp gallons) standard, 182 litres (48 US gallons; 40 Imp gallons) optional. Overwing refuelling point for each tank. Oil capacity 4.5 litres (1.2 US gallons; 1 Imp gallon).
ACCOMMODATION: Side by side seats, adjustable fore and aft, for pilot and observer/passenger in enclosed and extensively glazed cabin. Right hand seat is removable, and aircraft can be flown with both forward opening fully glazed doors removed. Space for 22.7 kg (50 lb) of baggage aft of seats.
ELECTRICAL SYSTEM: 24V 35A alternator standard.
AVIONICS AND EQUIPMENT: VOR, ADF and dual VHF com. Wing hardpoints for external stores. Quick-change photo/survey modules, stretcher or 100 litre (26.4 US gallon; 22 Imp gallon) spraytank in place of right hand seat.

First prototype of the Seabird SB-4 Sentinel lightweight observation aircraft

DIMENSIONS, EXTERNAL:	
Wing span	10.60 m (34 ft 9¼ in)
Wing chord, constant	1.22 m (4 ft 0 in)
Wing aspect ratio	8.8
Length overall	6.70 m (21 ft 11¾ in)
Fuselage: Max width	1.12 m (3 ft 8 in)
Height overall	1.83 m (6 ft 0 in)
Tailplane span	3.05 m (10 ft 0 in)
Wheel track	1.83 m (6 ft 0 in)
Propeller diameter	1.73 m (5 ft 8 in)
DIMENSIONS, INTERNAL:	
Cabin: Max length	1.83 m (6 ft 0 in)
Max width	1.09 m (3 ft 7 in)
Max height	1.12 m (3 ft 8 in)
Baggage compartment volume	0.23 m³ (8.0 cu ft)

AREA:	
Wings, gross	12.77 m² (137.46 sq ft)
WEIGHTS AND LOADINGS:	
Basic operating weight empty (prototype)	405 kg (893 lb)
Max fuel	113 kg (250 lb)
Max T-O weight: Utility	650 kg (1,433 lb)
Normal	750 kg (1,653 lb)
Max wing loading	50.90 kg/m² (10.43 lb/sq ft)
Max power loading	9.70 kg/kW (15.92 lb/hp)
PERFORMANCE (first prototype, NR 642 engine):	
Never-exceed speed	127 knots (235 km/h; 146 mph)
Max level speed at 1,525 m (5,000 ft)	104 knots (193 km/h; 120 mph)

Max cruising speed at 1,525 m (5,000 ft)	90 knots (166 km/h; 103 mph)
Stalling speed, flaps down, engine idling	38 knots (71 km/h; 44 mph)
Max rate of climb at S/L	244 m (800 ft)/min
Service ceiling	4,875 m (16,000 ft)
T-O and landing run	92 m (300 ft)
T-O to 15 m (50 ft)	305 m (1,000 ft)
Landing from 15 m (50 ft)	365 m (1,200 ft)
Min ground turning radius	12.2 m (40 ft 0 in)
Range, 45 min reserves:	
standard fuel and max payload	380 nm (704 km; 437 miles)
max optional fuel	800 nm (1,480 km; 920 miles)
g limits	+4.4/−2.23 (Utility category)

SEAIR
SEAIR PACIFIC PTY LTD
PO Box 166, Airlie Beach, Queensland 4802
Telephone: 61 (79) 46 9133
Telex: 46489
MANAGING DIRECTOR: Shane O'Hare

This company reported in late 1988 that, subject to availability of funding, it was committed to building a full size prototype of an eight-passenger commercial seaplane powered by twin pusher engines, built of composite materials, and having a maximum level speed of 150 knots (278 km/h; 173 mph). Initial design work has been completed, and it was hoped to fly the prototype by 1991. Seair Pacific has a requirement for 20 such aircraft for its own operations. No recent news of progress has been received.

TRANSAVIA
TRANSFIELD CONSTRUCTION PTY LTD, TRANSAVIA DIVISION
73 Station Road, Seven Hills, NSW 2147
Telephone: 61 (2) 624 4400
Telex: AA 170300 TRANSAC
Fax: 61 (2) 624 2548
AVIATION SALES MANAGER: Neil McDonald

Transavia, formed in 1964, is a division of Transfield Construction Pty Ltd, one of Australia's largest construction companies.

TRANSAVIA SKYFARMER
The original PL-12 **Airtruk**, designed by Mr Luigi Pellarini for agricultural use and first flown on 22 April 1965, was type certificated on 10 February 1966. A general purpose version, the **PL-12-U** for passenger/cargo/aerial survey/cropspraying, flew in December 1970, and received certification in February 1971. Deliveries of production aircraft began in December 1966, and by early 1990 about 120 of all versions (including 18 assembled by Flight Engineers Ltd in New Zealand) had been sold for use in Australia, New Zealand, China, Denmark, Malaysia, South Africa, Taiwan, Thailand, the USA and Yugoslavia.

The **Skyfarmer T-300** (first flight July 1978) differs chiefly in having a Textron Lycoming IO-540 engine, and was followed in 1981 by an improved **Skyfarmer T-300A**. Significant changes in the latter include a larger upper-fuselage structure (providing a roomier cockpit and larger hopper throat), and new aerodynamically balanced ailerons, horn balanced elevators and electromechanical flaps to reduce pilot workload. This version received FAA certification in 1986. A **PL-12/M300** military utility version, adapted from the T-300, was under development in 1989.

Five Skyfarmers provided to China in 1986 are of a **Skyfarmer T-400** version, powered by a Textron Lycoming IO-720 engine, for which FAA certification was being sought in 1989.

Details of the original PL-12 and PL-12-U can be found in earlier editions of *Jane's*. The following description applies to the Skyfarmer T-300A, except where indicated:
TYPE: Single-engined agricultural aircraft.
WINGS: Strut braced sesquiplane. Wing section NACA 23012. Dihedral 1° 30′ on upper wings. Incidence (upper wings) 3° 30′, stub-wings 4°. Conventional all-metal structure, covered with Alclad sheet. All-metal trailing-edge flaps and ailerons, covered with ribbed Alclad sheet, and operated manually. Upper-wing fence on each side of each tailboom to ensure full aileron control, even below stalling speeds. Small stub-wings at base of fuselage, constructed on a 4130 steel leading-edge D box section welded to the integral hopper frame and braced to the upper wings by a V strut on each side.

FUSELAGE: Pod shaped structure comprising 4130 welded steel frame with stainless steel and 2024 Alclad covering. Hopper is integrally structured. Entire one-piece rear cabin is of glassfibre to eliminate corrosion and withstand hard wear and tear.
TAIL UNIT: Twin units, each comprising a fin, rudder and separate T tailplane with elevator, and each carried on a cantilever tapered tubular Alclad boom extending from the upper wings.
LANDING GEAR: Non-retractable tricycle type. Mainwheels carried on pivoted trailing legs supported by Transavia short stroke, heavy duty oleo-pneumatic shock absorbing suspension units. Port and starboard main units are interchangeable. Nosewheel carried on a heavy duty, long stroke straight oleo-suspension unit. All wheels and tyres same size (8.00-6); tyre pressure 1.72 bars (25 lb/sq in) (nose); 2.07 bars (30 lb/sq in) (main). Cleveland disc brakes with parking lock.
POWER PLANT: One 224 kW (300 hp) Textron Lycoming IO-540-K1A5 flat-six engine, driving a Hartzell three-blade constant-speed metal propeller with spinner (298 kW; 400 hp IO-720-D1BD in Skyfarmer 400). Two upper-wing fuel tanks, total capacity 189 litres (50 US gallons; 41.5 Imp gallons). Optional long-range installation of second tank in each upper mainplane (standard in T-400), increasing total usable capacity to 364 litres (96.2 US gallons; 80.1 Imp gallons). Refuelling point above upper wings. Oil capacity 11.4 litres (3 US gallons; 2.5 Imp gallons).
ACCOMMODATION: Single-seat cockpit, with door on starboard side. Two-seat cabin aft of chemical hopper/tank for carriage of ground crew, with door at rear of lower deck. Accommodation heated and ventilated.
SYSTEM: 24V electrical system standard, 12V optional.
AVIONICS AND EQUIPMENT: Optional VHF, HF, ADF, artificial horizon and directional gyro. Standard hopper aft of cockpit for 907 kg (2,000 lb) of dry chemical or 818 litres (216 US gallons; 180 Imp gallons) of liquid. Optional Powermist spray system, Transavia safety take-off weight (STOW) checking system, wire cutter, seed spreader attachment, and cockpit heater.

DIMENSIONS, EXTERNAL:	
Upper wing span: 300A, 400	11.98 m (39 ft 3½ in)
Upper wing chord (300A):	
constant portion	1.76 m (5 ft 9¼ in)
at tip	1.27 m (4 ft 2 in)
Stub-wing span	4.93 m (16 ft 2 in)
Length overall: 300A	6.35 m (20 ft 10 in)
400	7.37 m (24 ft 2 in)
Length of fuselage: 300A	4.19 m (13 ft 9 in)
Height overall: 300A	2.79 m (9 ft 2 in)
400	2.87 m (9 ft 5 in)
Fuselage: Max width	0.97 m (3 ft 2 in)
Tailplane span (each)	2.13 m (7 ft 0 in)

Distance between tailplanes:	
300A, 400	3.48 m (11 ft 5 in)
Wheel track	2.44 m (8 ft 0 in)
Wheelbase	1.64 m (5 ft 4½ in)
Propeller diameter: 300A	2.13 m (7 ft 0 in)
400	2.18 m (7 ft 2 in)
Min propeller ground clearance: 300A	0.36 m (1 ft 2 in)
Passenger door: Height	0.97 m (3 ft 2 in)
DIMENSIONS, INTERNAL:	
Rear passenger cabin: Length	1.83 m (6 ft 0 in)
Max width	0.97 m (3 ft 2 in)
Max height	2.03 m (6 ft 8 in)
Floor area	0.37 m² (4 sq ft)
Volume: Passenger cabin	0.85 m³ (30 cu ft)
Hopper: 300A, 400	1.05 m³ (37 cu ft)
AREAS:	
Wings, gross: 300A	24.53 m² (264.0 sq ft)
400	26.76 m² (288.0 sq ft)
Ailerons, total	1.67 m² (18.0 sq ft)
Trailing-edge flaps, total	1.67 m² (18.0 sq ft)
Fins, total	1.30 m² (14.0 sq ft)
Rudders, total	0.56 m² (6.0 sq ft)
Tailplanes, total	2.60 m² (28.0 sq ft)
Elevators, total, incl tabs	1.30 m² (14.0 sq ft)
WEIGHTS AND LOADINGS:	
Typical weight empty: 300A	953 kg (2,101 lb)
400	1,111 kg (2,450 lb)
Max T-O weight (agricultural category):	
300A	1,925 kg (4,244 lb)
400	2,227 kg (4,910 lb)
Max T-O weight (normal category):	
300A	1,724 kg (3,800 lb)
400	1,814 kg (4,000 lb)
Max landing weight: 300A	1,723 kg (3,800 lb)
400	1,814 kg (4,000 lb)
Max wing loading: 300A	78.5 kg/m² (16.1 lb/sq ft)
400	83.2 kg/m² (17.0 lb/sq ft)
Max power loading: 300A	8.6 kg/kW (14.15 lb/hp)
400	7.5 kg/kW (12.28 lb/hp)

PERFORMANCE (at max agricultural T-O weight, ISA at S/L, except where indicated):

Never-exceed speed:	
300A and 400	148 knots (274 km/h; 170 mph)
Max level speed:	
300A at 915 m (3,000 ft)	106 knots (196 km/h; 122 mph)
400	109 knots (202 km/h; 125 mph)
Max cruising speed (75% power):	
300A	102 knots (188 km/h; 117 mph)
400	103 knots (191 km/h; 118 mph)
Stalling speed, power on (300A and 400):	
flaps up	47 knots (88 km/h; 55 mph)
flaps down	39 knots (73 km/h; 45 mph)
Stalling speed, power off (300A and 400):	
flaps up	52 knots (97 km/h; 60 mph)
flaps down	50 knots (93 km/h; 58 mph)
Max rate of climb at S/L: 300A	156 m (514 ft)/min
400	168 m (550 ft)/min
* Max light-weight rate of climb:	
300A	457 m (1,500 ft)/min
400	488 m (1,600 ft)/min
Service ceiling: 300A and 400	3,810 m (12,500 ft)
* Light-weight service ceiling:	
300A and 400	6,890 m (22,600 ft)
T-O run: 300A	329 m (1,080 ft)
400	275 m (900 ft)
* Light-weight T-O run: 300A	77 m (252 ft)
400	72 m (234 ft)
* Light-weight landing run: 300A	82 m (270 ft)
400	78 m (255 ft)

* *Weight of empty aircraft plus pilot and 50 per cent standard fuel*

Transavia Skyfarmer T-300A agricultural aircraft (Textron Lycoming IO-540 engine)

VTOL

VTOL AIRCRAFT PTY LTD

123 Marshall Street, Kotara Heights, NSW 2288
Telephone: 61 (49) 43 5348
CHAIRMAN: Duan A. Phillips

VTOL PHILLICOPTER Mk 1

The prototype Phillicopter, a photograph of which can be found in the 1989-90 *Jane's*, made its first flight in 1971. Its original 74.5 kW (100 hp) O-200-C engine was later replaced by a 108 kW (145 hp) Rolls-Royce Continental O-300.

The Phillicopter was granted Australian type certification in mid-1984. Development of a modified pre-production example, begun some years ago, was continuing in early 1990. Compared with the prototype (see description in 1989-90 and earlier *Jane's*), this has a new high-inertia stabilised main rotor system, incorporating a micro self-balancing unit, and a 134 kW (180 hp) Textron Lycoming O-360 flat-four engine. No illustration or other details were available at the time of going to press.

AUSTRIA

HB

HB-AIRCRAFT INDUSTRIES LUFTFAHRZEUG AG

Postfach 27, Dr Adolf-Schärf-Strasse 42, A-4053 Haid
Telephone: 43 (7) 229 88375/88355
Telex: 21909
Fax: 43 (7) 229 80118
DIRECTORS:
  Willy Reinhardt
  Heribert Katzenberger
  Heino Brditschka

HB-AIRCRAFT HB-23 HOBBYLINER and SCANLINER

The Hobbyliner and Scanliner are registered in Austria as motor gliders, with numerical instead of alphabetical registrations. The manufacturer, however, wishes them to be regarded as light aircraft, hence their removal from their former location in the Sailplanes section.

The following versions were in production in 1989:

HB-23/2400 Hobbyliner. Basic side by side two-seat light aircraft; 40 built by January 1989. Certificated in Austria, West Germany, Italy, Switzerland and the USA.

HB-23/2400 Scanliner. Version of HB-23 with bubble canopy to provide optimum air to ground forward view. Suitable for oil and powerline inspection, coastal and border patrol, policing, observation, survey, fish spotting, pollution control, and communications platform roles. Provision for hardpoint under each wing, on which can be carried a miniature FLIR or SLAR pod, LLL TV, searchlight or other stores. In production, with 10 built by January 1989. Certificated in Austria, Italy, Spain and the USA.

Both models are also being produced under licence by Ciskei Aircraft Industries (which see).

TYPE: Two-seat utility light aircraft.
WINGS: Cantilever high-wing monoplane. Wortmann wing sections: FX-61-184 at root, FX-60-126 at tip. Dihedral 2° on outer panels. Incidence 3°. No sweep. Single main box spar of PhBu 7 (laminated beechwood) and plywood, wooden ribs, and overall plywood covering. All-wood ailerons. Spoilers on upper surface.
FUSELAGE: Main fuselage pod has a welded steel tube frame with glassfibre skin; rear fuselage comprises upper and lower tailbooms, covered in plywood except for triangular cutout in area of propeller arc.
TAIL UNIT: Plywood covered wooden structure comprising fin, rudder, fixed incidence T tailplane, and elevators. Trim tab in starboard elevator.
LANDING GEAR: Non-retractable tricycle type. Mainwheels have self-sprung cantilever glassfibre legs, size 5.00-5 or 6.00-6 tyres (pressure 2.5 bars; 36.3 lb/sq in). Steerable nosewheel, with size 3.00-4, 3.50 or 4.00-4 tyre.
POWER PLANT: One 74.2 kW (98 hp) 2,400 cc Porsche modified Volkswagen G/2 four-cylinder motorcar engine, mounted aft of cabin with rubber belt drive to a Mühlbauer MT 172LD 130 2C or Hoffmann

Prototype of the HB-Aircraft HB-202 general purpose aircraft

HO-14C/172 130LD two-blade fixed-pitch pusher propeller (constant-speed three-blade propeller optional). Single fuel tank in wing centre-section, capacity 76 litres (20 US gallons; 16.7 Imp gallons) in Hobbyliner, 100 litres (26.4 US gallons; 22 Imp gallons) in Scanliner.
ACCOMMODATION: Fully enclosed cabin for two persons, on side by side adjustable seats; 0.23 m³ (8.1 cu ft) of baggage space aft of seats. One-piece fixed canopy forward, aft of which are twin window/doors hinged on centreline and opening upward. VFR instrumentation standard, IFR panel optional.

DIMENSIONS, EXTERNAL:
Wing span	16.40 m (53 ft 9¾ in)
Wing chord: at root	1.538 m (5 ft 0½ in)
at tip	0.60 m (1 ft 11½ in)
Wing aspect ratio	14.1
Width, outer wing panels removed	7.15 m (23 ft 5½ in)
Length overall: Hobbyliner	8.00 m (26 ft 3 in)
Scanliner	7.35 m (24 ft 1½ in)
Height overall	2.45 m (8 ft 0½ in)
Wheel track	1.80 m (5 ft 11 in)
Wheelbase	2.46 m (8 ft 1 in)

AREA:
Wings, gross	19.067 m² (205.2 sq ft)

WEIGHTS AND LOADINGS:
Weight empty, equipped: both versions	560 kg (1,234 lb)
Max T-O weight: Hobbyliner	760 kg (1,676 lb)
Scanliner	850 kg (1,874 lb)

Max wing loading:	
Hobbyliner	39.86 kg/m² (8.16 lb/sq ft)
Scanliner	44.58 kg/m² (9.13 lb/sq ft)
Max power loading:	
Hobbyliner	10.24 kg/kW (17.10 lb/hp)
Scanliner	11.46 kg/kW (19.12 lb/hp)

PERFORMANCE, UNPOWERED:
Best glide ratio at 53 knots (98 km/h; 61 mph):	
Hobbyliner	22
Scanliner	19
Min rate of sink at 50 knots (92 km/h; 57 mph):	
Hobbyliner	1.20 m (3.94 ft)/s
Scanliner	1.40 m (4.59 ft)/s
Stalling speed	41 knots (75 km/h; 47 mph)
g limits (both versions):	
semi-aerobatic, up to T-O weight of 750 kg; 1,653 lb	+5.3/-3
Utility category	+4.4/-3

PERFORMANCE, POWERED:
Never-exceed speed:	
both versions	108 knots (200 km/h; 124 mph) IAS
Max cruising speed (75% power):	
both versions	97 knots (180 km/h; 112 mph)
Min patrol speed:	
both versions	54 knots (100 km/h; 62 mph)
Stalling speed:	
both versions	43 knots (80 km/h; 50 mph)
Max rate of climb at S/L:	
Hobbyliner	228 m (748 ft)/min
Scanliner	216 m (709 ft)/min
Service ceiling: both versions	5,000 m (16,400 ft)
T-O to 15 m (50 ft):	
Hobbyliner	160 m (525 ft)
Scanliner	290 m (950 ft)
Landing run: both versions	210 m (689 ft)
Range with max fuel, no reserves:	
Hobbyliner	432 nm (800 km; 497 miles)
Scanliner	693 nm (1,285 km; 798 miles)
Endurance: Hobbyliner	6 h
Scanliner	10 h

HB-AIRCRAFT HB-202

HB-Aircraft Industries has flown the prototype (OE-AHB) of this derivative of the HB-23 series, which is intended for certification under European JAR VLA (very light aircraft) regulations and to US FAR Pt 23 standards, with a VW-Porsche or Textron Lycoming flat-four engine respectively. The fuselage and landing gear are substantially similar to those on the Hobbyliner/Scanliner, but the HB-202 has a shorter span one-piece wing (with Fowler trailing-edge flaps instead of spoilers) and a shorter, sweptback fin and rudder with low-set tailplane and elevators. Wingtips and parts of the tail unit are of reinforced glassfibre. The JAR VLA version is available also in kit form. Applications for the HB-202 include pilot training, touring and reconnaissance.

HB-Aircraft HB-23/2400 Hobbyliner two-seat light utility aircraft

POWER PLANT: One 82 kW (110 hp) 2,400 cc Volkswagen-Porsche VW-HB-2400 G/2 or 119 kW (160 hp) Textron Lycoming O-320 flat-four engine, in installation similar to that of HB-23, driving a three-blade constant-speed pusher propeller.

DIMENSIONS, EXTERNAL:
Wing span	10.00 m (32 ft 9¾ in)
Wing aspect ratio	7.78
Length overall	7.40 m (24 ft 3⅓ in)
Height overall	2.60 m (8 ft 6½ in)

AREA:
Wings, gross	12.86 m² (138.4 sq ft)

WEIGHT:
Max T-O weight	750 kg (1,653 lb)

PERFORMANCE (estimated. A with VW engine, B with O-320):
Never-exceed speed: A, B	155 knots (288 km/h; 178 mph)
Max cruising speed: A	102 knots (190 km/h; 118 mph)
B	132 knots (245 km/h; 152 mph)

Stalling speed (A and B):
flaps up	46 knots (85 km/h; 53 mph)
30° flap	37 knots (67 km/h; 42 mph)
Max rate of climb at S/L: A	270 m (886 ft)/min
B	360 m (1,181 ft)/min
T-O run: A	180 m (591 ft)
B	120 m (394 ft)
Range with max fuel: A	701 nm (1,300 km; 808 miles)
B	593 nm (1,100 km; 683 miles)

BELGIUM

PROMAVIA
PROMAVIA SA

Chaussée de Fleurus 181, B-6200 Gosselies-Aéroport
Telephone: 32 (71) 35 08 29
Telex: 51872 SQUAL B
Fax: 32 (71) 35 79 54
PRESIDENT: André L. Delhamende
VICE-PRESIDENT: Philippe Delhamende
MARKETING MANAGER: Joseph Bernas

Promavia SA was formed by a number of industrialists, investment companies and a bank, with offices and facilities at Charleroi-Gosselies Airport. Following a market survey completed in 1983, the company initiated the Jet Squalus programme, commissioning Dott Ing Stelio Frati to undertake design and prototype construction. Substantial financial backing was obtained from the Belgian government in 1985 to contribute towards prototype research and development. Marketing and support of the production Jet Squalus, including training programmes, will be undertaken by Promavia; production is intended to be undertaken in various countries worldwide, in addition to Belgium.

Promavia has proposed the Jet Squalus to the USAF and US Navy as a potential replacement for, respectively, the Cessna T-37 and Beechcraft T-34C. For this purpose, it has established contacts with US manufacturers to build any examples ordered for the US market. Promavia is also developing a three-seat Jet Squalus for an all-jet system for civilian airline pilot training. This version will have a 'business jet' cockpit incorporating the latest displays and avionics, including EFIS.

PROMAVIA JET SQUALUS F1300 NGT

The Jet Squalus (Latin for 'shark') was designed to cover all stages of flying training, from ab initio to part of the advanced syllabus, and to be powered by a small, modern, fuel-efficient and quiet turbofan engine. A side by side seating arrangement was chosen for instructor and trainee, and four underwing attachment points enable it also to undertake weapons training or light tactical missions.

Marketing programmes have been developed to offer the Jet Squalus to airlines and other civilian customers through leasing companies, to establish a new 'jet air academy' concept. The Jet Squalus has also been proposed as an 'air ward system' (AWS), in the following four versions:

AWS-MS/SAR. Maritime surveillance/search and rescue, with SLAR and VHF-FM com radio.

AWS-R. Reconnaissance, with photographic equipment and a VLF/Omega R/Nav system.

AWS-W. For bombing and gunnery training, police and border defence missions.

AWS-TT. For target towing.

In addition, Promavia was marketing internationally in 1990 a proposed military training package which would combine the Jet Squalus NGT with the ATTA 3000 (see following entry) to offer complete primary, basic and full advanced training enabling young trainee pilots to graduate to such advanced combat aircraft as the F-16, F/A-18 and Tornado.

First prototype of the Promavia Jet Squalus next generation trainer

Two prototypes have been built, the first of which made its first flight on 30 April 1987 and is powered by a Garrett TFE109-1 turbofan. The second prototype (OO-JET, now scheduled to fly in August 1990) is equipped with air-conditioning and anti-icing systems. Static, flutter and other testing of major components has been completed, as have drawings for the production version. A third prototype, which will have a new pressurised cockpit and advanced design features, is under construction.

In June 1989, at which time the first prototype had completed approx 250 hours' flying, an agreement was announced for 100 or more Jet Squalus NGT trainers to be built by OGMA in Portugal, for use by the Portuguese Air Force (approx 30-35) and civilian agencies. No date for the start of this programme had been announced at the time of going to press.

The following description applies to the first prototype, except where indicated:

TYPE: Two-seat aircraft for pilot screening, primary, basic and part of advanced jet training.

AIRFRAME: Composite materials are used for fairings and some non-structural components; otherwise the aircraft is basically of metal construction throughout.

WINGS: Cantilever low-wing monoplane, with supercritical wing section (thickness/chord ratio 13%, constant). Dihedral 6° from roots. Incidence 1° at root, –1° 45′ at tip. Single-spar structure in light alloy with flush riveted stressed skin. Differentially operated Frise ailerons with servo-tabs, airbrakes, and hydraulically operated trailing-edge flaps.

FUSELAGE: Semi-monocoque structure with press-formed light alloy frames, linked by stringers and stiffeners; flush riveted aluminium alloy skin. Hydraulically operated two-piece light alloy airbrake in lower central part of fuselage, in line with flaps. Avionics and equipment bay in nose. Large quick-disconnect panel in lower rear fuselage permits rapid engine access or removal.

TAIL UNIT: Cantilever structure with flush riveted skin. Sweptback fin and rudder; fixed incidence non-swept tailplane, with elevators. Electrically operated trim tab in port elevator.

LANDING GEAR: Retractable tricycle type, with single wheel and oleo-pneumatic shock absorber on each unit. Mainwheels retract inward, nosewheel rearward. Hydraulic actuation, with built-in emergency system. Main gear of trailing-arm type. Nosewheel steerable 18° left and right. Mainwheels and tyres size 6.00-6, nosewheel 5.00-5.

POWER PLANT: One Garrett TFE109-1 turbofan mounted in rear fuselage of first prototype, rated initially at 5.92 kN (1,330 lb st); a TFE109-3 engine, uprated to 7.12 kN (1,600 lb st), was to be installed in this aircraft in early 1989. Alternative engine under consideration is an 8.01 kN (1,800 lb st) Williams International FJ44 turbofan. Semi-integral metal fuel tank in centre-fuselage, max usable capacity 720 litres (190 US gallons; 158 Imp gallons). Single gravity refuelling point on top of fuselage, aft of canopy. Electric fuel pump for engine starting and emergency use.

ACCOMMODATION: Two persons side by side in air-conditioned cockpit, on Martin-Baker Mk 11 lightweight ejection seats capable of operation at altitudes up to 12,200 m (40,000 ft) and at any speed between 60 and 400 knots (111-741 km/h; 69-461 mph), including ejection through canopy. One-piece framed canopy is hinged at rear and opens upward.

SYSTEMS: Environmental control system for cockpit air-conditioning. Hydraulic system (operating pressure 117 bars; 1,700 lb/sq in) for actuation of airbrake, landing gear and flaps. System incorporates electrically driven oil pump, with two air/oil accumulators (one for normal and one for emergency operation); separate standby system for emergency lowering of landing gear. Electrical system is 28V DC, using an engine driven starter/generator and nickel-cadmium or lead-acid battery. Negretti Aviation oxygen system.

AVIONICS AND EQUIPMENT: Include dual Collins Pro Line II EFIS avionics and radio equipment.

Promavia ATTA 3000 tandem-seat trainer (left) and ARA 3600 single-seat light strike aircraft *(Jane's/Mike Keep)*

ARMAMENT: Four underwing attachment points, each of 150 kg (331 lb) capacity, capable of carrying a variety of weapons or auxiliary fuel tanks.

DIMENSIONS, EXTERNAL:

Wing span	9.04 m (29 ft 8 in)
Wing chord: at root	1.90 m (6 ft 2¾ in)
at tip	1.00 m (3 ft 3¼ in)
mean aerodynamic	1.575 m (5 ft 2 in)
Wing aspect ratio	6.0
Length of fuselage	9.36 m (30 ft 8½ in)
Height overall	3.60 m (11 ft 9¾ in)
Tailplane span	3.80 m (12 ft 5½ in)
Wheel track	3.59 m (11 ft 9¼ in)
Wheelbase	3.58 m (11 ft 9 in)

AREAS:

Wings, gross	13.58 m² (146.17 sq ft)
Ailerons (total)	1.122 m² (12.08 sq ft)
Trailing-edge flaps (total)	1.784 m² (19.20 sq ft)
Fin	1.256 m² (13.52 sq ft)
Rudder	0.782 m² (8.42 sq ft)
Tailplane	2.04 m² (22.00 sq ft)
Elevators (total, incl tab)	1.61 m² (17.33 sq ft)

WEIGHTS AND LOADINGS (A: TFE 109-1 engine, B: uprated TFE109-3):

Weight empty: A	1,300 kg (2,866 lb)
B	1,400 kg (3,086 lb)
Max external stores load	600 kg (1,323 lb)
Max T-O weight: A (Aerobatic)	2,000 kg (4,409 lb)
A (Normal), B	2,400 kg (5,291 lb)
Max wing loading:	
A (Aerobatic)	147.27 kg/m² (30.18 lb/sq ft)
A (Normal), B	176.73 kg/m² (36.21 lb/sq ft)
Max power loading:	
A (Aerobatic)	337.75 kg/kN (3.31 lb/lb st)
A (Normal), B (TFE109-3)	
	337.21 kg/kN (3.30 lb/lb st)
A·(Normal), B (FJ44)	300.00 kg/kN (2.94 lb/lb st)

PERFORMANCE (at max T-O weight, TFE109-1 engine):

Never-exceed speed	
	Mach 0.70 (345 knots; 638 km/h; 397 mph)
Max level speed at 4,265 m (14,000 ft)	
	280 knots (519 km/h; 322 mph)
Normal operating speed	260 knots (482 km/h; 299 mph)
Max speed for landing gear extension	
	150 knots (278 km/h; 173 mph)
Max speed for flap extension (landing position)	
	130 knots (241 km/h; 150 mph)
Stalling speed, flaps down	67 knots (124 km/h; 77 mph)
Max rate of climb at S/L	762 m (2,500 ft)/min
Service ceiling	11,275 m (37,000 ft)
Max operating ceiling	7,620 m (25,000 ft)
T-O run	335 m (1,100 ft)
T-O to 15 m (50 ft)	396 m (1,300 ft)
Landing from 15 m (50 ft)	427 m (1,400 ft)
Landing run	366 m (1,200 ft)
Ferry range at 6,100 m (20,000 ft), max internal fuel	
	1,000 nm (1,850 km; 1,150 miles)
g limits	+2.8 sustained, at 3,050 m (10,000 ft)
	+7/−3.5 Aerobatic

PROMAVIA ATTA 3000

The ATTA 3000 (Advanced Trainer/Tactical Aircraft) is a twin-engined design with 6.67 kN (1,500 lb st) TFE109-2 turbofans. A tandem two-seater, it has stepped cockpits, McDonnell Douglas Minipac zero/zero ejection seats and EFIS instrumentation; like the Jet Squalus, it has been proposed for the US JPATS (Joint Primary Air Training System) requirement. In the weapons training/tactical role, it could be armed with 7.62 mm or 20 mm guns, 70 mm rocket launchers, infra-red air-to-air missiles, or bombs of up to Mk 82 size.

DIMENSIONS, EXTERNAL:

Wing span	9.20 m (30 ft 2¼ in)
Length overall	9.96 m (32 ft 8 in)
Height overall	3.60 m (11 ft 9¾ in)

AREA:

Wings, gross	13.81 m² (148.65 sq ft)

WEIGHTS:

Weight empty, equipped	1,769 kg (3,900 lb)
Max T-O weight	3,265 kg (7,198 lb)
Max landing weight	2,520 kg (5,555 lb)

PERFORMANCE (estimated):

Max level speed	485 knots (899 km/h; 558 mph)
Stalling speed, flaps down	72 knots (134 km/h; 83 mph)
Max rate of climb at S/L	2,165 m (7,100 ft)/min
Service ceiling	12,200 m (40,000 ft)
T-O run	244 m (800 ft)
Landing run	366 m (1,200 ft)
Ferry range	950 nm (1,760 km; 1,094 miles)

PROMAVIA ARA 3600

The ARA 3600 (Attack/Reconnaissance Aircraft) is a single-seat light strike aircraft design, with an intended power plant of two 8.01 kN (1,800 lb st) TFE109-3 turbofans and the same 757 litres (200 US gallons; 166.5 Imp gallons) internal fuel capacity as the ATTA 3000. It would be capable of carrying 1,000 kg (2,205 lb) of external stores including two 20 mm or four 7.62 mm guns, four 7-tube 70 mm rocket launchers, or up to four Mk 82 or smaller bombs.

DIMENSIONS AND WEIGHTS: As for ATTA 3000

PERFORMANCE (estimated): As for ATTA 3000 except:

Max rate of climb at S/L	2,440 m (8,000 ft)/min
Service ceiling	13,715 m (45,000 ft)

SABCA

SOCIÉTÉ ANONYME BELGE DE CONSTRUCTIONS AÉRONAUTIQUES

Chaussée de Haecht 1470, B-1130 Brussels
Telephone: 32 (2) 246 25 11
Telex: 21 237 SABCA B
Fax: 32 (2) 216 15 70
CHAIRMAN: J. Groothaert
DIRECTOR/GENERAL MANAGER: J. Detemmerman
MARKETING MANAGERS:
  J. E. Versmessen (Aerospace)
  P. Johansen (Electronic Defence)
OTHER WORKS: Aéroport de Gosselies-Charleroi, B-6200 Gosselies
Telephone: 32 (71) 25 42 11
Telex: 51 251 SABGO B
Fax: 32 (71) 34 42 14

Founded in 1920, Sabca is the major aerospace company in Belgium. Since the Second World War, it has participated in various European aircraft programmes. At Haren, Sabca is manufacturing major structures such as wings and nose sections, and other structural components and equipment, for the General Dynamics F-16; Alpha Jet; Mirage III/5/F1

and Atlantic 1/Atlantique 2; Airbus A310; Fokker 50 and F28; 330 Puma; Spacelab; and Ariane launchers. Servo controls are produced for the F-16 and the Ariane launchers.

At Gosselies, Sabca assembles and tests F-16s for Belgium; modifies Belgian Air Force and USAFE F-16s; and is responsible for final assembly of Agusta A 109B helicopters for Belgium, including installing and integrating HeliTOW 2 and all other avionics systems.

Sabca's Electronic Division produces IFF components and aircraft electronic ground equipment, as well as maintaining Doppler equipment.

For many years Sabca has been responsible for the maintenance and overhaul of Belgian and other armed forces' military aircraft, their electronic components and accessories, as well as commercial fixed-wing aircraft and helicopters. It is currently integrating ECM devices in Belgian aircraft.

Sabca is a member of various European industrial consortia; Dassault-Breguet and Fokker have parity holdings in the company. The company's works occupy a total area of approx 82,000 m² (882,640 sq ft) and in early 1990 employed an average of 1,600 people.

Construction of a new plant for the Sabca-Limburg NV subsidiary began in 1990. This new factory, due to be operational by mid-1991, will produce components in high grade composite materials for aircraft and aerospace applications.

MIRAGE SAFETY IMPROVEMENT PROGRAMME

Sabca has been selected as prime contractor for the Belgian Air Force's Mirage Safety Improvement Programme (MIRSIP), under which 15 single-seat Mirage 5-BAs and five two-seat Mirage 5-BD operational trainers are to be upgraded and redelivered by the end of 1994. In addition to life-extending modifications and maintenance, the 20 aircraft are to be fitted with canard control surfaces and pressure refuelling (both Dassault-Breguet systems), and a new weapons delivery and navigation system (Sagem Uliss 92 INS, Sagem Tercor terrain contour matching system with 3D digital map database, Thomson-CSF laser rangefinder and Ferranti HUD) operating via a MIL-STD-1553B databus. (See also page 68.)

SONACA

SOCIÉTÉ NATIONALE DE CONSTRUCTION AEROSPATIALE SA

Parc Industriel, Route Nationale Cinq, B-6200 Gosselies
Telephone: 32 (71) 34 22 11
Telex: 51241
Fax: 32 (71) 34 40 35
GENERAL MANAGER: M. Harmant
MANUFACTURING DIRECTOR: P. Wacquez
SALES AND MARKETING DIRECTOR: Claude Loriaux

Sonaca SA, formerly Fairey SA (established in 1931), was incorporated on 1 May 1978. Its capital is held 90 per cent by public institutions. Built on 22 ha (54 acres) of ground adjacent to Charleroi Airport, Sonaca's facility covers 87,661 m² (943,574 sq ft). Workforce in early 1990 was 1,380.

Sonaca participates in civil and military aviation manufacturing programmes, co-producing the General Dynamics F-16 (rear fuselage, vertical fin, dorsal fairing and final mating) and components (leading-edge moving surfaces) for the Airbus A310, A320 and A330/340. It supplies parts for various aircraft, including Aerospatiale

and Agusta A 109 helicopters, the Dassault-Breguet Atlantique 2, Lockheed C-130, Saab 340 and Dassault-Breguet/Dornier Alpha Jet. The company designed and sells aircraft galley polycarbonate containers.

Sonaca's association in large international military and civil programmes has resulted in a significant increase in its capability to develop and manufacture metallic and composite aerospace structures. R & D resources include an IBM Cadam (2D, 3D) and Catia (3D) scientific data processing system. Sonaca is developing structural elements for the Hermes spacecraft.

BRAZIL

CTA

CENTRO TÉCNICO AEROESPACIAL

PO Box 6001, 12225 São José dos Campos, SP
Telephone: 55 (123) 21 1311
Telex: 123 3393 CTAE BA
PROGRAMME MANAGER: Dilson Faria Pessoa

The CTA (see earlier editions of *Jane's*) IFI (Instituto de Fomento e Coordenação Industrial) and IPD (Instituto de Pesquisa e Desenvolvimento) co-ordinated the development of a re-engined version of the Neiva Paulistinha P-56, last described fully in the 1968-69 edition. No information has been received since 1988. All known details of the

re-engined version, and an illustration, can be found in the 1989-90 *Jane's*.

EMBRAER

EMPRESA BRASILEIRA DE AERONÁUTICA SA

Av Brig Faria Lima 2170, Caixa Postal 343, 12225 São José dos Campos, SP
Telephone: 55 (123) 25 1711
Telex: (391) 1233589 EBAE BR
RIO OFFICE: Aeroporto Santos-Dumont, Sobreloja, Salão de Embarque No. 2, 20021 Rio de Janeiro, RJ

Telephone: 55 (21) 262 6411
CHAIRMAN: Eng Ozires Silva
CHIEF EXECUTIVE OFFICER: Eng Ozilio Carlos da Silva
COMMERCIAL DIRECTOR: Heitor Fernandes Serra
TECHNICAL DIRECTOR: Eng Guido Fontegalante Pessotti
PRESS OFFICER: Mario B. de M. Vinagre
US SUBSIDIARY:
  Embraer Aircraft Corporation, 276 Southwest 34th Street, PO Box 21623, Fort Lauderdale, Florida 33315

Telephone: 1 (305) 524 5755 and 5744
Telex: (230) 522318 EMBRAER FORT LAUDERDALE
PARIS OFFICE:
  Embraer Aviation International, BP 74, Aéroport du Bourget, Zone d'Aviation d'Affaires, 93350 Le Bourget, France
Telephone: 33/48 35 94 20
Telex: 213498F EBAE PAR

Embraer, which celebrated its 20th anniversary and delivered its 4,000th aircraft in 1989, was created on 19 August 1969, and came into operation on 2 January 1970. The Brazilian government owns 63.81 per cent of the voting shares, 36.19 per cent of the subscribed capital being held by private shareholders. Embraer had a workforce in January 1990 of 12,607 persons and a factory area of 275,198.55 m² (2,962,210 sq ft). By the end of 1989 Embraer had built a total of 4,064 aircraft.

Since August 1974, Embraer has had an agreement with Piper Aircraft Corporation to manufacture various Piper types under licence. Agreements concluded in 1983-84 with Sikorsky provide for development of Embraer's capability to manufacture aircraft components in composite materials, initially for the S-70C helicopter, the EMB-120 Brasilia and the AMX attack aircraft. A 1987 agreement with McDonnell Douglas provides for the supply of 200 sets of wing flaps, in composites material, for the MD-11 airliner, with a further 100 sets on option. Deliveries began on 29 October 1988.

Embraer has in current production the EMB-120 Brasilia commuter transport and the EMB-312 Tucano military trainer, and is developing a new regional transport known as the EMB-145. The AMX tactical fighter is produced jointly with Aeritalia and Aermacchi of Italy, and the CBA-123 commuter transport is being developed with FAMA of Argentina. Manufacture of the EMB-201A Ipanema agricultural aircraft, and licence produced versions of Piper twin-engined light aircraft, is the responsibility of Neiva (which see), which became a subsidiary of Embraer in March 1980. Neiva production and marketing of these aircraft are co-ordinated with the licence manufacture and sale of single-engined Piper types by Chincul of Argentina (which see).

AMX

Details of this military aircraft programme with Aeritalia and Aermacchi are given in the International section.

EMBRAER MFT/LF

Following submission of a concept to the Brazilian Air Force in 1987, Embraer has begun project design of a tandem two-seat aircraft provisionally designated MFT/LF (modern fighter trainer/light fighter). The intention is to develop it in the former category first, but to make the same design the basis for an advanced light fighter. The MFT would be a replacement for the EMB-326 Xavante in the Brazilian Air Force, and the LF a successor to its Mirages and Northrop F-5s.

Initial design parameters include a conventional configuration, a top speed of about Mach 1.8 with a 40 kN (9,000 lb st) class afterburning engine, extensive use of advanced composites, low gross weight, and high agility. The Brazilian requirement is reportedly for 60-70 trainers and 70-80 light fighters. Development with an international partner is under consideration.

EMBRAER EMB-110 BANDEIRANTE (PIONEER)

Brazilian Air Force designations: C-95, EC-95, R-95 and SC-95

The first of three EMB-100 prototypes (described in the 1970-71 Jane's) made its initial flight on 26 October 1968, followed by the first production EMB-110 Bandeirante (C-95/2133) on 9 August 1972. Following Brazilian certification to FAR Pt 23 in December 1972, the first three Bandeirantes were delivered to the Brazilian Air Force on 9 February 1973.

Bandeirantes of various models have been sold to more than 80 operators in 36 countries worldwide. By 1 January 1990 the worldwide fleet of Bandeirantes had logged more than 5.2 million flying hours; at that time Embraer had delivered 481 Bandeirantes and military EMB-111 maritime surveillance aircraft. Production was terminated with the 500th aircraft, a C-95C for the Brazilian Air Force, which was due to be delivered during the first half of 1990. With its delivery, that service will then have received 156 Bandeirantes, as follows: 60 C-95, 20 C-95A and 28 C-95B transports; two EC-95Bs for navaid calibration; one XC-95B for artificial rain research; five search and rescue SC-95Bs; six aerial photogrammetry R-95s; 12 dihedral-tailed, EFIS-equipped C-95Cs; and 22 EMB-111s (see separate entry: 12 P-95s and 10 P-95Bs).

Details of early production models can be found in the 1984-85 and previous editions of Jane's. Principal later models were:

EMB-110P1A. Updated version of P1 with 10° tailplane dihedral and other detail changes (listed in 1987-88 and earlier editions). First two delivered in December 1983. Replaced P1 as standard version from c/n 439 onwards. Weights and performance as listed in 1989-90 Jane's.

EMB-110P1K. Military utility, cargo and paradropping version of P1. No tailplane dihedral.

EMB-110P1K SAR. Search and rescue version of P1K, equipped for inland and overwater search, paradropping and aeromedical evacuation. Max T-O weight 6,000 kg (13,230 lb). Further details in 1989-90 Jane's.

EMB-110P2A. Replaced former P2 (1984-85 Jane's) as third-level commuter transport version, carrying up to 21 passengers. Incorporates same changes as P1A. Description applies to this version.

Embraer EMB-110P1A Bandeirante (two P&WC PT6A-34 turboprops)

EMB-110P1A/41 and EMB-110P2A/41. Replaced P1/41 and P2/41 from 1983, certificated under SFAR Pt 41 for a max T-O weight of 5,900 kg (13,010 lb). Power plant and dimensions unchanged; weights and performance as listed in 1989-90 Jane's.

EMB-111. Maritime surveillance version, described separately.

The following description, except where indicated, applies to the EMB-110P2A:

TYPE: Twin-turboprop general purpose transport.

AIRFRAME: As described in 1989-90 and earlier editions.

POWER PLANT: Two 559 kW (750 shp) Pratt & Whitney Canada PT6A-34 turboprops, each driving a Hartzell HC-B3TN-3C/T10178H-8R constant-speed three-blade metal propeller with autofeathering and full reverse-pitch capability. Four integral fuel tanks in wings, with total capacity of 1,720 litres (454 US gallons; 378 Imp gallons).

ACCOMMODATION: Pilot and co-pilot side by side on flight deck. Seats for up to 21 passengers in main cabin of P2A, at 74 cm (29 in) pitch. P1A has quick-change cabin seating up to 18 persons. Crew/passenger door at front and passenger/baggage door at rear, both on port side; emergency exit over wing on each side, and opposite crew/passenger door on starboard side. Crew/passenger door can also be used as emergency exit. Cabin floor stressed for uniformly distributed loads of up to 488 kg/m² (100 lb/sq ft). Baggage compartment at rear of cabin. Windscreen de-icing optional.

SYSTEMS, AVIONICS AND EQUIPMENT: See 1989-90 and earlier editions.

DIMENSIONS, EXTERNAL:

Wing span	15.33 m (50 ft 3½ in)
Wing aspect ratio	8.1
Length overall	15.10 m (49 ft 6½ in)
Length of fuselage	14.59 m (47 ft 10½ in)
Height overall	4.92 m (16 ft 1¾ in)
Fuselage: Max width	1.72 m (5 ft 7¾ in)
Tailplane span	7.54 m (24 ft 9 in)
Wheel track	4.94 m (16 ft 2½ in)
Wheelbase	5.10 m (16 ft 8¾ in)
Propeller diameter	2.36 m (7 ft 9 in)

DIMENSIONS, INTERNAL:

Cabin: Max length	9.53 m (31 ft 3¼ in)
Width	1.60 m (5 ft 3 in)
Height	1.60 m (5 ft 3 in)
Floor area	12.00 m² (129.2 sq ft)
Volume	20.4 m³ (720.4 cu ft)
Baggage compartment volume	2.0 m³ (70.6 cu ft)

AREA:

Wings, gross	29.10 m² (313.23 sq ft)

WEIGHTS AND LOADINGS (P2A):

Weight empty, equipped	3,516 kg (7,751 lb)
Fuel weight	1,308 kg (2,883 lb)
Max payload	1,681 kg (3,706 lb)
Max T-O weight	5,670 kg (12,500 lb)
Max ramp weight	5,700 kg (12,566 lb)
Max landing weight	5,670 kg (12,500 lb)

Max zero-fuel weight	5,450 kg (12,015 lb)
Max wing loading	195.52 kg/m² (40.04 lb/sq ft)
Max power loading	5.07 kg/kW (8.33 lb/shp)

PERFORMANCE (P2A at max T-O weight, ISA, except where indicated):

Max level speed at 2,440 m (8,000 ft)	248 knots (460 km/h; 286 mph)
Max cruising speed at 2,440 m (8,000 ft)	223 knots (413 km/h; 257 mph)
Long-range cruising speed at 3,050 m (10,000 ft)	181 knots (335 km/h; 208 mph)
Stalling speed at max landing weight	70 knots (130 km/h; 81 mph) CAS
Max rate of climb at S/L	545 m (1,788 ft)/min
Rate of climb at S/L, one engine out	131 m (430 ft)/min
Time to 3,050 m (10,000 ft)	6 min
Time to 4,575 m (15,000 ft)	10 min
Service ceiling	6,860 m (22,500 ft)
Service ceiling, one engine out	3,385 m (11,100 ft)
T-O run, FAR 23.135A	675 m (2,215 ft)
Landing run (non-factored) at max landing weight	850 m (2,790 ft)
Range with max fuel (long-range cruising speed, 45 min reserves)	1,080 nm (2,001 km; 1,244 miles)

EMBRAER EMB-111

Brazilian Air Force designation: P-95

This land based maritime surveillance aircraft, based on the EMB-110 Bandeirante, was designed to meet specifications issued by the Comando Costeiro, the Brazilian Air Force's Coastal Command. Main external differences are the large nose radome, housing search radar, and the addition of wingtip fuel tanks.

The EMB-111 flew for the first time on 15 August 1977, and 12 were delivered initially, as P-95s, to the Brazilian Air Force. Six delivered to the Chilean Navy in 1978 and 1979 have some mission equipment changes, including full de-icing system, and passive ECM antennae under the nose and at the tail. One EMB-111 was delivered in August 1981 to the Gabonese Air Force, and two were ordered in 1986 by the air force of Angola. Delivery dates for the Angolan pair were still awaiting financial approval in 1990.

In December 1987, the Brazilian Air Force ordered a further 10 EMB-111s, deliveries of which began in October 1989. The new aircraft, designated **P-95B**, are similar to those currently in service, except for structural improvements and updated avionics which include MEL Super Searcher radar and Thomson-CSF DR 2000A Mk II/Dalia 1000A Mk II ESM; Collins EFIS-74 electronic flight instrument system, ADI-84 and APS-65 autopilot; and a Canadian Marconi CMA 771 Mk III Omega navigation system. The earlier P-95s will be brought up to a similar standard. Brazilian Air Force EMB-111s serve with the 1st and 2nd Squadrons of the 7th Aviation Group (GAv 1°/7° and 2°/7°).

A full description of the EMB-111 can be found in the 1985-86 and earlier editions of Jane's.

Embraer EMB-111 maritime surveillance aircraft of the Brazilian Air Force

Embraer EMB-120 Brasilia twin-turboprop passenger transport in the insignia of Air Littoral of France

EMBRAER EMB-120 BRASILIA
Brazilian Air Force designation: VC-97

Design of this twin-turboprop passenger and cargo transport started in September 1979. The first of three flying prototypes (PT-ZBA) made its initial flight on 27 July 1983; Nos 2 and 5 were static and fatigue test aircraft; No 6 was a pre-series demonstration aircraft. On 4 January 1989, the first prototype began flight trials as a testbed for the engine installation of the CBA-123 transport (see International section), with a Garrett TPE331-12B turboprop mounted on the port side of its rear fuselage.

Certification of the standard Brasilia by the Brazilian CTA was granted on 10 May 1985, and FAA (FAR Pt 25) type approval on 9 July 1985. Type certification by the British CAA, French DGAC and German LBA was granted in 1986. The first customer, Atlantic Southeast Airlines of the USA, received its first Brasilia in June 1985. By 6 March 1990 firm orders totalled 291, with 135 more on option. By that date, a total of 166 had been delivered, including four **VC-97** VIP transports for the Brazilian Air Force. The first order for the corporate version was received from United Technologies Corporation (USA) in August 1985. Furnished for 18 passengers, it was delivered in September 1986. Production rate was five aircraft per month in 1989.

From Brasilia c/n 120028, delivered in October 1986, composite materials equivalent to 10 per cent of the aircraft's basic empty weight have been used in the airframe, as noted in the following descriptive details:

TYPE: Twin-turboprop general purpose transport.
WINGS: Cantilever low-wing monoplane. Wing section NACA 23018 (modified) at root, NACA 23012 at tip. Dihedral 6° 30′ from roots at 66 per cent chord. Incidence 2°. Sweepback 0° at 66 per cent chord. Single continuous fail-safe structure, attached to underside of fuselage on three special frames. Main wing box has three spars (at 15, 28 and 66 per cent chord), ribs, stiffeners and skin. Spar caps machined from 2024 or 7050 aluminium alloy extrusions; skin panels are of 2024 or 7475 laminations, chemically milled. Leading-edges, wingtips and root fairings of Kevlar reinforced glassfibre. Hydraulically actuated electrically controlled double-slotted Fowler trailing-edge flap, of carbonfibre construction, inboard and outboard of each engine nacelle; small plain flap beneath each nacelle. No slats, slots, spoilers or airbrakes. Small fence on each outer wing between outboard flap and aileron. Internally balanced all-metal ailerons. Lateral trimming by tabs (two in starboard aileron, one in port aileron). Ailerons actuated by dual irreversible mechanical actuators operated manually by cable controls. Pneumatic boot de-icing of leading-edges, using engine bleed air.
FUSELAGE: Semi-monocoque pressurised structure, of circular cross-section throughout most of its length. Chemically milled skin, reinforced by extruded stiffeners; C frames attached to skin by shear clips. Entire structure is of 2024, 7050 and 7475 aluminium alloys, and meets the damage tolerance requirements of FAR Pt 25 (Transport category) up to Amendment 25-54. Nosecone of Kevlar reinforced glassfibre; tailcone also of Kevlar reinforced glassfibre on aircraft without APU. Pressurised area contained within flat bulkhead forward of flight deck and hemispherical rear bulkhead aft of baggage compartment. Twin ventral strakes under rear fuselage.
TAIL UNIT: Cantilever T tail, of three-spar metal construction except for leading-edges and tips, which are of Kevlar reinforced glassfibre. Fixed incidence swept tailplane, with horn balanced elevators. Sweptback fin, with

Kevlar reinforced glassfibre dorsal fin. Serially hinged two-segment rudder actuated hydraulically by Bertea CSD unit. Mechanically actuated trim tab in each elevator. Pneumatic boot de-icing of leading-edges, using engine bleed air.
LANDING GEAR: Retractable tricycle type, with Goodrich twin wheels and oleo-pneumatic shock absorber on each unit (main units 12 in, nose unit 8 in). Hydraulic actuation; all units retract forward (main units into engine nacelles). Hydraulically powered nosewheel steering. Goodyear tyres, size 24 × 7.25 in (main), 18 × 5.5 in (nose); pressure 6.90-7.58 bars (100-110 lb/sq in) on main units, 4.14-4.83 bars (60-70 lb/sq in) on nose unit. Goodrich carbon brakes standard (steel optional). Hydro Aire anti-skid system standard; autobrake optional.
POWER PLANT: Two Pratt & Whitney Canada PW118 turboprops, each rated at 1,342 kW (1,800 shp) for T-O and max continuous power, and driving a Hamilton Standard 14RF-9 four-blade constant-speed reversible-pitch fully-feathering propeller with glassfibre blades containing aluminium spars. Fuel in two-cell 1,670 litre (441 US gallon; 367.2 Imp gallon) integral tank in each wing; total capacity 3,340 litres (882 US gallons; 734.4 Imp gallons), of which 3,312 litres (875 US gallons; 728.6 Imp gallons) are usable. Single-point pressure refuelling (beneath outer starboard wing), plus gravity point in upper surface of each wing. Oil capacity 9 litres (2.4 US gallons; 2 Imp gallons).
ACCOMMODATION: Two-pilot flight deck. Main cabin accommodates cabin attendant and 30 passengers in three-abreast seating at 79 cm (31 in) pitch, with overhead lockable baggage racks, in pressurised and air-conditioned environment. Passenger seats are made of carbonfibre and Kevlar, floor and partitions of carbonfibre and Nomex sandwich, side panels and ceiling of glassfibre/Kevlar/Nomex/carbonfibre sandwich. Provisions for wardrobe, galley and toilet. Downward opening main passenger door, with airstairs, forward of

wing on port side. Type II emergency exit on starboard side at rear. Overwing Type III emergency exit on each side. Pressurised baggage compartment aft of passenger cabin, with large door on port side. Also available with all-cargo interior; executive or military transport interior; or in mixed-traffic version with 24 or 26 passengers (toilet omitted in latter case), and 900 kg (1,984 lb) of cargo in enlarged rear baggage compartment.
SYSTEMS: AiResearch air-conditioning/pressurisation system (differential 0.48 bars; 7 lb/sq in), with dual packs of recirculation equipment. Duplicated hydraulic systems (pressure 207 bars; 3,000 lb/sq in), each powered by an engine driven pump, for landing gear, flap, rudder and brake actuation, and nosewheel steering. Emergency standby electric pumps on each system, plus single standby handpump, for landing gear extension. Main electrical power supplied by two 28V 400A DC starter/generators; two 28V 100A DC auxiliary brushless generators for secondary and/or emergency power; one 24V 40Ah nickel-cadmium battery for assisted starting and emergency power. Main and standby 450VA static inverters for 26/115V AC power at 400Hz. Single high-pressure (127.5 bars; 1,850 lb/sq in) oxygen cylinder for crew; individual chemical oxygen generators for passengers. Pneumatic de-icing for wing and tail leading-edges, and engine air intakes; electrically heated windscreens, propellers and pitot tubes; bleed air de-icing of engine air intakes. Optional Garrett GTCP36-150(A) APU in tailcone, for electrical and pneumatic power supply (fitted to second and third prototypes).
AVIONICS: Collins Pro Line II digital avionics package includes as standard dual VHF-22 com transceivers, dual VIR-32 VHF nav receivers, one ADF-60A, one TDR-90 transponder, CLT-22/32/62/92 control heads, one DME-41, one WXR-270 weather radar, dual AHRS-85 digital strapdown AHRS, dual ADI-84, dual EHSI-74, dual RMI-36, one Dorne & Margolin DMELT-81 emergency locator transmitter, dual Avtech audio/interphones,

Embraer EMB-120 Brasilia twin-turboprop transport *(Pilot Press)*

Second EMB-120 operated as a VC-97 VIP transport by the Brazilian Air Force *(Ivo Sturzenegger)*

Avtech PA and cabin interphone, Fairchild voice recorder, and IET standby attitude indicator. Optional avionics include third VHF com, second transponder and DME, WXR-300 weather radar, two EFIS-86 electronic flight instrument systems, one MFD-85 multi-function display, one or two J.E.T. RNS-8000 3D or Racal Avionics RN 5000 nav, one APS-65 digital autopilot, one or two FCS-65 digital flight directors, flight entertainment music, one or two Canadian Marconi CMA-771 Alpha VLF/Omega, one or two ALT-55 radio altimeters, altitude alerter/preselect, microwave landing system, ground proximity warning system, flight recorder, and·Motorola Selcal. Second (Bendix/King) avionics package is available optionally. Other types of avionics, for special versions of the aircraft, as required for the missions concerned.

DIMENSIONS, EXTERNAL:
Wing span	19.78 m (64 ft 10¾ in)
Wing chord: at root	2.81 m (9 ft 2¾ in)
at tip	1.40 m (4 ft 7 in)
Wing aspect ratio	9.9
Length overall	20.00 m (65 ft 7½ in)
Length of fuselage	18.73 m (61 ft 5½ in)
Fuselage: Max diameter	2.28 m (7 ft 5¾ in)
Height overall	6.35 m (20 ft 10 in)
Elevator span	6.94 m (22 ft 9¼ in)
Wheel track (c/l of shock struts)	6.58 m (21 ft 7 in)
Wheelbase	6.97 m (22 ft 10½ in)
Propeller diameter	3.20 m (10 ft 6 in)
Propeller ground clearance (min)	0.48 m (1 ft 7 in)
Passenger door (fwd, port): Height	1.70 m (5 ft 7 in)
Width	0.774 m (2 ft 6½ in)
Height to sill	1.47 m (4 ft 10 in)
Cargo door (rear, port): Height	1.36 m (4 ft 5½ in)
Width	1.30 m (4 ft 3¼ in)
Height to sill	1.67 m (5 ft 5¾ in)
Emergency exit (rear, stbd): Height	1.37 m (4 ft 6 in)
Width	0.51 m (1 ft 8 in)
Height to sill	1.56 m (5 ft 1½ in)
Emergency exits (overwing, each):	
Height	0.91 m (3 ft 0 in)
Width	0.51 m (1 ft 8 in)
Emergency exits (flight deck side windows, each):	
Min height	0.48 m (1 ft 7 in)
Min width	0.51 m (1 ft 8 in)

DIMENSIONS, INTERNAL:
Cabin, excl flight deck and baggage compartment:
Length	9.35 m (30 ft 8 in)
Max width	2.10 m (6 ft 10¾ in)
Max height	1.76 m (5 ft 9¼ in)
Floor area	14.97 m² (161.14 sq ft)

Rear baggage compartment volume:
30-passenger version	6.40 m³ (226 cu ft)
all-cargo version	2.70 m³ (95 cu ft)
passenger/cargo version	11.00 m³ (388 cu ft)

Cabin, incl flight deck and baggage compartment:
Total volume	approx 41.8 m³ (1,476 cu ft)

Max available cabin volume (all-cargo version)
31.10 m³ (1,098 cu ft)

AREAS:
Wings, gross	39.43 m² (424.42 sq ft)
Ailerons (total)	2.88 m² (31.00 sq ft)
Trailing-edge flaps (total)	3.23 m² (34.77 sq ft)
Fin, incl dorsal fin	5.74 m² (61.78 sq ft)
Rudder	2.59 m² (27.88 sq ft)
Tailplane	6.10 m² (65.66 sq ft)
Elevator, incl tabs	3.90 m² (41.98 sq ft)

WEIGHTS AND LOADINGS:
Weight empty, equipped	7,070 kg (15,586 lb)
Max fuel	2,659 kg (5,862 lb)
Max payload	3,470 kg (7,650 lb)
Max T-O weight	11,500 kg (25,353 lb)
Max ramp weight	11,580 kg (25,529 lb)
Max landing weight	11,250 kg (24,802 lb)
Max zero-fuel weight	10,500 kg (23,148 lb)
Max wing loading	292 kg/m² (59.8 lb/sq ft)
Max power loading	4.29 kg/kW (7.04 lb/shp)

PERFORMANCE (at max T-O weight, ISA, except where indicated):
Max operating speed
272 knots (504 km/h; 313 mph) EAS
Max level speed at 6,100 m (20,000 ft)
328 knots (608 km/h; 378 mph)
Max cruising speed at 6,100 m (20,000 ft)
298 knots (552 km/h; 343 mph)
Long-range cruising speed at 7,620 m (25,000 ft)
260 knots (482 km/h; 299 mph)
Stalling speed, power off:
flaps up	117 knots (217 km/h; 135 mph) CAS
flaps down	87 knots (162 km/h; 100 mph) CAS

Max rate of climb at S/L 646 m (2,120 ft)/min
Rate of climb at S/L, one engine out 206 m (675 ft)/min
Service ceiling 9,085 m (29,800 ft)
Service ceiling, one engine out 5,240 m (17,200 ft)
FAR Pt 25 T-O field length 1,420 m (4,660 ft)
FAR Pt 135 landing field length, max landing weight at S/L 1,370 m (4,495 ft)
Min ground turning radius 15.76 m (51 ft 8½ in)
Range at 7,620 m (25,000 ft), reserves for 100 nm (185 km; 115 mile) diversion and 45 min hold:
with max (30) passenger payload (2,721 kg; 6,000 lb)
945 nm (1,750 km; 1,088 miles)
with max fuel and 1,920 kg (4,233 lb) payload (21 passengers) 1,610 nm (2,983 km; 1,854 miles)
OPERATIONAL NOISE LEVELS (FAR Pt 36, BCAR-N and ICAO Annex 16):
T-O	78.6 EPNdB
Approach	89.1 EPNdB
Sideline	76.8 EPNdB

EMBRAER/FAMA CBA-123

Details of this twin-turboprop airliner, which is being developed jointly by Embraer and FAMA of Argentina, can be found in the International section.

EMBRAER EMB-145

Embraer revealed its plans to develop this new 45/48-seat twin-turbofan regional transport on 12 June 1989. The fuselage will be based on that of the EMB-120 Brasilia.

First flight is planned for late 1991, and first production deliveries in mid-1993, following international certification to FAR/JAR 25, FAR 121 and FAR 36 (ICAO Annex 16).
TYPE: Twin-turbofan regional transport.
WINGS: Cantilever low-wing monoplane. Wing sections: Embraer EA 270414 at root, EA 370410 at tip, with thickness/chord ratios of 14 and 10 per cent respectively.

Dihedral 6° 30′ from roots. Incidence 2°. Sweepback 4° 54′ at quarter-chord. Semi-monocoque fail-safe main wing box of aluminium alloy with Kevlar/glassfibre skins; leading-edges have a Nomex honeycomb core. Hydraulically assisted plain ailerons, each with trim/servo tab. Two-segment Fowler flap on each trailing-edge. Ground spoiler and speed brake on each wing, forward of flaps. Winglet at each wingtip.
FUSELAGE: Semi-monocoque fail-safe structure of aluminium alloy, of circular cross-section throughout most of its length. Fully pressurised except for nosecone and tailcone.
TAIL UNIT: Cantilever T tail, with main boxes of semi-monocoque aluminium alloy and leading-edges of composite sandwich construction. Fixed incidence tailplane, with trim tab in each elevator. Serially hinged two-segment rudder, with Bertea duplicated hydraulic actuation.
LANDING GEAR: Hydraulically retractable tricycle type, with twin wheels and ERAM oleo-pneumatic shock absorber on each unit. All units retract forward, main units into rear of engine nacelles. Nose unit steerable ±57°.
POWER PLANT: Two 30.03 kN (6,750 lb st) Allison GMA 3007 turbofans, one mounted above and ahead of each wing. Integral fuel tank, with gravity refuelling point, in each wing; pressure refuelling point in starboard wing, outboard of nacelle.
ACCOMMODATION: Flight crew of three, plus a flight observer and a cabin attendant. Standard accommodation for 45 passengers (48 maximum), in three-abreast layout at seat pitch of 79 cm (31 in). Two carry-on baggage cabinets and a toilet at front of cabin; galley and main baggage compartment at rear of cabin; overhead bins along starboard side of cabin. Alternative location for toilet at rear of cabin. Downward opening passenger door at front, and upward sliding baggage door at rear, both on port side. Sideways opening service door at rear on starboard side. Inward opening emergency exit above wing on each side. Entire accommodation, including baggage compartments, pressurised and air-conditioned.
SYSTEMS, AVIONICS AND EQUIPMENT: To be defined.

DIMENSIONS, EXTERNAL:
Wing span	22.57 m (74 ft 0¾ in)
Wing chord: at root	3.22 m (10 ft 6¾ in)
at tip	1.47 m (4 ft 10 in)
Wing aspect ratio	10.19
Length overall	27.08 m (88 ft 10¼ in)
Fuselage: Length	25.47 m (83 ft 6¾ in)
Max diameter	2.28 m (7 ft 5¾ in)
Height overall	6.30 m (20 ft 8 in)
Elevator span	6.94 m (22 ft 9¼ in)
Wheel track	6.58 m (21 ft 7 in)
Wheelbase	10.92 m (35 ft 10 in)
Passenger door (fwd, port):	
Height	1.70 m (5 ft 7 in)
Width	0.77 m (2 ft 6¼ in)
Height to sill (max)	1.57 m (5 ft 1¾ in)
Baggage door (rear, port):	
Height	1.36 m (4 ft 5½ in)
Width	1.30 m (4 ft 3¼ in)
Height to sill (max)	1.89 m (6 ft 2½ in)
Service door (rear, stbd):	
Height	1.38 m (4 ft 6¼ in)
Width	0.67 m (2 ft 2¼ in)
Height to sill (max)	1.76 m (5 ft 9¼ in)
Emergency exits (overwing, each):	
Height	0.92 m (3 ft 0¼ in)
Width	0.51 m (1 ft 8 in)

DIMENSIONS, INTERNAL:
Cabin (excl flight deck, incl galley and toilet):
Length	14.99 m (49 ft 2¼ in)
Max width	2.10 m (6 ft 10¾ in)
Max height	1.82 m (5 ft 11¾ in)

General arrangement of the Embraer EMB-145 twin-turbofan regional transport *(Pilot Press)*

Floor area	24.00 m² (258.3 sq ft)
Volume	48.00 m³ (1,695.1 cu ft)
Baggage volume:	
Rear of cabin	10.2 m³ (360.2 cu ft)
Front of cabin (total)	1.2 m³ (42.38 cu ft)
Overhead bins (total)	1.4 m³ (49.44 cu ft)
AREAS:	
Wings, gross	50.00 m² (538.2 sq ft)
Ailerons (total)	2.88 m² (31.00 sq ft)
Trailing-edge flaps (total)	3.23 m² (34.77 sq ft)
Winglets (total)	2.18 m² (23.47 sq ft)
Ground spoilers (total)	1.30 m² (13.99 sq ft)
Speed brakes (total)	0.78 m² (8.40 sq ft)
Fin	4.68 m² (50.38 sq ft)
Rudder	2.59 m² (27.88 sq ft)
Tailplane	10.00 m² (107.64 sq ft)
Elevators (total, incl tabs)	3.90 m² (41.98 sq ft)
*WEIGHTS AND LOADING (estimated):	
Weight empty, equipped	9,820 kg (21,649 lb)
Max payload	4,500 kg (9,921 lb)
Max fuel weight (usable)	4,130 kg (9,105 lb)
Max ramp weight	17,100 kg (37,700 lb)
Max T-O weight	17,000 kg (37,478 lb)
Max zero-fuel weight	14,320 kg (31,570 lb)
Max landing weight	16,500 kg (36,376 lb)
Max wing loading	340.0 kg/m² (69.64 lb/sq ft)
*PERFORMANCE (estimated, at max T-O weight, ISA):	
Max cruising speed at 6,700 m (22,000 ft)	
	436 knots (808 km/h; 502 mph)
Econ cruising speed at 10,670 m (35,000 ft)	
	365 knots (676 km/h; 420 mph)
Stalling speed, flaps down, power off	
	91 knots (169 km/h; 105 mph)
Max rate of climb at S/L	1,280 m (4,200 ft)/min
Rate of climb at S/L, one engine out	244 m (800 ft)/min
Service ceiling	12,200 m (40,000 ft)
Service ceiling, one engine out	5,180 m (17,000 ft)
T-O field length	1,330 m (4,365 ft)
Landing field length	1,400 m (4,595 ft)
Min ground turning radius	13.00 m (42 ft 8 in)
Range, with reserves for 100 nm (185 km; 115 mile)	
diversion, 10% block fuel remaining, and 30 min hold:	
with 45 passengers (4,082 kg; 9,000 lb payload)	
	870 nm (1,612 km; 1,001 miles)
with max fuel	1,340 nm (2,483 km; 1,543 miles)

See Addenda for revised data

EMBRAER EMB-312 TUCANO (TOUCAN)
Brazilian Air Force designation: T-27

Design of the EMB-312 began in January 1978 as part of a programme to develop a new basic trainer for the Brazilian Air Force. On 6 December that year a contract was received from the Departamento de Pesquisas e Desenvolvimento (Department of Research and Development) of the Brazilian Ministry of Aeronautics, for two flying prototypes plus two airframes for static and fatigue testing.

Characteristics of the EMB-312 include high manoeuvrability, short take-off and landing, the ability to operate from unprepared runways, and a high degree of stability. In addition to meeting the requirements of FAR Pt 23 Appendix A, the aircraft meets MIL and CAA Section K specifications.

The first prototype (Brazilian Air Force serial number 1300) first flew on 16 August 1980, and the second (1301) on 10 December 1980. A third prototype (PP-ZDK), modified to production standard, flew on 16 August 1982.

The EMB-312 is designated **T-27** by the Brazilian Air Force (FAB), to which the 118 Tucanos ordered originally were delivered between September 1983 and September 1986. In January 1990 the FAB ordered a further 10, for delivery by April 1990; it has options on a further 40.

EMB-312 Tucano tandem two-seat trainer of the Venezuelan Air Force

The Egyptian government ordered 120 Tucanos in September 1983: 40 for its own air force and 80 for Iraq, with options on 60 more, of which 20 would be for Iraq. Embraer built the first 10 of these, which were ferried to Egypt from October 1984 in flyaway condition. Kits for the remaining 110 have been delivered to AOI in Egypt (which see), which is completing these aircraft under licence. Egypt ordered an additional 14 Tucano kits in early 1989. By 1 February 1990 deliveries had also been made to the air forces of Argentina (30), Honduras (12), Iran (five of 15 on order), Paraguay (six), Peru (20) and Venezuela (31). Tucano deliveries then totalled 396 out of 507 firm orders; options were held for a further 115. The French government has announced its intention to order 60 Tucanos, with options on a further 15. These are expected to have strengthened wings similar to those of the Tucanos being built for the RAF.

The version selected for the Royal Air Force, with British equipment and a more powerful 820 kW (1,100 shp) Garrett TPE331 engine, is being built by Short Brothers and is described under that company's entry in the UK section. The Garrett engined prototype (PP-ZTC) made its first of six flights in Brazil on 14 February 1986. It was then dismantled and airfreighted to the UK for continued testing. This aircraft, and kits for 25 of the 130 ordered by the RAF, are included in the 396 delivery total in the preceding paragraph.

The following description applies to the standard Embraer version, production of which was at the rate of four to five per month in 1989-90:

TYPE: Tandem two-seat basic trainer.

WINGS: Cantilever low-wing monoplane. Wing section NACA 63₂A-415 at root, NACA 63A-212 at tip. Dihedral 5° 30′ at 30 per cent chord. Incidence 1° 25′.

Geometric twist 2° 13′. Sweepback 0° 43′ 26″ at quarter-chord. Aluminium alloy two-spar torsion box structure of 2024-T3511 extrusions and 2024-T3 sheet. Single-slotted electrically actuated trailing-edge flaps of 2024-T3, supported on 4130 steel tracks. Frise constant chord balanced ailerons. Electrically actuated trim tab in, and small geared tab on, each aileron.

FUSELAGE: Conventional semi-monocoque structure of 2024-T3 aluminium alloy.

TAIL UNIT: Cantilever all-metal structure, of similar construction to wings. Non-swept fin, with dorsal fin, and horn balanced rudder. Non-swept fixed incidence tailplane and balanced elevators. Small fillet forward of tailplane root on each side. Electromechanically actuated spring trim in rudder and port elevator.

LANDING GEAR: Hydraulically retractable tricycle type, with single wheel and Piper oleo-pneumatic shock absorber on each unit. Accumulator for emergency extension in the event of hydraulic system failure. Shimmy damper on nose unit. Rearward retracting steerable nose unit; main units retract inward into wings. Parker Hannifin 40-130 mainwheels, Oldi-DI-1.555-02-OL nosewheel. Tyre sizes 6.50-10 (Type III, 8-ply rating) on mainwheels, 5.00-5 (Type III, 6-ply rating) on nosewheel. Tyre pressures (plus or minus 0.21 bars; 3 lb/sq in in each case) are 5.17 bars (75 lb/sq in) on mainwheels, 4.48 bars (65 lb/sq in) on nosewheel. Parker Hannifin 30-95A hydraulic mainwheel brakes.

POWER PLANT: One 559 kW (750 shp) Pratt & Whitney Canada PT6A-25C turboprop, driving a Hartzell HC-B3TN-3C/T10178-8R three-blade constant-speed fully-feathering reversible-pitch propeller with spinner. Single-lever combined control for engine throttling and propeller pitch adjustment. Two integral fuel tanks in each wing, total capacity 694 litres (183.3 US gallons; 152.7 Imp gallons). Fuel tanks lined with anti-detonation plastics foam. Gravity refuelling point in each wing upper surface. Fuel system allows nominally for up to 30 s of inverted flight. (Aircraft has been test flown inverted for up to 10 min.) Provision for two underwing ferry fuel tanks, total capacity 660 litres (174.4 US gallons; 145 Imp gallons).

ACCOMMODATION: Instructor and pupil in tandem, on Martin-Baker BR8LC lightweight ejection seats, in air-conditioned cockpit. One-piece fully transparent vacuum formed canopy, opening sideways to starboard, with internal and external jettison provisions. Rear seat elevated. Dual controls standard. Baggage compartment in rear fuselage, with access via door on port side. Cockpit heating and canopy demisting by engine bleed air.

SYSTEMS: Freon cycle air-conditioning system, with engine driven compressor. Single hydraulic system, consisting basically of (a) control unit, including reservoir with usable capacity of 1.9 litres (0.5 US gallon; 0.42 Imp gallon); (b) an engine driven pump with nominal pressure of 131 bars (1,900 lb/sq in) and nominal flow rate of 4.6 litres (1.22 US gallons; 1.01 Imp gallons)/min at 3,800 rpm; (c) landing gear and gear door actuators; (d) filter; (e) shutoff valve; and (f) hydraulic fluid to MIL-H-5606. Under normal operation, hydraulic system actuates landing gear extension/retraction and control of gear doors. Landing gear extension can be performed under

Embraer EMB-312 Tucano basic trainer (Pratt & Whitney Canada PT6A-25C turboprop) *(Pilot Press)*

emergency operation; emergency retraction may also be possible during landing and T-O with engine running. Reservoir and system are suitable for aerobatics. No pneumatic system. 28V DC electrical power provided by a 6kW starter/generator, 26Ah battery and, for 115V and 26V AC power at 400Hz, a 250VA inverter. Diluter-demand oxygen system conforms to MIL-C-5887 and is supplied individually to each occupant by six MS 21227 D2 type cylinders (total capacity approx 1,200 litres; 317 US gallons; 264 Imp gallons) at a pressure of 31 bars (450 lb/sq in).

AVIONICS AND EQUIPMENT: Standard avionics include two Collins VHF-20A transceivers; two Collins 387C-4 audio systems, one Embraer radio transferring system; Telephonics audio control panel; one Collins VIR-31A VOR/ILS/marker beacon receiver; one Collins TDR-90 ATC transponder; one Collins DME-40; one Collins PN-101 gyromagnetic compass; and one Collins ADF-60A. Landing light in each wing leading-edge; taxiing lights on nosewheel unit.

ARMAMENT: Two hardpoints under each wing, each stressed for a max load of 250 kg (551 lb). Typical loads, on GB100-20-36B pylons, include two 0.30 in C2 machine-gun pods, each with 500 rds; four 25 lb Mk 76 practice bombs; four 250 lb Mk 81 general purpose bombs; or four LM-37/7A or LM-70/7 launchers, each with seven rockets (Avibras SBAT-37 and SBAT-70 respectively). Fixed reflex-type gunsight.

DIMENSIONS, EXTERNAL:

Wing span	11.14 m (36 ft 6½ in)
Wing chord: at root	2.30 m (7 ft 6½ in)
at tip	1.07 m (3 ft 6⅛ in)
Wing aspect ratio	6.4
Length overall	9.86 m (32 ft 4¼ in)
Length of fuselage (excl rudder)	8.53 m (27 ft 11⅞ in)
Fuselage: Max width	1.00 m (3 ft 3¼ in)
Max depth	1.55 m (5 ft 1 in)
Height overall (static)	3.40 m (11 ft 1¾ in)
Tailplane span	4.66 m (15 ft 3½ in)
Wheel track	3.76 m (12 ft 4 in)
Wheelbase	3.16 m (10 ft 4½ in)
Propeller diameter	2.36 m (7 ft 9 in)
Propeller ground clearance (static)	0.33 m (1 ft 1 in)
Baggage compartment door:	
Height	0.60 m (1 ft 11⅝ in)
Width	0.54 m (1 ft 9¼ in)
Height to sill	1.25 m (4 ft 1¼ in)

DIMENSIONS, INTERNAL:

Cockpits: Combined length	2.90 m (9 ft 6⅛ in)
Max height	1.55 m (5 ft 1 in)
Max width	0.85 m (2 ft 9½ in)
Baggage compartment volume	0.17 m³ (6.0 cu ft)

AREAS:

Wings, gross	19.40 m² (208.82 sq ft)
Ailerons (total)	1.97 m² (21.20 sq ft)
Trailing-edge flaps (total)	2.58 m² (27.77 sq ft)
Fin, incl dorsal fin	2.29 m² (24.65 sq ft)
Rudder, incl tab	1.38 m² (14.85 sq ft)
Tailplane, incl fillets	4.77 m² (51.34 sq ft)
Elevators, incl tab	2.00 m² (21.53 sq ft)

WEIGHTS AND LOADINGS:

Basic weight empty	1,810 kg (3,991 lb)
Max internal fuel load (usable)	529 kg (1,166 lb)
Max external stores load	1,000 kg (2,205 lb)
Max T-O weight: clean	2,550 kg (5,622 lb)
with external load	3,175 kg (7,000 lb)
Max ramp weight	3,195 kg (7,044 lb)
Max landing weight: clean	2,800 kg (6,173 lb)
Max zero-fuel weight	2,050 kg (4,519 lb)
Max wing loading: clean	131.4 kg/m² (26.92 lb/sq ft)
with external stores	163.7 kg/m² (33.52 lb/sq ft)
Max power loading: clean	4.56 kg/kW (7.50 lb/shp)
with external stores	5.68 kg/kW (9.33 lb/shp)

PERFORMANCE (at max clean T-O weight except where indicated):

Never-exceed speed	
	280 knots (519 km/h; 322 mph) EAS
Max level speed at 3,050 m (10,000 ft)	
	242 knots (448 km/h; 278 mph)
Max cruising speed at 3,050 m (10,000 ft)	
	222 knots (411 km/h; 255 mph)
Econ cruising speed at 3,050 m (10,000 ft)	
	172 knots (319 km/h; 198 mph)
Stalling speed, power off:	
flaps and landing gear up	
	72 knots (133 km/h; 83 mph) EAS
flaps and landing gear down	
	67 knots (124 km/h; 77 mph) EAS
Max rate of climb at S/L	680 m (2,231 ft)/min
Service ceiling	9,150 m (30,000 ft)
T-O run	380 m (1,250 ft)
T-O to 15 m (50 ft)	710 m (2,330 ft)
Landing from 15 m (50 ft)	605 m (1,985 ft)
Landing run	370 m (1,214 ft)
Range at 6,100 m (20,000 ft) with max fuel, 30 min reserves	995 nm (1,844 km; 1,145 miles)
Ferry range at 6,100 m (20,000 ft) with underwing tanks	1,797 nm (3,330 km; 2,069 miles)
Endurance on internal fuel at econ cruising speed at 6,100 m (20,000 ft), 30 min reserves	approx 5 h

g limits: fully Aerobatic category, at max clean T-O

weight	+6/−3
at max T-O weight with external stores	+4.4/−2.2

EMBRAER EMB-201A IPANEMA

The original version of this agricultural aircraft was designed to Brazilian Ministry of Agriculture specifications, and the EMB-200 prototype (PP-ZIP) made its first flight on 30 July 1970. A type certificate was granted on 14 December 1971.

Details of the EMB-200/200A (73 built), EMB-201 (200 built) and EMB-201R (three built) can be found in the 1977-78 and previous editions of *Jane's*. The current production version, first flown on 10 March 1977, is the EMB-201A, of which 355 had been sold by 1 January 1990, bringing total Ipanema sales (all versions) to 631. The 600th aircraft was delivered on 23 March 1988.

Manufacture of the EMB-201A was transferred to Embraer's Neiva subsidiary during the second half of 1981.

An improved version was launched at the end of 1988 with an enlarged windscreen; redesigned canopy in glassfibre composites, with two overhead windows; doors with built-in side windows, fitted with triple-lock and jettison provisions; an airscoop at the top of the canopy front edge, to improve cockpit ventilation, and one on the fin leading-edge to pressurise the interior of the rear fuselage; an ergonomically improved cockpit and instrument layout; and new engine exhaust mufflers. New optional items include a Hartzell three-blade variable-pitch propeller; ram air pressure generator for use with the liquid spray system; improved lightweight spraybooms; smaller and lighter Micronair AU5000 rotary atomisers; and a trapezoidal spreader with adjustable inlet to improve application of dry chemicals.

TYPE: Single-seat agricultural aircraft.

WINGS: Cantilever low-wing monoplane. Wing section NACA 23015 (modified), with cambered leading-edges. Dihedral 7° from roots. Incidence 3°. All-metal single-spar structure of 2024 aluminium alloy with all-metal Frise ailerons outboard and all-metal slotted flaps on trailing-edge, and detachable cambered leading-edges. No tabs. Cambered wingtips standard.

FUSELAGE: Rectangular section all-metal safe-life structure, of welded 4130 steel tube with removable skin panels of 2024 aluminium alloy. Structure is specially treated against chemical corrosion.

TAIL UNIT: Cantilever two-spar all-metal structure of 2024 aluminium alloy. Slight sweepback on fin and rudder. Fixed incidence tailplane. Trim tab in starboard elevator.

LANDING GEAR: Non-retractable main- and tailwheels, with oleo shock absorbers in main units. Tailwheel has tapered spring shock absorber. Mainwheels and tyres size 8.50-10. Tyre pressures: main, 2.07-2.41 bars (30-35 lb/sq in); tailwheel, 3.79 bars (55 lb/sq in). Hydraulic disc brakes on mainwheels.

POWER PLANT: One 224 kW (300 hp) Textron Lycoming IO-540-K1J5D flat-six engine, driving a Hartzell two-blade constant-speed metal propeller with spinner. Integral fuel tanks in each wing leading-edge, with total capacity of 292 litres (77.1 US gallons; 64.2 Imp gallons). Refuelling point on top of each tank. Oil capacity 12 litres (3.2 US gallons; 2.6 Imp gallons).

ACCOMMODATION: Single horizontally/vertically adjustable seat in fully enclosed cabin with bottom-hinged window/door on each side. Ventilation system in cabin. Inertial shoulder harness standard.

SYSTEM: 28V DC electrical system supplied by a 24Ah BB639/U battery and a Bosch K.1 28V 35A alternator. Power receptacle for external battery (AN-2552-3A type) on port side of forward fuselage.

AVIONICS AND EQUIPMENT: Standard VFR avionics include 720-channel Collins VHF-251S transceiver and Collins RCR-650 ADF transceiver. Hopper for agricultural chemicals has capacity of 680 litres (179.6 US gallons; 149.5 Imp gallons) liquid or 750 kg (1,653 lb) dry. Dusting system below centre of fuselage. Spraybooms or Micronair atomisers aft of or above wing trailing-edges respectively.

DIMENSIONS, EXTERNAL:

Wing span	11.20 m (36 ft 9 in)
Wing chord (constant)	1.71 m (5 ft 7½ in)
Wing aspect ratio	6.3
Length overall (tail up)	7.43 m (24 ft 4½ in)
Height overall (tail down)	2.20 m (7 ft 2½ in)
Fuselage: Max width	0.93 m (3 ft 0½ in)
Tailplane span	3.66 m (12 ft 0 in)
Wheel track	2.20 m (7 ft 2½ in)
Wheelbase	5.20 m (17 ft 7¼ in)
Propeller diameter	2.20 m (7 ft 2½ in)

DIMENSIONS, INTERNAL:

Cockpit: Max length	1.20 m (3 ft 11¼ in)
Max width	0.85 m (2 ft 9½ in)
Max height	1.34 m (4 ft 4¾ in)

AREAS:

Wings, gross	19.94 m² (214.63 sq ft)
Ailerons (total)	1.60 m² (17.22 sq ft)
Trailing-edge flaps (total)	2.30 m² (24.76 sq ft)
Fin	0.58 m² (6.24 sq ft)

Embraer Ipanema agricultural aircraft, the 600th to be built

Embraer EMB-201A Ipanema single-seat agricultural aircraft *(Pilot Press)*

Rudder	0.63 m² (6.78 sq ft)					
Tailplane	3.17 m² (34.12 sq ft)					
Elevators (total, incl tab)	1.50 m² (16.15 sq ft)					

WEIGHTS AND LOADINGS (N: Normal; R: Restricted category):

Weight empty: N, R	1,011 kg (2,229 lb)
Max payload: N, R	750 kg (1,653 lb)
Max T-O and landing weight: N	1,550 kg (3,417 lb)
R	1,800 kg (3,968 lb)
Max wing loading: N	77.75 kg/m² (15.92 lb/sq ft)
R	90.29 kg/m² (18.49 lb/sq ft)
Max power loading: N	6.92 kg/kW (11.39 lb/hp)
R	8.03 kg/kW (13.23 lb/hp)

PERFORMANCE (at max T-O weight, clean configuration, ISA):

Never-exceed speed:	
N	147 knots (272 km/h; 169 mph)
R	113 knots (209 km/h; 130 mph)
Max level speed at S/L:	
N	124 knots (230 km/h; 143 mph)
R	121 knots (225 km/h; 140 mph)

Max cruising speed (75% power) at 1,830 m (6,000 ft):	
N	115 knots (212 km/h; 132 mph)
R	110 knots (204 km/h; 127 mph)
Stalling speed, power off (N):	
flaps up	56 knots (103 km/h; 64 mph)
8° flap	54 knots (100 km/h; 62 mph)
30° flap	50 knots (92 km/h; 57 mph)
Stalling speed, power off (R):	
flaps up	60 knots (110 km/h; 68 mph)
8° flap	58 knots (107 km/h; 66 mph)
30° flap	53 knots (99 km/h; 61 mph)
Max rate of climb at S/L, 8° flap:	
N	283 m (930 ft)/min
R	201 m (660 ft)/min
Service ceiling, 8° flap: R	3,470 m (11,385 ft)
T-O run at S/L, 8° flap, asphalt runway:	
N	200 m (656 ft)
R	354 m (1,160 ft)
T-O to 15 m (50 ft), conditions as above:	
N	333 m (1,093 ft)
R	564 m (1,850 ft)

Landing from 15 m (50 ft) at S/L, 30° flap, asphalt runway: N	440 m (1,444 ft)
R	500 m (1,640 ft)
Landing run, conditions as above: N	153 m (502 ft)
R	170 m (558 ft)
Range at 1,830 m (6,000 ft), no reserves:	
N	506 nm (938 km; 583 miles)
R	474 nm (878 km; 545 miles)

EMBRAER-PIPER LIGHT AIRCRAFT PROGRAMME

Detailed descriptions of Piper aircraft built under licence by Embraer can be found in the US section of this and earlier editions of *Jane's*. Manufacture is undertaken by Embraer's subsidiary, Neiva. The following types were in production in 1990:

EMB-720D Minuano. Piper PA-32-301 Saratoga.
EMB-810D Seneca III. Piper PA-34-220T Seneca III.

HELIBRAS
HELICÓPTEROS DO BRASIL S/A

Rua Projetada Um 200, Distrito Industrial, Caixa Postal 184, 37500 Itajubá, MG

Telephone: 55 (35) 622 3366 and 622 2455

Telex: 31 2602 HLBR BR

PRESIDENT: Fernando Antonio Rainho Thomaz Ribeiro
COMMERCIAL DIRECTOR: Hilton Amaral
PUBLIC RELATIONS: Odilon Martins de Andrade

Formed in 1978 and owned jointly by Engesa of Brazil (60 per cent), Aerospatiale of France (28 per cent), the state government of Minas Gerais (11 per cent) and Aerofoto of Brazil (0.18 per cent), Helibras is assembling and moving towards local manufacture of Aerospatiale SA 315B Lama, SA 350B and B₁ Ecureuil single-engined helicopters, the twin-engined AS 355F₂ Ecureuil, and the AS 565AA (formerly AS 365K) Panther. Of the total assembly hours per helicopter, approx 30 per cent involve the incorporation of locally manufactured items. The first assembly hall was officially inaugurated on 28 March 1980. The complete facility will extend over an area of 206,650 m² (2,224,360 sq ft), of which 9,747 m² (104,916 sq ft) is covered at present. A total of 320 people was employed in 1989.

HELIBRAS HB 315B GAVIÃO

These are the Brazilian name and designation of the SA 315B Lama assembled by Helibras, the first of which was completed during the latter half of 1979. Production by May 1989 included six for the Bolivian Air Force and one civil example for a customer in Chile.

HELIBRAS HB 350B, HB 350B1, HB 350L1 and HB 355F2 ESQUILO

All Brazilian models of the Ecureuil have the name Esquilo, the HB 350B and B1 corresponding to the French single-engined AS 350B and B₁ and the HB 355F2 to the twin-engined AS 355F₂. Deliveries began in 1979, and by early 1990 totalled more than 200 Esquilos including the twin-engined version. These included 41 HB 350B/B1s and HB 355F2s for the Brazilian Air Force (designations **CH-50**, **TH-50**, **CH-55** and **VH-55**), 20 for the Brazilian Navy (nine **UH-12** and 11 **UH-12B**), 16 HB 350L1s for the Brazilian Army, and others for the Brazilian police and civilian customers. The Brazilian Navy Esquilos, which serve with the 1° Esquadrão de Helicópteros de Emprego Geral (squadron of general purpose helicopters), are equipped to carry two Avibrás LM-70/7 pods each containing seven SBAT 70 mm rockets, or two FN twin 7.62 mm MAG machine-gun pods, and a door mounted MAG

pedestal. Those for the Brazilian Army, delivered to the 1st Aviation Battalion at Taubaté, São Paulo, in 1989, are equipped for tactical support and reconnaissance. Equipment can include a 20 mm gun and 2.75 in unguided rockets, or anti-tank missiles and a HeliTOW sighting system. HB 350Bs have been sold to foreign civil customers in Argentina (three), Bolivia (four), and Venezuela (three), and six military examples to Paraguay (Air Force four, Navy two).

An aeromedical version of the Esquilo was launched in February 1989. Equipment includes an electrocardiograph, respirator, pacemaker, stretchers, battery operated incubator, oxygen and compressed air cylinders, first aid kit, and a four-way electrical socket for 115V AC (60Hz) and 12V DC power. Apart from the pilot, this version can carry a doctor, nurse and two stretcher patients.

HELIBRAS AS 565 PANTHER

Deliveries of the first 10 Panthers in the present 36-aircraft Brazilian Army contract began at the end of 1989, with a further 16 following in 1990; these 26 aircraft are of Aerospatiale manufacture. Helibras will assemble the final 10 from French built kits, delivering them by mid-1991. Brazilian Army designation is **HM-1**

Left: An HB 350B Esquilo of the Paraguayan Air Force. Helibras production also includes the twin-engined HB 355F2 Esquilo, illustrated on the right, which has the FAB designation VH-55

IPE
INDÚSTRIA PARANAENSE DE ESTRUTURAS

Rua Jeronimo Durski 357, 80430 Curitiba, Paraná
Telephone: 55 (41) 242 2324
MANAGER: Eng J. C. Boscardin

IPE 04

No news of this two-seat training aircraft has been received since 1987. All known details, and a three-view drawing, can be found in the 1989-90 *Jane's*.

NEIVA
INDÚSTRIA AERONÁUTICA NEIVA S/A (Subsidiary of Embraer)

Rua Nossa Senhora de Fátima 360, Vila Antártica, Caixa Postal 10, 18600 Botucatu, SP
Telephone: 55 (149) 22 1010
Telex: 142 423 SOAN BR
PRESIDENT: Eng Antonio Garcia da Silveira
ENGINEERING MANAGER: Luíz Carlos Benetti

Neiva, which in January 1990 had a workforce of 519 and factory area of 20,580 m² (221,521 sq ft), was formed in 1954 and became a wholly owned subsidiary of Embraer on 10 March 1980. It designed and built the U-42/L-42 Regente utility/liaison light aircraft and the T-25/AT-25 Universal trainer/light attack aircraft, which continue in

service with the Brazilian Air Force. Currently, Neiva participates in Embraer's general aviation programme, being responsible for all production of the EMB-720D Minuano and EMB-810D Seneca III. It had delivered 1,421 licence-built Piper aircraft of these and other types by January 1990. For many years Neiva has built fuselages for the Embraer Ipanema, and since 1981 has been entirely responsible for Ipanema engineering, manufacture and assembly. The 597th Ipanema, completed in November 1987, was the 2,000th aircraft to be produced at the Neiva facility. The company also produces subassemblies and components for the Embraer Bandeirante (wings, engine nacelles, pilots' seats, hoses and tubing) and Tucano (wing flaps, elevators, tailplanes, fins, rudders, fuselage rear sections and engine exhaust stacks).

NEIVA NE-821 CARAJÁ

Responsibility for the EMB-820C Navajo was transferred to Neiva in mid-1983, and in 1984 (first flight 9 March) four of the last five Embraer assembled examples were converted to Comanchero 500B eight-seat executive configuration (see Schafer entry in US section), in which form they are designated NE-821 Carajá. Deliveries began in November of that year. A total of 36 had been delivered by 1 January 1990. Brazilian certification covers the use of either PT6A-27 or PT6A-34 engines, flat rated in both cases at 410 kW (550 shp) and driving Hartzell three-blade constant-speed propellers. Further details of the Carajá, and a photograph, can be found in the 1989-90 *Jane's*.

SUPER ROTOR

M.M. SUPER ROTOR INDÚSTRIA AERONÁUTICA LTDA

Rua Itapeti 541, Tatuapé, 03324 São Paulo, SP
Telephone: 55 (11) 295 8187
DIRECTOR: José Montalvá Perez

SUPER ROTOR AC-4 ANDORINHA

This all-Brazilian single-seat autogyro was designed in 1970, as a private venture, by Eng Altair Coelho. The prototype first flew in December 1972, being sold subsequently to Sr Francisco Mattos Jr, who introduced a number of modifications before obtaining Brazilian CTA certification in January 1985. It is produced in both ready to fly and kit forms. By early 1990 domestic and foreign orders for the AC-4, including kits, totalled 307.

TYPE: Single-seat autogyro.
ROTOR SYSTEM AND DRIVE: Single rotor, with two blades of NACA H-12 (modified) section, each attached to hub by 10 bolts. Aluminium alloy blades (6061-T6 spars and 0.8 mm sheet skins), each with tab inset from tip. No blade folding or rotor brake. Engine power take-off for pre-spinning rotor before T-O.
FUSELAGE: Welded truss structure of SAE 1025 carbon steel tube, with nose fairing and windscreen.
TAIL UNIT: Fin and rudder only, latter with trim tab.
LANDING GEAR: Non-retractable unsprung tricycle type, with belt type mainwheel brakes and steerable nosewheel. Goodyear tyres, size 5.00-5 (main) and 3.50-5 (nose); pressure (all three tyres) 1.38 bars (20 lb/sq in). Streamline fairing on nosewheel.
POWER PLANT: One 63 kW (85 hp) modified VW 1600 motorcar engine, driving a two-blade wooden pusher propeller. Single aluminium fuel tank beneath engine, capacity 40 litres (10.5 US gallons; 8.8 Imp gallons). Oil capacity 3 litres (0.8 US gallon; 0.66 Imp gallon).
ACCOMMODATION: Single open seat for pilot.
EQUIPMENT: 7.5Ah battery.
DIMENSIONS, EXTERNAL:

Main rotor diameter	7.44 m (24 ft 5 in)
Main rotor blade chord	0.185 m (7.3 in)
Length overall, excl rotors	3.75 m (12 ft 3¾ in)
Height to top of rotor head	2.36 m (7 ft 9 in)
Width overall, excl main rotor	1.70 m (5 ft 7 in)
Wheel track	1.446 m (4 ft 9 in)
Propeller diameter	1.51 m (4 ft 11½ in)

AREAS:

Main rotor blades, each	0.63 m² (6.78 sq ft)
Main rotor disc	43.47 m² (467.9 sq ft)
Fin	0.21 m² (2.26 sq ft)
Rudder	0.36 m² (3.88 sq ft)

WEIGHTS AND LOADINGS:

Basic weight empty	190 kg (419 lb)
Max T-O weight	310 kg (683 lb)
Max disc loading	7.13 kg/m² (1.46 lb/sq ft)
Max power loading	4.92 kg/kW (8.04 lb/hp)

Super Rotor M-1 Montalvá 1 two-seat autogyro

PERFORMANCE (at max T-O weight):

Never-exceed speed	97 knots (180 km/h; 112 mph)
Max level speed	86 knots (160 km/h; 99 mph)
Max cruising speed	70 knots (130 km/h; 81 mph)
Econ cruising speed	59 knots (110 km/h; 68 mph)
Max rate of climb at S/L	366 m (1,200 ft)/min
Service ceiling	3,660 m (12,000 ft)
T-O run	35 m (115 ft)
T-O to 15 m (50 ft)	100 m (328 ft)
Landing from 15 m (50 ft)	30 m (99 ft)
Landing run	10 m (33 ft)
Range with max fuel	243 nm (450 km; 280 miles)

SUPER ROTOR M-1 MONTALVÁ

Design of this two-seat development of the AC-4 started in June 1984, and it flew for the first time in March 1985. Production aircraft became available in the Summer of that year, and 75, all to firm orders, had been completed by January 1990.

TYPE: Tandem two-seat autogyro.
ROTOR SYSTEM AND DRIVE: As described for AC-4, but rotor is of increased diameter.
AIRFRAME: As described for AC-4, except for longer fuselage and increased mainwheel tyre pressure of 1.72 bars (25 lb/sq in).

POWER PLANT: One 72 kW (97 hp) modified VW 1600 engine and 27 litre (7 US gallon; 6 Imp gallon) fuel tank; otherwise as described for AC-4.
ACCOMMODATION: Two open seats in tandem.
EQUIPMENT: 7.5Ah battery.
DIMENSIONS, EXTERNAL: As for AC-4 except:

Main rotor diameter	8.14 m (26 ft 8½ in)
Main rotor blade chord	0.21 m (8¼ in)
Length overall, excl rotors	4.38 m (14 ft 4½ in)
Height to top of rotor head	2.68 m (8 ft 9½ in)
Wheel track	1.90 m (6 ft 3 in)

AREAS: As for AC-4 except:

Main rotor blades, each	0.77 m² (8.29 sq ft)
Main rotor disc	52.04 m² (560.2 sq ft)

WEIGHTS AND LOADINGS:

Basic weight empty	174 kg (383 lb)
Max T-O weight	374 kg (825 lb)
Max disc loading	7.19 kg/m² (1.47 lb/sq ft)
Max power loading	5.19 kg/kW (8.50 lb/hp)

PERFORMANCE (at max T-O weight): As for AC-4 except:

Max level speed	75 knots (140 km/h; 87 mph)
Max cruising speed	65 knots (120 km/h; 75 mph)
Econ cruising speed	54 knots (100 km/h; 62 mph)
Max rate of climb at S/L	213 m (700 ft)/min
T-O run	160 m (525 ft)
T-O to 15 m (50 ft)	250 m (820 ft)
Range with max fuel	118 nm (220 km; 136 miles)

CANADA

AIRTECH

AIRTECH CANADA

Peterborough Municipal Airport, PO Box 415, Peterborough, Ontario K9J 6Z3
Telephone: 1 (705) 743 9483
Telex: 06-962912
Fax: 1 (705) 749 0841
PRESIDENT: John O'Dwyer
CHIEF ENGINEER: James C. Mewett
PRESS RELATIONS: Alison M. Mewett

Airtech specialises in retrofitting versions of the de Havilland Canada Otter and Beaver with more powerful Polish built engines that offer increased climb rates and considerably greater fuel economy, at lower power settings, than the original engines which they replace. It has also designed, manufactured, tested and installed modifications (in particular, auxiliary fuel tanks and medevac equipment) for various types of aircraft including the Cessna 401, 414 and 421, Piper PA-31 and PA-42, Mitsubishi MU-2 and Fairchild Metro IIB.

AIRTECH CANADA DHC-3/1000 OTTER

Airtech Canada refitted eight de Havilland Canada DHC-3 Otters with Polish PZL-3S radial engines. Details of this DHC-3/PZL-3S version can be found in the 1983-84 *Jane's*.

Following the first flight of a prototype on 25 August 1983, the Otter conversion is now offered with a 746 kW (1,000 hp) Polish ASz-62IR engine instead of the 447 kW (600 hp) PZL-3S. Seven of these conversions, designated DHC-3/1000, were flying in North and South America by February 1989.

POWER PLANT: One 746 kW (1,000 hp) PZL Kalisz ASz-62IR nine-cylinder aircooled radial engine, driving a PZL Warszawa AW-2-30 four-blade constant-speed propeller. Fuel capacity as for standard DHC-3; oil capacity 41 litres (10.8 US gallons; 9 Imp gallons).

Airtech Canada's DHC-3/1000 Otter conversion, powered by a PZL Kalisz ASz-62IR radial engine

WEIGHTS:

Weight empty, equipped	2,200 kg (4,850 lb)
Max T-O weight	3,628 kg (8,000 lb)

PERFORMANCE (at max T-O weight): As for standard DHC-3 except:

Never-exceed speed	157 knots (291 km/h; 181 mph)
Max level speed and max cruising speed at S/L	
	125 knots (232 km/h; 144 mph)
Econ cruising speed at 1,525 m (5,000 ft)	
	117 knots (217 km/h; 135 mph)

Max rate of climb at S/L:

at T-O power	552 m (1,810 ft)/min
at 602 kW (808 hp) max continuous power	
	421 m (1,380 ft)/min
Service ceiling	5,945 m (19,500 ft)
T-O run	91 m (300 ft)
T-O to 15 m (50 ft)	182 m (600 ft)

Max range, allowances for 10 min warm-up, T-O, climb to 1,525 m (5,000 ft), and reserves for 45 min at cruise power 800 nm (1,482 km; 921 miles)

AIRTECH CANADA DHC-2/PZL-3S BEAVER

Airtech Canada introduced a conversion of the DHC-2 Beaver with the PZL-3S engine at the request of operators who wanted an increase in power to provide improved performance and safer operation from short airstrips. Four such conversions had been completed by early 1989.

POWER PLANT: One 447 kW (600 hp) PZL-3S seven-cylinder aircooled radial engine, driving a PZL US132000A four-blade constant-speed propeller. Fuel capacity 359 litres (95 US gallons; 79 Imp gallons), or 523 litres (138 US gallons; 115 Imp gallons) with auxiliary tank in each wingtip.

WEIGHTS:

Weight empty	1,419 kg (3,129 lb)
Useful load with full fuel	636 kg (1,402 lb)
Max T-O weight	2,313 kg (5,100 lb)

PERFORMANCE:

Normal operating speed and max cruising speed	
	126 knots (233 km/h; 145 mph) IAS
Max rate of climb at S/L	488 m (1,600 ft)/min
T-O to 15 m (50 ft)	305 m (1,000 ft)

AIRTECH CANADA DC-3/2000

In an attempt to prolong the useful life of the already long-lived DC-3, Airtech Canada successfully replaced the existing 895 kW (1,200 hp) Pratt & Whitney R-1830 engines of an ex-Spanish Air Force C-47, converted to a DC-3C, with 746 kW (1,000 hp) PZL ASz-62IR radials driving PZL AW-2 four-blade propellers modified by Airtech to provide full feathering capability. As the prototype DC-3/2000 (C-CJDM), it made its first flight on 6 March 1987. Flight testing was completed in 1987, indicating a lower single-engine climb performance than with the original engines. Airtech feels that the resultant decreased payload

Airtech Canada DHC-2 Beaver converted to a Polish PZL-3S radial engine and four-blade propeller

makes the 1,000 hp engine conversion commercially unviable, and planned to install a pair of 895 kW (1,200 hp) engines currently being developed by WSK-PZL Kalisz.

Delivery of these engines, which are externally identical to the ASz-62IR, was expected in mid-1989.

BELL
BELL HELICOPTER TEXTRON
(a Division of Textron Canada Ltd)

12800 rue de l'Avenir, St Janvier, Quebec J0N 1L0
Telephone: 1 (514) 437 3400
PRESIDENT: Fred Hubbard III
EXECUTIVE VICE-PRESIDENT: Jack Cadieux
VICE-PRESIDENT, OPERATIONS: E. H. Barnett

On 7 October 1983 the Canadian government announced the signing of a memorandum of understanding under which Bell had been selected to establish a helicopter industry in Canada, the second largest user of helicopters outside the Soviet bloc. The new 34,560 m² (372,000 sq ft) facility at Mirabel, Quebec, some 32 km (20 miles) from Montreal, opened in late 1985 and employed 805 people in early 1990.

US civil production of the Model 206B JetRanger and 206L LongRanger had been transferred to the Canadian factory by early 1987, followed by the Model 212 in August 1988 and Model 412 in February 1989. About half of each helicopter is now made in Canada and product support for the Model 206 series is based there. The JetRanger and Models 212/412 are also produced under licence by Agusta in Italy (which see).

Bell 206B JetRanger III (Allison 250-C20J turboshaft) *(Pilot Press)*

BELL MODEL 206B JETRANGER III

In the Summer of 1977, Bell began delivery of the Model 206B JetRanger III, which subsequently replaced in production the lower-powered JetRanger II, of which 1,619 were delivered. The uprated power plant of the JetRanger III is installed with minimal modification of the original airframe, enabling Bell to offer modification kits to convert JetRanger IIs to JetRanger III standard.

By January 1990, Bell and its licensees had manufactured well over 7,000 helicopters of the Model 206 series, more than 4,600 of them for commercial customers. The Model 206B was transferred to Mirabel in 1986. The first Canadian built example was delivered at the end of 1986 and 120 had been completed at Mirabel by January 1990.

TYPE: Turbine powered general purpose light helicopter.

ROTOR SYSTEM: Two-blade semi-rigid teetering main rotor, employing pre-coning and underslinging to ensure smooth operation. Blades are of standard Bell 'droop snoot' section. They have a D-shape aluminium spar, bonded aluminium alloy skin, honeycomb core and a trailing-edge extension. Each blade is connected to the head by means of a grip, pitch change bearings and a tension-torsion strap assembly. Two tail rotor blades have bonded aluminium skin but no core. Main rotor blades do not fold, but modification to permit manual folding is possible. Rotor brake available as optional kit.

ROTOR DRIVE: Rotors driven through tubular steel alloy shafts with spliced couplings. Initial drive from engine through 90° spiral bevel gear to single-stage planetary main gearbox. Shaft to tail rotor single-stage bevel gearbox. Freewheeling unit ensures that main rotor continues to drive tail rotor when engine is disengaged. Main rotor/engine rpm ratio 1 : 15; main rotor rpm 374-394. Tail rotor/engine rpm ratio 1 : 2.3.

FUSELAGE: Forward cabin section is made up of two aluminium alloy beams and 25 mm (1 in) thick

aluminium honeycomb sandwich. Rotor, transmission and engine are supported by upper longitudinal beams. Upper and lower structures are interconnected by three fuselage bulkheads and a centrepost to form an integrated structure. Intermediate section is of aluminium alloy semi-monocoque construction. Aluminium monocoque tailboom.

TAIL UNIT: Fixed stabiliser of aluminium monocoque construction, with inverted aerofoil section. Fixed vertical tail fin in sweptback upper and ventral sections, of aluminium honeycomb with aluminium alloy skin.

LANDING GEAR: Aluminium alloy tubular skids bolted to extruded cross-tubes. Tubular steel skid on ventral fin to protect tail rotor in tail-down landing. Special high skid gear (0.25 m; 10 in greater ground clearance) available for use in areas with high brush. Pontoons or stowed floats, capable of in-flight inflation, available as optional kits.

POWER PLANT: One 313 kW (420 shp) Allison 250-C20J turboshaft, flat rated at 236 kW (317 shp). Rupture resistant fuel tank below and behind rear passenger seat, capacity 344 litres (91 US gallons; 75.75 Imp gallons). Refuelling point on starboard side of fuselage, aft of cabin. Oil capacity 5.2 litres (11 US pints; 9 Imp pints).

ACCOMMODATION: Two seats side by side in front and three-seat rear bench. Dual controls optional. Two forward-hinged doors on each side, made of formed aluminium alloy with transparent panels (bulged on rear pair). Baggage compartment aft of rear seats, capacity 113 kg (250 lb), with external door on port side.

SYSTEMS: Hydraulic system, pressure 41.5 bars (600 lb/sq in), for cyclic, collective and directional controls. Maximum flow rate 7.57 litres (2 US gallons; 1.65 Imp gallons)/min. Open reservoir. Electrical supply from 150A starter/generator. One 24V 13Ah nickel-cadmium battery.

AVIONICS AND EQUIPMENT: Full range of avionics available in form of optional kits, including VHF communications

and omni navigation kit, ADF, DME, R/Nav, transponder and intercom and speaker system. Standard equipment includes cabin fire extinguisher, first aid kit, door locks, night lighting, and dynamic flapping restraints. Optional items include clock, engine hour meter, turn and slip indicator, custom seating, internal litter kit, cabin heater, environmental control system, camera access door, high intensity night lights, engine fire detection system, and external cargo sling of 680 kg (1,500 lb) capacity.

DIMENSIONS, EXTERNAL:

Main rotor diameter	10.16 m (33 ft 4 in)
Tail rotor diameter	1.65 m (5 ft 5 in)
Main rotor blade chord	0.33 m (1 ft 1 in)
Distance between rotor centres	5.96 m (19 ft 6½ in)
Length: overall, rotors turning	11.82 m (38 ft 9½ in)
fuselage, incl tailskid	9.50 m (31 ft 2 in)
Height: over tail fin	2.54 m (8 ft 4 in)
overall	2.91 m (9 ft 6½ in)
Stabiliser span	1.97 m (6 ft 5¾ in)
Width over skids	1.92 m (6 ft 3½ in)

DIMENSIONS, INTERNAL:

Cabin: Length	2.13 m (7 ft 0 in)
Max width	1.27 m (4 ft 2 in)
Max height	1.28 m (4 ft 3 in)
Volume	1.13 m³ (40 cu ft)
Baggage compartment volume	0.45 m³ (16 cu ft)

AREAS:

Main rotor blades (each)	1.68 m² (18.05 sq ft)
Tail rotor blades (each)	0.11 m² (1.18 sq ft)
Main rotor disc	81.07 m² (872.7 sq ft)
Tail rotor disc	2.14 m² (23.04 sq ft)
Stabiliser	0.90 m² (9.65 sq ft)

WEIGHTS:

Weight empty, standard configuration	742 kg (1,635 lb)
Max T-O weight	1,451 kg (3,200 lb)

PERFORMANCE (at max T-O weight, ISA):

Never-exceed speed at S/L	122 knots (225 km/h; 140 mph)
Max cruising speed:	
at 1,525 m (5,000 ft)	116 knots (216 km/h; 134 mph)
at S/L	115 knots (214 km/h; 133 mph)
Max rate of climb at S/L	384 m (1,260 ft)/min
Vertical rate of climb at S/L	91 m (300 ft)/min
Service ceiling	4,115 m (13,500 ft)
Hovering ceiling: IGE	3,900 m (12,800 ft)
OGE	2,680 m (8,800 ft)
Range with max fuel and max payload:	
at S/L, no reserves	364 nm (674 km; 419 miles)
at 1,525 m (5,000 ft), no reserves	
	404 nm (748 km; 465 miles)

BELL MODEL 206L-3 LONGRANGER III

Announced on 25 September 1973, Bell's LongRanger was developed to fill the size and performance gap between the five-seat JetRanger II and 15-seat Model 205A-1. Rotor-induced vibration is greatly reduced by Bell's Noda-Matic cabin suspension system.

Detail improvements first introduced in the LongRanger II included a redesigned rear cabin to provide 0.05 m (2 in) more headroom for passengers in aft cabin seats; new cowlings, firewall, engine mountings, and engine deck area structure; new freewheeling unit, input shaft, forward tail rotor driveshaft, and increased-thrust tail rotor; a rupture resistant fuel system; new engine oil system, oil tank, cooler, and transition duct; deletion of the water/alcohol system required formerly; and increased capacity 17Ah battery. Optional kits include emergency flotation gear, a 907 kg (2,000 lb) cargo hook, and an engine bleed air environmental control system.

The current production Model 206L-3 LongRanger III, developed during 1981, has a 485 kW (650 shp) Allison 250-C30P engine with a max continuous rating of 415 kW (557 shp). The transmission is rated at 324 kW (435 shp) for take-off, with a continuous rating of 276 kW (370 shp); 340 kW (456 shp) transmission optional. Main rotor rpm is 394. Fuel capacity is 416 litres (110 US gallons; 91 Imp gallons).

Cabin volume of the LongRanger III is 2.35 m³ (83 cu ft), representing a considerable increase over that of the original JetRanger. The port forward passenger seat has a folding back to allow loading of a 2.44 × 0.91 × 0.30 m (8 × 3 × 1 ft) container, making possible the carriage of such items as survey equipment, skis, and long components that cannot be accommodated in any other light helicopter. Double doors on the port side of the cabin provide an opening 1.52 m (5 ft 0 in) wide, for easy straight-in loading of litter patients or utility cargo; in an ambulance or rescue role two litter patients and two ambulatory patients/attendants may be carried. With a crew of two, the standard cabin layout accommodates five passengers in two canted rearward facing seats and three forward facing seats. An optional executive cabin layout has four individual passenger seats.

Standard avionics fit of Collins MicroLine equipment includes dual nav/com, ADF, DME, transponder and marker beacon receiver. R/Nav, radio altimeter and encoding altimeter are optional. A Collins AP-107H autopilot can be fitted, to provide single-pilot IFR capability. A Sfena autopilot is also available, featuring automatic heading, altitude navigation, approach and basic stabilisation modes of operation.

By January 1990 more than 1,100 LongRangers (all versions) had been delivered. They have proved particularly popular in an ambulance role, far outnumbering any other type in the fleet of more than 130 helicopters used by 112 US emergency medical service (EMS) centres at that time. Canadian production of the LongRanger began in January 1987, deliveries beginning in May of that year and totalling 120 by January 1990.

The following details apply to the LongRanger III:

DIMENSIONS, EXTERNAL:

Main rotor diameter	11.28 m (37 ft 0 in)
Tail rotor diameter	1.65 m (5 ft 5 in)
Length overall, both rotors turning	
	13.02 m (42 ft 8½ in)
Height: over tail fin	2.90 m (9 ft 6¼ in)
to top of rotor head	3.14 m (10 ft 3¾ in)
Fuselage: Max width	1.32 m (4 ft 4 in)
Stabiliser span	1.98 m (6 ft 6 in)

DIMENSION, INTERNAL:

Cabin volume	2.35 m³ (83 cu ft)

AREAS:

Main rotor disc	99.89 m² (1,075.2 sq ft)
Tail rotor disc	2.14 m² (23.04 sq ft)

WEIGHTS:

Weight empty, standard	998 kg (2,200 lb)
Max external load	907 kg (2,000 lb)
Max T-O weight: normal	1,882 kg (4,150 lb)
external load	1,927 kg (4,250 lb)

PERFORMANCE (at max normal T-O weight, ISA):

Never-exceed speed:	
at S/L	130 knots (241 km/h; 150 mph)
at 1,525 m (5,000 ft)	133 knots (246 km/h; 153 mph)
Max cruising speed at 1,525 m (5,000 ft)	
	110 knots (203 km/h; 126 mph)
Max rate of climb at S/L	408 m (1,340 ft)/min
Service ceiling at max cruise power	6,100 m (20,000 ft)

Bell Model 206L-3 LongRanger III seven-seat general purpose helicopter

Hovering ceiling: IGE	5,030 m (16,500 ft)
OGE	1,645 m (5,400 ft)
Range, no reserves: at S/L	320 nm (592 km; 368 miles)
at 1,525 m (5,000 ft)	360 nm (666 km; 414 miles)

BELL MODEL 212 TWIN TWO-TWELVE
US military designation: UH-1N
Canadian military designation: CH-135

Bell announced on 1 May 1968 that the Canadian government had approved development of a twin-engined UH-1 helicopter to be powered by a Pratt & Whitney Canada PT6T-3 power plant. Subsequently, the Canadian government ordered 50 of these aircraft (designated CUH-1N) for the Canadian Armed Forces. Now designated **CH-135**, they were delivered in 1971-72. Simultaneously, the US services ordered 79 **UH-1Ns** for the US Air Force, 40 for the US Navy and 22 for the US Marine Corps. Subsequent orders covered the delivery of 159 more UH-1Ns to the US Navy and Marine Corps in 1973-78. Initial deliveries to USAF began in 1970, when UH-1Ns joined UH-1Ps (modified UH-1Fs) in support of Special Operations Force counter-insurgency activities, psychological warfare and unconventional warfare operations worldwide. Deliveries to the US Navy and US Marine Corps also began during 1971.

Foreign military deliveries have been made to the Argentine Air Force (eight), Bangladesh Air Force (nine), Mexican Air Force (16, with nine more due for delivery in 1990), Panamanian Air Force (two) and Royal Thai Army (nine).

A commercial version, known as the **Twin Two-Twelve**, received FAA type certification with PT6T-3 power plant in October 1970, and FAA Transport Type Category A certification on 30 June 1971. The PT6T-3B engine was introduced in June 1980, offering improved single-engine performance and, consequently, additional safety margins.

The Twin Two-Twelve has been certificated for IFR operations by the FAA, UK's CAA, Norwegian DCA

and Canadian DoT. Conversion from VFR to IFR configuration requires a new avionics package, new instrument panel and aircraft stabilisation controls. In June 1977, the Model 212 became the first helicopter FAA certificated for single-pilot IFR operations with fixed floats.

Deliveries of civil Model 212s have included nine to the People's Republic of China in 1979-81 (see 1987-88 and earlier *Jane's* for details) and four to the Japanese Maritime Safety Agency. Five were delivered in 1988 to customers in Australia and Saudi Arabia (one each) and Japan (three).

Production of the Model 212 continues, having been transferred to Bell's Canadian factory in August 1988.

TYPE: Twin-turbine utility helicopter.

ROTOR SYSTEM: Two-blade all-metal semi-rigid main rotor with interchangeable blades, built up of extruded aluminium spars and laminates. Stabilising bar above and at right angles to main rotor blades. Underslung feathering axis head. Two-blade all-metal tail rotor. Main rotor blades do not fold. Rotor brake optional.

ROTOR DRIVE: Shaft drive to both main and tail rotors.

FUSELAGE: Conventional all-metal semi-monocoque structure.

TAIL UNIT: Small fixed stabiliser on rear fuselage.

LANDING GEAR: Tubular skid type. Lock-on ground handling wheels, fixed floats and inflatable nylon float bags optional.

POWER PLANT: Pratt & Whitney Canada PT6T-3B Turbo Twin-Pac, comprising two PT6 turboshafts coupled to a combining gearbox with a single output shaft. Producing 1,342 kW (1,800 shp), the Twin Pac is flat rated at 962 kW (1,290 shp) for T-O and 843 kW (1,130 shp) for continuous operation. In the event of an engine failure, the remaining engine can deliver 764 kW (1,025 shp) for 2½ min, 723 kW (970 shp) for 30 min, or 596 kW (800 shp) continuously. Five interconnected rubber fuel cells, total usable capacity 814 litres (215 US gallons; 179 Imp gallons). Auxiliary fuel tanks optional, to provide a max total capacity of 1,495 litres (395 US gallons; 329 Imp gallons). Single-point refuelling on starboard side of

Bell Model 212 Twin Two-Twelve helicopter in Japanese offshore oil rig support service

cabin. Oil capacity 11.5 litres (3 US gallons; 2.5 Imp gallons) for engines, 8.5 litres (2.25 US gallons; 1.87 Imp gallons) for transmission.

ACCOMMODATION: Pilot and up to 14 passengers. Dual controls optional. In cargo configuration there is a total internal volume of 7.02 m³ (248 cu ft), including baggage space in tailboom, capacity 181 kg (400 lb). Forward opening crew door on each side of fuselage. Two doors on each side of cabin; forward door hinged to open forward, rear door sliding aft. Accommodation heated and ventilated. AiResearch air-cycle environmental control unit optional.

SYSTEMS: Dual hydraulic systems, pressure 69 bars (1,000 lb/sq in), max flow rate 22.7 litres (6 US gallons; 5 Imp gallons)/min. Open reservoir. 28V DC electrical system supplied by two completely independent 30V 200A starter/generators. Secondary AC power supplied by two independent 250VA single-phase solid state inverters. A third inverter can acquire automatically the load of a failed inverter. 34Ah nickel-cadmium battery.

AVIONICS AND EQUIPMENT: Optional IFR avionics include dual Bendix/King KTR 900A com transceivers, dual KNR 660A VOR/LOC/RMI receivers, KDF 800 ADF, KMD 700A DME, KXP 750A transponder and KGM 690 marker beacon/glideslope receiver; dual Honeywell Tarsyn-444 three-axis gyro units; stability control augmentation system; and an automatic flight control system. Flight director and weather radar optional. Other optional equipment includes a litter kit, cargo hook, cargo sling, rescue hoist, fixed float gear, emergency pop-out flotation gear and high skid gear.

DIMENSIONS, EXTERNAL:

Main rotor diameter (with tracking tips)	
	14.69 m (48 ft 2¼ in)
Tail rotor diameter	2.59 m (8 ft 6 in)
Main rotor blade chord	0.59 m (1 ft 11¼ in)
Tail rotor blade chord	0.292 m (11½ in)
Length:	
overall (main rotor fore and aft)	
	17.46 m (57 ft 3¼ in)
fuselage	12.92 m (42 ft 4¾ in)
Height: to top of rotor head	3.91 m (12 ft 10 in)
overall	4.53 m (14 ft 10¼ in)
Width: over skids	2.64 m (8 ft 8 in)
overall (main rotor fore and aft)	2.86 m (9 ft 4½ in)
Stabiliser span	2.86 m (9 ft 4½ in)
Rear sliding doors (each): Height	1.24 m (4 ft 1 in)
Width	1.88 m (6 ft 2 in)
Height to sill	0.76 m (2 ft 6 in)
Baggage compartment door: Height	0.53 m (1 ft 9 in)
Width	1.71 m (2 ft 4 in)
Emergency exits (centre cabin windows, each):	
Height	0.76 m (2 ft 6 in)
Width	0.97 m (3 ft 2 in)

DIMENSIONS, INTERNAL:

Cabin, excl flight deck: Length	2.34 m (7 ft 8 in)
Max width	2.44 m (8 ft 0 in)
Max height	1.24 m (4 ft 1 in)
Volume	6.23 m³ (220 cu ft)
Baggage compartment volume	0.78 m³ (28 cu ft)

AREAS:

Main rotor disc	173.90 m² (1,871.91 sq ft)
Tail rotor disc	5.27 m² (56.74 sq ft)

WEIGHTS:

VFR empty weight plus usable oil	2,720 kg (5,997 lb)
Max external load: 212	2,268 kg (5,000 lb)
UH-1N	1,814 kg (4,000 lb)
Max T-O weight and mission weight	
	5,080 kg (11,200 lb)

PERFORMANCE (at max T-O weight):

Never-exceed speed and max cruising speed at S/L	
	100 knots (185 km/h; 115 mph)
Max rate of climb at S/L	402 m (1,320 ft)/min
Service ceiling	3,960 m (13,000 ft)
Max altitude for T-O and landing	1,430 m (4,700 ft)
Hovering ceiling IGE	3,350 m (11,000 ft)
Max range with standard fuel at S/L, no reserves	
	227 nm (420 km; 261 miles)

BELL MODEL 412SP

Bell announced on 8 September 1978 its intention to develop a variant of the twin-turbine Model 212 with an

Bell Military 412SP of the Royal Norwegian Air Force (*Ivo Sturzenegger*)

advanced four-blade main rotor, Bell's first production helicopter with a four-blade rotor. A pendulum absorber kit, to reduce internal vibration levels, became standard in mid-1984, and is available for retrofit to earlier Model 412s.

Details of the Model 412 development programme have been given in earlier editions of *Jane's*. FAA type approval, in accordance with FAR Pt 29, for VFR operation was received on 9 January 1981, and IFR certification on 13 February 1981. The first (civil) delivery to a customer was made on 18 January 1981. Two military Model 412s are operated by the Venezuelan Air Force, three by the Botswana Defence Force, two by the Public Security Flying Wing of the Bahrain Defence Force, four by Sri Lanka's armed forces and two by the Nigerian Police Air Wing. The Mexican government has ordered two for VIP transport duties, and one is on order by the South Korea Coast Guard. By January 1990 a total of 182 Model 412s (all versions) had been delivered.

The current commercial **Model 412SP** (Special Performance) features an increased max T-O weight, new interior seating options and a 55 per cent increase in standard fuel capacity.

The Indonesian aircraft industry (IPTN) is producing 100 Model 412SPs, with progressive increase of manufacturing content. Other orders for the SP have been received from the Republic of Honduras (10) and Royal Norwegian Air Force (18). Seventeen of the latter are being assembled by Helikopter Services A/S of Stavanger, using subassemblies and components supplied by Bell. These helicopters will replace Bell UH-1Bs with 339 Squadron at Bardufoss and 720 Squadron at Rygge.

In June 1986 Bell announced the **Military 412SP**, equipped with a 600 rds/min 0.50 in calibre machine-gun in a Lucas Aerospace undernose turret, guided by a Honeywell Head Tracker helmet sight system similar to that used in the AH-1S. The installation carries 875 rounds of ammunition, weighs 188 kg (414 lb) including the helmet sight, and can be installed or removed in less than 30 minutes. The turret mounted gun can be fired through a 110° arc in azimuth, at a maximum elevation of 15° and a maximum depression of 45° to the horizontal. With the turret, the 412SP has a max level speed of 120 knots (222 km/h; 138 mph); in addition, it can be equipped with twin dual FN 7.62 mm machine-gun pods, a single FN 0.50 in machine-gun pod, pods of seven or nineteen 2.75 in rockets, M24OE1 pintle-mounted door guns, an FN four-round 70 mm rocket launcher and a 0.50 in machine-gun, or two GIAT M621 20 mm cannon pods.

Bell's Italian licensee, Agusta (which see), has developed its own multi-role military version, known as the **Griffon**, capable of performing medical evacuation, armed tactical support, logistic transport, SAR and patrol missions.

Model 412 production was transferred to the Canadian factory in February 1989. The description of the Model 212 applies also to the Model 412SP, except as follows:

ROTOR SYSTEM: Four-blade flex-beam soft-in-plane main rotor. Blades are of similar construction to those described for the Model 214ST (see US section), but are interchangeable and have lightning protection mesh moulded into the structure and provisions for inclusion of de-icing heater elements. New design main rotor head of steel and light alloy construction, with elastomeric bearings and dampers. Main rotor can be folded. Rotor

brake standard. Two-blade all-metal tail rotor. Main rotor rpm 314.

ROTOR DRIVE: As for Model 212, except for shorter main rotor mast. Transmission rating 1,044 kW (1,400 shp) for T-O, 846 kW (1,134 shp) max continuous.

LANDING GEAR: Non-retractable tricycle gear available optionally.

POWER PLANT: Pratt & Whitney Canada PT6T-3B-1 Turbo Twin-Pac, comprising two 671 kW (900 shp) turboshafts, rated to produce a total of 1,044 kW (1,400 shp) for take-off and 843 kW (1,130 shp) for continuous operation. In the event of an engine failure the remaining engine can deliver up to 764 kW (1,025 shp) for 2½ min, or 723 kW (970 shp) for 30 min. Seven interconnected rupture resistant fuel cells, with automatic shut-off valves (breakaway fittings), have a combined capacity of 1,249 litres (330 US gallons; 275 Imp gallons). Optional auxiliary fuel tanks can increase maximum total capacity to 1,870 litres (494 US gallons; 411 Imp gallons). Single-point refuelling on starboard side of cabin.

AVIONICS AND EQUIPMENT: Optional IFR avionics include Bendix/King Gold Crown III equipment and dual Honeywell automatic flight control systems. Optional equipment includes a cargo sling, rescue hoist, emergency pop-out flotation gear and high skid gear.

DIMENSIONS, EXTERNAL:

Main rotor diameter	14.02 m (46 ft 0 in)
Tail rotor diameter	2.59 m (8 ft 6 in)
Main rotor blade chord: at root	0.40 m (1 ft 3.9 in)
at tip	0.22 m (8½ in)
Tail rotor blade chord	0.29 m (11½ in)
Length: overall, rotors turning	17.07 m (56 ft 0 in)
fuselage, excl rotors	12.92 m (42 ft 4¾ in)
Height: to top of rotor head	3.29 m (10 ft 9½ in)
overall, tail rotor turning	4.32 m (14 ft 2¼ in)
Stabiliser span	2.86 m (9 ft 4½ in)
Width over skids	2.59 m (8 ft 6 in)
Door sizes	as Model 212

AREAS:

Main rotor disc	154.40 m² (1,661.9 sq ft)
Tail rotor disc	5.27 m² (56.75 sq ft)

WEIGHTS:

Weight empty with utility seating, plus usable oil	
	2,946 kg (6,495 lb)
Max T-O weight	5,397 kg (11,900 lb)

PERFORMANCE (at max T-O weight except where indicated):

Never-exceed speed at S/L	
	140 knots (259 km/h; 161 mph)
Max cruising speed at S/L	
	124 knots (230 km/h; 143 mph)
Max rate of climb at S/L	411 m (1,350 ft)/min
Service ceiling	5,030 m (16,500 ft)
Max altitude for T-O and landing	427 m (1,400 ft)
Hovering ceiling: IGE	2,805 m (9,200 ft)
OGE, AUW of 4,762 kg (10,500 lb)	
	2,805 m (9,200 ft)
Range with max payload, standard fuel, at 118 knots (219 km/h; 136 mph) at 3,200 m (10,500 ft), 30 min fuel reserves	375 nm (695 km; 432 miles)
Max range with standard fuel at S/L, no reserves	
	354 nm (656 km; 408 miles)

BOEING CANADA
BOEING OF CANADA LTD
(de Havilland Division)

Garratt Boulevard, Downsview, Ontario M3K 1Y5
Telephone: 1 (416) 633 7310
PRESIDENT: Ronald B. Woodard
EXECUTIVE VICE-PRESIDENT: W. Daniel Heidt
VICE-PRESIDENT, MARKETING AND SALES:
Thomas E. Appleton
DIRECTOR, MARKETING: John Giraudy
MANAGER, PUBLIC RELATIONS: Colin S. Fisher

The de Havilland Aircraft of Canada Ltd was established in early 1928 as a subsidiary of The de Havilland Aircraft Co Ltd, and became subsequently a member of the Hawker Siddeley Group. On 26 June 1974 ownership was transferred

to the Canadian government, continuing until 31 January 1986 when purchase was completed by The Boeing Company, and de Havilland Canada became a Division of Boeing of Canada Ltd.

Approximately 5,500 people were employed by the Division in early 1990. Repair and overhaul services for the Buffalo, Twin Otter, Dash 7 and Dash 8, by a newly formed Aero Services organisation, were introduced in 1981.

DHC-8 DASH 8 SERIES 100

The first of four flying prototypes of the Dash 8 Series 100 (C-GDNK) made its first flight on 20 June 1983, followed by the second (C-GGMP) on 26 October and the third in November 1983. The fourth aircraft (first with production PW120 engines) was flying by early 1984, followed by the

first Dash 8 with production interior in June. Certification by the Canadian DoT, to FAR Pts 25 and 36 and SFAR No. 27, was awarded on 28 September 1984, and FAA type approval before the end of that year. Certification has since been granted by Austria, West Germany and the UK. The first customer Dash 8, one of two Series 100s for NorOntair (c/n 6), was delivered on 23 October 1984, and entered service on 19 December that year.

The Series 100 is available with PW120A or PW121 engines (as **Model 102** and **Model 103** respectively), and in the following two basic versions:

Commuter. Standard local service version, to which the detailed description mainly applies. With full IFR fuel reserves for a 100 nm (185 km; 115 mile) diversion, plus 45 min at long-range cruising speed at 1,525 m (5,000 ft), this

DHC-8 Dash 8 Series 100 twin-turboprop transport in the insignia of Talair Tourist Airlines of Papua New Guinea

DHC-8 Dash 8 Series 100, with additional side view (bottom) and wingtip of Series 300 *(Pilot Press)*

version has enough fuel to fly four 100 nm stages without refuelling, carrying a 3,102 kg (6,840 lb) payload of 36 passengers and their baggage.

Corporate. Marketed in North America exclusively by Innotech Aviation of Montreal, outside North America by Boeing, the corporate version has an extended range capability of up to 2,000 nm (3,706 km; 2,303 miles), plus IFR reserves, with a 544 kg (1,200 lb) payload. In a more typical mission it can carry 17 passengers and their baggage for up to 1,320 nm (2,446 km; 1,520 miles), with reserves, at a max cruising speed of 270 knots (500 km/h; 311 mph). An APU is standard in this version. Alternative layouts can include a single cabin with first class accommodation for about 24 passengers; the standard commuter interior is also available for corporate customers.

By mid-February 1990 a total of 230 firm orders had been received for the Series 100, of which 167 had been delivered.

The military **Dash 8M** and stretched **Dash 8 Series 300 and 400** are described separately. The following description applies to the standard Dash 8 Series 100:

TYPE: Twin-turboprop quiet short-range transport.

WINGS: Cantilever high-wing monoplane, with constant chord centre-section and tapered outer panels. Thickness/chord ratio 18 per cent at root, 13 per cent at tip. Sweepback 3° 1′ 48″ at quarter-chord. Dihedral 2° 30′ on outer panels. Drooped inboard leading-edges. Tip to tip torsion box formed by front and rear spars, ribs and skin. Single-slotted Fowler trailing-edge flaps inboard and outboard of engine nacelles. Hydraulically actuated roll control spoilers/lift dumpers forward of each outer flap segment; independent ground spoiler/lift dumper inboard and outboard of each engine nacelle. Mechanically actuated balanced ailerons, with inset tabs. Small stall strip on each wing leading-edge outboard of engine. Pneumatic rubber boot de-icing of leading-edges. Composite materials used for construction of leading-edges, wingtip fairings, flap shrouds, flap trailing-edges and other components.

FUSELAGE: Conventional flush riveted semi-monocoque pressurised structure, of near-circular cross-section. Extensive use of adhesively bonded stringers and

cutout reinforcements. Radome, nose bay, wing/fuselage fairings and tailcone of Kevlar and other composites.

TAIL UNIT: Cantilever T tailplane; full span horn balanced elevator, with tabs. Sweptback fin (integral with rear fuselage), large dorsal fin, and two-segment serially hinged hydraulically actuated rudder with yaw damper. Composites used in construction of dorsal fin, fin leading-edge, fin/tailplane fairings, tailplane leading-edges and elevator tips. Pneumatic rubber boot de-icing of tailplane and fin leading-edges.

LANDING GEAR: Retractable tricycle type, by Dowty Equipment of Canada Ltd, with twin wheels on each unit. Steer by wire nose unit retracts forward, main units rearward into engine nacelles. Goodrich mainwheels and brakes; Hydro-Aire Mk 3 anti-skid system. Standard tyre pressures: main 7.93 bars (115 lb/sq in), nose 5.52 bars (80 lb/sq in). Low pressure tyres optional, pressure 4.48 bars (65 lb/sq in) on main units, 3.31 bars (40 lb/sq in) on nose unit. Wheel doors of Kevlar and other composites.

POWER PLANT: Two 1,491 kW (2,000 shp) Pratt & Whitney Canada PW120A turboprops in Model 102, each driving a Hamilton Standard 14SF-7 four-blade constant-speed fully-feathering propeller with reversible pitch. Model 103 has 1,603 kW (2,150 shp) PW121 engines. Propeller blades have a solid aluminium spar, glassfibre outer shell, nickel erosion sheath outboard, electric de-icing, and Beta control. Engine cowlings, produced by British Hovercraft Corporation, have lower panels, air intakes and rear panels of Kevlar/Nomex sandwich, aluminium side panels, and a titanium firewall. Standard usable fuel capacity (in-wing tanks) of 3,160 litres (835 US gallons; 695 Imp gallons); optional auxiliary tank system increases this maximum to 5,700 litres (1,506 US gallons; 1,254 Imp gallons). Pressure refuelling point in rear of starboard engine nacelle; overwing gravity point in each outer wing panel. Oil capacity 21 litres (5.5 US gallons; 4.6 Imp gallons) per engine.

ACCOMMODATION: Crew of two on flight deck, plus one attendant in cabin. Dual controls standard, although aircraft will be certificated for single-pilot operation. Standard commuter layout in main cabin provides

four-abreast seating, with central aisle, for 37 passengers at 79 cm (31 in) pitch, plus buffet, toilet and large rear baggage compartment. Wardrobe at front of passenger cabin, in addition to overhead lockers and underseat stowage, provides additional carry-on capacity for passengers' baggage. Alternative 40-passenger, mixed passenger/cargo or corporate layouts available at customer's option. Movable bulkhead to facilitate conversion to mixed-traffic or all-cargo configuration. Port side airstair door at front provides access for crew as well as passengers; large inward opening port side door aft of wing for cargo loading. Emergency exit each side, in line with wing leading-edge, and opposite passenger door on starboard side. Entire accommodation pressurised and air-conditioned.

SYSTEMS: Air cycle air-conditioning system provides heating, cooling, ventilation and pressurisation (cabin max differential 0.38 bars; 5.5 lb/sq in). Normal hydraulic installation comprises two independent systems, each having an engine driven variable displacement pump and an electrically driven standby pump; accumulator and handpump for emergency use. Electrical system DC power provided by two starter/generators, two transformer-rectifier units, and two nickel-cadmium batteries. Variable frequency AC power provided by two engine driven AC generators and three static inverters. Ground power receptacles in port side of nose (DC) and rear of starboard nacelle (AC). De-icing system consists of pneumatic system plus electric heating. APU standard in corporate version.

AVIONICS AND EQUIPMENT: Standard factory installed avionics include Bendix/King Gold Crown III com/nav (KTR 908 VHF com, KNR 634 VHF nav, KDF 806 ADF, KDM 706A DME and KXP 756 transponder), Honeywell SPZ-800 dual-channel digital AFCS with integrated fail-operational flight director/autopilot system, dual digital air data system, electromechanical flight instruments, and Primus 800 colour weather radar. Honeywell electronic flight instrumentation system (EFIS) optional on commuter, standard on corporate version. Avtech audio integrating system. Telephonics PA system. Simmonds fuel monitoring system.

DIMENSIONS, EXTERNAL:

Wing span	25.91 m (85 ft 0 in)
Wing aspect ratio	12.4
Length overall	22.25 m (73 ft 0 in)
Fuselage: Max diameter	2.69 m (8 ft 10 in)
Height overall	7.49 m (24 ft 7 in)
Elevator span	7.92 m (26 ft 0 in)
Wheel track (c/l of shock struts)	7.87 m (25 ft 10 in)
Wheelbase	7.95 m (26 ft 1 in)
Propeller diameter	3.96 m (13 ft 0 in)
Propeller ground clearance	0.94 m (3 ft 1 in)
Propeller/fuselage clearance	0.76 m (2 ft 6 in)
Passenger/crew door (fwd, port):	
Height	1.77 m (5 ft 9¾ in)
Width	0.76 m (2 ft 6 in)
Height to sill	1.09 m (3 ft 7 in)
Baggage door (rear, port):	
Height	1.52 m (5 ft 0 in)
Width	1.27 m (4 ft 2 in)
Height to sill	1.09 m (3 ft 7 in)

DIMENSIONS, INTERNAL:

Cabin: Length	9.17 m (30 ft 1 in)
Max width	2.49 m (8 ft 2 in)
Width at floor	2.03 m (6 ft 8 in)

Max height	1.94 m (6 ft 4½ in)
Volume	36.8 m³ (1,300 cu ft)
Baggage compartment volume	8.5 m³ (300 cu ft)

AREAS:

Wings, gross	54.35 m² (585.0 sq ft)
Vertical tail surfaces (total)	14.12 m² (152.0 sq ft)
Horizontal tail surfaces (total)	13.94 m² (150.0 sq ft)

WEIGHTS AND LOADINGS:

Operating weight empty	10,024 kg (22,100 lb)
Max usable fuel: standard	2,576 kg (5,678 lb)
optional	4,646 kg (10,244 lb)
Max payload: passengers	4,037 kg (8,900 lb)
cargo	4,467 kg (9,849 lb)
Max ramp weight	15,785 kg (34,800 lb)
Max T-O weight	15,650 kg (34,500 lb)
Max landing weight	15,375 kg (33,900 lb)
Max zero-fuel weight	14,060 kg (31,000 lb)
Max wing loading	287.95 kg/m² (58.97 lb/sq ft)
Max power loading:	
Model 102	5.25 kg/kW (8.62 lb/shp)
Model 103	4.88 kg/kW (8.02 lb/shp)

PERFORMANCE (Model 102 at 95% MTOGW except where indicated):

Max cruising speed:	
at 4,575 m (15,000 ft)	265 knots (491 km/h; 305 mph)
at 6,100 m (20,000 ft)	264 knots (489 km/h; 304 mph)
Stalling speed, flaps down	
	72 knots (134 km/h; 83 mph)
Max rate of climb at S/L	475 m (1,560 ft)/min
Rate of climb at S/L, one engine out	137 m (450 ft)/min
Certificated ceiling	7,620 m (25,000 ft)
Service ceiling, one engine out	4,575 m (15,000 ft)
FAR Pt 25 T-O field length at S/L, 15° flap:	
ISA	960 m (3,150 ft)
ISA + 15°C	1,052 m (3,450 ft)
FAR Pt 25 landing field length at S/L, 35° flap, at max landing weight	908 m (2,979 ft)
Range with standard fuel, IFR reserves:	
full passenger load	1,085 nm (2,010 km; 1,249 miles)
2,721 kg (6,000 lb) payload	
	1,190 nm (2,205 km; 1,370 miles)
max cargo payload	550 nm (1,019 km; 633 miles)

OPERATIONAL NOISE LEVELS (FAR Pt 36 Stage 3 and ICAO Annex 16):

T-O	81 EPNdB
Sideline	86 EPNdB
Approach	95 EPNdB

One of the two CC-142 passenger/cargo transports delivered to the Canadian Forces *(David Godfrey)*

Newly completed and unpainted Boeing Canada CT-142 navigation trainer version of the DHC-8 Dash 8M *(David Godfrey)*

DHC-8 DASH 8M
CF designations: CC-142 and CT-142
US Air Force designation: E-9A

The Dash 8 is adaptable to a wide range of missions, and is currently in service or on order in a number of variants including military transport, flight calibration, missile range control and navigation training. Other potential missions include medevac, surveillance, search and rescue, early warning and ASW/ASV/maritime patrol.

Two Dash 8M-100s are in service with the Canadian Dept of Transport for airways calibration duties. The Canadian Dept of National Defence operates two as **CC-142** passenger/cargo transports, based at Lahr in West Germany, and four others configured as **CT-142** navigation trainers with an extended nose. These DND aircraft have long-range fuel tanks, rough-field landing gear, high-strength floors and mission-related avionics. Two other Dash 8M-100s, delivered in Spring 1988, were outfitted by Sierra Research in the USA as USAF missile range control aircraft with the designation **E-9A**. They are equipped as flying data links that can relay telemetry, voice communications and drone and fighter control data while simultaneously performing radar surveillance functions. Equipment includes a large, electronically steerable phased-array radar antenna in a starboard-side fuselage fairing, an AN/APS-128D sea surveillance radar in a ventral radome, and extensive internal avionics and electronics. All 10 of these aircraft are included in the order total given for the Dash 8 Series 100.

Other special mission versions of the Dash 8 have been proposed, notably **Triton** maritime patrol versions of the Series 100 and 300, and a fully equipped **Triton ASW** version based on the Series 300, with equipment that would include a nose mounted maritime surveillance radar, FLIR, MAD, ESM, inertial navigation system, sonobuoy processing equipment, a universal display and control system, and wing and fuselage weapon attachment points.

ARMAMENT (Trition ASW): Alternative loads can include four ASW torpedoes on fuselage pylons, with 50 sonobuoys carried internally; four 1,500 lb anti-ship mines on fuselage pylons; eight 500 lb mines (four on fuselage and four on underwing pylons); four underwing short-range air-to-surface missiles, plus 20 sonobuoys; four fuselage mounted torpedoes, two outer-wing short-range air-to-surface missiles and 20 sonobuoys; or four fuselage mounted long-range air-to-surface missiles. Sonobuoys are launched from eight pressurised chutes, and there is a single free-fall chute for low level dropping of flares or special sonobuoys.

WEIGHTS (Triton ASW):

Typical operating weight empty (maritime patrol)	
	12,009 kg (26,475 lb)
Max T-O weight	19,504 kg (43,000 lb)
Max zero-fuel weight	17,916 kg (39,500 lb)

PERFORMANCE (Trition ASW, estimated):

Max cruising speed	274 knots (508 km/h; 316 mph)
Service ceiling, one engine out	4,265 m (14,000 ft)

DHC-8 DASH 8 SERIES 300

Announced in mid-1985, the Series 300 is a stretched version of the Dash 8 Series 100 with fore and aft plugs totalling 3.43 m (11 ft 3 in) inserted to increase seating capacity to 50 (standard) at a seat pitch of 81 cm (32 in) or 56 passengers (optional). Other fuselage/cabin changes include enlarging the galley and moving it aft, with a separate galley service door on the starboard side, an additional wardrobe, larger lavatory, dual air-conditioning packs, and an optional Turbomach T-40 APU. Wing span is increased by tip extensions, and the Series 300 is powered by 1,775 kW (2,380 shp) PW123 engines driving Hamilton Standard 14SF-15 propellers. The rear cargo compartment and fuel tankage are as for the Series 100.

The Series 300 prototype (converted from the No. 1 Series 100 aircraft C-GDNK) flew on 15 May 1987. Canadian DoT certification was obtained on 14 February 1989, and deliveries began (with the first of six aircraft for Time Air) on 27 February. FAA type approval followed in June 1989, and German LBA certification was anticipated in early 1990. Firm orders for the Series 300 totalled 100 by mid-February 1990, of which 13 had been delivered.

DIMENSIONS, EXTERNAL: As for Series 100 except:

Wing span	27.43 m (90 ft 0 in)
Wing aspect ratio	13.4
Length overall	25.68 m (84 ft 3 in)
Wheelbase	10.01 m (32 ft 10 in)

DIMENSIONS, INTERNAL: As for Series 100 except:

Cabin: Length	12.60 m (41 ft 4 in)
Volume	48.7 m³ (1,720 cu ft)
Baggage compartment volume	9.06 m³ (320 cu ft)

AREAS:

Wings, gross	56.21 m² (605.0 sq ft)
Tail surfaces	as for Series 100

WEIGHTS AND LOADINGS:

Operating weight empty	11,657 kg (25,700 lb)
Max usable fuel	as for Series 100

The first Series 300 stretched version of the DHC Dash 8 during its initial flight on 15 May 1987

Max payload (passengers)	5,216 kg (11,500 lb)
* Max T-O weight (basic)	18,642 kg (41,100 lb)
Max landing weight	18,144 kg (40,000 lb)
Max zero-fuel weight	16,873 kg (37,200 lb)
Max wing loading	331.65 kg/m² (67.93 lb/sq ft)
Max power loading	5.25 kg/kW (8.63 lb/shp)

* *Alternative gross weight options of 18,996 kg (41,880 lb) and 19,504 kg (43,000 lb) available: see Addenda*

PERFORMANCE (at basic max T-O weight except where indicated):

Max cruising speed at 95% of MTOGW:	
at 4,575 m (15,000 ft)	286 knots (530 km/h; 329 mph)
at 6,100 m (20,000 ft)	282 knots (522 km/h; 325 mph)
Stalling speed, flaps down	77 knots (141 km/h; 88 mph)
Max rate of climb at S/L	549 m (1,800 ft)/min
Rate of climb at S/L, one engine out	137 m (450 ft)/min
Certificated ceiling	7,620 m (25,000 ft)
Service ceiling, one engine out	4,115 m (13,500 ft)
FAR Pt 25 T-O field length at S/L, 15° flap:	
ISA	1,150 m (3,775 ft)
ISA + 15°C	1,220 m (4,000 ft)
FAR Pt 25 landing field length at S/L, 35° flap, at max landing weight	1,110 m (3,642 ft)
Range with standard fuel, IFR reserves:	
full passenger load	890 nm (1,649 km; 1,025 miles)
2,721 kg (6,000 lb) payload	
	930 nm (1,723 km; 1,071 miles)

DHC-8 DASH 8 SERIES 400

The Series 400 represents a further stretch of the Dash 8 with a passenger capacity in the 66/70-seat range. Power plant selection (candidates are the General Electric/Textron Lycoming GLC38 and Allison GMA 2100, with six-blade propellers) was expected to be made in the Autumn of 1990. First flight is anticipated in late 1993, and first customer delivery about a year later. A 59-seat Dash 8-300-A has been proposed as an interim model pending availability of the 400.

The following provisional data for the Series 400 were released in February 1990:

Triton ASW proposed anti-submarine version of the Dash 8M Series 300 *(Pilot Press)*

WEIGHTS:

Standard operational weight empty	14,515 kg (32,000 lb)
Payload	7,484 kg (16,500 lb)
Max usable fuel	4,646 kg (10,244 lb)
Max T-O weight	25,174 kg (55,500 lb)
Max landing weight	24,494 kg (54,000 lb)
Max zero-fuel weight	22,000 kg (48,500 lb)

PERFORMANCE (estimated):

Nominal cruising speed	350 knots (648 km/h; 403 mph)
Service ceiling, one engine out, at 95% of max T-O weight, ISA	5,485 m (18,000 ft)
T-O and landing field length	1,280 m (4,200 ft)
Range with 68 passengers and baggage:	
at max cruising speed	1,120 nm (2,075 km; 1,289 miles)
at long-range cruising speed	1,300 nm (2,409 km; 1,497 miles)

BRISTOL AEROSPACE
BRISTOL AEROSPACE LTD

PO Box 874, 660 Berry Street, Winnipeg, Manitoba R3C 2S4

Telephone: 1 (204) 775 8331

Telex: 0757774

Fax: 1 (204) 885 3195

PRESIDENT: H. R. Beattie

NORTHROP CF-5 UPGRADE PROGRAMME

As the designated support centre for the Canadian Forces' Northrop CF-5, Bristol Aerospace is to upgrade and extend the life of these aircraft into the 21st century. About 50 CF-5A fighters and CF-5D fighter/trainers are to be modified for pilot familiarisation and lead-in training for CF-18 Hornets. Significant features of the programme include the repair, overhaul and re-skinning of the wings and vertical fin; inspection and reinforcement of the dorsal longeron; replacement of rear fuselage formers and landing gear; total aircraft rewiring and repainting; and a major avionics upgrade.

As a part of the avionics update, Bristol Aerospace awarded contracts to Ferranti Defence Systems of the UK to supply two prototype HUDWACs (head-up displays and weapon aiming computers) for a flight test programme due to begin in early 1990, and to GEC Avionics for two prototype air data computers. Substantial production orders are expected to follow.

CANADAIR
CANADAIR GROUP, BOMBARDIER INC

Cartierville Airport, 1800 Laurentien Boulevard, St Laurent, Quebec H4R 1K2

POSTAL ADDRESS: PO Box 6087, Station A, Montreal, Quebec H3C 3G9

Telephone: 1 (514) 744 1511

Telex: 05-826747

Fax: 1 (514) 744 6586

PRESIDENT: Robert E. Brown
PRESIDENT, CHALLENGER DIVISION: Bryan T. Moss
PRESIDENT, REGIONAL JET DIVISION: Robert A. Wohl
VICE-PRESIDENTS/GENERAL MANAGERS:
　Trevor F. Young (CL-215 Division)
　Roland Gagnon (Manufacturing Division)
　Walter Niemy (Military Aircraft Division)
　Yvon Lafortune (Surveillance Systems Division)
　Keith Garner (Canadair Challenger Inc)
PUBLIC RELATIONS: Catherine Chase

Canadair has manufactured more than 4,000 military and commercial aircraft since 1944. It has also been employed in the research, design, development and production of missile components, pilotless surveillance systems and a variety of non-aerospace products. It currently has three plants in the St Laurent complex at Cartierville Airport, and a fourth is being expanded at Dorval International Airport to accommodate Challenger and Regional Jet assembly. New facilities have opened at Montreal International Airport, Mirabel, to house the CF-18 Hornet programme and other military aircraft services; and at St Laurent to house the Regional Jet Division. Total covered floor space at the beginning of 1990 was 292,181 m² (3,145,000 sq ft). Total workforce at that time was 6,600.

Canadair became a wholly owned Bombardier subsidiary on 23 December 1986. Restructuring into a corporate group and four major business divisions took place in 1987, as detailed in the 1988-89 *Jane's*. On 5 August 1988 Canadair merged with its parent company and is now known as the Canadair Group of Bombardier Inc. The Group comprises six divisions: Challenger, Regional Jet, CL-215, Manufacturing, Military Aircraft, and Surveillance Systems.

The Challenger entered production during 1978, with advanced design of a stretched version starting in 1987, leading to programme go-ahead for the Regional Jet variant in March 1989. Manufacture of the fifth series of CL-215 tanker/utility amphibians (c/n 1081-1125) ended in 1989; certification of the CL-215 turboprop conversion kit was scheduled for mid-1990. Major subcontracts concern outer wing boxes, wing stubs, rear fuselages, forward and aft radomes and main electrical load centres for US Navy and other Lockheed P-3C Orions and the CP-140 Aurora Canadian version of this aircraft; aluminium bulkheads, frames and other machined parts for the McDonnell Douglas F-15; nose barrel assemblies for the McDonnell Douglas F/A-18 Hornet; six major fuselage components for 600 Airbus A330/A340 aircraft (for Aerospatiale), and inboard wing leading-edge assemblies for these aircraft (for BAe); and rear fuselage sections for the Boeing 767. Engineering support for the CF's CF-18 Hornet fleet is provided under a 1986 four-year contract by a team comprising Canadair, CAE Electronics (Montreal) and NWI (Edmonton), with Canadair as prime contractor. Production of aircraft spares, and the modification, repair and overhaul of aircraft, are also included in the current work programme.

CANADAIR CHALLENGER 600 and 601
CF designations: CC-144 and CE-144A

The first of three pre-production Challengers (C-GCGR-X, c/n 1001) made its first flight on 8 November 1978. The first production Challenger flew on 21 September 1979. Powered by Textron Lycoming ALF 502L-2 turbofans, this version, known as the **Challenger 600**, received Canadian DoT type approval on 11 August 1980, and FAA certification on 7 November of that year. A total of 83 Challenger 600s was delivered, of which 69 had been retrofitted with winglets by February 1990. The Canadian Dept of National Defence received 12 Challenger 600s (seven CE-144As for electronic support and training, four CC-144s for government transport duties and one for testbed programmes). The Model 600 was described in the 1989-90 and earlier *Jane's*. Production has stopped for the present.

The basic Challenger production model since 1982 has been the **Challenger 601**, which has General Electric CF34 series turbofans, increased fuel capacity, and winglets. The prototype flew on 10 April 1982, and the following variants are currently available:

601-1A. Basic version, with CF34-1A engines. First production example (C-GBUU) flew for first time on 17 September 1982. Certificated by Canadian DoT on 25 February 1983 and FAA on 11 March 1983. Deliveries totalled 66 by 1 February 1990, including four to the Canadian DND as VIP transports, two to the DoT for flight inspection, seven to the West German Luftwaffe for various missions (12/16-passenger transport, passenger/cargo combi and air ambulance), the People's Republic of China (three as VIP transports) and the Royal Malaysian Air Force (two).

601-3A. Current standard version, with 'glass cockpit' and upgraded engines. First flight 28 September 1986; Canadian and US type certification received on 21 and 30 April 1987 respectively, and Category II certification five months later. Incorporates four main improvements: CF34-3A engines, flat rated to 21°C, for better climb and hot day take-off performance; fully integrated digital flight guidance and flight management system; a power assisted passenger door; and twin landing lights in nose. First delivery 6 May 1987; total of 60 delivered by 1 February 1990.

601-3A/ER. An extended range option, available from 1989 on new production 601-3As and as retrofit for existing 601-1As and 601-3As, increasing range to 3,600 nm (6,667 km; 4,142 miles) with NBAA IFR reserves. First flown 8 November 1988; received Canadian certification 16 March 1989. Option requires replacing existing tail fairing with a conformal tailcone fuel tank and an extended fairing, increasing fuselage length by about 46 cm (18 in) and adding 113 kg (250 lb) to aircraft empty weight. Max ramp weight increased by minor modification of main landing gear. Customers not requiring extended range option can request the 680 kg (1,500 lb) increase in gross weight. Eighteen modification kits ordered by October 1989.

601-S. New version, launched in June 1989. Designed for transcontinental rather than intercontinental routes, its weight and price are reduced mainly through removal of auxiliary fuselage fuel tanks, deletion of some avionics, and introduction of a new standard 12-passenger interior configuration. First examples due to be delivered in mid-1990.

Total Challenger deliveries (all versions) had reached 209 by 1 February 1990, of which 27 were delivered during the 1989-90 financial year.

Canadair CE-144A (Challenger 600) electronic support and training aircraft of the Canadian Forces
(Ivo Sturzenegger)

The following description applies to the 601-1A and 601-3A, except where indicated otherwise:

TYPE: Twin-turbofan business, cargo and commuter transport.

WINGS: Cantilever low-wing monoplane, built in one piece. Advanced technology section, with winglets at tips. Thickness/chord ratio 14 per cent at root, 12 per cent at leading-edge sweep break and 10 per cent at tip. Dihedral 2° 20′. Incidence 3° at root. Sweepback at quarter-chord 25°. Two-spar structure, primarily of aluminium alloy; spars covered with skin/stringer panels to form rigid torsion box. Two-section double-slotted trailing-edge flaps. Hydraulically powered aluminium plain ailerons. Inboard spoilers for descent control and ground lift dumping. No tabs. Thermal anti-icing of leading-edges by engine bleed air.

FUSELAGE: Aluminium alloy damage-tolerant semi-monocoque pressurised structure of circular cross-section. Chemically milled aluminium alloy skins with riveted frames and stringers, providing optimum strength characteristics while minimising aircraft weight.

TAIL UNIT: Cantilever multi-spar aluminium alloy T tail, with swept vertical and horizontal surfaces. All control surfaces hydraulically powered. Tailplane incidence adjusted by electric trim motor. No tabs.

LANDING GEAR: Hydraulically retractable tricycle type, with twin wheels and Dowty Rotol oleo-pneumatic shock absorber on each unit. Mainwheels retract inward into wing centre-section, nose unit forward. Nose unit steerable and self-centring. Mainwheels have Goodyear 25 × 6.65 tyres, pressure 13.17 bars (191 lb/sq in); nosewheels have Goodyear 18 × 4.4 tyres, pressure 10.0 bars (145 lb/sq in). Goodyear hydraulically operated multiple-disc carbon brakes with fully modulated anti-skid system.

POWER PLANT: Two General Electric CF34-1A turbofans in Challenger 601-1A or CF34-3A in 601-3A, each rated at 40.66 kN (9,140 lb st) with automatic power reserve, or 38.48 kN (8,650 lb st) without APR. One engine is pylon mounted on each side of rear fuselage, fitted with cascade type fan-air thrust reversers. Nacelles and thrust reversers produced by LTV Aircraft Products Group. Integral fuel tank in centre-section (capacity 2,839 litres; 750 US gallons; 624 Imp gallons), one in each wing (each 2,725 litres; 720 US gallons; 600 Imp gallons) and auxiliary tank beneath cabin floor; total capacity 9,278 litres (2,451 US gallons; 2,041 Imp gallons). Optional tank in tailcone (601-3A/ER), capacity 696.5 litres (184 US gallons; 153 Imp gallons). Pressure and gravity fuelling and defuelling. Oil capacity 13.6 litres (3.6 US gallons; 3 Imp gallons).

ACCOMMODATION: Pilot and co-pilot side by side on flight deck with dual controls. Blind-flying instrumentation standard. Interiors are installed to customer's specifications. A maximum of 19 passenger seats is approved. Typical installations include toilet, buffet, bar and wardrobe. Medevac version can carry up to seven stretcher patients, an infant incubator, a full complement of medical staff and comprehensive intensive care equipment. The baggage compartment, with its own loading door, is accessible in flight. Downward opening, power assisted door on port side, forward of wing. Overwing emergency exit on starboard side. Entire accommodation heated, ventilated and air-conditioned.

SYSTEMS: Sundstrand pressurisation and AiResearch air-conditioning systems, max pressure differential 0.62 bars (9.0 lb/sq in). Three independent hydraulic systems, each of 207 bars (3,000 lb/sq in). No. 1 system powers flight controls (via servo-actuators positioned by cables and pushrods); No. 2 system for flight controls and brakes; No. 3 system for flight controls, landing gear extension/retraction, brakes and nosewheel steering. Nos. 1 and 2 systems each powered by an engine driven pump, supplemented by an AC electric pump; No. 3 system by two AC pumps. Two 30kVA engine driven generators supply primary 115/200V three-phase AC electric power at 400Hz. Three transformer-rectifiers to convert AC power to 28V DC; one 43Ah nickel-cadmium battery. Alternative primary power provided by APU and an air driven generator, the latter being deployed automatically if the engine driven generators and APU are inoperative. Stall warning system, with stick shakers

and stick pusher. Garrett GTCP-100E gas turbine APU for engine start, ground air-conditioning and other services. Electric anti-icing of windscreen, flight deck side windows and pitot heads; Sundstrand bleed air anti-icing of wings, tailplane, engine intake cowls and guide vanes. Gaseous oxygen system, pressure 124 bars (1,800 lb/sq in). Continuous-element fire detectors in each engine nacelle and APU; two-shot extinguishing system for engines, single-shot system for APU.

AVIONICS (601-1A): Standard avionics include dual Collins VHF-20A com, dual Collins VIR-30A VOR/ILS/marker beacon receiver, dual Honeywell SPZ 600 flight directors, SPZ 600 autopilot with dual servos, dual TDR-90 transponders, dual DME (with HSI display), one ALT-55B radio altimeter, dual C-14 compasses, standby compass, one ADF-60, dual intercom system, comparator warning system, RCA Primus 400 weather radar, HF and other antennae. Space provision, at customer's option, for HF com, third VHF com, second ADF, VLF nav, INS, GPWS, ELT, flight data recorder and cockpit voice recorder. Flight Dynamics HGS (head-up guidance system) due to become available as option in late 1990.

AVIONICS (601-3A): Honeywell digital avionics include SPZ-8000 five-tube electronic flight instrument system (EFIS) including a single multi-function display (MFD); dual Honeywell laser inertial reference systems (LIRS); dual flight management systems; digital automatic flight control system, with dual channel fail-operational autopilot and flight director; Mach trim and auto trim; dual digital air data system; Honeywell four-colour digital weather radar; radio altimeter; Collins Pro Line II nav/coms, including dual VHF com; dual VHF nav; dual DME; dual ATC transponders; dual ADF; dual HF com; cockpit voice recorder; standby instruments (artificial horizon, airspeed indicator and altimeter). Systems certificated for Cat. II operations. Space provisions for flight data recorder, ELT, VLF/Omega, GPWS, and full provisions for third LIRS.

AVIONICS (601-S): Honeywell digital avionics include SPZ-8000 four-tube electronic flight instrument system (EFIS); dual Honeywell laser inertial reference systems (LIRS); single flight management system; digital automatic flight control system, with dual channel fail-operational autopilot and flight director; Mach trim and auto trim; dual digital air data system; Honeywell four-colour digital weather radar; radio altimeter; Collins Pro Line II nav/coms, including dual VHF com; dual VHF nav; dual DME; dual ATC transponders; dual ADF; cockpit voice recorder; standby instruments (artificial horizon, airspeed indicator and altimeter). Systems certificated for Cat. II operations. Space provisions for flight data recorder, ELT, VLF/Omega and GPWS.

EQUIPMENT (Medevac version): Includes a cardio-pulmonary resuscitation unit; a physio control lifepack comprising a heart defibrillator, ECG and cardioscope; an ophthalmoscope; respirators and resuscitators; an infant monitor; X-ray viewer; cardiostimulator; foetal heart monitor; and an anti-shock suit.

DIMENSIONS, EXTERNAL:

Wing span over winglets	19.61 m (64 ft 4 in)
Wing chord: at fuselage c/l	4.89 m (16 ft 0½ in)
at tip	1.27 m (4 ft 1.9 in)
Wing aspect ratio	7.96
Length overall	20.85 m (68 ft 5 in)
Fuselage: Max diameter	2.69 m (8 ft 10 in)
Height overall	6.30 m (20 ft 8 in)
Tailplane span	6.20 m (20 ft 4 in)
Wheel track (c/l of shock struts)	3.18 m (10 ft 5 in)
Wheelbase	7.99 m (26 ft 2½ in)
Passenger door (port, fwd): Height	1.78 m (5 ft 10 in)
Width	0.91 m (3 ft 0 in)
Height to sill	1.61 m (5 ft 3½ in)
Baggage door (port, rear): Height	0.84 m (2 ft 9 in)
Width	0.71 m (2 ft 4 in)
Height to sill	1.61 m (5 ft 3½ in)
Overwing emergency exit (stbd):	
Height	0.91 m (3 ft 0 in)
Width	0.51 m (1 ft 8 in)

DIMENSIONS, INTERNAL:

Cabin: Length, incl galley, toilet and baggage area, excl flight deck	8.61 m (28 ft 3 in)
Max width	2.49 m (8 ft 2 in)
Width at floor level	2.18 m (7 ft 2 in)
Max height	1.85 m (6 ft 1 in)
Floor area	18.77 m² (202 sq ft)
Volume	32.6 m³ (1,150 cu ft)

AREAS:

Wings, gross (excl winglets)	48.31 m² (520.0 sq ft)
Ailerons (total)	1.39 m² (15.0 sq ft)
Trailing-edge flaps (total)	7.80 m² (84.0 sq ft)
Fin	9.18 m² (98.8 sq ft)
Rudder	2.03 m² (21.9 sq ft)
Tailplane	6.45 m² (69.4 sq ft)
Elevators (total)	2.15 m² (23.1 sq ft)

WEIGHTS:

Manufacturer's weight empty:	
601-1A	9,049 kg (19,950 lb)
601-3A	9,292 kg (20,485 lb)
601-3A/ER	9,405 kg (20,735 lb)
601-S (with interior)	10,909 kg (24,050 lb)
Typical operating weight empty:	
601-1A	11,151 kg (24,585 lb)
601-3A	11,197 kg (24,685 lb)
601-3A/ER	11,310 kg (24,935 lb)
601-S	11,371 kg (25,070 lb)
Max fuel: 601-1A, 601-3A	7,559 kg (16,665 lb)
601-3A/ER	8,119 kg (17,900 lb)
601-S	6,740 kg (14,860 lb)
Max payload: 601-1A	2,229 kg (4,915 lb)
601-3A	2,184 kg (4,815 lb)
601-3A/ER	2,070 kg (4,565 lb)
601-S	2,690 kg (5,930 lb)
Payload with max fuel: 601-1A	907 kg (2,000 lb)
601-3A	862 kg (1,900 lb)
601-3A/ER	868 kg (1,915 lb)
601-S	1,506 kg (3,320 lb)
Max T-O weight:	
601-1A, 601-3A, 601-S	19,550 kg (43,100 lb)
601-3A/ER	20,230 kg (44,600 lb)
Max ramp weight:	
601-1A, 601-3A, 601-S	19,618 kg (43,250 lb)
601-3A/ER	20,300 kg (44,750 lb)
Max landing weight:	
all 601 versions	16,329 kg (36,000 lb)
Max zero-fuel weight:	
all 601 versions	13,381 kg (29,500 lb)*
Max wing loading:	
601-1A, 601-3A, 601-S	404.7 kg/m² (82.88 lb/sq ft)
601-3A/ER	418.8 kg/m² (85.77 lb/sq ft)
Max power loading (without APR):	
601-1A, 601-3A, 601-S	254.03 kg/kN (2.49 lb/lb st)
601-3A/ER	262.86 kg/kN (2.58 lb/lb st)

*14,061 kg (31,000 lb) available optionally

PERFORMANCE (at max T-O weight except where indicated):

Max cruising speed:	
601-1A	459 knots (851 km/h; 529 mph)
601-3A, 601-3A/ER, 601-S	
	476 knots (882 km/h; 548 mph)

Canadair Challenger 601-3A/ER demonstrator, with additional tailcone fuel tank and extended rear fuselage fairing

Normal cruising speed:
601-1A   442 knots (819 km/h; 509 mph)
601-3A, 601-3A/ER, 601-S
    459 knots (851 km/h; 529 mph)
Long-range cruising speed:
all 601 versions   424 knots (786 km/h; 488 mph)
Time to initial cruise altitude: 601-1A   21 min
601-3A, 601-S   24.7 min
601-3A/ER   24 min
Max operating altitude (all)   12,500 m (41,000 ft)
Service ceiling, one engine out (all) 7,315 m (24,000 ft)
Balanced T-O field length (ISA at S/L):
601-1A, 601-3A, 601-S   1,645 m (5,400 ft)
601-3A/ER   1,791 m (5,875 ft)
Landing distance at S/L at max landing weight:
all 601 versions   1,006 m (3,300 ft)
Min ground turning radius:
all 601 versions   20.27 m (66 ft 6 in)
Range with max fuel and five passengers, NBAA IFR
reserves (200 nm; 370 km; 230 mile alternate) at
long-range cruising speed:
601-1A   3,440 nm (6,371 km; 3,959 miles)
601-3A   3,430 nm (6,356 km; 3,950 miles)
601-3A/ER   3,650 nm (6,764 km; 4,203 miles)
601-3S   3,038 nm (5,630 km; 3,498 miles)
Design g limit: all 601 versions   +2.6
OPERATIONAL NOISE LEVELS (FAR Pt 36):
T-O: 601-1A   79.9 EPNdB
601-3A, 601-S   79.4 EPNdB
601-3A/ER   79.8 EPNdB
Sideline: 601-1A   84.8 EPNdB
601-3A, 601-S   85.9 EPNdB
601-3A/ER   85.7 EPNdB
Approach: all 601 versions   89.4 EPNdB

CANADAIR REGIONAL JET

The Regional Jet, or RJ, is a stretched commuter version of the Challenger 601 for which design studies began in Autumn 1986. A one-year advanced design phase had been substantially completed by December 1988, and when programme go-ahead was announced on 31 March 1989 Canadair had received launch commitments for 62 aircraft. By September of that year orders and options had increased to 126, from nine customers in seven countries.

The RJ has fuselage extensions of 3.25 m (10 ft 8 in) forward of the wings and 2.84 m (9 ft 4 in) aft, which increase passenger capacity to 50, while retaining a generous baggage capacity. Emergency exits are increased to four: one overwing each side, plus one opposite the port side second passenger door. To meet field length requirements, the wing area has been increased by about 15 per cent, by chordwise and wingtip extension. The RJ wing also has a strengthened box, heavier gauge skins, modified outboard leading-edges, modified inboard spoilers, plus flight spoilers and outboard 'spoilerons', both fly by wire. Short Brothers (see UK section) will manufacture the fuselage central section, fore and aft fuselage extension plugs, wing flaps, ailerons, spoilerons and inboard spoilers.

Options to be offered include an increased max T-O weight of 23,133 kg (51,000 lb); additional fuel capacity, extending the range to 1,418 nm (2,627 km; 1,633 miles); and a max certificated altitude raised to 12,500 m (41,000 ft).

Two development aircraft are being built. First flight is scheduled for mid-1991 and certification for Spring 1992.

TYPE: Twin-turbofan regional transport.

WINGS: Of generally similar planform to Challenger 601, but with some design and structural changes. Wing sections NACA 0010-64 (mod) at root, NACA 0008-64 (mod) at tip, with respective thickness/chord ratios of 13.3 and 10.0 per cent. Dihedral 2° 20'. Incidence 3° 27' 36" at root. Sweepback at quarter-chord 24° 51' 36". Eemco electro-mechanical flap drive system. Flap vanes of composite material. Spoilers increased to four on each

wing, inner two each side functioning as ground spoilers, outer two comprising one proportional spoiler and a spoileron.

FUSELAGE: Generally as for Challenger except for increased length.

TAIL UNIT: As Challenger except for slightly modified tailplane leading-edges. Tailplane manufactured by Canadian Aircraft Products. Aviac electro-mechanical tailplane actuation.

LANDING GEAR: Hydraulically retractable tricycle type, with nosewheel unit generally as described for Challenger. Inward retracting main units each have Dowty floating piston type shock absorption, and 15 in ABS wheels with 29 × 9-15 Goodyear tyres, pressure 10.55 bars (153 lb/sq in). ABS steel multi-disc brakes and fully modulated Hydro Aire Mk III anti-skid system. Dowty Canada nosewheel steering.

POWER PLANT: Two General Electric CF34-3A1 turbofans, each rated at 41.0 kN (9,220 lb st) with APR and 38.83 kN (8,729 lb st) without. Nacelles produced by LTV Aircraft Products Group. Fuel in two integral wing tanks, combined capacity 5,300 litres (1,400 US gallons; 1,166 Imp gallons). Pressure refuelling point in starboard leading-edge wingroot; two gravity points on each wing.

ACCOMMODATION: Pilot, co-pilot and one or two cabin attendants. Main cabin seats up to 50 people, four-abreast at 79 cm (31 in) pitch, with centre aisle. Downward opening passenger door at front, port side, with plug type outward opening forward exit/service door (Class I emergency exit) opposite on starboard side. Inward opening baggage door on port side at rear. Overwing emergency exit each side. Outward opening equipment bay door at rear, and avionics equipment bay door on underside of forward fuselage. Crew hatch in flight deck roof. Entire accommodation pressurised, including rear baggage compartment.

SYSTEMS: Generally as for Challenger 601. Max cabin pressure differential 0.57 bars (8.3 lb/sq in). Hamilton Standard air-conditioning system. Garrett GTCP36-150RJ APU.

AVIONICS: 650 weather radar; Collins Pro Line 4 integrated avionics system standard, incorporating a six-CRT panel and EICAS.

DIMENSIONS, EXTERNAL: As for Challenger 601 except:
Wing span over winglets   21.44 m (70 ft 4 in)
Wing chord at fuselage c/l   5.13 m (16 ft 10 in)
Wing aspect ratio   8.51
Length overall   26.95 m (88 ft 5 in)
Length of fuselage   24.38 m (80 ft 0 in)
Wheelbase   11.39 m (37 ft 4½ in)
Passenger door (port, fwd):
  Height to sill   1.52 m (5 ft 0 in)
Service door (stbd, fwd): Height 1.22 m (4 ft 0 in)
  Width   0.61 m (2 ft 0 in)
  Height to sill   1.61 m (5 ft 3½ in)
Baggage door (port, rear): Width 1.09 m (3 ft 7 in)
DIMENSIONS, INTERNAL:
Cabin: Length, incl galley and toilet, excl flight deck
    14.71 m (48 ft 3 in)
  Cross-section   as Challenger 601
  Floor area   32.05 m² (345.0 sq ft)
  Volume   56.27 m³ (1,987 cu ft)
Stowage volume:
  Main (rear) baggage compartment
    9.17 m³ (324.0 cu ft)
  Wardrobes/bins/underseat (total)
    5.89 m³ (208.0 cu ft)
AREAS:
Wings, gross   53.99 m² (581.1 sq ft)
Ailerons (total)   1.93 m² (20.8 sq ft)
Trailing-edge flaps (total)   10.60 m² (114.1 sq ft)
Spoilers (total)   2.23 m² (24.0 sq ft)
Winglets (total)   1.38 m² (14.9 sq ft)
Fin   9.13 m² (98.3 sq ft)
Rudder   2.03 m² (21.9 sq ft)

Tailplane   11.15 m² (120.0 sq ft)
Elevators (total)   2.15 m² (23.1 sq ft)
WEIGHTS AND LOADINGS:
Manufacturer's weight empty   13,236 kg (29,180 lb)
Operating weight empty   13,653 kg (30,100 lb)
Max payload (structural)   5,488 kg (12,100 lb)
Max fuel   4,254 kg (9,380 lb)
Max T-O weight   21,523 kg (47,450 lb)
Max ramp weight   21,636 kg (47,700 lb)
Max zero-fuel weight   19,141 kg (42,200 lb)
Max landing weight   20,275 kg (44,700 lb)
Max wing loading   398.4 kg/m² (81.6 lb/sq ft)
Max power loading (APR rating)
    262.48 kg/kN (2.57 lb/lb st)
PERFORMANCE (estimated, at max T-O weight except where indicated):
Max operating speed   Mach 0.85
  or 335 knots (621 km/h; 386 mph) CAS
Max cruising speed at 11,000 m (36,000 ft) Mach 0.80
  or 459 knots (851 km/h; 529 mph)
Long-range cruising speed at 11,000 m (36,000 ft)
    Mach 0.74
  or 424 knots (786 km/h; 488 mph)
Stalling speed, 45° flap 100 knots (185 km/h; 115 mph)
Max rate of climb at S/L   1,190 m (3,900 ft)/min
Max operating altitude   12,500 m (41,000 ft)
FAR T-O field length at S/L, ISA 1,585 m (5,200 ft)
FAR landing field length at S/L, ISA, at max landing
  weight   1,631 m (5,350 ft)
Min ground turning radius   22.86 m (75 ft 0 in)
Range, at long-range cruising speed, FAR Pt 121
  reserves:
  with max payload   845 nm (1,566 km; 973 miles)
OPERATIONAL NOISE LEVELS (estimated):
T-O   81.0 EPNdB
Approach   91.0 EPNdB
Sideline   87.0 EPNdB

CANADAIR CL-215

The Canadair CL-215 twin-engined amphibian is used primarily for firefighting but is adaptable to a wide variety of other duties. It first flew from land on 23 October 1967 and water on 2 May 1968. Canadian DoT certification in the Utility and Restricted categories was obtained on 7 March 1969, followed by FAA certification in the Restricted category on 15 May of the same year.

By 1 March 1990, 124 had been delivered to the governments of France (15); Greece (16); Italy (5); Spain (30); Thailand (2); Venezuela (2); Yugoslavia (5); and eight Canadian provinces and territories (Alberta 4, Manitoba 5, Newfoundland 4, Northwest Territories 2, Ontario 9, Quebec 19, Saskatchewan 4 and Yukon 2). The 125th and last CL-215, a 17th aircraft for Greece, was due for delivery in April 1990. All aircraft are capable of firefighting and other roles: Spain has eight equipped for SAR and coastal patrol, and Thailand two; the Venezuelan pair are configured as passenger transport aircraft.

The first 80 aircraft were produced in batches of 30, 20, 15 and 15. Details of the first and second series can be found in the 1977-78 Jane's, and of the third in the 1979-80 edition. The fifth and final series involved 45 aircraft, the last of which (c/n 1125) was completed in November 1989. Fifth series aircraft have nosewheel steering, and a retrofit kit is available. Single CL-215s have frequently made over 100 drops in a day, and total drops by all those in service had exceeded 800,000 by January 1990.

A full description of the fifth production series CL-215 can be found in the 1989-90 and earlier editions, but the following amended weight figures are now applicable:

WEIGHTS AND LOADINGS: As listed in 1989-90 Jane's, except:
Manufacturer's weight empty   12,337 kg (27,200 lb)
Typical operating weight empty 12,854 kg (28,340 lb)
Max payload: Utility version   3,746 kg (8,260 lb)

CANADAIR CL-215T

In August 1986 Canadair announced its intention to develop this turboprop version of the CL-215. Firefighting/aerial spraying are expected to account for some 44 per cent of CL-215T sales, but a larger share of the potential market is envisaged for various maritime, military or paramilitary versions (33 per cent, including surveillance, ASV/ASW coastal defence, SAR and customs/immigration patrol), and for civil personnel or utility transport versions (23 per cent).

The CL-215T utilises the well proven basic airframe of the piston engined CL-215, with a number of improvements. These include an upgraded and air-conditioned flight deck, a new fuel system with both pressure and gravity refuelling, increased after-scooping weights, wingtip endplates, auxiliary fins, and a larger capacity four-tank drop system for firefighting missions. An extensive list of options will be available for specialised applications, including underwing hardpoints. Various military and commercial versions have been defined, including variants equipped with airborne radar for maritime operations.

Two CL-215s were modified as CL-215T prototypes. The first of these (C-FASE) made its initial flight on 8 June 1989, followed on 20 September 1989 by the second, which is fitted with powered ailerons. Retrofit kits for existing CL-215s became available in early 1990; new-build CL-215Ts, to which the detailed description applies, will

Canadair Regional Jet transport (two General Electric CF34-3A1 turbofans) *(Pilot Press)*

Canadair CL-215T prototype during its first flight on 8 June 1989

enter production when sufficient orders have been obtained. Co-production or licence manufacture agreements are open for negotiation. The Government of Quebec is launch customer for the retrofit programme, with an initial contract to convert two of its existing CL-215s. Fifteen conversion kits, including powered ailerons, were ordered by the Spanish Government on 3 August 1989.

TYPE: Twin-turboprop multi-purpose amphibian.

WINGS: Cantilever high-wing monoplane. No dihedral. All-metal one-piece fail-safe structure, with front and rear spars at 16 and 49 per cent chord. Spars of conventional construction, with extruded caps and webs stiffened by vertical members. Aluminium alloy skin, with riveted spanwise extruded stringers, is supported at 762 mm (30 in) pitch by interspar ribs. Leading-edge consists of aluminium alloy skin attached to pressed nose-ribs and spanwise stringers. Hydraulically operated all-metal single-slotted flaps, supported by four external hinges on interspar ribs on each wing. Powered ailerons, with Jacottet actuators, standard on new-build aircraft. Trim tab and geared tab in port aileron, rudder/aileron interconnect tab in starboard aileron. Metal endplates, which improve lateral stability and permit use of full engine ratings.

FUSELAGE: All-metal single-step flying-boat hull of conventional fail-safe construction.

TAIL UNIT: Cantilever all-metal fail-safe structure with horizontal surfaces mounted midway up fin. Structure of aluminium alloy sheet, honeycomb panels, extrusions and fittings. 'Arrowhead' auxiliary fin on each half of tailplane. Elevators and rudder fitted with dynamic balance, trim tab (port elevator only), spring tabs and geared tabs. Provision for de-icing of leading-edges.

LANDING GEAR: Hydraulically retractable tricycle type. Fully castoring, self-centring twin-wheel nose unit retracts rearward into hull and is fully enclosed by doors. Nosewheel steering standard on new-build aircraft. Main gear support structures retract into wells in sides of hull. A plate mounted on each main gear assembly encloses bottom of wheel well. Mainwheel tyre pressure 5.31 bars (77 lb/sq in); nosewheel tyre pressure 6.55 bars (95 lb/sq in). Hydraulic disc brakes. Non-retractable stabilising floats are each carried on a pylon cantilevered from wing box structure, with breakaway provision.

POWER PLANT: Two 1,775 kW (2,380 shp) Pratt & Whitney Canada PW123AF turboprops, in damage-tolerant nacelles, each driving a Hamilton Standard 14SF-17 four-blade constant-speed fully-feathering reversible-pitch propeller with spinner. Two fuel tanks, each of eight identical flexible cells, in wing spar box, with total usable capacity of 5,796 litres (1,531 US gallons; 1,275 Imp gallons). Single-point pressure refuelling (rear fuselage, starboard side), plus gravity point above each tank. Pneumatic/electric intake de-icing system.

ACCOMMODATION: Normal crew of two side by side on flight deck, with dual controls. Additional stations in maritime patrol/SAR versions for flight engineer, navigator and two observers. For water bomber cabin installation, see under Equipment paragraph. With water tanks removed, transport configurations can include layout for 30 passengers plus toilet, galley and baggage area, with seat pitch of 79 cm (31 in). Combi layout offers cargo at front, full firefighting capability, plus 11 seats at rear. Other quick-change interiors available for medevac (12 stretchers and two medical attendants), utility/paratroop (up to 14 foldup troop-type canvas seats in cabin, in two inward facing rows), all-cargo, or other special missions according to customer's requirements. Flush doors to main cabin on port side of fuselage forward and aft of wings. Emergency exit on starboard side aft of wing

trailing-edge. Crew emergency hatch in flight deck roof on starboard side. Mooring hatch in upper surface of nose. Large cargo loading door optional; provision for additional cabin windows.

SYSTEMS: Casey vapour cycle air-conditioning system and Janitrol heater. Hydraulic system, pressure 207 bars (3,000 lb/sq in), utilises two engine driven pumps (max flow rate 45.5 litres; 12 US gallons; 10 Imp gallons/min) to actuate nosewheel steering, landing gear, flaps, water drop doors, pickup probes and wheel brakes. Unpressurised air/oil reservoir. Electrically driven third pump provides hydraulic power for emergency actuation of landing gear and brakes and closure of water doors. Electrical system includes two 800VA 115V 400Hz static inverters, two 28V 400A DC engine driven starter/generators, two 40Ah nickel-cadmium batteries, and one aircooled petrol engine driven 28V 200A generator GPU. Ice protection system optional.

AVIONICS: Standard installation includes dual VHF transceivers, single VHF/FM com, dual VOR/ILS receivers, dual ADF, two marker beacon receivers, ATC transponder and ELT. Optional avionics include autopilot, VLF/Omega nav system, search radar and colour weather radar.

EQUIPMENT (water bomber): Four integral water tanks in main fuselage compartment, near CG (combined capacity 6,132 litres; 1,620 US gallons; 1,350 Imp gallons), with seven inward facing seats. Hydraulically actuated scoop on each side, aft of hull step, fillable also on ground by hose adapter on each side of fuselage. Four independently openable water drop doors in hull bottom. Improved drop pattern and drop door sequencing compared with CL-215. Optional spray kit can be coupled with firefighting tanks for large scale spraying of oil dispersants and insecticides. In a typical mission profile, with a fire 85 nm (157 km; 98 miles) from the CL-215T's base, a water source 10 nm (18.5 km; 11.5 miles) from the fire, and 45 min fuel reserves, aircraft could make 23 water scoop and drop circuits before having to return to base to refuel. Water tanks can be scoop-filled completely (on smooth water in ISA conditions) in an on-water distance of only 564 m (1,850 ft); partial water loads can

be scooped on smaller bodies of water. Minimum safe water depth for scooping operations is only 1.40 m (4 ft 7 in).

EQUIPMENT (other versions): Stretcher kits, passenger or troop seats, cargo tiedowns, searchlight, and other equipment according to mission and customer requirements. Provision for two underwing pylon attachment points for auxiliary fuel tanks or other stores.

DIMENSIONS, EXTERNAL:

Wing span	28.60 m (93 ft 10 in)
Wing chord (constant)	3.54 m (11 ft 7½ in)
Wing aspect ratio	8.2
Length overall	19.82 m (65 ft 0¼ in)
Beam (max)	2.59 m (8 ft 6 in)
Length/beam ratio	7.5
Height overall: on land	8.98 m (29 ft 5½ in)
on water	6.88 m (22 ft 7 in)
Draught: wheels up	1.12 m (3 ft 8 in)
wheels down	2.03 m (6 ft 8 in)
Tailplane span	10.97 m (36 ft 0 in)
Wheel track	5.28 m (17 ft 4 in)
Wheelbase	7.23 m (23 ft 9 in)
Propeller diameter	3.97 m (13 ft 0¼ in)
Propeller/fuselage clearance	0.59 m (1 ft 11¼ in)
Propeller/water clearance	1.30 m (4 ft 3¼ in)
Propeller/ground clearance	2.77 m (9 ft 1 in)
Forward door: Height*	1.37 m (4 ft 6 in)
Width	1.03 m (3 ft 4 in)
Height to sill	1.68 m (5 ft 6 in)
Rear door: Height	1.12 m (3 ft 8 in)
Width	1.03 m (3 ft 4 in)
Height to sill	1.83 m (6 ft 0 in)
Water drop door: Length	1.60 m (5 ft 3 in)
Width	0.81 m (2 ft 8 in)
Emergency exit: Height	0.91 m (3 ft 0 in)
Width	0.51 m (1 ft 8 in)

incl 25 cm (10 in) removable sill

DIMENSIONS, INTERNAL:

Cabin, excl flight deck: Length	9.38 m (30 ft 9½ in)
Max width	2.39 m (7 ft 10 in)
Max height	1.90 m (6 ft 3 in)
Floor area	19.69 m² (212 sq ft)
Volume	35.59 m³ (1,257 cu ft)

AREAS:

Wings, gross	100.33 m² (1,080.0 sq ft)
Ailerons (total)	8.05 m² (86.6 sq ft)
Flaps (total)	22.39 m² (241.0 sq ft)
Fin	11.22 m² (120.75 sq ft)
Rudder, incl tabs	6.02 m² (64.75 sq ft)
Tailplane	20.55 m² (221.2 sq ft)
Elevators (total, incl tabs)	7.88 m² (84.8 sq ft)

WEIGHTS (A: water bomber; B: utility, land or water based):

Typical operating weight empty:	
A	12,043 kg (26,550 lb)
B	11,789 kg (25,990 lb)
Max internal fuel weight: A, B	4,649 kg (10,250 lb)
Max payload: A (disposable)	6,123 kg (13,500 lb)
B	4,790 kg (10,560 lb)
Max ramp weight: A (land)	19,890 kg (43,850 lb)
A (water), B	17,236 kg (38,000 lb)
Max T-O weight:	
A, production (land)	19,890 kg (43,850 lb)
A (water), B (land and water)	17,100 kg (37,700 lb)
Max touchdown weight for water scooping:	
A	16,102 kg (35,500 lb)
Max flying weight after water scooping:	
A, new production	20,865 kg (46,000 lb)
A, retrofit	20,411 kg (45,000 lb)
Max landing weight:	
A, new production (land)	16,783 kg (37,000 lb)
A, retrofit (land)	15,603 kg (34,400 lb)
A, new production (water), B (water), and retrofit from	
c/n 1056	16,783 kg (37,000 lb)

Canadair CL-215T twin-turboprop general purpose amphibian *(Pilot Press)*

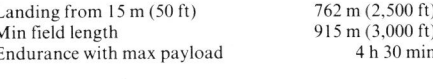

A (water), B (water), retrofit c/n 1001-1055
15,603 kg (34,400 lb)
Max zero-fuel weight:
A, new production 19,051 kg (42,000 lb)
A, retrofit 17,917 kg (39,500 lb)
B 16,511 kg (36,400 lb)
PERFORMANCE (estimated at weights shown):
Max cruising speed at 3,050 m (10,000 ft), AUW of
14,741 kg (32,500 lb) 203 knots (376 km/h; 234 mph)
Long-range cruising speed at 3,050 m (10,000 ft), AUW
of 14,741 kg (32,500 lb)

155 knots (287 km/h; 178 mph)
Patrol speed at S/L, AUW of 15,876 kg (35,000 lb)
110 knots (204 km/h; 127 mph)
Stalling speed:
15° flap, AUW of 20,865 kg (46,000 lb)
76 knots (141 km/h; 88 mph) CAS
25° flap, AUW of 16,783 kg (37,000 lb)
65 knots (121 km/h; 75 mph) CAS
Max rate of climb at S/L, AUW of 20,865 kg (46,000 lb)
390 m (1,280 ft)/min

T-O distance at S/L, ISA:
land, AUW of 19,890 kg (43,850 lb) 701 m (2,300 ft)
water, AUW of 17,168 kg (37,850 lb) 677 m (2,220 ft)
Landing distance at S/L, ISA:
land, AUW of 16,783 kg (37,000 lb) 768 m (2,520 ft)
water, AUW of 16,783 kg (37,000 lb) 838 m (2,750 ft)
Scooping distance at S/L, ISA (incl safe clearance
heights) 1,189 m (3,900 ft)
Ferry range with 884 kg (1,950 lb) payload
1,125 nm (2,085 km; 1,295 miles)
Design g limits (15° flap) +3.25/–1

CONAIR
CONAIR AVIATION LTD
PO Box 220, Abbotsford, British Columbia V2S 4N9
Telephone: 1 (604) 853 1171
Telex: 04-363529
Fax: 1 (604) 853 9017
PRESIDENT: L. G. (Les) Kerr
VICE-PRESIDENT AND GENERAL MANAGER:
K. B. (Barry) Marsden
MARKETING REPRESENTATIVE: Robert M. Stitt
CORPORATE COMMUNICATIONS: Lorna Thomassen

Conair specialises in aerial control services such as forest fire control, oil spill control, insect control, forest fertilisation, and salmonid enhancement. It designs and manufactures many speciality aviation systems such as fire retardant delivery systems, dispersal equipment, and various spray systems. Among these are underbelly retardant tanks for a range of helicopters including the Bell 205 and 212 and Aerospatiale Ecureuil, Lama and Puma, and an 11,365 litre (3,002 US gallon; 2,500 Imp gallon) ventral retardant tank for a firefighting version of the Douglas DC-6B. Since 1978 Conair has undertaken 34 conversions of Grumman or Canadian built S-2 Tracker aircraft to Conair Firecat or Turbo Firecat air tanker configuration.

Orders due for delivery in 1990 include a Turbo Firecat and an F27 Firefighter for France. Production was also to begin of a follow-on order for four 7,560 litre (1,997 US gallon; 1,663 Imp gallon) modular spray systems for Lockheed C-130s, to be operated by the 356th Tactical Airlift Squadron of USAF. Two such systems had been delivered previously to this operator, the second in late 1989. In addition to the C-130 spray system, Conair produces similar modifications for the Douglas DC-6, Fokker F27 and Aeritalia G222.

In 1986 Conair was awarded a five-year contract to maintain and operate the four Canadair CL-215 water bombers of the Yukon and Northwest Territories. These aircraft are equipped with Conair foam injection systems.

CONAIR FIRECAT
The Firecat is converted from standard Grumman S-2A (S2F-1) or de Havilland Canada CS2F-1/2/3 Tracker aircraft for specialised fire control operation, and the aircraft so converted are part of the Conair fleet as well as being available for export. The Canadian type certificate for the S2F/CS2F was transferred to Conair in 1984, and special purpose Canadian type approval A-107 was awarded for the Firecat on 1 January 1984. A total of 31 Firecat conversions had been delivered by the beginning of 1990.

The Conair conversion includes raising the cabin floor by 20.3 cm (8 in) and installing a 3,296 litre (870 US gallon; 725 Imp gallon) retardant tank in the fuselage; modifying the landing gear by fitting larger wheels with low pressure tyres, for soft field operation; inspecting the wing spar caps for corrosion, and repairing or replacing them as necessary; removing 1,361 kg (3,000 lb) of military equipment; completely rewiring the aircraft; and rebuilding/updating the flight deck instrument panels. Options include a hydraulic or pneumatic system for discharging the retardant, and a microcomputer system to control the drop pattern. The retardant tank has four compartments which can be discharged in a single salvo, two two-door salvos, or

Conair 1,360 litre (359 US gallon; 299 Imp gallon) helitanker system on a Bell 212

four single-door drops. A 173 litre (45.7 US gallon; 38 Imp gallon) foam injection system is available for enhancing water drops.
POWER PLANT: Two 1,100 kW (1,475 hp) Wright 982C9HE2 (R-1820-82) Cyclone nine-cylinder aircooled radial engines, each driving a Hartzell five-blade propeller. Total internal fuel capacity 1,968 litres (520 US gallons; 433 Imp gallons).
ACCOMMODATION: Minimum crew: one pilot.
WEIGHTS:
Operating weight empty 6,895 kg (15,200 lb)
Max payload 3,300 kg (7,275 lb)
Max fuel 1,418 kg (3,126 lb)
Max T-O weight 11,793 kg (26,000 lb)
Max landing weight 11,113 kg (24,500 lb)
PERFORMANCE (at max T-O weight):
Never-exceed speed 240 knots (444 km/h; 276 mph)
Max level speed at 1,220 m (4,000 ft)
220 knots (408 km/h; 253 mph)
Normal cruising speed 180 knots (333 km/h; 207 mph)
Normal drop speed 120 knots (222 km/h; 138 mph)
Stalling speed, flaps down, power off
82 knots (152 km/h; 95 mph)
Max rate of climb at S/L 366 m (1,200 ft)/min
Rate of climb at S/L, one engine out 107 m (350 ft)/min
Service ceiling 6,100 m (20,000 ft)
T-O to 15 m (50 ft) 915 m (3,000 ft)

Landing from 15 m (50 ft) 762 m (2,500 ft)
Min field length 915 m (3,000 ft)
Endurance with max payload 4 h 30 min

CONAIR TURBO FIRECAT
This turboprop version of the Firecat, which flew for the first time on 7 August 1988, has two P&WC PT6A-67AF turboprops instead of Wright Cyclone piston engines. The turbine engines allow more precise speed control and greater manoeuvrability at the fire site, particularly during steep descents in mountainous terrain.

The Turbo Firecat offers several other improvements over the piston engined Firecat, including turbine reliability, better fuel availability, improved aircraft performance, greater speed for increased productivity, and reduced operating and maintenance costs. It also has a single-point refuelling station on the starboard engine nacelle, and a modern stall warning system.

The four-door, four-compartment retardant tank is 3.25 m (10 ft 8 in) long, 1.27 m (4 ft 2 in) wide and 0.86 m (2 ft 10 in) deep, and has a maximum capacity of 3,455 litres (913 US gallons; 760 Imp gallons). Retardant can be discharged at a max flow rate of 3,955 litres (1,045 US gallons; 870 Imp gallons)/min.

Canadian certification for the Turbo Firecat was granted on 22 December 1989, the first conversion having previously been delivered to the French Sécurité Civile in August 1988. Two more were delivered to France in 1989, and a fourth was to be delivered during 1990.
POWER PLANT: Two 1,062 kW (1,424 shp) Pratt & Whitney Canada PT6A-67AF turboprops, each driving a Hartzell HC-B5MA-3BXI/M11296SX five-blade propeller. Total fuel capacity of 2,936 litres (775.6 US gallons; 645.8 Imp gallons), consisting of 1,972 litres (521 US gallons; 433.8 Imp gallons) internally and 964 litres (254.7 US gallons; 212 Imp gallons) in two underwing pylon tanks.
ACCOMMODATION: Minimum crew: one pilot.
WEIGHTS:
Operating weight empty 6,884 kg (15,177 lb)
Max payload 3,300 kg (7,275 lb)
Max fuel 2,339 kg (5,158 lb)
Max T-O weight 12,473 kg (27,500 lb)
Max landing weight 11,113 kg (24,500 lb)
PERFORMANCE (at max T-O weight except where indicated; interim figures, based on original six-blade Hartzell propellers):
Never-exceed speed 240 knots (444 km/h; 276 mph)
Max level speed at 1,220 m (4,000 ft)
220 knots (408 km/h; 253 mph)
Normal cruising speed 220 knots (408 km/h; 253 mph)
Normal drop speed 120 knots (222 km/h; 138 mph)
Stalling speed, flaps down, power off
82 knots (152 km/h; 95 mph)
Max rate of climb at S/L 366 m (1,200 ft)/min
Rate of climb at S/L, one engine out:
at max T-O weight 61 m (200 ft)/min
at 9,072 kg (20,000 lb) gross weight 227 m (745 ft)/min
Service ceiling 6,100 m (20,000 ft)
T-O to 15 m (50 ft) 1,220 m (4,000 ft)
* Landing from 15 m (50 ft) 762 m (2,500 ft)
Min field length 1,220 m (4,000 ft)
Endurance with max payload 5 h
* *Without propeller reversal*

CONAIR F27 FIREFIGHTER
Conair has modified two Fokker F27 Mk 600 commuter transports for firefighting roles, for which it received Canadian DoT type approval on 5 June 1986. The world's first turboprop conversion dedicated to forest fire suppression and resource protection, the first aircraft has undertaken firefighting contracts in British Columbia, France and Australia. A second F27 Firefighter conversion was completed for the Sécurité Civile in 1988 and a third was due for delivery to this operator in 1990.

The modification includes installing a Conair delivery system which can carry 6,364 litres (1,681 US gallons; 1,400 Imp gallons) of long-term retardant. A 455 litre (120 US gallon; 100 Imp gallon) foam injection system is also available. The converted aircraft are readily adaptable to other functions such as transporting cargo and fire crews, infra-red fire detection and mapping, aerial survey, aerial spraying and pararescue operations. Unnecessary internal items such as cabin insulation, bulkheads, pressurisation equipment and galleys are deleted, modern avionics installed, and the eight-compartment retardant delivery system fitted ventrally as an integral part of the fuselage.

Prototype Conair Turbo Firecat (two P&WC PT6A-67AF turboprops)

The tank is blended to the fuselage with Kevlar fairings, and can be loaded at a rate of 1,514 litres (400 US gallons; 333 Imp gallons)/min. Door sequencing is computer controlled, and the entire vent system is integral with the modified fuselage floor so that the aircraft's cargo-carrying capabilities are retained. The aircraft is crewed by two pilots, and seating for 19 support crew members is retained, together with the large forward (port) freight door.

WEIGHTS:

Operating weight empty	10,646 kg (23,471 lb)
Max payload	6,731 kg (14,840 lb)
Max fuel	4,152 kg (9,153 lb)
Max T-O weight	20,411 kg (45,000 lb)
Max landing weight	18,143 kg (40,000 lb)

PERFORMANCE (at max T-O weight except where indicated):

Never-exceed speed	259 knots (480 km/h; 298 mph)
Max cruising speed	230 knots (426 km/h; 265 mph)
Normal drop speed	125 knots (232 km/h; 144 mph)
Min control speed	80 knots (149 km/h; 92 mph)
Stalling speed, flaps down, power off	77 knots (143 km/h; 89 mph)
Max rate of climb at S/L	366 m (1,200 ft)/min
Rate of climb at S/L, one engine out, AUW of 14,060 kg (31,000 lb)	177 m (580 ft)/min
Service ceiling	7,620 m (25,000 ft)
Service ceiling, one engine out, AUW of 14,060 kg (31,000 lb)	5,640 m (18,500 ft)
T-O to 10.7 m (35 ft)	1,600 m (5,250 ft)
Landing from 15 m (50 ft) at max landing weight	987 m (3,240 ft)
Min field length	1,525 m (5,000 ft)
Max endurance	3 h 24 min

CONAIR HELITANKERS

Conair has developed a growing number of helicopter-mounted fire control systems known as helitankers. Of semi-monocoque construction, the belly-mounted tanks feature individually operated, full-length rigid doors which may be opened in various combinations over a wide range of airspeeds to permit variable retardant line lengths and drop concentrations. A self-loading hover-fill system allows the tank to be filled while the helicopter hovers above a remote water source, and an offload feature allows the water payload to be pumped to a portable ground reservoir for the use of ground-based firefighters. A foam injection system permits the fire suppressing qualities of a water payload to be greatly enhanced. A reversible pump allows single-point loading injection into the tank and single-point offloading.

Helitanker system sales to date have included 21 Bell 205/212s, 11 Aerospatiale AS 350B₁ Ecureuils, eight SA 315B Lamas and one AS 330 Puma. System capacities are 1,360 litres (359 US gallons; 299 Imp gallons) for the Bell 205/212; 900 litres (238 US gallons; 198 Imp gallons) for the Lama; 800 litres (211 US gallons; 176 Imp gallons) for the Ecureuil; and 2,355 litres (622 US gallons; 517.5 Imp gallons) for the Puma. The Puma system features an 800 litre (211 US gallon; 176 Imp gallon) two-door belly tank, and a 1,296 litre (342 US gallon; 285 Imp gallon) fuselage main tank with two internal doors for reloading the external tank via a 261 litre (69 US gallon; 57 Imp gallon) chute. Foam tank capacity is 173 litres (46 US gallons; 38 Imp gallons). The Bell 205 and 212 helitankers are available with a rappelling system to deliver firefighters to remote fire sites.

DE HAVILLAND CANADA — *see Boeing Canada*

KFC

KELOWNA FLIGHTCRAFT AIR CHARTER LTD

Kelowna Airport, RR2, Kelowna, British Columbia V1Y 7R1
Telephone: 1 (604) 765 1481
Telex: 048 5217
Fax: 1 (604) 765 1489
PRESIDENT: Barry Lapointe
OPERATIONS MANAGER: Greg Carter

Kelowna Flightcraft is currently upgrading Canadair CC-109 Cosmopolitan (Canadian built Convair 580) aircraft of the Canadian Forces, in a programme which includes retrofit of a Honeywell SPZ-4500 digital automatic flight control system. The first updated aircraft was redelivered to the CF in December 1989. As an extension of this activity, KFC plans to modify its own fleet of five civil Convair 580s, and to offer a similar retrofit package to other Convairliner operators.

KFC STRETCH 580

This modification includes a 4.34 m (14 ft 3 in) extension of the fuselage, and incorporation of a Honeywell SPZ-4500 digital AFCS, EDZ-803 electronic flight instrumentation system, and Primus II nav/com/ident radio package. These avionics will include dual FZ-450 flight guidance computers, manually switchable into a single control surface servo drive system; a four-tube EFIS; Primus 650 weather radar; a dual VG-14A/C-14A attitude/heading package; and an AA-300 radio altimeter. Thus modified, the Stretch 580 will be a totally refurbished and reconditioned aircraft meeting Stage 3 noise and Cat. II landing standards.

A prototype avionics package was due for delivery to KFC in October 1990, and FAA certification of the Stretch 580 is anticipated in April 1991. The modification is applicable to any serviceable Convair 340, 440 or 580 airframe, and is claimed to extend aircraft life by a further 100,000 hours.

MBB

MBB HELICOPTER CANADA LIMITED
(Subsidiary of Messerschmitt-Bölkow-Blohm GmbH)

HEAD OFFICE: PO Box 250, 1100 Gilmore Road, Fort Erie, Ontario L2A 5M9
Telephone: 1 (416) 871 7772
Telex: 061-5250
Fax: 1 (416) 871 3320
VICE-PRESIDENT AND GENERAL MANAGER:
Richard W. Harwood
GOVERNMENT MARKETING OFFICE: Suite 1202, 60 Queen Street, Ottawa, Ontario K1P 5Y7
Telephone: 1 (613) 232 1557
Telex: 053-4109
Fax: 1 (613) 232 5454
DIRECTOR, GOVERNMENT PROGRAMMES: Donald P. Chambers

MBB Helicopter Canada Limited began operations as Canada's first helicopter manufacturer in April 1984 as a result of a contract between Messerschmitt-Bölkow-Blohm GmbH (MBB) of West Germany and the Federal and Ontario governments of Canada. In mid-1986, MBB Helicopter Canada opened a 7,897 m² (85,000 sq ft) manufacturing plant in Fort Erie, Ontario.

MBB Helicopter Canada Limited has the world product mandate and design authority for the manufacture in Canada of the BO 105 LS variant of this light twin-engined helicopter. Production began with the BO 105 LS A-3 version. The first customer delivery was made in February 1987, and 22 of the LS model had been delivered by January 1990.

MBB Helicopter Canada is responsible for sales and completion of all MBB helicopters in Canada, including the BO 105 CBS (see German section) and the larger MBB/Kawasaki BK 117 (see International section).

MBB BO 105 LS

This 'hot and high' version of the BO 105 (L for Lift and S for Stretch) combines the enlarged cabin of the CBS version with more powerful engines and an uprated transmission, permitting operation at a higher gross weight. It was first flown on 23 October 1981. Certification by the German LBA was granted in July 1984, and extended in April 1985 to cover 'hot and high' take-offs and landings at altitudes up to 6,100 m (20,000 ft). It was extended again on 7 July 1986 to cover the A-3 version of the BO 105 LS, with FAA and Canadian DoT certification granted subsequently.

A BO 105 LS B-1 (C-FMCL) was chosen as the testbed to prove Pratt & Whitney Canada's PW200 turboshaft engine series, and the first flight test, with two 307 kW (412 shp) PW205B engines, took place on 13 October 1988. Further details of this aircraft, and an illustration, appeared in the 1989-90 *Jane's*. No indication was given of this programme's current (1990) status. Follow-on derivative

MBB BO 105 LS five/six-seat helicopter (two Allison 250-C28C turboshafts)

MBB Helicopter Canada Ltd BO 105 LS 'hot and high' helicopter *(Pilot Press)*

engines for other MBB helicopters, as well as widespread application in the light to medium classes of helicopter, are seen as the most probable areas for the PW200 engine series.

The description of the BO 105 CBS in the German section applies also to the BO 105 LS A-3, except as follows:

ROTOR DRIVE: Main transmission, type ZF-FS 112, is rated for independent restricted input of 310 kW (416 shp) per engine at T-O power or 294 kW (394 shp) per engine for max continuous operation; or a single-engine restricted input of 368 kW (493 shp) at max continuous power, or 410 kW (550 shp) for 2.5 min at T-O power.

POWER PLANT: Two Allison 250-C28C turboshafts, each rated at 410 kW (550 shp) for 2.5 min, and with 5 min T-O and max continuous power ratings of 373 kW (500 shp) and 368 kW (493 shp) respectively. Fuel capacity as for

CB/CBS. Oil capacity 5 litres (1.3 US gallons; 1.1 Imp gallons) per engine.

ACCOMMODATION: Pilot, and co-pilot or passenger, on two front seats; three or four passengers in main cabin. Cargo space behind rear seats, plus additional 20 kg (44 lb) in baggage compartment. Crew door and passengers' sliding door each side; clamshell rear cargo doors, removable for carriage of extra-long cargo. Cabin heating and air-conditioning available optionally.

SYSTEMS: As for BO 105 CBS, except stability augmentation system is standard, bleed air anti-icing optional.

WEIGHTS (LS A-3):
Weight empty, basic	1,430 kg (3,152 lb)
Fuel weight	456 kg (1,005 lb)
Max T-O weight	2,600 kg (5,732 lb)

PERFORMANCE (LS A-3 at T-O weight of 2,400 kg; 5,291 lb, ISA):
Never-exceed speed at S/L	145 knots (270 km/h; 167 mph)
Max cruising speed at S/L	131 knots (243 km/h; 151 mph)
Max rate of climb at S/L	634 m (2,080 ft)/min
Vertical rate of climb at S/L	427 m (1,400 ft)/min
Max operating altitude	6,100 m (20,000 ft)
Service ceiling, one engine out, 30.5 m (100 ft)/min climb	
reserve	2,590 m (8,500 ft)
Hovering ceiling: IGE	4,265 m (14,000 ft)
OGE	3,385 m (11,100 ft)
Range at S/L, standard fuel, max internal payload, no	
reserves	281 nm (522 km; 324 miles)

NWI
NORTHWEST INDUSTRIES LIMITED
(a Division of CAE Industries Ltd)
PO Box 9864, Edmonton International Airport, Edmonton, Alberta T5J 2T2
Telephone: 1 (403) 890 6300
Telex: 037-41574
Fax: 1 (403) 890 7773
PRESIDENT: L. H. Prokop
VICE-PRESIDENT AND GENERAL MANAGER: F. A. Maybee

NWI is one of Canada's largest aircraft maintenance, repair, overhaul and modification centres for military and commercial aircraft, including the Lockheed C-130

Hercules, Dassault-Breguet Falcon, Lockheed T-33, Canadair CL-41 (CT-114) and CF-104 Starfighter. In addition to its major in-plant aircraft programmes, mobile repair parties are stationed at CFB Cold Lake in support of CF-5 and CF-18 aircraft of the Canadian Forces. The manufacturing shops produce structural, mechanical and electronic components for its aircraft overhaul and modification programmes and, under subcontract, for North America's principal aerospace manufacturers.

In 1987 NWI completed a major structural upgrade of the CF's fleet of 22 Lockheed C-130E Hercules, as described in the 1989-90 and previous editions of *Jane's*. In addition, two new C-130H-84 and two used C-130H-73 aircraft,

purchased by the CF, required extensive avionics upgrading, modification, repair and repaint to achieve commonality with the remainder of the fleet. A progressive structural inspection (PSI) programme for CF C-130s, begun in Autumn 1987, will result in the complete fleet being cycled through NWI every three years. Depot level inspection and repair, as well as sampling inspections, will continue to be carried out on CF T-33A Silver Star jet trainers. A prototype rewiring programme on CL-41 (CT-114) Tutor jet trainers was scheduled to begin in early 1990, and will be incorporated into a complete fleet depot level inspection and repair forecast for late 1991.

VENGA
VENGA AIRCRAFT INC
666 Sherbrooke Street West, Suite 700, Montreal, Quebec H3A 1E7
Telephone: 1 (514) 842 2724
Telex: 055-60500
Fax: 1 (514) 849 8367

PRESIDENT: J. Gregory Gooch
VICE-PRESIDENT AND DIRECTOR OF MARKETING:
Jay Lumiere
Venga Aircraft was incorporated in May 1985 to develop, manufacture and market a new, all-composites high-performance jet trainer known as the TG-10. No recent news has been received and the TG-10 is not thought to have flown by the forecast date.

VENGA TG-10
Rollout of the TG-10 prototype was anticipated in the Summer of 1989, subject to funding availability, and joint venture arrangements made earlier that year were claimed to have ensured funding to completion at about that time, but no subsequent news of this venture has been received. A description and three-view drawing of the TG-10 can be found in the 1989-90 *Jane's*.

CHILE

CARDOEN
INDUSTRIAS CARDOEN LTDA
HEADQUARTERS: Aeropuerto Los Cerrillos, Los Conquistadores 1700, Piso 28, Santiago
Telephone: 56 (2) 2313420
Telex: 340997 INCAR CK
Fax: 56 (2) 2316366
WORKS: Planta Macul, Exequiel Fernandez 3397, Santiago
Telephone: 56 (2) 5574513 or 5573828
Telex: 241377 INCAR CK
Fax: 56 (2) 5574513
PROJECT MANAGER, C206L-III: Rene M. Gonzalez

Cardoen has been well known for many years as a major manufacturer of weapons and other military equipment. It has abandoned development of a single-seat gunship version of the MBB BO 105 and is currently developing a multi-purpose helicopter based on the Bell LongRanger.

CARDOEN C 206L-III
Development of this modified variant of the Bell LongRanger began in 1988, replacing an earlier abortive proposal to undertake a similar conversion based on the use of an MBB BO 105 airframe. Modification, using an imported civil example of the Bell 206L-III, began in August 1989, and the converted aircraft made its first flight on 8 December that year. Changes mainly concern the front fuselage, which has a narrower cross-section with flat-plate cockpit transparencies, an indication of the project's intended potential as a gunship. However, Cardoen says that the stronger cockpit structure and symmetrical field of view should also make the C 206L-III suited for cropdusting, firefighting, police work, powerline inspection and highway survey work, and is seeking US (FAR Pt 27) certification for a civil utility version. Bell Helicopter Textron, which currently produces the LongRanger at its Canadian facility, is not thought to be involved in the Cardoen programme. The prototype, at least initially, is unarmed, and no details of any proposed armament have been received.

The following details have been supplied by Cardoen:

ROTOR SYSTEM AND DRIVE: Two-blade all-metal semi-rigid main rotor, bolted to hub, and two-blade tail rotor. No blade or tail folding; no rotor brake. Main rotor/engine rpm ratio 394 : 6,016.

FUSELAGE: Aluminium alloy semi-monocoque fail-safe structure.

LANDING GEAR: Skid type.

POWER PLANT: One Allison 250-C30P turboshaft, with max rating of 485 kW (650 shp). Max internal fuel capacity 372.5 litres (98.4 US gallons; 82 Imp gallons).

ACCOMMODATION: Pilot only in cockpit; up to five passengers in main cabin. Forward opening door on each side.

Prototype of the Cardoen C 206L-III multi-purpose helicopter

SYSTEMS: Single-pump hydraulic system, operating at pressure of 41.37 bars (600 lb/sq in); capacity 4.7 litres (1.25 US gallons; 1.04 Imp gallons), plus 0.5 litre (1 US pint; 0.8 Imp pint) in reservoir. 28V DC electrical system, with 30V 150A starter/generator and 13Ah nickel-cadmium battery.

AVIONICS: Prototype fitted with Bendix/King VHF com, VOR and ATC transponder. Blind-flying instrumentation standard.

DIMENSIONS, EXTERNAL:
Main rotor diameter	11.28 m (37 ft 0 in)
Tail rotor diameter	1.65 m (5 ft 5 in)
Length overall, rotors turning	12.95 m (42 ft 6 in)
Length of fuselage, excl rotors	10.49 m (34 ft 5 in)
Height of top of rotor head	3.66 m (12 ft 0 in)
Tailplane span	1.98 m (6 ft 6 in)
Cabin doors (each): Height	0.58 m (1 ft 11 in)
Width	0.94 m (3 ft 1 in)
Baggage door: Height	0.55 m (1 ft 9½ in)
Width	1.07 m (3 ft 6 in)

DIMENSIONS, INTERNAL:
Cabin, excl flight deck: Max width	1.19 m (3 ft 10¾ in)
Max height	1.16 m (3 ft 9½ in)
Floor area	0.98 m² (10.57 sq ft)
Volume	0.82 m³ (29.0 cu ft)

AREAS:
Main rotor disc	99.89 m² (1,075.2 sq ft)
Tail rotor disc	2.14 m² (23.04 sq ft)

WEIGHTS:
Weight empty, equipped	1,095 kg (2,414 lb)
Max payload	approx 454 kg (1,000 lb)
Max fuel weight	299 kg (659 lb)
Max T-O weight: normal	1,882 kg (4,150 lb)
with external load	1,928 kg (4,250 lb)

PERFORMANCE (at max T-O weight, ISA):
Never-exceed speed at S/L	130 knots (241 km/h; 149 mph)
Max cruising speed at S/L	112 knots (207 km/h; 129 mph)
Max rate of climb at S/L	408 m (1,340 ft)/min
Service ceiling	6,100 m (20,000 ft)
Hovering ceiling: IGE	5,030 m (16,500 ft)
OGE	1,645 m (5,400 ft)
Range at S/L with max fuel	322 nm (596 km; 370 miles)
Max loiter endurance	3 h 42 min

ENAER
EMPRESA NACIONAL DE AERONÁUTICA DE CHILE

Avenida José Miguel Carrera 11087, P. 36 ½, Santiago
Telephone: 56 (2) 5282735 and 5282823
Telex: 645115 ENAER CT
Fax: 56 (2) 5282815
PRESIDENT: Caupolicán Boisset
DIRECTOR OF MARKETING: Alejandro Vargas

ENAER is a state owned company formed in 1984 from the IndAer industrial organisation set up by the Chilean Air Force in 1980. Aircraft manufacturing started in 1980 with the assembly of 27 Piper PA-28 Dakota light aircraft for Chilean Air Force and flying club use. With a 1989 workforce of about 1,900 people, ENAER's current activities are the design and production of aircraft and electronic warfare equipment.

ENAER's major current programmes are production of the T-35 Pillán trainer and T-36/A-36 Halcón (CASA C-101) jet trainer/attack aircraft, plus development of Chile's first lightplane of indigenous design, the Ñamcu (Eaglet). It also undertakes upgrade programmes for the Chilean Air Force which include conversion of Beechcraft 99s for maritime surveillance (see 1987-88 *Jane's*), retrofitting FACh Hawker Hunters with a Caiquen II radar warning receiver system, and an airframe/avionics upgrade for the service's Mirage 50s.

ENAER T-35 PILLÁN (DEVIL)
Spanish Air Force designation: E.26 Tamiz

The Pillán is a tandem two-seat, fully aerobatic aircraft for basic, intermediate and instrument flying training. It is cleared to FAR Pt 23 (Aerobatic category) and military standards. Design was based on the Piper Cherokee series, utilising in particular many components of the PA-28 Dakota and PA-32 Saratoga.

Two prototypes were developed by Piper, the first of these making its initial flight on 6 March 1981 and the second at the end of that year. Three further aircraft were delivered by Piper as kits for assembly by ENAER: the first of these (FACh serial number 101) flew on 30 January 1982 and the third in September of that year. After replacement of the original all-moving tailplane by an electrically trimmable tailplane with a conventional elevator, increasing rudder mass balance, and deepening the canopy, series production began in September 1984.

The following versions have been announced:

T-35A. Primary trainer version for Chilean Air Force (60 ordered, including the three assembled from Piper kits). First flight 28 December 1984, first delivery (two aircraft) 31 July 1985. All (and all T-35Bs) delivered by Spring 1990. In service with Escuela de Aviación Capitan Avalos at El Bosque, Santiago.

T-35B. Instrument trainer version for Chilean Air Force (20 ordered), with more comprehensive instrumentation.

T-35C. Primary trainer version for Spanish Air Force (40), first flown on 12 May 1986. These have the Spanish designation **E.26 Tamiz**, and were assembled by CASA (which see) from components supplied by ENAER. Kit deliveries to CASA began on 27 December 1985 and were completed in September 1987. One replacement aircraft supplied subsequently. All are now in service.

T-35D. Instrument trainer version for Panamanian Air Force: 10 delivered in 1988-89.

T-35S. Single-seat version, first flown (CC-PZB) on 5 March 1988 with IO-540-K1K5 piston engine; 313 kW (420 shp) Allison 250-B17 turboprop intended for production version. Prototype evaluation continuing in 1990.

T-35T Aucán. Turboprop version, described in 1988-89 *Jane's*. Prototype only; since modified to have new one-piece canopy, opening sideways to starboard, oxygen

Prototype of the T-35S single-seat aerobatic version of the Pillán

system, and some new avionics. Now known as **Turbo Pillán**; being offered in military armed trainer market.

The following description applies to the basic T-35A except where indicated:

TYPE: Two-seat fully aerobatic basic (T-35A/C) and instrument (T-35B/D) military trainer.

WINGS: Cantilever low-wing monoplane. Wing section NACA 65$_2$-415 on constant chord inboard panels, NACA 65$_2$-415 (modified) at tips. Dihedral 7°. Incidence 2° at root, −0° 30′ at tip. Single-spar fail-safe structure of light alloy, steel and glassfibre, with components mainly from PA-28-236 Dakota (leading-edges) and PA-32R-301 Saratoga (trailing-edges), modified to shorter span. Slotted aluminium ailerons and electrically operated single-slotted trailing-edge flaps of riveted construction, identical to those of Saratoga. Electrically actuated trim tab in port aileron.

FUSELAGE: Semi-monocoque fail-safe structure of aluminium alloy frames and longerons, with riveted skin. Tailcone assembled from Cherokee components, modified to fit narrower fuselage. Two-piece engine cowling of GRP.

TAIL UNIT: Cantilever structure of light alloy with sweptback (38° 43′) vertical surfaces, identical to those of Dakota except for heavier gauge skins, minor reinforcement of fin, and increased rudder mass balance. One-piece non-swept variable incidence tailplane, with electric trim and glassfibre tips. Full span mass balanced elevator. Tailplane incorporates some standard PA-28 (Dakota) and PA-31 (Navajo/Cheyenne) components; elevator is of all-new design. No tabs; rudder trimmed electrically.

LANDING GEAR: Hydraulically retractable tricycle type, with single wheel on each unit. Main gear legs and doors identical to those on PA-32R-301; nose gear assembled from PA-32R-301 and PA-28R-200 components. Main

units retract inward, steerable nosewheel rearward. Piper oleo-pneumatic shock absorber in each unit. Emergency free-fall extension. Cleveland mainwheels and McCreary tyres size 6.00-6 (8 ply), nosewheel and tyre size 5.00-5 (6 ply). Tyre pressures: 2.62 bars (38 lb/sq in) on mainwheels, 2.41 bars (35 lb/sq in) on nosewheel. Single-disc aircooled hydraulic brake on each mainwheel. Parking brake.

POWER PLANT: One 224 kW (300 hp) Textron Lycoming IO-540-K1K5 flat-six engine, driving a Hartzell HC-C3YR-4BF/FC7663R three-blade constant-speed metal propeller with spinner. Fuel contained in two integral aluminium tanks in wing leading-edges, total capacity 291.5 litres (77 US gallons; 64.1 Imp gallons), of which 272.5 litres (72 US gallons; 60 Imp gallons) are usable. Overwing gravity refuelling point on each wing. Oil capacity 11.4 litres (3 US gallons; 2.5 Imp gallons). Fuel and oil systems permit unlimited inverted flight (up to 40 min flight tested).

ACCOMMODATION: Vertically adjustable seats for two persons, with seat belts and shoulder harnesses, in tandem beneath one-piece transparent jettisonable canopy which opens sideways to starboard. One-piece acrylic windscreen, and one-piece window in glassfibre fairing aft of canopy. Rear (instructor's) seat 22 cm (8.7 in) higher than front seat. Dual controls standard. Baggage compartment aft of rear cockpit, with external access on port side. Cockpits ventilated; cockpit heating and canopy demisting are by engine bleed air.

SYSTEMS: Electrically operated hydraulic system, at 124 bars (1,800 lb/sq in) pressure for landing gear retraction and 44.8 bars (650 lb/sq in) for gear extension; separate system at 20.7 bars (300 lb/sq in) for wheel brakes. Electrical system is 24V DC, powered by a 28V 70A engine driven Prestolite alternator and 24V 10Ah battery, with an inverter for AC power at 400Hz to operate RMIs and attitude indicators. External power socket. No oxygen or de-icing provisions.

AVIONICS AND EQUIPMENT: (*T-35A*) Two Collins VHF-251 com transceivers, two Collins AMR-350 audio panels, one Clark Isocom, and one each Collins VIR-351 VOR, ADF-650A and TOR-950 IFF. (*T-35C*) One Bendix/King KTR 908, two KFS 598A control units, two KMA 244 audio panels and two KR 87 ADF. Blind-flying instrumentation and full IFR capability in T-35B and D.

DIMENSIONS, EXTERNAL:

Wing span	8.84 m (29 ft 0 in)
Wing chord: at root	1.88 m (6 ft 2 in)
at tip	1.26 m (4 ft 1½ in)
inboard (constant)	1.60 m (5 ft 3 in)
mean aerodynamic	1.55 m (5 ft 1 in)
Wing aspect ratio	5.7
Length overall	8.00 m (26 ft 3 in)
Height overall	2.64 m (8 ft 8 in)
Fuselage: Length	7.66 m (25 ft 1¾ in)
Max width	0.86 m (2 ft 9¾ in)
Max depth	1.56 m (5 ft 1¼ in)
Tailplane span	3.05 m (10 ft 0 in)
Wheel track	3.02 m (9 ft 11 in)
Wheelbase	2.09 m (6 ft 10¼ in)
Propeller diameter	1.93 m (6 ft 4 in)

DIMENSIONS, INTERNAL:

Cockpit: Length	3.24 m (10 ft 7½ in)
Max width	1.04 m (3 ft 5 in)
Max height	1.48 m (4 ft 10¼ in)

ENAER T-35B Pillán instrument trainer of the Chilean Air Force

AREAS:

Wings, gross	13.69 m² (147.34 sq ft)
Ailerons (total)	1.135 m² (12.22 sq ft)
Trailing-edge flaps (total)	1.36 m² (14.64 sq ft)
Fin	0.69 m² (7.43 sq ft)
Rudder	0.38 m² (4.09 sq ft)
Tailplane	1.57 m² (16.90 sq ft)
Elevator	0.77 m² (8.29 sq ft)

WEIGHTS AND LOADINGS:

Weight empty, equipped	930 kg (2,050 lb)
Fuel	210 kg (462 lb)
Max aerobatic T-O weight	1,315 kg (2,900 lb)
Max T-O and landing weight	1,338 kg (2,950 lb)
Max wing loading	97.73 kg/m² (20.03 lb/sq ft)
Max power loading	5.98 kg/kW (9.83 lb/hp)

PERFORMANCE (at max T-O and landing weight, ISA):

Never-exceed speed	241 knots (446 km/h; 277 mph)
Max level speed at S/L	168 knots (311 km/h; 193 mph)
Cruising speed:	
75% power at 2,680 m (8,800 ft)	
	144 knots (266 km/h; 166 mph) IAS
55% power at 5,120 m (16,800 ft)	
	138 knots (255 km/h; 159 mph) IAS
Max speed for flap extension	
	118 knots (218 km/h; 136 mph) IAS
Max speed for landing gear extension	
	138 knots (256 km/h; 159 mph) IAS
Approach speed over 15 m (50 ft) obstacle	
	80 knots (148 km/h; 92 mph)
Landing speed	65 knots (120 km/h; 75 mph)
Stalling speed: flaps up	67 knots (125 km/h; 78 mph)
flaps down	62 knots (115 km/h; 72 mph)
Max rate of climb at S/L	465 m (1,525 ft)/min
Time to: 1,830 m (6,000 ft)	4 min 42 s
3,050 m (10,000 ft)	8 min 48 s
Service ceiling	5,840 m (19,160 ft)
Absolute ceiling	6,250 m (20,500 ft)
T-O run	287 m (940 ft)
T-O to 15 m (50 ft)	494 m (1,620 ft)
Landing from 15 m (50 ft)	509 m (1,670 ft)
Landing run	238 m (780 ft)
Min ground turning radius	6.20 m (20 ft 4 in)
Range with 45 min reserves:	
75% power at 2,440 m (8,000 ft)	
	590 nm (1,093 km; 679 miles)
55% power at 3,660 m (12,000 ft)	
	650 nm (1,204 km; 748 miles)
Range, no reserves:	
75% power at 2,440 m (8,000 ft)	
	680 nm (1,260 km; 783 miles)
55% power at 3,660 m (12,000 ft)	
	735 nm (1,362 km; 846 miles)
Endurance at S/L: 75% power	4 h 24 min
55% power	5 h 36 min
g limits	+6/−3

ENAER T-35 Pillán tandem two-seat basic/intermediate trainer *(Pilot Press)*

ENAER T-36/A-36 HALCÓN (HAWK)

In 1980 the Chilean Air Force (FACh) ordered 14 C-101 Aviojet trainers from CASA of Spain, the contract including a licence for local manufacture by ENAER in a progressive programme advancing from assembly of CASA built components to partial manufacture of major components in Chile. The first four were built in Spain as C-101BB-02s, then delivered to the FACh to serve as pattern aircraft in organising the production line. A further 10 of this version were completed by ENAER.

Designated **T-36** Halcón by the FACh, the C-101BB-02 differs from the Spanish Air Force C-101EB in having a more powerful (16.46 kN; 3,700 lb st) Garrett TFE731-3 turbofan instead of the 15.57 kN (3,500 lb st) TFE731-2. Deliveries began in late 1983; they are in service with the Escuela de Aviación Capitan Avalos at El Bosque, Santiago.

During 1982 ENAER and CASA initiated a programme to develop an attack version of the C-101 with a higher thrust turbofan. Designated C-101CC-02 by CASA and **A-36** by the FACh, this flew for the first time in November 1983. Chile ordered 23 of this version, to replace the Cessna A-37 in FACh service. The A-36 is powered by a TFE731-5 of 19.13 kN (4,300 lb st), with a military power reserve (MPR) system which allows the thrust to be increased to 20.91 kN (4,700 lb).

Four of the C-101CC-02s/A-36s from the follow-on order are Spanish built aircraft; the remaining 19, built by ENAER, currently progressing through phase 3B (Chilean manufacture of electrical and hydraulic systems and small subassemblies) to phase 4 (manufacture of front fuselage). The A-36 is in service with the 1° Squadron of Brigada Aérea I at Los Cóndores, in northern Chile, and the 12° Squadron of Brigada Aérea IV at Carlos Ibánez air base in the extreme south.

ENAER PANTERA 50C

With technical assistance from Israel Aircraft Industries, ENAER is upgrading the Chilean Air Force's 16 Dassault-Breguet Mirage 50s (eight 50FCs, six 50CHs and two 50DCHs), serving with the 4° Squadron of Brigada Aérea IV at Carlos Ibánez, by fitting them with non-moving canard surfaces, an inertial navigation system, computerised head-up display, modified electrical, hydraulic and armament control systems, ENAER Caiquen III radar

ENAER A-36 Halcón in Fuerza Aérea de Chile insignia *(Kenneth Munson)*

First ENAER Pantera, a modified Mirage 50 with foreplanes and upgraded nav/attack system *(Kenneth Munson)*

warning receiver and Eclipse chaff/flare dispensing system. Flight testing, with foreplanes only, began in 1986. The first fully upgraded aircraft, known as Pantera (Panther) 50C, was rolled out in November 1988. The second Pantera was expected to be completed during 1990.

ENAER ÑAMCU (EAGLET)

Launched in June 1986 under the project name Avión Liviano (light aircraft), the Ñamcu was designed as a small, inexpensive club aircraft, initially for domestic use and later for export. Prototype construction began in February 1987. It has been designed for use also as a trainer, with full capability for aerobatic flying, and conforms to FAR Pt 23 in the Utility category.

The first ENAER aircraft of all-Chilean design, the prototype (CC-PZI) made its initial flight in April 1989. A second prototype (CC-PZJ) was flown in March 1990. The third, which will be fully aerobatic, may have a more powerful Textron Lycoming engine and variable-pitch propeller. It was hoped to begin series production of the Ñamcu in the Summer of 1990.

TYPE: Two-seat light aircraft.

WINGS: Cantilever low-wing monoplane. Wing section NACA 63₂-415. Dihedral 5° from roots. Incidence 3° at root, 0° 30′ at tip. Tapered, non-swept all-composites structure (glassfibre/foam sandwich with carbonfibre spar caps). Plain trailing-edge flaps and plain ailerons also of glassfibre/foam sandwich construction.

FUSELAGE: All-composites stressed skin structure of glassfibre/foam sandwich, with four bulkheads.

TAIL UNIT: Conventional assembly, with swept vertical and non-swept horizontal surfaces, of similar construction to wings. Balanced elevators and rudder; trim tab in starboard elevator.

LANDING GEAR: Non-retractable tricycle type. Cantilever spring steel main units; steerable nose unit, with oleo-pneumatic shock absorber. Cleveland wheel and Goodyear 6-ply tyre on each unit; all three tyres size 5.00-5. Cleveland hydraulic mainwheel brakes.

POWER PLANT: One 85.75 kW (115 hp) Textron Lycoming O-235-N2C flat-four engine, driving a fixed-pitch propeller with spinner and two composites blades. Single fuel tank in fuselage, capacity 100 litres (26.4 US gallons; 22 Imp gallons), with refuelling point in fuselage side.

ACCOMMODATION: Seats for two persons side by side in fully enclosed cockpit, with adjustable headrests and four-piece safety harnesses. Dual controls. Two

ENAER Namcu first prototype two-seat light aircraft during an early test flight

independent 'gull wing' window/doors, hinged on centre-line to open upward. Cockpit heated and ventilated. Electric defrosting of windscreen.

SYSTEMS: Hydraulic system for brakes only. Electrical power supplied by 12V 70A alternator and 12V 35Ah battery.

AVIONICS AND EQUIPMENT: VFR flight and engine instrumentation, Walter Dittel FSG 71M 760-channel VHF com transceiver, and intercom, are standard; IFR instrumentation optional.

DIMENSIONS, EXTERNAL:

Wing span	8.31 m (27 ft 3¼ in)
Wing chord: at root	1.53 m (5 ft 0¼ in)
at tip	0.84 m (2 ft 9 in)
Wing aspect ratio	7.6
Length overall	7.05 m (23 ft 1½ in)
Height overall	2.42 m (7 ft 11¼ in)
Tailplane span	3.00 m (9 ft 10 in)
Wheel track	2.54 m (8 ft 4 in)
Wheelbase	1.50 m (4 ft 11 in)
Propeller diameter	1.78 m (5 ft 10 in)

DIMENSIONS, INTERNAL:

Cockpit: Max width	1.16 m (3 ft 9½ in)

AREAS:

Wings, gross	10.01 m² (107.75 sq ft)
Ailerons (total)	0.44 m² (4.74 sq ft)
Trailing-edge flaps (total)	0.92 m² (9.90 sq ft)
Fin	0.88 m² (9.47 sq ft)
Rudder	0.34 m² (3.66 sq ft)
Tailplane	2.08 m² (22.39 sq ft)
Elevators (total)	0.76 m² (8.18 sq ft)

WEIGHTS AND LOADINGS:

Basic weight empty	546 kg (1,204 lb)
Max fuel	72 kg (159 lb)
Max T-O and landing weight	800 kg (1,763 lb)
Max wing loading	79.92 kg/m² (16.38 lb/sq ft)
Max power loading	9.33 kg/kW (15.33 lb/hp)

PERFORMANCE (at max T-O weight except where indicated):

Never-exceed speed	177 knots (328 km/h; 204 mph)
Max level speed at S/L	127 knots (235 km/h; 146 mph)
Max cruising speed, 75% power at 2,440 m (8,000 ft)	103 knots (191 km/h; 119 mph)

Stalling speed, power off:

flaps up	56 knots (104 km/h; 65 mph)
flaps down	50 knots (93 km/h; 58 mph)
Max rate of climb at S/L	295 m (968 ft)/min
Service ceiling	4,270 m (14,000 ft)
T-O run	304 m (998 ft)
T-O to 15 m (50 ft)	412 m (1,352 ft)
Landing from 15 m (50 ft)	364 m (1,195 ft)
Landing run	177 m (581 ft)
Range at 75% power at 2,440 m (8,000 ft) with max fuel, 10% reserves	500 nm (926 km; 575 miles)
g limits	+4.4/−2.2

CHINA, PEOPLE'S REPUBLIC

MAS
MINISTRY OF AERO-SPACE INDUSTRY
PO Box 33, Beijing
Telephone: 86 (1) 440517
Telex: 211244 MAS CN
MINISTER: Lin Zongtang
INTERNATIONAL MARKETING:
CATIC (China National Aero-Technology Import and Export Corporation)
5 Liang Guo Chang Road, East City District (PO Box 1671), Beijing
Telephone: 86 (1) 445831
Telex: 22318 AEROT CN
Fax: 86 (1) 4015381
PRESIDENT: Sun Zhaoqing
EXECUTIVE VICE-PRESIDENT: Tang Xiaoping

All Chinese aircraft factories function under the jurisdiction of the Ministry of Aero-Space Industry. There are design and development centres at Shenyang, Beijing, Harbin and elsewhere. Xian, Harbin and other Chinese factories also carry out subcontract work on the Airbus

A300, ATR 42, BAe 146, Boeing 737 and 747, Canadair CL-215, McDonnell Douglas MD-80 and Shorts 360. Total workforce of the aerospace industry was estimated at no fewer than 350,000 in 1984, although most of its factories are engaged also in manufacturing non-aerospace products.

Output of older fighters and bombers is now diminishing, with increasing emphasis being placed on the development of new aircraft making use of China's growing technological capability. The reduction of 1 million personnel in China's armed forces manpower was intended to make more funds available during the seventh Five-Year Plan (1986-90) for the purchase of modern weapons and technology, while at the same time shifting emphasis in the aviation industry towards a target of a 60-40 per cent bias in favour of civil aircraft production.

In addition to continuing with production and new versions of the Y-7, Y-8 and Y-12, an international partner is being sought for a 30/40-passenger commuter airliner programme (existing type or new design). A larger transport, designated MPC-75, is being undertaken by CATIC and the German company MBB (see MPC-75 entry

in the International section). To follow the Y-8 a 150-passenger 'Trunkliner' is being sought, for service entry in about 1995. Derivatives of the Boeing 737 and McDonnell Douglas MD-90 have been proposed, and a selection was expected during 1990. Chinese partner companies would be XAC and SAMF respectively. Up to 150 of the selected type are said to be required.

Increasing attention is also being given to helicopter development. China's modern helicopter design and manufacturing experience is restricted chiefly to development of the Changhe Z-8, a Chinese derivative of the Aerospatiale Super Frelon, and licence production at Harbin of the same company's Dauphin as the Z-9. To extend this range, an agreement was signed with Aerospatiale in 1987 (and, later, with Singapore Aerospace, which see) for joint development of a small (2,500 kg; 5,500 lb class) type for agricultural and forestry work. The latter could also fulfil a current requirement for a small military helicopter. The PLA is said to need about 50 for anti-tank duties. Currently designated P 120L, this programme is further described in the International section.

CAC
CHENGDU AIRCRAFT CORPORATION
PO Box 800, Chengdu, Sichuan
Telephone: 86 (28) 669629
Telex: 60132 CCDAC CN
Fax: 86 (28) 69816
GENERAL MANAGER: Hou Jianwu
DEPUTY GENERAL MANAGER: Li Shaoming

Founded in 1958, Chengdu Aircraft Corporation is a major centre for the development and production of fighter aircraft. Current activity includes several models of the J-7/F-7 fighter series, and limited batch production also continues of the JJ-5/FT-5 fighter/trainer developed from the Soviet MiG-17. Chengdu is subcontracted by McDonnell Douglas of the USA to manufacture nosecones for MD-80 series airliners, both for the Shanghai MD-82 programme (see SAMF entry in this section) and for the US production line. The CAC facility occupies a site area of 510 ha (1,260 acres), and had a 1989 workforce of about 20,000. Output includes a number of non-aerospace products.

CAC (MIKOYAN) JJ-5
Chinese name: Jianjiji Jiaolianji-5 (Fighter training aircraft 5) or Jianjiao-5
Westernised designation: FT-5
This tandem two-seat version of the J-5 (Chinese built MiG-17) was developed at Chengdu in 1965 and flew for the first time on 8 May 1966. In essence, it combines the tandem cockpits and forward fuselage of the MiG-15UTI with the rest of the airframe of the J-5A (Chinese MiG-17PF), though retaining the latter's lipped intake, the small fairing indicating provision for a radar ranging gunsight in the front cockpit. Other changes include use of a non-afterburning Xian (XAE) WP5D turbojet, rated at 26.48 kN (5,952 lb st); and reduction of the armament to a single Type 23-1 (23 mm) gun, carried in a removable belly pack, with the barrel to the starboard side of the nosewheel doors.

Certificated for mass production at the end of 1966, the JJ-5 is still the standard advanced trainer of the Chinese air

forces, to which pupil pilots graduate after basic training on the NAMC CJ-6 (which see). A total of 1,061 had been built by the end of 1986, and limited batch production was continuing in 1989-90. More than 100, designated FT-5, have been exported to Bangladesh, Pakistan, Sudan and Tanzania.

WEIGHTS:

Weight empty, equipped	4,080 kg (8,995 lb)
Normal T-O weight	5,401 kg (11,907 lb)
Max T-O weight	6,215 kg (13,700 lb)

PERFORMANCE:

Normal operating speed	418 knots (775 km/h; 482 mph)
Max rate of climb at S/L	1,620 m (5,315 ft)/min
Service ceiling	14,300 m (46,900 ft)
T-O run	760 m (2,493 ft)
Landing run	780-830 m (2,559-2,723 ft)
Range with max fuel at 12,000 m (39,370 ft)	664 nm (1,230 km; 764 miles)
Max endurance at 13,700 m (45,000 ft) with two 400 litre (105.5 US gallon; 88 Imp gallon) drop tanks	2 h 38 min

CAC (MIKOYAN) J-7
Chinese name: Jianjiji-7 (Fighter aircraft 7) or Jian-7
Westernised designations: F-7A, F-7B, F-7M, F-7MP and F-7P
NATO reporting name: Fishbed
A Soviet licence to manufacture the MiG-21F-13 fighter and its Tumansky R-11F-300 engine was granted to the Chinese government in 1961, and some pattern aircraft and CKD (component knocked-down) kits for both were delivered, but due to the severing of relations between the two countries the necessary technical documentation was not completed. Assembly of the first J-7, at Shenyang, thus did not begin until early 1964, and the first flight of this aircraft eventually took place on 17 January 1966. Static testing had by then been completed (in November 1965), and approval for production was granted in June 1967. Earlier, in 1964-65, it had been planned to make factories at Chengdu and Guizhou the main centres for J-7 airframe

and engine production, backed up by Shenyang until the former two locations were fully productive. However, the planned programme was seriously affected by the onset of the 'cultural revolution', at which time relatively few examples of the original J-7 had been delivered by Shenyang. Some of this version were supplied (as **F-7A**) to Albania and Tanzania.

The following subsequent variants have been developed by Chengdu:

J-7 I. Initial Chengdu production version for PLA Air Force (1967). Not accepted in large numbers, due mainly to unsatisfactory escape system (front-hinged canopy, to which ejection seat was attached).

F-7B. Export counterpart of J-7 I, supplied to Egypt and Iraq.

J-7 II. Much modified and improved development of J-7 I, with WP7B turbojet of increased thrust (43.15 kN; 9,700 lb st dry, 59.82 kN; 13,448 lb st with afterburning); variable intake shock cone; 720 litre (190.2 US gallon; 158.4 Imp gallon) centreline drop tank for increased range; brake-chute relocated at base of rudder to improve landing performance and shorten run; rear-hinged canopy, jettisoned before ejection seat deploys; new Chengdu Type II seat offering ejection at zero height and speeds down to 135 knots (250 km/h; 155 mph); second 30 mm gun; and new Lanzhou compass system. Development began 1975; first flight 30 December 1978. Approved for production in September 1979. In service. Small batch production (14 in 1989) is continuing.

F-7M Airguard. Upgraded export version, developed from J-7 II and equipped with GEC Avionics HUDWAC (head-up display and weapon aiming computer); new ranging radar, air data computer, radar altimeter and IFF; more secure com radio; improved electrical power generation system to cater for the new avionics; two additional underwing stores points; an improved WP7B (BM) engine; birdproof windscreen; strengthened landing gear; ability to carry PL-7 air-to-air missiles; and a relocated nose probe. Development began in 1981, and production approval was issued in December 1984. Supplied to

F-7M Airguard Chinese built export version of the MiG-21 ('Fishbed')

Chengdu F-7M Airguard single-seat fighter and close support aircraft *(Jane's/Mike Keep)*

Pakistan (60, from 1986), Bangladesh (16), Iran (12-18 or more) and Zimbabwe (48). In production.

F-7P Skybolt. Variant of F-7M, embodying 24 modifications to meet specific requirements of Pakistan Air Force, in particular the ability to carry four air-to-air missiles underwing instead of two. Martin-Baker Mk 10L ejection seat. Twenty delivered to PAF in mid-1989.

F-7MP. Variant of F-7M for Pakistan, which has ordered 75. Improved cockpit layout and navigation system incorporating Collins AN/ARN-147 VOR/ILS receiver, AN/ARN-149 ADF and Pro Line II digital DME-42.

J-7 III. Much redesigned from J-7 II for PLA Air Force, with all-weather, day/night capability. Main improvements are more powerful WP13 engine (40.21 kN; 9,039 lb st dry, 64.72 kN; 14,550 lb st with afterburning); additional fuel in deeper dorsal spine; JL-7 (J-band) interception radar, with correspondingly larger nose intake and centrebody radome; sideways (instead of rearward) hinged canopy, with centrally located rearview mirror; improved (zero/zero?) ejection seat; more advanced fire control system; twin-barrel 23 mm gun under fuselage (with optical gunsight); broader-chord vertical tail surfaces, incorporating antennae for radar warning receivers; and increased weapon/stores capability (four underwing stations), similar to that of F-7M. Other features include 'Odd Rods' IFF, similar angle of attack vane and air data probe to those of F-7M, and a Beijing Aeronautical Instruments Factory KJ-11 autopilot. Joint development by Chengdu and Guizhou (GAIC): design began in 1981, and first flight was made on 26 April 1984. In production and service.

J-7E. Latest version, with redesigned wing. Due to fly in April 1990: no other details known at time of going to press.

Super-7. Proposed export development of F-7M for Pakistan; joint programme with Grumman (USA). Described separately.

JJ-7/FT-7. Tandem two-seat operational trainer, based on J-7 II. Developed at Guizhou and described separately under GAIC entry.

Total exports of the F-7 (all models) have exceeded 500. Current Soviet versions of the MiG-21 are fully described and illustrated in the USSR section of this edition. The following description applies to the standard Chengdu F-7M:

TYPE: Single-seat day fighter and close support aircraft.

WINGS: As for standard MiG-21, with 57° sweepback on leading-edges, 2° anhedral, slotted flaps and balanced ailerons.

FUSELAGE: Generally as MiG-21F except for automatically operated, continuously adjustable shock cone in centre of nose intake. Nose probe relocated above intake, offset to starboard, as on Soviet built MiG-21PFM 'Fishbed-J'.

TAIL UNIT: All-swept surfaces, with all-moving tailplane, as for MiG-21.

LANDING GEAR: Inward retracting mainwheels, with 660 × 220 tyres and LS-16 disc brakes; forward retracting nosewheel, with 500 × 180 tyre and LS-15 double-acting brake. Tail braking parachute at base of vertical tail.

POWER PLANT: One Chengdu WP7B(BM) turbojet (43.15 kN/4,400 kg; 9,700 lb st dry, 59.82 kN/6,100 kg; 13,448 lb st with afterburning). Total internal fuel capacity of 2,385 litres (630 US gallons; 524.5 Imp gallons), contained in six flexible tanks in fuselage and two integral tanks in each wing. Provision for carrying a 500 or 800 litre (132 or 211.3 US gallon; 110 or 176 Imp gallon) centreline drop tank, and/or a 500 litre drop tank on each outboard underwing pylon. Max possible internal/external fuel capacity 4,185 litres (1,105.6 US gallons; 920.5 Imp gallons).

ACCOMMODATION: Pilot only, on Chengdu Aircraft Corporation zero-height/low-speed ejection seat operable between 70 and 459 knots (130-850 km/h; 81-528 mph) IAS. One-piece canopy, hinged at rear to open upward.

SYSTEMS: Improved electrical system, using three static inverters, to cater for additional avionics. Jianghuai YX-3 oxygen system.

AVIONICS: GEC Avionics suite includes Type 956 HUD-WAC, AD 3400 two-band UHF/VHF multi-function com system, Type 226 Skyranger ranging radar with ECCM, and an air data computer. Other avionics include Type 602 IFF transponder, Type 0101 HR A/2 radar altimeter, WL-7 radio compass, and XS-6A marker beacon receiver. The HUDWAC (head-up display and weapon aiming computer) provides the pilot with displays for instrument flying, with air-to-air and air-to-ground weapon aiming symbols integrated with flight-instrument symbology. It can store 32 weapon parameter functions, allowing for both current and future weapon variants. In air-to-air combat its four modes (missiles, conventional gunnery, snapshoot gunnery, dogfight and standby aiming reticle) allow for all eventualities. The navigation function includes an approach mode.

ARMAMENT: Two 30 mm Type 30-1 belt-fed cannon, with 60 rds/gun, in fairings under front fuselage just forward of wingroot leading-edges. Two hardpoints under each wing, of which the outer ones are wet for the carriage of drop tanks. The centreline pylon is used for a drop tank only. Each inboard pylon is capable of carrying a PL-2, -2A, -5B or -7 air-to-air missile or, at customer's option, a Matra R.550 Magic; one 18-tube pod of Type 57-2 (57 mm) air-to-air and air-to-ground rockets; one Type 90-1 (90 mm) 7-tube pod of air-to-ground rockets; or a 50, 150, 250 or 500 kg bomb. Each outboard pylon can carry one of the above rocket pods, a 50 or 150 kg bomb, or a 500 litre drop tank.

DIMENSIONS, EXTERNAL:
Wing span	7.154 m (23 ft 5⅝ in)
Wing aspect ratio	2.2
Length overall: excl nose probe	13.945 m (45 ft 9 in)
incl nose probe	14.885 m (48 ft 10 in)
Height overall	4.103 m (13 ft 5½ in)
Tailplane span	3.74 m (12 ft 3¼ in)
Wheel track	2.692 m (8 ft 10 in)
Wheelbase	4.807 m (15 ft 9¼ in)

AREA:
Wings, gross	23.00 m² (247.6 sq ft)

WEIGHTS AND LOADINGS:
Weight empty	5,275 kg (11,629 lb)
Normal max T-O weight with two PL-2 or PL-7 air-to-air missiles	7,531 kg (16,603 lb)
Wing loading at normal max T-O weight	327.43 kg/m² (67.10 lb/sq ft)
Power loading at normal max T-O weight	125.5 kg/kN (1.23 lb/lb st)

PERFORMANCE (at normal max T-O weight with two PL-2 or PL-7 air-to-air missiles, except where indicated):
Max level speed between 12,500 and 18,500 m (41,010-60,700 ft)	Mach 2.05 (1,175 knots; 2,175 km/h; 1,350 mph)
Unstick speed	167-178 knots (310-330 km/h; 193-205 mph)
Touchdown speed	162-173 knots (300-320 km/h; 186-199 mph)
Max rate of climb at S/L	10,800 m (35,435 ft)/min
Acceleration from Mach 0.9 to 1.2 at 5,000 m (16,400 ft)	35 s
Max sustained turn rate: Mach 0.7 at S/L	14.7°/s
Mach 0.8 at 5,000 m (16,400 ft)	9.5°/s
Service ceiling	18,200 m (59,710 ft)
Absolute ceiling	18,700 m (61,350 ft)
T-O run	700-950 m (2,297-3,117 ft)
Landing run with brake-chute	600-900 m (1,969-2,953 ft)

Model of the proposed Super-7 advanced development of the Chengdu F-7M (see next page)

Typical mission profiles:

Combat air patrol at 11,000 m (36,000 ft) with two air-to-air missiles and three 500 litre drop tanks, incl 5 min combat 45 min

Long-range interception at 11,000 m (36,000 ft) at 351 nm (650 km; 404 miles) from base, incl Mach 1.5 dash and 5 min combat, stores as above

Hi-lo-hi interdiction radius, out and back at 11,000 m (36,000 ft), with three 500 litre drop tanks and two 150 kg bombs 324 nm (600 km; 373 miles)

Lo-lo-lo close air support radius with four rocket pods, no external tanks 200 nm (370 km; 230 miles)

Range: two PL-7 missiles and three 500 litre drop tanks 939 nm (1,740 km; 1,081 miles)

self-ferry with one 800 litre and two 500 litre drop tanks, no missiles

1,203 nm (2,230 km; 1,385 miles)

g limit +8

CAC/GRUMMAN SUPER-7

An agreement was signed on 21 October 1988 between CATIC and Grumman (USA) to produce a further developed export version of the F-7M known as the Super-7.

The agreement covered a preliminary design phase, which was completed by early 1990. If sufficient customer interest is shown, it will progress to a second (detail design and development) stage and a production third stage.

As proposed, the Super-7 would have lateral air intakes for a more powerful engine (candidates are the General Electric F404/RM12 and Turbo-Union RB199) and a 'solid' ogival nosecone for a Westinghouse APG-66 radar, but other changes would be more extensive. The wings would be enlarged in span and area, fitted with leading-edge slats, and equipped with an additional pair of inboard hardpoints for Sidewinder air-to-air missiles. The fuselage would incorporate an enlarged dorsal spine to house additional fuel, single-point pressure refuelling, an easier-access engine compartment, an arrester hook and a revised ventral fin. Strengthened main landing gear, with larger

tyres, would be combined with a new straight-leg steerable nosewheel unit. The F-7M's two internal 30 mm cannon would be replaced by a belly mounted twin-barrel 23 mm gun. A new cockpit, under a Northrop F-20 windscreen and canopy, would incorporate an F-16 type head-up display and a new ejection seat, and a revised environmental control system would cool the avionics.

Subject to receipt of a firm customer order, Phase 2 would involve the completion of three prototypes, but the Super-7 programme was suspended by the US government in mid-1989 and had not been reinstated at the time of going to press.

DIMENSIONS, EXTERNAL:
Wing span	7.92 m (26 ft 0 in)
Length overall	15.04 m (49 ft 4 in)

AREA:
Wings, gross	approx 24.62 m² (265 sq ft)

WEIGHTS (estimated):
Design gross weight	8,800 kg (19,400 lb)
Max T-O weight	10,800 kg (23,810 lb)

CAF
CHANGHE AIRCRAFT FACTORY
PO Box 109, Jingdezhen, Jiangxi
Telephone: 3019
Telex: 95027 CHAF CN
DIRECTOR: Li Wanxin

Changhe Aircraft Factory, built on a 234 ha (578 acre) site at Jingdezhen, began producing coaches and commercial road vehicles in 1974. These and other automotive products still account for most of its output, but since being placed under MAS jurisdiction it has developed a capability for batch production of helicopters and is one of three members (the others being Harbin Aircraft Manufacturing Co and the Helicopter Design and Research Institute) which form the China Helicopter Industry Corporation. CAF had a 1989 workforce of 6,000, of whom nearly 1,700 are engineers and technicians.

CAF Z-8
Chinese name: Zhishengji-8 (Vertical take-off aircraft 8) or Zhi-8

Design work on this Chinese version of the Aerospatiale AS 321Ja Super Frelon (see 1982-83 *Jane's*) began as long ago as 1975, but development was suspended between 1979 and mid-1984 and the first prototype did not make its initial flight until 11 December 1985. A second prototype has since flown. Domestic type approval of the Z-8 was granted on 8 April 1989, and on 5 August that year the first Z-8 was handed over to the PLA Naval Air Force for service trials. Eventual applications are expected to include troop transport, ASW/ASV, search and rescue, minelaying/sweeping, aerial survey and firefighting.

TYPE: Multi-role military and civil helicopter.

ROTOR SYSTEM AND DRIVE: Six-blade main rotor and five-blade tail rotor. Main rotor head consists basically of two six-armed star plates carrying the drag and flapping hinges for each blade. The root of each main rotor blade carries a fitting for pitch control, and each blade has an individual hydraulic drag damper. Gearboxes are manufactured by Zhongnan Transmission Machinery Factory.

FUSELAGE AND TAIL UNIT: Boat-hull fuselage of conventional semi-monocoque construction, with riveted watertight compartments inside planing bottom. Stabilising float attached to stub-wing at rear on each side. Small, strut braced fixed horizontal stabiliser on starboard side of tail rotor pylon.

LANDING GEAR: Non-retractable tricycle type, with twin wheels and low-pressure oleo-pneumatic shock absorber on each unit. Small tripod tailskid under rear of tailboom. Boat hull and side floats permit emergency water landings and take-offs.

POWER PLANT: Three Changzhou (CLXMW) WZ6 turboshafts, each having a max emergency rating of 1,156 kW (1,550 shp) and 20 per cent power reserve at S/L, ISA. Two engines side by side in front of main rotor shaft and one aft of shaft. Fuel in flexible tanks under floor of centre fuselage. Auxiliary fuel tanks can be carried inside cabin for extended range or self-ferry missions.

ACCOMMODATION: Crew of two or three on flight deck. Fully redundant flight control system. Dong Fang KJ-8 autopilot. Accommodation in main cabin for up to 27 fully armed troops, or 39 without equipment; up to 15

Second prototype of the Changhe Z-8 Chinese version of the Aerospatiale Super Frelon

stretchers in ambulance configuration; a BJ-212 jeep and its crew; or other configurations according to mission. Forward opening crew door on each side of flight deck. Rearward sliding door at front of cabin on starboard side. Hydraulically actuated rear loading ramp/door.

EQUIPMENT: Equipment for SAR role can include a 275 kg (606 lb) capacity hydraulic rescue hoist and two five-person liferafts. Can also be equipped with sonar, sonobuoys and torpedoes for ASW; with search radar and air-to-surface missiles for anti-shipping missions; with gear for minelaying (eight 250 kg mines) or minesweeping; or with appropriate equipment for oceanography, geological survey and forest firefighting.

DIMENSIONS, EXTERNAL:
Main rotor diameter	18.90 m (62 ft 0 in)
Tail rotor diameter	4.00 m (13 ft 1½ in)
Length overall, rotors turning	23.035 m (75 ft 7 in)
Height overall, rotors turning	6.66 m (21 ft 10¼ in)
Width over main gear sponsons	5.20 m (17 ft 0¾ in)

AREAS:
Main rotor disc	280.48 m² (3,019.1 sq ft)
Tail rotor disc	12.57 m² (135.3 sq ft)

WEIGHTS:
Max hovering weight OGE at S/L	12,480 kg (27,513 lb)
Max T-O weight	13,000 kg (28,660 lb)

PERFORMANCE (A at T-O weight of 9,000 kg; 19,841 lb, B at 11,000 kg; 24,251 lb, C at 13,000 kg; 28,660 lb):

Never-exceed speed: A 170 knots (315 km/h; 195 mph)
B 159 knots (296 km/h; 183 mph)
C 148 knots (275 km/h; 170 mph)

Max cruising speed: A 143 knots (266 km/h; 165 mph)
B 140 knots (260 km/h; 161 mph)
C 134 knots (248 km/h; 154 mph)

Econ cruising speed: A 137 knots (255 km/h; 158 mph)
B 132 knots (246 km/h; 153 mph)
C 125 knots (232 km/h; 144 mph)

Rate of climb at S/L (15° 30′ collective pitch, one engine out): A 690 m (2,263 ft)/min
B 552 m (1,811 ft)/min
C 396 m (1,299 ft)/min

Service ceiling: A 6,000 m (19,685 ft)
B 4,900 m (16,075 ft)
C 3,050 m (10,000 ft)

Hovering ceiling IGE: A 5,500 m (18,045 ft)
B 3,600 m (11,810 ft)
C 1,900 m (6,235 ft)

Hovering ceiling OGE: A 4,400 m (14,435 ft)
B 2,300 m (7,545 ft)

Range with max standard fuel, one engine out, no reserves: A 232 nm (430 km; 267 miles)
B 442 nm (820 km; 509 miles)
C 431 nm (800 km; 497 miles)

Ferry range with auxiliary fuel tanks, one engine out, no reserves: C 755 nm (1,400 km; 870 miles)

Endurance with max standard fuel, one engine out, no reserves: A 2 h 31 min
B 4 h 43 min
C 4 h 10 min

GAIC
GUIZHOU AVIATION INDUSTRY CORPORATION
PO Box 38, Anshun, Guizhou
Telephone: 86 (34) 551027; or 86/Anshun 22228
Telex: 66018 AIMGA CN
GENERAL MANAGER: Sun Ruisheng

GAIC incorporates a number of enterprises, factories and institutes which between them are engaged in many

aerospace and non-aerospace activities. The former include the JJ-7/FT-7 fighter/trainer described in this entry, two series of turbojet engines, air-to-air missiles and rocket launchers. It also participates in production of the single-seat J-7/F-7 described under the Chengdu (CAC) heading. GAIC describes its total group workforce as "dozens of thousands", including some 18,000 with professional or technical qualifications.

GAIGC JJ-7
Chinese name: Jianjiji Jiaolianji-7 or Jianjiao-7 (Fighter training aircraft 7)
Westernised designation: FT-7

First flown on 5 July 1985, the JJ-7 or FT-7 is a tandem two-seat trainer version of the Chengdu J-7 II, outwardly similar to its Soviet counterpart, the MiG-21U (NATO 'Mongol-A'), and is capable of providing most of the training necessary for the Shenyang J-8 fighter as well as the full syllabus for all versions of the J-7/F-7. Avionics and power plant are generally as described for the single-seat version under the CAC heading.

Differences from the single-seat J-7 and MiG-21U include sideways opening (to starboard) twin canopies, the rear one fitted with a retractable periscope, twin ventral strakes of modified shape, and a removable saddleback fuel tank aft of the second cockpit. A 480 or 800 litre (127 or 211 US gallon; 105.5 or 176 Imp gallon) drop tank can be carried under the centre-fuselage, and there is a single underwing pylon each side for such stores as PL-2 or -2B air-to-air missiles, an HF-5A 18-round launcher for 57 mm rockets, or bombs of up to 250 kg size. The JJ-7 can also be fitted with a Type 23-3 twin-barrel 23 mm gun in an underbelly pack.

DIMENSIONS, EXTERNAL: As J-7 except:
Length overall, incl probe   14.874 m (48 ft 9½ in)
WEIGHTS:
Weight empty   5,330 kg (11,750 lb)
Internal fuel   1,891 kg (4,169 lb)
Normal max T-O weight with two PL-2 air-to-air missiles   7,590 kg (16,733 lb)
Max T-O weight with two PL-2 missiles and one 800 litre drop tank   8,600 kg (18,960 lb)
PERFORMANCE:
Max level speed   as for J-7/F-7
Unstick speed   170-181 knots (315-335 km/h; 196-208 mph)
Touchdown speed   165-175 knots (305-325 km/h; 190-202 mph)
Service ceiling   17,300 m (56,760 ft)
Absolute ceiling   17,700 m (58,070 ft)
T-O run   900-1,100 m (2,953-3,609 ft)
Landing run with brake-chute and wheel braking   850-1,100 m (2,789-3,609 ft)

GAIC JJ-7/FT-7 two-seat trainer version of the CAC J-7/F-7 (Brian M. Service)

Range at 11,000 m (36,000 ft):
internal fuel only   545 nm (1,010 km; 627 miles)
with 800 litre drop tank   701 nm (1,300 km; 808 miles)
g limit with two PL-2B missiles   +7

GOHL
GUANGZHOU ORLANDO HELICOPTERS LTD
Hoben, Jiahe, Guangzhou, Guangdong
Telephone: 86 (20) 628201
Telex: 44526 EECCG CN
Fax: 86 (20) 342203
GENERAL MANAGER: Kelly Robinson
VICE-GENERAL MANAGER: Zhao Shuxin

GUANGZHOU (ORLANDO) PANDA
Orlando Helicopter Airways (see US section) initiated a venture in 1985 in which its OHA-S-55 Bearcat is now being assembled, and will later be part-built, in China, by a jointly owned company known as Guangzhou Orlando Helicopters Ltd. A 2,323 m² (25,000 sq ft) factory was built for the purpose at an airfield near the city of Guangzhou.

The 20-year contract, signed on 27 October 1985, provides for the initial assembly in China, from Orlando kits, of ten aircraft. Kits for five of these had been shipped to China by early 1989, first flight took place in Spring 1987, and Chinese type certification has been granted. Crop and forestry spraying trials were conducted in 1988, and the OHA-S-55 is expected to replace some Y-5 (Chinese An-2) biplanes with these duties. Second and third stage batches of 20 and 30 aircraft respectively will include a proportion of OHA-S-55T Challenger and/or Phoenix turbine powered versions, with 671 kW (900 shp) Pratt & Whitney Canada PT6T engines. Chinese built OHA-S-55s are to be

One of the first five Guangzhou assembled Orlando OHA-S-55 helicopters to be completed

marketed, under the name Panda, by Orlando Helicopter Far East Ltd, based in Hong Kong. The contract also contains options for co-production of the Orlando modified

S-58T Viking. The Sikorsky S-76 has been deleted from the original programme.

HAMC
HARBIN AIRCRAFT MANUFACTURING COMPANY
PO Box 201, Harbin, Heilongjiang
Telephone: 86 (451) 62951
Telex: 87082 HAF CN
Fax: 86 (451) 227491
GENERAL MANAGER: Yang Shouwen

Harbin had its origin in the plant of the Manshu Aeroplane Manufacturing Company, one of several aircraft and aero engine factories established in Manchukuo (Manchuria) by the Japanese in 1938. After the Communist regime came to power in mainland China in 1949 it was re-established in 1952 and re-equipped with Soviet assistance, and since then has been responsible for production of the H-5 twin-jet light bomber, a reverse engineered version of the Soviet Ilyushin Il-28, and the nationally designed SH-5 amphibian and Y-11 and Y-12 agricultural and utility light twins. Details of the H-5 and Y-11 can be found in earlier editions of Jane's. A new version of the Y-11, designated Y-11B, is reportedly under development. Landing gear doors for the British Aerospace 146 are produced under a 1981 agreement with BAe, and doors and wing components for the Shorts 360.

Harbin is also the chief centre for helicopter production, which began with the Mil Mi-4 (Chinese Z-5, first flown on 14 December 1958; total of 545 built. Described in 1985-86 and earlier Jane's). It is currently responsible for the Aerospatiale Dauphin 2 (Z-9) manufacturing and assembly programme, and is producing components for China's Mil Mi-8s. The workforce numbers about 15,000.

Latest known Harbin product is the SH-5 (PS-5) maritime patrol amphibian.

HAMC SH-5
Chinese name: Shuishang Hongzhaji 5 (Maritime bomber 5) or Shuihong-5
Westernised designation: PS-5
Design of this four-turboprop flying-boat amphibian was undertaken jointly by HAMC and the Seaplane Design Institute, but its development became one of many victims of the 'cultural revolution'. Detail design was completed in February 1970, but static testing of the first complete airframe was not achieved until August 1974, nearly three years after its completion. The first flying prototype, completed in December 1973, underwent water taxi trials totalling some 30 hours, between May 1975 and March 1976, before achieving its first flight on 3 April 1976.

Four more SH-5s were completed and flown in 1984-85, subsequently being handed over to the PLA Naval Air Force on 3 September 1986, for service at Tuandao naval air station, Qingdao.

The SH-5 is intended for a wide range of maritime duties including anti-submarine and anti-surface-vessel warfare, patrol and surveillance, minelaying, search and rescue, and the carriage of bulk cargo. A firefighting water-bomber version has already been evaluated.

The Chinese are reportedly seeking an ASW and avionics upgrade for the SH-5, possibly similar to that now under way for the Dassault-Breguet Atlantique 2.

TYPE: Maritime patrol and anti-submarine bomber, surveillance, SAR and transport amphibian.

WINGS: All-metal cantilever high-wing monoplane. Constant chord centre-section; outer panels tapered, with anhedral outboard of outer engine nacelles. Non-retractable stabilising float, on N struts with twin I struts inboard, beneath each wing near tip. Spoiler forward of each outer flap segment. Trim tab in each aileron.

FUSELAGE: Unpressurised all-metal semi-monocoque hull, with high length/beam ratio and single-step planing bottom. Curved spray suppression strakes along sides of nose; spray suppression slots in lower sides, aft of inboard propeller plane. Small water rudder at rear of hull. 'Thimble' radome on nose; MAD in extended tail 'sting'.

TAIL UNIT: High mounted dihedral tailplane, with oval endplate fins and rudders, mounted on fairing above rear fuselage. Trim tabs in each rudder and each elevator.

LANDING GEAR: Retractable tricycle type, with single mainwheels and twin-wheel nose unit. Oleo-pneumatic shock absorbers. Main units retract upward and rearward into wells in hull sides; nose unit retracts rearward.

POWER PLANT: Four 2,349 kW (3,150 ehp) Dongan (DEMC) WJ5A turboprops, each driving a Baoding four-blade propeller with spinner.

ACCOMMODATION: Standard eight-person crew includes a flight crew of five (pilot, co-pilot, navigator, flight engineer and radio operator), plus systems/equipment operators according to mission. Three freight compartments in front portion of hull. Mission crew cabin amidships, aft of which are two further compartments, one for communications and other electronic equipment and the rear one for specialised mission equipment. All

HAMC SH-5 (PS-5) patrol and anti-submarine bomber amphibian, in service with the Chinese PLA Naval Air Force

HAMC SH-5 (four Harbin WJ5A turboprops) *(Pilot Press)*

compartments connected by corridor, with watertight doors aft of flight deck and between each compartment.

AVIONICS AND EQUIPMENT: Include inertial navigation system, air data computer, radio altimeter and radio compass.

ARMAMENT AND OPERATIONAL EQUIPMENT: Doppler search radar in 'thimble' radome forward of nose transparencies. Magnetic anomaly detector (MAD) in extended tail 'sting'. Four underwing hardpoints for C-101 sea skimming supersonic anti-shipping or other missiles (one on each inboard pylon), lightweight torpedoes (up to three on each outer pylon), or other stores. Depth charges, mines, bombs, sonobuoys, SAR gear or other mission equipment and stores in rear of hull, as required.

DIMENSIONS, EXTERNAL:

Wing span	36.00 m (118 ft 1¼ in)
Wing aspect ratio	9.0
Length overall	38.90 m (127 ft 7½ in)
Height overall	9.79 m (32 ft 1½ in)
* Span over tail-fins	11.40 m (37 ft 4¾ in)
* Wheel track	3.70 m (12 ft 1¾ in)
* Wheelbase	10.50 m (34 ft 5½ in)
* Propeller diameter	3.80 m (12 ft 5½ in)
* *estimated*	

AREA:

Wings, gross	144.0 m² (1,550.0 sq ft)

WEIGHTS AND LOADINGS:

Weight empty, equipped:	
SAR and transport	less than 25,000 kg (55,115 lb)
ASW	26,500 kg (58,422 lb)
Fuel load (max)	16,500 kg (36,376 lb)
Max internal weapons load	6,000 kg (13,228 lb)
Max payload (bulk cargo)	10,000 kg (22,045 lb)
Normal T-O weight	36,000 kg (79,366 lb)
Max T-O weight	45,000 kg (99,208 lb)
Wing loading:	
at normal T-O weight	250.0 kg/m² (51.2 lb/sq ft)
at max T-O weight	312.5 kg/m² (64.0 lb/sq ft)
Power loading:	
at normal T-O weight	3.31 kg/kW (5.44 lb/ehp)
at max T-O weight	4.14 kg/kW (6.80 lb/ehp)

PERFORMANCE:

Max level speed	299 knots (555 km/h; 345 mph)
Max cruising speed	243 knots (450 km/h; 280 mph)
Min patrol speed	124 knots (230 km/h; 143 mph)
T-O speed (water)	87 knots (160 km/h; 100 mph)
Landing speed (water)	92 knots (170 km/h; 106 mph)
Service ceiling	7,000 m (22,965 ft)
T-O run (water)	548 m (1,798 ft)
Landing run (water)	240 m (788 ft)
Range with max fuel	2,563 nm (4,750 km; 2,951 miles)
Endurance (2 engines)	12 to 15 h

HAMC Y-12 II

Chinese name: Yunshuji-12 (Transport aircraft 12) or Yun-12

This STOL general purpose transport was developed in order to improve upon the modest payload/range capabilities of the piston engined nine/ten-seat Harbin Y-11 (see 1986-87 and earlier *Jane's*). Design and construction are to FAR Pt 23 and Pt 135 (Appendix A) standards. Three prototype **Y-12 Is** and about 30 production examples of this PT6A-11 engined version were built, the first flight taking place on 14 July 1982. Details of this version can be found in the 1987-88 and earlier *Jane's*.

Current version is the **Y-12 II**, which has higher rated PT6A-27 engines and no leading-edge slats. First flight of a

Y-12 II took place on 16 August 1984. Domestic certification was received in December 1985, and 35 production Y-12 IIs had been completed by 1 January 1988. First deliveries (of four, to the Sri Lanka government for patrol duties) were made in early 1987, and a further two for this customer were delivered subsequently. Lao Aviation ordered two in early 1990, with options for two more. It is hoped to obtain international certification with assistance from the British Civil Aviation Authority. A licence agreement for P&WC PT6 engines to be assembled in China was announced in May 1986, and kits for 300 engines have been ordered initially. China is developing its own turboprop, the 507 kW (680 shp) WJ9, as a power plant for the Y-12 and other aircraft. China has a domestic requirement for more than 200 Y-12s. Future plans include a stretched version and one with a pressurised cabin.

The description applies to the current production version:

TYPE: Twin-turboprop STOL general purpose transport.

WINGS: Braced high-wing monoplane, with constant chord from root to tip. Wing section LS(1)-0417, with thickness/chord ratio of 17 per cent. Anhedral 1° 41'. Incidence 4°. No sweep. Two-spar fail-safe structure, with aluminium alloy skin; Ziqiang-2 resin bonding on 70 per cent of structure and integral fuel tankage in wing spar box. All-metal drooping ailerons and electrically actuated two-section double-slotted flaps along full span of trailing-edges. Trim tab in starboard aileron. Type 29S-7D 5178 anti-icing of leading-edges. Small stub-wings at cabin floor level support the main landing gear units; bracing strut from each stub-wing out to approx one-third span.

FUSELAGE: Conventional semi-monocoque all-metal fail-safe structure of basically rectangular cross-section, swept upward at rear. Ziqiang-2 resin bonding on 40 per cent of structure.

TAIL UNIT: Cantilever non-swept metal structure, with low-set constant chord tailplane and large dorsal fin. Horn balanced rudder and elevators. Trim tab in rudder and each elevator. Ventral fin under tailcone. Type 29S-7D 5178 anti-icing of leading-edges.

LANDING GEAR: Non-retractable tricycle type, with oleo-pneumatic shock absorber in each unit. Single-wheel main units, attached to underside of stub-wings. Single steerable nosewheel. Mainwheel tyres size 640 × 230 mm, pressure 5.5 bars (80 lb/sq in); nosewheel tyre size 480 × 200 mm, pressure 3.5 bars (51 lb/sq in). Pneumatic brakes.

POWER PLANT: Two Pratt & Whitney Canada PT6A-27 turboprops, each flat rated at 507 kW (680 shp) and driving a Hartzell HC-B3TN-3B/T10173B-3 three-blade

Water-bomber version of the HAMC SH-5 in action *(Brian M. Service)*

constant-speed reversible-pitch propeller with spinner. All fuel in tanks in wing spar box, total capacity 1,616 litres (427 US gallons; 355.5 Imp gallons), with overwing gravity filling point each side.

ACCOMMODATION: Crew of two on flight deck, access to which is via a forward opening door on the port side. Four-way adjustable crew seats. Dual controls. Main cabin can accommodate up to 17 passengers in commuter configuration, in three-abreast layout (with aisle), at seat pitch of 79 cm (31 in). Alternative layouts for up to 16 parachutists, or an all-cargo configuration with 11 tiedown rings. Passenger/cargo double door on port side at rear, the rear half of which opens outward and the forward half inward; foldout steps in passenger entrance. Emergency exits on each side at front of cabin and opposite passenger door on starboard side at rear. Baggage compartments in nose and at rear of passenger cabin, for 100 kg (220 lb) and 260 kg (573 lb) respectively.

SYSTEM: R70-3WG environmental control system.

AVIONICS AND EQUIPMENT: Avionics include VHF-251 and HF-230 com radio, AUD-251H, ADF-650A radio compass, VIR-351 and Bendix 1400C weather radar. Standard instrumentation includes BK-450 airspeed indicator, BDP-1 artificial horizon, BG10-1A altimeter, ZGW-3G altitude indicator, ZHZ-4A radio magnetic heading indicator, BC10 rate of climb indicator, ZWH-1 outside air temperature indicator, and ZEY-1 flap position indicator; dual engine torquemeters, interturbine temperature indicators, gas generator tachometers, oil temperature and pressure indicators, and fuel pressure and quantity indicators; HSZ-2 clock; and XDH-10B warning light box.

EQUIPMENT: Hopper for 1,200 litres (317 US gallons; 264 Imp gallons) of dry or liquid chemical in agricultural version. Appropriate specialised equipment for fire-fighting, geophysical survey and other missions.

DIMENSIONS, EXTERNAL:
Wing span	17.235 m (56 ft 6½ in)
Wing chord, constant	2.00 m (6 ft 6¾ in)
Wing aspect ratio	8.7
Length overall	14.86 m (48 ft 9 in)
Height overall	5.575 m (18 ft 3½ in)
Elevator span	5.365 m (17 ft 7¼ in)
Wheel track	3.60 m (11 ft 9¾ in)
Wheelbase	4.698 m (15 ft 5 in)
Propeller diameter	2.49 m (8 ft 2 in)
Distance between propeller centres	
	4.937 m (16 ft 2⅜ in)
Fuselage/ground clearance	0.65 m (2 ft 1½ in)
Crew door: Height	1.35 m (4 ft 5¼ in)
Width	0.65 m (2 ft 1½in)
Passenger/cargo door: Height	1.38 m (4 ft 6¼ in)
Width (passenger door only)	0.65 m (2 ft 1½ in)
Width (double door)	1.45 m (4 ft 9 in)
Emergency exits (three, each):	
Height	0.68 m (2 ft 2¾ in)
Width	0.68 m (2 ft 2¾ in)
Baggage door (nose, port):	
Max height	0.56 m (1 ft 10 in)
Width	0.75 m (2 ft 5½ in)

DIMENSIONS, INTERNAL:
Cabin, excl flight deck and rear baggage compartment:	
Length	4.82 m (15 ft 9¾ in)
Max width	1.46 m (4 ft 9½ in)
Max height	1.70 m (5 ft 7 in)
Volume	12.9 m³ (455.5 cu ft)
Baggage compartment volume:	
nose	0.77 m³ (27.20 cu ft)
rear	1.89 m³ (66.75 cu ft)

AREAS:
Wings, gross	34.27 m² (368.88 sq ft)
Vertical tail surfaces (total)	5.064 m² (54.51 sq ft)
Horizontal tail surfaces (total)	7.024 m² (75.61 sq ft)

WEIGHTS AND LOADINGS:
Weight empty, equipped	2,840 kg (6,261 lb)
Operating weight empty	3,000 kg (6,614 lb)
Max fuel load	1,233 kg (2,718 lb)
Max payload	1,700 kg (3,748 lb)
T-O weight for agricultural operation	
	4,500 kg (9,921 lb)
Max T-O and landing weight	5,300 kg (11,684 lb)
Max ramp weight	5,330 kg (11,750 lb)
Max zero-fuel weight	4,700 kg (10,362 lb)
Max cabin floor loading (cargo)	
	750 kg/m² (153.7 lb/sq ft)
Max wing loading	145.9 kg/m² (29.90 lb/sq ft)
Max power loading	5.23 kg/kW (8.59 lb/shp)

PERFORMANCE (at max T-O weight, ISA):
Never-exceed speed at 3,000 m (9,840 ft)	
	177 knots (328 km/h; 204 mph)
Max cruising speed at 3,000 m (9,840 ft)	
	157 knots (292 km/h; 181 mph)
Econ cruising speed at 3,000 m (9,840 ft)	
	135 knots (250 km/h; 155 mph)
Max rate of climb at S/L	504 m (1,655 ft)/min
Rate of climb at S/L, one engine out	
	101 m (331 ft)/min
Service ceiling	7,000 m (22,960 ft)
Service ceiling, one engine out, 15 m (50 ft)/min rate of climb, max continuous power	3,000 m (9,840 ft)
T-O run, 15° flap	340 m (1,115 ft)

Harbin Y-12 II twin-turboprop utility transport with newly enlarged ventral fin *(Brian M. Service)*

HAMC Y-12 II STOL general purpose transport *(Pilot Press)*

T-O to 15 m (50 ft), 15° flap	425 m (1,395 ft)
Landing from 15 m (50 ft), with braking and propeller reversal	500 m (1,640 ft)
Landing run with braking and propeller reversal	
	200 m (656 ft)
Min ground turning radius	16.75 m (54 ft 11½ in)
Range at 135 knots (250 km/h; 155 mph) at 3,000 m (9,840 ft) with max fuel, 45 min reserves	
	723 nm (1,340 km; 832 miles)
Endurance, conditions as above	5 h 12 min

HAMC (AEROSPATIALE) Z-9 HAITUN (DOLPHIN)
Chinese name: Zhishengji-9 (Vertical take-off aircraft 9) or Zhi-9

A licence agreement was signed on 2 July 1980 between Aerospatiale and CATIC for the former's AS 365N Dauphin 2 twin-turboshaft helicopter (which see) to be manufactured in China. The first (French built) example for China made its initial acceptance flight in the Beijing area on 6 February 1982. Current examples, designated **Z-9A**, are to the upgraded standard of the AS 365N₁ French version, and have a substantial proportion of locally manufactured components.

The agreement is for an initial batch of 50, which was due to be completed in 1990. These have been delivered for both civil and military duties. Helicopter units flying Z-9s were established with two PLA group armies in January (Beijing Military Region) and February 1988 (Shenyang Military Region), and others may have been formed subsequently. Some Z-9s are allocated to the PLA Naval Air Force, some to offshore oil rig support work, and some are configured as air ambulances accommodating four stretchers and two seats or two stretchers and five seats. The transmission

system is manufactured by the Dongan Engine Manufacturing Company at Harbin, while the aircraft's Arriel IC and IC₁ turboshafts are produced by SMPMC at Zhuzhou, as the WZ8 and WZ8A; the Baoding Propeller Factory manufacturers the hubs and tail rotor blades. Fuel capacity is 1,140 litres (301 US gallons; 251 Imp gallons).

It has been reported that China is seeking a suitable magnetic anomaly detector for installation on naval versions of the Z-9, and that the first anti-tank version (which carries Norinco 'Red Arrow 8' missiles) made its initial flight in late 1988 or early 1989.

China has an option to continue producing the Dauphin 2 on a licence basis, after completion of the original 50.

The following Chinese figures have been published for the Z-9 and Z-9A:

WEIGHTS:
Weight empty, equipped: Z-9	1,975 kg (4,354 lb)
Z-9A	2,050 kg (4,519 lb)
Max payload: Z-9	1,863 kg (4,107 lb)
Z-9A	2,038 kg (4,493 lb)
Max load on cargo sling: Z-9, Z-9A	1,600 kg (3,527 lb)
Max T-O weight, internal or external load:	
Z-9	3,850 kg (8,488 lb)
Z-9A	4,100 kg (9,039 lb)

PERFORMANCE (at max T-O weight):
Max cruising speed at S/L:	
Z-9	158 knots (293 km/h; 182 mph)
Z-9A	154 knots (285 km/h; 177 mph)
Max vertical rate of climb at S/L:	
Z-9	252 m (827 ft)/min
Z-9A	246 m (805 ft)/min
Max forward rate of climb at S/L:	
Z-9	462 m (1,515 ft)/min
Z-9A	456 m (1,495 ft)/min

HAMC Z-9A Haitun twin-turbine light helicopter

Service ceiling: Z-9	4,500 m (14,765 ft)	Max range at 140 knots (260 km/h; 161 mph) normal			with 180 litre (47.5 US gallon; 39.6 Imp gallon)	
Z-9A	6,000 m (19,685 ft)	cruising speed, no reserves:			auxiliary tank:	
Hovering ceiling IGE: Z-9	1,950 m (6,400 ft)	standard tanks: Z-9	491 nm (910 km; 565 miles)		Z-9	572 nm (1,060 km; 658 miles)
Z-9A	2,600 m (8,530 ft)	Z-9A	464 nm (860 km; 534 miles)		Z-9A	539 nm (1,000 km; 621 miles)
Hovering ceiling OGE: Z-9	1,020 m (3,350 ft)					
Z-9A	1,600 m (5,250 ft)					

NAMC
NANCHANG AIRCRAFT MANUFACTURING COMPANY

PO Box 5001-506, Nanchang, Jiangxi
Telephone: 86/Nanchang 41112/41512
Telex: 95068 NHMC CN
Fax: 86/Nanchang 41112 ext 2272
GENERAL MANAGER: Wu Mingwang
INFORMATION: Feng Jinghua

Created in 1951, Nanchang was responsible for licence production of the Soviet Yak-18 trainer, of which it built 379 (as the CJ-5) between 1953 and 1958, and continues to manufacture its own CJ-6A development of that aircraft. In the 1960s it shared in the large production programme for the J-6 fighter (Chinese development of the MiG-19), from which it subsequently developed the Q-5 attack aircraft series. In 1957-68, NAMC produced 727 examples of the Y-5 (Chinese An-2) biplane, now described under the SAP heading in this section, including 114 as local service transports and 229 for agricultural use. Its latest design, the N-5A, is a dedicated agricultural aircraft which made its first flight at the end of 1989. Two upgrade programmes for the Q-5 are under way, and a jet trainer is being developed jointly with Pakistan. NAMC occupies a 500 ha (1,235 acre) site, with 10,000 m² (107,639 sq ft) of covered space, and had a 1989 workforce of more than 20,000. About 80 per cent of its activities are non-aerospace.

NAMC Q-5
Chinese name: Qiangjiji-5 (Attack aircraft 5) or Qiang-5
Westernised designation: A-5
NATO reporting name: Fantan

Development of this twin-jet attack aircraft, derived from the J-6/MiG-19 produced in China, began with a design proposal submitted by Shenyang in August 1958. Responsibility for the programme was assigned to Nanchang, but the prototype programme was cancelled in 1961. It was, however, kept alive by a small team of enthusiasts, and was officially resumed two years later, the first prototype eventually making its initial flight on 4 June 1965. On receipt of a preliminary design certificate, a pre-production batch was authorised at the end of that year, but further modifications, to the fuel, armament, hydraulic and other systems, were found necessary, leading to the flight testing of two much modified prototypes beginning in October 1969. Series production of the Q-5 was approved at the end of that year, and deliveries began in 1970. A number of these initial production aircraft were adapted for nuclear weapon delivery tests in the early 1970s.

Details of the adaptation of the J-6 airframe can be found in the 1989-90 and earlier editions of *Jane's*. Major variants of the Q-5 are as follows:

Q-5. Initial production version, with internal fuselage bay approx 4.00 m (13 ft 1½ in) long for two 250 kg or 500 kg bombs, two underfuselage attachments adjacent to bay for two similar bombs, and two stores pylons beneath each wing; Series 6 WP6 turbojets; brake-chute in tailcone, between upper and lower 'pen-nib' fairings.

Q-5 I. Extended payload/range version, first proposed in 1976; flight tested in late 1980 and certificated for

NAMC A-5C 'Fantan' single-seat twin-jet combat aircraft, with scrap views showing nose configurations of Q-5K (left) and A-5M (right) *(Pilot Press)*

production on 20 October 1981. Internal bomb bay blanked off; space used to enlarge main fuselage fuel tank and add a flexible tank, and underfuselage stores points increased to four; improved series WP6 engines; modified landing gear; brake-chute relocated under base of rudder; improved Type I rocket ejection seat; HF/SSB transceiver added. Some Q-5 Is adapted for PLA Naval Air Force to carry two underfuselage torpedoes; these reportedly have Doppler type nose radar and 20 m (66 ft) sea-skimming capability with C-801 anti-shipping missiles.

Q-5 IA/Q-5 II. Improved Q-5 I, certificated as Q-5 IA in January 1985 with additional underwing hardpoint each side (increasing stores load by 500 kg; 1,102 lb), new gun/bomb sighting systems, pressure refuelling, and added warning/countermeasures systems. Forty Q-5 IAs exported to North Korea. Current production version designated Q-5 II.

Q-5K Kong Yun. Upgraded version for Chinese armed forces, under development. Described separately.

A-5C. Export version for Pakistan Air Force, involving 32 modifications from Q-5 I, notably upgraded avionics, Martin-Baker PKD10 zero/zero ejection seats, and adaptation of hardpoints for 356 mm (14 in) lugs compatible with PAF weapons, including Sidewinder missiles. Three prototypes built. Original order for 52, placed in April 1981, delivered between January 1983 and January 1984, equipping Nos. 7, 16 and 26 Squadrons of PAF. Further 98, ordered in 1984, also now delivered. Bangladesh has ordered 20.

A-5M. Upgraded export version of Q-5 II, under development. Described separately.

Including some 200 for export, nearly 1,000 Q-5s (all versions) have been built to date. A design study has been carried out by FRL in the UK to equip the Q-5 as a receiver for in-flight refuelling, with a Xian H-6 bomber adapted to

act as the tanker aircraft. Go-ahead for such a modification had not been given up to the Spring of 1990.

The following description applies to the Q-5 II and A-5C, except where otherwise indicated:

TYPE: Single-seat close air support and ground attack aircraft, with capability also for air-to-air combat.

WINGS: Cantilever all-metal mid-wing monoplane, of low aspect ratio, with 4° anhedral from roots. Sweepback at quarter-chord 52° 30'. Multi-spar basic structure with ribs and stressed skin, with three-point attachment to fuselage. Deep, full chord boundary layer fence on each upper surface at mid span. Inboard of each fence is a hydraulically actuated Gouge flap, the inner end of which is angled to give a trailing-edge at right angles to side of fuselage. Hydraulically actuated (by irreversible servo) internally balanced aileron outboard of each fence. Electrically operated inset trim tab at inboard end of port aileron.

FUSELAGE: Conventional all-metal structure of longerons, stringers and stressed skin, built in forward and rear portions which are detachable aft of wing trailing-edge to provide access to engines. Air intake on each side of fuselage, abreast of cockpit; twin jetpipes side by side at rear. Top and bottom 'pen nib' fairings aft of nozzles. Centre-fuselage is 'waisted' in accordance with area rule. Dorsal spine fairing between rear of cockpit and leading-edge of fin. Forward hinged, hydraulically actuated door type airbrake under centre of fuselage, forward of bomb attachment points. Shallow ventral strake under each jetpipe.

TAIL UNIT: Cantilever all-metal stressed skin structure, with sweepback on all surfaces. Mechanically actuated mass balanced rudder, with electrically operated inset trim tab. One-piece hydraulically actuated (by irreversible servo) all-moving tailplane, with 6° 30' anhedral and anti-flutter weight projecting forward from each tip. Tail warning antenna in tip of fin.

LANDING GEAR: Hydraulically retractable wide-track tricycle type, with single wheel and oleo-pneumatic shock

Nanchang Q-5 II of PLA Air Force with stores on all ten stations *(Brian M. Service)*

Q-5 II with ECM pods on its centre underwing stations

absorber on each unit. Main units retract inward into wings, non-steerable nosewheel forward into fuselage, rotating through 87° to lie flat in gear bay. Mainwheels have size 830 × 205 mm tubeless tyres, and disc brakes. Tail braking parachute, deployed when aircraft is 1 m (3.3 ft) above the ground, in bullet fairing at root of vertical tail trailing-edge beneath rudder.

POWER PLANT: Two Shenyang WP6 turbojets, each rated at 25.50 kN (5,732 lb st) dry and 31.87 kN (7,165 lb st) with afterburning, mounted side by side in rear of fuselage. Improved WP6A engines (see A-5M entry for details) available optionally. Lateral air intake, with small splitter plate, for each engine. Hydraulically actuated nozzles. Internal fuel in three forward and two rear fuselage tanks with combined capacity of 3,648 litres (964 US gallons; 802.5 Imp gallons). Provision for carrying a 760 litre (201 US gallon; 167 Imp gallon) drop tank on each centre underwing pylon, to give max internal/external fuel capacity of 5,168 litres (1,366 US gallons; 1,136.5 Imp gallons). When centre wing stations are occupied by bombs, a 400 litre (105.7 US gallon; 88 Imp gallon) drop tank can be carried instead on each outboard underwing pylon.

ACCOMMODATION: Pilot only, under one-piece jettisonable canopy which is hinged at rear and opens upward. Downward view over nose, in level flight, is 13° 30'. Low-speed seat allows for safe ejection within speed range of 135-458 knots (250-850 km/h; 155-528 mph) at zero height or above. Aircraft in Pakistan service have been refitted with Martin-Baker PKD10 zero/zero seats. Armour plating in some areas of cockpit to protect pilot from anti-aircraft gunfire. Cockpit pressurised and air-conditioned.

SYSTEMS: Dual air-conditioning systems, one for cockpit environment and one for avionics cooling. Two independent hydraulic systems, each operating at pressure of 207 bars (3,000 lb/sq in). Primary system actuates landing gear extension and retraction, flaps, airbrake and afterburner nozzles; auxiliary system supplies power for aileron and all-moving tailplane boosters. Emergency system, operating pressure 108 bars (1,570 lb/sq in), for actuation of main landing gear. Electrical system (28V DC) powered by two 6kW engine driven starter/generators, with two inverters for 115V single-phase and 36V three-phase AC power at 400Hz.

AVIONICS AND EQUIPMENT: Include CT-3 VHF com transceiver, WL-7 radio compass, WG-4 low altitude radio altimeter, LTC-2 horizon gyro, YD-3 IFF, Type 930 radar warning receiver and XS-6 marker beacon receiver. Combat camera in small 'teardrop' fairing on starboard side of nose (not on export models). 'Odd Rods' type IFF aerials under nose on Q-5 variants, replaced on A-5C by a single blade antenna. Space provision in nose and centre-fuselage for additional or updated avionics, including an attack radar. Landing light under fuselage, forward of nosewheel bay and offset to port; taxying light on nosewheel leg.

ARMAMENT AND OPERATIONAL EQUIPMENT: Internal armament consists of one 23 mm cannon (Norinco Type 23-2K), with 100 rds, in each wingroot. Ten attachment points normally for external stores: two pairs in tandem under centre of fuselage, and three under each wing (one inboard and two outboard of mainwheel leg). Fuselage stations can each carry a 250 kg bomb (Chinese 250-2 or 250-3, US Mk 82 or Snakeye, French Durandal, or similar). Inboard wing stations can carry 6 kg or 25 lb practice bombs, or a pod containing eight Chinese 57-2 (57 mm), seven 68 mm, or seven Norinco 90-1 (90 mm) or four 130-1 (130 mm) rockets. Centre wing stations can carry a 500 kg or 750 lb bomb, a BL755 600 lb cluster bomb, a Chinese 250-2 or -3 bomb, US Mk 82 or Snakeye, French Durandal, or similar, or a C-801 anti-shipping missile. Normal bomb carrying capacity is 1,000 kg (2,205 lb), max capacity 2,000 kg (4,410 lb). Instead of bombs, the centre wing stations can each carry a 760 litre drop tank (see Power Plant paragraph) or an ECM pod. The outboard wing stations can each be occupied by a 400 litre drop tank (when the larger tank is not carried on the centre wing station) or by air-to-air missiles such as the Chinese PL-2, PL-2B, PL-7, AIM-9 Sidewinder and Matra R.550 Magic. Within the overall max T-O weight, all stores mentioned can be carried provided that CG shift remains within the allowable operating range of 31 to 39 per cent of mean aerodynamic chord, and more than 22 external stores configurations are possible. The aircraft carries an SH-1J or ABS1A optical sight for level and dive bombing, or for air-to-ground rocket launching. Aircraft in Chinese service can carry a single 5-20 kT nuclear bomb.

DIMENSIONS, EXTERNAL (Q-5 II):
Wing span	9.70 m (31 ft 10 in)
Wing chord (mean aerodynamic)	3.097 m (10 ft 2 in)
Wing aspect ratio	3.37
Length overall: incl nose probe	16.255 m (53 ft 4 in)
excl nose probe	15.415 m (50 ft 7 in)
Height overall	4.516 m (14 ft 9¾ in)
Wheel track	4.40 m (14 ft 5¼ in)
Wheelbase	4.01 m (13 ft 2 in)

AREAS:
Wings, gross	27.95 m² (300.85 sq ft)
Vertical tail surfaces (total)	4.64 m² (49.94 sq ft)

Horizontal tail surfaces:
movable	5.00 m² (53.82 sq ft)
total, incl projected fuselage area	8.62 m² (92.78 sq ft)

WEIGHTS AND LOADINGS:
Weight empty	6,494 kg (14,317 lb)
Fuel: max internal	2,827 kg (6,232 lb)
two 400 litre drop tanks	620 kg (1,367 lb)
two 760 litre drop tanks	1,178 kg (2,597 lb)
max internal/external	4,005 kg (8,829 lb)
Max external stores load	2,000 kg (4,410 lb)
Max T-O weight: clean	9,530 kg (21,010 lb)
with max external stores	12,000 kg (26,455 lb)
Max wing loading: clean	341 kg/m² (69.9 lb/sq ft)
with max external stores	429 kg/m² (87.9 lb/sq ft)
Max power loading: clean	149.5 kg/kN (1.47 lb/lb st)
with max external stores	188.3 kg/kN (1.85 lb/lb st)

PERFORMANCE (at max clean T-O weight, with afterburning, except where indicated):
Max limiting Mach number (VNE)	Mach 1.5
Max level speed:	
at 11,000 m (36,000 ft)	Mach 1.12 (643 knots; 1,190 km/h; 740 mph)
at S/L	653 knots (1,210 km/h; 752 mph)
T-O speed:	
clean, 15° flap	162 knots (300 km/h; 186 mph)
with max external stores, 25° flap	178 knots (330 km/h; 205 mph)
* Landing speed:	
25° flap, brake-chute deployed	150-165 knots (278-307 km/h; 172-191 mph)
* Max rate of climb at 5,000 m (16,400 ft)	4,980-6,180 m (16,340-20,275 ft)/min
Service ceiling	15,850 m (52,000 ft)
T-O run:	
*clean, 15° flap	700-750 m (2,300-2,460 ft)
with max external stores, 25° flap	1,250 m (4,100 ft)
Landing run:	
25° flap, brake-chute deployed	1,060 m (3,480 ft)

Combat radius with max external stores, afterburners off:
lo-lo-lo (500 m; 1,640 ft)	216 nm (400 km; 248 miles)
hi-lo-hi (8,000/500/8,000 m; 26,250/1,640/26,250 ft)	324 nm (600 km; 373 miles)

Range at 11,000 m (36,000 ft) with max internal and external fuel, afterburners off
nearly 1,080 nm (2,000 km; 1,243 miles)

g limits:
with full load of bombs and/or drop tanks	5
with drop tanks empty	6.5
clean	7.5

* *depending upon airfield elevation and temperature*

NAMC Q-5K KONG YUN (CLOUD)
In a programme similar to that of the A-5M (see next entry), initiated in June 1987, a French team led by Thomson-CSF has carried out prototype upgrading of the Q-5 by installing an avionics package that includes a Thomson-CSF head-up display and laser rangefinder, Sagem inertial navigation system, TRT radio altimeter, Crouzet air data sensor, Thomson/Jaeger/Sfim/Sfena new

instrument panel, Omera HUD, video camera, new wiring by Labinal, and a Thomson-CSF/Auxilec electrical generation system.

The first of two prototypes was flown for the first time on 17 September 1988, with the second due to join it in February or March 1989. This programme is to fulfil a requirement of the PLA Air Force.

NAMC A-5M
This improved version of the Q-5 II, intended only for export is the subject of a development programme started on 1 August 1986 between CATIC and Aeritalia to upgrade the aircraft's avionics by incorporating a new all-weather nav/attack system similar to that used in the AMX aircraft. The M (for Modified) version also has improved WP6A turbojets with dry and afterburning ratings of 29.42 kN (6,614 lb st) and 36.78 kN (8,267 lb st) respectively.

Two A-5M prototypes were ordered, and the first of these (converted from Q-5 IIs) made its initial flight on 30 August 1988, but was lost in a crash on 17 October 1988. The second prototype flew on 8 March 1989, and a replacement for the first has since been completed.

The nav/attack system is designed around two Singer central digital computers and a dual-redundant MIL-STD-1553B databus with plenty of growth potential. Other new sensors and equipment include a ranging radar, inertial navigation system, Selenia 58 head-up display, air data computer, three-axis gyro package, RW-30 radar warning receiver, chaff/flare dispenser, HSI, attitude indicator, static inverters, mode controls, and an interface unit linking these with the aircraft's existing AR-3201 VHF com radio, radio altimeter, radio compass, marker beacon receiver, IFF and armament system.

The number of external stores stations is increased to 12 by adding a fourth pylon beneath each outer wing, with some redistribution of the weapons carried on each wing station, and the PL-5B is added to the range of air-to-air missiles. External stores configurations are otherwise essentially the same as for the Q-5 II/A-5C, except that the underwing drop tanks can be of 1,140 litre (301 US gallon; 251 Imp gallon) capacity. The max external stores load of 2,000 kg (4,410 lb) remains unchanged.

DIMENSIONS, EXTERNAL: As for Q-5 II/A-5C except:
Length overall	15.366 m (50 ft 5 in)
Height overall	4.53 m (14 ft 10¼ in)

WEIGHTS:
Weight empty	6,728 kg (14,833 lb)
T-O weight clean	9,769 kg (21,537 lb)
Max T-O weight	12,200 kg (26,869 lb)

PERFORMANCE (estimated):
Max level speed at S/L at clean T-O weight	658 knots (1,220 km/h; 758 mph)
Max level flight Mach number at 11,000 m (36,000 ft) at clean T-O weight	1.205
Unstick speed, with afterburning:	
no external stores, 15° flap	162 knots (300 km/h; 187 mph)
full external stores, 25° flap	174 knots (322 km/h; 200 mph)
Landing speed, 25° flap, brakes on and brake-chute	

First prototype Q-5K, a modified version of the Q-5 II for the PLAAF with upgraded French avionics

Prototype A-5M improved-capability attack aircraft, with new nav/attack system and digital avionics

Nanchang N-5A agricultural monoplane (Textron Lycoming IO-720 flat-eight engine) *(Jane's/Mike Keep)*

deployed (depending upon AUW)
	150-166 knots (278-307 km/h; 173-191 mph)

Max vertical rate of climb at 5,000 m (16,400 ft) at clean
T-O weight, with afterburning	6,900 m (22,638 ft)/min
Service ceiling at clean T-O weight	16,000 m (52,500 ft)

T-O run, with afterburning:
no external stores, 15° flap	911 m (2,989 ft)
full external stores, 25° flap	1,250 m (4,101 ft)

Landing run, 25° flap, brakes on and brake-chute
deployed	1,060 m (3,478 ft)

Combat radius with full external stores:
out at 8,000 m (26,250 ft), combat at 500 m (1,640 ft)
and back at 11,000 m (36,000 ft)
280 nm (518 km; 322 miles)
out, combat and back all at 500 m (1,640 ft)
174 nm (322 km; 200 miles)
Range at 11,000 m (36,000 ft) with two 760 litre (200 US gallon; 167 Imp gallon) drop tanks
1,080 nm (2,000 km; 1,243 miles)

NAMC K-8 KARAKORUM 8

This tandem two-seat jet trainer (originally L-8) is the subject of a collaborative programme between NAMC and the Pakistan Aeronautical Complex, and is described under the NAMC/PAC heading in the International section.

NAMC N-5A

First details of this specialised farming and forestry aircraft, design of which began in November 1987, were revealed at the Farnborough International air show in September 1988. The N-5A, of which three prototypes are being built, is designed to meet FAA certification requirements and is expected to be offered eventually for export. A domestic market for more than 300, as a Y-5 replacement, has been estimated. It first flew on 26 December 1989.

TYPE: Single-/two-seat agricultural aircraft.

WINGS: Cantilever low-wing monoplane. Non-swept two-spar structure, of mainly constant chord (wing section L9(1)-0417 Mod at inboard end) except for root portions, which are sweptforward 18°. Dihedral 4° 30′ from roots. Incidence 2°. Electrically actuated single-slotted trailing-edge flaps. Differential ailerons, actuated by pushrods.

FUSELAGE: Forward fuselage is a metal-skinned stainless steel tube truss structure, joined aft of cabin to a thin-walled aluminium alloy rear fuselage. Skin panels at rear removable for maintenance and cleaning.

TAIL UNIT: Cantilever non-swept structure of aluminium alloy. Mass balanced, pushrod actuated rudder, with fixed tab; mass balanced, cable controlled elevators, each with electrically actuated trim tab.

LANDING GEAR: Non-retractable tricycle type, with single wheel on each unit. Nose unit has a telescopic strut and size 400 × 150 mm tyre, pressure 2.5 bars (36.3 lb/sq in). Main gear legs are of trailing-link type, with wheel tyres size 500 × 200 mm, pressure 3.0 bars (43.5 lb/sq in). Hydraulic mainwheel brakes.

POWER PLANT: One 298 kW (400 hp) Textron Lycoming IO-720-D1B flat-eight engine, driving a Hartzell HC-C3YR-1RF/F8475R three-blade metal propeller.

ACCOMMODATION: Tandem seats for pilot and, when required, a loader/mechanic, under hard-top framed canopy with all-round field of view. Downward opening door on each side. Cockpit heated, by engine bleed air, and ventilated.

SYSTEMS: Hydraulic system for brakes only. No pneumatic system. Electrical system employs a Prestolite 28V 100A AC generator, an SBL-40 inverter and a 12HK-30 battery to power onboard avionics, plus as SBL-125 inverter and a 1B 250-10-1 static inverted for other functions.

AVIONICS AND EQUIPMENT: Bendix/King KY 96A VHF and KHF 950 HF com radio; WG-4 radio altimeter; WL-7A radio compass; XS-6B marker beacon receiver. Hopper for chemical in front fuselage, between cockpit and engine firewall, plus appropriate spraygear. Wire cutters on main landing gear and in front of cockpit canopy.

DIMENSIONS, EXTERNAL:
Wing span	13.418 m (44 ft 0¼ in)
Wing chord: at root	2.319 m (7 ft 7½ in)
at tip	1.877 m (6 ft 2 in)
Wing aspect ratio	6.80
Length overall	10.487 m (34 ft 4⅞ in)
Height overall	3.733 m (12 ft 3 in)
Wheel track	3.528 m (11 ft 7 in)
Wheelbase	2.713 m (8 ft 10¾ in)
Tailplane span	4.59 m (15 ft 0¾ in)
Fuselage: Max width	1.01 m (3 ft 3¾ in)
Max depth	1.735 m (5 ft 8¼ in)
Propeller diameter	2.184 m (7 ft 2 in)

DIMENSIONS, INTERNAL:
Cockpit: Length	2.29 m (7 ft 6¼ in)
Max width	1.00 m (3 ft 3¼ in)
Max height	1.26 m (4 ft 1½ in)

AREAS:
Wings, gross	26.0 m² (279.86 sq ft)
Ailerons (total)	2.08 m² (22.39 sq ft)
Trailing-edge flaps (total)	4.06 m² (43.70 sq ft)
Fin	2.28 m² (24.54 sq ft)
Rudder, incl tab	1.57 m² (16.90 sq ft)
Tailplane	4.68 m² (50.38 sq ft)
Elevators (total, incl tabs)	2.20 m² (23.68 sq ft)

WEIGHTS:
Weight empty	1,328 kg (2,928 lb)
Fuel weight: normal	85 kg (187 lb)
max	233 kg (513 lb)
Payload: normal	705 kg (1,554 lb)
max	905 kg (1,995 lb)
T-O weight: normal	2,250 kg (4,960 lb)
max overload	2,450 kg (5,401 lb)

PERFORMANCE (estimated, with agricultural equipment installed):
Max level speed	118 knots (220 km/h; 136 mph)
Normal operating speed	92 knots (170 km/h; 105 mph)
Econ cruising speed	75 knots (139 km/h; 86 mph)
Stalling speed	47 knots (86 km/h; 54 mph)
Max rate of climb at S/L	281 m (922 ft)/min

Service ceiling	4,280 m (14,040 ft)
Min air turning radius	140 m (459 ft)
T-O run	296 m (971 ft)
T-O to 15 m (50 ft)	553 m (1,814 ft)
Landing from 15 m (50 ft)	379 m (1,243 ft)
Landing run	252 m (827 ft)
Normal range with standard fuel	
	152 nm (282 km; 175 miles)
Ferry range with max fuel	528 nm (979 km; 608 miles)

NAMC CJ-6A

Chinese name: Chuji Jiaolianji-6A (Basic training aircraft 6A) or Chujiao-6A
Westernised designation: PT-6A

The CJ-6's predecessor, the CJ-5, one of the first aircraft to be mass produced in post-1949 China, was a licence built version of the Soviet Yak-18 basic trainer. The first flight of a CJ-5 took place on 3 July 1954, and 379 were built at Nanchang between 1954 and 1958, for Air Force, Navy and CAAC use.

Design of the CJ-6, as a Chinese engineered successor to the CJ-5, was initiated at Shenyang in the Autumn of 1956, a prototype powered by a 108 kW (145 hp) Mikulin M-11ER radial engine flying for the first time on 27 August 1958. Flight trials with this power plant proving disappointing, a modified version was tested (first flight 18 July 1960) with a 194 kW (260 hp) Ivchenko AI-14R engine. Responsibility for the CJ-6 was subsequently transferred to Nanchang, where further redesign preceded the first flight of a production-standard prototype on 15 October 1961. Production go-ahead was given in 1962 for the aircraft (in January) and the Chinese HS6 version of the AI-14R engine (in June), and a total of 1,796 CJ-6s (all versions) had been built by the end of 1986, including exports to Albania, Bangladesh, Cambodia, Korea, Tanzania and Zambia.

Standard version since December 1965 has been the **CJ-6A**, signifying introduction of the uprated HS6A engine. Ten examples were built in 1964-66 of an armed version, designated **CJ-6B**. The prototype of a civil agricultural version known as the **Haiyan** (see following entry) has been developed, and a six-seat utility version has been proposed. The details which follow apply to the standard CJ-6A basic trainer:

AIRFRAME: All-metal cantilever low-wing monoplane. Two-spar wings, with detachable, tapered and dihedralled outer panels. Retractable tricycle landing gear, with low-pressure mainwheel tyres, suitable for operation from grass strips.

POWER PLANT: One 213 kW (285 hp) Zhuzhou (SMPMC) HS6A nine-cylinder air-cooled radial engine, driving a Baoding J9-G1 two-blade constant-speed propeller. Fuel capacity (two tanks) 100 litres (26.4 US gallons; 22 Imp gallons).

DIMENSIONS, EXTERNAL:
Wing span	10.18 m (33 ft 4¾ in)
Length overall	8.46 m (27 ft 9 in)
Height overall	3.25 m (10 ft 8 in)

WEIGHTS:
Weight empty	1,172 kg (2,584 lb)
Max fuel	110 kg (243 lb)
Max T-O weight	1,419 kg (3,128 lb)

PERFORMANCE:
Max level speed	155 knots (286 km/h; 178 mph)
Landing speed	62 knots (115 km/h; 72 mph)
Max rate of climb at S/L	380 m (1,248 ft)/min
Service ceiling	5,080 m (16,665 ft)
T-O run	280 m (920 ft)
Landing run	350 m (1,150 ft)
Endurance	3 h 36 min

NAMC HAIYAN (PETREL)

To meet a national requirement for a multi-purpose agricultural and forestry aircraft, NAMC began work on a conversion of its CJ-6 basic trainer (see preceding entry) in April 1985, this **Haiyan A** prototype flying for the first time on 17 August that year. It was fitted with a more powerful (257 kW; 345 hp) HS6E engine and a new-design propeller. Removal of the rear seat allowed a 400 kg (882 lb) insecticide tank to be installed, and another 200 kg (441 lb) of chemical was accommodated in the leading-edge of the wing centre-section.

Further details of the Haiyan A and of two proposed production versions (Haiyan B and C) can be found in the 1989-90 and earlier *Jane's*. No news of this programme has been received for some years, and it may now have been superseded by the N-5A.

SAC
SHAANXI AIRCRAFT COMPANY
PO Box 35, Chenggu, Shaanxi
Telephone: 86/Hanzhong 2974 ext 309
Telex: 70141 STAF CN
GENERAL MANAGER: Yan Guangming
DEPUTY MARKETING MANAGER: Li Yousheng

Founded in the late 1970s, SAC is responsible for the Y-8 transport aircraft programme; non-aerospace products include coaches and small trucks. The company occupies a 204 ha (504 acre) site and had a 1989 workforce of about 10,000 people; its covered area includes the largest final assembly building in China.

SAC (ANTONOV) Y-8
Chinese name: Yunshuji-8 (Transport aircraft 8) or Yun-8
NATO reporting name: Cub

The Shaanxi Aircraft Company is building a Chinese version of the Antonov An-12B four-turboprop civil/military transport aircraft. Redesign of this version was carried out at Xian, beginning in March 1969; the first Y-8 (B-3102) made its initial flight on 25 December 1974, followed by a second (the first built by SAC) on 29 December 1975.

Outwardly, the Y-8 can be distinguished from the An-12 by its more pointed nose transparencies, which extend the overall length of the aircraft by 0.92 m (3 ft 0¼ in). The aircraft's engines, derived from the Ivchenko AI-20M, are produced at Zhuzhou; landing gear and all hydraulic components for the Y-8 are manufactured by Shaanxi Aero-Hydraulic Component Factory (SAHCF).

Prototype Y-8 MPA (maritime patrol aircraft) version of the Shaanxi Y-8

The decision to put the Y-8 into production was taken in January 1980, and 31 had been completed for CAAC and the PLA Air Force by February 1989. Two Y-8s have been supplied to the Sri Lanka Air Force. The Y-8 is a major production priority programme, including the development of a 100-passenger fully pressurised version: the current version has a small pressurised forward cabin for up to 14 passengers in addition to the five-man crew, but the rear cargo hold is unpressurised. An in-flight refuelling tanker study for the Y-8 has been made by FRL of the UK. Alternative power plants (one candidate being the General Electric CT7) are also under consideration.

On 4 September 1985 the first Y-8MPA maritime patrol version cleared its technical qualification tests. This aircraft (see an accompanying photograph) has a large chin radome housing the antenna for a search radar. The maritime surveillance version is expected to be used for both anti-submarine patrol and civilian offshore duties such as fishery patrol, pollution monitoring, and support of the oil exploration industry. Other versions of the Y-8 are under development as drone carrier, helicopter (for example, Black Hawk) transport, and (reportedly with Israeli assistance) for airborne early warning.

The following description applies to the standard Y-8 transport, unless otherwise indicated:

TYPE: Four-turboprop transport aircraft.

WINGS: Cantilever high-wing monoplane. All-metal two-spar box structure in five panels, comprising centre-section, intermediate portions and tip sections. Wing sections C-5-18 at root, C-3-16 at rib 15 and C-3-14 at tip, with respective thickness/chord ratios of 18, 16 and 14 per cent. Anhedral 1° on intermediate panels, 4° on outboard sections. Incidence 4°. Sweepback 6° 50′ at quarter-chord. Mechanically actuated, aerodynamically balanced aluminium ailerons, capable of differential operation and fitted with trim tabs. All-metal double-slotted Fowler flaps, actuated hydraulically, in two segments on each trailing-edge. Comb-shaped all-metal spoilers forward of flaps. Hot-air de-icing of leading-edges.

FUSELAGE: All-metal semi-monocoque circular-section structure of frames and stringers. Forward section and tail turret pressurised.

TAIL UNIT: Cantilever all-metal two-spar box structure, with fixed incidence tailplane. Elevators and rudder are manually operated and aerodynamically balanced. Trim tabs in rudder and each elevator. Electric de-icing of fin and tailplane leading-edges.

LANDING GEAR: Hydraulically retractable tricycle type, with Shaanxi (SAHCF) nitrogen/oil shock struts on all units. Four-wheel main bogie on each side retracts inward and upward into blister on side of fuselage. Twin-wheel nose unit, hydraulically steerable ± 35°, retracts rearward. Mainwheel tyres size 1,050 × 300 mm, pressure 28.4 bars (412 lb/sq in); nosewheel tyres size 900 × 300 mm, pressure 16.7 bars (242 lb/sq in). Hydraulic disc brakes and Xingping inertial anti-skid sensor.

POWER PLANT: Four 3,169 kW (4,250 ehp) Zhuzhou (SMPMC) WJ6 turboprops, each driving a Baoding four-blade J-17 G-13 constant-speed propeller. All fuel in two integral tanks and 29 bag-type tanks in wings (20,102 litres; 5,310.5 US gallons; 4,422 Imp gallons) and fuselage (10,075 litres; 2,661.5 US gallons; 2,216 Imp gallons), giving total capacity of 30,177 litres (7,972 US gallons; 6,638 Imp gallons). Refuelling points in starboard side of fuselage (between frames 14 and 15), mainwheel fairing, and in wing upper surface.

ACCOMMODATION: Flight crew of five (pilot, co-pilot, navigator, engineer and radio operator). Forward portion of fuselage (up to frame 13) is pressurised, and can accommodate up to 14 passengers in addition to crew. Cargo compartment (between frames 13 and 43) is unpressurised. Max accommodation for up to 96 troops;

or 58 paratroops; or 60 severe casualties plus 20 slightly wounded, with three medical attendants; or two 'Liberation' army trucks. Crew door and two emergency exits in forward fuselage. Three additional emergency exits in cargo compartment, access to which is via a large rear-loading ramp/door in underside of rear fuselage. Entire accommodation heated and ventilated.

SYSTEMS: Forward fuselage pressurised to maintain a differential of 0.20 bars (2.84 lb/sq in) at altitudes above 4,300 m (14,100 ft). Two independent hydraulic systems, with operating pressures of 152 bars (2,200 lb/sq in) (port) and 147 bars (2,130 lb/sq in) (starboard), plus hand and electrical standby pumps, for actuation of landing gear extension/retraction, nosewheel steering, flaps, brakes and rear ramp/door. Electrical DC power (28.5V) supplied by eight 12kW generators, an 18kW (24 hp) Xian Aero Engine Co APU (mainly for engine starting) and four 28Ah batteries. Four 12kVA alternators provide 115V AC power at 400Hz. Gaseous oxygen system for crew. Electric de-icing of windscreen, propellers and fin/tailplane leading-edges; hot air de-icing for wing leading-edges.

AVIONICS AND EQUIPMENT (Y-8MPA): Collins VHF, dual HF (DF-2 and DS-3) and HF/SSB radios; HAL-2 navigational radar; Litton Canada APS-504(V)3 search radar; Litton Canada LTN-72 INS and LTN-211 Omega navigation system; Collins ADF, DME-42, TRD-90 ATC transponder, VOR-32, HSI-85, ADI-85A, 520-3337 RMI, IFF and autopilot. Operational equipment includes optical and infra-red cameras, IR submarine detection system and sonobuoys.

DIMENSIONS, EXTERNAL:

Wing span	38.00 m (124 ft 8 in)
Wing chord: at root	4.73 m (15 ft 6¼ in)
at tip	1.69 m (5 ft 6½ in)
Wing aspect ratio	11.85

Shaanxi Y-8 four-turboprop multi-purpose medium-range transport of the PLA Air Force

Model of the Shaanxi Y-8 with two WZ-5 high-altitude reconnaissance RPVs under the wings

Length overall	34.25 m (111 ft 7½ in)	Floor area	55.0 m² (592.0 sq ft)	
Fuselage: Max diameter of circular section		Volume	123.3 m³ (4,354.3 cu ft)	
	4.10 m (13 ft 5½ in)			
Height overall	11.16 m (36 ft 7½ in)	AREAS:		
Wheel track	4.92 m (16 ft 1¾ in)	Wings, gross	121.86 m² (1,311.7 sq ft)	
Wheelbase	9.576 m (31 ft 5 in)	Ailerons (total)	7.84 m² (84.39 sq ft)	
Propeller diameter	4.50 m (14 ft 9¼ in)	Trailing-edge flaps (total)	26.91 m² (289.66 sq ft)	
Propeller ground clearance	1.89 m (6 ft 2½ in)	Rudder	6.537 m² (70.36 sq ft)	
Crew door: Height	1.455 m (4 ft 9¼ in)	Tailplane	27.05 m² (291.16 sq ft)	
Width	0.80 m (2 ft 7½ in)	Elevators (total)	7.101 m² (76.43 sq ft)	
Rear loading hatch: Length	7.67 m (25 ft 2 in)			
Width: min	2.16 m (7 ft 1 in)	WEIGHTS AND LOADINGS:		
max	3.10 m (10 ft 2 in)	Weight empty, equipped	35,500 kg (78,265 lb)	
Emergency exits (each): Height	0.55 m (1 ft 9¾ in)	Max fuel load	22,909 kg (50,505 lb)	
Width	0.60 m (1 ft 11½ in)	Max payload: containerised	16,000 kg (35,275 lb)	
DIMENSIONS, INTERNAL:		bulk cargo	20,000 kg (44,090 lb)	
Cabin (incl flight deck, galley and toilet):		Max T-O weight	61,000 kg (134,480 lb)	
Length	13.50 m (44 ft 3½ in)	Max ramp weight	61,500 kg (135,585 lb)	
Width: min	3.00 m (9 ft 10 in)	Max landing weight	58,000 kg (127,870 lb)	
max	3.50 m (11 ft 5¾ in)	Max zero-fuel weight	36,266 kg (79,955 lb)	
Height: min	2.40 m (7 ft 10½ in)	Max wing loading	500.6 kg/m² (102.5 lb/sq ft)	
max	2.60 m (8 ft 6½ in)	Max power loading	4.81 kg/kW (7.91 lb/ehp)	

PERFORMANCE (at max T-O weight except where indicated):
Max level speed at 7,000 m (22,965 ft)
357 knots (662 km/h; 411 mph)
Max cruising speed at 8,000 m (26,250 ft)
297 knots (550 km/h; 342 mph)
Econ cruising speed at 8,000 m (26,250 ft)
286 knots (530 km/h; 329 mph)
Max rate of climb at S/L   473 m (1,552 ft)/min
Rate of climb at S/L, one engine out 231 m (758 ft)/min
Service ceiling, AUW of 51,000 kg (112,435 lb)
10,400 m (34,120 ft)
Service ceiling, one engine out, AUW of 51,000 kg
(112,435 lb)   8,100 m (26,575 ft)
T-O run   1,270 m (4,167 ft)
T-O to 15 m (50 ft)   3,007 m (9,866 ft)
Landing from 15 m (50 ft)   2,174 m (7,133 ft)
Landing run   1,050 m (3,445 ft)
Range: with max payload 687 nm (1,273 km; 791 miles)
with max fuel   3,030 nm (5,615 km; 3,490 miles)
Max endurance   10 h 40 min

SAC
SHENYANG AIRCRAFT CORPORATION
PO Box 328, Shenyang, Liaoning
Telephone: 86 (24) 462680
Telex: 80018 SAMC CN
GENERAL MANAGER: Tang Qiansan
DEPUTY MANAGER: Xu Guosheng

One of the pioneer centres of fighter design in China, Shenyang now occupies a site area of more than 800 ha (1,976 acres) and has a workforce of over 20,000 people. Between 1956 and 1959 it produced 767 examples of the J-5 (licence MiG-17F), and from 1963 was the major producer (others were produced at Nanchang) of the J-6 series (Chinese versions of the MiG-19), including 634 tandem two-seat JJ-6 fighter/trainers. Initial development and production of the J-7 series (see Chengdu Aircraft Corporation entry) began at Shenyang, and SAC's principal current programme concerns the J-8 air superiority fighter. Aerospace products account for about 30 per cent of SAC's present activities, and include subcontract manufacture of cargo doors for the Boeing 757 and Boeing de Havilland Dash 8; rudders for the British Aerospace ATP; wing ribs and emergency exit hatches for the Airbus A320; tailcone, landing gear door and pylon components for the Lockheed C-130 Hercules; and other machined parts for BAe, Boeing, MBB and Saab-Scania.

SAC J-?
A new fighter, for entry into service by the year 2000, is in the early design definition stages at Shenyang. Although various alternative configurations are under consideration, studies are understood at present to favour a single-seater with swept wings, close-coupled canards, single or twin engines, and a gross weight in the 10-15 tonne (22,045-33,070 lb) class. Other objectives include extensive use of composites, a fly by wire flight control system, and foreign co-operation in developing the power plant and/or avionics.

SAC J-8
Chinese name: Jianjiji-8 (Fighter aircraft 8) or Jian-8
Westernised designation: F-8
NATO reporting name: Finback
Development of the J-8 began at Shenyang in 1964, the first of two original prototypes making its first flight on 5 July 1969. Although all other J-8 activity was suspended during the 'cultural revolution', flight trials were allowed to continue, and these prototypes accumulated 663 hours of flying, in 1,025 flights, before production was eventually authorised in 1979. The following versions have since been produced:
J-8 ('Finback-A'). Initial clear-weather day fighter, powered by two Liyang (LMC) WP7B turbojets (each 43.15 kN; 9,700 lb st dry and 59.82 kN; 13,448 lb st with afterburning) and armed with single twin-barrel 23 mm cannon and four wing-mounted PL-2B air-to-air missiles. Single intake in nose, with conical centrebody. Approved for production in 1979, but built in small numbers only. Retrofitted from 1984 with Sichuan SR-4 fire control radar in intake centrebody. In service.
J-8 I ('Finback-A'). Improved version of J-8, with same power plant and armament but fitted from outset with Sichuan SR-4 radar in intake centrebody. Three prototypes built, one being lost before flight testing; first flight, by second aircraft, made on 24 April 1981. Initial batch production authorised in July 1985. Described in 1985-86 *Jane's*. More than 100 now in service, including upgraded J-8s, by early 1990, but gradually being supplanted by J-8 II.
J-8 II ('Finback-B'). All-weather dual-role version (high altitude interceptor and ground attack), embodying some 70 per cent redesign compared with J-8 I. Main configuration change is to 'solid' nose and twin lateral air intakes, to provide nose space for fire control radar and

Fourth prototype of the J-8 II single-seat multi-role fighter *(Paul Jackson)*

J-8 II version of the 'Finback' twin-jet air superiority fighter *(Pilot Press)*

other avionics, and increased airflow for more powerful WP13A II turbojets. Four prototypes built (first flight 12 June 1984), plus two for static/fatigue testing. In production and service: 'several dozen' built by early 1990, but being manufactured in small economic batches rather than at a steady monthly rate.
Peace Pearl. Title under which, in a joint Chinese/US programme, USAF's Aeronautical Systems Division is sponsoring an FMS (foreign military sales) avionics upgrade for the J-8 II. A 5 August 1987 contract to Grumman Aerospace Corporation, due for completion in January 1995, calls for 50 shipsets, plus five spare kits, of an avionics suite comprising a fire control system, inertial navigation system, HUD, mission and air data computers, and a databus. Under subcontract to Grumman, Westinghouse is developing the fire control system (modified AN/APG-66 radar, fire control computer, backup control and interface unit, CW illuminator, fire control software, variable-speed constant-frequency power generation system and logistics support), while Litton will supply the LN-39 INS and the HUD. Two J-8 IIs have been delivered to Grumman for flight test (at Edwards AFB), followed by certification of the upgrade package, with kit deliveries scheduled for 1991-95. The Peace Pearl version is intended for service in Manchuria and along China's northern border with the USSR.

The following description applies to the J-8 II:
TYPE: Single-seat twin-engined air superiority fighter, with secondary ground attack capability.
WINGS: Cantilever mid-wing monoplane. Thin-section delta wings, with slight anhedral and 60° sweepback on leading-edges. Small fence on each upper surface near tip. Two-segment single-slotted trailing-edge flaps on each wing inboard of aileron. Main wing structure is of aluminium alloy and high tensile steel. Control surfaces, which have hydraulically boosted actuation, are of aluminium honeycomb with skins of sheet aluminium.
FUSELAGE: Conventional semi-monocoque structure, 'waisted' between air intakes and tail section in accordance with area rule. Construction is mainly of aluminium alloy, with high tensile steel for main load-bearing members and titanium in high-temperature areas. Dielectric nosecone. Rear fuselage detachable for access to engines. Four door-type underfuselage airbrakes, one under each engine air intake trunk and one immediately aft of each mainwheel well. Spine fairing along top of fuselage from cockpit to fin, with small airscoop at foot of fin leading-edge. Additional airscoop at top of rear fuselage on each side, above tailplane.
TAIL UNIT: Cantilever sweptback all-metal surfaces, comprising broad chord fin and rudder and low-set all-moving tailplane; 60° sweepback on tailplane leading-

Line-up of early J-8 ('Finback-A') day fighters

edges. Ventral fin similar to that of MiG-23, main portion of which folds sideways to starboard during take-off and landing, to provide additional directional stability. Rudder and rear part of tailplane are of aluminium honeycomb, with sheet aluminium skins; actuation is hydraulically boosted. Dielectric panels at tip of main fin (radar warning receiver antenna) and on non-folding portion of ventral fin leading-edge.

LANDING GEAR: Hydraulically retractable tricycle type, with single wheel and oleo-pneumatic shock absorber on each unit. Nose unit (which is steerable) retracts forward, main units inward into centre-fuselage; mainwheels turn to stow vertically inside fuselage, resulting in a slight overwing bulge. Brake-chute in bullet fairing at base of rudder.

POWER PLANT: Two Liyang (Guizhou Engine Co) WP13A II turbojets, each rated at 42.7 kN (9,590 lb st) dry and 65.9 kN (14,815 lb st) with afterburning, mounted side by side in rear fuselage with 'pen nib' fairing above and between exhaust nozzles. Lateral, non-swept air intakes, with automatically regulated ramp angle and large splitter plates similar in shape to those of MiG-23. Internal fuel capacity (four integral wing tanks plus fuselage tanks) approx 5,400 litres (1,426 US gallons; 1,188 Imp gallons). Single-point pressure refuelling. Provision for auxiliary

fuel tanks on fuselage centreline and each outboard underwing pylon.

ACCOMMODATION: Pilot only, on ejection seat under one-piece canopy hinged at rear and opening upward. Cockpit pressurised, heated and air-conditioned. Heated windscreen.

SYSTEMS: Two simple air-cycle environmental control systems, one for cockpit heating and air-conditioning and one for radar cooling; cooling air bled from engine compressor. Two 207 bar (3,000 lb/sq in) independent hydraulic systems (main utility system plus one for flight control surfaces boost), powered by engine driven pumps. 28.5V DC primary electrical power from two 12kW engine driven starter/generators, with two 6kVA alternators for 115/200V three-phase AC at 400Hz. Pneumatic bottles for emergency landing gear extension. Pop-out ram air emergency turbine under fuselage.

AVIONICS AND OPERATIONAL EQUIPMENT: VHF/UHF and HF/SSB com radio, Tacan, radio compass, radar altimeter, ILS, marker beacon receiver, 'Odd Rods' type IFF, radar warning receiver and ECM. Autopilot for attitude and heading hold, altitude hold and stability augmentation. Existing fire control system comprises a monopulse radar, optical gyro gunsight and gun camera. Enlarged avionics bays in nose and fuselage provide

room for modernised fire control system and other upgraded avionics now under development for Peace Pearl programme.

ARMAMENT: One 23 mm Type 23-3 twin-barrel cannon, with 200 rds, in underfuselage pack immediately aft of nosewheel doors. Seven external stations (one under fuselage and three under each wing) for a variety of stores which can include PL-2B infra-red air-to-air missiles, PL-7 medium-range semi-active radar homing air-to-air missiles, 18-round pods of 57 mm Type 57-2 unguided air-to-air rockets, launchers for 90 mm air-to-surface rockets, bombs, or (centreline and outboard underwing stations only) auxiliary fuel tanks. Chaff/flare dispensers in tailcone.

DIMENSIONS, EXTERNAL:
Wing span	9.344 m (30 ft 7⅞ in)
Wing aspect ratio	2.1
Length overall, incl nose probe	21.59 m (70 ft 10 in)
Height overall	5.41 m (17 ft 9 in)
Wheel track	approx 3.80 m (12 ft 7 in)
Wheelbase	approx 7.25 m (23 ft 9½ in)

AREA:
Wings, gross	42.2 m² (454.2 sq ft)

WEIGHTS AND LOADINGS:
Weight empty	9,820 kg (21,649 lb)
Normal T-O weight	14,300 kg (31,526 lb)
Max T-O weight	17,800 kg (39,242 lb)
Wing loading:	
at normal T-O weight	338.9 kg/m² (69.4 lb/sq ft)
at max T-O weight	421.8 kg/m² (86.4 lb/sq ft)
Power loading:	
at normal T-O weight	110.5 kg/kN (1.08 lb/lb st)
at max T-O weight	137.5 kg/kN (1.35 lb/lb st)

PERFORMANCE:
Design max operating Mach number	2.2
Design max level speed	701 knots (1,300 km/h; 808 mph) IAS
Unstick speed	175 knots (325 km/h; 202 mph)
Landing speed	156 knots (290 km/h; 180 mph)
Max rate of climb at S/L	12,000 m (39,370 ft)/min
Acceleration from Mach 0.6 to 1.25 at 5,000 m (16,400 ft)	54 s
Service ceiling	20,000 m (65,620 ft)
T-O run, with afterburning	670 m (2,198 ft)
Landing run, brake-chute deployed	1,000 m (3,280 ft)
Combat radius	432 nm (800 km; 497 miles)
Max range	1,187 nm (2,200 km; 1,367 miles)
g limit in sustained turn at Mach 0.9 at 5,000 m (16,400 ft)	+4.83

SAMF
SHANGHAI AIRCRAFT MANUFACTURING FACTORY (Subsidiary of Shanghai Aviation Industrial Corporation)

PO Box 814, Shanghai
Telephone: 86 (21) 383311
Telex: 33136 SHAIR CN
DIRECTOR: Jing Deyuan

SAMF occupies a site area of 135 ha (333.5 acres) and has a total workforce of about 7,000, of whom some 3,000 are engaged in the present MD-82 programme. The factory has produced main and nose landing gear doors for the McDonnell Douglas MD-80 series since 1979, and had delivered 825 sets by the end of 1988. Other MD-80 components now produced include cargo and service doors, and tooling for tailplane production was under way in early 1989. SAMF is also responsible for the Q-2 microlight aircraft.

SAMF (MCDONNELL DOUGLAS) MD-82

McDonnell Douglas Corporation announced on 11 January 1984 the signing of a letter of intent with SAMF on a co-production programme for MD-82 jet transports. Details of this new programme were confirmed in an April 1985 announcement of the sale of 26 MD-82s to China, of which 25 are being assembled in Shanghai, all for Chinese airlines.

One Douglas built aircraft was delivered in October 1985, and assembly at Shanghai began in April 1986. Complete major subassemblies were supplied by Douglas for the first three MD-82s to be assembled at Shanghai; since then, the Chinese industry has taken a gradually increasing share in manufacturing the remaining 22, producing its own landing gear doors, cargo and service doors and aileron supports

Shanghai assembled McDonnell Douglas MD-82 of CAAC

from aircraft No. 7. Starting with the 20th aircraft, SAMF will produce tailplanes for both its own and Douglas built MD-82s. Nosecones for the Chinese MD-82s are manufactured by Chengdu Aircraft Corporation.

Rollout of the first Chinese assembled MD-82 took place on 8 June 1987, with first flight following on 2 July. Delivery to the Shenyang branch of CAAC was made on the last day of that month, and the aircraft entered service with China

Northeast Airlines on 4 August. By 1 January 1989, six aircraft had been delivered to CAAC (Shenyang branch) and China Eastern Airlines based at Shanghai. Seven more MD-82s were delivered during 1989. Eight more were due for delivery in 1990, with the remaining four to follow by July 1991. Extension of the programme into 1994 with 20 more MD-82s received Chinese government approval in the Spring of 1990.

SAP
SHIJIAZHUANG AIRCRAFT PLANT

PO Box 164, Shijiazhuang, Hebei
Telephone: 86/Shijiazhuang 744251
Telex: 26236 HBJXC CN
DIRECTOR: Zhou Enqing

This factory began producing the An-2 transport aircraft in 1970, and had a 1989 workforce of more than 4,000, including some 570 engineers and technicians. Its principal

aircraft products are the Y-5 transport/agricultural biplane and the W-5 and W-6 microlight series.

SAP (ANTONOV) Y-5
Chinese name: Yunshuji-5 (Transport aircraft 5) or Yun-5
NATO reporting name: Colt

The Antonov An-2 general purpose biplane was supplied to, and since 1957 has been built under licence in, China in considerable numbers (nearly 1,000). The Y-5 was

manufactured initially at Nanchang, which built 727 between 1957-68 (first flight 7 December 1957). A further 221 had been built by SAP by the end of 1986, and small scale production was continuing in 1990. The Y-5 continues to be used extensively by the PLA Air Force, which has about 300, and in a civil capacity for agricultural and general transport work. Nanchang production included 229 Y-5s for agricultural duties and 114 for regional transport use.

A description of the basic An-2 can be found under the

Y-5 (licence An-2) general purpose biplane produced by Shijiazhuang Aircraft Plant

AVIONICS: Include Bendix/King KHF 950 HF and KY 196 VHF com radios, KR 87 ADF and KMA 24 audio control panel.

WEIGHTS (A with dry chemical spreader, B with liquid spray system):

Max payload: A, B	1,500 kg (3,307 lb)
Max T-O weight: A, B	5,205 kg (11,574 lb)

PERFORMANCE (A and B as for Weights):

Max level speed at S/L:

A	110 knots (205 km/h; 127 mph)
B	108 knots (200 km/h; 124 mph)

Max level speed at 1,700 m (5,575 ft):

A	119 knots (220 km/h; 137 mph)
B	116 knots (215 km/h; 133 mph)
Operating speed: A, B	86 knots (160 km/h; 99 mph)
Stalling speed: A, B	52 knots (95 km/h; 59 mph)
Max rate of climb at S/L: A, B	114 m (374 ft)/min

Rate of climb at 1,600 m (5,250 ft):

A	132 m (433 ft)/min
B	126 m (413 ft)/min
Service ceiling: A	3,500 m (11,480 ft)
B	3,300 m (10,825 ft)
Air turning radius: A, B	350 m (1,150 ft)
T-O run: A	170 m (558 ft)
B	180 m (591 ft)
Landing run: A	160 m (525 ft)
B	150 m (493 ft)
Range at S/L with fuel load of 670 litres (177 US gallons; 147 Imp gallons): A, B	456 nm (845 km; 525 miles)
Endurance, conditions as above: A, B	5 h 39 min
Swath width	20-50 m (66-165 ft)

WSK-PZL Mielec heading in the Polish section of this edition. The standard Chinese civil version is designated **Y-5N**, but a more recent development is a specialised agricultural and forestry version known as the **Y-5B**, which first flew on 2 June 1989 and conforms to the Chinese equivalent of FAR Pt 23.

The Y-5B retains the airframe, power plant and multi-purpose adaptability of the basic aircraft, but has a corrosion resistant structure and specially developed role equipment. This comprises a large hopper/tank with emergency jettison of contents; a high flow rate wind-driven pump; and spraybars with various nozzle sizes depending on the spray volume required. Cabin heating and ventilation are improved by a new environmental control system, the cabin doors are sealed against ingress of chemical, and some electrical and instrument installations are also improved. The Y-5B can be crewed by one or two persons.

The following details apply to the Y-5B:

POWER PLANT: One 746 kW (1,000 hp) Zhuzhou (SMPMC) HS5 nine-cylinder radial engine, driving a Baoding four-blade propeller.

XAC
XIAN AIRCRAFT MANUFACTURING COMPANY
PO Box 140, Xian, Shaanxi
Telephone: 86 (29) 61971
Telex: 70101 XAC CN
Cables: 2401 Yanliang Shaanxi
GENERAL MANAGER: Shao Guobin
SALES MANAGER: Fei Yu

Established in 1958, the Xian aircraft factory has a covered area of some 850,000 m² (9,149,315 sq ft). The 1989 workforce numbered about 15,000, of whom about 10,000 were engaged in aircraft production. Aircraft built at Xian include Chinese versions of the Soviet Tupolev Tu-16 bomber (Chinese designation H-6) and Antonov An-24 (Y7-100) and An-26 (Y-7H-500) transports. It is also developing a new two-seat supersonic strike aircraft, the H-7, powered by two large turbofan engines.

Since 1980 XAC has manufactured glassfibre header tanks, water float pylons, ailerons and various doors for the Canadair CL-215 amphibian; other subcontract work has included various components for the Airbus A300, Boeing 737 and 747, and ATR 42. It is expected to be the main Chinese centre for the MBB/CATIC MPC-75 airliner (see International section).

XAC (TUPOLEV) H-6
Chinese name: Hongzhaji-6 (Bomber aircraft 6) or Hong-6
Westernised designation: B-6
NATO reporting name: Badger

A Soviet licence to produce the Tupolev Tu-16 twin-jet bomber in China was granted in September 1957, two pattern aircraft (one disassembled, one in component knocked-down form) being delivered in 1959 and the former of these making its first flight in China on 27 September 1959. It was originally intended that both Harbin (HAMC) and Xian would be involved in the production programme, but in 1961 all work on the H-6, as the Chinese version was designated, was transferred to XAC. The first entirely Chinese built **H-6A** made its initial flight on 24 December 1968.

Production has been relatively slow, but it is continuing at a low rate (three or four per year), and the number in service with the PLA Air Force and Navy is now believed to be about 120, the current version being designated **H-6 IV** or **B-6D**. Development of this version began in 1975, although its first flight did not take place until 29 August 1981. China has supplied spares for the Tu-16 bombers of the Egyptian Air Force, and the sale of four B-6Ds to Iraq was reported in mid-1987. Those in PLA Air Force service are reportedly being updated with more modern bombing and navigation systems, and the possibility remains that ECM, reconnaissance or other variants may be developed in the future. A probe and drogue aerial tanker design study for the H-6 has been carried out by FRL of the UK, followed by a memorandum of understanding in September 1986 for FRL to assist CATIC in converting a number of H-6s to the tanker role. This version, which had not received a go-ahead up to early 1990, would serve primarily as a refuelling tanker for the Q-5 attack aircraft; there are no plans for a receiver version of the H-6.

As with other Chinese developments of original Soviet designs, some local modifications have been noted: some B-6Ds carrying C-601 missiles, for example, have a bigger and cylindrical chin fairing, housing a Chinese radar associated with cruise missile guidance; other H-6/B-6s have no chin radome at all.

TYPE: Twin-jet strategic bomber, tactical or maritime strike and reconnaissance aircraft.

POWER PLANT: Two 93.17 kN (20,944 lb st) Xian (XAE) WP8 turbojets. WQJ-1 starter motor. Fuel in total of 27 tanks in wings and fuselage.

ACCOMMODATION: Crew of six, including pilot and co-pilot. Ejection seats for all crew members.

AVIONICS: 20-channel VHF//UHF communications system. Automatic navigation system, based on Doppler radar, INS and AHRS, linked to autopilot.

ARMAMENT: Defensive armament of six or seven guns in nose (not on B-6D), dorsal, ventral and tail positions. Conventional or nuclear bombs in internal bay. Two underwing C-601 anti-shipping missiles on B-6D. Chute for flares and marine markers aft of bomb bay.

DIMENSIONS, EXTERNAL:

Wing span	34.189 m (112 ft 2 in)
Length overall	34.800 m (114 ft 2 in)
Height overall	10.355 m (33 ft 11¾ in)
Wheel track	9.755 m (32 ft 0 in)
Wheelbase	10.913 m (35 ft 9¾ in)

AREAS:

Wings, gross: H-6A	164.65 m² (1,772.3 sq ft)
B-6D	167.55 m² (1,803.5 sq ft)

WEIGHTS (A: H-6A, B: B-6D):

Weight empty: A	37,729 kg (83,178 lb)
B	38,530 kg (84,944 lb)
Max fuel load: A, B	approx 33,000 kg (72,752 lb)
Normal bomb load: A, B	3,000 kg (6,614 lb)
Max bomb load: B	9,000 kg (19,841 lb)
Two C-601 missiles: B	4,880 kg (10,758 lb)
Normal T-O weight: B	72,000 kg (158,733 lb)
Max T-O weight: A	72,000 kg (158,733 lb)
B	75,800 kg (167,110 lb)
Max landing weight: A, B	55,000 kg (121,254 lb)
Normal landing weight: B	48,000 kg (105,822 lb)

Xian B-6D maritime strike bomber, showing underwing C-601 missile carriage

PERFORMANCE (B-6D with two underwing C-601 anti-shipping missiles):

Max cruising speed	424 knots (786 km/h; 488 mph)
T-O speed with full load	163 knots (302 km/h; 188 mph)
Normal landing speed	126 knots (233 km/h; 145 mph)
Max rate of climb at S/L	1,140 m (3,740 ft)/min
Service ceiling	12,000 m (39,370 ft)
T-O run with full load	2,100 m (6,890 ft)
Normal landing run	1,540 m (5,050 ft)
Combat radius	971 nm (1,800 km; 1,118 miles)
Max range	2,320 nm (4,300 km; 2,672 miles)
Max endurance	5 h 41 min

XAC H-7
Chinese name: Hongzhaji-7 (Bomber aircraft 7) or Hong-7
Westernised designation: B-7

This new multi-role combat aircraft, of Chinese design, was first shown in model form in September 1988 at the Farnborough Air Show. In the same class as the Soviet Su-24 'Fencer', the H-7 is being developed as an all-weather interdictor/strike aircraft for the PLA Air Force and in maritime attack form for the Naval Air Force, and has the highest priority of any current Chinese military aircraft programme. The first of two prototypes was rolled out in August 1988 and made its first flight in late 1988 or early 1989.

In 1988 the prototypes were said to be powered by twin 91.2 kN (20,515 lb st) Rolls-Royce Spey Mk 202 augmented turbofans (Xian WS9), but in October 1989 a senior PLA Air Force official was quoted as saying that the aircraft had "a more powerful version of the WP7 Chinese built engine", presumably a reference to the WP13A II that currently powers the J-8 II fighter. The eventual intention is believed to be to power production H-7s with the Liming (LEMC) WS6A turbofan (71.3 kN; 16,027 lb st dry, 138.3 kN; 31,085 lb st with afterburning) of Chinese design.

The general appearance of the H-7 is shown in the accompanying illustrations. It is a shoulder-wing monoplane, with compound-swept wings, 'dog-tooth' leading-edges, all-moving tailplane, lateral engine air intakes, and tandem seating for the crew of two on HTY-4 ejection seats operable at speeds from zero to 540 knots (1,000 km/h; 621 mph) and heights from sea level to 20,000 m (65,600 ft). The wings are fitted with leading-edge slats. The large fin is supplemented by a single ventral fin. On the model, the four underwing stores pylons were shown with two C-801 sea-skimming anti-shipping missiles inboard and auxiliary fuel tanks outboard. A 23 mm twin-barrel gun in the nose, and close-range air-to-air missile on each wingtip, are claimed to give the H-7 a secondary air-to-air capability. Terrain following radar and avionics on the prototypes are claimed to be of Chinese design and manufacture. Entry into service is scheduled for 1992-93.

DIMENSIONS, EXTERNAL (estimated):

Wing span	12.65 m (41 ft 6 in)
Length overall, incl probe	18.60 m (61 ft 0 in)

WEIGHT (estimated):

Max T-O weight	27,500 kg (60,627 lb)

PERFORMANCE (estimated):

Max level speed at altitude	Mach 1.8

XAC (ANTONOV) Y7-100
Chinese name: Yunshuji-7 (Transport aircraft 7) or Yun-7
NATO reporting name: Coke

Civil and military examples of the Antonov An-24 twin-turboprop transport aircraft (40 of which were purchased from the USSR) have been in service with CAAC and the PLA Air Force since about 1970. A reverse engineered version of this 48/52-passenger aircraft, known as the Y-7, received its Chinese certificate of airworthiness in 1980, following the completion of three prototypes (first flight 25 December 1970) plus two additional airframes for static and fatigue testing.

Provisional three-view *(Pilot Press)* **and model of XAC H-7 in maritime attack form**

Public debut by a pre-production Y-7 took place on 17 April 1982, and production started later that year. First flight of a production Y-7 was announced on 1 February 1984, and the initial delivery to CAAC was made shortly afterwards. Scheduled passenger services began on 29 April 1986. The PLA Naval Air Force operates one Y-7 in the transport role and another as a navigation trainer. Twenty of the initial Y-7 version were built, on one of which (B-3499) Hong Kong Aircraft Engineering Company (HAECO) undertook 'prototype' refurbishment in 1985. This programme called for a new three-person flight deck layout, all-new cabin interior with 52 reclining seats, windscreen de-icing, new HF/VHF communications, new navigation equipment, and installation of oxygen, air data and environmental control systems. The aircraft was also fitted with winglets. In this new form the aircraft meets BCAR standards, and is known as the **Y7-100**. The winglet modification is being applied to the original batch of Y-7s. The first production Y7-100 was flown in late 1985, and certification was awarded on 23 January 1986. About 33 had been delivered by March 1990.

China estimates a requirement for 120 Y-7s by 1995, and plans an ongoing development programme intended to lead to a more fuel-efficient **Y7-200A** in 1991, with a reduced-weight **Y7-200B** appearing later. Boeing Commercial Airplanes is assisting in the Y-7 modification programme. XAC is now producing a military and civil cargo version, derived from the Antonov An-26, under the designation **Y-7H-500**; this is described separately. The following description is based on that of the An-24RV, modified where possible to refer to the Y7-100. Further details of the original Y-7 can be found in the 1988-89 and earlier *Jane's*.

TYPE: Twin-turboprop short/medium-range transport.

WINGS: Cantilever high-wing monoplane, with 2° 12′ 2″ anhedral on outer panels. Incidence 3°. Sweepback at quarter-chord on outer panels 6° 50′. All-metal two-spar structure, built in five sections: constant chord centre-section, two tapered inner wings and two tapered outer panels. Mass balanced servo-compensated ailerons, with large glassfibre trim tabs. Hydraulically operated Fowler flaps along entire wing trailing-edges inboard of unpowered ailerons; single-slotted flaps on centre-section, double-slotted outboard of nacelles. Servo tab and trim tab in each aileron. Winglet at each tip (being retrofitted also on Y-7).

FUSELAGE: All-metal semi-monocoque structure in front, centre and rear portions, of bonded/welded construction.

TAIL UNIT: Cantilever all-metal structure, with single ventral fin. Tailplane dihedral 9°. All controls operated manually. Balance tab in each elevator, trim tab and spring tab in rudder.

LANDING GEAR (An-24RV): Retractable tricycle type with twin wheels on all units. Hydraulic actuation, with emergency gravity extension. All units retract forward. Mainwheels are size 900 × 300 mm, tyre pressure 5.39-5.88 bars (78.2-85.3 lb/sq in); nosewheels size 700 × 250 mm, tyre pressure 3.92 bars (56.8 lb/sq in). (Mainwheel tyre pressures variable to cater for different types of runway.) Disc brakes on mainwheels; steerable and castoring nosewheel unit.

POWER PLANT: Two Dongan (DEMC) WJ5A I turboprops, each rated at 2,080 kW (2,790 shp) for T-O and 1,976 kW (2,650 shp) at ISA + 23°C; Baoding four-blade constant-speed fully-feathering propellers with elongated spinners. Fuel in integral wing tanks immediately outboard of nacelles, and four bag-type tanks in centre-section, total capacity 5,550 litres (1,466 US gallons; 1,220 Imp gallons). Provision for four additional tanks in centre-section. Pressure refuelling point in starboard engine nacelle; gravity fuelling point above each tank. One 8.83 kN (1,985 lb st) Type RU 19-300 auxiliary turbojet in starboard engine nacelle for engine starting, to improve take-off and in-flight performance,

XAC Y-7 (Chinese development of the Antonov An-24) after modification by HAECO of Hong Kong as the prototype Y7-100 *(HAECO)*

and to reduce stability and handling problems if one turboprop engine fails in flight.

ACCOMMODATION: Crew of three (Y7-100) on flight deck, plus cabin attendant. Standard layout has four-abreast seating, with centre aisle, for 52 passengers in air-conditioned, soundproofed (by Tracor) and pressurised cabin. Galley (by Lermer) and toilet at rear on starboard side. Baggage compartments forward and aft of passenger cabin, plus overhead stowage bins in cabin. Passenger door on port side, at rear of cabin, is of airstair type. Doors to forward and rear baggage compartments on starboard side. All doors open inward. Electric windscreen de-icing.

SYSTEMS: Hamilton Standard environmental control system (cabin pressure differential in An-24RV is 0.29 bars; 4.27 lb/sq in). Main and emergency hydraulic systems, pressure 152 bars (2,200 lb/sq in), for landing gear actuation, nosewheel steering, flaps, brakes, windscreen wipers and propeller feathering. Electrical system in An-24RV includes two 27V DC starter/generators, two alternators to provide 115V 400Hz AC supply, and two inverters for 36V 400Hz three-phase AC. Puritan-Bennett passenger oxygen system optional in Y7-100.

AVIONICS AND EQUIPMENT: Standard communications equipment comprises Collins 618M-3 dual VHF, Collins 628T-3 single HF, Becker audio selection and intercom, and Sundstrand AV-557C cockpit voice recorder. Standard navigation equipment comprises dual ADI-84A, dual EHSI-74 electronic HSI, dual RMI-36, FGS-65 flight guidance system, dual 51RV-4B VOR/ILS, dual DME-42, dual DF-206 ADF, 860F-4 radio altimeter, 621A-6A ATC transponder, 51Z-4 marker beacon receiver and CWC-80 instrument warning system, all by Collins; Litton LTN-211 VLF/Omega navigation system; Honeywell MHRS dual compass system, dual attitude reference and Primus 90 colour weather radar; IDC air data system; Sundstrand UFDR flight data recorder; and KJ-6A autopilot. Gables control units. Other instrumentation by Gould, IDC, Sfena and Smiths.

DIMENSIONS, EXTERNAL:
Wing span (over winglets)	29.637 m (97 ft 2¾ in)
Wing chord: at root	3.50 m (11 ft 5¾ in)
at tip	1.095 m (3 ft 7 in)
Wing aspect ratio	11.7
Length overall	23.708 m (77 ft 9½ in)
Height overall	8.553 m (28 ft 0¾ in)
Fuselage: Max width	2.90 m (9 ft 6¼ in)
Max depth	2.50 m (8 ft 2½ in)
Tailplane span	9.08 m (29 ft 9½ in)
Wheel track (c/l of shock struts)	7.90 m (25 ft 11 in)
Wheelbase	7.90 m (25 ft 11 in)
Passenger door (port, rear):	
Height	1.40 m (4 ft 7 in)
Width	0.75 m (2 ft 5½ in)
Height to sill	1.40 m (4 ft 7 in)
Baggage compartment door (starboard, fwd):	
Height	1.10 m (3 ft 7¼ in)
Width	1.20 m (3 ft 11¼ in)
Height to sill	1.30 m (4 ft 3 in)
Baggage compartment door (starboard, rear):	
Height	1.41 m (4 ft 7½ in)
Width	0.75 m (2 ft 5½ in)

DIMENSIONS, INTERNAL:
Cabin:	
Length, incl flight deck	10.50 m (34 ft 5½ in)
Max width	2.80 m (9 ft 2¼ in)
Max height	1.90 m (6 ft 2¾ in)
Volume	56.0 m³ (1,978 cu ft)
Baggage compartment volume:	
fwd	4.50 m³ (159 cu ft)
rear	6.70 m³ (237 cu ft)

AREAS:
Wings, gross	74.98 m² (807.1 sq ft)
Vertical tail surfaces (total)	13.38 m² (144.0 sq ft)
Horizontal tail surfaces (total)	17.23 m² (185.5 sq ft)

WEIGHTS AND LOADINGS:
Operating weight empty	14,900 kg (32,849 lb)
Max fuel	4,790 kg (10,560 lb)
Max payload	5,500 kg (12,125 lb)
Max T-O and landing weight	21,800 kg (48,060 lb)
Max zero-fuel weight	19,655 kg (43,332 lb)
Max wing loading	290.7 kg/m² (59.6 lb/sq ft)
Max power loading	5.24 kg/kW (8.61 lb/shp)

PERFORMANCE:
Max level speed	279 knots (518 km/h; 322 mph)
Max cruising speed at 4,000 m (13,125 ft)	
	261 knots (484 km/h; 301 mph)
Econ cruising speed at 6,000 m (19,685 ft)	
	228 knots (423 km/h; 263 mph)
Max rate of climb at S/L	458 m (1,504 ft)/min
Service ceiling	8,750 m (28,700 ft)
Service ceiling, one engine out	3,900 m (12,800 ft)
T-O run at S/L, FAR Pt 25: ISA	1,248 m (4,095 ft)
ISA + 20°C	1,398 m (4,590 ft)
Landing run	620 m (2,035 ft)
Range:	
max (52-passenger) payload	
	491 nm (910 km; 565 miles)
max standard fuel	1,025 nm (1,900 km; 1,180 miles)
standard and auxiliary fuel	
	1,306 nm (2,420 km; 1,504 miles)

XAC Y7-100 current production version of this twin-turboprop transport aircraft *(Pilot Press)*

XAC Y-7H-500
NATO reporting name: Curl

XAC has developed its own derivative of the Soviet Antonov An-26 medium-range military transport for both domestic use and export. Originally referred to as the Y-14-100, it first flew in prototype form in late 1988 and is now in production as the Y-7H-500.

Commonality with the Y7-100 includes the wings (with added winglets), forward fuselage, twin military versions of the WJ5A I turboprop (each driving a Baoding J16-G10 four-blade constant-speed metal propeller), and a turbojet APU for take-off assistance in hot and high conditions. It carries a crew of five (pilot, co-pilot, navigator, flight engineer and radio operator) and has accommodation for up to 38 fully equipped troops or 19 paratroops, or 24 stretcher cases and one medical attendant in a medevac role. Up to 2,000 kg (4,409 lb) of external stores, such as weapons or supply containers, can be carried on fuselage attachment points. The fuselage, like that of the An-26, has a rear-loading ramp/door in the underside. Other features include a nose-mounted weather radar, rough-field landing gear, enlarged flight deck windows, and modern avionics comprising navaids, an AHRS and autopilot.

DIMENSIONS, EXTERNAL:
Wing span	29.20 m (95 ft 9½ in)
Length overall	23.98 m (78 ft 8 in)
Height overall	8.89 m (29 ft 2 in)
Wheel track	7.90 m (25 ft 11 in)
Wheelbase	8.03 m (26 ft 4¼ in)
Crew door: Height	1.40 m (4 ft 7 in)
Width	0.60 m (1 ft 11½ in)

DIMENSIONS, INTERNAL:
Cargo hold: Length	11.10 m (36 ft 5 in)
Width	2.78 m (9 ft 1½ in)
Height	1.91 m (6 ft 3¾ in)

AREA:
Wings, gross	74.98 m² (807.08 sq ft)

WEIGHTS:
Operating weight empty	15,400 kg (33,950 lb)
Max fuel weight	5,500 kg (12,125 lb)
Max payload	5,500 kg (12,125 lb)
Max ramp weight	24,230 kg (53,420 lb)
Max T-O and landing weight	24,000 kg (52,910 lb)

Model of XAC Y-7H-500 medium-range military transport *(Brian M. Service)*

Xian Y-7H-500 rear-loading transport (two WJ5A I turboprops) *(Pilot Press)*

PERFORMANCE (estimated, at max T-O weight except where indicated):
Max cruising speed at 6,000 m (19,685 ft) at AUW of
22,500 kg (49,600 lb)   240 knots (445 km/h; 276 mph)
Max rate of climb at S/L   480 m (1,575 ft)/min
Rate of climb at S/L, one engine out   144 m (472 ft)/min

Service ceiling   8,200 m (26,900 ft)
Service ceiling, one engine out 3,800 m (12,465 ft)
T-O run   857 m (2,812 ft)
Landing run   634 m (2,080 ft)
Range at 236 knots (438 km/h; 272 mph) at 6,000 m
(19,685 ft):

with max payload   560 nm (1,038 km; 645 miles)
with 3,300 kg (7,275 lb) payload
                      1,187 nm (2,200 km; 1,367 miles)
Max endurance   5 h 23 min

CISKEI

CAI
CISKEI AIRCRAFT INDUSTRIES (PTY) LTD
PO Box 1, Kidds Beach, Bisho 5264
Telephone: (04323) 69402 or (011) 8024342
In a newly built factory at Bisho's Bulembu Airport, CAI is producing under licence the Austrian **HB-Aircraft**

Hobbyliner and Scanliner (which see), manufacture having started at the end of 1987 following initial orders from the Wonderboom Flying School in Pretoria, South Africa.
The first aircraft completed by CAI, a Hobbyliner, first flew in December 1988, when 16 other HB-23 series aircraft

were in various stages of fabrication. Certification by the South African Division of Aviation was under way in early 1989. Orders received by CAI include one from Taiwan, for four aircraft with an option for 16.

COLOMBIA

AERO MERCANTIL
AERO MERCANTIL SA
Carrera 3 No. 56-19, Apartado Aéreo 6781, Bogotá
Telephone: 57 (1) 211 8100
Telex: 44 581 LAVE CO
Fax: 57 (1) 212 8952
PRESIDENT: James G. Leaver
PROJECTS MANAGER: Eric Leaver
Aero Mercantil has been associated with Piper Aircraft Corporation since 1952, first as a dealer and then as a distributor. Currently, it markets the aircraft produced by AICSA (see entry on next page) and provides the quality assurance at the latter's assembly plant. It is currently developing and building a prototype aircraft of its own design, known as the Gavilán.

AERO MERCANTIL EL1 GAVILÁN (SPARROWHAWK)
Construction of the Gavilán prototype began in May 1987. By December 1989 the fuselage was virtually complete, with engine, landing gear and tail surfaces all in place; and all systems had been installed. Wing attachment was scheduled for February 1990, and first flight was expected during April. Certification under FAR Pt 23 is planned.
TYPE: Eight-seat light transport.
WINGS: Braced high-wing monoplane. Wing section NACA 4412. Dihedral 2°. Incidence 1° 30'. Unswept, two-spar structure of 2024-T3 aluminium alloy, with constant chord and single-strut bracing each side. Piano hinged ailerons and offset hinged single-slotted trailing-edge flaps also of 2024-T3. No tabs.
FUSELAGE: Mainframe of 4130N steel tube, with 2024-T3 aluminium alloy skin.
TAIL UNIT: Two-spar fin and fixed incidence tailplane; trim tab in starboard elevator. Entire structure of 2024-T3 aluminium alloy.
LANDING GEAR: Non-retractable tricycle type, with elastomeric shock absorption and single wheel on each unit. Tyre sizes 700 × 6-6 (main) and 600 × 6-6 (nose). Cleveland mainwheel brakes.
POWER PLANT: One 261 kW (350 hp) Textron Lycoming TIO-540-W2A flat-six engine, driving a three-blade constant-speed Hartzell propeller. Fuel tank in each wing, combined capacity 273 litres (72 US gallons; 60 Imp gallons), increasable optionally to 454 litres (120 US gallons; 100 Imp gallons). Refuelling point in each tank. Oil capacity 7.6 litres (2 US gallons; 1.7 Imp gallons).
ACCOMMODATION: Pilot and co-pilot or one passenger at front. Two rows of three seats to rear of these; middle row faces aft. Door at front on each side, plus larger cargo double door at rear on port side.

Aero Mercantil EL1 Gavilán eight-seat light utility transport *(Jane's/Mike Keep)*

SYSTEMS: Pneumatic system, vacuum pump driven at 0.34 bar (5 lb/sq in). 12V 70A electrical system. Oxygen system optional.
AVIONICS: Bendix/King KX 155 VHF/VOR and KR 87 ADF, and blind-flying instrumentation, are standard.
DIMENSIONS, EXTERNAL:

Wing span	12.19 m (40 ft 0 in)
Wing chord, constant	1.55 m (5 ft 1 in)
Wing aspect ratio	6.67
Length overall	9.22 m (30 ft 3 in)
Height overall	3.35 m (11 ft 0 in)
Tailplane span	3.10 m (10 ft 2 in)
Wheelbase	3.35 m (11 ft 0 in)
Propeller diameter	2.13 m (7 ft 0 in)
Propeller ground clearance	0.36 m (1 ft 2 in)
Crew/passenger doors (each): Height	0.91 m (3 ft 0 in)
Width	0.97 m (3 ft 2 in)
Height to sill	1.02 m (3 ft 4 in)
Cargo double door: Height	1.17 m (3 ft 10 in)
Width	1.02 m (3 ft 4 in)
Height to sill	1.02 m (3 ft 4 in)

DIMENSIONS, INTERNAL:

Cabin: Length	3.66 m (12 ft 0 in)
Max width	1.37 m (4 ft 6 in)
Max height	1.22 m (4 ft 0 in)
Floor area	5.02 m² (54.0 sq ft)

AREAS:

Wings, gross	22.30 m² (240.0 sq ft)
Tailplane	5.57 m² (60.0 sq ft)

WEIGHTS AND LOADINGS:

Weight empty, equipped	1,134 kg (2,500 lb)
Max fuel	212 kg (468 lb)
Max payload	862 kg (1,900 lb)
Max T-O and landing weight	1,905 kg (4,200 lb)
Max wing loading	100.6 kg/m² (20.6 lb/sq ft)
Max power loading	7.30 kg/kW (12.0 lb/hp)

PERFORMANCE (estimated, at max T-O weight):

Never-exceed speed	203 knots (376 km/h; 233 mph)
Max level speed at 5,500 m (18,000 ft)	145 knots (269 km/h; 167 mph)
Max cruising speed at 5,500 m (18,000 ft)	135 knots (250 km/h; 155 mph)
Econ cruising speed at 5,500 m (18,000 ft)	130 knots (241 km/h; 150 mph)
Stalling speed, 40° flap, engine idling	58 knots (108 km/h; 67 mph)
Max rate of climb at S/L	366 m (1,200 ft)/min
Service ceiling	7,620 m (25,000 ft)
T-O run	275 m (900 ft)
T-O to 15 m (50 ft)	475 m (1,500 ft)
Landing from 15 m (50 ft)	366 m (1,200 ft)
Landing run	183 m (600 ft)
Range with max fuel, no reserves	580 nm (1,075 km; 668 miles)

AGRO-COPTEROS
AGRO-COPTEROS LTDA
Calle 20 N 8A-18, Apartado Aéreo 1789, Cali
Telephone: 57 (3) 825110, 833519
Telex: 51138 DIEGO CO
PRESIDENT: Maximo Tedesco Kappler
This company assembles various North American light aircraft and rotorcraft kits, notably those suitable for agricultural work. Details of its sprayplane version of the Aerosport Scamp B can be found in the 1984-85 *Jane's*.

AGRO-COPTEROS (ZENAIR) STOL CH 701
This is a licence built version of the Zenair STOL CH 701 side by side two-seat all-metal Experimental category aircraft of which details and an illustration can be found in the Canadian part of the Sport Aircraft section. It is powered by a 47.7 kW (64 hp) Rotax 532 engine and has a standard fuel capacity of 42 litres (11 US gallons; 9.25 Imp gallons). By July 1988, sales in Latin America and the USA totalled 40 aircraft. No later information has been received.
WEIGHTS:

Weight empty	193 kg (425 lb)
Max T-O weight	430 kg (948 lb)

PERFORMANCE (A, pilot only; B, at max T-O weight):

Never-exceed speed: A, B	86 knots (161 km/h; 100 mph)
Max level speed: A, B	69 knots (128 km/h; 80 mph)
Cruising speed: A, B	over 52 knots (96 km/h; 60 mph)

Stalling speed, flaps down:

A	20 knots (37 km/h; 23 mph)
B	23 knots (42 km/h; 26 mph)
Max rate of climb at S/L: A	426 m (1,400 ft)/min
B	250 m (820 ft)/min
Service ceiling: A	4,265 m (14,000 ft)
B	3,650 m (12,000 ft)
T-O run: A on hard surface	16 m (53 ft)
A on grass	24 m (79 ft)
B on hard surface	30 m (99 ft)
B on grass	40 m (131 ft)
Range: A	200 nm (370 km; 230 miles)
B	160 nm (296 km; 184 miles)

AICSA
AERO INDUSTRIAL COLOMBIANA SA
Aeropuerto Guaymaral, Bogotá
GENERAL MANAGER: Pedro Alberto Gil

AICSA has been assembling Piper aircraft since 1968, when the Colombian Air Force permitted these aircraft to be imported in kit form, enabling some locally produced materials and skilled local labour to be used in their completion. AICSA was created to assemble Pipers not only for Colombia but also for member countries of the Andean Pact, although in the event exports of Colombian assembled aircraft have been limited to Bolivia, Chile and Ecuador. Currently, through another subsidiary, the Colombian Air Force owns 51 per cent of AICSA; the other major shareholder is the Instituto de Fomento Industrial (IFI), whose 48 per cent holding was due to be placed on the open stock market during 1990.

From 1968 to the end of 1985, AICSA assembled 492 Piper aircraft (275 single-engined and 217 twin-engined), as listed in the 1987-88 *Jane's*. No aircraft were built in 1986, but production was resumed in 1987 with 12 Seneca IIIs, one Cheyenne 400 and a Turbo Saratoga. Three Seneca IIIs and a Cheyenne 400 were assembled during 1989.

In mid-1989, AICSA entered into an agreement with Pezetel of Poland for the PZL Mielec (Antonov) An-2 (which see) to be assembled in Colombia. Two An-2s had been completed by the end of that year.

Piper Cheyenne 400 assembled under licence by AICSA

AVIONES DE COLOMBIA
AVIONES DE COLOMBIA SA
Eldorado International Airport, Entrance No 1, PO Box 6876, Bogotá
Telephone: 57 (1) 413 8300, 9857 and 9223
Telex: 45 220
Fax: 57 (1) 413 8075
WORKS: Aeropuerto Guaymaral, Apartado Aéreo 6876, Bogotá
Telephone: 57 (1) 676 0478, 0101 and 0326
Fax: 57 (1) 676 0458
COMMERCIAL MANAGER: Rafael Urdaneta

This company, established in the 1950s and known formerly as Urdaneta y Galvez Ltda, has been a South American distributor for Cessna aircraft since 1961. In 1969 it began assembling and partly building selected Cessna types under licence (see 1981-82 and earlier editions of *Jane's*), and is now qualified to manufacture complete airframes. Facilities include a new 1,330 m² (14,316 sq ft) fixed base operation at Eldorado International Airport; and 13,935 m² (150,000 sq ft) of assembly plant and a maintenance service station, recently approved by the US FAA, located at the Guaymaral general aviation airport in Bogotá.

On 31 January 1990 the company had a workforce of 170 persons, and had assembled a total of 1,047 Cessna aircraft.

AVIONES DE COLOMBIA/CESSNA AGTRAINER
Illustrated in the accompanying photograph, the AgTrainer is modified by Aviones de Colombia from the Cessna Model 188 Ag Truck (1984-85 *Jane's*). The cabin is widened to accommodate two persons side by side, increasing the empty weight by approx 91 kg (200 lb). Flight characteristics remain unchanged. Two prototypes were flown (the first of them on 16 September 1976), and the first prototype has since been operated by Aeroandes, a local cropspraying flying school.

Eight AgTrainers had been produced by early 1990, of which four were operating in Colombia, three in Central America and one in Ecuador.
TYPE: Two-seat agricultural monoplane.
WINGS: Braced low-wing monoplane, with single streamline section bracing strut each side. Wing section NACA 2412, modified. Dihedral 9°. Incidence 1° 30′ at root, −1° 30′ at tip. All-metal structure with NACA all-metal single-slotted flaps inboard of Frise all-metal ailerons. Aileron leading-edge gaps sealed. Wing fences immediately outboard of bracing strut attachments.
FUSELAGE: Rectangular section welded steel tube structure with removable metal skin panels forward of cabin. All-metal semi-monocoque rear fuselage.
TAIL UNIT: Cantilever all-metal structure. Fixed incidence tailplane. Trim tab in starboard elevator. Tailplane abrasion boots standard.

Aviones de Colombia AgTrainer two-seat agricultural aircraft

LANDING GEAR: Non-retractable tailwheel type. Land-O-Matic cantilever main legs of heavy duty spring steel. Tapered tubular tailwheel spring shock absorber. Mainwheel tyres size 22 × 8.00-8, 6-ply rating, pressure 2.41 bars (35 lb/sq in). Oversize tyres optional, size 8.50-10, 6-ply rating, pressure 1.72 bars (25 lb/sq in). Tailwheel tyre size 3.50-10, 4-ply rating, pressure 3.45-4.14 bars (50-60 lb/sq in). Steerable tailwheel. Hydraulic disc brakes and parking brake.
POWER PLANT: One 224 kW (300 hp) Continental IO-520-D flat-six engine, driving a McCauley three-blade constant-speed propeller. Fuel capacity 204 litres (54 US gallons; 45 Imp gallons). Oil capacity 11.4 litres (3 US gallons; 2.5 Imp gallons).
ACCOMMODATION: Side by side seats for two persons, in enclosed cabin with steel overturn structure. Combined window and door on each side, hinged at bottom. Ventilation standard. Air-conditioning, heating and windscreen defrosting optional.
SYSTEM: Electrical system powered by a 28V 60A alternator and 24V 12.75Ah battery as standard. 28V 95A alternator and 24V 15.5Ah heavy duty battery optional.
EQUIPMENT: Standard equipment includes a 1,060 litre (280 US gallon; 233 Imp gallon) hopper with shatter-resistant window, engine driven hydraulic spray system and manually controlled spray valve and gearbox without agitator, hopper side loading system on port side, pilot's four-way adjustable seat, control stick lock, wire cutters, cable deflector, navigation lights, tailcone lift handles, quick drain oil valve, remote fuel strainer drain control, and auxiliary fuel pump.
DIMENSIONS, EXTERNAL:
Wing span | 12.70 m (41 ft 8 in)

Length overall	8.00 m (26 ft 3 in)
Height overall	2.44 m (8 ft 0 in)
Propeller diameter	2.03 m (6 ft 8 in)
DIMENSIONS, INTERNAL:	
Cabin: Max width	1.09 m (3 ft 7 in)
Hopper volume	0.85 m³ (30.0 cu ft)
AREA:	
Wings, gross	19.05 m² (205.0 sq ft)
WEIGHTS:	
Weight empty:	
without dispersal equipment	1,017 kg (2,242 lb)
with dispersal equipment	1,099 kg (2,424 lb)
Max T-O weight:	
Normal category	1,497 kg (3,300 lb)
Restricted category	1,905 kg (4,200 lb)
Max landing weight	1,497 kg (3,300 lb)
PERFORMANCE (at max T-O weight):	
Max level speed at S/L	105 knots (195 km/h; 121 mph)
Max cruising speed (75% power) at 1,980 m (6,500 ft)	
	98 knots (182 km/h; 113 mph)
Stalling speed, power off:	
flaps up	53 knots (98 km/h; 61 mph) IAS
flaps down	50 knots (92 km/h; 57 mph) IAS
Max rate of climb at S/L	210 m (690 ft)/min
Service ceiling	3,385 m (11,100 ft)
T-O run	207 m (680 ft)
T-O to 15 m (50 ft)	332 m (1,090 ft)
Landing from 15 m (50 ft)	386 m (1,265 ft)
Landing run	128 m (420 ft)
Range, reserves for start, taxi, T-O and 45 min at 45%	
power	256 nm (474 km; 295 miles)
Endurance, conditions as above	2 h 36 min

CZECHOSLOVAKIA

The Czechoslovak aircraft industry is centrally controlled by the Aero Concern of the Aeronautical Industry, Prague-Letnany, whose General Director is Zdeněk Hořčík.

About 29,000 people are employed by the Czechoslovak aircraft industry. Principal factories concerned with aircraft manufacture are the Aero Vodochody, Let Kunovice and Zlin Aircraft Moravan Otrokovice, whose current products appear under the appropriate headings in this section. Other Czechoslovak factories engaged in the production of aero engines and sailplanes are listed in the relevant sections of this edition.

Sales of all aircraft products outside Czechoslovakia are handled by the Omnipol Foreign Trade Corporation.

OMNIPOL
FOREIGN TRADE CORPORATION
Nekázanka 11, 112 21 Prague 1
Telephone: 42 (2) 2140111
Telex: 121297 and 121299

Fax: 42 (2) 226792
GENERAL DIRECTOR: Ing František Háva
COMMERCIAL DIRECTOR: Ing Josef Stibor
PUBLICITY MANAGER: Ing Eduard Dopita

This concern handles the sales of products of the Czechoslovak aircraft industry outside Czechoslovakia and furnishes all information requested by customers with regard to export goods.

AERO
AERO VODOCHODY NÁRODNÍ PODNIK
(Aero Vodochody National Corporation)
250 70 Odolena Voda
Telephone: 42 (2) 843641
Telex: 121169 AERO C
MANAGING DIRECTOR: Ing Václav Klouda
CHIEF DESIGNER: Ing Vlastimil Havelka

This factory was established on 1 July 1953. Aero produced about 3,600 L-29 Delfin jet trainers between 1963 and 1974 and has since produced the L-39.

Aero L-39 Z0 trainers of the Libyan Arab Air Force *(Ivo Sturzenegger)*

AERO L-39 ALBATROS

The L-39 basic and advanced jet trainer first flew on 4 November 1968. The prototypes (see earlier *Jane's*) were followed by ten pre-production aircraft from 1971, and series production started in late 1972, following official selection of the L-39 to succeed the L-29 Delfin (1974-75 *Jane's*) as the standard jet trainer for the air forces of the Soviet Union, Czechoslovakia and East Germany. Service trials took place in 1973 in Czechoslovakia and the USSR, and by the Spring of 1974 the L-39 had begun to enter service with the Czechoslovak Air Force. Other recipients now include Afghanistan (18), Algeria (16), Bulgaria (18), Cuba (30), Ethiopia (12), Iraq (80), Libya (170), Nigeria (10), Romania (35), Syria (100) and Vietnam (25).

Production totalled more than 2,350 by 1 January 1989, and was expected to continue for at least five more years, at the rate of 200 a year. The Albatros is used in Czechoslovakia for all pilot training, including that of helicopter pilots. On average, pupils solo after approx 14 hours' dual instruction on the L-39 C.

The following variants have been produced:

L-39 C. Basic version, for basic and advanced flying training, to which the detailed description chiefly applies. Two underwing stations only. In service with the air forces of Afghanistan, Cuba, Czechoslovakia, East Germany and USSR. In production.

L-39 V. As basic L-39 C, but modified as single-seater for target towing (see 1987-88 and earlier editions). Two delivered to East Germany. No longer in production.

L-39 Z0. Jet trainer with four underwing weapon stations (Z = Zbrojní: armed) and reinforced wings. Prototype (X-09) first flown 25 August 1975. Customers include the air forces of East Germany (52), Iraq (80), Libya (170) and Syria (100). In production.

L-39 ZA. Ground attack and reconnaissance version of L-39 Z0, with underfuselage gun pod and four underwing weapon stations; reinforced wings and landing gear. Prototypes (X-10 and X-11) first flown 1975-76. In service with the air forces of Bulgaria (18), Czechoslovakia and Romania (35). In production.

L-39 MS. New advanced training version with improved airframe, more powerful engine and upgraded avionics; described separately.

The following description applies to the current production L-39 C basic version, except where indicated:

TYPE: Two-seat basic and advanced jet trainer; L-39 ZA also has ground attack and reconnaissance capability.

WINGS: Cantilever low-wing monoplane, with 2° 30′ dihedral from roots. Wing section NACA 64A012 mod. 5. Incidence 2°. Sweepback 6° 26′ on leading-edges, 1° 45′ at quarter-chord. One-piece all-metal stressed skin structure, with main spar and auxiliary spar; four-point attachment to fuselage. All-metal double-slotted trailing-edge flaps, operated by push/pull rods actuated by a

single hydraulic jack. Flaps retract automatically when airspeed reaches 167 knots (310 km/h; 193 mph). Small fence above and below each trailing-edge between flap and aileron. Mass balanced ailerons, each with electrically operated servo tab; port tab, used also for trim, is operated by electromechanical actuator. Non-jettisonable wingtip fuel tanks, incorporating landing/taxying lights.

FUSELAGE: Metal semi-monocoque structure, built in two portions. Front portion consists of three sections, the first of which is a laminated glassfibre nosecone housing avionics, antennae, battery, compressed air and oxygen bottles and the nose landing gear. Next comes the pressurised compartment for the crew. The third section incorporates the fuel tanks, air intakes and the engine bay. The rear fuselage, carrying the tail unit, is attached by five bolts and can be removed quickly to provide access for engine installation and removal. Two airbrakes side by side under fuselage, just forward of wing leading-edge, actuated by single hydraulic jack; these are lowered automatically as airspeed nears a maximum of Mach 0.8.

TAIL UNIT: Conventional all-metal cantilever structure, with sweepback on vertical surfaces. Variable incidence tailplane. Control surfaces actuated by pushrods. Electrically operated trim tab in each elevator; servo tab in rudder. Elevators deflect 30° up, 20° down; rudder 30° to right and left.

LANDING GEAR: Retractable tricycle type, with single wheel and oleo-pneumatic shock absorber on each unit. Gear is designed for a touchdown sink rate of 3.4 m (11.15 ft)/s at AUW of 4,600 kg (10,141 lb). Retraction/extension is operated hydraulically, with electrical control. All wheel well doors close automatically after wheels are lowered, to prevent ingress of dirt and debris. Mainwheels retract inward into wings (with automatic braking during retraction), nosewheel forward into fuselage. K24 mainwheels, fitted with Barum tubeless tyres size 610 × 215 mm (610 × 185 mm on early production aircraft), pressure 5.88 bars (85.34 lb/sq in). K25 castoring and self-centring nosewheel, fitted with Barum tubeless tyre size 450 × 165 mm (430 × 150 mm on early production aircraft), pressure 3.92 bars (56.89 lb/sq in). Hydraulic

disc brakes and anti-skid units on mainwheels; shimmy damper on nosewheel leg. The L-39 is capable of operation from grass strips (with a bearing strength of 6 kg/cm²; 85 lb/sq in) at up to 4,600 kg (10,141 lb) T-O weight, or from unprepared runways. Landing gear of L-39 ZA reinforced to cater for higher operating weights.

POWER PLANT: One 16.87 kN (3,792 lb st) Ivchenko AI-25 TL turbofan mounted in rear fuselage, with semi-circular lateral air intake, fitted with splitter plate, on each side of fuselage above wing centre-section. Fuel in five rubber main bag tanks aft of cockpit, with combined capacity of 1,055 litres (279 US gallons; 232 Imp gallons), and two 100 litre (26.5 US gallon; 22 Imp gallon) non-jettisonable wingtip tanks. Total internal fuel capacity 1,255 litres (332 US gallons; 276 Imp gallons). Gravity refuelling points on top of fuselage and on each tip tank. Provision for two 350 litre (92.5 US gallon; 77 Imp gallon) drop tanks on inboard underwing pylons, increasing total overall fuel capacity to a maximum of 1,955 litres (517 US gallons; 430 Imp gallons). Fuel system permits up to 20 s of inverted flight.

ACCOMMODATION: Crew of two in tandem, on Czechoslovak VS-1-BRI rocket assisted ejection seats, operable at zero height and at speeds down to 81 knots (150 km/h; 94 mph), beneath individual transparent canopies which hinge sideways to starboard and are jettisonable. Rear seat elevated. One-piece windscreen hinges forward to provide access to front instrument panel. Internal transparency between cockpits. Dual controls standard.

SYSTEMS: Cabin pressurised (standard pressure differential 0.227 bars; 3.29 lb/sq in, max overpressure 0.29 bars; 4.20 lb/sq in) and air-conditioned, using engine bleed air and cooling unit. Air-conditioning system provides automatic temperature control from 10° to 25°C at ambient air temperatures from −55°C to +45°C. Main and standby interconnected hydraulic systems, the main system having a variable flow pump with an operating pressure of 147 bars (2,133 lb/sq in) for actuation of landing gear, flaps, airbrakes, ram air turbine and (at 34.3 bars; 500 lb/sq in pressure) wheel brakes. Emergency system, for all of above except airbrakes, incorporates three accumulators. Pneumatic canopy seals supplied by a 2 litre compressed air bottle in nose (pressure 147 bars; 2,133 lb/sq in). Electrical system (27V DC) is powered by a 7.5kVA engine driven generator. If primary generator fails, a V 910 ram air turbine is extended automatically into the airstream and generates up to 3kVA of emergency power for essential services. 12V 28Ah SAM 28 lead-acid battery for standby power and for APU starting. Two 800VA static inverters (the first for radio equipment, ice warning lights, engine vibration measurement and air-conditioning, the second for navigation and landing systems, IFF and air-to-air missiles) provide 115V single-phase AC power at 400Hz. A second circuit incorporates a 500VA rotary inverter and 40VA static inverter to provide 36V three-phase AC power, also at 400Hz. Saphir 5 APU and SV-25 turbine for engine starting. Air intakes and windscreen anti-iced by engine bleed air; normally, anti-icing is sensor-activated automatically, but a manual standby system is also provided. Six-bottle oxygen system for crew, pressure 147 bars (2,133 lb/sq in).

AVIONICS AND EQUIPMENT: Standard avionics include R-832 M two-band com radio (VHF 118-140MHz; UHF 220-389MHz); SPU-9 crew intercom; RKL-41 ADF (150-1,800kHz); RV-5 radar altimeter; MRP-56 P/S marker beacon receiver; SRO-2 IFF; and RSBN-5S navigation and landing system. VOR/ILS system available at

Aero L-39 Z0 Albatros two-seat basic and advanced jet trainer *(Pilot Press)*

customer's option. Landing and taxying light in forward end of each tip tank.

ARMAMENT (L-39 Z0 and ZA): Underfuselage pod on ZA only, below front cockpit, housing a single 23 mm Soviet GSh-23 two-barrelled cannon; ammunition for this gun (max 150 rds) is housed in fuselage, above gun pod. Gun/rocket firing and weapon release controls, including electrically controlled ASP-3 NMU-39 Z gyroscopic gunsight and FKP-2-2 gun camera, in front cockpit only (no FKP-2-2 in L-39 V). Z0 and ZA have four underwing hardpoints, the inboard pair each stressed for loads of up to 500 kg (1,102 lb) and the outer pair for loads of up to 250 kg (551 lb) each; max underwing stores load 1,100 kg (2,425 lb). Non-jettisonable pylons, each comprising a D3-57D stores rack. Typical underwing stores can include various combinations of bombs (two 500 kg, four 250 kg or six 100 kg); four UB-16-57 M pods each containing sixteen S-5 57 mm air-to-surface rockets; infra-red air-to-air missiles (outer pylons only); a five-camera day reconnaissance pod (port inboard pylon only); or (on inboard stations only) two 350 litre (92.5 US gallon; 77 Imp gallon) drop tanks.

DIMENSIONS, EXTERNAL:

Wing span	9.46 m (31 ft 0½ in)
Wing chord (mean)	2.15 m (7 ft 0½ in)
Wing aspect ratio: geometric	4.4
incl tip tanks	5.2
Length overall	12.13 m (39 ft 9½ in)
Height overall	4.77 m (15 ft 7¾ in)
Tailplane span	4.40 m (14 ft 5 in)
Wheel track	2.44 m (8 ft 0 in)
Wheelbase	4.39 m (14 ft 4¾ in)

AREAS:

Wings, gross	18.80 m² (202.36 sq ft)
Ailerons (total)	1.23 m² (13.26 sq ft)
Trailing-edge flaps (total)	2.68 m² (28.89 sq ft)
Airbrakes (total)	0.50 m² (5.38 sq ft)
Fin	2.60 m² (27.99 sq ft)
Rudder, incl tab	0.91 m² (9.80 sq ft)
Tailplane	3.93 m² (42.30 sq ft)
Elevators, incl tabs	1.14 m² (12.27 sq ft)

WEIGHTS AND LOADINGS:

Weight empty, equipped: C	3,455 kg (7,617 lb)
Z0	3,480 kg (7,672 lb)
ZA	3,565 kg (7,859 lb)
Fuel load: fuselage tanks	824 kg (1,816 lb)
wingtip tanks	156 kg (344 lb)
Max external stores load: C	284 kg (626 lb)
Z0	1,150 kg (2,535 lb)
ZA	1,290 kg (2,844 lb)
T-O weight clean: C	4,525 kg (9,976 lb)
Z0	4,550 kg (10,031 lb)
ZA	4,635 kg (10,218 lb)
Max T-O weight: C	4,700 kg (10,362 lb)
Z0 and ZA	5,600 kg (12,346 lb)
Max wing loading: C	250.0 kg/m² (51.23 lb/sq ft)
Z0 and ZA	297.9 kg/m² (61.01 lb/sq ft)
Max power loading: C	278.6 kg/kN (2.73 lb/lb st)
Z0 and ZA	332.0 kg/kN (3.25 lb/lb st)

PERFORMANCE (C at clean T-O weight of 4,500 kg; 9,921 lb, Z0 and ZA at max T-O weight):

Max limiting Mach number	0.80
Max level speed at S/L:	
C	378 knots (700 km/h; 435 mph)
Z0 and ZA	329 knots (610 km/h; 379 mph)
Max level speed at 5,000 m (16,400 ft)	
C	405 knots (750 km/h; 466 mph)
Z0 and ZA	340 knots (630 km/h; 391 mph)
Stalling speed: C	90 knots (165 km/h; 103 mph)
Z0 and ZA	103 knots (190 km/h; 118 mph)
Max rate of climb at S/L: C	1,260 m (4,130 ft)/min
Z0 and ZA	810 m (2,657 ft)/min

Time to 5,000 m (16,400 ft): C	5 min
Z0 and ZA	10 min
Service ceiling: C	11,000 m (36,100 ft)
Z0 and ZA	7,500 m (24,600 ft)
T-O run (concrete): C	530 m (1,740 ft)
Z0 and ZA	970 m (3,182 ft)
Landing run (concrete): C	650 m (2,135 ft)
Z0 and ZA	800 m (2,625 ft)

Range at 7,000 m (22,975 ft):
C, 980 kg (2,160 lb) max internal fuel
593 nm (1,100 km; 683 miles)
C, 1,524 kg (3,360 lb) max internal and external fuel
944 nm (1,750 km; 1,087 miles)

Endurance at 7,000 m (22,975 ft):

C, max internal fuel as above	2 h 30 min
C, max internal/external fuel as above	3 h 50 min

g limits:

operational, at 4,200 kg (9,259 lb) AUW	+8/-4
ultimate, at 4,200 kg (9,259 lb) AUW	+12
operational, at 5,500 kg (12,125 lb) AUW	+5.2/-2.6

AERO L-39 MS

The L-39 MS first prototype X22 (OK-184) first flew on 30 September 1986. Two further prototypes, designated X24 and X25, flown on 26 June and 6 October 1987, and the first production L-39 MS flew on 1 October 1989.

Major changes concern the wings, power plant and avionics.

TYPE: Two-seat advanced jet trainer.

WINGS: Similar in planform and construction to L-39 C, main differences being a NACA 64₁A012 (modified) aerofoil section and shorter span. Ailerons and trailing-edge flaps are of light alloy/sandwich construction, ailerons having a Czechoslovak designed irreversible power control system and no tabs.

FUSELAGE: Generally as described for L-39 C, but with more pointed nose section.

TAIL UNIT: Similar to that of L-39 C, but fixed incidence tailplane and irreversible power control system for elevators.

LANDING GEAR: Czechoslovak design gas/oil shock absorption; K 36 mainwheels (610 × 215 mm) and K 37 nosewheel (460 × 180 mm). Mainwheel tyre pressures 6.0 bars (87 lb/sq in) on training version, 8.0 bars (116 lb/sq in) on combat version; corresponding nosewheel tyre pressures are 3.5 bars (51 lb/sq in) and 4.5 bars (65 lb/sq in) respectively. Nose unit steerable ±60°. Six-piston, aircooled hydraulic disc brakes on mainwheels, plus electronic anti-skid units. Otherwise generally as described for L-39 C.

POWER PLANT: One 21.57 kN (4,850 lb st) Lotarev/ZVL DV-2 turbofan. Internal fuel in fuselage tanks and two 115 litre (30.4 US gallon; 25.3 Imp gallon) non-jettisonable wingtip tanks. Provision for two underwing (inboard) 350 litre (92.5 US gallon; 77 Imp gallon) drop tanks.

ACCOMMODATION: Crew of two in tandem, on Czechoslovak VS-2 zero/zero ejection seats. Individual canopies hinged at rear and open upward.

SYSTEMS: Air-conditioning and pressurisation as described for L-39 C. Main and standby interconnected hydraulic systems (two pumps), operating pressure 150 bars (2,175 lb/sq in). No pneumatic system. Main and standby generators for electrical power, plus DC battery. Gaseous oxygen system for crew. Saphir APU for engine starting and standby drive of hydraulic pump and generator.

AVIONICS AND EQUIPMENT: Include LPR-80 two-band com radio, LUN-3524 standby radio, RKL-52 ADF, RSBN radio navigation and landing system, and head-up/head-down display.

ARMAMENT: As described for L-39 Z0 and ZA.

DIMENSIONS, EXTERNAL: As for L-39 C except:

Wing span: excl tip tanks	9.16 m (30 ft 0½ in)
incl tip tanks	9.54 m (31 ft 3½ in)
Wing chord: at root	2.80 m (9 ft 2¼ in)
at tip	1.40 m (4 ft 7 in)

AREA: As for L-39 C except:

Ailerons (total)	1.52 m² (16.36 sq ft)

WEIGHTS:

Manufacturer's bare weight	4,150 kg (9,149 lb)
Basic operating weight empty	5,510 kg (12,147 lb)
Max fuel load:	
internal, incl wingtip tanks	1,200 kg (2,645 lb)
external (2 drop tanks)	544 kg (1,199 lb)
Max T-O weight	7,000 kg (15,432 lb)
Max landing weight	5,500 kg (12,125 lb)

PERFORMANCE (at max T-O weight):

Max limiting Mach number	0.82
Max level speed at 5,000 m (16,400 ft)	473 knots (876 km/h; 544 mph)
Stalling speed: flaps up	111 knots (205 km/h; 128 mph)
flaps down	92 knots (170 km/h; 106 mph)
Max rate of climb at S/L	1,560 m (5,120 ft)/min
Service ceiling	11,730 m (38,500 ft)
Min ground turning radius (from nosewheel)	2.50 m (8 ft 2 in)
T-O run	620 m (2,035 ft)
Landing run	650 m (2,135 ft)

Range at 9,000 m (29,530 ft) with max internal and external fuel 809 nm (1,500 km; 932 miles)

Aero L-39 MS, the latest variant of this successful Czechoslovak jet trainer (*Jane's/Mike Keep*, **redrawn** from *Letectvi + Kosmonautika*)

LET

LET KONCERNOVÝ PODNIK (Let Concern Enterprise)

Uherské Hradiste-Kunovice
Telephone: 42 (5) 411111
Telex: 060387 and 060388
MANAGING DIRECTOR: Ing Stanislav Boura
TECHNICAL DIRECTOR: Ing Zdeněk Karásek
CHIEF DESIGNER: Ing Vlastimil Mertl

The Let plant at Kunovice was established in 1950, its early activities including licence production of the Soviet Yak-11 trainer under the Czechoslovak designation C-11. It is currently responsible for the L-410UVP-E light transport aircraft and development of the larger L-610. The factory also produces equipment for radar and computer technology.

LET L-410UVP-E

Details of the prototypes and initial production versions of the Turbolet can be found in the 1980-81 and earlier editions of *Jane's*.

The L-410UVP, first flown on 1 November 1977, introduced a number of major changes (see previous editions for details), becoming in 1980 the first non-USSR aircraft to receive a type certificate under Soviet NLGS-2 airworthiness regulations. Stringent Aeroflot requirements

included the ability to operate in temperatures ranging from −50°C to +45°C; systems were required to be survivable in temperatures as low as −60°C. Production of the UVP, in four models, ended in late 1985 and totalled 495.

A prototype of the improved L-410UVP-E (OK-120) was flown on 30 December 1984 and went into production in 1985, replacing the UVP. It received NLGS-2 Soviet certification in March 1986, and Let had delivered 287 examples by 1 January 1990. In this version the rear fuselage has the baggage and toilet compartments moved further aft, creating space for four additional seats without increasing overall length. The wings are reinforced to support two optional streamlined wingtip tanks, enabling range to be increased by more than 40 per cent. Maximum flap deflection is increased compared with the UVP, and the spoilers have two fixed deflection angles: 25° (for use in flight) and 72°. Power plant associated changes include a vacuum sintered oil cooler of new design, an oil-to-fuel heat exchanger on each engine firewall to avoid the need for fuel additives at low ambient temperatures, relocation of the engine fire extinguishing bottles under the port rear wing/fuselage fairing, and on the instrument panel, separate speed indicators for each engine and propeller. Cabin improvements include installation of portable oxygen equipment and an improved PA system; a fire extinguishing system is installed in the nose baggage compartment. The

aircraft can be operated in temperatures ranging from −50°C to +50°C. Its design life is 20,000 flying hours or 20,000 landings.

Altogether, 937 L-410s of all versions had been produced for civil and military use by 1 January 1990. Several hundred more are believed to be required by the Soviet Union.

The following description applies to the L-410UVP-E:

TYPE: Twin-turboprop general purpose light transport.

WINGS: Cantilever high-wing monoplane. Wing section NACA 63A418 at root, NACA 63A412 at tip. Dihedral 1° 45′. Incidence 2° at root, −0° 30′ at tip. No sweepback at front spar. Conventional all-metal two-spar torsion box structure, attached to fuselage by four-point mountings. Chemically machined skin with longitudinal reinforcement. Hydraulically actuated two-section double-slotted metal flaps. Spoiler forward of each flap. All-metal ailerons, forward of which are 'pop-up' bank control surfaces that come into operation automatically during single-engine operation and decrease the lift on the side of the running engine. Tab in port aileron. Kléber-Colombes pneumatic de-icing of leading-edges.

FUSELAGE: Conventional all-metal semi-monocoque spot welded and riveted structure, built in three main portions.

TAIL UNIT: Conventional cantilever structure, of all-metal construction except for elevators and rudder, which are

Polish-registered L-410UVP-E twin-turboprop transport, in air ambulance configuration

Let L-410UVP-E twin-turboprop 19-passenger light transport (*Pilot Press*)

fabric covered. Vertical tail surfaces sweptback 35°; shallow dorsal fin and deeper ventral fin. One-piece tailplane, with 7° dihedral from roots, mounted part-way up fin. Balance tab in rudder and each elevator. Kléber-Colombes pneumatic de-icing of leading-edges.

LANDING GEAR: Retractable tricycle type, with single wheel on each unit. Hydraulic retraction, nosewheel forward, mainwheels inward to lie flat in fairing on each side of fuselage. Technometra Radotin oleo-pneumatic shock absorbers. Non-braking nosewheel, with servo-assisted steering, fitted with 548 × 221 mm (9.00-6) tubeless tyre, pressure 4.5 bars (65 lb/sq in). Nosewheel is also steerable by rudder pedals. Mainwheels fitted with 718 × 306 mm (12.50-10) tubeless tyres, pressure 4.5 bars (65 lb/sq in). All wheels manufactured by Moravan Otrokovice, tyres by Rudy Rijen, Gottwaldow. Moravan Otrokovice K38-3200.00 hydraulic disc brakes, parking brake and anti-skid units on mainwheels. Metal ski landing gear, with plastics undersurface, optional.

POWER PLANT: Two 559 kW (750 shp) Motorlet Walter M 601 E turboprops, each driving an Avia V 510 five-blade constant-speed reversible-pitch metal propeller with manual and automatic feathering and Beta control. At higher ambient temperatures, engine power can be increased to 603 kW (809 ehp) for short periods by water injection into compressor. De-icing for propeller blades (electrical) and lower intakes (bleed air); anti-icing flaps inside each nacelle. Eight bag fuel tanks in wings, total capacity 1,290 litres (341 US gallons; 284 Imp gallons), plus additional optional 200 litres (52.8 US gallons; 44 Imp gallons) of fuel in each wingtip tank. Fuel system operable after failure of electrical system. Total oil capacity (incl oil in cooler) 22 litres (5.8 US gallons; 4.8 Imp gallons). Water tank capacity (for injection into compressor) 11 litres (2.9 US gallons; 2.4 Imp gallons).

ACCOMMODATION: Crew of one or two on flight deck, with dual controls. Electric de-icing for windscreen. Standard accommodation in main cabin for 19 passengers, with pairs of adjustable seats on starboard side of aisle and single seats opposite, all at 76 cm (30 in) pitch. Baggage compartment (at rear, accessible from cabin), toilet and wardrobe standard. Cabin heated by engine bleed air. Alternative layouts include all-cargo; ambulance, accommodating six stretchers, five sitting patients and a medical attendant; accommodation for 18 parachutists and a dispatcher/instructor; firefighting configuration, carrying 16 firefighters and a pilot/observer. All-cargo version has protective floor covering, crash nets on each side of cabin, and tiedown provisions; floor is at truckbed height. Aircraft can also be equipped for aerial photography or for calibration of ground navigation aids. Double upward opening doors aft on port side, with stowable steps; right hand door serves as passenger entrance and exit. Both doors open for cargo loading, and can be removed for paratroop training missions.

Rearward opening door, forward on starboard side, serves as emergency exit.

SYSTEMS: No APU, air-conditioning or pressurisation systems. Duplicated hydraulic systems, No. 1 system actuating landing gear, flaps, spoilers, automatic pitch trim surfaces, mainwheel brakes, nosewheel steering and windscreen wipers. No. 2 system for emergency landing gear extension, flap actuation and parking brake. 28V DC electrical system supplied by two 5.6kW starter/generators, connected for autonomous starting, plus two 25V 25Ah batteries for emergency power. Two input systems for AC power (three-phase 200V/115Hz, variable frequency), incorporating two 3.7kW alternators with alternator control unit. Port alternator provides for windscreen heating, starboard one for propeller blade de-icing. Two static inverters provide three-phase 36V/400Hz AC. Two 115V/400Hz inverters. One three-phase 36V/400Hz static inverter for standby horizon. Two portable oxygen breathing sets on flight deck and two in passenger cabin. Fire extinguishing system for engines and nose baggage compartment.

AVIONICS AND EQUIPMENT: Standard instrumentation provides for flight in IMC conditions, with all basic instruments duplicated and three artificial horizons.

Communications include two VHF transceivers with a range of 65 nm (120 km; 75 miles) at 1,000 m (3,280 ft) altitude, passenger address system and crew intercom. Standard instruments include LUN 1205 horizon gyros, rate of climb indicators, LUN 1215 turn and bank indicator, RMIs, gyro compasses, ILS/SP-50A instrument landing system with marker beacon receiver, dual ARK-22 ADF, A-037 radio altimeter, SO-69 SSR transponder with encoding altimeter, ASI with stall warning, magnetic compass, GMK-1GE VOR, and BUR-1-2G flight data recorder. Cockpit, instrument and passenger cabin lights, navigation lights, three landing lights in nose (each with two levels of light intensity), crew and cabin fire extinguishers, windscreen wipers, and alcohol spray for windscreen and wiper de-icing, are also standard. Weather radar and VZLU autopilot optional.

DIMENSIONS, EXTERNAL:

Wing span: over tip tanks	19.98 m (65 ft 6½ in)
excl tip tanks	19.48 m (63 ft 11 in)
Wing chord at root	2.534 m (8 ft 3¾ in)
Length overall	14.424 m (47 ft 4 in)
Fuselage: Max width	2.08 m (6 ft 10 in)
Max depth	2.10 m (6 ft 10¾ in)
Height overall	5.83 m (19 ft 1½ in)
Tailplane span	6.74 m (22 ft 1¼ in)
Wheel track	3.65 m (11 ft 11½ in)
Wheelbase	3.67 m (12 ft 0¼ in)
Propeller diameter	2.30 m (7 ft 6½ in)
Propeller ground clearance	1.26 m (4 ft 1½ in)
Distance between propeller centres	4.82 m (15 ft 9½ in)
Passenger/cargo door (port, rear):	
Height	1.46 m (4 ft 9½ in)
Width overall	1.25 m (4 ft 1¼ in)
Width (passenger door only)	0.80 m (2 ft 7½ in)
Height to sill	0.70 m (2 ft 3½ in)
Emergency exit door (stbd, fwd):	
Height	0.97 m (3 ft 2¼ in)
Width	0.66 m (2 ft 2 in)
Height to sill	0.80 m (2 ft 7½ in)

DIMENSIONS, INTERNAL:

Cabin, excl flight deck:	
Length	6.345 m (20 ft 9¾ in)
Max width	1.95 m (6 ft 4¾ in)
Max height	1.66 m (5 ft 5¼ in)
Aisle width at 0.4 m (1 ft 3¾ in) above cabin floor	
	0.34 m (1 ft 1½ in)
Floor area	10.0 m² (107.6 sq ft)
Volume	17.9 m³ (632.1 cu ft)
Baggage compartment volume:	
nose	0.60 m³ (21.19 cu ft)
rear	0.77 m³ (27.19 cu ft)

AREAS:

Wings, gross	35.18 m² (378.67 sq ft)
Ailerons (total)	2.89 m² (31.11 sq ft)
Automatic bank control flaps (total)	
	0.49 m² (5.27 sq ft)
Trailing-edge flaps (total)	5.92 m² (63.72 sq ft)
Spoilers (total)	0.87 m² (9.36 sq ft)
Fin	4.49 m² (48.33 sq ft)
Rudder, incl tab	2.81 m² (30.25 sq ft)
Tailplane	6.41 m² (69.00 sq ft)
Elevators, incl tabs	3.15 m² (33.91 sq ft)

WEIGHTS AND LOADINGS:

Weight empty	3,985 kg (8,785 lb)
Operating weight empty, equipped	4,160 kg (9,171 lb)
Max fuel	1,300 kg (2,866 lb)
Max payload	1,615 kg (3,560 lb)
Max ramp weight	6,420 kg (14,154 lb)
Max T-O weight	6,400 kg (14,110 lb)
Max zero-fuel weight	5,775 kg (12,732 lb)

Hungarian-registered L-410UVP with blister window at rear of flight deck. Fairings and pods on rear fuselage, beneath the rudder and at the wingtips, are for aerial photogrammetry equipment

First prototype of the Let L-610 (two Motorlet M 602 turboprops), expected to achieve certification by the end of 1990

Max landing weight	6,200 kg (13,668 lb)
Max wing loading	181.9 kg/m² (37.26 lb/sq ft)
Max power loading	5.38 kg/kW (8.93 lb/ehp)

PERFORMANCE (at max T-O weight):
Never-exceed speed
192 knots (357 km/h; 222 mph) EAS
Max level speed at 4,200 m (13,780 ft)
168 knots (311 km/h; 193 mph) EAS
Max cruising speed at 4,200 m (13,780 ft)
205 knots (380 km/h; 236 mph)
Econ cruising speed at 4,200 m (13,780 ft)
197 knots (365 km/h; 227 mph)
Stalling speed:
flaps up   84 knots (155 km/h; 97 mph) EAS
flaps down   66 knots (121 km/h; 76 mph) EAS
Max rate of climb at S/L   444 m (1,455 ft)/min
Rate of climb at S/L, one engine out   108 m (354 ft)/min
Service ceiling: practical   6,320 m (20,725 ft)
theoretical   7,050 m (23,125 ft)
Service ceiling, one engine out:
practical   2,700 m (8,860 ft)
theoretical   3,980 m (13,050 ft)
T-O run   445 m (1,460 ft)
T-O to 10.7 m (35 ft)   685 m (2,250 ft)
Landing from 9 m (30 ft)   480 m (1,575 ft)
Landing run   240 m (787 ft)
Min ground turning radius   13.40 m (43 ft 11½ in)
Range at 4,200 m (13,780 ft), max cruising speed, 30 min
reserves:
with max payload   294 nm (546 km; 339 miles)
with max fuel and 885 kg (1,951 lb) payload
744 nm (1,380 km; 857 miles)

LET L-610

Intended for certification in 1990 under Soviet ENLG-S civil airworthiness requirements, the L-610 is designed for short-haul operations over stage lengths of 216-324 nm (400-600 km; 248-373 miles). The first prototype (OK-130) flew on 28 December 1988. Five development aircraft have been built: the first, third and fifth for flight trials, the second for static test and the fourth for fatigue testing. Certification was expected in late 1990, with deliveries (initially to Aeroflot) beginning in 1991. There is said to be a Soviet requirement for 600 L-610s, to replace Aeroflot Yak-40s and An-24s.

General Electric has an agreement to supply its CT7-9B turboprop to Czechoslovakia, and an L-610 fitted with this power plant is expected to make its first flight in mid-1991, followed by certification in 1992.

TYPE: Twin-turboprop transport aircraft.
WINGS: Cantilever high-wing monoplane. Wing sections MS(1)-0318D at root, MS(1)-0312 at tip, with respective thickness/chord ratios of 18.29 and 12 per cent. Dihedral 2°. Incidence 3.144° at root, 0° at tip. Sweepback 1° at quarter-chord. All-metal fail-safe stressed skin structure, built of high grade aluminium alloys and high strength steel and incorporating sandwich panels. All-metal horn balanced ailerons and single-slotted Fowler trailing-edge flaps. Spoiler, of sandwich construction, forward of each outer flap segment. Electro-mechanically actuated trim tab in port aileron. Pneumatic boot de-icing of leading-edges.
FUSELAGE: Pressurised all-metal semi-monocoque structure (except for nose and tailcones), incorporating fail-safe principles. Central portion has a constant circular cross-section.
TAIL UNIT: All-metal structure, with sweptback fin and rudder and long dorsal fin. Non-swept tailplane and elevators mounted near top of fin. Trim tab and spring

balance tab in rudder, trim tab and geared tab in each elevator. Pneumatic boot de-icing of fin and tailplane leading-edges.
LANDING GEAR: Retractable tricycle type, with single wheel on each unit. Hydraulic actuation, mainwheels retracting inward to lie flat in fairing each side of fuselage, nosewheel retracting forward. Oleo-pneumatic shock absorber in each unit. Mainwheels are type XK 34-3000.00, with 1,050 × 390 × 480 mm tyres; type XR 25-1000.00 nosewheel has a 720 × 310 × 254 mm tyre. Hydraulic disc brakes and electronically controlled anti-skid units.
POWER PLANT: Two 1,358 kW (1,822 shp) Motorlet M 602 turboprops, each driving an Avia V 518 five-blade fully-feathering metal propeller with reversible pitch. Fuel in two integral wing tanks, combined usable capacity 3,500 litres (925 US gallons; 770 Imp gallons). Pressure refuelling point in fuselage, gravity points in wings. Oil capacity 30 litres (7.9 US gallons; 6.6 Imp gallons).
ACCOMMODATION: Crew of two on flight deck, plus one cabin attendant. Standard accommodation for 40 passengers, four-abreast at seat pitch of 75 cm (29.5 in). Aisle width 51 cm (20 in). Galley, two wardrobes, toilet, freight and baggage compartment, all located at rear of cabin. Alternative mixed (passenger/cargo) and all-cargo layouts available. Passenger door at rear of fuselage, freight door at front, both opening outward on port side. Outward opening service door on starboard side, opposite passenger door, serving also as emergency exit; outward opening emergency exit beneath wing on each side. Entire accommodation pressurised and air-conditioned.
SYSTEMS: Bootstrap type air-conditioning system. Max operating cabin pressure differential 0.3 bars (4.35 lb/sq in). Duplicated hydraulic systems (one main and one standby), operating at pressure of 210 bars (3,045 lb/sq in). APU in tailcone, for engine starting and auxiliary on-ground and in-flight power. Electrical system powered by two 115/200V 25kVA variable frequency AC generators, plus a third 8kVA 115/200V three-phase AC generator driven by APU. System also includes two 115V 400Hz inverters (each 1.5kVA), two 27V DC

transformer-rectifiers (each 4.5kW), and a 25Ah nickel-cadmium battery for APU starting and auxiliary power supply. Portable oxygen equipment for crew and 10 per cent of passengers. Pneumatic de-icing of wing and tail unit leading-edges, engine inlets and oil cooler; electric de-icing of propeller blade roots, windscreen, pitot static system and horn balances.
AVIONICS AND EQUIPMENT: Equipped with dual 760-channel VHF com, single HF com (optional), intercom, cabin address system, weather radar, blind-flying instrumentation, dual ILS with two LOC/glideslope receivers and two marker beacon receivers, single or dual ADF, Doppler radar, navigation computer, dual compasses, single or dual radio altimeters, transponder, autopilot, voice recorder, flight recorder, and Cat. II approach aids.

DIMENSIONS, EXTERNAL:
Wing span	25.60 m (84 ft 0 in)
Wing chord: at root	2.917 m (9 ft 6⅞ in)
at tip	1.458 m (4 ft 9½ in)
Wing aspect ratio	11.7
Length overall	21.419 m (70 ft 3¼ in)
Fuselage: Length	20.533 m (67 ft 4⅜ in)
Max diameter	2.70 m (8 ft 10¼ in)
Distance between propeller centres	7.00 m (22 ft 11½ in)
Height overall	7.608 m (24 ft 11½ in)
Tailplane span	7.908 m (25 ft 11⅓ in)
Wheel track	4.59 m (15 ft 0¾ in)
Wheelbase	6.596 m (21 ft 7¾ in)
Propeller diameter	3.50 m (11 ft 5¾ in)
Propeller/fuselage clearance	0.59 m (1 ft 11¼ in)
Propeller ground clearance	1.64 m (5 ft 4½ in)
Passenger door: Height	1.625 m (5 ft 4 in)
Width	0.76 m (2 ft 6 in)
Height to sill	1.448 m (4 ft 9 in)
Freight door: Height	1.30 m (4 ft 3¼ in)
Width	1.25 m (4 ft 1¼ in)
Height to sill	1.448 m (4 ft 9 in)
Service door: Height	1.286 m (4 ft 2⅔ in)
Width	0.61 m (2 ft 0 in)
Emergency exits (underwing, each):	
Height	0.915 m (3 ft 0 in)
Width	0.515 m (1 ft 8¼ in)

Let L-610 twin-turboprop 40-seat commuter transport *(Pilot Press)*

DIMENSIONS, INTERNAL:
Cabin (excl flight deck): Length	11.10 m (36 ft 5 in)
Max width	2.54 m (8 ft 4 in)
Width at floor	2.02 m (6 ft 7½ in)
Max height	1.825 m (5 ft 11⅞ in)
Floor area	22.4 m² (241.1 sq ft)
Volume	44.1 m³ (1,557.4 cu ft)
Wardrobe volume (total)	1.0 m³ (35.3 cu ft)
Baggage/freight hold volume (total)	4.3 m³ (151.8 cu ft)

AREAS:
Wings, gross	56.0 m² (602.8 sq ft)
Ailerons (total)	3.27 m² (35.20 sq ft)
Trailing-edge flaps (total)	11.29 m² (121.52 sq ft)
Spoilers (total)	3.54 m² (38.10 sq ft)
Fin	8.30 m² (89.34 sq ft)
Rudder, incl tabs	5.54 m² (59.63 sq ft)
Tailplane	7.68 m² (82.67 sq ft)
Elevators (total, incl tabs)	5.82 m² (62.65 sq ft)

WEIGHTS AND LOADINGS:
Weight empty, equipped	8,730 kg (19,246 lb)

Operating weight empty	9,000 kg (19,841 lb)
Max fuel	2,650 kg (5,842 lb)
Max payload	3,800 kg (8,377 lb)
Max T-O weight	14,000 kg (30,865 lb)
Max ramp weight	14,040 kg (30,953 lb)
Max landing weight	13,500 kg (29,762 lb)
Max zero-fuel weight	12,800 kg (28,219 lb)
Max wing loading	250 kg/m² (51.2 lb/sq ft)
Max power loading	5.147 kg/kW (8.47 lb/shp)

PERFORMANCE (estimated at max T-O weight):
Never-exceed speed	216 knots (400 km/h; 248 mph) EAS
Max level and max cruising speed at 7,200 m (23,620 ft)	264 knots (490 km/h; 304 mph)
Long-range cruising speed at 7,200 m (23,620 ft)	220 knots (408 km/h; 253 mph)
Approach speed	92 knots (170 km/h; 106 mph)

Stalling speed:
flaps up	93 knots (172 km/h; 107 mph) EAS
flaps down	75 knots (139 km/h; 87 mph) EAS
Max rate of climb at S/L	570 m (1,870 ft)/min

Rate of climb at S/L, one engine out	150 m (492 ft)/min

Service ceiling:
theoretical	10,750 m (35,270 ft)
practical	10,250 m (33,630 ft)

Service ceiling, one engine out (30.5 m; 100 ft/min rate of climb):
theoretical	4,750 m (15,585 ft)
practical	3,980 m (13,060 ft)
Min ground turning radius	18.33 m (60 ft 1¾ in)
T-O run	370 m (1,214 ft)
T-O to 10.7 m (35 ft)	613 m (2,011 ft)
Balanced T-O distance	752 m (2,467 ft)

Balanced T-O field length:
hard runway	875 m (2,870 ft)
unpaved surface	1,030 m (3,380 ft)
Landing from 9 m (30 ft)	545 m (1,788 ft)
Landing run	340 m (1,115 ft)

Range, reserves for 45 min hold:
with max payload	469 nm (870 km; 540 miles)
with max fuel	1,298 nm (2,406 km; 1,495 miles)

ZLIN

MORAVAN NÁRODNÍ PODNIK (Zlin Aircraft Moravan National Corporation)

76581 Otrokovice
Telephone: 42/Gottwaldov 92 2041/44
Telex: Gottwaldov 067 240
MANAGING DIRECTOR: Ing Josef Panáček
CHIEF DESIGNER: Ing Vojtěch Vraj
VICE-DIRECTOR, SALES: František Mužný

The Moravan Company was formed on 18 September 1934 as Zlinská Letecká Akciová Spolecnost (Zlin Aviation Joint Stock Co) in Zlin, although manufacture of Zlin aircraft was actually started in 1933 by the Masarykova Letecká Liga (Masaryk League of Aviation). The factory was renamed Moravan after the Second World War. Moravan also manufactures items of aircraft equipment.

ZLIN 142

The Zlin 142 is employed for basic and advanced flying training, aerobatic flying and the training of aerobatic pilots, glider towing, and (when equipped with appropriate instrumentation) for night and IFR flying training. It is a progressive development of the Zlin 42 M (1980-81 *Jane's*), and first flew on 29 December 1978. In 1980 it received FAR Pt 23 certification in the Aerobatic, Utility and Normal categories, and production began in 1981. A total of 269 had been built by 1 January 1989. Exports have been made to Algeria (32), Bulgaria, Cuba, Germany (Democratic and Federal Republics), Hungary, Poland and Romania. Licence production in Algeria began in 1989.

TYPE: Two-seat fully aerobatic (A), light training (U) and touring (N) aircraft.

WINGS: Cantilever low-wing monoplane. Wing section NACA 63₂416.5. Dihedral 6° from roots. Sweepforward 4° 20′ at quarter-chord. All-metal structure with single main spar and auxiliary spar; skins (fluted on control surfaces) of aluminium plated duralumin sheet. All-metal slotted ailerons and flaps all have same dimensions. Mass balanced flaps and ailerons, operated mechanically by control rods. Ground adjustable tab on each aileron.

FUSELAGE: Engine cowlings of sheet metal. Centre-fuselage of welded steel tube truss construction, covered with laminated glassfibre panels. Rear fuselage is all-metal semi-monocoque structure.

TAIL UNIT: Cantilever all-metal structure with skins (fluted on control surfaces) of duralumin sheet. Control surfaces have partial mass and aerodynamic balance. Trim tabs on elevator and rudder. Rudder actuated by control cables, elevator by control rods.

LANDING GEAR: Non-retractable tricycle type, with nosewheel offset to port. Oleo-pneumatic nosewheel shock absorber. Mainwheels carried on flat spring steel legs. Nosewheel steered by rudder pedals. Mainwheels and Barum tyres size 420 × 150, pressure 1.90 bars (27.6 lb/sq in); nosewheel and Barum tyre size 350 × 135, pressure 2.50 bars (36.3 lb/sq in). Hydraulic disc brakes on mainwheels can be operated from either seat. Parking brake standard.

POWER PLANT: One 156.5 kW (210 hp) Avia M 337 AK inverted six-cylinder aircooled inline engine, with supercharger and low-pressure injection pump, driving a two-blade Avia V 500 A constant-speed metal propeller. Fuel tanks in each wing leading-edge, with combined capacity of 125 litres (33 US gallons; 27.5 Imp gallons). Normal category version has auxiliary 50 litre (13.2 US gallon; 11 Imp gallon) tank at each wingtip, increasing total fuel capacity to 225 litres (59.4 US gallons; 49.5 Imp gallons). Fuel and oil systems permit inverted flying for up to 3 min. Oil capacity 12 litres (3.2 US gallons; 2.6 Imp gallons).

ACCOMMODATION: Individual side by side seats for two persons, the instructor's seat being to port. Both seats are adjustable and permit the use of back-type parachutes. Baggage space aft of seats. Cabin and windscreen heating and ventilation standard. Forward sliding cockpit canopy. Dual controls standard.

Photograph and three-view drawing *(Pilot Press)* **of the two-seat Zlin 142**

SYSTEMS: Electrical system includes a 600W 27V engine driven generator and 24V 25Ah Teledyne battery. External power source can be used for starting the engine.

AVIONICS AND EQUIPMENT: VHF radio with IC (Mesit LUN 3524.20) and IFR instrumentation optional. Standard equipment includes cockpit, instrument and cabin lights; navigation lights; landing and taxying lights; and anti-collision light. Towing gear, for gliders of up to 500 kg (1,102 lb) weight, optional.

DIMENSIONS, EXTERNAL:
Wing span	9.16 m (30 ft 0½ in)
Wing aspect ratio	6.4
Wing chord (constant portion)	1.42 m (4 ft 8 in)
Length overall	7.33 m (24 ft 0½ in)
Height overall	2.75 m (9 ft 0¼ in)
Elevator span	2.904 m (9 ft 6⅓ in)
Wheel track	2.33 m (7 ft 7¾ in)
Wheelbase	1.66 m (5 ft 5¼ in)
Propeller diameter	2.00 m (6 ft 6¾ in)
Propeller ground clearance	0.40 m (1 ft 3¾ in)

DIMENSIONS, INTERNAL:
Cabin: Length	1.80 m (5 ft 10¾ in)
Max width	1.12 m (3 ft 8 in)
Max height	1.20 m (3 ft 11¼ in)
Baggage space	0.2 m³ (7.1 cu ft)

AREAS:
Wings, gross	13.15 m² (141.5 sq ft)
Ailerons (total)	1.408 m² (15.16 sq ft)
Trailing-edge flaps (total)	1.408 m² (15.16 sq ft)
Fin	0.54 m² (5.81 sq ft)
Rudder, incl tab	0.81 m² (8.72 sq ft)
Tailplane	1.23 m² (13.24 sq ft)
Elevator, incl tabs	1.36 m² (14.64 sq ft)

WEIGHTS AND LOADINGS (A: Aerobatic; U: Utility; N: Normal category):
Basic weight empty (all versions)	730 kg (1,609 lb)
Max T-O weight: A	970 kg (2,138 lb)
U	1,020 kg (2,248 lb)
N	1,090 kg (2,403 lb)
Max landing weight: A	970 kg (2,138 lb)
U	1,020 kg (2,248 lb)
N	1,050 kg (2,315 lb)
Max wing loading: A	73.76 kg/m² (15.11 lb/sq ft)
U	77.57 kg/m² (15.89 lb/sq ft)
N	82.89 kg/m² (16.98 lb/sq ft)
Max power loading: A	6.19 kg/kW (10.17 lb/hp)
U	6.51 kg/kW (10.69 lb/hp)
N	6.96 kg/kW (11.43 lb/hp)

PERFORMANCE (at max T-O weight):
Never-exceed speed (all versions)	179 knots (333 km/h; 206 mph) IAS

Max level speed at 500 m (1,640 ft):
A, U	125 knots (231 km/h; 143 mph)
N	122 knots (227 km/h; 141 mph)

Max cruising speed at 500 m (1,640 ft):
A, U	106 knots (197 km/h; 122 mph)
N	102 knots (190 km/h; 118 mph)

Econ cruising speed at 500 m (1,640 ft):
A	97 knots (180 km/h; 112 mph)

Stalling speed, flaps up:
A	56 knots (103 km/h; 64 mph) IAS
U	58 knots (107 km/h; 67 mph) IAS
N	60 knots (110 km/h; 69 mph) IAS

Stalling speed, T-O flap setting:
A	54 knots (99 km/h; 62 mph) IAS
U	56 knots (102 km/h; 64 mph) IAS
N	57 knots (105 km/h; 66 mph) IAS

Stalling speed, flaps down:
A	48 knots (88 km/h; 55 mph) IAS
U	50 knots (91 km/h; 57 mph) IAS
N	52 knots (95 km/h; 60 mph) IAS

Max rate of climb at S/L, ISA:
A	330 m (1,082 ft)/min
U	306 m (1,004 ft)/min
N	264 m (866 ft)/min

Service ceiling: A	5,000 m (16,400 ft)
U	4,700 m (15,425 ft)
N	4,300 m (14,100 ft)
T-O run: A	220 m (722 ft)
T-O to 15 m (50 ft): A	440 m (1,444 ft)
U	475 m (1,560 ft)
N	540 m (1,772 ft)
Landing from 15 m (50 ft): A	400 m (1,313 ft)
U	425 m (1,395 ft)
N	460 m (1,510 ft)
Landing run: A	190 m (624 ft)

Range at max cruising speed:
A, U	283 nm (525 km; 326 miles)
N	513 nm (950 km; 590 miles)
Max range: N	566 nm (1,050 km; 652 miles)
g limits: A	+6/−3.5
U	+5/−3
N	+3.8/−1.5

ZLIN 242 L

Introduced in 1990, the Zlin 242 L is a modified version of the Z 142 aimed at the North American market, subject to obtaining certification under FAR Pt 35. It is powered by a 149 kW (200 hp) Textron Lycoming AEIO-360-A1B6 flat-six engine, resulting in a shorter nose and non-sweptforward wings to offset the resultant shift in CG. A Hartzell two-blade propeller is fitted, and total fuel capacity is 220 litres (58 US gallons; 48.4 Imp gallons). Other known data include:

WEIGHTS (Aerobatic category):
Weight empty	710 kg (1,565 lb)
Max T-O weight	1,090 kg (2,403 lb)

PERFORMANCE (Aerobatic category):
Max level speed at 500 m (1,640 ft)
	113 knots (209 km/h; 130 mph)
Service ceiling	4,785 m (15,700 ft)
Range with max fuel	581 nm (1,077 km; 669 miles)
g limits	+6/−3.5

ZLIN Z 50 L

Full details of the original **Z 50 L**, with 194 kW (260 hp) Textron Lycoming AEIO-540-D4B5 engine, can be found in the 1982-83 *Jane's*. Series production is continuing of the more powerful **Z 50 LS**, and of the **Z 50 LA**, which is a modified L with propeller pitch control and a propeller speed governor. The LS was flown for the first time on 29 June 1981, and in the following year received FAR Pt 23 certification in the Aerobatic and Normal categories. It won the European Aerobatic Championships in 1983 and the World Championships in 1984 and 1986; in 1985 it came 1st and 2nd in the European Championships, and won nine of the first 22 places. A total of 57 Z 50 L, LA and LS had been delivered by 1 June 1989. Exports have been made to Bulgaria, Germany (Federal and Democratic Republics), Hungary, Italy, Poland, Romania and Spain.

Zlin 50 M single-seat aerobatic aircraft (Avia M 137 AZ inline engine) *(Vaclav Jukl/Letectvi + Kosmonautika)*

The following description applies to the Z 50 LS:

TYPE: Single-seat aerobatic aircraft.

WINGS: Cantilever low-wing monoplane. Wing section NACA 0018 at root, NACA 0012 at tip. Dihedral 1° 7′ 24″. All-metal structure, with single continuous main spar, rear auxiliary spar, and aluminium-clad duralumin skin. All-metal mass balanced ailerons, actuated by pushrods, occupy most of each trailing-edge. Ground adjustable tab on port outer aileron; automatic trim tab on each inboard aileron. No flaps. Provision for fitting wingtip fuel tanks for cross-country flights.

FUSELAGE: All-metal semi-monocoque structure with stressed duralumin skin.

TAIL UNIT: Conventional metal structure. Braced tailplane and fin duralumin covered, elevators and rudder fabric covered. One mechanically adjustable balance tab and one automatic trim tab on elevators; automatic balance tab on rudder. Elevators actuated by pushrods, rudder by cables.

LANDING GEAR: Non-retractable tailwheel type. Mainwheels carried on flat-spring titanium cantilever legs. Mechanical mainwheel brakes actuated by rudder pedals. Fully castoring tailwheel, with flat-spring shock absorption, has automatic locking device to maintain aircraft on a straight track during taxying, take-off and landing. Mainwheel tyres size 350 × 135 mm, pressure 2.5 bars (36 lb/sq in); tailwheel tyre size 200 × 80 mm, pressure 1.0 bar (14.5 lb/sq in). Mainwheel fairings optional.

POWER PLANT: One 224 kW (300 hp) Textron Lycoming AEIO-540-L1B5D flat-six engine, driving a Hoffmann HO-V123K-V/200AH three-blade constant-speed wooden propeller with spinner. Single main fuel tank in fuselage, aft of firewall, capacity 60 litres (15.9 US gallons; 13.2 Imp gallons). Auxiliary 50 litre (13.2 US gallon; 11 Imp gallon) tank can be attached to each wingtip for cross-country flights only. Fuel and oil systems designed for full aerobatic manoeuvres, including inverted flight. Oil capacity 12 litres (3.2 US gallons; 2.6 Imp gallons).

ACCOMMODATION: Single seat under fully transparent sideways opening (to starboard) bubble canopy, which can be jettisoned in an emergency. Seat and backrest are adjustable, and permit the use of a back type parachute. Cockpit ventilated by sliding panel in canopy.

SYSTEM: Electrical system includes a 24V LUN 2111 alternator as main power source and two 12Ah batteries. External power socket in fuselage side for engine starting.

AVIONICS: VHF radio optional.

DIMENSIONS, EXTERNAL:
Wing span	8.58 m (28 ft 1¾ in)
Wing span over tip tanks	9.03 m (29 ft 7½ in)
Wing chord: at root	1.73 m (5 ft 8¼ in)
at tip	1.21 m (3 ft 11¾ in)
Wing aspect ratio	5.9
Length overall (tail up)	6.62 m (21 ft 8¾ in)
Height over tail (static)	2.075 m (6 ft 9¾ in)
Elevator span	3.44 m (11 ft 3½ in)
Wheel track	1.90 m (6 ft 2¾ in)
Wheelbase	5.05 m (16 ft 7 in)
Propeller diameter	2.00 m (6 ft 6¾ in)
Propeller ground clearance (tail up)	0.31 m (1 ft 0¼ in)

AREAS:
Wings, gross	12.50 m² (134.55 sq ft)
Ailerons (total)	2.80 m² (30.14 sq ft)
Fin	0.59 m² (6.35 sq ft)
Rudder, incl tab	0.81 m² (8.72 sq ft)
Tailplane	1.66 m² (17.87 sq ft)
Elevators (total, incl tabs)	1.20 m² (12.92 sq ft)

WEIGHTS AND LOADINGS (A: Aerobatic, N: Normal category):
Weight empty: A	600 kg (1,322 lb)
N	610 kg (1,345 lb)
Max T-O weight: A	760 kg (1,675 lb)
N	840 kg (1,852 lb)
Max wing loading: A	60.8 kg/m² (12.45 lb/sq ft)
N	67.2 kg/m² (13.76 lb/sq ft)
Max power loading: A	3.40 kg/kW (5.58 lb/hp)
N	3.75 kg/kW (6.17 lb/hp)

PERFORMANCE (at max Aerobatic T-O weight):
Never-exceed speed
	181 knots (337 km/h; 209 mph) CAS

Max level speed at 500 m (1,640 ft), ISA
	166 knots (308 km/h; 191 mph)

Max cruising speed at 500 m (1,640 ft), ISA
	148 knots (275 km/h; 171 mph)

Stalling speed, engine idling
	56 knots (103 km/h; 81 mph) CAS
Max rate of climb at S/L, ISA	840 m (2,755 ft)/min
Service ceiling, ISA	8,175 m (26,820 ft)
T-O run	150 m (492 ft)
T-O to 15 m (50 ft)	300 m (985 ft)
Landing from 15 m (50 ft)	530 m (1,740 ft)
Landing run	300 m (985 ft)
g limits: A	+8/−6
N	+3.8/−1.5

ZLIN Z 50 M

Intended as a successor to the Z 526AFS Akrobat (1975-76 *Jane's*), the Z 50 M has a longer and slimmer nose than the L series, accommodating a 134 kW (180 hp) Avia M 137 AZ six-cylinder inline engine driving an Avia V 503 A two-blade constant-speed propeller. First flight was made on 25 April 1988. One prototype (OK-080) and two production examples (of 15 ordered) had been built by 1 January 1989. Certification (Aerobatic and Normal categories) was granted in February 1989.

The description of the Z 50 LS applies also to the Z 50 M, except as follows:

DIMENSION, EXTERNAL:
Length overall	6.96 m (22 ft 10 in)

AREA:
Tailplane	2.24 m² (24.1 sq ft)

WEIGHTS AND LOADINGS (A: Aerobatic, N: Normal category):
Weight empty: A	540 kg (1,190 lb)
N	550 kg (1,212 lb)
Max T-O and landing weight: A	700 kg (1,543 lb)
N	780 kg (1,719 lb)
Max wing loading: A	56.0 kg/m² (11.48 lb/sq ft)
N	62.4 kg/m² (12.78 lb/sq ft)
Max power loading: A	5.22 kg/kW (8.57 lb/hp)
N	5.81 kg/kW (9.55 lb/hp)

Zlin Z 50 LS single-seat aerobatic light aircraft

PERFORMANCE (at max Aerobatic T-O weight):
Never-exceed speed
170 knots (315 km/h; 195 mph) CAS
Max level speed at S/L 136 knots (252 km/h; 156 mph)
Max cruising speed at 1,000 m (3,280 ft)
114 knots (211 km/h; 131 mph)
Stalling speed 54 knots (100 km/h; 63 mph)
Max rate of climb at S/L 450 m (1,476 ft)/min
Service ceiling 5,200 m (17,060 ft)
T-O run 200 m (656 ft)
T-O to 15 m (50 ft) 360 m (1,181 ft)
Landing from 15 m (50 ft) 640 m (2,100 ft)
Landing run 360 m (1,181 ft)
Ferry range with wingtip tanks
372 nm (690 km; 429 miles)
g limits +7/−4.5

ZLIN Z 61 L

This new trainer was being designed in 1988 for a first flight in 1989. Powered by a 224 kW (300 hp) Textron Lycoming AEIO-540-L1B5D engine, with a Hoffmann HO-V123K-V/200 AH propeller, the Z 61 L is intended for aerobatics and training and has tandem seats, the rear one elevated. The wings have MS(1)-0317 root and MS(1)-0313 tip sections, full span flaperons, and tip winglets.

ZLIN Z 37T AGRO TURBO

The piston engined Z-37A Cmelák (Bumble-bee) agricultural aircraft, of which more than 700 were built by Let (651 plus 26 two-seaters) and Moravan, was last described in the 1976-77 Jane's. Let then built an XZ-37T prototype (OK-146) of a turboprop version, powered by a 515 kW (691 shp) Walter M 601 B engine, which flew for the first time on 6 September 1981. Brief details of this prototype appeared in the 1982-83 Jane's.

In 1982 Moravan began the design and construction of a lower powered turbine engined version known as the Z 37T. Two prototypes (OK-072 and OK-074) made their first flights on 12 July and 29 December 1983; a third was completed in 1985. Certification under BCAR Section K was received in 1984, followed by the start of series production in 1985. First delivery of a production aircraft, to Slov-Air for operational trials, was made in 1985, and 24 had been delivered to this operator by 1 January 1989.

A two-seat Z 37T-2, for training agricultural pilots, was certificated in 1986. Two had been built by 1 January 1989.
TYPE: Single/two-seat agricultural aircraft.
WINGS: Cantilever low-wing monoplane. Wing section NACA 33015 at root, NACA 44012A at tip. Dihedral 7° on outer panels only. Incidence 3° at root, 0° at tip. All-metal single-spar structure, with auxiliary rear spar, comprising centre-section, built integrally with fuselage, and two outer panels. Linen covered duralumin ailerons, each with ground adjustable tab. All-metal duralumin skinned double-slotted trailing-edge flaps. Leading-edge fixed slats. Outward canted winglet at each tip.
FUSELAGE: Welded steel tube structure, with part-metal, part-linen covering.
TAIL UNIT: Cantilever all-metal two-spar structure, with fabric covering on control surfaces. Elevator aerodynamically and mass balanced. Trim tabs in rudder and centre of elevator.
LANDING GEAR: Non-retractable tailwheel type, with Technometra oleo-pneumatic mainwheel shock absorbers, Moravan light alloy wheels and Barum tyres. Steerable tailwheel. Mainwheel tyres size 556 × 163 × 254 mm, tailwheel tyre size 290 × 110 mm; pressure 3.45 bars (50 lb/sq in) on all units. Moravan hydraulic drum brakes on mainwheels.

Zlin Z 37T Agro Turbo fitted with underwing fuel tanks

Zlin Z 37T Agro Turbo agricultural aircraft (Motorlet M 601 Z turboprop) (Pilot Press)

POWER PLANT: One 365 kW (490 shp) Motorlet Walter M 601 Z turboprop, driving an Avia VJ7-508Z three-blade constant-speed propeller. Two metal fuel tanks in wing centre-section, combined capacity 350 litres (92.5 US gallons; 77 Imp gallons). Fuel can be transported to distant airstrips in four auxiliary tanks with a combined capacity of 500 litres (132 US gallons; 110 Imp gallons). Gravity refuelling point in top of each wing. Oil capacity 7 litres (1.8 US gallons; 1.5 Imp gallons). Air intake filter.

ACCOMMODATION: Pilot in enclosed cockpit, with forward opening window/door on starboard side. Auxiliary seat to rear for one passenger (mechanic or loader). Cockpit heated, and provided with filtered fresh air intake, contoured seat with headrest, rearview mirror and windscreen wiper and washer. Door can be jettisoned in an emergency. Two-seat training version available.

SYSTEMS: Pneumatic system of 50 bars (725 lb/sq in) pressure, reduced to 30 bars (435 lb/sq in) for agricultural equipment and flaps. Electrical power supplied by 28V 5.6kW DC starter/generator.
AVIONICS AND EQUIPMENT: LUN 3524 VHF radio standard. Hopper/tank capacity (max) 1,000 litres (264 US gallons; 220 Imp gallons) of liquid or 900 kg (1,984 lb) of dry chemical. Distribution system for both liquid and dry chemicals is operated pneumatically. Chemicals can be jettisoned in 5 s in emergency. Steel cable cutter on windscreen and each mainwheel leg; steel deflector cable runs from tip of windscreen cable cutter to tip of fin. Windscreen washer and wiper standard. Other equipment includes gyro compass, clock, rearview mirror, second (mechanic's) seat, cockpit air-conditioning, ventilation and heating, and anti-collision light. Can be modified for firefighting role.
DIMENSIONS, EXTERNAL:
Wing span 13.63 m (44 ft 8½ in)
Wing chord: at root 2.39 m (7 ft 10 in)
at tip 1.224 m (4 ft 0¼ in)
Wing aspect ratio 7.0
Length overall (flying attitude) 10.46 m (34 ft 4 in)
Fuselage: Max width 1.70 m (5 ft 7 in)
Height overall 3.505 m (11 ft 6 in)
Elevator span 5.294 m (17 ft 4½ in)
Wheel track 3.30 m (10 ft 10 in)
Wheelbase 6.375 m (20 ft 11 in)
Propeller diameter 2.50 m (8 ft 2½ in)
Propeller ground clearance (min) 0.45 m (1 ft 5¾ in)
AREAS:
Wings, gross 26.69 m² (287.3 sq ft)
Ailerons (total) 2.428 m² (26.13 sq ft)
Trailing-edge flaps (total) 4.37 m² (47.04 sq ft)
Fin 1.185 m² (12.76 sq ft)
Rudder, incl tab 1.054 m² (11.35 sq ft)
Tailplane 2.776 m² (29.88 sq ft)
Elevator, incl tab 3.008 m² (32.38 sq ft)
WEIGHTS AND LOADINGS:
Weight empty with basic agricultural equipment
1,250 kg (2,756 lb)
Max payload 900 kg (1,984 lb)
Max fuel 280 kg (617 lb)
Max T-O weight: ferry flights 2,260 kg (4,982 lb)
agricultural, forestry and waterways work
2,525 kg (5,566 lb)

Tandem cockpits distinguish the two-seat Z 37T-2 agricultural pilot trainer
(Vaclav Jukl/Letectvi + Kosmonautika)

Max zero-fuel weight		2,250 kg (4,960 lb)
Max wing loading		89.9 kg/m² (18.41 lb/sq ft)
Max power loading		6.67 kg/kW (10.95 lb/shp)

PERFORMANCE (at 2,525 kg; 5,566 lb max T-O weight):

Never-exceed speed		153 knots (285 km/h; 177 mph)
Max level speed at 500 m (1,640 ft)		
		118 knots (218 km/h; 135 mph)
Max cruising speed at 500 m (1,640 ft)		
		103 knots (190 km/h; 118 mph)

Working speed 78-89 knots (145-165 km/h; 90-103 mph)		
Stalling speed:		
flaps up		48 knots (88 km/h; 55 mph)
flaps down		42 knots (77 km/h; 48 mph)
Max rate of climb at S/L		252 m (827 ft)/min
T-O run		265 m (870 ft)
T-O to 15 m (50 ft)		580 m (1,905 ft)
Landing from 15 m (50 ft)		720 m (2,365 ft)
Landing run		300 m (985 ft)

Range with max internal fuel 188 nm (350 km; 217 miles)		
Swath width: granules		30 m (98 ft)
liquid		40 m (131 ft)
g limits		+3.2/–1.28

EGYPT

AOI
ARAB ORGANISATION FOR INDUSTRIALISATION
PO Box 770, Cairo
CHAIRMAN: Lt General Ibrahim Al Orabi
Aircraft Factory (36), Helwan
CHAIRMAN: Ahmed Heiba
Engine Factory (135), Helwan
CHAIRMAN: Hassen El Gebali
Kader Factory (72), Heliopolis
SAKR Factory (333), Heliopolis
Avionics Factory
SUBSIDIARIES:
Arab American Vehicle Co (AAVCo)
Arab British Dynamics Co (ABDCo)
Arab British Engine Co (ABECo), Helwan
Arab British Helicopter Co (ABHCo)

The AOI was set up in November 1975 by Egypt, Saudi Arabia, Qatar and the United Arab Emirates, to provide the basis for an Arab military industry. It is organised into five

divisions, which between them have a workforce of about 20,000 people, including approximately 3,000 employed in its four subsidiaries. Rockets, missiles and other weapons are produced by the SAKR Factory (except for the Swingfire programme, which is managed by ABDCo).

The main AOI centre is at Helwan, south of Cairo. Nearby is a large industrial complex, the chief elements of which are an aircraft factory (No. 36) and an aero-engine factory (No. 135), with about 3,000 and 3,500 employees respectively. Helwan also accommodates the Arab British Helicopter Company and the Arab British Engine Company. By reverse engineering, ABECo has also manufactured components for, and overhauled, Soviet TV2-117A turbo-shaft engines for Egypt's Mil Mi-8 helicopter fleet.

Details of the AOI Gazelle and Alpha Jet programmes can be found in the 1986-87 *Jane's*. Other more recent aircraft and engine programmes are as follows:

Aerospatiale Super Puma. Protocol signed on 10 November 1983, providing for component manufacture (now in progress) and possible ultimate assembly.

Dassault-Breguet Falcon 50. Component manufacture.

Dassault-Breguet Mirage 2000. Egyptian Air Force has received 20 (French built), and has a further 20 on option. Some components for first batch are of Egyptian manufacture; first deliveries made in second half of 1986.

Embraer EMB-312 Tucano. October 1983 contract for 120 Tucanos (80 for Iraq, 40 for Egypt), of which first ten were delivered complete by Embraer. Remainder being assembled from Brazilian built kits; PT6A-25 engines for these aircraft also being assembled in Egypt. Deliveries of Egyptian assembled Tucanos to the Egyptian Air Force began with three aircraft in November 1985, and totalled 42 by 1 January 1987, the latest date for which details have been received. Contract option for further 14 taken up in early 1989; kits for these have been delivered.

ETHIOPIA

EAL
ETHIOPIAN AIRLINES S.C.
PO Box 1755, Addis Ababa
Telephone: 251 (1) 612222
Telex: 21012 ETHAIR ADDIS
Fax: 251 (1) 611474
GENERAL MANAGER: Capt Mohammed Ahmed
DIRECTOR, AGRO AIRCRAFT MANUFACTURING:
Col Taddele Mekuria

Under licence from Schweizer Aircraft Corporation in the USA (which see), Ethiopian Airlines is producing for domestic use and eventual export the former's Ag-Cat Super B Turbine agricultural aircraft under the Ethiopian name **Eshet**. Nine had been completed by early 1990, the first example (ET-AIY) having been rolled out on 20 December 1986. Ethiopian Eshets are powered by a 559 kW (750 shp) PT6A-34AG turboprop with a 2.69 m (8 ft 10 in) Hartzell HC-B3TN-3D three-blade propeller, have an optional max fuel load of 435 litres (115 US gallons; 95.75 Imp gallons), and an oil capacity of 10.6 litres (2.8 US gallons; 2.3 Imp gallons). Mainwheels are as for the US built version, but with a higher tyre pressure of 3.83 bars (55.58 lb/sq in). Empty equipped weight is 1,500 kg (3,307 lb). EAL has the sole rights to build, market and service this aircraft throughout the African continent with the exceptions of Algeria, Tunisia and South Africa.

Ethiopian Airlines Eshet licence built version of the Schweizer Ag-Cat Super B Turbine

FINLAND

VALMET
VALMET AVIATION INDUSTRIES
Punanotkonkatu 2, PO Box 155, 00131 Helsinki
Telephone: 358 (0) 13291
Telex: 124427 VALP SF
Fax: 358 (0) 179677 or 605323
CHIEF EXECUTIVE: Heikki Mäntylä
GENERAL MANAGER: Juhani Mäkinen
SALES DIRECTOR: Matti Hämäläinen

Since 1922, Valmet Aviation Industries and its predecessors have built 30 different types of aircraft, of which 18 have been of Finnish design.

Current activities include the overhaul and repair of military and civil aircraft, piston engines and instruments. The factory has a covered production area of approximately 18,000 m² (193,750 sq ft) and a workforce of about 600 people. Linnavuori Works, at Siuro, is concerned primarily with the overhaul and repair of aircraft jet engines.

The latest aircraft of Finnish design to be built by Valmet is the L-90 Redigo turboprop primary and basic trainer. Under a contract signed on 14 October 1988, it will design and develop components for future aircraft built by Mooney Aircraft Corporation of the USA. Valmet is to manufacture the fin, rudder, tailplane and elevators for the Saab 2000 regional transport, under a 1989 contract from Saab-Scania of Sweden.

VALMET L-90 TP REDIGO
The L-90 TP is developed from, and is slightly larger than, the L-70 (1986-87 *Jane's*), from which it differs primarily in having a turboprop power plant, new wings and retractable landing gear. The first prototype (OH-VTP) made its initial flight on 1 July 1986. Valmet first flew the second prototype (OH-VTM) in early December 1987. This was powered by a 373 kW (500 shp) Turbomeca TP 319 turboprop, derated to 313 kW (420 shp), instead of the Allison 250 of the first prototype. The second prototype was lost in a flying accident on 29 August 1988. The TP 319, and a West German (Becker) avionics fit, will be offered on production Redigos. With the TP 319, the Redigo has a more compact nose contour.

Suitable for primary and basic flying training, aerobatic training, night and instrument flight training, tactical training, observation and liaison missions, the Redigo is designed to fit a training system that can produce combat-ready pilots within minimum time and cost levels, pupils proceeding directly from the L-90 TP to a demanding advanced trainer such as the BAe Hawk used by the Finnish Air Force. Additional roles can include search and rescue, weapons training, photographic reconnaissance and target towing. An alternative wing, built of Kevlar and carbon-fibre, has been successfully fatigue tested; its development is continuing.

The Finnish Air Force placed a contract for 10 of the Allison engined version on 6 January 1989. These are to be delivered in 1991-92.

TYPE: Two/four-seat multi-purpose military primary and basic training aircraft, designed to airworthiness requirements of FAR Pt 23 and BCAR Section K. Minimum fatigue life of 10,000 flight hours (fatigue spectrum MIL-A-8866B), and 30,000 landings in heavy military use.

WINGS: Cantilever low-wing monoplane of tapered planform, with forward-swept inboard leading-edges. Wing section NACA 63-218 (mod B3) at root, NACA 63-412 (mod B3) at tip. Dihedral 6° from roots. Incidence 3° at root; –3° washout at tip. Fail-safe structure comprising main spar, auxiliary spar, ribs and stringers, bolted to fuselage. Construction mainly of aluminium alloy, with riveted skin (fluted on flaps and ailerons). In-wing fuel tanks are of Valmet load bearing sandwich construction. Wingroot fairings are of CFRP, wingtips of glassfibre. All-metal single-slotted trailing-edge flaps, actuated electrically by screwjack. Ailerons, also all-metal, are of modified Frise type, mass balanced, and actuated by cables. Geared tab and spring tab in each aileron; starboard geared tab can be operated also as a trim tab.

FUSELAGE: Conventional aluminium alloy semi-monocoque fail-safe structure of frames and longerons, with riveted

First prototype of the Valmet L-90 TP Redigo two/four-seat military trainer, now modified to have non-swept vertical tail surfaces

Valmet L-90 TP Redigo turboprop powered multi-stage trainer *(Pilot Press)*

skin; CFRP and glassfibre used in tailcone and engine cowling panels.

TAIL UNIT: Cantilever non-swept aluminium alloy structure, with riveted skin (fluted on rudder and elevators). CFRP dorsal fin. Elevators and rudder horn balanced and cable operated. Geared tab in rudder and each elevator, all three operable also as trim tabs.

LANDING GEAR: AP Precision Hydraulics electro-hydraulically retractable tricycle type, with single wheel and oleo-pneumatic shock absorber on each unit. Nosewheel, which is centred by a spring, retracts rearward; main units retract inward into wings. Spring assisted lowering of all units in event of emergency. Mainwheel tyres size 17.5 × 6.3-6.0 in, pressure 3.79 bars (55 lb/sq in); nosewheel tyre size 14.2 × 4.95-5.0 in, pressure 3.45 bars (50 lb/sq in). Differential brakes on mainwheels. Parking brake.

POWER PLANT: One Allison 250-B17F turboprop (max power 373 kW; 500 shp), flat rated at 313 kW (420 shp), or a similarly rated Turbomeca TP 319 turboprop, each driving a Hartzell HC-B3TF-7A/T10173-15 three-blade constant-speed reversible-pitch propeller with spinner. Fuel in four wing tanks and a fuselage collector tank, total usable capacity 360 litres (95 US gallons; 79 Imp gallons). Collector tank of 15 litres (4 US gallons; 3.3 Imp gallons) can be used for up to 30 s of inverted flight. Gravity refuelling point in top of each wing tank. Oil capacity 5.7 litres (1.5 US gallons; 1.25 Imp gallons). Anti-icing for engine air intake, spinner and propeller blades.

ACCOMMODATION: Instructor and pupil, side by side, beneath one-piece rearward sliding jettisonable canopy with steel tube turnover windscreen frame. Canopy can be locked in partially open position if required. Zero/zero rocket assisted escape system optional. Dual controls standard, but instructor's or pupil's control column can be removed if desired. Both front seats are adjustable longitudinally and for rake, and are fitted with five-point seat belts and inertia reel shoulder harnesses. Provision for two more seats at rear, with four-point harnesses, which can be removed to make room for up to 200 kg (440 lb) of baggage. As ambulance, can accommodate one stretcher patient, and a medical attendant or sitting patient, in addition to pilot. Accommodation heated and ventilated by heat exchanger, fresh air intake and mixer unit. Auxiliary fresh air intake in fin leading-edge. Air-conditioning system optional.

SYSTEMS: No hydraulic or pneumatic systems. Electrical system is 28V DC, powered normally by a 150A engine driven starter/generator, with a 23Ah nickel-cadmium battery for emergency supply and engine starting. Ground power receptacle. Emergency battery for main artificial horizon. Oxygen system available to customer's requirements.

AVIONICS AND EQUIPMENT: Dual controls and instrumentation for day and night VFR and IFR operation, including VHF com radios (two), ADF, DME, transponder, RMI, HSI, marker beacon receiver, standby compass, airspeed indicator, attitude indicator, altimeter, turn and bank indicator, vertical speed indicator, outside

air temperature gauge, and clock. Twin landing lights in starboard wing leading-edge.

OPERATIONAL EQUIPMENT: Six underwing attachments, each inner point stressed for 250 kg (551 lb) and the other four for 150 kg (331 lb) each; max external stores load 800 kg (1,764 lb). When flown solo, can carry up to four photographic, TV, radar or reconnaissance pods plus two flares. As two-seater, typical loads can include five liferafts or emergency packs and one searchlight pod; and photo and TV pods. Provision for target towing with winch and hit counters.

DIMENSIONS, EXTERNAL:
Wing span	10.373 m (34 ft 0½ in)
Wing chord: at root	1.83 m (6 ft 0 in)
mean aerodynamic	1.50 m (4 ft 11 in)
at tip	1.098 m (3 ft 7¼ in)
Wing aspect ratio	7.25
Length overall	7.90 m (25 ft 11 in)
Fuselage: Max width	1.22 m (4 ft 0 in)
Height overall	2.85 m (9 ft 4¼ in)
Elevator span	3.68 m (12 ft 1 in)
Wheel track	3.367 m (11 ft 0½ in)
Wheelbase	2.13 m (7 ft 0 in)
Propeller diameter	2.19 m (7 ft 2¼ in)
Propeller ground clearance	0.29 m (11½ in)

DIMENSIONS, INTERNAL:
Cockpit: Length	1.81 m (5 ft 11¼ in)
Max width	1.14 m (3 ft 9 in)
Height (seat cushion to canopy)	1.02 m (3 ft 4¼ in)

AREAS:
Wings, gross	14.75 m² (158.8 sq ft)
Ailerons (total, incl tabs)	1.98 m² (21.31 sq ft)
Trailing-edge flaps (total)	1.76 m² (18.94 sq ft)
Fin	0.97 m² (10.44 sq ft)
Rudder, incl tab	0.99 m² (10.66 sq ft)
Tailplane	1.56 m² (16.79 sq ft)
Elevators (total, incl tabs)	1.53 m² (16.47 sq ft)

WEIGHTS AND LOADINGS (A: Aerobatic category; U: Utility; N: Normal category):
Weight empty, equipped: A	890 kg (1,962 lb)
Max fuel	296 kg (652 lb)
External stores: max	800 kg (1,764 lb)
with max fuel	600 kg (1,323 lb)
Max T-O weight: A	1,350 kg (2,976 lb)
U	1,470 kg (3,241 lb)
U (with external stores)	1,900 kg (4,189 lb)
N	1,600 kg (3,527 lb)
Max wing loading: A	91.5 kg/m² (18.75 lb/sq ft)
U	99.7 kg/m² (20.42 lb/sq ft)
U (with external stores)	128.8 kg/m² (26.40 lb/sq ft)
N	108.5 kg/m² (22.23 lb/sq ft)
Max power loading: A	5.03 kg/kW (8.27 lb/shp)
U	5.48 kg/kW (9.00 lb/shp)
U (with external stores)	7.08 kg/kW (11.64 lb/shp)
N	5.96 kg/kW (9.80 lb/shp)

PERFORMANCE (at max Aerobatic T-O weight, ISA):
Max permissible speed in dive	280 knots (520 km/h; 323 mph)
Never-exceed speed	251 knots (465 km/h; 289 mph)
Max level speed at 1,525 m (5,000 ft)	181 knots (335 km/h; 208 mph)
Cruising speed (75% power) at 3,000 m (9,840 ft)	164 knots (305 km/h; 189 mph)
Max speed for flap extension	129 knots (240 km/h; 149 mph)
Stalling speed, engine idling:	
flaps up	57 knots (105 km/h; 65 mph)
10° flap	54 knots (100 km/h; 62 mph)
40° flap	50 knots (93 km/h; 58 mph)
Max rate of climb at S/L	588 m (1,929 ft)/min
Time to height: 3,000 m (9,840 ft)	5 min
5,000 m (16,400 ft)	11 min 30 s
Service ceiling (engine limited)	7,620 m (25,000 ft)
T-O run	195 m (640 ft)
T-O to 15 m (50 ft)	310 m (1,017 ft)
Landing from 15 m (50 ft)	360 m (1,181 ft)
Landing run (without propeller reversal)	210 m (689 ft)
Min ground turning radius	10.80 m (35 ft 5 in)
Range at 6,000 m (19,685 ft) with max internal fuel, 30 min reserves	approx 809 nm (1,500 km; 932 miles)
Endurance, conditions as above	more than 5 h
g limits	+7/−3.5 aerobatic
	+2.7 max sustained

FRANCE

A.C.E.
A.C.E. INTERNATIONAL
MEMBER COMPANIES:
Avions Marcel Dassault-Breguet Aviation, BP 32, 92420 Vaucresson
Telephone: 33 (1) 47 41 79 21
SNECMA, 2 boulevard Victor, 75724 Paris Cédex 15
Telephone: 33 (1) 45 54 92 00
Thomson-CSF, 173 boulevard Hausmann, 75379 Paris Cédex 08
Telephone: 33 (1) 45 61 96 00

Electronique Serge Dassault, 55 quai Carnot, BP 301, 92214 Saint-Cloud Cédex
Telephone: (1) 46 02 50 00
MANAGING DIRECTOR: Bruno Revellin-Falcoz

On 8 April 1987, the Chairmen of the four member companies listed signed documents creating the A.C.E. International Groupement d'Intérêt Economique. Its purpose is to co-ordinate the launch of the future Avion de Combat Européen (A.C.E.) programme. The consortium is open to foreign companies interested in becoming members.

In addition to its own management bodies, the consortium will have a Technical Co-ordination Committee and a Finance and Contract Committee. As a first step, A.C.E. International is co-ordinating work undertaken by its member companies, with government authorities and military staff of concerned countries, to determine the common technical definition of the A.C.E.

AEROSPATIALE
AEROSPATIALE SNI
37 boulevard de Montmorency, 75781 Paris Cédex 16
Telephone: 33 (1) 42 24 24 24
Telex: AISPA 620059 F
PRESIDENT AND CHIEF EXECUTIVE OFFICER:
  Henri Martre
DIRECTOR OF INFORMATION AND COMMUNICATIONS:
  Patrice Kreis
AIRCRAFT DIVISION
DIVISION MANAGER: Jacques Plenier
AIRBUS PROGRAMME DIRECTOR: Alain Bruneau
ATR 42 PROGRAMME DIRECTOR: Jean-Paul Perrais
HYPERSONIC PROGRAMMES DIRECTOR: Jean-Marc Thomas
COMMERCIAL DIRECTOR: Henri Paul Puel
WORKS AND FACILITIES:
  Toulouse. PLANT MANAGER: Jean-Marie Mir
  Nantes-Bouguenais. PLANT MANAGER: Christian Beugnet
  Saint-Nazaire.
    PLANT MANAGER: Jean-Claude Chaussonnet
  Méaulte. PLANT MANAGER: Jacques Crusson
HELICOPTER DIVISION
DIVISION MANAGER: Jean François Bigay
DIRECTOR OF RESEARCH AND DEVELOPMENT:
  René Mouille
COMMERCIAL DIRECTOR: Lucien Lordereau
WORKS AND FACILITIES:
  Marignane and La Courneuve. FACTORY DIRECTOR:
  Paul Chandez
SUBSIDIARIES
SOGERMA-SOCEA
Société de Construction d'Avions de Tourisme et d'Affaires (SOCATA)
Société d'Exploitation et de Constructions Aéronautiques (SECA)
Sextant Avionique (50:50 with Thomson-CSF)
Unilaser
Aerospatiale Helicopter Corporation (USA)

Aerospatiale was formed on 1 January 1970, by decision of the French government, as a result of the merger of the former Sud-Aviation, Nord-Aviation and SEREB companies. It had a registered capital of 3,747,070,000 francs, facilities extending over a total covered area of 1,802,253 m² (gross area not available) and a staff (including subsidiary companies) of 32,800 persons on 1 January 1990. By December 1988 Aerospatiale had delivered some 7,670 helicopters of French design, excluding licensed production abroad, plus 328 assembled under licence.

In addition to the programmes of which details follow, Aerospatiale is a partner in the European Airbus programmes (see International section), and participates financially in Helibras (Brazil), Samaero (Singapore) and Maroc Aviation (Morocco). Out of Fr66,000 million new orders taken during 1989, 45.6% was for aircraft, 23.6% for helicopters, 14.3% for tactical missiles and 16.5% for ballistic missiles and space. Total order backlog at end of year was Fr90,000 million, equivalent to two years' work, and of that 65% was for export. In 1989 Aerospatiale and Lockheed agreed to a joint venture for identification, development and execution of R&D, licensing and/or production projects in several areas of technology, including missiles and space.

Most Aerospatiale helicopter designations were amended in January 1990, the changes being applied retrospectively. The prefix 'AS' (for Aerospatiale) now replaces 'SA' (referring to the former Sud-Aviation) in most cases. Additionally, military versions add 200 to their former numerical designation and adopt a standardised role suffix (except for the Gazelle): A – Armed, land-based; C – anti-tank; M – maritime, non-combatant; S – maritime, armed; and U – utility.

AEROSPATIALE AS 100
In 1988, Aerospatiale revealed details of a 96/124-seat airliner powered by two propfans or UDFs and designed to bridge the gap between the ATR 42/72 and European Airbus families. Intended to cruise at Mach 0.76 at 9,145 m (30,000 ft) over ranges up to 1,500 nm (2,780 km; 1,727

Artist's impression of Aerospatiale AS 100 projected 96/124-seat propfan powered airliner

miles), the AS 100 could enter service in about 1995, given a go-ahead for development before late 1990.

AEROSPATIALE ATSF and AGV
Long-term studies are in hand by Aerospatiale for both supersonic and hypersonic airliners. The ATSF (Avion de Transport Supersonique Futur) is foreseen as a 200-seat, Mach 2+ aircraft which would be available for service in 2005, replacing the Concorde. Intended for 2015 service-entry, the AGV (Avion à Grande Vitesse) would transport 150 passengers at Mach 5. Development, almost certainly in conjunction with foreign partners, has yet to be authorised.

In 1989, the official aerospace research office, ONERA, was authorised by the French government to study the practical possibilities of a hypersonic passenger aircraft, working from studies previously undertaken by Aerospatiale, Dassault, SNECMA and SEP.

AEROSPATIALE EPSILON
Marketing responsibility for the Epsilon was transferred in 1989 to the manufacturer's Socata division (which see).

AEROSPATIALE/MBB HAP and PAH-2/HAC TIGER/TIGRE
Details of this Franco-German anti-tank helicopter programme can be found under the Eurocopter heading in the International section.

AEROSPATIALE/AERITALIA ATR 42/72
Details of the ATR 42/72 programme can be found in the International section.

AEROSPATIALE SA 315B LAMA
Indian Army name: Cheetah
Design of the SA 315B Lama began in late 1968, initially to meet a requirement of the Indian armed forces, and a prototype was flown for the first time on 17 March 1969. French certification was granted on 30 September 1970 and FAA type approval on 25 February 1972.

The Lama combines features of the Alouette II and III, having the airframe (with some reinforcement) of the former and the dynamic components, including the Artouste power plant and rotor system, of the SA 316 Alouette III.

During demonstration flights in the Himalayas in 1969 a Lama, carrying a crew of two and 140 kg (308 lb) of fuel, made the highest landings and take-offs ever recorded, at a height of 7,500 m (24,600 ft). On 21 June 1972, a Lama set a helicopter absolute height record of 12,442 m (40,820 ft).

The production Lama is capable of transporting an external load of 1,135 kg (2,500 lb) at an altitude of more than 2,500 m (8,200 ft). In an agricultural role, it can be fitted with spraybars and an underbelly tank of 1,135 litres

(300 US gallons; 250 Imp gallons) capacity, developed jointly by Aerospatiale Helicopter Corporation and Simplex Manufacturing Company.

A total of 407 Lamas had been sold and delivered for operation in 31 countries by 1 January 1989. In addition to manufacture by Aerospatiale, the SA 315B is produced under licence by HAL for the Indian Army, under the name Cheetah; and is assembled by Helibras in Brazil under the name Gavião.

TYPE: Turbine-driven general purpose helicopter.
ROTOR SYSTEM: Three-blade main and anti-torque rotors. Folding main rotor blades, of NACA 63A section and constant chord, on articulated hinges, with hydraulic drag dampers. Each blade has aluminium alloy spar with steel cuff, aluminium alloy sheet skin, with stainless steel protective strips, and sandwich type Moltoprene block filling. Rotor brake standard. Tail rotor blades are hollow aluminium alloy aerofoils, with stainless steel leading-edge strip.
ROTOR DRIVE: Main rotor driven through planetary gearbox, with freewheel for autorotation. Take-off drive for tail rotor at lower end of main gearbox, from where a torque shaft runs to a small gearbox which supports the tail rotor and houses the pitch change mechanism. Steel alloy shafts. Cyclic and collective pitch controls are powered. Main rotor rpm 353. Tail rotor rpm 2,001.
FUSELAGE: Glazed cabin has light metal frame. Centre and rear fuselage have triangulated steel tube framework.
LANDING GEAR: Skid type, with removable wheels for ground manoeuvring. Pneumatic floats for normal operation from water, and emergency flotation gear, inflatable in the air, are available.
POWER PLANT: One 640 kW (858 shp) Turbomeca Artouste IIIB turboshaft, derated to 404 kW (542 shp). Fuel tank in fuselage centre-section, with capacity of 575 litres (152 US gallons; 126.5 Imp gallons), of which 573 litres (151.5 US gallons; 126 Imp gallons) are usable. Oil capacity 7 litres (1.85 US gallons; 1.55 Imp gallons).
ACCOMMODATION: Glazed cabin seats pilot and co-pilot or passenger side by side in front and three passengers behind. Jettisonable door on each side. Provision for external sling for loads of up to 1,135 kg (2,500 lb). Can be equipped for rescue (hoist capacity 160 kg; 352 lb), liaison, observation, training, agricultural, photographic and other duties. As an ambulance, can accommodate two stretchers and a medical attendant. Cabin heating optional.
SYSTEMS: Single hydraulic system. Electrical system includes engine starter/generator, 36Ah battery and external power socket. Oxygen system optional.
DIMENSIONS, EXTERNAL:
Main rotor diameter	11.02 m (36 ft 1¾ in)
Tail rotor diameter	1.91 m (6 ft 3¼ in)
Distance between rotor centres	6.435 m (21 ft 1½ in)

Models of current concepts for the Aerospatiale ATSF (left) and AGV (right) *(Brian M. Service)*

Main rotor blade chord (constant)	0.35 m (13.8 in)
Length overall, both rotors turning	
	12.91 m (42 ft 4¼ in)
Length of fuselage	10.23 m (33 ft 6¾ in)
Height overall	3.09 m (10 ft 1¾ in)
Skid track	2.38 m (7 ft 9¾ in)

DIMENSIONS, INTERNAL:

Cabin: Length	2.10 m (6 ft 10½ in)
Max width	1.40 m (4 ft 7 in)
Max height	1.28 m (4 ft 2¼ in)
Volume	3.10 m³ (109.5 cu ft)

AREAS:

| Main rotor disc | 95.38 m² (1,026.7 sq ft) |
| Tail rotor disc | 2.87 m² (30.84 sq ft) |

WEIGHTS:

Weight empty	1,021 kg (2,251 lb)
Max T-O weight: normal	1,950 kg (4,300 lb)
with externally slung cargo	2,300 kg (5,070 lb)

PERFORMANCE (A, at AUW of 1,950 kg; 4,300 lb. B, at AUW of 2,300 kg; 5,070 lb with slung load):

Never-exceed speed at S/L:	
A	113 knots (210 km/h; 130 mph)
Max cruising speed: A	103 knots (192 km/h; 119 mph)
B	65 knots (120 km/h; 75 mph)
Max rate of climb at S/L: A	330 m (1,080 ft)/min
B	234 m (768 ft)/min
Service ceiling: A	5,400 m (17,715 ft)
B	3,000 m (9,840 ft)
Hovering ceiling IGE: A	5,050 m (16,565 ft)
B	2,950 m (9,675 ft)
Hovering ceiling OGE: A	4,600 m (15,090 ft)
B	1,550 m (5,085 ft)
Range with max fuel: A	278 nm (515 km; 320 miles)

AEROSPATIALE ALOUETTE III

The seven-seat Alouette III helicopter was produced by Aerospatiale in two major versions, details of which can be found in the 1981-82 and previous editions of *Jane's*:

SA 316B. Powered by 649 kW (870 shp) Turbomeca Artouste IIIB turboshaft, derated to 425 kW (570 shp). Prototype flew for first time on 28 February 1959.

SA 319B. Powered by 649 kW (870 shp) Turbomeca Astazou XIV turboshaft, derated to 447 kW (600 shp). Prototype completed in 1967.

A total of 1,455 Alouette IIIs were produced by Aerospatiale by 1 May 1985. Production in France, and by ICA of Brasov, Romania, which built 230, has ended, but SA 316B production by HAL in India, as the Chetak, continues (see Indian section for full description).

AEROSPATIALE AS 330 PUMA

Details of six early versions of the Puma can be found in the 1976-77 *Jane's*. The final French production versions were as follows:

AS 330J/L. Civil (J) and military (L) versions introduced in 1976 with main rotor blades of composite materials. Increased max T-O weight, including certification at 7,500 kg (16,535 lb) for cargo-sling mission. Last described fully in 1982-83 *Jane's*.

A total of 697 AS 330 Pumas had been built by March 1989 for delivery to 46 countries. This total includes 145 built by ICA of Brasov, Romania (which see), which began manufacture under licence in 1977, as IAR-330s, and is now the sole producer of this helicopter. Nurtanio of Indonesia (see IPTN) completed the assembly of 11 from knocked-down components in the second quarter of 1983.

During 1989, OGMA began refurbishment of 10 Portuguese Air Force AS 330Cs, used for SAR and transport. These are receiving an upgrade to AS 330L standard, but also involving replacement of Turmo IIIC power plants by two Makila turboshafts, as in the Super Puma.

Aerospatiale AS 332L, Super Puma, with lengthened cabin *(Pilot Press)*

AS 532L Super Puma of the Ecole d'Application, French Army Aviation *(Ivo Sturzenegger)*

AEROSPATIALE AS 332/532 SUPER PUMA

Brazilian Air Force designation: CH-34
Spanish Air Force designations: HD.21/HT.21
Swedish Air Force designation: Hkp 10

The early history of the Super Puma, a list of its improved features compared with the original AS 330 Puma, and details of earlier versions, can be found in the 1985-86 edition of *Jane's*. The prototype AS 332 Super Puma (F-WZJA) flew on 13 September 1978. The current versions introduced in 1986, with uprated Turbomeca Makila IA1 engines, are as follows:

AS 532UC. Military utility short version; unarmed. Seating for up to 21 troops and two crew. Cabin floor reinforced for loads of 1,500 kg/m² (307 lb/sq ft).

AS 532UL. Military utility stretched version; unarmed. Cabin lengthened by 0.76 m (2 ft 6 in); additional fuel capacity and two additional windows. Up to 25 troops and two crew.

AS 532AC. Armed AS 532UC.
AS 532AL. Armed AS 532UL.

AS 532SC. Naval short version with armament and ASW/ASV equipment. Folding tail rotor pylon and deck landing assistance device.

AS 532MC. Naval utility short version; unarmed.

AS 332L. Civil stretched version. As AS 532UL, but 24 passengers.

Super Puma Mk II. This improved version is described separately.

The air component of the French Army (ALAT) has started to replace its current AS 330B Pumas with AS 532L Super Pumas. An initial 22 AS 532Ls are on order for the Army's Force d'Action Rapide, comprising six ordered in 1987 and eight funded in each of the two years 1988-89. The first was handed over on 13 December 1988 and became operational on 1 July 1989 with 5e Escadrille of 4e RHCM at Phalsbourg. Deliveries to ALAT totalled 12 by December 1989.

All Super Puma variants are certificated for IFR category A and B operation, to FAR Pt 29 standards. The first Super Puma (an AS 332L) equipped for operation to IFR Cat II standards was certificated by the DGAC on 7 July 1983 and delivered to Lufttransport of Norway in September 1983. Certification of this version for flight into known icing conditions was granted on 29 June 1983. Corresponding FAA certifications cover Cat II automatic approach, using a SFIM CDV 85 P4 four-axis flight director coupler, and flight into known icing conditions under FAR Pt 25 Appendix C.

Orders for 350 Super Pumas (including 255 military, but excluding six prototypes), for service in 34 countries, had been received by January 1990. They include five for operation by the French Air Force in support of nuclear test facilities in the Pacific (three) and for VIP transport (two); and others for Abu Dhabi (eight including two VIP), Argentina (three, Army), Brazil (16 including six AS 532SCs), Cameroon (one), Chile (one, Army; four AS 532SCs), China (six), Ecuador (eight, including six Army), Finland (two, border police), West Germany (three, border police), Indonesia (built under licence), Iraq (six AS 532SCs), Japan (three, Army/VIP), Jordan (eight), South Korea (three, Army/VIP), Mexico (two VIP), Nigeria (two), Oman (two, Royal Flight), Panama (one VIP), Saudi Arabia (12 AS 532SCs), Singapore (22), Spain (10 SAR HD.21s, two VIP HT.21s and 18 Army tactical transport HT.21s), Sweden (10 SAR), Switzerland (15) and Zaïre (one VIP). A further 31 AS 332Ls were ordered by Bristow Helicopters, whose 19-passenger aircraft, serving offshore oil platforms, are known as **Tigers**. Special equipment on the Tigers includes foldable seats, large rear baggage

Portuguese Puma refurbished to AS 330L airframe standards and re-engined with Makila turboshafts *(Paul Jackson)*

compartment, in-flight music, public address system, automatic emergency door jettison, and large capacity liferafts. By 1989, 60 Super Pumas were in service with petroleum support operators.

Deliveries of the Super Puma from French production began in mid-1981. IPTN of Indonesia (which see) is manufacturing several versions under licence, and 12 of the Spanish tactical transports are being assembled in Spain by CASA.

TYPE: Twin-turbine multi-role helicopter.

ROTOR SYSTEM: Four-blade main rotor, with a fully articulated hub and integral rotor brake. Each drag hinge is fitted with an elastomeric frequency adaptor. Blade pitch is controlled by twin-cylinder hydraulic powered control units. Each of the moulded blades is made up of a glassfibre roving spar and a composite glassfibre and carbonfibre fabric skin, with Moltoprene filler. The leading-edge is covered with a titanium protective section. The tips are swept. Attachment of each blade to its sleeve by means of two quick-disconnect pins enables the blades to be folded back quickly by hand. The five-blade tail rotor has flapping hinges only, and is located on the starboard side of the tailboom. Optional de-icing system, with heating mat on leading-edge of each main and tail rotor blade.

ROTOR DRIVE: Mechanical shaft and gear drive. Modular main gearbox is fitted with two torquemeters and has two separate lubrication circuits. It is mounted on top of the cabin behind the engines, has two separate inputs from the engines and five reduction stages. The first stage drives, from each engine, an intermediate shaft directly driving the alternator and indirectly driving the two hydraulic pumps, with a further shaft drive to the ventilation fan. At the second stage the action of the two units becomes synchronised on a single main driveshaft by means of freewheeling spur gears. If one or both engines are stopped, this enables the drive gears to be rotated by the remaining turbine or the autorotating rotor, thus maintaining drive to the ancillary systems when the engines are stopped. Drive to the tail rotor is via shafting and an intermediate angle gearbox, terminating at a right-angle tail rotor gearbox. Turbine output 23,840 rpm; main rotor shaft 265 rpm, tail rotor shaft 1,278 rpm. The hydraulically controlled rotor brake, installed on the main gearbox, permits stopping of the rotor 15 s after engine shutdown.

FUSELAGE: Conventional all-metal semi-monocoque structure, embodying anti-crash features. Local use of titanium alloy under engine installation, which is outside the main fuselage shell. Monocoque tailboom supports the tail rotor on the starboard side and a horizontal stabiliser with fixed leading-edge slat (and optional pneumatic de-icing) on the port side. Large ventral fin. Optional folding tailboom for naval versions.

LANDING GEAR: Retractable tricycle type, of Messier-Hispano-Bugatti high energy absorbing design. All units retract rearward hydraulically, mainwheels into sponsons on sides of fuselage. Dual-chamber oleo-pneumatic shock absorbers. Optional 'kneeling' capability for main units. Twin-wheel self-centring nose unit, tyre size 466 × 176, pressure 7.0 bars (102 lb/sq in). Single wheel on each main unit with tyre size 615 × 225-10 or 640 × 230-10, pressure 9.0 bars (130 lb/sq in). Hydraulic differential disc brakes, controlled by foot pedals. Lever operated parking brake. Emergency pop-out flotation units can be mounted on main landing gear fairings and forward fuselage.

POWER PLANT: Two Turbomeca Makila 1A1 turboshafts, each with max contingency rating of 1,400 kW (1,877 shp) and max continuous rating of 1,184 kW (1,588 shp). Air intakes protected by a grille against ingestion of ice, snow and foreign objects; but Centrisep multi-purpose intake is necessary for flight into sandy areas. AS 532UC/AC has five flexible fuel tanks under cabin floor, with total usable capacity of 1,497 litres (395 US gallons; 329 Imp gallons). AS 532SC/MC has total basic capacity

Orchidée battlefield surveillance radar extended in operational position under Puma test aircraft
(Paul Jackson)

of 2,141 litres (565 US gallons; 471 Imp gallons). AS 332L₁/532UL/532AL have a basic fuel system of six flexible tanks with total capacity of 2,020 litres (533 US gallons; 444 Imp gallons) in the 332; 2,003 litres (529 US gallons; 440 Imp gallons) in the 532. Provision for additional 1,900 litres (502 US gallons; 418 Imp gallons) in four auxiliary ferry tanks installed in cabin. Two external auxiliary tanks are standard on the AS 532SC/MC, optional on other versions, with total capacity of 650 litres (172 US gallons; 143 Imp gallons). For long range missions (mainly offshore), a special internal auxiliary tank can be fitted in cargo sling well, in addition to the two external tanks, to raise the total usable fuel capacity to 2,994 litres (791 US gallons; 658 Imp gallons) in AS 332L₁. Refuelling point on starboard side of cabin. Fuel system is designed to avoid leakage following a crash. Self-sealing tanks are standard on military versions, optional on other versions. Other options include a fuel dumping system and pressure refuelling.

ACCOMMODATION: One pilot (VFR) or two pilots side by side (IFR) on flight deck, with jump seat for third crew member or paratroop dispatcher. Provision for composite light alloy/Kevlar armour for crew protection on military models. Door on each side of flight deck and internal doorway connecting flight deck to cabin. Dual controls, co-pilot instrumentation and crashworthy flight deck and cabin floors. Max accommodation for 21 passengers in AS 532UC/MC, 24 in AS 332L₁ and 25 in AS 532UL. Variety of interiors available for VIP use, or for air ambulance duty carrying six stretchers and eleven seated casualties/attendants, or nine stretchers and three seated. Strengthened floor for cargo carrying, with lashing points. Jettisonable sliding door on each side of main cabin; or port side door with built-in steps and starboard side double door in VIP or airline configurations. Removable panel on underside of fuselage, at rear of main cabin, permits longer loads to be accommodated, and also serves as emergency exit. Removable door with integral steps for access to baggage

racks optional. A hatch in the floor below the centreline of the main rotor is provided for carrying loads of up to 4,500 kg (9,920 lb) on an internally mounted cargo sling. A fixed or retractable rescue hoist (capacity 275 kg; 606 lb) can be mounted externally on the starboard side of the fuselage. Cabin and flight deck are heated, ventilated and soundproofed. Demisting, de-icing, washers and wipers for pilots' windscreens.

SYSTEMS: Two independent hydraulic systems, supplied by self-regulating pumps driven by the main gearbox. Each system supplies one set of servo unit chambers, the left-hand system supplying in addition the autopilot, landing gear, rotor brake and wheel brakes. Freewheels in main gearbox ensure that both systems remain in operation, for supplying the servo controls, if the engines are stopped in flight. Other hydraulically actuated systems can be operated on the ground from the main gearbox (when a special disconnect system is installed to permit running of port engine with rotors stationary), or by external power through the ground power receptacle. Independent auxiliary system, fed through a handpump, can be used in an emergency to lower the landing gear. Three-phase 200V AC electrical power supplied by two 20kVA 400Hz alternators, driven by the port side intermediate shaft from the main gearbox and available on the ground under the same conditions as the hydraulic ancillary systems. 28.5V DC power provided from the AC system by two transformer-rectifiers. Main aircraft battery used for self starting and emergency power in flight.

AVIONICS AND EQUIPMENT: Optional communications equipment includes VHF, UHF, tactical HF and HF/SSB radio installations and intercom system. Navigational equipment includes radio compass, radio altimeter, VLF Omega, Decca navigator and flight log, Doppler, and VOR/ILS with glidepath. SFIM 155 autopilot, with provision for coupling to self contained navigation and microwave landing systems. Full IFR instrumentation available optionally. Offshore models have nose mounted radar. The search and rescue version has nose mounted Bendix RDR 1400 or RCA Primus 500 search radar, Doppler, and Crouzet Nadir or Decca self contained navigation system, including navigation computer with SAR patterns, polar indicator, roller map display, hover indicator, route mileage indicator and ground speed and drift indicator. Nadir Mk 2 in French Army version. A SFIM CDV 155 autopilot coupler makes possible automatic nav track including search patterns, transitions and hover. A multifunction video display shows radar and route images, SAR patterns and hover indication. For naval ASW and ASV missions, aircraft can be fitted with nose mounted Thomson-CSF Varan radar, linked to a tactical table in the cabin, and an Alcatel/Thomson-Sintra HS 312 sonar station at the rear of the cabin.

ARMAMENT AND OPERATIONAL EQUIPMENT (optional): Typical alternatives for army/air force missions are one 20 mm gun, two 7.62 mm machine-guns, or two pods each containing twenty-two 68 mm rockets or nineteen 2.75 in rockets. Armament and equipment for naval missions includes two AM39 Exocet missiles, or two lightweight torpedoes and sonar, or MAD and sonobuoys.

DIMENSIONS, EXTERNAL:

Main rotor diameter	15.60 m (51 ft 2¼ in)
Tail rotor diameter	3.05 m (10 ft 0 in)
Main rotor blade chord	0.60 m (1 ft 11½ in)

Aerospatiale AS 532UL Super Puma VIP helicopter of the Japanese Army's Special Transport Squadron at Kisarazu *(Ivo Sturzenegger)*

Aerospatiale AS 532MC Super Puma of the Brazilian Navy

Length overall, rotors turning	18.70 m (61 ft 4¼ in)
Length of fuselage, incl tail rotor:	
AS 532UC/AC/SC/MC	15.53 m (50 ft 11½ in)
AS 332L₁/532UC/UL	16.29 m (53 ft 5½ in)
Width, blades folded:	
AS 532UC/AC/AL/UL/332L₁	3.79 m (12 ft 5¼ in)
AS 532SC/MC	4.04 m (13 ft 3 in)
Height overall	4.92 m (16 ft 1¾ in)
Height, blades and tail pylon folded:	
AS 532UC/AC	4.80 m (15 ft 9 in)
Height to top of rotor head	4.60 m (15 ft 1¼ in)
Width overall, blades folded	3.79 m (12 ft 5¼ in)
Wheel track	3.00 m (9 ft 10 in)
Wheelbase: AS 532UC/AC/SC/MC	4.49 m (14 ft 8¾ in)
AS 332L₁/532AL/UL	5.28 m (17 ft 4 in)
Passenger cabin doors, each:	
Height	1.35 m (4 ft 5 in)
Width	1.30 m (4 ft 3¼ in)
Floor hatch, rear of cabin:	
Length	0.98 m (3 ft 2¾ in)
Width	0.70 m (2 ft 3½ in)
DIMENSIONS, INTERNAL:	
Cabin: Length: AS 532UC/AC	6.05 m (19 ft 10½ in)
AS 332L₁/532AL/UL	6.81 m (22 ft 4 in)
Max width	1.80 m (5 ft 11 in)
Max height	1.55 m (5 ft 1 in)
Floor area: AS 532UC/AC/SC/MC	7.80 m² (84 sq ft)
AS 332L₁/532AL/UL	9.18m² (98.8 sq ft)
Usable volume: AS 532UC/AC	11.40 m³ (403 cu ft)
AS 332L₁/532AL/UL	13.30 m³ (469.5 cu ft)
AREAS:	
Main rotor disc	191.1 m² (2,057.4 sq ft)
Tail rotor disc	7.31 m² (78.64 sq ft)
WEIGHTS:	
Weight empty (standard aircraft):	
AS 532UC/AC	4,330 kg (9,546 lb)
AS 532SC/MC	4,550 kg (10,031 lb)
AS 332L₁/532AL/UL	4,460 kg (9,832 lb)
Max T-O weight:	
AS 532UC/AC/AL/UL/SC/MC, internal load	9,000 kg (19,841 lb)
AS 332L₁, internal load	8,600 kg (18,960 lb)
all versions, with slung load	9,350 kg (20,615 lb)
PERFORMANCE (at max T-O weight):	
Never-exceed speed	150 knots (278 km/h; 172 mph)
Cruising speed at S/L:	
AS 532UC/AC/AL/UL	141 knots (262 km/h; 163 mph)
AS 532SC/MC	130 knots (240 km/h; 149 mph)
AS 332L₁	144 knots (266 km/h; 165 mph)
Max rate of climb at S/L:	
AS 532UC/AC/AL/UL	420 m (1,378 ft)/min

AS 532SC/MC	372 m (1,220 ft)/min
AS 332L₁	486 m (1,594 ft)/min
Service ceiling: AS 332L₁	4,600 m (15,090 ft)
AS 532UC/AC/SC/MC/AL/UL	3,500 m (11,480 ft)
Hovering ceiling IGE:	
AS 532AC/UC/SC/MC/AL/UL	2,800 m (9,185 ft)
AS 332L₁	3,100 m (10,170 ft)
Hovering ceiling OGE:	
AS 532AC/UC/SC/MC/AL/UL	1,650 m (5,415 ft)
AS 332L₁	2,300 m (7,545 ft)
Range at S/L, standard tanks, no reserves:	
AS 532UC/AC	334 nm (618 km; 384 miles)
AS 532SC/MC/332L₁	470 nm (870 km; 540 miles)
AS 532AL/UL	455 nm (842 km; 523 miles)
Range at S/L with external (2 × 338 litre) and auxiliary (320 litre) tanks, no reserves:	
AS 532AL/UL	672 nm (1,245 km; 773 miles)

AEROSPATIALE AS 332/532 SUPER PUMA Mk II

This developed version of the AS 332 M₁ Super Puma introduces new main and tail rotors which offer improved performance and economy without changes to the standard power plant of two Makila turboshafts, although the main transmission is upgraded to transmit increased power. Slightly longer main rotor blades with parabolic tips are fitted to a Spheriflex head, which is lighter and simpler than the current type. The rear fuselage is lengthened by 45 cm (1 ft 5¾ in), to provide adequate clearance between the new main rotor and the tail rotor. Similarly, the tail rotor is increased in size, the main change being to four blades, instead of five, and use of a Spheriflex head. Compared with the Mk 1, the new variant offers a 300 kg (661 lb) increase in useful load; high speed cruise increased by 6-27 knots (8-50 km/h; 5-31 mph), according to altitude and weight; and a hovering performance improved by 500 kg (1,102 lb) at the same altitude, or 500 m (1,640 ft) at the same weight.

There are no short-fuselage versions of the Mk II. Those proposed are:

AS 532U₂. Military utility version.
AS 532A₂. Armed version.
AS 332L₂. Civil version.

Internally, the Mk II has the rear cabin bulkhead moved rearwards by 0.55 m (1 ft 9⅝ in), increasing troop capacity from 25 to 29. In the civil version, maximum passenger capacity is 23 plus a flight attendant. Luggage storage space is increased by 15 per cent.

Following testing of the Spheriflex head on a Puma, a Super Puma Mk II development vehicle flew for the first time on 6 February 1987. Bristow Helicopters, a major Super Puma operator, ordered 20 Mk IIs in June 1989 for

delivery between April 1992 and 1995, representing the first commercial contract. The Mk II will be the carrier vehicle for the Orchidée radar system, for which trials began with a smaller Orphée II antenna beneath an AS 330B Puma (No. 1052/F-ZKCQ) in 1986. By 1989, the helicopter had received a Super Puma rotor head and nose-mounted Omera ORB 37 radar and was undertaking trials at the CEV as F-ZVLH. French Army Aviation (ALAT) has a requirement for 25 Orchidée-equipped Super Puma Mk IIs to be delivered from 1996 onwards.

Orchidée (Observatoire Radar Cohérent Héliporté d'Investigation Des Eléments Ennemis) is a battlefield surveillance system, intended as a key system for co-ordinating the actions of all French ground forces by the mid-1990s. As can be seen in an accompanying illustration, the radar scanner is carried on a rotating mount under the rear of the helicopter's cabin. For take-off and landing, it is retracted upward to stow transversely under the junction of the rear fuselage and tailboom. For transit flying, the 3.50 m (11 ft 5¾ in) antenna is deployed longitudinally. Orchidée, which will have a 5.0 m (16 ft 4¾ in) long antenna, includes an LCTAR high-performance Doppler radar, capable of detecting and pinpointing troops and vehicles up to 54 nm (100 km; 62 miles) behind enemy lines while the helicopter is 27 nm (50 km; 31 miles) inside friendly territory at an altitude of around 3,000 m (9,850 ft). Aerospatiale is industrial prime contractor for Orchidée, in conjunction with Le Centre Thomson d'Applications Radar, which supplies the radar and is responsible for the surveillance system. This transmits data in real time via an Agatha downlink to a Mistigri mobile ground station, both of which are built by Electronique Serge Dassault. Thomson-CSF and Matra are responsible for associated countermeasures.

Data generally as for AS 332/532, except:
FUSELAGE: New, multi-purpose sponsons with liferaft, luggage space or extra fuel tank, air-conditioning system and emergency floats.
POWER PLANT: Two Turbomeca Makila 1A2 turboshafts, each with take-off rating of 1,374 kW (1,843 shp) and max contingency 1,236 kW (1,658 shp). Emergency ratings are 2 min at 1,461 kW (1,959 shp) and 30 s 'super emergency' at 1,569 kW (2,104 shp).
ACCOMMODATION: Up to 29 commandos; or six stretchers, six sitting wounded and three attendants. Civilian version, 23 passengers.
SYSTEMS: Integrated Flight Data System including two AHRS primary references, a digital dual duplex four-axis autopilot and new IFIS control panel with four 15.25 cm (6 in) square screens. Electrical system simplified. Built-in test equipment.
DIMENSIONS, EXTERNAL:

Main rotor diameter	16.20 m (53 ft 1¾ in)
Tail rotor diameter	3.15 m (10 ft 4 in)
Length overall, rotors turning	19.50 m (63 ft 11¾ in)
Length of fuselage, incl tail rotor	16.79 m (55 ft 1 in)
Height overall	4.97 m (16 ft 3⅝ in)
Width overall, blades folded	3.86 m (12 ft 8 in)

WEIGHTS:

Weight empty	4,700 kg (15,420 lb)
Max T-O weight: military	9,500 kg (20,944 lb)
civil	9,070 kg (19,996 lb)
with external load	10,000 kg (22,046 lb)
Max underslung load	4,500 kg (9,921 lb)

PERFORMANCE (at max T-O weight):

Never-exceed speed	177 knots (432 km/h; 268 mph)
Cruising speed at S/L	149 knots (276 km/h; 172 mph)
Max rate of climb at S/L	390 m (1,279 ft)/min
Service ceiling	4,000 m (13,123 ft)
Hovering ceiling: IGE	2,500 m (8,202 ft)
OGE	1,550 m (5,085 ft)
Range at S/L	449 nm (832 km; 517 miles)
Range with 23 passengers and full reserves	up to 200 nm (371 km; 230 miles)
Range with 19 passengers and full reserves	350 nm (649 km; 403 miles)

AEROSPATIALE SA 342 GAZELLE

The first prototype of the Gazelle (designated SA 340) made its first flight on 7 April 1967, powered by an Astazou III engine. Details of early versions of the helicopter can be found in the 1979-80 and 1984-85 *Jane's*. Versions currently available are as follows:

SA 342L₁. Current basic military version, with higher max T-O weight than earlier models. Powered by Astazou XIVM turboshaft with max rating of 640 kW (858 shp) and max continuous rating of 441 kW (592 shp). In 1988, 12 Egyptian SA 342Ls were fitted with SFIM Osloh I laser designation systems for artillery co-operation.

SA 342M. For ALAT (French Army Light Aviation Corps). Differs from SA 342L₁ in having an ALAT instrument panel. Optional equipment specified as standard by ALAT includes SFIM PA 85G autopilot, Crouzet Nadir self-contained navigation system, Decca 80 Doppler and night flying equipment. An exhaust deflector remains optional. Max T-O weight initially 1,900 kg (4,188 lb), the current limit for SA 342F. By February 1989, French orders totalled 188 SA 342Ms, each armed with four Hot missiles and gyro stabilised sight for anti-tank warfare. Deliveries to the ALAT trials unit (GALSTA) began on 1 February 1980, and to an operational unit on 9 June 1980.

Aerospatiale Super Puma Mk II development vehicle

Aerospatiale AS 342M Gazelle of the 1st Combat Helicopter Regiment at Phalsbourg *(AGPPA)*

Aerospatiale Gazelle five-seat light utility helicopter *(Pilot Press)*

Two new SA 342M versions were under development at the CEV trials unit in 1990: an escort helicopter with a turret-mounted 20 mm cannon, Sextant Avionique HUD and rate gyro unit; and an anti-helicopter conversion with four Matra Mistral missiles. ALAT plans to acquire 67 cannon and 30 Mistral Gazelles.

A two-stretcher ambulance configuration has received FAA supplemental type certification. No major modification is necessary to convert the aircraft to carry two patients longitudinally on the port side of the cabin, one above the other, leaving room for the pilot and a medical attendant in tandem on the starboard side. The dual spineboard arrangement weighs 27 kg (60 lb) and stows into the baggage compartment when not in use.

Under an Anglo-French agreement signed in 1967, Gazelles are produced jointly with Westland Helicopters Ltd; they have been assembled in Egypt, and built under licence in Yugoslavia. A total of 1,253 had been ordered from Aerospatiale and Westland for civil and military operation in 41 countries by 1 January 1989, of which 1,223 had been delivered, plus 220 built in Yugoslavia. Westland manufacture of complete Gazelles ended in March 1984 with the 294th example, of which 12 were for civilian use.

Military customers for the Gazelle include Abu Dhabi (12), Angola (seven), Burundi (three), Cameroon (four), Chad (one), China (eight), Cyprus (six), Egypt (90 including local assembly of 30), Ecuador (28), France (357), Gabon (five), Guinea Republic (one), Iraq (81), Ireland (two), Kenya (two), Kuwait (24), Lebanon (seven), Morocco (30), Qatar (16), Rwanda (four), Senegal (one), Syria (65), Trinidad and Tobago (two), United Kingdom (282) and Yugoslavia (21 French-built). Civilian sales total some 170.

TYPE: Five-seat light utility helicopter.

ROTOR SYSTEM: Three-blade semi-articulated main rotor and 13-blade shrouded fan anti-torque tail rotor (known as a fenestron or fan-in-fin). Rotor head and rotor mast form a single unit. Main rotor blades are NACA 0012 section, attached to NAT hub by flapping hinges. No drag hinges. Each blade has a single leading-edge spar of GFRP, a laminated glass-fabric skin and honeycomb filler. Tail rotor blades of die-forged light alloy, with articulation for pitch change only. Main rotor blades can be folded manually for stowage. Rotor brake standard.

ROTOR DRIVE: Main reduction gearbox forward of engine, which is mounted above the rear cabin. Intermediate gearbox beneath engine, rear gearbox supporting the tail rotor. Main rotor/engine rpm ratio 387 : 6,334. Tail rotor/engine rpm ratio 5,918 : 6,334.

FUSELAGE: Cockpit structure is based on a welded light alloy frame which carries the windows and doors. This is mounted on a conventional semi-monocoque lower structure consisting of two longitudinal box sections connected by frames and bulkheads. Central section, which encloses the baggage hold and main fuel tank and supports the main reduction gearbox, is constructed of light alloy honeycomb sandwich panels. Rear section, which supports the engine and tailboom, is of similar construction. Honeycomb sandwich panels are also used for the cabin floors and transmission platform. Tailboom is of conventional sheet metal construction, as are the horizontal tail surfaces and the tail fin.

TAIL UNIT: Small horizontal stabiliser on tailboom, ahead of tail rotor fin.

LANDING GEAR: Steel tube skid type. Wheel can be fitted at rear of each skid for ground handling. Provision for alternative float or ski landing gear.

POWER PLANT: One Turbomeca Astazou XIVM turboshaft, installed above fuselage aft of cabin and rated at 640 kW (858 shp). Two standard fuel tanks in fuselage (one beneath baggage compartment) with total usable capacity of 545 litres (144 US gallons; 120 Imp gallons). Provision for 200 litre (53 US gallon; 44 Imp gallon) ferry tank inside rear cabin. Total possible usable fuel capacity 745 litres (197 US gallons; 164 Imp gallons). Refuelling point on starboard side of cabin. Oil capacity 14.6 litres (4 US gallons; 3.2 Imp gallons) for engine, 3.5 litres (0.9 US gallon; 0.77 Imp gallon) for gearbox.

ACCOMMODATION: Crew of one or two side by side, with bench seat to the rear for a further three persons. Bench can be folded into floor wells to leave a completely flat cargo floor. Access to baggage compartment via rear cabin bulkhead, or via optional starboard door. Cargo tiedown points in cabin floor. Forward opening car type door on each side of cabin, immediately behind which are rearward opening auxiliary cargo loading doors. Baggage compartment at rear of cabin. Ventilation standard. Dual controls optional.

SYSTEMS: Hydraulic system, pressure 40 bars (570 lb/sq in), serves three pitch change jacks for main rotor head and one for tail rotor. 28V DC electrical system supplied by

4kW engine driven generator and 40Ah battery. Optional 26V AC system, supplied by 0.5kVA alternator at 115/200V 400Hz.

AVIONICS AND EQUIPMENT: Optional communications equipment includes UHF, VHF, HF, intercom systems and homing aids. Optional navigation equipment includes radio compass, radio altimeter and VOR. Blind-flying instrumentation and autopilot optional. A variety of operational equipment can be fitted, according to role, including a 700 kg (1,540 lb) cargo sling, 135 kg (300 lb) rescue hoist, one or two stretchers (internally), or photographic and survey equipment.

ARMAMENT: Military loads can include two pods of Brandt 68 mm or FZ 2.75 in rockets, four or six Hot wire guided missiles with APX M397 gyro stabilised sight, two forward firing 7.62 mm machine-guns, or one GIAT M.621 20 mm gun on starboard side. Yugoslav SA 342Ls are fitted with dual-role carriers for a total of four AT-3 'Sagger' ATMs and two SA-7 'Grail' AAMs. During late 1980s, Gazelles of UK Army Air Corps and Royal Marines retrofitted with Ferranti AF 532 magnifying roof sights for unarmed scout duties. Some French Army Gazelles were simultaneously equipped with similar Athos scouting sight. Ferranti AWARE-3 radar warning receivers ordered in 1989 for British Army Gazelles.

DIMENSIONS, EXTERNAL:
Main rotor diameter	10.50 m (34 ft 5½ in)
Tail rotor diameter	0.695 m (2 ft 3⅜ in)
Distance between rotor centres	5.85 m (19 ft 2¼ in)
Main rotor blade chord (constant)	0.30 m (11.8 in)
Length overall (main rotor turning)	11.97 m (39 ft 3⁵⁄₁₆ in)
Length of fuselage, incl tail rotor	9.53 m (31 ft 3³⁄₁₆ in)
Width, rotors folded	2.04 m (6 ft 8½ in)
Height to top of rotor head	2.72 m (8 ft 11⅛ in)
Height overall	3.19 m (10 ft 5½ in)
Skid track	2.015 m (6 ft 7⁵⁄₁₆ in)
Main cabin doors, each: Height	1.05 m (3 ft 4⁹⁄₁₆ in)
Width	1.00 m (3 ft 3¼ in)
Height to sill	0.63 m (2 ft 0¾ in)
Auxiliary cabin doors, each: Height	1.05 m (3 ft 4⁹⁄₁₆ in)
Width	0.48 m (1 ft 6¾ in)
Height to sill	0.63 m (2 ft 0¾ in)

DIMENSIONS, INTERNAL:
Cabin: Length	2.20 m (7 ft 2⁹⁄₁₆ in)
Max width	1.32 m (4 ft 4 in)
Max height	1.21 m (3 ft 11⅝ in)
Floor area	1.50 m² (16.1 sq ft)
Volume	1.80 m³ (63.7 cu ft)
Baggage hold volume	0.45 m³ (15.9 cu ft)

AREAS:
Main rotor blades, each	1.57 m² (16.9 sq ft)
Tail rotor blades, each	0.007 m² (0.075 sq ft)
Main rotor disc	86.59 m² (932.05 sq ft)
Tail rotor disc	0.37 m² (3.98 sq ft)
Fin	0.45 m² (4.84 sq ft)
Tailplane	1.80 m² (19.4 sq ft)

WEIGHTS AND LOADINGS:
Weight empty: 342L₁	997 kg (2,198 lb)
Max T-O and landing weight:	
342L₁	2,000 kg (4,410 lb)
342M	2,100 kg (4,630 lb)
Max disc loading: 342L₁	23.1 kg/m² (4.73 lb/sq ft)
342M	21.94 kg/m² (4.49 lb/sq ft)

PERFORMANCE (SA 342L₁ at max T-O weight):
Never-exceed speed at S/L	151 knots (280 km/h; 174 mph)
Max cruising speed at S/L	140 knots (260 km/h; 161 mph)
Max rate of climb at S/L	468 m (1,535 ft)/min
Service ceiling	4,100 m (13,450 ft)
Hovering ceiling: IGE	3,040 m (9,975 ft)
OGE	2,370 m (7,775 ft)
Range at S/L with standard fuel	383 nm (710 km; 440 miles)

AEROSPATIALE AS 350/550 ECUREUIL/ASTAR
Brazilian Air Force designation: CH-50 Esquilo

Developed as a successor to the Alouette, the AS 350 Ecureuil (Squirrel) embodies Aerospatiale's Starflex type of main rotor hub, made of glassfibre, with elastomeric spherical stops and visco-elastic frequency adaptors. The first prototype (F-WVKH) flew on 27 June 1974, powered by a Textron Lycoming LTS 101 turboshaft. It was followed on 14 February 1975 by a second prototype (F-WVKI) with a Turbomeca Arriel turboshaft.

The Textron Lycoming powered version is marketed only in North America, as the **AStar**; and the Arriel powered **Ecureuil** is marketed throughout the rest of the world. Initial production of the latter included the basic AS 350B, with 478 kW (641 shp) Arriel 1B, for which French certification was received on 27 October 1977. Current production versions are as follows:

AS 350B₂ Ecureuil. With 540 kW (724 shp) Arriel 1D1 turboshaft; uprated transmission, with gearbox able to absorb max input of 440 kW (590 shp); and wide-chord, new section main and tail rotor blades developed originally for the Ecureuil 2/TwinStar. Certification in progress in Spring 1989. Known as **SuperStar** in North America.

AS 350B₁ Ecureuil water bomber of France's Securité Civile *(AGPPA)*

On 14 May 1985 an AS 350B₁, at an AUW of 1,270 kg (2,800 lb) with a crew of two, set three official class E1c records by climbing to 3,000 m in 2 min 59.3 s, 6,000 m in 6 min 54.9 s, and 9,000 m in 13 min 51.5 s.

AS 350D AStar. Current AStar Mk III has 459 kW (615 shp) Textron Lycoming LTS 101-600A-3 turboshaft. Otherwise as AS 350B₂.

AS 550 Ecureuil. (Previously AS 350L₂.) Military version of AS 350B₂, with Arriel 1D1 turboshaft rated at 546 kW (732 shp). Standard features include a taller landing gear, sliding doors, extended instrument panel and airframe reinforcement for axial armament. Provision for armoured seats. Individual versions are utility **AS 550U₂**; armed **AS 550A₂**; and anti-tank **AS 550C₂**.

Deliveries of the basic AS 350B began in March 1978. FAA certification of the original AS 350C AStar was obtained on 21 December 1977 and the first production delivery was made in April 1978. The AS 350C was superseded in 1978 by the AS 350D. By 1 January 1990 a total of 1,395 AS 350 Ecureuils and AStars had been ordered for service in 46 countries; 1,276 had been delivered. Customers include the Singapore armed forces, which have six, and the Australian government, which has taken delivery of 18 AS 350Bs for RAAF pilot training, liaison, search and rescue, and six more for survey and utility duties with the Royal Australian Navy. In mid-1987, the Danish Army ordered 12 AS 550Cs, equipped with the Saab/Emerson Electric HeliTOW anti-tank missile system, for delivery in 1990. Ecureuils are also produced under licence by Helibras of Brazil, with the name Esquilo, 16 being ordered in 1988 as initial equipment of the newly-formed army aviation branch, following 30 ordered for the air force. The French Army has a requirement for up to 100 AS 550s to replace its Alouette IIs.

During 1986, an AS 350B₁ Ecureuil with taller landing gear was fitted with a firefighting kit purchased from Conair of Canada (which see), to test its effectiveness in dealing with forest fires in Southern France. The kit consists of a streamlined tank which can be refilled in 30 s through a snout while the helicopter hovers over a stretch of water.

Under a French government contract, Aerospatiale flew in 1986 an AS 350 fitted with a fenestron shrouded tail rotor, but this is not expected to become a feature of production Ecureuils of the current series.

Aerospatiale has teamed with Hughes Training Systems to offer the aircraft for the US Army's New Training Helicopter (NTH) programme.

TYPE: Five/six-seat light general purpose helicopter.

ROTOR SYSTEM: Three-blade main rotor, with Starflex glassfibre hub in which the three conventional hinges for each blade are replaced by a single balljoint of rubber/steel sandwich construction, requiring no maintenance. Glassfibre blades, with stainless steel leading-edge sheath, produced by an entirely mechanised process. Symmetrical blade section on AS 350B; OA 209 section on wider-chord blades of AS 350B₂ and 550. Two-blade tail rotor; each blade comprises a sheet metal skin around a glassfibre spar, the flexibility of which obviates the need for hinges.

ROTOR DRIVE: Simplified transmission, with single epicyclic main gear train. Tail rotor driveshaft coupling on engine.

FUSELAGE: Basic structure of light alloy pressings, with skin mainly of thermoformed plastics, including baggage compartment doors.

TAIL UNIT: Horizontal stabiliser, of inverted aerofoil section, mid mounted on tailboom. Sweptback fin, in two sections above and below tailboom.

LANDING GEAR: Steel tube skid type. Taller version standard on military aircraft. Emergency flotation gear optional.

POWER PLANT: One turboshaft (for type see individual model listings) mounted above fuselage to rear of cabin. Plastics fuel tank (self sealing on AS 550) with capacity of 540 litres (142.6 US gallons; 119 Imp gallons).

ACCOMMODATION: Two individual bucket seats at front of cabin and two two-place bench seats are standard. In the alternative layout the two benches are replaced by three armchair seats. Optional ambulance layout. Large forward hinged door on each side of versions for civil use. Optional sliding door at rear of cabin on port side. (Sliding doors standard on military version.) Baggage compartment aft of cabin, with full-width upward hinged door on starboard side. Top of baggage compartment reinforced to provide platform on each side for inspecting and servicing rotor head.

SYSTEMS: Hydraulic system includes four single-body servo units, operating at 40 bars (570 lb/sq in) pressure, and accumulators to protect against a hydraulic power supply failure. Electrical system includes a 4.5kW engine driven starter/generator, a 24V 16Ah nickel-cadmium battery and a ground power receptacle connected to the busbar which distributes power to the electrical equipment. Cabin air-conditioning system optional.

AVIONICS AND EQUIPMENT: Optional com/nav radio equipment includes VHF/AM, ICS, VOR/LOC/glideslope, marker beacon indicator, radio compass, HF/SSB, transponder and DME. IFR instrumentation optional. Available equipment includes a SFIM PA 85T31, Honeywell HelCis or Collins APS-841H autopilot, a 907 kg (2,000 lb) cargo sling (1,160 kg; 2,557 lb for B₂ and 550 versions), a 135 kg (297 lb) electric hoist, a TV camera for aerial filming, and a 735 litre (194 US gallon; 161 Imp gallon) Simplex agricultural spraytank and boom system.

ARMAMENT (AS 550): Provision for wide range of weapons, including 20 mm GIAT M621 gun, FN Herstal TMP twin 7.62 mm machine-gun pods, Thomson Brandt 68.12 launchers for twelve 68 mm rockets, Forges de Zeebrugge launchers for seven 2.75 in rockets, and Saab/Emerson Electric HeliTOW anti-tank missile systems.

DIMENSIONS, EXTERNAL:

Main rotor diameter	10.69 m (35 ft 0¾ in)
Main rotor blade chord: AS 350B/D	0.30 m (11.8 in)
AS 350B₂/550	0.35 m (13.8 in)
Tail rotor diameter	1.86 m (6 ft 1¼ in)
Tail rotor blade chord: AS 350B/D	0.185 m (7.28 in)
AS 350B₂/550	0.205 m (8.07 in)
Length overall (rotors turning)	12.94 m (42 ft 5½ in)
Length of fuselage	10.93 m (35 ft 10½ in)
Width of fuselage	1.80 m (5 ft 10¾ in)
Width overall, blades folded (ie, horizontal stabiliser span)	2.53 m (8 ft 3¾ in)
Height overall: AS 350B/B₂/D	3.14 m (10 ft 3½ in)
AS 550	3.34 m (10 ft 11½ in)
Skid track: AS 350B/B₂/D	2.17 m (7 ft 1½ in)
AS 550	2.28 m (7 ft 5¾ in)
Cabin doors (civil versions, standard, each):	
Height	1.15 m (3 ft 9¼ in)
Width	1.10 m (3 ft 7¼ in)

DIMENSIONS, INTERNAL:

Cabin: Length	2.42 m (7 ft 11¼ in)
Width at rear	1.65 m (5 ft 5 in)
Height	1.35 m (4 ft 5 in)
Baggage compartment volume	1.00 m³ (35.31 cu ft)

AREAS:

Main rotor disc	89.75 m² (966.1 sq ft)
Tail rotor disc	2.72 m² (29.25 sq ft)

WEIGHTS:

Weight empty: 350B	1,102 kg (2,430 lb)
350B₂	1,133 kg (2,500 lb)
350D	1,070 kg (2,359 lb)
550	1,180 kg (2,601 lb)
Max T-O weight: normal: 350B/D	1,950 kg (4,300 lb)
350B₂/550	2,250 kg (4,960 lb)
with max slung load: 350B/D	2,100 kg (4,630 lb)
350B₂/550	2,500 kg (5,511 lb)
in anti-tank configuration: 550C₂	2,350 kg (5,181 lb)

PERFORMANCE (B/D at normal max T-O weight, B₂/550 at 2,200 kg; 4,850 lb):

Never-exceed speed at S/L:	
350B/D	147 knots (272 km/h; 169 mph)
350B₂/550	155 knots (287 km/h; 178 mph)
Max cruising speed at S/L:	
350B	125 knots (232 km/h; 144 mph)
350B₂	133 knots (246 km/h; 153 mph)
350D	124 knots (230 km/h; 143 mph)
550	134 knots (248 km/h; 154 mph)
Max rate of climb at S/L:	
350B/D	475 m (1,558 ft)/min
350B₂/550	607 m (1,990 ft)/min
Service ceiling: 350B/D	4,750 m (15,600 ft)
350B₂/550	5,600 m (18,375 ft)
Hovering ceiling IGE: 350B	2,950 m (9,675 ft)
350B₂/550	4,055 m (13,300 ft)
350D	2,500 m (8,200 ft)
Hovering ceiling OGE: 350B	2,250 m (7,380 ft)
350B₂/550	3,415 m (11,200 ft)
350D	1,800 m (5,900 ft)
Range with max fuel at S/L, at econ cruising speed, no reserves:	
350B	389 nm (720 km; 447 miles)
350D	410 nm (760 km; 472 miles)
350B₂/550	370 nm (686 km; 426 miles)

AEROSPATIALE AS 355/555 ECUREUIL 2/TWINSTAR
Brazilian Air Force designations: CH-55 and VH-55 Esquilo

The AS 355 and 555 are twin-engined versions of the AS 350 Ecureuil/AStar family. Many components, such as the main rotor mast and head, tail rotor hub, servo units, cabin and landing gear, are identical to those of the AS 350. The main and tail rotor blades are also identical to those of the current AS 350B₂/550 versions. Major changes apply to the

AS 550C₂ Ecureuil in anti-tank configuration, with HeliTOW system

power plant, transmission, fuel system and fuselage structure.

The first of two prototypes (F-WZLA) flew on 28 September 1979. Details of the AS 355E/F initial production versions, with Allison engines, can be found in the 1984-85 and earlier editions of *Jane's*.

From January 1984, the AS 355F was superseded by the **AS 355F₁**, incorporating three significant modifications. Addition of a laminated tab increased the tail rotor blade chord. The max power transmitted to the main gearbox was increased, by setting the torque limiter to 2 × 78 per cent instead of 2 × 73 per cent. Addition of a rotor overspeed alarm set to 410 rpm represented a complementary function of the normal alarm system. These changes permitted increased max T-O weight and payload.

A further increase in max T-O weight is offered by the **AS 355F₂**, which received DGAC certification on 10 December 1985. This version introduced a load compensator in the yaw channel and an extension of the CG limits.

The AS 355F₂ is intended primarily for the civil market, in particular for use by companies working in the oil industry. It received French civil certification in the Summer of 1989. McAlpine Helicopters of the United Kingdom has developed a dedicated law enforcement version of the AS 355F₂ known as the **Police Twin Squirrel**. It is equipped with a nose-mounted GEC thermal imaging camera, with cabin monitor screen and real-time transmission capability; 30 million candlepower SX 16 'Night Sun' searchlight mounted in a fully articulated pod aft of the cabin; and 'Skyshout' public address speakers mounted on the landing gear skids, which are taller than standard to provide ground clearance for camera and searchlight. The Police Twin Squirrel is fitted with non-standard sliding cabin doors to facilitate air-to-ground observation and photography, and for fast entry and exit. Several Police Twin Squirrels are in service with police forces in the UK. Certification is anticipated in 1990 of the **AS 355F₂R**, which will replace the current 355F₂ in production.

Since January 1990, military Ecureuil 2s (formerly known as AS 355Ms) have been designated AS 555, as follows:
AS 555UR. Utility version.
AS 555AR. Armed version.
AS 555AN. French Air Force version (formerly AS 355N).
AS 555MR. Naval utility version.
AS 555SR. Naval armed version.

All AS 555s will be fitted with C20R marks of the Allison 250 turboshaft. The AS 555SR is intended for operation from small vessels (600 t and above) in the anti-submarine and over-horizon targeting roles. Operational equipment

Aerospatiale AS 355F₂ Ecureuil 2 equipped with Wescam gyro-stabilised camera *(Paul Jackson)*

includes a 360° Bendix 1500 radar beneath the nose; Crouzet Mk 3 MAD beneath the tailboom; Crouzet Nadir Mk 10 navigation system (including ESD RDN 85 Doppler and auto-hold); and SFIM 85 T31 three-axis autopilot. Armament comprises two homing torpedoes (Mk 44, Mk 46 or Murène), or the cannon, missiles and rockets of land-based versions. The Brazilian Air Force has 13 AS 555s, of which 11 with armament are designated **CH-55** and two VIP transports are designated **VH-55**. A further 11 H-55s are being acquired by the Brazilian Navy. Brazilian Esquilos are assembled by Helibras (which see).

The French Air Force has 50 Ecureuil 2s on order, the last six of which were funded in 1989. An initial six, delivered by 1987, were originally AS 355F₁s, used for communications by the 67e Escadre d'Hélicoptères at Villacoublay and in the security role with a starboard-side GIAT M621 20 mm cannon by EHOM 68 in French Guyana. The remaining 44, of which the first was delivered to training school, Centre d'Instruction des Equipages d'Hélicoptères 341 at Chambéry on 19 January 1990, are powered by Turbomeca TM 319 turboshafts and designated AS 555AN. From the 24th onwards, provision is being made for a centrally mounted 20 mm cannon and T-100 sight, plus Matra Mistral missiles for anti-helicopter roles.

By 1 January 1990, a total of 443 AS 355/555s had been ordered for service in 31 countries; 389 had been delivered. The version for the North American market is known as the **TwinStar**; aircraft marketed elsewhere are named **Ecureuil 2**.

The following details apply to the AS 355F₂ and 555 versions:
TYPE: Twin-turbine light general purpose helicopter.
ROTOR SYSTEM: As for AS 350B₂/550.
ROTOR DRIVE: Single main gearbox, made up of three modules (coupling gearbox with freewheel, angle gearing with spiral bevel gears, and epicyclic gear train including five oscillating planetary gears). Power take-offs for the accessories and tail rotor.
FUSELAGE: Light alloy centre fuselage structure, with deep drawn sheet metal forms of simple geometric design. Cabin skin of thermoformed plastics. Tapered tailboom of light alloy sheet wrapped and riveted around deep drawn sheet metal cylindrical frames.
TAIL UNIT AND LANDING GEAR: As for AS350B₂/550.
POWER PLANT: Two Allison 250-C20F turboshafts, each rated at 313 kW (420 shp) for take-off and 276 kW (370 shp) max continuous, mounted above fuselage to rear of cabin. From 1990, AS 555 has two Allison 250-C20R turboshafts, each rated at 343 kW (460 shp) for take-off and 283 kW (380 shp) max continuous. (AS 555AN has two Turbomeca TM 319 turboshafts, each rated at 340 kW; 456 shp for take-off and 295 kW; 395 shp max continuous with full authority digital engine control (FADEC).) Two structural fuel tanks, with total usable capacity of 730 litres (193 US gallons; 160 Imp gallons), in body structure.
ACCOMMODATION: As for AS 350B₂, except sliding doors are optional on both sides (standard on military aircraft), and there are three baggage holds with external doors.
SYSTEMS, AVIONICS AND EQUIPMENT: As for AS 350B₂/550, except that twin-body servo command units and a second electrical generator are standard. Options include a second VHF/AM, radio altimeter and casualty installations. Provisions for IFR instrumentation, and SFIM 85 T31 three-axis autopilot and CDV 85 T3 nav coupler.
ARMAMENT (AS 555): Optional alternative weapons include Brandt or Forges de Zeebrugge rocket packs, Matra or FN machine-gun pods, a GIAT M621 20 mm gun, and Hot or TOW anti-tank missiles. Naval version carries two homing torpedoes in ASW role, or SAR winch.
DIMENSIONS, EXTERNAL AND INTERNAL:
As for AS 350B₂/550 except:

Height: 555	3.34 m (10 ft 11½ in)
Skid track: 555	2.08 m (6 ft 10 in)

WEIGHTS:

Weight empty: 355F₂	1,315 kg (2,900 lb)
555	1,370 kg (3,020 lb)
Max sling load: 355F₂/555	1,134 kg (2,500 lb)
Max T-O weight:	
355F₂/555, internal load	2,540 kg (5,600 lb)
355F₂/555, max slung load	2,600 kg (5,732 lb)

PERFORMANCE (AS 355F₂/555 at max T-O weight, ISA):

Never-exceed speed (structural limitation)	150 knots (278 km/h; 172 mph)
Max cruising speed at S/L	119 knots (221 km/h; 137 mph)
Max rate of climb at S/L	408 m (1,340 ft)/min
Service ceiling	3,400 m (11,150 ft)
Hovering ceiling: IGE	2,000 m (6,560 ft)
OGE	1,500 m (4,920 ft)
Radius, SAR, two survivors	70 nm (129 km; 80.5 miles)
Range with max fuel at S/L, no reserves	375 nm (695 km; 432 miles)

Endurance, AS 555, no reserves:

two torpedoes	1 h
one torpedo, or cannon or rocket pods	2 h 20 min
cannon plus rockets	1 h 50 min

Naval AS 555SR with nose radar, homing torpedoes and flotation bags

Aerospatiale AS 555AR Ecureuil 2, with additional side elevation (top) of single-engined AS 350 and scrap view of AS 355F₁ *(Pilot Press)*

AEROSPATIALE AS 365F/565 DAUPHIN 2

On 13 October 1980, the government of Saudi Arabia placed in France orders for four frigates and associated naval equipment including 24 SA 365F Dauphin 2 helicopters, based on the SA 365N. The first four of these are equipped with an Omera ORB 32 radar for search and rescue duties. The remaining 20 are anti-ship helicopters, equipped with Thomson-CSF Agrion 15 radar, Aerospatiale AS.15TT all-weather air-to-surface missiles and Crouzet MAD, for operation from both shore bases and frigates. Subsequent orders include five for Ireland, equipped with Bendix RDR 1500 search radar, SFIM 155 autopilot, CDV 155 four-axis flight director/coupler, Crouzet Nadir Mk II nav computer, ESD Cina B Doppler, Crouzet ONS 200A long-distance nav system and five-screen EFIS instrumentation, for fishery surveillance and SAR from ship and shore bases. Irish Dauphins have no AS.15 capability, but may be fitted with other forms of light armament. Early in 1988, the French Navy ordered three AS 365Fs in SAR configuration for plane guard duties on board its two aircraft carriers. Four have been ordered by the Chilean Navy. Further orders include up to 10 in utility configuration for Angola.

An AS 365N (c/n 5100) was modified to flight test the equipment and weapon systems of the AS 365F, and made its first flight in the new configuration on 22 February 1982. It was followed by the first production AS 365F (c/n 6014) on 2 July 1982, equipped as a search and rescue helicopter with arrester hook, search radar, searchlight, self-contained navigation system, automatic hover/transition coupler and rescue winch.

The latest version is designated AS 565S (formerly SA 365F₁), and is intended for search and rescue and anti-shipping and anti-submarine roles. In anti-shipping configuration it is equipped with the Agrion Plan Position radar on a roll-stabilised pivot mounting under its nose to ensure a 360° field of sweep, a total of four AS.15TT radar-guided missiles in pairs on an outrigger on each side of the fuselage, and the MAD bird on the port side of the rear fuselage. Range of the AS.15TT missile is greater than 8 nm (15 km; 9.3 miles). In addition to locating and attacking hostile warships, the AS 565S/AS.15TT can be used for coastal surveillance and ship escort duties, and to provide over-the-horizon target designation for long-range anti-ship missiles launched from ship or shore. The anti-submarine version is equipped with MAD, Thomson-Sintra ASM HS12 sonar and two homing torpedoes. The sea surveillance/SAR version is equipped with a rescue hoist, sea search radar, self-contained navigation system and automatic hover-transition coupler. All versions can be equipped with the Harpoon fast-mooring system to enable them to operate from mobile platforms.

The AS 365F₁ carries a normal crew of two, has provision for 10 passengers and is powered by two Turbomeca Arriel 1M turboshafts, each rated at 584 kW (783 shp) for take-off and with a max continuous rating of 487 kW (653 shp). Standard fuel capacity of 1,135 litres (300 US gallons; 250 Imp gallons) can be augmented by a 180 litre (47.5 US gallon; 39.6 Imp gallon) auxiliary tank. Like the current AS 365N₂, it has a larger, carbonfibre 11-blade fenestron to improve hovering performance, particularly in the most severe condition of hovering with the wind from three-quarters aft.

DIMENSIONS, EXTERNAL:
As for AS 365N₂, except:
Length overall, main rotor turning	13.68 m (44 ft 10½ in)
Length of fuselage	12.11 m (39 ft 8¾ in)
Height overall	3.99 m (13 ft 1 in)
Width over missiles	4.20 m (13 ft 9½ in)

WEIGHTS:
Weight empty	2,240 kg (4,938 lb)
Max slung load	1,600 kg (3,527 lb)
Max T-O weight, internal or external load	4,250 kg (9,370 lb)

PERFORMANCE (at average mission weight 4,000 kg; 8,819 lb):
Never-exceed speed	160 knots (296 km/h; 184 mph)
Max cruising speed at S/L	148 knots (274 km/h; 170 mph)
Max rate of climb at S/L	540 m (1,770 ft)/min
Hovering ceiling: IGE	2,600 m (8,530 ft)
OGE	1,860 m (6,100 ft)
Range with max standard fuel at S/L	432 nm (800 km; 497 miles)

Radius of action: anti-shipping, with four missiles, 120 knots cruising speed at 3,000 ft, ISA −20°C, 30 min reserves
	135 nm (250 km; 155 miles)
with two missiles	150 nm (278 km; 173 miles)

SAR, ISA +20°C, 30 mins reserves, carrying six survivors
130 nm (241 km; 150 miles)

AEROSPATIALE AS 365N₂ DAUPHIN 2

The AS 365N₂ is the current production version of the civil Dauphin. Compared with the AS 365N, described in previous editions of *Jane's*, it has improved engines and a larger carbonfibre fenestron tail rotor with eleven blades.

Orders for all versions of AS 365/366 totalled 504 for civil and military use in 40 countries by 1 January 1990. The totals included production in China (as the Harbin Z-9), as well as AS 366Gs for the US Coast Guard and AS 365F/AS.15TTs with special equipment for search and rescue, and for attacking surface ships. These last two variants are described separately.

A special aeromedical version of the AS 365N₂, with a flight crew of two, is available in two forms. An intensive care layout is arranged to carry two patients, one on each side of the cabin on a standard NATO stretcher, with space between for the doctor's seat and medical equipment. One of the stretchers can be replaced by seats for two patients, if required. The alternative ambulance configuration provides space for two stretchers on each side of the cabin, one above the other, plus room for the doctor; or a single pair of stretchers, with room for four seated persons on the other

Aerospatiale AS 365N, emergency medical services helicopter operated in the United Kingdom and sponsored by Express Newspapers *(Kenneth Munson)*

side, and a doctor. Stretchers are loaded through nose doors, with 180° opening, on both models. Those in the ambulance layout are fixed to the sides of the cabin, and the patients are carried to them on special mattresses. Six ambulance versions of the earlier AS 365N₁ were delivered to the State of Maryland in 1989, bringing to 22 the total of Dauphin 2s in US EMS (emergency medical service) use.

The latest version, designated AS 365N₂, received French certification for VFR and IFR operations in November 1989. It features uprated Arriel 1C2 turboshafts, improved gearbox, a 150 kg (331 lb) increase in max T-O weight, redesigned cabin doors, interior improvements, and optional EFIS avionics. Aerospatiale had received orders for 30 AS 365N₂s by late 1989, and expected to deliver the first production aircraft in August 1990 to Bond Helicopters of the United Kingdom, which has ordered 12 for offshore support operations in the North Sea.

The following structural description refers to the standard AS 365N₂, but is generally applicable to all versions:

TYPE: Twin-turbine commercial general purpose helicopter.
ROTOR SYSTEM: Four-blade main rotor. Blades attached by quick disconnect pins to Starflex glassfibre/carbonfibre hub, in which the three conventional hinges for each blade are replaced by a single main elastomeric bearing and inboard locator bearing, requiring no maintenance. Blades of new OA 2 section, developed in collaboration with Onera: varying from OA 212 (thickness/chord ratio 12%) at root to OA 207 (7%) at tip, with 10° twist from root to tip. Each blade comprises two Z section carbonfibre spars and carbonfibre skin, a solid glassfibre-resin leading-edge covered with a stainless steel sheath, and Nomex honeycomb filling. Leading-edge of carbonfibre tip is swept back at 45°. Ground adjustable tab on trailing-edge of each blade towards tip. Blade chord extended outboard of tab to align with tab trailing-edge. Rotor brake standard. Eleven-blade fenestron type of carbonfibre ducted fan anti-torque tail rotor.
ROTOR DRIVE: Mechanical shaft and gear drive. Transmission shaft from each engine extends forward, through freewheel, to helical and epicyclic reduction stages of main gearbox. Shaft to fenestron driven off bottom of main rotor shaft. Main rotor rpm 350. Fenestron rpm 3,665.
FUSELAGE: Semi-monocoque structure. Bottom structure and framework of front fuselage, primary machined frames fore and aft of the main gearbox platform and at the rear of the centre fuselage, floors under main gearbox and engines, cabin doors and fin are all of light alloy (AU4G). Nose and power plant fairings and fin tip of glassfibre/Nomex sandwich. Centre and rear fuselage assemblies, flight deck floor, roof, walls and bottom skins of fuel tanks of light alloy/Nomex sandwich.
TAIL UNIT: Horizontal stabiliser mid-set on rear fuselage, forward of fenestron; swept endplate fins offset 10° to

port. Construction of carbonfibre and Nomex/Rohacell sandwich.
LANDING GEAR: Hydraulically retractable tricycle type. Twin-wheel steerable and self-centring nose unit retracts rearward. Single wheel on each rearward retracting main unit, fully enclosed by doors of Kevlar/Nomex sandwich when retracted. All three units embody oleo-pneumatic shock absorber. Mainwheel tyres size 15 × 6.00, pressure 8.6 bars (125 lb/sq in); nosewheel tyres size 5.00-4, pressure 5.5 bars (80 lb/sq in). Hydraulic disc brakes.
POWER PLANT: Two Turbomeca Arriel 1C2 turboshafts, each rated at 547 kW (733 shp) for T-O and 471 kW (631 shp) max continuous, side by side aft of main rotor driveshaft, with stainless steel firewall between them. Standard fuel in four tanks under cabin floor and a fifth tank in the bottom of the centre-fuselage; total capacity 1,135 litres (300 US gallons; 249.5 Imp gallons). Provision for auxiliary tank in baggage compartment, with capacity of 180 litres (47.5 US gallons; 39.5 Imp gallons); or ferry tank in place of rear seats in cabin, capacity 475 litres (125.5 US gallons; 104.5 Imp gallons). Refuelling point above landing gear door on port side. Oil capacity 14 litres (3.7 US gallons; 3 Imp gallons).
ACCOMMODATION: Standard accommodation for pilot and co-pilot or passenger in front, and two rows of four seats to rear. High density seating for one pilot and 13 passengers. VIP configurations for four to six persons in addition to pilot. Three forward opening doors on each side. Freight hold aft of cabin rear bulkhead, with door on starboard side. Cabin heated and ventilated.
SYSTEMS: Air-conditioning system optional. Duplicated hydraulic system, pressure 60 bars (870 lb/sq in). Electrical system includes two 4.8kW starter/generators, one 24V 43Ah battery and two 250VA 115V 400Hz inverters.
AVIONICS AND EQUIPMENT: Two-pilot IFR instrument panel and SFIM 155 duplex autopilot standard. Optional avionics include EFIS, VHF and HF com/nav, VOR, ILS, ADF, transponder, DME, radar and self-contained nav system. Optional equipment includes a SFIM CDV 85 nav coupler, a 1,600 kg (3,525 lb) capacity cargo sling, and 275 kg (606 lb) capacity hoist with 90 m (295 ft) cable length.
ARMAMENT: HJ-8 anti-tank missiles flown experimentally on a Chinese Z-9 in 1988.

DIMENSIONS, EXTERNAL:
Main rotor diameter	11.94 m (39 ft 2 in)
Diameter of fenestron	1.10 m (3 ft 5⁵⁄₁₆ in)
Main rotor blade chord: basic	0.385 m (1 ft 3¼ in)
outboard of tab	0.405 m (1 ft 4 in)
Length overall, main rotor turning	13.68 m (44 ft 10⅝ in)
Length of fuselage	11.63 m (38 ft 1⅞ in)
Width, rotor blades folded	3.21 m (10 ft 6½ in)
Height to top of rotor head	3.52 m (11 ft 6½ in)
Height overall (tip of fin)	3.98 m (13 ft 0¾ in)

Aerospatiale AS 365N, Dauphin, with rescue boat hoist, serving in Japan

Wheel track	1.90 m (6 ft 2¾ in)
Wheelbase	3.61 m (11 ft 10¼ in)
Main cabin door (fwd, each side):	
Height	1.16 m (3 ft 9½ in)
Width	1.14 m (3 ft 9 in)
Main cabin door (rear, each side):	
Height	1.16 m (3 ft 9½ in)
Width	0.87 m (2 ft 10¼ in)
Baggage compartment door (stbd):	
Height	0.51 m (1 ft 8 in)
Width	0.73 m (2 ft 4¾ in)

DIMENSIONS, INTERNAL:

Cabin: Length	2.30 m (7 ft 6½ in)
Max width	1.92 m (6 ft 3½ in)
Max height	1.40 m (4 ft 7 in)
Floor area	4.20 m² (45.20 sq ft)
Volume	5.00 m³ (176 cu ft)
Baggage compartment volume	1.00 m³ (35.3 cu ft)

AREAS:

Main rotor disc	111.9 m² (1,204.5 sq ft)
Fenestron disc	0.95 m² (10.23 sq ft)

WEIGHTS:

Weight empty, equipped	4,970 kg (10,957 lb)
Max T-O weight:	
internal or external load	9,370 kg (20,657 lb)

PERFORMANCE (at max T-O weight):

Never-exceed speed at S/L	
	160 knots (296 km/h; 184 mph)
Max cruising speed at S/L	
	154 knots (285 km/h; 177 mph)
Econ cruising speed at S/L	
	140 knots (260 km/h; 161 mph)
Max rate of climb at S/L	420 m (1,379 ft)/min
Service ceiling	4,300 m (14,100 ft)
Hovering ceiling: IGE	2,550 m (8,365 ft)
OGE	1,800 m (5,905 ft)
Max range with standard fuel at S/L	
	484 nm (897 km; 557 miles)
Endurance with standard fuel	4 h

AEROSPATIALE AS 366 DAUPHIN 2
US Coast Guard designation: HH-65A Dolphin

At the 1979 Paris Air Show, Aerospatiale announced that it had won with this aircraft the competition for a helicopter to perform SRR (Short Range Recovery) duties from 18 shore bases, and from icebreakers and cutters, of the US Coast Guard. Current orders for the Coast Guard are for a total of 99 AS 366Gs, basically similar to the AS 365N but with engines and equipment of US manufacture accounting for about 60 per cent of the total cost of each aircraft.

The AS 366G (known to the Coast Guard as the HH-65A Dolphin) is powered by two Textron Lycoming LTS 101-750A-1 turboshafts, each rated at 507 kW (680 shp) and fitted with a Lucas SDS 300 full authority digital electronic control system. It normally carries a crew of three (pilot, co-pilot and aircrewman/hoist operator). Rockwell Collins is prime contractor for the advanced communications, navigation and all-weather search equipment. The communications package includes dual UHF/VHF transceivers and single UHF/FM and HF systems, plus a data link for automatic transmission of data, such as aircraft position, flight path, ground speed, wind and fuel state, to ship or shore base. A nose mounted Northrop See Hawk forward looking infra-red sensor aids rescue operations in bad weather, darkness or high seas. Important design features include the passive failure characteristics of the Dolphin's automatic flight control system, and an omnidirectional airspeed system able to provide information while the aircraft is hovering. Inflatable flotation bags are effective up to sea state 5. Under a 1988 contract, three HH-65As are to be fitted by Grumman with a prototype Fairey Hydraulics Talon lightweight decklock system.

In February 1990 the USCG signed a contract with the Light Helicopter Turbine Company for flight testing an HH-65A with an 895 kW (1,200 shp) T800 turboshaft, with a view to replacing the standard LTS 101s. Flight trials with the T800 are due to start in early 1991 and to last for 21 months. The Arriel 1C2 turboshaft which powers the AS 365N₂ Dauphin is also being considered as a possible replacement for the Textron Lycoming power plants, to which new power turbine wheels were to be installed by the manufacturer during 1990 to improve reliability.

The first AS 366G flew for the first time at Marignane on 23 July 1980. It was later shipped to Aerospatiale Helicopter Corporation in Texas for installation of avionics, and flight testing for FAA certification. DGAC certification was received on 20 July 1982. As on the AS 365F/555, the size of the tail fin and carbonfibre fenestron is increased on the operational Coast Guard aircraft, designated **AS 366G-1**. Deliveries began on 19 November 1984, and were completed on 24 April 1989. The first life-saving medevac mission was completed on 20 September 1985. In 1985, the Israel Defence Force purchased two ex-USCG trials AS 366s for an 18-month evaluation. This was completed successfully in 1987 when a contract was placed with Aerospatiale Helicopter Corporation for 20 more to HH-65A standards, bought with FMS funds. Duties will include fire control, ASW and SAR duties from 'Sa'ar' missile boats.

WEIGHTS:

Weight empty, incl mission equipment	
	2,718 kg (5,992 lb)
Max T-O weight	4,050 kg (8,928 lb)

PERFORMANCE (at max T-O weight):

Never-exceed speed	175 knots (324 km/h; 201 mph)
Max cruising speed	139 knots (257 km/h; 160 mph)
Hovering ceiling: IGE	2,290 m (7,510 ft)
OGE	1,627 m (5,340 ft)
Range: SRR	166 nm (307 km; 191 miles)
with max passenger load	216 nm (400 km; 248 miles)
with max fuel	410 nm (760 km; 471 miles)
Endurance with max fuel	4 h

AEROSPATIALE AS 565 PANTHER
Brazilian Army designation: HM-1

This multi-role military development of the Dauphin 2 was first flown in prototype form (AS 365M F-WZJV) on 29 February 1984. It has since undergone considerable refinement, and was first shown in production form, as the Panther, on 30 April 1986. Armament integration and firing trials were completed successfully in late 1986, and a second, improved prototype (F-ZVLO) was flown in April 1987.

Originally designated SA 365K, the Panther has been known since January 1990 as the AS 565:

AS 565AA. Armed version.

AS 565UA. Utility version.

Initial orders include six 565AAs and 12 UAs for Angola and 36 AAs, delivered from 1989 onwards, for Brazil's 1 BAvEx (Army Aviation Battalion) at Taubaté.

The airframe of the Panther is basically similar to that of the AS 365N₁, but with greater emphasis on survivability in combat areas. Composite materials are used exclusively for the dynamic components and for an increased (15 per cent) proportion of the fuselage structure. The crew seats are armoured, and similar protection is extended to the flying control servos and engine controls of production Panthers. Other features include a cable cutter, self-sealing fuel tanks and redundant hydraulic circuits. Further development is expected to permit continued operation of the main transmission after total loss of lubricating oil.

Aerospatiale AS 565AA Panther, armed with two 20 mm gun pods

Aerospatiale AS 565UA of the Angolan Air Force *(Ivo Sturzenegger)*

Aerospatiale AS 565AA Panther, with added side views of HH-65A Dolphin (AS 366G-1) for US Coast Guard (centre) and AS 365N₂ Dauphin 2 (top) *(Pilot Press)*

Similar attention has been paid to crashworthiness. The crew seats will tolerate 20g. The entire basic airframe is designed to withstand an impact at a vertical speed of 7 m (23 ft)/s at max T-O weight; the fuel system is capable of withstanding a 14 m (46 ft)/s crash.

The AS 565 Panther is powered by two Turbomeca Arriel 1M1 turboshafts, each rated at 558 kW (748 shp) for take-off with a contingency rating of 584 kW (783 shp) and max continuous rating of 487 kW (653 shp). Full FADEC control gives automatic engine-start sequencing and automatic limiting of power according to a variety of preselected limits. The SFIM 155 autopilot has special tactical fly-through modes. It utilises the larger carbonfibre fenestron of the AS 365F. The airframe is finished in low IR reflecting paint. Noise level is low, and radar signature is minimised by the aircraft's composite structure and special paints. The cockpit is adapted for night vision goggles. Equipment can include a Thomson-CSF TMV 011 Sherloc radar warning receiver, IR jammer and chaff dispenser.

Two world helicopter records were established by the prototype Panther on 15 September 1987 when, at a weight of 2,774 kg (6,116 lb), it achieved an altitude of 3,000 m in 2 min 54 s and 6,000 m in 6 min 14 s. It is also cleared for aerobatics.

As a high speed assault transport, the Panther will carry a crew of two and eight to ten troops over a radius of action of 215 nm (400 km; 248 miles), or 60 troops per hour over 11 nm (20 km; 12 miles). For close support missions of three-hour duration, the fuselage-side outriggers can each carry a pack of 22 Thomson-Brandt 68 mm rockets, a launcher for 19 Forges de Zeebrugge 2.75 in rockets or a 20 mm GIAT M621 gun pod with 180 rounds. Operations against fixed-wing aircraft or other helicopters are envisaged, using either 20 mm guns or four two-round packs of Matra Mistral infra-red homing air-to-air missiles. Secondary roles could include armed or unarmed reconnaissance, electronic warfare, target designation, aerial command post, search and rescue, casualty evacuation (four stretchers) and transport of up to 1,600 kg (3,525 lb) of external freight.

DIMENSIONS, EXTERNAL: As for AS 365F
WEIGHTS:

Weight empty	2,193 kg (4,835 lb)
Max slung load	1,600 kg (3,527 lb)
Max T-O weight, internal or external load	
	4,250 kg (9,369 lb)

PERFORMANCE (at average mission weight 4,000 kg; 8,818 lb):

Never-exceed speed	160 knots (296 km/h; 184 mph)
Max cruising speed at S/L	
	150 knots (278 km/h; 173 mph)
Max rate of climb at S/L	420 m (1,378 ft)/min
Hovering ceiling: IGE	2,600 m (8,531 ft)
OGE	1,850 m (6,070 ft)
Range with max standard fuel at S/L	
	472 nm (875 km; 544 miles)

AEROSPATIALE DAUPHIN X 380, DGV and FBW

On 20 March 1989, Aerospatiale flew a modified Dauphin (F-WDFK) designated X 380DTP (indicating Probationary Technical Development) fitted with a five-blade Spheriflex rotor head in place of the standard production Starflex assembly. Combining the advantages of higher flight speeds with a reduced quantity of components, Spheriflex is an integrated hub/mast unit constructed of filament-wound carbonfibre, coated with a Kevlar safety layer. The hub allows for blade attachment

Dauphin X 380DTP flying testbed for the Spheriflex five-blade rotor hub/mast unit *(Michel Isaac/GIFAS)*

Artist's impression of Hermès aerospacecraft aboard the STAR-H reusable launch vehicle

and movement through an elastomeric thrust bearing, so that reduced drag may be achieved by mounting blades close to the rotor axis. Inter-blade dampers replace the conventional drag dampers. Connection of the hub/mast to the transmission unit is via a single large diameter bearing (replacing two normally used). Blades of the X 380 have turned-down tips with leading-edge taper. The whole rotor hub is faired and integrated with a high-speed fairing for transmission and engines.

On the power of two Arriel 1C1 turboshaft engines, the X 380 is expected to achieve 181 knots (335 km/h; 208 mph), compared with a limit of 159 knots (295 km/h; 183 mph) for the production Dauphin. It will be followed by a Dauphin Grande Vitesse (DGV) fitted with two Arriel 1X power plants, each developing 624 kW (836 shp). Also employing a Spheriflex rotor, and with a reinforced structure and new servo-controls, the DGV is planned to break the 200 knot (371 km/h; 230 mph) barrier by mid-1990.

The Dauphin FBW (Fly By Wire) is a conversion of prototype No. 6001/F-WZJJ, which first flew in this new guise on 6 April 1989 and completed an initial series of tests in October. These were to be followed by an evaluation of more complex attitude control laws, initially using conventional cockpit controls, and with a sidestick controller commencing in April 1990. Traditional controls have been retained for a safety pilot on the left.

AEROSPATIALE P.120

Details of this demonstrator for a future light helicopter to be developed jointly with the People's Republic of China and Singapore may be found in the International section of this edition.

HERMÈS AEROSPACECRAFT

On 18 October 1985 it was announced that the French Centre National d'Études Spatiales (CNES) had appointed Aerospatiale as industrial prime contractor for the Hermès aerospacecraft programme. Aerospatiale will build two of the vehicles over a ten-year period. Dassault-Breguet will be responsible for the work required to achieve successful flight in the atmosphere.

The Hermès vehicle is envisaged as a delta-wing aircraft with winglets, able to carry three persons and up to three tonnes of payload. It will have a crew escape system, and a pressurised cargo compartment linked by an airlock tunnel to the rear docking port. The cargo compartment will be enclosed at the top by large sideways opening solar panels. Placed in low (460 km; 286 mile) Earth orbit by an Ariane 5 launcher, Hermès' primary mission will be to service space stations.

In late 1988, while detail design of the Hermès remained fluid, it was revealed that 1,500 kg (3,307 lb) will be saved from the previously calculated re-entry weight by housing the manoeuvring motors, radiators and docking mechanism in a truncated cone-shaped structure attached to the rear of the craft. This, the Module de Resources Hermès (MRH), would be detached from immediately behind the wing trailing-edge prior to re-entry.

During 1989 crew escape systems for Hermès were evaluated, including an ejectable crew compartment, individual ejection seats, and a launch tower escape system. The European Space Agency and CNES have recommended ejection seats, which must be able to operate during the 126 s burn time of the Ariane 5 launcher, up to an altitude of 50 km (31 miles) and Mach 5 velocity.

In preparation for subsonic flights in 1997 and a manned orbital flight in 1999, Dassault-Breguet is proposing an adapted Mystère-Falcon 900 for crew training. As an alternative to the Ariane rocket, the same firm is studying a horizontal take-off and landing vehicle for the aerospacecraft under the designation STAR-H (Système de Transport Aérobie Récupérable - Hermès). This would be powered by five turbo-rockets, each rated at some 392.27 kN (88,185 lb st), and weigh 400,000 kg (881,848 lb).

DIMENSIONS (approximate):

Wing span (winglet tip to winglet tip)	
	9.01 m (29 ft 6¾ in)
Length:	
in orbit (incl MRH)	18.29 m (60 ft 0 in)
on re-entry (Hermès only)	12.69 m (41 ft 7⅝ in)

WEIGHTS:

Launch weight	29,000 kg (63,934 lb)
Orbiting weight	23,000 kg (50,705 lb)
Re-entry weight	15,000 kg (33,069 lb)
Payload:	
outbound (incl MRH)	3,000 kg (6,614 lb)
outbound, useful load	1,600 kg (3,527 lb)
Earthbound (incl fixtures)	1,500 kg (3,307 lb)
Earthbound, useful load	580 kg (1,279 lb)
Fuel	1,500 kg (3,307 lb)

CAGNY
RAYMOND DE CAGNY
5 square des Bégonias, 91370 Verrières le Buisson
Telephone: 33 (1) 60 11 98 02

CAGNY PERFORMANCE 2000

M de Cagny is developing a unique side-by-side three-seat light aircraft, which was first displayed in the form of a full-scale mockup at the 1985 Paris Air Show.

The prototype Performance 2000 was scheduled to fly in January 1988. However, this was postponed, partly as the result of a re-design which transferred the power plant from

the leading edge of the fin (as shown in mockup form) to a pylon immediately to the rear of the cockpit, and replaced the shrouded tractor propeller with an unshrouded pusher unit.

No recent news has been received of progress on the Performance 2000. A full description and photograph may be found in the 1989-90 and earlier editions of *Jane's*.

DASSAULT AVIATION

DASSAULT AVIATION
9 Rond-Point des Champs-Elyseés, 75008 Paris
Telephone: 33 (1) 47 95 85 85
Telex: 203944 AMADAS
Fax: 33 (1) 47 41 67 89
PRESS INFORMATION OFFICE: 46 avenue Kléber, 75116 Paris
Telephone: 33 (1) 47 27 61 19
Telex: AMDPARI 643758 F
Fax: 33 (1) 47 55 10 24
WORKS: 92214 Saint-Cloud, 95100 Argenteuil,
    78140 Vélizy-Villacoublay, 33610 Martignas,
    33700 Bordeaux-Mérignac, 91120 Brétigny,
    33630 Cazaux, 64600 Biarritz-Anglet,
    64200 Biarritz-Parme, 13800 Istres,
    74370 Argonay, 59113 Lille-Seclin, 86000 Poitiers
CHAIRMAN AND CHIEF EXECUTIVE OFFICER: Serge Dassault
VICE-PRESIDENT, RESEARCH: Bruno Revellin-Falcoz
VICE-PRESIDENT, MILITARY EXPORTS: Paul-Emile Jaillard
VICE-PRESIDENT, CIVIL AIRCRAFT: Bernard Latreille
DIRECTOR, COMMUNICATIONS: Pierre Pacalon

Avions Marcel Dassault-Breguet Aviation resulted from
the merger in December 1971 of Avions Marcel Dassault
with Breguet Aviation. In January 1979, 20 per cent of its
stock was assigned to the French State, and in November
1981 the State shareholding was raised to 46 per cent. Due
to a double voting right of some of its shares, the French
State holds a majority control of the company. The name
was changed to Dassault Aviation in April 1990.

Dassault is engaged in the development and production
of military and civil aircraft, flight control system
components, maintenance and support equipment, and
CAD/CAM software. Series production of its aircraft is
undertaken under a widespread subcontracting programme,
with final assembly and flight testing handled by the
company.

Dassault has established close links with the industries of
other countries. The programme for the Atlantique
maritime patrol aircraft associates manufacturers in
Belgium, France, West Germany and Italy under the overall
responsibility of their respective governments. In the same
way the British and French governments are associated in
the SEPECAT concern, formed to control the Dassault/
BAe Jaguar programme; and the West German and French
governments are associated in the Dassault/Dornier Alpha
Jet programme. The A.C.E. International consortium has
been formed to co-ordinate the launch programme for the
future Avion de Combat Européen. Purchase of Mirage
fighters by Belgium and Spain led to Belgian and Spanish
participation in production of Dassault aircraft. Similarly,
purchase of Mirage 2000 fighters by Greece and Egypt has
led to co-production of components for this aircraft by the
Hellenic Aerospace Industry and the AOI. Dassault's
Biarritz-Parme factory manufactures fuselages for Fokker.
Since 1945, Dassault has produced more than 6,000 aircraft,
including 92 prototypes and 78 pre-series.

MIRAGE ADVANCED TECHNOLOGY UPDATE PROGRAMME

Although the first-generation Mirage (types III, 5 and 50)
remains available to special order, series production has
now ended. At the beginning of 1989, orders totalled 1,422,
of which 1,415 had been delivered, including 949 exported.
Many of these remain in service, or are in storage awaiting
re-sale.

Since 1977, Dassault has been involved in programmes to
update the navigation and attack systems, flight aids, radio
com/nav, power plant and other features of in-service
Mirage III/5/50 aircraft. In particular, several air forces
have awarded Dassault contracts to install an inertial
platform, digital computer, CRT head-up display, air-to-
ground laser rangefinder and other equipment for improved
navigational accuracy, easier target acquisition, and high
bombing precision in the various CCIP (continuous
computation of the impact point) or CCRP (continuous
computation of the release point) modes, including standoff
capability through the introduction of CCRP with initial
point. Combat efficiency in the air-to-air gunnery mode is
improved considerably by display of a highly accurate
hot-line on the HUD.

Another major improvement available for the Mirage
III/5/50 series is a flight refuelling kit able to offer an
increase of 30 to more than 100 per cent in radius of action.
Already ordered by several air forces for their Mirage 5s,
this system was demonstrated in flight before becoming
generally available to Mirage operators in 1986. It involves
lengthening the nose of the aircraft by 90 mm (3½ in) to
accommodate system changes associated with a non-
retractable probe on the starboard side, forward of the
windscreen, and a single-point pressure refuelling port for
both internal and external tanks. With the addition of a
pressure refuelling system, time for refuelling on the ground
is reduced from 15 to three minutes.

Over half the air forces operating Mirage III/5/50s have
now opted for update programmes, some of which are
undertaken at least partly by local organisations and are of
sufficient complexity to warrant mention in other national
sections in this book. Brief details are listed below.
Argentina: from 1982 onwards, up to 26 IAI Daggers

Updated Mirage III of the Brazilian Air Force

(Israeli-built Mirage 5s) underwent three-phase 'Fingir Ia',
'IIa' and 'IIIa' upgrade programme, eventually receiving a
laser rangefinder, INS, HUD, ECM equipment and
refuelling probe. **Belgium:** a 'Mirage Safety Improvement
Programme' will be applied to 15 Mirage 5BAs and five
two-seat 5BDs which will serve with No 8 Squadron until
2005. A further 36 aircraft, including 5BR recce versions,
will be withdrawn by 1993. Additions, incorporated by
SABCA as main contractor, include a Ferranti HUD,
Thomson-CSF TMV 630 laser-ranger, SAGEM nav/attack
avionics (ULISS 92 INS and UTR 90 computer), fixed
canard foreplanes, single-point pressure refuelling, pilot's
liquid oxygen system, strobe anti-collision lights and
complete re-wiring. Martin-Baker Mk 10L ejection seats
are being installed under a separate contract. **Brazil:** first of
seven ex-French Mirage IIIEs (including two converted to
tandem-seat trainers) handed over by Dassault on 30
September 1988 following a complete overhaul and
addition of foreplanes; 10 existing Mirage IIIEBRs and two
IIIDBRs being modified in Brazil from December 1989.
Chile: Mirage 50C update with foreplanes and Israeli
avionics in progress. (See ENAER Pantera.) **Colombia:**
a requirement exists for Mirage 5 updating. **Egypt:**
improvement programme for some Mirages has been
completed. **Pakistan:** update programme completed.
Peru: some 12 Mirage 5P/P3s and three 5DP/DP3s fitted
with refuelling probe, laser-ranger and other improvements,
as 5P4 and 5DP4. **South Africa:** Mirage IIIs being fitted
with foreplanes and Israeli avionics as Atlas Cheetah (which
see). **Spain:** CESELSA, with CASA as subcontractor, will
install Emerson Electric AN/APQ-159 radar, Honeywell
AN/AYK-1 mission computer, a HUD, radar warning
receiver, tactical navigation equipment and multi-function
displays, plus pressure refuelling and in-flight refuelling
probes. Re-work involves 18 Mirage IIIEEs and five
two-seat IIIBEs — the latter with provision for buddy
refuelling pods. **Switzerland:** foreplanes and avionics
improvements being installed locally in Mirage IIIS/RS
fleet by F + W (which see). **Venezuela:** six single-seat and
two two-seat aircraft to receive Atar 9K-50 power plants
and improved avionics, under designations Mirage 50EV
and 50DV respectively, deliveries beginning in June 1990.
Venezuelan aircraft have canards, a ULISS 81 INS, Cyrano
IVM3 radar and an in-flight refuelling probe. Armament
options will include Magic 2 AAMs and AM 39 Exocet
anti-ship missiles. These aircraft are being supplemented by
six new Mirage 50EVs, one new Mirage 50DV and three
refurbished second-hand Mirage 50EVs. No modification
programmes have been announced for Abu Dhabi, Gabon,
Libya or Zaïre. The type has been withdrawn from use in
Australia, Israel and Lebanon.

Several standards of equipment for modified or new
airframes have been offered by Dassault in recent years,

including the Mirage 3NG and Mirage 50M, last described
in the 1989-90 *Jane's*. Most recent of these, the **Mirage
IIIEX**, was revealed in 1989 as a modified IIIE (being
replaced in French service) with a longer, Mirage F1-type
nose; underfuselage strakes (as on Mirage 5D series); an
in-flight refuelling probe, offset to port, ahead of the
cockpit; and fixed canards. The Doppler fairing below the
forward fuselage is deleted. No purchases had been
recorded at the time of going to press.

DASSAULT AVIATION MIRAGE F1

Spanish Air Force designation: C.14

Details of the early history of the Mirage F1 can be found
in the 1977-78 *Jane's*. The prototype flew for the first time
on 23 December 1966 and was followed by three pre-series
aircraft.

The primary role of the single-seat Mirage **F1-C**
production version, to which the detailed description
applies, is that of all-weather interception at any altitude. It
is equally suitable for visual ground attack missions,
carrying a variety of external loads beneath the wings and
fuselage. Other versions include the **F1-B** two-seat version
of F1-C, the first of which made its first flight on 26 May
1976; the **F1-D** two-seat version of F1-E; the single-seat
F1-E multi-role air superiority/ground attack/
reconnaissance version for export customers, with an
inertial navigation system, nav/attack central computer,
CRT head-up display, and a large inventory of external
stores; and the single-seat **F1-R** (French Air Force **F1-CR**)
day and night reconnaissance variant. Production of the
F1-A ground attack version, with reduced equipment, a
retractable flight refuelling probe and increased fuel, has
been completed.

Many F1-Cs of the French Air Force were delivered or
modified to **F1-C-200** standard by installation of an 8 cm
(3.15 in) fuselage plug for a removable flight refuelling
probe. Export customers who have F1s equipped with
refuelling probes include Iraq, Libya, Morocco, South
Africa and Spain.

By January 1990, a total of 731 Mirage F1s had been
ordered and deliveries made to: France (251 including five
prototypes), Ecuador (two F1-JE and 16 JA, equivalent to
F1-B and E), Greece (40 F1-CG), Iraq (98 F1-EQs and 15
BQs), Jordan (two F1-BJ, 17 CJ — to be upgraded to EJ —
and 17 EJ), Kuwait (six F1-BK and 27 CK), Libya (six
F1-BD, 16 AD and 16 ED), Morocco (30 F1-CH and 20
EH), Qatar (two F1-DDA and 13 EDA), South Africa (32
F1-AZ and 16 CZ) and Spain (six F1-BE, 45 CE and 22 EE).
Production was due to end in 1990 with the last of a
follow-on batch of 16 for Iraq.

The first production F1 flew on 15 February 1973 and

Dassault Aviation Mirage IIIEX upgraded version of the basic Mirage IIIE

Dassault Aviation Mirage F1-C-200 reconnaissance fighter, with additional side view (upper) of Mirage F1-B *(Pilot Press)*

was delivered officially to the French Air Force on 14 March 1973. The first unit to receive the F1 was the 30e Escadre at Reims, which became operational in early 1974. This now has two and a half squadrons of F1-Cs (the half detached to Djibouti) and an OCU squadron of F1-Bs, whilst the 12e Escadre de Chasse at Cambrai has three squadrons of F1-Cs. A further 55 F1-C-200s, made surplus by conversion of units to Mirage 2000Cs, are to be issued to Mirage IIIE, 5F and/or Jaguar squadrons in the tactical attack role. Designated **Mirage F1-CT**, they will receive a radar upgrade to Cyrano IVMR standard, INS and navigation computer, as described for the Mirage F1-CR below, plus Martin-Baker F10M ejection seats, radar warning receivers and air-to-ground ordnance. The 1990 defence budget includes funding for the first 19 conversions, plus authorisation for a further 22, deliveries being due from late 1991. A prototype conversion was begun at Biarritz-Parme in 1989 and will begin trials at Istres in 1991. Remaining aircraft will be re-worked at the Atelier Industriel de l'Air at Clermont-Ferrand.

Deliveries of the F1-C series to the French Air Force totalled 162, made up of 83 F-1Cs and 79 F1-C-200s. Twenty tandem-seat F-1Bs were delivered to an OCU squadron, initially at Orange, from June 1980; each aircraft is equipped with the same radar, weapon system and air-to-air missiles as the F1-C, but has no internal guns. Fuel capacity is reduced by 450 litres (119 US gallons; 99 Imp gallons); empty weight increased by 200 kg (441 lb); and the forward fuselage extended by 30 cm (11¾ in).

The French Air Force also purchased F1-CRs to re-equip the three squadrons of the 33e Escadre de Reconnaissance, at Strasbourg. These aircraft are designated **F1-CR-200** (having a fixed in-flight refuelling probe) and differ from the F1-C in being fitted with the IVMR model of Cyrano radar (with additional ground mapping, contour mapping, air-ground ranging and blind let-down modes), a Sagem Uliss 47 inertial platform and ESD 182 navigation computer. An SAT SCM2400 Super Cyclope infra-red linescan reconnaissance system replaces the starboard gun, and an undernose bay houses either a 75 mm Thomson-TRT 40 panoramic camera or a 150 mm Thomson-TRT 33 vertical camera. French aircraft have a secondary ground attack role and may also carry a centreline podded sensor in the form of a Thomson-CSF Raphaël TH SLAR or a Thomson-CSF Astac electronic reconnaissance system for detection of ground radars. Several types of sensor pod are available for fitment to export Mirage F1-Es. The first of two F1-CR-200 prototypes flew on 20 November 1981. Sixty-four (including the prototypes) were ordered for the French Air Force. The first production F1-CR-200 flew on 10 November 1982, and

Chaff/flare dispenser on rear fuselage of Moroccan Mirage F1-EH *(AGPPA)*

the first squadron (2/33) became operational in July 1983. Deliveries were completed in 1987 and the third and last squadron of 33e Escadre converted from Mirage III-Rs in 1988.

Export F1-Cs have a radar similar to Cyrano IV or IVM. Export F1-Es have radar similar to Cyrano IVMR but repackaged to save space. Mirage F1-EQ5s and EQ6s of the Iraqi Air Force are equipped to carry Exocet anti-ship missiles and laser guided weapons such as the AS.30L missile and Matra 400 kg laser guided bomb. They have Thomson-CSF Agave radar.

The Mirage F1 is produced by Dassault Aviation in co-operation with the Belgian company Sabca, in which Dassault Aviation has a parity interest, and CASA of Spain, which is building fuselage sections for all Mirage F1s ordered. Dassault Aviation also has a technical and industrial co-operation agreement with the Armaments Development and Production Corporation of South Africa Ltd (Armscor), whereby the latter company has rights to build the Mirage F1 under licence. Mirage F1 flying hours passed 1,000,000 in June 1989.

The following abbreviated description applies to the F1-C-200 production version for the French Air Force, except where indicated:

TYPE: Single-seat multi-mission fighter and attack aircraft.

WINGS: All-metal two-spar torsion box structure. Trailing-edge control surfaces of honeycomb sandwich construc-

tion, with carbonfibre aileron skin. Entire leading-edge can be drooped hydraulically (manually for T-O and landing, automatic in combat). Two differentially operating double-slotted flaps and one aileron on each trailing-edge. Two spoilers on each wing, ahead of flaps.

FUSELAGE: Conventional all-metal semi-monocoque structure. Titanium alloy is used for landing gear trunnions, engine firewall and certain other major structures. High tensile steel wing attachment points. Large hydraulically actuated door type airbrake in forward underside of each intake trunk.

TAIL UNIT: Single-spar fin. All-moving tailplane mid-set on fuselage, and actuated hydraulically by electric or manual control.

LANDING GEAR: Retractable tricycle type, by Messier-Hispano-Bugatti. Hydraulic retraction, nose unit rearward, main units upward into rear of intake trunk fairings. Twin wheels on each unit. Messier-Hispano-Bugatti brakes and anti-skid units. Brake parachute in bullet fairing at base of rudder.

POWER PLANT: One SNECMA Atar 9K-50 turbojet, rated at 70.6 kN (15,873 lb st) with afterburning. Fuel in integral tanks in wings (combined capacity 375 litres; 99 US gallons; 82.5 Imp gallons), and three main tanks and one inverted-flight supply tank (combined capacity 3,925 litres; 1,037 US gallons; 863.5 Imp gallons) in fuselage. Total internal fuel capacity 4,300 litres (1,136 US gallons; 946 Imp gallons). Provision for two jettisonable auxiliary fuel tanks (each 1,200 litres; 317 US gallons; 264 Imp gallons) to be carried on inboard wing pylons, plus a single tank of 2,200 litres (581 US gallons; 484 Imp gallons) capacity on the underfuselage station. Non-retractable, but removable, flight refuelling probe on starboard side of nose optional.

ACCOMMODATION: SEM Martin-Baker F1RM4 ejection seat for pilot, under rearward hinged canopy (SEM Martin-Baker F10M rocket seat in latest F1-Cs and in F1-E and F1-CR. Two Mk 10 seats with inter-seat sequence system in F1-B). No-delay through-the-canopy escape system.

SYSTEMS: Two independent hydraulic systems, pressure 207 bars (3,000 lb/sq in), for landing gear actuation, flaps and flying controls. Electrical system includes two Auxilec 15kVA variable speed alternators. DC power provided by two transformer-rectifiers operating in conjunction with battery.

AVIONICS AND EQUIPMENT: Thomson-CSF Cyrano IV fire control radar in nose. LMT Tacan, LMT NR-AI-4-A IFF, remote setting interception system, three-axis generator, central air data computer, SFIM spherical indicator with ILS pointers, Crouzet Type 63 navigation indicator, SFENA 505 autopilot and CSF head-up display, with wide field-of-view double-converter. (Standard equipment on F-1E includes Sagem Uliss 47 INS, EMD 182 central digital computer for nav/attack computations, TH C8F VE-120C CRT head-up display, Crouzet air data computer and digital armament/nav control panels.)

ARMAMENT AND OPERATIONAL EQUIPMENT: Standard installed armament of two 30 mm DEFA 553 cannon, with 135 rds/gun, mounted in lower central fuselage. Max theoretical external combat load 6,300 kg (13,890 lb), comprising 2,100 kg (4,630 lb) on centreline pylon; 1,300 kg (2,866 lb) on each inner wing pylon; 550 kg (1,213 lb) on each outer wing pylon; 150 kg (331 lb) on each wingtip AAM rail (Matra 550 Magic or AIM-9 Sidewinder) and 100 kg (220 lb) of chaff/flare dispensers on each fuselage shoulder position. Practical max operational load is 4,000 kg (8,818 lb). Externally mounted weapons for interception role include Matra Super 530 air-to-air missiles under inboard wing pylons. For ground attack, typical loads may include one ARMAT anti-radar missile, or one AM39 Exocet anti-ship missile, or up to fourteen 250 kg bombs, thirty anti-runway bombs or 144 Thomson-Brandt rockets. Other possible external loads include auxiliary fuel tanks, a Thomson-CSF Atlis laser designator pod with AS.30L missiles or 400 kg laser guided bombs, air-to-surface missiles, and sensor pods comprising a Thomson-CSF Raphaël SLAR, a Thomson-TRT/Dassault Harold long-range oblique photographic unit (1,700 mm Thomson-TRT 38), a Thomson-TRT/Dassault COR2 multi-purpose pod (visual spectrum and IR linescan), a Thomson-CSF TMV 018 Syrel real-time electro-optical reconnaissance pod, a Dassault Nora real-time video pod and a Thomson-CSF Astac ground radar detector unit. A Thomson-CSF BF radar warning receiver is standard, and a range of jamming (Barracuda, Barem, Barrax) and chaff/flare (Phimat, Sycomor) pods may be fitted. Some Moroccan F1-EHs and Spanish F1-CEs have chaff/flare dispensers scabbed to each side of rear fuselage.

DIMENSIONS, EXTERNAL (F1-C):

Wing span: without missiles	8.40 m (27 ft 6¾ in)
over Magic missiles	approx 9.32 m (30 ft 6¾ in)
Length overall: F1-C	15.23 m (49 ft 11¾ in)
F1-C-200	15.30 m (50 ft 2½ in)
F1-B	15.53 m (50 ft 11½ in)
Height overall	4.50 m (14 ft 9 in)

AREA:

Wings, gross	25.00 m² (269.1 sq ft)

Dassault Aviation Mirage F1-EDA of the Qatar Emiri Air Force with COR2 reconnaissance pod
(Ivo Sturzenegger)

WEIGHTS AND LOADING (F1-C):

Weight empty	7,400 kg (16,314 lb)
T-O weight, clean	10,900 kg (24,030 lb)
Max T-O weight	16,200 kg (35,715 lb)

PERFORMANCE (F1-C):

Max level speed: high altitude	Mach 2.2
low altitude	Mach 1.2
(800 knots; 1,480 km/h; 920 mph EAS)	
Max rate of climb at S/L (with afterburning)	
	12,780 m (41,930 ft)/min
Service ceiling	20,000 m (65,600 ft)
Stabilised supersonic ceiling	16,000 m (52,500 ft)
T-O run (AUW of 11,500 kg; 25,355 lb)	
	600 m (1,970 ft)
Landing run (AUW of 8,500 kg; 18,740 lb)	
	670 m (2,200 ft)

Combat radius:
hi-lo-hi at Mach 0.75/0.88, with fourteen 250 kg bombs and max internal fuel, with reserves
230 nm (425 km; 265 miles)
lo-lo with one Exocet and two external tanks, with reserves and including missile flight path
378 nm (700 km; 435 miles)
Combat air patrol endurance, with two Super 530 missiles and underbelly tank, with reserves, incl one attack at ceiling
2 h 15 min

DASSAULT AVIATION MIRAGE 2000
Indian Air Force name: Vajra

The Mirage 2000 was selected on 18 December 1975 as the primary combat aircraft of the French Air Force from the mid-1980s. Under French government contract, it was developed initially as an interceptor and air superiority fighter, powered by a single SNECMA M53 turbofan and with Thomson-CSF RDM multi-mode Doppler radar. The Mirage 2000 is equally suitable for reconnaissance, close support, and low altitude attack missions in areas to the rear of a battlefield. Its early history has been outlined in previous editions of *Jane's*. On the basis of structural testing, the Mirage 2000 airframe was approved for a load factor of +9g and rate of roll of 270°/s in subsonic and supersonic flight, clean or with four air-to-air missiles.

A SNECMA M53-2 turbofan, rated at 83.4 kN (18,740 lb st), was fitted for early prototype testing, and was replaced in 1980 by the uprated M53-5 which also powers early production aircraft. Export aircraft have the more powerful M53-P2, which was introduced on French Air Force Mirage 2000Cs from No. 38 onwards (and 2000Bs from c/n 516 -the sixteenth) in 1987 in conjunction with Thomson-CSF RDI pulse-Doppler radar. These aircraft are sometimes referred to as **2000 RDIs**.

The first production **Mirage 2000C** flew on 20

Two-seat Dassault Aviation Mirage 2000B in slow-speed/high-AoA configuration *(Paul Jackson)*

November 1982 and deliveries began in 1983. The first production **Mirage 2000B** two-seat trainer flew on 7 October 1983. Escadron de Chasse (EC) 1/2 'Cigognes' was the first French Air Force unit to become operational, at Dijon on 2 July 1984. EC 3/2 'Alsace' followed in 1986 and Escadron de Chasse et de Transformation (ECT) 2/2 'Côte d'Or', the OCU with Mirage 2000Bs and three 2000Cs, in early 1987. Eventually, Mirage 2000Cs will equip four wings (escadres), each with three interceptor squadrons. Deliveries of 2000Cs with RDI radar and M53-P2 engines began on 20 July 1988 to EC 1/5 'Vendée' at Orange, the squadron being declared operational on 1 April 1989. The second component of 5e Escadre de Chasse (EC 2/5 'Ile de France') followed on 1 April 1990. The designation **'2000DA'** (Défense Aérienne) is used loosely in collective reference to Mirage 2000Bs and Cs.

Following a mid-1979 go-ahead, the first of two prototypes of the **Mirage 2000N** two-seat low-altitude penetration version made its first flight on 3 February 1983; the second flew on 21 September 1983. Strengthened for flight at a typical 600 knots (1,110 km/h; 690 mph) at 60 m (200 ft) above the terrain, this version was intended basically as a vehicle for the ASMP medium-range air-to-surface nuclear missile, and has ESD Antilope V terrain following radar, two Sagem inertial platforms, improved TRT AHV-12 radio altimeter, Thomson-CSF colour CRT, an Omera vertical camera, special ECM and two Magic air-to-air missiles for self defence. Currently the 2000N is cleared for automatic terrain-following at 91 m

(300 ft). A reduction to the design altitude is expected after further trials. Production deliveries began on 19 February 1987, and EC 1/4 'Dauphiné' at Luxeuil received its first on 30 March 1988, being declared operational on 1 July 1988. EC 2/4 'La Fayette' followed on 1 July 1989. Third squadron was EC 3/4 'Limousin', which is detached to Istres, on 1 July 1990. The aircraft of this unit are ASMP-capable, but will be used in conventional roles only.

Excluding seven prototypes, France plans to fund 372 Mirage 2000s by 1994, taking delivery of the last 2000C in 1998 and the final 2000N' in 2000. The latter — N Prime — is an attack version not equipped to carry ASMP. A 1989 government decision to reduce nuclear delivery systems resulted in a change of emphasis between the N and N' variants, the Armée de l'Air targets now being 23 2000Bs, 169 2000Cs, 75 2000Ns and 105 2000N's, of which 23, 136, 75 and 39, respectively, were on firm order at 1 January 1990. A further 10 2000C and 18 N' aircraft were due to be funded in 1990. Production of the N will be completed in 1992 before N' deliveries begin. Wings are manufactured at Martignas, fuselages at Argenteuil; final assembly and flight testing take place at Mérignac. Origin of contents, by value, of a Mirage 2000C include SNECMA 27 per cent, Dassault 26 per cent, Thomson-CSF 12 per cent, Aerospatiale 5 per cent and ESD 5 per cent. By January 1990, 255 Mirage 2000s (including 126 for export) had been delivered from 442 on firm order.

Export customers for 169 Mirage 2000s comprise Abu Dhabi, Egypt, India, Peru and Greece, some of which have chosen the **Mirage 2000E** multi-role variant. A compatible trainer variant is designated **2000D**. The Egyptians placed an initial firm contract for 20 (16 2000EM and 4 BM, all with M53-P2 engines) in January 1982. The first was delivered on 30 June 1986. India placed an initial order for 40 in October 1982 (36 2000H and 4 TH), the last of which were delivered in 1986. The four THs and 26 of the Hs had M53-5 engines temporarily; the final 10 Hs were powered from the start by the M53-P2. First flight by a 2000H (KF-101) was made on 21 September 1984, followed in early 1985 by the first TH (KT-201). The first of two Indian squadrons (No. 7 'Battle Axe') was formed at Gwalior AB on 29 June 1985, when the Mirage 2000 received the Indian name **Vajra** (Divine Thunder). A follow-on order for nine aircraft (six Hs and three THs) was signed in March 1986 and executed by late 1988 to complete No.1 'Tigers' Squadron. Peru ordered 26 aircraft in December 1982 (24 2000P and 2 DP), but reduced the total subsequently to 12 (10 2000P and 2 DP). The first 2000DP was handed over on 7 June 1985 to begin pilot training in France and is now with Escuadrón 214 of Grupo Aéreo de Caza 4 at La Joya. Abu Dhabi has ordered 36 (22 2000EAD, 8 RAD and 6 DAD); deliveries were due to begin in 1986 but were delayed for fitment of additional equipment, including provision for carrying US weapons, such as Sidewinder AAMs. Deliveries to Maqatra/Al Dhafra began on 7 November 1989. The RAD reconnaissance version for this customer is fitted with a COR2 multi-camera pod, but may alternatively carry SLAR 2000 (Raphaël type) or Harold pods. The second 18 for Abu Dhabi are fitted with Elettronica ELT/158 threat-warning receivers and ELT/558 self-protection jammers. Greece ordered 40 (36 2000EGM and four 2000BGM) in July 1985, and received the first on 21 March 1988. They serve 331 and 332 Mire within 114 Pterix at Tanagra. Jordan ordered 10 2000EJs and two DJs in April 1988 and will take delivery from early 1991 onwards.

A two-stage private venture update programme announced by Dassault in 1987 includes the **2000-3** with Rafale-type cockpit multifunction displays, flown in 1988. Addition of Thomson-CSF RDY radar and a new central processing unit will produce the **2000-5** air defence variant or APSI (advanced pilot-system interface) Mirage, which will also feature a Thomson-CSF VEH 3020 holographic HUD and compatibility with Matra Mica air-to-air missiles. A prototype of the -3 (BX1 ex-No. 501) flew on 10 March 1988, and the RDY radar flew in a Mirage 2000 (BY1 ex-No. B01) for the first time in May 1988. The 2000-5 is intended for export, as is the **2000S** (strike), a

Dassault Aviation Mirage 2000C of current series with M53-P2 engine and RDI radar *(SIRPA "AIR")*

Dassault Aviation Mirage 2000N, with added side view (bottom) of Mirage 2000C *(Pilot Press)*

conventional attack version of the 2000N' announced in April 1989. Both versions will become available in 1993.

The following description applies to the single-seat Mirage 2000C, except where indicated:

TYPE: Single-seat interceptor, air superiority and multi-role fighter.

WINGS: Cantilever multi-spar low-wing monoplane of delta planform, with cambered profile. Leading-edge sweepback 58°; trailing-edge sweepforward 3° 30'. Large radius root fairings. Full span two-segment automatic leading-edge slats provide variable camber in combat, but are retracted during all phases of acceleration and low altitude cruise, to reduce drag. Slat downward depression, 17° 30' for inboard section; 30° outboard. Two-section elevons, forming entire trailing-edge of each wing, have carbonfibre skin, with AG5 light alloy honeycomb core. Elevon movement range −16° to +25°. Fly by wire control system for elevons and slats, with surfaces actuated by hydraulic servo units. No tabs. Retractable airbrake above and below each wing.

FUSELAGE: Conventional semi-monocoque structure, waisted in accordance with area rule; of conventional all-metal construction except for glassfibre radome and carbonfibre/light alloy honeycomb panel over avionics compartment, immediately aft of canopy. Small fixed strake, with marked dihedral, near leading-edge of each air intake trunk.

TAIL UNIT: Cantilever, twin-spar fin and inset rudder only; latter actuated by fly by wire control system via hydraulic servo units. Much of fin skin and all rudder skin of boron/epoxy/carbon composites with a light alloy structure for the fin and light alloy honeycomb core for the rudder. Sweepback on fin leading-edge 53°; trailing-edge 17°. No tab.

LANDING GEAR: Retractable tricycle type by Messier-Hispano-Bugatti, with twin nosewheels, and single wheel on each main unit. Hydraulic retraction, nosewheels rearward, main units inward. Oleo-pneumatic shock absorbers. Electro-hydraulic nosewheel steering, through 45° to each side. Manual disconnect permits nosewheel unit to castor through 360° for ground towing. Light alloy wheels and tubeless tyres, size 360 × 135-6, pressure 8.0 bars (116 lb/sq in) on nosewheels, size 750 × 230-15, pressure 15.0 bars (217 lb/sq in) on mainwheels. Messier-Hispano-Bugatti hydraulically actuated polycrystalline graphite disc brakes on mainwheels, with anti-skid units. Runway arrester gear standard. Brake-chute in canister above jet nozzle.

POWER PLANT: One SNECMA M53-P2 turbofan, rated at 64.3 kN (14,462 lb st) dry and 95.1 kN (21,385 lb st) with afterburning. Movable half-cone centrebody in each air intake. Internal fuel capacity 4,000 litres (1,057 US gallons; 880 Imp gallons) in 2000C, 3,920 litres (1,035 US gallons; 862 Imp gallons) in 2000B. Provision for one jettisonable 1,300 litre (343 US gallon; 286 Imp gallon) fuel tank under centre of fuselage, and a 1,700 litre (449 US gallon; 374 Imp gallon) drop tank under each wing. Total internal/external fuel capacity 8,700 litres (2,298 US gallons; 1,914 Imp gallons) in 2000C, 8,620 litres (2,276 US gallons; 1,896 Imp gallons) in 2000B. Detachable flight refuelling probe forward of cockpit on starboard side. Drop tanks of 2,000 litres (528 gallons; 440 Imp gallons) are available for the 2000N.

ACCOMMODATION: Pilot only in 2000C, on SEMB licence-built Martin-Baker F10Q zero/zero ejection seat, under transparent canopy, in air-conditioned and pressurised cockpit. Canopy hinged at rear to open upward.

SYSTEMS: ABG-Semca air-conditioning and pressurisation system. Two independent hydraulic systems, pressure 280 bars (4,000 lb/sq in), to actuate flying control servo units, landing gear and brakes. Hydraulic flow rate 110 litres (29 US gallons; 24 Imp gallons)/min. Electrical system includes two Auxilec 20110 aircooled 20kVA 400Hz constant frequency alternators, two Bronzavia DC transformers, a SAFT 40Ah battery and ATEI static inverter. Fly by wire flight control system. Eros oxygen system.

AVIONICS AND EQUIPMENT: Thomson-CSF RDM multi-mode radar or RDI pulse-Doppler radar, each with operating range of 54 nm (100 km; 62 miles). (Mirage 2000N has ESD/Thomson-CSF Antilope V terrain-following and ground mapping radar.) Sagem Uliss 52 inertial platform, ESD Type 2084 central digital computer and Digibus digital data bus, Thomson-CSF TMV-980 data display system (VE-130 head-up and VMC-180 head-down) (two head-down in 2000N), Sfena 605 autopilot, Thomson-CSF/ESD ECM with VCM-65 display (jammers on leading-edge of fin and in bullet fairing at base of rudder; chaff/flare dispenser under fuselage at wing trailing-edge), Matra Spirale passive counter-measures, LMT Deltac Tacan, LMT NRAI-7A IFF transponder, Socrat 8900 solid-state VOR/ILS and IO-300-A marker beacon receiver, TRT radio altimeter (AHV-6 in 2000B and C, AHV-9 in export aircraft, AHV-12 in 2000N), TRT ERA 7000 V/UHF com transceiver, TRT ERA 7200 UHF or EAS secure voice com, Thomson-CSF Serval radar warning receiver (antennae at each wingtip and on trailing-edge of fin, near tip), Crouzet type 90 air data computer, and Thomson-CSF Atlis laser designator and marked target seeker (in pod on forward starboard underfuselage station). Omera vertical camera in 2000N.

Dassault Aviation Mirage 2000N, externally representative of 2000S, fitted with ATLIS laser/designator and AS 30L ASMs

Dassault Aviation Mirage 2000EGM of the Greek Air Force (*Aviaplans*)

ARMAMENT: Two 30 mm DEFA 554 guns in 2000C and 2000E (not fitted in B, D or N), with 125 rds/gun. Nine attachments for external stores, five under fuselage and two under each wing. Fuselage centreline and inboard wing stations each stressed for 1,800 kg (3,968 lb) loads; other four fuselage points for 400 kg (882 lb) each, and outboard wing points for 300 kg (661 lb) each. Typical interception weapons comprise two Matra Super 530D or (with RDM radar) 530F missiles (inboard) and two Matra 550 Magic or Magic 2 missiles (outboard) under wings. Alternatively, each of the four underwing hardpoints can carry a Magic. Primary weapon for 2000N is ASMP tactical nuclear missile. In an air-to-surface role, the Mirage 2000 can carry up to 6,300 kg (13,890 lb) of external stores, including eighteen Matra 250 kg retarded bombs or Thomson-Brandt BAP 100 anti-runway bombs; sixteen Durandal penetration bombs; one or two Matra BGL 1,000 kg laser guided bombs; five or six Matra Belouga cluster bombs or Thomson-Brandt BM 400 400 kg modular bombs; one Rafaut F2 practice bomb launcher; two Aerospatiale AS 30L, Matra Armat anti-radar, or Aerospatiale AM39 Exocet anti-ship, air-to-surface missiles; four Matra LR F4 rocket launchers, each with eighteen 68 mm rockets; two packs of 100 mm rockets; a Dassault CC 630 gun pod, containing two 30 mm cannon and ammunition; a Dassault COR2 multi-camera pod or Dassault AA-3-38 Harold long-range oblique photographic (Lorop) pod; a Thomson-CSF Atlis laser designator/marked target seeker pod; two Thomson-CSF DB 3141/3163 self-defence ECM pods; one Thomson-CSF Caiman offensive or intelligence ECM pod; or an Intertechnique 231-300 buddy type in-flight refuelling pod. Fuselage centreline and inboard underwing stations are wet for carriage of fuel drop tanks (see Power Plant paragraph for details). For air defence weapon training, a Cubic Corpn AIS (airborne instrumentation subsystem) pod, externally resembling a Magic missile, can replace the Magic on its launch rail, enabling pilot to simulate a firing without carrying the actual missile.

DIMENSIONS, EXTERNAL:

Wing span	9.13 m (29 ft 11½ in)
Wing aspect ratio	2.03
Length overall: 2000C	14.36 m (47 ft 1¼ in)
2000B, N	14.55 m (47 ft 9 in)
Height overall: 2000C	5.20 m (17 ft 0¾ in)
2000B, N	5.15 m (16 ft 10¾ in)
Wheel track	3.40 m (11 ft 1¾ in)
Wheelbase	5.00 m (16 ft 4¾ in)

AREA:

Wings, gross	41.0 m² (441.3 sq ft)

WEIGHTS AND LOADING:

Weight empty: 2000C	7,500 kg (16,534 lb)
2000B	7,600 kg (16,755 lb)
Max internal fuel: 2000C	3,160 kg (6,967 lb)
2000B	3,095 kg (6,823 lb)
Max external fuel: 2000C	3,720 kg (8,201 lb)
2000B	3,715 kg (8,190 lb)
Max external stores load	6,300 kg (13,890 lb)
T-O weight clean: 2000C	10,860 kg (23,940 lb)
2000B	10,960 kg (24,165 lb)
Max T-O weight: 2000C and B	17,000 kg (37,480 lb)
Max wing loading:	
2000C and B	414.63 kg/m² (84.97 lb/sq ft)

PERFORMANCE (Mirage 2000C):

Max level speed	over Mach 2.2
Max continuous speed	Mach 2.2
	(800 knots; 1,482 km/h; 921 mph IAS)

Max speed at low altitude without afterburning, carrying eight 250 kg bombs and two Magic missiles
over 600 knots (1,110 km/h; 690 mph)

Min speed in stable flight	100 knots (185 km/h; 115 mph)
Max rate of climb at S/L	17,060 m (56,000 ft)/min

Time to 15,000 m (49,200 ft) and Mach 2   4 min
Time from brake release to intercept target flying at Mach 3 at 24,400 m (80,000 ft)   less than 5 min

Service ceiling	18,000 m (59,000 ft)

Range: with four 250 kg bombs
more than 800 nm (1,480 km; 920 miles)
with two 1,700 litre drop tanks
more than 1,000 nm (1,850 km; 1,150 miles)
with one 1,300 litre and two 1,700 litre drop tanks
1,800 nm (3,335 km; 2,073 miles)

g limits:	+9 normal
	+13.5 ultimate

DASSAULT AVIATION SUPER ÉTENDARD

Production of the original, carrier-based, version of this single-seat transonic strike fighter for the navies of France (71 aircraft) and Argentina (14 aircraft) ended in 1983. However, in late 1986 the French Navy signed a contract to initiate study of a weapon system modernisation, including replacement of the existing Agave radar by ESD Anémone, having twice the detection range against surface targets; a new SAGEM INS and UAT 90 computer; a Thomson-CSF wide-angle HUD with TV or IR overlay, and cockpit modernisation, including an electronic warfare display screen, HOTAS controls and provision for pilot's night vision goggles. An additional fuselage stores pylon will be added. Minimal structural changes are required for the aircraft to achieve an extended life of 6,500 hours by 2005, when replacement by Rafale Ms is to begin.

The first two of an eventual 56 re-worked aircraft will be delivered by Dassault late in 1992, the remainder being modified by the navy's Atelier Aéronautique at Cuers. Initial conversions will temporarily retain Agave radar, as Anémone will not be available until mid-1994. Thomson-CSF TMV 011 Sherloc radar warning receivers will also be a later retrofit.

Offers by Dassault to re-launch Super Étendard production for land-based operations, and to transfer production to IPTN of Indonesia, have not been taken up. A full description appeared in the 1982-83 edition of *Jane's*, and expanded weapon options for the land-based version in 1989-90.

DASSAULT AVIATION RAFALE A

Known initially as the ACX (advanced combat experimental), the **Rafale A** ('Squall') is an experimental prototype that was built to demonstrate technologies applicable to the tactical combat aircraft (ACT) needed to replace French Air Force Jaguars in the 1990s, and to the ship-based combat aircraft (ACM: avion de combat marine) proposed for deployment on the French Navy's nuclear powered aircraft carrier. The production versions will be known as **Rafale D** and **M** and are described separately. The design philosophy and early history of the Rafale programme are explained in the 1989-90 edition of *Jane's*.

Rafale A was rolled out of the Saint-Cloud assembly plant on 14 December 1985, and exceeded Mach 1.3 during its first test flight on 4 July 1986. Mach 1.8 was achieved during the sixth flight. After completion of 90 flights, on 13 January 1987, the aircraft's test instrumentation was updated. Subsequent performance measurements on 4 March 1987 demonstrated a stabilised speed of Mach 2 at 13,000 m (42,650 ft). On 30 April 1987, the prototype performed successfully a series of carrier approaches to the French Navy's aircraft carrier *Clémenceau*, without touchdown. The aircraft has been subjected to load factors of +9*g*/-3.6*g* and angles of attack up to 32°. By July 1989 the Rafale A had completed some 440 flights totalling 363 hours, including 300 simulated deck landings by day and night on the runway at Istres and 92 practice approaches (without contact) to the carriers *Clémenceau* and *Foch*. Twenty-one pilots had flown it (five from Dassault, six from the CEV, six from the Armeé de l'Air, three from Aéronavale, and one from SNECMA). Rafale A began trials in April 1989 with digital flight controls and optical fibre transmission. The aircraft was laid-up in late 1989 for installation of a SNECMA M88-2 reheated turbofan in the port engine bay. It resumed flying on 27 February 1990, although no plans exist for fitment of a second M88.

Brief details of Rafale A appear below.

TYPE: Single-seat twin-engined experimental combat aircraft.
WINGS, FUSELAGE, FOREPLANES, TAIL UNIT, LANDING GEAR: Similar to Rafale D and M.
POWER PLANT: Two General Electric F404-GE-400 augmented turbofans, in 71.2 kN (16,000 lb st) class, mounted side by side in rear fuselage. Port F404 replaced by trials SNECMA M88 Mk 2 in 1990. Kidney shape plain air intakes, with splitter plates, mounted low on centre-fuselage. Integral tanks in fuselage and wings for more than 4,250 kg (9,370 lb) of fuel.
DIMENSIONS, EXTERNAL:
Wing span	11.20 m (36 ft 9 in)
Length overall	15.80 m (51 ft 10 in)
Wheel track	2.675 m (8 ft 9¼ in)
Wheelbase	5.185 m (17 ft 0¼ in)

AREA:
Wings, gross	47.0 m² (506.0 sq ft)

DASSAULT AVIATION RAFALE D and M

Production versions of the Rafale will be slightly smaller and lighter than the prototype, although the general configuration is to be identical except for deletion of the air intake at the base of the tail fin. Dassault foresees a market for 800 to 1,200 Rafales, of which 250 are required by the French Air Force and 86 by the French Navy. International partners have been sought for the development and production phases, although none had come forward by early 1990.

Five prototypes are planned of the three production versions. The air force is to receive the **Rafale D** (for Discret, or 'Stealthy') in both single and two-seat trainer form which, following Mirage precedent, will be the **C** and **B** sub-types, respectively. Naval aviation is assigned the monoplace **Rafale M** (Marine). The first prototype, single-seat C01, was ordered on 21 April 1988 and will fly in February 1991 as the first Rafale with M88 engines in both engine bays. Second prototype M01, ordered December 1988, is to follow soon afterwards, and both these aircraft will have basic avionics only. A third prototype was ordered on 12 July 1989 as two-seat B01, being the first with RBG radar fitted when it flies in 1992.

Dassault Aviation Rafale A twin-engined experimental combat aircraft (*Katsuhiko Tokunaga DACT*)

Dassault Aviation Rafale A experimental combat aircraft (*Pilot Press*)

Aircraft C02 and M02 will complete the programme, but had not been authorised by early 1990. The five prototypes are intended to contribute a total of 5,000 hours to the flight test programme by 1998.

First production orders will be placed in the 1992 budget, and between 1995 and 2007 it is intended to order 28 Rafales per year against a current requirement for 336: 225 Cs and 25 Bs for the air force and 86 Ms for the navy. Further aircraft will be required if the Rafale is selected to replace the Mirage F1-CR in reconnaissance roles and supplant Mirage IVPs as strategic nuclear strike aircraft. In order to accelerate service entry — particularly to the navy for urgent replacement of LTV Crusader interceptors — the first 20 Rafales for each service will be to the interim S01

standard, lacking ASMP, automatic terrain-following, automatic defensive subsystems, helmet-mounted sight, forward sector electro-optics and voice-commanded controls. Subsequent deliveries will be in definitive S02 configuration, although an avionics upgrade may be introduced in 2005.

Production deliveries will begin on 1 July 1996, the Aéronavale receiving 20 in 1996-99 for re-equipment of 12 Flottille. Initially deployed aboard the current-generation aircraft carrier *Foch*, the aircraft will be limited by catapult restrictions to a take-off weight of 16,500 kg (36,376 lb), pending availability of the new *Charles de Gaulle*. After gaining one Rafale in 1996, the Armée de l'Air will receive 41 in 1997-99 to convert the 30ème Escadre de Chasse at

Reims. Production will then continue at 28 per year until 2009, with the navy sharing output between 2005 and the end of production for its balance of 66. Rafale Ms suffer a weight penalty of 760 kg (1,675 lb) for naval features including a strengthened main landing gear to absorb sink rates of up to 6.5 m (21 ft)/s; twin nosewheels for nose gear launch; and hydraulic arrester hook. Carbonfibre construction will not permit wings to be hinged for folding aboard ship.

Rafale radar will be the two-axis electronic scanning Thomson-CSF/ESD RBE2 (Radar à Balayage Electronique Deux Plans) for which a development contract was awarded in November 1989. Parameters include a 54 nm (100 km; 62 mile) air-to-air detection range. RBG will first fly in a Mystère 20 testbed in Spring 1991.

TYPE: Single-seat interceptor and multi-role fighter.

WINGS: Cantilever multi-spar mid-wing monoplane of compound delta planform. Most of wing components made from carbonfibre, including two-segment (three on Rafale A) full span elevons on each trailing-edge. Wing spar/fuselage attachment fittings of aluminium-lithium alloy. Elevons can be deflected simultaneously or differentially. Full span two-segment (three on Rafale A) leading-edge slats on each wing operate automatically with the elevons to alter wing camber and provide high lift. Slats made from titanium. Wingroot tip fairings of Kevlar. All movable surfaces actuated by fly by wire control system, via hydraulic actuators.

FUSELAGE: Conventional semi-monocoque structure; 50 per cent carbonfibre, including entire front fuselage and dorsal spine fairings. Kevlar fibre nosecone and jetpipe fairings. Most centre and side fuselage skin panels of aluminium-lithium alloy. Wheel doors and engine doors of carbonfibre. Dorsal spine fairing from rear of canopy to jet nozzles. Forward hinged door type airbrake above engine duct on each side of fin leading-edge.

FOREPLANES: Shoulder-mounted active foreplanes of swept-back planform, actuated hydraulically by fly by wire control system. Made primarily of carbonfibre with honeycomb core and Kevlar tips. Foreplanes automatically raised to 20° on selection of landing gear down, to provide additional lift.

TAIL UNIT: Fin and inset rudder only, of sweptback form, made primarily of carbonfibre, with honeycomb core in rudder. Aramid fibre fin tip. (Air intake in base of fin leading-edge on Rafale A). Rudder actuated hydraulically by fly by wire control system. No tabs.

LANDING GEAR: Hydraulically retractable tricycle type supplied by Messier-Bugatti, with single wheel on each unit. Hydraulically steerable nosewheel. All wheels retract forward. Designed for impact at vertical speed of 4 m (13 ft)/s, without flare-out. Michelin radial tyres. Mainwheel tyres size 810 × 275-15, pressure 16.0 bars (232 lb/sq in). Nosewheel tyre size 550 × 200-10. Carbon brakes on all three wheels, controlled by fly by wire system. Brake-chute for emergency use in cylindrical container at base of rudder. Rafale M has twin nosewheels and a 'jump strut' nosewheel leg which releases energy stored in the shock-absorber at the end of the deck take-off run, changing the aircraft's attitude for climb-out without need for a ski-jump ramp.

POWER PLANT: Two SNECMA M88-2 augmented turbofans, each rated at 48.7 kN (10,950 lb st) dry and 72.9 kN (16,400 lb st) with afterburning. M88-3 of 87 kN (19,558 lb st) max rating in production aircraft. Kidney shape plain air intakes, with splitter plates, mounted low on centre fuselage. Internal tanks for more than 5,325 litres (1,406 US gallons; 1,171 Imp gallons) of fuel. One 1,700 litre (449 US gallon; 374 Imp gallon) drop tank on centreline; 2,000 litre (528 US gallon; 440 Imp gallon) drop tanks on each inboard underwing pylon; and/or 1,300 litre (343 US gallon; 286 Imp gallon) tanks on each centre underwing pylon. Max external fuel 6,600 litres (1,742 US gallons; 1,452 Imp gallons). Fixed (detachable) in-flight refuelling probe on Rafale D; retractable probe on Rafale M.

ACCOMMODATION: Pilot only, on Martin-Baker Mk 10 zero/zero ejection seat, reclined at angle of 29°. One-piece blister windscreen/canopy, hinged to open sideways to starboard. HOTAS (hands on throttle and stick) controls, with sidestick controller on starboard console and small-travel throttle lever.

SYSTEMS: Bootstrap cockpit air-conditioning system. Dual hydraulic circuits, pressure 280 bars (4,000 lb/sq in), each with two Messier-Hispano-Bugatti pumps. Variable frequency electrical system, with two 30/40kVA Auxilec alternators. Triplex digital plus one dual analog fly by wire flight control system, integrated with engine controls and linked with weapons system. Eros oxygen system.

AVIONICS AND EQUIPMENT: Provision for more than 780 kg (1,720 lb) of avionics equipment and racks, including Thomson-CSF/ESD RBG lookdown/shootdown radar, able to track up to eight targets simultaneously, with automatic threat assessment and allocation of priority. Sagem Uliss 52X INS. Digital CRT display of fuel, engine, hydraulic, electrical, oxygen and other systems information. Wide-angle diffractive optics HUD, collimated eye-level display and lateral multi-function colour displays by Thomson-CSF/SFENA. TRT com. SOCRAT VOR/ILS. Crouzet voice activated radio controls and voice alarm warning system. LMT SC25 Mk

XII IFF. Internal ECM suite by Thomson-CSF, ESD and Matra; Crouzet Navstar/GPS; EAS V/UHF and TRT Saturn UHF radios; Microturbo APU; Thomson-CSF helmet sight; TRT radio altimeter. Communications via SINTAC/JTIDS.

ARMAMENT: One 30 mm GIAT M791B cannon in side of port engine duct. Fourteen external stores attachments: two on fuselage centreline, two beneath engine intakes, two astride rear fuselage, six under wings and two at wingtips. Forward centreline position deleted on Rafale M. Normal external load 6,000 kg (13,228 lb); max permissible, 8,000 kg (17,637 lb). In interception role, up to eight Matra Mica AAMs and two underwing fuel tanks; or six Micas and 5,700 litres (1,505 US gallons; 1,254 Imp gallons) of external fuel. In air-to-ground role, typically sixteen 227 kg (500 lb) bombs, two Micas and two 1,300 litre (343 US gallon; 286 Imp gallon) tanks; or two Apache stand-off weapon dispensers, two Micas and 5,700 litres of external fuel; or FLIR pod, Atlis laser designator pod, two 1,000 kg (2,205 lb) laser-guided bombs, two AS 30L laser ASMs, four Micas and single 1,700 litre (449 US gallon; 374 Imp gallon) tank. In anti-ship role, two sea-skimming missiles, four Micas and 4,300 litres (1,135 US gallons; 946 Imp gallons) of external fuel. Various reconnaissance and ECM pods.

DIMENSIONS, EXTERNAL:

Span, including wingtip missiles	10.90 m (35 ft 9⅛ in)
Length, overall	15.30 m (50 ft 2⅜ in)
Height (Rafale D)	5.34 m (17 ft 6¼ in)

AREA:

Wings, gross	46.00 m² (495 sq ft)

WEIGHTS (estimated):

Basic empty weight, equipped:	
Rafale D	9,060 kg (19,973 lb)
Rafale M	9,800 kg (21,605 lb)
Max external load	6,000 kg (13,228 lb)
Max ramp weight: initial version	19,500 kg (42,990 lb)
developed version	21,500 kg (47,399 lb)

PERFORMANCE (estimated):

Max level speed: at altitude	Mach 2
at low level	750 knots (1,390 km/h; 864 mph)
Approach speed	115 knots (213 km/h; 132 mph)
T-O distance: air defence	400 m (1,312 ft)
attack	600 m (1,969 ft)

Radius of action: low-level penetration with twelve 250 kg (551 lb) bombs, four Mica AAMs and 4,300 litres (1,135 US gallons; 946 Imp gallons) of external fuel in three tanks   590 nm (1,093 km; 679 miles)

Air-to-air, long-range with eight Mica AAMs and 6,600 litres (1,742 US gallons; 1,452 Imp gallons) of external fuel in four tanks, 12,200 m (40,000 ft) transit   1,000 nm (1,853 km; 1,152 miles)

g limits   +9.0/−3.6

DASSAULT AVIATION ATLANTIQUE 2 (ATL2)

The Atlantique 2, or ATL2 (formerly ANG: Atlantique Nouvelle Génération), is a twin-turboprop maritime patrol aircraft derived directly from the earlier Atlantic that was produced in 1964-73 for operation by the armed services of France (40, of which 3 were sold subsequently to Pakistan), the German Federal Republic (20, including 5 special-purpose elint/sigint aircraft), Italy (18) and the Netherlands (9, of which five survivors transferred to French Navy and one sold back to Dassault for transfer to Pakistan in October 1988). Comprehensive avionics update programmes have been undertaken on 14 Atlantics of the German Navy by Dornier in 1979-84 and on 18 Italian aircraft by Aeronavali (see under Aeritalia heading).

Design definition of the ATL2 was initiated by the French government in July 1977, with the aim of providing a replacement for the first generation Atlantic (now known retrospectively as the Atlantic 1) during the period from 1988 to 1996. This led to launch of the development phase of the ATL2 programme in September 1978.

Two ATL2 prototypes were produced by modification of

Atlantic 1 airframes. Work started in January 1979, and the first prototype flew for the first time in its new form on 8 May 1981, followed by the second on 26 March 1982. Series production was authorised on 24 May 1984 and the first production aircraft flew on 19 October 1988. This was formally accepted by the French Navy two days later, at the start of a 100-hour flight trials programme. The aircraft, No. 1, was delivered to Lann-Bihoué for acceptance by 23 Flottille on 26 October 1989. Also at Lann, 24 F will equip with eight Atlantiques from 1992 onwards, followed by 21 F and 22 F at Nimes-Garons, on the Mediterranean seaboard, from 1995-96.

The French Navy requirement is for 42 aircraft, of which two were funded in 1985, followed by three, five, six, five and three in 1986-90. Economies have forced a future ceiling of three orders per year, delaying the final delivery until 2001. The work is being shared by most members of the European SECBAT (Société d'Etude et de Construction du Breguet Atlantic) consortium that was responsible for the earlier programme, with some modification of the work-split to reflect varying national interests in the ATL2 aircraft. Companies involved, under Dassault Aviation direction, are Sabca and Sonaca of Belgium, MBB and Dornier of Federal Germany, Aeritalia of Italy and Aerospatiale of France. The Tyne engines are being produced by SNECMA of France, Rolls-Royce of the UK, FN of Belgium and MTU of Federal Germany; and propellers by Ratier of France and British Aerospace. Production Atlantique No. 2 flew on 29 December 1989. Subsequent aircraft will be built at Bordeaux, following closure of the Toulouse-Colomiers plant.

Structural changes by comparison with the Atlantic 1 include use of a refined bonding technique, improved anti-corrosion protection, better sealing between skin panels, and design improvements offering longer fatigue life and more economical maintenance. These are intended to ensure increased serviceability, with at least 75 per cent of squadron aircraft permanently available for operations; readiness to take off within 30 minutes of an order to go; and an aircraft life of 30 years.

The basic mission performance requirements envisaged for the ATL2 are similar to those of the Atlantic 1: a high cruising speed to the operational area, quick descent from cruising altitude to patrol height, lengthy patrol endurance at low altitude, and a high degree of manoeuvrability at sea level. It is able to carry a wide variety of weapons and equipment for finding and attacking both submarines and surface targets in all weathers. In particular, its Thomson-CSF Iguane search radar can detect large ships at a range of 150-200 nm (275-370 km; 170-230 miles), and small targets such as submarine schnorkels over 'several dozen nautical miles' in rough seas.

Like the original Atlantic, the ATL2 is able to perform minelaying, logistic support, and passenger and freight transport missions. It could be adapted for advanced AEW duties, and is suitable for civilian tasks such as air/sea rescue and patrol of offshore fishing and oil interests.

During 1988, Dassault announced that it is considering an Atlantique 3 development programme. The company would also be responsible for installing Atlantique 2 detection systems in the prospective ATR 42/72 Petrel (see International section).

TYPE: Twin-turboprop maritime patrol aircraft.

WINGS: Cantilever mid-wing monoplane, with streamlined ESM pods on tips. Wing section NACA 64 series. Dihedral 6° on outer panels only. Incidence 3°. Tapered planform, with 9° sweepback on leading-edge. All-metal three-spar fail-safe structure, with bonded light alloy honeycomb skin panels on torsion box and on main landing gear doors. Two conventional all-metal ailerons on each wing, actuated by SAMM twin-cylinder jacks. All-metal slotted flaps, with bonded light alloy honeycomb filling, in three segments on each wing, over 75 per cent of span. Three hinged spoilers on upper surface of each outer wing, forward of flaps. Metal airbrake above and below each wing. No trim tabs. Air Equipement/Kléber-Colombes pneumatic de-icing system on leading-edges.

Model of the Rafale M naval version showing 'jump strut' nosewheel with launch bar (*Paul Jackson*)

FUSELAGE: All-metal double-bubble fail-safe structure, with bonded honeycomb sandwich skin on pressurised central section of upper lobe, upward sliding weapons bay doors and nosewheel door. Large air intake and duct for air-conditioning system on each side of nose.

TAIL UNIT: Cantilever all-metal structure, with bonded honeycomb sandwich skin panels on torsion boxes. Slightly bulged housing for ESM antennae at top of fin leading-edge. Fixed incidence tailplane, with dihedral. Control surfaces operated through SAMM twin-cylinder jacks. No trim tabs. Air Equipement/Kléber-Colombes pneumatic de-icing system on leading-edges.

LANDING GEAR: Retractable tricycle type, supplied by Messier-Hispano-Bugatti, with twin wheels on each unit. Hydraulic retraction, nosewheels rearward, main units forward into engine nacelles. Kléber-Colombes or Dunlop tyres; size 39 × 13-20 on mainwheels, pressure 12 bars (170 lb/sq in), 26 × 7.75-13 on nosewheels, pressure 6.5 bars (94 lb/sq in). New Messier-Hispano-Bugatti disc brakes with higher braking energy, and Modistop anti-skid units.

POWER PLANT: Two 4,549 kW (6,100 ehp) Rolls-Royce Tyne RTy.20 Mk 21 turboprops, each driving a four-blade Ratier/British Aerospace constant-speed metal propeller type PD 249/476/3 on prototypes. Four pressure-refuelled integral fuel tanks in wings, with total capacity of 23,120 litres (6,108 US gallons; 5,085 Imp gallons). Updated gauging system. Oil capacity 100 litres (26.5 US gallons; 22 Imp gallons).

ACCOMMODATION: Normal flight crew of 10-12, comprising observer in glazed nose; pilot, co-pilot and flight engineer on flight deck; a radio-navigator, ESM-ECM-MAD operator, radar-IFF operator, tactical co-ordinator and two acoustic sensor operators at stations on the starboard side of the tactical compartment; and two optional observers in beam positions at the rear. Rest/relief crew compartment in centre of fuselage. Primary access via extending airstair door in bottom of rear fuselage. Emergency exits above and below flight deck and on each side of fuselage, above wing trailing-edge.

SYSTEMS: Air-conditioning system supplied by two compressors driven by gearboxes. Heat exchangers and bootstrap system for cabin temperature control. Duplicated hydraulic system, pressure 186 bars (2,700 lb/sq in), to operate flying controls, landing gear, flaps, weapons bay doors and retractable radome. Hydraulic flow rate 17.85 litres (4.7 US gallons; 3.9 Imp gallons)/min. Three basic electrical systems: variable frequency three-phase 115/200V AC system, with two 60/80kVA Auxilec alternators and modernised control and protection equipment; fixed frequency three-phase 115/200V 400Hz AC system, with four 15kVA Auxilec Auxivar generators, two on each engine; 28V DC system, with four 6kW transformer-rectifiers supplied from the variable frequency AC system, and one 40Ah battery. One 60kVA emergency AC generator, driven at constant speed by APU. Individual oxygen bottles for emergency use. Electric anti-icing for engine air intake lips, propeller blades and spinners. Turbomeca/ABG/SEMCA Astadyne gas turbine APU for engine starting, emergency electrical supply, and air-conditioning on ground.

ARMAMENT, AVIONICS AND OPERATIONAL EQUIPMENT: Main weapons bay, 2.1 m x 9.0 m x 1.0 m (6 ft 10¾ in x 29 ft 6¼ in x 3 ft 3¼ in) in unpressurised lower fuselage can accommodate all NATO standard bombs, depth charges, up to eight Mk 46 homing torpedoes, seven French Murène advanced torpedoes or two air-to-surface missiles (typical load comprises three torpedoes and one AM39 Exocet or AS37 Martel missile). Max internal weapons load 2,500 kg (5,500 lb). Four underwing attachments for up to 3,500 kg (7,716 lb) of stores, including future air-to-surface and air-to-air missiles or pods. More than 100 sonobuoys, with Alkan pneumatic launcher, in compartment aft of weapons bay, where whole of upper and lower fuselage provides storage for sonobuoys and 160 smoke markers and flares. SAT/TRT Tango forward looking infra-red sensor in turret under nose. Thomson-CSF Iguane retractable radar immediately forward of weapons bay, with integrated LMT IFF interrogator and SECRE decoder. Thomson-TRT 35 cameras in starboard side of nose and in bottom of rear fuselage. Crouzet MAD in lengthened tail sting. Thomson-CSF Arar 13A radar detector for ESM. Thomson-CSF Sadang system for processing active and passive acoustic detection data. A distributed data processing system around a databus, with a CIMSA Mitra 125X tactical computer (512K words memory), two ESD bus computers, two Sagem magnetic bubble mass memories and Thomson-CSF display subsystem. Other equipment includes IFF transponder and HF com by LMT, UHF AM/FM by Sintra, Tacan and DME by Thomson-CSF, VHF AM/FM com by Socrat, VOR/ILS by EAS, TRT radio altimeter, Collins MF radio compass, ADF, HSI and autopilot/flight director by SFENA, dual Sagem Uliss 53 inertial navigation systems coupled to a GPS/Navstar receiver, Sagem high-speed printer and terminal display, Crouzet navigation table and air data computer.

DIMENSIONS, EXTERNAL:
Wing span, incl wingtip pods   37.42 m (122 ft 9¼ in)

First production Dassault Aviation Atlantique 2 (ATL2) maritime patrol aircraft

Dassault Aviation Atlantique 2 (ATL2) twin-turboprop maritime patrol aircraft (*Pilot Press*)

Wing aspect ratio	10.9
Length overall	33.63 m (110 ft 4 in)
Height overall	10.89 m (35 ft 8¾ in)
Fuselage: Max depth	4.00 m (13 ft 1½ in)
Tailplane span	12.31 m (40 ft 4½ in)
Wheel track (c/l of shock struts)	9.00 m (29 ft 6¼ in)
Wheelbase	9.40 m (30 ft 10 in)
Propeller diameter	4.88 m (16 ft 0 in)
Distance between propeller centres	
	9.00 m (29 ft 6¼ in)
Main weapons bay: Length	9.00 m (29 ft 6¼ in)
Width	2.10 m (6 ft 10¾ in)

DIMENSIONS, INTERNAL:
Cabin, incl rest compartment, galley, toilet, aft observers'	
stations: Length	18.50 m (60 ft 8½ in)
Max width	3.60 m (11 ft 9½ in)
Max height	2.00 m (6 ft 6¾ in)
Floor area	155.0 m² (1,668 sq ft)
Volume	92.0 m³ (3,250 cu ft)

AREAS:
Wings, gross	120.34 m² (1,295.3 sq ft)
Ailerons (total)	5.26 m² (56.62 sq ft)
Flaps (total)	26.42 m² (284.38 sq ft)
Spoilers (total)	1.66 m² (17.87 sq ft)
Vertical tail surfaces (total)	16.64 m² (179.11 sq ft)
Rudder	5.96 m² (64.15 sq ft)
Horizontal tail surfaces (total)	32.50 m² (349.83 sq ft)
Elevators	8.30 m² (89.34 sq ft)

WEIGHTS AND LOADINGS:
Weight empty, equipped, standard mission	
	25,600 kg (56,438 lb)
Military load:	
ASW or ASSW mission	3,000 kg (6,600 lb)
Max fuel	18,500 kg (40,785 lb)
Standard mission T-O weight:	
ASW or ASSW mission	44,200 kg (97,440 lb)
combined ASW/ASSW mission	
	45,000 kg (99,200 lb)

Max T-O weight	46,200 kg (101,850 lb)
Normal design landing weight	36,000 kg (79,365 lb)
Max landing weight	46,000 kg (101,400 lb)
Max zero-fuel weight	32,500 kg (71,650 lb)
Max wing loading	385 kg/m² (78.96 lb/sq ft)
Max power loading	5.07 kg/kW (8.34 lb/ehp)

PERFORMANCE (with metal propellers, at T-O weight of 45,000 kg; 99,200 lb except where indicated):
Never-exceed speed	Mach 0.73
Max level speed at optimum height	
	350 knots (648 km/h; 402 mph)
Max level speed at S/L	320 knots (592 km/h; 368 mph)
Max cruising speed at 7,620 m (25,000 ft)	
	300 knots (555 km/h; 345 mph)
Normal patrol speed, S/L to 1,525 m (5,000 ft)	
	170 knots (315 km/h; 195 mph)
Stalling speed, flaps down	
	90 knots (167 km/h; 104 mph)
Max rate of climb at S/L:	
AUW of 30,000 kg (66,140 lb)	884 m (2,900 ft)/min
AUW of 40,000 kg (88,185 lb)	610 m (2,000 ft)/min
Rate of climb at S/L, one engine out:	
AUW of 30,000 kg (66,140 lb)	365 m (1,200 ft)/min
AUW of 40,000 kg (88,185 lb)	213 m (700 ft)/min
Service ceiling	9,145 m (30,000 ft)
Runway LCN at max T-O weight	60
T-O to 10.7 m (35 ft)	1,840 m (6,037 ft)
Landing from 15 m (50 ft)	1,500 m (4,922 ft)
170 knot turning radius at AUW of 40,000 kg (88,185 lb)	
at: 30° bank	1,380 m (4,530 ft)
45° bank	800 m (2,625 ft)
60° bank	460 m (1,510 ft)

Typical mission profiles, with reserves of 5% total fuel, 5% of fuel consumed and 20 min hold-off:

Anti-ship mission: T-O with max fuel and one AM39 missile; fly 1,800 nm (3,333 km; 2,071 miles) to target area; descend for two-hour search and attack at 90 m (300 ft); return to base

Anti-submarine mission: T-O at 44,300 kg (97,665 lb) AUW with 15,225 kg (33,565 lb) of fuel, four Mk 46 torpedoes, 78 sonobuoys, and a full load of markers and flares; cruise to search area at 290 knots (537 km/h; 333 mph) at 7,620 m (25,000 ft); descend for 8 h low altitude patrol at 600 nm (1,110 km; 690 miles) from base, or 5 h patrol at 1,000 nm (1,850 km; 1,150 miles) from base; return to base at 9,145 m (30,000 ft). Total mission time 12 h 31 min

Ferry range with max fuel
4,900 nm (9,075 km; 5,635 miles)
Max endurance 18 h

DASSAULT AVIATION PETREL

Details of this maritime patrol adaptation by Dassault-Breguet of the ATR 42/72 regional airliner will be found in the International section.

DASSAULT AVIATION ALIZÉ

In the early 1980s, 28 Aéronavale Alizé shipboard maritime patrol aircraft were modernised, as last described in the 1985-86 *Jane's*. A further, less extensive re-work for 24 of these was begun at the Cuers naval workshops in 1990, involving addition of a SAGEM MTP16 micro-computer integrated with a system of tactical data processing and transmission, improved decoy systems and INS data links. The Alizé will be retained in land- and sea-based service until early in the next century.

DASSAULT AVIATION/DORNIER ALPHA JET

Details of the Alpha Jet programme can be found in the International section of this edition.

DASSAULT AVIATION/BAe JAGUAR

Details of the Jaguar programme can be found under SEPECAT in the International section of this edition.

CRUSADER

Originally due to have been retired on 30 June 1993, the French Navy's Vought F-8E(FN) Crusader carrier-based interceptors will be updated for up to five more years of service before their operating squadron, 12 Flottille at Landivisiau, has completed conversion to Rafale Ms. In 1989, Dassault was contracted to determine the required changes, although work will be performed by the navy's own Cuers workshops, Atelier d'Aviation de Cuers on 17 of the 21 Crusaders remaining from 42 delivered. Apart from a radar warning receiver, modifications are expected to concentrate on alleviation of airframe fatigue, replacement of wiring and ejection seats. Re-deliveries will begin in 1992.

DASSAULT AVIATION MYSTÈRE-FALCON 20 and 200
US Coast Guard designation: HU-25 Guardian

The Mystère-Falcon 200 twin-turbofan light transport was based on the Mystère 20 design, first flown in prototype form on 4 May 1963. Manufacture of the Mystère-Falcon 200 began with aircraft c/n 401, first flown on 30 April 1980, concurrent with the production rundown of the earlier Mystère-Falcon 20F series, the last of which (c/n 486) came off the assembly line in late 1983. The model 200 had been introduced, originally as the Mystère-Falcon 20H, at the 1981 Paris Air Show, with Garrett turbofans in place of the F's General Electric CF700s, larger integral fuel tankage in the rear fuselage, redesigned wingroot fairings, automatic slat extension, and many important systems changes. Certification was achieved on 21 June 1981.

One aircraft was built in 1988, completing production of 473 Mystère-Falcon 20s and 35 Mystère-Falcon 200s. Several have been, and are being, converted for specific duties, as listed below, while Mystère-Falcon 20s are eligible for re-engining to 20-5 standard (described separately under the Garrett entry in USA section).

Calibration: Ten Mystère-Falcons, in several different variants, have been delivered to the French DGAC, French Air Force, and authorities in Spain (designation TM.11), Indonesia and Iran, for navaid calibration. Most are equipped with Dassault-designed high/low level navigation facility calibration systems, some in the form of a removable console.

Airline crew training: Mystère-Falcon 20s have been used by Air France to train pilots for its jet airliners, with up to five aircraft being used simultaneously. Japan Air Lines also used three of this version.

Quick-change and cargo: A quick-change kit, consisting of an assembly of nets and supports keeps the centre aisle free and allows direct access to nine freight compartments. Total usable volume of these compartments is 6.65 m³ (235 cu ft), and transformation from executive configuration to cargo configuration, or vice versa, takes less than one hour. Another specific cargo conversion was performed on 33 aircraft in the USA. For both versions the maximum zero-fuel weight of 9,980 kg (22,000 lb) allows a payload of up to 3,000 kg (6,615 lb).

Target towing: A Mystère-Falcon 20 is used by the French Air Force for target towing. It carries a Secapem target on an inboard hardpoint under each wing and a pod containing a winch and cable on each of two outboard hardpoints. Missions of up to 2 h duration can be flown, cruising at up to 300 knots (555 km/h; 345 mph) at 450 m

Mystère-Falcon 20 modified by Flight Refuelling Ltd with underwing ECM training pods

(1,500 ft) or 270 knots (500 km/h; 310 mph) at 4,500 m (15,000 ft). The hardpoints (650 kg; 1,433 lb inboard, 750 kg; 1,650 lb outboard) can be used to carry alternative stores if required. Sixteen former Federal Express cargo aircraft operated by Flight Refuelling Ltd of the UK provide Royal Navy target facilities with equipment including an RM30A target winch, ALQ-167 radar jammer, BOZ-3 chaff dispenser, ALE-43 chaff/flare dispenser and ATRS-5 radar simulator, all mounted under the wings.

Aerial photography: This version has two ventral camera bays fitted with optical glass windows. It is operated for high altitude photography, survey and scientific research in several countries. The camera installation can be supplemented by a multispectral scanner and other scientific loads.

Systems trainer: Five aircraft fitted with the combat radar and navigation systems of various Mirage types are in service with the French Air Force for training pilots. These comprise two Mystère **20SNA**s (Système de Navigation-Attaque — equivalent to the Mirage IIIE); and single examples of the **20SNR** (Système de Navigation-Reconnaissance — Mirage F1-CR) and versions equivalent to the Mirage 2000N and Mirage IV-P.

Ambulance: Up to three stretchers can be accommodated, together with a large supply of oxygen and equipment for intensive care and monitoring of patients. Cabinets near the door are removed to facilitate the loading of stretchers.

Electronic warfare: Norway, Canada and Morocco have been followed by several other nations, including Pakistan and Spain, in operating Mystère-Falcon 20 aircraft modified for ECM duties such as radar and communications intelligence and jamming.

Remote sensing: In 1988, a Falcon 20 owned by Innotech was fitted with infra-red mapping equipment supplied by the Canada Centre for Remote Sensing and used for fire-spotting by the forestry authorities in Idaho, USA.

Versions of the Falcon 20 supplied to the US Coast Guard have the following designations:

HU-25A Guardian. Basic version delivered in 1982-83 for search and rescue and offshore surveillance (described fully in 1985-86 *Jane's*). Total of 41 includes modified HU-25Bs and Cs.

HU-25B. Retrospective designation for variant tasked with location of sea pollution and identification of vessels responsible. Equipment comprises one of the six Aerojet Aireye detection systems ordered for the Guardian in the form of a Motorola APS-131 SLAR pod under the forward fuselage, offset, starboard; a Texas Instruments RS-18C linescan unit in a starboard underwing pod; and a laser illuminated TV under the port wing.

HU-25C. Designation of eight Guardians converted to identify and track air or seaborne drug smugglers by means of a fighter type Westinghouse AN/APG-66 radar in the nose, and turret-mounted Texas Instruments WF-360 FLIR. Also fitted with secure HF/UHF/VHF-FM radio communications. Entered service 30 May 1988.

Two aircraft supplied to the Chilean Navy (the first in 1983) are standard Falcon 200s, slightly modified for maritime survey.

Full data on the Mystère-Falcon 200 appeared in the 1988-89 and previous editions of *Jane's*. An abbreviated specification follows:

TYPE: Twin-turbofan executive transport.

WINGS: Cantilever low-wing monoplane. Thickness/chord ratio varies from 10.5 to 8 per cent. Dihedral 2°. Incidence 1° 30′, Sweepback at quarter-chord 30°. All-metal (copper bearing alloys) fail-safe torsion box structure with machined stressed skin. Hydraulically actuated airbrakes forward of the hydraulically actuated two-section, single-slotted flaps. Leading-edges anti-iced by engine bleed air.

FUSELAGE: All-metal semi-monocoque structure of circular cross-section, built on fail-safe principles.

TAIL UNIT: Cantilever all-metal structure, with variable-incidence tailplane mounted halfway up fin. No trim tabs.

LANDING GEAR: Retractable tricycle type, by Messier-Hispano-Bugatti, with twin wheels on all three units. Hydraulic retraction. Max steering angle of nosewheel ±50° for taxying, ±180° for towing.

POWER PLANT: Two Garrett ATF 3-6A-4C turbofans (each rated at 23.13 kN; 5,200 lb st). Optional thrust reversers are produced by Hurel-Dubois. Fuel in two integral tanks in wings and large integral tank in rear fuselage, with total capacity of 6,000 litres (1,585 US gallons; 1,320 Imp gallons).

ACCOMMODATION: Flight deck for crew of two, with airline type instrumentation. Airstair door, with handrail, on port side. Main cabin normally seats nine passengers. Alternative arrangement provides 12 compact seats at a pitch of 76 cm (30 in).

SYSTEMS: Duplicated air-conditioning and pressurisation system. Two independent hydraulic systems. Electrical system includes a 9kW 28V DC starter/generator on each engine, three 750VA inverters and two 36Ah batteries. Solar T40 APU optional. Wing leading-edges and engine air inlets anti-iced with LP compressor bleed air.

AVIONICS AND EQUIPMENT: Collins FCS-80 flight control system standard, with dual Collins EFIS-86C electronic flight instrument system using colour CRTs. Standard avionics include duplicated VHF, VOR, ADF, DME and ATC transponder, one weather radar and one radio altimeter.

DIMENSIONS, EXTERNAL:
Wing span	16.32 m (53 ft 6½ in)
Wing aspect ratio	6.5
Length overall	17.15 m (56 ft 3 in)
Length of fuselage	15.55 m (51 ft 0 in)
Height overall	5.32 m (17 ft 5 in)
Wheel track	3.34 m (10 ft 11½ in)
Wheelbase	5.74 m (18 ft 10 in)
Passenger door: Height	1.52 m (5 ft 0 in)
Width	0.80 m (2 ft 7½ in)
Height to sill	1.09 m (3 ft 7 in)

DIMENSIONS, INTERNAL:
Cabin, incl fwd baggage space and rear toilet:
Length	7.26 m (23 ft 10 in)
Max width	1.79 m (5 ft 10½ in)
Max height	1.70 m (5 ft 7 in)
Volume	20.0 m³ (706 cu ft)
Baggage space (cabin)	0.65 m³ (23 cu ft)
Baggage compartment (rear fuselage)	0.80 m³ (28.2 cu ft)

AREA:
Wings, gross	41.00 m² (440 sq ft)

WEIGHTS:
Weight empty, equipped	8,250 kg (18,190 lb)
Payload with max fuel	1,265 kg (2,790 lb)
Max fuel	4,845 kg (10,680 lb)
Max T-O and ramp weight	14,515 kg (32,000 lb)
Max zero-fuel weight	10,200 kg (22,500 lb)
Max landing weight	13,100 kg (28,800 lb)

PERFORMANCE:
Max operating Mach No.	0.865
Max operating speed:	
at S/L	350 knots (648 km/h; 402 mph) IAS
at 6,100 m (20,000 ft)	
	380 knots (704 km/h; 438 mph) IAS

Dassault Aviation Mystère-Falcon 20 converted to a radar testbed for CEV, France *(AGPPA)*

Max cruising speed at 9,150 m (30,000 ft) at AUW of
   11,340 kg (25,000 lb)   470 knots (870 km/h; 541 mph)
Econ cruising speed at 12,500 m (41,000 ft)
                420 knots (780 km/h; 485 mph)
Stalling speed   84 knots (156 km/h; 97 mph)
Service ceiling   13,715 m (45,000 ft)
Min ground turning radius about nosewheel
                       12.8 m (42 ft)
FAR 25 balanced T-O field length with 8 passengers and
   full fuel   1,420 m (4,660 ft)
FAR 121 landing distance with 8 passengers, FAR 121
   reserves   1,130 m (3,710 ft)
Range with max fuel and 8 passengers at long-range
   cruising speed, 45 min reserves
              2,510 nm (4,650 km; 2,890 miles)

DASSAULT AVIATION GARDIAN 2

The Gardian 2 is a Falcon 200 fitted with a Thomson-CSF Varan radar for maritime detection, a Crouzet Omega navigation system and four underwing hardpoints. With additional equipment, it can perform the following missions:

Target designation: This includes over-the-horizon targeting for maritime forces or coastal missile batteries; missile midcourse retargeting; control of surface operations; and strike guidance against surface ships or land objectives. Equipment includes a navigation table, UHF modem to transmit data, V/UHF DF, and IFF interrogator. Options include ESM, search windows, inertial platform, VHF/FM, HF and track-while-scan radar system.

AM39 Exocet attack: As well as two Exocet sea-skimming air-to-surface missiles, this requires an inertial platform, Omega/INS interface, AM39 interface and controls, and IFF interrogator. Options are track-while-scan, navigation table and ESM.

Electronic surveillance and countermeasures: This requires either Thomson-CSF DR 2000 ESM and navigation table, or an integrated system including a Thomson-CSF DR 4000 ESM, a computer, the Varan radar, an inertial platform and tactical visualisation elements from the Atlantique 2 system. Options include an IFF interrogator, AM39 installation, track-while-scan, countermeasures or decoy pods, elint equipment, HF/VHF/UHF comint equipment and V/UHF DF.

Target towing: As for Falcon 200.

In all cases, the cabin can be arranged to permit secondary transport missions.

DASSAULT AVIATION MYSTÈRE-FALCON 100

The Mystère-Falcon 100 is the latest version of the Mystère-Falcon 10 series, which it has replaced in production. Like its predecessors, it is a small executive jet for five to eight passengers, with compound swept wings fitted with high-lift devices, and powered by Garrett TFE731-2 turbofans.

Details of the early history of the Mystère-Falcon 10 series can be found in the 1982-83 *Jane's*. By January 1990, a total of 223 Mystère-Falcon 10s and 100s had been delivered, of which 182 had gone to Falcon Jet in the USA, 16 to French customers, and 25 to other export customers.

Fuselages are provided by Potez at Aire-sur-Adour, which assembles components built by Sogerma, Socea and Socata. Wings come from CASA of Spain; tail units and nose assemblies from IAM of Italy; and many other components such as tail fins, doors and emergency exits from Latécoère at Toulouse.

By comparison with the Mystère-Falcon 10, the 100 has an increase of 225 kg (496 lb) in max T-O weight and higher max ramp weight; a fourth cabin window on the starboard side, opposite the door; a larger heated, unpressurised rear baggage compartment; and a Collins five-CRT EFIS-85 instrument package.

In December 1986, the Falcon 100 was certificated by the DGAC for Cat II approaches in commercial operation.

Under a state sponsored research and development programme, Aerospatiale and Dassault Aviation manufactured a set of resin-impregnated carbonfibre wings for a Falcon 10 designated **V10F**. Dassault Aviation made the port wing, Aerospatiale the starboard wing, retaining the aerodynamic form of the standard metal wings. The V10F (F-WVPR, c/n 5) flew for the first time on 21 May 1985 and

received DGAC certification on 16 December 1985. It made a total of 40 test flights and built up flying hours subsequently as one of the aircraft in the charter fleet of Europe Falcon Service.

The following details apply to the standard production Mystère-Falcon 100:

TYPE: Twin-turbofan executive transport.

WINGS: Cantilever low-wing monoplane with increased sweepback on inboard leading-edges. All-metal torsion box structure, with leading-edge slats and double-slotted trailing-edge flaps and plain ailerons. Two-section spoilers above each wing, forward of flaps.

FUSELAGE: All-metal semi-monocoque structure, designed to fail-safe principles.

TAIL UNIT: Cantilever all-metal structure, similar to that of Falcon 200.

LANDING GEAR: Retractable tricycle type, manufactured by Messier-Hispano-Bugatti, with twin wheels on each main gear unit, single wheel on nose gear. Hydraulic retraction, main units inward, nosewheel forward. Oleo-pneumatic shock absorbers. Mainwheel tyres size 22 × 5.75 in, pressure 9.31 bars (135 lb/sq in). Nosewheel tyre size 18 × 5.75 in, pressure 6.55 bars (95 lb/sq in).

POWER PLANT: Two Garrett TFE731-2 turbofans (each 14.4 kN; 3,230 lb st), pod mounted on sides of rear fuselage. Thrust reversers optional. Fuel in two integral tanks in wings and two integral feeder tanks in rear fuselage, with total capacity of 3,340 litres (882 US gallons; 735 Imp gallons). Separate fuel system for each engine, with provision for cross-feeding. Pressure refuelling system.

ACCOMMODATION: Crew of two on flight deck, with dual controls and airline type instrumentation. Provision for

third crew member on a jump seat. Seating arrangements differ from aircraft to aircraft in accordance with customer preference. All have a two/three-place sofa in the rear of the cabin, with further seats for a total of up to eight passengers. There is an internal baggage compartment behind the sofa, and a small galley and toilet forward of the passenger accommodation. Clamshell door at the front, on the port side, with built-in steps.

SYSTEMS: Duplicated air-conditioning and pressurisation systems supplied with air bled from both engines. Pressure differential 0.61 bars (8.8 lb/sq in). Two independent hydraulic systems, each of 207 bars (3,000 lb/sq in) pressure and with twin engine driven pumps and emergency electric pump, to actuate primary flight controls, flaps, landing gear, wheel brakes, spoilers, yaw damper and nosewheel steering. Plain hydraulic reservoir, pressurised at 1.47 bars (21 lb/sq in). 28V DC electrical system with a 9kW DC starter/generator on each engine, three 750VA 400Hz 115V inverters and two 23Ah batteries. Automatic emergency oxygen system.

AVIONICS AND EQUIPMENT: Standard avionics include Collins APS 80 autopilot and EFIS-85, ADC 80 air data computer and electrical instruments, dual VHF, VOR, DME, transponders, ADF and intercom systems, Collins weather radar, and radio altimeter. Optional avionics are a 718 U5M HF transceiver, Collins APS 85 autopilot and EFIS-86C, and Global GNS 500 flight management system and long-range navigation system.

DIMENSIONS, EXTERNAL:

Wing span	13.08 m (42 ft 11 in)
Wing chord (mean)	2.046 m (6 ft 8½ in)
Wing aspect ratio	7.1
Length overall	13.86 m (45 ft 5¾ in)
Length of fuselage	12.47 m (40 ft 11 in)
Height overall	4.61 m (15 ft 1½ in)
Tailplane span	5.82 m (19 ft 1 in)
Wheel track	2.86 m (9 ft 5 in)
Wheelbase	5.30 m (17 ft 4¾ in)
Passenger door: Height	1.47 m (4 ft 10 in)
Width	0.80 m (2 ft 7 in)
Height to sill	0.884 m (2 ft 10¾ in)
Emergency exit (stbd side, over wing):	
Height	0.914 m (3 ft 0 in)
Width	0.508 m (1 ft 8 in)

DIMENSIONS, INTERNAL:

Cabin, excl flight deck: Length	4.70 m (15 ft 5 in)
Max width	1.55 m (5 ft 1 in)
Max height	1.45 m (4 ft 9 in)
Volume	7.11 m³ (251 cu ft)

Dassault Aviation Mystère-Falcon 100 of Lyon-Air, equipped for operations to Cat II landing minima

Dassault Aviation Mystère-Falcon 100 four/eight-passenger executive transport *(Pilot Press)*

Baggage compartment volume:

cabin	0.72 m³ (25.4 cu ft)
rear	0.81 m³ (28.6 cu ft)

AREAS:

Wings, gross	24.1 m² (259.4 sq ft)
Vertical tail surfaces (total)	4.54 m² (48.87 sq ft)
Horizontal tail surfaces (total)	6.75 m² (72.65 sq ft)

WEIGHTS:

Weight empty, equipped	5,055 kg (11,145 lb)
Max payload	1,305 kg (2,875 lb)
Payload with max fuel	840 kg (1,852 lb)
Max fuel	2,680 kg (5,910 lb)
Max T-O weight	8,755 kg (19,300 lb)
Max ramp weight	8,800 kg (19,400 lb)
Max zero-fuel weight	6,540 kg (14,420 lb)
Max landing weight	8,000 kg (17,640 lb)

PERFORMANCE (at AUW of 8,280 kg; 18,254 lb):

Never-exceed speed at S/L	350 knots (648 km/h; 402 mph)
Max operating Mach No.	0.87
Max cruise Mach No. at 10,670 m (35,000 ft)	0.84
Max cruising speed at 7,620 m (25,000 ft)	492 knots (912 km/h; 566 mph)
Approach speed	100 knots (185 km/h; 115 mph)
Operational ceiling (four passengers, full fuel)	13,715 m (45,000 ft)

FAR 25 balanced T-O field length with four passengers and fuel for a 1,000 nm (1,850 km; 1,150 mile) stage, 45 min reserves 960 m (3,150 ft)

FAR 25 balanced T-O field length, with four passengers and max fuel 1,325 m (4,350 ft)

FAR 121 landing field length, with four passengers and 45 min reserves 1,065 m (3,495 ft)

Range with four passengers and 45 min reserves 1,565 nm (2,900 km; 1,802 miles)

DASSAULT AVIATION MYSTÈRE-FALCON 50

The Mystère-Falcon 50 three-turbofan executive transport has the same external fuselage cross-section as the Mystère-Falcon 200, but is an entirely new design, featuring area ruling and advanced wing aerodynamics. Normal layout is for a crew of two and eight or nine passengers, with provision for up to 12 passengers.

The original prototype (F-WAMD) flew for the first time on 7 November 1976, followed by a second prototype (F-WINR) on 18 February 1978 and the third (and sole pre-production) aircraft on 13 June 1978. DGAC certification was received on 27 February 1979, followed by FAA type approval on 7 March. Falcon 50 c/n 4, flown on 2 March 1979, was the first built on Dassault's Mérignac assembly line and became Falcon Jet's US demonstrator. Deliveries began in July 1979 and totalled 200 aircraft, registered in 30 countries, by the beginning of 1990. Since delivery of the fifth aircraft to the Armée de l'Air's GLAM (Groupe de Liaisons Aériennes Ministérielles) in early 1980, for use by the President of the French Republic, Mystère-Falcon 50s have been purchased for state VIP transportation in Djibouti, Iraq, Jordan, Libya, Morocco, Portugal, South Africa, Spain (designation T.16) and Yugoslavia. Three supplied to the Italian Air Force are equipped for both VIP and air ambulance duties.

On 31 March 1979 a Falcon 50 set the current straight-line distance record for Class C1h (business aircraft of 12,000-16,000 kg AUW) in the USA, by flying 3,293.69 nm (6,099.91 km; 3,790.31 miles). Two current records in Class C1i (16,000-20,000 kg) were set in France on 24 April 1980, with a sustained level flight at 13,716 m (45,000 ft), which qualified also as the altitude record in this class.

Fuselages for the Mystère-Falcon 50 are produced at Aerospatiale's Saint-Nazaire works, tail units by Aerospatiale at Méaulte, and cowlings by Hurel-Dubois at Vélizy-Villacoublay.

TYPE: Three-turbofan executive transport.

WINGS: Cantilever low-wing monoplane, with compound leading-edge sweepback and optimised section. Each wing is attached to the central box structure by multiple bolts and forms an integral fuel tank. Full span leading-edge slats, of which the outboard sections are slotted. Double-slotted trailing-edge flaps and ailerons, latter with carbonfibre skin. Three-section two-position airbrakes on top surface of each wing.

FUSELAGE: All-metal semi-monocoque structure of circular cross-section, with aft baggage compartment included in pressure cell.

TAIL UNIT: Cantilever all-metal structure. Horizontal surfaces, with anhedral, mounted partway up fin. Tailplane incidence adjustable by screwjack, driven by two electric motors controlled by normal and emergency controls located respectively on the control wheels and pedestal.

LANDING GEAR: Retractable tricycle type by Messier-Hispano-Bugatti, with twin wheels on each unit. Hydraulic retraction, main units inward, nosewheels forward. Nosewheel steerable ±60° for taxying, ±180° for towing. Mainwheel tyres size 26 × 6.6-14 in, pressure 14.34 bars (208 lb/sq in). Nosewheel tyres size 14.5 × 5.5-6 in, pressure 8.96 bars (130 lb/sq in). Four-disc brakes designed for 400 landings with normal energy braking.

Dassault Aviation Mystère-Falcon 50 of the Iraqi government *(Ivo Sturzenegger)*

POWER PLANT: Three Garrett TFE731-3 turbofans, each rated at 16.5 kN (3,700 lb st) for take-off. Two engines pod mounted on sides of rear fuselage, the third attached by two top mounts. Thrust reverser on centre engine. Fuel in integral tanks, with capacity of 5,787 litres (1,529 US gallons; 1,273 Imp gallons) in wings and 2,976 litres (786 US gallons; 655 Imp gallons) in fuselage tanks. Total fuel capacity 8,763 litres (2,315 US gallons; 1,928 Imp gallons). Single point pressure fuelling.

ACCOMMODATION: Crew of two side by side on flight deck, with full dual controls and airline type instrumentation. Third seat to rear of co-pilot. Various cabin configurations available, based on two alternative toilet locations. An aft cabin toilet allows an eight/nine-passenger arrangement, with four chairs in forward cabin, facing each other in pairs, and a three-place sofa and two facing chairs in the rear cabin. A wardrobe, galley and crew toilet are located forward, in the entrance area. Alternatively, a forward toilet, facing the door, makes possible a lounge in the rear cabin, furnished with a four/five-place angle sofa and a chair. This rear lounge is separated from the forward cabin by either a wardrobe and refreshment/recreation console, or by two additional seats, raising the cabin accommodation to 12 persons. After removing forward cabin equipment (wardrobe and galley) and seats, the cabin will accommodate up to three stretchers, two doctors and medical equipment, or freight. The rear baggage compartment is pressurised and air-conditioned, and has a capacity of 1,000 kg (2,200 lb). Access is by a separate door on the port side.

SYSTEMS: Air-conditioning system utilises bleed air from all three engines. Max pressure differential 0.61 bars (8.8 lb/sq in). Pressurisation maintains a max cabin altitude of 2,440 m (8,000 ft) to a flight altitude of 13,700 m (45,000 ft). Two independent hydraulic systems, pressure 207 bars (3,000 lb/sq in), with three engine driven pumps and one emergency electric pump, actuate primary flying controls, flaps, slats, landing gear, wheel brakes, airbrakes and nosewheel steering. Plain reservoir, pressurised by bleed air at 1.47 bars (21 lb/sq in). 28V DC electrical system, with a 9kW 28V DC starter/generator on each engine and two 23Ah batteries. Automatic emergency oxygen system. Optional 9kW Garrett APU.

AVIONICS: Standard fit provides Collins FCS 80F autopilot in conjunction with dual five-CRT EFIS-85 system, ADC 80 air data computer, dual VHF, VOR, DME, ADF, transponders, radar altimeter and Honeywell Primus 400 weather radar. Main options provide for advanced symbology EFIS-86C, digital radio controllers used in conjunction with autotune FMS (Global GNS 1000 or UNS 1), Honeywell laser inertial systems, which may also replace gyro reference systems, and Omega. Installation of Collins digital avionics including APS-85 autopilot, EFIS-86, ADS-82, AHS-85 AHRS and Pro Line II com/nav/pulse makes possible certificated Cat II operation.

DIMENSIONS, EXTERNAL:

Wing span	18.86 m (61 ft 10½ in)
Wing chord (mean)	2.84 m (9 ft 3¾ in)
Wing aspect ratio	7.6
Length overall	18.52 m (60 ft 9¼ in)
Length of fuselage	17.66 m (57 ft 11 in)
Height overall	6.97 m (22 ft 10½ in)
Tailplane span	7.74 m (25 ft 4¾ in)
Wheel track	3.98 m (13 ft 0¾ in)
Wheelbase	7.24 m (23 ft 9 in)
Passenger door: Height	1.52 m (4 ft 11¾ in)
Width	0.80 m (2 ft 7½ in)
Height to sill	1.30 m (4 ft 3¼ in)

Emergency exits (each side, over wing):

Height	0.92 m (3 ft 0¼ in)
Width	0.51 m (1 ft 8 in)

DIMENSIONS, INTERNAL:

Cabin, incl forward baggage space and rear toilet:

Length	7.16 m (23 ft 6 in)
Max width	1.86 m (6 ft 1¼ in)
Max height	1.79 m (5 ft 10½ in)
Volume	20.15 m³ (711.6 cu ft)
Baggage space	0.75 m³ (26.5 cu ft)
Baggage compartment (rear)	2.55 m³ (90 cu ft)

AREAS:

Wings, gross	46.83 m² (504.1 sq ft)
Horizontal tail surfaces (total)	13.35 m² (143.7 sq ft)
Vertical tail surfaces (total)	9.82 m² (105.7 sq ft)

WEIGHTS:

Weight empty, equipped	9,150 kg (20,170 lb)

Dassault Aviation Mystère-Falcon 50 long-range three-turbofan executive transport *(Pilot Press)*

Dassault Aviation Mystère-Falcon 900 three-turbofan executive transport of United Arab Emirates *(Ivo Sturzenegger)*

Max payload: normal	1,570 kg (3,461 lb)	
optional	2,170 kg (4,784 lb)	
with max fuel	1,130 kg (2,491 lb)	
Max fuel	7,040 kg (15,520 lb)	

Max T-O and ramp weight:
standard 17,600 kg (38,800 lb)
optional 18,500 kg (40,780 lb)
Max zero-fuel weight: standard 11,000 kg (24,250 lb)
optional 11,600 kg (25,570 lb)
Max landing weight 16,200 kg (35,715 lb)
PERFORMANCE:
Max operating Mach No. 0.86
Max operating speed:
at S/L 350 knots (648 km/h; 402 mph) IAS
at 7,225 m (23,700 ft)
370 knots (685 km/h; 425 mph) IAS
Max cruising speed
Mach 0.82 or 475 knots (880 km/h; 546 mph)
Long-range cruising speed at 10,670 m (35,000 ft)
Mach 0.75 (430 knots; 797 km/h; 495 mph)
Max operating altitude 13,715 m (45,000 ft)
Min ground radius about nosewheels
13.54 m (44 ft 5 in)
FAR 25 balanced field length with 8 passengers and fuel
for 3,500 nm (6,480 km; 4,025 miles)
1,365 m (4,480 ft)
FAR 121 landing distance with 8 passengers and 45 min
LR reserves 1,080 m (3,545 ft)
Approach speed, as above
99.5 knots (184 km/h; 115 mph)
Range at Mach 0.75 with 8 passengers and 45 min LR
reserves 3,500 nm (6,480 km; 4,025 miles)

DASSAULT AVIATION GARDIAN 50

A maritime surveillance and environmental protection version of the Falcon 50 is offered by the manufacturer, equipped with Thomson-CSF Varan sea search radar, Crouzet Omega and a Sagem INS. Crew of three includes a radar operator located in the rear of the cabin, although the aircraft is otherwise able to undertake transport and air ambulance missions. Extras include a navigation table,

search windows and a dropping hatch, and additional reconnaissance and electronic surveillance roles may be undertaken by fitment of appropriate external pods.

Data as Mystère-Falcon 50 except:
WEIGHTS:
Weight empty, equipped 11,640 kg (25,662 lb)
PERFORMANCE:
Balanced field length at max T-O weight
1,600 m (5,250 ft)
FAR 25 landing distance with 3 crew 1,050 m (3,445 ft)
Range at sea level with 3 crew and 5% +30 min fuel
reserves 3,448 nm (6,390 km; 3,970 miles)
Endurance at 7,620 m (25,000 ft), no reserves 10 h

DASSAULT AVIATION MYSTÈRE-FALCON 900
Spanish military designation: T.18

On 27 May 1983, at the Paris Air Show, Dassault announced a programme to develop an intercontinental three-turbofan executive transport to be known as the Mystère-Falcon 900. The prototype (F-GIDE *Spirit of Lafayette*) made its first flight on 21 September 1984. The second development aircraft (F-GFJC) flew on 30 August 1985. In the following month it made a nonstop flight of 4,305 nm (7,973 km; 4,954 miles) from Paris to Little Rock, Arkansas, USA, for demonstration at the NBAA Convention and at 30 other locations. The return trans-Atlantic flight from Teterboro, New Jersey, to Istres, France, was made at Mach 0.84.

DGAC certification was received on 14 March 1986, and FAA type approval on 21 March. Deliveries began in December 1986. By 1 January 1990, 74 aircraft had been delivered, all but two to export customers. Outfitting for American customers is undertaken by Falcon Jet Corporation at Little Rock, Arkansas, to customers' requirements. Government/VIP aircraft are operated in Australia, France, Malaysia, Nigeria and Spain. An example registered F-WWFJ, which left the production line on 17 June 1988, was the 1,000th aircraft in the Mystère-Falcon series. Five Falcon 900s are in VIP service with the Royal Australian Air Force.

In February 1987, a Mystère-Falcon 900 (c/n 10) set three class C1g records (subject to FAI homologation) by climbing to 9,000 m in 5 min 24.5 s, and to 15,000 m in 21 min 0.5 s, and by maintaining a height of 51,000 ft (15,545 m) in horizontal flight.

As can be seen in the accompanying illustrations, the Mystère-Falcon 900 is similar in configuration to the Mystère-Falcon 50, but with increased overall dimensions, notably a larger fuselage. Design and manufacturing programmes are computer assisted, and extensive use is made of carbonfibre and aramid composite (Kevlar) materials. Certification is to FAR Pt 25 and 55 requirements, including qualification of the entire airframe to damage tolerance standards. A secondary pressure bulkhead, while allowing in-flight access to the large baggage compartment at the rear, isolates the latter in the event of pressure loss. In a belly landing, the bottom fuselage fuel tanks would be protected by ventral skids and energy absorbing honeycomb pads which form an integral part of the fuselage structure.

The first two examples of a long-range maritime surveillance Falcon 900 were ordered by the Japan Maritime Safety Agency in September 1987, and entered service on 27 September 1989. These aircraft have observation windows and observers' seats of the kind fitted on US Coast Guard HU-25As, a drop hatch for sonobuoys, markers and flares, an operations control station with a US search radar and special communications equipment.

TYPE: Three-turbofan executive transport.
WINGS: Cantilever low-wing monoplane, with profile optimised for Mach 0.84 cruise. Dihedral 0° 30'. Sweepback at quarter-chord 29° inboard, 24° 30' on outer panels. Constructional details as for Falcon 50, apart from three-position airbrakes.
FUSELAGE: All-metal semi-monocoque damage tolerant structure, with less riveting than in Falcon 50. Kevlar nosecone over radar. Kevlar fairing on each side of fuselage in area of wingroots. Twelve windows each side standard; further six optional.
TAIL UNIT: Cantilever structure, with horizontal surfaces mounted partway up fin at anhedral of 8°. All surfaces swept. Tailplane incidence adjustable by screwjack, driven by two electric motors controlled by normal and emergency controls located respectively on the pilots' control wheels and pedestal. All-metal construction, except for rear portion of fin below rudder, and tailcone, which are of Kevlar. Rudder and elevators operated hydraulically.
LANDING GEAR: Retractable tricycle type by Messier-Hispano-Bugatti, with twin wheels on each unit. Hydraulic retraction, main units inward, nosewheels forward. Oleo-pneumatic shock absorbers. Mainwheels fitted with Michelin radial tyres size 29 × 7.7-15, pressure 13.0 bars (189 lb/sq in). Nosewheel tyres size 17.5 × 5.75-8, pressure 10.0 bars (145 lb/sq in). Hydraulic nosewheel steering (±60° for taxying, ±180° for towing). MHB triple-disc carbon brakes and anti-skid system. Nosewheel doors of Kevlar; mainwheel doors of carbonfibre.
POWER PLANT: Three Garrett TFE731-5AR-1C turbofans, each rated at 20 kN (4,500 lb st). Thrust reverser on centre engine. Fuel in two integral tanks in wings, centre-section tank, and two tanks under floor of forward and rear fuselage. Total fuel capacity 10,735 litres (2,835 US gallons; 2,361 Imp gallons). Kevlar air intake trunk for centre engine, and rear cowling for side engines. Carbonfibre central cowling around all three engines.
ACCOMMODATION: A Type III emergency exit on the starboard side of the cabin permits a wide range of layouts for up to 19 passengers. Flight deck for two pilots, with a central jumpseat. The flight deck is separated from

Dassault Aviation Mystère-Falcon 900 (three Garrett TFE731-5AR-1C turbofans) *(Pilot Press)*

the cabin by a door, with a crew wardrobe and baggage locker on either side. At the front of the main cabin, on the starboard side opposite the main cabin door, is a galley. The passenger area is divided into three lounges. The forward zone has four armchairs in facing pairs with tables. The centre zone contains a four-place sofa on the port side, facing a longitudinal table. On the starboard side, a bar cabinet contains a foldaway longitudinal bench, allowing five to six persons to be seated around the table for dinner, while leaving the emergency exit clear. In the rear zone, an inward facing settee on the starboard side converts into a bed. On the port side, two armchairs are separated by a table. At the rear of the cabin, a door leads to the toilet compartment, on the starboard side, and a second structural plug door to the large rear baggage area. The baggage door is electrically actuated. Other interior configurations include Dreyfuss human engineered designs in the USA and IDEI travel ergonomics concepts in France. The Dreyfuss interior features patented seating and galley innovations. It includes a crew lavatory forward, a transverse table with four chairs and two stowable lateral seats in a central conference area, a sofa bed on the port side and an executive work station opposite. An alternative eight-passenger configuration has a bedroom at the rear and three personnel seats in the forward zone. A 15-passenger layout divides a VIP area at the rear from six (three-abreast) chairs forward. The 18-passenger scheme has four rows of three-abreast airline type seats forward, and a VIP lounge with two chairs and a settee aft. Many optional items, including stereo, video and hot running water, are available. Windscreens anti-iced electrically.

SYSTEMS: Air-conditioning system uses engine bleed air or air from Garrett GTCP36-150 APU installed in rear fuselage. Softair pressurisation system, with max differential of 0.64 bars (9.3 lb/sq in), maintains sea level cabin environment to a height of 7,620 m (25,000 ft), and a cabin equivalent of 2,440 m (8,000 ft) at 15,550 m (51,000 ft). Cold air supply is by a single oversize air cycle unit. Two independent hydraulic systems, pressure 207 bars (3,000 lb/sq in), with three engine driven pumps and one emergency electric pump, actuate primary flying controls, flaps, slats, landing gear retraction, wheel brakes, airbrakes, nosewheel steering and thrust reverser. Bootstrap hydraulic reservoirs. DC electrical system supplied by three 9kW 28V Auxilec starter/generators and two 23Ah batteries. Eros (SFIM/Intertechnique) oxygen system.

AVIONICS AND EQUIPMENT: Dual bi-directional Honeywell ASCB digital databus operating in conjunction with dual SPZ 800 flight director/autopilot and EFIS. Dual Honeywell FMZ 605 flight management system, associated with two AZ 810 air data computers and Honeywell laser gyro inertial platforms. Collins Pro Line II ARINC 429 series com/nav receivers. Honeywell Primus 800 colour radar.

DIMENSIONS, EXTERNAL:

Wing span	19.33 m (63 ft 5 in)
Wing chord: at root	4.08 m (13 ft 4¾ in)
at tip	1.12 m (3 ft 8 in)
Wing aspect ratio	7.6
Length overall	20.21 m (66 ft 3¾ in)
Fuselage: Max diameter	2.50 m (8 ft 2½ in)
Height overall	7.55 m (24 ft 9¼ in)
Tailplane span	7.74 m (25 ft 4¾ in)
Wheel track	4.45 m (14 ft 7¼ in)
Wheelbase	7.93 m (26 ft 0¼ in)
Passenger door: Height	1.72 m (5 ft 7¾ in)
Width	0.80 m (2 ft 7½ in)
Height to sill	1.79 m (5 ft 10½ in)
Emergency exit (overwing, stbd):	
Height	0.91 m (2 ft 11¾ in)
Width	0.53 m (1 ft 8¾ in)

DIMENSIONS, INTERNAL:

Cabin, excl flight deck, incl toilet and baggage compartments:	
Length	11.90 m (39 ft 0½ in)
Max width	2.34 m (7 ft 8 in)
Width at floor	1.86 m (6 ft 1¼ in)
Max height	1.87 m (6 ft 1½ in)
Volume	35.79 m³ (1,264 cu ft)
Rear baggage compartment volume	3.60 m³ (127 cu ft)
Flight deck volume	3.75 m³ (132 cu ft)

AREAS:

Wings, gross	49.03 m² (527.75 sq ft)
Vertical tail surfaces (total)	9.82 m² (105.7 sq ft)
Horizontal tail surfaces (total)	13.35 m² (143.7 sq ft)

WEIGHTS:

Weight empty, equipped (typical)	10,240 kg (22,575 lb)
Operating weight empty	10,545 kg (23,248 lb)
Max payload	1,815 kg (4,000 lb)
Payload with max fuel	1,405 kg (3,097 lb)
Max fuel	8,620 kg (19,004 lb)
Max T-O weight	20,640 kg (45,500 lb)
Max landing weight	19,050 kg (42,000 lb)
Normal landing weight	12,250 kg (27,000 lb)
Max zero-fuel weight: standard	12,430 kg (27,400 lb)
optional	14,000 kg (30,865 lb)

PERFORMANCE (at AUW of 12,250 kg; 27,000 lb, except where indicated):

Max operating speed:	
at S/L Mach 0.87; 350 knots (648 km/h; 402 mph) IAS	
between 3,050-7,620 m (10,000-25,000 ft)	
Mach 0.84; 370 knots (685 km/h; 425 mph) IAS	
Max cruising speed at 8,230 m (27,000 ft)	
	500 knots (927 km/h; 575 mph)
Econ cruising speed	Mach 0.75
Stalling speed: clean	101 knots (188 km/h; 117 mph)
landing configuration	79 knots (147 km/h; 91 mph)
Approach speed, eight passengers and fuel reserves	
	103 knots (191 km/h; 119 mph)
Max cruising height	15,550 m (51,000 ft)
Min ground turning radius: nosewheels	
	13.54 m (44 ft 5 in)
Balanced T-O field length with full tanks, eight passengers and baggage	1,515 m (4,970 ft)
FAR 91 landing field length at AUW of 12,250 kg (27,000 lb)	700 m (2,300 ft)
Range with max payload, NBAA IFR reserves	
	3,460 nm (6,412 km; 3,984 miles)
Range at Mach 0.75 with max fuel and NBAA IFR reserves:	
15 passengers	3,760 nm (6,968 km; 4,329 miles)
8 passengers	3,900 nm (7,227 km; 4,491 miles)

DASSAULT AVIATION MYSTÈRE FALCON 2000

At the 1989 Paris Air Show, Dassault revealed preliminary details and a full-scale cabin mockup of a new business twin-jet intended to replace the Mystère/Falcon 20/200 series, then known provisionally as the Falcon X, but later designated Falcon 2000. Based substantially on the Falcon 900, and retaining the same cabin cross-section, the prototype is expected to fly in 1992, with French and US certification scheduled for 1994. Dassault anticipate sales of 300 Falcon 2000s over a nine-year period.

The description for the Falcon 900 applies also to the Falcon 2000 except as follows:

TYPE: Twin-turbofan executive transport.

WINGS: As Falcon 50/900, except for removal of inboard slats and modification of leading-edge.

FUSELAGE: As Falcon 900, but reduced in length by 1.98 m (6 ft 6 in) and redesigned at the rear for two turbofan engines.

POWER PLANT: Two turbofan engines, either GE/Garrett CFE738 of 24.91 kN (5,600 lb st) or Pratt & Whitney PW305 of approximately 24.02 kN (5,400 lb st).

ACCOMMODATION: Up to 12 passengers and two flight crew. Baggage volume 4.00 m³ (141.3 cu ft).

AVIONICS AND EQUIPMENT: EFIS cockpit, with avionics by either Collins or Honeywell.

DIMENSIONS, EXTERNAL:

Length overall	19.23 m (63 ft 1 in)
Height	6.98 m (22 ft 10¾ in)

DIMENSIONS, INTERNAL:

Cabin:	
Length	7.98 m (26 ft 2¼ in)
Max width	2.34 m (7 ft 8¼ in)
Height	1.97 m (6 ft 5½ in)
Volume	28.00 m³ (989.6 cu ft)

AREA:

Wings, gross	49.02 m² (527.65 sq ft)

WEIGHTS AND LOADINGS:

Weight empty, equipped	8,250 kg (18,188 lb)
Max payload	1,390 kg (3,064 lb)
Max fuel weight	5,513 kg (12,154 lb)
Max T-O weight	15,875 kg (35,000 lb)
Max landing weight	14,970 kg (33,000 lb)

PERFORMANCE (at max T-O weight, ISA, except where indicated):

Max operating speed	Mach 0.85
Max cruising speed at 11,890 m (39,000 ft)	
	Mach 0.83-0.85
Certificated ceiling	12,500 m (41,000 ft)
T-O run	1,615 m (5,300 ft)
Landing run	1,550 m (5,085 ft)
Range with max fuel, 8 passengers and NBAA IFR reserves	
	2,995 nm (5,550 km; 3,448 miles)

HERMÈS AEROSPACECRAFT

Dassault Aviation is responsible for all work required to achieve successful re-entry atmospheric flight by the Hermès aerospacecraft, of which brief details can be found under the Aerospatiale entry in this section.

Cabin mockup and three-view drawing (*Pilot Press*) **of Dassault Aviation Mystère Falcon 2000 twin-engined business jet**

MICROJET

MICROJET SA (Member company of Groupe Creuzet)

Aérodrome de Marmande-Virazeil, 47200 Marmande
Telephone: 33 53 64 53 50
Telex: 550 777 F
Fax: 33 53 64 54 55
CHAIRMAN: Robert Creuzet
INFORMATION OFFICER: Jérôme Creuzet

MICROJET 200 B

The early history of the Microjet programme was recorded in the 1984-85 and previous editions of *Jane's*. Aim of the programme is to offer economies in military pilot training by use of very small high-performance jet aircraft with comparatively low initial and operating costs.

First flight of a pre-production aircraft (F-WDMT) took place on 19 May 1983. Together with the earlier, wooden, prototype, it then underwent technical evaluation by pilots of the CEV, but was lost on 13 March 1985. The second pre-production Microjet (F-WDMX), manufactured entirely by Marmande Aéronautique, flew on 5 January 1985 and has significance in that it is the first Microjet with underwing hardpoints for expanded military applications. A third pre-production aircraft (also F-WDMT) flew on 4 November 1986. The fourth pre-production airframe was built for static tests at the CEAT, Toulouse.

The following description applies to the planned initial production version of the Microjet 200 B. Take-off rating of each engine will be increased progressively to 1.80 kN (405 lb st), to improve performance and payload, with particular emphasis on the aircraft's potential in an anti-helicopter combat role.

TYPE: Two-seat lightweight training aircraft.
WINGS: Cantilever low-wing monoplane of tapered planform. Wing section RA 16.3c3. Thickness/chord ratio 16 per cent. Dihedral 5° 2′ constant from roots. Incidence 3°. Sweepback 0° at 30 per cent chord. Wings, Frise ailerons and electrically operated single-slotted trailing-edge flaps all of glassfibre/epoxy, with carbonfibre wing spars. Small airbrake forward of outer end of flap on upper surface of each wing. Ailerons embody adjustable artificial feel. Ground adjustable tab on starboard aileron.
FUSELAGE: Conventional light alloy semi-monocoque structure. NACA flush engine air intake on each side of fuselage aft of cockpit; exhaust through lateral jetpipes forward of tail unit.
TAIL UNIT: Cantilever V type, comprising interchangeable fixed surfaces and elevators of glassfibre/epoxy, with carbonfibre spars. Sweepback 26° at 50 per cent chord. Included angle 110°. Controllable tab at root end of each elevator. Shallow ventral fin. Small vertical extensions added to fins in 1989 to assist spin recovery.
LANDING GEAR: Retractable tricycle type, with single wheel on each unit. Electric retraction, nosewheel rearward, main units inward to fuselage. Manual emergency extension. All wheels fully enclosed by doors when retracted. Microjet oleo-pneumatic shock absorber in all three units. Nosewheel offset 149 mm (6 in) to starboard. Goodyear wheels, tyres and two-disc hydraulic brakes. Mainwheel tyres size 386 × 172-150, pressure 4.2 bars (61 lb/sq in); nosewheel tyre size 361 × 120-125, pressure 1.8 bars (26 lb/sq in). Parking brake.
POWER PLANT: Two Microturbo TRS 18-1 turbojets, each rated at 1.30 kN (293 lb st) for normal operation, uprated automatically to the T-O rating of 1.45 kN (326 lb st) on surviving engine if the other should fail during take-off. Ratings will be increased to 1.60 kN (360 lb st) and 1.80 kN (405 lb st) respectively in TRS 18-2 form for series production aircraft. Fuel in two structural tanks behind cockpit and one in each wing, with total capacity of 440 litres (116 US gallons; 97 Imp gallons). Two refuelling points, one aft of cockpit on each side. Total oil capacity 1.6 litres (0.42 US gallon; 0.35 Imp gallon).
ACCOMMODATION: Pupil and instructor on side by side adjustable seats, under one-piece rearward hinged jettisonable tinted transparent canopy. Starboard (instructor's) seat staggered 55 cm (1 ft 9¾ in) aft of port seat. Adjustable rudder pedals. Cockpit heated and

Third pre-production Microjet 200 B lightweight training aircraft

Microjet 200 B in production configuration *(Pilot Press)*

ventilated by ram air and exhaust heat exchanger, but not pressurised.
SYSTEMS: Electrical system comprises two 1.6kW engine driven generators and a 15Ah nickel-cadmium battery which actuate the landing gear and flaps through non-reversible mechanical jacks. Gaseous oxygen supply for two crew for four hours, from one 1,400 litre (50 cu ft) bottle.
AVIONICS AND EQUIPMENT: Blind-flying instrumentation and avionics for IFR flight standard, including ADI, HSI and RMI. Typical installation would include VHF, VOR, ILS, DME, marker beacon receiver, transponder, ADF and intercom. Military version would have UHF, Tacan and IFF.

DIMENSIONS, EXTERNAL:

Wing span	7.56 m (24 ft 9¾ in)
Wing chord at root	0.85 m (2 ft 9½ in)
Wing aspect ratio	9.1
Length overall	6.665 m (21 ft 10½ in)
Fuselage: Length	6.56 m (21 ft 6¼ in)
Width	1.10 m (3 ft 7¼ in)
Height overall	2.76 m (9 ft 0⅝ in)
Tailplane span	3.07 m (10 ft 1 in)
Wheel track	1.92 m (6 ft 3½ in)
Wheelbase	2.64 m (8 ft 8 in)

AREAS:

Wings, gross	6.28 m² (67.60 sq ft)
Ailerons (total)	0.446 m² (4.80 sq ft)
Trailing-edge flaps (total)	0.69 m² (7.43 sq ft)
Tail surfaces (total)	2.52 m² (27.13 sq ft)

WEIGHTS AND LOADINGS:

Weight empty	780 kg (1,719 lb)
Max fuel	340 kg (750 lb)
Max T-O weight: Aerobatic	1,140 kg (2,513 lb)
Utility	1,300 kg (2,866 lb)
Max ramp weight	1,300 kg (2,866 lb)
Max zero-fuel weight	960 kg (2,116 lb)
Max landing weight	1,280 kg (2,822 lb)
Max wing loading	207 kg/m² (42.4 lb/sq ft)
Max power loading	448 kg/kN (4.40 lb/lb st)

PERFORMANCE (at max T-O weight with 1.45 kN engines):

Never-exceed speed	300 knots (555 km/h; 345 mph)
Max level speed and max cruising speed at 5,500 m	
(18,045 ft)	250 knots (463 km/h; 287 mph)
Econ cruising speed	210 knots (389 km/h; 241 mph)
Stalling speed, flaps down, engines idling	
	79 knots (146 km/h; 91 mph)
Max rate of climb at S/L	540 m (1,772 ft)/min
Rate of climb at S/L, one engine out	90 m (295 ft)/min
Service ceiling	9,150 m (30,000 ft)
Service ceiling, one engine out	3,050 m (10,000 ft)
T-O run	750 m (2,461 ft)
T-O to 15 m (50 ft)	1,150 m (3,773 ft)
Landing from 15 m (50 ft)	675 m (2,215 ft)
Landing run	435 m (1,427 ft)
Range with max internal fuel, 20 min hold	
	400 nm (741 km; 461 miles)
Max endurance	2 h
g limits:	+7/-3.5 Aerobatic
	+4/-1.8 Utility

MUDRY

AVIONS MUDRY et CIE

Aérodrome de Bernay, BP 214, 27300 Bernay
Telephone: 33 32 43 47 34
Telex: MUDRY 180 587 F
Fax: 33 32 43 47 90
DIRECTORS GENERAL: A. Mudry (President) and D. Baron
CHIEF DESIGNER: M. Dozieres
Mudry Aviation Ltd
Dutchess County Airport, Wappingers Falls, NY 12590, USA
Telephone: 1 (914) 462 5009
Fax: 1 (914) 462 0258
PRESIDENT: Daniel Heligoin

M Auguste Mudry established this company in 1958 in the works of the former Société Aéronautique Normande at Bernay, and operated it in parallel with his other aircraft manufacturing company, C.A.A.R.P. of Beynes (see

1977-78 *Jane's*). All activities of C.A.A.R.P. were subsequently combined with those of Avions A. Mudry, at Bernay, where some 50 persons are employed, divided between the Courcelles design office and the manufacturing plant at Bernay Aerodrome.

MUDRY CAP 10 B

Developed from the Piel Emeraude two-seat light aircraft (see Sport Aircraft section), via the prototype C.P. 100 aerobatic version built by C.A.A.R.P., the CAP 10 is designed for use as a training, touring or aerobatic aeroplane. The prototype was flown for the first time in August 1968, and certification of the CAP 10 was granted on 4 September 1970. Later production aircraft, with ventral fin and enlarged rudder, are designated **CAP 10 B**. Construction is to French AIR 2052 (CAR 3) Category A standards for aerobatic flying. FAA certification for day and night VFR operation was received in 1974.

A total of 245 CAP 10/10 Bs had been delivered to customers in 24 countries by January 1990, including 56 for the French Air Force and eight for the French Navy. The Air Force aircraft are operated currently by EFIPN 307 (École de Formation Initiale du Personnel Navigant) at Avord and the École de l'Air at Salon de Provence. The Navy CAP 10s serve with 51 Escadrille de Servitude at Rochefort/Soubise. Overseas operators include the Mexican Air Force's flying training school, whose 20 aircraft are equipped almost to IFR standard. Recent deliveries include two aircraft for the Australian Aviation College at Parafield, South Australia.

To extend the potential market for the CAP 10, Mudry produced the prototype of a version equipped for glider towing, under the designation **CAP 10 R** (for remorqueur). In 1988, however, it was decided to delay marketing of this model.

TYPE: Two-seat aerobatic light aircraft.

WINGS: Cantilever low-wing monoplane. Wing section NACA 23012. Dihedral 5° from roots. Incidence 0°. No sweepback. All-spruce single-spar torsion box structure, with trellis ribs, rear auxiliary spar and okoumé plywood covering, with outer skin of polyester fabric. Inner section of each wing is rectangular in plan, outer section semi-elliptical. Wooden trailing-edge plain flaps and slotted ailerons.

FUSELAGE: Conventional spruce girder structure, built in two halves and joined by three main frames. Of basically rectangular section with rounded top decking. Polyester fabric covering. Forward section also has an inner plywood skin for added strength. Engine cowling panels of non-flammable laminated plastics.

TAIL UNIT: Conventional cantilever structure. All-wood single-spar fin, integral with fuselage, and tailplane. All surfaces covered with both plywood and polyester fabric. Tailplane incidence adjustable on ground. Trim tab in each elevator. Automatic rudder trim. Small ventral fin.

LANDING GEAR: Non-retractable tailwheel type. Mainwheel legs of light alloy, with ERAM type 9 270 C oleo-pneumatic shock absorbers. Single wheel on each main unit, tyre size 380 × 150. Solid tailwheel tyre, size 6 × 200. Tailwheel is steerable by rudder linkage but can be disengaged for ground manoeuvring. Hydraulically actuated mainwheel disc brakes (controllable from port seat) and parking brake. Streamline fairings on mainwheels and legs.

POWER PLANT: One 134 kW (180 hp) Textron Lycoming AEIO-360-B2F flat-four engine, driving a Hoffmann two-blade fixed-pitch wooden propeller. Standard fuel tank aft of engine fireproof bulkhead, capacity 72 litres (19 US gallons; 16 Imp gallons). Optional auxiliary tank, capacity 75 litres (20 US gallons; 16.5 Imp gallons), beneath baggage compartment. Inverted fuel and oil (Christen Industries) systems permit continuous inverted flight.

ACCOMMODATION: Side by side adjustable seats for two persons, with provision for back parachutes, under rearward sliding and jettisonable moulded transparent canopy. Special aerobatic shoulder harness standard. Space for 20 kg (44 lb) of baggage aft of seats in training and touring models.

SYSTEMS: Electrical system includes Delco-Rémy 40A engine driven alternator and STECO ET24 nickel-cadmium battery.

AVIONICS: King avionics standard.

DIMENSIONS, EXTERNAL:
Wing span	8.06 m (26 ft 5¼ in)
Wing aspect ratio	6.0
Length overall	7.16 m (23 ft 6 in)
Height overall	2.55 m (8 ft 4½ in)
Tailplane span	2.90 m (9 ft 6 in)
Wheel track	2.06 m (6 ft 9 in)

DIMENSION, INTERNAL:
Cockpit: Max width	1.054 m (3 ft 5½ in)

AREAS:
Wings, gross	10.85 m² (116.79 sq ft)
Ailerons (total)	0.79 m² (8.50 sq ft)
Vertical tail surfaces (total)	1.32 m² (14.25 sq ft)
Horizontal tail surfaces (total)	1.86 m² (20.0 sq ft)

WEIGHTS (A: Aerobatic, U: Utility):
Weight empty, equipped: A, U	550 kg (1,213 lb)
Fuel load: A	54 kg (119 lb)
U	108 kg (238 lb)
Max T-O weight: A	760 kg (1,675 lb)
U	830 kg (1,829 lb)

PERFORMANCE (at max T-O weight):
Never-exceed speed	183 knots (340 km/h; 211 mph)
Max level speed at S/L	146 knots (270 km/h; 168 mph)
Max cruising speed (75% power)	135 knots (250 km/h; 155 mph)
Stalling speed:	
flaps up	51.5 knots (95 km/h; 59 mph) IAS
flaps down	43 knots (80 km/h; 50 mph) IAS
Max rate of climb at S/L	480 m (1,575 ft)/min
Service ceiling	5,000 m (16,400 ft)
T-O run	350 m (1,149 ft)

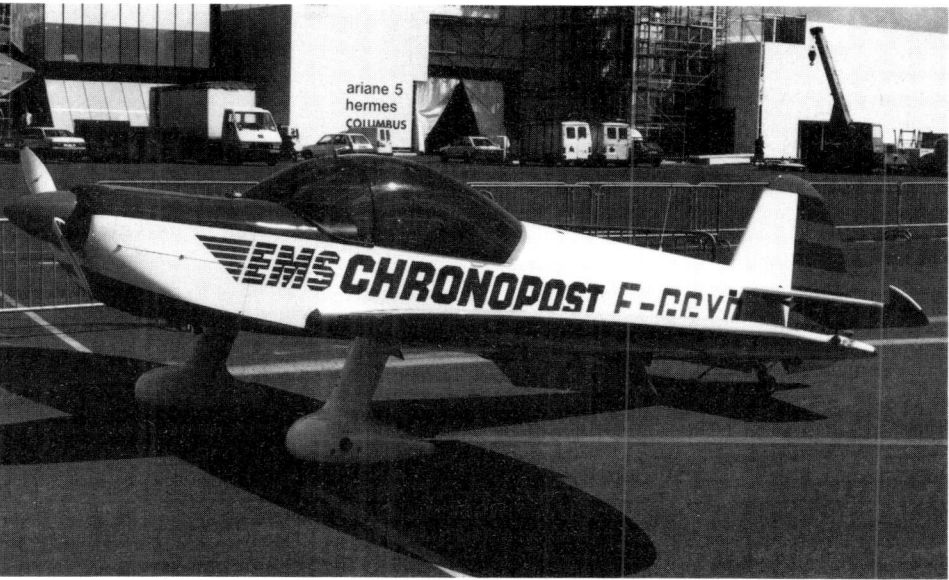

Mudry CAP 10 B two-seat aerobatic light aircraft *(Mike Jerram)*

T-O to 15 m (50 ft)	450 m (1,477 ft)
Landing from 15 m (50 ft)	600 m (1,968 ft)
Landing run	360 m (1,182 ft)
Range with max fuel	539 nm (1,000 km; 621 miles)
g limits	+6/−4.5

MUDRY CAP 21

The CAP 21 is a single-seat aerobatic competition aircraft which retains the fuselage and tail unit of the earlier CAP 20LS-200, but has cantilever main landing gear legs and an entirely new wing, which has improved the rate of roll to 180°/s at 135 knots (250 km/h; 155 mph) by comparison with the CAP 20L's 130°/s, and enhanced snap rolling capability.

The prototype (F-WZCH) was displayed at the 1979 Paris Air Show. It flew for the first time on 23 June 1980, and work was started on a first batch of ten production CAP 21s. Deliveries began in May 1982, and Mudry began manufacture of a second series in 1983. By January 1990, a total of 39 CAP 20/21s had been delivered to 30 customers. No further production is planned.

An earlier aircraft, registered in Italy (I-SIVM), has been retrofitted with a 194 kW (260 hp) engine by its Italian owner, Sig Sergio Dallan. Known as the CAP **21-260**, the aircraft embodies several other modifications, including a main wing spar which permits load factors of ± 10g; larger wingroot fairings on both the leading- and trailing-edges; longer exhaust pipes which reduce noise; repositioned main landing gear legs with root fairings to reduce airflow disturbance at the wingroot leading-edge; a larger rudder; improved aileron control linkage; substitution of a one-piece canopy; movement of the reclined pilot's seat further aft to offset the effect on CG of a heavier power plant; replacement of the standard 40 litre (10.5 US gallon; 8.8 Imp gallon) fuel tank with a 60 litre (15.8 US gallon; 13.2 Imp gallon) tank; and installation of a ferry tank under the pilot's seat.

The following details apply to the standard CAP 21 production aircraft:

TYPE: Single-seat aerobatic light aircraft.

WINGS: Cantilever low-wing monoplane. Wing section V16F. Thickness/chord ratio 16 per cent. Dihedral 1° 30′. No twist. All-wood single-spar structure, with flaps. Automatic tab in each aileron to reduce stick forces.

FUSELAGE: Conventional all-wood structure, of basically triangular section with rounded top decking. Wood covering, except for laminated plastics engine cowling.

TAIL UNIT: Cantilever all-wood structure. Trim tab in each elevator.

LANDING GEAR: Non-retractable tailwheel type. Cantilever glassfibre main legs, with streamline fairings over wheels. Disc brakes.

POWER PLANT: One 149 kW (200 hp) Textron Lycoming AEIO-360-A1B flat-four engine, driving a two-blade Hartzell variable-pitch propeller. Fixed-pitch propeller optional. Normal fuel tank capacity 40 litres (10.5 US gallons; 8.8 Imp gallons). Max fuel capacity 75 litres (20 US gallons; 16.5 Imp gallons), with 15 litre (4 US gallon; 3.3 Imp gallon) gravity tank for inverted flying. Christen inverted oil system.

ACCOMMODATION: Single glassfibre seat under rearward sliding transparent canopy. Special aerobatic shoulder harness.

DIMENSIONS, EXTERNAL:
Wing span	8.08 m (26 ft 6 in)
Wing aspect ratio	7.0
Length overall	6.46 m (21 ft 2½ in)
Height overall	1.52 m (5 ft 0 in)

AREAS:
Wings, gross	9.40 m² (101.18 sq ft)
Ailerons (total)	1.42 m² (15.28 sq ft)
Fin	0.780 m² (8.40 sq ft)
Rudder	0.725 m² (7.80 sq ft)
Elevators	1.18 m² (12.70 sq ft)

WEIGHTS AND LOADINGS:
Weight empty	500 kg (1,103 lb)
Max T-O weight: Aerobatic	620 kg (1,367 lb)
Normal	750 kg (1,653 lb)
Max wing loading (Aerobatic)	65.95 kg/m² (13.5 lb/sq ft)
Max power loading (Aerobatic)	4.16 kg/kW (6.84 lb/hp)

PERFORMANCE:
Never-exceed speed	200 knots (372 km/h; 231 mph)
Max level speed at S/L	151 knots (280 km/h; 174 mph)
Max cruising speed (75% power)	135 knots (250 km/h; 155 mph)
Stalling speed	49 knots (90 km/h; 56 mph)
Max rate of climb at S/L	780 m (2,560 ft)/min
Range (with supplementary tank)	431 nm (800 km; 497 miles)
g limits	+8/−6
Rate of roll	200°/s

MUDRY CAP 230

The CAP 230 is a version of the CAP 21 powered by a 224 kW (300 hp) Textron Lycoming AEIO-540-L1-B5D flat-six engine. Its development was announced in January 1985, simultaneously with news of an initial order for four CAP 230s to equip the Royal Moroccan Air Force's aerobatic team. A prototype first flew on 8 October 1985. Four were ordered for the French Air Force's Équipe de Voltige Aérienne (EVA) at Salon de Provence, to replace the team's CAP 20s. The first of these (actually prototype F-WZCH) was delivered on 13 June 1986 but no more were supplied to customers until 1988, when the EVA received three (c/n 02-04); the AFVA (French Aerobatic Association) one; and the Moroccan Air Force 'Green March' team four (c/n 06-09). The tenth CAP 230 was delivered to the Aéro Club de l'Hérault at Montpellier. Avions Mudry expects to build a further 10 aircraft during 1990, of which three are destined for customers in France, the United Kingdom and United States. The Moroccan Air Force holds an option for two further CAP 230s. In August 1988, a CAP 230 flown by Patrick Paris and Claude Bessiere won two gold medals at the World Aerobatic Championships.

Mudry CAP 21 (Textron Lycoming AEIO-360-A1B engine) *(Mike Jerram)*

The following details apply to the CAP 230 in production form:

DIMENSIONS, EXTERNAL:
Wing span	8.08 m (26 ft 6 in)
Length overall	6.75 m (22 ft 1¾ in)
Height overall	1.80 m (5 ft 11 in)

AREAS:
Wings, gross	9.66 m² (103.98 sq ft)

WEIGHTS:
Weight empty	630 kg (1,389 lb)
Max T-O weight: Aerobatic	730 kg (1,609 lb)
Normal	820 kg (1,808 lb)

PERFORMANCE:
Never-exceed speed	215 knots (400 km/h; 248 mph)
Max level speed at S/L	183 knots (340 km/h; 211 mph)
Max cruising speed (75% power)	
	156 knots (290 km/h; 180 mph)
Stalling speed	51.5 knots (95 km/h; 59 mph)
Max rate of climb at S/L	1,020 m (3,350 ft)/s
g limits	±10

MUDRY CAP X4

Having postponed indefinitely production of the CAP X tricycle lightplane (see 1987-88 *Jane's*), Mudry resuscitated the aircraft as a tailwheel design in response to interest expressed by three French civilian pilot training schools. The classical landing gear, and an increase in engine power from the original 59 kW (80 hp) Mudry-Buchoux MB-4-80 to an 83.5 kW (112 hp) Textron Lycoming O-235-N2A, meet the need for students to perform basic aerobatics in a demanding tailwheel aircraft before beginning airline training.

CAP X1 and X2 are retrospective designations applied to the two nosewheel prototypes, of which X2 has been adapted for ground demonstration of X4 aspects. These aircraft were due to be joined in February 1990 by a CAP X3 featuring a redesigned airframe with wing attachment points farther forward and 70 per cent span ailerons. Depending on market response, this will be followed by the definitive CAP X4, which will have a fuselage widened and modified for increased visibility; and improved comfort and soundproofing.

TYPE: Two-seat trainer and aerobatic aircraft.

WINGS: Cantilever low-wing single-spar monoplane of wood construction. Wing section ONERA OAAG04. Dihedral 5° from root; incidence 1° 52'. Wing attached to fuselage at four points. 70 per cent span ailerons.

FUSELAGE: Conventional wooden structure based upon two trellis longerons.

TAIL UNIT: Cantilever wooden structure. Single-spar tailplane with elevators; single-spar vertical fin.

LANDING GEAR: Non-retractable tailwheel type. Disc brakes on mainwheels. Parking brake.

POWER PLANT: One 83.5 kW (112 hp) Textron Lycoming O-235-N2A piston engine, driving a two-blade fixed-pitch propeller. Two fuselage fuel tanks with total capacity of 144 litres (38 US gallons; 31.7 Imp gallons).

ACCOMMODATION: Two persons side by side under one-piece canopy.

DIMENSIONS, EXTERNAL:
Wing span	8.41 m (27 ft 7⅛ in)
Wing aspect ratio	7.524
Length overall	6.10 m (20 ft 0¼ in)
Height overall	1.55 m (5 ft 1 in)

Mudry CAP 230 single-seat aerobatic aircraft of the Équipe de France de Voltige

Tailplane span	2.84 m (9 ft 3¾ in)
Wheel track	2.60 m (8 ft 6⅜ in)
Wheelbase	4.05 m (13 ft 3½ in)

DIMENSIONS, INTERNAL:
Cabin: Width	1.17 m (3 ft 10 in)
Length	1.38 m (4 ft 6⅜ in)

AREAS:
Wings, gross	9.4 m² (101.2 sq ft)
Horizontal tail surfaces (total)	2.06 m² (22.2 sq ft)
Fin	1.18 m² (12.7 sq ft)

WEIGHTS (estimated):
Weight empty	415 kg (914 lb)
Max T-O weight: Aerobatic	660 kg (1,455 lb)
Utility	695 kg (1,532 lb)

PERFORMANCE (estimated. A, Aerobatic; U, Utility):
Never-exceed speed: A	170 knots (315 km/h; 195 mph)
U	156 knots (290 km/h; 180 mph)
Design manoeuvring speed:	
A	127 knots (235 km/h; 146 mph)
U	113 knots (210 km/h; 130 mph)
Cruising speed: A	138 knots (255 km/h; 158 mph)
U	130 knots (240 km/h; 149 mph)

Rate of climb at S/L	213 m (700 ft)/min
Service ceiling	4,575 m (15,000 ft)
T-O run	240 m (787 ft)
T-O to 15 m (50 ft)	340 m (1,225 ft)
Landing from 15 m (50 ft)	330 m (1,083 ft)
Landing run	180 m (591 ft)
Range	691 nm (1,280 km; 795 miles)
g limits: A	+6/−4.5
U	+4.4/−2

MUDRY CAP '92'

This is the provisional designation of an aerobatic aircraft commissioned from Mudry by the French Air Force for its entry in the 1992 World Aerobatic Championships. Partners in the venture include Socata, the Air Force, a technical school and an engine manufacturer. In early 1990, the last-mentioned had yet to be selected, two firms having been requested to submit proposals for developing a 298 kW (400 hp) piston engine to be installed in the CAP '92'.

REIMS AVIATION

REIMS AVIATION SA

Aérodrome de Reims-Prunay, BP 2745, 51062 Reims Cédex
Telephone: 33 26 06 96 55
Telex: REMAVIA 830754
Fax: 33 26 49 13 60
PRESIDENT DIRECTOR-GENERAL AND PRODUCTION
 DIRECTOR: Jean Pichon
PUBLIC RELATIONS OFFICER: Christian Jousset

Reims Aviation is the successor to the former Société Nouvelle des Avions Max Holste, which had been founded in 1956. It has the right to manufacture under licence Cessna designs for sale in Europe, Africa and Asia; but the suspension of Cessna production of piston engined aircraft applies also to Reims Aviation. By 1 January 1990 Reims had assembled a total of 6,317 aircraft of all types, including 2,518 Reims-Cessna F150/152s and 2,496 F172s.

As an extension of its collaboration with Cessna, Reims Aviation developed and is manufacturing a twin-turboprop light transport aircraft known as the Reims-Cessna F 406 Caravan II. Manufacture of this aircraft continues, but Cessna sold its former 49 per cent interest in Reims Aviation to Compagnie Française Chanfour Investissement (CFCI) of Paris in early 1989.

Reims Aviation is a subcontractor to Dassault-Breguet in the Mystère-Falcon programmes; and a subcontractor to Aerospatiale in the ATR 42/72 and Airbus programmes and for miscellaneous parts. It had 530 employees in 1989. Its offices and factory at Reims-Prunay Airport have an area of 28,300 m² (304,618 sq ft).

REIMS-CESSNA F 406 CARAVAN II

It was announced in mid-1982 that, with financial support from the French government, Reims Aviation and

Reims-Cessna F 406 Caravan II with ventral cargo pod

Cessna were collaborating in the development of an unpressurised twin-turboprop transport known as the F 406 Caravan II. Intended for business and utility use, it is a variant of Cessna's 400 series of light twins. A prototype (F-WZLT), constructed by Reims Aviation, was exhibited at the Paris Air Show prior to its first flight on 22 September 1983. Certification was achieved on 21 December 1984, and the F 406 is now being manufactured and marketed exclusively by Reims, using wings supplied by Cessna. By January 1990, 56 aircraft had been ordered from the initial production batch of 85, and 41 had been delivered.

The first production F 406 to fly was c/n 4 (F-ZBEO) on 20 April 1985, this being one of four F 406s for the French Customs Service, with full Bendix/King Gold Crown IFR avionics, Gemini navigation system (including Crouzet Nadir computer) and a Bendix 1500 radar with 360° scan in an underbelly radome. Next to fly, on 3 May, was c/n 1 (N406CE), which was used as Cessna's demonstrator following FAA certification to SFAR 41 standard. Two others are operated by No. 3 GHL of the French Army at Rennes as target tugs, with underbelly tow equipment, the first delivered on 18 May 1987. Largest fleet is that of Aviation Lease Holland BV, which has acquired 28 for use primarily as cargo transports throughout Europe.

In 1987, flight testing began of a coastal surveillance and pollution detection version of the F 406. Primary sensors housed in a long underfuselage fairing are a Terma side-looking airborne radar (SLAR) and an SAT infra-red linescan. These are claimed to detect ships over a range of 40 nm (74 km; 46 miles) and oil spills up to about half that distance.

A ventral cargo pod has recently been developed for the Caravan II, expanding baggage volume to 3.52 m³ (124.3 cu ft).

TYPE: Twin-turboprop light business and utility transport.

WINGS: Cantilever low-wing monoplane. Wing section NACA 23018 at root, NACA 23012 at tip. Dihedral 3° 30′ on wing centre-section, 4° 55′ on outer panels. Incidence 2° at root, −1° at construction tip. All-metal three-spar centre-section structure to meet SFAR 41C fail-safe requirements: two-spar structure for outer wing panels. Hydraulically operated Fowler trailing-edge flaps of light alloy construction. Plain ailerons of light alloy construction. Trim tab in port aileron. Goodrich pneumatic de-icing system optional.

FUSELAGE: All-metal semi-monocoque structure of light alloy.

TAIL UNIT: Cantilever all-metal two-spar structure, with horizontal surfaces mounted on sweptback fin. Fin offset 1° to port to counter torque of non-handed engines. Tailplane dihedral 9°. Goodrich pneumatic de-icing of leading-edges optional.

LANDING GEAR: Hydraulically retractable tricycle type with single wheel on each unit. Main units retract inward into wing, nosewheel rearward. Emergency extension by means of a 138 bar (2,000 lb/sq in) rechargeable nitrogen bottle. Cessna oleo-pneumatic shock absorbers. Main units of articulated (trailing link) type. Single-disc hydraulic brakes. Parking brake.

POWER PLANT: Two Pratt & Whitney Canada PT6A-112 turboprops (each 373 kW; 500 shp), driving McCauley 9910535-2 three-blade reversible-pitch and automatically feathering metal propellers. Fuel capacity 1,823 litres (481 US gallons; 401 Imp gallons).

ACCOMMODATION: Crew of two and up to 12 passengers, in pairs, facing forward, with centre aisle, except at rear of cabin in 12/14-seat versions. Alternative basic configurations for six VIP passengers in reclining seats in executive version, and for operation in mixed passenger/freight role. Executive version has a partition between cabin and flight deck, and toilet on starboard side at rear. Split main door immediately aft of wing, on port side, with built-in airstair in downward hinged lower portion. Optional cargo door forward of this door to provide single large opening. Overwing emergency exit on each side. Passenger seats removable for cargo carrying, or for conversion to ambulance, air photography, maritime surveillance and other specialised roles. Baggage compartments in nose, with three doors, at rear of cabin and in rear of each engine nacelle. Ventral cargo pod optional. Electric windscreen de-icing optional.

SYSTEMS: Freon air-conditioning system of 17,500 BTU capacity, plus engine bleed air and electric boost heating. Pressurisation system with max differential of 0.35 bars (5.0 lb/sq in). Electrical system includes a 28V 250A starter/generator on each engine and a 39Ah nickel-cadmium battery. Hydraulic system, pressure 120 bars (1,750 lb/sq in), for operation of landing gear. Separate hydraulic system for brakes.

AVIONICS AND EQUIPMENT: Standard avionics comprise Bendix/King Silver Crown equipment consisting of dual nav/com, ADF and marker beacon receiver. Bendix/King Gold Crown avionics and autopilot. Provision for equipment to FAR Pt 135A standards, including dual controls and instrumentation for co-pilot, IFR com/nav, Bendix RDS 82 weather radar and additional emergency exit. Optional cargo interior includes heavy duty sidewalls, utility floorboards, cabin floodlighting and cargo restraint nets.

Reims-Cessna F 406 Caravan II target tug of the French Army

Reims-Cessna F 406 Caravan II light business and utility transport *(Pilot Press)*

DIMENSIONS, EXTERNAL:

Wing span	15.08 m (49 ft 5½ in)
Wing aspect ratio	9.7
Length overall	11.89 m (39 ft 0¼ in)
Height overall	4.01 m (13 ft 2 in)
Tailplane span	5.87 m (19 ft 3 in)
Wheel track	4.28 m (14 ft 0½ in)
Wheelbase	3.81 m (12 ft 5⅞ in)
Propeller diameter	2.36 m (7 ft 9 in)
Cabin door: Height	1.27 m (4 ft 2 in)
Width	0.58 m (1 ft 10¾ in)
Cargo double door (optional):	
Total width	1.24 m (4 ft 1 in)

DIMENSIONS, INTERNAL:

Cabin (incl flight deck): Length	5.71 m (18 ft 8¾ in)
Max width	1.42 m (4 ft 8 in)
Max height	1.31 m (4 ft 3¼ in)
Min height (at rear)	1.21 m (3 ft 11½ in)
Width of aisle	0.29 m (11½ in)
Volume	8.64 m³ (305 cu ft)
Baggage compartment (nose):	
Length	2.00 m (6 ft 6¾ in)
Volume	0.74 m³ (26.0 cu ft)
Nacelle lockers:	
Length	1.55 m (5 ft 1¼ in)
Width	0.73 m (2 ft 4¾ in)
Baggage volume (total, internal)	2.22 m³ (78.5 cu ft)
incl cargo pod	3.52 m³ (124.3 cu ft)

AREAS:

Wings, gross	23.48 m² (252.75 sq ft)
Ailerons (total)	1.36 m² (14.64 sq ft)
Trailing-edge flaps	3.98 m² (42.84 sq ft)
Fin	4.05 m² (43.59 sq ft)
Rudder, incl tab	1.50 m² (16.15 sq ft)
Tailplane	5.81 m² (62.54 sq ft)
Elevators, incl tabs	1.66 m² (17.87 sq ft)

WEIGHTS:

Weight empty, equipped	2,460 kg (5,423 lb)
Max payload	1,563 kg (3,446 lb)
Max fuel	1,444 kg (3,183 lb)
Max ramp weight	4,502 kg (9,925 lb)
Max T-O and landing weight	4,468 kg (9,850 lb)
Max zero-fuel weight	3,856 kg (8,500 lb)

PERFORMANCE:

Max operating Mach No.	0.52
Max operating speed	229 knots (424 km/h; 263 mph) IAS
Max cruising speed	246 knots (455 km/h; 283 mph)
Econ cruising speed	200 knots (370 km/h; 230 mph)
Stalling speed:	
clean	94 knots (174 km/h; 108 mph) IAS
wheels and flaps down	81 knots (150 km/h; 93 mph) IAS
Max rate of climb at S/L	564 m (1,850 ft)/min
Rate of climb at S/L, one engine out	121 m (397 ft)/min
Service ceiling	9,145 m (30,000 ft)
Service ceiling, one engine out	4,935 m (16,200 ft)
T-O run	526 m (1,725 ft)
T-O to 15 m (50 ft)	803 m (2,635 ft)
Landing from 15 m (50 ft), without reverse pitch	674 m (2,212 ft)
Range with max fuel, at max cruising speed, 45 min reserves	1,153 nm (2,135 km; 1,327 miles)

ROBIN
AVIONS PIERRE ROBIN

BP 87, Aérodrome de Dijon Val-Suzon, Darois, 21121 Fontaine-les-Dijon Cédex
Telephone: 33 80 35 61 01
Telex: 350 818 Robin F
Fax: 33 80 35 60 80
PRESIDENT DIRECTOR GENERAL: Georges Megrelis
DOMESTIC SALES MANAGER: Michel Pelletier
EXPORT SALES MANAGER: Serge Darroux
PUBLIC RELATIONS: Jacques Bigenwald
This company was formed in October 1957 as Centre Est Aéronautique. In 1969 the company name was changed to Avions Pierre Robin. It was acquired by Aéronautique Service in mid-1988.

Since 1973, Avions Pierre Robin has manufactured the DR 400 series of wooden light aircraft, which represent highly refined developments of the company's earlier Jodel designs. A new variant, the Cadet, was introduced in 1987. Production of 'DR' aircraft of all designations and models totalled more than 3,000 by January 1990.

A total of 73 aircraft was delivered in 1989, comprising 68 DR 400s, four R 3000s and one ATL.

The company's works cover an area of about 11,500 m² (123,785 sq ft) and it employed 130 people in 1988.

ROBIN DR 400/100 CADET

Deliveries began in 1987 of a two-seat DR 400 based on the series 120 Dauphin, but with rear seating removed and max weight reduced by 100 kg (220 lb). The 1988 refinements to the Dauphin (revised instrument panel and toe-operated brakes) are included in the current Cadet. A total of 10 Cadets had been delivered by January 1990.

Data as DR 400/120, except:
TYPE: Two-seat training and touring aircraft.
WEIGHTS AND LOADINGS:

Useful load (incl baggage)	270 kg (595 lb)
Max T-O and landing weight	800 kg (1,764 lb)

Max wing loading	58.8 kg/m² (12.04 lb/sq ft)
Max power loading	9.58 kg/kW (15.75 lb/hp)

PERFORMANCE (at max T-O weight):

Max level speed at S/L	129 knots (239 km/h; 149 mph)
Max rate of climb at S/L	249 m (817 ft)/min
Service ceiling	5,030 m (16,500 ft)
T-O run	190 m (623 ft)
T-O to and landing from 15 m (50 ft)	425 m (1,395 ft)
Landing run	180 m (591 ft)
Range with standard fuel at 1,830 m (6,000 ft) and 116 knots (215 km/h; 133 mph) max cruising speed, no reserves	510 nm (945 km; 587 miles)

ROBIN DR 400 DAUPHIN

The prototype of this DR 400 series aircraft first flew on 15 May 1972 and received French and British certification that year. The original version had a 93 kW (125 hp) engine and was manufactured as the DR 400/125 Petit Prince. It was superseded in 1975 by the DR 400/120 Petit Prince, with 88 kW (118 hp) engine, as described in the 1979-80 *Jane's*. The current version has a fine-pitch propeller, and entered production in 1979 as the Dauphin. A redesigned instrument panel, toe brakes, an enlarged baggage compartment and additional windows were introduced in 1988. Twenty-three of this **DR400/120 Dauphin 2+2** version (implying two adults and two children) were built in 1989.

Also in 1989, Robin delivered 10 examples of the **DR400/140B Dauphin 4**, a genuine four-seat variant possessing additional power sufficient to transport four adults.

TYPE: Three/four-seat light training and touring aircraft.

WINGS: Cantilever low-wing monoplane. Wing section NACA 23013.5 (modified). Centre-section has constant chord and no dihedral; outer wings have a dihedral of 14°. All-wood one-piece structure, with single box spar. Leading-edge plywood covered; Dacron covering overall. Wooden ailerons, covered with Dacron. Aluminium alloy flaps. Ailerons and flaps interchangeable port and starboard. Manually operated airbrake under spar outboard of landing gear on each side. Picketing ring under each wingtip.

FUSELAGE: Wooden semi-monocoque structure of basic rectangular section, plywood covered.

TAIL UNIT: Cantilever all-wood structure, covered with Dacron. Sweptback fin and rudder. All-moving one-piece horizontal surface, with tab.

LANDING GEAR: Non-retractable tricycle type, with oleo-pneumatic shock absorbers and hydraulically actuated disc brakes. All three wheels and tyres are size 380 × 150, pressure 1.57 bars (22.8 lb/sq in) on nose unit, 1.77 bars (25.6 lb/sq in) on main units. Nosewheel steerable via rudder bar. Fairings over all three legs and wheels. Tailskid with damper. Toe brakes and parking brake.

POWER PLANT: Dauphin 2+2: One 83.5 kW (112 hp) Textron Lycoming O-235-L2A flat-four engine, driving a Sensenich 72 CKS 6-0-56 two-blade fixed-pitch metal propeller, or Hoffmann two-blade fixed-pitch wooden propeller. Dauphin 4: One Textron Lycoming O-320-D flat-four engine developing 104.4 kW (140 hp) at 2,300 rpm and 119 kW (160 hp) at 2,700 rpm. Fuel tank in fuselage, usable capacity 100 litres (26.4 US gallons; 22 Imp gallons); optional 50 litre (13.2 US gallon; 11 Imp gallon) auxiliary tank. Oil capacity 5.7 litres (1.5 US gallons; 1.25 Imp gallons).

ACCOMMODATION: Enclosed cabin, with seats for three or four persons. Max weight of 154 kg (340 lb) on front pair and 136 kg (300 lb), including baggage, at rear in Dauphin 2+2. Additional 55 kg (121 lb) of disposable load in Dauphin 4. Access via forward sliding jettisonable transparent canopy. Dual controls standard. Cabin heated and ventilated. Baggage compartment with internal access.

SYSTEMS AND EQUIPMENT: Standard equipment includes a 12V 50A alternator, 12V 32Ah battery, push-button starter, audible stall warning, and windscreen de-icing. Radio, blind-flying equipment, and navigation, landing and anti-collision lights, to customer's requirements.

DIMENSIONS, EXTERNAL:

Wing span	8.72 m (28 ft 7¼ in)
Wing chord:	
centre-section (constant)	1.71 m (5 ft 7½ in)
at tip	0.90 m (3 ft 0 in)
Wing aspect ratio	5.6
Length overall	6.96 m (22 ft 10 in)
Height overall	2.23 m (7 ft 3¾ in)
Tailplane span	3.20 m (10 ft 6 in)
Wheel track	2.60 m (8 ft 6¼ in)
Wheelbase	5.20 m (17 ft 0¾ in)
Propeller diameter	1.78 m (5 ft 10 in)

DIMENSIONS, INTERNAL:

Cabin: Length	1.62 m (5 ft 3¾ in)
Max width	1.10 m (3 ft 7¼ in)
Max height	1.23 m (4 ft 0½ in)
Baggage volume	0.39 m³ (13.75 cu ft)

AREAS:

Wings, gross	13.60 m² (146.39 sq ft)
Ailerons, total	1.15 m² (12.38 sq ft)
Flaps, total	0.70 m² (7.53 sq ft)
Fin	0.61 m² (6.57 sq ft)
Rudder	0.63 m² (6.78 sq ft)
Horizontal tail surfaces, total	2.88 m² (31.00 sq ft)

Robin DR 400/100 Cadet two-seat light training aircraft *(Mike Jerram)*

WEIGHTS AND LOADINGS (A: Dauphin 2+2; B: Dauphin 4):

Weight empty, equipped: A	535 kg (1,179 lb)
B	580 kg (1,279 lb)
Max baggage: A, B	40 kg (88 lb)
Max T-O and landing weight: A	900 kg (1,984 lb)
B	1,000 kg (2,205 lb)
Max wing loading: A	66.2 kg/m² (13.56 lb/sq ft)
B	73.5 kg/m² (15.05 lb/sq ft)
Max power loading: A	10.78 kg/kW (17.71 lb/hp)
B	8.38 kg/kW (13.78 lb/hp)

PERFORMANCE (at max T-O weight):

Never-exceed speed: A, B	166 knots (308 km/h; 191 mph)
Max level speed at S/L:	
A	130 knots (241 km/h; 150 mph)
B	143 knots (265 km/h; 165 mph)
Max cruising speed: A	116 knots (215 km/h; 133 mph)
B	117 knots (216 km/h; 134 mph)
Stalling speed, flaps down:	
A	45 knots (82 km/h; 51 mph)
B	47 knots (87 km/h; 54 mph)
Max rate of climb at S/L: A	183 m (600 ft)/min
B	264 m (865 ft)/min
Service ceiling: A	3,660 m (12,000 ft)
B	4,265 m (14,000 ft)
T-O run: A	235 m (771 ft)
B	245 m (804 ft)
T-O to 15 m (50 ft): A	535 m (1,755 ft)
B	485 m (1,591 ft)
Landing from 15 m (50 ft): A	460 m (1,510 ft)
B	470 m (1,542 ft)
Landing run: A	200 m (656 ft)
B	220 m (722 ft)
Range with standard fuel at max cruising speed, no reserves: A, B	464 nm (860 km; 534 miles)

ROBIN DR 400/160 MAJOR

The first DR 400/160 flew on 29 June 1972. It was certificated in France and Britain in 1972 and was manufactured as the Chevalier (see 1979-80 *Jane's*). The current version, with wingroot fuel tanks, a baggage hold door and a propeller of finer pitch, has been in production since 1980 as the Major. A total of 114 had been built by January 1990, including six delivered during 1989.

TYPE: Four-seat light aircraft.

WINGS, FUSELAGE, TAIL UNIT, LANDING GEAR: Generally as for DR 400/120, but with external baggage door aft of cabin, on port side.

POWER PLANT: One 119 kW (160 hp) Textron Lycoming O-320-D flat-four engine, driving a Sensenich two-blade metal fixed-pitch propeller. Fuel tank in fuselage, capacity 110 litres (29 US gallons; 24 Imp gallons), and two tanks in wingroot leading-edges, giving total capacity of 190 litres (50 US gallons; 41.75 Imp gallons), of which 182 litres (48 US gallons; 40 Imp gallons) are usable. Provision for auxiliary tank, raising total capacity to 250 litres (66 US gallons; 55 Imp gallons). Oil capacity 7.5 litres (2 US gallons; 1.6 Imp gallons).

ACCOMMODATION: Seating for four persons, on adjustable front seats (max load 154 kg; 340 lb total) and rear bench seat (max load 154 kg; 340 lb total). Forward sliding transparent canopy. Up to 40 kg (88 lb) of baggage can be stowed aft of rear seats when four occupants are carried.

SYSTEMS AND EQUIPMENT: As for DR 400/120.

DIMENSIONS AND AREAS: As for DR 400/120, except:

Propeller diameter	1.83 m (6 ft 0 in)
Baggage door: Height	0.47 m (1 ft 6½ in)
Width	0.55 m (1 ft 9½ in)
Wing area	14.20 m² (152.8 sq ft)

WEIGHTS AND LOADINGS:

Weight empty, equipped	570 kg (1,257 lb)
Max T-O and landing weight	1,050 kg (2,315 lb)
Max wing loading	74.2 kg/m² (15.20 lb/sq ft)
Max power loading	8.82 kg/kW (14.47 lb/hp)

PERFORMANCE (at max T-O weight):

Never-exceed speed	166 knots (308 km/h; 191 mph)
Max level speed at S/L	146 knots (271 km/h; 168 mph)

Max cruising speed (75% power) at 2,440 m (8,000 ft)	132 knots (245 km/h; 152 mph)
Econ cruising speed (65% power) at 3,200 m (10,500 ft)	130 knots (241 km/h; 150 mph)
Stalling speed: flaps up	56 knots (103 km/h; 64 mph)
flaps down	50 knots (93 km/h; 58 mph)
Max rate of climb at S/L	255 m (836 ft)/min
Service ceiling	4,115 m (13,500 ft)
T-O run	295 m (968 ft)
T-O to 15 m (50 ft)	590 m (1,936 ft)
Landing from 15 m (50 ft)	545 m (1,788 ft)
Landing run	250 m (820 ft)
Range with standard fuel at econ cruising speed, no reserves	825 nm (1,530 km; 950 miles)

ROBIN DR 400/180 RÉGENT

First flown on 27 March 1972, this most powerful, four/five-seat member of the wooden DR 400 series received DGAC certification on 10 May 1972, and CAA certification in December 1972. A total of 222 had been built by January 1990, including 19 delivered in 1989.

At the 1989 Paris Air Show Robin exhibited a prototype (F-WGXT) **DR 400NGL Régent III** which featured a wider fuselage with cabin width increased by 10 cm (4 in); cabin height at the rear seat positions increased by 5 cm (2 in); new ergonomically designed control columns; raised engine mounting to increase propeller ground clearance; and max T-O weight increased to 1,150 kg (2,535 lb). This variant has not been produced.

The DR 400/180 is generally similar to the DR 400/160 Major, except in the following details:

POWER PLANT: One 134 kW (180 hp) Textron Lycoming O-360-A flat-four engine. Fuel tankage as for DR 400/160.

ACCOMMODATION, SYSTEMS AND EQUIPMENT: Basically as for DR 400/160, but optional seating for three persons on rear bench seat. Baggage capacity 60 kg (132 lb).

DIMENSIONS AND AREAS: As for DR 400/160, except:

Propeller diameter	1.93 m (6 ft 4 in)

WEIGHTS AND LOADINGS:

Weight empty, equipped	600 kg (1,322 lb)
Max T-O and landing weight	1,100 kg (2,425 lb)
Max wing loading	77.7 kg/m² (15.91 lb/sq ft)
Max power loading	8.21 kg/kW (13.47 lb/hp)

PERFORMANCE (at max T-O weight):

Never-exceed speed	166 knots (308 km/h; 191 mph)
Max level speed at S/L	150 knots (278 km/h; 173 mph)
Max cruising speed (75% power) at 2,285 m (7,500 ft)	140 knots (260 km/h; 162 mph)
Econ cruising speed (60% power) at 3,660 m (12,000 ft)	132 knots (245 km/h; 152 mph)
Stalling speed: flaps up	57 knots (105 km/h; 65 mph)
flaps down	52 knots (95 km/h; 59 mph)
Max rate of climb at S/L	252 m (825 ft)/min
Service ceiling	4,720 m (15,475 ft)
T-O run	315 m (1,035 ft)
T-O to 15 m (50 ft)	610 m (2,000 ft)
Landing from 15 m (50 ft)	530 m (1,740 ft)
Landing run	249 m (817 ft)
Range with standard fuel at 65% power, no reserves	783 nm (1,450 km; 900 miles)

ROBIN DR 400 REMORQUEUR

A glider-towing version of the DR 400 first flew and was certificated in France in 1972. Designated **DR 400/180R** (now abbreviated to **Remo 180**) it is powered by a Textron Lycoming flat-four engine and may also be used as a normal four-seat tourer.

In 1985, a prototype was flown of a variant fitted with a Porsche PFM 3200 flat-six engine. Known at first as the DR 400/180RP, it is now designated **DR 400RP** or **Remo 212**. The Remo 212 was delivered from 1987 onward, becoming the first aircraft with a Porsche engine to receive German certification.

Remorqueur production totalled 260 by January 1990, including six Remo 180s and one Remo 212 delivered in 1989.

Specification details of the standard Remorqueur are the same as the DR 400/180 Régent except for the following items:

FUSELAGE: No external baggage door. The baggage compartment is covered with transparent Plexiglas as an extension of the canopy, allowing optimum rearward view.

POWER PLANT: Remo 180: One 134 kW (180 hp) Textron Lycoming O-360-A flat-four engine, driving (for glider towing) a Sensenich 76 EM 8S5 058 or Hoffmann HO-27-HM-180/138 two-blade propeller. For touring, a Sensenich 76 EM 8S5 064 propeller of the same diameter is fitted. Fuel capacity 110 litres (29 US gallons; 24.2 Imp gallons); optional 60 litre (15.9 US gallon; 13.2 Imp gallon) auxiliary tank. Remo 212: One 158 kW (212 hp) Porsche PFM 3200 flat-six engine with forced-fan cooling driving a Hoffman three-blade constant-speed pitch propeller. Fuel capacity 115 litres (30.4 US gallons; 25.3 Imp gallons); optional 50 litre (13.2 US gallon; 11 Imp gallon) auxiliary tank.

DIMENSIONS AND AREAS: As for DR 400/120, except:
Length: 212	7.45 m (24 ft 5¼ in)
Propeller diameter	1.83 m (6 ft 0 in)

WEIGHTS AND LOADINGS:
Weight empty, equipped: 180	560 kg (1,234 lb)
212	680 kg (1,499 lb)
Max T-O and landing weight: 180	1,000 kg (2,205 lb)
212	1,100 kg (2,425 lb)
Max wing loading: 180	73.5 kg/m² (15.05 lb/sq ft)
212	80.9 kg/m² (16.57 lb/sq ft)
Max power loading: 180	7.46 kg/kW (12.25 lb/hp)
212	6.96 kg/kW (11.44 lb/hp)

PERFORMANCE (glider tug, at max T-O weight):
Never-exceed speed:	
180, 212	166 knots (308 km/h; 191 mph)
Max level speed: 180	146 knots (270 km/h; 168 mph)
212	158 knots (292 km/h; 181 mph)
Cruising speed at 2,440 m (8,000 ft):	
180 (70% power)	124 knots (230 km/h; 143 mph)
212 (75% power)	146 knots (270 km/h; 168 mph)
Stalling speed, flaps down:	
180	47 knots (87 km/h; 54 mph)
212	48 knots (88 km/h; 55 mph)
Max rate of climb at S/L: 180	336 m (1,100 ft)/min
212	420 m (1,380 ft)/min
Max rate of climb at S/L, towing two-seat sailplane:	
180, 212	210 m (690 ft)/min
Service ceiling: 180	6,100 m (20,000 ft)
212	5,335 m (17,500 ft)
T-O to 15 m (50 ft), towing single-seat sailplane:	
180	375 m (1,230 ft)
212	330 m (1,083 ft)
Landing from 15 m (50 ft): 180	470 m (1,542 ft)
212	447 m (1,467 ft)

Robin DR 400RP Remo 212 glider towing aircraft (Porsche PFM 3200 engine) *(Roland Eichenberger)*

Range at econ cruising speed, with auxiliary fuel, no reserves:
180	647 nm (1,200 km; 745 miles)
212	785 nm (1,455 km; 904 miles)

ROBIN R 3000 SERIES

Development of this series of all-metal light aircraft began in 1978, to replace types then in production. Two prototypes, with the designation R 3140 flew in 1980 and 1981, the second having the compound-taper wing.

Marketing of R 3000s was assigned to the Socata division of Aerospatiale from 1 September 1983 until 1 February 1988, when Robin resumed responsibility. Deliveries totalled 41 by 1 January 1990, including four in 1988. The basic series 140 (formerly R 3140E and certificated by DGAC on 13 October 1983) remains in production, but manufacture of the series 120 ended in 1987, being replaced by the series 160. A further seven projected versions, listed in the 1983-84 *Jane's*, have not been built to date.

Robin is investigating the practicability of replacing the present engines of the R 3000 series with engines based on the more modern and fuel-efficient PRV six-cylinder engines built in France for Peugeot, Renault and Volvo motorcars. First aircraft to be fitted with a PRV engine, an R 3140, first flew in 1983.

Robin has had engineering assistance from Renault. The power plant currently being evaluated is a three-litre PRV on which the belted reduction drive has been replaced by a

gearbox, reduction ratio 0.442:1. The engine features dual electronic ignition and electronic fuel injection and is rated at 134 kW (180 hp). Ground running trials were continuing in early 1990 in anticipation of flight tests by the middle of the year with the engine installed in an R 3000. A new company, France Aéromoteur (which see), has been established to produce an aviation certificated PRV engine.

At the 1989 Paris Air Show Robin exhibited an R 3000 equipped with an Aerospatiale ATAL underwing surveillance pod containing black-and-white, colour or LLTV video camera. The camera is steered with a joystick and the picture viewed in the cockpit. The system, which weighs 8.6 kg (19 lb), permits real-time transmission of video images to mobile or fixed ground stations at ranges of 2.7-27 nm (5-50 km; 3.1-31 miles) and 64.75-97 nm (120-180 km; 74.6-112 miles) respectively.

The following details apply to the R 3000/140 except where indicated:

TYPE: Four-seat all-metal light aircraft.

WINGS: Cantilever low-wing monoplane, with upturned tips. Wing section NACA 43013.5 on constant chord inner wings, NACA 43010.5 at tip of each tapered outer panel. Dihedral 6° from roots. Incidence 3°. Conventional single-spar aluminium alloy structure. Entire trailing-edge of each constant chord panel comprises an electrically controlled slotted flap. Ailerons and flaps of aluminium alloy.

FUSELAGE: Conventional aluminium alloy semi-monocoque structure, except for glassfibre engine cowling.

TAIL UNIT: Cantilever T tail of aluminium alloy construction, with dorsal fin. Elevator trim with anti-tabs.

LANDING GEAR: Non-retractable tricycle type. Nosewheel, steerable via rudder pedals, is self-centring and locks automatically after take-off. Robin long-stroke low pressure oleo-pneumatic shock absorbers. Mainwheel tyres size 380 × 150-6. Nosewheel tyre size 5.00-5. Cleveland disc brakes. Streamline polyester fairings on all three legs and wheels. Hydraulic disc brakes. Parking brake.

POWER PLANT: Srs 140: One 119.3 kW (160 hp) Textron Lycoming O-320-D2A flat-four engine, driving a Sensenich 74DMS5-2-64 two-blade fixed-pitch metal propeller. Two integral fuel tanks in wing leading-edges, with total capacity of 160 litres (42.25 US gallons; 35.2 Imp gallons) standard, or 200 litres (52.8 US gallons; 44 Imp gallons) optional. Oil capacity 7.5 litres (2 US gallons; 1.6 Imp gallons). Srs 160: One 134 kW (180 hp) Textron Lycoming O-320-A flat-four engine. Standard fuel capacity 225 litres (59.4 US gallons; 49.5 Imp gallons).

ACCOMMODATION: Four seats in pairs in enclosed cabin, with dual controls and brakes. Adjustable front seats, with inertia reel safety belts. Removable rear seats, with belts. Carpeted floor. Forward sliding jettisonable and tinted transparent canopy, with safety lock, accessible from both sides. Automatically retracting step on each side. Baggage capacity 40 kg (88 lb). Cabin heated and ventilated. Windscreen demister.

SYSTEM: Electrical system includes 12V 60A alternator and 12V 32Ah battery.

AVIONICS AND EQUIPMENT: Standard equipment includes hour meter, audible stall warning system and towbar. Three standards of optional avionics and equipment available. Series I includes horizon and directional gyros with vacuum pump, type 9100 electric turn co-ordinator, rate of climb indicator, C 2400 magnetic compass (exchange for standard C 2300), position lights and two beacons, anti-collision light and instrument panel lighting. Series II adds to Series I either Becker AR 2009/25 720-channel VHF, with NR 2029 VOR/LOC receiver and indicator; or Bendix/King KX 155/08 nav/com with audio and KI 203 VOR indicator. Series III adds to Series II either a Becker ATC 2000 transponder and type 2079 ADF; or King KT 76A transponder and KR 87 digital ADF. Optional equipment includes agricultural spraygear with underwing spraybars and chemical tank, capacity 350 litres (92.5 US gallons; 77 Imp gallons).

Photograph and three-view drawing *(Pilot Press)* **of Robin R 3000/140 four-seat light aircraft (Textron Lycoming O-320-D2A engine)**

DIMENSIONS, EXTERNAL:

Wing span	9.81 m (32 ft 2¼ in)
Wing chord: at root	1.72 m (5 ft 7¾ in)
at tip	0.655 m (2 ft 1¾ in)
Wing aspect ratio	6.6
Length overall	7.51 m (24 ft 7¾ in)
Height overall	2.66 m (8 ft 8¾ in)
Tailplane span	3.20 m (10 ft 6 in)
Wheel track	2.64 m (8 ft 8 in)
Wheelbase	1.74 m (5 ft 8½ in)
Propeller diameter	1.83 m (6 ft 0 in)
Propeller ground clearance	0.30 m (11¾ in)

DIMENSIONS, INTERNAL:

Cabin: Length	2.70 m (8 ft 10¼ in)
Max width	1.14 m (3 ft 8¾ in)
Max height	1.20 m (3 ft 11¼ in)
Floor area	2.60 m² (28.0 sq ft)
Volume (incl baggage space)	2.4 m³ (84.75 cu ft)
Baggage space	0.43 m³ (15.2 cu ft)

AREAS:

Wings, gross	14.47 m² (155.75 sq ft)
Ailerons (total)	1.32 m² (14.21 sq ft)
Trailing-edge flaps (total)	2.02 m² (21.74 sq ft)
Vertical tail surfaces (total)	1.30 m² (14.00 sq ft)
Horizontal tail surfaces (total)	2.44 m² (26.26 sq ft)

WEIGHTS AND LOADINGS:

Weight empty: 140	600 kg (1,323 lb)
160	650 kg (1,433 lb)
Max T-O and landing weight: 140	1,050 kg (2,315 lb)
160	1,150 kg (2,535 lb)
Max wing loading: 140	72.6 kg/m² (14.86 lb/sq ft)
160	79.5 kg/m² (16.28 lb/sq ft)
Max power loading: 140	10.10 kg/kW (16.54 lb/hp)
160	8.58 kg/kW (14.08 lb/hp)

PERFORMANCE (at max T-O weight):

Max level speed at S/L:	
140	135 knots (250 km/h; 155 mph)
160	146 knots (270 km/h; 168 mph)
Max cruising speed (75% power) at optimum height:	
140	130 knots (240 km/h; 149 mph)
160	138 knots (255 km/h; 158 mph)
Econ cruising speed (65% power):	
140	119 knots (220 km/h; 136 mph)
160	128 knots (238 km/h; 148 mph)
Stalling speed, flaps down:	
140	47 knots (87 km/h; 54 mph)
160	49 knots (91 km/h; 57 mph)
Max rate of climb at S/L: 140	258 m (846 ft)/min
160	267 m (875 ft)/min
Service ceiling: 140	4,265 m (14,000 ft)
160	4,570 m (15,000 ft)
T-O run: 140	280 m (920 ft)
160	310 m (1,017 ft)
T-O to 15 m (50 ft): 140	525 m (1,725 ft)
160	565 m (1,854 ft)
Landing from 15 m (50 ft): 140	490 m (1,610 ft)
160	540 m (1,772 ft)
Landing run: 140	190 m (625 ft)
160	210 m (690 ft)
Range with max standard fuel, no reserves:	
75% power: 140	605 nm (1,120 km; 696 miles)
160	804 nm (1,490 km; 925 miles)
65% power: 140	640 nm (1,185 km; 736 miles)
160	868 nm (1,610 km; 1,000 miles)
Range with max optional fuel, no reserves:	
75% power: 140	756 nm (1,400 km; 870 miles)
65% power: 140	799 nm (1,480 km; 919 miles)

ROBIN ATL

Avions Pierre Robin began design of the ATL (avion très léger) in 1981 to meet the requirement of French flying clubs for a very lightweight two-seat monoplane that would, in the tradition of the veteran Jodel D.112, be economical to buy and to operate. The prototype (F-WFNA) flew initially, on 17 June 1983, with a 35 kW (47 hp) JPX PAL 1,300 three-cylinder aircooled radial two-stroke engine. To speed certification, it was re-engined subsequently with a 41.5 kW (56 hp) JPX converted 1,835 cc Volkswagen motorcar engine, and a 2,050 cc version of this engine was the standard power plant of production ATLs up to the end of 1988. The increased power plant weight necessitated sweeping the wings forward to maintain an acceptable CG.

A first order, for 30, was placed by the French National Aeronautical Federation (FNA) on 28 November 1983.

A second ATL flew for the first time on 7 December 1984. Deliveries began on 27 April 1985, when the Coulommiers Aero Club received a production ATL (F-WFNC). Twenty-five more were delivered (one to Australia) with a DGAC 'laissez-passer' before certification was received on 15 January 1986. All of these aircraft were called back to Dijon for modification to full certification standards.

By January 1990, a total of 131 ATLs had been delivered, including one in 1989. The initial production model, to which the detailed description applies, is known as **ATL Club** in France and **Bijou** in the UK. The **ATL Club Model 88** had a new propeller of smaller diameter (1.50 m; 4 ft 11 in), to increase ground clearance, improvements to the cabin, equipment and systems, and increased fuel capacity, giving a max range of 594 nm (1,100 km; 683 miles). Deliveries began in 1987.

Robin ATL Club very light two-seat personal and club aircraft

Robin ATL Club Model 88 (JPX 4T 60A converted Volkswagen engine) *(Pilot Press)*

A version of the ATL was developed, initially for the German market, with a 52.2 kW (70 hp) Limbach four-cylinder engine, achieving German certification in January 1989. The Limbach is now the standard engine on all ATLs, beginning with the **ATL Club Model 89**, which received French certification on 6 June 1989.

The following data apply to the initial version of the ATL Club, except where indicated:

TYPE: Two-seat very light personal and club aircraft.

WINGS: Cantilever mid-wing monoplane. Wing section NACA 43015 modified. Dihedral 6° from roots. Incidence 3° at root, −1° at tip. Sweepforward at front spar 7° 30′. Conventional wood single-spar structure in two halves, with plywood covered leading-edge torsion box, light auxiliary rear spar, girder ribs and Dacron covering. Frise ailerons, actuated by cables, and electrically actuated flaps of light alloy along entire trailing-edges. No tabs.

FUSELAGE: Pod and boom configuration, made of glassfibre/Nomex honeycomb/epoxy sandwich.

TAIL UNIT: Cantilever V structure, with fixed surfaces of Dacron covered wood, and rod actuated light alloy control surfaces. Spring trim in elevator control.

LANDING GEAR: Non-retractable tricycle type. Cantilever main legs. Nosewheel has rubber shock absorption and is steerable via rudder pedals. Mainwheel tyres size 300-130, pressure 2.2 bars (32 lb/sq in); nosewheel tyre size 270-100, pressure 1.6 bars (23 lb/sq in). Hydraulic disc brakes on mainwheels. Parking brake. Wheel fairings optional.

POWER PLANT: One JPX 4T 60A (converted 2,050 cc Volkswagen) aircooled flat-four engine, rated at 48 kW (65 hp) and driving an EVRA two-blade wooden propeller. Current Model 89 powered by 52 kW (70 hp) Limbach four-cylinder engine, with Muhlbauer MT two-blade fixed-pitch propeller. Fuel tank in each wingroot; total capacity 70 litres (18.5 US gallons; 15.4 Imp gallons).

ACCOMMODATION: Two glassfibre seats side by side under large canopy which hinges upward and forward. Dual controls, with adjustable rudder pedals, cabin heating and ventilation standard. All-transparent canopy optional. Baggage shelf behind seats, capacity 10 kg (22 lb).

SYSTEM: Electrical system includes 12V alternator and 12V 15Ah battery. Anti-collision, navigation, cabin and instrument lights optional.

AVIONICS AND EQUIPMENT: Optional avionics include 720 channel VHF transceiver, VOR, ADF and transponder. Standard equipment includes basic instruments, inertia reel safety belts and tiedown rings. Optional items include horizon and directional gyros, rate of climb indicator, turn co-ordinator, outside air temperature gauge, hourmeter, exhaust gas temperature gauge, four-strap safety harness, tinted canopy, leather furnishing, faired main landing gear legs and canopy cover.

DIMENSIONS, EXTERNAL:

Wing span	10.25 m (33 ft 7½ in)
Wing mean aerodynamic chord	1.25 m (4 ft 1¼ in)
Wing aspect ratio	8.65
Length overall	6.72 m (22 ft 0½ in)
Height: to tip of tail unit	2.00 m (6 ft 6¾ in)
cockpit canopy open	2.45 m (8 ft 0½ in)
Tailplane span	3.82 m (12 ft 6½ in)
Wheel track	3.00 m (9 ft 10 in)

AREAS:

Wings, gross	12.15 m² (130.8 sq ft)
Ailerons (total)	0.49 m² (5.27 sq ft)
Trailing-edge flaps	0.49 m² (5.27 sq ft)
Fixed V-tail surfaces	2.60 m² (27.99 sq ft)
Elevons (total)	0.96 m² (10.33 sq ft)

WEIGHTS AND LOADINGS (JPX 4T 60A engine):

Weight empty	360 kg (794 lb)
Max T-O weight	580 kg (1,278 lb)
Max wing loading	47.7 kg/m² (9.77 lb/sq ft)
Max power loading	12.1 kg/kW (19.7 lb/hp)

PERFORMANCE (Model 89 with Limbach engine, at max T-O weight):

Max level speed at S/L	105 knots (195 km/h; 121 mph)
Max cruising speed (70% power) at 1,675 m (5,500 ft)	
	90 knots (167 km/h; 104 mph)
Econ cruising speed (60% power) at 2,590 m (8,500 ft)	
	90 knots (167 km/h; 104 mph)
Stalling speed, flaps down	41 knots (75 km/h; 47 mph)
Max rate of climb at S/L	183 m (600 ft)/min
Service ceiling	4,265 m (14,000 ft)
T-O run	200 m (656 ft)
T-O to 15 m (50 ft)	405 m (1,330 ft)
Landing from 15 m (50 ft)	475 m (1,560 ft)
Landing run	170 m (558 ft)
Range with max fuel at econ cruising speed, no reserves	
	542 nm (1,004 km; 624 miles)

SECA

SOCIÉTÉ D'EXPLOITATION ET DE CONSTRUCTIONS AÉRONAUTIQUES
(Subsidiary of Aerospatiale)

Aéroport du Bourget, 93350 Le Bourget
Telephone: 33 (1) 48 35 99 77
Telex: SECAVIA BRGET 235710 F
Fax: 33 (1) 48 35 96 27

SECA/FOKKER F27 FRIENDSHIP ARAT

SECA, the aircraft overhaul and modification centre at Paris Le Bourget, has converted a Friendship Mk 100 to a flying laboratory for the Institut Géographique National. Known as the F27 ARAT (Avion de Recherche Atmosphérique et de Télédétection), it differs substantially from standard in the following ways: addition of Thomson-CSF Varan radar in a ventral radome; a removable nose-probe; two survey camera windows in the lower fuselage; a laser window in the upper starboard rear fuselage; a 30kVA APU for the operation of scientific equipment during flight; four attachments for various small sensor pods around the forward fuselage; underwing pylons; and three multi-purpose equipment panels above (two) and below the forward fuselage.

Friendship Mk 100 F-W(B)YAO converted by SECA as a flying laboratory for the French National Geographic Institute *(Paul Jackson)*

SELLET-PELLETIER

SELLET-PELLETIER HÉLICOPTÈRE

c/o Lange SA, 35 rue de Naples, 75008 Paris
Telephone: 33 (1) 45 22 66 68
Telex: 640 627

M Christian Sellet and M Jacques Pelletier, engineers, are responsible for a small helicopter known as the Grillon 120, which was designed and built by M Sellet. His partner is handling the administrative, commercial and public relations aspects of the project.

SELLET-PELLETIER GRILLON 120

The general appearance of the Grillon 120 (Cricket) is shown in an accompanying illustration. It was designed primarily for training helicopter pilots at much reduced cost. Thus, although the prototype was completed in single-seat form, production Grillons could have one or two seats, with single or dual controls.

Design of the Grillon began in August 1984; construction of the prototype started three months later. It was almost complete when exhibited at the 1985 Paris Air Show, and flew for the first time on 8 September 1987. In early 1989 it was converted to two-seat configuration.

TYPE: Prototype light helicopter.
ROTOR SYSTEM: Three-blade fully articulated main rotor and two-blade tail rotor. Boeing Helicopters Vertol VR7 blade section. NACA 0012 tail rotor blade section. Each main rotor blade has carbonfibre reinforced plastics skin (three laminations at 45°), polyurethane foam filler and steel weight adjustment bar in leading-edge. Carbonfibre tail rotor blades. Main rotor/engine rpm ratio 1:8.4. Tail rotor/engine rpm ratio 1:2.1.
FUSELAGE: Extensively glazed cabin pod, with aluminium alloy structure and aluminium alloy skin. Tail rotor carried on aluminium alloy tube supported by mast structure at rear of cabin.
LANDING GEAR: Non-retractable tubular skid type.
POWER PLANT: One 89.5 kW (120 hp) Mazda twin-rotor engine, mounted above cabin, forward of main rotor mast. Two fuel tanks under seats, total capacity 50 litres (13.2 US gallons; 11 Imp gallons) on prototype, 100 litres (26.4 US gallons; 22 Imp gallons) planned for production aircraft. Oil capacity 5 litres (1.3 US gallons; 1.1 Imp gallons) for engine; 2 litres (0.53 US gallon; 0.44 Imp gallon) for main gearbox.

Prototype Sellet-Pelletier Grillon 120 light helicopter in two-seat form

ACCOMMODATION: Prototype was flown initially with single semi-reclining seat and conventional helicopter controls, comprising collective and cyclic sticks and rudder pedals. It now has two seats, side by side. Dual controls will be standard in certificated version.

DIMENSIONS, EXTERNAL:
Main rotor diameter	5.18 m (17 ft 0 in)
Main rotor blade chord	0.18 m (7 in)
Tail rotor diameter	1.08 m (3 ft 6½ in)
Distance between rotor centres	4.05 m (13 ft 3½ in)
Length overall, rotors turning	6.70 m (21 ft 11¾ in)
Length of fuselage, excl rotors	5.10 m (16 ft 8¾ in)
Width, between skids	1.85 m (6 ft 0¾ in)
Height to top of rotor head	2.30 m (7 ft 6½ in)
Height overall	2.38 m (7 ft 9¾ in)

AREAS:
Main rotor blades (each)	0.32 m² (3.44 sq ft)
Tail rotor blades (each)	0.034 m² (0.366 sq ft)
Main rotor disc	21.07 m² (226.8 sq ft)
Tail rotor disc	0.968 m² (10.42 sq ft)

WEIGHTS (single-seat):
Weight empty	270 kg (595 lb)
Max T-O weight	510 kg (1,124 lb)

PERFORMANCE (estimated):
Max level speed at S/L	108 knots (200 km/h; 124 mph)
Max cruising speed at S/L	92 knots (170 km/h; 106 mph)
Econ cruising speed at S/L	62 knots (115 km/h; 71 mph)
Max rate of climb at S/L	360 m (1,180 ft)/min
Service ceiling	3,500 m (11,500 ft)
Range: with max fuel	243 nm (450 km; 280 miles)
with max payload	191 nm (355 km; 220 miles)

SOCATA

SOCIÉTÉ DE CONSTRUCTION D'AVIONS DE TOURISME ET D'AFFAIRES
(Subsidiary of Aerospatiale)

12 rue Pasteur, 92150 Suresnes
Telephone: 33 (1) 45 06 37 60
Telex: SOCATAS 614 549 F
WORKS AND AFTER-SALES SERVICE: Aérodrome de Tarbes-Ossun-Lourdes, BP 38, 65001 Tarbes Cédex
Telephone: 33 62 51 73 00
Telex: SOCATA 520 828 F
PRESIDENT AND DIRECTOR GENERAL: Pierre Gautier
TECHNICAL DIRECTOR: Denis Legrand
COMMERCIAL DIRECTOR: A. Aubry
MANAGER, PROMOTION AND COMMUNICATION: Gérard Maoui

This company, formed in 1966, is a subsidiary of Aerospatiale, responsible for producing all of the group's piston engined light aircraft, as well as the Epsilon primary/basic trainer. By the end of 1989 sales of the TB series of light aircraft totalled 1,009.

Socata also produces components for the Airbus A300, ATR 42, Mystère-Falcon 100, 200 and 50 business aircraft, and Super Puma, Dauphin and Ecureuil helicopters. It is responsible for overhaul and repair of MS 760 Paris light jet aircraft.

Socata's works cover an area of 56,000 m² (602,775 sq ft).

SOCATA TB 30 EPSILON

First details of the **Epsilon** tandem two-seat primary/basic trainer were released in September 1978. Purpose of the project was to meet a French Air Force requirement for a propeller driven aircraft for use in the initial stages of a more cost-effective pilot training scheme than that then operated.

A development contract from the Air Force, for two prototypes and two ground test airframes, was announced by Aerospatiale in June 1979. The first prototype flew on 22 December that year, followed by the second prototype on 12 July 1980. On 6 January 1982, a manufacturing programme was approved, covering delivery of 150 Epsilons at the rate of 30 a year. A contract for the first production batch of 30 aircraft was received on 5 March 1982. The first production Epsilon flew on 29 June 1983; deliveries to the Centre d'Expériences Aériennes Militaires (CEAM) at Mont-de-Marsan began on 29 July 1983, and to Groupement École 315 at Cognac/Chateaubernard in June 1984. Following abandonment of plans to equip other flying schools, GE 315 had been issued with 150 Epsilons by late 1989.

Until 1989 the Epsilon programme was handled by the Aircraft Division of Aerospatiale, as prime contractor responsible for the entire programme. Design and manufacture were subcontracted to Socata, the company's light aircraft subsidiary at Tarbes, which now has full marketing responsibility. In October 1987, an order was announced for 18 Epsilons for Esquadra 104 of the Portuguese Air Force at Sintra. The first of these was handed over at Tarbes on 18 January 1989; the remainder have been assembled by OGMA in Portugal, to provide the first 120 hours of pilot training.

An armed version is available to export customers, with four underwing hardpoints for a total 300 kg (661 lb) of external stores with pilot only, or 200 kg (441 lb) with crew of two. Empty weight of this version is 929 kg (2,048 lb), max T-O weight 1,400 kg (3,086 lb), and *g* limits +6/−3. An Epsilon armed with two twin 7.62 mm machine-gun pods could loiter for 30 min at low altitude over a combat area 170 nm (315 km; 195 miles) from its base. First export order, for three armed Epsilons, was placed by the Togolese Air Force in the Autumn of 1984. These aircraft (c/n 51, 55 and 59) were delivered in August 1986 and were followed by a single attrition replacement ordered in 1987. Sales of Epsilons by Spring 1989 totalled 172, plus two demonstrator/trials aircraft.

The first prototype Epsilon was used as testbed for the 335 kW (450 shp) TP 319 turboprop developed by Turbomeca from the TM 319 turboshaft, and was subsequently further modified under the new name **Oméga**, described separately.

The following description applies mainly to the basic version of the Epsilon, as operated by the French Air Force:

TYPE: Two-seat military primary/basic trainer.

WINGS: Cantilever low-wing monoplane. Wing section RA 1643 at root, RA 1243 at tip. Thickness/chord ratio 16 per cent at root, 12 per cent at tip. Dihedral 5°. Incidence 2°. All-metal light alloy structure, with single main spar and rear auxiliary spar, built in two panels attached directly to sides of fuselage. Press-formed ribs and heavy gauge skin without stringers. Slightly upturned wingtips. Electrically actuated single-slotted flaps. Light alloy ailerons, with spring tabs.

FUSELAGE: Light alloy semi-monocoque structure of four longerons, frames and heavy gauge skin, without stringers.

TAIL UNIT: Cantilever single-spar light alloy structure. Fixed surfaces metal covered; elevators and rudder covered with polyester fabric. Fixed incidence tailplane, with dihedral. Balanced elevators and rudder, with spring tab in each elevator and ground adjustable tab on rudder. Shallow ventral fin.

LANDING GEAR: Electro-hydraulically retractable tricycle type, with single wheel on each unit. Inward retracting main units and rearward retracting castoring nosewheel. Mainwheel tyres size 380 × 150; nosewheel tyre size 330 × 130. Independent hydraulic single-disc brake on each mainwheel. Parking brake.

POWER PLANT: One 224 kW (300 hp) Textron Lycoming AEIO-540-L1B5D flat-six engine, driving a Hartzell HC-C2YR-4()F/FC 8475-6R two-blade constant-speed metal propeller, with spinner. Fuel in two wing leading-edge tanks, with total capacity of 210 litres (55.5 US gallons; 46 Imp gallons). Refuelling points on wing upper surface. Christen system to permit up to 2 min inverted flight.

ACCOMMODATION: Two seats in tandem, with rear seat raised by 70 mm (2.7 in). Rudder pedals are mechanically adjustable fore and aft. Two-component sliding Plexiglas canopy, with emergency jettison system, plus sideways hinged (to port) windscreen, providing access to instruments for servicing. Full dual controls. Baggage compartment aft of cabin, with door on port side.

SYSTEMS: Hydraulic systems for actuating landing gear and brakes. 28V electrical system includes engine driven alternator; battery for engine starting and emergency use; ground power socket in port side of rear fuselage. Cabin heated and ventilated. Windscreen demister.

AVIONICS AND EQUIPMENT: Standard installation includes blind-flying instrumentation, standby artificial horizon, VHF, UHF, automatic and manual VOR, transponder, ILS capability and Tacan. Optional equipment includes a Rockwell-Collins ETC-500F electronic tactical control unit providing centralised control and display of all radio communications and radio navigation equipment.

ARMAMENT AND OPERATIONAL EQUIPMENT (not on French Air Force Epsilons): Four underwing hardpoints; outboard points each able to carry 80 kg (176 lb), inboard points 160 kg (352 lb). Alternative loads include two Matra CM pods each containing two 7.62 mm machine-guns, four Matra F2D launchers for six XF1 68 mm rockets, six Bavard F4B practice bombs, two 125 kg bombs, two Alkan 500 grenade launchers with 10 Lacroix rounds each, and four land or sea survival kit containers. Associated equipment includes Alkan 663 stores racks, SFOM 83A3 sight and Alkan E105C firing control box.

DIMENSIONS, EXTERNAL:

Wing span	7.92 m (25 ft 11¾ in)
Wing chord: at root	1.46 m (4 ft 9½ in)
at tip	0.92 m (3 ft 0¼ in)
Wing aspect ratio	7.0
Length overall	7.59 m (24 ft 10¾ in)
Height overall	2.66 m (8 ft 8¾ in)
Tailplane span	3.20 m (10 ft 6 in)
Wheel track	2.30 m (7 ft 6½ in)
Wheelbase	1.80 m (5 ft 10¾ in)
Propeller diameter	1.98 m (6 ft 6 in)
Propeller ground clearance	0.25 m (10 in)

AREAS:

Wings, gross	9.00 m² (96.9 sq ft)

Socata Epsilon of the Portuguese Air Force

Socata Epsilon tandem two-seat primary/basic trainer with underwing weapon pylons *(Pilot Press)*

Fin	1.02 m² (10.98 sq ft)
Tailplane	2.00 m² (21.53 sq ft)

WEIGHTS AND LOADINGS:

Weight empty, equipped	932 kg (2,055 lb)
Fuel weight	150 kg (330 lb)
Max T-O and landing weight	1,250 kg (2,755 lb)
Max wing loading	139 kg/m² (28.4 lb/sq ft)
Max power loading	5.58 kg/kW (9.18 lb/hp)

PERFORMANCE (at max T-O weight):

Never-exceed speed	281 knots (520 km/h; 323 mph)
Max level speed at S/L	204 knots (378 km/h; 236 mph)
Max cruising speed (75% power) at 1,830 m (6,000 ft)	
	193 knots (358 km/h; 222 mph)
Approach speed	80 knots (148 km/h; 92 mph)
Stalling speed, flaps and landing gear down, power off	
	62 knots (115 km/h; 72 mph)
Max rate of climb at S/L	564 m (1,850 ft)/min
Service ceiling	7,010 m (23,000 ft)
T-O run	410 m (1,345 ft)
T-O to 15 m (50 ft)	640 m (2,100 ft)
Landing from 15 m (50 ft)	440 m (1,444 ft)
Landing run	250 m (820 ft)
Endurance (65% power)	3 h 45 min
g limits	+6.7/−3.35

SOCATA TB 31 OMÉGA

The Oméga turboprop development of the Epsilon primary/basic trainer is a Socata private venture based on the Turbomeca TP 319. The prototype (F-WOMG) first flew on 30 April 1989 as a conversion of the TP 319 testbed Epsilon (see 1987-88 *Jane's*), itself the original No. 01 prototype. Additional features include optional lightweight Martin-Baker Mk 15FC ejection seats beneath a revised two-piece canopy. There is 60 per cent similarity in components between Epsilon and Oméga which has a wider manoeuvre envelope and greater fatigue tolerance.

Details as for Epsilon except:

WINGS: Local strengthening; four weapons hardpoints standard. Hardpoints stressed for same weapon loads as Epsilon.

FUSELAGE: Revised nose contours, resulting in transfer of landing lights to main landing gear legs. Airframe anti-corrosion protection to MIL-C-81773 and 83286 standards.

POWER PLANT: One 364 kW (488 shp) Turbomeca TP 319 1A2 turboprop, derated to 268 kW (360 shp) and fitted with a hydromechanical Hartzell propeller. Rated speed 2,377 rpm. Fuel capacity in wing leading-edges of 278 litres (73.3 US gallons; 61.2 Imp gallons). Provision for two minutes of inverted flying.

ACCOMMODATION: Two-piece single-unit canopy of Poly 76, hinged to starboard and including transparent separator between cockpits. MDC at junction of canopy frame for manual emergency evacuation. Martin-Baker 15FC through-canopy ejection seats with zero altitude, 60 knot (111 km/h; 69 mph) capability.

AVIONICS AND EQUIPMENT: CRT display of radio/navigation data (as on Portuguese Epsilons). Alkan E105-E200 armament selection indicator and E105-C02 control panel in front cockpit.

DIMENSIONS:

Length overall	7.81 m (25 ft 7½ in)
Height overall	2.68 m (8 ft 9½ in)

Epsilon of GE 315 Flying School, French Air Force *(AGPPA)*

WEIGHTS (approximate):
Weight empty, equipped	860 kg (1,896 lb)
Fuel weight	222 kg (489 lb)
Max T-O and landing weight	1,400 kg (3,086 lb)

PERFORMANCE (calculated):
Never-exceed speed	321 knots (595 km/h; 370 mph) CAS
Max level speed at S/L	280 knots (519 km/h; 322 mph) CAS
Max cruising speed at 3,050 m (10,000 ft)	234 knots (434 km/h; 269 mph)
Econ cruising speed (75% power)	191 knots (354 km/h; 220 mph)
Stalling speed, power off, 25° flap, landing gear up or down	64 knots (119 km/h; 74 mph)
Max rate of climb at S/L	640 m (2,100 ft)/min
Service ceiling	9,145 m (30,000 ft)
T-O to 15 m (50 ft)	570 m (1,870 ft)
Range at 75% power with 20 min reserves	706 nm (1,308 km; 813 miles)
g limits	+7/−3.5

Socata Oméga turboprop trainer (Turbomeca TP 319 engine)

SOCATA TB 9 TAMPICO and TB 10 TOBAGO

The prototype for this series of all-metal light aircraft was the original TB 10 (F-WZJP), of which design was initiated by Socata's Research and Development Department in February 1975. Construction began in February 1976, and it made a 25 min first flight at Tarbes on 23 February 1977, powered by a 119 kW (160 hp) Textron Lycoming O-320-D2A engine. The second prototype of the TB 10 was fitted with a 134 kW (180 hp) Lycoming engine.

Current production versions are as follows:

TB 9 Tampico Club. From 1989, this single model has superseded the Tampico FP (to which it is similar) and Tampico CS (Hartzell constant-speed propeller) of which details can be found in the 1988-89 *Jane's*. It is a four-seater, with 119 kW (160 hp) Textron Lycoming O-320-D2A engine, Sensenich 74 DM6 S8-0-54 fixed-pitch propeller, fuel capacity of 158 litres (41.75 US gallons; 34.75 Imp gallons), and non-retractable landing gear. First flown on 9 March 1979 and received DGAC certification on 27 September 1979. Socata held orders for 30 Tampico Clubs in February 1990.

TB 10 Tobago. Four/five-seater, with 134 kW (180 hp) engine and non-retractable landing gear. DGAC certification received on 26 April 1979, followed by FAA approval on 27 November 1985. Eight are used by SFACT to provide flying training for French air traffic control officers.

In February 1990 Socata held orders for 10 Tobagos, including a further three for SFACT and 10 for the Australian Aviation College at Parafield, South Australia, delivery of which was due to be completed in June 1990.

The more powerful **TB 20/21 Trinidad**, with retractable landing gear, is described separately.

The following description applies specifically to the TB 10 Tobago, but the Tampico is generally similar in basic construction.

TYPE: Four/five-seat all-metal light aircraft.

WINGS: Cantilever low-wing monoplane. Wing section RA 16.3C3. Thickness/chord ratio 16 per cent. Dihedral 4° 30' from roots. No incidence at root. No sweep. Conventional light alloy single-spar structure of constant chord, with glassfibre tips. Balanced ailerons and electrically actuated slotted flaps, of light alloy. Ground adjustable tabs.

FUSELAGE: Light alloy semi-monocoque structure. Shallow strake under each side of fuselage immediately aft of wing root fillet. Glassfibre engine cowlings.

TAIL UNIT: Cantilever all-metal type, with sweptback vertical surfaces and constant chord all-moving horizontal surfaces mounted at extreme tail, aft of rudder. Ground adjustable tab at top of rudder. Anti-tab in horizontal surfaces.

LANDING GEAR: Non-retractable tricycle type, with steerable nosewheel. Oleo-pneumatic shock absorber in all three units. Mainwheel tyres size 6.00-6, 6-ply rating, pressure 2.3 bars (33 lb/sq in). Glassfibre wheel fairings on all three units. Hydraulic disc brakes. Parking brake.

POWER PLANT: One 134 kW (180 hp) Textron Lycoming O-360-A1AD flat-four engine, driving a Hartzell two-blade constant-speed propeller with spinner. Two integral fuel tanks in wing leading-edges; total capacity 210 litres (55.5 US gallons; 46 Imp gallons), of which 204 litres (54 US gallons; 45 Imp gallons) are usable. Oil capacity 7.5 litres (2 US gallons; 1.6 Imp gallons).

ACCOMMODATION: Four/five seats in enclosed cabin, with dual controls. Adjustable front seats with inertia reel seat belts. Removable rear bench seat with safety belts. Sharply inclined low-drag windscreen. Access via upward hinged window/doors of glassfibre. Baggage compartment aft of cabin, with external door on port side. Cabin carpeted, soundproofed, heated and ventilated. Windscreen defrosting standard.

SYSTEMS: Electrical system includes 12V 60A alternator and 12V 32A battery, landing and navigation lights, four individual cabin lights and instrument panel lighting. Hydraulic system for wheel brakes only.

AVIONICS AND EQUIPMENT: Bendix/King Silver Crown avionics to customer's specification. Current aircraft are equipped without extra charge with a basic nav pack that includes a rate of climb indicator, electric turn and bank indicator, horizontal and directional gyro, true airspeed indicator, EGT and outside air temperature indicator. Standard equipment includes armrests for all seats, map pockets, anti-glare visors, stall warning indicator, tiedown fittings and towbar.

DIMENSIONS, EXTERNAL (Tampico Club and Tobago):
Wing span	9.76 m (32 ft 0¼ in)
Wing chord (constant)	1.22 m (4 ft 0 in)
Wing aspect ratio	8.0
Length overall	7.63 m (25 ft 0½ in)
Height overall	3.20 m (10 ft 6 in)
Tailplane span	3.20 m (10 ft 6 in)
Wheelbase	1.96 m (6 ft 5 in)
Propeller diameter	1.88 m (6 ft 2 in)
Propeller ground clearance	0.10 m (4 in)
Cabin doors (each): Width	0.90 m (2 ft 11½ in)
Height	0.76 m (2 ft 6 in)
Baggage door: Width	0.64 m (2 ft 1¼ in)
Height	0.44 m (1 ft 5¼ in)

DIMENSIONS, INTERNAL (Tampico Club and Tobago):
Cabin: Length:	
firewall to rear bulkhead	2.53 m (8 ft 3½ in)
panel to rear bulkhead	2.00 m (6 ft 6¾ in)
Max width: at rear seats	1.28 m (4 ft 2¼ in)
at front seats	1.15 m (3 ft 9¼ in)
Max height, floor to roof	1.12 m (3 ft 8 in)

AREAS (Tampico Club and Tobago):
Wings, gross	11.90 m² (128.1 sq ft)
Ailerons (total)	0.91 m² (9.80 sq ft)
Trailing-edge flaps (total)	3.72 m² (40.04 sq ft)
Fin	0.88 m² (9.47 sq ft)
Rudder	0.63 m² (6.78 sq ft)
Horizontal tail surfaces (total)	2.56 m² (27.56 sq ft)

WEIGHTS (A: Tampico Club, B: Tobago):
Weight empty, with unusable fuel and oil:	
A	655 kg (1,444 lb)
B	700 kg (1,543 lb)
Baggage: B	45 kg (100 lb)
Max T-O weight: A	1,058 kg (2,332 lb)
B	1,150 kg (2,535 lb)

PERFORMANCE (at max T-O weight, A and B as above):
Max level speed: A	122 knots (226 km/h; 140 mph)
B	133 knots (247 km/h; 153 mph)
Max cruising speed (75% power):	
A	107 knots (198 km/h; 123 mph)
B	127 knots (235 km/h; 146 mph)
Econ cruising speed (65% power):	
A	100 knots (185 km/h; 115 mph)
B	117 knots (217 km/h; 135 mph)
Stalling speed, flaps up:	
A	58 knots (107 km/h; 67 mph)
B	61 knots (112 km/h; 70 mph)
Stalling speed, flaps down:	
A	48 knots (89 km/h; 56 mph)
B	52 knots (97 km/h; 60 mph)
Max rate of climb at S/L: A	229 m (750 ft)/min
B	240 m (790 ft)/min
Service ceiling: A	3,810 m (12,500 ft)
B	3,960 m (13,000 ft)

Socata TB 9 Tampico Club training aircraft (Textron Lycoming O-320 engine)

Socata Tobago, with additional side view (bottom) of Trinidad *(Pilot Press)*

T-O run: A	340 m (1,115 ft)
B	325 m (1,066 ft)
T-O to 15 m (50 ft): A	520 m (1,705 ft)
B	505 m (1,657 ft)
Landing from 15 m (50 ft): A	420 m (1,378 ft)
B	425 m (1,395 ft)
Landing run: A	195 m (640 ft)
B	190 m (623 ft)

Range with max standard fuel, allowances for T-O, climb, econ power cruise and descent, 45 min reserves:

A	450 nm (834 km; 518 miles)
B	653 nm (1,210 km; 752 miles)

SOCATA TB 20/21 TRINIDAD

The Trinidad is a four/five-seat touring and IFR training aircraft, basically similar to the TB 10 Tobago (which see) but with a more powerful engine and retractable landing gear. The prototype (F-WDBA) flew for the first time, at Tarbes, on 14 November 1980. French certification was received on 18 December 1981, and the first production Trinidad (F-WDBB) was delivered on 23 March 1982. FAA type approval was obtained on 27 January 1984. A significant number of TB 20/21s has been delivered to civilian pilot training organisations SFACT (42 aircraft), IAAG and CIPRA in France; and equivalents in Australia, China (28 aircraft, deliveries completed in October 1989), India and Tunisia. In February 1990 Socata held orders for 69 TB 20s and 11 TB 21s, including six TB 20s for the Australian Aviation College, and three for IAAG.

There are two current versions of the Trinidad, as follows:

TB 20 Trinidad. Basic version with 186 kW (250 hp) Textron Lycoming IO-540-C4D5D engine.

TB 21 Trinidad TC. Turbocharged version, first flown on 24 August 1984, with 186 kW (250 hp) Textron Lycoming TIO-540-AB1AD engine and oxygen system.

DGAC certification received on 23 May 1985, followed by FAA type approval on 5 March 1986. The first production Trinidad TC (F-GENI), displayed at the 1985 Paris Air Show, was the 500th aircraft of the TB 9/10/20/21 series produced by Socata.

The description of the Tobago applies also to both versions of the Trinidad, except as follows:

WINGS: Dihedral 6° 30′ from roots. Flap preselector standard.

TAIL UNIT: Span and chord of horizontal tail surfaces increased. Mechanical rudder trim standard.

LANDING GEAR: Hydraulically retractable tricycle type, with single wheel on each unit. Free fall emergency extension. Steerable nosewheel retracts rearward. Main units retract inward into fuselage. Hydraulic disc brakes. Parking brake.

POWER PLANT: One Textron Lycoming flat-six engine, as described in individual model listings, driving a Hartzell HC-C2YK-1BF/F8477-4 two-blade metal propeller. Fuel tanks in wings; total usable capacity 326 litres (86 US gallons; 71.75 Imp gallons). Oil capacity 12.6 litres (3.3 US gallons; 2.8 Imp gallons).

SYSTEMS: Self-contained electro-hydraulic system for landing gear actuation. Eros oxygen system is standard in TB 21.

EQUIPMENT: In addition to basic nav pack described in the Tampico/Tobago entry, current aircraft have as standard equipment a heated pitot, emergency static vent, cylinder head temperature gauge, emergency lighting systems, tinted windows and a storm window.

DIMENSIONS:
As for Tobago, except:

Length overall	7.71 m (25 ft 3½ in)
Height overall	2.85 m (9 ft 4¼ in)
Tailplane span	3.64 m (11 ft 11¼ in)
Wheelbase	1.91 m (6 ft 3¼ in)
Propeller diameter	2.03 m (6 ft 8 in)

AREAS:
As for Tobago, except:

Horizontal tail surfaces (total)	3.06 m² (32.94 sq ft)

WEIGHTS (A: TB 20, B: TB 21):

Weight empty: A	800 kg (1,763 lb)
B	844 kg (1,861 lb)
Max baggage: A, B	65 kg (143 lb)
Max T-O weight: A, B	1,400 kg (3,086 lb)

PERFORMANCE (at max T-O weight, A and B as above):

Max level speed: A	167 knots (310 km/h; 192 mph)
B at 4,575 m (15,000 ft)	200 knots (370 km/h; 230 mph)

Max cruising speed (75% power) at 2,440 m (8,000 ft):

A	164 knots (303 km/h; 188 mph)

Best power cruising speed (75% power) at 7,620 m (25,000 ft): B 190 knots (352 km/h; 219 mph)

Econ cruising speed (65% power):

A at 3,660 m (12,000 ft)	160 knots (296 km/h; 184 mph)
B at 7,620 m (25,000 ft)	170 knots (315 km/h; 195 mph)

Stalling speed: flaps up:

A	64 knots (118 km/h; 74 mph)
B	66 knots (121 km/h; 75 mph)

flaps and wheels down:

A	54 knots (99 km/h; 62 mph)
B	55 knots (101 km/h; 63 mph)
Rate of climb: A at S/L	384 m (1,260 ft)/min
B at 610 m (2,000 ft)	332 m (1,090 ft)/min
B at 5,180 m (17,000 ft)	244 m (800 ft)/min
Service ceiling: A	6,100 m (20,000 ft)
Certification ceiling: B	7,620 m (25,000 ft)
T-O run: A	295 m (968 ft)
B	330 m (1,083 ft)
T-O to 15 m (50 ft): A	479 m (1,572 ft)
B	540 m (1,772 ft)
Landing from 15 m (50 ft): A	530 m (1,739 ft)
B	540 m (1,772 ft)
Landing run: A	230 m (755 ft)

Range with max fuel, allowances for T-O, climb, cruise at best econ setting and descent, 45 min reserves:

A at 75% power at 2,135 m (7,000 ft)	885 nm (1,640 km; 1,019 miles)
A at 65% power at 3,050 m (10,000 ft)	963 nm (1,785 km; 1,109 miles)

Range with max fuel, no reserves:

B at 75% power at 7,620 m (25,000 ft)	890 nm (1,648 km; 1,024 miles)
B at 65% power at 7,620 m (25,000 ft)	1,030 nm (1,907 km; 1,185 miles)

Max ferry range at 6,100 m (20,000 ft):

A	1,158 nm (2,145 km; 1,332 miles)

Socata TB 21 Trinidad TC, with retractable landing gear *(G. Maoui)*

TBM 700

This Socata/Mooney single-turboprop business aircraft is described under TBM SA in the International section.

GERMANY, WEST

CCE
COLANI/COMPOSITE ENGINEERING
Josef-Baumann-Strasse 29, 4630 Bochum 1
Telephone: 49 (234) 865346
Telex: 825 828 LEMAB D
Fax: 49 (234) 864125
HEAD OF DEVELOPMENT: Dipl-Ing Walter Schulze

COLANI CORMORAN CCE-208
Conceived by industrial designer Luigi Colani and sponsored by the Tohshin Company of Japan, the Cormoran is a four/five-seat light aircraft of which a prototype (D-EBCN) was built by Composite Engineering in West Germany. No recent news has been received from the company. Full details and an illustration of the CCE-208 can be found in the 1989-90 *Jane's*.

CLAUDIUS DORNIER
CLAUDIUS DORNIER SEASTAR GmbH & Co KG
Werksflugplatz Oberpfaffenhofen, 8031 Wessling
Telephone: 49 (8153) 4010
Telex: 5270288 CDS D
Fax: 49 (8153) 3636
MANAGING DIRECTOR: Dipl Ing Hannes Lucas

This company was founded by the late Prof Dipl Ing Claudius Dornier Jr to produce the Seastar utility amphibian, of which design was initiated in January 1982. The VT 01 first prototype (D-ICDS), assembled by Lufthansa and described in the 1984-85 *Jane's*, made its first flight on 17 August 1984, but in mid-1985 was retired after being damaged. In October 1986 the company moved to Oberpfaffenhofen where, with an initial development team of ten people, work began on an improved version known as the CD2.

Funding for production came originally from the West German government, Daimler-Benz (20 per cent shareholder), banks and the Dornier family. The use of about 100,000 m² (1,076,390 sq ft) of the Dornier airfield at Oberpfaffenhofen, plus a hangar for final assembly of the

Seastar, resulted from an agreement between Daimler-Benz/Dornier GmbH and the Dornier family. However, on 3 November 1989 the company filed for bankruptcy, while continuing to operate and work towards certification by the German LBA and FAA type approval under FAR Pt 23. In early 1990 it had about 170 employees.

Seastar production had begun in October 1989 and delivery of the first of 38 aircraft then held on option was expected in December 1990. In January 1990 two rival offers were made to the receiver, one from Conrado Dornier and the Dresdner Bank, and the other from Claudio Dornier who had the support of a West German aerospace company and Albert Blum. In February Claudius Dornier Seastar was finally purchased by Dornier Composite Aircraft, owned by Conrado Dornier. The Dresdner Bank has a 40 per cent shareholding.

Prior to this, and at the invitation of the Latvian-based Aeroprogress organisation, talks had been held regarding the possible licence production of the Seastar in the Soviet Union, where up to 250 could be required over 10 years. However, this would follow initial West German manufacture. Other interest has come from Japan. World Import Mart Co Ltd and Japan Airlines System Trading Inc are Seastar agents in Japan.

CLAUDIUS DORNIER SEASTAR CD2
The only portion of the VT 01 prototype to suffer serious damage in 1985 was the strut braced metal wing, and this was replaced in the first pre-series CD2 Seastar by a larger wing manufactured entirely from composite materials, with carbonfibre reinforcement in two spars that eliminates the need for strut bracing of the outer panels. Hull design was improved by a flatter planing bottom, enlarged cockpit, reprofiled nose and extended sponsons, and the original PT6A-11 turboprops were replaced by 373 kW (500 shp) PT6A-112s driving four-blade instead of three-blade propellers. The virtually all-composites airframe thus offered both light weight and a high degree of corrosion resistance, with an airframe life of 30,000 flight hours.

The Seastar is suitable for a variety of missions, including feeder transport from water bases to airports; missions for which helicopters would be restricted by range, economics or safety factors; search and rescue; law enforcement; air ambulance; maritime patrol; EEZ surveillance; and civil or military special missions, accommodating four people over a range of 1,000 nm (1,850 km; 1,150 miles). Its ability to operate from land, water, snow or ice enables it to perform such other roles as sightseeing and hunting tours, fire control and firefighting. A typical maritime patrol or law enforcement mission could involve an outward flight to a distance of 80 nm (148 km; 92 miles) taking 30 min; a search pattern lasting 2 h 45 min at a speed of 120 knots (222 km/h; 138 mph), altitude of 610 m (2,000 ft) and taking the aircraft to a distance of 330 nm (612 km; 380 miles); a sea landing and 4 h surveillance of ships with power off and loading of 500 kg (1,102 lb) of seized cargo; and flight back to base with an intermediate stop to unload the cargo, taking 1 h. Total mission time 8 h 15 min. The Seastar can operate in wave heights of up to 1.0 m (3.3 ft), in sea-state 1-2.

The first CD2 (also registered D-ICDS) made its first flight on 24 April 1987. Seaworthiness trials in the Baltic, off Kiel, and on Lake Constance were completed successfully, and a second pre-production aircraft (D-ICKS) joined the certification flight test programme in October 1988. It differs from D-ICDS only in having larger cabin windows and a fully furnished interior, a max T-O weight increased to 4,600 kg (10,141 lb), and the use of production type PT6A-135A turboprop engines.

The following description applies to the second pre-production CD2 and planned production model:

TYPE: Twin-turboprop STOL utility amphibian.

WINGS: Cantilever parasol monoplane, with modified NACA 23015 aerofoil section. The high-lift wing has drooped outboard leading-edges. Three-spar fail-safe structure constructed of GFRP with a foam core, with carbonfibre reinforcement of the front and rear spars. Single-slotted trailing-edge flaps and horn balanced ailerons. Flotation compartments are embodied. Leading-edge de-icing.

HULL: Conventional unpressurised flying-boat hull, constructed almost entirely of glassfibre. Large chined sponson on each side. Flotation compartments are embodied.

TAIL UNIT: Conventional unit, constructed of glassfibre and incorporating a variable incidence tailplane. Leading-edge de-icing. Horn balanced elevators and rudder, each with trim tab. Shallow dorsal fin on maritime patrol version.

LANDING GEAR: Hydraulically retractable tricycle type, with twin wheels on each main unit and single nosewheel. All wheels size 6.00-6. Main units retract forward into hull sponsons, nose unit forward into bow.

POWER PLANT: Two 485 kW (650 shp) Pratt & Whitney Canada PT6A-135A turboprops, mounted in tandem above wing in continuous nacelle and driving one tractor and one pusher propeller. Each is a four-blade McCauley C-760 series constant-speed metal propeller with spinner. Fuel tank in each sponson, combined max usable capacity 1,869 litres (494 US gallons; 411 Imp gallons).

ACCOMMODATION: Max accommodation for two pilots and 12 passengers in four rows of three in wide body cabin, at 81 cm (32 in) seat pitch, with single aisle. Dual controls standard. Alternative layouts for six executives in VIP seating, with a lavatory at rear of cabin and galley in part of baggage compartment; or nine passengers, with lavatory. By utilising entire baggage compartment space, aircraft can accommodate six stretchers plus two attendants and medical equipment; or can be configured for all-cargo use with front and rear loading access, providing 10.00 m³ (353.1 cu ft) of space able to transport items up to 5.50 m (18 ft 0½ in) in length. Crew door on port side, plus roof hatch to observe water manoeuvres. Passenger doors at front of cabin on starboard side and at rear on port side; latter has an optional airstair incorporated in the adjacent sponson structure. Baggage compartment at rear of cabin, with optional external door on starboard side, capacity 180 kg (397 lb). All accommodation heated and ventilated; air-conditioning optional. Crew of three and 450 kg (992 lb) of mission equipment in maritime patrol role.

SYSTEMS: Hydraulic system for landing gear actuation. Electrical system. Pneumatic de-icing for wing and tail leading-edges and engine intakes.

AVIONICS: Complete single-pilot IFR installation standard. For maritime roles, can carry nose-mounted Bendix RDR 1400 weather radar and Swedish Space Corporation SLAR.

WEAPONS: Four underwing stations available for loads of 250 kg (551 lb) each.

DIMENSIONS, EXTERNAL:

Wing span	17.80 m (58 ft 4¾ in)
Wing chord, mean	1.89 m (6 ft 2½ in)
Wing aspect ratio	10.35
Width over sponsons	4.20 m (13 ft 9½ in)
Length overall: normal	12.46 m (40 ft 10½ in)
with radar nose	12.85 m (42 ft 2 in)
Fuselage: Max width	1.90 m (6 ft 2¾ in)
Max depth	1.80 m (5 ft 10¾ in)
Height overall (on land)	4.60 m (15 ft 1 in)
Tailplane span	5.56 m (18 ft 3 in)

Second pre-production Claudius Dornier Seastar CD2 amphibian (two P&WC PT6A-135A turboprops)

Claudius Dornier Seastar in its planned production form (*Pilot Press*)

Wheel track	2.45 m (8 ft 0½ in)
Propeller diameter: front	2.40 m (7 ft 10½ in)
rear	2.35 m (7 ft 8½ in)
Crew door: Height	0.85 m (2 ft 9½ in)
Width	0.70 m (2 ft 3½ in)
Passenger door (fwd, stbd):	
Height	1.00 m (3 ft 3¼ in)
Width	0.80 m (2 ft 7½ in)
Passenger door (rear, port):	
Height	1.15 m (4 ft 11 in)
Width	0.95 m (3 ft 1½ in)
Baggage compartment door:	
Height	0.50 m (1 ft 7¾ in)
Width	0.90 m (2 ft 11½ in)

DIMENSIONS, INTERNAL:

Cabin, excl flight deck:	
Length: excl baggage compartment	5.00 m (16 ft 5 in)
incl baggage compartment	5.50 m (18 ft 0½ in)
Max width	1.68 m (5 ft 6 in)
Max height	1.45 m (4 ft 9 in)
Floor area: excl baggage compartment	
	6.30 m² (67.8 sq ft)
Volume:	
excl baggage compartment	
	8.30 m³ (293.1 cu ft)
incl baggage compartment	
	10.00 m³ (353.1 cu ft)
Rear baggage compartment volume	
	1.70 m³ (60.0 cu ft)

AREAS:

Wings, gross	30.60 m² (329.38 sq ft)
Vertical tail surfaces (total)	3.15 m² (33.9 sq ft)
Horizontal tail surfaces (total)	6.32 m² (68.0 sq ft)

WEIGHTS AND LOADINGS:

Weight empty, equipped (standard)	2,400 kg (5,291 lb)
Max payload	1,460 kg (3,218 lb)
Max usable fuel	1,495 kg (3,296 lb)
Max T-O weight	4,600 kg (10,141 lb)
Max wing loading	150.3 kg/m² (30.79 lb/sq ft)
Max power loading	4.75 kg/kW (7.80 lb/shp)

PERFORMANCE (preliminary, PT6A-135A engines, at 4,000 kg; 8,818 lb AUW):

Max cruising speed at 3,000 m (9,840 ft):	
both engines	190 knots (352 km/h; 219 mph)
one engine	134 knots (248 km/h; 154 mph)
Surveillance speed	
	81-182 knots (150-338 km/h; 93-210 mph)
Stalling speed at S/L	62 knots (115 km/h; 72 mph)
Max rate of climb at S/L	480 m (1,575 ft)/min
Rate of climb at S/L, one engine out	150 m (492 ft)/min
Service ceiling	8,600 m (28,215 ft)
Service ceiling, one engine out	4,200 m (13,780 ft)
T-O distance (land)	410 m (1,345 ft)
T-O to 15 m (50 ft)	640 m (2,100 ft)
Landing from 15 m (50 ft)	480 m (1,575 ft)
Landing distance (land)	270 m (886 ft)
Range:	
with 12 passengers at max cruising speed, at 3,050 m (10,000 ft), 10% reserves	
	220 nm (407 km; 253 miles)
with 454 kg (1,000 lb) payload, one pilot, at max cruising speed, no reserves	
	907 nm (1,680 km; 1,044 miles)
with 1,116 kg (2,460 lb) payload	
	220 nm (407 km; 253 miles)
Ferry range	1,460 nm (2,705 km; 1,681 miles)
Max endurance: two engines	11 h 30 min
one engine	12 h 30 min
Time on station: at 200 nm radius	5 h 30 min
in waterborne mode, power off	over 24 h

DEUTSCHE AEROSPACE GROUP
DEUTSCHE AEROSPACE AG
Leopaldstrasse, 8000 Munich 40
Telephone: 49 (89) 381990
Telex: 528 576 DASAM D
Fax: 49 (89) 38 199890
CHAIRMAN - Deutsche Aerospace supervisory board:
 Edzard Reuter

PRESIDENT - Deutsche Aerospace executive board:
 Jürgen E. Schrempp
DEPUTY PRESIDENT: Dr Johann Schäffler (Chairman of Aircraft Group)
EXECUTIVES:
 Dr Manfred Bischoff
 Karl J. Dersch
 Hubert Dunkler (Chairman of Engine Group)

 Dr Gerhard Jäger (Chairman of Defence Systems Group)
 Dr Hartwig Knitter
 Dr-Ing Helmut Ulke (Chairman of Space Technology Group)
 Deutsche Aerospace AG (DASA) was founded on 19 May 1989 to oversee the future aerospace activities of the Daimler-Benz group, which simultaneously assumed a 57.5 per cent shareholding in Dornier GmbH and a 100 per cent

shareholding of MTU (Motoren und Turbinen-Union). MTU produces aero engines and diesel engines. At that time Deutsche Aerospace corporations employed a total workforce of about 38,000.

Deutsche Aerospace capital was thereafter raised to acquire all shares in TST (Telefunken Systemtechnik GmbH), and in September 1989 the West German Economic Minister, Helmut Haussmann, authorised DASA's take-over of MBB, in which it now has a 50.24 per

cent shareholding. Conditions imposed by the West German government when allowing the integration of MBB into DASA included a commitment by MBB to take over the 20 per cent shareholding of the Kreditanstalt für Wideraufbau bank in Deutsche Airbus by 1996; that DASA should terminate its naval business activities (involving work by MBB and TST); and that MBB should discontinue production of RPVs and armoured vehicle work.

The combined DASA workforce now stands at over

80,000 people, although the four main companies still operate under individual identities. DASA activities are themselves placed in four groups, namely Aircraft, Space Technology, Defence Systems and Engines. Foreign collaboration is expected to expand, with talks already under way with several French and Japanese companies, plus British Aerospace.

DORNIER
DORNIER LUFTFAHRT GmbH (Subsidiary of Dornier GmbH -part of Deutsche Aerospace AG)

HEADQUARTERS: Werksflugplatz, Oberpfaffenhofen, 8031 Wessling
Telephone: 49 (8153) 300
Telex: 52 64 12 DORW D
Fax: 49 (8153) 30 29 01
MANAGING DIRECTOR: Dr Hans Blume
DIRECTOR, MARKETING AND SALES: Dipl-Ing Klaus Neuhaus
DIRECTOR OF AIRCRAFT SALES: Reinhold Orthmann
CHAIRMAN OF DORNIER GMBH: Dr-Ing Helmut Ulke
PRESS AND INFORMATION: Andrea Schuster
Postfach 2160, 8000 Munich 66
Telephone: 49 (89) 87 153484
Telex: 52 35 43 DOWN D
Fax: 49 (89) 87 15230

Dornier GmbH, formerly Dornier-Metallbauten, was formed in 1922 by the late Professor Claude Dornier. It has operated as a GmbH since 22 December 1972. Daimler-Benz AG acquired a majority holding (65.5 per cent) in Dornier GmbH in 1985, but had reduced this to 57.55 per cent by 1 January 1989, when a new three-group Dornier company structure came into being with Silvius Dornier (21.22 per cent) and the Claudius Dornier heirs (21.22 per cent) as the other shareholders. The Daimler-Benz shareholding has since been assumed by Deutsche Aerospace AG (which see), which was formed in May 1989 and now brings together the activities of Dornier, MBB, MTU and TST.

The former Dornier System GmbH no longer exists, its activities having been transferred to the parent Dornier GmbH, which is based at Friedrichshafen. Dornier GmbH is thus responsible for space systems, defence technology, electronics and informatics, new technologies and planning consulting within the overall Deutsche Aerospace organisation. All of Dornier's aviation activities are undertaken by Dornier Luftfahrt GmbH (formerly Dornier Reparaturwerft GmbH) at Oberpfaffenhofen, which is a wholly owned subsidiary of Dornier GmbH. The third member of the group is Dornier Medizintechnik GmbH of Munich, also a wholly owned subsidiary of Dornier GmbH. The total group workforce was about 10,000 in late 1989.

Dornier Luftfahrt undertakes research and development at Friedrichshafen (workforce of 900), parts production at Munich-Neuaubing (workforce of about 1,800), and systems integration, final assembly, test flying, marketing, maintenance and customer services at Oberpfaffenhofen (workforce of about 1,700).

Dornier Luftfahrt developed the Alpha Jet training/light attack aircraft, described in the International section, in partnership with Dassault-Breguet of France. It is responsible for industrial support of Luftwaffe Alpha Jets and is to modernise the fleet to meet the requirements of the 1990s. It is one of the European aerospace companies defining and developing the multi-nation Eurofighter EFA (see International section), and is participating, under subcontract from Deutsche Airbus GmbH, in the manufacturing and development programmes for the Airbus Industrie family of transport aircraft. It was responsible for integrating the operational avionics in the 18 Boeing E-3A Sentry AWACS aircraft acquired by NATO for use in Europe, and now conducts depot-level maintenance of these aircraft under NATO contract. Dornier was prime contractor for planning and implementation of the NATO Trainer/Cargo Aircraft (TCA) programme (see 1989-90 *Jane's*). It also assisted in the design of the Argentine IA 63 Pampa trainer. In April 1989 Dornier signed a memorandum of understanding with Aermacchi of Italy for the joint definition of a future integrated military Pilot Training System (PTS-2000), including related airborne and ground-based training means to take student pilots from initial screening up to conversion onto operational aircraft. The company's latest activities in aviation technology encompass future low-drag aeroplane fuselages, a new transonic laminated wing, Eureca research items (with Aeritalia) towards an advanced amphibious aircraft, and hypersonic aircraft technologies.

Dornier Luftfahrt undertakes technical and logistic servicing of the Breguet Br 1150 Atlantic 1 aircraft operated by the West German Navy. It also became prime contractor for modernisation of the German Atlantics, which are expected to continue in service until replaced (probably by Lockheed P-7As) around 1997. Details of the modernisation programme appeared in the 1989-90 *Jane's*.

DORNIER 228
The design of the Dornier 228 complies with US FAR Pt 23 requirements, including Amendment 23, and Appendix

Dornier 228-200 in the insignia of the Nigerian Air Force *(Ivo Sturzenegger)*

A of FAR Pt 135. One prototype of each initial version was built; the first of these, the Dornier 228-100 (D-IFNS) made its first flight on 28 March 1981. The 228-200 (D-ICDO) flew for the first time on 9 May 1981. A static test airframe of the 228-200 was also completed. Service life is for 62,500 flights without major structural repair.

British CAA and American FAA certification were granted on 17 April and 11 May 1984 respectively, followed by Australian certification on 11 October 1985; in addition, LBA certification has been accepted by the licensing authorities of Bhutan, Canada, India, Japan, Malaysia, Nigeria, Norway, Sweden and Taiwan.

Excluding Indian licence production, firm orders for the Dornier 228 (all versions) totalled 181 by February 1990 from 65 customers in 35 countries; deliveries at that time had reached 150.

The Dornier 228 is available in the following versions:

228-100. Basic version, with standard accommodation for 15 passengers in airline seats at 76 cm (30 in) pitch. German (LBA) certification awarded on 18 December 1981. Deliveries began in February 1982; entered service, with A/S Norving Flyservice in Norway, in late Summer of 1982. Suitable for a wide range of other duties, including freight or mixed cargo/passenger transport, executive travel, air taxi service, photogrammetry, airways calibration, training, ambulance or search and rescue operations, and paramilitary missions. Details of two 228-100s specially equipped for polar research were given in the 1986-87 *Jane's*. Two ordered for SAR and other special duties by Australia's National Safety Council in 1987 are fitted with bubble windows each side of the cabin, a wide roller cabin door for SAR or firefighting operations, lightweight 360° Bendix radar, an Omega Loran system, 20-man liferaft, a rear fuselage launch chute for smoke or colour markers and flares, and provision for two stretchers.

228-101. Identical to 228-100 except for reinforced fuselage and different mainwheel tyres, to permit higher operating weights, and installation of engine fire extinguishing system to conform to SFAR Pt 41b. Introduced in 1984.

228-200. Lengthened fuselage, providing standard accommodation for 19 passengers at 76 cm (30 in) seat pitch and a larger rear baggage compartment, but otherwise generally similar to 228-100. Certificated by German LBA on 6 September 1982. One delivered to Japan's National Aerospace Laboratory in 1988 was specially equipped by AAR Oklahoma Inc, USA, for use as an in-flight simulator to evaluate aerodynamic and flight control system characteristics for future aircraft, including an automatic landing system for a future spaceplane.

228-201. Introduced in 1984. Identical to 228-200 except for changes noted under 228-101. Accommodation for 19 passengers with two pilots, 20 passengers with one pilot, 15-17 passengers with two pilots plus galley and lavatory, or nine passengers as a corporate transport. One (98 + 78) evaluated by MFG 5 of the German Navy and by German Air Force during 1986-87. Two specially equipped -201s, delivered in 1985-86 to DLR for meteorological (remote sensing) and environmental forestry and pollution control work, have ventral camera/scanner apertures and numerous attachments for special sensors and other equipment under the wings and fuselage.

228-202. Designed to offer increases in payload/range performance, compared with 228-201, for only a slight

difference in empty weight. Certificated by LBA and FAA in August and September 1986 respectively; available since Autumn 1987.

228-203F Freight Liner. Freighter version, with higher payload and operating weights. Additional crew door on starboard side. Wing, propeller and windscreen de-icing. Colour weather radar for all-weather operation. Primary structural life expectancy of at least 56,000 flights. Five dome lights in main cabin and six partitioning cargo nets. Floor rails. In addition to main cabin, forward and aft baggage compartments have capacities of 120 kg (265 lb) and 210 kg (463 lb) respectively.

228-212. Generally as -201, but with 6,400 kg (14,110 lb) and 6,100 kg (13,448 lb) take-off and landing weights respectively, allowing increased payload on short route segments. Reduced empty weight. Max fuel weight 1,885 kg (4,155 lb). Increased engine T-O rating (to 579 kW; 776 shp at S/L, ISA). Strengthened landing gear (with modified anti-skid system and carbon brakes), wing boxes and fuselage; two underfuselage fins to improve STOL and low-speed flying; increase in max flaps extended speed from 150 to 160 knots IAS; modification of elevator and rudder control (electrically actuated rudder trim); and relocating the battery from the nose to the landing gear bay. Modernised avionics and equipment. Certificated by the LBA in April 1989.

228 Troop, Paratroop and Ambulance. Based on the 228-200. Troop accommodates 17, 20 or 22 fully equipped troops, and can be adapted quickly for paratroop operations. Fold-up seats along sides. Lightweight toilet, roller door, military nav/com, and loadmaster intercom. Paratroop accommodates 16, 19 or 21 persons, plus jumpmaster. Similar equipment to Troop, but no toilet. Ambulance also has roller door and accommodates six stretchers in pairs and nine sitting casualties/attendants. Optional small galley, toilet, refrigerator, oxygen system and cabin intercom. Can carry full casevac load at cruising speed over a distance of 850 nm (1,575 km; 978 miles).

228 Maritime Patrol. Described separately.

228 Sigint. Described separately.

On 29 November 1983 contracts were signed covering the transfer of technology in a progressive programme to manufacture versions of the Dornier 228 under licence in India, by Hindustan Aeronautics Ltd. A production run of about 150 aircraft is envisaged, for various Indian organisations and customers, and was prefaced by the delivery of five 228-201s to Vayudoot, the Indian regional airline, in 1984-85, and three 228-101s to the Indian Coast Guard in 1986-87. Meanwhile, Dornier began delivery of complete sets of aircraft assemblies to India in early 1985, and the first flight of an HAL assembled 228 was made on 31 January 1986. Further details of this licence programme can be found in the HAL entry in the Indian section.

TYPE: Twin-turboprop STOL light transport.

WINGS: Cantilever high-wing monoplane, comprising two-spar rectangular centre-section and two tapered outer panels ending in raked tips. Dornier Do A-5 supercritical wing section. No dihedral or anhedral. Sweepback on leading-edge of outer panels 8°. Wingtips of CFRP; Kevlar used in construction of wing rib webs, wingroot fairings and ailerons. Remainder of wing of light alloy construction. Fowler single-slotted trailing-edge flaps and ailerons of carbonfibre composites. Ailerons can be

Dornier 228-100 light transport, with additional side view (bottom) of 228-200 *(Pilot Press)*

drooped symmetrically to augment trailing-edge flaps, and are operated differentially to serve as conventional ailerons. Trim coupling of flaps and tailplane optional.

FUSELAGE: Conventional stressed skin unpressurised structure of light alloy, built in five sections. GFRP nosecone and Kevlar landing gear fairings.

TAIL UNIT: Cantilever structure, with rudder and horizontal surfaces partly Eonnex covered. CFRP used for tips of tailplane and elevators; GFRP used for tips of rudder and fin, and hybrid composites used for fin leading-edges. All-moving tailplane, with horn balanced elevators. Trim tab in rudder.

LANDING GEAR: Retractable tricycle type, with single mainwheels and twin-wheel nose unit. Main units retract forward and inward into fairings built on to the lower fuselage. Hydraulically steerable nosewheels retract forward. Goodyear wheels and tyres, size 8.50-10 on mainwheels (12 ply rating on 228-100, 10 ply rating on 228-200); size 6.00-6, 6 ply rating, on nosewheels. Low pressure tyres optional. Goodyear brakes on mainwheels.

POWER PLANT: Two 533 kW (715 shp) Garrett TPE331-5-252D turboprops in -100/-101, each driving a Hartzell HC-B4TN-5ML/LT10574 four-blade constant-speed fully-feathering reversible-pitch metal propeller; -200 series have 578.7 kW (776 shp) version of same engine. Primary wing box forms an integral fuel tank with a total usable capacity of 2,386 litres (630 US gallons; 525 Imp gallons). Oil capacity per engine 5.9 litres (1.56 US gallons; 1.30 Imp gallons). Optional APU.

ACCOMMODATION: Crew of one or two, and accommodation for 15 to 20 passengers as described under model listings, or 16, 19 or 21 paratroops plus jumpmaster, or 17, 20 or 22 fully equipped troops in military transport configuration. Pilots' seats adjustable fore and aft. Individual seats down each side of the cabin with a central aisle. Flight deck door on port side (both sides on -203F). Combined two-section passenger and freight door, with integral steps, on port side of cabin at rear. One emergency exit on port side of cabin, two on starboard side (deleted on -203F). Baggage compartment at rear of cabin, accessible externally and from cabin; capacity 210 kg (463 lb). Enlarged baggage door optional. Additional baggage space in fuselage nose, with separate access; capacity 120 kg (265 lb). Modular units using seat rails for rapid changes of role. In air ambulance configuration, six stretchers carried in three double units plus nine seated patients/medical attendants.

SYSTEMS: Entire accommodation heated and ventilated. Air-conditioning system optional. Heating by engine bleed air. Hydraulic system, pressure 207 bars (3,000 lb/sq in), for landing gear, brakes and nosewheel steering. Handpump for emergency landing gear extension. Primary 28V DC electrical system, supplied by two 28V 250A engine driven starter/generators and two 24V 25Ah nickel-cadmium batteries. Two 350VA inverters supply 115/26V 400Hz AC system. APU optional. Air intake anti-icing standard. De-icing system optional for wing and tail unit leading-edges, windscreen and propellers.

AVIONICS AND EQUIPMENT: Instrumentation for IFR flight standard. Autopilot optional, to permit single-pilot IFR operation. Standard avionics include dual Bendix/King KY 196 VHF com, dual KN 53 VOR/ILS and KN 72 VOR/LOC converters; KMR 675 marker beacon receiver, dual or single KR 87 ADF and KT 76A transponder; dual or single Aeronetics 7137 RMI; dual or single DME; two Honeywell GH14B gyro horizons; two King KPI 552 HSIs; dual ASIs; dual altimeters; dual ADIs; dual VSIs; Becker audio selector and intercom. Standard equipment includes complete internal and external lighting, hand fire extinguisher, first aid kit, gust control locks and tiedown kit. Wide range of optional avionics and equipment available, including weather radar. For geophysical role, equipment includes VLF magnetometer in nose probe, VLF or protomagneto-

meter in port wing fairing, gamma ray detector, camera in rear of cabin with the operator's position in forward section of cabin, navigation telescope, emergency equipment, and magnetometer in tail 'sting'; operator's position for magnetometers on port side of cabin.

DIMENSIONS, EXTERNAL:

Wing span	16.97 m (55 ft 8 in)
Wing aspect ratio	9.0
Length overall: 100 series	15.04 m (49 ft 4⅛ in)
200 series	16.56 m (54 ft 4 in)
Height overall	4.86 m (15 ft 11½ in)
Tailplane span	6.45 m (21 ft 2 in)
Wheel track	3.30 m (10 ft 10 in)
Wheelbase: 100 series	5.53 m (18 ft 1¾ in)
200 series	6.29 m (20 ft 7½ in)
Propeller diameter	2.73 m (8 ft 11½ in)
Propeller ground clearance	1.08 m (3 ft 6½ in)
Passenger door (port, rear):	
Height	1.34 m (4 ft 4¾ in)
Width	0.64 m (2 ft 1¼ in)
Height to sill	0.60 m (1 ft 11½ in)
Freight door (port, rear):	
Height	1.34 m (4 ft 4¾ in)
Width, incl passenger door	1.28 m (4 ft 2½ in)
Emergency exits (each): Height	0.66 m (2 ft 2 in)
Width	0.48 m (1 ft 7 in)
Baggage door (nose): Height	0.50 m (1 ft 7½ in)
Width	1.20 m (3 ft 11¼ in)
Standard baggage door (rear):	
Height	0.90 m (2 ft 11½ in)
Width	0.53 m (1 ft 9 in)

DIMENSIONS, INTERNAL:

Cabin, excl flight deck and rear baggage compartment:	
Length: 100 series	6.33 m (20 ft 9 in)
200 series	7.08 m (23 ft 2¾ in)
Max width	1.346 m (4 ft 5 in)
Max height	1.55 m (5 ft 1 in)
Floor area: 100 series	8.50 m² (91.49 sq ft)
200 series	9.56 m² (102.9 sq ft)
Volume: 100 series	13.00 m³ (459.1 cu ft)
200 series	14.70 m³ (519.1 cu ft)
Rear baggage compartment volume:	
100 series, standard	1.20 m³ (42.4 cu ft)
100 series, optional; 200 series, standard	
	2.60 m³ (91.8 cu ft)
Nose baggage compartment volume	0.89 m³ (31.4 cu ft)
Cargo volume (203F):	
main cabin	14.70 m³ (519.1 cu ft)
nose	0.89 m³ (31.4 cu ft)
rear fuselage	2.60 m³ (91.8 cu ft)

AREAS:

Wings, gross	32.00 m² (344.3 sq ft)
Ailerons (total)	2.708 m² (29.15 sq ft)
Trailing-edge flaps (total)	5.872 m² (63.21 sq ft)
Fin, incl dorsal fin	4.50 m² (48.44 sq ft)
Rudder, incl tab	1.50 m² (16.15 sq ft)
Horizontal tail surfaces (total)	8.33 m² (89.66 sq ft)

WEIGHTS AND LOADINGS:

Weight empty, standard: 100	2,980 kg (6,570 lb)
101	2,990 kg (6,592 lb)
200	3,086 kg (6,803 lb)
201	3,096 kg (6,825 lb)
202	3,221 kg (7,101 lb)
Operating weight empty: 100	3,413 kg (7,524 lb)
101	3,423 kg (7,546 lb)
200	3,547 kg (7,820 lb)
201	3,737 kg (8,238 lb)
202	3,698 kg (8,153 lb)
212	3,742 kg (8,249 lb)
Max payload: 100	2,127 kg (4,689 lb)
101	2,117 kg (4,667 lb)
200	1,853 kg (4,085 lb)
201	1,903 kg (4,195 lb)
202	1,895 kg (4,178 lb)
203F	2,300 kg (5,070 lb)
212	1,848 kg (4,074 lb)
Max ramp weight: 100, 200	5,730 kg (12,632 lb)
101, 201	6,010 kg (13,250 lb)
202	6,230 kg (13,735 lb)
212	6,430 kg (14,175 lb)
Max T-O weight: 100, 200	5,700 kg (12,566 lb)
101, 201	5,980 kg (13,183 lb)
202	6,200 kg (13,668 lb)
203F	6,500 kg (14,330 lb)
*212	6,400 kg (14,110 lb)
Max landing weight: 100, 101, 200	5,700 kg (12,566 lb)
201, 202	5,900 kg (13,007 lb)
212	6,100 kg (13,448 lb)
Max wing loading:	
100, 200	178.1 kg/m² (36.48 lb/sq ft)
101, 201	186.9 kg/m² (38.28 lb/sq ft)
202	193.7 kg/m² (39.67 lb/sq ft)
203F	203.1 kg/m² (41.60 lb/sq ft)
212	200.0 kg/m² (40.96 lb/sq ft)
Max power loading:	
100, 200	5.35 kg/kW (8.79 lb/shp)
101, 201	5.17 kg/kW (8.49 lb/shp)
202	5.36 kg/kW (8.81 lb/shp)
203F	4.19 kg/kW (9.23 lb/shp)
212	5.53 kg/kW (9.09 lb/shp)

*Increasable to 6,600 kg (14,550 lb) in special cases

PERFORMANCE (at max T-O weight, S/L, ISA, except where indicated):

Never-exceed speed (all)	
	255 knots (472 km/h; 293 mph) IAS
Max operating speed (VMO):	
212	223 knots (413 km/h; 256 mph) IAS
Max cruising speed at 3,050 m (10,000 ft) (all)	
	231 knots (428 km/h; 266 mph)
Cruising speed at 4,575 m (15,000 ft), average cruise weight of 5,300 kg (11,684 lb):	
212	220 knots (408 km/h; 253 mph)
Max cruising speed at S/L (all)	
	199 knots (370 km/h; 230 mph)
Econ cruising speed (all)	
	180 knots (333 km/h; 207 mph)
Stalling speed, flaps up:	
100	79 knots (146 km/h; 91 mph) IAS
200	81 knots (150 km/h; 93 mph) IAS
Stalling speed, flaps down:	
100	63 knots (117 km/h; 73 mph) IAS
200	67 knots (124 km/h; 77 mph) IAS
Max rate of climb at S/L:	
100, 200	618 m (2,025 ft)/min
101, 201	582 m (1,910 ft)/min
202	546 m (1,790 ft)/min
203F	516 m (1,695 ft)/min
212	570 m (1,870 ft)/min
Rate of climb at S/L, one engine out:	
100, 200	162 m (531 ft)/min
101, 201	138 m (450 ft)/min
202	126 m (413 ft)/min
212	134 m (440 ft)/min
Service ceiling, 30.5 m (100 ft)/min rate of climb:	
100, 200	9,020 m (29,600 ft)
101, 201	8,535 m (28,000 ft)
Service ceiling, one engine out, 30.5 m (100 ft)/min rate of climb: 100, 200	4,265 m (14,000 ft)
202	4,210 m (13,810 ft)
203F	4,116 m (13,500 ft)
Service ceiling, one engine out, 15 m (50 ft)/min rate of climb	3,962 m (13,000 ft)
T-O run: 100	411 m (1,350 ft)
101	442 m (1,450 ft)
202	686 m (2,250 ft)
T-O to 10.7 m (35 ft): 203F	732 m (2,400 ft)
T-O to 15 m (50 ft): 100	564 m (1,850 ft)
101	592 m (1,945 ft)
200	750 m (2,461 ft)
201	625 m (2,050 ft)
202	686 m (2,250 ft)
Landing from 15 m (50 ft) at max landing weight:	
100	600 m (1,968 ft)
200	620 m (2,034 ft)
202, max braking	536 m (1,760 ft)
203F	558 m (1,831 ft)
212	512 m (1,680 ft)
Range at 3,050 m (10,000 ft) with max passenger payload, max cruising speed:	
100	724 nm (1,343 km; 834 miles)
101	939 nm (1,740 km; 1,081 miles)
200	323 nm (600 km; 372 miles)
202	540 nm (1,000 km; 621 miles)
Max range at 3,050 m (10,000 ft) at econ cruising speed, reserves for 85 nm (157 km; 98 mile) diversion, 45 min hold and 15% fuel remaining:	
201	164 nm (305 km; 189 miles)
203F (max payload)	
	over 400 nm (741 km; 460 miles)
203F (1,360 kg; 3,000 lb) payload	
	over 1,200 nm (2,224 km; 1,380 miles)
Max range at 3,050 m (10,000 ft) at econ cruising speed, max passenger load and 45 min reserves:	
202	610 nm (1,130 km; 702 miles)

Range at 3,050 m (10,000 ft) at econ cruising speed, max
fuel load and 45 min reserves:
202   1,460 nm (2,704 km; 1,680 miles)
Range at 3,050 m (10,000 ft) with 19 passengers, reserves
for 50 nm (93 km; 57 mile) diversion, 45 min hold and
5% fuel remaining:
212 at max cruising speed
                       560 nm (1,038 km; 645 miles)
212 at max range speed   630 nm (1,167 km; 725 miles)
Range with 775 kg (1,708 lb) payload, conditions as
above:
212 at max cruising speed
                       1,160 nm (2,150 km; 1,335 miles)
212 at max range speed
                       1,320 nm (2,446 km; 1,520 miles)

DORNIER 228 MARITIME PATROL

Dornier has developed three specialised versions of the
Dornier 228-200 for maritime patrol. Other uses can include
SAR.

Version A: Intended for surveillance of EEZ and
foreign fisheries; territorial tasks and activities of national
safety relating to infiltration, prohibited border traffic and
smuggling; and SAR. Ordered by Indian Coast Guard
(three German built 228-101s, two delivered in July 1986
and one in July 1987, plus 33 by HAL, from 1987). The
Indian Navy has ordered from HAL the first four of 24
required for coastal patrol and anti-ship operations.
Primary surveillance sensor is an underfuselage MEL
Marec 2 radar with 360° scan (replaced on 15 aircraft by
Super Marec ordered in early 1987). The cabin is laid out to
accommodate an observer on a lateral sliding seat adjacent
to a bubble window on each side, with a radar operator's
station situated on the port side in a mid-cabin position
(with a radar rack forward). Stowage position for Agiflite
hand-held camera. There is a toilet towards the rear of the
cabin on the starboard side. Optional galley, camera
operator's seat, photo window, observer's desk/worktop
and intercom, Spectrol Sk-16 Nightscan steerable searchlight (mounted externally), 20-man liferaft for SAR, wide
roller door, and smoke/colour markers and flares with
stowage and chute at rear of fuselage. Two 300A Lear
Siegler starter/generators are standard to supply power for
specialised equipment which, in addition to the Marec or
alternative Eaton AN/APS-128 radar, can include SSC
IR/UV scanner without cutout and rack, high resolution
optical equipment, underwing Micronair spraypods for
oil spill/chemical pollution control, Litton LTN 211
VLF/Omega, Global Navigation GNS 500-4M VLF/
Omega, Collins DF-301E direction finder system, Collins
IND-41A DME, vertical gyro system, UNS1 integrated
special mission flight management system, Collins HF-230
HF com, Collins ARC-182 V/UHF com, Wulfsberg RT
9600 VHF/FM com, and Becker IC 3100-(2) interphone.
Additional equipment in the radar operator's console
includes an airspeed indicator, altimeter and clock;
Aeronetics Model 7137 RMI; VLF/Omega control unit;
and a Becker AS-3100 interphone. Wet outboard wing
sections increase fuel capacity to 2,250 kg (4,960 lb).

Version B: Intended for surveillance of coastal waters
to locate oil spills and chemical dumping, survey sea traffic
and protect fisheries. Secondary tasks include SAR.
Primary surveillance source is an Ericsson/Swedish Space
Corporation SLAR, with an underfuselage antenna. Basic
mission equipment also includes an Omega navigation
system (ONS), Swedish Space Corporation Daedalus 1221
IR/UV linescanner system, Nikon hand-held camera with
interface to nav system, and the wet wing of Version A.
Other equipment can include Decca Racal Mk 19 nav
system with TANS, or Type 72 Doppler nav system with
TANS, SOC microwave radiometer, SOC image link
system, Barco TV monitor, Honeywell Primus 500 colour
weather radar; steerable searchlight; loudhailer; galley;
observer's desk/worktop and intercom; smoke/colour
markers and flares, stowage and chute (for SAR); wide
roller door; 20-man liferaft; and photo window. SLAR
operator adjacent to optional photo window on port side of
cabin. Two observers' seats forward, staggered and with
bubble windows. Repositioned crew liferaft.

Version C: Intended for fishery control, customs and
coastguard operations, plus SAR and casevac. Bendix
RDR 1500 360° scan radar, with CRT display installed in
cabin or, alternatively, in cockpit to allow two-crew
missions. Radar operator's seat on forward starboard side
of cabin, opposite observer's seat with bubble window. To
rear is second observer's position. Crew liferaft, toilet and
chute as for Version B. Wet wings as for Versions A and B.
Omega navigation system. Major options include small
galley, double stretchers and attendant's seat, smoke/colour
markers and flares with stowage and chute for SAR,
20-man liferaft for SAR, wide roller door, steerable
searchlight, photo window, interfaced hand-held camera
system, and observer's desk/worktop and intercom.
WEIGHTS:
Fuel weight   2,250 kg (4,960 lb)
Max T-O weight   6,500 kg (14,330 lb)
Max landing weight   6,100 kg (13,448 lb)
PERFORMANCE (ISA, at 6,200 kg; 13,668 lb AUW):
Max rate of climb at S/L   546 m (1,790 ft)/min
Rate of climb at S/L, one engine out 126 m (413 ft)/min
Service ceiling, one engine out   4,330 m (14,200 ft)

Dornier 228 in Maritime Patrol configuration for fisheries protection

Dornier 228 Reconnaissance showing FLIR pod but with SLOS retracted

T-O to 15 m (50 ft)   686 m (2,250 ft)
Landing from 15 m (50 ft)   536 m (1,760 ft)
MISSION ENDURANCE (at max T-O weight):
At max range   9 h 31 min
At 100 nm from base   8 h 20 min
Max   11 h 1 min

DORNIER 228 RECONNAISSANCE

This version of the 228-200 is specially equipped to enable
civil or military agencies to carry out a wide range
of surveillance and reconnaissance missions, including
customs and border patrol, ground target detection by day
or night, maritime patrol, SAR support, ground target
recognition and identification, and aerial survey and
mapping. In addition to a comprehensive avionics suite, it
carries FLIR, ASC (aerial survey camera) system and SLOS
(stabilised long-range observation system). The SLOS
permits visual detection of targets up to 27 nm (50 km; 31
miles) and identification up to 16 nm (30 km; 18.6 miles).
The gyro-stabilised telescope is controlled by a remote
joystick and twin TV monitors, and is coupled to a video
recorder. An interface is incorporated for a C-band
real-time air-to-ground data link. Other mission equipment
includes a four-man liferaft, flare/markers and chute, VLF
Omega navigation system, and colour WX. A typical
mission could be a flight out to a search area 100 nm (185
km; 115 miles) from base and a 7½ hour search time.
Dimensions, weights and performance are similar to those
for the 228-200 transport.

DORNIER 228 SIGINT

Dornier offers a signal intelligence (sigint) version of the
228-200, with communications intelligence (comint) and
electronic intelligence (elint) constituent parts. Two to four
mission operators can be accommodated, with the basic
elint and comint operators being joined by an additional
comint operator and/or supervisor. Sigint data can be
recorded to form a threat library enabling comparison and
evaluation during ESM and ECM operations. Comint
operator's station on starboard side of rear fuselage, joined
by a second station on the port side if required. As part of
the AEG sigint suite, comint operator's subsystem is used
for search and interception of communications, direction
finding, preliminary analysis, and recording of signals in the
20-1,000 MHz frequency range. The search operation uses
frequency scan, memory scan, automatic signal detection

and demodulation of microwave links. Direction finding
has a 360° azimuth coverage. Audio and video signals
are recorded, together with time and comments. Elint
operator's subsystem is used for similar functions to comint
subsystem, but aimed at electronic emissions and recording
of radar signals in the 0.5-18 GHz frequency range for
subsequent analysis. Direction finding azimuth is ±135°,
and on-line analysis is for type of modulation, pulse
duration, pulse repeat time and agility, scanning type and
scanning period. The elint operator's station is on the
forward port side of the cabin. Slightly to its rear and on the
starboard side is the supervisor's station, controlling and
co-ordinating the activities of the other operators. It
comprises a terminal computer which automatically depicts
an emitter activity presentation, identifies known signals,
determines the location of the emitters and stores the results
of the mission. The supervisor may also establish contact
with the ground-based control and analysis station via a
secure radio link. A lightweight toilet is provided in the rear
of the cabin, and a tape recorder is situated between the
supervisor's and first comint operator's stations. Elint and
comint antennae are housed in underfuselage fairings.
WEIGHTS:
Fuel weight   1,300 kg (2,866 lb)
Max T-O weight   6,400 kg (14,110 lb)
Max landing weight   6,100 kg (13,448 lb)
PERFORMANCE:
*Max cruising speed   231 knots (428 km/h; 266 mph)
*Econ cruising speed   178 knots (330 km/h; 205 mph)

*ISA, at 3,050 m (10,000 ft), at average cruising weight of
5,700 kg (12,566 lb)

DORNIER 328

On 3 August 1988, the partners of Dornier GmbH took
the decision to resume full development of the Dornier 328
twin-turboprop pressurised regional transport, this phase
starting that December. The 328 is intended to offer
take-off, climb and landing characteristics comparable to
those of the company's earlier utility and commuter
aircraft, including the capability to operate from STOL-
ports and rough unprepared airstrips. Other criteria include
a 78 dBA noise level in 75 per cent of the passenger cabin,
stand-up cabin height, and a seat width per passenger better
than that in the average Boeing 727 or 737. It is expected to
replace 19-seat aircraft on routes with growing traffic, and

Dornier 328 30-33 passenger airliner (two PW119 turboprops) *(Pilot Press)*

supersede uneconomical 40/50-seat aircraft on steady traffic routes by making more departures.

The basic TNT wing profile of the Dornier 228 is retained, with an enlarged centre-section housing more fuel, and a new flap system incorporating ground and flight spoilers. This is combined with a new and enlarged circular-section fuselage, developed using data from the Federal Ministry of Research and Technology's NRT (Neue Rumpf-technologien: new fuselage technologies) programme, and a T tail unit of new design. The centre section of the fuselage has been designed by British consultants, SAC International.

First flight is scheduled for July 1991, with 13-nation JAR certification set for late 1992 and FAA certification to FAR Pts 135 and 121 following three months later in early 1993. Launch customers are Sunshine Aviation of Switzerland (one) and Contact Air of West Germany (four), with contracts signed in April and May 1989 respectively. Largest order by early 1990 had come from Midway Airlines, for 33, with another 40 on option. Dornier sees a potential market for up to 400 by the year 2006.

Daewoo Heavy Industries of the Republic of Korea will manufacture fuselage shells for the Dornier 328. These will be assembled by Aermacchi of Italy (a risk sharing partner in the 328), which will also be involved in structural testing, engineering and manufacturing work to a total of about 10 per cent of the manufacturing hours per aircraft. The Daewoo share represents about 20 per cent of the total manufacturing time.

TYPE: Twin-turboprop pressurised regional transport.

WINGS: Cantilever high-wing monoplane, essentially scaled up from that of Dornier 228 by enlarging centre-section, enabling it to accommodate an additional fuel tank. Flight spoiler (outboard) and two ground spoilers added forward of trailing-edge flaps on each wing. Wing skins mainly of aluminium-lithium alloy, with Kevlar-CFRP sandwich trailing-edges. Stringers and precision forgings of aluminium-lithium alloy. Flaps, ailerons and wingtips of CFRP.

FUSELAGE: Circular-section semi-monocoque pressurised structure, with conical nosecone and tailcone. Primary structure is of aluminium alloy, with aluminium-lithium used for longerons, stringers, window frames and skin panels. Rear fuselage of CFRP, tailcone of Kevlar/CFRP sandwich; nosecone of CFRP sandwich. Doors of superplastic formed aluminium alloy. Long Kevlar/CFRP wing/fuselage fairing, offering space for systems installation outside main pressure shell.

TAIL UNIT: Cantilever T tail, comprising sweptback fin and rudder and tapered, non-swept horizontal surfaces. Entire structure is of CFRP except for dorsal fin (Kevlar/CFRP sandwich) and tailplane leading-edge (aluminium alloy). Trim tab in rudder and each elevator.

LANDING GEAR: ERAM/SHL retractable tricycle type, with twin wheels on each unit. Nose unit retracts forward, main units into long Kevlar/CFRP sandwich unpressurised fairings on fuselage sides. Tyre pressures 3.72 bars (54 lb/sq in) on nose unit, 6.55 bars (95 lb/sq in) on main units.

POWER PLANT: Two Pratt & Whitney Canada PW119 turboprops, each rated at 1,353 kW (1,815 shp) for normal take-off and 1,625 kW (2,180 shp) for short-field take-off, each driving a Hartzell six-blade composites propeller with electronic synchrophasing. Improved performance kit will be available. Nacelles of superplastic formed titanium and carbon composite. All fuel in wing tanks, total capacity of 3,400 litres (898 US gallons; 748 Imp gallons). Propeller brakes standard.

ACCOMMODATION: Flight crew and cabin attendant(s). Main cabin seats 30-33 passengers, three-abreast at 79 cm (31 in) or 76 cm (30 in) pitch, with single aisle. Galley to rear of passenger seats; toilet at front of cabin. Large

baggage hold between passenger cabin and rear pressure bulkhead, with access from cabin and externally via baggage door in port side. Additional overhead and underseat baggage stowage in main cabin. Crew/passenger airstair door at front on port side, with Type III emergency exit opposite; Type III emergency exit on port side at rear of cabin, with service door Type II exit at rear on starboard side. Cargo restraint nets and pallet/container system for freight carrying.

SYSTEMS: Air-conditioning and pressurisation systems standard (max differential 0.45 bar; 6.53 lb/sq in). Hydraulic and two independent AC/DC electrical systems housed in main landing gear fairings. APU optional.

AVIONICS: Standard fit comprises Honeywell SPZ-8800 'glass cockpit' with integrated EFIS, AFCS and EICAS (electronic flight instrument system, automatic flight control system, and electronic indication, caution and advisory system); digital air data computer; AHRS with advanced fibre-optic laser gyros; radar altimeter; Primus 650 weather radar; and Primus II digital radio system. Standard options include Honeywell flight management system (FMS), traffic alert and collision avoidance system (TCAS), GPS, MLS, and laser inertial reference system.

DIMENSIONS, EXTERNAL (provisional):

Wing span	20.98 m (68 ft 10 in)
Length overall	21.22 m (69 ft 7½ in)
Fuselage: Length	20.85 m (68 ft 4¾ in)
Max width	2.415 m (7 ft 11 in)
Max depth	2.426 m (7 ft 11½ in)
Height overall	7.199 m (23 ft 7½ in)
Elevator span	6.389 m (20 ft 11½ in)
Wheel track (c/l of shock struts)	3.22 m (10 ft 6¾ in)
Wheelbase	7.156 m (23 ft 5¾ in)
Propeller diameter	3.50 m (11 ft 5¾ in)
Propeller/fuselage clearance	0.785 m (2 ft 7 in)
Passenger door (fwd, port): Height	1.70 m (5 ft 7 in)
Width	0.70 m (2 ft 3½ in)
Service door (rear, stbd): Height	1.25 m (4 ft 1¼ in)
Width	0.50 m (1 ft 7¾ in)
Baggage door (rear, port): Height	1.40 m (4 ft 7 in)
Width	0.92 m (3 ft 0¼ in)

DIMENSIONS, INTERNAL:

Cabin, excl flight deck:	
Length	10.26 m (33 ft 8 in)
Max width	2.18 m (7 ft 2 in)
Width at floor	1.84 m (6 ft 0½ in)
Max height	1.86 m (6 ft 1¼ in)
Baggage hold volume	6.0 m³ (211.9 cu ft)

DESIGN WEIGHTS:

Max payload	3,450 kg (7,605 lb)
Max baggage load	600 kg (1,322 lb)
Max T-O weight	12,500 kg (27,557 lb)
Max zero-fuel weight	11,625 kg (25,629 lb)
Max landing weight	12,250 kg (27,006 lb)

DESIGN PERFORMANCE:

Max cruising speed	345 knots (639 km/h; 397 mph)
Max rate of climb at S/L	740 m (2,430 ft)/min
Design cruise altitude:	
normal	7,620 m (25,000 ft)
with improved performance kit	9,145 m (30,000 ft)
Required runway length:	
normal	1,006 m (3,300 ft)
with improved performance kit	823 m (2,700 ft)
Range with 30 passengers, with allowance for 100 nm (185 km; 115 mile) diversion and 45 min hold	
	701 nm (1,300 km; 808 miles)

MBB
MESSERSCHMITT-BÖLKOW-BLOHM
GmbH (part of Deutsche Aerospace AG)

Postfach 801109, 8000 Munich 80
Telephone: 49 (89) 6070
Telex: 5287-310 MBB D

In May 1969 the former Messerschmitt-Bölkow GmbH and Hamburger Flugzeugbau GmbH (see 1968-69 *Jane's*) merged to form a new group known as Messerschmitt-Bölkow-Blohm GmbH. MBB acquired all shares of VFW on 1 January 1981. In 1989 Daimler-Benz AG, through Deutsche Aerospace AG, acquired a 50.24 per cent share holding in MBB. Other shareholders are the State of Bavaria (17.44 per cent), City of Hamburg (12.75 per cent), City State of Bremen (6.99 per cent), Fides Industrie-Beteiligungsgesellschaft GmbH (12.21 per cent), and the Messerschmitt, Bölkow and Blohm families (0.37 per cent). Federal government conditions for the takeover of shares are detailed under Deutsche Aerospace AG. The MBB group employed approx 40,000 people in early 1990.

HELICOPTER AND MILITARY AIRCRAFT GROUP
(Helicopter Division and Military Aircraft Division)

See next page

Helicopter activities of this Group include civil and military versions of the MBB BO 105 and MBB/Kawasaki BK 117, development of the BO 108, participation in the

Two-tone grey camouflage Sea King Mk 41 of MFG 5, West German Navy, after conversion from SAR to ASV configuration

Eurocopter and NH 90 programmes (described in the International section), and the ALH programme in co-operation with Hindustan Aeronautics Ltd (see Indian section). Main centre for the BO 105 and BK 117 is MBB's Donauwörth factory. The Division also overhauls and repairs Sikorsky CH-53G and Westland Sea King Mk 41 helicopters in service with the West German armed forces, and the Speyer factory is currently upgrading 22 German Navy Sea Kings of Marinefliegergeschwader 5 with Ferranti Seaspray Mk 3 radar for target acquisition, a Ferranti Link II target data transformer, AEG ALR-68 radar warning receiver, Tracor M130 chaff/flare dispenser and four BAe Sea Skua missiles for anti-surface vessel attack.

Major military aircraft activities of the Group involve the Panavia Tornado (see International section), for which MBB is the German prime contractor; modifications to improve the combat capability of Luftwaffe F-4F and RF-4E Phantoms; and a major role in the development of the European Fighter Aircraft, for which MBB became German prime contractor, with Dornier as its co-contractor (see International section). MBB is also partnered with Rockwell International in development of the X-31A (see International section). Additional fields of MBB activity include aircraft armament and airborne reconnaissance systems, simulation and training systems, and research into advanced aircraft systems, materials and manufacturing technologies.

DEUTSCHE AIRBUS GmbH
See page 99

Deutsche Airbus, formerly known as MBB's Transport Aircraft Group, with more than 16,000 employees in six factories in northern Germany, is involved in manufacture and development for several international European collaborative programmes, including the Airbus A300/310/320/321/330/340 (63 per cent of the group's workload), Fokker 100 (11 per cent), Panavia Tornado (17 per cent), MPC 75, and miscellaneous programmes. Maintenance and conversion work on Airbus and other aircraft, for customers throughout the world, is carried out at the Aircraft Service Centre in Lemwerder as part of MBB's product support activities. Airspares in Hamburg provides a worldwide 24 h spares service for the company. Spoilers and rudders of carbonfibre reinforced plastics (CFRP) are produced for Airbus aircraft, and the fin box for the A310, designed and manufactured by MBB, is currently the largest CFRP aircraft component made in Europe. The A320 is fitted with CFRP horizontal and vertical tail surfaces, which save 25 per cent in weight compared to metal equivalents and also minimise corrosion.

Early in 1990 Airbus agreed that the A321 should be assembled and equipped by Deutsche Airbus in Hamburg.

DEFENCE SYSTEMS GROUP
(Guided Missiles Division, Ballistic and Dispenser Systems Division, and Special Products Division)
GUIDED MISSILES DIVISION AND BALLISTIC & DISPENSER SYSTEMS DIVISION:
Postfach 801149, 8000 Munich 80
Telephone: 49 (89) 6000 6056
Telex: 5287-0 MBB D
SPECIAL PRODUCTS DIVISION:
Postfach 107845, 2800 Bremen 1
Telephone: 49 (421) 538-1
Telex: 245821 MBB D
WORKS: Ottobrunn, Bremen, Kassel, Nabern/Teck and Schrobenhausen

Missile programmes on which the Defence Systems Group is engaged include those for the air-launched MBB Kormoran, Euromissile Hot and Aerospatiale/MBB ANS. Others include the surface-launched Hot, Milan, MLRS, Patriot, Roland and RAM. The Group also produces the MW-1 submunition dispenser which is carried by the Tornado.

Special Products Division is involved in diversified MBB activities which include airborne subsystems, training systems and simulators, measuring and tracking systems, test and automation systems, and logistics.

SPACE SYSTEMS GROUP (MBB/ERNO)
Postfach 105909, 2800 Bremen 1
Telephone: 49 (421) 539 4348
Telex: 245548A ERNO D
Postfach 801169, 8000 Munich 80
Telephone: 49 (89) 6000 3738
Telex: 5287-0 MBB D
WORKS: Bremen and Ottobrunn

Details of this Group's recent and current space programme activities can be found in the Spaceflight section of the 1983-84 and earlier editions of *Jane's*, and currently in *Interavia Space Directory*. Current programmes include the proposed Sänger II two-stage space transportation system.

INDUSTRIAL PRODUCTS GROUP
Postfach 801109, 8000 Munich 80

ENERGY AND PROCESS TECHNOLOGY DIVISION
Postfach 801109, 8000 Munich 80

HELICOPTER AND MILITARY AIRCRAFT GROUP
Postfach 801160, 8000 Munich 80
Helicopter Division:
Telephone: 49 (89) 607 22539
Telex: 5287-027 MBB D
Military Aircraft Division:
Telephone: 49 (89) 6070
Telex: 5287-095 MBB D
Fax: 49 (89) 607 28740
WORKS: Ottobrunn, Donauwörth, Augsburg, Manching, Laupheim and Speyer
PUBLIC RELATIONS:
  Christina Gotzhein (Helicopter Division)
  Wolfram Wolff (Military Aircraft Division)

MBB/KAWASAKI BK 117
MBB is building in conjunction with Kawasaki of Japan the BK 117 8/11-seat multi-purpose helicopter. The main description of this aircraft can be found in the International section; details of the all-German military BK 117 M are given in this entry, after the description of the BO 105.

EUROCOPTER TIGER
The programme for this Franco-German common anti-tank helicopter, also known as PAH-2/HAC/HAP, is described under the Eurocopter heading in the International section.

NH 90
This four-nation programme (NATO helicopter for the 1990s) is described under the NH 90 heading in the International section.

MBB BO 105
The first prototype of this light utility helicopter was fitted with an existing conventional rotor and two Allison 250-C18 turboshafts; subsequent aircraft, of which the first one flew on 16 February 1967, have had a rotor system based on a single-piece titanium hub, with bearings only for pitch change, and flexible glassfibre blades.

Details of prototypes, early BO 105C and D production helicopters and special variants can be found in previous editions of *Jane's*. Production of 100 BO 105 M (VBH) and 212 BO 105 P (PAH-1) military versions for the Federal German Army ended in 1984, and details of these versions can be found in the 1985-86 edition. MBB is currently preparing for a PAH-1 upgrade programme in two phases that include retrofit with new rotor blades of improved aerofoil section, a Hot 2 or later missile system with digital guidance, and new lightweight launching system and racks. Changes would allow a max T-O weight increase from 2,400 kg (5,291 lb) to 2,500 kg (5,511 lb), effectively increasing payload capacity by 180 kg (397 lb). This would permit either an increase in fuel load or integration of a night vision system for the pilot and gunner. Upgrading of 209 in-service PAH-1s under phase one began in 1990, with the night vision system and improved self-defence capability following in 1992 under phase two.

BO 105s in use as military testbeds include one being used by MBB to flight test an AEG mast mounted radar system, and one fitted by Lucas Aerospace in the UK with a bolt-on undernose turret to permit off-axis firing of Stinger

CBS version of the BO 105 operated by the Devon and Cornwall Police in the UK

BO 105 CB five-seat light helicopter (two Allison 250-C20B turboshafts) *(Pilot Press)*

Length, incl main and tail rotors	11.86 m (38 ft 11 in)
Length, excl rotors: CB	8.56 m (28 ft 1 in)
CBS	8.81 m (28 ft 11 in)
Length of fuselage pod: CB	4.30 m (14 ft 1 in)
CBS	4.55 m (14 ft 11 in)
Height to top of main rotor head	3.00 m (9 ft 10 in)
Width over skids: unladen	2.53 m (8 ft 3½ in)
laden	2.58 m (8 ft 5½ in)
Rear loading doors: Height	0.64 m (2 ft 1 in)
Width	1.40 m (4 ft 7 in)

DIMENSIONS, INTERNAL:

Cabin, incl cargo compartment:	
Max width	1.40 m (4 ft 7 in)
Max height	1.25 m (4 ft 1 in)
Volume	4.80 m³ (169 cu ft)
Cargo compartment: Length	1.85 m (6 ft 0¾ in)
Max width	1.20 m (3 ft 11¼ in)
Max height	0.57 m (1 ft 10½ in)
Floor area	2.25 m² (24.2 sq ft)
Volume	1.30 m³ (45.9 cu ft)

AREAS:

Main rotor disc	76.05 m² (818.6 sq ft)
Tail rotor disc	2.835 m² (30.5 sq ft)

WEIGHTS AND LOADING:

Weight empty, basic: CB	1,276 kg (2,813 lb)
CBS	1,301 kg (2,868 lb)
Standard fuel (usable)	456 kg (1,005 lb)
Max fuel, incl auxiliary tanks	776 kg (1,710 lb)
Standard T-O weight	2,400 kg (5,291 lb)
Max T-O weight	2,500 kg (5,511 lb)
Max disc loading	32.9 kg/m² (6.74 lb/sq ft)

PERFORMANCE (A at 2,400 kg; 5,291 lb standard T-O weight,
B at 2,500 kg; 5,511 lb max T-O weight):

Never-exceed speed at S/L:		
A		145 knots (270 km/h; 167 mph)
B		131 knots (242 km/h; 150 mph)
Max cruising speed at S/L:		
A, B		131 knots (242 km/h; 150 mph)
Best range speed at S/L:		
A, B		110 knots (204 km/h; 127 mph)
Max rate of climb at S/L, max continuous power:		
A		480 m (1,575 ft)/min
B		419 m (1,375 ft)/min
Vertical rate of climb at S/L, T-O power:		
A		183 m (600 ft)/min
B		91 m (300 ft)/min
Max operating altitude: A		5,180 m (17,000 ft)
B		3,050 m (10,000 ft)
Service ceiling, one engine out (30.5 m; 100 ft/min climb		
reserve, T-O power): A		890 m (2,920 ft)
Hovering ceiling IGE, T-O power:		
A		2,560 m (8,400 ft)
B		1,525 m (5,000 ft)
Hovering ceiling OGE, T-O power:		
A		1,615 m (5,300 ft)
B		457 m (1,500 ft)
Range with standard fuel and max payload, no reserves:		
at S/L: A		310 nm (575 km; 357 miles)
B		307 nm (570 km; 354 miles)
at 1,525 m (5,000 ft): A		355 nm (657 km; 408 miles)
B		321 nm (596 km; 370 miles)
Ferry range with auxiliary tanks, no reserves:		
at S/L: A		540 nm (1,000 km; 621 miles)
B		537 nm (995 km; 618 miles)
at 1,525 m (5,000 ft):		
A		600 nm (1,112 km; 691 miles)
B		550 nm (1,020 km; 634 miles)
Endurance with standard fuel and max payload, no		
reserves:		
at S/L: A		3 h 30 min
B		3 h 24 min

Upgraded version of the PAH-1, with new weapons system and new rotor blades

air-to-air missiles, controlled by a Ferranti helmet pointing system. This latter helicopter has joined one German Army BO 105 M and two Army BO 105 Ps (PAH-1s) being flown at test and operational training centres to evaluate the weapon and sighting systems needed to convert 54 current PAH-1 anti-tank helicopters into interim first-generation fire support and escort helicopters. Each BSH-1 (Begleitschutz-Hubschrauber der 1 Generation) would be armed with four Stingers for engaging other helicopters or aeroplanes and for self defence. Although initially for day operation only, BSH-1s could later be given night sights. Conversion of the PAH-1s to BSH-1 standard will begin in 1994. A BO 105 is being flown to test the OPST-1 DLR-MBB-Liebherr full-authority, intelligent triplex, optically signalled yaw control that relieves the pilot of the task of yaw/collective axis co-ordination.

By January 1990 more than 1,300 BO 105s of all models had been delivered, to 37 countries in five continents. All BO 105 helicopters for the world market are manufactured and assembled at the company's Donauwörth facility, with the exceptions of those for the Spanish market which are assembled in Spain by CASA, those for the Indonesian market which are manufactured and assembled in that country by IPTN, and BO 105 LS helicopters produced at MBB's Fort Erie facility in Ontario, Canada. Current models are as follows:

BO 105 CB. Standard production version since 1975, with two Allison 250-C20B engines, operable in air temperatures ranging from –45° to +54°C. LBA certification received in November 1976. Details of specially equipped versions for the Mexican Navy (12) and Swedish Army (20, delivered by September 1988) were given in the 1987-88 *Jane's*. In Spain, CASA assembled 57 of an initial 60 for the Spanish Army for armed reconnaissance (18), observation (14) and anti-tank missions (28), and is currently assembling a further undisclosed number.

BO 105 CBS. Version with increased seating or cargo capacity in a 0.25 m (10 in) longer fuselage. Available in five-seat executive or six-seat high density configurations. Identified by small additional window aft of rear door on each side. Marketed in the USA, by MBB Helicopter Corporation, under the name **Twin Jet II**. Certificated in early 1983 by FAA for IFR operation in accordance with SFAR Pt 29-4, requiring two pilots, radar, Loran-C and a separate battery, but not a stability augmentation system, though SAS is available as an option. The Swedish Air Force has four BO 105 CBSs, equipped for IFR search and rescue configuration.

BO 105 LS. Produced in Canada and described separately under MBB entry in Canadian section. Five pre-production models produced in Germany during 1984.

The description which follows applies to the BO 105 CB except where indicated:

TYPE: Five-seat light helicopter.

ROTOR SYSTEM: Four-blade main rotor, comprising rigid titanium head and GFRP blades, with titanium anti-erosion strip forming leading-edge and vibration damper on each blade. MBB designed 'droop-snoot' blades of NACA 23012 asymmetrical section, having a specially designed trailing-edge giving improved control in pitching moment. Flexible tension/torsion blade retention, to take up centrifugal forces. Roller bearings for pitch change. Main rotor brake standard. Main rotor blade folding optional. Two-blade semi-rigid tail rotor; blades of GFRP, with stainless steel anti-erosion strip on leading-edge. Main rotor rpm 424. Tail rotor rpm 2,220.

ROTOR DRIVE: Main transmission utilises two bevel gear input stages with freewheeling clutches and a spur collector gear stage. Planetary reduction gear; three auxiliary drives for accessories. Main transmission rated

for twin-engine input of 257 kW (345 shp) per engine, or a single-engine input of 283 kW (380 shp). Tail rotor gearbox on fin. Main rotor/engine rpm ratio 1 : 14.2. Tail rotor/engine rpm ratio 1 : 2.7.

FUSELAGE: Conventional light alloy semi-monocoque structure of pod and boom type. Glassfibre reinforced cowling over power plant. Titanium sheet engine deck.

TAIL UNIT: Horizontal stabiliser of conventional light alloy construction with small endplate fins.

LANDING GEAR: Skid type, with cross-tubes designed for energy absorption by plastic deformation in the event of a heavy landing. Inflatable emergency floats can be attached to skids.

POWER PLANT: Two 313 kW (420 shp) Allison 250-C20B turboshafts, each with a max continuous rating of 298 kW (400 shp). Bladder fuel tanks under cabin floor, capacity 580 litres (153.2 US gallons; 127.5 Imp gallons), of which 570 litres (150.6 US gallons; 125.3 Imp gallons) are usable. Fuelling point on port side of cabin. Auxiliary tanks in freight compartment available optionally. Oil capacity: engine 12 litres (3.2 US gallons; 2.6 Imp gallons), gearbox 11.6 litres (3.06 US gallons; 2.55 Imp gallons).

ACCOMMODATION: Pilot and co-pilot or passenger on individual longitudinally adjustable front seats with safety belts and automatic locking shoulder harnesses. Optional dual controls. Bench seat at rear for three persons, removable for cargo and stretcher carrying. Both cabin and cargo compartment have panelling, sound insulation and floor covering. Entire rear fuselage aft of seats and under power plant available as freight and baggage space, with access through two clamshell doors at rear. Two standard stretchers can be accommodated side by side in ambulance role. One forward opening hinged and jettisonable door and one sliding door on each side of cabin. Ram air and electrical ventilation system. Heating system optional.

SYSTEMS: Tandem fully redundant hydraulic system, pressure 103.5 bars (1,500 lb/sq in), for powered main rotor controls. System flow rate 6.2 litres (1.64 US gallons; 1.36 Imp gallons)/min. Bootstrap/oil reservoir, pressurised at 1.7 bars (25 lb/sq in). Electrical system powered by two 150A 28V DC starter/generators and a 24V 25Ah nickel-cadmium battery; external power socket.

AVIONICS AND EQUIPMENT: Standard equipment includes basic flight instruments, engine instruments, heated pitot, tiedown rings in cargo compartment, cabin and cargo compartment dome lights, position lights and collision warning lights. A wide range of optional avionics and equipment is available, including stability augmentation system, Doppler navigation, search radar, dual controls, heating system, windscreen wiper, rescue winch, landing light, searchlight, externally mounted loudspeaker, fuel dump valve, external load hook, settling protectors, snow skids, and main rotor blade folding. GEC Avionics AD 2780 Tacan in aircraft of Royal Netherlands Air Force. A completely equipped ambulance version is available.

ARMAMENT (military versions): Provision for a variety of alternative military loads, including six Hot or eight TOW anti-tank missiles and associated stabilised sight, or a Saab/Emerson HeliTOW installation. Lucas Aerospace turret system for use on BO 105 and NBO-105 has also been qualified. Turret mounts an FN gun and is aimed by a Ferranti helmet sight.

DIMENSIONS, EXTERNAL:

Main rotor diameter	9.84 m (32 ft 3½ in)
Tail rotor diameter	1.90 m (6 ft 2¾ in)
Main rotor blade chord	0.27 m (10⅝ in)
Tail rotor blade chord	0.18 m (7 in)
Distance between rotor centres	5.95 m (19 ft 6¼ in)

MBB BK 117 M

Shown publicly for the first time at the 1985 Paris Air Show, this multi-role military version of the MBB/Kawasaki BK 117 (see International section) is a purely German development by MBB. The airframe and power plant are virtually unchanged from the commercial 117, except for a new high-skid landing gear to provide clearance for an underfuselage Lucas turret housing a 0.50 in or 12.7 mm Browning automatic machine-gun, with 450 rounds of ammunition, controlled by a helmet mounted sight. Typical weapons load is eight Hot 2 anti-tank missiles, mounted on outrigger pylons (four missiles each side of cabin), with which are associated a SFIM APX-M397 stabilised roof mounted sight and digital weapons control avionics. Provisions exist for a mast mounted sight of up to 120 kg (264 lb) weight, infra-red jamming and chaff/flare ECM, a Racal Prophet radar warning system, and a Racal RAMS 3000 Series avionics management system which uses a dual MIL-STD-1553B databus and multifunction cockpit displays. In this configuration the BK 117 M has an empty equipped weight of 2,560 kg (5,644 lb), carries a crew of two and 460 kg (1,014 lb) of fuel, for a max T-O weight of 3,200 kg (7,055 lb). Alternative ordnance can include TOW anti-tank missiles, air-to-air missiles, unguided rockets, machine-gun pods, fixed forward-firing cannon, or a doorway gunner's position with a 0.50 in machine-gun. The capacity to serve instead as an 11-troop or cargo transport helicopter is the same as for the commercial BK 117. Weapon system qualification trials began in Summer 1988, initially with Forges de Zeebrugge FZ-100 rocket pods. Equipment included a Crouzet pilot reflex sight and a SFIM stabilised gunner's sight.

Market studies and customer reactions are still being evaluated by MBB, and flight tests with various sights and weapons systems are continuing.

MBB BO 108

This new helicopter incorporates all the advances individually developed by MBB in recent years. Two prototypes were funded, the first of which (D-HBOX) flew initially on 15 October 1988 and made its public debut on 13 December that year. The BO 108 programme is being financed by MBB and various equipment manufacturers, with support from the Federal Ministry of Economics and the Federal Ministry of Research and Technology.

The BO 108 was at first considered as a technology exercise, but may be put into production. New features include completely hingeless main rotor, shallow transmission with special vibration absorbers, low-drag aerodynamics, composite structures, and advanced electrical and avionics systems, cockpit installations and engine integration. One aim is to achieve single-pilot IFR with a cost-effective stability augmentation system. Other objectives are to develop the means to improve handling and simplify maintenance procedures (including provision of a diagnostic system if economical) and reduce the direct operating costs (25 per cent lower than those of the BO 105) and life cycle costs for future helicopters while increasing performance (by improving the payload/empty weight ratio). Improvements in direct operating costs are achieved partly by better aerodynamics; wind tunnel tests revealed that the fuselage of the BO 108 has almost 30 per cent less drag than that of the BO 105. This is achieved by a 5° rotor installation angle (fuselage aerodynamics optimised to pitch position in cruising flight), optimised nose and tail configurations, and increased usable volume without enlargement of the frontal area (increased interior height, width and cargo volume, plus increased internal fuel capacity and equipment space). All essential dynamically loaded components are to be qualified to 3,000 h MTBR or 'on condition'.

The initial basic flight test programme using the first BO 108 prototype was completed by the end of March 1989, followed, after evaluation of the results, by testing within an extended flight envelope until the end of 1989. A second prototype featuring some modifications to the cabin and

MBB BK 117 M with pods of FZ-100 rockets mounted on cabin sides

TM 319 engines was expected to begin flight testing by the end of 1990. A third prototype may use PW205B/1s (see Power Plant).

TYPE: Four/five-seat experimental light helicopter.

ROTOR SYSTEM AND DRIVE: Four-blade FVW hingeless main rotor, with rigid cuffs to transmit pitch-change commands from hub to main blade section. Blades of glassfibre construction, with foam core; new DM-H3 and -H4 aerofoil sections, non-linear twist, and tapered transonic tips. Two-blade hingeless tail rotor with FEL (fibre-elastomeric bearings in hub) and composite blades, mounted on port side of tail pylon. FVW tail rotor has been designed for later testing. Lightweight rotor drive chain. Transmission system of new flat design, with two-stage reduction gearing. ARIS (anti-resonance isolation system), providing dynamic separation of rotor/shaft transmission unit from airframe structure.

AIRFRAME: Constructed mainly of Kevlar/carbonfibre sandwich composites, except for aluminium alloy sidewalls, pod lower module and cabin floor, tailboom and around cargo area, and some titanium components in region of engine bay. Composites horizontal stabiliser with endplate fins.

LANDING GEAR: Skid type, inclined rearward by 1°.

POWER PLANT: First prototype has two 335.5 kW (450 shp) class Allison 250-C20R-3 turboshafts, mounted side by side above cabin. Second prototype will be fitted with Turbomeca TM 319-1Bs. Other engines could be Pratt & Whitney Canada PW205B/1s, as may be installed in a third BO 108 prototype. Two separate cooling systems, fans and oil reservoirs. Large volume for fuel in underfloor tanks.

ACCOMMODATION: Four/five persons on crashproof seats. Forward hinged doors for crew. Sliding doors for passengers. Rear of pod clamshell doors for bulky items/cargo; flights permissible with clamshell doors removed. Unobstructed cabin interior. Rear loading cargo volume 1.60 m³ (56.50 cu ft). Total cabin volume 5.00 m³ (176.57 cu ft).

SYSTEMS: Redundant electrical supply systems to FAR Pt 29 standards (2 × 260 kW continuous operation). Fully redundant dual hydraulic system attached to main rotor transmission with integrated SAS input.

AVIONICS: IFR capability. Provisions for integrated weather radar. Radio/nav systems. Future developments can include liquid-crystal display flat panel instrumentation, centralised data dialogue systems and appropriate computers, and GPS.

DIMENSIONS, EXTERNAL:
Main rotor diameter	10.00 m (32 ft 9¾ in)
Tail rotor diameter	1.90 m (6 ft 2¾ in)
Distance between rotor centres	6.148 m (20 ft 2½ in)
Length, incl main and tail rotors	10.637 m (34 ft 10½ in)
Length of fuselage	9.525 m (31 ft 3 in)
Length of fuselage pod	5.816 m (19 ft 1 in)
Height to top of main rotor head	3.062 m (10 ft 0¾ in)
Width of fuselage	1.50 m (4 ft 11 in)
Tailplane span	2.347 m (7 ft 8½ in)
Width over skids	2.20 m (7 ft 2¾ in)

WEIGHTS:
Weight empty	1,225 kg (2,700 lb)
Max T-O weight	2,400 kg (5,291 lb)

PERFORMANCE (at max T-O weight, at 1,500 m; 4,920 ft altitude):
Max cruising speed	approx 146 knots (270 km/h; 168 mph)
Econ cruising speed	445 knots (240 km/h; 149 mph)
Max rate of climb	552 m (1,810 ft)/min
Hovering ceiling: IGE	3,850-5,000 m (12,630-16,400 ft)
OGE	3,350 m (11,000 ft)
Range with max fuel	431 nm (800 km; 497 miles)
Max endurance, no reserves	4 h 45 min

First prototype of the MBB BO 108 experimental light helicopter

General arrangement of the BO 108 (two Allison 250-C20R-3 turboshafts) *(Pilot Press)*

MBB F-4F ICE PROGRAMME

Under a German Defence Ministry programme known as ICE (improved combat effectiveness), 110 Luftwaffe F-4F Phantom IIs, primarily those of fighter wings JG 71 and JG 74, are to be upgraded to give them a lookdown/shootdown capability against multiple targets. The programme, for which MBB is the prime contractor, was initiated in late 1983 and reached the end of the definition phase some two years later. It entered the full scale development phase in December 1986, with first test flight scheduled for Summer 1989; redelivery of 'production' ICE Phantoms is planned to begin in November 1991.

Main ingredient of this retrofit programme involves replacement of the existing Westinghouse AN/APQ-120 radar with the all-digital multi-mode Hughes AN/APG-65, built under licence in Germany by AEG. This advanced I-band system has 30 air-to-air and air-to-ground modes, with a ten-target track-while-scan capability, of which eight can be displayed simultaneously. AN/APG-65 subsystems include a low sidelobe planar array antenna, a 16-bit (250K) memory, receiver-exciter containing the analog-to-digital converter, liquid-cooled transmitter, LCU heat exchanger,

and a fully software programmable signal processor with advanced ECCM. Armament capability of the ICE Phantoms will be extended to include up to four Hughes AIM-120 (AMRAAM) air-to-air missiles. Other new avionics in the full ICE package are to include a new AEG radar control console, optimisation (by Hughes) of the cockpit display, installation of a new Litef digital fire control computer, Honeywell H-423 laser inertial platform, GEC Avionics CPU-143/A digital air data computer, new IFF system, a Frazer-Nash AMRAAM launcher, a

MIL-1553B digital databus with advanced operational software, and improved resistance to electronic jamming and other countermeasures.

A further 40 Luftwaffe F-4Fs, serving in the fighter-bomber role with JaboGs 35 and 36, were to undergo partial update (databus, INS and ADC only, initially), with the option of a full ICE installation later. Deliveries were expected to begin in May 1990.

DEUTSCHE AIRBUS GmbH
PO Box 950109, Kreetslag 10, 2103 Hamburg 95
Telephone: 49 (40) 7437 1
Telex: 21950-0 MBBH D
WORKS: Hamburg-Finkenwerder, Bremen, Einswarden, Varel, Lemwerder and Stade
DIRECTOR, PUBLIC RELATIONS: Josef Grendel

MBB VFW 614 ATTAS
A twin-turbofan VFW 614 transport (s/n G-017, D-ADAM) was converted for use by the DLR research establishment in developing and evaluating future flight control concepts for civil air transports. Details of the modifications and the planned programme appeared in the 1989-90 *Jane's.*

EXTRA

EXTRA-FLUGZEUGBAU GmbH
Flugplatz Dinslaken, 4224 Hünxe
Telephone: 49 (2858) 6851
MANAGING DIRECTOR: Walter Extra

EXTRA 230
This single-seat aerobatic monoplane was designed by Walter Extra for high performance competition work. First flight was made on 14 July 1983 by the second aircraft (D-EJNC), with the first (D-EKEW) following shortly after. The third Extra 230 (D-EHLE) was purchased by members of the Swiss national aerobatic team. A considerable number of completed aircraft have since been sold, plus a smaller number in kit form.

TYPE: Single-seat aerobatic aircraft.

WINGS: Cantilever mid-wing monoplane. Tapered wings, with square-cut tips and thick trailing-edge. Root and tip aerofoil sections of MA 15S and MA 12S respectively, resulting in a wing with virtually no curvature except on leading-edge. Incidence 0°. Structure comprises a box spar of high strength Polish pine, with pine capstrips and 'solid' ribs, covered with birch plywood and doped with an acrylic urethane paint. Long span ailerons (±26° deflection) occupy approx three-quarters of each trailing-edge. No flaps.

FUSELAGE: Steel tube mainframe, with aluminium alloy skin at front and on top-decking. Rear section covering is Ceconite.

TAIL UNIT: Conventional wire braced structure of steel tube and bent sheet metal ribs; all parts fabric covered. Horn balanced rudder. Trim tab and servo tab in elevators. All control surfaces ±26° deflection.

LANDING GEAR: Non-retractable tailwheel type, with main-wheel units essentially similar to those of Christen Pitts Special, and Haigh steerable tailwheel. Mainwheel fairings optional.

POWER PLANT: One 149 kW (200 hp) Textron Lycoming AEIO-360-A1E flat-four engine (DeMars modification). Mühlbauer two-blade constant-speed propeller, with composites-skinned wooden blades, McCauley hub, and large spinner. 12V battery for electric engine starting. Fuel capacity 80 litres (21.1 US gallons; 17.5 Imp gallons).

ACCOMMODATION: Single seat, under one-piece canopy which opens sideways to starboard.

DIMENSIONS, EXTERNAL:

Wing span	7.40 m (24 ft 3⅓ in)
Length overall	5.82 m (19 ft 1¼ in)
Height overall	1.73 m (5 ft 8¼ in)

UK-registered Extra 230, sponsored by Jaguar Cars *(Dr Alan Beaumont)*

WEIGHTS:

Weight empty	440 kg (970 lb)
Max T-O weight	560 kg (1,234 lb)

PERFORMANCE:

Never-exceed speed	220 knots (407 km/h; 253 mph)
Max level speed	190 knots (352 km/h; 218 mph) IAS
Stalling speed	38 knots (71 km/h; 44 mph) IAS
Max rate of climb at S/L	900 m (2,950 ft)/min
Roll rate at 160 knots (296 km/h; 184 mph) IAS	200°/s
T-O run	50 m (164 ft)
Endurance with max fuel	2 h 30 min
g limits	±10

EXTRA 300
The latest aerobatic aircraft from Walter Extra is the two-seat Extra 300, the design of which started in January 1987. Construction of a prototype began that August, and this aircraft (D-EAEW) was first flown on 6 May 1988. Although the general configuration remains similar to the Extra 230, the new and larger aircraft introduces important changes. Still using the familiar steel tube fuselage structure with aluminium alloy and fabric covering, the wings use

carbonfibre for the box spars, caps, webs and honeycomb sandwich skins. The tail surfaces are mostly glassfibre, with carbonfibre spar caps and elevators. Trim tab on starboard elevator. Mainwheels size 5.00-5, on glassfibre legs. Parker hydraulic disc brakes. Power is provided by a 224 kW (300 hp) Textron Lycoming AEIO-540-L1B5D engine, driving a Mühlbauer MTU-9-B-C/C200-15 three-blade constant-speed propeller with large spinner. Fuel capacity is 120 litres (31.7 US gallons; 26.4 Imp gallons) in wing tanks plus a 40 litre (10.6 US gallon; 8.8 Imp gallon) fuselage tank. Standard equipment includes a Becker AR 3201 com.

Series production began in July 1988. On 2 November 1989 the Chilean Air Force received the first two of six Extra 300s purchased to replace Pitts Specials of the Halcónes High Aerobatics Team.

Known technical details follow:

TYPE: Two-seat aerobatic aircraft.

DIMENSIONS, EXTERNAL:

Wing span	8.00 m (26 ft 3 in)
Wing chord: at root	1.25 m (4 ft 1¼ in)
at tip	0.83 m (2 ft 8¾ in)
Wing aspect ratio	6
Length overall	7.28 m (23 ft 10½ in)
Height overall	2.62 m (8 ft 7¼ in)
Tailplane span	3.20 m (10 ft 6 in)
Wheelbase	1.80 m (5 ft 11 in)
Propeller ground clearance	2.00 m (6 ft 6¾ in)

AREA:

Wings, gross	10.72 m² (115.4 sq ft)

WEIGHTS AND LOADINGS:

Weight empty	630 kg (1,389 lb)
Max T-O weight: Aerobatic	820 kg (1,808 lb)
Normal	905 kg (1,995 lb)
Max wing loading	84.4 kg/m² (17.29 lb/sq ft)
Max power loading	4.04 kg/kW (6.65 lb/hp)

PERFORMANCE:

Never-exceed speed	220 knots (407 km/h; 253 mph)
Max level speed	185 knots (343 km/h; 213 mph)
Max cruising speed	170 knots (315 km/h; 196 mph)
Stalling speed	58 knots (108 km/h; 67 mph)
Max rate of climb at S/L	1,005 m (3,300 ft)/min
T-O to 15 m (50 ft)	approx 250 m (820 ft)
Landing from 15 m (50 ft)	about 450 m (1,476 ft)
g limits	±10 Aerobatic

Extra 300 two-seat aerobatic aircraft of the Chilean Air Force's Halcónes display team *(Kenneth Munson)*

FFT

FFT GESELLSCHAFT FÜR FLUGZEUG- UND FASERVERBUND-TECHNOLOGIE mbH

PO Box 85, Flugplatz, 7947 Mengen
Telephone: 49 (7572) 6050
Telex: 732 543 SCAV D
Fax: 49 (7572) 605400
PRESIDENT: Dipl-Ing Justus Dornier
MANAGING DIRECTOR: Joachim Rechtsteiner
VICE-PRESIDENT, MARKETING: Dipl-Ing Gunter Merz
CHIEF ENGINEER: Dipl-Ing Rudolf Voit-Nitschmann

Dipl-Ing Peter Krauss and Herr Jörg Elzenbeck built, and in April 1977 flew for the first time, the first Rutan VariEze two-seat homebuilt aircraft to be completed in Europe (D-EEEZ). They decided to develop, manufacture and market a similar aircraft, known as the Speed Canard, as a ready to fly, certificated production aircraft that would conform to the requirements of FAR Pt 23. In August 1978, with Dipl-Ing Wolfgang Schiller, they formed Gyroflug, called FFT, as above, since 1989. At the end of 1984 the company became a member of the Justus Dornier Group. In September 1987 Gyroflug moved to its present location in Mengen, where a new factory complex was built. The 80 person workforce moved into its new production quarters in May 1988.

In late 1988 Gyroflug signed an agreement with Litton Industries of the USA covering the use of the Speed Canard as a platform for an Advanced Tactical Surveillance System (ATSS). Three demonstration aircraft have been completed and an RPV version is under development. A second agreement with TRW-ESL (USA) and Dornier Luftfahrt GmbH (West Germany), signed in 1989, covers the integration of a comint payload in the SC 01 B-160 platform, named Light Aircraft Surveillance System (LASS). One prototype system, including ground station, is in operation.

In 1989 all design and development of the FFA-2000 (Switzerland), as described in the 1989-90 *Jane's*, was transferred to FFT. The programme was renamed Eurotrainer 2000.

FFT SC 01 B SPEED CANARD

As well as being slightly larger overall than the Rutan VariEze, the Speed Canard differs in a number of important details, as noted in the 1987-88 *Jane's*. Wings and other GFRP/CFRP components, manufactured initially by Glaser-Dirks, are now produced by FFT.

Construction of the first prototype (D-EEEX, c/n A-1) began in late 1978, and this aircraft first flew on 2 December 1980. Initial test flights revealed the need for a number of design changes before it could be approved for series production. Of these, the principal one was the adoption of a new Eppler aerofoil section, and a new 'first' flight with this modified wing was made by D-EEEX on 10 July 1981. A second airframe was completed for static testing, followed by a second flying prototype (D-EEEW, c/n A-3), which made its initial flight on 17 April 1983 and enabled the Speed Canard to receive German LBA type certification on 30 September that year.

Series production began with the fourth aircraft (D-EELZ, c/n S-4), and 20 examples of this initial version were built by September 1985 for customers in Germany (17), Switzerland (2), and Belgium (1). As built with the standard O-235 engine, they are designated **SC-01**; some examples have been retrofitted with the more powerful O-320 engine, in which form they are known as the **SC 01-160** and described in *Jane's 1987-88*.

Beginning with c/n S-24, current production models are designated **SC 01 B** (O-235 engine) and **SC 01 B-160** (O-320 engine). These versions, which first flew in the Summer of 1985 and received LBA certification on 26 March 1986, have winglets of increased area, plus other minor improvements. A number of earlier Speed Canards have also been modified to the current B/B-160 standard. A **GT** version of the SC 01 B-160 was introduced in 1987; this has VFR avionics as standard.

The Speed Canard is certificated in France, West Germany, Switzerland, Scandinavia, UK, USA and the Benelux countries. A total of 50 B/B-160s had been ordered by January 1990.

TYPE: Two-seat sporting and surveillance aircraft.
WINGS: Cantilever mid-wing monoplane. Short-span centre-section strakes, sweptback approx 60° on leading-edges, without anhedral or dihedral. Main wings have an Eppler E793 aerofoil section, with 15.6 per cent thickness/chord ratio, anhedral angle of 5° 54', and 22° sweepback at quarter-chord. Single-spar structure of GFRP and CFRP, without ribs. Each wingtip is upswept at nearly 90° to form a slightly outward canted NASA type winglet with inset rudder. Centrally located aileron in each wing trailing-edge. No flaps. No aileron or rudder tabs. Main wings are detachable for transportation and storage.
FOREPLANE: Narrow-chord cantilever structure, of Eppler E1231 aerofoil section, mounted high on nose. Balanced elevator, with fixed tab near inboard end, on each trailing-edge. Construction (GFRP and CFRP) similar to that of wings.
FUSELAGE: Non-pressurised oval-section nacelle type, of GFRP composites construction.
LANDING GEAR: Tricycle type, with fixed main units and

FFT SC 01 B-160 M LASS demonstrator

electrically retractable nosewheel which is carried on a carbon/Kevlar strut moulded to conform to the outside contour of the fuselage, eliminating need for a fairing door. Main units, carried on cantilever self-sprung carbon/Kevlar struts, are fitted with Cleveland wheels (tyre size 5.00-5), Cleveland disc brakes, and speed fairings. The Scott nosewheel, which retracts rearward, is fitted with a size 10 × 3.5-4 tyre. Nosewheel strut is hinged to allow aircraft to be parked in a kneeling position with only the wheel exposed.
POWER PLANT (SC 01 B): One 86.5 kW (116 hp) Textron Lycoming O-235-P2A flat-four engine, mounted in the rear fuselage and driving a Hoffmann HO-V113B-L/LD 150+2A three (composites)-blade constant-speed pusher propeller with spinner. Fuel in two integral tanks (one in each wing centre-section strake) with combined capacity of 160 litres (42.3 US gallons; 35.2 Imp gallons). Oil capacity 6 litres (1.58 US gallons; 1.32 Imp gallons).
POWER PLANT (SC 01 B-160): One 119 kW (160 hp) Textron Lycoming O-320-D1A flat-four engine, driving an MT-Propeller (Mühlbauer) MTV-6-C/LD 152-07 three-blade constant-speed propeller. Fuel capacity as for lower powered version. Oil capacity 8 litres (2.11 US gallons; 1.76 Imp gallons).
ACCOMMODATION: Pilot and passenger in tandem, on semi-reclining seats in individual cockpits. Side-stick controls. Separate one-piece moulded canopies, both opening sideways to starboard. Space for 15 kg (33 lb) of baggage aft of rear seat. Both cockpits heated and ventilated.
ELECTRICAL SYSTEM: Alternator to provide power to actuate nosewheel extension/retraction mechanism.
AVIONICS AND EQUIPMENT: To customer's requirements except for GT, which has VFR instrumentation as standard. Can be equipped to full IFR standard, including autopilot, two com/nav, ILS, ADF, artificial horizon, turn and bank indicator and heading gyro.
DIMENSIONS, EXTERNAL:

Wing span	7.77 m (25 ft 6 in)
Foreplane span	3.60 m (11 ft 9¾ in)
Foreplane chord, constant	0.34 m (1 ft 1¾ in)
Wing aspect ratio	7.7
Foreplane aspect ratio	10.6
Length overall	4.70 m (15 ft 5 in)
Fuselage: Length	4.40 m (14 ft 5¼ in)
Max width	0.74 m (2 ft 5 in)
Max depth	1.06 m (3 ft 5¾ in)
Height overall	1.81 m (5 ft 11¼ in)
Wheel track	1.66 m (5 ft 5¼ in)
Wheelbase	2.47 m (8 ft 1¼ in)
Propeller diameter	1.52 m (5 ft 0 in)
Propeller ground clearance	0.31 m (1 ft 0¼ in)

DIMENSIONS, INTERNAL:

Cockpits: Max combined length	2.80 m (9 ft 2¼ in)

Max width	0.64 m (2 ft 1¼ in)
Max height	0.99 m (3 ft 3 in)

AREAS:

Wings, gross	7.84 m² (84.39 sq ft)
Foreplane, gross	1.22 m² (13.13 sq ft)
Ailerons (total)	0.376 m² (4.05 sq ft)
Winglets (total)	2.20 m² (23.68 sq ft)
Rudders (total)	0.168 m² (1.81 sq ft)
Elevators (total, incl tabs)	0.33 m² (3.55 sq ft)

WEIGHTS AND LOADINGS (A: with O-235, B: with O-320 engine):

Weight empty: A	420 kg (926 lb)
B	440 kg (970 lb)
Max fuel: A, B	115 kg (253 lb)
Max payload with 100 litres (26.4 US gallons) fuel: A	188 kg (414.5 lb)
B	204 kg (450 lb)
Max T-O weight: A	680 kg (1,499 lb)
B	715 kg (1,576 lb)
Max landing weight: A, B	680 kg (1,499 lb)
Max wing/foreplane loading:	
A	75.05 kg/m² (15.38 lb/sq ft)
B	78.92 kg/m² (16.16 lb/sq ft)
Max power loading: A	7.86 kg/kW (12.92 lb/hp)
B	6.01 kg/kW (9.85 lb/hp)

PERFORMANCE (at max T-O weight, A and B as above):

Never-exceed speed:	
A, B	197 knots (365 km/h; 226 mph) IAS
Max level speed at S/L:	
A	146 knots (270 km/h; 168 mph)
B	159 knots (295 km/h; 183 mph)
Max cruising speed, 75% power:	
A at 1,830 m (6,000 ft)	143 knots (265 km/h; 165 mph)
B at 2,135 m (7,000 ft)	154 knots (285 km/h; 177 mph) IAS
Econ cruising speed, 65% power:	
A at 3,050 m (10,000 ft)	138 knots (257 km/h; 160 mph)
B at 3,350 m (11,000 ft)	148 knots (275 km/h; 171 mph)
Stalling speed: A, B	57 knots (105 km/h; 66 mph) IAS
Max rate of climb at S/L: A	300 m (985 ft)/min
B	396 m (1,300 ft)/min
Service ceiling: A	4,420 m (14,500 ft)
B	5,640 m (18,500 ft)
T-O run: A	450 m (1,475 ft)
B	350 m (1,150 ft)
T-O to 15 m (50 ft): A	700 m (2,300 ft)
B	540 m (1,770 ft)
Landing from 15 m (50 ft): A, B	700 m (2,300 ft)
Landing run: A, B	300 m (985 ft)
Range with max fuel, no reserves:	
55% power: A	1,025 nm (1,900 km; 1,180 miles)
B	815 nm (1,510 km; 938 miles)

Model of the FFT Eurotrainer 2000

Range at S/L with max fuel, 45 min reserves:

75% power: A		728 nm (1,350 km; 839 miles)
B		553 nm (1,025 km; 637 miles)
45% power: A		1,011 nm (1,875 km; 1,165 miles)
B		715 nm (1,325 km; 823 miles)
g limits: A		+4.4/–2.2
B		+3.8/–2.2

FFT EUROTRAINER 2000

On 25 April 1988 FFA announced the receipt of a contract from Swissair for eight trainers of advanced design, designated FFA-2000 (now Eurotrainer 2000), to replace the Piaggio P.149s of the airline's flying school, which have been in service for 25 years. The airline has an option on a further four of these trainers. Development began in 1987, with design assistance from the Swiss ALR group (see 1987-88 *Jane's*). Development has been taken over by FFT, and the first flight is scheduled for late 1990. Delivery of the first aircraft to Swissair is scheduled for early 1992.

The prototypes and the eight aircraft for Swissair's civil aviation flying school (SLS) will be powered by the 182.7 kW (245 hp) Porsche turbocharged PFM 3200-T03, which produces extremely low noise and pollution. The aircraft will sustain +6/–3 g and high-stress parts of the glassfibre airframe are reinforced with carbonfibre. A Christen-type fuel and oil system will permit negative-g manoeuvres.

TYPE: Two/four-seat training and touring aircraft, capable of limited aerobatics.

WINGS: Cantilever low-wing monoplane. Horstmann-Quast advanced laminar wing section, with thickness/chord ratio of 16 per cent. Dihedral 6° 30′ from roots. Fail-safe structure of composites (mainly glassfibre), including ailerons and Fowler trailing-edge flaps. No tabs.

FUSELAGE: Conventional structure, constructed of same materials as wings.

TAIL UNIT: Conventional structure, built in same way as wings. Fixed incidence tailplane. Trim tab in rudder and each elevator.

LANDING GEAR: Hydraulically retractable tricycle type, with single wheel on each unit. Mainwheels retract inward, nosewheel rearward.

POWER PLANT: One 182.7 kW (245 hp) Porsche PFM 3200-T03 turbocharged engine, driving a constant-speed, three-blade Mühlbauer composite propeller. Fuel capacity 260 litres (68.7 US gallons; 57.2 Imp gallons).

ACCOMMODATION: Seats for two or four persons, in pairs, under one-piece forward-hinged canopy. Dual controls and pedal brakes standard. Baggage space aft of seats. Cockpit heated and ventilated.

AVIONICS AND EQUIPMENT: From simple VFR to dual control IFR, according to customer's requirements.

DIMENSIONS, EXTERNAL:

Wing span	10.38 m (34 ft 0¾ in)
Wing aspect ratio	7.7
Length overall	8.14 m (26 ft 8½ in)
Height overall	3.20 m (10 ft 6 in)
Elevator span	3.87 m (12 ft 8½ in)
Propeller diameter	2.10 m (6 ft 10¾ in)

AREA:

Wings, gross	14.00 m² (150.7 sq ft)

WEIGHT AND LOADINGS:

Max T-O weight	1,480 kg (3,262 lb)
Max wing loading	105.7 kg/m² (21.6 lb/sq ft)
Max power loading	8.1 kg/kW (13.31 lb/hp)

PERFORMANCE (estimated, at two-seat trainer T-O weight):

Max level speed at S/L	more than 170 knots (315 km/h; 196 mph)
Max cruising speed at 6,100 m (20,000 ft)	218 knots (404 km/h; 251 mph)
Econ cruising speed (65% power) at S/L	160 knots (296 km/h; 184 mph)
Rate of climb at 600 m (1,970 ft)	366 m (1,200 ft)/min
Service ceiling	7,925 m (26,000 ft)
T-O to 15 m (50 ft) at 600 m (1,970 ft)	500 m (1,640 ft)
Endurance, with 45 min reserves	4 h

GROB

BURKHART GROB LUFT- UND RAUMFAHRT GmbH & Co KG
(Division of Grob-Werke GmbH & Co KG)

Postfach 1257, 8948 Mindelheim
Telephone: 49 (8268) 9980
Telex: 5 39 623
Fax: 49 (8268) 998-14 or 998-24
CHAIRMAN: Dr hc Dipl-Ing Burkhart Grob
DEPUTY CHAIRMAN:
Dipl-Ing Klaus Harald Fischer

Grob was founded in 1972, employs about 180 people, and has built about 3,500 aircraft.

The name of the company was changed from Burkhart Grob Flugzeugbau to Burkhart Grob Luft- und Raumfahrt GmbH, with the aviation activities divided into light and heavy aircraft sections. In addition to the G 115, G 116 and GF 200 programmes, further batches of gliders were put in hand (see Sailplanes).

Grob's 'heavy aircraft' section is also concerned with development of the Egrett-1, described in the International section. The company co-operates with the Weltraum-Institut Berlin space institute on programmes concerned with microgravity and other space research.

GROB G 115

The first prototype of this light aircraft made its initial flight in November 1985, powered by an O-235 engine with fixed-pitch propeller. The second prototype, which flew in the Spring of 1986, was similarly powered, but had a constant-speed propeller, a taller fin and rudder and relocated tailplane. The latter version is now in production as the **G 115-A**. The third prototype, first flown in 1986, represented the **G 115-B**, having an uprated (O-320) engine. The production version with an O-320-E2A engine is known as the **G 115-C**.

The G 115-A was certificated to FAR Pt 23 standards by the LBA on 31 March 1987 and by the British CAA in May 1988. The G 115 later gained full public transport certification and then LBA spinning approval. This has allowed the company to plan a 119 kW (160 hp) model for 1990, and then an aerobatic version with a 134 kW (180 hp) engine as the Sport-Acro. New models will feature control columns in place of present yokes. Deliveries of production aircraft began in mid-1987. Most are G 115-As. The G 115-C has glider towing capability.

TYPE: Two-seat light aircraft.

WINGS: Cantilever low-wing monoplane. Wing section Eppler E 696. Dihedral 5°. Incidence 2°. Ailerons and flaps; anti-servo tab on port flap deleted from current models. GFRP construction.

FUSELAGE: Conventional GFRP structure.

TAIL UNIT: Conventional GFRP structure, with tailplane, elevators (trim tab on port elevator), fin and horn balanced rudder.

LANDING GEAR: Non-retractable tricycle type, with wheel fairings. Steerable nosewheel, size 5.00-5. Mainwheels size 6.00-5. Cantilever spring suspension. Hydraulic toe-operated brakes. Parking brake.

POWER PLANT: One 85.8 kW (115 hp) Textron Lycoming O-235-H2C flat-four engine in G 115-A, driving a Hoffmann HO 14-175 120 two-blade fixed-pitch propeller with spinner; 86.5 kW (116 hp) O-235-P1 and constant-speed propeller optional. One 112 kW (150 hp) Textron Lycoming O-320-E2A with constant-speed propeller in G 115-C. Fuel capacity 100 litres (26.4 US gallons; 22 Imp gallons). Oil capacity for O-235 engine 5.7 litres (1.5 US gallons; 1.25 Imp gallons).

ACCOMMODATION: Two seats side by side under one-piece rearward sliding framed canopy, with dual controls.

Four-seat Grob G 116 (Textron Lycoming IO-360 engine) *(Peter F. Selinger)*

Grob GF 200 projected all-composites four-seat light aircraft *(Jane's/Mike Keep)*

Baggage space behind seats, with restraining net. Heating.

SYSTEMS: Electrical, with 14V battery. Hydraulic system for brakes only.

AVIONICS: To customer's requirements. Instrument panel will accommodate full IFR instrumentation. Optional avionics include VOR nav system, ADF 2079 with indicator and ATC 2000 transponder.

DIMENSIONS, EXTERNAL:

Wing span	10.00 m (32 ft 9½ in)
Wing aspect ratio	8.19
Length overall	7.36 m (24 ft 1¾ in)
Height overall: A	2.75 m (9 ft 0¼ in)
C	2.82 m (9 ft 3 in)
Wheel track: A, C	1.61 m (5 ft 3½ in)
Wheelbase: A, C	2.50 m (8 ft 2½ in)

AREA:

Wings, gross	12.21 m² (131.43 sq ft)

WEIGHTS AND LOADINGS (Normal category):

Basic weight empty: A	590 kg (1,301 lb)
C	620 kg (1,367 lb)
Fuel weight: A, C	72 kg (159 lb)
Max T-O and landing weight: A, C	850 kg (1,874 lb)
Max wing loading: A, C	69.61 kg/m² (14.26 lb/sq ft)

Max power loading:

A (115 hp)	9.91 kg/kW (16.30 lb/hp)
A (116 hp)	9.83 kg/kW (16.15 lb/hp)
C	8.04 kg/kW (13.23 lb/hp)

PERFORMANCE (at max T-O weight):

Max level speed: A	119 knots (220 km/h; 137 mph)
C	135 knots (250 km/h; 155 mph)

Cruising speed, 75% power:

A	110 knots (205 km/h; 127 mph)
C	120 knots (222 km/h; 138 mph)
Stalling speed: A	45 knots (83 km/h; 52 mph)
C	47 knots (87 km/h; 54 mph)
Max rate of climb at S/L: A	210 m (690 ft)/min
C	305 m (1,000 ft)/min
T-O run: A	250 m (820 ft)
C	210 m (690 ft)
T-O to 15 m (50 ft): A	420 m (1,378 ft)
C	390 m (1,280 ft)

Grob G 115-A two-seat light aircraft *(Peter F. Selinger)*

Range with max fuel (approx):	
A	540 nm (1,000 km; 621 miles)
C	394 nm (730 km; 453 miles)
g limits: Normal	+3.8/−1.52
Utility	+4.4/−1.76

GROB G 116

The G 116 is essentially a four-seat (2 + 2) version of the G 115, with a higher powered engine. The prototype (D-EGRF) had flown for about 30 hours since 29 April 1988 when development and certification were suspended for the present, in favour of the GF 200.

POWER PLANT: One 149 kW (200 hp) Textron Lycoming IO-360 flat-four engine, driving a three-blade propeller with spinner. Fuel capacity 200 litres (52.8 US gallons; 44 Imp gallons).

DIMENSIONS, EXTERNAL:

Wing span	11.00 m (36 ft 1 in)
Wing aspect ratio	7.8
Length overall	8.00 m (26 ft 3 in)
Height overall	3.00 m (9 ft 10 in)

AREA:

Wings, gross	15.50 m² (166.8 sq ft)

WEIGHTS AND LOADINGS:

Weight empty	710 kg (1,565 lb)
Fuel weight	144 kg (317 lb)
Max T-O weight	1,198 kg (2,641 lb)
Max wing loading	77.3 kg/m² (15.83 lb/sq ft)
Max power loading	8.93 kg/kW (14.67 lb/hp)

PERFORMANCE (estimated, at max T-O weight):

Max level speed	148 knots (274 km/h; 170 mph)
Cruising speed, 75% power	
	132 knots (245 km/h; 152 mph)
Stalling speed	49 knots (91 km/h; 57 mph)
Max rate of climb at S/L	300 m (985 ft)/min
T-O run	265 m (869 ft)
T-O to 15 m (50 ft)	410 m (1,345 ft)
Range with max fuel	539 nm (1,000 km; 621 miles)

GROB GF 200

Grob announced this new four-seat all-composites high-performance aircraft in early 1988, displaying a full size mockup that May at the Hanover Air Show. The aircraft will have a pressurised cabin, a choice of a Porsche PFM 3200-N03 or -T03 flat-six engine (162 kW; 217 hp or 180 kW; 241 hp respectively), three-blade pusher propeller, and standard fuel capacity of 250 litres (66 US gallons; 55 Imp gallons) in integral wing tanks. Optional long-range tanks (combined capacity 340 litres; 90 US gallons; 74.8 Imp gallons) will be available for the turbocharged version.

General appearance of the GF 200 is shown in the accompanying three-view drawing.

DIMENSIONS, EXTERNAL:

Wing span	9.60 m (31 ft 6 in)
Wing aspect ratio	6.4
Length overall	8.25 m (27 ft 0¾ in)
Height overall	3.20 m (10 ft 6 in)
Cabin door: Height	1.20 m (3 ft 11¼ in)
Width	0.60 m (1 ft 11½ in)

DIMENSIONS, INTERNAL:

Cabin: Max width	1.22 m (4 ft 0 in)
Max height	1.20 m (3 ft 11¼ in)

AREA:

Wings, gross	14.40 m² (155.0 sq ft)

WEIGHTS:

Basic weight empty	850 kg (1,874 lb)
Max fuel weight	180 kg (397 lb)
Max T-O weight	1,350 kg (2,976 lb)

PERFORMANCE (at max T-O weight: T 03 engine and normal fuel capacity, unless stated otherwise):

Max level speed at 6,700 m (22,000 ft)	
	218 knots (404 km/h; 251 mph)
Max cruising speed at 5,485 m (18,000 ft), 75% power	
	195 knots (361 km/h; 224 mph)
Cruising speed, 65% power	
	188 knots (348 km/h; 216 mph)
Econ cruising speed at 5,485 m (18,000 ft), 55% power	
	175 knots (324 km/h; 201 mph)
Max rate of climb at S/L	396 m (1,300 ft)/min
Service ceiling	8,535 m (28,000 ft)
T-O run	290 m (950 ft)
T-O to 15 m (50 ft)	450 m (1,476 ft)
Landing from 15 m (50 ft)	480 m (1,575 ft)
Landing run	220 m (722 ft)
Range at 5,485 m (18,000 ft), 75% power, with 340 litres of fuel	1,274 nm (2,361 km; 1,467 miles)

GYROFLUG — *see FFT*

HOFFMANN
WOLF HOFFMANN FLUGZEUGBAU KG
Sportflugplatz, D-8870 Günzburg/Ulm
Telephone: 49 (8221) 1417
Telex: 531625 HOFBG D
Fax: 49 (8221) 32034
DIRECTOR: Dipl-Ing Wolf D. Hoffmann

Mr Hoffmann, designer of the Dimona motor glider (see Sailplanes section), has developed a two-seat light aircraft known as the H 40.

HOFFMANN H 40

Design of the H 40 began in January 1986 and construction started in August 1987. The first of two prototypes (D-EIOF) was exhibited at the Hanover Air Show in May 1988 and flew for the first time on 28 August 1988. The H 40 was then modified to meet FAR Pt 23 requirements (Normal category), first flying in this form on 8 February 1990.

TYPE: Two-seat light aircraft.

WINGS: Cantilever low-wing monoplane. Wortmann FX-63-137 section. Dihedral 4°. Incidence 2°. Sweepforward 3° at quarter-chord. Carbonfibre single-spar structure, with glassfibre and PVC foam sandwich skins. Carbonfibre ailerons and trailing-edge split flaps. No tabs.

FUSELAGE: Glassfibre/carbonfibre semi-monocoque structure using bulkheads, with sandwich tailboom of same materials.

TAIL UNIT: Cantilever T tail, of similar CFRP/GFRP sandwich construction to wings. Fixed incidence tailplane. Trim tab in elevator.

LANDING GEAR: Non-retractable tricycle type, with steel plate spring shock absorption on main units. All units have Cleveland wheels and Goodyear tyres, size 380 × 150 (6.00-5) on main gear, 40-78 (5.00-5) on nose unit. Cleveland 30-5 mainwheel brakes.

POWER PLANT: One 86.5 kW (116 hp) Textron Lycoming O-235-P2A engine, driving a Mühlbauer MTV-6-F/160-03 three-blade constant-speed propeller with spinner. Fuel in two wing tanks, combined capacity 100 litres (26.4 US gallons; 22 Imp gallons). Overwing gravity refuelling. Oil capacity 3.5 litres (0.92 US gallon; 0.77 Imp gallon).

ACCOMMODATION: Side by side seats for pilot and passenger. Gull wing window/doors, hinged on centreline and opening upward. Heated and ventilated. Baggage compartment.

AVIONICS: Options include Becker AR 3201 radio, Becker ATC 2000 transponder, and Becker NR 3301 VOR/LOC.

Prototype Hoffmann H 40 (Textron Lycoming O-235-P2A engine)

DIMENSIONS, EXTERNAL:

Wing span	10.84 m (35 ft 6¾ in)
Wing chord: at root	1.34 m (4 ft 4¾ in)
at tip	0.94 m (3 ft 1 in)
Wing aspect ratio	8.6
Length overall	6.99 m (22 ft 11¼ in)
Fuselage: Max width	1.20 m (3 ft 11¼ in)
Height overall	2.39 m (7 ft 10 in)
Tailplane span	3.00 m (9 ft 10 in)
Wheel track	2.00 m (6 ft 6¾ in)
Propeller diameter	1.60 m (5 ft 3 in)
Propeller ground clearance	0.20 m (8 in)

AREAS:

Wings, gross	13.62 m² (146.6 sq ft)
Ailerons (total)	0.912 m² (9.82 sq ft)
Trailing-edge flaps (total)	1.072 m² (11.54 sq ft)
Fin	1.17 m² (12.59 sq ft)
Rudder	0.47 m² (5.06 sq ft)
Tailplane	1.80 m² (19.38 sq ft)
Elevators (total)	0.54 m² (5.81 sq ft)

WEIGHTS AND LOADINGS (2nd prototype and production aircraft):

Basic weight empty	560 kg (1,235 lb)
Max fuel weight	72 kg (159 lb)
Max T-O weight	850 kg (1,874 lb)
Max wing loading	62.4 kg/m² (12.78 lb/sq ft)
Max power loading	9.83 kg/kW (16.16 lb/hp)

PERFORMANCE (71 kW; 95 hp Limbach L 2400 DB1 engine, at max T-O weight):

Never-exceed speed	148 knots (275 km/h; 171 mph)
Max cruising speed	113 knots (210 km/h; 130 mph)
Econ cruising speed	97 knots (180 km/h; 112 mph)
Stalling speed, power on, flaps up	
	42 knots (78 km/h; 49 mph)
Max rate of climb at S/L	240 m (787 ft)/min
Service ceiling	4,575 m (15,000 ft)
T-O and landing run	180 m (591 ft)
T-O to and landing from 15 m (50 ft)	290 m (951 ft)
Range with max fuel	647 nm (1,200 km; 745 miles)

RFB
RHEIN-FLUGZEUGBAU GmbH
(Subsidiary of MBB)

Flugplatz (Postfach 408), 4050 Mönchengladbach 1
Telephone: 49 (2161) 6820
Telex: 852 506
Fax: 49 (2161) 682200
OTHER WORKS: Lübeck-Blankensee and Hamburg
PRESIDENT: Dipl Ing Alfred Schneider
COMMERCIAL DIRECTOR AND VICE-PRESIDENT:
   Dipl Betriebsw Norbert Frentzen
CHIEF DESIGNER: Christoph Fischer
MARKETING MANAGER: Michael Specht

This company, founded in 1956, is an independent subsidiary of MBB. Its own former subsidiary, Elektro-Mechanischer Fluggerätebau of Hamburg, becoming a branch of RFB in 1981.

RFB specialises in the development and manufacture of airframe structural components, especially wings and fuselages made entirely of glassfibre reinforced plastics. Recent production has also included components and assemblies of light alloy, steel and GFRP for aircraft in quantity production by other West German companies, as well as spare parts and ground equipment.

Under contract to the West German government, RFB services military aircraft, and provides target towing flights and other services with special aircraft. It has Luftfahrt-Bundesamt (LBA) approval as an organisation for aircraft development, manufacture, maintenance and overhaul. It also operates a factory certificated service centre for Piper and Mitsubishi aircraft, as well as for Bendix, Becker and King avionics. General servicing of other types of all-metal aircraft is undertaken.

In the aircraft propulsion field, RFB has been engaged for many years in developing specialised applications for ducted propellers, one of which led to the Fantrainer multi-purpose training aircraft. In early 1990 it was reported that Fanstar Partners was expected to contract RFB to build two Fanstar 200 T civil aircraft prototypes (see US section).

RFB FANTRAINER 400 and 600

Early development history of the Fantrainer was given in the 1987-88 and previous editions of *Jane's*. There are two versions: the **Fantrainer 400**, powered by an Allison 250-C20B turboshaft, and the **Fantrainer 600**, which has an Allison 250-C30. About 92 per cent of the airframe is common to the 400 and the 600.

The first German built production Fantrainer, a 600, flew for the first time on 12 August 1984. This aircraft and one prototype were allocated to the certification programme, and LBA approval of the 600 was granted on 23 May 1985.

In August 1982 RFB received a contract covering the production of 31 Fantrainer 400s and 16 Fantrainer 600s for the Royal Thai Air Force. The first two aircraft were built in Germany and delivered to Thailand in October 1984; the remaining 45 were supplied in CKD form for assembly in Thailand by RTAF (which see), all kits having been delivered by RFB by early 1988. All Fantrainer 600s have light composite wings, the Fantrainer 400s having metal wings designed and manufactured by RTAF. The Fantrainer 600s began regular flight operations in January 1987, and all 16 are in service. Assembly of Fantrainer 400s will be completed in 1991. RTAF student pilots are now transferring directly from the Fantrainer to operational F-5 aircraft, without first being trained on a dedicated jet.

One Fantrainer 400 and two 600s underwent evaluation by the Luftwaffe in 1985, as a result of which some modifications were recommended, including a revised instrument layout. The airline Lufthansa has chosen the Fantrainer 600 to complement its training fleet, mainly to train instructors in aerobatics and special flight attitudes. RFB is also studying a possible **Fantrainer 1000** advanced trainer version with a 746 kW (1,000 shp) ducted fan. In early 1990 this remained a drawing board project only. A modified Fantrainer, named Fanranger, is being considered for the USAF/USN JPATS programme.

The following description applies to the Fantrainer 400 and 600 as built by RFB.

TYPE: Two-seat primary and basic training aircraft (IFR).
WINGS: Cantilever mid-wing monoplane. Wing section Eppler 502. Thickness/chord ratio 15.7 per cent. Dihedral 3°. No incidence. Sweepforward 2° 30′ at quarter-chord. Wings constructed of GFRP and plastics tube sandwich. Conventional ailerons and electrically actuated trailing-edge split flaps. Trim tab in port aileron.
FUSELAGE: The load-carrying fail-safe structure of the forward and centre-fuselage is of light alloy, with non-load-bearing GFRP skin, sections of which are removable for servicing purposes. Cruciform metal rear fuselage is connected to the centre-fuselage at three points. The integral fan duct is free of structural loads. Large airbrake on each side of fan duct, operation of which causes no lift or stability changes.
TAIL UNIT: All-metal T tail of light alloy, with conventional rudder and elevators. Trim tab in each elevator; rudder trim tab optional.
LANDING GEAR: Retractable tricycle type, with single wheel on each unit. Hydraulic actuation, with manual emergency extension. Fully castoring nosewheel retracts forward, main units inward and upward into wing roots.

RFB Fantrainer 600 operated by Lufthansa

RFB Fantrainer 600 (Allison 250-C30 turboshaft) *(Pilot Press)*

Steel tube legs, acting as torsional/bending springs. Cleveland mainwheels, size 15 × 6.00-6, tyre pressure 4.14 bars (60 lb/sq in). Goodyear nosewheel, size 5.00-5, tyre pressure 2.76 bars (40 lb/sq in). Cleveland wheel brakes.
POWER PLANT: One turboshaft, driving a Hoffmann five-blade constant-speed ducted fan. Fantrainer 400 has a 313 kW (420 shp) Allison 250-C20B, Fantrainer 600 a 485 kW (650 shp) Allison 250-C30. Air intakes above wings. Four integral fuel tanks in wings, with combined capacity of 480 litres (127 US gallons; 105.5 Imp gallons). Refuelling points in wing upper surface. Provision to carry 440 litres (116 US gallons; 97 Imp gallons) of auxiliary fuel externally. Oil capacity 16 litres (4.2 US gallons; 3.5 Imp gallons).
ACCOMMODATION: Two seats in tandem cockpit, meeting US MIL specifications in terms of dimensions and layout. Rear (instructor's) seat elevated 8 cm (3 in). Seats and rudder pedals adjustable. UPC (Stencel) Ranger zero/zero rocket assisted escape system standard; ejection seats optional. Fighter type side consoles. Canopy over each seat hinges sideways (to starboard) independently. Accommodation heated and ventilated.
SYSTEMS: Electrical system includes a starter/generator and battery. Hydraulic system for operation of landing gear and airbrakes.

DIMENSIONS, EXTERNAL:
Wing span	9.74 m (31 ft 11½ in)
Wing chord: at root	1.89 m (6 ft 2½ in)
at tip	1.02 m (3 ft 4 in)
Wing aspect ratio	6.8
Length overall: incl probe	9.48 m (31 ft 1¼ in)
excl probe	9.20 m (30 ft 2¼ in)
Height overall	3.16 m (10 ft 4½ in)
Tailplane span	3.59 m (11 ft 9½ in)
Wheel track	1.94 m (6 ft 4¼ in)
Wheelbase	3.89 m (12 ft 9 in)
Fan diameter	1.20 m (3 ft 11¼ in)

AREAS:
Wings, gross	14.00 m² (150.7 sq ft)
Ailerons (total)	1.68 m² (18.08 sq ft)
Trailing-edge flaps (total)	1.22 m² (13.13 sq ft)
Rudder, incl tab	0.87 m² (9.36 sq ft)
Tailplane	3.12 m² (33.58 sq ft)
Elevators, incl tabs	0.92 m² (9.90 sq ft)

WEIGHTS AND LOADINGS (A: Aerobatic; U: Utility category):
Weight empty: 400: A, U	1,114 kg (2,456 lb)
600: A, U	1,160 kg (2,557 lb)
Fuel weight: A	176 kg (388 lb)
U, internal fuel only	384 kg (847 lb)
U, with drop tanks	736 kg (1,623 lb)
Max T-O weight: 400: A	1,600 kg (3,527 lb)
U	1,800 kg (3,968 lb)
600: A	1,600 kg (3,527 lb)
U	2,300 kg (5,070 lb)
Max landing weight: 600: A	1,600 kg (3,527 lb)
U	2,000 kg (4,409 lb)
Max wing loading: 400	128.6 kg/m² (26.34 lb/sq ft)
600	164.3 kg/m² (33.65 lb/sq ft)
Max power loading: 400	5.75 kg/kW (9.45 lb/shp)
600	4.74 kg/kW (7.80 lb/shp)

PERFORMANCE (at max Aerobatic T-O weight, S/L, ISA, except where indicated):
Max permissible diving speed:	
400, 600	300 knots (555 km/h; 345 mph)
Max operating speed:	
400, 600	250 knots (463 km/h; 288 mph)
Max level speed:	
400 at 3,050 m (10,000 ft)	
	200 knots (370 km/h; 230 mph)
600 at 5,490 m (18,000 ft)	
	225 knots (417 km/h; 259 mph)
Cruising speed at 3,050 m (10,000 ft):	
400	175 knots (325 km/h; 201 mph)
600	200 knots (370 km/h; 230 mph)
Stalling speed at AUW of 1,800 kg (3,968 lb):	
400, 600	61 knots (113 km/h; 71 mph)
Max rate of climb at S/L: 400	472 m (1,550 ft)/min
600	914 m (3,000 ft)/min
Service ceiling: 400	6,100 m (20,000 ft)
600	7,620 m (25,000 ft)
T-O run: 400	280 m (920 ft)
600	250 m (820 ft)
Landing run: 400, 600	250 m (820 ft)
Range with max internal fuel, optimum cruising speed at 3,050 m (10,000 ft), 45 min reserves:	
400	640 nm (1,186 km; 737 miles)
600	560 nm (1,037 km; 645 miles)
Endurance, conditions as above: 400	4 h 36 min
600	4 h 6 min
Range with drop tanks, at 3,050 m (10,000 ft):	
600	1,250 nm (2,316 km; 1,439 miles)
Endurance, conditions as above:	
600	7 h
g limits (both): A	+6/–3
U	+4.4/–1.76

RUSCHMEYER

RUSCHMEYER LUFTFAHRTTECHNIK GmbH

Flugplatz, 4520 Melle 1
Telephone: 49 (5422) 6566
Telex: 941 500 RULUF D
GENERAL MANAGER: Horst Ruschmeyer

RUSCHMEYER MF-85 SERIES

The MF-85 all-composites four-seat light aircraft was begun in 1985. The prototype, an MF-85P-RG model (D-EEHE), was rolled out on 24 March 1988 and first flew on 8 August that year. The P-RG designation indicates a Porsche engine and retractable landing gear, and the design meets LBA and FAR Pt 23 Normal and Utility requirements. A second (P-FG) prototype is powered by a 134 kW (180 hp) Porsche NN engine using Auto Super fuel, and was followed in June 1989 by the first flight of the third prototype, a PT-RG variant with a 183 kW (245 hp) PFM 3200 Turbo engine and retractable landing gear. Max cruising speed of the latter was expected to be about 230-235 knots (426-435 km/h; 265-270 mph). Production was expected to begin in 1990.

The following details apply to the first prototype MF-85 P-RG:

TYPE: Four-seat cabin monoplane.
AIRFRAME: Cantilever low-wing monoplane, with modified Wortmann FX 184-61/163-61 wing aerofoil sections. Dihedral 6°. Incidence 2°. No sweepback. Ailerons and slotted flaps. Conventional fuselage and tail unit, latter with sweptback vertical surfaces. Adjustable trim tabs in port elevator and rudder. Construction of glassfibre and VE-resin sandwich.
LANDING GEAR: Electro-hydraulically retractable tricycle type, main units retracting inward, nose unit rearward. Mainwheels size 6.00-6; nosewheel 5.00-5. Goodyear tyres, pressure 2.07 bars (30 lb/sq in). Cleveland disc brakes.
POWER PLANT: One 156 kW (212 hp) Porsche PFM 3200 N 01 flat-six engine, driving an MT-Propeller MTV9 three-blade constant-speed composites propeller with spinner. Fuel (Avgas 100LL) capacity 200 litres (52.75 US gallons; 44 Imp gallons) standard in wing tanks. Refuelling points in wings. Oil capacity 8 litres (2.1 US gallons; 1.76 Imp gallons).
ACCOMMODATION: Seats for pilot and three passengers in pairs in fully enclosed and heated cabin, with space for up to 70 kg (154 lb) of baggage aft of seats. Two gull wing window/doors, hinged on centreline to open upward.
SYSTEMS: Electro-hydraulic system for retractable landing gear. Dual independent 28V electrical systems, with two 55A/28V alternators and two 12Ah/28V batteries.
AVIONICS: Becker nav/com in prototype.
DIMENSIONS, EXTERNAL (all models):
Wing span   9.50 m (31 ft 2 in)

Prototype Ruschmeyer MF-85P-RG four-seat light aircraft

Wing chord: at root	1.87 m (6 ft 1½ in)
at tip	0.98 m (3 ft 2½ in)
Wing aspect ratio	6.97
Length overall	7.88 m (25 ft 10¼ in)
Height overall	2.73 m (8 ft 11½ in)
Tailplane span	3.20 m (10 ft 6 in)
Wheel track	3.00 m (9 ft 10 in)
Wheelbase	1.93 m (6 ft 4 in)
Propeller diameter	2.00 m (6 ft 6¾ in)
Propeller ground clearance	0.25 m (9¾ in)
DIMENSIONS, INTERNAL:	
Cabin: Length	2.26 m (7 ft 5 in)
Max width	1.15 m (3 ft 9¼ in)
Max height	1.12 m (3 ft 8 in)
AREAS:	
Wings, gross	12.94 m² (139.28 sq ft)
Ailerons	0.614 m² (6.61 sq ft)
Flaps	1.60 m² (17.22 sq ft)
Fin	1.00 m² (10.76 sq ft)
Rudder	0.60 m² (6.46 sq ft)
Tailplane	1.20 m² (12.92 sq ft)
Elevators	0.816 m² (8.78 sq ft)

WEIGHTS AND LOADINGS:	
Weight empty, standard	814 kg (1,795 lb)
Max payload	394 kg (868 lb)
Max fuel weight	142 kg (313 lb)
Max T-O weight	1,350 kg (2,976 lb)
Max wing loading	104.3 kg/m² (21.36 lb/sq ft)
Max power loading	8.65 kg/kW (14.04 lb/hp)
PERFORMANCE:	
Never-exceed speed	194 knots (360 km/h; 223 mph)
Max level speed at S/L	173 knots (320 km/h; 199 mph)
Max cruising speed at S/L	
	157 knots (290 km/h; 180 mph)
Econ cruising speed at S/L	
	140 knots (260 km/h; 162 mph)
Stalling speed	48 knots (89 km/h; 56 mph)
Max rate of climb at S/L	518 m (1,700 ft)/min
Service ceiling	6,100 m (20,000 ft)
T-O run	200 m (656 ft)
T-O to 15 m (50 ft)	266 m (873 ft)
Landing from 15 m (50 ft)	480 m (1,575 ft)
Range, 45 min reserves	
	863 nm (1,600 km; 994 miles)

GREECE

HAI

HELLENIC AEROSPACE INDUSTRY LTD

Athens Tower, Messogion 2-4, 115 27 Athens
Telephone: 30 (1) 77 99 678
Telex: 219528 HAI GR
WORKS: Tanagra, PO Box 23, 320 09 Schimatari
Telephone: 30 (262) 52000
Telex: 299372 HAI GR
CHAIRMAN AND MANAGING DIRECTOR:
Air Marshal G. Vayiakakos (Ret'd)
COMMERCIAL DIRECTOR: D. G. Sarlis

Hellenic Aerospace Industry is owned 100 per cent by the Greek government, headed by a board of directors. A total of 3,000 people were employed in 1988.

HAI covers Greece's own needs for manufacture and repair in both military and civil aviation fields, and is proving its capability in the international market by signing contracts with such customers as Dassault-Breguet, SNECMA, Thomson-CSF, Dornier, Airbus Industrie, USAFE, British Aerospace, the RAF, Aeritalia, Agusta, General Dynamics and Jordan. These include production of flaps for the BAe ATP, fuselage components for the

Agusta A 109A, and components for the Dassault Mirage 2000, Dornier 228, General Dynamics F-16 and Aeritalia G222 aircraft, as well as for SNECMA M53 aero engines and Thomson-CSF airborne radars.

The HAI facility comprises an Aircraft Division, Engine Division, Electronics/Avionics Division and Manufacturing Division. The Directorate of Engineering, Research and Development provides support, maintenance and modification of equipment as well as production of new electronic and aeronautical systems.

HUNGARY

GANZAVIA

GANZAVIA GT

Dunyov u. 6, H-1134 Budapest
Telephone: 36 (1) 209 020
Telex: 4 22 7951 H
CHIEF DESIGNER: Eng Gyula Kovács

GANZAVIA GA-K-22 DINO

Displayed in model form at the June 1987 Paris Air Show, the Dino is a small, side by side two-seat biplane designed to FAR Pt 23 standards and suitable for training, aerobatics, aerial photography, glider towing and (as the GA-K-22A with 200 kg; 441 lb of spray chemicals) light agricultural duties. It was preceded by a proof-of-concept aircraft (HA-XAD), which was illustrated in the 1987-88 *Jane's*.

Design started in late 1986, and construction of a full size prototype began in early 1987. This aircraft was scheduled to make its first flight in the Autumn of 1990. The following description applies to the full size prototype:
TYPE: Two-seat light general purpose biplane.
WINGS: Negative-stagger biplane, with both wings fully cantilevered. Constant chord single-spar wings, with

aerofoil sections NACA 23018 at root, NACA 23012 at tip. Incidence 4° (upper) and 3° (lower). Wingtip washout (both wings) 1° 12′. Tips sweptback 30° on leading-edges. Near full span flaperons, on lower wings only, are interconnected with elevator and pushrod operated (upward movement of elevator produces downward movement of flaperons). Trim tab in each flaperon. Wings and control surfaces are of corrosion resistant aluminium alloy; wingtips are of glassfibre.
FUSELAGE: Welded steel tube structure, duralumin covered at front and fabric covered at rear. Glassfibre engine cowling.
TAIL UNIT: Conventional configuration, of similar construction to wings. Rudder and elevator tips are of glassfibre. All controls pushrod operated.
LANDING GEAR: Non-retractable tricycle type, with single-spring mainwheel legs and elastomerically sprung nose unit. Mainwheels (340 mm diameter) from Jantar 2B sailplane; nosewheel (300 × 125 mm) from Ka-26 helicopter. Jantar 2B double-disc brakes; parking brake. Nosewheel steerable ±35°.
POWER PLANT: One 85.7 kW (115 hp) Textron Lycoming O-235-H2C flat-four engine, driving an MT178R117-2C

two-blade fixed-pitch wooden propeller with spinner. Fuel tank in lower part of fuselage, capacity 100 litres (26.4 US gallons; 22 Imp gallons). Alternative 40 litre (10.6 US gallon; 8.8 Imp gallon) tank in GA-K-22A. Refuelling point in port side of fuselage. Oil capacity 6.8 litres (1.8 US gallons; 1.5 Imp gallons).
ACCOMMODATION: Side by side adjustable seats for pilot and one passenger in fully enclosed cockpit, with upward opening window/door on each side. Baggage space aft of seats, capacity 30 kg (66 lb). Accommodation heated and/or ventilated.
SYSTEMS AND EQUIPMENT: 24V battery standard. Radio optional. Chemical spraygear for GA-K-22A.
DIMENSIONS, EXTERNAL:

Wing span (both)	7.60 m (24 ft 11¼ in)
Wing chord: constant portion	1.00 m (3 ft 3¼ in)
at tip	0.25 m (9.8 in)
Wing stagger	1.09 m (3 ft 7 in)
Length overall	6.40 m (21 ft 0 in)
Fuselage: Max width	1.185 m (3 ft 10¾ in)
Height overall	2.60 m (8 ft 6½ in)
Elevator span	2.80 m (9 ft 2¼ in)
Wheel track	2.30 m (7 ft 6½ in)

Wheelbase	1.60 m (5 ft 3 in)
Propeller diameter	1.78 m (5 ft 10 in)
Propeller ground clearance	0.36 m (1 ft 2¼ in)
DIMENSIONS, INTERNAL:	
Cabin: Length	1.40 m (4 ft 7 in)
Max width	1.13 m (3 ft 8½ in)
Max height	1.00 m (3 ft 3¼ in)
Baggage compartment volume	0.1 m³ (3.53 cu ft)
AREAS:	
Wings, gross	14.04 m² (151.13 sq ft)
Flaperons (total)	1.37 m² (14.75 sq ft)
Rudder	0.88 m² (9.47 sq ft)
Tailplane	0.53 m² (5.70 sq ft)
Elevator	1.27 m² (13.67 sq ft)

WEIGHTS AND LOADINGS (A: Aerobatic, B: agricultural version):

Weight empty, equipped: A	360 kg (794 lb)
B	385 kg (849 lb)
Max fuel weight: A	80 kg (176 lb)
B	35 kg (77 lb)
Max T-O weight: A	650 kg (1,433 lb)
B	710 kg (1,565 lb)
Max wing loading: A	46.3 kg/m² (9.49 lb/sq ft)
B	50.6 kg/m² (10.36 lb/sq ft)
Max power loading: A	7.58 kg/kW (12.46 lb/hp)
B	8.28 kg/kW (13.61 lb/hp)

PERFORMANCE (estimated, at max Aerobatic T-O weight):

Never-exceed speed	188 knots (350 km/h; 217 mph)
Max level speed at S/L	100 knots (186 km/h; 116 mph)
Max cruising speed at S/L 97 knots (180 km/h; 112 mph)	
Stalling speed, flaperons up 45 knots (83 km/h; 52 mph)	
Max rate of climb at S/L	282 m (925 ft)/min
T-O run	110 m (361 ft)
T-O to 15 m (50 ft)	235 m (771 ft)
Landing from 15 m (50 ft)	285 m (935 ft)

Model of the Ganzavia GA-K-22 Dino two-seat light biplane

Landing run	90 m (295 ft)
Range with max fuel	378 nm (700 km; 435 miles)

INDIA

HAL
HINDUSTAN AERONAUTICS LIMITED
CORPORATE OFFICE: PO Box 5150, 15/1 Cubbon Road, Bangalore 560 001
Telephone: 91 (812) 76901
Telex: 845 2266 HAL IN
Fax: 91 (812) 258758
CHAIRMAN: I. M. Chopra
CHIEF OF MARKETING: B. S. Jaswal

Hindustan Aeronautics Limited (HAL) was formed on 1 October 1964, and has 14 Divisions (eight at Bangalore and one each at Nasik, Koraput, Hyderabad, Kanpur, Lucknow and Korwa), plus a Design Complex. The total workforce is about 42,000.

Kanpur Division is producing the HPT-32 and HTT-34 ab initio trainers and assembles, under licence, the Dornier 228. Nasik and Koraput Divisions are manufacturing airframes and engines of the Soviet MiG-27 in collaboration with the USSR. Hyderabad Division manufactures avionics

for all aircraft produced by HAL, as well as airport radars. Lucknow Division is producing aircraft accessories under licence from manufacturers in the UK, France and the USSR, and Korwa manufactures inertial navigation systems.

In addition to HAL's manufacturing programmes, major design and development activities include the Light Combat Aircraft (LCA) and Advanced Light Helicopter (ALH) programmes.

BANGALORE COMPLEX
Post Bag 1785, Bangalore 560 017
Telephone: 91 (812) 565201 and 561020
Telex: 845 2234
MANAGING DIRECTOR: Dr C. G. Krishnadas Nair

Aircraft Division
Post Bag 1788, Bangalore 560 017
Telephone: 91 (812) 565201 and 561020
Telex: 845 2234
Fax: 91 (812) 565188
GENERAL MANAGER: S. N. Sachindran

Helicopter Division
Post Bag 1790, Bangalore 560 017
Telephone: 91 (812) 565201 and 561020
Telex: 845 2764
GENERAL MANAGER: K. N. Murthy

The Bangalore Complex is subdivided into an Aircraft Division, Helicopter Division, Aerospace Division, Engine Division, Overhaul Division, Services Division, Foundry and Forge Division, Flight Operations, and Design Complex. It is engaged in the manufacture of the SEPECAT Jaguar International combat aircraft and its Adour engine. The Complex also undertakes repair and overhaul of airframes, engines, and allied instruments and accessories. A contract to supply up to 150 sets of tailplanes for the British Aerospace ATP transport aircraft was signed in May 1987.

HAL (SEPECAT) JAGUAR INTERNATIONAL
Indian Air Force name: Shamsher (Assault sword)
HAL is producing SEPECAT Jaguar International combat aircraft (see International section) and their Adour Mk 811 engines for the Indian Air Force. Initial orders were for 76 aircraft: 45 assembled from European built components (now completed) and 31 of virtually all-Indian manufacture. The first of the latter batch was completed in early 1988, and IAF Jaguar Squadrons include Nos. 5 and 14. Jaguars of No. 6 Squadron assigned to anti-shipping duty have nose mounted Thomson-CSF Agave radar, a Smiths Industries Darin nav/attack system, and air-to-surface missiles. The first of an initial six aircraft so modified was delivered during January 1986. An additional order for 15 Jaguars has since been received.

SEPECAT Jaguar International single-seat strike aircraft of the Indian Air Force

LIGHT COMBAT AIRCRAFT
In 1983 the Indian government sanctioned development of an all-weather air superiority and light close air support aircraft for service in the 1990s, known as the LCA (light combat aircraft). A single-seat, single-engined compound-delta-wing aircraft, it will embody some 35 per cent (by weight) of composite materials in its construction, and have a quadruplex fly by wire flight control system, an Ericsson/Ferranti PS-05 multi-function radar, a ring laser gyro, digital databus and engine controls, and a central weapons management system. Empty and max T-O weights are 5,365 kg (11,828 lb) and 12,900 kg (28,440 lb) respectively, and there will be seven attachment points for up to 4,000 kg (8,814 lb) of external stores. An indigenous afterburning engine of about 83.4 kN (18,740 lb st), designated GTX-35 VS, is under development by the Gas Turbine Research Establishment at Bangalore, but variants of the General Electric F404/RM12 turbofan have been ordered to power the seven prototypes (including one two-seater) until this is ready. The project definition stage, which began in the Spring of 1987, was completed in late 1988, and design engineering is now in progress. A first flight is not expected before 1992, and service entry not

earlier than 1996. Between 200 and 300 production LCAs are required by the Indian Air Force, and a carrier based version for service at the end of the 1990s is being studied.

HAL HJT-16 KIRAN Mk II
This version of the Kiran, for armament training and counter-insurgency duties, was developed from the Mks I/IA (1982-83 *Jane's*) and first flew on 30 July 1976. Principal differences include improved weapon carrying capability, a more powerful engine, updated avionics, an improved hydraulic system and a Rolls-Royce Orpheus 701-01 turbojet.

Sixty-one Kiran Mk IIs were ordered, of which deliveries were completed in 1989. A full description can be found in the 1987-88 *Jane's*, and a shortened version in the 1988-89 and 1989-90 editions.

MBB/HAL ADVANCED LIGHT HELICOPTER
In July 1984 the Indian government and MBB signed a contract for the development of an advanced twin-turboshaft light helicopter (ALH), initially for Indian national requirements, which are said to be in the order

Naval version of the MBB/HAL Advanced Light Helicopter, with additional side view (centre) of air force/army variant *(Jane's/Mike Keep)*

of 200 for the armed forces and Coast Guard as Chetak/Cheetah replacements. Development of the ALH basic version is by HAL with MBB consultancy. MBB is providing support during design, development and preparations for production of the helicopter in Bangalore.

The preliminary design phase has been completed, configuration has been frozen, and overall design of critical components has been completed. A civil version is under consideration. A full-scale engineering mockup was completed in 1987, and prototype first flight was expected to take place in late 1990 or early 1991; production is expected to start in 1993.

TYPE: Multi-role civil and military light helicopter.

ROTOR SYSTEM AND DRIVE: Four-blade hingeless main rotor, with all-composites (carbonfibre) blades of advanced aerofoil section, incorporating sweptback tips. Blades are attached to hub by flexible collars, and are foldable on naval version. Rotor head is of composites and metal, with elastomeric bearings. Integrated drive system, with direct input to main gearbox from both engines. Four-blade bearingless tail rotor, also with composite blades, mounted on starboard side of tail fin.

FUSELAGE: Conventional pod and boom structure, of metal and composites construction (Kevlar nosecone and carbonfibre tailboom). Tailboom foldable on naval variant.

TAIL UNIT: Single sweptback main fin/tail rotor pylon, plus constant chord tailplane with smaller sweptback endplate fins.

LANDING GEAR: Fully retractable tricycle type standard, with twin nosewheels and single mainwheels, latter retracting into fuselage-side fairings which also house flotation gear and battery. Harpoon decklock system on naval variant. Non-retractable tubular skid gear optional on all except naval variant. Spring skid under rear of tailboom, to protect tail rotor.

POWER PLANT: Two 746 kW (1,000 shp) Turbomeca TM 333-2B turboshafts, with full authority digital electronic control (FADEC). Pressure refuelling standard.

ACCOMMODATION: Seating capacity for up to 12 persons, including a crew of two. Crew door and rearward sliding passenger door on each side; clamshell cargo doors at rear of cabin section.

AVIONICS AND EQUIPMENT: V/UHF, HF/SSB and standby UHF com radio, plus intercom. Four-axis AFCS. Doppler navigation system, TAS system, ADF, radio altimeter, heading reference and IFF standard. Oxygen system. Other avionics and equipment, according to role, can include Omega nav system, weather radar, two stretchers, and external hoist.

DIMENSIONS, EXTERNAL:
Main rotor diameter	approx 13.30 m (43 ft 7½ in)
Tail rotor diameter	approx 2.50 m (8 ft 2½ in)
Length overall, both rotors turning	15.87 m (52 ft 0¾ in)
Height overall, tail rotor turning	4.91 m (16 ft 1¼ in)
Tail unit span (over fins)	3.19 m (10 ft 5½ in)
Wheel track	2.80 m (9 ft 2¼ in)

WEIGHTS (A: Army/Air Force versions, B: naval variant):
Weight empty: A	2,216 kg (4,885 lb)
B	2,352 kg (5,185 lb)
Max fuel: A	1,032 kg (2,275 lb)
B	1,100 kg (2,425 lb)
Max sling load: A	1,000 kg (2,205 lb)
B	1,500 kg (3,307 lb)
Max T-O weight: A	4,000 kg (8,818 lb)
B	5,000 kg (11,023 lb)

PERFORMANCE (estimated, at design gross weight, ISA):
Max level speed at S/L	156 knots (290 km/h; 180 mph)
Hovering ceiling OGE	above 3,000 m (9,850 ft)
Range at S/L with 700 kg (1,543 lb) payload	216 nm (400 km; 248 miles)
Endurance at S/L	more than 3 h

HAL (AEROSPATIALE) SA 315B LAMA
Indian name: Cheetah

The last known details of HAL's Lama licence production were given in the 1987-88 *Jane's*. Indian production continues. A description of the SA 315B appears under the Aerospatiale heading in the French section.

HAL (AEROSPATIALE) SA 316B ALOUETTE III
Indian name: Chetak

The first French built SA 316B made its initial flight on 27 June 1968, and deliveries began in 1970. The sale of Alouette IIIs to India, Romania and Switzerland included licence agreements for manufacture of the aircraft in those countries, the quantities involved being 250, 180 and 60 respectively. Romanian and Swiss manufacture has ended, but Indian production was continuing in 1990.

TYPE: Turbine driven general purpose helicopter.

ROTOR SYSTEM: Three-blade main and anti-torque rotors. All-metal main rotor blades, of constant chord, on articulated hinges, with hydraulic drag dampers. Main rotor brake and blade folding standard.

ROTOR DRIVE: Main rotor driven through planetary gearbox, with freewheel for autorotation. Take-off drive

for tail rotor at lower end of main gearbox, from where a torque shaft runs to a small gearbox which supports the tail rotor and houses the pitch change mechanism. Cyclic and collective pitch controls are powered.

FUSELAGE: Welded steel tube centre-section, carrying the cabin at the front and a semi-monocoque tailboom.

TAIL UNIT: Cantilever all-metal fixed tailplane, with twin endplate fins, mounted on tailboom.

LANDING GEAR: Non-retractable tricycle type, manufactured under Messier-Hispano-Bugatti licence. Hydraulic shock absorption. Nosewheel is fully castoring. Provision for skis or emergency pontoon landing gear.

POWER PLANT: One 649 kW (870 shp) Turbomeca Artouste IIIB turboshaft, derated to 410 kW (550 shp) for max continuous operation. Fuel in single tank in fuselage centre-section, with capacity of 575 litres (152 US gallons; 126.5 Imp gallons), of which 573 litres (151 US gallons; 126 Imp gallons) are usable.

ACCOMMODATION: Normal accommodation for pilot and six persons, with three seats in front and a four-person folding seat at the rear of the cabin. Two baggage holds in centre-section, on each side of the welded structure and enclosed by the centre-section fairings. Provision for carrying two stretchers athwartships at rear of cabin, and two other persons, in addition to pilot. All passenger seats removable to enable aircraft to be used for freight carrying. Can also be adapted for cropspraying or aerial survey roles. Provision for external sling for loads of up to 750 kg (1,650 lb). One forward opening door on each side, immediately in front of two rearward sliding doors. Dual controls and cabin heating optional.

OPERATIONAL EQUIPMENT (military version): In the assault role, the Alouette III can be equipped with a wide range of weapons. A 7.62 mm machine-gun (with 1,000 rds) can be mounted athwartships on a tripod behind the pilot's seat, firing to starboard, either through a small window in the sliding door or through the open doorway with the door locked open. The rear seat is removed to allow the gun mounting to be installed. In this configuration, max accommodation is for pilot, co-pilot, gunner and one passenger, although normally only the pilot and gunner would be carried. Alternatively, a 20 mm cannon (with 480 rds) can be carried on an open turret-type mounting on the port side of the cabin. For this installation all seats except that of the pilot are removed, as is the port side cabin door, and the crew consists of pilot and gunner. Instead of these guns, the Alouette III can be equipped with two or four wire-guided missiles on external jettisonable launching rails, a gyro-stabilised sight, or 68 mm rocket pods.

DIMENSIONS, EXTERNAL:
Main rotor diameter	11.02 m (36 ft 1¾ in)
Main rotor blade chord (each)	0.35 m (13.8 in)
Tail rotor diameter	1.912 m (6 ft 3¼ in)
Spraybar span (agricultural version)	10.00 m (32 ft 9¾ in)
Length overall, rotors turning	12.84 m (42 ft 1½ in)
Length of fuselage, tail rotor turning	10.17 m (33 ft 4½ in)
Width overall, blades folded	2.60 m (8 ft 6¼ in)
Height to top of rotor head	2.97 m (9 ft 9 in)
Wheel track	2.602 m (8 ft 6½ in)

AREAS:
Main rotor disc	95.38 m² (1,026.6 sq ft)
Tail rotor disc	2.87 m² (30.9 sq ft)

WEIGHTS:
Weight empty: standard version	1,050 kg (2,315 lb)
agricultural version	1,300 kg (2,866 lb)
Max payload (agricultural version)	685 kg (1,510 lb)
Max T-O weight	2,200 kg (4,850 lb)

PERFORMANCE (standard version at max T-O weight, except where indicated):
Never-exceed speed at S/L	113 knots (210 km/h; 130 mph)
Max cruising speed at S/L	100 knots (185 km/h; 115 mph)
Operating speed (agricultural version)	32-76 knots (60-140 km/h; 37-87 mph)
Max rate of climb at S/L	260 m (850 ft)/min
Service ceiling	3,200 m (10,500 ft)
Hovering ceiling: IGE	2,850 m (9,350 ft)
OGE	1,500 m (4,920 ft)
Range with max fuel at S/L	267 nm (495 km; 307 miles)
Range at optimum altitude	290 nm (540 km; 335 miles)
Swath width (agricultural version)	30-40 m (98-131 ft)

KANPUR DIVISION
Post Bag 225, Kanpur 208 008
Telephone: 91 (512) 43071 to 43074
Telex: 325 243 HALK IN
GENERAL MANAGER: S. K. Ohri

HAL (DORNIER) 228
Under a November 1983 contract with Dornier of West Germany, HAL is undertaking licence assembly and manufacture of up to 150 Dornier 228 twin-turboprop utility transports in a ten-year technology transfer programme. Kanpur Divison is responsible for the airframe,

final assembly and flight testing; the Engine Division at Bangalore manufactures the Garrett TPE331-5 turboprops; instrumentation and accessories are supplied by Lucknow Division; and Hyderabad Division provides various items of avionics including the colour weather radar and Omega navigation system.

The 228, in several versions, is used for a wide variety of civil and military duties in India, and while Kanpur Division was preparing for its manufacture a number of Dornier built aircraft were supplied to meet urgent Indian customer needs, as detailed in earlier editions of *Jane's*.

In early 1985 Dornier began delivering complete shipsets of aircraft assemblies to HAL, and the first Kanpur

assembled 228 made its initial flight on 31 January 1986. First deliveries from Kanpur, of five 228-201s for Vayudoot, were made in March 1986. The initial three Coast Guard 228-101s being followed by 30 more from the Kanpur assembly line, the first of which were delivered in 1987. In service with No. 750 Squadron at Daman, they are used for a wide variety of coastal patrol, environmental control and anti-smuggling missions with equipment that includes a 360° MEL Marec 2 underfuselage search radar, Litton Omega navigation system, a Swedish infra-red/ultraviolet linescanner for pollution detection, search and rescue liferafts, a 1 million candlepower searchlight, side mounted loudhailer, marine markers, and

HAL built Dornier 228-101 of the Indian Coast Guard *(John Fricker)*

HAL HPT-32 two-seat basic training aircraft in Indian Navy insignia

provision for two Micronair underwing spraypods to combat oil spills and chemical pollution. The standard cabin door is replaced by a sliding door to permit airdropping of the 20-man liferaft. Normal crew comprises a pilot, co-pilot, radar operator and observer. The Marec 2 radar will eventually be replaced on 15 aircraft by Super Marec, ordered in 1987. Armament (optional) can include two 7.62 mm multi-barrel machine-guns and underwing air-to-surface missiles.

In Phase 2 of the manufacturing programme, 50 Dornier 228s are being built for the Indian Air Force, of which four had been delivered by the beginning of 1988. In various utility and logistic support roles they will eventually replace all of the IAF's Otters, Devons and remaining C-47s currently serving with Nos. 41 and 59 Squadrons.

For maritime surveillance and anti-shipping tasks, the Indian Navy will also add specially equipped Dornier 228s to its shore based fixed-wing fleet. Twenty-four have been ordered, and are expected to have anti-ship missile carrying capability. The first four were reported to have been ordered, with MEL Super Marec radar, in mid-1988.

The Indian National Aeronautical Laboratory and German DLR have jointly developed a carbonfibre rudder for the Dornier 228, flight testing of which was to take place in 1989, followed by certification and commercial production.

HAL HPT-32

The HPT-32 is a fully aerobatic piston engined basic trainer, with side by side seats for instructor and pupil. It can be used for a wide range of ab initio training, including instrument, navigation, night flying and formation flying; for armed patrol; for observation, liaison or sport flying; or for weapon training, light strike duties, supply dropping, search and rescue, reconnaissance, or glider or target towing. The all-metal airframe is designed to FAR Pt 23.

The first prototype (X2157) made its initial flight on 6 January 1977. The third, flown on 31 July 1981, represented the production version, substantially lighter in weight and with aerodynamic refinements. By 31 March 1987 a total of 40 had been delivered to the Indian Air Force and eight to the Indian Navy. Production of a further 40, against anticipated IAF orders, was in progress in 1988, the last date for which any information has been received.

TYPE: Two-seat ab initio, aerobatic, night flying, instrument flying and navigation trainer.

WINGS: Cantilever low-wing monoplane. Wing section NACA 64A$_1$-212. Dihedral 5° from roots. Incidence 2° 30′ at root. No sweepback. Light alloy safe-life wings, of tapered planform, with stressed skin. Light alloy plain ailerons and plain trailing-edge flaps. Balance tab in, and ground adjustable tab on, each aileron. Pitot static tube can be heated.

FUSELAGE: Semi-monocoque safe-life structure of light alloy, with stressed skin.

TAIL UNIT: Cantilever light alloy stressed skin structure, with sweptback vertical surfaces. One-piece elevator. Trim tabs in rudder and starboard half of elevator; balance tabs in rudder and port half of elevator.

LANDING GEAR: Non-retractable tricycle type, with HAL oleo-pneumatic shock absorber in each unit. Dunlop UK single mainwheels and nosewheel. Dunlop UK mainwheel tyres, size 446 × 151 × 166 mm, pressure 3.10 bars (45 lb/sq in); Dunlop India nosewheel tyre, size 361 × 126 × 127 mm, pressure 2.41 bars (35 lb/sq in). Dunlop UK aircooled hydraulic disc brakes on mainwheels.

POWER PLANT: One 194 kW (260 hp) Textron Lycoming AEIO-540-D4B5 flat-six engine, driving a Hartzell two-blade constant-speed metal propeller with spinner. Total of 220 litres (58.1 US gallons; 48.4 Imp gallons) of fuel in four flexible tanks (two in each wing), plus a 9 litre (2.4 US gallon; 2 Imp gallon) metal collector tank in fuselage. Total fuel capacity 229 litres (60.5 US gallons; 50.4 Imp gallons). Overwing refuelling points. Oil capacity 13.6 litres (3.6 US gallons; 3 Imp gallons).

ACCOMMODATION: Side by side seats for two persons under rearward sliding jettisonable framed canopy. Seats adjustable in height by 127 mm (5 in). Full dual controls, and adjustable rudder pedals, for instructor and pupil. Cockpits ventilated.

SYSTEMS: Hydraulic system for brakes only. Electrical system (28V DC earth return type) powered by 70A alternator, with SAFT 24V nickel-cadmium standby battery. No air-conditioning, pneumatic, de-icing or oxygen systems.

AVIONICS: HAL (Hyderabad Divn) COM-150 main UHF and COM-104A standby VHF com; directional gyro. No blind-flying instrumentation.

DIMENSIONS, EXTERNAL:

Wing span	9.50 m (31 ft 2 in)
Wing chord: at root	2.24 m (7 ft 4¼ in)
at tip	0.92 m (3 ft 0¼ in)
Wing aspect ratio	6.0
Length overall	7.72 m (25 ft 4 in)
Fuselage: Max width	1.25 m (4 ft 1¼ in)
Height overall	2.88 m (9 ft 5½ in)
Tailplane span	3.60 m (11 ft 9¾ in)
Wheel track	3.45 m (11 ft 4 in)
Wheelbase	2.10 m (6 ft 10¾ in)
Propeller diameter	2.03 m (6 ft 8 in)
Propeller ground clearance (static)	0.23 m (9 in)

AREAS:

Wings, gross	15.00 m² (161.5 sq ft)
Ailerons (total)	1.04 m² (11.19 sq ft)
Trailing-edge flaps (total)	1.82 m² (19.59 sq ft)
Vertical tail surfaces (above fuselage reference line)	2.06 m² (22.17 sq ft)
Rudder (aft of hinge line), incl tabs	0.869 m² (9.35 sq ft)
Tailplane	3.024 m² (32.55 sq ft)
Elevator (aft of hinge line), incl tabs	1.34 m² (14.42 sq ft)

WEIGHTS AND LOADINGS:

Basic weight empty	890 kg (1,962 lb)
Fuel and oil (guaranteed minimum)	164 kg (361 lb)
Max T-O and landing weight	1,250 kg (2,756 lb)

First production example of the HAL HTT-34 ab initio trainer

Hindustan Aeronautics HTT-34 military trainer (Allison 250-B17D turboprop) *(Pilot Press)*

Max wing loading	83.33 kg/m² (17.07 lb/sq ft)
Max power loading	6.44 kg/kW (10.60 lb/hp)

PERFORMANCE (at max T-O weight, ISA):

Never-exceed speed (structural)
240 knots (445 km/h; 276 mph)

Max level speed at S/L
143 knots (265 km/h; 164 mph) IAS

Max cruising speed at 3,050 m (10,000 ft)
115 knots (213 km/h; 132 mph)

Econ cruising speed   95 knots (176 km/h; 109 mph)

Stalling speed, 20° flap, engine idling
60 knots (110 km/h; 69 mph)

Max rate of climb at S/L	335 m (1,100 ft)/min
Service ceiling	5,500 m (18,045 ft)
T-O run	345 m (1,132 ft)
T-O to 15 m (50 ft)	545 m (1,788 ft)
Landing from 15 m (50 ft)	487 m (1,598 ft)
Landing run	220 m (720 ft)
Min ground turning radius	6.50 m (21 ft 4 in)

Range at 3,050 m (10,000 ft) at econ cruise power
401 nm (744 km; 462 miles)

g limits   +6/–3

HAL HTT-34

Exhibited publicly for the first time at the 1984 Farnborough International air show, the HTT-34 is a private venture development of the piston engined HPT-32. First flown on 17 June 1984, the prototype was the third HPT-32 (X2335) refitted with an Allison 250-B17D turboprop engine. The airframe is virtually unchanged aft of the firewall.

The HTT-34 is designed to FAR 23 standards, is fully aerobatic, and can be used for a wide range of ab initio training duties. In addition, it can be used for instrument, night and formation flying training, or for reconnaissance, observation, liaison or sport flying.

No news of the HTT-34 had been received for several years until early 1989, when HAL rolled out the first pre-production example and revealed that 48 had been ordered by the Nigerian Air Force. As Kanpur Division did not supply information for this year's edition, it is not known what changes may be embodied in the production HTT-34.

TYPE: Two-seat ab initio trainer.

AIRFRAME: As described for HPT-32.

LANDING GEAR: Non-retractable tricycle type, with HAL oleo-pneumatic shock absorber in each unit. Dunlop tyres on all wheels (mainwheel size 6.00-6.5, nose size 5.00-5); pressure 2.76-3.10 bars (40-45 lb/sq in) on main units, 2.07-2.41 bars (30-35 lb/sq in) on nose unit. Hydraulic disc brakes on mainwheels.

POWER PLANT: One 313 kW (420 shp) Allison 250-B17D turboprop, driving a Hartzell three-blade constant-speed fully-feathering propeller with reverse pitch capability. Total of 220 litres (58.1 US gallons; 48.4 Imp gallons) of fuel in four flexible tanks (two in each wing), plus a 10 litre (2.6 US gallon; 2.2 Imp gallon) collector tank in fuselage. Total fuel capacity 230 litres (60.8 US gallons; 50.6 Imp gallons).

ACCOMMODATION: Side by side seats for two persons in front, with provision at rear under separately hinged canopy for 20 kg (44 lb) of baggage with tiedown facilities. Rearward sliding jettisonable framed canopy. Seats adjustable in height by 127 mm (5 in). Full dual controls, and adjustable rudder pedals, for instructor and pupil. Cockpits ventilated.

AVIONICS: VHF and UHF com radio; ADF and pictorial navigation.

DIMENSIONS, EXTERNAL: As for HPT-32, except:

Length overall	8.07 m (26 ft 5¾ in)
Propeller diameter	2.13 m (7 ft 0 in)
Propeller ground clearance (static)	0.24 m (9½ in)

AREAS: As for HPT-32, except:

Ailerons (total)	0.80 m² (8.60 sq ft)
Rudder (aft of hinge line), incl tabs	0.75 m² (8.07 sq ft)
Tailplane	3.02 m² (32.51 sq ft)

Elevators (aft of hinge line), incl tabs
1.08 m² (11.63 sq ft)

WEIGHTS AND LOADINGS:

Weight empty (prototype)	866 kg (1,909 lb)
Max T-O weight	1,300 kg (2,866 lb)
Max wing loading	86.7 kg/m² (17.7 lb/sq ft)
Max power loading	4.15 kg/kW (6.82 lb/shp)

PERFORMANCE (at max T-O weight, ISA):

Max level speed at 3,000 m (9,845 ft)
149 knots (276 km/h; 171 mph)

Stalling speed, engine idling:

flaps up	61 knots (112 km/h; 70 mph)
flaps down	58 knots (107 km/h; 67 mph)
Max rate of climb at S/L	640 m (2,100 ft)/min
Service ceiling	7,925 m (26,000 ft)
T-O to 15 m (50 ft)	247 m (810 ft)
Landing from 15 m (50 ft)	380 m (1,247 ft)

Range with max fuel at 3,500 m (11,485 ft)
380 nm (700 km; 435 miles)

Endurance with max fuel at 3,500 m (11,485 ft)   3 h

g limits   +6/–3

MiG COMPLEX

Ojhar Township Post Office, Nasik 422 207, Maharashtra
Telephone: 91 (22) 77901
Telex: 0752 241 and 0752 256
Fax: 91 (22) 77907
MANAGING DIRECTOR:
Wg Cdr A. C. Sood (Ret'd)
GENERAL MANAGER, NASIK DIVISION:
V. M. Akolkar
GENERAL MANAGER, KORAPUT DIVISION:
N. R. Mohanty

The MiG Complex was originally formed with the Nasik, Koraput and Hyderabad Divisions of HAL, which, under an agreement concluded in 1962, built respectively the airframes, power plants and avionics of MiG-21 series fighters under licence from the USSR. Indian production of MiG-21s was phased out in 1986-87, as production of the

MiG-27M increased. The Hyderabad Division is now a part of the Accessories Complex.

HAL (MIKOYAN) MiG-27M
Indian Air Force name: Bahadur (Valiant)
NATO reporting name: Flogger-J

Licence assembly of some 165 MiG-27Ms (see USSR section) began at HAL in 1984, and the first example assembled by HAL was rolled out in October of that year. These aircraft supplement Soviet built MiG-23s and MiG-27s already supplied to the Indian Air Force, and are the first MiG-27s to be assembled outside the USSR. Since 1988, MiG-27Ms assembled at Nasik are thought to incorporate components manufactured in India. First IAF unit to receive Bahadurs was No. 32 ('Tiger Sharks') Squadron, the type being formally inducted into IAF service on 11 January 1986.

POWER PLANT: One Tumansky R-29B-300 turbojet, rated at 78.65 kN (17,681 lb st) dry and 112.78 kN (25,353 lb st) with afterburning.

AVIONICS: Include an advanced integrated nav/attack system and active/passive ECM systems.

ARMAMENT: One ventrally mounted six-barrel 30 mm cannon, and seven external hardpoints for up to 3,000 kg (6,614 lb) of stores which can include 500 kg bombs, 57 mm S-24 rockets, two 'Kerry' air-to-surface or four R-60 air-to-air missiles.

WEIGHT:

Max T-O weight   18,000 kg (39,685 lb)

PERFORMANCE:

T-O run at S/L	800 m (2,625 ft)
Combat radius (low level)	210 nm (390 km; 242 miles)
Ferry range	1,349 nm (2,500 km; 1,553 miles)

INDONESIA

IPTN
INDUSTRI PESAWAT TERBANG NUSANTARA (Nusantara Aircraft Industries Ltd)

PO Box 563, Jalan Pajajaran 154, Bandung
Telephone: 62 (22) 611081/2
Telex: 28295 IPTN BD
HEAD OFFICE: PO Box 3752, 8 Jalan M.H. Thamrin, Jakarta
Telephone: 62 (21) 322395 and 336651
Telex: 46141 ATP JAKARTA
PRESIDENT DIRECTOR: Prof Dr-Ing B. J. Habibie
DIRECTOR, COMMERCIAL AFFAIRS: Ir S. Paramajuda
CHIEF ENGINEER: Ir Budiarta Suradiningrat
PUBLIC RELATIONS MANAGER: Suripto Sugondo

This company was officially inaugurated as PT Industri Pesawat Terbang Nurtanio (Nurtanio Aircraft Industry Ltd) on 23 August 1976, when the government of Indonesia implemented a decision to centralise all existing facilities in the establishment of a single new aircraft industry. The original capital was provided by combining the assets of Pertamina's Advanced Technology and Aeronautical Division with those of the former Nurtanio Aircraft Industry (LIPNUR: see 1977-78 *Jane's*). The present name of the company was adopted in late 1985. A weapons system division, located in Menang Tasikmalaya, West Java, develops and produces the weaponry fitted to aircraft built by the company for military customers. By mid-1989, the company had delivered approximately 260 fixed-wing aircraft and helicopters.

IPTN is jointly responsible with CASA of Spain for development and production of the Airtech CN-235 (see International section), as well as continuing licence manufacture of the NC-212 Aviocar, NBO-105, NAS-332 Super Puma, NBell-412 and MBB/Kawasaki NBK-117, as described in the following entries. Major subcontracting includes the manufacture of components for the Boeing 737 and 767, Fokker 100 and General Dynamics F-16. The company had a workforce of approx 15,500 employees in mid-1989, and occupies a 69 ha (170.5 acre) site with 365,000 m² (3,928,824 sq ft) of covered accommodation. It did not supply any updated information for 1988, 1989 or 1990.

With MBB of West Germany, IPTN has set up a joint company known as NTT (New Transport Technologies), with its headquarters in Munich. Its first venture is a small helicopter (the N-442).

AIRTECH (CASA/IPTN) CN-235

Details of this joint transport programme can be found under the Airtech heading in the International section.

IPTN N-250

Indonesia's first entirely indigenously designed transport, the N-250 is a national programme for a 50/54-seat pressurised aircraft powered by twin turboprops in the

2,237 kW (3,000 shp) class, for entry into service in 1996. First flight is planned for early 1995. The N-250's appearance, illustrated in the accompanying three-view drawing, is generally similar to that of the Airtech (CASA/IPTN) CN-235, but it will have a modified fuselage cross-section, longer cabin, and no rear loading ramp. The engine selected had not been decided at the time of going to press, but the choice then reportedly lay between the Pratt & Whitney Canada PW130, Allison GMA 2100 and General Electric/Textron Lycoming GLC38.

Indonesian airlines Merpati and Bouraq have announced an intention to purchase 106 N-250s (44 and 62 respectively), and FFV Aerotech of Sweden 24.

IPTN N-250 twin-turboprop regional transport aircraft *(Pilot Press)*

ACCOMMODATION: Cabin seating (four-abreast with central aisle) for 50 passengers at 81 cm (32 in) pitch or 54 passengers at 76 cm (30 in) pitch. One or two cabin attendants. Storage compartments at front of cabin on port side and at rear on starboard side; galley and toilet at rear. Passenger door at front on port side, and service door at rear on starboard side, each with Type III emergency exit on opposite side. Large baggage compartment aft of main cabin, with baggage door on port side. Additional bulk storage in underfloor compartment, also with external access. Aisle headroom 1.90 m (6 ft 2¾ in).

DIMENSIONS, EXTERNAL:
Wing span	28.00 m (91 ft 10¼ in)
Length overall	26.23 m (86 ft 0¾ in)
Fuselage: Max diameter	2.90 m (9 ft 6¼ in)
Height overall	8.20 m (26 ft 10¾ in)

DIMENSIONS, INTERNAL:
Main baggage compartment	10.30 m³ (363.7 cu ft)
Underfloor bulk storage	0.60 m³ (21.2 cu ft)

DESIGN WEIGHTS (basic):
Max payload	6,000 kg (13,227 lb)
Max T-O weight	20,850 kg (45,966 lb)
Max landing weight	20,650 kg (45,525 lb)
Max zero-fuel weight	18,565 kg (40,929 lb)

PERFORMANCE (estimated):
Max cruising speed at 6,100 m (20,000 ft), ISA 300 knots (556 km/h; 345 mph)
FAR T-O and landing field length 1,220 m (4,000 ft)
Max range with 50 passengers:
basic 800 nm (1,482 km; 921 miles)
optional 1,100 nm (2,038 km; 1,266 miles)

IPTN (CASA) NC-212-200 AVIOCAR

The C-212 Aviocar twin-turboprop multi-purpose transport aircraft has been manufactured in Indonesia since 1976, under licence from CASA of Spain (which see). Indonesian built Aviocars have the designation NC-212.

Contracts were placed for 114 NC-212s, and IPTN built 29 NC-212-100 series Aviocars before switching production to the NC-212-200 version, of which 81 had been delivered by February 1987 for duties which include civil passenger and cargo carrying (including a quick-change VIP interior), LAPES airdropping (low altitude parachute extraction system), military transport, search and rescue, maritime patrol, medical evacuation, photographic, survey, and rainmaking. Domestic and foreign operators were listed in the 1985-86 Jane's. Recent deliveries include five to the Indonesian Navy (making eight in all) in January 1989.

IPTN (MBB) NBO-105

The BO 105 helicopter has been manufactured in Indonesia since 1976, under licence from MBB (see German section). Indonesian designation is NBO-105. All components for the NBO-105 are now of Indonesian manufacture.

By February 1987 a total of 100 NBO-105s had been delivered, and from the 101st aircraft production has continued with the NBO-105 S, which has a 25 cm (10 in) longer fuselage and optional radar. An armed version, designated NBO-105MPDS (multi-purpose delivery system), can be equipped with unguided rockets (50 mm to 81 mm calibre), machine-gun pods (single or twin 0.30 in or 0.50 in), reconnaissance pods or FLIR pods. Customers for the NBO-105 include the Indonesian Army, Navy (4) and Police (6), Pelita Air Service, the Indonesian Forestry Department, Indonesian Immigration Department, Indonesian Search and Rescue Agency, Gudang Garam, Gunung Madu, and the Indonesian Civil Aviation Training Centre.

Indonesian Army NBO-105 helicopter, built by IPTN (John Fricker)

NAS-332 Super Puma assembled by IPTN

IPTN (MBB/KAWASAKI) NBK-117

Under a contract signed with MBB in November 1982, IPTN is manufacturing the BK 117 helicopter (see International section) under licence. Indonesian aircraft, which have been ordered by government agencies and private operators, are designated NBK-117; three had been completed by 1 January 1987, the latest date for which any information has been received.

NTT N-442

MBB and IPTN have suspended development of this small four-seat helicopter, known previously as the BN-109. All available details were given under the NTT heading in the International section of the 1989-90 Jane's.

IPTN (AEROSPATIALE) NAS-332 SUPER PUMA

IPTN began assembling the NSA 330J Puma in 1981, completing 11 before switching production to the AS 332C and L Super Puma in early 1983.

Rollout of the first IPTN assembled NAS-332 for Pelita Air Service took place on 22 April 1983. Eight had been purchased by Indonesian customers by late 1988, including four as commando and general purpose transports by the Indonesian Navy. One, for use as a VIP transport, was delivered to the Malaysian Ministry of Finance in November 1988. From the 19th NAS-332, the Super Puma was due to become available from IPTN in its stretched versions, with a 0.765 m (2 ft 6 in) longer cabin.

IPTN (BELL) NBELL-412SP

A licence agreement for IPTN to manufacture the Bell Model 412 (see Canadian section) was signed in November 1982. It covers the partial manufacture and assembly of more than 100 Bell 412s, the first of which was flown for the first time in April 1986. Orders have been placed by the Indonesian armed forces (including four for the Navy) and private operators. IPTN built aircraft, three of which had been completed by mid-1987, are designated NBell-412SP. Four were delivered to the Indonesian Army in September 1988.

INTERNATIONAL PROGRAMMES

AEROSPATIALE/CATIC/SA

Aerospatiale (France), CATIC (People's Republic of China) and Singapore Aerospace (SA) are teamed in the development and production of a new four/five-seat light helicopter for civil and military applications. The definition phase was launched on 15 February 1990. ASTA of Australia, a signatory to the original agreement, withdrew from the programme in late 1989.

P 120 L

Known provisionally as the P 120 L, this helicopter will be single-engined and compete with the Lama, Gazelle and JetRanger. Design features include a fenestron tail rotor with a stator, Aerospatiale Spheriflex four-blade main rotor and skid landing gear. Its general appearance is shown in the accompanying illustration. Main and tail rotor blades and much of the fuselage will be built of composites. Aerospatiale is programme leader, with a 54 per cent share of the work; CATIC will be responsible for 30 per cent and Singapore Aerospace for 16 per cent. Singapore will be responsible for the upper fuselage, tailboom and fin, with the main front fuselage structure produced by CATIC's Harbin Aircraft Manufacturing Company. Aerospatiale

Model of the P 120 L light helicopter under development by France, China and Singapore

will be responsible for rotors and transmission system, final assembly, flight test and certification.

The definition phase is scheduled for completion in December 1990, first flight early 1993, and first deliveries in early 1996. Two versions are to be developed: a basic economy model, and one with a more powerful engine for improved performance under hot and high conditions.

POWER PLANT: One turboshaft of 559 kW (750 shp) in basic version, 655 kW (879 shp) in high performance version.

ACCOMMODATION: Pilot and four passengers.

DIMENSIONS: Not yet known.

WEIGHTS: (A: basic version, B: high performance version):

Max sling load: A	1,000 kg (2,205 lb)	
B	1,160 kg (2,557 lb)	

Max T-O weight: A	2,000 kg (4,409 lb)	
B	2,300 kg (5,070 lb)	

PERFORMANCE (estimated, at max T-O weight except where indicated; A and B as under Weights):

Max cruising speed at S/L, ISA:		
A	147 knots (272 km/h; 169 mph)	
B	151 knots (280 km/h; 174 mph)	
B at 2,000 kg (4,409 lb) AUW		
	157 knots (291 km/h; 181 mph)	
Hovering ceiling OGE:		
A, ISA	3,500 m (11,480 ft)	
B, ISA	3,250 m (10,660 ft)	
B, ISA, at 2,000 kg (4,409 lb) AUW		
	4,500 m (14,760 ft)	

A, ISA +20°C	2,850 m (9,350 ft)	
B, ISA +20°C	2,550 m (8,365 ft)	
B, ISA +20°C, at 2,000 kg (4,409 lb) AUW		
	3,900 m (12,795 ft)	
Range at S/L with 600 litres (158.5 US gallons; 132 Imp gallons) fuel:		
A	442 nm (820 km; 509 miles)	
B	405 nm (750 km; 466 miles)	

AIRBUS
AIRBUS INDUSTRIE

1 Rond Point Maurice Bellonte, 31707 Blagnac Cédex, France
Telephone: 33 61 93 33 33
Telex: AIRBU 530526 F
Fax: 33 61 93 37 92
PARIS OFFICE: 12bis avenue Bosquet, 75007 Paris, France
Telephone: 33 (1) 45 51 40 95
AIRFRAME PRIME CONTRACTORS:

Aerospatiale, 37 boulevard de Montmorency, 75781 Paris Cédex 16, France

Deutsche Airbus GmbH, Postfach 950109, Kreetslag 10, 2103 Hamburg 95, West Germany

British Aerospace PLC, 11 Strand, London WC2N 5JT, UK

Construcciones Aeronauticas SA, Rey Francisco 4, Apartado 193, 28008 Madrid, Spain

MANAGING DIRECTOR AND CHIEF EXECUTIVE OFFICER:
Jean Pierson

CHIEF OPERATING OFFICER: Heribert Flosdorff

SENIOR VICE-PRESIDENT, COMMERCIAL: Stuart Iddles

MANAGER, TECHNICAL PRESS: David Velupillai

Airbus Industrie was set up in December 1970 as a Groupement d'Intérêt Economique to manage the development, manufacture, marketing and support of the A300 twin-engined large-capacity short/medium-range transport. This management now extends to the A300-600, A310, A320, A321 and A340/A330 included in this entry. Airbus Industrie is responsible for all work on these programmes by the partner companies, made up of Aerospatiale of France, which has a 37.9 per cent interest in Airbus Industrie, Deutsche Airbus of West Germany (37.9 per cent), British Aerospace PLC (20 per cent), and CASA of Spain (4.2 per cent). Fokker (Netherlands) is an associate in the A300 and A310 programmes; and Belairbus (Belgium) in the programmes for the A310, A320 and A330/A340. Among the major partners, a total workforce of about 30,000 is engaged on Airbus Industrie programmes. Some of the Deutsche Airbus work on the A300/A310 is subcontracted to the Italian aerospace industry, and some BAe work to the Australian industry. Canadair is an Aerospatiale subcontractor on the A330/A340.

Large, fully equipped and inspected airframe sections are flown from their places of manufacture in Europe to the final assembly line in Toulouse on board four Super Guppy outsize cargo aircraft. After assembly, painting in customers' colour scheme is usually carried out at Toulouse. Aircraft are then flown to Hamburg for installation of interior furnishings and cabin and cargo hold equipment before returning to Toulouse for final customer acceptance.

In 1989 Airbus Industrie won firm orders for a total of 421 aircraft, comprising 87 A300s and A310s, 126 A320s, 20 A321s, 107 A330s and 81 A340s. The European consortium delivered 105 aircraft during the same period: 47 A300s and A310s, and 58 A320s.

AIRBUS A300-600

The early history of the A300 programme has appeared in previous editions of *Jane's*.

The first A300, a B1 (F-WUAB, later F-OCAZ) first flew on 28 October 1972, and was followed by the second B1 (F-WUAC) on 5 February 1973. The B1 was described in detail in the 1971-72 *Jane's*. Detailed descriptions of the B2 and B4 series (248 built) can be found in the 1984-85 and earlier editions. A300B4 production ended in Autumn 1984.

The major production versions since early 1984 are:

A300-600. Advanced version of B4-200, first flown (F-WZLR) on 8 July 1983 and certificated (with JT9D-7R4H1 engines) on 9 March 1984. French certification for Category IIIB take-offs and landings awarded on 26 March 1985. Increased passenger and freight capacity. Modifications include use of rear fuselage developed for A310, shorter by two frame pitches in unpressurised section than that of 100/200 series A300s, with three frame pitches extension of parallel section of fuselage to restore tail moment arm. Passenger capacity thus increased by two seat rows for increase in overall length equivalent to only one frame pitch. Other improvements include increased wing trailing-edge camber and installation of simple Fowler flaps, forward facing two-man cockpit with CRT displays, new digital avionics, new braking control system, and new APU.

An extensive weight reduction programme, including simplified systems and the use of composite materials for some secondary structural components, allows greater payload capacity with very little change in empty weight. Performance improvements, offering better payload/range capability and greater fuel economy, result from a comprehensive drag clean-up programme.

First delivery (to Saudia) was made on 26 March 1984. September 1985 certification was obtained for the improved version (first flown on 20 March 1985) with CF6-80C2 engines, carbon brakes, wingtip fences and 'New World' cockpit. The improved version subsequently became available with Pratt & Whitney PW4000 engines. Improved versions of the A300-600 have been ordered by Thai Airways International (six), the Abu Dhabi Private Flight (one), Korean Air (five), LATUR of Mexico (one) and Lufthansa (10); first delivery (to Thai Airways) was made on 26 September 1985. The basic equipment fit of aircraft for delivery from late 1991 will be improved relative to earlier deliveries by the incorporation of standard options.

A300-600R. Extended range version of -600 (formerly known as -600ER), first flown on 9 December 1987. European and FAA certification granted on 10 and 28 March 1988 respectively. Principal differences from the improved A300-600 are incorporation of tailplane trim tank (already in service on the A310-300) and increased max T-O weight. Deliveries began on 21 April 1988 to launch customer American Airlines, which has ordered 32. Other customers include Ansett (six), China Airlines (five), China Eastern (three), Egyptair (nine), Emirates (four), ILFC (five), Japan Air System (seven), JFS-S (four), Korean Air

(15), LATUR (one), Monarch Airlines (four), Polaris Aircraft Leasing (five) and Thai Airways International (five).

A300-600 Convertible. Convertible passenger/cargo version of the A300-600; described separately.

By 28 February 1990 orders for the A300-600 and -600R, including Convertibles, totalled 142, of which 73 had been delivered, by 31 January.

Aerospatiale is responsible for the entire nose section (including the flight deck), lower centre fuselage, two inboard spoilers on each wing, wing/body fairings and engine pylons, and for final assembly. Deutsche Airbus builds the forward fuselage between the flight deck and wing box, the upper centre fuselage, rear fuselage, vertical tail surfaces, tailcone, five outboard spoilers on each wing, some cabin doors, and also installs the commercial interior, including seats. British Aerospace has design responsibility for the wings, builds the wing box, and collaborates with Fokker, which is building the wingtips, leading-edge slats, ailerons, trailing-edge flaps, and main landing gear leg fairings. Wing equipping is done by Deutsche Airbus. CASA manufactures all horizontal tail surfaces, port and starboard forward passenger doors, mainwheel doors and nosewheel doors.

The following description applies to the A300-600, except where otherwise indicated:

TYPE: Large-capacity wide-bodied medium/long-range transport.

WINGS: Cantilever mid-wing monoplane. Thickness/chord ratio 10.5 per cent. Sweepback 28° at quarter-chord. Primary two-spar box structure, integral with fuselage and incorporating fail-safe principles, built of high strength aluminium alloy except for spoilers and outer flap deflector doors (carbonfibre); flap track fairings and rear wing/body fairings (aramid fibre); and upper surface panels above mainwheel bays (glassfibre). All CFRP moving surfaces have aluminium or titanium trailing-edges. Third spar across inboard sections. Machined skin with open-sectioned stringers. Each wing has three-section metal leading-edge slats (no slat cutout over the engine pylon), and three cambered tabless metal flaps on trailing-edge; a Krueger flap on the leading-edge wingroot; and an all-speed metal aileron between inboard flap and outer pair. Seven spoilers on each wing, forward of flaps, all of which are used as lift dumpers. The five outboard spoilers are used for roll control; the five inboard spoilers are used as airbrakes. The flaps extend over 84 per cent of each half span, and increase the wing chord by 25 per cent when fully extended. The aileron is deflected downward automatically 9° 2′ on each side when the flaps are operated. Drive mechanisms for flaps and slats are similar to one another, each powered by twin motors driving ball screwjacks on each surface with built-in protection against asymmetric operation. Two slat positions for take-off and landing. Pre-selection of the spoiler/lift dump lever allows automatic extension of the lift dumpers on touchdown. Ailerons are fully powered by mechanically controlled hydraulic servos (three per surface); secondary control surfaces (spoilers, flaps and slats) fully hydraulically powered, with electrical control. Wingtip fences introduced 1985. Anti-icing of wing leading-edges, outboard of engines, is by engine bleed air.

FUSELAGE: Semi-monocoque pressurised structure of circular cross-section, with frames and open Z-section stringers. Built of damage-tolerant aluminium alloy, with steel or titanium for some major components; cooling air inlet fairings and radome of AFRP. Skin panels integrally machined in areas of high stress. Honeycomb panels or selected glassfibre laminates for secondary structures.

TAIL UNIT: Cantilever structure, with sweepback on all surfaces. Construction mainly of metal except for fin leading/trailing-edges, fin tip, fin/fuselage fairings, rudder, tailplane trailing-edge and elevator leading-edge panels, tailplane and elevator tips, and access panels to elevator actuator, which are made of GFRP (with CFRP in case of elevators and rudder). Fin box made of carbonfibre since mid-1987. Variable incidence tailplane is actuated by a fail-safe ball screwjack, driven by two independent hydraulic motors which are electrically controlled with an additional mechanical input. Elevators and rudder are fully powered by mechanically controlled hydraulic servos (three per surface). No anti-icing of leading-edges.

Airbus A300-600R wide-bodied medium-range transport (JT9D engines) *(Pilot Press)*

Airbus A300-600R twin-turbofan extended range transport in the insignia of Emirates, the IATA airline of Dubai

LANDING GEAR: Hydraulically retractable tricycle type, of Messier-Hispano-Bugatti design, with Messier-Hispano-Bugatti/Liebherr/Dowty shock absorbers and wheels standard. Twin-wheel nose unit retracts forward, main units inward into fuselage. Free-fall extension. Nosewheel doors and mainwheel leg fairing doors are of CFRP. Nose gear is structurally identical to B2/B4/A310; main gear is generally reinforced, with a new-design hinge arm and a new pitch damper hydraulic and electrical installation. Each four-wheel main unit comprises two tandem mounted bogies, interchangeable left with right. Standard bogie size is 927 × 1,397 mm (36½ × 55 in); wider bogie of 978 × 1,524 mm (38½ × 60 in) is optional. Mainwheel tyres size 49 × 17-20 (standard) or 49 × 19-20 (wide bogie), with respective pressures of 12.4 and 11.1 bars (180 and 161 lb/sq in). Nosewheel tyres size 40 × 14-16, pressure 9.4 bars (136 lb/sq in). Steering angles 65°/95°. Messier-Hispano-Bugatti/Liebherr/Dowty hydraulic disc brakes standard on all mainwheels. Normal braking powered by 'green' hydraulic system, controlled electrically through two master valves and monitored by a brake system control box to provide anti-skid protection. Standby braking (powered automatically by 'yellow' hydraulic system if normal 'green' system supply fails) controlled through a dual metering valve; anti-skid protection is ensured through same box as normal system, with emergency pressure supplied to brakes by accumulators charged from 'yellow' system. Automatic braking system optional. Duplex anti-skid units fitted, with a third standby hydraulic supply for wheel brakes. Bendix or Goodrich wheels and brakes available optionally.

POWER PLANT: Two turbofans in underwing pods. A300-600 was launched with the 249 kN (56,000 lb st) Pratt & Whitney JT9D-7R4H1 and is currently available with the 249 kN (56,000 lb st) Pratt & Whitney PW4156 or 262.4 kN (59,000 lb st) General Electric CF6-80C2A1. A300-600R is offered with the 273.6 kN (61,500 lb st) CF6-80C2A5 or 258 kN (58,000 lb st) PW4158. The CF6-80C2A5 and PW4158 are also available as options on the A300-600. The PW4160 (267 kN; 60,000 lb st) is available as an option on both the A300-600 and A300-600R. Nacelles have CFRP cowling panels and are subcontracted to Rohr (California); pylon fairings are of AFRP. Fuel in two integral tanks in each wing, and fifth integral tank in wing centre-section, giving standard usable capacity of 62,000 litres (16,379 US gallons; 13,638 Imp gallons). Additional 6,150 litre (1,625 US gallon; 1,353 Imp gallon) fuel/trim tank in tailplane (-600R only) increases this total to 68,150 litres (18,004 US gallons; 14,991 Imp gallons). Optional extra fuel cell in aft cargo hold can increase total to 75,350 litres (19,906 US gallons; 16,575 Imp gallons) in -600R. Two standard refuelling points beneath starboard wing; similar pair optional under port wing.

ACCOMMODATION: Crew of two on flight deck, plus two observers' seats. Passenger seating in main cabin in six, seven, eight or nine-abreast layout with two aisles. Typical mixed class layout has 267 seats (26 first class and 241 economy), six/eight abreast at 96/86 cm (38/34 in) seat pitch with two galleys and two toilets forward, one galley and two toilets in mid-cabin, and one galley and two toilets at rear. Typical economy class layout for 289 passengers eight-abreast at 86 cm (34 in) pitch. Max capacity (subject to certification) 375 passengers. Closed overhead baggage lockers on each side (total capacity 10.48 m³; 370 cu ft) and in double-sided central 'super-bin' installation (total capacity 14.50 m³; 512 cu ft), giving 0.03 to 0.09 m³ (1.2 to 3.2 cu ft) per passenger in typical economy layout. Two outward parallel-opening Type A plug type passenger doors ahead of wing on each side, and one on each side at rear. Type I emergency exit on each side aft of wing. Underfloor baggage/cargo holds

fore and aft of wings, with doors on starboard side. Forward hold will accommodate twelve LD3 containers, or four 2.24 × 3.17 m (88 × 125 in) or, optionally, 2.43 × 3.17 m (96 × 125 in) pallets, or engine modules. Rear hold will accommodate ten LD3 containers. Additional bulk loading of freight provided for in an extreme rear compartment with usable volume of 17.3 m³ (611 cu ft). Alternatively, the rear hold can be arranged optionally to carry eleven LD3 containers, with bulk cargo capacity reduced to 8.6 m³ (303 cu ft). The bulk cargo compartment can be used for the transport of livestock. Entire accommodation is pressurised, including freight, baggage and avionics compartments.

SYSTEMS: Air supply for air-conditioning system taken from engine bleed and/or APU via two high pressure points. Conditioned air can also be supplied direct to cabin by two low pressure ground connections. Ram air inlet for fresh air ventilation when packs not in use. Pressure control system (max differential 0.574 bars; 8.32 lb/sq in) consists of two identical, independent, automatic systems (one active, one standby). Switchover from one to the other is automatic after each flight and in case of active system failure. In each system, pressure is controlled by two electric outflow valves, its function depending on pre-programmed cabin pressure altitude and rate of change of cabin pressure, aircraft altitude, and preselected landing airfield elevation. Automatic pre-pressurisation of cabin before take-off is provided, to prevent noticeable pressure fluctuation during take-off. Hydraulic system comprises three fully independent circuits, operating simultaneously. Each system includes a reservoir of the direct air/fluid contact type, pressurised at 3.5 bars (51 lb/sq in); fluid used is a fire resistant phosphate ester type. Nominal output flow of 136 litres (35.9 US gallons; 30 Imp gallons)/min is delivered at pressure of 207 bars (3,000 lb/sq in). 'Blue' and 'yellow' systems have one pump each, 'green' system has two pumps. The three circuits provide triplex power for primary flying controls; if any circuit fails, full control of the aircraft is retained without any necessity for action by the crew. All three circuits supply the ailerons, rudder and elevators; 'blue' circuit additionally supplies spoiler 7, spoiler/airbrake 4, airbrake 1, yaw damper and slats; 'green' circuit additionally supplies spoiler 6, flaps, Krueger flaps, slats, landing gear, wheel brakes, steering, tailplane trim, artificial feel, and roll/pitch/yaw autopilot; 'yellow' circuit additionally supplies spoiler 5, spoiler/airbrake 3, airbrake 2, flaps, wheel brakes, cargo doors, artificial feel, yaw damper, tailplane trim, and roll/pitch/yaw autopilot. Ram air turbine driven pump provides standby hydraulic power should both engines become inoperative. Main electrical power is supplied under normal flight conditions by two integrated drive generators, one on each engine. A third (auxiliary) generator, driven by the APU, can replace either of the main generators, having the same electromagnetic components but not the constant-speed drive. Each generator is rated at 90kVA, with overload ratings of 112.5kVA for 5 min and 150kVA for 5 s. The APU generator is driven at constant speed through a gearbox. Three unregulated transformer-rectifier units (TRUs) supply 28V DC power. Three 25Ah nickel-cadmium batteries are used for emergency supply and APU starting. Emergency electrical power taken from main aircraft batteries and an emergency static inverter, providing single-phase 115V 400Hz output for flight instruments, navigation, communications and lighting when power is not available from normal sources. Hot air anti-icing of engines, engine air intakes, and outer segments of leading-edge slats. Electrical heating for anti-icing flight deck front windscreens, demisting flight deck side windows, and for sensors, pitot probes and static ports, and waste water drain masts. Garrett GTCP

331-250F APU in tailcone, exhausting upward. The installation incorporates APU noise attenuation. Fire protection system is self-contained, and firewall panels protect main structure from an APU fire. APU provides bleed air to pneumatic system, and drives an auxiliary AC generator during ground and in-flight operation. APU drives a 90kVA oil spray cooled generator, and supplies bleed air for main engine start or air-conditioning system. For current deliveries of A300-600, APU has an improved relight capability, with starting capability throughout the flight envelope. Modular box system provides passenger oxygen to all installation areas. For new A300-600s and -600Rs, two optional modifications are offered for compliance with full extended-range operations (EROPS) requirements: a hydraulically driven fourth generator, and an increased cargo hold fire suppression capability. EROPS kit is already qualified for aircraft with CF6-80C2 and JT9D-7R series engines, and was qualified from mid-1988 for those with PW4000 series.

AVIONICS AND EQUIPMENT: Standard communications avionics include two VHF sets, one HF, one Selcal system, interphone and passenger address systems, groundcrew call system, and voice recorder. Radio navigation avionics include two DME interrogators, two VOR receivers, two ATC transponders, one ADF, two marker beacon receivers, two ILS receivers, weather radar, and two radio altimeters. Full provisions for second weather radar and GPWS; space provisions for one or two HF, third VHF; structural provision for such future systems as a discrete address beacon system. Two Honeywell digital air data computers standard. Most other avionics are to customer's requirements, only those related to the blind landing system (ILS and radio altimeter) being selected and supplied by the manufacturer. Six identical and interchangeable CRT electronic displays (four EFIS and two ECAM: electronic flight instrument system and electronic centralised aircraft monitor), plus digitised electromechanical instruments with liquid crystal displays. The basic digital AFCS comprises a single flight control computer (FCC) for flight director and autopilot functions, a single thrust control computer (TCC) for speed and thrust control, and two flight augmentation computers (FACs) to provide yaw damping, electric pitch trim, and flight envelope monitoring and protection. Options include second FCC (for Cat III automatic landing); second TCC; two flight management computers (FMCs) and two control display units for full flight management system; windscreen guidance display by adding optical device in glareshield; and addition of delayed flap approach (DFA) to TCC for decelerated approach. Basic aircraft is also fitted with an ARINC 717 data recording system, comprising a digital flight data acquisition unit, digital flight data recorder, three-axis linear accelerometer, and flight data entry panel. An optional speed reference system with built-in windshear protection is available. Dual automatic landing system provides coupled approach and automatic landing facilities suitable for Category II operation.

DIMENSIONS, EXTERNAL:

Wing span	44.84 m (147 ft 1 in)
Wing aspect ratio	7.7
Length overall	54.08 m (177 ft 5 in)
Fuselage: Length	53.30 m (174 ft 10½ in)
Max diameter	5.64 m (18 ft 6 in)
Height overall	16.62 m (54 ft 6½ in)
Tailplane span	16.26 m (53 ft 4 in)
Wheel track	9.60 m (31 ft 6 in)
Wheelbase (c/l of shock absorbers)	18.60 m (61 ft 0 in)
Passengers doors (each): Height	1.93 m (6 ft 4 in)
Width	1.07 m (3 ft 6 in)
Height to sill: fwd	4.60 m (15 ft 1 in)

centre	4.80 m (15 ft 9 in)
rear	5.50 m (18 ft 0½ in)
Emergency exits (each): Height	1.60 m (5 ft 3 in)
Width	0.61 m (2 ft 0 in)
Height to sill	4.87 m (15 ft 10 in)
Underfloor cargo door (fwd):	
Height	1.71 m (5 ft 7½ in)
Width	2.69 m (8 ft 10 in)
Height to sill	3.07 m (10 ft 1 in)
Underfloor cargo door (rear):	
Height	1.71 m (5 ft 7½ in)
Width	1.81 m (5 ft 11¼ in)
Height to sill	3.41 m (11 ft 2¼ in)
Underfloor cargo door (extreme rear):	
Height (projected)	0.95 m (3 ft 1 in)
Width	0.95 m (3 ft 1 in)
Height to sill	3.56 m (11 ft 8 in)

DIMENSIONS, INTERNAL:

Cabin, excl flight deck:	
Length	40.21 m (131 ft 11 in)
Max width	5.28 m (17 ft 4 in)
Max height	2.54 m (8 ft 4 in)
Underfloor cargo hold:	
Length: fwd	10.60 m (34 ft 9¼ in)
rear	7.95 m (26 ft 1 in)
extreme rear	3.40 m (11 ft 2 in)
Max height	1.76 m (5 ft 9 in)
Max width	4.20 m (13 ft 9¼ in)
Underfloor cargo hold volume:	
fwd	75.1 m³ (2,652 cu ft)
rear	55.0 m³ (1,942 cu ft)
extreme rear	17.3 m³ (611 cu ft)

AREAS:

Wings, gross	260.0 m² (2,798.6 sq ft)
Leading-edge slats (total)	30.30 m² (326.15 sq ft)
Krueger flaps (total)	1.115 m² (12.00 sq ft)
Trailing-edge flaps (total)	47.30 m² (509.13 sq ft)
All-speed ailerons (total)	7.06 m² (75.99 sq ft)
Spoilers (total)	5.396 m² (58.08 sq ft)
Airbrakes (total)	12.59 m² (135.52 sq ft)
Fin	45.20 m² (486.53 sq ft)
Rudder	13.57 m² (146.07 sq ft)
Horizontal tail surfaces (total)	64.0 m² (688.89 sq ft)

*WEIGHTS AND LOADINGS (A: CF6-80C2A1/A5 engines; B: PW4156/4158 engines, all in 267-seat configuration):

Manufacturer's weight empty:	
A (600)	79,210 kg (174,628 lb)
A (600R)	79,403 kg (175,053 lb)
B (600)	79,151 kg (174,498 lb)
B (600R)	79,318 kg (174,866 lb)
Operating weight empty:	
A (600)	89,445 kg (197,192 lb)
A (600R)	89,669 kg (197,686 lb)
B (600)	89,397 kg (197,086 lb)
B (600R)	89,595 kg (197,523 lb)
Max payload (structural): A (600)	40,555 kg (89,408 lb)
A (600R)	40,331 kg (88,914 lb)
B (600)	40,603 kg (89,514 lb)
B (600R)	40,405 kg (89,077 lb)
Underfloor cargo capacity (A and B):	
containerised	31,300 kg (69,005 lb)
bulk	2,800 kg (6,173 lb)
Max usable fuel:	
600: standard	49,777 kg (109,740 lb)
600R: standard	54,712 kg (120,620 lb)
with optional cargo hold tank	58,604 kg (129,200 lb)
Max T-O weight (A and B):	
600	165,000 kg (363,765 lb)
600R (standard)	170,500 kg (375,885 lb)
600R (option)	171,700 kg (378,535 lb)
Max ramp weight (A and B):	
600	165,900 kg (365,745 lb)
600R (standard)	170,500 kg (375,885 lb)
600R (option)	172,600 kg (380,520 lb)
Max landing weight (A and B):	
600	138,000 kg (304,240 lb)
600R (standard)	140,000 kg (308,645 lb)
Max zero-fuel weight (A and B):	
600, 600R (standard)	130,000 kg (286,600 lb)
Max wing loading: 600	635 kg/m² (130.0 lb/sq ft)
600R (standard)	656 kg/m² (134.4 lb/sq ft)

Production aircraft from late 1991 onward. See 1989-90 and previous editions for earlier versions

PERFORMANCE (at max T-O weight except where indicated: A and B as for Weights):

Max operating speed (VMO) from S/L to 8,075 m (26,500 ft)	335 knots (621 km/h; 386 mph) CAS
Max operating Mach number (MMO) above 8,075 m (26,500 ft)	0.82
Max cruising speed at 7,620 m (25,000 ft)	480 knots (890 km/h; 553 mph)
Typical high-speed cruise at 9,150 m (30,000 ft)	Mach 0.82 (484 knots; 897 km/h; 557 mph)
Typical long-range cruising speed at 9,450 m (31,000 ft)	Mach 0.80 (472 knots; 875 km/h; 543 mph)
Approach speed: 600	134.5 knots (249 km/h; 155 mph)
600R	135.5 knots (251 km/h; 156 mph)
Max operating altitude	12,200 m (40,000 ft)
Min ground turning radius (effective, aft CG):	

wingtips	34.75 m (114 ft 0 in)
nosewheel	22.00 m (72 ft 2¼ in)
Runway ACN for flexible runway, category B:	
standard bogie & tyres: 600	56
600R	59
600R (option)	60
optional bogie & tyres: 600	52
600R	55
600R (option)	56
T-O field length at S/L, ISA + 15°C:	
600: A	2,384 m (7,820 ft)
B	2,332 m (7,650 ft)
600R: A (C2A5 engines)	2,451 m (8,040 ft)
B (PW4158 engines)	2,500 m (8,200 ft)
Landing field length: 600	1,536 m (5,040 ft)
600R	1,555 m (5,100 ft)

Range (1991 deliveries) at typical airline OWE with 267 passengers and baggage, reserves for 200 nm (370 km; 230 miles):

600: A	3,680 nm (6,820 km; 3,195 miles)
B	3,750 nm (6,949 km; 3,256 miles)
600R (standard fuel):	
A	4,050 nm (7,505 km; 3,517 miles)
B	4,150 nm (7,690 km; 3,604 miles)
600R (MTOGW option and additional fuel):	
A	4,210 nm (7,802 km; 3,656 miles)
B	4,310 nm (7,987 km; 3,743 miles)

OPERATIONAL NOISE LEVELS (A300-600, ICAO Annex 16, Chapter 3):

T-O (flyover): A, B	91.3 EPNdB (96.2 limit)
T-O (sideline): A, B	97.1 EPNdB (99.8 limit)
Approach: A, B	99.1 EPNdB (103.3 limit)

AIRBUS A300-600 CONVERTIBLE and A300-600 FREIGHTER

The Convertible is a version of the A300-600, with the same range of power plant options. Main differences are a large forward upper deck cargo door, a reinforced cabin floor, a smoke detection system in the main cabin, and an interior trim adaptable to the freighter role. The upper deck cargo door is on the opposite side to that of the forward underfloor hold, enabling loading or unloading to be carried out simultaneously at all positions. Three are operated by Kuwait Airways and one by the Private Flight of Abu Dhabi.

The A300-600 Convertible can be converted to passenger or mixed passenger/cargo configuration. Typical options include accommodation (in mainly eight-abreast seating) for up to 375 passengers (subject to certification) on the upper deck; or 145 passengers (seven/eight abreast) plus six 2.44 × 3.17 m (96 × 125 in) pallets; or 83 passengers plus nine 96 × 125 in pallets; up to twenty 2.24 × 3.17 m (88 × 125 in) pallets; or five 88 × 125 in plus nine 96 × 125 in pallets.

The A300-600 Freighter is designed for freighting only, and no passenger systems are provided. Various systems options give airlines the ability to adapt the basic aircraft to their specific freight requirements.

DIMENSIONS, EXTERNAL: As A300-600, plus:

Upper deck cargo door (fwd, port):	
Height (projected)	2.57 m (8 ft 5¼ in)
Width	3.58 m (11 ft 9 in)
Height to sill	4.91 m (16 ft 1 in)

DIMENSIONS, INTERNAL:

Cabin upper deck usable for cargo:	
Length	33.45 m (109 ft 9 in)
Min height	2.01 m (6 ft 7 in)
Max height:	
ceiling trim panels in place	2.22 m (7 ft 3½ in)
without ceiling trim panels	2.44 m (8 ft 0 in)
Volume	192-203 m³ (6,780-7,169 cu ft)

WEIGHTS (basic Convertible. A: with CF6-80C2A5 engines, B: with PW4158 engines):

Manufacturer's weight empty:	
A, passenger mode	81,900 kg (180,558 lb)
B, passenger mode	81,820 kg (180,382 lb)
A, freight mode	81,640 kg (179,985 lb)
B, freight mode	81,560 kg (179,809 lb)
Operating weight empty:	
A, passenger mode	92,160 kg (203,178 lb)
B, passenger mode	92,100 kg (203,045 lb)
A, freight mode	83,470 kg (184,020 lb)
B, freight mode	83,410 kg (183,887 lb)
Max payload (structural):	
A, passenger mode	37,840 kg (83,423 lb)
B, passenger mode	37,900 kg (83,555 lb)
A, freight mode	46,530 kg (102,581 lb)
B, freight mode	46,590 kg (102,713 lb)
Max T-O weight (A and B)	170,500 kg (375,900 lb)
Max landing weight (A and B)	140,000 kg (308,650 lb)
Max zero-fuel weight (A and B)	130,000 kg (286,600 lb)

WEIGHTS (basic Freighter variant of -600R):

As for Convertible except:

Manufacturer's weight empty:	
A	78,550 kg (173,173 lb)
B	78,470 kg (172,997 lb)
Operating weight empty:	
A	80,120 kg (176,634 lb)
B	80,040 kg (176,458 lb)
Max payload (structural):	
A	49,880 kg (109,966 lb)
B	49,940 kg (110,099 lb)

PERFORMANCE:

Range with max (structural) payload, allowances for 30 min hold at 460 m (1,500 ft) and 200 nm (370 km; 230 mile) diversion:

A	2,680 nm (4,960 km; 3,090 miles)
B	2,720 nm (5,040 km; 3,130 miles)

AIRBUS A310

The A310 was launched in July 1978. Compared with the A300B2/B4-100 and 200 series, the cabin is shorter by 11 frames and the overall fuselage by 13 frames. The cabin thus normally seats from 210 to 250 passengers, although the aircraft is certificated for up to 280 persons. The A310 retains the same fuselage cross-section as the A300, thus being able to carry standard LD3 containers two abreast, and/or standard pallets installed crosswise. Convertible and Freighter versions are available.

The A310 also has new, advanced technology wings, of reduced span and area; new and smaller horizontal tail surfaces; common pylons able to support all types of General Electric and Pratt & Whitney engines offered; and landing gear modified to cater for these changes in size and weight. It features Airbus Industrie's advanced digital two-man cockpit.

Manufacturing breakdown of the A310 differs in minor respects from that of the A300. Aerospatiale builds the nose section (including flight deck), lower centre-fuselage and wing box, rear wing/body fairings, engine pylons and airbrakes, and is responsible for final assembly. Deutsche Airbus is responsible for the forward fuselage, upper centre-fuselage, rear fuselage and associated doors, tailcone, fin and rudder, flaps and spoilers; for wing assembly, and for commercial installation. BAe Chester produces the wing fixed structures. CASA's contribution includes the horizontal tail surfaces, nose-gear doors and mainwheel doors, and forward passenger doors. Fokker manufactures the main landing gear leg doors, wingtips, all-speed ailerons and flap track fairings. The wing leading-edge slats and forward wing/fuselage fairings are produced by Belairbus.

Airbus A310 medium/extended-range transport aircraft (*Pilot Press*)

A310-300 in the livery of the East German airline Interflug, the first East European operator of Airbus aircraft

The prototype A310 (F-WZLH) flew for the first time on 3 April 1982. Simultaneous French and German certification was awarded on 11 March 1983, UK certification in January 1984 and FAA type approval in early 1985. The first aircraft (for Lufthansa and Swissair) were handed over on 29 March 1983, entering service on 12 and 21 April respectively. Certification to JAR Category IIIA was awarded by the French and German authorities on 28 and 29 September 1983, and Category IIIB on 28 November 1984.

The following versions have been announced:

A310-200. Basic passenger version. Wingtip fences introduced as standard from Spring 1986 (first delivery: Thai Airways on 7 May).

A310-200C. Convertible version; first delivered to Martinair on 29 November 1984.

A310-200F. Freighter version.

A310-300. Extended-range version. First flown on 8 July 1985 with JT9D-7R4E engines; certificated with these engines on 5 December 1985 and delivered to launch customer Swissair on 17 December. Second member of Airbus family to introduce as standard the delta shaped wingtip fences (for drag reduction) developed by BAe and test flown in 1983 on an A310-200 testbed. Version with CF6-80C2 engines first flew on 6 September 1985, followed by certification and first delivery (to Air-India) in April 1986. Certificated with PW4152 engines and first delivered (to Pan American) in June 1987. Extra range is provided by an increased basic max T-O weight (150,000 kg; 330,695 lb) and greater fuel capacity. Higher max T-O weights optional. The standard extra fuel capacity is in the tailplane, which allows in-flight CG control for improved fuel efficiency; for extra long range, one or two ACTs (additional centre tanks) can be installed in part of the cargo hold. First customer for this version, certificated in November 1987, is Wardair of Canada. Other customers include Aeroflot, Air France, Balair, CSA, Hapag-Lloyd Flug, Interflug, TEA and THY.

By 14 February 1990 firm orders for 229 A310s had been received, of which 165 had been delivered by 31 January.

TYPE: Large-capacity wide-bodied medium/extended-range transport.

WINGS: Cantilever mid-wing monoplane. Thickness/chord ratio 15.2 per cent at root, 11.8 per cent at kink in trailing-edge, and 10.8 per cent at tip. Dihedral at trailing-edge 11° 8′ (inboard), 4° 3′ (outboard). Incidence 5° 3′ at root. Sweepback 28° at quarter-chord. Construction is mainly of high strength aluminium alloy except for outer shroud (structure in place of low-speed aileron), airbrakes, spoilers, leading-edge lower access panels and outer deflector doors (CFRP); flap track fairings, flap access doors and rear wing/body fairings (AFRP); and leading-edge top panels, panel aft of rear spar, upper surface skin panel above mainwheel bay, and forward wing/body fairings (GFRP). Wing box is two-spar multi-rib metal structure, with top and bottom load-carrying skins. Three-section leading-edge slats on each wing over almost full span, with no cutout over engine pylon; Krueger flap between inboard slat and wingroot. Fowler trailing-edge flap on outboard section of each wing; vaned Fowler flap inboard. All-speed metal aileron between flaps on each wing. Electrically signalled spoilers for roll control. Two independent computer systems with different software provide redundancy and operational safety. Two airbrakes between root and engine, two airbrakes outboard of engine, and three spoilers outboard of outer airbrakes, on each wing; all 14 surfaces are used also as lift dumpers. Delta shaped wingtip fences

standard from 1985. Outer slat leading-edges de-iced by engine bleed air.

FUSELAGE: Generally similar to A300B4, except for reduced length (see introductory copy), resulting in deletion of two passenger doors. Rear fuselage reprofiled and shortened between pressure bulkhead and tailcone. Construction generally as described for A300-600, with AFRP radome and cooling air inlet fairings, GFRP cover panel over glideslope antenna.

TAIL UNIT: Generally as described for A300-600, with CFRP fin box standard since Spring 1985. GFRP fin leading-/trailing-edges and fin tip. Metal tailplane, with GFRP tips, CFRP trailing-edge actuator access panel and AFRP trailing-edge panels. Rudder of CFRP and GFRP; CFRP elevators introduced on A310s delivered from Autumn 1988 onward.

LANDING GEAR: Hydraulically retractable tricycle type. Twin-wheel steerable nose unit (steering angle 65°/95°) as for A300. Main gear by Messier-Hispano-Bugatti, each bogie comprising two tandem mounted twin-wheel units. Retraction as for A300. Nosewheel doors and mainwheel leg fairing doors of CFRP. Undertail bumper beneath rear fuselage, to protect structure against excessive nose-up attitude during T-O and landing. Standard tyre sizes: main, 46 × 16-20, pressure 11.2 bars (163 lb/sq in); nose, 40 × 14-16, pressure 9.0 bars (131 lb/sq in). Two options for low-pressure tyres on main units: (1) size 49 × 17-20, pressure 9.8 bars (143 lb/sq in); (2) size 49 × 19-20, pressure 8.9 bars (129 lb/sq in). Messier-Hispano-Bugatti brakes and anti-skid units standard; Bendix type optional on A310-200. Carbon brakes standard from Spring 1986.

POWER PLANT: Currently ordered or available with the following turbofan engines:
Launched with two 213.5 kN (48,000 lb st) Pratt & Whitney JT9D-7R4D1 or 222.4 kN (50,000 lb st) General Electric CF6-80A3; currently available with 238 kN (53,500 lb st) CF6-80C2A2, or two 231.2 kN (52,000 lb st) Pratt & Whitney PW4152. To become available from late 1991 with two 262.4 kN (59,000 lb st) CF6-80C2A8 or two 249.1 kN (56,000 lb st) PW4156A. CFRP cowling panels and AFRP pylon fairings. Total usable fuel capacity 55,000 litres (14,530 US gallons; 12,098 Imp gallons) in A310-200. Increased to 61,100 litres (16,141 US gallons; 13,440 Imp gallons) in A310-300, with additional fuel in tailplane trim tank. Further 7,200 litres (1,902 US gallons; 1,584 Imp gallons) can be carried in each additional centre tank (ACT) in forward part of aft cargo hold. Two refuelling points, one beneath each wing outboard of engine.

ACCOMMODATION: Crew of two on flight deck. Provision for third and fourth crew seats. Cabin can be configured with six/seven/eight and nine-abreast seating. Typical two-class layout is for 218 passengers: 18 first class, six-abreast at 96.5 cm (38 in) seat pitch, plus 200 economy class mainly eight-abreast at 86 cm (34 in) pitch. Max capacity is for up to 280 passengers nine-abreast in high-density configuration at pitch of 76 cm (30 in). Standard layout has two galleys and toilet at forward end of cabin, plus two galleys and four toilets at rear. Depending upon customer requirements, a second toilet can be added forward, and toilets and galleys can be located at the forward end at the class divider position. Overhead baggage stowage as for A300, rising to 0.09 m³ (3.2 cu ft) per passenger in typical economy layout. Four passenger doors, one forward and one aft on each side. Oversize Type I emergency exit over wing on each side. Underfloor baggage/cargo holds fore and aft of wings, each with door on starboard side. Forward hold will

accommodate eight LD3 containers or three 2.24 × 3.17 m (88 × 125 in) standard or three 2.44 × 3.17 m (96 × 125 in) optional pallets. Rear hold will accommodate six LD3 containers, with an optional seventh LD3 or LD1 position.

SYSTEMS: Garrett GTCP 331-250 APU. Air-conditioning system, powered by compressed air from engines, APU, or a ground supply unit, comprises two separate packs; air is distributed to flight deck, three separate cabin zones, electrical and electronic equipment, avionics bay and bulk cargo compartment. Ventilation of forward cargo compartments optional. Pressurisation system has a max normal differential of 0.57 bars (8.25 lb/sq in). Air supply for wing ice protection, engine starting and thrust reverser system is bled from various stages of the engine compressors, or supplied by the APU or a ground supply unit. Hydraulic system (three fully independent circuits operating at 207 bars; 3,000 lb/sq in: details as described for A300-600). Electrical system, similar to that of A300-600, consists of a three-phase 115/200V 400Hz constant frequency AC system and a 28V DC system. Two 90kVA engine driven brushless generators for normal single-channel operation, with automatic transfer of busbars in the event of a generator failure. Each has an overload rating of 135kVA for 5 min and 180kVA for 5 s. A third (identical) AC generator, directly driven at constant speed by the APU, can be used during ground operations, and also in flight to compensate for the loss of one or both engine driven generators. Current production A310s have APU with improved relight capability, which can be started and operated throughout the flight envelope. Any one generator can provide sufficient power to operate all equipment and systems necessary for an indefinite period of safe flight. DC power is generated via three 150A transformer-rectifiers. Three nickel-cadmium batteries are supplied. Flight crew oxygen system fed from rechargeable pressure bottle of 2,166 litres (76.5 cu ft) capacity. Standard options are a second 76.5 cu ft bottle, a 3,256 litre (115 cu ft) bottle, and an external filling connection. Emergency oxygen sets for passengers and cabin attendants. Anti-icing of outer wing leading-edge slats and engine air intakes by hot air bled from engines; and of pitot probes, static ports and plates, and sensors, by electric heating. For current production A310s, an EROPS (extended-range operations) modification kit, as for the A300-600, is available.

AVIONICS AND EQUIPMENT: Basic standard flight deck displays include flight guidance, navigation, configuration and engine management/monitoring information presented by electro-mechanical indicators, and an electronic centralised aircraft monitoring (ECAM) system unique to Airbus Industrie; warning information presented by conventional warning lights and on a master warning CRT; system information presented on a system CRT. Electronic flight instrument system comprises a CRT primary flight display, replacing the ADI and radio altimeter, and a CRT navigation display replacing the HSI and weather radar. The latter displays data from the flight management system (map mode, flight data display). A flight data recorder is also installed. Head-up display is optional. The basic aircraft is fitted with an AIDS (airborne integrated data system) providing a basic 80-parameter system (40 mandatory plus 40 additional) with an option to extend the system to 160 parameters. Standard com system includes HF radio (ARINC 719) (full provision); two VHF transceivers and space provision for a third (all to ARINC 716); Selcal system (ARINC 714); passenger address system (the amplifier conforming to ARINC 715); audio systems, comprising service interphone, audio integrating and flight interphone systems, and a ground crew call circuit. Digital navigation system, to ARINC 429 and ARINC 600, includes ADF (ARINC 712); two radio altimeters (ARINC 707); two DME (ARINC 709); two ATC transponders (ARINC 718); two VOR, one including marker beacon receiver (ARINC 711); weather radar (ARINC 708); two ILS (ARINC 710); and three AHRS (ARINC 705). Options include a second ADF; two or three IRS (ARINC 704); Omega system; and a second weather radar. The digital automatic flight control system (AFCS), in its basic definition, comprises a single flight control computer (FCC) for automatic flight control (to ARINC 701); a single thrust control computer (TCC) for speed and thrust control (to ARINC 703); and a duplicated flight augmentation computer (to ARINC 701). The flight management system (to ARINC 702) comprises a computer unit and control display unit. The FCC, functioning as autopilot, flight director and speed reference system, has the following basic modes: pitch hold, heading/roll altitude hold, altitude hold, altitude acquire, level change, vertical speed select and hold, heading select, VOR, heading, take-off and go-around. The installation of a second FCC will provide Cat. III autolands. The TCC provides the following functions: permanent computation of N1 or EPR limits, autothrottle functions, throttle pusher with windshear protection, speed and angle of attack protection, and a test function. A delayed flap approach mode is available as an option.

DIMENSIONS, EXTERNAL:

Wing span	43.89 m (144 ft 0 in)
Wing chord: at root	8.38 m (27 ft 6 in)
at tip	2.18 m (7 ft 1¾ in)
Wing aspect ratio	8.8
Length overall	46.66 m (153 ft 1 in)
Length of fuselage	45.13 m (148 ft 0¾ in)
Fuselage: Max diameter	5.64 m (18 ft 6 in)
Height overall	15.80 m (51 ft 10 in)
Tailplane span	16.26 m (53 ft 4¼ in)
Wheel track	9.60 m (31 ft 6 in)
Wheelbase (c/l of shock absorbers)	
	15.21 m (49 ft 10¾ in)
Passenger door (fwd, port): Height	1.93 m (6 ft 4 in)
Width	1.07 m (3 ft 6 in)
Height to sill at OWE	4.54 m (14 ft 10¾ in)
Passenger door (rear, port): Height	1.93 m (6 ft 4 in)
Width	1.07 m (3 ft 6 in)
Height to sill at OWE	4.85 m (15 ft 11 in)
Servicing doors (fwd and rear, stbd)	
as corresponding passenger doors	
Upper deck cargo door (A310C/F)	as A300-600
Emergency exits (overwing, port and stbd, each):	
Height	1.39 m (4 ft 6¾ in)
Width	0.67 m (2 ft 2½ in)
Underfloor cargo door (fwd):	
Height	1.71 m (5 ft 7½ in)
Width	2.69 m (8 ft 10 in)
Height to sill at OWE	2.611 m (8 ft 6¾ in)
Underfloor cargo door (rear):	
Height	1.71 m (5 ft 7½ in)
Width	1.81 m (5 ft 11¼ in)
Height to sill at OWE	2.72 m (8 ft 11 in)
Underfloor cargo door (aft bulk hold):	
Height	0.95 m (3 ft 1½ in)
Width	0.95 m (3 ft 1½ in)
Height to sill at OWE	2.751 m (9 ft 0¼ in)

DIMENSIONS, INTERNAL:

Cabin, excl flight deck: Length	33.24 m (109 ft 0¾ in)
Max width	5.28 m (17 ft 4 in)
Max height	2.33 m (7 ft 7¾ in)
Volume	210.0 m³ (7,416.1 cu ft)
Fwd cargo hold: Length	7.63 m (25 ft 0½ in)
Max width	4.18 m (13 ft 8½ in)
Height	1.71 m (5 ft 7¼ in)
Volume	50.3 m³ (1,776.3 cu ft)
Rear cargo hold: Length	5.033 m (16 ft 6¼ in)
Max width	4.17 m (13 ft 8¼ in)
Height	1.67 m (5 ft 5¾ in)
Volume	34.5 m³ (1,218.4 cu ft)
Aft bulk hold: Volume	17.3 m³ (610.9 cu ft)
Total overall cargo volume	102.1 m³ (3,605.6 cu ft)

AREAS:

Wings, gross	219 m² (2,357.3 sq ft)
Leading-edge slats (total)	28.54 m² (307.20 sq ft)
Trailing-edge flaps (total)	36.68 m² (394.82 sq ft)
Ailerons (total)	6.86 m² (73.84 sq ft)
Spoilers (total)	7.36 m² (79.22 sq ft)
Airbrakes (total)	6.16 m² (66.31 sq ft)
Fin	45.20 m² (486.53 sq ft)
Rudder	13.57 m² (146.07 sq ft)
Tailplane	44.80 m² (482.22 sq ft)
Elevators (total)	19.20 m² (206.67 sq ft)

WEIGHTS (218-seat configuration. A: CF6-80C2A2 engines; B: PW4152s; C: CF6-80C2A8s; D: PW4156As):
Manufacturer's weight empty:

200: A	71,490 kg (157,608 lb)
B	71,430 kg (157,476 lb)
300: A	71,670 kg (158,005 lb)
B	71,610 kg (157,873 lb)

Operating weight empty: 200: A

Operating weight empty: 200: A	79,840 kg (176,017 lb)
B	79,790 kg (175,907 lb)
300: A	80,050 kg (176,480 lb)
B	80,000 kg (176,370 lb)
C	80,500 kg (177,472 lb)
D	80,450 kg (177,362 lb)
Max payload: 200: A	34,160 kg (75,310 lb)
B	34,210 kg (75,420 lb)
300: A	33,950 kg (74,847 lb)
B	34,000 kg (74,957 lb)
* Max usable fuel: 200	44,089 kg (97,200 lb)
300	49,029 kg (108,090 lb)
Max T-O weight: 200	142,000 kg (313,055 lb)
300 (basic)	150,000 kg (330,695 lb)
300 (options)	153,000 kg (337,305 lb)
or	157,000 kg (346,125 lb)
or	164,000 kg (361,560 lb)
Max landing weight: 200, 300	123,000 kg (271,170 lb)
options (200 and 300)	124,000 kg (273,375 lb)
Max zero-fuel weight: 200, 300	113,000 kg (249,120 lb)
options (200 and 300)	114,000 kg (251,330 lb)

optional additional tank in aft cargo hold adds 5,779 kg (12,740 lb) of fuel and increases OWE/reduces max payload by 757 kg (1,670 lb). Two additional tanks add 11,560 kg (25,485 lb) of fuel and increase OWE/reduce max payload by 1,300 kg (2,866 lb)

PERFORMANCE (at basic max T-O weight except where indicated; engines as under Weights):

Typical long-range cruising speed at 9,450-12,500 m (31,000-41,000 ft): A, B, C, D	Mach 0.80
Approach speed at max landing weight:	
A, B, C, D	135 knots (250 km/h; 155 mph)
Min ground turning radius (effective, aft CG):	
wingtips	33.00 m (108 ft 3¼ in)
nosewheel	18.75 m (61 ft 6 in)
T-O field length at S/L, ISA + 15°C:	
200: A	1,860 m (6,100 ft)
B	1,799 m (5,900 ft)
300: A (at 150 tonne MTOGW)	2,408 m (7,900 ft)
B (at 150 tonne MTOGW)	2,225 m (7,300 ft)
C (at 164 tonne MTOGW)	2,560 m (8,400 ft)
C (at 164 tonne MTOGW)	2,400 m (7,875 ft)
Landing field length at S/L, at max landing weight (200 and 300): A	1,479 m (4,850 ft)
B	1,555 m (5,100 ft)
Runway ACN for flexible runway, category B:	
standard tyres: 200	43
300	49
optional tyres: 200	41
300	47

Range (1990 deliveries) at typical airline OWE with 218 passengers and baggage, international reserves for 200 nm (370 km; 230 mile) diversion:

200: A	3,820 nm (7,079 km; 4,399 miles)
B	3,870 nm (7,172 km; 4,456 miles)
300 at basic MTOGW:	
A	4,420 nm (8,191 km; 5,090 miles)
B	4,480 nm (8,300 km; 5,160 miles)
300 at 164 tonne MTOGW with two additional fuel tanks: C	5,280 nm (9,785 km; 6,080 miles)
D	5,360 nm (9,933 km; 6,172 miles)

OPERATIONAL NOISE LEVELS (ICAO Annex 16, Chapter 3):

T-O (flyover): 200	89.0 EPNdB (95.1 limit)
300	91.2 EPNdB (95.6 limit)
T-O (sideline): 200	96.1 EPNdB (99.1 limit)
300	96.3 EPNdB (99.4 limit)
Approach: 200, 300	98.6 EPNdB (102.7 limit)

AIRBUS A320

The A320 is a short/medium-range, single-aisle, twin-turbofan commercial transport aircraft, making optimum use of advanced design concepts, modern production techniques, new materials, advanced digital avionics, and efficient systems design. Among a number of technological 'firsts', it is the first subsonic commercial aircraft to have fly by wire (FBW) control throughout normal flight; a centralised maintenance system; side-stick controllers in the cockpit, in place of control columns; and composites materials for major elements of primary structure, including the fin and horizontal tailplane. Wing design incorporates the latest advances in technology (including a gust load alleviation system), as well as experience from the wing of the A310, and the A320 offers significant commonality with other Airbus Industrie aircraft where this is cost-effective.

Compared with existing single-aisle aircraft, the fuselage cross-section is significantly increased, permitting the use of wider triple seats to provide higher standards of passenger comfort; five-abreast business class seating provides a standard equal to that offered as first class on major competitive aircraft. In addition, the wider aisle permits quicker turnrounds. Overhead stowage space is superior to that available on existing aircraft of similar capacity, and provides ample carry-on baggage space; best use of the underseat space for baggage is provided by improved seat design and optimised positioning of the seat rails. The fuselage double-bubble cross-section provides increased baggage/cargo hold volume and working height, and the ability to carry containers derived from the standard interline LD3 type. As the base is the same as that of the LD3, all existing wide-body aircraft and ground handling

equipment can accept these containers without modification.

Full go-ahead to develop and build the A320 was confirmed on 2 March 1984. The **A320-100** (21 ordered) was offered originally (see 1987-88 *Jane's*), but was replaced from Autumn 1988 by the **A320-200**, which has wingtip fences, a wing centre-section fuel tank and higher max T-O weight.

Four aircraft were used in the flight test programme, the first of which (F-WWAI) made its first flight on 22 February 1987. European (UK, French, German and Dutch) JAA certification of the A320-100 with CFM56-5 engines, for two-crew operation, was achieved on 26 February 1988. First deliveries, initially to Air France and British Airways (previously British Caledonian), took place on 28 and 31 March 1988 respectively. Certification of the A320-200 was received on 8 November 1988, followed by FAA certification of both models, with CFM56-5 engines, on 15 December. The first A320 with IAE V2500 engines made its initial flight on 28 July 1988. Joint European certification with this power plant was received on 20 April 1989, and deliveries (to Adria Airways) began on 18 May. FAA certification was awarded on 6 July 1989. On 19 November 1988, A320 No. 2 resumed flight testing after replacement of the twin-wheel main landing gear units by four-wheel bogies, suitable for operation from low-strength runways. Indian Airlines is the first customer for A320s with this option.

On 9 November 1989, Airbus Industrie's A320 was test flown for the first time after receiving a coating of drag-reducing 'riblets' (a plastic film with microscopic grooves) over 75 per cent of the airframe. The test programme is expected to demonstrate an appreciable reduction in fuel consumption.

Aerospatiale is building the entire front fuselage (forward of the wing leading-edge), cabin rear doors, nosewheel doors, the centre wing box and engine pylons, and is responsible for final assembly. The centre and rear fuselage, tailcone, wing flaps, fin, rudder, and commercial furnishing are undertaken by Deutsche Airbus. British Aerospace builds the main wings, including ailerons, airbrakes, spoilers and wingtips, and the main landing gear leg fairings. Belairbus produces the leading-edge slats. CASA is responsible for the tailplane, elevators, mainwheel doors, and sheet metal work for parts of the rear fuselage.

Firm orders for the A320 (-100 and -200) totalled 530, from 26 customers, by 14 February 1990, of which 79 had been delivered by 31 January.

TYPE: Twin-turbofan short/medium-range transport.

WINGS: Cantilever low/mid-wing monoplane, with 5° 6′ 36″ dihedral and 25° sweepback at quarter-chord. Five-segment leading-edge slats (one inboard and four outboard of engine pylon) over almost full span. These and most of fixed portion of wing are of aluminium alloy construction. CFRP materials are used for the fixed leading/trailing-edge bottom access panels and deflectors, trailing-edge flaps, flap track fairings, spoilers and ailerons. Spoilers, in five segments on each wing, are located forward of the flaps. The four outer spoilers are used in roll, the three middle ones as speed brakes, and all five for lift dumping. Ailerons, spoilers, flaps and slats are controlled electrically by the fly by wire control system, acting via hydraulic actuators. Slat and flap controls manufactured by Liebherr and Lucas. Wingtip fences standard on A320-200.

FUSELAGE: Semi-monocoque pressurised structure, of double bubble cross-section. Construction generally as described for A310, but belly fairing skins are of AFRP.

TAIL UNIT: Cantilever structure, with sweepback on all surfaces (35° on fin, 28° on tailplane) and 6° dihedral on tailplane. Entire fin and tailplane are fabricated from CFRP, except for fin leading-edge and fin/fuselage fairing (GFRP); rudder and elevators are of CFRP. Elevators are fly by wire, while the rudder and tailplane trim are signalled by conventional mechanical means (to provide backup control in direction and pitch). All surfaces are actuated hydraulically. Electric trim (with connection to FBW system) of rudder and tailplane.

LANDING GEAR: Hydraulically retractable tricycle type, with twin wheels and oleo-pneumatic shock absorber on each unit (four-wheel main gear bogies optional). Dowty main units retract inward into wing/body fairing; steerable Messier-Hispano-Bugatti nose unit retracts forward. Nosewheel steering angle ±75° (effective turning angle ±70°). Nosewheel doors, main gear leg fairing doors and mainwheel doors are of CFRP. Radial tyres are standard, size 45 × 16-R20 on main gear and 30 × 8.8-R15 on nose gear. Optional tyres for main gear are 49 × 19-R20 radials or 46 × 16-20 crossplies, and for nose gear 32 × 11.5-15 crossplies. Carbon brakes standard.

POWER PLANT: Two 104.5-111.2 kN (23,500-25,000 lb st) class CFM International CFM56-5A1 turbofans for first aircraft delivery in Spring 1988, with 111.2 kN (25,000 lb st) IAE V2500-A1 engines becoming available for aircraft delivered from May 1989. Nacelles by Rohr Industries; thrust reversers by Hispano-Suiza for CFM56 engines, by IAE for V2500s. Dual-channel FADEC (full authority digital engine control) system on each engine standard. For A320-200, standard fuel capacity in wing and wing centre-section tanks is 23,859 litres (6,303 US gallons;

Airbus A320 short/medium-range commercial transport for Air Canada, for use on routes within Canada and to the USA from 1990

Airbus A320-200 twin-turbofan single-aisle 150/179-seat transport *(Pilot Press)*

5,248 Imp gallons); for A320-100, standard fuel capacity without centre-section tank is 15,843 litres (4,185 US gallons; 3,485 Imp gallons). Composites materials used in construction of engine cowlings and pylon fairings.

ACCOMMODATION: Standard crew of two on flight deck, with one (optionally two) forward facing folding seats for additional crew members; seats for four cabin attendants. Seating for up to 179 passengers, depending upon layout, with locations at front and rear of cabin for galley(s) and toilet(s). Typical two-class layout would have 12 seats four-abreast at 91.5 cm (36 in) pitch in 'super first' and 138 six-abreast at 81 cm (32 in) pitch economy class; or 152 six-abreast seats (84 business + 68 economy) at 86 and 78 cm (34 and 31 in) pitch respectively. Single class economy layout could offer 164 seats at 81 cm (32 in) pitch, or up to 179 in high-density configuration. Passenger doors at front and rear of cabin on port side, forward one having optional integral airstairs; service door opposite each of these on starboard side. Two overwing emergency exits each side. Forward and rear underfloor baggage/cargo holds, plus overhead lockers; with 164 seats, overhead stowage space per seat is 0.056 m³ (2.0 cu ft). Mechanised cargo loading system will allow up to seven LD3-46 containers to be carried in freight holds (three forward and four aft).

SYSTEMS: The A320 is the first subsonic commercial aircraft to be equipped for fly by wire (FBW) control throughout the entire normal flight regime, and the first to have a side-stick controller (one for each pilot) instead of a control column and hand wheel. The Thomson-CSF/ Sfena digital FBW system features five main computers and operates, via hydraulic jacks, all primary and secondary flight controls, except for the rudder and tailplane trim. The pilot's pitch and roll commands are applied through the side-stick controller via two different types of computer. These have a redundant architecture to provide safety levels at least as high as those of the

mechanical systems they replace. The Thomson-CSF/ Sfena flight control system incorporates flight envelope protection features to a degree that cannot be achieved with conventional mechanical control systems, and the system's computers will not allow the aircraft's structural and aerodynamic limitations to be exceeded: even if the pilot pushes the side-stick fully forward, it is impossible to go beyond the aircraft's maximum design speed. Similarly, the A320 has angle of attack protection: if the pilot pulls the side-stick fully back, he will just achieve maximum lift from the wing and no more, and therefore cannot stall the aircraft. Nor is it possible to exceed *g* limits while manoeuvring. Other systems include Liebherr/ABG-Semca air-conditioning, Hamilton Standard/Nord-Micro pressurisation, hydraulic, Sundstrand electrical system, and a new and more efficient Garrett APU. Primary electrical system is powered by two Sundstrand 90kVA constant frequency generators, providing 115/200V three-phase AC at 400Hz. A third generator of the same type, directly driven at constant speed by the APU, can be used during ground operations and, if required, during flight.

AVIONICS: Fully equipped digital avionics fit, to ARINC 700 series specification, including advanced digital automatic flight control and flight management systems. AFCS integrates functions of Sfena autopilot and Honeywell FMS. Each pilot has two Thomson-CSF/VDO electronic flight instrumentation system (EFIS) displays: a primary flight display and a navigation display. Primary flight display is first on an airliner to incorporate speed, altitude and heading. Between these two pairs of displays are two Thomson-CSF/VDO electronic centralised aircraft monitor (ECAM) displays unique to Airbus Industrie and developed from the ECAM systems on the A310 and A300-600. The larger size of the A320 displays allows the upper one to incorporate engine performance and warnings. The lower display carries warning and system

synoptic diagrams. Honeywell air data and inertial reference system.

DIMENSIONS, EXTERNAL:
Wing span	33.91 m (111 ft 3 in)
Wing aspect ratio	9.4
Length overall	37.57 m (123 ft 3 in)
Fuselage: Max width	3.95 m (12 ft 11½ in)
Max depth	4.14 m (13 ft 7 in)
Height overall	11.80 m (38 ft 8½ in)
Tailplane span	12.45 m (40 ft 10 in)
Wheel track (c/l of shock struts)	7.59 m (24 ft 11 in)
Wheelbase	12.63 m (41 ft 5 in)
Passenger doors (port, fwd and rear), each:	
Height	1.85 m (6 ft 1 in)
Width	0.81 m (2 ft 8 in)
Height to sill	3.415 m (11 ft 2½ in)
Service doors (stbd, fwd and rear), each:	
Height	1.85 m (6 ft 1 in)
Width	0.81 m (2 ft 8 in)
Height to sill	3.415 m (11 ft 2½ in)
Overwing emergency exits (two port and two stbd), each:	
Height	1.02 m (3 ft 4¼ in)
Width	0.51 m (1 ft 8 in)
Underfloor baggage/cargo hold doors (stbd, fwd and rear), each: Height	1.249 m (4 ft 1¼ in)
Width	1.82 m (5 ft 11½ in)

DIMENSIONS, INTERNAL:
Cabin, excl flight deck: Length	27.38 m (89 ft 10 in)
Max width	3.696 m (12 ft 1½ in)
Max height	2.22 m (7 ft 4 in)
Baggage/cargo hold volume:	
front	13.28 m³ (469 cu ft)
rear	25.48 m³ (900 cu ft)

AREAS:
Wings, gross	122.4 m² (1,317.5 sq ft)
Leading-edge slats (total)	12.64 m² (136.1 sq ft)
Trailing-edge flaps (total)	21.10 m² (227.1 sq ft)
Ailerons (total)	2.74 m² (29.49 sq ft)
Spoilers (total)	8.64 m² (93.00 sq ft)
Airbrakes (total)	2.35 m² (25.30 sq ft)
Vertical tail surfaces (total)	21.5 m² (231.4 sq ft)
Horizontal tail surfaces (total)	31.0 m² (333.7 sq ft)

WEIGHTS AND LOADINGS (A: CFM56-5A1 engines, B: V2500-A1s):
Operating weight empty: 100	39,450 kg (86,972 lb)
200: A	39,750 kg (87,634 lb)
B	39,980 kg (88,141 lb)
Max payload: 100	17,550 kg (38,691 lb)
200: A	20,750 kg (45,746 lb)
B	20,520 kg (45,239 lb)
Max fuel: 100	12,722 kg (28,047 lb)
200	19,159 kg (42,238 lb)
Max T-O weight: 100	68,000 kg (149,915 lb)
200	73,500 kg (162,040 lb)
Max landing weight: 100	63,000 kg (138,890 lb)
200	64,500 kg (142,195 lb)
Max zero-fuel weight: 100	57,000 kg (125,665 lb)
200	60,500 kg (133,380 lb)
Max wing loading: 100	555.5 kg/m² (113.8 lb/sq ft)
200	600.5 kg/m² (123.0 lb/sq ft)

PERFORMANCE (at max T-O weight except where indicated; engines A and B as for Weights):
T-O distance at S/L, ISA + 15°C:	
100	1,970 m (6,465 ft)
200: A	2,330 m (7,645 ft)
B	2,290 m (7,513 ft)

Landing distance at max landing weight:

100	1,500 m (4,920 ft)
200: A	1,460 m (4,790 ft)
B	1,440 m (4,725 ft)

Min width of pavement for 180° turn

23.1 m (75 ft 9½ in)

Runway ACN (flexible runway, category B):

twin-wheel, standard 45 × 16-16R20 tyres: 100		36
200		40
four-wheel bogie option, 36 × 11-16 Type VII or 900 × 315-R16: 200		22

Range with 150 passengers and baggage in two-class layout, typical international reserves and 200 nm (370 km; 230 mile) diversion:

100	1,750 nm (3,243 km; 2,015 miles)
200: A, B	2,870 nm (5,318 km; 3,305 miles)

OPERATIONAL NOISE LEVELS (ICAO Annex 16, Chapter 3):

T-O (flyover): 100	85.7 EPNdB (90.1 limit)
200: A	88.0 EPNdB (91.5 limit)
B	86.6 EPNdB (91.5 limit)
T-O (sideline): 100	94.6 EPNdB (96.5 limit)
200: A	94.4 EPNdB (96.8 limit)
B	92.8 EPNdB (96.8 limit)
Approach: 100	96.5 EPNdB (100.2 limit)
200: A	96.2 EPNdB (100.5 limit)
B	96.6 EPNdB (100.5 limit)

Airbus A340-300 four-turbofan long-range transport, with additional side view (top) of A340-200
(Pilot Press)

AIRBUS A321-100

On 22 May 1989 Airbus Industrie announced that a stretched version of the A320 would become available for service from 1994, typically offering 24 per cent more seats and 40 per cent more hold volume than the present A320-200. Designated A321-100 and launched on 24 November 1989, this version will have a 4.27 m (14 ft 0 in) fuselage plug inserted immediately forward of the wings and a 2.67 m (8 ft 9 in) plug immediately aft, each plug incorporating a pair of 1.52 × 0.66 m (5 ft 0 in × 2 ft 2 in) emergency exits instead of the A320's overwing pair.

The A321-100 will be capable of seating 186 passengers in a typical two-class layout (16 first class at 91 cm; 36 in pitch and 170 economy class at 81 cm; 32 in pitch), or 200 passengers in an all-economy configuration, while retaining maximum design commonality with the A320. In addition to the fuselage plugs the lengthened version will have local structural reinforcement of existing assemblies, a modified wing trailing-edge with double-slotted flaps, and an uprated landing gear with 49 × 18R-22 tyres and increased energy brakes. It will be powered by developed versions of the turbofans fitted to the current A320, namely the CFM56-5B1 and V2500-A5, both rated at 133.4 kN (30,000 lb st). Fuel capacity will be 23,700 litres (6,261 US gallons; 5,213 Imp gallons).

Four development aircraft are expected to be built, of which the first is planned to make its initial flight in March 1993 and the second, with the alternative type of engine, three months later. It has not yet been decided which power plant will be used to begin the flight test programme, but the third and fourth development aircraft will also utilise the alternative power plants. Initial certification with the lead engine is planned for December 1993, with service entry in January 1994; tne version with the alternative engine will follow three months later. Firm orders for the A321 totalled 109 by 14 February 1990, with a further 74 on option.

DIMENSIONS, EXTERNAL:

Wing span	34.09 m (111 ft 10 in)
Length overall	44.51 m (146 ft 0 in)
Height overall	11.81 m (38 ft 9 in)

DIMENSIONS, INTERNAL:

Cabin, excl flight deck: Length	34.39 m (112 ft 10 in)
Baggage/cargo hold volume:	
front	23.22 m³ (820 cu ft)
rear	30.16 m³ (1,065 cu ft)

WEIGHTS:

Operating weight empty: CFM56-5B1

45,822 kg (101,020 lb)

V2500-A5	45,846 kg (101,073 lb)
Max T-O weight	82,200 kg (181,220 lb)
Max landing weight	73,000 kg (160,985 lb)
Max zero-fuel weight	69,000 kg (152,120 lb)

PERFORMANCE (estimated):

T-O distance at max T-O weight, S/L, ISA +15°C:

CFM56-5B1	2,400 m (7,874 ft)
V2500-A5	2,370 m (7,776 ft)

Landing distance at max landing weight:

CFM56-5B1/V2500-A5	1,570 m (5,151 ft)

Range with 186 passengers and baggage at typical airline OWE, FAR domestic reserves and 200 nm (370 km; 230 mile) diversion:

CFM56-5B1	2,320 nm (4,299 km; 2,671 miles)
V2500	2,390 nm (4,429 km; 2,752 miles)

AIRBUS A340 and A330

Airbus Industrie launched the A340 and A330 as a combined programme on 5 June 1987, at which time it had 130 commitments (89 A340s and 41 A330s) from ten customers—Lufthansa, Air France, Northwest, Air Inter, Thai Airways International, UTA, International Lease Finance Corporation, Royal Jordanian, TAP-Air Portugal and Sabena. By 1 February 1990 total commitments for the A330 and A340 stood at almost 400 from 28 customers, including firm orders for 110 A330s and 94 A340s.

In launching the A340/A330 as a single programme, Airbus Industrie is capitalising on commonality (an identical wing, cockpit and tail unit and the same basic fuselage) to create aircraft for different markets. This approach is made possible by the similar size and shape of the two aircraft, which differ mainly in the number of engines and engine-related systems. In addition, the A340 and A330 have much in common with the present range of Airbus aircraft: both will employ existing wide-body fuselage cross-sections, the A310/A300-600 fin, and advanced versions of the A320 cockpit and systems.

The high level of commonality and simplicity in fly by wire controls and cockpit design will allow Airbus Industrie to offer common pilot type ratings between the A330 and A340, and between the A330 and A320.

In addition to sharing basic airframe components and systems, the A340 and A330 will incorporate technological advances introduced in the A320, such as fly by wire

flight control and state of the art avionics design with multi-function cockpit displays. Work sharing will be along lines similar to those for the A310 and A300-600, with percentages similar to those held in the consortium. Aerospatiale will thus be responsible for the cockpit, engine pylons, part of the centre-fuselage, and final assembly; British Aerospace (with Textron Aerostructures, USA, as subcontractor) for the wings; Deutsche Airbus for the bulk of the fuselage, fin and interior; and CASA for the tailplane. Belairbus of Belgium will make the wing leading-edge slats and slat tracks. As with the rest of the Airbus family, final assembly will be carried out in Toulouse.

The following versions have been announced:

A340-300. Four-engined long-range version, carrying up to 375 passengers (standard) or 440 (optional) and powered initially by CFM56-5C2 turbofans, a more powerful and efficient version of the engine fitted on the A320. Due to enter service in late 1992.

A340-300 Combi. Passenger/freight version of A340-300; described separately.

A340-200. Longer-range version of A340-300, with same initial power plant and shorter fuselage. Exit-limited seating capacities as for A340-300. Due to enter service in late 1992.

A330. Twin-engined, medium/long-range version, with CF6-80E1A1 turbofans initially and seating capacities as for A340-300. Alternative power plants will include Rolls-Royce Trent (already specified by Cathay Pacific) and growth versions of Pratt & Whitney PW4000. Due to enter service in late 1993.

TYPE: Large-capacity wide-bodied medium- to long-range transport.

WINGS: Of new design (by BAe), some 40 per cent larger than those of A300-600, with 30° sweepback and 2.74 m (9 ft) wingtip devices. Movable surfaces comprise seven-segment leading-edge slats, two-segment trailing-edge flaps, two-segment ailerons, single airbrake (forward of inboard flap) and five-segment spoilers (forward of outboard flap) on each wing. Wing is virtually identical for A340 and A330, but A340 is strengthened in area of outboard engine pylon with appropriate modification of leading-edge slats 4 and 5. Main three-spar wing box structure, and leading/trailing-edge ribs and fittings, are of aluminium alloy, and Al-Li is under consideration for some secondary structures. Approx 13 per cent (by weight) will be of CFRP, AFRP or GFRP, including outer flap pair, ailerons, spoilers, flap track fairings, all leading/trailing-edge fixed surface panels, and (possibly) wingtip devices. Slat support structures are of steel or titanium; flap supports are of aluminium alloy with titanium elements. Fly by wire aileron actuators supplied by Allied-Signal Aerospace, USA.

FUSELAGE: Is of existing Airbus wide-body cross-section, and of generally similar construction to that of A310 and A300-600, but with new centre-section to accept the new wing. Common fuselage for all three current versions, except in overall length, with A340-300 and A330 the same size (and longest), and the A340-200 eight frames shorter.

TAIL UNIT: Common to all versions; utilises same carbonfibre vertical fin as A300-600 and A310. New tailplane includes trim tank and features outer main boxes of carbonfibre bridged by centre-section of aluminium alloy.

LANDING GEAR: Main (four-wheel bogie) and twin-wheel nose units identical on all versions. A340 has additional twin-wheel auxiliary unit on fuselage centreline amidships. Goodyear tyres on all units.

POWER PLANT (A330): Launched with two 291.4 kN (65,500 lb st) General Electric CF6-80E1A1 turbofans. Alternative engines, using a common pylon and mount, will include developments of the Pratt & Whitney

A321-100 stretched development of the Airbus A320 *(Pilot Press)*

Airbus A330 twin-turbofan transport, launched as a joint programme with the A340 *(Pilot Press)*

PW4000 and Rolls-Royce Trent series. Fuel capacity 93,500 litres (24,700 US gallons; 20,568 Imp gallons).
POWER PLANT (A340): Four 138.8 kN (31,200 lb st) CFM56-5C2 turbofans initially. Max fuel capacity (-200 and -300) 135,000 litres (35,664 US gallons; 29,697 Imp gallons).
ACCOMMODATION: Crew of two on flight deck (all versions). Passenger seating typically six-abreast in first class, seven-abreast in business class and eight-abreast in economy (nine-abreast optional), all with twin aisles. Two-class configurations seat 335 passengers in A330 and A340-300, and 303 passengers in A340-200. More typically, a three-class layout would seat 295 in A340-300 and 262 in the A340-200. Underfloor cargo holds have capacity for up to 32 LD3 containers or 11 standard 2.24 × 3.17 m (88 × 125 in) pallets in A340-300 and A330, and 26 LD3s or 9 pallets in A340-200. Both front and rear cargo holds have doors wide enough to accept 2.44 × 3.17 m (96 × 125 in) pallets. In addition, all models have a 19.68 m³ (695 cu ft) bulk cargo hold aft of the rear cargo hold.
DIMENSIONS, EXTERNAL:
Wing span (all versions) 58.65 m (192 ft 5 in)

Wing aspect ratio (all versions)	9.5
Wing sweepback (all versions)	30°
Length overall:	
A340-200	59.39 m (194 ft 10 in)
A330, A340-300	63.65 m (208 ft 10 in)
Fuselage: Max diameter (all versions)	5.64 m (18 ft 6 in)
Height overall (all versions)	16.74 m (54 ft 11 in)
Wheel track (all versions)	10.49 m (34 ft 5 in)

AREA:
Wings, gross (all versions) 363.1 m² (3,908.4 sq ft)

WEIGHTS (engines for A330: A, CF6-80E1; B, PW4164; C, Trent 768. Seating: A330 two-class, 335 passengers, A340 three-class with 262 passengers in -200 and 295 in -300):
Typical airline operating weight empty:

A330: A	118,511 kg (261,272 lb)
B	118,502 kg (261,252 lb)
C	118,234 kg (260,661 lb)
A340-200	122,111 kg (269,209 lb)
A340-300	126,061 kg (277,917 lb)
Max payload: A330: A	45,489 kg (100,286 lb)
B	45,498 kg (100,306 lb)
C	45,766 kg (100,897 lb)
A340-200	46,889 kg (103,372 lb)
A340-300	47,939 kg (105,687 lb)
Max T-O weight: A330	212,000 kg (467,380 lb)
A340-200, -300	253,500 kg (558,870 lb)
Max landing weight: A330	174,000 kg (383,605 lb)
A340-200	181,000 kg (399,040 lb)
A340-300	186,000 kg (410,060 lb)
Max zero-fuel weight: A330	164,000 kg (361,560 lb)
A340-200	169,000 kg (372,580 lb)
A340-300	174,000 kg (383,605 lb)

PERFORMANCE (estimated, definitions as for Weights):
Max operating speed Mach 0.84 to 0.86
Typical operating speed Mach 0.82
Range at typical OWE, with allowances for 200 nm (370 km; 230 mile) diversion and international reserves:
A330 with 335 passengers and baggage:

A	4,740 nm (8,785 km; 5,460 miles)
B	4,770 nm (8,840 km; 5,490 miles)
C	4,660 nm (8,635 km; 5,365 miles)

A340-200 with 262 passengers and baggage
7,550 nm (13,990 km; 8,695 miles)
A340-300 with 295 passengers and baggage
6,750 nm (12,510 km; 7,770 miles)

AIRBUS A340-300 COMBI

Launch and future customers for the Airbus A340 are being offered an A340-300 Combi, typically carrying 194 passengers (in a three-class layout) and six 2.44 × 3.17 m (96 × 125 in) freight pallets on the main deck. The A340-300 Combi features a large port-side cargo door in the rear fuselage, with a clear opening on to a main deck flat floor (the rear part of the floor slopes upward very slightly in the standard aircraft). It thus has the ability to carry the same pallets and containers as other wide-body combis, freighters and convertibles, allowing the 'interlining' of freight between different aircraft types. In addition, the A340-300 Combi can accommodate even larger cargo, such as the outsize AMA container or an assembled large turbofan.

Customers for the A340-300 Combi will also be able to obtain a kit to replace one, two or all of the main deck pallet positions by seats, giving them the added flexibility of additional layouts.
DIMENSIONS, EXTERNAL:

Cargo door: Height	2.57 m (8 ft 5 in)
Width	3.58 m (11 ft 9 in)

WEIGHTS:

Max T-O weight	251,000 kg (553,400 lb)
Max landing weight	186,000 kg (410,000 lb)
Max zero-fuel weight	178,000 kg (392,400 lb)

PERFORMANCE (estimated):
Range with 194 passengers and 33,700 kg (74,400 lb) of freight (six pallets) 4,600 nm (8,525 km; 5,297 miles)

AIRTECH
AIRCRAFT TECHNOLOGY INDUSTRIES
PRESIDENT: Prof Dr-Ing B. J. Habibie (IPTN)
VICE-PRESIDENT: Javier Alvarez Vara (CASA)
PARTICIPATING COMPANIES:
Construcciones Aeronauticas SA, Rey Francisco 4, Apartado 193, 28008 Madrid, Spain
Telephone: 34 (1) 247 2500
Telex: 27418 CASA E
IPTN (Industri Pesawat Terbang Nusantara), PO Box 563, Jalan Pajajaran 154, Bandung, Indonesia
Telephone: 62 (22) 611081/2
Telex: 28295 IPTN BD
Airtech is a joint company formed by CASA and IPTN to develop a twin-turboprop transport known as the CN-235. Design and production work is shared 50-50 between the two companies.

AIRTECH (CASA/IPTN) CN-235 SERIES 100

Preliminary design of the CN-235 was initiated in January 1980, and prototype construction in May 1981. Two prototypes were built, one in each country (ECT-100 and PK-XNC), plus static and fatigue test airframes. Simultaneous rollouts were made on 10 September 1983, and first flights took place on 11 November (CASA) and 30 December 1983 (IPTN).

The first production CN-235 made its initial flight on 19 August 1986. Spanish and Indonesian certification was received on 20 June 1986, and FAA type approval to FAR Pts 25 and 121 on 3 December that year. First delivery, of an IPTN aircraft to Merpati Nusantara Airlines, was made on 15 December 1986; the first two CN-235s from the CASA assembly line, equipped as VIP transports for the Royal Saudi Air Force, were handed over on 4 February 1987, with two more (in **CN-235 M** military transport configuration) following in April 1987. Commercial operation, by the first Merpati aircraft, began on 1 March 1988.

Firm orders for the CN-235 totalled 126 by 1 January 1990 (48 civil and 78 military), of which nine civil and 25 military examples had been delivered. Civil customers are Merpati (15), Pelita (10), Binter Canarias (four), Binter Mediterraneo (five), and other Spanish regional carriers (14). Military customers comprise the Botswana Defence Force (two), Brunei (three), Chilean Air Force (three), Ecuadorean Army and Navy (one each), French Armée de l'Air (eight), Indonesian Air Force and Navy (24), Royal Moroccan Air Force (seven), Panamanian National Guard (one), Royal Saudi Air Force (four) and Spanish Air Force (24). In January 1990, CASA announced a preliminary agreement under which 52 CN-235 Ms would be assembled under licence by TAI in Turkey (which see) for the Turkish Air Force, progressing gradually to local manufacture in that country.

CASA builds the wing centre-section, inboard flaps, forward and centre fuselage and engine nacelles; the outer wings, outboard flaps, ailerons, rear fuselage and tail unit are built by IPTN. Numerical control machinery is used extensively in the CN-235's manufacture. Design has been optimised for short-haul operations, enabling the CN-235 to fly four 100 nm (185 km; 115 mile) stage lengths, with reserves, before needing to refuel, and to operate from paved runways and unprepared strips.

Initial production CN-235s have General Electric CT7-7A engines, as described in previous editions of *Jane's*, and are designated **Series 10**. The following description applies to the **Series 100** version, with CT7-9C engines in new composites nacelles, which replaced it in 1988 from the 31st (and 16th Spanish) production aircraft.
TYPE: Twin-turboprop commuter and utility transport.
WINGS: Cantilever high-wing monoplane. NACA 65₃-218 wing section. Constant chord centre-section, without dihedral; 3° dihedral on tapered outer panels. Incidence 3°. Sweepback 3° 51′ 36″ at quarter-chord on outer panels. Three main assemblies each consist of a machined fail-safe box structure of aluminium/copper alloy, with main spars at 15 and 55 per cent chord, plus leading- and trailing-edge structures. Inboard flaps on centre-section, outboard flap segments and ailerons on outer panels.

Airtech (CASA/IPTN) CN-235 twin-turboprop commuter and utility transport *(Pilot Press)*

Spanish built Airtech CN-235 M transport aircraft in the insignia of the Royal Moroccan Air Force

Fail-safe attachment of centre-section to top of fuselage; large wing/fuselage fairing, made of composites. Chemically milled skins. Leading-edges each made up of a false spar, ribs and skin panels. Flap segments each have a machined aluminium spar, two sheet metal ribs of aluminium/zinc alloy, and leading/trailing-edges of glassfibre laminates with honeycomb core. Inboard and outboard pairs are interchangeable port/starboard. Flaps are single-slotted and actuated hydraulically by Dowty Aerospace irreversible jacks. Ailerons, of similar construction to flaps, are statically and dynamically balanced and have duplicated flight controls. Mechanically operated servo tab and electrically actuated trim tab in each aileron. Raked wingtips are of glassfibre. Pneumatic boot anti-icing of outer leading-edges.

FUSELAGE: Conventional fail-safe pressurised semi-monocoque structure (including baggage compartment), built mainly of aluminium/copper and aluminium/zinc alloy longerons, frames, stringers and skin panels. Flattened circular cross-section, upswept at rear. Glassfibre nose radome, reinforced with glassfibre/Nomex honeycomb/glassfibre sandwich, forward of front pressure bulkhead. Forward pressurised section includes flight deck and bulkhead at front of passenger cabin. Central (passenger cabin) section is 19 frames long, at 508 mm (20 in) pitch. Rear fuselage, 15 frames long, includes rear cargo ramp and door, baggage compartment, and the tailcone, which incorporates the rear pressure bulkhead. Composite fairings on fuselage sides house some equipment and systems, in addition to retracted main landing gear.

TAIL UNIT: Sweptback fin and statically and dynamically balanced rudder, large dorsal fin, two small honeycomb ventral fins, and non-swept fixed incidence tailplane with statically and dynamically balanced elevators. Main fin and tailplane boxes are two-spar aluminium/copper alloy structures, with detachable leading-edges and glassfibre tips. Rudder and elevators have glassfibre skin, Nomex honeycomb core, and leading-edge vortex generators. Rudder and elevators actuated mechanically. Mechanically operated servo tab and electrically actuated trim tab in rudder and starboard elevator; trim tab only in port elevator. Pneumatic boot anti-icing of fin and tailplane leading-edges.

LANDING GEAR: Messier-Hispano-Bugatti retractable tricycle type with levered suspension, suitable for operation from semi-prepared runways. Electrically controlled hydraulic extension/retraction, with mechanical backup for emergency extension. Oleo-pneumatic shock absorber in each unit. Each main unit comprises two wheels in tandem, retracting rearward into fairing on side of fuselage. Mainwheels semi-exposed when retracted. Single steerable nosewheel (±48°) retracts forward into unpressurised bay under flight deck. Dunlop 28 × 9.00-12 (12 ply rating) tubeless mainwheel tyres standard, pressure 5.17 bars (75 lb/sq in) on civil version, 5.58 bars (81 lb/sq in) on military version; low pressure mainwheel tyres optional, size 11.00-12/10, pressure 3.45 bars (50 lb/sq in). Dunlop 24 × 7.7 (10/12 ply rating) tubeless nosewheel tyre, pressure 5.65 bars (82 lb/sq in) on civil version, 6.07 bars (88 lb/sq in) on military version. Dunlop hydraulic differential disc brakes; Dunlop anti-skid units on main gear.

POWER PLANT: Two General Electric CT7-9C turboprops, each flat rated at 1,305 kW (1,750 shp) (S/L, to 41°C) for take-off and 1,394.5 kW (1,870 shp) up to 31°C with automatic power reserve. Hamilton Standard 14-RF21 four-blade constant-speed propellers, with full feathering and reverse-pitch capability. Blades are of glassfibre, with

Maritime patrol version of the CN-235, under development by IPTN for the Indonesian Navy
(John Fricker)

metal spar and urethane foam core. Lightweight low-drag composites nacelles. Fuel in two 1,042 litre (275 US gallon; 229 Imp gallon) integral main tanks in wing centre-section and two 1,592 litre (421 US gallon; 350 Imp gallon) integral outer-wing auxiliary tanks; total fuel capacity 5,268 litres (1,392 US gallons; 1,158 Imp gallons), of which 5,128 litres (1,355 US gallons; 1,128 Imp gallons) are usable. Single pressure refuelling point in starboard main landing gear fairing; gravity filling point in top of each tank. Propeller braking permits engine to be used as an on-ground APU. Oil capacity 13.97 litres (3.69 US gallons; 3.07 Imp gallons).

ACCOMMODATION: Crew of two on flight deck, plus cabin attendant (civil version) or third crew member (military version). Accommodation in commuter version for up to 45 passengers in four-abreast seating, at 76 cm (30 in) pitch, with 22 seats each side of central aisle. Toilet, galley and overhead luggage bins standard. Pressurised baggage compartment at rear of cabin, aft of movable bulkhead; additional stowage in rear ramp area and in overhead lockers. Can also be equipped as mixed passenger/cargo combi (eg, 19 passengers and two LD3 containers), or for all-cargo operation, with roller loading system, carrying four standard LD3 containers, five LD2s, or two 2.24 × 3.18 m (88 × 125 in) and one 2.24 × 2.03 m (88 × 80 in) pallets; or for military duties, carrying up to 48 troops or 46 paratroops. Other options include layouts for aeromedical (24 stretchers and four medical attendants), ASW/maritime patrol (with 360° search radar and Exocet missiles or Mk 46 torpedoes), electronic warfare, geophysical survey or aerial photographic duties. Main passenger door, outward and forward opening with integral stairs, aft of wing on port side, serving also as a Type I emergency exit. Type III emergency exit facing this door on starboard side. Crew/service downward opening door (forward, starboard) has built-in stairs, and serves also as a Type I emergency exit, or as passenger door in combi version; a second Type III exit is provided, opposite this door, on the port side. Wide ventral door/cargo ramp in underside of upswept rear fuselage, for loading of bulky cargo. Accommodation fully air-conditioned and pressurised.

SYSTEMS: Hamilton Standard air-conditioning system, using engine compressor bleed air. AiResearch electropneumatic pressurisation system (max differential 0.25 bars;

3.6 lb/sq in) giving cabin environment of 2,440 m (8,000 ft) up to operating altitude of 5,485 m (18,000 ft). Hydraulic system, operating at nominal pressure of 207 bars (3,000 lb/sq in), comprises two engine driven, variable displacement axial electric pumps, a self pressurising standby mechanical pump, and a modular unit incorporating connectors, filters and valves; system is employed for actuation of wing flaps, landing gear extension/retraction, wheel brakes, emergency and parking brakes, nosewheel steering, cargo ramp and door, and propeller braking. Accumulator for backup braking system. No pneumatic system. 28V DC primary electrical system powered by two 400A Auxilec engine driven starter/generators, with two 24V 37Ah nickel-cadmium batteries for engine starting and 30 min (minimum) emergency power for essential services. Constant frequency single-phase AC power (115/26V) provided at 400Hz by three 600VA static inverters (two for normal operation plus one standby); two three-phase engine driven alternators for 115/200V variable frequency AC power. Fixed oxygen installation for crew of three (single cylinder at 124 bars; 1,800 lb/sq in pressure); three portable units and individual masks for passengers. Pneumatic boot anti-icing of wing (outboard of engine nacelles), fin and tailplane leading-edges. Electric anti-icing of propellers, engine air intakes, flight deck windscreen, pitot tubes and angle of attack indicators. No APU: starboard engine, with propeller braking, can be used to fulfil this function. Hand type fire extinguishers on flight deck (one) and in passenger cabin (two); smoke detector in baggage compartment. Engine fire detection and extinguishing system.

AVIONICS AND EQUIPMENT: Standard avionics include two Collins VHF-22B com radios, one Avtech DADS crew interphone, one Collins TDR-90 ATC transponder, two Collins VIR-32 VOR/ILS/marker beacon receivers, one Collins DME-42, one Collins ADF-60A, one Collins WXR-300 weather radar, two Collins 332D-11T vertical gyros, two Collins MCS-65 directional gyros, two Collins ADI-85A, two Collins HSI-85, two Collins RMI-36, one Collins APS-65 autopilot/flight director, one Collins ALT-55B radio altimeter, one Fairchild/Teledyne flight data recorder, one Fairchild A-100A cockpit voice recorder, one Avtech PACIS PA system, two Collins 345A-7 rate of turn sensors, one Sfena H-301 APM standby attitude director indicator, one Dorne & Margolin ELT 8-1 emergency locator transmitter, and one Sundstrand Mk II GPWS. Collins EFIS-85 five-tube CRT system optional. Other options include Collins EFIS-85B; second TDR-90, DME-42 and ADF-60A; plus Collins HF-230 com radio, Collins RNS-325 radar nav, Litton LTN-72R inertial nav or Global GNS-500A Omega navigation system. Navigation lights, anti-collision strobe lights, 600W landing light in front end of each main landing gear fairing, taxi lights, ice inspection lights, emergency door lights, flight deck and flight deck emergency lights, cabin and baggage compartment lights, individual passenger reading lights, and instrument panel white lighting, are all standard.

ARMAMENT (military version): Three attachment points under each wing. Indonesian Navy ASW version can be fitted with two AM39 Exocet anti-shipping missiles.

DIMENSIONS, EXTERNAL:

Wing span	25.81 m (84 ft 8 in)
Wing chord: at root	3.00 m (9 ft 10 in)
at tip	1.20 m (3 ft 11¼ in)
Wing aspect ratio	11.3
Length overall	21.353 m (70 ft 0¾ in)
Length of fuselage	20.90 m (68 ft 7 in)
Fuselage: Max width	2.90 m (9 ft 6 in)
Max depth	2.615 m (8 ft 7 in)
Height overall	8.177 m (26 ft 10 in)
Tailplane span	11.00 m (36 ft 1 in)
Wheel track (c/l of mainwheels)	3.90 m (12 ft 9½ in)
Wheelbase	6.919 m (22 ft 8½ in)
Propeller diameter	3.35 m (11 ft 0 in)
Propeller ground clearance	1.66 m (5 ft 5¼ in)
Distance between propeller centres	7.00 m (22 ft 11½ in)

Passenger door (port, rear), paratroop door (stbd, rear) and service door (stbd, fwd): Height   1.70 m (5 ft 7 in)

Width	0.73 m (2 ft 4¾ in)
Height to sill	1.22 m (4 ft 0 in)
Ventral upper door (rear): Length	2.366 m (7 ft 9¼ in)
Width	2.349 m (7 ft 8½ in)
Height to sill	1.22 m (4 ft 0 in)
Ventral ramp/door (rear): Length	3.042 m (9 ft 11¾ in)
Width	2.349 m (7 ft 8½ in)
Height to sill	1.22 m (4 ft 0 in)

Type III emergency exits (port, fwd, and stbd, rear):

Height	0.91 m (3 ft 0 in)
Width	0.51 m (1 ft 8 in)

DIMENSIONS, INTERNAL:

Cabin, excl flight deck: Length	9.65 m (31 ft 8 in)
Max width	2.70 m (8 ft 10½ in)
Width at floor	2.366 m (7 ft 9 in)
Max height	1.88 m (6 ft 2 in)
Floor area	22.822 m² (245.65 sq ft)
Volume	43.24 m³ (1,527.0 cu ft)

Baggage compartment volume:

ramp	5.30 m³ (187.2 cu ft)
overhead bins	1.68 m³ (59.3 cu ft)

AREAS:

Wings, gross	59.10 m² (636.1 sq ft)
Ailerons (total, incl tabs)	3.07 m² (33.06 sq ft)
Trailing-edge flaps (total)	10.87 m² (117.0 sq ft)
Fin, incl dorsal fin	11.38 m² (122.49 sq ft)
Rudder, incl tabs	3.32 m² (35.74 sq ft)
Tailplane	21.20 m² (228.2 sq ft)
Elevators (total, incl tabs)	6.17 m² (66.41 sq ft)

WEIGHTS AND LOADINGS:

Operating weight empty:	
passenger version	9,400 kg (20,725 lb)
cargo and military versions	8,600 kg (18,960 lb)
Max fuel	4,230 kg (9,325 lb)
Max payload: passenger version	4,200 kg (9,260 lb)
cargo and military versions	5,000 kg (11,025 lb)
Max weapon load (CN-235 M)	3,500 kg (7,716 lb)
Max T-O weight	15,100 kg (33,290 lb)
Max landing weight	15,050 kg (33,180 lb)
Max zero-fuel weight	13,600 kg (29,980 lb)
Cabin floor loading:	
cargo and military versions	1,504 kg/m² (308.0 lb/sq ft)
Max wing loading	255.5 kg/m² (52.36 lb/sq ft)
Max power loading without APR	5.78 kg/kW (9.51 lb/shp)

PERFORMANCE (civil versions at max T-O weight, ISA, except where indicated):

Max operating speed at S/L
240 knots (445 km/h; 276 mph) IAS
Max cruising speed at 4,575 m (15,000 ft)
244 knots (452 km/h; 280 mph)
Stalling speed at S/L:

flaps up	100 knots (186 km/h; 116 mph) IAS
flaps down	84 knots (156 km/h; 97 mph) IAS
Max rate of climb at S/L	465 m (1,527 ft)/min
Rate of climb at S/L, one engine out	128 m (420 ft)/min
Service ceiling	8,110 m (26,600 ft)
Service ceiling, one engine out	4,550 m (14,925 ft)
T-O run	554 m (1,818 ft)
T-O to 10.7 m (35 ft) at S/L	687 m (2,254 ft)
Landing from 15 m (50 ft) at S/L	585 m (1,920 ft)
Min ground turning radius	18.98 m (62 ft 3¼ in)

Range at 5,485 m (18,000 ft), reserves for 87 nm (161 km; 100 mile) diversion and 45 min hold:

with max payload	208 nm (385 km; 239 miles)
with max fuel	2,110 nm (3,910 km; 2,429 miles)

OPERATIONAL NOISE LEVELS (civil versions):

T-O	84.0 EPNdB
Approach	87.0 EPNdB
Sideline	86.0 EPNdB

PERFORMANCE (CN-235 M at max T-O weight, ISA, except where indicated):
As for civil versions except:

Max rate of climb at S/L	579 m (1,900 ft)/min
Rate of climb at S/L, one engine out	156 m (512 ft)/min
Service ceiling	7,620 m (25,000 ft)
Service ceiling, one engine out	4,665 m (15,300 ft)
Min ground turning radius:	
nosewheel	9.50 m (31 ft 2 in)
wingtip	18.98 m (62 ft 3¼ in)
T-O to 15 m (50 ft)	732 m (2,400 ft)
Landing from 15 m (50 ft)	772 m (2,530 ft)
Landing run, with propeller reversal	286 m (939 ft)

Range at 6,100 m (20,000 ft), long-range cruising speed, reserves for 45 min hold:

with max payload	669 nm (1,240 km; 770 miles)
with 2,400 kg (5,291 lb) payload	2,304 nm (4,270 km; 2,653 miles)

AMX

AMX INTERNATIONAL LTD

PRESIDENT: Ing Giandomenico Cantele (Aeritalia)
PARTICIPATING COMPANIES:

Aeritalia (Defence Aircraft Group), Corso Marche 41, 10146 Turin, Italy
Telephone: 39 (11) 71811
Telex: 221076 AERITOR

Aermacchi SpA, Via Sanvito Silvestro 80 (Casella Postale 246), 21100 Varese, Italy
Telephone: 39 (332) 254111
Telex: 380070 AERMAC I

Embraer (Empresa Brasileira de Aeronáutica SA), Av Brig Faria Lima 2170, Caixa Postal 343, 12200 São José dos Campos, SP, Brazil
Telephone: 55 (123) 251000
Telex: 1233589 EBAE BR

AMX

Brazilian Air Force designation: A-1

The AMX is the outcome of an Italian Air Force specification drawn up in 1977 for a small tactical fighter-bomber, optimised for direct air reconnaissance and weapons support of friendly ground and naval forces but capable also, when required, of carrying out missions which would otherwise require use of both the Tornado and F-104S. The early background to the AMX programme has been described in the 1987-88 and previous *Jane's*.

In March 1980, soon after completion of the definition phase by Aeritalia and Aermacchi, the Brazilian government confirmed its intention of taking part in the programme, and four months later Embraer became an industrial partner of the two Italian manufacturers.

Seven prototypes were built (three by Aeritalia, two each by Aermacchi and Embraer), plus one airframe (by Aeritalia at Turin) for static testing. In addition, selected components for fatigue testing were completed by each of the three manufacturers. The Aeritalia-assembled A01 first prototype made its initial flight on 15 May 1984 and was destroyed in an accident in June 1984. First Brazilian assembled (YA-1) prototype to fly, on 16 October 1985, was A04, and the final prototype (Embraer's A06) made its initial flight on 16 December 1986. Further details of the prototypes can be found in the 1987-88 and earlier editions. In all, the prototypes had accumulated more than 2,500 hours, in more than 1,500 flights, by January 1990.

The AMX work split gives Aeritalia, the programme leader, 46.5 per cent (fuselage centre-section, nose radome, fin and rudder, tailplane, elevators, ailerons and spoilers); Aermacchi has 23.8 per cent (forward fuselage, including gun and avionics integration, canopy and tailcone); and Embraer 29.7 per cent (air intakes, wings, wing leading-edge slats, flaps, wing pylons, external fuel tanks and reconnaissance pallets). There is single source component manufacture only, but there are final assembly lines in both Italy and Brazil.

Two AMX of the Italian Air Force's 51° Stormo, the first operational unit to fly this single-seat close support aircraft

Based on present stated requirements for the air forces of Italy and Brazil, series production of the AMX is expected to continue until 1994. Manufacture of the first 30 production aircraft (21 for Italy and nine for Brazil) began on schedule in July 1986, and the first of these was rolled out at Turin on 29 March 1988, making its first flight on 11 May. The first production A-1 for the Brazilian Air Force (serial number 5500) was flown for the first time on 12 August 1989, and all 30 were due for delivery by the end of 1990. Deliveries began to the Italian Air Force (six aircraft for the Reparto Sperimentale Volo at Pratica di Mare) in April 1989, and two aircraft to the 1° Esquadrão (16° Grupo de Aviação) of the Brazilian Air Force at Santa Cruz in November 1989. A second contract, signed in 1988, provides for a further 84 aircraft (59 including six two-seaters for Italy, and 25 including three two-seaters for Brazil).

The series production phase is expected to involve 252 single-seat AMXs (187 for the Aeronautica Militare Italiana and 65 for the Força Aérea Brasileira) and 65 two-seaters (51 for Italy and 14 for Brazil). In the Italian Air Force the AMX is intended to take over duties performed at present by the G91R, the G91Y interdictor, and the F-104G and S Starfighter. The close air support and interdiction tasks will be undertaken fully by the AMX, while counter-air duties will be shared with the longer-range Tornado; the 187 aircraft to be ordered will be sufficient to equip eight squadrons. In the Brazilian Air Force, the AMX is intended to replace the EMB-326GB Xavante (Aermacchi MB-326) for close air support and interdiction missions, with counter-air duties carried out by the Northrop F-5 and Dassault Mirage. The Brazilian Air Force aircraft differ

primarily in avionics and weapon delivery systems, and have two internally mounted 30 mm cannon instead of the single multi-barrel 20 mm weapon of the Italian version.

An in-flight refuelling test programme was completed by Embraer in August-September 1989. Rolls-Royce is developing a 58.38 kN (13,125 lb st) Mk 821 variant of the RB168 (Spey) turbofan for possible use in future production AMXs, and was expected to test fly this engine in an AMX during 1990.

The AMX is capable of carrying out missions at high subsonic speed and very low altitude, by day and night, in poor visibility, and if necessary from bases with poorly equipped or partially damaged runways. Basic requirements included good take-off and landing performance, good penetration capability, and a proven, in-production power plant requiring a minimum of adaptation to the AMX airframe. The primary flying control surfaces have manual reversion, to provide a fly-home capability even if both of the two independent hydraulic systems become inoperative.

Work on a tandem two-seat version of the AMX began in mid-1986, and one Brazilian and two Italian prototypes have been built. The first flight was made on 14 March 1990, with the second aircraft scheduled to fly in July and the third (Brazilian) prototype in late 1990. The two-seat version is envisaged both as an operational trainer (**AMX-T**) and, with suitable specialist equipment, for such roles as electronic warfare or maritime attack. The second two-seat AMX was expected to begin flight trials in late 1990 after being fitted with a FIAR Grifo ASV and maritime search radar, to evaluate such a version for anti-shipping missions, armed with an Exocet missile. In the two-seater, the second cockpit occupies the area vacated by the forward fuselage fuel tank, with virtually no significant change to the remainder of the airframe. Embraer designed the dual controls, canopy, and integration of the Ferranti rear cockpit HUD monitor; and redesigned the environmental control and oxygen systems.

The following description applies to the single-seat AMX:

TYPE: Single-seat close air support, battlefield interdiction and reconnaissance aircraft, with secondary capability for offensive counter-air.

WINGS: Cantilever shoulder-wing monoplane, with sweep-back of 31° on leading-edges, 27° 30′ at quarter chord, and thickness/chord ratio of 12 per cent. Three-spar torsion box structure, machined from solid aluminium alloy with integrally stiffened skins. Three-point attachment of each wing to fuselage main frames. Leading-edge slats (two segments each side) over most of span, and two-segment double-slotted Fowler flaps over approx two-thirds of each trailing-edge, are operated electrically and actuated hydraulically. Forward of each pair of flaps is a pair of hydraulically actuated spoilers, deployed separately in inboard and outboard pairs. These are controlled electronically by Aeritalia/GEC Avionics flight control computer, and serve also as airbrakes/lift dumpers. Hydraulically actuated ailerons, with manual reversion. No tabs.

FUSELAGE: Conventional semi-monocoque oval-section structure, built chiefly of aluminium alloy. Forward section incorporates main avionics and equipment bays, airborne systems, gun(s), nose landing gear and cockpit; central section includes engine air intake ducts, main landing gear and engine bay. Extreme rear fuselage, complete with tailplane, detachable for access to engine.

TAIL UNIT: Sweptback fin (of carbonfibre) and rudder. Variable incidence tailplane, mid-mounted on fuselage. Tailplane and rudder movement controlled electronically by Aeritalia/GEC Avionics flight control computer. Hydraulically actuated carbonfibre elevators, with manual reversion. No elevator or rudder tabs.

LANDING GEAR: Hydraulically retractable tricycle type, of Messier-Hispano-Bugatti levered suspension design, built in Italy by Magnaghi (nose unit) and ERAM (main units). Single wheel and oleo-pneumatic shock absorber on each unit. Nose unit retracts forward; main units retract forward and inward, turning through approx 90° to lie almost flat in underside of engine air intake trunks. Nosewheel is hydraulically steerable (60° to left and right), self-centring, and fitted with anti-shimmy device. Mainwheel tyres size 670 × 210-12, pressure 9.65 bars (140 lb/sq in); nosewheel tyre size 18 × 5.5-8, pressure 10.7 bars (155 lb/sq in). Hydraulic brakes and anti-skid system. No brake-chute. Runway arrester hook.

POWER PLANT: One 49.1 kN (11,030 lb st) Rolls-Royce Spey Mk 807 non-afterburning turbofan, built under licence in Italy by Fiat, Piaggio and Alfa Romeo Avio, in association with Companhia Eletro-Mecânica (CELMA) in Brazil. Fuel in compartmented fuselage tank and two integral wing tanks with combined capacity of 3,440 litres (909 US gallons; 757 Imp gallons). Auxiliary fuel tanks of up to 1,100 litres (290 US gallons; 242 Imp gallons) capacity can be carried on each of the inboard underwing pylons, and up to 580 litres (153 US gallons; 128 Imp gallons) on each of the outboard pylons. Single-point pressure or gravity refuelling of internal and external tanks. In-flight refuelling capability (probe and drogue system) is provided.

ACCOMMODATION: Pilot only, on Martin-Baker Mk 10L zero/zero ejection seat; 18° downward view over nose. One-piece wraparound windscreen; one-piece hinged canopy, opening sideways to starboard. Cockpit pressurised and air-conditioned. Tandem two-seat combat trainer/special missions version under development.

SYSTEMS: Microtecnica environmental control system (ECS) provides air-conditioning of cockpit, avionics and reconnaissance pallets, cockpit pressurisation, air intake and inlet guide vane anti-icing, windscreen demisting, and anti-g systems. Duplicated redundant hydraulic systems, driven by engine gearbox, operate at pressure of 207 bars (3,000 lb/sq in) for actuation of primary flight control system, flaps, spoilers, landing gear, wheel brakes, anti-skid system, nosewheel steering and gun operation. Primary electrical system AC power (115/200V at fixed frequency of 400Hz) supplied by two 30kVA IDG generators, with two transformer-rectifier units for conversion to 28V DC; 36Ah nickel-cadmium battery for emergency use, to provide power for essential systems in the event of primary and secondary electrical system failure. Aeroeletrônica (Brazil) external power control unit. Fiat FA 150 Argo APU for engine starting. An APU driven electrical generator for ground operation is planned. Liquid oxygen system.

AVIONICS AND EQUIPMENT: Avionics and equipment are divided into six main subsystems: (1) UHF and VHF com, and IFF; (2) navigation (Litton Italia inertial system, with standby AHRS, and with Tacan and VOR/ILS, for Italian Air Force; VOR/ILS for Brazil); (3) Aeritalia computer based weapons aiming and delivery, incorporating an Elta/FIAR range-only radar and Selenia stores management system; (4) digital data displays (OMI/Selenia head-up, Aeritalia multi-function head-down, and weapons/nav selector); (5) data process-

Rollout of the first AMX-T two-seat trainer prototype

Aeritalia/Aermacchi/Embraer AMX, in production for the air forces of Italy and Brazil
(Pilot Press)

ing, with Microtecnica air data computer; and (6) Elettronica active and passive ECM, including fin mounted radar warning receiver. The ranging radar in Italian AMXs, known as Pointer, is an I band set modified from the Elta (Israel) EL/M-2001B and built in Italy by FIAR. Brazilian aircraft will have a Technasa/SMA SCP-01 radar. Ferranti MED 2067 video monitor display in rear cockpit of two-seater, for use as HUD monitor by instructor/navigator. Modular design and space provisions within the aircraft permit retrofitting of alternative avionics systems, FLIR and provisions for the use of night vision goggles if and when required. All avionics/equipment packages are pallet mounted and positioned to allow rapid access.

ARMAMENT AND OPERATIONAL EQUIPMENT: One M61A1 multi-barrel 20 mm cannon, with 350 rds, in port side of lower forward fuselage of aircraft for Italian Air Force (one 30 mm DEFA 554 cannon on each side in aircraft for Brazilian Air Force). Single stores attachment point on fuselage, centreline, plus two attachments under each wing, and wingtip rails for two AIM-9L Sidewinder or similar infra-red air-to-air missiles (MAA-1 Piranha on Brazilian aircraft). Fuselage and all four underwing points can be fitted with twin carriers and are each stressed for loads of up to 907 kg (2,000 lb); outboard underwing points stressed for 454 kg (1,000 lb) each. Triple carriers can be fitted to inboard underwing pylons. Total external stores load 3,800 kg (8,377 lb). Attack weapons can include free-fall or retarded Mk 82/83/84 bombs, cluster bombs, air-to-surface missiles (including area denial, anti-radiation and anti-shipping weapons), electro-optical precision guided munitions, and rocket launchers. For reconnaissance missions, any one of three interchangeable Aeroeletrônica (Brazil) pallet mounted photographic systems can be carried, installed internally in forward fuselage; an external infra-red/electro-optical pod can be carried on the centreline pylon. Each of these systems is fully compatible with the aircraft, and will not affect operational capability; the aircraft will therefore be able to carry out reconnaissance missions without effect upon its normal navigation/attack and self defence

capabilities. Camera bay is in lower starboard side of fuselage, forward of mainwheel bay.

DIMENSIONS, EXTERNAL:

Wing span:	
excl wingtip missiles and rails	8.874 m (29 ft 1½ in)
over missiles	9.97 m (32 ft 8½ in)
Wing aspect ratio	3.75
Wing taper ratio	0.5
Length overall	13.575 m (44 ft 6½ in)
Length of fuselage	12.55 m (41 ft 2 in)
Height overall	4.576 m (15 ft 0¼ in)
Tailplane span	5.20 m (17 ft 0¾ in)
Wheel track	2.15 m (7 ft 0¾ in)
Wheelbase	4.70 m (15 ft 5 in)

AREAS:

Wings, gross	21.00 m² (226.04 sq ft)
Ailerons (total)	0.88 m² (9.47 sq ft)
Trailing-edge flaps (total)	3.86 m² (41.55 sq ft)
Leading-edge slats (total)	2.066 m² (22.24 sq ft)
Spoilers (total)	1.30 m² (13.99 sq ft)
Fin (exposed)	4.265 m² (45.91 sq ft)
Rudder	0.833 m² (8.97 sq ft)
Tailplane (total exposed)	5.10 m² (54.90 sq ft)
Elevators (total)	1.00 m² (10.76 sq ft)

WEIGHTS AND LOADINGS:

Operational weight empty	6,640 kg (14,638 lb)
Max fuel weight: internal	2,762 kg (6,089 lb)
external	1,760 kg (3,880 lb)
Max external stores load	3,800 kg (8,377 lb)
T-O weight clean	9,600 kg (21,164 lb)
Typical mission T-O weight	10,750 kg (23,700 lb)
Max T-O weight	13,000 kg (28,660 lb)
Normal landing weight	7,000 kg (15,432 lb)
Combat wing loading (clean)	
	457.1 kg/m² (93.62 lb/sq ft)
Max wing loading	619.05 kg/m² (126.79 lb/sq ft)
Max power loading	265.14 kg/kN (2.60 lb/lb st)

PERFORMANCE (A at typical mission weight of 10,750 kg; 23,700 lb with 907 kg; 2,000 lb of external stores, B at max T-O weight with 2,721 kg; 6,000 lb of external stores, ISA in both cases):

Max level speed	Mach 0.86
Max rate of climb at S/L	3,124 m (10,250 ft)/min
Service ceiling	13,000 m (42,650 ft)
T-O run at S/L: A	631 m (2,070 ft)
B	982 m (3,220 ft)
T-O to 15 m (50 ft) at S/L: B	1,442 m (4,730 ft)
Landing from 15 m (50 ft) at S/L: B	753 m (2,470 ft)
Landing run at S/L	464 m (1,520 ft)

Min ground turning radius: A, B   7.53 m (24 ft 8½ in)
Attack radius, allowances for 5 min combat over target and 10% fuel reserves:

lo-lo-lo: A	300 nm (556 km; 345 miles)
B	285 nm (528 km; 328 miles)
hi-lo-hi: A	480 nm (889 km; 553 miles)
B	500 nm (926 km; 576 miles)

Ferry range with two 1,000 litre (264 US gallon; 220 Imp gallon) drop tanks, 10% reserves
    1,800 nm (3,336 km; 2,073 miles)
g limits   +7.33/−3

ATR
AVIONS DE TRANSPORT RÉGIONAL
316 route de Bayonne (BP 31107), 31060 Toulouse Cédex 03, France
Telephone: 33 61 93 51 80
Telex: 531 546 F
CHAIRMAN AND CHIEF EXECUTIVE OFFICER (alternate):
Henri Martre (Aerospatiale)
Fausto Cereti (Aeritalia)
EXECUTIVE VICE-PRESIDENT: Gérard Hibon (Aerospatiale)
VICE-PRESIDENT, SALES ENGINEERING:
P. Lebouc
GENERAL MANAGER: Henri-Paul Puel

Launch of the initial ATR 42 programme, by Aerospatiale (France) and Aeritalia (Italy), was confirmed on 4 November 1981 and a Groupement d'Intérêt Economique (a 50:50 joint management company) was formally established on 5 February 1982. ATR corresponds to the initial letters of the French and Italian words for regional transport aircraft, and 42 to the seating capacity of the basic aircraft.

ATR 42
The ATR 42 is a twin-turboprop transport designed to FAR Pt 25 and European Joint Airworthiness Requirement JAR 25. Choice of the Pratt & Whitney Canada PW120 turboprop as the aircraft's original power plant was announced on 8 June 1981.

Aeritalia is responsible for the entire fuselage, including the tail unit and installation of the landing gear; and for the hydraulic, air-conditioning and pressurisation systems. Aerospatiale undertakes design and construction of the wings; layout of the flight deck and cabin; and is also responsible for power plant, electrical system, flight controls and de-icing system installation, and for final assembly and flight testing of the civil passenger versions. Aeritalia will assemble and flight test any cargo/military variants with a rear loading ramp.

Two development aircraft were built, plus airframes for static and fatigue test. First flight was made by F-WEGA on 16 August 1984, with the second aircraft (F-WEGB) following on 31 October 1984. The first production aircraft (F-WEGC) made its initial flight on 30 April 1985. French DGAC certification of the ATR 42-200 and -300 to JAR 25 was granted on 24 September 1985, with concurrent type approval by the Italian RAI. FAA certification (FAR Pt 25) followed on 25 October 1985, German LBA approval on 12 February 1988 and UK CAA certification on 31 October 1989. Deliveries began on 2 December 1985 with the fourth aircraft (to Air Littoral), and services with this airline began seven days later.

By late March 1990 firm orders and options totalled 287 for the ATR 42, of which about half had been delivered.

Initial production is centred on the **ATR 42-300**, which has an increased maximum take-off weight and payload/range capability by comparison with the prototypes. With optional PW121 engines, it is designated **ATR 42-320**, OWE being increased (and max payload decreased) by 5 kg (11 lb). Details are otherwise identical for both versions. The following other variants are being studied or produced:

ATR 42 F. Commercial freighter version, capable of carrying 3,800 kg (8,377 lb) or 42 passengers over 1,250 nm (2,316 km; 1,439 miles). Modified interior, reinforced cabin floor, port side flight-openable cargo/airdrop door. One delivered to Gabonese Presidential Guard in 1989.

Petrel. Proposed maritime patrol version (of ATR 42 or 72). Described separately.

ATR 72. Stretched version, launched in mid-1985. Described separately.

The following description applies to the standard ATR 42-300:
TYPE: Twin-turboprop regional transport aircraft.
WINGS: Cantilever high-wing monoplane. Aerospatiale RA-XXX-43 wing section, derived from NACA 43 series, with thickness/chord ratio of 18 per cent at root and 13 per cent at tip. Constant chord centre-section and tapered outer panels. Dihedral 2° 30′ and sweepback 3° 6′ at quarter-chord on outer panels. Incidence 2° at root. Two-spar fail-safe wings, constructed mainly of aluminium alloys, with leading-edges of Kevlar/Nomex sandwich, and skin panels of Kevlar/Nomex with carbon reinforcement on upper surface aft of rear spar. Two-segment double-slotted single-rotation flaps, each segment with a Ratier-Figeac hydraulic actuator, on each trailing-edge. Spoiler forward of outer end of each outer flap segment. Ailerons actuated mechanically by cables and push/pull rods; no servos. Flaps and ailerons of carbonfibre/Nomex and carbon/epoxy construction respectively, with aluminium frames and spars. Electri-

Aerospatiale/Aeritalia ATR 42 twin-turboprop regional transport aircraft *(Pilot Press)*

cally actuated automatic trim tab in each aileron. Kléber-Colombes pneumatic de-icing of leading-edges outboard of engine nacelles.
FUSELAGE: Conventional semi-monocoque fail-safe structure mainly of light alloy unit construction, employing main and secondary frames and longitudinally disposed skin panels. Nosecone, tailcone, wing/body fairings, nosewheel doors and main landing gear fairings of Kevlar/Nomex sandwich. Crew, passenger and baggage/cargo compartments pressurised.
TAIL UNIT: Cantilever structure, with sweptback vertical surfaces (attached to rearmost fuselage frame) and non-swept horizontal surfaces. Fixed incidence tailplane mounted near tip of fin. Fin and tailplane construction mainly of aluminium alloys, with dorsal fin of Kevlar/Nomex and glassfibre/Nomex sandwich. Mechanically actuated mass balanced rudder and elevators, of carbonfibre/Nomex sandwich construction. Electrically actuated automatic trim tab in rudder and each elevator. Kléber-Colombes pneumatic de-icing of tailplane leading-edges.
LANDING GEAR: Hydraulically retractable tricycle type, of Messier-Hispano-Bugatti/Magnaghi/Nardi trailing-arm design, with twin wheels and oleo-pneumatic shock absorber on each unit. Nose unit retracts forward, main units inward into fuselage and large underfuselage fairing. Goodyear multi-disc brakes and Hydro-Aire anti-skid units on main gear. No brake cooling. Goodyear mainwheels and tubeless tyres, size 32 × 8.8-10PR, pressure 7.17 bars (104 lb/sq in). Low pressure tyres optional. Goodyear nosewheels and tubeless tyres, size 450 × 190-5TL, pressure 4.14 bars (60 lb/sq in).
POWER PLANT: Two Pratt & Whitney Canada PW120 turboprops, each flat rated at 1,342 kW (1,800 shp) and driving a Hamilton Standard 14SF four-blade constant-speed fully-feathering and reversible-pitch propeller with spinner. Blades have metal spars and glassfibre/polyurethane skins. Two PW121 turboprops, each flat rated at 1,454 kW (1,950 shp), optional. Fuel in two integral tanks formed by wing spar box, total capacity 5,700 litres (1,506 US gallons; 1,254 Imp gallons). Single pressure refuelling point in starboard wing leading-edge. Gravity refuelling points in wing upper surface. Oil capacity 40 litres (10.6 US gallons; 8.8 Imp gallons). Cowlings of carbonfibre/Nomex and Kevlar/Nomex sandwich, reinforced with carbonfibre in nose and underside.
ACCOMMODATION: Crew of two on flight deck, with optional third seat for observer. Seating for 42 passengers at 81 cm (32 in) pitch; or 46, 48 or 50 passengers at 76 cm (30 in) pitch, in four-abreast layout with central aisle. Passenger door, with integral steps, at rear of cabin on port side. Main baggage/cargo compartment between flight deck and passenger cabin, with access from inside cabin and separate loading door on port side. Rear baggage/cargo compartment, toilet, galley, wardrobe, and seat for cabin attendant, aft of passenger cabin, with service door on starboard side. Additional baggage space provided by overhead bins and underseat stowage. Entire accommodation, including baggage/cargo compartments, pressur-

ised and air-conditioned. Emergency exit via rear passenger and service doors, and by window exits on each side at front of cabin.
SYSTEMS: AiResearch air-conditioning and Softair pressurisation systems, utilising engine bleed air. Pressurisation system (nominal differential 0.41 bars; 6.0 lb/sq in) provides cabin altitude of 2,000 m (6,560 ft) at flight altitudes of up to 7,620 m (25,000 ft), and a sea level cabin environment at flight levels up to 4,025 m (13,200 ft). Two independent hydraulic systems, each at system pressure of 207 bars (3,000 lb/sq in), driven by an electrically operated Abex pump and separated by an interconnecting valve controlled from the flight deck. System flow rate 7.9 litres (2.09 US gallons; 1.74 Imp gallons)/min. One system actuates wing flaps, spoilers, propeller braking, emergency wheel braking and nosewheel steering; second system for landing gear and normal braking system. Kléber-Colombes pneumatic system for de-icing of outer wing leading-edges, tailplane leading-edges and engine air intakes. Main electrical system is 28V DC, supplied by two Auxilec 12kW engine driven starter/generators and two nickel-cadmium batteries (27Ah and 16Ah) with two solid state static inverters for 115/26V single-phase AC supply, and a third (standby) inverter for 115V only. A 115/200V three-phase supply from two 20kVA frequency-wild engine driven alternators is used for anti-icing of windscreen, flight deck side windows, stall warning and airspeed indicator pitots, pitot tubes, propeller blades and control surface horns. Eros/Puritan oxygen system. No APU.
AVIONICS: Bendix/King Gold Crown III com/nav equipment standard, Collins Pro Line II optional. Other standard avionics include Honeywell DFZ-600 autopilot/flight director, Honeywell P-800 weather radar, dual Honeywell AZ-800 digital air data computers and dual AH-600 attitude/heading reference systems with ASCB (avionics standard communication bus), GPWS, radio altimeter, and digital flight deck recorder. EDZ-820 electronic flight instrumentation system (R/Nav, microwave landing system, Omega nav and HF com) optional. Standard avionics package includes two VHF, two VOR/ILS/marker beacon receivers, radio compass, radio altimeter, DME, ATC transponder, cockpit voice recorder, intercom, PA system, and equipment to FAR Pt 121.
DIMENSIONS, EXTERNAL:

Wing span	24.57 m (80 ft 7½ in)
Wing chord: at root	2.57 m (8 ft 5¼ in)
at tip	1.41 m (4 ft 7½ in)
Wing aspect ratio	11.08
Length overall	22.67 m (74 ft 4½ in)
Fuselage: Max width	2.865 m (9 ft 4½ in)
Height overall	7.586 m (24 ft 10¾ in)
Elevator span	7.31 m (23 ft 11¾ in)
Wheel track (c/l of shock struts)	4.10 m (13 ft 5½ in)
Wheelbase	8.78 m (28 ft 9¾ in)
Propeller diameter	3.96 m (13 ft 0 in)
Distance between propeller centres	8.10 m (26 ft 7 in)
Propeller/fuselage clearance	0.82 m (2 ft 8¼ in)
Propeller ground clearance	1.20 m (3 ft 11¼ in)

Aerospatiale/Aeritalia ATR 42 short-haul transport in the insignia of Continental Express commuter services, USA

Passenger door (rear, port): Height	1.75 m (5 ft 9 in)
Width	0.75 m (2 ft 5½ in)
Height to sill (at OWE)	1.375 m (4 ft 6¼ in)
Service door (rear, stbd): Height	1.22 m (4 ft 0 in)
Width	0.61 m (2 ft 0 in)
Height to sill	1.375 m (4 ft 6¼ in)
Cargo/baggage door (fwd, port):	
Height	1.52 m (5 ft 0 in)
Width	1.275 m (4 ft 2¼ in)
Height to sill (at OWE)	1.15 m (3 ft 9¼ in)
Emergency exits (fwd, each): Height	0.91 m (3 ft 0 in)
Width	0.51 m (1 ft 8 in)
Crew emergency hatch (flight deck roof):	
Length	0.51 m (1 ft 8 in)
Width	0.483 m (1 ft 7 in)

DIMENSIONS, INTERNAL:
Cabin:

Length (excl flight deck, incl toilet and baggage compartments)	13.85 m (45 ft 5¼ in)
Max width	2.57 m (8 ft 5¼ in)
Max width at floor	2.263 m (7 ft 5⅛ in)
Max height	1.91 m (6 ft 3¼ in)
Floor area	31.0 m² (333.7 sq ft)
Volume	58.0 m³ (2,048.25 cu ft)
Baggage/cargo compartment volume:	
front (max)	6.2 m³ (219 cu ft)
front (50 passengers)	3.5 m³ (123.6 cu ft)
rear (max)	2.9 m³ (102.4 cu ft)
overhead bins	1.5 m³ (53 cu ft)

AREAS:

Wings, gross	54.50 m² (586.6 sq ft)
Ailerons (total)	3.12 m² (33.58 sq ft)
Flaps (total)	11.00 m² (118.40 sq ft)
Spoilers (total)	1.12 m² (12.06 sq ft)
Fin, excl dorsal fin	8.48 m² (91.28 sq ft)
Rudder, incl tab	4.00 m² (43.05 sq ft)
Tailplane	7.81 m² (84.07 sq ft)
Elevators (total, incl tabs)	3.92 m² (42.19 sq ft)

WEIGHTS AND LOADINGS:

Operating weight empty (incl FAR 121 equipment)	10,285 kg (22,674 lb)
Max fuel weight	4,500 kg (9,920 lb)
Max payload	4,915 kg (10,835 lb)
Max T-O weight	16,700 kg (36,817 lb)
Max ramp weight	16,720 kg (36,860 lb)
Max zero-fuel weight	15,200 kg (33,510 lb)
Max landing weight	16,400 kg (36,156 lb)
Max wing loading	306.4 kg/m² (62.79 lb/sq ft)
Max power loading	6.22 kg/kW (10.23 lb/shp)

PERFORMANCE (at max T-O weight, to FAR Pt 25, incl Amendment 42, ISA, except where indicated):

Never-exceed speed	
Mach 0.55 (250 knots; 463 km/h; 287 mph CAS)	
Max cruising speed at 5,180 m (17,000 ft)	
	267 knots (495 km/h; 307 mph)
Econ cruising speed at 7,620 m (25,000 ft)	
	243 knots (450 km/h; 279 mph)
Stalling speed: flaps up	104 knots (193 km/h; 120 mph)
30° flap	81 knots (151 km/h; 94 mph)
Max rate of climb at S/L, AUW of 15,000 kg (33,069 lb)	
	640 m (2,100 ft)/min
Rate of climb at S/L, one engine out, AUW as above	
	191 m (625 ft)/min
Max operating altitude	7,620 m (25,000 ft)
Service ceiling, one engine out, at 97% of max T-O weight, ISA + 10°C	2,515 m (8,250 ft)
FAR Pt 25 T-O balanced field length:	
at S/L	1,090 m (3,576 ft)
at 915 m (3,000 ft), ISA + 10°C	1,300 m (4,265 ft)
FAR Pt 25 landing field length at S/L at max landing weight	1,030 m (3,380 ft)
Runway LCN at max T-O weight:	
rigid pavement, 200 cm radius of relative stiffness:	

standard tyres	19
low pressure tyres	16
76 cm flexible pavement, standard tyres	20
83 cm flexible pavement, low pressure tyres	16
Min ground turning radius	17.08 m (56 ft 0½ in)
Max range with 46 passengers, reserves for 87 nm (161 km; 100 mile) diversion and 45 min hold	1,050 nm (1,946 km; 1,209 miles)
Range with max fuel, reserves as above:	
max cruising speed	2,420 nm (4,481 km; 2,785 miles)
long-range cruising speed	2,700 nm (5,003 km; 3,109 miles)
Block time for 200 nm (370 km; 230 mile) stage length at max cruising speed at 6,100 m (20,000 ft), IFR reserves	58 min
Block fuel for above	469 kg (1,034 lb)

OPERATIONAL NOISE CHARACTERISTICS:

Take-off	83.1 EPNdB
Approach	96.7 EPNdB
Sideline	83.7 EPNdB

PETREL 42/72

Announced in the Autumn of 1988, the Petrel is a joint ATR/Dassault-Breguet proposed for a maritime patrol aircraft combining the airframe of either the ATR 42 or the ATR 72 with an avionics suite similar to that of the Atlantique 2. Although their exact configurations would depend upon a customer's requirements, in general terms the Petrel 42 would be an anti-surface-vessel aircraft armed with AM39 Exocet missiles, while the Petrel 72 would be a two or four torpedo carrying version optimised for anti-submarine warfare. Common to both would be an undernose FLIR turret, Iguane 360° scan radar, active and passive sonobuoys, and electronic support measures.

WEIGHTS (estimated):

Operational weight empty: 42	12,139 kg (26,762 lb)
72	14,753 kg (32,525 lb)
Max usable fuel: 42	4,500 kg (9,921 lb)
72	5,000 kg (11,023 lb)
Max T-O weight: 42	16,700 kg (36,817 lb)
72	21,500 kg (47,399 lb)
Max zero-fuel weight: 42	15,200 kg (33,510 lb)
72	19,700 kg (43,431 lb)

PERFORMANCE (estimated):
Time on station at 200 nm (370 km; 230 miles) from base:

42	8 h 0 min
72	8 h 48 min
Max endurance, no reserves: 42	11 h 30 min
72	13 h 36 min

ATR 72

Go-ahead for this stretched version of the ATR 42 was announced at the 1985 Paris Air Show. Powered by 1,611 kW (2,160 shp) PW124/2 engines with Hamilton Standard 14SF-11 four-blade propellers, it has a greater wing span and area, and the lengthened fuselage can accommodate 64-74 passengers. The pressure refuelling point is in the starboard main landing gear fairing. The new wings outboard of the engines have carbonfibre front and rear spars, self-stiffening carbon skin panels and light alloy ribs, each outer wing box forming an additional 1,500 litre (396 US gallon; 330 Imp gallon) fuel tank. Customers have a choice of passenger or cargo door at the front on the port side.

The first ATR 72 (F-WWEY) made its initial flight on 27 October 1988, followed by the second aircraft on 20 December and the third in April 1989. French and US certification were received on 25 September and 15 November 1989 respectively. Customer deliveries began on 27 October 1989 with the first aircraft for Kar-Air of Finland. Orders and options totalled 128 by late March 1990.

WINGS: Generally as described for ATR 42 except for increased span, and wing spar box of new outer panels (with 2° 18′ sweepback at quarter-chord) manufactured from carbonfibre/epoxy.

FUSELAGE: As ATR 42, but of increased length.

TAIL UNIT: As ATR 42.

LANDING GEAR: Main units of improved type, fitted with Dunlop mainwheels and structural carbon brakes. Mainwheel tyres size 34 × 10 R-16, pressure 7.86 bars (114 lb/sq in). Nose gear as ATR 42.

ACCOMMODATION: Crew of two on flight deck. Cabin seating for 64, 66, 70 or (high density) 74 passengers, at respective seat pitches of 81/79/76/76 cm (32/31/30/30 in), plus cabin attendant's seat. Single baggage compartment at rear of cabin; one or two at front, depending on seating layout and type of port forward door fitted. This can be a passenger or cargo door, with a service door opposite on starboard side. Second passenger door at rear of cabin, also with service door opposite. Two additional emergency exits (one each side); both rear doors also serve as emergency exits. All doors are of plug type. Passenger cabin equipped with folding tables on seats, individual air outlets and reading lights, and increased-capacity air-conditioning system.

AVIONICS AND EQUIPMENT: Flight deck equipment and layout generally as for ATR 42. Additions/improvements

Artist's impression of the proposed Petrel 72 maritime patrol aircraft

ATR 72 stretched version of this twin-turboprop transport aircraft in the insignia of Kar-Air of Finland

ATR 72 (two Pratt & Whitney Canada PW124/2 turboprops) *(Pilot Press)*

include engine monitoring mini-aids, and fuel repeater on refuelling panel.

DIMENSIONS, EXTERNAL: As ATR 42 except:

Wing span	27.05 m (88 ft 9 in)
Wing chord at tip	1.59 m (5 ft 2½ in)
Wing aspect ratio	12.0
Length overall	27.166 m (89 ft 1½ in)
Height overall	7.65 m (25 ft 1¼ in)
Wheelbase	10.70 m (35 ft 1¼ in)
Passenger door (fwd, port): Height	1.75 m (5 ft 9 in)
Width	0.82 m (2 ft 8¼ in)
Height to sill	1.12 m (3 ft 8 in)
Alternative cargo door (fwd, port):	
Height	1.52 m (5 ft 0 in)
Width	1.275 m (4 ft 2½ in)
Height to sill	1.12 m (3 ft 8 in)

DIMENSIONS, INTERNAL:

Cabin:

Length (excl flight deck, incl toilet and baggage compartments)	19.21 m (63 ft 0¼ in)
Cross-section	as for ATR 42
Floor area	41.7 m² (449 sq ft)
Volume	76.0 m³ (2,684 cu ft)

Baggage volume (total, incl overhead bins and stowage):

74 pass, front pass door	8.60 m³ (304 cu ft)
70 pass, front pass door	11.85 m³ (418 cu ft)
66 pass, front pass door	11.70 m³ (413 cu ft)
66 pass, front cargo door	13.20 m³ (466 cu ft)
64 pass, front pass door	12.00 m³ (424 cu ft)

AREAS: As ATR 42 except:

Wings, gross	61.0 m² (656.6 sq ft)
Ailerons (total)	3.75 m² (40.36 sq ft)
Flaps (total)	12.28 m² (132.18 sq ft)
Spoilers (total)	1.34 m² (14.42 sq ft)

WEIGHTS AND LOADINGS (A: basic, B: optional):

Operating weight empty:	
A, B	12,200 kg (26,896 lb)
Max fuel weight: A, B	5,000 kg (11,023 lb)
Max payload:	
A	7,150 kg (15,763 lb)
B	7,500 kg (16,535 lb)
Max T-O weight: A	19,990 kg (44,070 lb)
B	21,500 kg (47,400 lb)
Max ramp weight: A	20,020 kg (44,136 lb)
B	21,530 kg (47,465 lb)
Max zero-fuel weight: A	19,350 kg (42,660 lb)
B	19,700 kg (43,430 lb)
Max landing weight: A	19,900 kg (43,872 lb)
B	21,350 kg (47,068 lb)
Max wing loading: A	327.7 kg/m² (67.12 lb/sq ft)
B	352.5 kg/m² (72.20 lb/sq ft)
Max power loading: A	5.58 kg/kW (9.18 lb/shp)
B	6.01 kg/kW (9.88 lb/shp)

PERFORMANCE (at max basic or optional T-O weight except where indicated):

Max cruising speed at 7,620 m (25,000 ft):	
A	286 knots (530 km/h; 329 mph)
B	284 knots (526 km/h; 327 mph)
Econ cruising speed at 7,620 m (25,000 ft)	
	248 knots (460 km/h; 286 mph)
Max operating altitude	7,620 m (25,000 ft)

Service ceiling, one engine out, at 97% MTOGW and ISA + 10°C: A 3,385 m (11,100 ft)

B	2,650 m (8,695 ft)

T-O balanced field length at S/L, ISA:

A	1,270 m (4,167 ft)
B	1,525 m (5,000 ft)
Landing field length at S/L, ISA: A	1,010 m (3,314 ft)
B	1,065 m (3,495 ft)
Min ground turning radius	19.76 m (64 ft 10 in)

Still air range at max optional T-O weight (ISA), reserves for 87 nm (161 km; 100 mile) diversion and 45 min continued cruise:

max optional payload 645 nm (1,195 km; 742 miles)	
66 passengers	1,440 nm (2,666 km; 1,657 miles)
max fuel and zero payload	
	2,370 nm (4,389 km; 2,727 miles)

DASSAULT/DORNIER

AIRFRAME PRIME CONTRACTORS:

Dassault Aviation, 33 Avenue Prof Pauchet, 92420 Vaucresson, France
Telephone: 33 (1) 47 95 85 85
Telex: 203944 AMADAS F
Dornier Luftfahrt GmbH, Werksflugplatz Oberpfaffenhofen, 8031 Wessling, West Germany
Telephone: 49 (8153) 300
Telex: 52 64 12 DORW D

The French and Federal German governments announced on 22 July 1969 a joint requirement for a new subsonic basic/advanced training and light attack aircraft to enter service with their armed forces in the 1970s. The Alpha Jet was selected in 1970 to meet this requirement, and production was authorised in March 1975. Dassault was named as main contractor and Dornier as industrial collaborator, the total workload being shared primarily between the two groups.

DASSAULT/DORNIER ALPHA JET

All initial production Alpha Jets had essentially identical structure, power plant, landing gear and standard equipment. For all aircraft, the outer wings, tail unit, rear fuselage, landing gear doors and cold-flow exhaust were manufactured in West Germany; the forward and centre fuselage (with integrated wing centre-section) were manufactured in France. Fuselage nosecones and wing flaps were manufactured in Belgium by Sabca. The power plant prime contractors were Turbomeca and SNECMA in France, and MTU and KHD in West Germany; and, for the landing gear, Messier-Hispano-Bugatti in France and Liebherr Aero Technik in West Germany.

The Alpha Jet made its first flight, at Istres, on 26 October 1973. Details of the four prototypes can be found in the 1978-79 and earlier editions of *Jane's*, and of Dornier's DSFC and TST national experimental programmes in the 1982-83 edition. Existing prototypes continue to be used as testbeds for various programmes, including armament testing, a CFRP wing, and development of the Larzac 04-C20 engine.

There are five current versions of the Alpha Jet, as follows; the Lancier version (1989-90 and earlier *Jane's*) has been abandoned:

Advanced trainer/light attack version (formerly Alpha Jet E). Ordered for the air forces of France (176), Belgium (33), Egypt (30, designated **MS1**), Ivory Coast (7), Morocco (24), Nigeria (24), Qatar (6) and Togo (6). Those for Nigeria were from German assembly line, others from French production; 26 of Egyptian MS1s assembled in Egypt by AOI (which see). Additional order anticipated in Spring 1990. Further details in 1988-89 and earlier editions.

Close support version (formerly Alpha Jet A). Ordered for Federal German Luftwaffe (175). First flown (A1) on 12 April 1978. Delivered in 1979-83 for JaboGs 41, 43 and 49 (51 aircraft each) and the Luftwaffe base at Beja in Portugal (18) for weapons training; these are earmarked to form an additional combat unit (JaboG 44) in the event of an emergency. An update programme for the armament and avionics of Luftwaffe Alpha Jets, due to be implemented in 1989-92, will include improved instruments, navigation and air data sensors; a stall warning indicator; improved wheel/tyre/brake cooling; a three-axis damping system; and provision for two AIM-9L Sidewinder missiles and a jettisonable pod containing a 27 mm Mauser gun. Under a separate programme, these aircraft have been refitted with Larzac 04-C20 engines.

Alternative close support version, developed by Dassault and first flown on 9 April 1982. Equipped with new nav/attack system which includes inertial platform, head-up display, laser rangefinder in modified nosecone, and radar altimeter. Ordered by Egypt (15, including 11 co-produced by AOI) and Cameroun (7). Egyptian Air Force version is designated **MS2**.

Alpha Jet 2 (formerly NGEA: Nouvelle Génération pour l'Ecole et l'Appui). Improved attack version, incorporating nav/attack system developed for MS2; uprated Larzac 04-C20 engines; capability of carrying Magic 2 air-to-air missiles, plus auxiliary fuel tanks of up to 625 litres (165 US gallons; 137.5 Imp gallons) on inboard underwing stations and 450 litres (119 US gallons; 99 Imp gallons) on inboard or outboard stations. No orders announced up to Spring 1990.

Alpha Jet 3. Advanced training system version fitted with state of the art cockpit controls, and displays such as CRT raster HUD combined with collimated head-level display, rear cockpit TV monitor, and lateral multi-function displays and multi-function keyboards in each cockpit. Proposed for training in the use of nav/attack systems of future combat aircraft, including training in the operation of such sensors as radar, FLIR, laser and ECM systems. No orders announced up to Spring 1990.

TYPE: Tandem two-seat basic, low-altitude and advanced jet trainer and close support and battlefield reconnaissance aircraft.

WINGS: Cantilever shoulder-wing monoplane, with 6° anhedral from roots. Thickness/chord ratio 10.2 per cent at root, 8.6 per cent at tip. Sweepback 28° at quarter-chord. All-metal numerically or chemically milled structure, consisting of two main wing panels bolted to a centre frame. Extended chord on outer wings. Hydraulically actuated Fowler slotted flaps on each trailing-edge. Ailerons actuated by double-body irreversible hydraulic servo, with trimmable artificial feel system.

FUSELAGE: All-metal semi-monocoque structure, numerically or chemically milled, of basically oval cross-section. Built in three sections: nose (including cockpit), centre-section (including engine air intake trunks and main landing gear housings) and rear (including engine mounts and tail assembly). Narrow strake on each side of nose of aircraft with no nav/attack system. Pointed nose, with pitot probe, on Luftwaffe version. Electrically controlled, hydraulically actuated airbrake on each side of rear upper fuselage, of carbonfibre reinforced epoxy resin.

TAIL UNIT: Cantilever type, of similar construction to wings, with 45° sweepback on fin leading-edge and 30° on tailplane leading-edge. Dorsal spine fairing between cockpit and fin. Aircraft equipped with radio compass have a long, narrow strake above the dorsal spine fairing to house the antenna for this equipment. All-flying tailplane, with trimmable and IAS-controlled artificial feel system. Glassfibre fin tip and tailplane tips. Double-body irreversible hydraulic servo-actuated rudder, with trimmable artificial feel system. Yaw damper on close support versions. A rudder and tailplane of CFRP have been developed and flight tested.

LANDING GEAR: Forward retracting tricycle type, of Messier-Bugatti/Liebherr design. All units retract hydraulically, main units into underside of engine air intake trunks. Single wheel and low-pressure tyre (approx 4 bars; 58 lb/sq in at normal T-O weight) on each unit. Tyre sizes 615 × 255-10 on main units, 380 × 150-4 on nose unit. Steel disc brakes and anti-skid units on main gear (Minispad or Modistop). Emergency braking system. Hydraulic nosewheel steering and arrester hook on close support version. Nosewheel offset to starboard to permit ground firing from gun pod.

POWER PLANT: Standard installation of two SNECMA/Turbomeca Larzac 04-C6 turbofans, each rated at 13.24 kN (2,976 lb st), mounted on sides of fuselage. Alternative option (on any Alpha Jet) for 14.12 kN (3,175 lb st) Larzac 04-C20 turbofans, which are retrofitted to Luftwaffe aircraft and are standard on the Alpha Jet 2. Splitter plate in front of each intake. Fuel in two integral tanks in outer wings, one in centre-section and three fuselage tanks. Internal fuel capacity 1,900 litres (502 US gallons; 418 Imp gallons) or 2,040 litres (539 US gallons; 449 Imp gallons). Provision for 310 or 450 litre (82 or 119 US gallon; 68 or 99 Imp gallon) capacity drop tank on each outer wing pylon, plus (on Alpha Jet 2) a 450 or 625

Dassault/Dornier Alpha Jet 2, with uprated Larzac engines and Sagem inertial nav/attack system

litre (119 or 165 US gallon; 99 or 137.5 Imp gallon) tank on each inboard wing pylon. Pressure refuelling standard for all tanks, including drop tanks. Gravity system for fuselage tanks and drop tanks. Pressure refuelling point near starboard engine air intake. Fuel system incorporates provision for inverted flying.

ACCOMMODATION: Two persons in tandem, in pressurised cockpit under individual upward opening canopies. Dual controls standard. Rear seat (for instructor in trainer versions) is elevated. French trainer versions fitted with Martin-Baker AJRM4 ejection seats, operable (including ejection through canopy) at zero height and speeds down to 90 knots (167 km/h; 104 mph). Martin-Baker B10N zero/zero seats in aircraft for Belgium, F10N in those for Egypt and Qatar. Aircraft for West Germany fitted with licence built (by MBB) Stencel S-III-S3AJ zero/zero ejection seats. Baggage compartment in tailcone, with door on starboard side.

SYSTEMS: Cockpit air-conditioning and demisting system. Cabin pressure differential 0.30 bars (4.3 lb/sq in). Two independent and redundant hydraulic systems, each 207 bars (3,000 lb/sq in), with engine driven pumps (emergency electric pump on one circuit), for actuating control surfaces, landing gear, brakes, flaps, airbrakes, and (when fitted) nosewheel steering. Pneumatic system, for cockpit pressurisation and air-conditioning, occupants' pressure suits and fuel tank pressurisation, is supplied by compressed air from engines. Main electric power supplied by two 28V 9kW starter/generators, one on each engine. Circuit includes a 36Ah nickel-cadmium battery for self-starting and two static inverters for supplying 115V AC power at 400Hz to auxiliary systems. External ground DC power receptacle in port engine air intake trunk. Hydraulic and electrical systems can be sustained by either engine in the event of the other engine becoming inoperative. De-icing by electric heater mats. Oxygen mask for each occupant, supplied by lox converter of 10 litres (0.35 cu ft) capacity. Emergency gaseous oxygen bottle for each occupant.

AVIONICS AND EQUIPMENT: Large avionics bays in rear fuselage, containing most of the radio and navigation equipment. Standard avionics, according to version, include V/UHF and VHF or UHF transceivers, IFF/SIF, VOR/ILS/marker beacon receiver, Tacan, radio compass, gyro platform and intercom. Landing light on starboard mainwheel leg, taxying light on port leg. Avionics of basic French and German Air Force versions as listed in 1987-88 and earlier *Jane's*, except that IFF/SIF is Thomson-CSF NRAI 4A. Alpha Jet 2 has Sagem Uliss 81 inertial platform (replacing SFIM 550)

and Una 81 nav/attack unit, Thomson-CSF VE 110C head-up display with film or video camera (VEM 130 in Lancier), Thomson-CSF TMV 630 laser rangefinder, TRT AHV 9 radar altimeter and ESD Digibus digital multiplexed avionics databus.

ARMAMENT AND OPERATIONAL EQUIPMENT: More than 75 different basic weapon configurations for training and tactical air support missions have been qualified for Alpha Jet users. For armament training and close support, the Alpha Jet can be equipped with an underfuselage jettisonable pod containing a 30 mm DEFA or 27 mm Mauser cannon with 150 rds; or an underfuselage pylon for one 250 kg bomb, one 400 kg modular bomb, or a target towing system. Provision also for two hardpoints under each wing, with non-jettisonable adaptor pylons. On these can be carried M155 launchers for eighteen 68 mm rockets; HE or retarded bombs of 125, 250 or 400 kg; 625 lb cluster dispensers; 690 or 825 lb special purpose tanks; practice launchers for bombs or rockets; Dassault CC-420 underwing 30 mm gun pods, each with 180 rds; or two drop tanks (see Power Plant paragraph). Provision for air-to-air or air-to-surface missiles such as Sidewinder, Magic or Maverick, or reconnaissance pod. Total load for all five stations more than 2,500 kg (5,510 lb). Dassault CEM-1 (combined external multistore) carriers can be attached to inboard underwing pylons, permitting simultaneous carriage of mixed fuel/bomb/rocket loads, including six rockets and four practice bombs, or 18 rockets with one 500 lb bomb, or six penetration bombs, or grenades or other stores. A special version of the CEM-1 allows carriage of a reconnaissance pod containing four cameras (three Omera 61 cameras and an Omera 40 panoramic camera) and a decoy launcher. Luftwaffe aircraft equipped with ML Aviation twin stores carriers, CBLS 200 practice bomb and rocket launcher carriers, and ejector release units. Fire control system for air-to-air or air-to-ground firing, dive bombing and low-level bombing. Firing by pupil pilot (in front seat) is governed by a safety interlock system controlled by the instructor, which energises the forward station trigger circuit and illuminates a fire clearance indicator in the pupil's cockpit. Thomson-CSF 902 sight and film or video gun camera in French version; Kaiser/VDO KM 808 sight and gun camera in West German attack version.

DIMENSIONS, EXTERNAL:

Wing span	9.11 m (29 ft 10¾ in)
Wing aspect ratio	4.8
Length overall: trainer	11.75 m (38 ft 6½ in)
close support version, incl probe	13.23 m (43 ft 5 in)
Height overall (at normal T-O weight)	4.19 m (13 ft 9 in)
Tailplane span	4.33 m (14 ft 2½ in)
Wheel track	2.71 m (8 ft 10¾ in)
Wheelbase	4.72 m (15 ft 5¾ in)

AREAS:

Wings, gross	17.50 m² (188.4 sq ft)
Ailerons (total)	1.04 m² (11.19 sq ft)
Trailing-edge flaps (total)	2.86 m² (30.78 sq ft)
Airbrakes (total)	0.74 m² (7.97 sq ft)
Fin	2.97 m² (31.97 sq ft)
Rudder	0.62 m² (6.67 sq ft)
Horizontal tail surfaces (total)	3.94 m² (42.41 sq ft)

WEIGHTS:

Weight empty, equipped:	
trainer	3,345 kg (7,374 lb)
close support version	3,515 kg (7,749 lb)
Fuel (internal)	1,520 kg (3,351 lb)
	or 1,630 kg (3,593 lb)
Fuel (external)	500 kg (1,102 lb)
	or 720 kg (1,587 lb)
	or 1,440 kg (3,174 lb)
Max external load	more than 2,500 kg (5,510 lb)
Normal T-O weight:	
trainer, clean	5,000 kg (11,023 lb)

Alpha Jet close support version, with scrap views showing noses of advanced trainer/light attack version (centre left) and MS2 (centre right), plus rear fuselage with dorsal antenna fairing
(Pilot Press)

Max T-O weight:
with external stores   8,000 kg (17,637 lb)
PERFORMANCE (at normal clean T-O weight, except where indicated):
Max level speed at 10,000 m (32,800 ft):
    Larzac 04-C6   Mach 0.85
    Larzac 04-C20   Mach 0.86
Max level speed at S/L:
    Larzac 04-C6   540 knots (1,000 km/h; 621 mph)
    Larzac 04-C20   560 knots (1,038 km/h; 645 mph)
Max speed for flap and landing gear extension
                    200 knots (370 km/h; 230 mph)
Approach speed   110 knots (204 km/h; 127 mph)
Landing speed at normal landing weight
                     92 knots (170 km/h; 106 mph)
Stalling speed: flaps and landing gear up
                     116 knots (216 km/h; 134 mph)
    flaps and landing gear down
                     90 knots (167 km/h; 104 mph)

Max rate of climb at S/L   3,660 m (12,000 ft)/min
Rate of climb at S/L, one engine out, at 4,782 kg (10,542 lb) AUW, in landing configuration
                     330 m (1,085 ft)/min
Time to 9,150 m (30,000 ft)   less than 7 min
Service ceiling   14,630 m (48,000 ft)
T-O run: Larzac 04-C6   370 m (1,215 ft)
    Larzac 04-C20   320 m (1,050 ft)
Landing run at usual landing weight
                 approx 500 m (1,640 ft)
Low altitude radius of action (trainer):
    clean, max internal fuel   291 nm (540 km; 335 miles)
    with external tanks   361 nm (670 km; 416 miles)
High altitude radius of action (trainer), reserves of 15% internal fuel:
    clean, max internal fuel
                664 nm (1,230 km; 764 miles)
    with external tanks   782 nm (1,450 km; 901 miles)
Lo-lo-lo mission radius (close support version), incl

combat at max continuous thrust and 54 nm (100 km; 62 mile) dash:
    with belly gun pod and underwing weapons
                210 nm (390 km; 242 miles)
    with belly gun pod, underwing weapons and external tanks   340 nm (630 km; 391 miles)
Hi-lo-hi mission radius (close support version), incl combat at max continuous thrust and 54 nm (100 km; 62 mile) dash:
    with belly gun pod and underwing weapons
                315 nm (583 km; 363 miles)
    with belly gun pod, underwing weapons and external tanks   580 nm (1,075 km; 668 miles)
Ferry range (internal fuel and four 450 litre external tanks)   more than 2,160 nm (4,000 km; 2,485 miles)
Endurance (internal fuel only):
    low altitude   more than 2 h 30 min
    high altitude   more than 3 h 30 min
g limits   +12/−6.4 ultimate

EGRETT

PARTICIPATING COMPANIES:

E-Systems Inc, PO Box 660248, 6250 LBJ Freeway, Dallas, Texas 75266-0248, USA
Telephone: 1 (214) 661 1000
Telex: 703365

Burkhart Grob Luft- und Raumfahrt GmbH & Co KG, Postfach 1257, 8948 Mindelheim, West Germany
Telephone: 49 (8268) 9980
Telex: 539623
Fax: 49 (8268) 998-14 or 998-24

Garrett Turbine Engine Company, Sky Harbor Airport, 111 South 34th Street (PO Box 5217), Phoenix, Arizona 85010, USA
Telephone: 1 (602) 231 1000
Telex: 667337

EGRETT/D-500

Described as being "adaptable to a broad spectrum of market requirements", the Egrett derives its name from those of the three companies collaborating in its development. The first announcement of its existence, in April 1987, revealed that overall design had been formulated by the Greenville Division of E-Systems Inc, the project's programme leader. Detail airframe design, and prototype construction, were undertaken by Grob of West Germany; Garrett provided the aircraft's turboprop engine. Systems integration, related to individual customers' mission requirements, is the responsibility of E-Systems.

An **Egrett-1** proof of concept aircraft (D-FGEI) made its first flight on 24 June 1987, at Manching in West Germany, in the hands of E-Systems' senior test pilot Einar Enevoldson. On 1 September 1988 this pilot flew the Egrett-1 to three new Class C1e (Type II) records: a maximum altitude of 16,394 m (53,787 ft), an altitude in sustained level flight of 16,226 m (53,236 ft), and a time to climb to 15,000 m (49,210 ft) of 42 min 37 s. This aircraft, re-registered N14ES, is continuing its use on environmental research missions in the USA and had accumulated about 250 hours' flying by late 1989. This included participation in a German research programme called Stratolab, involving overflights of the North Sea in September/October 1989 as part of the International Cirrus Experiment. Equipment installed for this operation included an infra-red scanner, a pyranometer (to register thermal radiation), a pyrgeometer (to collect radio wave radiations) and a motorised camera.

E-Systems claims that the Egrett can provide outstanding opportunities for radio communication spanning vast areas of the Earth's surface or mountainous regions, such a capability having been the basic objective behind its design and creation. Its capacious fuselage—very large for a single-seater—and long-span, high aspect ratio wings, clearly place it in the HALE (high altitude, long endurance) category, and extensive use of radio- and radar-transparent materials in its construction contribute considerably to its ability to act as a platform for data communications equipment, or for systems transmitting and receiving radio waves from different frequency bands. The rear portion of the fuselage can accept a variety of payloads according to individual customer requirements. These can be mounted in modular packages to facilitate straightforward installation, servicing and removal; large underfuselage doors provide easy access to all installed equipment.

On-station endurance can be extended by installing optional auxiliary internal fuel tanks. Equipped with a microwave relay payload (eg, two computer-pointed antennae, a receiver and a power amplifier, transmitting broadband signals over long distances), Egrett could provide quick response in emergency situations where other long-term communications facilities might become overloaded. One or more Egrett-1s could be deployed carrying payload packages to establish a radio based data communications network over a very large area. The Egrett is also potentially suitable for unmanned operation.

Official announcements about the Egrett programme have referred mainly to civil applications, but the aircraft is equally suitable for covert military roles such as tactical reconnaissance or surveillance and sigint/elint collection,

E-Systems/Grob/Garrett Egrett-1 proof of concept and research aircraft

Three-view drawing *(Pilot Press)* **and photograph of the D-500 high altitude surveillance aircraft**

and the West German Luftwaffe is expected to acquire 14 or 15 such aircraft to fulfil a requirement known as EASysLuft (Erfassungs- und Auswertesystem Luft: airborne data gathering and evaluation system). A modified prototype (D-FGEE), designated **D-500**, made its first flight on 20 April 1989 and had completed more than 120 hours' flying by the end of that year. Main differences from the proof of concept Egrett-1 are a 5.00 m (16 ft 4¾ in) increase in wing span to house additional antennae, a pressurised cockpit, retractable main landing gear to avoid masking its underfuselage D/F antenna, a modified rear fuselage, and higher gross weight. The D-500, which is likely to be more representative of any eventual production version, is expected to be followed in 1991 by a fully outfitted sigint example for operational evaluation; production aircraft should enter service during the period 1994-97, and are expected to be based at Pferdsfeld. The original partners were joined in late 1989 by Hughes Aircraft of the USA, and three German companies (MBB, Elekluft and Telefunken Systemtechnik), to develop a variety of sensor packages for civil and military applications ranging from environmental monitoring to disarmament verification.

TYPE: Multi-purpose high-altitude surveillance and relay aircraft.

AIRFRAME: Cantilever three-spar mid-wing monoplane, constructed largely of glassfibre, carbonfibre and Kevlar reinforced composites. Split flaps on wing inboard trailing-edges. Large, deep fuselage, underside of which is upswept at rear on Egrett-1, 'stepped' on D-500. Very tall, angular fin and rudder, latter with inset trim tab. Low-set tailplane and elevators.

LANDING GEAR: Tricycle type, with single wheel on each unit. Nose unit retracts rearward; main units on Egrett-1 are non-retractable, but on D-500 retract rearward into underwing pods.

POWER PLANT: One Garrett TPE331-14F turboprop, flat rated at 731 kW (980 shp), driving a constant-speed, fully feathering, reversible-pitch spinnered propeller with four composite blades and electric de-icing. Integral fuel tank occupying almost the whole of each wing, combined capacity approx 1,105 litres (292 US gallons; 243 Imp gallons).

ACCOMMODATION: Egrett-1 has air-conditioned accommodation for pilot only, but D-500 has a pressurised cockpit. Large fairing aft of cockpit appears to offer ample space for a second crew member such as a systems operator.

SYSTEM: Electrical DC power provided by 28V 300A generator and 24V 19Ah battery.

AVIONICS AND EQUIPMENT (Egrett-1): Dual VHF radios, dual VOR/ILS/marker beacon receivers, ADF, magnetic slaved compass system and vertical gyro standard; Tacan and UHF radio optional. Instrumentation includes vertical gyro indicator, standby attitude indicator, HSI, magnetic standby compass, sensitive altimeter/altitude alerter, ASI, instantaneous VSI, RMI, clock, and engine instruments.

DIMENSIONS, EXTERNAL (A: Egrett-1, B: D-500):

Wing span: A	28.00 m (91 ft 10½ in)
B	33.00 m (108 ft 3¼ in)
Length overall: A, B	12.00 m (39 ft 4½ in)
Height overall: A, B	6.00 m (19 ft 8¼ in)
* Wheel track: A, B	4.80 m (15 ft 9 in)
* Wheelbase: A, B	3.66 m (12 ft 0 in)
* Propeller diameter: A, B	2.74 m (9 ft 0 in)

* *estimated*

DIMENSIONS, INTERNAL: A, B

Cockpit volume: A, B	2.83 m³ (100 cu ft)
Max payload volume: A, B	2.83 m³ (100 cu ft)

AREAS (estimated):

Wings, gross: A	41.81 m² (450 sq ft)
B	46.45 m² (500 sq ft)

WEIGHTS:

Max payload: A, B	more than 408 kg (900 lb)
Max T-O weight: A	more than 3,630 kg (8,000 lb)
B	4,200 kg (9,259 lb)

PERFORMANCE:

Max level speed: A, B	more than 190 knots (352 km/h; 219 mph)
Cruising speed: B	162 knots (300 km/h; 186 mph)
Stalling speed: A, B	61 knots (113 km/h; 71 mph)
Max rate of climb at S/L: A	more than 457 m (1,500 ft)/min
Max operating altitude: B	approx 17,000 m (55,775 ft)
Time to 12,200 m (40,000 ft): A	45 min
T-O distance: A	488-610 m (1,600-2,000 ft)
Endurance, depending on payload, speed and altitude:	
manned	6-9 h
as RPV	more than 15 h
g limits	+5/-3

EHI

EH INDUSTRIES LIMITED

500 Chiswick High Road, London W4 5RG, England
Telephone: 44 71 995 8221
Telex: 291600 EHILON
CO-CHAIRMEN:
  A. Jones
  Dott R. D'Alessandro
MANAGING DIRECTOR: G. Bologna
PARTICIPATING COMPANIES:
  Agusta SpA, Via Caldera 21, 20153 Milan, Italy
  Telephone: 44 (2) 452751
  Telex: 333280 AGUMI I
  Westland Helicopters Ltd, Yeovil, Somerset BA20 2YB, England
  Telephone: 44 (935) 75222
  Telex: 46277

EH Industries was formed in June 1980 by Westland Helicopters and Agusta to undertake the joint development of a new anti-submarine warfare helicopter, for which the Royal Navy and Italian Navy both have a requirement. Such a programme was initiated by Westland in the UK in 1977 in response to Naval Staff Requirement 6646, leading to the WG 34 design described under that company's heading in the 1979-80 *Jane's*. Following extensive market research and project definition, it was established that civil and military requirements were compatible with the naval requirements.

British and Italian government approval for the nine-month project definition phase was given on 12 June 1981, and full programme go-ahead was announced by the two governments on 25 January 1984. A formal contract for full development was signed on 7 March 1984. The programme is being handled on behalf of both governments by the British Ministry of Defence. Technical responsibility rests with Westland Helicopters and Agusta, each of which has a 50 per cent interest in EHI. Westland has design leadership for the commercial version, and Agusta for the rear loading military/utility version; the naval version is being developed jointly by the two companies for their respective navies and export customers.

EH INDUSTRIES EH 101
Royal Navy name: Merlin

In the Spring of 1977 the British MoD (Navy) completed a series of feasibility studies for a new ASW helicopter, and examined what sensors and performance standards it would require. Westland's WG 34 design, marginally smaller than the Sea King but with substantially more disposable load capability, was selected by the MoD (Navy) for development in the late Summer of 1978. The Italian Navy, although it would place more emphasis on shore-based than shipboard operation, has a requirement broadly similar to that of the Royal Navy, and in 1980 Westland and Agusta combined forces in a joint design, the EH 101, to meet the requirements of both services. Subsequent market research indicated that commercial payload/range and military tactical transport/logistics requirements for a medium sized helicopter were also compatible with the basic airframe design requirements of the naval version, and it was decided to develop all three variants, based on a common aircraft.

Nine pre-production aircraft, numbered PP1 to PP9, are being produced; in addition, an iron bird airframe is being used in Italy for ground tests. Aircraft PP1 (ZF641) made its initial flight at Yeovil on 9 October 1987, and PP2 flew at Cascina Costa on 26 November 1987. These two aircraft are being used for basic development. PP3 (G-EHIL), which

PP5, the fifth pre-production EH 101, development aircraft for the Royal Navy Merlin ASW variant

made its first flight on 30 September 1988, will be used to speed the award of civil certification, planned for 1992. Aircraft PP4 (ZF644), first flown on 15 June 1989, is being used for development of a basic naval variant; PP5 (ZF649) and PP6 (first flights 24 October and late April 1989 respectively) are devoted to development of the Royal Navy and Italian Navy versions. PP7 (first flight 18 December 1989) represents the rear ramp variant; PP8 and PP9, both due to fly in 1990, will be used for reliability proving and as demonstrators for the commercial (Heliliner) and utility versions.

Series production will be by single source manufacture of components, with a final assembly line in each country. Major design responsibilities include Westland for the front fuselage, cabin, cockpit and main rotor blades; Agusta for the rear fuselage, tail, rotor head and drive system, hydraulic system and part of the electrical system. The airframe, power plant, rotor and transmission systems, flight controls and utility systems are common to all three variants. The design philosophy is to provide significant improvements in performance, integrity, availability, operating cost, and crew/passenger acceptability. Design features include the use of three engines, providing higher power margins; fail-safe, damage-tolerant airframe structure and rotating components; greater system redundancy; and onboard monitoring of the engines, transmission, avionics and utility systems.

The **naval EH 101** (to be known as the **Merlin** by the Royal Navy) is designed for fully autonomous all-weather operations, and will operate from land bases, large and small vessels (including merchant ships), and oil rigs. It is specifically designed for operation from a 3,500 tonne frigate, and its physical dimensions are designed for compatibility with frigate hangar size. It will be capable of launch and recovery from a frigate in sea state 5/6, with the ship on any heading and in wind speeds, from any direction, of up to 50 knots (93 km/h; 57 mph). It will have the greater endurance and carrying capacity necessary to meet the expanding maritime tactical requirements of the 21st century, with the ability to operate distantly for up to 5 hours with all the new technology detection equipment and weaponry currently under development. Initial orders will comprise 50 for the Royal Navy and 42 for the Italian Navy.

Primary roles of the maritime version will be anti-submarine warfare, anti-ship surveillance and tracking, anti-surface-vessel, amphibious operations, and search and rescue. Other roles include airborne early warning, vertical replenishment, and electronic countermeasures (deception, jamming and missile seduction). For the Royal Navy, the EH 101 Merlin has been specified as equipment for its Type 23 general purpose frigates; it has also been announced that the helicopter will operate from 'Invincible' class aircraft carriers, Royal Fleet Auxiliaries and other ships, as well as from land bases.

The Canadian government confirmed in August 1987 its selection of the EH 101 to meet the Canadian Navy's **NSA** (new shipborne aircraft) need for a Sea King replacement. In April 1988 it awarded a contract to define the EH 101 to meet the exact specifications of the NSA programme. Canada is expected eventually to buy up to 35 NSA EH 101s, and EHI is joined in the contract definition phase by five Canadian companies (Bell Helicopter Canada, Canadian Marconi, the AMTEK Group, IMP Group, and Paramax Electronics). Intended to operate from patrol frigates and destroyers as a fully autonomous weapons system, the Canadian Navy EH 101 will have three to four times the capability of the service's present CH-124A Sea Kings when it enters service in the mid-1990s. To co-ordinate the international team and manage the Canadian programme, EHI has formed a new, Ottawa-based company known as EH Industries (Canada) Inc.

The **Heliliner** commercial variant, based on the common aircraft but with detail design tailored to meet civil requirements, will offer a range of 550 nm (1,019 km; 633 miles), with full IFR reserves, carrying 30 passengers and their baggage. The three-engine configuration gives the EH 101 a Category A VTO performance, capable of offshore and oil rig operations or scheduled flights into inner cities at high all-up weights under the more rigorous civil operating rules of the future. It will be operated by a crew of two, with provision for a cabin attendant, and will offer airline standards of comfort with stand-up headroom, airline style seating, overhead baggage storage, full environmental control, passenger entertainment, plus a toilet and galley. It will also be available, if required, with a large rear-loading ramp. Certification is planned for late 1991.

The **military variant**, in a tactical transport or logistic configuration, will have a rear-loading ramp and be able to airlift 6 tons or up to 35 combat equipped troops. Initially, 25 of this version are required by the Royal Air Force, to provide air mobility for the British Army. A **civil/utility version** will also be available to commercial operators requiring a rear-loading facility.

TYPE: Multi-role helicopter.

ROTOR SYSTEM: Five-blade main rotor, with hub designed on multiple load path concept, incorporating fail-safe principles, and formed from composite materials surrounding a metal core. Blades, also of composites, have an advanced aerofoil section, special high-speed tips resulting from British Experimental Rotor Programme (BERP), and are attached by multi-path loading including elastomeric bearings. Naval version has fully automatic power folding of main rotor blades (optional on other versions) and tail rotor pylon, with manual system for emergency backup. Electric de-icing of main and tail rotor blades (Lucas Spraymat system) standard on naval version, optional on other versions. Four-blade tail rotor, mounted on port side of tail rotor pylon.

ROTOR DRIVE: Front drive directly into main gearbox from all three engines, with all gears straddle mounted for greater rigidity. Transmission has 45 min 'run-dry' capability.

FUSELAGE AND TAIL UNIT: Main fuselage structure is of aluminium alloy, with composites used for such complex shapes as forward fuselage, windscreen structure, entire tail-fin and tailplane, and upper fuselage cowling panels. Main fuselage panels are of bonded honeycomb. Fuselage is divided into four major modules, with front and centre modules common to all three variants. Modified rear fuselage and slimmer tailboom on military version, to accommodate rear-loading ramp/door in underside. Tailcone and tail rotor pylon of naval version fold forward and downward so that starboard half of tailplane stows underneath rear fuselage.

LANDING GEAR: Hydraulically retractable tricycle type, with single mainwheels and steerable twin-wheel nose unit, designed and manufactured by AP Precision Hydraulics in association with Officine Meccaniche Aeronautiche. Main units retract into fairings on sides of fuselage. Goodrich wheels, tyres and brakes: main units have size 8.50-10 wheels with 24 × 7.7 tyres, unladen pressure 6.96 bars (101 lb/sq in); nosewheels have size 19.5 × 6.75 tyres, unladen pressure 8.83 bars (128 lb/sq in). A twin-mainwheel gear has been designed for the military and civil variants.

POWER PLANT: Three General Electric T700-GE-401A turboshafts in naval variant, rated at 1,278 kW (1,714 shp) max contingency, 1,254 kW (1,682 shp) intermediate and 1,071 kW (1,437 shp) max continuous at S/L, ISA. Engines for naval variant will be assembled by Alfa Romeo Avio and Fiat. Commercial and military variants powered by three General Electric CT7-6 turboshafts (CT7-6A in PP3) with ratings of 1,432 kW (1,920 shp) max and intermediate contingency, 1,230 kW (1,649 shp) max continuous. An alternative engine, already specified by British MoD if additional power is required for naval and military variants, is the Rolls-Royce Turbomeca RTM 322, with max contingency and intermediate contingency ratings of 1,724 kW (2,312 shp) and 1,566 kW (2,100 shp) respectively. Computerised fuel management system. Pressure refuelling point on starboard side; three gravity positions on port side. Dunlop electric anti-icing of engine air intakes, which are of Kevlar reinforced with aero-web honeycomb.

ACCOMMODATION: One or two pilots on flight deck (naval version will be capable of single-pilot operation, commercial variant will be certificated for two-pilot operation). ASW version will normally also carry observer and acoustic systems operator. Martin-Baker crew seats in naval version, able to withstand 10.7 m (35 ft)/s impact. Socea or Ipeco crew seats in commercial variant. Commercial version able to accommodate 30

passengers, four abreast at approx seat pitch of 76 cm (30 in), plus cabin attendant, with toilet, galley and baggage facilities (including overhead bins). Military variant can accommodate up to 35 combat equipped troops, 16 stretchers plus a medical team, or equivalent cargo. Main passenger door/emergency exit at front on port side with additional emergency exits on starboard side and on each side of cabin at rear, above main landing gear sponson. Large sliding door at mid-cabin position on starboard side, with inset emergency exit. Commercial variant has baggage bay aft of cabin, with external access via door on port side. Cargo loading ramp/door at rear of cabin on utility version. Cabin floor loading 976 kg/m² (200 lb/sq ft) on PP1.

SYSTEMS: Hamilton Standard/Microtecnica environmental control systems. Dual redundant integrated hydraulic system, pressurised by three Vickers pumps each supplying fluid at 207 bars (3,000 lb/sq in) nominal working pressure, with flow rates of 55, 59 and 60 litres (14.5, 15.6 and 15.9 US gallons; 12.1, 13.0 and 13.2 Imp gallons)/min respectively. Hydraulic system reservoirs are of the piston load pressurised type, with a nominal pressure of 0.97 bars (14 lb/sq in). Primary electrical system is 115/200V three-phase AC, powered by two Lucas brushless, oilspray-cooled 45kVA generators (90kVA if Lucas Spraymat blade ice protection system fitted), with one driven by main gearbox and the other by accessory gearbox, plus a third, separately driven standby alternator. APU for main engine air-starting, and to provide electric power, plus air for ECS, without running main engines or using external power supplies. Fire detection and suppression systems by Graviner and Walter Kidde respectively. BAJ Ltd four-float emergency flotation system.

AVIONICS: Integrated avionics system of naval and military variants based on two MIL-STD-1553B multiplex databases that link the basic aircraft management, avionics and mission systems. Integrated avionics system of commercial variant based on ARINC 429 data transfer bus. On naval variant, main processing element of the management system is a dual redundant aircraft management computer, which carries out navigation, control and display management, performance computation and health and usage monitoring of the principal systems (engines, drive systems, avionics and utilities); it also controls the basic bus. On civil variant, a Canadian Marconi CMA-900 flight management system will include a colour CRT display with graphics and alphanumeric capability; fuel flow, fuel quantity and specific range computations; tuning of nav/com radios; interfaces with electronic instrument systems; two-dimensional multi-sensor navigation; and built-in navigational database with update service. Smiths Industries/OMI SEP 20 dual redundant digital AFCS is standard, providing fail-operational autostabilisation and four-axis autopilot modes (auto hover, auto transitions to/from hover standard on naval variants, optional on commercial and military variants). AFCS sensors on naval variant include British Aerospace LINS 300 ring laser gyro inertial reference unit (IRU) and Litton Italia LISA-4000 strapdown AHRS; IRU also provides self-contained navigation, with Racal Doppler 91E velocity sensor; Plessey GPS receiver selected for Royal Navy variant, Euronav GPS for Italian Navy aircraft. AFCS sensors on commercial variant include two Litton Italia LISA-4000 strapdown AHRS. Advanced flight deck incorporates standard Smiths Industries/OMI electronic instrument system (EIS) providing colour flight instrument, navigation and power systems displays. Other avionics on naval variants include Plessey/Elettronica PA 5015 I-band radar altimeters, GEC Avionics low airspeed sensing and air data system, MEL pilot's mission display unit, Selenia/Racal cabin mission display unit, and Selenia/Ferranti aircraft management computer. Elm... HF and V/UHF com radios and radio/nav equipm... on Italian Navy variant. On commercial variant, standard avionics include Penny and Giles air data system, Racal intercom system, optional Collins or Bendix/King communications and navigation systems, optional Honeywell or Bendix weather radar.

ARMAMENT AND OPERATIONAL EQUIPMENT (naval and military utility versions): Naval version able to carry up to four homing torpedoes (probably Marconi Sting Ray on RN Merlin) or other weapons. ASW version will have 360° search radar (Ferranti Blue Kestrel in Merlin) in a chin radome, plus dipping sonar, two sonobuoy dispensers, advanced sonobuoy processing equipment, Racal ESM and an external rescue hoist. GEC Avionics AQS-903 acoustic processor system, NGL mission recorder and Fairey Hydraulics deck lock have been selected for Royal Navy Merlin. ASST (anti-ship surveillance and tracking) version will carry equipment for tactical surveillance and OTH (over the horizon) targeting, to locate and relay to a co-operating frigate the position of a target vessel, and for midcourse guidance of the frigate's missiles. On missions involving the patrol of an exclusive economic zone it can also, with suitable radar, monitor every hour all surface contacts within an area of 77,700 km² (30,000 sq miles); can patrol an EEZ 400 × 200 nm (740 × 370 km; 460 × 230 miles) twice in one sortie; and can effect

Basic naval ASW version of the EH 101 multi-role helicopter *(Jane's/Mike Keep)*

Mockup of the EH 101 military variant in tactical support configuration

boarding and inspection of surface vessels during fishery protection and anti-smuggling missions. ASV version is designed to carry air-to-surface missiles and other weapons, for use as appropriate, from strikes against major units using sea-skimming anti-ship missiles to small-arms deterrence of smugglers. Various duties in amphibious operations could include personnel/stores transportation, casualty evacuation, surveillance over the beachhead, and logistic support. The military tactical transport or logistic support variant can seat up to 35 troops; alternatively, palleted internal loads or external slung loads up to a total of 5,443 kg (12,000 lb) can be carried. Armament and self-protection systems are optional.

DIMENSIONS, EXTERNAL:
Main rotor diameter	18.59 m (61 ft 0 in)
Tail rotor diameter	4.01 m (13 ft 2 in)
Length:	
overall, both rotors turning	22.81 m (74 ft 10 in)
main rotor and tail pylon folded (naval variant)	
	16.00 m (52 ft 6 in)
Width: excl main rotor	4.52 m (14 ft 10 in)
main rotor and tail pylon folded (naval variant)	
	5.49 m (18 ft 0 in)
Height: overall, both rotors turning	6.65 m (21 ft 10 in)
main rotor and tail pylon folded (naval variant)	
	5.21 m (17 ft 1 in)
Passenger door (fwd, port):	
Height	1.70 m (5 ft 7 in)
Width	0.97 m (3 ft 2 in)
Sliding cargo door (mid-cabin, stbd):	
Height	1.63 m (5 ft 4 in)
Width	1.83 m (6 ft 0 in)

Baggage compartment door (rear, port, commercial variant):	
Height	1.63 m (5 ft 4 in)
Width	0.79 m (2 ft 7 in)
Rear-loading ramp/door (rear, military/utility variant):	
Height	1.80 m (5 ft 11 in)
Width	2.11 m (6 ft 11 in)

DIMENSIONS, INTERNAL:
Cabin:	
Length: naval variant	7.09 m (23 ft 3 in)
commercial/utility variant	6.50 m (21 ft 4 in)
Max width	2.49 m (8 ft 2 in)
Width at floor	2.39 m (7 ft 10 in)
Max height	1.83 m (6 ft 0 in)
Volume: naval variant	29.0 m³ (1,024 cu ft)
commercial variant	27.5 m³ (970 cu ft)
Baggage compartment volume (commercial variant)	
	3.82 m³ (135 cu ft)

AREAS:
Main rotor disc	271.51 m² (2,922.5 sq ft)
Tail rotor disc	12.65 m² (136.2 sq ft)

WEIGHTS (A: naval variant, B: commercial variant, C: military/utility variant):
Basic weight empty (estimated): A	7,121 kg (15,700 lb)
B	6,967 kg (15,360 lb)
C	7,284 kg (16,060 lb)
Operating weight empty (estimated):	
A	9,298 kg (20,500 lb)
B (IFR, offshore equipped)	8,718 kg (19,220 lb)
C	8,618 kg (19,000 lb)
Max fuel weight (four internal tanks, total):	
A	3,438 kg (7,580 lb)
B, C	3,370 kg (7,430 lb)

Max fuel weight with optional auxiliary tank:	
A	4,298 kg (9,475 lb)
B, C	4,213 kg (9,288 lb)
Disposable load/payload:	
A (four torpedoes)	960 kg (2,116 lb)
B (30 passengers plus baggage)	2,721 kg (6,000 lb)
C (30 combat equipped troops)	4,309 kg (9,500 lb)
Max T-O weight: A	13,000 kg (28,660 lb)
	or 13,530 kg (29,830 lb)
B, C	14,288 kg (31,500 lb)

PERFORMANCE (estimated):
Never-exceed speed at S/L, ISA	
	167 knots (309 km/h; 192 mph) IAS
Average cruising speed	160 knots (296 km/h; 184 mph)
Best range cruising speed	
	147 knots (272 km/h; 169 mph)
Best endurance speed	90 knots (167 km/h; 104 mph)
Range (B, estimated):	
standard fuel, offshore IFR equipped, with reserves, 30 passengers	550 nm (1,019 km; 633 miles)
auxiliary fuel, offshore IFR equipped, with reserves, 30 passengers	625 nm (1,158 km; 720 miles)
with zero T-O distance (Category A rules)	
	330 nm (611 km; 380 miles)
Ferry range:	
B (standard fuel, IFR equipped, with reserves)	
	630 nm (1,167 km; 725 miles)
B (auxiliary fuel, IFR equipped, with reserves)	
	800 nm (1,482 km; 921 miles)
C (standard fuel plus internal auxiliary tanks)	
	1,130 nm (2,094 km; 1,301 miles)

EMBRAER/FAMA

PARTICIPATING COMPANIES:
Empresa Brasileira de Aeronáutica SA, Caixa Postal 343, 12225 São José dos Campos, SP, Brazil
Telephone: 55 (123) 25 1711
Telex: 12 33589 EBAE BR
Fábrica Argentina de Materiales Aero-espaciales, Avenida Fuerza Aérea Argentina Km 5½, 5103 Córdoba, Argentina
Telephone: 54 (1) 45011
Telex: AMCOR AR 51965

Following a co-operation agreement with the Fábrica Militar de Aviones (FMA) of Argentina, signed in January 1986, Embraer revealed in April 1986 provisional details of a proposed new commuter and business transport then known as the EMB-123. Details of the early stages of the design were given in the Addenda to the 1986-87 *Jane's*.

On 21 May 1987 Embraer formally joined forces with FMA (as FAMA) to develop and produce the aircraft as a fully international programme. As a result, it was redesignated CBA-123 (for Co-operation Brazil-Argentina).

EMBRAER/FAMA CBA-123

Due for rollout in June 1990, the CBA-123 utilises a shortened version of the Embraer EMB-120 Brasilia fuselage, and will share with that aircraft approximately 60 per cent commonality of components, including almost the same flight deck, as well as common maintenance and cabin and crew procedures. Combined with a new supercritical wing, a T tail, and two rear mounted pusher turboprops, the CBA-123 is expected to offer an optimum combination of fuel efficiency and speed, as well as an extremely smooth and quiet ride. Certification will be to FAR/JAR Pt 25 (Transport Category), with noise certification to FAR Pt 36 (ICAO Annex 16). The programme is divided two-thirds to Embraer, one-third to FAMA, with assembly lines in both countries. FAMA will manufacture the front section of the centre-fuselage, sections 1 and 2 of the rear fuselage (including the dorsal fin and ventral tail bumper), tailcone, vertical fin, fin/tailplane junction fairings, tailplane, elevators and engine pylons. Embraer will be responsible for the remainder of the airframe structure. The first two prototypes are being built in Brazil and the third in Argentina. Paid option contracts for 127 aircraft were held in the Spring of 1990. These included 70 for regional airlines in the USA, Canada, France and Finland; 20 for the Argentine Air Force; and 22 for corporate customers in Brazil. The CBA-123 is expected to enter service in June 1991, replacing such types as the EMB-110 Bandeirante.

TYPE: Twin-propfan regional and corporate transport aircraft.

AIRFRAME (general): Extensive use of chemical milling and 7000 series aluminium alloys.

WINGS: Cantilever low-wing monoplane. High aspect ratio wings with taper increased on inboard portions by extending chord and sweeping trailing-edges forward. Aerofoil section Embraer EA 160316 at root, EA 160313 at tip (thickness/chord ratios 16 per cent and 13 per cent). Dihedral 3°. Incidence 2° at root, 0° at tip. Sweepback 4° 8′ at quarter-chord. Basic damage-tolerant structure of riveted aluminium alloy, with composites leading-edges. Three-segment, mechanically actuated double-slotted Fowler flaps and single electrically actuated aileron (aerodynamically sealed internally) on each trailing-edge.

Embraer/FAMA CBA-123 twin-propfan transport under development by Brazil and Argentina
(Jane's/Mike Keep)

Hydraulically actuated two-segment ground spoilers forward of inboard flaps. Ailerons, flaps and spoilers all of composites construction. Pneumatic inflatable anti-icing boots on leading-edges.

FUSELAGE: Pressurised semi-monocoque damage-tolerant structure of circular cross-section; generally as for EMB-120 Brasilia (which see), but of reduced length and area ruled at rear. Basic structure is of riveted aluminium alloy, with composites fairings.

TAIL UNIT: Broad chord sweptback fin, with dorsal fin, and electrically actuated tandem dual rudders. Sweptback, electrically actuated variable incidence tailplane with mechanically actuated balanced elevators. Riveted aluminium alloy tailplane and fin, with composites leading-edges; all-composites rudders and elevators. Pneumatic inflatable anti-icing boots on leading-edges. Ventral tail bumper beneath rear fuselage, to protect propellers during take-off rotation.

LANDING GEAR: Hydraulically retractable tricycle type, with twin wheels and oleo-pneumatic shock absorber on each unit. Mainwheels retract inward into wing/underfuselage fairing; nose unit retracts forward. Emergency free-fall extension capability. Electrically actuated nosewheel steering. Mainwheel tyres size 22 × 6.75-10, pressure 7.24 bars (105 lb/sq in); nosewheel tyres size 16 × 4.1-8, pressure 5.17 bars (75 lb/sq in). Hydraulic carbon brakes with anti-skid provision. Backup braking system for use if one hydraulic system fails. Mechanical emergency and parking brake systems. High flotation tyres optional.

POWER PLANT: Two 1,552 kW (2,081 shp) Garrett TPF351-20 propfans, each derated to 969 kW (1,300 shp) and driving a Hartzell slow-turning constant-speed pusher propeller with reversible pitch, autofeathering, synchrophasing, and six scimitar blades. Engines are pylon mounted in carbonfibre nacelles at rear of fuselage, and have a

cruise/climb rating of 746 kW (1,000 shp). Fuel in integral wing tanks and auxiliary tank with combined capacity of 2,612 litres (690 US gallons; 574.5 Imp gallons). Single-point underwing pressure fuelling/defuelling, and two overwing gravity points. Oil capacity 9.5 litres (2.5 US gallons; 2.1 Imp gallons) per engine. Pneumatic inflatable de-icing boots on pylon leading-edges and engine air inlets.

ACCOMMODATION: Crew of two on flight deck, with dual controls; optional seat to rear for observer. Standard commuter cabin layout for 19 passengers, in five rows of three and a final four-seat row, at 79 cm (31 in) pitch. Wardrobe, toilet, galley, jump seat and seat for cabin attendant at front of cabin. Underseat and overhead bin stowage for carry-on baggage; main baggage/cargo compartment aft of rear row of seats. Executive interiors, to customer's requirements, available optionally. Plug type passenger door and baggage door on port side, at front and rear of cabin respectively. Plug type passenger emergency exit above wing on each side; flight deck side windows serve as emergency exits for crew. Entire accommodation pressurised and air-conditioned. Electric anti-icing of windscreens.

SYSTEMS: Dual air-conditioning and pressurisation systems (max differential 0.56 bars; 8.2 lb/sq in), giving a S/L cabin atmosphere up to 6,400 m (21,000 ft) and a 2,440 m (8,000 ft) environment at altitudes up to 12,200 m (40,000 ft). Two independent hydraulic systems (each 207 bars; 3,000 lb/sq in). Primary electrical power supply is 28V DC, provided by two 400A engine driven starter/generators and two nickel-cadmium batteries. Additional 400A starter/generator driven by APU. Two solid state inverters for 115V and 26V single-phase AC power at 400Hz. Digital fly by wire system provides electric signalling of flap and rudder actuation. High pressure

(127.5 bars; 1,850 lb/sq in) gaseous oxygen system for crew and passengers. Garrett APU for air-conditioning and electrical power generation.

AVIONICS: Generally similar to those for EMB-120 Brasilia. Standard basic Collins EFIS-86/EICAS fit will include two Pro Line II VHF com, audio distribution system, two VHF nav (VOR/ILS/marker beacon receiver), DME, WXR-350 colour weather radar, ADF, two ATC transponders with altitude encoders, two EADI, ALI-850 multifunction display system (CRT altimeter/preselector/VSI), two AHS-85 AHRS, two RMI, standby attitude indicator, standby magnetic compass, ELT, PA system, cabin interphone and dual APS-65 autopilots. Options include GPWS, flight data recorder, Selcal, MLS and FMS.

DIMENSIONS, EXTERNAL:

Wing span	17.72 m (58 ft 1½ in)
Wing chord: at root	2.50 m (8 ft 2½ in)
at tip	0.99 m (3 ft 3 in)
Wing aspect ratio	11.5
Length overall	18.09 m (59 ft 4¼ in)
Fuselage: Length	16.90 m (55 ft 5½ in)
Max diameter	2.28 m (7 ft 5¾ in)
Height overall	5.97 m (19 ft 7 in)
Elevator span	6.31 m (20 ft 8½ in)
Wheel track (c/l of shock struts)	3.56 m (11 ft 8¼ in)
Wheelbase	7.53 m (24 ft 8½ in)

Propeller diameter	2.59 m (8 ft 6 in)
Propeller ground clearance: min	1.58 m (5 ft 2¼ in)
max	1.62 m (5 ft 3¾ in)
Distance between propeller centres	4.50 m (14 ft 9¼ in)
Passenger door (fwd, port): Height	1.70 m (5 ft 7 in)
Width	0.77 m (2 ft 6¼ in)
Baggage door (rear, port): Height	1.35 m (4 ft 5¼ in)
Width	0.80 m (2 ft 7½ in)
Emergency exits (two, each):	
Height	0.92 m (3 ft 0¼ in)
Width	0.51 m (1 ft 8 in)

DIMENSIONS, INTERNAL:

Cabin: Length	6.47 m (21 ft 2¾ in)
Max width	2.11 m (6 ft 11 in)
Max height	1.76 m (5 ft 9¼ in)
Baggage compartment volume	4.25 m³ (150 cu ft)

AREAS:

Wings, gross	27.2 m² (292.8 sq ft)
Ailerons (total)	1.20 m² (12.92 sq ft)
Trailing-edge flaps (total)	4.63 m² (49.84 sq ft)
Spoilers (total)	1.49 m² (16.00 sq ft)
Fin	4.23 m² (45.53 sq ft)
Rudder	1.79 m² (19.27 sq ft)
Tailplane	8.01 m² (86.22 sq ft)
Elevators (total)	2.40 m² (25.83 sq ft)

WEIGHTS:

Basic operating weight empty	6,045 kg (13,327 lb)

Max fuel weight	1,980 kg (4,365 lb)
Max payload	2,155 kg (4,750 lb)
Max T-O weight	9,000 kg (19,841 lb)
Max ramp weight	9,040 kg (19,930 lb)
Max zero-fuel weight	8,200 kg (18,078 lb)
Max landing weight	8,750 kg (19,290 lb)

PERFORMANCE (estimated):

Max cruising speed at 7,315 m (24,000 ft)	351 knots (650 km/h; 404 mph)
Max rate of climb at S/L	777 m (2,549 ft)/min
Rate of climb at S/L, one engine out	189 m (620 ft)/min
Service ceiling	11,890 m (39,000 ft)
Service ceiling, one engine out	6,705 m (22,000 ft)
T-O to 15 m (50 ft):	
FAR 25 at S/L, ISA	1,160 m (3,806 ft)
at 1,525 m (5,000 ft), ISA + 20°C	1,720 m (5,643 ft)
Landing from 15 m (50 ft):	
FAR 135 at S/L, ISA	1,150 m (3,773 ft)
at 1,525 m (5,000 ft), ISA + 20°C	1,320 m (4,331 ft)
Min ground turning radius	10.04 m (32 ft 11 in)

Range at max cruising speed (ISA), reserves for 100 nm (185 km; 115 mile) diversion and 45 min hold:

with 19 passengers	780 nm (1,445 km; 898 miles)
with max fuel	1,653 nm (3,063 km; 1,903 miles)

EUROCOPTER

Eurocopter GIE
Chemin de la Piste, Bonneuil-en-France, 95500 Gonesse, France
Telephone: 33 (1) 48 35 94 76
Telex: 235632 F
Fax: 33 (1) 48 35 90 57

Eurocopter GmbH
Gustav Heinemann Ring 135 (Postfach 830356), 8000 Munich 83, West Germany
Telephone: 49 (89) 638250-0
Fax: 49 (89) 638250-50

CHIEF EXECUTIVE OFFICERS (both Eurocopter companies):
Bernard Darrieus
Frank Dorn

PARTICIPATING COMPANIES:
Messerschmitt-Bölkow-Blohm GmbH, Helicopter and Military Aircraft Group, Postfach 801160, 8000 Munich 80, West Germany
Telephone: 49 (89) 607 26488
Telex: 5287-027 MBB D
Fax: 49 (89) 607 29033
Aerospatiale, 37 boulevard de Montmorency, 75781 Paris Cédex 16, France
Telephone: 33 (1) 42 24 24 24
Telex: AISPA 620059 F

Following approval of a Franco-German co-operation programme on the basis of industry proposals, the defence ministers of West Germany and France signed on 13 November 1987 an amendment to their 1984 memorandum of understanding covering the development of a new anti-tank helicopter for service with their two armies in the 1990s. The main development contract was awarded to Eurocopter GmbH on 30 November 1989, when the name Tiger (for Germany) or Tigre (France) was adopted. Leadership and work is being shared between MBB and Aerospatiale.

Eurocopter GIE is the instrument of co-operation in the field of helicopters between Aerospatiale and MBB. For the purpose of managing the Franco-German battlefield helicopter programme, Eurocopter GmbH was established in Munich on 18 September 1985 as a wholly owned subsidiary of Eurocopter GIE in Paris. Executive authority for the programme is the DFHB (Deutsch-Französisches Hubschrauberbüro) in Koblenz; procurement agent is the BWB (Bundesamt für Wehrtechnik und Beschaffung).

Estimated costs for the three variants originally proposed (see 1986-87 *Jane's*) caused the programme to be temporarily halted in mid-1986 pending a reappraisal of requirements and aircraft specifications. It was re-launched in March 1987 on the basis of an anti-tank version common to both countries, plus an HAP version for France, and full-scale development was approved on 8 December 1987.

EUROCOPTER TIGER/TIGRE
The HAP and PAH-2/HAC programme, which is intended to provide 427 aircraft for the two countries, utilises a single basic helicopter design, from which the following versions will be developed:

HAP Tigre (Hélicoptère d'Appui Protection). Escort and fire support version for French Army, for delivery from 1997. Armed with a 30 mm GIAT AM-30781 automatic cannon in undernose turret, with 150-450 rds of ammunition. Releasable weapons, mounted on stub-wings, comprise four Matra Mistral infra-red homing air-to-air missiles and two pods each with twenty-two 68 mm unguided SNEB rockets. A 12-round rocket pod can be carried instead of each pair of Mistrals, making a total of 68 rockets. Roof mounted TV, FLIR, laser rangefinder and direct-optics sensors.

Eurocopter PAH-2 Tiger/HAC Tigre anti-tank helicopter, with additional side view (bottom) of the Tigre HAP escort and support version *(Jane's/Mike Keep)*

PAH-2 Tiger (Panzerabwehr-Hubschrauber, 2nd generation). Variant of the common anti-tank version for West German Army, for delivery from 1998. Underwing pylons for up to eight Hot 2 or Trigat long-range anti-tank missiles, or four Hot 2 plus four Trigat (inboard), and four Stinger 2 air-to-air missiles for self-defence (outboard). Mast mounted TV/FLIR/tracker/laser rangefinder sighting system for gunner; nose mounted FLIR night vision device for piloting.

HAC Tigre (Hélicoptère Anti-Char). Anti-tank variant for French Army, for delivery from 1998. Wing pylons for up to eight Hot 2 or Trigat missiles, or four Hot 2 and four Trigat, inboard and four Matra Mistral air-to-air missiles outboard. Mast mounted sight and pilot FLIR system similar to PAH-2.

Five development aircraft are to be built, including three unarmed aerodynamic prototypes (PT1, 2 and 3) to flight test the common basic airframe and systems. First flight is expected to take place in the first half of 1991, with PT2 flying for the first time in 1992 and the remaining prototypes at six-monthly intervals thereafter. PT2 and PT3 will become avionics testbeds, PT4 will be completed in HAP configuration, and PT5 as a PAH-2/HAC prototype. After their initial flight testing is completed, PT2 and PT3 will be retrofitted to HAP and PAH-2/HAC standard respectively, to participate in the weapon trials programme.

The agreed work sharing gives Aerospatiale responsibility for the tail rotor, centre-fuselage (including engine installation), transmission, fuel and electrical systems, aerodynamics, weight control, maintainability, reliability and survivability. MBB is responsible for the front and rear fuselage (including cockpits), main rotor, hydraulic and flight control systems, prototype assembly, flight performance, flight characteristics, stress, vibration testing, and simulation. Jointly staffed teams will be based at Marignane for flight testing the basic helicopter, updating the avionics fit during trials, and testing the HAP version; and at Ottobrunn for basic avionics, the Euromep mission equipment (armament) package, and weapons system integration.

Requirements have been estimated at 212 PAH-2s for Germany, 75 HAPs and 140 HACs for France.

TYPE: Twin-engined anti-tank and ground support helicopter.

ROTOR SYSTEM AND DRIVE: Four-blade semi-rigid main rotor, with composite blades and two elastomeric bearings per blade. Rotor head consists of two fibre composite starplates bolted together with a titanium spacer, a configuration which permits installation of a mast mounted sight. Main features are a compact, robust construction, low aerodynamic drag, a very small number of parts, and ease of maintenance. Development of new DMH blade aerofoil sections and geometries promises performance improvements of about 10 per cent over most present-day systems, and will provide the agility needed in typical anti-tank missions. Three-blade Aerospatiale Spheriflex composite tail rotor, mounted on starboard side, has OA aerofoil section. Principal features of main transmission are separate load paths, high run-dry capability (up to 30 min), compatibility with the mast mounted sight, and ability to withstand 12.5 mm hits. Subcontractors include SAMM/Liebherr (main and tail rotor servo controls) and Labinal/Electrométal (servo trim).

WINGS, FUSELAGE AND TAIL UNIT: Composites structures, meeting criteria for safety, crash resistance (to MIL-STD-1290 standards), and damage tolerance (survivable against hits from weapons of up to 23 mm calibre). Fuselage and wings mainly of carbonfibre, with glassfibre or Kevlar fairings. Stub wings, with anhedral on outer panels, for releasable weapons. Sweptback fin/tail rotor pylon and underfin; horizontal stabiliser, with sweptback endplate auxiliary fins.

LANDING GEAR: Non-retractable tailwheel type, with single wheel on each unit. Designed to absorb impacts of up to 6 m (20 ft)/s. Main gear by Messier-Hispano-Bugatti, tail gear by Liebherr Aerotechnik.

POWER PLANT: Two 958 kW (1,285 shp) MTU/Rolls-Royce/Turbomeca MTR 390 turboshafts, mounted side by side above centre-fuselage. Infra-red exhaust suppressors, using ram air. Self-sealing crashworthy fuel tanks, with explosion suppression and total capacity of 1,360 litres (359 US gallons; 299 Imp gallons).

ACCOMMODATION: Crew of two in tandem, with pilot in front and weapons system operator at rear. Armoured, impact-absorbing seats. Stepped cockpits, with flat-plate transparencies.

SYSTEMS: Redundant hydraulic, electrical and fuel systems.

AVIONICS: Essential characteristics will be common to both French and German versions, and European in origin. Flight controls are mechanical, comprising duplex primary hydraulic servocontrols (controlled by autopilot and trim), and duplex main hydraulic servocontrols to generate control loads towards rotors. Support is provided by a redundant, four-axis duplex AFCS with stabilisation and autopilot functions. Systems architecture is based on a dual MIL-STD-1553B databus. Via two central computers with symbol generation, information for pilot and gunner is shown on multifunction displays in cockpit. Essential flight data for pilot are also displayed by backup conventional instruments. Navigation subsystem consists of two identical strapdown units together with such sensors as ASI, Doppler radar, radar altimeter and magnetic sensor. Subsystem conducts functions of autonomous navigation as well as flight path computation, and supplies data necessary for AFCS and mission equipment packages. An integrated radar/laser warning subsystem will be installed to recognise, identify and classify specific threats. Provisions are made for comprehensive additional active ECM. Subcontractors so far announced include Rohde und Schwarz/Sextant Avionique (control and display unit); Teldix GmbH (licence for Canadian Marconi CMA 2012 Doppler velocity sensor); and Dornier/VDO-L (digital map display system). *Anti-tank mission* equipment package, based on a MIL-STD-1553B redundant databus, comprises visionic system with mast mounted sight, piloting vision system and gunner's sight, and combined helmet mounted sight and display, plus armament according to variant. Mast mounted sight, controlled by gunner, is a multi-sensor system with TV and infra-red channels and various fields of view. Visionic system is stabilised, includes tracker for single and multiple targets, a laser rangefinder, and cockpit display. Nose mounted IR sensor (piloting vision system, or PVS) image is displayed and steered via helmet sight display; in the event of PVS loss, the gunner's redundant IR image can be used. Mission equipment of HAP *escort/combat support version* is also based on MIL-STD-1553B redundant databus, which interconnects firing control and redundant bus management computer, gunner's sight, HUD, gun turret, rockets, air-to-air missiles, pilot's and gunner's helmet sights, and pilot's and gunner's armament control unit. Between all three versions some equipment (eg com radios, sand filters) will vary according to individual operator's specifications.

ARMAMENT: As listed under model descriptions.

DIMENSIONS, EXTERNAL:

Main rotor diameter	13.00 m (42 ft 7¾ in)
Tail rotor diameter	2.70 m (8 ft 10¼ in)
Length of fuselage	14.00 m (45 ft 11¼ in)
Height to top of rotor head	3.81 m (12 ft 6 in)
Wheel track	2.40 m (7 ft 10½ in)
Wheelbase	approx 7.95 m (26 ft 1 in)

AREAS:

Main rotor disc	132.7 m² (1,428.7 sq ft)
Tail rotor disc	5.72 m² (61.63 sq ft)

WEIGHTS:

Basic weight empty	3,300 kg (7,275 lb)
Mission T-O weight	5,300 to 5,600 kg (11,685 to 12,346 lb)
Max overload T-O weight	6,000 kg (13,227 lb)

PERFORMANCE (estimated, at AUW of 5,400 kg; 11,905 lb):

Cruising speed	135-151 knots (250-280 km/h; 155-174 mph)
Max rate of climb at S/L	more than 600 m (1,970 ft)/min
Hovering ceiling OGE	more than 2,000 m (6,560 ft)
Endurance, incl 20 min reserves	2 h 50 min

EUROFAR
EUROPEAN FUTURE ADVANCED ROTORCRAFT

Six European aerospace companies (Aerospatiale, MBB, Agusta, Aeritalia, CASA and Westland) signed an accord in September 1986 to collaborate in a preliminary study of a European tilt-rotor convertiplane, initially for civil applications. Funding of the three-year study (1987-90) was provided in the approximate ratio of 75 per cent from the Eureka European technology research programme, which voted £31.5 million to the project in September 1987, and 25 per cent from the participating companies. Of the latter, the major share will be borne by Aerospatiale (France), MBB (Germany) and Agusta/Aeritalia (Italy), with 29 per cent each; CASA (Spain) and Westland (UK) each have 6.5 per cent. Agusta is leader of the working group assigned to define the aircraft.

Early parameters for the Eurofar aircraft envisage a twin-engined, 30-passenger design in the 13,000 kg (28,660 lb) gross weight class, with a 15 m (49.2 ft) wing span, 10-11 m (32.8-36.1 ft) rotor diameter, a cruising speed of 313 knots (580 km/h; 360 mph) and a range of 539 nm (1,000 km; 621 miles). This would require two engines in the 2,983 kW (4,000 shp) class, and various power plant options are being studied. A first flight is tentatively planned for 1994.

Artist's impression of a possible Eurofar civil tilt-rotor aircraft for the mid-1990s

EUROFIGHTER
EUROFIGHTER JAGDFLUGZEUG GmbH

Arabellastrasse 16 (Postfach 860366), 8000 Munich 86, West Germany
Telephone: 49 (89) 92803214
Telex: 5213908 or 5213744
Fax: 49 (89) 92803443
CHAIRMAN: I. R. Yates
MANAGING DIRECTOR: F. G. Willox
MARKETING: A French
PUBLICITY EXECUTIVE: Ursula Kruse
PUBLIC RELATIONS: E. Sanchez-Ulloa

EUROPEAN FIGHTER AIRCRAFT (EFA)

The chiefs of air staff of France, West Germany, Italy, Spain and the UK issued in December 1983 an outline staff target for a new combat aircraft to enter service with all five air forces in the mid-1990s. France withdrew in July 1985, participation by the remaining four countries then being set at 33 per cent each for the UK and Germany, 21 per cent for Italy and 13 per cent for Spain. National design teams from MBB (with Dornier as co-contractor), Aeritalia, CASA and British Aerospace are collaborating in developing and harmonising individual national requirements, incorporating some of the design aspects and technology from the BAe EAP programme (see UK section). The initial feasibility study, launched in July 1984, was followed by the project definition phase, completed in September 1986. In June 1986 Eurofighter GmbH, with headquarters in Munich, was formed to manage the EFA programme. Eurojet Turbo GmbH was formed shortly afterwards to manage the engine programme.

The project definition stage was followed by a definition refinement and risk reduction stage, which lasted until the end of 1987. In September of that year the four air staffs issued European Staff Requirement-Development (ESR-D), featuring the military requirements of the EFA in further detail. At the same time, industry delivered all necessary technical and economic data to the four governments for go-ahead negotiations. The full-scale development phase was initiated by the signing of main development contracts for the weapons system and engine on 23 November 1988, and this is scheduled to lead to a first flight in 1991 and initial deliveries in 1996.

Eight prototypes (including two two-seaters) are to be built, with flight testing in all four countries. First to fly will be P01, at Manching in West Germany, followed about three months later by P02 at BAe Warton. P03, the first two-seater (and first with EJ200 engines), will also be flown at Warton; P04 will be the first Italian prototype. The next two (P05 in the UK and P06 in Germany) will be the avionics testbeds, and the development batch will be completed by Spain's first EFA, the two-seat P07, and Italy's second, P08. All eight are to fly by 1993. Two additional airframes will be used for static and fatigue testing. The EFA programme is being supervised by an international agency known as NEFMA (NATO European Fighter Management Agency) independent of, but collocated with, the NAMMA agency for the Panavia Tornado, based in Munich.

The EFA will be configured primarily for the air defence and air superiority roles, but with a secondary capability for air-to-surface attack. A total of 765 EFAs is required by the partner nations, in the ratio of 250 for Germany, 165 for Italy, 100 for Spain and 250 for Great Britain; a proportion of two-seat trainer versions would be included in these totals. Export orders are also anticipated. The agreed workshare gives BAe responsibility for design and manufacture of the front fuselage and foreplanes; MBB (teamed with Dornier) will produce the centre-fuselage and fin; Aeritalia and CASA will build the rear fuselage; and wing production will be shared between Aeritalia, CASA and BAe, without any duplication of tooling. There will be a final assembly line at each of the four airframe companies. Most subsystems are being developed by multi-nation teams; in the following description, for the sake of clarity, only the name of the relevant team leader is given.

TYPE: Single-seat, extremely agile STOL-capable fighter, optimised for air defence and air superiority roles, with secondary ground attack capability.

AIRFRAME: Aerodynamically unstable design, incorporating low detectability technologies, a substantial proportion built of composites materials in conjunction with new lightweight metal alloys, using advanced manufacturing techniques such as superplastic forming and diffusion bonding. Joint structures team headed by CASA.

WINGS AND FOREPLANES: Cantilever low-mounted delta-wing monoplane of low aspect ratio, with 53° sweepback on leading-edges. Inboard and outboard flaperons on trailing-edges. All-moving titanium foreplanes mid-mounted on nose, in line with windscreen. Main wing structure built of CFC (carbonfibre composites), with Al-Li (aluminium-lithium) alloys for flaperons and two-segment leading-edge slats. Pitch control via foreplanes and flaperons, using advanced active control technology to provide artificial longitudinal stability (aircraft is otherwise aerodynamically unstable). Al-Li ECM pod at each wingtip. Liebherr flight control actuators.

FUSELAGE: Conventional semi-monocoque, built largely of CFC except for GFRP nose radome, aluminium canopy surround, Al-Li wing/body fairing and intake cowling, and titanium in exhaust nozzle area. Dorsal spine aft of cockpit incorporates airbrake.

TAIL UNIT: Vertical surfaces only, comprising sweptback Al-Li/CFC fin (with GFRP tip) and Al-Li inset rudder.

LANDING GEAR: Dowty Aerospace retractable tricycle type. Single-wheel main units retract inward into fuselage, steerable nosewheel unit forward.

POWER PLANT: First two prototypes each powered by two Turbo-Union RB199-122 afterburning turbofans (each more than 71.2 kN; 16,000 lb st). Later prototypes and the production aircraft will be powered by two Eurojet EJ200 advanced technology turbofans (each of 90 kN; 20,250 lb nominal thrust with afterburning), mounted side by side in rear fuselage with ventral intakes. Dornier digital engine control system. Lucas Aerospace fuel management system. Provision for up to three external fuel tanks and in-flight refuelling.

ENGINE AIR INTAKES: Side by side intakes in underfuselage box, each having a fixed upper wedge/ramp and a variable-position lower cowl lip (vari-cowl) with Dowty Aerospace actuators.

ACCOMMODATION: Pilot only, on zero/zero ejection seat. Smiths Industries glareshields.

SYSTEMS: Normalair-Garrett environmental control system. Magnaghi hydraulic system. Lucas Aerospace electrical system, with Ferranti-Bendix variable speed constant frequency generator and Ferranti transformer-rectifier units. Full authority four-channel ACT (active control technology) digital fly by wire flight control system (team leader MBB), combined with mission adaptive configuring and the aircraft's artificial longitudinal instability, will provide the EFA with the required 'carefree' handling, gust alleviation and high sustained manoeuvrability throughout the flight envelope. Pitch control effected via foreplane/flaperon ACT to provide artificial longitudinal stability; yaw control via rudder. The quadruplex AFCS, which will operate through a STANAG 3910 NATO standard databus, is intended to ensure that pilot cannot exceed aircraft's flying limits. Aeritalia-led utilities control system (UCS), controlled by microcomputer. Garrett APU for engine starting, systems running and NBC filtering. Microturbo UK air turbine starter motor.

AVIONICS: BAe has overall team leadership for avionics development and integration. Primary sensor will be a multi-mode pulse-Doppler radar with an interception range of 50-80 nm (92.5-148 km; 57.5-92 miles), able to acquire at least 85 per cent of probable targets (including eight targets simultaneously), and to direct lookdown/shootdown and snap-up weapons against them. Other radar requirements include velocity and single-target search, track-while-scan and range-while-scan, target priority processing, automatic weapons selection, and recommended combat tactics display. In attack mode, it will have capability for ground mapping/ranging and terrain avoidance, but not terrain following. Radar will form part of a comprehensive avionics suite which also includes extensive communications, and wingtip pods will house an advanced integrated defensive aids support system (DASS). All avionics, flight control and utilities control systems will be integrated through STANAG 3910 NATO standard databus highways with appropriate redundancy levels, using fibre optics and microprocessors. Special attention has been given to reducing pilot workload. New cockpit techniques will simplify flying the aircraft safely and effectively to the limits of the flight envelope while monitoring and managing the aircraft and its operational systems, and detecting/identifying/attacking desired targets while remaining safe from enemy defences. This will be achieved through a high level of system integration and automation, including HOTAS (hands on throttle

Three-view drawing of Eurofighter EFA (European Fighter Aircraft), under development for four European air forces *(Pilot Press)*

and stick); a wide-angle HUD able to display, in addition to other symbology, FLIR pictures from an infra-red search and track (IRST) sensor pod-mounted externally to the left of the cockpit; a helmet mounted sight (HMS), with direct voice input (DVI) for appropriate functions; and three Smiths Industries multi-function head-down (MFHD) colour CRT displays. Other cockpit instrumentation includes a Computing Devices video and voice recorder, Ferranti (Elmer) crash survival memory unit, and Teldix cockpit interface unit.

ARMAMENT: Interceptor will have an internally mounted 27mm gun on starboard side, plus a mix of AIM-120 AMRAAM and short-range (AIM-132 ASRAAM or Sidewinder) air-to-air missiles carried externally, four of the former being mounted in tandem pairs in a semi-recessed underfuselage installation similar to that of the ADV Tornado. The short-range missiles are carried on underwing pylons. The EFA will, if necessary, be able to carry a considerable overload of air-to-air weapons. For secondary role air-to-surface weapons, and/or auxiliary fuel tanks, it will have a total of 13 external stores stations.

DIMENSIONS, EXTERNAL:
Wing span	10.50 m (34 ft 5½ in)
Wing aspect ratio	2.205
Length overall	approx 14.50 m (47 ft 7 in)

AREA:
Wings, gross	50.0 m² (538.2 sq ft)

WEIGHTS (approx):
Weight empty	9,750 kg (21,495 lb)
Internal fuel load	4,000 kg (8,818 lb)
External stores load (weapons and/or fuel)	4,500 kg (9,920 lb)
Max T-O weight	17,000 kg (37,480 lb)

DESIGN PERFORMANCE:
Max level speed	more than Mach 1.8

T-O and landing distance with full internal fuel and two AMRAAM plus two ASRAAM or Sidewinder missiles, ISA + 15°C   500 m (1,640 ft)

Combat radius (estimated)   250-300 nm (463-556 km; 288-345 miles)

g limits with full internal fuel and two AMRAAM missiles   +9/-3

EUROFLAG
EUROPEAN FUTURE LARGE AIRCRAFT GROUP

A four-nation Future International Military Airlifter (FIMA) study group was set up in December 1982 to work towards development of a late-1990s replacement for the Lockheed C-130 Hercules and Transall C-160 transport aircraft with increased payload capacity, enhanced performance, and major savings in fleet operating costs and manpower.

The original group, consisting of Aerospatiale, British Aerospace, Lockheed Aeronautical Systems (Georgia Division) and MBB (now Deutsche Airbus), was joined in December 1987 by Aeritalia and CASA. In April 1989, by mutual agreement, Lockheed left the group and the FIMA Memorandum of Understanding was superseded by a new MoU signed by the five European companies under the title European Future Large Aircraft Group (Euroflag). The aim of Euroflag is to satisfy European and NATO requirements in a modern, common aircraft. Derivative variants may include air-refuelling tankers, surveillance/reconnaissance, long-range maritime patrol and airborne early warning aircraft. Hence, major economies could result from a 'large aircraft fleet rationalisation' policy which is one of the goals stated by NATO and in the IEPG's Future Large Aircraft (FLA) Outline European Staff Target (OEST) issued by European air forces in April 1988.

The European FLA tactical transport is emerging as a high-wing aircraft with a max T-O weight in the order of 80-110 tonnes (176,370-242,500 lb). It is likely to have a two-man flight deck, a T tail, rough-field landing gear, and a much larger cargo hold floor area and cross-section than those of the C-130 and Transall C-160. Design payload is likely to be 20-25 tonnes (44,090-55,115 lb) over a 2,000-2,500 nm (3,706-4,633 km; 2,303-2,879 mile) range. The large hold dimensions will allow room for low-density cargo. Economical cruising speed will be between Mach 0.70 and 0.75. Type and number of engines will be based on the availability of suitably sized new-generation civil or military engines in the mid-1990s, and all engine configuration options remain under study. Major reductions in maintenance man-hour requirements, and

New artist's impression of the five-nation Euroflag European Future Large Aircraft now powered by turbofans

increases in aircraft availability and survivability, will follow from the use of modern design and manufacturing techniques. The market is estimated at 700-1,000 aircraft.

First flight is planned for about 2,000, with deliveries beginning two years later, assuming a 1996 start for the full scale engineering development phase.

JEH

JOINT EUROPEAN HELICOPTER Srl

Via Sicilia 43, 00187 Rome, Italy
Telephone: 39 (6) 49801
Telex: 614398

Following industrial agreements between Agusta, CASA, Fokker and Westland, JEH was formed in November 1986 to manage the multi-national programme to produce a third-generation multi-role light attack helicopter (LAH) known as Tonal, based on the Agusta A 129 Mangusta. Shareholdings are 38 per cent each to Agusta and Westland, 19 per cent to Fokker and 5 per cent to CASA.

JEH A 129 LAH TONAL

The Tonal programme came into being to meet the requirements of the Italian, British, Dutch and Spanish armed forces for an advanced multi-role combat helicopter for the late 1990s. Named after an ancient Aztec deity, Tonal would have a structure based on that of the Mangusta (see Italian section), but with equipment and weapons systems to give it anti-tank, scout and anti-helicopter capability. Reported requirements of the four partner nations are: Italy 90, UK 125, Netherlands 50 and Spain 40.

An interim feasibility report put forward four basic options for development of the A 129 Mangusta to meet an internationally agreed LAH Staff Target. This was followed in February 1989 by authorisation of the second phase, in which one configuration was selected for further study, resulting in submission of a technical report by the four partners to their governments in March 1990. This report was to be considered by the four governments during the second half of the year, to be followed, if the report is accepted, by a one-year pre-development phase lasting from January to December 1991. At the time of going to press, continued Westland participation remained uncertain.

MBB/KAWASAKI

AIRFRAME PRIME CONTRACTORS:

Messerschmitt-Bölkow-Blohm GmbH (Helicopter and Military Aircraft Group), Postfach 801140, 8000 Munich 80, West Germany
Telephone: 49 (89) 6070
Telex: 5287-071/074 MBB D
Fax: 49 (89) 60728720
Kawasaki Heavy Industries Ltd, World Trade Center Building, 4-1 Hamamatsu-cho 2-chome, Minato-ku, Tokyo, Japan
Telephone: 81 (3) 435 2971
Telex: 242 4371 KAWAJU J
Fax: 81 (3) 436 3037

MBB/KAWASAKI BK 117 B-1

MBB and Kawasaki agreed on 25 February 1977 to develop jointly a multi-purpose helicopter known as the BK 117. This aircraft has a number of components and accessories interchangeable with those of the MBB BO 105, from which aircraft the principle of the hydraulic boost system is also adapted. The transmission is based on that developed by Kawasaki for its earlier KH-7 design.

The BK 117 is manufactured by the single source method, each company producing the components which it has developed, which are then exchanged. There are two final assembly lines, one at Donauwörth and one at Gifu. MBB is responsible for production of the main and tail rotor systems, tailboom and tail unit, skid landing gear, hydraulic system, engine firewall and cowlings, power-amplified controls and systems integration; Kawasaki is responsible for the fuselage, transmission, fuel and electrical systems, and standard items of equipment. An agreement was signed with MBB in November 1982 whereby IPTN of Indonesia (which see) is licensed to manufacture the BK 117, as the **NBK-117.**

Four prototypes (first flight 13 June 1979) and one pre-production BK 117 (first flight 6 March 1981) were built, as described in earlier editions of *Jane's*. The first production BK 117 to fly was a Kawasaki-built aircraft (JQ1001), which flew for the first time on 24 December 1981. The first MBB production aircraft flew on 23 April 1982. German LBA type certification was granted on 9 December 1982, followed by Japanese certification on 17 December 1982. Certification is to FAR Pt 29, Category A and B, including Amendments 29-1 to 29-16. FAA certification was granted on 29 March 1983.

Customer deliveries began in early 1983, the initial production model being known as the **BK 117 A-1** (described in the 1984-85 *Jane's*). On 15 March 1985 the LBA certificated the **BK 117 A-3** with max T-O weight increased from 2,850 kg (6,283 lb) to 3,200 kg (7,055 lb), and from January 1987 a **BK 117 A-4** model (certificated by the LBA on 29 July 1986 and JCAB on 29 August 1986) became available. The A-3 introduced an enlarged tail rotor with twisted blades; the A-4, with an increased transmission limit at T-O power, improved tail rotor head and (on German built examples) more standard fuel, offered enhanced performance. Details of the A-3 and A-4 can be found in the 1987-88 *Jane's*.

A new **BK 117 B-1** series was certificated in 1987 by the LBA (on 10 December) and FAA (11 December) and, on 31 March 1988, by the JCAB. This has LTS 101-750B-1 engines, enabling it to hover OGE, in ISA conditions, at a 427 m (1,400 ft) higher altitude than the A-4, with 140 kg (309 lb) more payload; and hover IGE with the same payload increase at altitudes increased by 457 m (1,500 ft) (ISA) and 549 m (1,800 ft) (ISA + 20°C). All current production BK 117s are to B-1 standard.

On behalf of, and subsidised by, the German Federal Ministry of Defence, MBB built an entire BK 117 airframe of fibre reinforced composite materials in a 3½ year research programme. This aircraft first flew on 27 April 1989, and the experience gained from the programme will assist the development of such new-generation helicopters as the Eurocopter Tiger and NH 90. The special BK 117 airframe was built 80 per cent in CFRP and 20 per cent in AFRP (Kevlar). The flight test programme was completed in July 1989.

By 1 January 1990 a total of 250 BK 117s had been delivered worldwide, including 36 by Kawasaki. Orders in 1989 included three for mission support duties with the US Customs Service, equipped with FLIR, an SX-16 searchlight and NVG lighting; and two for anti-drug surveillance with the Peruvian Ministry of the Interior. The following description applies to the BK 117 B-1:

Kawasaki built BK 117 B-1 in passenger executive configuration

MBB/Kawasaki BK 117 B-1 twin-turboshaft multi-purpose helicopter *(Pilot Press)*

TYPE: Twin-turbine multi-purpose helicopter.

ROTOR SYSTEM: Four-blade 'System Bölkow' rigid titanium main rotor head almost identical to that of BO 105; main rotor blades similar to those of BO 105, but larger. Two-blade teetering tail rotor. Fail-safe GFRP main rotor blades of NACA 23012/23010 (modified) section with a stainless steel anti-erosion strip. Optional folding of two blades of main rotor. Main rotor rpm: 383. Tail rotor mounted on port side of vertical fin; blades are of GFRP, with high impact resistance and MBB-S102E performance/noise-optimised section. Tail rotor rpm: 2,169.

ROTOR DRIVE: Each engine has separate drive input into Kawasaki KB 03 main transmission via single bevel gear and collector. Transmission rated at 736 kW (986 shp) for twin-engine take-off and 632 kW (848 shp) for max continuous operation; and, for single-engine operation, at 442 kW (592 shp) for 2½ min, 404 kW (542 shp) for 30 min, and 368 kW (493 shp) max continuous. Auxiliary drives for accessories. Dual redundant lubrication system.

FUSELAGE: Of typical pod shaped configuration, comprising flight deck, cabin, cargo compartment and engine deck. Main structural components are of semi-monocoque riveted aluminium alloy with single curvature sheets and bonded aluminium sandwich panels. Secondary components are compound curvature shells with sandwich panels and Kevlar skins. Level floor extends throughout cockpit, cabin and cargo compartment. Engine deck forms roof of cargo compartment and, adjacent to engine bays, is of titanium to serve as a firewall.

TAIL UNIT: Semi-monocoque tailboom, of tapered conical section, attached integrally to engine deck at forward end. Rear end, which is detachable, carries main fin/tail rotor support, and horizontal stabiliser with endplate fins set at an offset angle.

LANDING GEAR: Non-retractable tubular skid type, of aluminium construction. Skids are detachable from cross-tubes. Ground handling wheels standard. Emergency flotation gear, settling protectors and snow skids available optionally.

POWER PLANT: Two Textron Lycoming LTS 101-750B-1 turboshafts, each rated at 442 kW (592 shp) for 30 min for take-off and 410 kW (550 shp) max continuous power. Fuel in four flexible bladder tanks (forward and aft main tanks, with two supply tanks between), in compartments under cabin floor. Two independent fuel feed systems for the engines and a common main fuel tank. Total standard fuel capacity 708 litres (187 US gallons; 155.7 Imp gallons). A 200 litre (53 US gallon; 44 Imp gallon) auxiliary tank is available optionally, raising total capacity to 908 litres (240 US gallons; 199.7 Imp gallons).

ACCOMMODATION: Pilot and up to six (executive version), seven (MBB standard version) or nine passengers (Kawasaki standard version). High-density layouts available for up to 10 passengers in addition to pilot. Provision for two-pilot operation at customer's option. Jettisonable forward hinged door on each side of cockpit, pilot's door having an openable window. Jettisonable rearward sliding passenger door on each side of cabin, lockable in open position. Fixed steps on each side. Two hinged, clamshell doors at rear of cabin, providing access to cargo compartment. Rear cabin window on each side.

Aircraft can be equipped, according to mission, for offshore, medical evacuation (one or two stretchers side by side and up to six attendants), firefighting, search and rescue, law enforcement, cargo transport or other operations.

SYSTEMS: Ram air and electrical ventilation system. Fully redundant tandem hydraulic boost system (one operating and one standby), pressure 103.5 bars (1,500 lb/sq in), for flight controls. System flow rate 8.1 litres (2.14 US gallons; 1.78 Imp gallons)/min. Bootstrap/oil reservoir, pressure 1.7 bars (25 lb/sq in). Main DC electrical power from two 150A 28V starter/generators (one on each engine) and a 24V 25Ah nickel-cadmium battery. AC power is provided by an inverter; a second AC inverter is available optionally. Emergency busbar provides direct battery power to essential services in event of a double generator failure. External DC power receptacle.

AVIONICS AND EQUIPMENT: Basic aircraft has instrumentation for single-pilot VFR operation, including airspeed indicator with electrically heated pitot tube and static ports, encoding altimeter, instantaneous vertical speed indicator, 4 in artificial horizon, 3 in standby artificial horizon, gyro magnetic heading system, HSI, magnetic compass, ambient air thermometer, and clock. (The 4 in and 3 in artificial horizons and HSI are optional on Kawasaki built aircraft.) Dual controls and dual VFR instrumentation available optionally. Com/nav and other avionics available to customer's requirements, including VHF-AM/FM, UHF and HF transceivers, ADF, nav, R/Nav, Loran, Decca, VLF/Omega, LDNS and AHRS systems, radar altimeter, ATC/IFF transponder, encoding altimeter, DME, multi-mode radar, IFR instrumentation packages, pitch/roll stability augmentation system and Honeywell SPZ-7100 dual digital AFCS. Standard basic equipment includes rotor brake and yaw CSAS (both optional only on Kawasaki aircraft), annunciator panel, master caution light, rotor rpm/engine fail warning control unit, fuel quantity indicator and low level sensor, outside air temperature indicator, engine and transmission oil pressure and temperature indicators, two exhaust temperature indicators, dual torque indicator, triple tachometer, two N1 tachometers, mast moment indicator, instrument panel lights, cockpit/cabin/cargo compartment dome lights, utility lights, emergency exit lights, position lights, anti-collision warning light, retractable landing light, portable flashlight, ground handling wheels, pilot's and co-pilot's windscreen wipers, floor covering, interior panelling and sound insulation, ashtrays, map/document

case, tiedown rings in cabin and cargo compartment, engine compartment fire warning indicator, engine fire extinguishing system, portable fire extinguisher, first aid kit, and single colour exterior paint scheme. Optional equipment includes high-density seating arrangement, bleed air heating system, long-range fuel tank, emergency flotation gear, settling protectors, snow skids, main rotor blade folding kit, non-retractable landing light, dual pilot operation kit, stretcher installation, external cargo hook, rescue hoist, SX 16 remotely controlled searchlight, external loudspeaker, and sand filter. Special optional equipment, including special mission kits for rescue, law enforcement and VIP transport, available at customer's request.

DIMENSIONS, EXTERNAL:
Main rotor diameter	11.00 m (36 ft 1 in)
Tail rotor diameter	1.956 m (6 ft 5 in)
Main rotor blade chord	0.32 m (1 ft 0½ in)
Length: overall, both rotors turning	13.00 m (42 ft 8 in)
fuselage, tail rotor blades vertical	9.91 m (32 ft 6¼ in)
Fuselage: Max width	1.60 m (5 ft 3 in)
Height: overall, both rotors turning	3.85 m (12 ft 7½ in)
to top of main rotor head	3.36 m (11 ft 0¼ in)
Tailplane span (over endplate fins)	2.70 m (8 ft 10¼ in)
Tail rotor ground clearance	1.90 m (6 ft 2¾ in)
Width over skids	2.50 m (8 ft 2½ in)

DIMENSIONS, INTERNAL:
Combined cabin and cargo compartment:
Max length	3.02 m (9 ft 11 in)
Width: max	1.49 m (4 ft 10½ in)
min	1.21 m (3 ft 11½ in)
Height: max	1.28 m (4 ft 2½ in)
min	0.99 m (3 ft 3 in)
Useful floor area	3.70 m² (39.83 sq ft)
Volume	5.00 m³ (176.6 cu ft)

AREAS:
Main rotor blades (each)	1.76 m² (18.94 sq ft)
Tail rotor blades (each)	0.0975 m² (1.05 sq ft)
Main rotor disc	95.03 m² (1,022.9 sq ft)
Tail rotor disc	3.00 m² (32.24 sq ft)

WEIGHTS:
Basic weight empty	1,725 kg (3,803 lb)
Fuel: standard usable	558 kg (1,230 lb)
incl auxiliary tank	718 kg (1,583 lb)
Max T-O weight, internal and external payload	3,200 kg (7,055 lb)

*PERFORMANCE (ISA; A at gross weight of 2,800 kg; 6,173 lb, B at 3,000 kg; 6,614 lb, C at 3,200 kg; 7,055 lb):

Never-exceed speed at S/L:		
A, B, C	150 knots	(278 km/h; 172 mph)
Max cruising speed at S/L:		
A	137 knots	(254 km/h; 158 mph)
B	135 knots	(250 km/h; 155 mph)
C	134 knots	(248 km/h; 154 mph)
Max forward rate of climb at S/L:		
A	714 m (2,345 ft)/min	
B	660 m (2,165 ft)/min	
C	582 m (1,910 ft)/min	
Max certificated operating altitude:		
A, B	4,575 m (15,000 ft)	
C	3,050 m (10,000 ft)	
Service ceiling, one engine out, 46 m (150 ft)/min climb reserve: A	3,110 m (10,200 ft)	
B	2,440 m (8,000 ft)	
C	1,770 m (5,800 ft)	
Hovering ceiling IGE (zero wind):		
A	4,205 m (13,800 ft)	
B	3,565 m (11,700 ft)	
C	2,925 m (9,600 ft)	
Hovering ceiling IGE (17 knot; 32 km/h; 20 mph crosswind): A	2,865 m (9,400 ft)	
B	2,195 m (7,200 ft)	
C	1,495 m (4,900 ft)	
Hovering ceiling OGE: A	3,625 m (11,900 ft)	
B	2,955 m (9,700 ft)	
C	2,285 m (7,500 ft)	
Range at S/L with standard fuel, no reserves:		
A	315 nm (585 km; 363 miles)	
B	313 nm (580 km; 360 miles)	
C	307 nm (570 km; 354 miles)	
Ferry range at S/L with auxiliary fuel, no reserves:		
A	408 nm (756 km; 469 miles)	
B	404 nm (750 km; 466 miles)	
C	399 nm (740 km; 460 miles)	
Endurance at S/L, standard fuel, no reserves:		
A	3 h 15 min	
B	3 h 12 min	
C	3 h 6 min	

Data are for German built aircraft: those for Japanese models vary slightly

MBB BK 117 M
This multi-role military version of the BK 117 is a purely German development by MBB, and is therefore described in the German section of this edition.

MCDONNELL DOUGLAS/BAe

AIRFRAME PRIME CONTRACTORS:

McDonnell Douglas Corporation, Box 516, St Louis, Missouri 63166, USA
Telephone: 1 (314) 234 7019
Telex: 234 4857 MCDL DGLS STZ

British Aerospace PLC, Richmond Road, Kingston upon Thames, Surrey KT2 5QS, England
Telephone: 44 (1) 546 7741
Telex: 23726

VICE-PRESIDENT AND GENERAL MANAGER, AV-8:
Roger H. Mathews

PROGRAMME MANAGER, T45TS: Larry A. Lemke

MCDONNELL DOUGLAS/BRITISH AEROSPACE HARRIER II
US Marine Corps designations: AV-8B and TAV-8B
RAF designation: Harrier GR. Mk 5
Spanish Navy designation: VA.2 Matador II

The early background to the Harrier II programme has been given in several previous editions of *Jane's*. After McDonnell Douglas and BAe (then Hawker Siddeley) joined forces in the current collaborative programme, two AV-8As were modified as YAV-8B aerodynamic prototypes by McDonnell Douglas and the USMC, these flying for the first time on 9 November 1978 and 19 February 1979. The first of four full-scale development AV-8Bs made its initial flight on 5 November 1981.

Compared with the Harrier GR. Mk 3/AV-8A (see under BAe in UK section), features of the AV-8B include the use of graphite epoxy (carbonfibre) composite materials for the wings, and parts of the fuselage and tail unit; adoption of a supercritical wing section; addition of lift improvement devices (LIDs) comprising fuselage mounted or under-gun-pod strakes and a retractable fence panel forward of the pods, to augment lift for vertical take-off; larger wing trailing-edge flaps and drooped ailerons; redesigned forward fuselage and cockpit; redesigned engine air intakes to provide more VTO/STO thrust and more efficient cruise; two additional wing stores stations; and the Hughes Angle Rate Bombing Set. Wing outriggers are relocated at mid-span to provide better ground manoeuvring capability, and leading-edge root extensions (LERX) add considerably to the instantaneous turn rate. Combined with an expanded thrust vectoring envelope, the LERX also enhance air combat capability. The landing gear is strengthened to cater for higher operating weights and greater external stores loads made possible by these changes.

Work split on the airframe for the AV-8B (including those for Spain) is 60 per cent to McDonnell Douglas and 40 per cent to British Aerospace; the GR. Mk 5 work split is 50 per cent to each manufacturer. Each manufacturer is responsible for the systems in those parts of the airframe which are its concern, and for their installation. British Aerospace provides the complete reaction control system for all aircraft in the programme, and undertakes final assembly of aircraft for the RAF. McDonnell Douglas assembles the aircraft for the USMC. Planned peak production rates are four US and two UK aircraft per month. Pratt & Whitney manufactures up to 25 per cent by value of the engines for the USMC aircraft; Rolls-Royce builds the remainder.

The following variants of the Harrier II have been announced:

AV-8B. Single-seat close support version for US Marine Corps, which has a requirement for 304. First 12 pilot production aircraft (first flight on 29 August 1983) ordered in FY 1982; subsequent contracts placed in FYs 1983 to 1988 inclusive for a further 183 aircraft (21, 27, 30, 40, 36 and 29). Current multi-year procurement programme allows for 24 aircraft each year in FYs 1989, 1990 and 1991 (21 AV-8Bs and 3 TAV-8Bs in each of FYs 1989 and 1990, 24 AV-8Bs in FY 1991). Deliveries to USMC began on 12 January 1984. Intended to re-equip three fleet operational AV-8A/C squadrons, one training squadron and five A-4 Skyhawk squadrons, and already operated (Spring 1988) by

VMA-223, -231, -331, -513 and -542, and training squadron VMAT-203, with a sixth operational squadron due to form at MCAS Yuma, Arizona. First operational squadron (VMA-331) was commissioned on 30 January 1985 at MCAS Cherry Point, North Carolina, achieving IOC in August 1985. Total of 167 (including TAV-8Bs) delivered to USMC by September 1989. A programme to develop a **night attack** version of the AV-8B was announced by McDonnell Douglas in November 1984, and a USMC prototype of this version flew for the first time on 26 June 1987. New systems include a nose mounted GEC Sensors FLIR, Smiths Industries colour HDDs, a wide field of view HUD, Honeywell colour digital moving map system, displays, and pilot's night vision goggles. First production night attack AV-8B (the 167th USMC aircraft) delivered to USMC on 15 September 1989, and all subsequent USMC AV-8Bs will have this capability. In addition, aircraft delivered from 1990 will have both night attack capability and an uprated F402-RR-408 (Pegasus 11-61) engine of 105.87 kN (23,800 lb) thrust, first production example of which was due for delivery in May 1990.

TAV-8B. Two-seat operational trainer version for USMC, which has a requirement for 24. BAe is major subcontractor for this version, which first flew (BuAer No. 162747) on 21 October 1986. Total of 20 ordered in FYs 1985-1989 (2, 6, 6, 3 and 3), deliveries (to VMAT-203) beginning in August 1987. Three more approved for FY 1990. Longer forward fuselage and 0.43 m (1 ft 5 in) taller

McDonnell Douglas/BAe AV-8B Harrier II V/STOL close support aircraft *(Pilot Press)*

vertical tail than AV-8B, with two cockpits in tandem, and only two underwing stores stations. For weapons training, can carry six Mk 76 practice bombs, two LAU-68 rocket launchers or two 1,135 litre (300 US gallon; 250 Imp gallon) external fuel tanks.

EAV-8B. US designation of single-seat export (FMS) version for Spanish Navy. Twelve ordered, all of which were delivered in 1987-88. In service with No. 9 Squadron of Spanish Navy, under the designation **VA.2 Matador II.** At sea, operate from the aircraft carrier *Principe de Asturias*, which was commissioned on 31 May 1988.

Harrier GR. Mk 5. Single-seat close support and reconnaissance version for Royal Air Force. Two development aircraft (ZD318 and ZD319), first flown on 30 April and 31 July 1985, plus fatigue test airframe to clear aircraft for central European low-level operating environment. First of initial production order for 60 (ZD324) was officially handed over to RAF on 1 July 1987, first unit being No. 233 OCU at Wittering, where first course began in August 1988. Due to equip Nos. 1 and 3 Squadrons by 1991, No. 1 Squadron (Wittering) becoming NATO declared in October 1989. Pilot conversion for No. 3 Squadron (Gütersloh) began in 1989. After completion of all 34 new-build GR. Mk 5s (see later paragraph), first 38 production GR. 5s will be retrofitted to Mk 7 standard, followed by Nos. 39-60 (which meanwhile will have been completed to an interim **GR. Mk 5A** specification).

Harrier GR. Mk 7. RAF single-seat night attack version, based on GR. Mk 5 with additional equipment including Smiths Industries HUD/HDD and GEC Sensors FLIR and digital colour map unit (DCMU), the latter replacing the GR. Mk 5's current moving map display. Cockpit compatible with image-intensifying night vision goggles (NVGs), a version of the Ferranti Nite-Op NVGs in production for rotary-wing elements of all three British services. Two GR. Mk 5 development aircraft converted as prototypes (first flight 29 November 1989), to be followed by 34 new-build GR. Mk 7s (ordered April 1988), after completion of which 38 GR. Mk 5s, then 22 GR. Mk 5As, will be retrofitted to Mk 7 standard. Night flying trials scheduled for Summer 1990; first RAF squadron will be No. 4 (in West Germany) in 1991.

Harrier T. Mk 10. Trainer version for GR. Mks 5/5A/7; 14 ordered in February 1990. Based on TAV-8B airframe, with addition of the FLIR and night vision equipment of GR. Mk 7.

The following description applies to the production AV-8B and the Harrier GR. Mk 5:

TYPE: Single-seat V/STOL close support, night attack and (RAF only) reconnaissance aircraft.

WINGS: Cantilever shoulder-wing monoplane. Low aspect ratio sweptback wings, with non-swept inboard trailing-edges and curved leading-edge root extensions (LERX). Span and area increased by approx 20 per cent and 14.5 per cent respectively compared with Harrier GR. Mk 3/AV-8A. Supercritical aerofoil section, with thickness/chord ratio of 11.5 per cent at root, 7.5 per cent at tip. Leading-edge sweep 10° less than that of GR. Mk 3/AV-8A. Marked anhedral. One-piece structure, of mixed construction, with extensive use of graphite epoxy (carbonfibre) and other composite materials in the main multi-spar torsion box, ribs, skins, flaps, ailerons, LERX, and outrigger pods and fairings. Leading-edges (reinforced against bird strikes on GR. Mk 5) and wingtips of aluminium alloy. Wide chord single-slotted trailing-edge flaps, with flap slot closure doors. Drooping ailerons, actuated by Fairey hydraulic jacks. Jet reaction control valve at each wingtip. All wing manufacture and assembly by McDonnell Douglas.

FUSELAGE: Conventional semi-monocoque safe-life structure of frames and stringers, generally similar to that of GR. 3 and AV-8A, but longer, due to provision of a new forward fuselage built largely of graphite epoxy composite material and a lengthened rear fuselage. Centre and rear fuselage mainly of aluminium alloy,

Prototype of the US night attack version of the AV-8B Harrier II, carrying laser guided Maverick missiles, 500 lb Mk 82 bombs and a 25 mm cannon

except for forward and rear underfuselage heatshields, and small area immediately forward of the windscreen, which are of titanium. Lift augmenting underfuselage devices consist of a fixed strake on each of the two ventral gun packs, plus a retractable fence between forward edges of gun packs, just aft of forward main landing gear unit. During VTOL modes the 'box' formed by these surfaces, which are made of composite materials, traps the cushion of air bounced off the ground by the engine exhaust, providing sufficient additional lift to enable the aircraft to take off vertically at a gross weight equal to its maximum hovering gross weight. Access to engine accessories through top of fuselage, immediately ahead of wing. Large forward hinged airbrake beneath fuselage, aft of rear main landing gear bay. Jet reaction control valves in nose and tailcone. McDonnell Douglas is responsible for manufacture of all front and forward centre-fuselages, including nosecones, air intakes, heatshields, engine access doors, and forward fuel tanks; and for the underfuselage fences and strakes. British Aerospace builds, for all aircraft, the rear centre and rear fuselages, including blast and heatshields, centre and rear fuel tanks, dorsal air intakes, and tail bullets. Fuselage assembly is by McDonnell Douglas for USMC and Spain and by BAe for RAF aircraft.

TAIL UNIT: One-piece variable incidence tailplane, with marked anhedral, differing in planform from that of AV-8A in having constant sweep on leading-edges and reduced sweep on trailing-edges. Tailplane is built mainly of graphite epoxy, with aluminium alloy tips and leading-edges, and is operated by Fairey tandem irreversible hydraulic jacks. Aluminium alloy fin, with dielectric tip; manually operated graphite epoxy composite rudder. Dorsal airscoop, at base of fin, for equipment bay cooling system. Ventral fin under rear fuselage. Fins and rudders for all aircraft, and tailplanes for RAF aircraft, built by BAe; tailplanes for USMC and Spanish aircraft built by McDonnell Douglas.

LANDING GEAR: Retractable bicycle type of Dowty design, permitting operation from rough unprepared surfaces of very low CBR (California Bearing Ratio). Hydraulic actuation, with nitrogen bottle for emergency extension. Single steerable nosewheel retracts forward, twin coupled mainwheels rearward, into fuselage. Small outrigger units, at approx mid span between flaps and ailerons, retract rearward into streamline pods. Telescopic oleo-pneumatic main and outrigger gear; levered suspension nosewheel leg. Dunlop wheels, tyres, multi-disc carbon brakes and anti-skid system. Mainwheel tyres (size 26.0 × 7.75-13.00) and nosewheel tyre (size 26.0 × 8.75-11)

all have pressure of 8.62 bars (125 lb/sq in). Outrigger tyres are size 13.5 × 6.00-4.00, pressure 10.34 bars (150 lb/sq in). McDonnell Douglas responsible for entire landing gear system.

POWER PLANT: One 95.42 kN (21,450 lb st) Rolls-Royce F402-RR-406A (Pegasus 11-21) vectored thrust turbofan in AV-8B (105.87 kN; 23,800 lb st F402-RR-408/Pegasus 11-61 in aircraft delivered from May 1990); one 96.75 kN (21,750 lb st) Pegasus Mk 105 in Harrier GR. Mk 5; Mk 152-42 in EAV-8B. Redundant digital engine control system (DECS), with mechanical backup, standard from March 1987. Zero-scarf front nozzles. Air intakes have an elliptical lip shape, leading-edges reinforced against bird strikes, and a single row of auxiliary intake doors. Integral fuel tanks in wings; total internal fuel capacity (fuselage and wing tanks) 4,163 litres (1,100 US gallons; 915 Imp gallons). AV-8B has water injection tank with capacity of approx 227 kg (500 lb); RAF, which does not use water injection, uses this tank to carry additional internal fuel. Retractable bolt-on in-flight refuelling probe optional. Each of the four inner underwing stations capable of carrying a 1,135 litre (300 US gallon; 250 Imp gallon) auxiliary fuel tank.

ACCOMMODATION: Pilot only, on zero/zero ejection seat (UPC/Stencel for USMC, Martin-Baker for RAF), in pressurised, heated and air-conditioned cockpit. AV-8B cockpit raised approx 30.5 cm (12 in) by comparison with AV-8A/YAV-8B, with redesigned one-piece wraparound windscreen (thicker on RAF aircraft than on those for USMC) and rearward sliding bubble canopy, to improve all-round field of view. Windscreen de-icing. Windscreens and canopies for all aircraft manufactured by McDonnell Douglas.

SYSTEMS: No. 1 hydraulic system has a flow rate of 43 litres (11.4 US gallons; 9.5 Imp gallons)/min; flow rate of No. 2 system is 26.5 litres (7.0 US gallons; 5.8 Imp gallons)/min. Reservoirs are nitrogen pressurised at 2.76-5.52 bars (40-80 lb/sq in). Other systems include Westinghouse variable speed constant frequency (VSCF) solid state electrical system, Lucas Mk 4 gas turbine starter/APU, Clifton Precision onboard oxygen generating system (OBOGS), and Graviner Firewire fire detection system.

AVIONICS AND EQUIPMENT: Include dual Collins RT-1250A/ARC U/VHF com (GEC Avionics AD3500 ECM-resistant U/VHF-AM/FM in GR. Mk 5), R-1379B/ARA-63 all-weather landing receiver, RT-1159A/ARN-118 Tacan, RT-1015A/APN-194(V) radar altimeter, Honeywell CV-3736/A com/nav/identification data converter, Bendix RT-1157/APX-100 IFF (Cossor IFF 4760 transponder in GR. Mk 5), Litton AN/ASN-130A inertial navigation system (being replaced by Ferranti FIN 1075 in GR. Mk 5), AiResearch CP-1471/A digital air data computer, Smiths Industries SU-128/A dual combining glass head-up display and CP-1450/A display computer, IP-1318/A CRT Kaiser digital display indicator, and (GR.Mk 5 only) Ferranti moving map display. Litton AN/ALR-67(V)2 fore/aft looking radar warning receiver, UK MoD AN/ARR-51 FLIR receiver, and Goodyear AN/ALE-39 flare/chaff dispenser (in lower rear fuselage) (Tracor AN/ALE-40 specified, but not at present fitted, in GR. Mk 5). Primary weapon delivery sensor system for AV-8B and GR.Mk 5 is the Hughes Aircraft AN/ASB-19(V)2 or (V)3 Angle Rate Bombing Set, mounted in the nose and comprising a dual-mode (TV and laser) target seeker/tracker. System functions in conjunction with Control Data Corporation CP-1429/AYK-14(V) mission computer (Computing Devices ACCS 2000 in GR. Mk 5), the Lear Siegler AN/AYQ-13 stores management system, the display computer, the head-up display, and the digital display indicator. Flight controls that interface with the reaction control system are provided by the Honeywell AN/ASW-46(V)2 stability augmentation and attitude hold system currently being updated to the high AOA capable configuration. RAF aircraft have an accident data recorder. Backup standby mechanical instrumentation

McDonnell Douglas/BAe Harrier GR. Mk 5s of No. 233 OCU, Royal Air Force (*Paul Jackson*)

Night attack Harrier GR. Mk 7, first development aircraft for Royal Air Force

includes airspeed indicator, altimeter, angle of attack indicator, attitude indicator, cabin pressure altitude indicator, clock, flap position indicator, horizontal situation indicator, standby compass, turn and slip indicator, and vertical speed indicator. Other equipment includes anti-collision, approach, formation, in-flight refuelling, landing gear position, auxiliary exterior lights, and console, instrument panel and other internal lighting.

ARMAMENT AND OPERATIONAL EQUIPMENT: Two under-fuselage packs, mounting on the port side a five-barrel 25 mm cannon based on the General Electric GAU-12/U, and a 300 round container on the starboard side, in the AV-8B; or two 25 mm Royal Ordnance Factories cannon with 100 rds/gun (derived from the 30 mm Aden) in the GR. Mk 5. Single 454 kg (1,000 lb) stores mount on fuselage centreline, between gun packs. Three stores stations under each wing on AV-8B, stressed for loads of up to 907 kg (2,000 lb) inboard, 907 kg (2,000 lb) on the intermediate stations, and 281 kg (620 lb) outboard. The four inner wing stations are wet, permitting the carriage of auxiliary fuel tanks. Including fuel, stores, weapons and ammunition, and water injection for the engine, the maximum useful load for vertical take-off is approximately 3,062 kg (6,750 lb), and for short take-off more than 7,710 kg (17,000 lb). Typical weapons include two or four AIM-9L Sidewinder, Magic or AGM-65E Maverick missiles, or up to six Sidewinders; up to sixteen 540 lb free-fall or retarded general purpose bombs, 12 BL 755 or similar cluster bombs, 1,000 lb free-fall or retarded bombs, ten Paveway laser guided bombs, eight fire bombs, 10 Matra 155 rocket pods (each with eighteen 68 mm SNEB rockets), or (in addition to the underfuselage gun packs) two underwing gun pods. Chaff/flare dispenser housings under fuselage. ML Aviation BRU-36/A bomb release units standard on all versions. Provision for Sanders AN/ALQ-164 defensive ECM pod on centreline pylon. GR. Mks 5/7 have two additional underwing weapon stations, for Sidewinder air-to-air missiles, ahead of the outrigger wheel fairings; a Marconi Defence Systems Zeus internal ECM system comprising an advanced radar warning receiver, and a multi-mode jammer with a Northrop RF transmitter; and provision for a nose mounted infra-red reconnaissance sensor. GR. Mk 5 is also to be equipped with a Plessey missile approach warning (MAW) equipment, mounted in the tailboom, which will automatically activate appropriate countermeasures upon detecting approach of enemy missiles.

DIMENSIONS, EXTERNAL:
Wing span	9.25 m (30 ft 4 in)
Wing aspect ratio	4.0
Length overall (flying attitude):	
AV-8B	14.12 m (46 ft 4 in)
TAV-8B	15.32 m (50 ft 3 in)
Height overall	3.55 m (11 ft 7¾ in)
Tailplane span	4.24 m (13 ft 11 in)
Outrigger wheel track	5.18 m (17 ft 0 in)

AREAS:
Wings, excl LERX, gross	21.37 m² (230 sq ft)
LERX (total)	0.81 m² (8.7 sq ft)
Ailerons (total)	1.15 m² (12.4 sq ft)
Trailing-edge flaps (total)	2.88 m² (31.0 sq ft)
Ventral fixed strakes (total)	0.51 m² (5.5 sq ft)
Ventral retractable fence (LIDs)	0.24 m² (2.6 sq ft)
Ventral airbrake	0.42 m² (4.5 sq ft)
Fin	2.47 m² (26.6 sq ft)
Rudder, excl tab	0.49 m² (5.3 sq ft)
Tailplane	4.51 m² (48.5 sq ft)

WEIGHTS (single-seaters, except where indicated):
Operating weight empty (incl pilot and unused fuel):	
AV-8B	5,936 kg (13,086 lb)
GR. Mk 5	6,343 kg (13,984 lb)
TAV-8B	6,451 kg (14,223 lb)
Max fuel: internal only	3,519 kg (7,759 lb)
internal and external	7,180 kg (15,829 lb)
Max external stores	4,173 kg (9,200 lb)
Basic flight design gross weight for 7g operation	10,410 kg (22,950 lb)
Max T-O weight:	
405 m (1,330 ft) STO	14,061 kg (31,000 lb)
S/L VTO, ISA	8,595 kg (18,950 lb)
S/L VTO, 32°C	8,142 kg (17,950 lb)
Design max landing weight	11,340 kg (25,000 lb)
Max vertical landing weight	8,459 kg (18,650 lb)

PERFORMANCE:
Max Mach number in level flight:		
at S/L	0.87 (575 knots; 1,065 km/h; 661 mph)	
at altitude		0.91
STOL T-O run at max T-O weight:		
ISA		405 m (1,330 ft)
32°C		518 m (1,700 ft)

Operational radius with external loads shown:
short T-O (366 m; 1,200 ft), twelve Mk 82 Snakeye bombs, internal fuel, 1 h loiter
90 nm (167 km; 103 miles)
hi-lo-hi, short T-O (366 m; 1,200 ft), seven Mk 82 Snakeye bombs, external fuel tanks, no loiter (payload of 1,814 kg; 4,000 lb)
480 nm (889 km; 553 miles)
deck launch intercept mission, two AIM-9 missiles and two external fuel tanks
627 nm (1,162 km; 722 miles)
Unrefuelled ferry range, with four 300 US gallon external tanks:
tanks retained 1,750 nm (3,243 km; 2,015 miles)
tanks dropped 2,100 nm (3,891 km; 2,418 miles)
Combat air patrol endurance at 100 nm (185 km; 115 miles) from base 3 h
g limits +7/-3

MCDONNELL DOUGLAS/BRITISH AEROSPACE HARRIER II PLUS

At the 1987 Paris Air Show, the two partners announced their intention to develop with company funds a version powered by a 105.87 kN (23,800 lb) thrust Pegasus 11-61 (F402-RR-408) engine and fitted with a pulse-Doppler radar. Such a version could also retain the FLIR if required, and would be able to deploy AMRAAM or other BVR (beyond visual range) missiles in the air defence role, or Sea Eagle or Harpoon sea skimming missiles in anti-shipping configuration.

As currently envisaged, the Harrier II Plus would be fitted with both night attack avionics and the pulse-Doppler radar. It would also be capable of carrying out ground mapping, terrain avoidance and ground attack functions. A cockpit simulator, complete with radar, has already been completed at St Louis. The USMC has a requirement (as yet unfunded) for this aircraft. It now seems most likely that the Harrier II Plus will be fitted with the Hughes AN/APG-65 radar. First flight of a development aircraft is envisaged for 1991.

PERFORMANCE (estimated, with 137 m; 450 ft short T-O deck run, 6.5° ski-jump, 20 knot; 37 km/h; 23 mph wind over deck, air temperature 32°C, optimum cruise conditions, incl reserves for landing):
Anti-shipping combat radius with two Harpoons, two Sidewinders and two 1,136 litre (300 US gallon; 250 Imp gallon) drop tanks

609 nm (1,128 km; 701 miles)
Combat air patrol (incl 2 min combat) with four AMRAAM and two 300 US gallon tanks: time on station:
at 100 nm (185 km; 115 mile) radius 2 h 42 min
at 200 nm (370 km; 230 mile) radius 2 h 6 min
Sea surveillance combat radius (incl 50 nm; 92 km; 57 mile dash at S/L) with two Sidewinders and two 300 US gallon tanks 608 nm (1,127 km; 700 miles)

MCDONNELL DOUGLAS/BRITISH AEROSPACE T-45A
US Navy designation: T-45A Goshawk

On 18 November 1981 a derivative of the British Aerospace Hawk (see UK section) was selected, out of six designs considered, as winner of the US Navy's VTXTS competition for an undergraduate jet pilot trainer, in which role it is to replace the T-2C Buckeye and TA-4J Skyhawk. The complete VTXTS system, since renamed T45TS (T-45 Training System), consists of modified Hawk aircraft (designated T-45A Goshawk) together with academic materials, flight simulators, computer aided training devices, a training integration system, and contractor operated logistics support.

The original plan for the US Navy to acquire an initial 54 'dry' (land based) T-45Bs followed by 253 carrier-capable 'wet' T-45As was amended in FY 1984 to eliminate the interim B model in favour of an 'all-wet' fleet of T-45As, and current plans are to acquire a total of 300 production examples of this version. To meet USN specifications, the T-45A has new main and nose landing gear, an arrester hook, and airframe strengthening to enable it to operate from aircraft carriers. The nose gear is twin-wheel, has a catapult launch bar, is steerable, and requires a slightly deeper nose contour to accommodate it when retracted. Two fuselage-side airbrakes replace the single large underfuselage airbrake of the standard Hawk. Avionics and cockpit displays are modified for carrier-compatible operations, and weapons delivery capability for advanced training is incorporated. Douglas Aircraft Company at Long Beach, California, designed and assembled the two flying full-scale development Goshawks and the initial production aircraft. On 19 December 1989 the decision was announced to transfer the entire programme to McDonnell Aircraft Co in St Louis, Missouri, from where future aircraft will be delivered. British Aerospace is principal T-45A subcontractor, its Brough, Samlesbury and Hamble factories being responsible for the wings, centre and rear fuselage, fin, tailplane, windscreen, canopy and flight controls. Rolls-Royce (Derby) supplies the Adour turbofan engines; Hughes manufactures the flight simulators at Reston, Virginia.

The T45TS programme entered the full-scale engineering development (FSED) phase in October 1984, and a contract with not-to-exceed prices for the first three production lots (including 60 T-45A aircraft and 15 flight simulators during FYs 1988-90) was signed on 16 May 1986. Twelve production T-45As are included in the FY 1988 Lot 1 contract, awarded on 26 January 1988. Production deliveries, which were scheduled to begin in October 1989, were delayed by changes recommended by US Navy testing conducted in November 1988. Production is now scheduled to reach 48 aircraft per year in 1993, with completion of the programme in 1999 if there are no additional sales.

The first non-flying airframe was successfully drop tested to design sink speed at Long Beach in 1988. A second, completed at BAe's Brough factory, began fatigue testing in 1989. The first of the two FSED T-45As (BuAer number 162787), construction of which had started in February 1986, made its first flight at Long Beach on 16 April 1988 and was joined in the 19-month test programme by the

First of two FSED examples of the US Navy T-45A Goshawk derivative of the BAe Hawk

second example in November 1988. Both aircraft were then transferred from the McDonnell Douglas test facility in Yuma, Arizona, to the US Naval Air Test Center at Patuxent River, Maryland. By 30 January 1990 these two aircraft had completed 322 flights and 318 hours of testing. The FSED aircraft are each powered by a 24.24 kN (5,450 lb st) F405-RR-400L (Adour Mk 861-49) turbofan, but this engine is replaced in production aircraft by the more powerful F405-RR-401, which produces 30 per cent more thrust in the low altitude/hot day regime.

The T45TS is scheduled to become operational initially, with the first 12 Goshawks and their associated equipment, at Kingsville Naval Air Station, Texas. The system will eventually be based also at NAS Chase Field, Texas, and NAS Meridian, Mississippi. The complete programme will involve 300 production aircraft, 32 flight simulators, 49 computer aided instructional devices, four training integration system mainframes and 200 terminals, as well as academic materials, to allow the training of up to 600 pilots a year. Introduction of the Goshawk system is expected to meet the USN's training requirements with 42 per cent fewer aircraft than at present, 25 per cent fewer flight hours, and 46 per cent fewer personnel, as well as saving up to 182 million litres (48 million US gallons; 40 million Imp gallons) of fuel per year.

The following description applies to the production T-45A, modified in accordance with US Navy recommendations:

TYPE: Two-seat basic and advanced jet trainer.
WINGS: Similar to BAe Hawk, but redesigned and strengthened to accommodate new main landing gear. Electrically actuated, hydraulically operated full span slat on each leading-edge, operation of which will be limited to landing configuration.
FUSELAGE: Similar to BAe Hawk, but strengthened for carrier operations, with composite airbrake on each side of rear fuselage, actuated by Dowty hydraulic jacks. New deeper and longer forward fuselage, to accommodate new nose landing gear. Underfuselage arrester hook, deployable 20° to each side of longitudinal axis.
TAIL UNIT: Fin and tailplane similar to BAe Hawk, but strengthened. Forward of each tailplane leading-edge root is a small curved horizontal surface ('smurf', or side mounted unit horizontal root tail fin) to eliminate pitch-down during low-speed flaps-down/gear-up manoeuvres.
LANDING GEAR: Wide-track hydraulically retractable tricycle type, stressed for vertical velocities of 7.47 m (24.5 ft)/s. Single wheel and long-stroke oleo (increased from 33 cm; 13 in of standard Hawk to 63.5 cm; 25 in) on each main unit; twin-wheel steerable nose unit with 40.6 cm (16

in) stroke. Articulated main gear, by AP Precision Hydraulics, is of levered suspension (trailing arm) type with a folding side-stay. Cleveland Pneumatic nose gear, with Sterer steering system. Nose gear has catapult towbar and holdback devices. Main units retract inward into wing, forward of front spar; nose unit retracts forward. All wheel doors are sequenced to close after gear lowering; inboard mainwheel doors are bulged to accommodate larger trailing arm and tyres. Gear emergency lowering by free fall. Goodrich wheels, tyres and brakes. Mainwheel tyres size 24 × 7.7-10; nosewheels have size 19 × 5.25-10 tyres. Tyre pressure (all units) 22.40 bars (325 lb/sq in) for carrier operation; reduced for land operation. Hydraulic multi-disc mainwheel brakes with Dunlop adaptive anti-skid system.
POWER PLANT: One 25.98 kN (5,840 lb st) Rolls-Royce Turbomeca F405-RR-401 (navalised Adour Mk 871) non-afterburning turbofan. Air intakes and engine starting as described for BAe Hawk. Fuel system similar to BAe Hawk, but with revision for carrier operation. Capacities are 840 litres (222 US gallons; 185 Imp gallons) in fuselage bag tank and 859 litres (227 US gallons; 189 Imp gallons) in integral wing tank, giving total internal capacity of 1,700 litres (449 US gallons; 374 Imp gallons). Provision for carrying one 591 litre (156 US gallon; 130 Imp gallon) drop tank on each underwing pylon.
ACCOMMODATION: Similar to BAe Hawk, except that ejection seats are of Martin-Baker Mk 14 NACES (Navy aircrew common ejection seat) zero/zero rocket assisted type.
SYSTEMS: Air-conditioning and pressurisation systems, using engine bleed air. Duplicated hydraulic systems, each 207 bars (3,000 lb/sq in), for actuation of control jacks, flaps, airbrakes, landing gear, arrester hook and anti-skid wheel brakes. No. 1 system has a flow rate of 36.4 litres (9.6 US gallons; 8.0 Imp gallons)/min, No. 2 system a rate of 22.7 litres (6.0 US gallons; 5.0 Imp gallons)/min. Reservoirs are nitrogen pressurised at 2.75-5.5 bars (40-80 lb/sq in). Hydraulic accumulator for emergency operation of wheel brakes. Pop-up Dowty Aerospace ram air turbine in upper rear fuselage provides emergency hydraulic power for flying controls in the event of an engine or No. 2 pump failure. No pneumatic system. DC electrical power from single brushless generator, with two static inverters to provide AC power and two batteries for standby power. Onboard oxygen generating system (OBOGS).
AVIONICS: AN/ARN-182 UHF/VHF com radios and AN/ARN-144 VOR/ILS by Rockwell Collins, Honeywell AN/APN-194 radio altimeter, Bendix APX-100

IFF, Sierra AN/ARN-136A Tacan, US Navy AN/USN-2 standard attitude and heading reference system (SAHRS), Smiths Industries Mini-HUD (front cockpit), Racal Acoustics avionics/com management system, GEC Avionics yaw damper computer, Electrodynamics airborne data recorder and Teledyne caution/warning system.
ARMAMENT: No built-in armament. Single pylon under each wing for carriage of practice multiple bomb rack, rocket pods or auxiliary fuel tank. Provision also for carrying single stores pod on fuselage centreline. CAI Industries gunsight in rear cockpit.

DIMENSIONS, EXTERNAL:
Wing span	9.39 m (30 ft 9¾ in)
Wing chord: at root	2.65 m (8 ft 8¼ in)
at tip	0.90 m (2 ft 11½ in)
Wing aspect ratio	5.3
Length: overall, incl nose probe	11.97 m (39 ft 3⅛ in)
fuselage	10.89 m (35 ft 9 in)
Height overall	4.09 m (13 ft 5 in)
Tailplane span	4.39 m (14 ft 4¾ in)
Wheel track (c/l of shock struts)	3.90 m (12 ft 9½ in)
Wheelbase	4.29 m (14 ft 1 in)

AREAS:
Wings, gross	16.69 m² (179.6 sq ft)
Ailerons (total)	1.05 m² (11.30 sq ft)
Trailing-edge flaps (total)	2.50 m² (26.91 sq ft)
Airbrakes (total)	0.79 m² (8.55 sq ft)
Fin	2.51 m² (27.02 sq ft)
Rudder, incl tab	0.58 m² (6.24 sq ft)
Tailplane	4.33 m² (46.61 sq ft)

WEIGHTS:
Weight empty	4,263 kg (9,399 lb)
Internal fuel	1,312 kg (2,893 lb)
Max T-O weight	5,787 kg (12,758 lb)

PERFORMANCE (estimated at max T-O weight):
Design limit diving speed at 1,000 m (3,280 ft)	610 knots (1,130 km/h; 702 mph)
Max true Mach number in dive	1.1
Max level speed at 2,440 m (8,000 ft)	538 knots (997 km/h; 620 mph)
Max level Mach number at 9,150 m (30,000 ft)	0.85
Max rate of climb at S/L	2,128 m (6,982 ft)/min
Time to 9,150 m (30,000 ft), clean	7 min 12 s
Service ceiling	12,875 m (42,250 ft)
T-O to 15 m (50 ft)	1,141 m (3,744 ft)
Landing from 15 m (50 ft)	1,189 m (3,900 ft)
Ferry range, internal fuel only	1,000 nm (1,850 km; 1,150 miles)
g limits	+7.33/-3

MPC
MPC AIRCRAFT GmbH

PARTICIPATING COMPANIES:
Deutsche Airbus GmbH, Kreetslag 10, Postfach 950109, 2103 Hamburg 95, West Germany
Telephone: 49 (40) 7437-3120 or 74202-0
Telex: 21950-0 MBB D
Fax: 49 (40) 7426366 and 74202-22
MANAGER, PRESS AND INFORMATION: Sigrid Schütz
China National Aero-Technology Import and Export Corporation, 5 Liang Guo Chang Road, East City District (PO Box 1671), Beijing, People's Republic of China
Telephone: 86 (1) 44 5831
Telex: 22318 AEROT CN

MPC 75

MBB (now Deutsche Airbus) and CATIC signed a memorandum of understanding on 3 October 1985 to explore together the possible development of a 60/85-seat regional transport aircraft. MPC Aircraft GmbH was set up subsequently in Hamburg to manage the programme.

Early studies appeared to favour a rear-mounted propfan configuration, but after comparative studies a wing-mounted turbofan propulsion system was selected in mid-1989, and since October 1989 pre-development of the MPC 75 has been concentrated upon a five-abreast aircraft with twin turbofans mounted under the wings. The five-abreast cabin layout was considered to offer optimum economy and comfort. An MPC-200 is also planned.

First flight is envisaged for late 1995, with series production beginning in 1996.

The following data, and the accompanying three-view drawing, reflect the MPC 75 as envisaged in early 1990.

AIRFRAME: Wing box, movable surfaces and tail will be made of composites, fuselage of aluminium-lithium. Advanced 'glass' cockpit and fly by wire control system.
POWER PLANT: Two 31.1 kN (7,000 lb st) class turbofans, pylon mounted under wings. All fuel in integral tanks in wings.
ACCOMMODATION: Typical mixed class layout for 73 passengers, with eight seats four-abreast at 91 cm (36 in) pitch and 65 seats five-abreast at 81 cm (32 in); or 80 seats in an all-economy layout; or up to 90 seats in single class high density configuration. Seats for three cabin

Provisional drawing of the MPC 75 twin-turbofan 80-seat transport *(Jane's/Mike Keep)*

attendants. Galley and toilet at front of cabin; second galley, toilet and wardrobes at rear.

DIMENSIONS, EXTERNAL:
Wing span	29.20 m (95 ft 9½ in)
Wing aspect ratio	10.03
Length overall	27.90 m (91 ft 6½ in)
Height overall	10.20 m (33 ft 5½ in)

AREA:
Wings, gross	85.0 m² (914.9 sq ft)

WEIGHTS:
Max payload	10,000 kg (22,046 lb)
Max fuel	7,055 kg (15,553 lb)
Max T-O weight	34,700 kg (76,500 lb)
Max landing weight	32,970 kg (72,686 lb)

PERFORMANCE (estimated):
Cruising speed at 10,670 m (35,000 ft)	Mach 0.76
Max operating altitude	11,890 m (39,000 ft)
T-O run (S/L, ISA) at max T-O weight	1,524 m (5,000 ft)
Landing run (S/L) at typical landing weight	1,372 m (4,500 ft)
Range with 80 passengers, with reserves	1,400 nm (2,595 km; 1,612 miles)

NAMC/PAC

PARTICIPATING COMPANIES:
Nanchang Aircraft Manufacturing Company,
  PO Box 5001-506, Nanchang, Jiangxi, People's
  Republic of China
Telephone: 86/Nanchang 41112
Telex: 95068 NAMC CN
Fax: 86/Nanchang 41112 2272
Pakistan Aeronautical Complex (Aircraft Manufacturing Factory), Kamra, District Attock, Pakistan
Telephone: 92 (51) 580260/5
Telex: 5601 PAC KAMRA PK

NAMC/PAC K-8 KARAKORUM 8

This tandem two-seat jet trainer was first disclosed in the form of a model at the 1987 Paris Air Show, where it was described as able to provide all basic flying training, plus parts of the primary and advanced training syllabi, with capability also for light air-to-ground close support. Known initially as the L-8, the project was launched by NAMC with the intention of being developed for export with an international partner. It is now under joint development by NAMC and PAC to fulfil the requirements of the Pakistan Air Force, and to compete in the international market. In recognition of this collaboration, it was redesignated K-8 and named after the mountain range forming part of the border between the two countries. Czechoslovakia has reportedly offered the Lotarev/ZVL DV-2 turbofan as a possible alternative to the Garrett TFE731.

Design of the K-8 began in July 1987. Wind tunnel testing had been completed by the Spring of 1988, and prototype construction started in January 1989. Five prototypes have been ordered, the first of which was expected to make its first flight in May or June 1990.
TYPE: Two-seat jet basic trainer and light ground attack aircraft.
WINGS: Cantilever low-wing monoplane. Tapered, non-swept wings, with NACA 64-A114 section at root and NACA 64-A412 at tip. Incidence 2° at root. Dihedral 3° from roots. Sweepback 0° at 40 per cent chord. All-metal damage-tolerant structure, including powered ailerons (of honeycomb) and Fowler trailing-edge flaps.
FUSELAGE: All-metal damage-tolerant semi-monocoque structure. Split airbrake under each side at rear.
TAIL UNIT: Sweptback vertical and non-swept horizontal surfaces, former of composites and latter of metal construction. Tailplane has variable incidence. Trim tab in rudder and port elevator.
LANDING GEAR: Retractable tricycle type, with single wheel and oleo-pneumatic shock absorber on each unit. Main units retract inward into underside of fuselage; nosewheel, which is steerable, retracts forward. Main-wheel tyres size 561 × 169 mm, pressure 6.9 bars (100 lb/sq in). Chinese hydraulic disc brakes. Anti-skid units.
POWER PLANT: One 16.01 kN (3,600 lb st) Garrett TFE731-2A-2A turbofan, mounted in rear fuselage, with intake and splitter plate on each side of fuselage. Fuel in two flexible tanks in fuselage and one integral tank in each wing, combined capacity 1,000 litres (264 US gallons; 220 Imp gallons); single refuelling point in

NAMC/PAC K-8 Karakorum 8 jet trainer and light attack aircraft *(Jane's/Mike Keep)*

fuselage. Provision for carring one 250 litre (66 US gallon; 55 Imp gallon) drop tank on inboard pylon under each wing.
ACCOMMODATION: Instructor and pupil in tandem, on Martin-Baker CN10LW zero/zero ejection seats; rear seat elevated. One-piece wraparound windscreen; sideways opening bubble canopy. Cockpits pressurised and air-conditioned.
SYSTEMS: AiResearch air-conditioning and pressurisation system, with max differential of 0.27 bars (3.91 lb/sq in). Hydraulic system, pressure 207 bars (3,000 lb/sq in), for operation of landing gear extension/retraction, wing flaps, airbrakes, aileron boost, nosewheel steering and wheel brakes. Flow rate 15 litres (3.96 US gallons; 3.30 Imp gallons)/min, with air pressurised reservoir, plus emergency backup hydraulic system. Abex AP09V-8-01 pump. Electrical systems 28.5V DC (primary) and 24V DC (auxiliary), with 115/26V single-phase AC and 36V three-phase AC available, both at 400Hz. Gaseous oxygen system for occupants. Demisting of cockpit transparencies.
AVIONICS: Collins EFIS-86 system in first 100 aircraft, incorporating CRT primary flight and navigation displays for each crew member plus dual display processing units and selector panels for tandem operation. Collins AN/ARC-186 VHF and Magnavox AN/ARC-164 UHF com radios. Interfaces to the EFIS system include KNR 634A VOR/ILS with marker beacon receiver, ADF, KTU-709 Tacan, Type 265 radio altimeter, WL-7 radio compass, AHRS and air data computer. Standby flight instruments include ASI, rate of climb indicator, barometric altimeter, emergency horizon and standby compass. Blind-flying instrumentation standard.
ARMAMENT: One 23 mm gun pod under centre-fuselage; self-computing optical gunsight in cockpit, plus gun camera. Two external stores points under each wing,

capable of carrying gun pods, rocket pods, bombs, missiles, auxiliary fuel tanks (inboard pair only), or a reconnaissance pod.

DIMENSIONS, EXTERNAL:
Wing span	9.63 m (31 ft 7¼ in)
Wing aspect ratio	5.45
Length overall, incl nose pitot	11.60 m (38 ft 0¾ in)
Height overall	4.21 m (13 ft 9¾ in)
Wheel track	2.54 m (8 ft 4 in)
Wheelbase	4.32 m (14 ft 2 in)

AREAS:
Wings, gross	17.02 m² (183.20 sq ft)
Ailerons (total, incl tab)	1.096 m² (11.80 sq ft)
Trailing-edge flaps (total)	2.69 m² (28.95 sq ft)
Fin	1.976 m² (21.27 sq ft)
Rudder, incl tab	1.06 m² (11.41 sq ft)
Tailplane	2.716 m² (29.23 sq ft)
Elevators (total, incl tab)	1.084 m² (11.67 sq ft)

WEIGHTS AND LOADINGS:
Weight empty, equipped	2,557 kg (5,637 lb)
Max fuel: internal	780 kg (1,720 lb)
external	390 kg (860 lb)
T-O weight clean	3,500 kg (7,716 lb)
Max T-O weight with external stores	4,200 kg (9,259 lb)
Max wing loading	246.8 kg/m² (50.57 lb/sq ft)
Max power loading	262.45 kg/kN (2.57 lb/lb st)

PERFORMANCE (estimated, at clean T-O weight):
Max level speed at S/L	432 knots (800 km/h; 497 mph)
Touchdown speed	89 knots (165 km/h; 103 mph)
Unstick speed	100 knots (185 km/h; 115 mph)
Max rate of climb at S/L	1,620 m (5,315 ft)/min
Service ceiling	13,000 m (42,650 ft)
T-O run	410-430 m (1,345-1,411 ft)
Landing run	510-520 m (1,674-1,706 ft)
Range with max internal fuel	755 nm (1,400 km; 870 miles)
Endurance	3 h

NH 90

PROGRAMME GENERAL CO-ORDINATOR: Gilbert Beziac
  (Aerospatiale), BP 13, 13725 Marignane Cédex, France
Telephone: 33 42 85 61 95
Telex: AISPA 410975 F

Following a September 1985 memorandum of understanding signed by the defence ministers of France, UK, Germany, Italy and Netherlands, a 14-month feasibility/pre-definition study was established, from which a new helicopter was proposed for the armed services of these countries, known as the NH 90 (NATO Helicopter for the '90s). British participation was terminated by the UK government in April 1987. The workshares were then: France and Italy 35 per cent each, West Germany 25 per cent and Netherlands 5 per cent, but in early 1990 Germany reduced its NH 90 budget from 394 million ECUs to 331 million and workshares were then adjusted accordingly.

One manufacturer from each country (Aerospatiale, MBB, Agusta and Fokker) make up the present industrial group, which has established a common basic configuration for the two major versions: an **NFH 90** (NATO frigate helicopter) for ASW, surface attack and SAR duties, and a land based tactical transport, SAR and special missions version known as the **TTH 90**. Estimated total requirements by the armed forces of the participating nations are 220 and 360 respectively; this total could be doubled if civil and export potential is realised. A multi-national team manages the NH 90 programme, with Aerospatiale as general co-ordinator.

The initial design phase was approved in December 1986. A second MoU in September 1987 led to completion of weapons system definition in 1988. The design and development phase was due to begin in mid-1990. First flight is envisaged for 1994, and initial deliveries for 1998.

The leading technology features of the helicopter have

Preliminary three-view of NH 90 NATO helicopter for the 1990s *(Jane's/Mike Keep)*

been defined as: mission weights between 8,000 and 9,100 kg (17,637-20,062 lb), according to version; twin 1,566 kW (2,100 shp) Rolls-Royce Turbomeca RTM 322-01/2 or 1,506 kW (2,020 shp) General Electric CT7-6 turboshafts; four-blade main and tail rotors, utilising composite blades of advanced aerofoil sections and tip planform; titanium main rotor hub with elastomeric bearings; a bearingless tail

rotor; cabin space for 20 commandos, or a 2 ton tactical vehicle loaded via a rear ramp (French Army version); a high level of composites utilised in the fuselage structure, with contours designed to reduce radar reflections; retractable crashworthy tricycle landing gear; automatic folding of main rotor blades and tail pylon in naval version; quadruplex fly by wire controls, with higher harmonic blade pitch control to minimise vibration; an APU; modern avionics with dual MIL-1553B digital databus; instrument panel with multi-function colour CRT displays; design features for low vulnerability and detectability; reduced maintenance requirements; and all-weather, day/night operability within temperature range of –40°C to + 50°C.

The naval variant will offer autonomy in ASW, ASV and anti-air warfare support operations, and will be designed for an all-weather, severe ship-motion environment. The payload capacity will meet a wide range of national requirements for such additional duties as vertical replenishment, SAR and personnel transport. The army/air force variant will offer a defensive weapons suite and low pilot workload.

The following data are provisional:

DIMENSIONS, EXTERNAL:

Main rotor diameter	16.00 m (52 ft 6 in)
Tail rotor diameter	3.20 m (10 ft 6 in)
Length overall, rotors turning	19.40 m (63 ft 7¾ in)
Length of fuselage, tail rotor turning	16.81 m (55 ft 1¾ in)
Length folded: NFH	13.20 m (43 ft 3¾ in)
Height folded: NFH	4.05 m (13 ft 3½ in)
Wheel track	3.20 m (10 ft 6 in)
Wheelbase	6.08 m (19 ft 11½ in)

DIMENSIONS, INTERNAL:

Cabin: Length, excl rear ramp	4.00 m (13 ft 1½ in)
Max width	2.20 m (7 ft 2½ in)
Max height	1.60 m (5 ft 3 in)
Max volume	16.0 m³ (565.0 cu ft)

WEIGHTS:

Weight empty, equipped: TTH	5,000 kg (11,023 lb)
NFH	5,400 kg (11,905 lb)
Standard fuel (usable)	2,000 kg (4,409 lb)
Max external sling load: NFH	4,000 kg (8,818 lb)
Max T-O weight: TTH	8,500 kg (18,739 lb)
NFH	9,100 kg (20,062 lb)

PERFORMANCE (NFH, estimated, at 8,500 kg; 18,739 lb AUW, ISA):

Never-exceed speed	167 knots (310 km/h; 192 mph)
Max cruising speed	154 knots (285 km/h; 177 mph)
Normal cruising speed	135 knots (250 km/h; 155 mph)
Service ceiling	6,000 m (19,685 ft)
Hovering ceiling: IGE	4,000 m (13,125 ft)
OGE	3,400 m (11,155 ft)
Max range, standard fuel	593 nm (1,100 km; 683 miles)
Time on station, 60 nm (111 km; 69 miles) from base, 20 min reserves	3 h
Max endurance at 75 knots (140 km/h; 87 mph)	5 h 30 min

NTT

NEW TRANSPORT TECHNOLOGIES LTD

Postfach 801304, 8000 Munich 80, West Germany
Telephone: 49 (89) 6070
Telex: 5287-740 MBB D

It was announced in April 1984 that MBB (West Germany) and IPTN (Indonesia) had signed an agreement to carry out a market development study (still in progress in 1989) for a small, four-seat light helicopter later designated N-442. A joint company, NTT, with headquarters in Munich, was set up, in which MBB and IPTN each hold 50 per cent of the shares. It was to study other forms of transport besides the helicopter. Responsibility for the N-442 was handed over to IPTN, and in early 1990 the programme was in suspension waiting for more favourable economic circumstances. All known details of the N-442 were given in the 1989-90 *Jane's*.

PANAVIA

PANAVIA AIRCRAFT GmbH

Arabellastrasse 16 (Postfach 860629), 8000 Munich 81, West Germany
Telephone: 49 (89) 9217 238/9
Telex: 05 29 825
Fax: 49 (89) 9217 903
PUBLIC RELATIONS: Ralf Wolf

Panavia was formed on 26 March 1969 to design, develop and produce an all-weather combat aircraft for the air forces of the United Kingdom, the Federal Republic of Germany and Italy, and the Federal German Navy. The name Tornado for this aircraft was adopted officially in March 1976. This programme is one of the largest European industrial programmes ever undertaken. The three component companies of Panavia are British Aerospace PLC (42.5 per cent participation), MBB (42.5 per cent) and Aeritalia (15 per cent).

The German, British and Italian governments set up a joint organisation known as NAMMO (NATO MRCA Management and production Organisation). This has its executive agency NAMMA (NATO MRCA Management Agency) in the same building as Panavia, in Munich.

On 29 July 1976 the three governments signed a memorandum of understanding for the production of 809 Tornados, manufactured under six successive contracts for a total of 805 aircraft, plus four pre-series Tornados brought up to production standard. Subsequent contracts have increased the total of 805 production aircraft to 921, comprising 697 of the IDS (interdictor strike) version for the air forces of the UK (228), West Germany (322), Italy (99) and Saudi Arabia (48); 35 of the ECR (electronic combat and reconnaissance) variant for the German Air Force; and 189 examples of the ADV (air defence variant) for the UK (165) and Saudi Arabia (24). To these are added the four pre-series aircraft brought up to IDS production standard (one for the UK, two for West Germany and one for Italy). More than 810 IDS and ADV Tornados had been delivered by 31 January 1990, the 800th aircraft (delivered on 9 January) being also the 150th production ADV.

PANAVIA TORNADO IDS

RAF designations: Tornado GR. Mks 1 and 1A

The Tornado is intended to fulfil six major requirements, some of which are shared by more than one of the partners. These are: close air support/battlefield interdiction; interdiction/counter air strike; air superiority; interception/air defence; naval strike; and reconnaissance.

Design was completed in August 1972. Nine flying prototypes were built—four in the UK, three in West Germany and two in Italy. The first prototype made its initial flight in West Germany on 14 August 1974. Details of the prototypes can be found in the 1978-79 and earlier editions of *Jane's*, and of the six pre-series Tornados in the 1980-81 and earlier editions. The first production Tornado made its initial flight on 10 July 1979, the first West German on 27 July 1979, and the first Italian on 25 September 1981.

Of the production IDS aircraft for the three partner nations, 129 will be dual control trainers with full operational capability. Export deliveries began in March 1986 with the first four IDS aircraft for Saudi Arabia, and the IDS Tornado now equips No. 7 Squadron of the Royal Saudi Air Force. Other commitments have been announced by Jordan (eight) and Malaysia (probably 12, including four ECR). Jordan indicated in Spring 1989 a postponement of its purchase for economic reasons.

The Tri-national Tornado Training Establishment (TTTE) at RAF Cottesmore received 53 Tornados initially (now reduced to 35). Weapons training is carried out at Tornado Weapons Conversion Units (TWCU) at RAF Honington (UK) and JaboG 38 at Jever (West Germany),

Panavia Tornado GR. Mk 1 of No. XV Squadron, RAF, with 1,500 litre drop tanks, BOZ chaff/flare dispenser and Sky Shadow ECM pod

Panavia Tornado IDS multi-role combat aircraft *(Pilot Press)*

and by the 154° Gruppo of the Italian Air Force at Brescia-Ghedi.

The RAF's planned total of 229 IDS Tornados includes, in addition to the standard **GR. Mk 1**, 50 **GR. Mk 1** dual-control trainers and 30 **GR. Mk 1A** all-weather day/night tactical reconnaissance variants, the latter including one development aircraft (ZA402, first flight 11 July 1985), 15 converted from GR. Mk 1s (delivered from 3 April 1987) and 14 built from the outset as GR. Mk 1As. Squadron deliveries began on 6 January 1982 to No. IX Squadron at RAF Honington, Suffolk, which became operational on 1 June 1982. It now also equips Nos. 27 and 617 at Marham (UK), Nos. XV, 16 and 20 at Laarbruch (West Germany), and Nos. 14, 17 and 31 at Brüggen (Germany). No. IX transferred to Brüggen in October 1986 to become the seventh Tornado GR. Mk 1 strike/attack squadron with RAF Germany. In 1984, RAF GR. Mk 1s based in Germany began to be modified to carry tactical nuclear weapons; they are also the first RAF Tornados to be equipped with the Hunting JP 233 anti-airfield weapon. The eighth RAFG Tornado squadron is No. 2 at Laarbruch, equipped with the GR. Mk 1A. The first UK based Tornado reconnaissance squadron is No. 13, at Honington, which was formed on 1 January 1990.

The RAF camera-less GR. Mk 1A retains its air-to-surface role except for deletion of guns. It is identifiable by a small underbelly blister fairing, immediately behind the laser rangefinder pod, and transparent side panels for a BAe sideways looking infra-red (SLIR) system and Vinten Linescan 4000 infra-red surveillance system. Its Computing Devices Company signal processing and video recording system is the first video-based tac/recce system with a replay facility, and offers the capability for future real-time reconnaissance data relay.

Luftwaffe IDS Tornados, all 212 of which have been delivered, now equip nine units: two each with JaboG 31 at Nörvenich, JaboG 32 at Lechfeld, JaboG 33 at Büchel and JaboG 34 at Memmingen, plus one with training unit JaboG 38. The 112 for the Federal German Navy are equipped for strike missions against sea and coastal targets, and for reconnaissance. Two squadrons of IDS Tornados are in service with Marinefliegergeschwader 1 at Jagel, and two with MFG 2 at Eggebeck, those of Staffel 1/MFG 2 being equipped with MBB multi-sensor reconnaissance pods. Sixty-seven of Germany's 324 Tornados are dual-control trainers.

The 100 Italian Air Force Tornados include 54 to replace F/RF-104G aircraft in the air superiority, ground attack and reconnaissance roles. Of the remainder, 34 will be kept in reserve and 12 are equipped as dual control trainers. First unit was the 154° Gruppo (Squadron) of 6° Stormo (Wing) at Brescia-Ghedi, which received its first Tornados in August 1982. By mid-1990 the Kormoran anti-shipping 156° Gruppo (36° Stormo) at Gioia del Colle (Bari), and the

First new-build Tornado GR. Mk 1A reconnaissance variant (ZG705) in the markings of No. 13 Squadron, RAF *(Paul Jackson)*

155° Gruppo (50° Stormo) at Piacenza, had also been equipped.

By the end of 1989, RAF Squadrons Nos. 27 and 617 were SACEUR declared, and all RAF Germany squadrons except the newly formed No. 2 Squadron had been assigned to NATO, as are the eight squadrons at German MFG. 1 and JaboGs 31, 32 and 33. The first operational batch of MW-1 weapons systems has been delivered to JaboG 31; and German Tornados have been cleared for in-flight refuelling by USAF KC-10A and KC-135 tanker aircraft.

The following details apply to the basic IDS production version:

TYPE: Twin-engined all-weather multi-purpose combat aircraft.

WINGS: Cantilever shoulder-wing monoplane. All-metal wings, of variable geometry, the outer panels having a leading-edge sweep of 25° in the fully forward position and 67° when fully swept. Fixed inboard portions have a leading-edge sweep of 60°. Wing carry-through box is of electron-beam-welded titanium alloy; majority of remaining wing structure is of aluminium alloy, with integrally stiffened skin. There is a Krueger flap on the leading-edge of each wing glove box. The wings each pivot hydraulically, on Teflon plated bearings, from a point in the centre-section just outboard of the fuselage. The root of the outer wing mates with the pivot pin through attachment members made of titanium alloy and fixed to the upper and lower light alloy panels of the outer wing box, and a so-called 'round rib', also of titanium alloy, transmitting the normal aerodynamic force. Sweep actuators are of the ballscrew type, with hydraulic motor drive. In the event of wing sweep failure, the aircraft can land safely with the wings fully swept. High-lift devices on the outer wings include full span leading-edge slats (three sections on each side), full span double-slotted fixed-vane trailing-edge flaps (four sections each side), and spoilers (two on upper surface on each side). Spoilers give augmented roll control at unswept and intermediate wing positions at low speed, and also act as lift dumpers after touchdown. All flying control surfaces actuated by electrically controlled tandem hydraulic jacks. No ailerons. Entire outer wings, including control surfaces, are Italian built, Aeritalia having prime responsibility for final assembly and production, assisted by Aermacchi, Aeronavali Venezia, Piaggio, Saca and SIAI-Marchetti as subcontractors. Microtecnica (Italy) is prime subcontractor for the wing sweep system.

FUSELAGE: Conventional all-metal semi-monocoque structure, mainly of aluminium alloy, built in three main sections. MBB is prime contractor for the centre fuselage section, including the engine air intake ducts and wing centre-section box and pivot mechanism. This task includes responsibility for the surface interface between the movable wing and the fixed portion, to ensure both a smooth and slender external contour and proper sealing against aerodynamic pressure over a range of wing sweep positions. The design uses fibre reinforced plastics in these areas, and an elastic seal between the outer wings and the fuselage sides. Responsibility for the front fuselage, including both cockpits, and for the rear fuselage, including the engine installation, is undertaken by BAe (Warton). Radar-transparent nosecone by AEG-Telefunken, assisted by Aeritalia and BAe, hinges sideways to starboard to provide access to ground mapping and terrain following radar antennae. Slice of fuselage immediately aft of nosecone also hinges sideways to starboard, to provide access to forward avionics bay and/or rear of radar. Door type airbrake on each side at top of rear fuselage.

TAIL UNIT: Cantilever all-metal structure, consisting of single sweptback two-spar fin and rudder, and low-set all-moving horizontal surfaces (tailerons) which operate together for pitch control and differentially for roll control, assisted by use of the wing spoilers when the wings are not fully swept. Rudder and tailerons actuated by electrically controlled tandem hydraulic jacks. Passive ECM antenna fairing near top of fin. Ram air intake for heat exchanger at base of fin. Entire tail unit is the responsibility of BAe. Four tailerons of carbonfibre

composite, 17 per cent lighter than the standard metal ones, were developed by MBB and BAe. Two were for structural and fatigue testing; the other pair were flight tested on prototype P07.

LANDING GEAR: Hydraulically retractable tricycle type, with forward retracting twin-wheel steerable nose unit. Single-wheel main units retract forward and upward into centre section of fuselage. Emergency extension system, using nitrogen gas pressure. Development and manufacture of the complete landing gear and associated hydraulics is headed by Dowty Aerospace (UK). Dunlop aluminium alloy wheels, hydraulic multi-disc brakes and low-pressure tyres (to permit operation from soft, semi-prepared surfaces) and Goodyear anti-skid units. Mainwheel tyres size 30 × 11.50-14.5, Type VIII (24 or 26 ply); nosewheel tyres size 18 × 5.5, Type VIII (12 ply). Runway arrester hook beneath rear of fuselage.

POWER PLANT: Two Turbo-Union RB199-34R turbofans, fitted with bucket type thrust reversers and installed in rear fuselage with opening doors for servicing and engine change. Mk 101 engines of early production aircraft rated at 38.7 kN (8,700 lb st) dry and 66.0 kN (14,840 lb st) with afterburning (uninstalled), except for TTTE aircraft, which have their engines down-rated to 37.0 kN (8,320 lb st) dry to extend service life. Mk 103 engines, introduced in May 1983 (engine number 761), are dry rated at 40.5 kN (9,100 lb st) uninstalled and provide 71.5 kN (16,075 lb st) with afterburning. RAF ordered 100 modification kits in 1983 to upgrade Mk 101 engined aircraft to Mk 103 standard. All internal fuel in multi-cell Uniroyal self-sealing integral fuselage tanks and/or wing box tanks, all fitted with press-in fuel sampling and water drain plugs, and all refuelled from a single-point NATO connector. Capacity of these tanks totals approx 6,090 litres (1,610 US gallons; 1,340 Imp gallons). Additional 551 litre (145.5 US gallon; 121 Imp gallon) tank in fin (on RAF aircraft only). Detachable and retractable in-flight refuelling probe can be mounted on starboard side of fuselage, adjacent to cockpit. Provision for one or two drop tanks to be carried beneath fuselage (1,500 litres; 396 US gallons; 330 Imp gallons) and single tanks on the shoulder pylons and inboard underwing pylons (1,500 or 2,250 litres; 396 or 594 US gallons; 330 or 495 Imp gallons). German Navy and Italian Air Force aircraft (96 aircraft so equipped by February 1990) adapted to carry a Sargent-Fletcher Type 28-300 1,135 litre (300 US gallon; 250 Imp gallon) buddy type hose/drogue refuelling pod. Dowty/Lucas/Microtecnica afterburning fuel control system. AEG-Telefunken intake de-icing system.

ACCOMMODATION: Crew of two on tandem Martin-Baker Mk 10A zero/zero ejection seats under Kopperschmidt/AIT one-piece canopy, which is hinged at rear and opens upward. Flat centre armoured windscreen panel and curved side panels, built by Lucas Aerospace, incorporate Sierracote electrically conductive heating film for windscreen anti-icing and demisting. Canopy (and windscreen in emergency) demisted by engine bleed air. Windscreen is hinged at front and can be opened forward and upward, allowing access to back of pilot's instrument panel. Seats provide safe escape at zero altitude and at speeds from zero up to 630 knots (1,166 km/h; 725 mph) IAS.

SYSTEMS: Cockpit air-conditioned and pressurised (max differential 0.36 bars; 5.25 lb/sq in) by Normalair-Garrett conventional air cycle system (with bootstrap cold air unit) using engine bleed air with ram air precooler, Marston intercooler, and Teddington temperature control system. Nordmicro/BAe/Microtecnica air intake control system, and Dowty Aerospace/Liebherr Aerotechnik engine intake ramp control actuators. Two independent hydraulic systems, each of 276 bars (4,000 lb/sq in pressure), are supplied from two separate, independently driven Vickers pumps, each mounted on an engine accessory gearbox. Each system is supplied from a separate bootstrap type reservoir. Systems provide fully duplicated power for primary flight control system, tailerons, rudder, flaps, slats, wing sweep, pitch Q-feel system, and refuelling probe. Port system also

supplies power for Krueger flaps, inboard spoilers, port air intake ramps, canopy, and wheel brakes; starboard system for airbrakes, outboard spoilers, starboard air intake ramps, landing gear, nosewheel steering, and radar stabilisation and scanning. Main system includes Dowty accumulators and Teves power pack. Fairey Hydraulics system for actuation of spoilers, rudder and taileron control. Provision for reversion to single-engine drive of both systems, via a mechanical cross-connection between the two engine auxiliary gearboxes, in the event of a single engine failure. In the event of a double engine flameout, an emergency pump in No. 1 system has sufficient duration for re-entry into the engine cold relight boundary. Flying control circuits are protected from loss of fluid due to leaks in other circuits by isolating valves which shut off the utility circuits if the reservoir contents drop below a predetermined safety limit level. Electrical system consists of a 115/200V AC three-phase 400Hz constant frequency subsystem and a 28V DC subsystem. Power is generated by two automatically controlled oil-cooled brushless AC generators integrated with a constant speed drive unit and driven by the engines via an accessory gearbox. Normally, each engine drives its own accessory gearbox, but provision is also made for either engine to drive the opposite gearbox through a cross-drive system. In the event of a generator failure, the remaining unit can supply the total aircraft load. Both gearboxes and generators can be driven by APU when aircraft is on ground. The generators supply two main AC busbars and an AC essential busbar. DC power is provided from two fan-cooled transformer/rectifier units (power being derived from the main AC system), these feeding power to two main DC busbars, one essential DC busbar and a battery busbar. Either TRU can supply total aircraft DC load. A fifth DC busbar is provided for maintenance purposes only. Battery is a rechargeable nickel-cadmium type, and provides power for basic flightline servicing and for starting APU. In the event of main electrical system or double TRU failure, it is connected automatically to the essential services busbar to supply essential electrical loads. Normalair-Garrett/Draegerwerk/OMI demand type oxygen system, using a 10 litre (2.6 US gallon; 2.2 Imp gallon) lox converter. Emergency oxygen system installed on each seat. KHD accessory drive gearboxes and Rotax/Lucas/Siemens integrated drive generator. GEC Avionics flow metering system. Eichweber fuel gauging system and Flight Refuelling flexible couplings. Graviner fire detection and extinguishing systems. Rotax contactors. Smiths engine speed and temperature indicators.

AVIONICS AND EQUIPMENT: Communications equipment includes Plessey PTR 1721 (UK and Italy) or Rohde und Schwarz (West Germany) UHF/VHF transceiver; AEG-Telefunken UHF/ADF (UK and West Germany only); SIT/Siemens emergency UHF with Rohde und Schwarz switch; BAe HF/SSB aerial tuning unit; Rohde und Schwarz (UK and West Germany) or Montedel (Italy) HF/SSB radio; Ultra communications control system; GEC Avionics central suppression unit (CSU); Leigh voice recorder; Chelton UHF communications and landing system aerials.

Primary self-contained nav/attack system includes a European built Texas Instruments multi-mode forward looking, terrain following ground mapping radar; Ferranti FIN 1010 three-axis digital inertial navigation system (DINS) and combined radar and map display; Decca Type 72 Doppler radar system, with Kalman filtering of the Doppler and inertial inputs for extreme navigational accuracy; Microtecnica air data computer; Litef Spirit 3 central digital computer (64K initially, 224K on current production aircraft); Aeritalia radio/radar altimeter (to be replaced on RAF aircraft by GEC Sensors AD1990 covert radar altimeter); Smiths/Teldix/OMI electronic head-up display with Davall camera; Ferranti nose mounted laser rangefinder and marked target seeker; GEC Avionics TV tabular display, produced in partnership with AEG and Selenia; Astronautics (USA) bearing distance and heading indicator and contour map display. Defensive equipment includes Siemens (West Germany) or Cossor SSR-3100 (UK and Saudi Arabia) IFF transponder; and Elettronica ARI 23284 radar warning receiver (being replaced in GR. Mk 1 from 1987 by MDSL Hermes RHWR).

Flight control system includes a GEC Avionics/Bodenseewerk triplex command stability augmentation system (CSAS), incorporating fly by wire and autostabilisation; GEC Avionics/Aeritalia autopilot and flight director (APFD), using two self-monitoring digital computers; GEC Avionics triplex transducer unit (TTU), with analog computing and sensor channels; GEC Avionics terrain following E-scope (TFE), produced in partnership with Selenia; Fairey/GEC Avionics quadruplex electro-hydraulic actuator; and Microtecnica air data set. The APFD provides preselected attitude, heading or barometric height hold, heading and track acquisition, and Mach number or airspeed hold with autothrottle. Flight director operates in parallel with, and can be used as backup for, the autopilot, as a duplex digital system with an extensive range of modes. Automatic approach, terrain following and radio height-holding modes are also available. Other instrumentation includes Smiths horizontal situation indicator, vertical speed indicator and standby altimeter; Lital standby attitude and heading reference system; SEL (with Setac) or (in UK aircraft) GEC Avionics AD2770 (without Setac) Tacan; Cossor CILS 75/76 ILS; Bodenseewerk attitude director indicator; Dornier flight data recorder.

ARMAMENT: Fixed armament comprises two 27 mm IWKA-Mauser cannon, one in each side of the lower forward fuselage, with 180 rds/gun. Other armament varies according to version, with emphasis on the ability to carry a wide range of advanced weapons. A GEC Avionics/Selenia stores management system is fitted; Sandall Mace 355 and 762 mm (14 and 30 in) ejector release units standard on UK Tornados; German and Italian aircraft use multiple weapon carriage system (MWCS) ejector release units. ML Aviation CBLS 200 practice bomb carriers are also standard. The battlefield interdiction version is capable of carrying weapons for hard or soft targets. Weapons are carried on seven fuselage and wing hardpoints: one centreline pylon fitted with a single ejection release unit (ERU), two fuselage shoulder pylons each with three ERUs, and, under each wing, one inboard and one outboard pylon each with a single ERU. For German Navy and Italian Air Force Tornados, MBB has developed a multi-sensor reconnaissance pod to be carried on the centreline pylon. RAF GR. Mk 1A fitted with infra-red cameras in ammunition bay. Among the weapons already specified for, or suitable for carriage by, the IDS Tornado are the Sidewinder air-to-air, and up to nine ALARM or up to four HARM anti-radiation missiles; JP 233 low-altitude airfield attack munition dispenser, CPU-123B Paveway laser guided bomb, AS.30, Maverick, GBU-15, Sea Eagle (UK) and Kormoran (Germany and Italy) air-to-surface missiles; napalm; BL755 cluster bombs (277 kg; 611 lb Mk 1 or 264 kg; 582 lb Mk 2); MW-1 munitions dispenser (German and Italian aircraft); 1,000 lb bombs; smart or retarded bombs; BLU-1B 750 lb fire bombs; Matra 250 kg ballistic and retarded bombs; Lepus flare bombs; LAU-51A and LR-25 rocket launchers; Marconi Sky Shadow (jamming/deception) and BOZ 100 (Germany), 102 (Italy) or 107 (UK) chaff/flare ECM pods. AEG Cerberus II or III jammer pods on German and Italian aircraft BAe TIALD (thermal imaging airborne laser designator) night/adverse visibility pods have been integrated for RAF Tornados. Various terrain reference navigation systems have also been developed, including BAe Terprom, GEC Spartan, and Ferranti Penetrate, as have night vision systems incorporating FLIR and NVGs. External fuel tanks (see Power Plant paragraph) can also be carried.

DIMENSIONS, EXTERNAL:

Wing span: fully spread	13.91 m (45 ft 7½ in)
fully swept	8.60 m (28 ft 2½ in)
Length overall	16.72 m (54 ft 10¼ in)
Height overall	5.95 m (19 ft 6¼ in)
Tailplane span	6.80 m (22 ft 3½ in)
Wheel track	3.10 m (10 ft 2 in)
Wheelbase	6.20 m (20 ft 4 in)

AREA:

Wings, gross (to fuselage c/l, 25° sweepback)	26.60 m² (286.3 sq ft)

WEIGHTS:

Weight empty, equipped	14,091 kg (31,065 lb)
Fuel (approx):	
internal: wing/fuselage tanks	4,862 kg (10,720 lb)
fin tank (RAF only)	440 kg (970 lb)
drop tanks (each): 1,500 litre	1,197 kg (2,640 lb)
2,250 litre	1,796 kg (3,960 lb)
Nominal max weapon load	more than 9,000 kg (19,840 lb)
Max T-O weight:	
clean, full internal fuel	20,411 kg (45,000 lb)
with external stores	more than 28,000 kg (61,730 lb)

PERFORMANCE:

Max Mach number in level flight at altitude, clean	2.2
Max level speed, clean	
above 800 knots (1,480 km/h; 920 mph) IAS	
Max level speed with external stores	
Mach 0.92 (600 knots; 1,112 km/h; 691 mph)	
Landing speed	approx 115 knots (213 km/h; 132 mph)
Time to 9,150 m (30,000 ft) from brake release	less than 2 min
Automatic terrain following	down to 61 m (200 ft)
Required runway length	less than 900 m (2,950 ft)
Landing run	370 m (1,215 ft)
Max 360° rapid roll clearance with full lateral control	4g
Radius of action with heavy weapons load, hi-lo-lo-hi	750 nm (1,390 km; 863 miles)
Ferry range	approx 2,100 nm (3,890 km; 2,420 miles)
g limit	+7.5

TORNADO IDS MID-LIFE IMPROVEMENT PROGRAMMES

In order to retain effective mission capability and survivability in the face of any increased threat in the 1990s and beyond, a mid-life improvement programme for the IDS version is currently being developed by the Tornado air arms and industry for the Luftwaffe, Marineflieger and Italian Air Force. It will confer more accurate navigation

First of two Tornado ECR (electronic combat and reconnaissance) development aircraft

for blind attacks, improved sortie generation capability, increased range for better target coverage, increased target acquisition capability, reduced penetration altitude, covert operation, improved electronic self-defence and threat suppression, and greater reliability and maintainability.

The first avionics upgrade modifications are already incorporated in the sixth Tornado production batch. They include a MIL-1553B databus, upgraded radar warning equipment and active ECM, an improved missile control unit, and integration of the Texas Instruments HARM anti-radar guided missile. HARM is already in service with German Navy Tornados.

Further updates for German and Italian Tornados may be based on the ECR variant (see next entry).

A contract for the development phase of the mid-life update (MLU) for RAF Tornado GR. Mk 1s was signed on 16 March 1989. Marconi Defence Systems will upgrade the electronic warfare suite, including the radar warning receiver and Sky Shadow jamming systems. In April 1989 GEC Avionics announced four contracts, to supply its Spartan TRN/TF (terrain referenced navigation/terrain following) system, which enables the aircraft to fly with great accuracy at low level without activating its radar or using external navigation sources; an updated weapon control system; an advanced video recording system with ground replay facility; and a computer loading system. Other MLU contracts have been awarded to Ferranti (HUD, computer generated HUD symbology, terrain following display 3D ground profile, and digital storage and image generating system for the moving map display); and Smiths Industries (colour CRT head-down display).

After receiving the mid-life update modifications, upgraded Tornado GR. Mk 1s will be redesignated **GR. Mk 4**. First flight of a GR. Mk 4 is expected in late 1991. The RAF plans to obtain a further 26 new GR. Mk 4s in the proposed 8th production batch.

PANAVIA TORNADO ECR

The Federal German Luftwaffe selected the ECR (electronic combat and reconnaissance) version of the IDS Tornado to replace tactical reconnaissance aircraft already in operation and to complement or supersede such NATO airborne electronic warfare types as the Wild Weasel F-4G Phantom. Development was authorised in June 1986.

Retaining its air-to-surface role, except for the removal of the two 27 mm guns, the ECR Tornado is intended for standoff reconnaissance and border control, reconnaissance via image-forming and electronic means, electronic support, and employment of anti-radar guided missiles. For this purpose, it has a Texas Instruments emitter location system

(ELS); a Honeywell/Sondertechnik infra-red linescanner system; Zeiss FLIR; onboard systems for processing, storing and transmitting reconnaissance data; and advanced tactical displays for the pilot and weapons officer. The external load stations on fuselage and wings may be used in ECR or fighter-bomber missions, or a combination of both.

The ECR version will normally be configured to carry two HARMs, two AIM-9L Sidewinders, an active ECM pod, chaff/flare dispenser pod, and two 1,500 litre (396 US gallon; 330 Imp gallon) underwing fuel tanks. A Mk 105 version of the RB199 engine will provide some 10 per cent more thrust than the Mk 103 in current IDS aircraft.

The seventh Tornado production contract, signed on 10 June 1986, included an order for 35 Tornado ECRs for the Luftwaffe, deliveries of which are being made to 3/JaboG 32 and 2/JaboG 38 in 1990-91. Pre-production Tornado P16 (serial number 98 + 03) and one other IDS aircraft (serial number 45 + 75) were converted for initial ECR flight trials, which began on schedule at Manching on 18 August 1988. First production ECR Tornado (serial 46 + 23) flew on 26 October 1989, and deliveries were due to begin in Spring 1990. Italy has expressed interest in acquiring about 16 ECR Tornados.

Panavia has teamed with Rockwell International to propose a variant of the Tornado to meet the USAF's Follow-on Wild Weasel requirement for an F-4G replacement in the early/mid-1990s. This would be based on the ECR version, with final assembly (from joint production) by Rockwell if selected for the USAF.

PANAVIA TORNADO ADV

RAF designations: Tornado F. Mks 2, 2A and 3

A possible air defence role for the Tornado was considered by the RAF when the interdictor/strike (IDS) programme was inaugurated in 1968, and studies leading to an air defence variant (ADV) were given impetus in 1971, when the Ministry of Defence issued Air Staff Target (AST) 395 covering the development of an interceptor with an advanced technology radar and Sky Flash air-to-air missiles. Changes from the IDS Tornado were to be minimal, and costs kept as low as possible. Full-scale development was authorised on 4 March 1976, and the RAF has ordered 165 of this long-range interceptor model to re-equip two former Lightning squadrons and three Phantom squadrons, as well as two new squadrons and an OCU. Of this total, 40 will be dual control trainers. Purchase is planned of 15 more ADVs in production batch 8.

The ADV is being procured primarily for air defence of the UK and to protect the northern and western approaches

Panavia Tornado F. Mk 3 all-weather air defence interceptor *(Pilot Press)*

Panavia Tornado F. Mk 3 in Royal Saudi Air Force insignia

of NATO. Equipped with a tactical display that can cover the entire North Sea, it also fulfils the RAF's commitments to provide long-range air defence of Britain's maritime forces, over a wide UK defence region extending from the Atlantic approaches to the Baltic and from Iceland to the English Channel; and to contribute towards air defence in the Central Region of Europe.

Two main airframe modifications distinguish the ADV from the IDS version. The principal one is an increase in fuselage length forward of the front cockpit, to accommodate the longer radome of the GEC Avionics AI Mk 24 Foxhunter radar, and a small stretch aft of the rear cockpit to allow the four Sky Flash missiles to be carried in two tandem pairs. The other is that the fixed inboard portions of the wings are extended forward at the leading-edges (sweep angle 67° instead of 60°), to give increased chord and compensate for the shift in the CG. These changes also benefit performance by reducing drag, especially at supersonic speed, compared with the IDS version. Extension of the fuselage provides additional space for avionics and for an additional 10 per cent of internal fuel. Other changes include deletion of one of the two IWKA-Mauser 27 mm cannon; and only the two inboard underwing pylons are used on the RAF's ADVs.

Two versions of the ADV have been produced for the Royal Air Force:

Tornado F. Mk 2. First 18 production aircraft, with RB199 Mk 103 engines. Further details in 1989-90 and earlier *Jane's*. These aircraft, the last of which was delivered on 9 October 1985, are currently in store. They are scheduled for return to BAe in the early 1990s, to be largely upgraded to F. 3 standard except for the Mk 104 engines, which could not be retrofitted without structural alterations to the rear fuselage. After upgrading, these F. 2s will be redesignated **F. Mk 2A.**

Tornado F. Mk 3. Current (and major) production version, with RB199 Mk 104 engines with extended nozzles, increased reheat combat thrust, and Lucas digital engine control; a ram air turbine, radar-dedicated cold air unit, and internally mounted retractable in-flight refuelling probe; added head-down display for the pilot, and a displayed data video recorder for the navigator instead of the original wet-film head-down display recorder; a second Ferranti 1010 INS platform; a new Cossor IFF interrogator; a Singer-Kearfott data link system (when development is completed); new cockpit displays and redesigned symbology, together with an increase in computer storage capacity. The F. Mk 3 also introduced automatic wing sweep (AWS) and automatic manoeuvre device system (AMDS).

The initial Tornado production contract included funding for three ADV prototypes. These made their first flights on 27 October 1979, 18 July 1980 and 18 November 1980.

The first two production F. Mk 2s made their initial flights on 12 April and 5 March 1984 respectively. The first F. Mk 3 (ZE154) made its initial flight on 20 November 1985. No. 229 OCU ('shadow' identity: No. 65 Squadron) received its first F. Mk 3 (ZE159) on 28 July 1986, and on 31 December that year was declared operational. No. 29 Squadron (Coningsby) became operational with the F. Mk 3 on 1 November 1987. No. 5 Squadron (Coningsby) and No. 11 (Leeming) did so on 1 May and 1 November 1988 respectively. They were followed by Nos. 23 and 25 (both at Leeming) on 1 August 1989 and 1 January 1990. Finally, Nos. 43 and 111 (both at Leuchars) were due to become operational by the end of 1990.

The 150th ADV Tornado was delivered at the beginning of 1990 when 15 F. Mk 2s and eight F. Mk 3s were held in store. Export orders were received in 1985 from the Royal Saudi Air Force (24, including six with dual control), to which the first ADV was handed over on 9 February 1989. The first two RSAF ADV squadrons are Nos. 29 and 34.

From 1990, a new data processor will be available to give the final standard of the F. Mk 3's Foxhunter radar considerably more capability than the earlier versions. In particular, more automation will be provided for the radar functions, to improve close combat capability. Modification kits will bring radars already in service up to the new standard.

The following description applies to the F. Mk 3:

TYPE: Twin-engined all-weather air defence interceptor.

WINGS: Similar to IDS version except that fixed inboard portions also have a leading-edge sweep of 67° and the Krueger leading-edge flaps are deleted. Automatic wing sweep (AWS) and automatic manoeuvre device system (AMDS). With AWS, four different wing sweeps can be scheduled (25° at speeds up to Mach 0.73, 45° from there up to Mach 0.88, 58° up to Mach 0.95, and 67° above Mach 0.95), enabling specific excess power at transonic speeds and turning capability at subsonic speeds to be maximised. Buffet-free handling can be maintained, to the limits defined by the SPILS (spin prevention and incidence limiting system), by use of the AMDS, which schedules with wing incidence to deploy either flaps and slats at 25° sweep angle or slats only at 45° sweep. Beyond 45°, both flaps and slats are scheduled in.

FUSELAGE: Generally as for IDS version, but lengthened forward of front cockpit and aft of rear cockpit, plus a 360 mm (14 in) extension of afterburner nozzles. Nosecone hinged in two places, providing access to front and rear of Foxhunter radar.

TAIL UNIT: As IDS version, except that base of rudder is recontoured to clear the repositioned thrust reversers, and tailerons to clear the revised rear fuselage outline.

LANDING GEAR: As IDS version. Nosewheel steering augmentation system to minimise wander on landing.

POWER PLANT: Two Turbo-Union RB199-34R Mk 104 turbofans, each with uninstalled rating of 40.5 kN (9,100 lb st) dry and 73.5 kN (16,520 lb st) with afterburning. Fuselage fuel capacity (incl fin tank) approx 7,250 litres (1,915 US gallons; 1,595 Imp gallons). Internally mounted, fully retractable in-flight refuelling probe in port side of nose, adjacent to cockpit. Provision for drop tanks of 1,500 or 2,250 litres (396 or 594 US gallons; 330 or 495 Imp gallons) capacity to be carried on the shoulder pylons and underwing pylons.

ACCOMMODATION: As for IDS version.

SYSTEMS: Generally as described for IDS version, with the addition of a radar-dedicated cold air unit to cool the Foxhunter radar, and a pop-up ram air turbine to assist recovery in the event of engine flameout at high altitude in a zoom climb.

AVIONICS AND EQUIPMENT: Among those in the IDS Tornado which are retained in the ADV are the communications equipment (Plessey VHF/UHF transceiver, SIT/Siemens emergency UHF, Rohde und Schwarz HF/SSB, Ultra communications control system and Epsilon cockpit voice recorder); GEC Avionics triplex fly by wire command stability augmentation system and autopilot/flight director system (modified for increased roll rate and reduced pitch stick forces); Litef Spirit 3 central digital computer (with capacity increased from 64K to 224K) and data transmission system; Smiths electronic

head-up and navigator's head-down display; Ferranti FIN 1010 inertial navigation system (to which is added a second 1010 to monitor the head-up display); GEC Sensors Tacan; Cossor ILS; and Cossor IFF transponder. Those deleted include the Texas Instruments nose radar, Decca 72 Doppler radar with terrain following, Ferranti laser rangefinder and marked target seeker, and Lital standby attitude and heading reference system.

Nose-mounted Marconi Defence Systems AI-24 Foxhunter multi-mode track-while-scan pulse-Doppler radar with FMICW (frequency modulated interrupted continuous wave), with which is integrated a new Cossor IFF-3500 interrogator and a radar signal processor to suppress ground clutter. This system is intended to enable the aircraft to detect targets more than 100 nm (185 km; 115 miles) away, and to track several targets simultaneously. A ground mapping mode for navigation backup is available. Ferranti is subcontractor for the Foxhunter transmitter and aerial scanning mechanism. A pilot's head-down display is added, a Ferranti displayed data video recorder (DDVR) replaces the navigator's wet-film display recorder, and an MDSL Hermes modular radar homing and warning receiver (RHWR) is added. Head-up/head-down displays are on front instrument panel only; radar control and data link presentations on rear panel only; both panels have weapon control and RHWR displays. A Ferranti FH 31A AC driven 3 in horizon gyro in the rear cockpit, in addition to providing an attitude display for the navigator, feeds pitch and roll signals to other avionics systems in the aircraft in certain modes. Lucas digital electronic engine control unit (DECU 500). ESM (electronic surveillance measures) and ECCM are standard; a Singer-Kearfott ECM-resistant data link system, interoperable with other NATO systems, is under development for installation later. Because of its comprehensive avionics the Tornado ADV can contribute significantly to the transfer of vital information over the entire tactical area and can, if necessary, partially fulfil the roles of both AEW and ground based radar.

ARMAMENT AND OPERATIONAL EQUIPMENT: Fixed armament of one 27 mm IWKA-Mauser cannon in starboard side of lower forward fuselage. Four BAe Sky Flash semi-active radar homing medium-range air-to-air missiles semi-recessed under the centre-fuselage, carried on internally mounted Frazer-Nash launchers; two European built NWC AIM-9L Sidewinder infra-red homing short-range air-to-air missiles on each underwing station. Smiths Industries/Computing Devices Company missile management system (MMS), which also controls tank jettison, has provision for pilot override, optimised for visual attack. The Sky Flash missiles, each fitted with an MSDS monopulse seeker head, can engage targets at high altitude or down to 75 m (250 ft), in the face of heavy ECM, and at standoff ranges of more than 25 nm (46 km; 29 miles). Release system permits the missile to be fired over the Tornado's full flight envelope. For the future, the ADV will be able to carry, instead of Sky Flash and Sidewinder, up to six Hughes AIM-20 AMRAAM or BAe Active Sky Flash medium-range and four BAe/Bodenseewerk ASRAAM short-range air-to-air missiles; studies are being undertaken for a 1553B multiplex digital databus associated with these weapons.

DIMENSIONS, EXTERNAL: As for IDS version, except:
Length overall   18.68 m (61 ft 3½ in)

WEIGHTS (approx):
Operational weight empty   14,500 kg (31,970 lb)
Fuel (approx):
   internal: wing/fuselage tanks   5,348 kg (11,790 lb)
    fin tank   as for IDS version
    drop tanks   as for IDS version
Max external fuel   5,806 kg (12,800 lb)
Nominal max weapon load   8,500 kg (18,740 lb)
Max T-O weight   27,986 kg (61,700 lb)

PERFORMANCE:
Max Mach number in level flight at altitude, clean   2.2
Max level speed, clean
   800 knots (1,480 km/h; 920 mph) IAS
Rotation speed, depending on AUW
   145-160 knots (269-297 km/h; 167-184 mph)
Normal touchdown speed
   115 knots (213 km/h; 132 mph)
Demonstrated roll rate at 750 knots (1,390 km/h; 864 mph) and up to 4g   180°/s
Operational ceiling   approx 21,335 m (70,000 ft)
T-O run:
  with normal weapon and fuel load   760 m (2,500 ft)
  ferry configuration (four 1,500 litre drop tanks and full weapon load)   approx 1,525 m (5,000 ft)
T-O to 15 m (50 ft)   under 915 m (3,000 ft)
Landing from 15 m (50 ft)   approx 610 m (2,000 ft)
Landing run with thrust reversal   370 m (1,215 ft)
Intercept radius:
  supersonic   more than 300 nm (556 km; 345 miles)
  subsonic   more than 1,000 nm (1,853 km; 1,151 miles)
Endurance
  2 h combat air patrol at 300-400 nm (555-740 km; 345-460 miles) from base, incl time for interception and 10 min combat

ROCKWELL INTERNATIONAL/MBB

PARTICIPATING COMPANIES:

Rockwell International Corporation (North American Aircraft Operations), PO Box 92098, Los Angeles, California 90009, USA
Telephone: 1 (213) 414 1092
Fax: 1 (213) 414 2677
Messerschmitt-Bölkow-Blohm GmbH, Postfach 801109, 8000 Munich 80, West Germany
Telephone: 49 (89) 6070

ROCKWELL INTERNATIONAL/MBB X-31A EFM

The X-31A is the first US 'X' series experimental aircraft to be developed jointly with another country. Known also by the programme title EFM (Enhanced Fighter Maneuverability), it was one of the first NATO co-operative efforts to be launched under the Nunn-Quayle research and development initiative, with a Phase 1 feasibility study which began in November 1984. This showed that close-in combat may continue to be necessary for future fighter aircraft, and that enhanced manoeuvring capabilities could lead to significant exchange ratio advantages. The X-31A programme is, therefore, intended to produce an aircraft that will break the so-called stall barrier, to allow close-in aerial combat beyond normal stall angles of attack.

The US Defense Advanced Research Projects Agency (DARPA), acting through US Naval Air Systems Command, is working with the German Federal Ministry of Defence to manage the X-31A development programme. An international memorandum of agreement was signed between the two countries in May 1986, and work on the year-long Phase 2 (vehicle preliminary design) started four months later. In the USA, Rockwell International has primary responsibility for the aircraft's configuration, aerodynamics and construction, while Messerschmitt-Bölkow-Blohm (MBB) in Germany is responsible for the control systems and thrust vectoring design. General Electric is propulsion subcontractor, and its Aerospace Business Group assisted in cockpit development. Other major subcontractors include Menasco (landing gear), Goodrich (wheels), Swedlow (canopy), Honeywell (flight control computers), Sundstrand (electrical power generator), and Allied Signal's Electrodynamics and AiResearch Divisions (fly by wire drive system for flight control surfaces).

The X-31A design integrates several technologies to expand the manoeuvring flight envelope, including vectored thrust, integrated control systems, and aircrew assistance. These advanced concepts are expected to enable extremely rapid target acquisition and fuselage pointing for addressing future low-speed, transonic and supersonic engagements. Earlier programmes such as the Rockwell HiMAT RPRV and MBB's TKF-90 contributed much useful data to the X-31A's design and development.

Two X-31A prototypes are being built under the 22-month Phase 3, funded in August 1988. These are assembled by Rockwell, with MBB providing a number of major components and subassemblies including the CFRP wings. The first X-31A (BuAer number 64584) was rolled out at Palmdale, California, on 1 March 1990, and was to fly during May. The second aircraft was due to be completed in June 1990, and the two-year, 400-hour flight test programme will involve an international team of pilots from Rockwell, MBB, the US Navy and the Federal German Luftwaffe. Funding between Rockwell and MBB is expected to be split approximately 80/20 per cent.

WINGS: Cantilever low-wing 'cranked delta' monoplane. Rockwell transonic aerofoil section (thickness/chord ratio 5 per cent), incorporating camber and twist. No dihedral or anhedral. Incidence 0°. Sweepback at quarter-chord 48° 6' inboard, 35° 36' outboard. Main wing constructed of aluminium spars and ribs, with graphite epoxy (carbonfibre) upper and lower skins. Plain ailerons and trailing-edge flaps, former of honeycomb, latter with aluminium ribs; all four surfaces have graphite epoxy skins. Two-segment flap on each leading-edge.

FOREPLANES: All-moving canard surfaces, rotating on steel spindle; honeycomb structure, with graphite epoxy skins. Bendix (modified V-22) actuators.

FUSELAGE: Conventional structure, with aluminium bulkheads and stringers. Glassfibre nose radome; aft of this, forward fuselage panels are graphite epoxy skins over honeycomb, mid-fuselage has aluminium skins, and rear 0.76 m (2 ft 6 in) of fuselage has titanium skin and bulkheads. Door type airbrake on each side of rear fuselage. Three thrust vectoring paddles attached to rear of exhaust nozzles which can act as additional airbrakes for rapid deceleration.

TAIL UNIT: Sweptback vertical fin and rudder only, of aluminium construction with graphite epoxy skin. Bendix (modified V-22) rudder actuator.

LANDING GEAR: Hydraulically retractable tricycle type adapted from GD F-16, with Cessna Citation III wheels and brakes and LTV A-7 tyre. Nosewheel and tyre are from F-16. Main units retract forward into fuselage, nosewheel unit rearward. Syndex tail braking parachute.

POWER PLANT: One 71.17 kN (16,000 lb st with afterburning) General Electric F404-GE-400 turbofan. Single fuel tank in fuselage, with gravity feed post just aft of canopy. Single ventral air intake, with movable lower lip. Three thrust-vectoring paddles can deflect the exhaust through approx 10° for additional yaw control.

ACCOMMODATION: Pilot only, on Martin-Baker SJU-5/6 ejection seat in pressurised, heated and air-conditioned cockpit. Windscreen and rear-hinged, upward opening canopy from McDonnell Douglas F/A-18 Hornet.

SYSTEMS: Include a Garrett (modified F-16 hydrazine system) emergency power unit to provide 4½ minutes of electrical hydraulic power, and a Garrett (hydrazine powered) emergency air start system from Northrop F-20.

DIMENSIONS, EXTERNAL:

Wing span	7.26 m (23 ft 10 in)
Wing aspect ratio	2.51
Foreplane span	2.64 m (8 ft 8 in)
Length: overall, incl nose probe	14.85 m (48 ft 8½ in)
fuselage, excl probe	12.39 m (40 ft 8 in)
Height overall	4.44 m (14 ft 7 in)
Wheel track	2.29 m (7 ft 6⅓ in)
Wheelbase	3.51 m (11 ft 6⅓ in)

AREAS:

Wings, gross	21.02 m² (226.3 sq ft)
Foreplanes (total)	2.19 m² (23.60 sq ft)
Ailerons (total)	1.29 m² (13.88 sq ft)
Trailing-edge flaps (total)	1.73 m² (18.66 sq ft)
Leading-edge flaps: inboard (total)	0.60 m² (6.42 sq ft)
outboard (total)	0.77 m² (8.28 sq ft)
Fin, incl dorsal fin	2.68 m² (28.87 sq ft)
Rudder	0.81 m² (8.68 sq ft)

WEIGHTS:

Weight empty, equipped	5,175 kg (11,410 lb)
Fuel weight	1,876 kg (4,136 lb)
Normal flying weight	6,622 kg (14,600 lb)
Max T-O weight	6,849 kg (15,099 lb)

PERFORMANCE (estimated, at max T-O weight):

Never-exceed and max level speed:	
S/L to 8,535 m (28,000 ft)	1,485 knots (2,752 km/h; 1,710 mph)
8,535-12,200 m (28,000-40,000 ft)	Mach 1.3
Max rate of climb at S/L	13,106 m (43,000 ft)/min
Max operating altitude	12,200 m (40,000 ft)
T-O run	457 m (1,500 ft)
T-O to 15 m (50 ft)	823 m (2,700 ft)
Landing from 15 m (50 ft)	1,128 m (3,700 ft)
Landing run	823 m (2,700 ft)
Design g limits	+9/-4

Rockwell/MBB X-31A EFM enhanced fighter manoeuvrability aircraft, showing exhaust deflection paddles and fully deflected control surfaces

SEPECAT
SOCIÉTÉ EUROPÉENNE DE PRODUCTION DE L'AVION E.C.A.T.

AIRFRAME COMPANIES:

British Aerospace PLC, Richmond Road, Kingston upon Thames, Surrey KT2 5QS, England
Telephone: 44 (1) 546 7741
Dassault Aviation,
33 Rue du Prof Pauchet, 92420 Vaucresson, France
Telephone: 33 (1) 47 95 85 85
Telex: 203944 AMADAS F
PRESIDENT: I. R. Yates (BAe)
VICE-PRESIDENT: P. E. Jaillard (Dassault)
PUBLIC RELATIONS: G. B. Hill (BAe)

This Anglo-French company was formed in May 1966 by Breguet Aviation and British Aircraft Corporation, to design and produce the Jaguar supersonic strike fighter/trainer.

SEPECAT JAGUAR INTERNATIONAL

Anglo-French production of the Jaguar and Jaguar International amounted to 497 aircraft for the Royal Air Force (203), Armée de l'Air (200), Ecuador (12), India (40), Nigeria (18) and Oman (24), as detailed in the 1987-88 and previous editions of *Jane's*. RAF Jaguars have since been re-engined with uprated Adour Mk 104 turbofans and refitted with a Ferranti FIN 1064 INS, as recorded in the 1989-90 edition. In January 1990 GEC Sensors announced a UK MoD order to supply its ATLANTIC (airborne targeting low altitude navigation thermal imaging and cueing) podded FLIR system for fitment underwing on the RAF Jaguar T. Mk 2A. Between 1985 and October 1989, major servicing and modification was carried out by BAe on 21 Omani Jaguar Internationals, including fitment of the Ferranti FIN 1064 INS.

The Jaguar International export version, first flown on 19 August 1976, has Adour Mk 804 or Mk 811 engines; customer options include overwing pylons compatible with Matra R.550 Magic or similar dogfight missiles; a multi-purpose radar such as the Thomson-CSF Agave; up to four anti-shipping weapons such as Sea Eagle, Harpoon, Exocet and Kormoran on the underwing and underfuselage hardpoints; and night sensors such as low light level TV.

Deliveries to India of 40 British built Jaguar Internationals with Adour Mk 804 engines were followed by a further 45 (with Mk 811 engines) assembled in India from European components, and Indian production is continuing with full manufacture of 31 additional aircraft under licence by Hindustan Aeronautics Ltd. Further details of this programme can be found under the HAL heading in the Indian section.

TYPE: Single-seat tactical support aircraft and two-seat operational or advanced trainer.

AIRFRAME: As described in 1985-86 and earlier *Jane's*.

POWER PLANT: Two Rolls-Royce Turbomeca Adour Mk 811 turbofans, each rated at 24.6 kN (5,520 lb st) dry and 37.4 kN (8,400 lb st) with afterburning, in current production aircraft for India. Fixed geometry air intake on each side of fuselage aft of cockpit. Fuel in six tanks, one in each wing and four in fuselage. Total internal fuel capacity 4,200 litres (1,110 US gallons; 924 Imp gallons). Armour protection for critical fuel system components. Provision for carrying three auxiliary drop tanks, each of 1,200 litres (317 US gallons; 264 Imp gallons) capacity, on fuselage and inboard wing pylons. Provision for in-flight refuelling, with retractable probe forward of cockpit on starboard side.

ACCOMMODATION (trainer): Crew of two in tandem on Martin-Baker 9B Mk II zero/zero ejection seats. Individual rearward hinged canopies. Rear seat 38 cm (15 in) higher than front seat. Windscreen bulletproof against 7.5 mm rifle fire.

ACCOMMODATION (single-seater): Enclosed cockpit for pilot, with rearward hinged canopy and Martin-Baker IN9B (India) ejection seat as in two-seaters. Bulletproof windscreen, as in two-seat version.

SYSTEMS: As detailed in 1985-86 *Jane's*.

AVIONICS AND OPERATIONAL EQUIPMENT: Indian assembled Jaguars have a raster cursive head-up display, Sagem inertial navigation and weapon aiming system, and a Ferranti COMED 2045 combined map and electronic display.

ARMAMENT: Two 30 mm Aden or DEFA 553 cannon in lower fuselage aft of cockpit in single-seater; single Aden gun on port side in two-seater. One stores attachment on fuselage centreline and two under each wing. Centreline and inboard wing points can each carry up to 1,134 kg (2,500 lb) of weapons, outboard underwing points up to 567 kg (1,250 lb) each. Maximum external stores load, including overwing loads, 4,763 kg (10,500 lb). Typical alternative loads include one Martel AS.37 anti-radar missile and two 1,200 litre (317 US gallon; 264 Imp gallon) drop tanks; eight 1,000 lb bombs; various combinations of free-fall, laser guided and retarded bombs, Hunting BL755 or Belouga cluster bombs, Matra R.550 Magic missiles and air-to-surface rockets, including the 68 mm SNEB rocket; a reconnaissance camera pack; or two drop tanks.

DIMENSIONS, EXTERNAL:

Wing span	8.69 m (28 ft 6 in)
Length overall, incl probe:	
single-seat	16.83 m (55 ft 2½ in)
two-seat	17.53 m (57 ft 6¼ in)
Height overall	4.89 m (16 ft 0½ in)
Wheel track	2.41 m (7 ft 11 in)
Wheelbase	5.69 m (18 ft 8 in)

AREA:

Wings, gross	24.18 m² (260.27 sq ft)

WEIGHTS AND LOADINGS:

Typical weight empty	7,000 kg (15,432 lb)
Normal T-O weight (single-seater, with full internal fuel and ammunition for built-in cannon)	
	10,954 kg (24,149 lb)
Max T-O weight with external stores	
	15,700 kg (34,612 lb)
Max wing loading	649.3 kg/m² (133 lb/sq ft)
Max power loading (Adour Mk 811)	
	209.9 kg/kN (2.06 lb/lb st)

PERFORMANCE:

Max level speed at S/L	
	Mach 1.1 (729 knots; 1,350 km/h; 840 mph)
Max level speed at 11,000 m (36,000 ft)	
	Mach 1.6 (917 knots; 1,699 km/h; 1,056 mph)
Landing speed	115 knots (213 km/h; 132 mph)

Last two of 21 Jaguar Internationals recently upgraded by BAe for the Sultan of Oman's Air Force

T-O run: clean	565 m (1,855 ft)	Typical attack radius, internal fuel only:	
with four 1,000 lb bombs	880 m (2,890 ft)	hi-lo-hi	460 nm (852 km; 530 miles)
with eight 1,000 lb bombs	1,250 m (4,100 ft)	lo-lo-lo	290 nm (537 km; 334 miles)
T-O to 15 m (50 ft) with typical tactical load		Typical attack radius with external fuel:	
	940 m (3,085 ft)	hi-lo-hi	760 nm (1,408 km; 875 miles)
Landing from 15 m (50 ft) with typical tactical load		lo-lo-lo	495 nm (917 km; 570 miles)
	785 m (2,575 ft)	Ferry range with external fuel	
Landing run:			1,902 nm (3,524 km; 2,190 miles)
normal weight, with brake-chute	470 m (1,540 ft)	g limits	+8.6/+12 ultimate
normal weight, without brake-chute			
	680 m (2,230 ft)		
overload weight, with brake-chute	670 m (2,200 ft)		

SOKO/CNIAR

PARTICIPANTS:

Sour Vazduhoplovna Industrija SOKO, 88000 Mostar, Yugoslavia
Telephone: 38 (88) 22121 and 21970
Telex: 46 180 and 46 181 YU SOKOMO
Centrul National al Industriei Aeronautice Române, 39 Bulevardul Aerogarii, Sector 1, Bucharest, Romania
Telephone: 40 (0) 50 27 14
Telex: 11648 AEROM

SOKO J-22 ORAO (EAGLE)/CNIAR IAR-93

This twin-jet close support and ground attack aircraft was developed to meet a joint requirement of the air forces of Romania and Yugoslavia. In the latter country it is known as the J-22 Orao (Eagle); in Romania it is known as the IAR-93. The joint programme is known as 'Yurom' (from *Yugoslavia-Rom*ania).

The Orao/IAR-93 was designed jointly by Yugoslav and Romanian engineers. Design began in 1970, and single-seat prototypes were started simultaneously in the two countries in 1972. A first flight in each country was made on 31 October 1974. SOKO and CNIAR each then completed a two-seat prototype, these making simultaneous first flights on 29 January 1977. In that year construction began in each country of a pre-production batch of 15 aircraft, the first of these making their initial flights in 1978. The IAR-93, which is built by IAv Craiova, entered the series production phase in 1979, and the Orao about a year later.

The following production versions have been announced:

IAR-93A. Romanian version with non-afterburning Viper Mk 632 turbojet engines, first flown in 1981. Twenty ordered for Romanian Air Force. Total includes single- and two-seat versions, the latter having almost the same operational capabilities despite a 0.41 m (1 ft 4¼ in) longer front fuselage.

IAR-93B. Romanian version with Viper Mk 633 engines and licence built afterburners. Total of 165 ordered by Romanian Air Force, including two-seaters. First flight of production version made in 1985.

Orao 1. Yugoslav non-afterburning equivalent of IAR-93A, produced both as single-seat tactical reconnaissance aircraft and two-seat operational conversion trainer. All two-seat Orao 1s have been converted to Orao 2D standard (which see).

Orao 2. Yugoslav afterburning version, in production as single-seat attack aircraft. First flight (aircraft serial number 25101) 20 October 1983. Increased external stores load. Fuel system and capacities differ slightly from other versions.

Orao 2D. Yugoslav afterburning version, in production as two-seat operational conversion trainer. Differs from two-seat Orao 1 in being powered by Viper Mk 633-41 engines, and equipped with wings (with integral fuel tanks) of Orao 2. Rear fuselage also identical to that of Orao 2, incorporating ventral fins and afterburner cooling air inlets. First flight 18 July 1986.

TYPE: Single-seat close support, ground attack and tactical reconnaissance aircraft, with secondary capability as low level interceptor. Combat capable two-seat versions used also for advanced flying and weapon training.

WINGS: Cantilever shoulder-wing monoplane, of NACA

Soko built Orao 2 single-seat ground attack aircraft of the Yugoslav Air Force *(Ivo Sturzenegger)*

Single-seat Orao 2 close support/ground attack aircraft, with additional scrap view of two-seat Orao 2D *(Pilot Press)*

65A-008 (modified) section and low aspect ratio. Anhedral 3° 30′ from roots. Incidence 0°. Sweepback 35° at quarter-chord and approx 43° on outer leading-edges. Inboard leading-edges extended forward (sweepback approx 70°) on production single-and two-seaters, but not on prototypes or pre-production aircraft. Two-spar structure of aluminium alloy, with ribs, stringers and partially machined skin. Wing spar box forms integral fuel tanks on IAR-93B/Orao 2; IAR-93A/Orao 1 have rubber fuel cells, forward of which are sandwich panels. Hydraulically actuated (EEMCO system) two-segment aluminium alloy leading-edge slats. Small boundary layer fence on upper surface of each outer panel. Hydraulically

operated wide chord plain ailerons and semi-Fowler trailing-edge flaps, all of aluminium alloy; ailerons have Dowty servo-actuators. No tabs.

FUSELAGE: Conventional all-metal, partially fail-safe semi-monocoque structure of aluminium alloy. Hydraulically actuated door type perforated airbrake under fuselage on each side, forward of mainwheel bays. Narrow strake on each side of nose (not on prototypes or current production Orao 2/2D). Dorsal spine fairing houses circuits, systems and flight controls. 'Pen nib' fairing above exhaust nozzles. Rear portion of fuselage is detachable to facilitate access for engine maintenance and removal.

TAIL UNIT: Cantilever all-metal structure, with sweepback on all surfaces. Low-set all-moving tailplane. Small dorsal fin. Auxiliary ventral fin on each side beneath rear fuselage (single-seat production versions and Orao 2D). Conventional stressed skin construction, of aluminium alloy on development aircraft and early production versions; current aircraft have honeycomb rudder and tailplane. Development and early production aircraft have anti-flutter weights on tailplane tips; these are deleted on definitive production models. Tailplane and rudder controlled by Dowty Aerospace servo-actuators. Trim tab in rudder on prototypes, deleted on pre-production and production models.

LANDING GEAR: Hydraulically retractable tricycle type of Messier-Hispano-Bugatti design, with single-wheel hydraulically steerable nose unit and twin-wheel main units. All units retract forward into fuselage. Two-stage oleo-pneumatic shock absorber in each unit. Mainwheels and tubeless tyres on all versions are size 615 × 225 × 254 mm; pressure is 4.5 bars (65.3 lb/sq in) on Orao 2/2D, 5.2 bars (75.4 lb/sq in) on other versions. Nosewheel and tubeless tyre are size 551 × 250 × 152 mm, pressure 3.1 bars (45.0 lb/sq in), on IAR-93A/Orao 1; and size 451 × 190 × 127 mm, pressure 3.8 bars (55.1 lb/sq in), on all afterburning versions except Orao 2, on which nosewheel tyre pressure is 5.0 bars (72.5 lb/sq in), and Orao 2D, which has a 551 × 250 × 152 mm tyre with pressure of 5.0 bars (72.5 lb/sq in). Hydraulic disc brakes on each mainwheel unit, and electrically operated anti-skid system. Bullet fairing at base of rudder contains a hydraulically deployed 4.2 m (13 ft 9½ in) diameter braking parachute.

POWER PLANT (non-afterburning versions): Two 17.79 kN (4,000 lb st) Turbomecanica/ORAO (licence built Rolls-Royce) Viper Mk 632-41R turbojets, mounted side by side in rear fuselage; air intake on each side of fuselage, below cockpit canopy. Fuel normally in seven fuselage tanks and two collector tanks, with combined capacity of 2,480 litres (655 US gallons; 545.5 Imp gallons), and two 235 litre (62 US gallon; 51.75 Imp gallon) wing tanks, giving total internal fuel capacity of 2,950 litres (779 US gallons; 649 Imp gallons). Provision for carrying three 500 litre (132 US gallon; 110 Imp gallon) auxiliary fuel tanks, one on underfuselage stores attachment and one inboard under each wing. Pressure refuelling point in fuselage; gravity refuelling points in fuselage and each external tank.

POWER PLANT (afterburning versions): Two Turbomecanica/ ORAO (licence built Rolls-Royce) Viper Mk 633-41 turbojets, each rated at 17.79 kN (4,000 lb st) dry and 22.24 kN (5,000 lb st) with afterburning. Orao 2 has six fuselage and two collector tanks, with two fuselage and both wing tanks enlarged, giving total internal capacity of 3,100 litres (819 US gallons; 682 Imp gallons). Three 500 litre (132 US gallon; 110 Imp gallon) drop tanks can be carried.

ACCOMMODATION: Single-seat or tandem two-seat cockpit(s), with Martin-Baker zero/zero seat for each occupant (RU10J in IAR-93, YU10J in Orao), capable of ejection through canopy. Canopy of single-seat IAR-93A and Orao 1/2 is hinged at rear and actuated electrically to open upward; single-seat IAR-93B, and all two-seaters, have manually operated canopies opening sideways to starboard. All accommodation pressurised, heated and air-conditioned. Dual controls in two-seat versions.

SYSTEMS: Bootstrap type environmental control system for cockpit pressurisation (max differential 0.214 bars; 3.1 lb/sq in), air-conditioning, and windscreen de-icing/ demisting. Two independent hydraulic systems, each of 207 bars (3,000 lb/sq in) pressure, for actuation of leading-edge slats, trailing-edge flaps, ailerons, tailplane, rudder, airbrakes, landing gear extension/retraction, mainwheel brakes, nosewheel steering, brake-chute, and afterburner nozzles. No pneumatic system. Main electrical system is 28V DC, supplied by two Lucas BC-0107 9kW engine driven starter/generators through two voltage regulators and a switching system, and a 36Ah battery; two 700VA static inverters (four 300VA in Orao 2/2D) for AC power at 400Hz. High pressure (150 bars; 2,175 lb/sq in) gaseous oxygen system for crew.

AVIONICS AND EQUIPMENT: Standard avionics include VHF/ UHF air-to-air and air-to-ground com radio (20W transmission power); gyro unit (Honeywell SGP500 twin-gyro platform in Orao), radio altimeter, ADF, radio compass and marker beacon receiver; IFF (Romanian aircraft only); and GEC Avionics three-axis stability augmentation system, incorporating a basic bank/ attitude hold autopilot and emergency wings-level facility. Orao 1 and 2 also have Collins VIR-30 VOR/ILS and Collins DME-40; Orao 2 fitted with Iskra SO-1 radar warning receiver. Landing light under nose, forward of nosewheel bay; taxying light on nosewheel shock strut.

Single-seat interceptor version of the Romanian Air Force's IAR-93B, with underwing air-to-air missiles

ARMAMENT (IAR-93 and Orao 1): Two 23 mm GSh-23L twin-barrel cannon in lower front fuselage, below engine air intakes, with 200 rds/gun. Gun camera and Ferranti D282 gyro gunsight. Five external stores stations, of which the inboard underwing pair and the fuselage centreline station are each stressed for loads up to 500 kg (1,102 lb); outboard underwing stations stressed for up to 300 kg (661 lb) each, giving a max external stores load of 1,500 kg (3,307 lb). Typical weapon loads can include two or three 500 kg bombs; four or five 250 kg bombs; four multiple carriers each with three 100 kg or 50 kg bombs; two such multiple carriers plus two L-57-16MD launchers each with sixteen 57 mm rockets; four L-57-16MD launchers; four launchers each with two 122 mm, one 128 mm or one 240 mm rocket (122 and 240 mm not used on Orao); a GSh-23L cannon pod with four L-57-16MD rocket launchers; four 160 kg KPT-150 or similar munition dispensers; or (Romanian aircraft only) four L-57-32 launchers each with thirty-two 57 mm rockets. Some IAR-93Bs equipped to carry up to eight air-to-air missiles, on twin launch rails, on the four underwing stations. Centreline and inboard underwing points are each plumbed to carry a 540 litre (142.7 US gallon; 119 Imp gallon) drop tank; centreline point also capable of carrying a camera or infra-red reconnaissance pod or (not yet available for Orao) a night illumination pod.

ARMAMENT (Orao 2): Guns, gun camera, drop tanks and centreline camera or infra-red reconnaissance pod as for Orao 1. Thomson-CSF VE-120T head-up display. All four wing stations stressed for 500 kg (1,102 lb), and fuselage station for 800 kg (1,763 lb), giving a max external stores capacity of 2,800 kg (6,173 lb). Typical weapon loads include five 50 kg, 100 kg, 250 kg or 500 kg bombs; four multiple carriers for a total of twelve 50 or 100 kg bombs or eight 250 kg bombs; four PLAB-340 napalm bombs (each 360 kg; 794 lb); five BL755 bomblet dispensers, or eight on four multiple carriers; sixteen BRZ-127 5 in HVAR rockets; four pods of L-57-16MD or L-128-04 (4 × 128 mm) rockets, or eight pods on multiple carriers; five 500 kg AM-500 sea mines; or two launch rails for AGM-65B Maverick or Yugoslav developed Grom air-to-surface missiles. The 100 kg and 250 kg bombs can be parachute retarded. Chaff and IR decoy launch pods (up to three per aircraft) can also be carried.

DIMENSIONS, EXTERNAL:

Wing span	9.62 m (31 ft 6¾ in)
Wing chord: at root	4.20 m (13 ft 9⅜ in)
at tip	1.40 m (4 ft 7⅛ in)
Wing aspect ratio	3.6
Length overall, incl probe:	
single-seater	14.90 m (48 ft 10⅝ in)
two-seater	15.38 m (50 ft 5½ in)
Length of fuselage:	
single-seater	13.96 m (45 ft 9⅝ in)
two-seater	14.44 m (47 ft 4½ in)
Fuselage: Max width	1.68 m (5 ft 6⅛ in)
Height overall	4.50 m (14 ft 9¼ in)
Tailplane span	4.72 m (15 ft 5⅞ in)
Wheel track (c/l of shock struts)	2.50 m (8 ft 2½ in)
Wheelbase: single-seater	5.42 m (17 ft 9⅜ in)
two-seater	5.88 m (19 ft 3½ in)

AREAS:

Wings, gross	26.00 m² (279.86 sq ft)
Ailerons (total)	1.92 m² (20.67 sq ft)
Trailing-edge flaps (total)	3.20 m² (34.44 sq ft)
Leading-edge slats (total)	1.56 m² (16.79 sq ft)
Fin	3.55 m² (38.21 sq ft)

Rudder, incl tab	0.88 m² (9.47 sq ft)
Tailplane	8.20 m² (88.26 sq ft)

WEIGHTS AND LOADINGS (A: IAR-93A, B: IAR-93B, C: Orao 2, D: Orao 2D):

Weight empty, equipped: A	6,150 kg (13,558 lb)
B, C	5,700 kg (12,566 lb)
D	5,975 kg (13,172 lb)
Max internal fuel: A	2,457 kg (5,416 lb)
B, C, D	2,450 kg (5,401 lb)
Max external stores load: A	1,500 kg (3,307 lb)
B, C, D	2,800 kg (6,173 lb)
Normal T-O weight clean: A	8,826 kg (19,458 lb)
B, C	8,400 kg (18,519 lb)
D	8,585 kg (18,926 lb)
Max T-O weight: A	10,326 kg (22,765 lb)
B, C	11,200 kg (24,692 lb)
D	11,520 kg (25,397 lb)
Max landing weight: A	8,826 kg (19,458 lb)
B	9,360 kg (20,635 lb)
C, D	11,000 kg (24,251 lb)
Max wing loading: A	397 kg/m² (81.3 lb/sq ft)
B, C	430.7 kg/m² (88.3 lb/sq ft)
D	443.1 kg/m² (90.75 lb/sq ft)
Max power loading: A	289.8 kg/kN (2.84 lb/lb st)
B, C	251.8 kg/kN (2.47 lb/lb st)
D	259.2 kg/kN (2.54 lb/lb st)

PERFORMANCE (A at max T-O weight; B and C at 8,450 kg; 18,629 lb T-O weight):

Max level speed at S/L:	
A	577 knots (1,070 km/h; 665 mph)
B, C	626 knots (1,160 km/h; 721 mph)
Max cruising speed:	
A at 7,000 m (22,965 ft)	394 knots (730 km/h; 453 mph)
B at 5,000 m (15,240 ft)	587 knots (1,089 km/h; 676 mph)
Stalling speed at S/L: A	130 knots (241 km/h; 150 mph)
B, C	148 knots (274 km/h; 171 mph)
Max rate of climb at S/L: A	2,040 m (6,693 ft)/min
B, C	4,500 m (14,764 ft)/min
Service ceiling: A	10,500 m (34,450 ft)
B, C	13,200 m (43,300 ft)
Min ground turning radius	7.00 m (22 ft 11½ in)
T-O run: A	1,500 m (4,921 ft)
B, C	595 m (1,952 ft)
T-O to 15 m (50 ft): A	1,600 m (5,249 ft)
B, C	950 m (3,117 ft)
Landing from 15 m (50 ft): A	1,650 m (5,413 ft)
B, C	1,520 m (4,987 ft)
Landing run: A	720 m (2,362 ft)
B, C	1,050 m (3,445 ft)
Landing run with brake chute: A, B, C	670 m (2,200 ft)

Mission radius, A, B, C:

lo-lo-lo with four rocket launchers, 5 min over target
140 km (260 km; 161 miles)

hi-hi-hi patrol with three 500 litre auxiliary fuel tanks, 45 min over target
205 nm (380 km; 236 miles)

lo-lo-hi with two rocket launchers, six 100 kg bombs and one 500 litre auxiliary fuel tank, 10 min over target
243 nm (450 km; 280 miles)

hi-hi-hi with four 250 kg bombs and one 500 litre auxiliary fuel tank, 5 min over target
286 nm (530 km; 329 miles)

Ferry range with three 500 litre auxiliary fuel tanks
1,025 nm (1,900 km; 1,180 miles)

g limits: A, B, C	+8/−4.2

SUKHOI/GULFSTREAM

PARTICIPANTS:

P.O. Sukhoi OKB, USSR

Gulfstream Aerospace Corporation, PO Box 2206, Savannah, Georgia 31402-2206, USA
Telephone: 1 (912) 964 3000
Telex: 546470

SUKHOI/GULFSTREAM SUPERSONIC BUSINESS JET

Sukhoi and Gulfstream began separate independent studies for a supersonic business jet in 1987 and 1988 respectively. After a meeting on 13 June 1989 they signed a memorandum of understanding to explore the feasibility of a joint venture for an aircraft able to carry at least 8-10

passengers and having a Mach 2 (or better) top speed and range of at least 4,342 nm (8,047 km; 5,000 miles). Meetings in Moscow and Savannah were followed on 15 November 1989 by the release to Sukhoi of Gulfstream's recommended specifications for the aircraft, a twin-engined design known by Sukhoi as the **S-21** and by Gulfstream as the **Gulfstream VI-SU**. Accommodation would be for a maximum of 12 passengers, at 98 cm (38.5 in) seat pitch, with 1.87 m (6 ft 1½ in) headroom and a 0.50 m (1 ft 7¾ in) central aisle. The propulsion system is expected to be a similar collaborative programme between Rolls-Royce of the UK and the Lyulka engine bureau in the USSR, although Lyulka AL-31F augmented turbofans are likely to power the prototype, which is expected to fly in 1993. A larger, 50/65-seat S-51 design, with an all-new engine, has also been projected.

The following provisional details refer to the S-21/Gulfstream VI-SU:

DIMENSIONS, EXTERNAL:
Fuselage: Max diameter 2.12 m (6 ft 11½ in)

WEIGHTS (estimated):
Weight empty 15,000 kg (33,070 lb)
Fuel weight 18,000 kg (39,685 lb)
T-O weight 35,000 kg (77,160 lb)

PERFORMANCE (estimated):
Cruise ceiling 14,000-17,000 m (45,925-55,775 ft)
T-O run 1,300 m (4,265 ft)
Landing run 850 m (2,790 ft)
Range (at Mach 0.9 or Mach 2.0)
3,510 nm (6,500 km; 4,040 miles)

Provisional drawing of Sukhoi S-21/Gulfstream VI-SU 12-passenger business jet *(Jane's/Mike Keep)*

TBM

TBM SA
12 rue Pasteur, 92150 Surèsnes, France
Telephone: 33 (1) 47 72 09 34
Telex: 614549
Fax: 33 (1) 45 06 71 76
PRESIDENT: Pierre Gautier
VICE-PRESIDENT, SALES AND MARKETING:
Alain Aubry
US SALES AND MARKETING:
TBM North America Inc, 8901 Wetmore Road, San Antonio, Texas 78216, USA
Telephone: 1 (512) 824 8383
Fax: 1 (512) 824 4221
PRESIDENT: Alec Couvelaire
VICE-PRESIDENT, SALES AND MARKETING:
Brant D. Dahlfors

TBM 700

The TBM 700, launched on 12 June 1987, is a pressurised single-engined business aircraft being developed by TBM SA, an association created jointly by Socata (France) and Mooney (USA), with one-third of its development cost being funded by a loan from the French government. Socata has full responsibility for technical development of the aircraft, including prototype manufacture and certification. Valmet (Finland) joined the programme in June 1988, but withdrew a year later.

Three prototypes have been built, the first of which (F-WTBM) made its initial flight on 14 July 1988. The second aircraft (F-WKPG) followed on 3 August 1989 and the third (F-WKDL) on 11 October. French DGAC type approval was granted on 31 January 1990, and certification under FAR and JAR Pt 23 (for one- or two-pilot operation) was expected in May or June 1990. Orders for 50 TBM 700s had been received by mid-February 1990. Socata builds the forward fuselage and tail unit, Mooney the rear fuselage and wings.

TYPE: Four/seven-passenger pressurised business aircraft.

WINGS: Cantilever low-wing monoplane, with 6° 30′ dihedral from roots. Wing section Aerospatiale RA 16-43 at root. Cambered leading-edges of laser drilled titanium. Two-spar wing torsion box, with light alloy skin, forms integral fuel tanks. Scaled-down 'ATR' electrically actuated single-slotted flaps, of Nomex honeycomb, occupy 71 per cent of each trailing-edge. Spoiler (forward of each flap at outer end) and aileron on each wing for roll control. Electrically actuated trim tab in port aileron. Rubber boot pneumatic de-icing of leading-edges.

FUSELAGE: Conventional stressed skin structure, mainly of light alloy construction except for Nomex honeycomb cowling.

TAIL UNIT: Sweptback fin (with dorsal fin) and balanced rudder; non-swept variable incidence tailplane (of Nomex honeycomb) with balanced elevators. Trim tab in rudder and each elevator. Pneumatic boot de-icing of leading-edges.

LANDING GEAR: Hydraulically retractable tricycle type, with emergency manual operation. Inward retracting main units of trailing-link type; rearward retracting nosewheel.

POWER PLANT: One 522 kW (700 shp) Pratt & Whitney Canada PT6A-64 turboprop, driving a McCauley four-blade constant-speed fully-feathering reversible-pitch metal propeller with spinner. Propeller de-icing optional. Fuel in integral tank in each wing, combined usable capacity 1,080 litres (285 US gallons; 237.5 Imp gallons). Gravity filling point in top of each tank.

ACCOMMODATION: Adjustable seats for one or two pilots at front. Dual controls standard. Four seats in club layout

Second prototype TBM 700 four/seven-passenger turboprop pressurised business aircraft

aft of these, with centre aisle, or six seats in high-density layout. Single door on port side aft of wing, with integral airstairs; overwing emergency exit on starboard side. Cabin pressurised by engine bleed air to 0.43 bars (6.2 lb/sq in). Individual emergency oxygen mask for each passenger. Pressurised baggage compartment at rear of cabin, with internal access only; additional compartment in nose, between engine and firewall, with external access via door on port side.

SYSTEMS: Hydraulic system for landing gear actuation. Two-generator electrical system, with three main and two emergency buses.

AVIONICS AND EQUIPMENT: Bendix/King Silver Crown digital IFR package, comprising KY 196 VHF com transceiver; KX 165 VHF2/NAV2 with KI 206 indicator; KMA 24H audio panel with interphone; KNS 81 R/Nav with KCS 55A HSI and KI 525A indicator; KR 21 marker beacon receiver; KR 87 ADF with KA 44B combined loop/sense antenna and KI 229 RMI; KN 63 DME with KDI 572 indicator; UI 5035 P encoding altimeter; KTS 79 transponder; and KFC 275 flight director/autopilot with KAS 297B altitude preselect/alerter. Wide range of alternative standard equipment to customer's requirements. Options include EFIS, GPS navigation system and weather radar.

DIMENSIONS, EXTERNAL:
Wing span 12.16 m (39 ft 10¾ in)
Wing chord (mean aerodynamic) 1.51 m (4 ft 11½ in)
Wing aspect ratio 8.21
Length overall 10.43 m (34 ft 2½ in)
Height overall 3.99 m (13 ft 1 in)
Elevator span 4.88 m (16 ft 0 in)
Propeller diameter 2.31 m (7 ft 7 in)

DIMENSIONS, INTERNAL:
Cabin: Length (between pressure bulkheads)
4.56 m (14 ft 11½ in)

Max width 1.24 m (4 ft 0¾ in)
Max height 1.24 m (4 ft 0¾ in)

AREAS:
Wings, gross 18.00 m² (193.75 sq ft)
Vertical tail surfaces (total) 2.56 m² (27.55 sq ft)
Horizontal tail surfaces (total) 4.76 m² (51.24 sq ft)

WEIGHTS:
Weight empty 1,790 kg (3,946 lb)
Fuel weight (usable) 866 kg (1,910 lb)
Baggage (two compartments, total) 60 kg (132 lb)
* Max T-O weight 2,835 kg (6,250 lb)
* Max ramp weight 2,850 kg (6,283 lb)
* incl 50 kg (110 lb) of optional equipment

PERFORMANCE (A at AUW of 2,500 kg; 5,511 lb, B at max T-O weight):
Max cruising speed at 7,925 m (26,000 ft):
A 300 knots (555 km/h; 345 mph)
Stalling speed, flaps and landing gear down
61 knots (113 km/h; 71 mph)
Max rate of climb at S/L: A 702 m (2,303 ft)/min
Service ceiling 9,150 m (30,000 ft)
Range (B):
at 300 knots (555 km/h; 345 mph), 45 min reserves:
6 persons and 850 litres (224.5 US gallons; 187 Imp gallons) fuel 850 nm (1,575 km; 978 miles)
3 persons and max fuel
1,335 nm (2,475 km; 1,538 miles)
at 248 knots (460 km/h; 286 mph) at 9,150 m (30,000 ft), 45 min reserves:
6 persons and 850 litres fuel
1,025 nm (1,900 km; 1,180 miles)
3 persons and max fuel
1,672 nm (3,100 km; 1,926 miles)
g limits +3.8/-1.5

IRAN

DORNA
H. F. DORNA
116 Karimkhan, Zand Avenue, Tehran 15847

In early 1990 discussions were under way between Operation Ability Ltd of the UK (which see) and H. F. Dorna concerning the possible sale of the former's G802/1 Spur two-seat light aircraft to H. F. Dorna. The Spur, a modified Aérodis G802 Orion, was being developed to meet the special disability needs of Mr Philip Scott, but has been replaced by a Piaggio P.149. It is understood that H. F. Dorna wished to develop the Spur prototype as a general aviation light jet aircraft, not associated with disability. A description and illustrations of the Spur in its present form appeared in the UK section of the 1989-90 *Jane's*.

IACI
IRAN AIRCRAFT INDUSTRIES
Karaj Road, PO Box 14155-1449, Tehran
Telephone: 98 (21) 9131
Telex: 213947 IACI IR
MANAGING DIRECTOR: A. Abdollahi Vighan
FOREIGN PROCUREMENT MANAGER: J. Nikanjam

FAJR (DAWN)
The first flight of this side by side two-seat light aircraft was announced in Tehran on 22 February 1988, together with the statement that it "could be used for military purposes" and was to be put into full scale production shortly afterwards. It is assumed that it will be used for primary training and, possibly, in a liaison or reconnaissance role.

Although claimed to be of Iranian design and manufacture, the Fajr is, to judge from its appearance, a Neico Lancair homebuilt of US origin (see description in Sport Aircraft section). It may embody some local modifications, but no details of the aircraft had been released at the time of going to press.

Prototype of the Iranian Fajr two-seat light aircraft *(IRNA)*

IRAQ

IAF
IRAQI AIR FORCE
Ministry of Defence, Bab Al-Muadam, Baghdad

BAGHDAD and ADNAN
At an exhibition in Baghdad in the Spring of 1989, Iraq displayed an AEW version of one of its Soviet Il-76MD ('Candid-B') standard transports, said to have been modified in-country by the Iraqi Air Force. Named **Baghdad 1**, it had a Thomson-CSF Tigre surveillance radar installed in an inverted position inside a large GFRP blister radome that replaced the standard rear fuselage clamshell doors and upward hinged panel. The Tigre radar is manufactured under licence in Iraq in its basic trailer-mounted form for ground use. Adaptation to airborne use in the Baghdad 1 involved modification of the signal processing to reduce ground clutter, and installation of radio and radar ESM. The navigation system was also modified, and a strake was added at each side of the new radome. Manned by four operators, the radar is claimed to have much more than 180° scan, and to have been used operationally during the final stages of the Gulf War. The system generator is of Iraqi design, and transmission by voice or real-time data link.

At the time of the exhibition, the Iraqi Air Force officer in charge of the programme indicated that plans were under way to upgrade the Baghdad 1 system by installing additional equipment to enable it to control friendly fighter aircraft as well as providing AEW cover. As revealed by a photograph taken later that year, the improved version carries an over-fuselage rotodome installation similar in appearance to that of the 'Mainstay' AEW&C version of the Il-76 described in the Soviet section. On this aircraft, named **Adnan 1** after a former Iraqi defence minister, a long strake is fitted on each side of the rear fuselage to offset instability created by the rotodome installation. The rotodome is estimated to be about 9 m (29.5 ft) in diameter and mounted about 4 m (13.1 ft) above the fuselage, housing a radar with a detection range reported to be "a few hundred kilometres".

Adnan 1 airborne early warning and control aircraft, modified from an Iraqi Air Force Il-76

Close-up of radome under rear fuselage of Baghdad 1 AEW conversion of an Il-76MD of the Iraqi Air Force, showing added strake
(Jane's Defence Weekly/Tony Banks)

ISRAEL

IAI
ISRAEL AIRCRAFT INDUSTRIES LTD
Ben-Gurion International Airport, Israel 70100
Telephone: 972 (3) 971 3111
Telex: ISRAVIA 381014, 381033 and 381002
Fax: 972 (3) 971 3131 and 971 2290
PRESIDENT AND CHIEF EXECUTIVE OFFICER: M. Keret
CORPORATE EXECUTIVE VICE-PRESIDENTS:
  A. Ostrinsky
  Dr M. Dvir
VICE-PRESIDENT, MARKETING: D. Onn
DIRECTOR OF CORPORATE COMMUNICATIONS: D. Suslik
FOREIGN PRESS AND CORPORATE ADVERTISING MANAGER:
  F. P. Hermann (Dept 9003)

This company was established in 1953 as Bedek Aviation. The change of name to Israel Aircraft Industries was made on 1 April 1967, and the number of Divisions was reduced in February 1988 from five to four: Aircraft, Electronics, Technologies, and Bedek Aviation. Corporate headquarters provides overall guidance and support of these Divisions, and supports the service and marketing activities of several overseas subsidiaries. IAI covered space totalled 680,000 m² (7.32 million sq ft) at the end of July 1988, when the total workforce numbered 16,500. The company is licensed by the Israel Civil Aviation Administration, US Federal Aviation Administration, British Civil Aviation Authority and the Israeli Air Force, among others, as an approved repair station and maintenance organisation.

In addition to aircraft of its own design (see Aircraft Division subsection), IAI markets a wide range of in-house developed airframe systems and avionics; and service, upgrading and retrofit packages, encompassing civil and military fixed-wing and rotating-wing aircraft. Several of these are described under the Bedek Aviation Division heading, and utilise many electronic and electro-optical equipments (hardware and software) of IAI design and manufacture. Additional corporate activities involve space technology, smart missiles and other ordnance, seaborne and ground equipment, and a wide range of component production and processing capability.

Aircraft Division
  Follows this entry
Bedek Aviation Division
  Follows Aircraft Division entry
Electronics Division
PO Box 105, Yahud Industrial Zone, Israel 56000
Telephone: 972 (3) 717450
Telex: ISRAVIA 341450
Fax: 972 (3) 536 5205
GENERAL MANAGER: M. Ortasse

The Electronics Division is now IAI's largest Division, with a 1988 workforce of 6,700 housed in 150,000 m² (1,614,585 sq ft) of covered accommodation. Operating plants of the Division are Elta Electronic Industries (a wholly owned subsidiary of IAI), MBT Systems and Space Technology, Tamam Precision Instruments Industries, and MLM System Engineering and Integration. Division capability covers electronic and electro-optical systems and

components, space technologies (including those applicable to an SDI environment), and manufacture/marketing of a wide range of military and civil hardware and software products and services.

Technologies Division
Follows Bedek Aviation Division entry.

AIRCRAFT DIVISION
Ben-Gurion International Airport, Israel 70100
Telephone: 972 (3) 9711415
Telex: ISRAVIA 381014 and 381033
Fax: 972 (3) 971 3131 and 971 2290
GENERAL MANAGER: Dr M. Dvir

Established in February 1988, the Aircraft Division consists of five autonomous plants: Lahav, military aircraft; Matan, civil aircraft; Malat, unmanned aerial vehicles (UAVs); Malkam, aeronautical manufacturing; and Tashan, engineering and testing. The military aircraft plant is currently engaged in operating the third prototype Lavi as an advanced combat technology demonstrator; designing and integrating upgrades of the Kfir; and proposals for developing and manufacturing, with overseas partners, customer-specified advanced combat aircraft such as the proposed supersonic multi-mission Nammer. Civil aircraft activity includes production of the Astra business aircraft, product support for the IAI Arava and Westwind (both now out of production), and development of future non-military airframes. The manufacturing plant produces structures and components for domestic and foreign customers. Engineering services include analysis, design, development, integration and testing of platforms and systems for domestic and international military and civil aerospace communities.

IAI SHAHAL (LION)
The Shahal is an IAI funded conceptual design study for a small, low-cost lightweight fighter with high agility and the capability to carry smart weapons. No other details were known at the time of going to press.

IAI LAVI (YOUNG LION) TECHNOLOGY DEMONSTRATOR
The Lavi multi-role combat aircraft received programme go-ahead in February 1980, and full scale development started in October 1982. First flight of prototype B-1 took place on 31 December 1986, the second (B-2) making its initial flight on 30 March 1987. The programme envisaged production of at least 300 aircraft, including about 60 combat-capable two-seat operational trainers, but was terminated by the Israeli government on 30 August 1987.

By early 1989, in about 80 test flights, the two prototypes had flown at speeds from 110 knots (204 km/h; 127 mph) up to Mach 1.45 at 23° angle of attack. Most systems, including digital flight control, were tested within that envelope.

Although the Lavi programme was discontinued due to severe budgetary constraints, IAI decided to continue the validation of the main tasks of the programme, utilising the B-3 (third prototype) as a Technology Demonstrator (TD). This airframe utilises some components from one of the Lavi prototypes, but is of two-seat configuration, with elevons approximately 15 per cent larger than on the Lavi prototypes. Its prime objective is to serve as a demonstrator of advanced systems and technologies developed and produced by the Israeli industry, and to act as a testbed for future developments. An immediate application involves the improved digital flight control system integrated with the advanced manoeuvre and attack system. The first flight of the TD was made on 25 September 1989.

The TD incorporates an advanced weapon delivery and navigation system, and carries a belly-mounted instrumentation and telemetry pod. The cockpit, with its three multi-function displays (including the tactical situation display) and a wide-angle holographic HUD, is designed to minimise pilot workload at high g and in a dense threat environment, and for full HOTAS (hands on throttle and stick) operation. Some of the avionics upgrading packages now offered by IAI for various aircraft derive from the TD systems and will have been tested and validated on the TD.

In the absence of specific details of the TD, the following shortened description of the B-1/B-2 single-seat prototypes is retained:
AIRFRAME: As described in 1988-89 *Jane's*.
POWER PLANT: One 91.7 kN (20,620 lb st) Pratt & Whitney PW1120 afterburning turbojet. Ventral single-shock intake based on that of General Dynamics F-16. Max fuel capacity 3,330 litres (880 US gallons; 732 Imp gallons) in integral wing tanks, plus 5,095 litres (1,346 US gallons; 1,121 Imp gallons) externally.
ACCOMMODATION: Two zero/zero ejection seats, in tandem, under teardrop cockpit canopy.
SYSTEMS: AiResearch environmental control system for air-conditioning, pressurisation and engine bleed air control. Pneudraulics bootstrap type hydraulic system, pressure 207 bars (3,000 lb/sq in), with Abex pumps. Electrical system powered by Sundstrand 60kVA integrated drive generator, for single-channel AC power at 400Hz. SAFT main and Marathon standby battery. AiResearch EPU and Garrett secondary power system.

First (B-1) prototype of the IAI Lavi multi-role combat aircraft

AVIONICS: Electronic warfare self-protection system, by Elta Electronics, to provide rapid threat identification (IFF) and flexible response (ECM). This computer-based, fully automatic system uses active and passive counter-measures, including internal and externally podded power-managed noise and deception jammers. Elbit Computers Ltd was prime contractor for the integrated display system, which includes a Hughes Aircraft wide angle holographic head-up display, three multi-function displays (two monochrome and one colour), display computers, and communications controller. Pilot can operate most systems through a single El-Op up-front control. Lear Siegler/MBT quadruple-redundant digital fly by wire flight control system, with stability augmentation, MBT control unit and Moog servo-actuators. No mechanical backup. Sundstrand actuation system, with geared rotary actuators, for leading-edge flaps. Cockpit designed to minimise pilot workload in high g and dense threat environment, with full HOTAS (hands on throttle and stick) operation. Elta EL/M-2035 multi-mode pulse-Doppler radar, incorporating automatic target acquisition and track-while-scan in the air-to-air mode, and beam-sharpened ground mapping/terrain avoidance and sea search in the air-to-surface mode. The radar's coherent transmitter and stable multi-channel receiver ensure reliable lookdown performance over a broad band of frequencies, as well as high resolution mapping. Elta programmable signal processor, backed by a network of distributed, embedded computers, provides optimum allocation of computer power and considerable flexibility for algorithm updating and system growth. Advanced versions of Elbit ACE-4 mission computer (128K memory) and SMS-86 stores management systems, both compatible with MIL-STD-1553B databus; SMS-86 capable of managing both conventional and smart weapons and sensors. Elta ARC-740 fully computerised onboard UHF com radio system, Elisra radar warning receiver and Astronautics air data computer. Tamam TINS 1700 advanced inertial navigation system.
ARMAMENT: Internally mounted 30 mm cannon, with helmet sight. Four underwing hardpoints for air-to-surface missiles, bombs, rockets and other stores; inboard pair wet for carriage of auxiliary fuel tanks. Seven underfuselage stores attachments (three tandem pairs plus one on centreline). Infra-red air-to-air missile at each wingtip.

DIMENSIONS, EXTERNAL:
Wing span	8.78 m (28 ft 9⅔ in)
Length overall	14.57 m (47 ft 9⅔ in)
Height overall	4.78 m (15 ft 8¼ in)
Wheel track	2.31 m (7 ft 7 in)
Wheelbase	3.86 m (12 ft 8 in)

AREA:
Wings, gross	33.05 m² (355.75 sq ft)

WEIGHTS AND LOADING:
Max fuel: internal	2,721 kg (6,000 lb)
external	4,164 kg (9,180 lb)
Max ordnance (excl air-to-air missiles)	2,721 kg (6,000 lb)
Max external load	7,257 kg (16,000 lb)
T-O weight: basic	9,990 kg (22,024 lb)
max	19,277 kg (42,500 lb)
Max wing loading	523 kg/m² (107 lb/sq ft)
Combat thrust/weight ratio	1.07

PERFORMANCE (estimated):
Max level speed above 11,000 m (36,000 ft)
  Mach 1.8 or 800 knots (1,482 km/h; 921 mph) CAS
Low-altitude penetration speed:
  two infra-red missiles and eight 750 lb M117 bombs
    538 knots (997 km/h; 619 mph)
  two infra-red missiles and two 2,000 lb Mk 84 bombs
    597 knots (1,106 km/h; 687 mph)

Air turning rate at Mach 0.8 at 4,575 m (15,000 ft):
sustained	13.2°/s
max	24.3°/s
T-O run	approx 305 m (1,000 ft)

Combat radius:
  air-to-ground, lo-lo-lo 600 nm (1,112 km; 691 miles)
  air-to-ground, hi-lo-hi with two Mk 84 or six Mk 82
    bombs 1,150 nm (2,131 km; 1,324 miles)
  air-to-air, combat air patrol
    1,000 nm (1,853 km; 1,151 miles)
g limit +9

IAI KFIR (LION CUB)
US Navy and Marine Corps designation: F-21A
A detailed history of the Kfir has appeared in the 1988-89 and many earlier editions of *Jane's*. A total of 212 was built, in the following versions:

C1. Initial production version: 27 built, most of which later retrofitted to interim C2 standard with small canards; all except two leased to US Navy (1985-88) and US Marine Corps (1987-89) as F-21A aggressor aircraft (which see).

C2. Modified and major production version, first flown in 1974. Changes included sweptback, detachable foreplanes on engine intake trunks, small strake each side of nose, and extended chord outer wings to improve airfield and combat performance. Late-production examples had lengthened nose to accommodate larger EL/M-2001B radar. Total of 185 built (including two-seat TC2s), of which (according to Defence Minister Yitzhak Rabin in 1987) 95 were then "no longer in Israeli Air Force service"; these are assumed to include those C2/C7s supplied to Ecuador and later to Colombia. Most other IAF C2s upgraded to C7 standard. Further details in 1983-84 *Jane's*.

TC2. Tandem two-seat operational trainer version of C2, with drooped and lengthened nose; first flown in February 1981. Further details in 1983-84 *Jane's*.

C7. Upgraded conversion of C2, with 'combat plus' increase in engine thrust and improved avionics, delivered to Israeli Air Force from Summer 1983. Other features include new HOTAS (hands on throttle and stick) cockpit installation and two additional external stores stations. Colombia ordered 13 in 1988, delivery of which was made in 1989.

TC7. Designation of TC2 when upgraded to C7 standard. Two exported to Colombia with C7s mentioned above. Further details in 1989-90 and earlier *Jane's*.

F-21A. Two versions leased to US Navy (12) and Marine Corps (13) as 'aggressor' trainers. Those for USN (1985-88) were of C1 configuration with small canards. USMC aircraft (leased 1987-89) were to similar airframe configuration. Further details in 1989-90 and earlier *Jane's*.

French government approval was given in the Autumn of 1989 for IAI to purchase five Snecma Atar 9K-50 turbojet engines for test installation in Kfirs as part of an upgrade and renewed export marketing programme that would be unhampered by US restrictions involving the aircraft's present J79 engines. First flight by an Atar engined Kfir was planned for the second half of 1990.

The following description applies to the Kfir-C7:
TYPE: Single-seat strike, ground attack and fighter aircraft.
AIRFRAME: See 1987-88 and earlier *Jane's*.
POWER PLANT: One General Electric J79-J1E turbojet (modified GE-17) in C7, with variable area nozzle, rated at 52.89 kN (11,890 lb st) dry and 83.41 kN (18,750 lb st) with afterburning. Adjustable half-cone centrebody in each air intake. Internal fuel in five fuselage and four integral wing tanks. Total internal capacity 3,243 litres (857 US gallons; 713.4 Imp gallons). Refuelling point on top of fuselage, above forward upper tank. Wet points for the carriage of one drop tank beneath each wing (inboard), and one under fuselage; these tanks may be of 500, 600, 825, 1,300 or 1,700 litres (132, 158.5, 218, 343.5

or 449 US gallons; 110, 132, 181.5, 286 or 374 Imp gallons) capacity; max external fuel capacity 4,700 litres (1,242 US gallons; 1,034 Imp gallons). Provision for boom/receptacle or probe/drogue in-flight refuelling system, and for single-point pressure refuelling.

ACCOMMODATION: Pilot only, on Martin-Baker IL10P zero/zero ejection seat, under rearward hinged upward opening canopy. Cockpit pressurised, heated and air-conditioned.

SYSTEMS: See 1987-88 *Jane's*.

AVIONICS AND EQUIPMENT: Compared with C2 (see 1987-88 *Jane's*), C7 differs in having an improved HOTAS (hands on throttle and stick) cockpit installation, facilitated by avionics which include a WDNS-341 weapons delivery and navigation system as standard, an Elbit System 82 computerised stores management and release system, video subsystems, smart weapons delivery capability, and updated electronic warfare systems. The EL-2001 ranging radar is replaced by an Elta EL/M-2001B, but the C7 can also mount Elta's EL/M-2021 advanced pulse-Doppler fire control radar, with lookup/lookdown capability, Doppler beam-sharpened mapping, terrain avoidance/following and sea search modes.

ARMAMENT: Fixed armament of one IAI built 30 mm DEFA 552 cannon in underside of each engine air intake (140 rds/gun). Nine hardpoints (five under fuselage and two under each wing) for external weapons, ECM pods or drop tanks. For interception duties, one Sidewinder, Python 3 or Shafrir 2 infra-red homing air-to-air missile can be carried under each outer wing. Ground attack version can carry a 3,000 lb M118 bomb, two 800 or 1,000 lb bombs, up to four 500 lb bombs, or a Shrike, Maverick or GBU-15 air-to-surface weapon under the fuselage, and two 1,000 lb or six 500 lb bombs (conventional, smart or concrete dibber type) under the wings. Alternative weapons can include Mk 82/83/84 and M117/118 bombs; CBU-24/49 and TAL-1/2 cluster bombs; LAU-3A/10A/32A rocket launchers; napalm, flares, chaff, Elta EL-L8202 ECM and other podded systems.

DIMENSIONS, EXTERNAL:

Wing span	8.22 m (26 ft 11½ in)
Foreplane span	3.73 m (12 ft 3 in)
Length overall, incl probe	15.65 m (51 ft 4¼ in)
Height overall	4.55 m (14 ft 11¼ in)
Wheel track	3.20 m (10 ft 6 in)
Wheelbase	4.87 m (15 ft 11¾ in)

AREAS:

Wings, gross	34.8 m² (374.6 sq ft)
Foreplanes (total)	1.66 m² (17.87 sq ft)

WEIGHTS AND LOADING:

Weight empty (interceptor, estimated)	
	7,285 kg (16,060 lb)
Max usable fuel: internal	2,572 kg (5,670 lb)
external	3,727 kg (8,217 lb)
Max external stores	6,085 kg (13,415 lb)
Typical combat weight:	
interceptor, 50% internal fuel, two Shafrir missiles	
	9,390 kg (20,700 lb)
interceptor, two 500 litre drop tanks, two Shafrir missiles	11,603 kg (25,580 lb)
combat air patrol, three 1,300 litre drop tanks, two Shafrir missiles	14,270 kg (31,460 lb)
ground attack, two 1,300 litre drop tanks, seven 500 lb bombs, two Shafrir missiles	14,670 kg (32,340 lb)
Max clean T-O weight	10,415 kg (22,961 lb)
Max T-O weight	16,500 kg (36,376 lb)
Wing/foreplane loading at 9,390 kg (20,700 lb) combat weight	257.5 kg/m² (52.8 lb/sq ft)
Thrust/weight ratio at 9,390 kg (20,700 lb) combat weight	0.91

PERFORMANCE:

Max level speed above 11,000 m (36,000 ft)	
over Mach 2.3 (1,317 knots; 2,440 km/h; 1,516 mph)	
Max sustained level speed at height, clean	Mach 2.0
Max level speed at S/L, clean	
	750 knots (1,389 km/h; 863 mph)
Max rate of climb at S/L	14,000 m (45,930 ft)/min
Time to 15,240 m (50,000 ft), full internal fuel, two Shafrir missiles	5 min 10 s
Height attainable in zoom climb	22,860 m (75,000 ft)
Stabilised ceiling (combat configuration)	
	17,680 m (58,000 ft)
Turn performance at 4,575 m (15,000 ft), combat weight of 9,390 kg (20,700 lb):	
turn rate: sustained	9.6°/s
instantaneous	18.9°/s
turn radius: sustained	1,326 m (4,350 ft)
instantaneous	671 m (2,200 ft)
T-O run at max T-O weight	1,450 m (4,750 ft)
Landing from 15 m (50 ft) at 11,566 kg (25,500 lb) landing weight	1,555 m (5,100 ft)
Landing run at 11,566 kg (25,500 lb) landing weight	
	1,280 m (4,200 ft)
*Combat radius, 20 min fuel reserves:	
high-altitude interception, one 825 litre and two 1,300 litre drop tanks, two Shafrir missiles	
	419 nm (776 km; 482 miles)
combat air patrol, one 1,300 litre and two 1,700 litre drop tanks, two Shafrir missiles, incl 60 min loiter	

IAI Kfir-C7 multi-mission combat aircraft, armed with Shafrir air-to-air missiles

IAI Kfir-C7 (General Electric J79-J1E afterburning turbojet) *(Pilot Press)*

IAI Nammer proposed upgraded version of the Mirage III and 5 *(Jane's/Mike Keep)*

	476 nm (882 km; 548 miles)
ground attack, hi-lo-hi, two 800 lb and two 500 lb bombs, two Shafrir missiles, one 1,300 litre and two 1,700 litre drop tanks	
	640 nm (1,186 km; 737 miles)
Ferry range:	
three 1,300 litre drop tanks	
	1,614 nm (2,991 km; 1,858 miles)
one 1,300 litre and two 1,700 litre drop tanks	
	1,744 nm (3,232 km; 2,008 miles)
g limit	+7.5

*Can be increased by 30 per cent with in-flight refuelling

IAI NAMMER (TIGER)

In addition to the Mirage III/5 upgrade programmes described under the Bedek Aviation Division, IAI has proposed the Nammer as a joint venture to be developed with one or more international partners.

Externally, the Nammer can be identified by a longer nose than the Mirage or single-seat Kfir, fitment of Kfir type canard surfaces on the engine air intake trunks, an additional fuselage plug aft of the cockpit, and a clean fin without the large dorsal airscoop of the Kfir. Like current Kfirs, it would be equipped with a contemporary weapon delivery and navigation system, HOTAS cockpit controls, and a related stores management and release system. There are two internally mounted 30 mm cannon, with 140 rds/gun, plus nine external wing and fuselage stations for weapons, drop tanks and other stores (similar to those listed for the Kfir, including capability for launching smart weapons). Elta EL/M-2032 lookup/lookdown pulse-Doppler multi-mode fire control radar would be standard; a radar warning system with information presented on the tactical display, automatic chaff/flare dispensers, and jamming system, would be optional. UHF/VHF com and radio navigation systems would be to customer's requirements.

POWER PLANT: One General Electric/Flygmotor F404/RM12 turbofan, rated at 55.6 kN (12,500 lb) dry and 80.7 kN (18,140 lb st) with afterburning. (See under Weights for fuel load.) In-flight and single-point ground pressure refuelling standard.

DIMENSIONS, EXTERNAL, AND AREAS: As listed for Kfir-C7 except:

Length overall	16.00 m (52 ft 6 in)
Wheel track	3.10 m (10 ft 2 in)

WEIGHTS:

Max fuel: internal	2,994 kg (6,600 lb)
external	3,719 kg (8,200 lb)
Max external stores	6,260 kg (13,800 lb)
T-O weight clean	10,251 kg (22,600 lb)
Typical combat weight	9,049 kg (19,950 lb)
Max T-O weight with external stores	16,511 kg (36,400 lb)

PERFORMANCE (estimated, at 9,049 kg; 19,950 lb combat weight except where indicated):

Max level speed:	
at S/L	750 knots (1,390 km/h; 863 mph)
at altitude	Mach 2.2
Stabilised ceiling	17,680 m (58,000 ft)

Max instantaneous turn rate at 4,575 m (15,000 ft) 21°/s
Combat radius (tanks dropped when empty):
interceptor, one 1,300 litre tank and four IR air-to-air missiles, out and back at 12,200 m (40,000 ft) at Mach 1.8, incl 2 min combat
250 nm (463 km; 288 miles)
combat air patrol at 9,150 m (30,000 ft) at Mach 0.85, one 1,300 litre and two 1,700 litre tanks and four IR air-to-air missiles, incl 60 min loiter and 2 min combat 746 nm (1,382 km; 859 miles)
ground attack (hi-lo-lo-hi) at 544 knots (1,008 km/h; 626 mph) attack speed, two 1,700 litre tanks, two Mk 82 bombs and two IR air-to-air missiles
537 nm (995 km; 618 miles)
ground attack (lo-lo-lo-hi) at 535 knots (991 km/h; 616 mph) attack speed, one 1,300 and two 1,700 litre tanks, four CBU-58 cluster bombs and two IR air-to-air missiles 573 nm (1,062 km; 660 miles)
g limit +9

IAI 1125 ASTRA

Known originally as the 1125 Westwind, the Astra was developed as a more fuel-efficient, environmentally acceptable aircraft in the Westwind mould, featuring an improved standard of passenger comfort. In effect, only the tail unit and engine nacelles remain virtually unchanged from the Westwind airframe. The major difference is in the wings, which have a new-design aerofoil section, are sweptback, and are mounted low on the fuselage. Whereas the Westwind features a mid-mounted wing passing aft of the passenger cabin, that of the Astra passes beneath the cabin floor, so avoiding interruption of the available internal space. The Astra has a deeper fuselage profile, allowing 20.3 cm (8 in) more cabin headroom than in the Westwind 2. The cabin is nearly 0.61 m (2 ft) longer and 5 cm (2 in) wider than in the Westwind, but otherwise the fuselage is little changed structurally except for a 50.8 cm (20 in) longer nose providing more space for avionics. The Sigma 2 wing section, a computer-assisted improvement by IAI of the Sigma 1 section employed in the Westwind 2, was designed to provide more efficient high-subsonic cruising flight over long ranges, with reduced operating costs. The one-piece Astra wing is constructed almost entirely of machined parts, including all skins (with integral stiffeners) and ribs, enabling a stronger, lighter, more precise structure. No demating or X-ray inspections are required for the 20,000 hour airframe life. Design and testing of the entire structure comply with FAR 25 requirements (up to Amendment 54) for fatigue and damage tolerance. Construction makes wider use than the Westwind of composite materials, notably for the control surfaces.

Construction of two flying prototypes began in April 1982. The first of these (4X-WIN, c/n 4001) was the first to fly, on 19 March 1984, being followed by c/n 4002 (4X-WIA) in August 1984. The third airframe was used for static and fatigue testing. First flight by a production Astra (4X-CUA) was made on 20 March 1985, and FAA certification to FAR Pts 25 and 36 was received on 29 August of that year. First delivery, to a US customer, was made on 30 June 1986.

Since January 1988, marketing and product support have been undertaken by IAI subsidiary Astra Jet Corporation in the USA. Atlantic Aviation maintains the principal inventory of Westwind and Astra spare parts for distribution worldwide.

At the NBAA convention in October 1989, IAI and Astra Jet Corporation announced an improved **Astra SP** with redesigned interior, upgraded avionics which include a Collins digital autopilot and EFIS, and aerodynamic refinements which improve high altitude performance and extend range with NBAA IFR reserves by 63 nm (117 km; 72 miles). No other details of the Astra SP were received.

The following description applies to the standard Astra:
TYPE: Twin-turbofan business transport.
WINGS: Cantilever low-wing monoplane, with sweptback leading-edges (34° inboard, 25° on outer panels) and outboard trailing-edges. Thin, high-efficiency Sigma 2 aerofoil section, of IAI design. One-piece two-spar fail-safe structure, mainly of aluminium alloys, incorporates machined ribs and wing skin panels and is attached to underfuselage by four main and five secondary frames.

IAI Astra twin-turbofan business transport

IAI 1125 Astra business transport (two Garrett TFE731-3A-200G turbofans) *(Pilot Press)*

Wing/fuselage fairings are of Kevlar, wingtips and inboard leading-edges of Kevlar and Nomex. Automatic extending leading-edge slats (outboard), interconnected with trailing-edge flaps; both flaps and slats are actuated electrically. Hydraulically actuated spoilers/lift dumpers forward of flaps. Ailerons, of Kevlar and honeycomb reinforced glassfibre, are hydraulically powered and pushrod operated. Port and starboard aileron control runs can be disconnected if a single aileron jams, allowing control of the aircraft by one aileron only. Pneumatic de-icing of leading-edge slats.
FUSELAGE: Metal semi-monocoque structure, mainly of aluminium alloy frames and chemically milled skins, with steel alloys or titanium in high stress or high temperature areas. Kevlar reinforced upward opening panel over nose avionics bay. Glassfibre tailcone fairing. Heated windscreens are of laminated polycarbonate, with an external layer of glass for scratch resistance.
TAIL UNIT: Cantilever all-sweptback structure, mainly of metal construction, with three-spar fin box and two-spar electrically actuated variable incidence tailplane. Fin and tailplane tips of glassfibre; small glassfibre ram air inlet at base of fin. Elevators and rudder operated manually via pushrods. Electrically driven rudder trim is via interconnected dual actuators. Pitch trim is by variable incidence tailplane. Pitch trim actuator has three separate electric motors, one for normal operation and a second for override operation in case of malfunction. All three motors operate together to provide emergency pitch control in the event of elevator jamming or disconnect. Pneumatic de-icing of tailplane leading-edges.
LANDING GEAR: SHL hydraulically retractable tricycle type, with oleo-pneumatic shock absorber and twin wheels on each unit. Trailing-link main units retract inward, nosewheels forward. Kevlar nosewheel doors. Tyre sizes 23 × 7 in (main), 16 × 4.4 in (nose). Hydraulic extension, retraction and nosewheel steering; hydraulic multi-disc anti-skid mainwheel brakes. Compressed nitrogen cylinder provides additional power source for emergency extension.
POWER PLANT: Two 16.23 kN (3,650 lb st) Garrett TFE731-3A-200G turbofans, with Grumman hydraulically actuated thrust reversers, pod-mounted in Grumman nacelle on each side of rear fuselage. Kevlar reinforced nacelle doors and panels. Thermal anti-icing of intakes. Standard fuel contained in integral tank in wing centre-section, two outer-wing tanks, and upper and lower tanks in centre-fuselage (combined usable capacity 4,910 litres; 1,297 US gallons; 1,080 Imp gallons). Additional fuel can be carried in a 378.5 litre (100 US gallon; 83.3 Imp gallon) removable auxiliary tank in

forward area of baggage compartment. Single pressure refuelling point in lower starboard side of fuselage aft of wing, or single gravity point in upper fuselage, allow convenient refuelling of all tanks from one position. Fuel sequencing is automatic, requiring no crew action to maintain safe supply of fuel to the engines and maintenance of correct CG.
ACCOMMODATION: Crew of two on flight deck. Dual controls standard. Sliding door between flight deck and cabin. Standard accommodation in pressurised cabin for six persons, two in forward facing seats at front and four in club layout; galley (port or starboard) at front of cabin, coat closet forward (stbd), toilet at rear. All six seats are individually adjustable fore and aft, laterally, and can be swivelled or reclined; all are fitted with armrests and headrests. Two wall mounted foldaway tables between club seat pairs. Coat closet houses stereo tape deck. Maximum accommodation for nine passengers. Plug type airstair door at front on port side; emergency exit over wing on each side. Heated baggage compartment aft of passenger cabin, with external access. A service compartment in the rear fuselage houses aircraft batteries (or optional APU), electrical relay boxes, inverters and miscellaneous equipment. Cabin soundproofing improved compared with Westwind 2.
SYSTEMS: AiResearch environmental control system, using engine bleed air, with normal pressure differential of 0.615 bars (8.9 lb/sq in). Garrett GTCP36-150(W) APU available optionally. Two independent hydraulic systems, each at pressure of 207 bars (3,000 lb/sq in). Primary system is operated by two engine driven pumps for actuation of brakes, anti-skid, landing gear, nosewheel steering, spoilers/lift dumpers and ailerons. Backup system, operated by electrically driven pump, provides power for emergency/parking brake, ailerons and thrust reversers. Electrical system comprises two 300A 28V DC engine driven starter/generators, with two 1kVA single-phase solid state inverters operating in unison to supply single-phase 115V AC power at 400Hz and 26V AC power for aircraft instruments. Two 24V nickel-cadmium batteries for engine starting and to permit operation of essential flight instruments and emergency equipment. 28V DC external power receptacle standard. Oxygen system for crew (pressure demand) and passengers (drop-down masks) supplied by single 1.35 m³ (48 cu ft) cylinder.
AVIONICS AND EQUIPMENT: Standard avionics suite comprises Collins EFIS-85A(1) five-tube electronic flight instrumentation system, dual FCS-80 flight director systems, dual VHF-22A com, dual VIR-32 nav, APS-80 autopilot, ADS-80 air data system, VNI-80D vertical nav system,

provisions for GNS-1000, GNS-X or UNS 1A flight management system, dual DME-42, ADF-60A, dual RMI-36, dual C-14 compass systems, dual TDR-90 transponders, ALT-50A radio altimeter, Baker dual audio systems, and WXT-250A colour weather radar. A two-bottle freon type engine fire extinguishing system is standard. Standard equipment includes electric windscreen wipers, electric (warm air) windscreen demisting, cockpit and cabin fire extinguishers, axe, first aid kit, wing ice inspection lights, landing light in each wingroot, taxying light inboard of each mainwheel door, navigation and strobe lights at wingtips and tailcone, rotating beacons under fuselage and on top of fin, and wing/tailplane static wicks.

DIMENSIONS, EXTERNAL:

Wing span	16.05 m (52 ft 8 in)
Wing aspect ratio	8.8
Length overall	16.94 m (55 ft 7 in)
Fuselage: Max width	1.57 m (5 ft 2 in)
Max depth	1.905 m (6 ft 3 in)
Height overall	5.54 m (18 ft 2 in)
Tailplane span	6.40 m (21 ft 0 in)
Wheel track (c/l of shock struts)	2.77 m (9 ft 1 in)
Wheelbase	7.34 m (24 ft 1 in)
Passenger door (fwd, port): Height	1.37 m (4 ft 6 in)
Width	0.66 m (2 ft 2 in)
Overwing emergency exits (each):	
Height	0.69 m (2 ft 3 in)
Width	0.48 m (1 ft 7 in)

DIMENSIONS, INTERNAL:

Cabin: Length: incl flight deck	6.86 m (22 ft 6 in)
excl flight deck	5.23 m (17 ft 2 in)
Max width	1.45 m (4 ft 9 in)
Max height	1.70 m (5 ft 7 in)
Baggage compartment volume	1.56 m³ (55 cu ft)

AREA:

Wings, gross	29.40 m² (316.6 sq ft)

WEIGHTS (A: without/B: with, long-range fuel tanks):

Basic operating weight empty, incl crew (typical):	
A	5,747 kg (12,670 lb)
B	5,801 kg (12,790 lb)
Max usable fuel: A	3,942 kg (8,692 lb)
B	4,248 kg (9,365 lb)
Fuel with max payload: A, B	3,470 kg (7,650 lb)
Max payload: A	1,510 kg (3,330 lb)
B	1,465 kg (3,230 lb)
Payload with max fuel: A	1,080 kg (2,380 lb)
B	730 kg (1,610 lb)
Max ramp weight: A, B	10,727 kg (23,650 lb)
Max T-O weight: A, B	10,659 kg (23,500 lb)
Max landing weight: A, B	9,389 kg (20,700 lb)
Max zero-fuel weight: A, B	7,257 kg (16,000 lb)

PERFORMANCE (at max T-O weight ISA except where indicated):

Max cruising speed at 10,670 m (35,000 ft), AUW of 7,257 kg (16,000 lb)

465 knots (862 km/h; 535 mph)

Max operating speed	
Mach 0.855 or 360 knots (667 km/h; 414 mph)	
Stalling speed at max landing weight:	
flaps and gear up	111 knots (206 km/h; 128 mph)
flaps and gear down	92 knots (171 km/h; 106 mph)
Max rate of climb at S/L	1,112 m (3,650 ft)/min
Rate of climb at S/L, one engine out	
	335 m (1,100 ft)/min
Max certificated altitude	13,715 m (45,000 ft)
Service ceiling, one engine out	5,790 m (19,000 ft)
FAR 25 T-O balanced field length at S/L at 10,296 kg	
(22,700 lb) T-O weight	1,518 m (4,980 ft)
FAR 25 landing field length at S/L at max landing weight	
	806 m (2,645 ft)
Range with long-range tanks and 4 passengers, 45 min reserves:	
at Mach 0.80	2,510 nm (4,651 km; 2,890 miles)
at Mach 0.72	3,110 nm (5,763 km; 3,581 miles)

OPERATIONAL NOISE LEVELS (FAR 36 at max T-O weight, estimated):

T-O: normal	89.9 EPNdB
with thrust cutback	84.1 EPNdB
Approach	89.8 EPNdB
Sideline	89.7 EPNdB

BEDEK AVIATION DIVISION

Ben-Gurion International Airport, Israel 70100
Telephone: 972 (3) 9711240
Telex: ISRAVIA 381014 and 381033
Fax: 972 (3) 971 3131 and 971 2290
GENERAL MANAGER: I. Geva (Brig-Gen Ret'd)

Bedek Aviation Division is internationally approved as a single-site civil and military airframe, power plant, systems and accessory service and upgrading centre. It has four operating plants: Matam, aircraft services and infrastructure; Shaham, aircraft maintenance and upgrading; Masham, engine maintenance; and Mashav, components maintenance; which, with the division headquarters, have a workforce of 3,200 housed in 110,000 m² (1,184,030 sq ft) of covered space. Bedek performs most of IAI's military and civil upgrading and retrofit programmes, current examples including the Phantom 2000 and Super Phantom programmes described in this entry and modification of a number of large transport aircraft to passenger/cargo, tanker, EW and reconnaissance mission configurations. Additional ongoing work includes the turnaround inspection, overhaul, repair, retrofit, outfitting and testing of more than 25 types of aircraft. Among these are various models of Boeing 707/727/737/747/767, McDonnell Douglas DC-8/DC-9/DC-10 and Lockheed C-130; combat aircraft that can be handled include the A-4 Skyhawk, F-4 Phantom, F-5, F-15 Eagle, F-16 Fighting Falcon, various MiG fighters and Mirage III/5. Power plants processed encompass 30 types of civil and military piston, turboprop, turbojet and turbofan engine and their components, including the JT3D, JT8D, JT9D, F100, J79, Atar 9C, TFE731, T56, PT6, C-250, T53 and T64. More than 6,000 types of accessories and instruments are serviced. The division provides total technical support to several international operators, and holds warranty and/or approved service centre appointments from domestic and foreign air regulatory agencies, air arms and a large number of leading aerospace manufacturers. Bedek is approved as a repair and overhaul agency by most major civil aviation authorities such as the Israeli CAA, Israeli Air Force, US military, FAA (USA), CAA (UK) and LBA (West Germany); these approvals cover aircraft, engine and accessory services.

IAI COMBAT AIRCRAFT UPGRADING

IAI's Bedek Aviation Division is currently offering a number of upgrade possibilities for existing combat aircraft. Modular modernisation packages include new avionics such as a computerised digital weapon delivery and navigation system (WDNS) with multiple weapon delivery in air-to-air and air-to-ground modes and navigation data for up to 40 waypoints; a stores management and release system (SMRS), integrated with the WDNS, for both conventional and smart weapons; various active and passive self-protection (ECM) systems such as podded or internally mounted jammers, radar warning, and flare/chaff dispensers; customised new digital ADI, HSI and ADC systems; and airframe and/or engine modifications and refits.

Typical programmes include the following:

Mirage III/5. Basic airframe modifications consist of the installation of Kfir type foreplanes and landing gear, the former permitting either a substantial reduction (305-457 m; 1,000-1,500 ft) in T-O run or a 907 kg (2,000 lb) increase in T-O gross weight, and the latter an increase in max T-O weight to 16,330 kg (36,000 lb). The foreplanes also offer a marked improvement in air turning radius (from 1,036 m; 3,400 ft to 610 m; 2,000 ft at 4,575 m; 15,000 ft altitude); improved sustained turn, a vastly extended usable angle of

Israeli Air Force Phantoms refuelling from a C-130 Hercules tanker converted by IAI's Bedek Aviation Division

attack and low-speed envelope; and much improved handling qualities. By reducing air loads on the wings and fuselage, they extend the fatigue life of the airframe. An additional fuselage fuel tank can be installed aft of the cockpit, and a Kfir type nose provides additional space for avionics such as control and stability augmentation systems. Other avionics include a radar warning system, with omnidirectional threat analysis and cockpit display, and a WDNS-391 fully inertial weapon delivery and navigation system with head-up operation in all air-to-surface and air-to-air modes. Martin-Baker Mk 10 ejection seats are another option, and missiles or ECM pods can be carried on reinforced wingtip stations. Two or four additional external stores stations are provided, and flare/chaff dispensers can be installed under the rear fuselage.

IAI is also offering two other concurrent remanufacturing/upgrading options for Mirage III and 5 airframes:

Option 1 involves replacement of the existing power plant with a General Electric/Flygmotor F404/RM12 turbofan (55.6 kN; 12,500 lb st dry, 80.7 kN; 18,140 lb st with afterburning), permitting a shorter interception reaction time, better air combat performance, enhanced payload/range capability and improved fleet serviceability. In addition to providing some 30 per cent more thrust and up to 20 per cent better sfc, this re-engining saves some 453.5 kg (1,000 lb) in the aircraft's weight and enables it to carry an additional 544 kg (1,200 lb) of internal fuel. Max T-O weight is increased by 2,721 kg (6,000 lb).

Option 2 offers integration of the Elta EL/M-2011 or M-2032 lightweight fire control radar, conferring the following performance benefits: a coherent pulse-Doppler radar with low and medium PRFs; lookup/lookdown capability; target tracking by monopulse technique and

tracking filter; ability to track low-altitude targets in heavy clutter; full utilisation of the launch envelopes and slaving capability of advanced missiles; all air target information presented on head-up display; improved air-to-ground ranging; extensive built-in testing and calibration; adaptability to other avionics systems; and growth potential through all-software-controlled LRUs and a MIL-STD-1553B interface.

Skyhawk. Major airframe improvements (already applied to Israeli Air Force A-4s) include a life extension overhaul, replacement of all wiring, provision of dual disc brakes on the mainwheels, a steerable nosewheel, addition of wing spoilers, an extra hardpoint under each wing, extension of the tailpipe (to change the heat signature and make the tailpipe more survivable and easier to repair), and addition of a brake-chute in a fairing beneath the rear fuselage. The wingroot cannon are of increased calibre (30 mm instead of 20 mm), and a modern WDNS is installed. Additional space for lighter-weight avionics is made available in an extended nose compartment and in the saddleback hump aft of the cockpit. Flare and chaff dispensers can be installed under the rear fuselage, forward of the brake-chute fairing. Bedek also offers a modification programme to convert single-seat A-4s into two-seat dual control trainers.

Phantom 2000. This programme relates specifically to Israeli Air Force F-4s, the major objectives being to extend service life, enhance mission capability, improve flight safety, and improve reliability and maintainability. These are being achieved by structural modifications, complete rewiring, and upgrading the avionics. A similar programme is available to other F-4 operators.

The Phantom 2000 prototypes were completed by the Israeli Air Force, the first of them flying for the first time on

Retouched photograph illustrating the Phalcon AEW aircraft based on a Boeing 707 airframe

IAI (Bedek) Super Phantom demonstrator, re-engined with PW1120 turbojets

11 August 1987. They are strengthened structurally (reinforced skins and fuel cells in fuselage and wings), to improve flight safety and fatigue life and to extend their service life well into the next century. The aircraft are completely rewired and are equipped with 1553B dual redundant digital databuses. Hydraulic lines are selectively replaced and rerouted, built-in test features added, and the number of line-replaceable units reduced. Small strakes above the intake flanks improve stability and manoeuvrability, and cockpit comfort and instrument layout embody the latest human engineering data.

The IAF Phantom 2000s are given a new, advanced and fully integrated avionics suite, the major items of which are a Norden/UTC multi-mode high-resolution radar, El-Op (Kaiser licence) wide-angle diffractive-optics head-up display, Elbit multi-function CRT displays for both crew members, a computerised WDNS, HOTAS (hands on throttle and stick) systems selection, Orbit integrated com and com/nav systems, and improved electronic warfare and self-protection (ECM) systems. Elbit Computers Ltd is overall integrator for the avionics refit, the core of which is a data processor derived from the company's ACE-3 currently fitted to all IAF F-16C/Ds. Redelivery of 'production' Phantom 2000 conversions to the Israeli Air Force began on 9 April 1989.

Super Phantom. This programme was launched in 1986, when an IAF F-4E (serial number 334) was refitted with a 60.3 kN (13,550 lb st) Pratt & Whitney PW1120 turbojet (91.7 kN; 20,620 lb st with afterburning) in place of one of its J79s, for use as an engine testbed in the Lavi development programme. It flew for the first time in this form on 30 July 1986, subsequently having the other J79 similarly replaced. Structural changes included modifying the air inlet ducts; new engine attachment points; new or modified engine bay doors; new airframe mounted gearbox with integrated drive generators and automatic throttle system; modified bleed management and air-conditioning ducting system; modified fuel and hydraulic systems; and an engine control/airframe interface.

By mid-1987 flight test results with this Super Phantom demonstrator (all in clean condition and at speeds of Mach 0.98 or below) had indicated significant performance improvements over the J79 powered F-4, as listed in the 1989-90 and earlier *Jane's.*

Super Phantom re-engineering is offered by IAI to F-4 operators worldwide. Options include canards and a conformal underfuselage auxiliary fuel tank.

F-5. The 'F-5 Plus' upgrade package can include upgraded avionics; improved mission systems (eg, weapons delivery and ECM); introduction of new weapon systems; and maintainability improvements. In early 1990, IAI received a contract to upgrade 12 F-5Es and two F-5Fs of the Chilean Air Force by installing new equipment that includes an Elta EL/M-2032 multi-mode fire control radar, an improved WDNS, El-Op HUD, HOTAS, central mission computer and multiple databus.

F-15. Upgrading effort for the McDonnell Douglas F-15 in which Bedek is involved includes structures, maintainability, and various utility and mission systems.

IAI TRACKER UPGRADING

Bedek has proposed a number of upgrades to the Grumman S-2 Tracker maritime patrol aircraft. They comprise refitting with modern turboprop engines; installation of modern avionics and flight systems; and introduction of such state of the art mission equipment as search radar, electro-optical systems, and EW, ESM and ECM systems.

IAI AMIT FOUGA
Israeli Air Force name: Tzukit (Thrush)

The AMIT Fouga (Advanced Multi-mission Improved Trainer) was engineered by the Bedek Aviation Division of IAI to Israeli Air Force requirements, to remain as the standard IAF trainer during the 1980s. It is, in effect, completely rebuilt and modernised, and is a dedicated trainer with all armament removed, although it retains capability for patrol and aerial photographic missions. Details of the modifications were given in the 1986-87 *Jane's.* The upgrade programme is available for other operators of this aircraft.

IAI LARGE TRANSPORT CONVERSIONS

Bedek Aviation Division has carried out, or can offer, a variety of configuration conversions for large transport aircraft, including the following:

Boeing 707/720. Bedek has refurbished and resold numerous Boeing 707s and 720s, often after conversion from passenger to cargo, sigint, hose or boom refuelling tanker or other configurations, and several of these have been recorded in previous editions of *Jane's.* A **sigint/tanker** conversion with wingtip refuelling pods and Elta EL/L-8300 sigint system was illustrated in the 1987-88 edition. Also under development is an **AEW** version mounting an Elta Electronics Phalcon solid state L band radar with six conformal phased array antennae: two on each side of the fuselage, one in an enlarged nose and one under the tail. In addition to the radar, the Phalcon system

incorporates a sophisticated monopulse IFF, wide-range ESM system and a comint data processing system for tactical situation display. A complete Phalcon system is expected to be flight tested in 1990 or 1991.

Modifications involved in the **tanker** conversion include local reinforcement of the outer wings, supports for additional fuel tanks where applicable, and fuselage reinforcement for the boom support point or tail reel hose exit; an additional hydraulic system to power the fuel pumps and boom or tail reel; adaptation of the fuel supply system to the tanker role; electrical system changes to add external illumination, refuelling system controls, boom operator's station with 3-D electro-optical viewing system, and director lights for pilots of receiver aircraft; and avionics to individual customer requirements.

Tanker combis, with a centreline boom and two probe/drogue underwing refuelling pods, have been delivered to the Israeli Air Force, and four similar conversions were ordered in 1989 for the Royal Australian Air Force.

WEIGHTS (707-320C tanker, approx):
Operational weight empty	65,770 kg (145,000 lb)
*Internal fuel weight	72,575 kg (160,000 lb)
**Additional fuel weight	up to 13,605 kg (30,000 lb)
Tanker T-O weight	151,950 kg (335,000 lb)

*90,300 litres (23,855 US gallons; 19,863 Imp gallons)
**17,034 litres (4,500 US gallons; 3,747 Imp gallons)

Boeing 747-100 and -200 Freighter. Bedek Aviation is converting a Boeing 747-100 to prototype Freighter configuration, for certification in 1990. Changes include installing a 3.05 × 3.40 m (10 ft 0 in × 11 ft 2 in) upward opening main deck cargo door aft of the wing on the port side, with local reinforcement of the fuselage; reinforcing the cabin floor to increase load carrying capacity; installing a fully powered ball mat/roller cargo handling system and restraint system, and a bulkhead between the passenger and cargo compartments; and interior modifications adapted to selected passenger/cargo combinations. Basic configuration options to be offered are (1) all-cargo, with up to 29 main deck standard pallets or containers; (2) Combi, with passengers at front and 7-13 pallets aft; and (3) all-passenger, with interior layout to customer's specification. Versions to accommodate non-standard containers, and similar conversions of the Model 747-200, can be produced.

WEIGHTS (747-100 Combi, estimated):
Operational weight empty	148,325 kg (327,000 lb)
Max payload	98,883 kg (218,000 lb)
Max T-O weight	334,750 kg (738,000 lb)
Max landing weight	265,350 kg (585,000 lb)
Max zero-fuel weight	247,435 kg (545,500 lb)

Lockheed C-130/L-100 Hercules. Bedek Aviation has already accomplished several successful conversions of C-130 series aircraft to such configurations as in-flight refuelling tanker and sigint platform, with appropriate airframe modifications and avionics refits. Operational configurations currently being offered for any C-130B to C-130H variant, or their L-100 commercial counterparts, include: (1) probe and drogue aerial refuelling tanker, with transfer fuel in an 11,356 litre (3,000 US gallon; 2,498 Imp gallon) cargo compartment tank plus two underwing fuel pods; (2) maritime surface patrol and ASW, with appropriate surveillance, acoustic, MAD, armament and stores management systems, and operator stations; (3) C³I and electronic warfare platform, with comint, elint, communications and EW systems to customer's requirements; (4) search and rescue, with a rescue kit, flare storage/launcher and operator station on a logistic pallet installed on the rear loading ramp; (5) emergency assistance, with an insulated cabin mounted on a logistic pallet for ambulance or flying hospital missions or in a firefighting configuration with up to 11,356 litres (3,000 US gallons; 2,498 Imp gallons) of water and retardant in pallet mounted tanks in the cargo hold; and (6) VIP, 65-seat passenger or passenger/cargo combi transport, with full airliner type seating, galley and toilet facilities, pallet-mounted in an air-conditioned environment.

WEIGHTS (C-130H tanker, approx):
Operational weight empty	35,380 kg (78,000 lb)
*Internal fuel weight	29,030 kg (64,000 lb)
**Additional fuel weight	10,885 kg (24,000 lb)
Tanker T-O weight	75,295 kg (166,000 lb)
Max overload T-O weight	79,380 kg (175,000 lb)

*36,643 litres (9,860 US gallons; 8,060 Imp gallons)
**13,627 litres (3,600 US gallons; 2,997 Imp gallons)

Cockpit upgrades. As future development programmes, Bedek Aviation intends to convert existing three-man flight decks of transport aircraft for two-man operation. Conversion will include advanced monitoring and control systems, including engine indicating and crew alerting system (EICAS). Candidate aircraft are the Boeing 727 and McDonnell Douglas DC-10.

Technologies Division
PO Box 190, Lod Industrial Zone 711101
Telephone: 972 (8) 239111
Telex: SHLD IL 381520
Fax: 972 (8) 222792

GENERAL MANAGER: Y. Shapira

This Division is the parent facility to four separate plants: SHL (Servo Hydraulics Lod), Ramta Structures and Systems, MATA Helicopters, and Golan Industries. SHL designs, develops and manufactures hydraulic system components, hydraulic flight control servo-systems, landing gears and brake systems; and produces air actuated chucks, miniature gears, clutches and brakes. Among others, its products equip the Kfir, Arava, Westwind and Astra, and IDF Sikorsky Black Hawk helicopters; manufacturing approvals are held from Boeing, Dornier, General Dynamics and General Electric, among others. Ramta undertakes metal and advanced composites fabrication for the F-4 Phantom, F-16 Fighting Falcon, E-2C Hawkeye, Kfir, Westwind and Astra, as well as manufacturing ground vehicles and patrol boats. MATA repairs, reconfigures and remanufactures helicopter structures and components, and produces equipment and systems for rotating-wing aircraft.

Golan designs and manufactures aircraft crew and passenger seats (including designing crashworthy troop seats for the Bell/Boeing V-22 Osprey), aircraft wheels and cockpit controls.

IAI CH-53 2000
Headed by MATA Helicopters, this programme is aimed

at upgrading the Israeli Air Force fleet of some 30 Sikorsky CH-53D heavy lift helicopters, with the first example due to be completed in 1993. The CH-53 2000 will embody structural changes to extend service life well into the next century, and improved avionics such as a new mission computer, moving map display, two multi-function displays and a new autopilot system. Elbit is avionics systems integrator for the CH-53 2000.

ITALY

AERITALIA

AERITALIA—SOCIETA AEROSPAZIALE ITALIANA p.A.
Piazzale Vincenzo Tecchio 51A (Casella Postale 3065), 80125 Naples

Telephone: 39 (81) 7252111

Telex: N. 710370 AERIT

CHAIRMAN: Amb Umberto La Rocca

DEPUTY CHAIRMAN AND MANAGING DIRECTOR: Ing Fausto Cereti

GENERAL MANAGERS: Ing Roberto Mannu and Dott Paolo Micheletta

PUBLIC AFFAIRS MANAGERS: Ing Federico Dalla Volta and Dott Fabio Dani

Aeritalia is a joint stock company formed on 12 November 1969 by an equal shareholding of Fiat and the state-controlled IRI-Finmeccanica, to combine Fiat's aerospace activities (except those which concerned aero engines) with those of Aerfer and Salmoiraghi of the Finmeccanica group. It became fully operational under that title on 1 January 1972. On 28 September 1976 IRI-Finmeccanica purchased the Aeritalia stock owned by Fiat, thus acquiring complete control of the company's stock capital. However, in 1990 IRI-Finmeccanica's shareholding stood at 84 per cent, with the remaining shares privately owned. In the Summer of 1981 Aeritalia acquired shareholdings of 100 per cent in Aeronavali Venezia, 60 per cent in Partenavia, and 50 per cent in Meteor. A 25 per cent holding in Aeronautica Macchi was acquired in 1983; in 1988 it acquired a 31 per cent holding in Rinaldo Piaggio (which see), a 44 (now 22) per cent share in FMA of Argentina, and 60 per cent in Dee Howard (see US section). Meteor is now 100 per cent owned by Aeritalia. The combined Aeritalia workforce is approx 17,000.

Organisation is based upon a centralised general management and five operational groups, as listed in this entry.

GAD - GRUPPO AEREI DIFESA (Defence Aircraft Group)
HEADQUARTERS AND TURIN WORKS: Corso Marche 41, 10146 Turin

Telephone: 39 (11) 71811

Telex: N. 221076 (AERITOR)

Fax: 39 (11) 710885
GENERAL MANAGER: Ing Mario Pellerei
CASELLE WORKS: Aeroporto Torino, 10072 Caselle

Telephone: 39 (11) 99601

Telex: 210411 (AERCAS)

Fax: 39 (11) 9963010

The Turin area factories (at Corso Marche, North Caselle and South Caselle) are responsible for work on the AMX combat aircraft; outer (movable) wings, final assembly and flight testing of the Panavia Tornado; definition, design and development of the Eurofighter European fighter aircraft, in partnership with other European companies; space vehicles; carbonfibre ailerons and rudders for the Boeing 767; and an improved weapons system for the F-104S. Current weapons under development by the Group include the Skyshark cluster bomb, first air-launched in 1988 from a Tornado. Other activities include extensive research in various fields of aerodynamics and advanced technologies, and the repair, overhaul and maintenance of aircraft. Flight testing is undertaken at the Decimomannu test centre. The 1988 workforce was 4,700.

GAT - GRUPPO AEREI TRASPORTO (Transport Aircraft Group)
HEADQUARTERS AND NAPLES AREA WORKS: Viale dell'Aeronautica, 80038 Pomigliano d'Arco, Naples

Telephone: 39 (81) 8451111

Telex: 710082 (AERITPOM)

Fax: 39 (81) 8843190
GENERAL MANAGER: Ing Pasquale D'Angelo

CAPODICHINO WORKS: Via del Riposo alla Doganella, Aeroporto di Capodichino, 80144 Naples

Telephone: 39 (81) 7817111

Telex: 710356 (AITCAP)

Fax: 39 (81) 7805661

CASORIA WORKS: Strada Statale 87, km 8.7, 80026 Casoria

Telephone: 39 (81) 7817111

Telex: 721583 (AITCAN)

Fax: 39 (81) 7583010

CASORIA WORKS: Via Giovanni Pascoli 7, 80026 Casoria

Telephone: 39 (81) 5502111

Telex: 720199 (PARTNA)

Fax: 39 (81) 7598229

FOGGIA WORKS: Zona ASI, Localita, Incoronata, 71100 Foggia

Telephone: 39 (881) 8185

Telex: 812096 (AITFG)

Fax: 39 (881) 81546

VENICE WORKS: Via Triestina 214, 30030 Venezia Tessera

Telephone: 39 (41) 666811

Telex: 410446 (AERONAV)

CIAMPINO WORKS: Via Mameli, Edificio 126, 00040 Aeroporto Ciampino, Rome

Telephone: 39 (6) 7240281

Telex: 616285 (AERNAC)

Fax: 39 (6) 7240602

Principal activities in the Naples area comprise construction of the complete series of fuselage structural panels and moving surfaces for the McDonnell Douglas MD-80; fuselage panels, vertical tail surfaces and winglets for the MD-11 airliner; components for the Rohr nacelle system for installation on the Airbus A320; numerous components for the Boeing 767; fuselage, outboard ailerons, trailing-edge flaps, spoilers and fin for the Aeritalia G222, plus assembly and flight testing; and manufacture of complete fuselage and tail unit of the ATR 42/72 regional transports. Aeritalia is also a risk-sharing contractor for the Airbus A321 programme, although not part of the Airbus Industrie consortium.

In January 1989 the Transport Aircraft Group took over the activities of the former Overhaul, Modification, Maintenance and General Aviation Group. By so doing, it undertook manufacture of Partenavia light aircraft (under which heading descriptions of current aircraft can be found), while being responsible also for the overhaul and maintenance of various Aeritalia-built and other aircraft including the Boeing 707 and E-3A Sentry, McDonnell Douglas DC-8, Breguet Atlantic and Douglas A-3 Skywarrior types.

The Group is responsible for full product support of Aeritalia aircraft, for support services such as training of crew members and technicians and for field service required by Aeritalia customers.

The Foggia Works is dedicated mainly to the manufacture of structural components in carbonfibre, aramid fibre and other composite materials. The Dee Howard company contributes to the activities of this Group (see introductory paragraph).

GST - GRUPPO SISTEMI TELEGUIDATI (Systems and RPVs Group)
HEADQUARTERS AND CASELLE WORKS: 10072 Caselle, Turin

Telephone: 39 (11) 99671

Telex: 210086 (AITCEA)

Fax: 39 (11) 9963357
GENERAL MANAGER: Ing Carlo Scaglia
NERVIANO WORKS: Viale Europa, 20014 Nerviano, Milan

Telephone: 39 (331) 587330

Telex: 330675

Fax: 39 (331) 588106
RONCHI WORKS: Via San Zanut - Zona Soleschiano, 34077 Ronchi dei Legionari (GO)

Telephone: 39 (481) 4791

Telex: 460369 (AITRDL)

Fax: 39 (481) 474321
ROME OFFICES: Via Vitorchiano 81, 00189 Rome

Telephone: 39 (6) 3330570

Telex: 622249

Fax: 39 (6) 3330648

Activities of this Group include research, development, production and integration of remotely piloted vehicles and associated ground stations, avionic systems and aircraft subsystems, ranging from nav/attack to computing and defensive aids, radio-communications/radio-navigation equipment, and integrated automatic test equipment.

GSS - GRUPPO SISTEMI SPAZIALI (Space Systems Group)
HEADQUARTERS AND TURIN WORKS: Corso Marche 41, 10146 Turin

Telephone: 39 (11) 71801

Telex: 221235
GENERAL MANAGER: Prof Ernesto Vallerani

The Space Systems Group, established as a separate body in 1984 and headquartered in Turin, has approximately 1,000 employees working in the areas of systems engineering, programme management, research, attitude control, design, structures, integration and systems, design and development of thermal control, quality control, software, technology, composite materials and control of ground simulation for space missions. It is the principal national company responsible for the systems in Italian Space Agency programmes (IRIS, Lageos II, Tethered Satellite System, SAX), and has various responsibilities in European Space Agency initiatives (Spacelab, Hipparcos, Eureca, IPS). The Group is also a member of the Columbus, Olympus and MESH consortia, and a principal shareholder in a number of companies: Italspazio (65 per cent), Space Software Italia (60 per cent), MARS (50 per cent), Carlo Gavazzi Spazio (33 per cent), Selenia Spazio (25 per cent), Società Italiana Avionica (25 per cent), Intospace (7.5 per cent), Spacehab (4 per cent), Eurospace (4 per cent), and Arianespace (1 per cent). It is also involved in the Eutelsat II and Carina programmes.

In addition to a series of modern laboratories, the Group's facilities include an integration complex (one of the largest and most complete in Europe) with a 100,000 class clean room, and a state-of-the-art Attitude Measurement and Control Simulation laboratory for the real-time testing of attitude control hardware. These facilities have allowed the Space Systems Group to progress from being a supplier of thermomechanic subsystems to being prime contractor, responsible for entire systems and their integration, at both a national and international level.

ALFA ROMEO AVIO
HEAD OFFICE: Viale dell'Aeronautica, 80038 Pomigliano d'Arco, Naples

Telephone: 39 (81) 8430111

Telex: 710082 AITPOM I
GENERAL MANAGER: Ing Filippo De Luca
See Aero Engines section

AIRBUS A321
Aeritalia is a risk-sharing contractor. Details can be found in the International section.

AMX
A description and illustration of this joint Italian-Brazilian attack aircraft programme, involving Aeritalia, Aermacchi and Embraer, can be found in the International section.

ATR 42/72
Aeritalia is an equal partner with Aerospatiale of France in developing these new regional transport aircraft, descriptions and illustrations of which appear under the ATR heading in the International section.

EUROFIGHTER
Aeritalia has a 21 per cent share in the development of this new generation fighter, details of which can be found in the International section.

NAMC A-5 MODERNISATION
Under a joint programme with CATIC, Aeritalia is modernising the avionics of the Nanchang A-5C ('Fantan') attack aircraft (see under NAMC in Chinese section). This upgrading encompasses all-weather autonomous and radio-assisted navigation, air and ground communications, IFF, weapon aiming for ground attack and air-to-air self-defence modes, and passive ECM. The avionics system is designed around central computers and a dual redundant MIL-STD-1553B databus. Having lost the first prototype, the second is flying and a replacement for the original aircraft is being built.

TORNADO

Aeritalia has a 15 per cent participation in the manufacturing programme for the Panavia Tornado (see International section), being responsible for the radomes, the entire outer wings, including control surfaces, and the final assembly of aircraft for the Italian Air Force. Assembly of Italian Tornados is now complete.

AERITALIA G222

Early history of the Aeritalia (originally Fiat) G222, the first prototype of which made its initial flight on 18 July 1970, can be found in the 1987-88 and previous editions of *Jane's*.

Several major Italian airframe companies have been involved in the construction programme, including Aermacchi (outer wings); Piaggio (wing centre-section); SIAI-Marchetti (tail unit); CIRSEA (landing gear); and IAM (miscellaneous airframe components). Wing flaps are contributed by Hellenic Aerospace Industries. Fuselages are built by Aeritalia's Transport Aircraft Group, in the Pomigliano d'Arco Works near Naples; final assembly takes place at the Capodichino Works, Naples.

Aeritalia has teamed with Chrysler Technologies Airborne Systems of the USA to offer the G222 as a competitor in the USAF's C-27A STOL mission support aircraft programme. If successful, deliveries could begin in the latter part of 1991.

The following versions have been built:

G222. Standard military transport, to which the detailed description mainly applies. The first of 44 G222s for the Italian Air Force (30 standard transports, eight G222SAA, four G222RM and two G222GE) flew on 23 December 1975, and deliveries began on 21 April 1978. Six quick-change kits, produced by Aeritalia, are held by the Italian Air Force for in-the-field conversions to the aeromedical configuration. Other customers included the Argentine Army (three), Dubai Air Force (one), Nigerian Air Force (five), Somali Air Force (two), and the Venezuelan Army (two) and Air Force (six). Five were ordered by the Italian Ministry for Civil Defence, to create a rapid-intervention squadron for firefighting, aeromedical evacuation, and airlift of supplies to earthquake and other disaster areas. Recent orders for G222s from Congo (three), Guatemala (two) and Yemen (four) are believed to be for this version.

G222RM. Flight inspection (radiomisure) version, detailed in the 1989-90 *Jane's*.

G222SAA. Firefighting version (Sistema Aeronautico Antincendio), detailed in the 1989-90 *Jane's*.

G222T. Version with Rolls-Royce Tyne turboprops, larger-diameter propellers and higher operating weights; details in 1986-87 *Jane's*.

G222VS (Versione Speciale). Electronic warfare version, detailed in the 1989-90 *Jane's*.

G222GE (Guerra Elettronica). Dimensions, weights and performance similar to those of the standard troop transport.

Total orders for the G222 (all versions) now stand at about 97.

The following abbreviated description applies to the standard G222 transport version, except where indicated. A full description can be found in the 1987-88 and many earlier editions.

TYPE: Twin-turboprop general purpose transport aircraft.

AIRFRAME: As described in 1987-88 *Jane's*.

POWER PLANT (except G222T): Two Fiat built General Electric T64-GE-P4D turboprops, each flat rated at 2,535 kW (3,400 shp) at ISA + 25°C and driving a Hamilton Standard 63E60-27 three-blade variable- and reversible-pitch propeller with spinner. Fuel in integral tanks: two in the outer wings, combined capacity 6,800 litres (1,796 US gallons; 1,495 Imp gallons), and two centre-section tanks, combined capacity 5,200 litres (1,374 US gallons; 1,143 Imp gallons), with cross-feed provision to either engine. Total overall fuel capacity 12,000 litres (3,170 US gallons; 2,638 Imp gallons).

ACCOMMODATION: Normal crew of three (two pilots and radio operator/flight engineer) on flight deck. Provision for loadmaster or jumpmaster when required. Standard troop transport version has 32 foldaway sidewall seats and 21 stowable seats for 53 fully equipped troops, and carries also two 20-man liferafts stowed in the wing/fuselage fairing and a single 9-man liferaft in the cargo compartment. Paratroop transport version can carry up to 40 fully equipped paratroops, and is fitted with the 32 sidewall seats and liferafts as in the troop transport version, plus eight stowable seats, door jump platforms and static lines. Five-person VIP lounge plus seats for 16 other passengers in VIP transport version. Cargo transport version can accept standard pallets of up to 2.24 m (88 in) wide, and can carry up to 9,000 kg (19,840 lb) of freight. Provision is made for 135 cargo tiedown points, on a 51 cm (20 in) square NATO standard grid, and a 1,500 kg (3,306 lb) capacity cargo hoist. Typical Italian military equipment loads can include two CL-52 light trucks; one CL-52 with a 105 mm L4 howitzer or one-ton trailer; Fiat AR-59 Campagnola reconnaissance vehicle with 106 mm recoilless gun or 250 kg (550 lb) trailer; or five standard A-22 freight pallets. In the aeromedical role the G222 can accommodate 36 stretchers and four medical attendants. A second toilet

Aeritalia G222RM for in-flight calibration of ground radio navigation and communications facilities, operated by the Italian Air Force

Aeritalia G222 twin-turboprop general purpose military transport aircraft *(Pilot Press)*

can be installed, and provision can be made to increase the water supply and to install electrical points and hooks for medical treatment bottles. In this version, the cabin oxygen system is available to all stretcher positions. Crew door is forward of cabin on port side. Passenger doors, at front and rear of main cabin on starboard side and at rear on port side, can be used also as emergency exits. Two emergency hatches in cabin roof, forward and aft of wing carry-through structure. Hydraulically operated rear loading ramp and upward opening door in underside of upswept rear fuselage, which can be opened in flight for airdrop operations. In cargo version, five pallets of up to 1,000 kg (2,205 lb) each can be airdropped from rear opening, or a single pallet of up to 5,000 kg (11,023 lb). Paratroop jumps can be made either from this opening or from the rear side doors. Windscreens and quarter-light panels are de-iced and demisted electrically. Wipers and screen wash for both windscreens. Entire accommodation pressurised and air-conditioned.

SYSTEMS: See 1987-88 and earlier *Jane's*.

AVIONICS AND EQUIPMENT: Standard communications equipment includes 3,500-channel UHF, two 1,360-channel VHF-AM, 920-channel VHF-FM, 28,000-channel HF/SSB, crew intercom and PA system. Navigation equipment includes Omega system, with TAS computer, autopilot, flight director, two compasses, and two vertical gyros; and an integrated ground based system incorporating two VOR, marker beacon receiver, two ILS, ADF, two Tacan or DME, and horizontal situation indicator. Other avionics include Meteo weather radar, with secondary terrain mapping mode; radar altimeter; and IFF/ATC transponder including altitude reporting. Provision for head-up display. Landing light on nosewheel leg.

DIMENSIONS, EXTERNAL:

Wing span	28.70 m (94 ft 2 in)
Wing aspect ratio	10.0
Length overall	22.70 m (74 ft 5½ in)
Height overall	9.80 m (32 ft 1¾ in)
Fuselage: Max diameter	3.55 m (11 ft 7¾ in)
Tailplane span	12.40 m (40 ft 8¼ in)
Wheel track	3.668 m (12 ft 0½ in)
Wheelbase (to c/l of main units)	6.23 m (20 ft 5¼ in)
Propeller diameter	4.42 m (14 ft 6 in)
Rear-loading ramp/door: Width	2.45 m (8 ft 0½ in)
Height	2.25 m (7 ft 4½ in)

DIMENSIONS, INTERNAL:

Main cabin: Length	8.58 m (28 ft 1¾ in)
Width	2.45 m (8 ft 0½ in)
Height	2.25 m (7 ft 4½ in)
Floor area: excl ramp	21.00 m² (226.0 sq ft)
incl ramp	25.68 m² (276.4 sq ft)
Volume	58.0 m³ (2,048 cu ft)

AREA:

Wings, gross	82.00 m² (882.6 sq ft)

WEIGHTS AND LOADINGS (standard version except where indicated):

Weight empty	14,590 kg (32,165 lb)
Weight empty, equipped	15,400 kg (33,950 lb)
Operating weight empty (standard and SAA)	15,700 kg (34,610 lb)
Max payload (cargo)	9,000 kg (19,840 lb)
Equipment module (SAA)	2,200 kg (4,850 lb)
Retardant (SAA)	6,800 kg (14,990 lb)
Max fuel load	9,400 kg (20,725 lb)
Fuel (SAA)	3,330 kg (7,340 lb)
Max T-O weight (standard and SAA)	28,000 kg (61,730 lb)
Max landing weight (standard and SAA)	26,500 kg (58,420 lb)
Max zero-fuel weight	24,400 kg (53,790 lb)
Max cargo floor loading	750 kg/m² (155 lb/sq ft)
Max wing loading	341.5 kg/m² (69.9 lb/sq ft)
Max power loading	5.52 kg/kW (9.08 lb/shp)

PERFORMANCE (standard transport, at max T-O weight except where indicated):

Max level speed at 4,575 m (15,000 ft)	291 knots (540 km/h; 336 mph)
Long-range cruising speed at 6,000 m (19,680 ft)	237 knots (439 km/h; 273 mph)
Airdrop speed (paratroops or cargo)	110-140 knots (204-259 km/h; 127-161 mph) IAS

Drop speed (G222SAA, T-O configuration)
              120 knots (222 km/h; 138 mph)
Stalling speed, flaps and landing gear down
              84 knots (155 km/h; 97 mph)
Time to 4,500 m (14,760 ft)   8 min 35 s
Max rate of climb at S/L   520 m (1,705 ft)/min
Rate of climb at S/L, one engine out   125 m (410 ft)/min
Service ceiling   7,620 m (25,000 ft)
Service ceiling, one engine out   5,000 m (16,400 ft)
Optimum height above ground during drop (G222SAA)
             50-100 m (165-330 ft)
T-O run   662 m (2,172 ft)
T-O to 15 m (50 ft)   1,000 m (3,280 ft)
Landing from 15 m (50 ft)   775 m (2,543 ft)
Landing run at max landing weight   545 m (1,788 ft)
Accelerate/stop distance   1,200 m (3,937 ft)
Range:
  with max payload, at optimum cruising speed and
    height   740 nm (1,371 km; 852 miles)
  with 36 stretchers and 4 medical attendants
        1,349 nm (2,500 km; 1,553 miles)
  with max retardant load (SAA)
        540 nm (1,000 km; 621 miles)
Ferry range with max fuel
        2,500 nm (4,633 km; 2,879 miles)
g limit   +2.5

AERITALIA (LOCKHEED) F-104S ASA

Aeritalia production of the F-104S ended in March 1979 after the manufacture of 246 aircraft, including 40 for the Turkish Air Force. Development was initiated in 1982 of a weapons system updating programme for 150 of the Italian Air Force's F-104Ss, to increase their capability in the interception and interdiction/strike roles.

Known as ASA (Aggiornamento Sistema d'Arma), this programme includes improved air-to-air self-defence and interception capability by the introduction of a FIAR R21G/M1 Setter lookdown/shootdown radar; advanced ECM; improved IFF and altitude reporting system; improved electrical power generation and distribution system; improved weapons delivery (armament computer and time delay unit); and a new automatic pitch control computer. Weapons include Aspide 1A medium-range and AIM-9L Sidewinder short-range air-to-air missiles.

An F-104S ASA demonstrator began flight testing in July 1983. Redelivery of the first ASA aircraft to the Italian Air Force took place on 19 November 1986 and the 100th was rolled out on 25 February 1990. The 150th and final ASA will be redelivered in 1991.

Rollout of the 100th Aeritalia F-104S ASA with upgraded weapons system, capable of carrying two Sidewinder and two Aspide air-to-air missiles

AERITALIA DC-8 FREIGHTER CONVERSION

Under a US programme launched in 1976, McDonnell Douglas converted 20 DC-8 passenger transports into specialised freighters, as recorded in the 1987-88 and earlier editions of *Jane's*. In 1982 responsibility for the DC-8 freighter conversion programme was taken over by Officine Aeronavali Venezia SpA (now a wholly owned subsidiary of Aeritalia), which delivered its first conversion, one of two DC-8-63Fs for Air Canada, in February 1986. Three further DC-8-63Fs were then produced for United Parcel Service of the USA, followed on 10 December 1987 by the first of about 17 DC-8-71Fs that are being produced for the GPA Group for lease to UPS under a three-year programme.

Modification includes removal of passenger installations and fitting a production freighter seven-track floor, and a 2.16 × 3.56 m (85 × 140 in) main deck cargo door. Cabin windows are replaced by metal plugs, and a cargo loading system is installed. The aircraft are then recertificated at a new max T-O weight of 161,025 kg (355,000 lb). Conversion to turbofan power is optional for turbojet models.

AERITALIA ATLANTIC 1 MODERNISATION

The navigation, radar, sonar dropping and intercom systems of 18 Italian Air Force Breguet Atlantic 1 maritime patrol aircraft are being upgraded under a contract awarded to the European SECBAT consortium. First, aircraft c/n 80 was upgraded by Dassault in France and first flew in the new configuration on 7 July 1987. It returned to service in March 1988. Aeritalia's Venice facility is updating the remainder, the first of which (c/n 83) was redelivered in 1988. Programme completion is scheduled for October 1992.

AERONAUTICA MACCHI

AERONAUTICA MACCHI SpA

Via Don Tornatore 6, 21100 Varese
Telephone: 39 (332) 287700
Telex: 380070
CHAIRMAN: Dott Fabrizio Foresio

The original Macchi company was founded in 1913 in Varese, and its first aeroplane was built in that year. On 1 January 1981 the Aeronautica Macchi group reorganised its structure, transforming itself into a holding company and transferring all of its operating activities to a newly formed, wholly owned company known as Aermacchi SpA. The group includes, besides Aermacchi SpA, the subsidiary companies Aero Engineering (aeronautical design), SICAMB (airframe and equipment manufacturing, including licence production of Martin-Baker ejection seats), OMG (precision machining), and Logic (electronics equipment). A 25 per cent holding in Aeronautica Macchi was acquired by Aeritalia in 1983.

AERMACCHI

AERMACCHI SpA (Subsidiary of Aeronautica Macchi SpA)

Via Sanvito Silvestro 80, CP 246, 21100 Varese
Telephone: 39 (332) 254111
Telex: 380070 AERMAC I
Fax: 39 (332) 254555
CHAIRMAN: Dott Fabrizio Foresio
MANAGING DIRECTOR: Dott Ing Giorgio Brazzelli
DIRECTOR, FINANCE AND ADMINISTRATION: Dott Alfonso Romagnoli
DIRECTOR, PROGRAMMES AND STRATEGIES: Dott Ing Bruno Cussigh
COMMERCIAL MANAGER: Dott Ing Giovanni Cattaneo
TECHNICAL MANAGER: Dott Ing Alberto Notari
PUBLIC RELATIONS MANAGER: Franca Grandi

Aermacchi, which celebrated its 75th anniversary in 1988, is the aircraft manufacturing company of the Aeronautica Macchi group. Its plants at Venegono airfield occupy a total area of 274,000 m² (2,949,310 sq ft), including 52,000 m² (559,720 sq ft) of covered space; the flight test centre has covered space of 5,100 m² (54,900 sq ft) in a total area of 28,000 m² (301,390 sq ft). Total workforce at the beginning of 1990 was approximately 2,750.

In addition to its aircraft programmes, Aermacchi is active in the field of aerospace ground equipment, with a complete line of hydraulic, electric and pneumatic ground carts for servicing civil and military aircraft, and also has important roles in the Ariane and EFA programmes. In April 1989 it announced the signature of a memorandum for co-operation on the Dornier 328 programme (see German section), under which Aermacchi will participate in manufacture and final assembly of the fuselage, as well as in structural testing and engineering work. In the same month Aermacchi and Dornier signed a memorandum of understanding for a joint effort in the definition of a future integrated military pilot training system (PTS-2000) to meet the challenging training requirements of the year 2000. That October, Aermacchi, Lockheed and Hughes signed a co-operation agreement to participate in the Joint Primary Aircraft Training System (JPATS) programme for the USAF and US Navy, using the MB-339 in their bid to replace T-37s and T-34Cs respectively. Lockheed would become prime contractor and system integrator for the JPATS programme, holding a manufacturing licence, with Hughes managing the training system with the intended supply of simulators.

AMX

Aermacchi is teamed with Aeritalia and Embraer in the AMX combat aircraft programme (see International section) for the Italian and Brazilian air forces.

AERMACCHI MB-339A

The first of two MB-339X prototypes (MM588) was flown for the first time on 12 August 1976. The second aircraft (MM589), which made its first flight on 20 May 1977, was built to pre-production standard; the third airframe was used for static and fatigue testing. The first production aircraft made its initial flight on 20 July 1978, and the first of an initial series of 51 aircraft for the Italian Air Force were handed over for pre-service trials on 8 August 1979. In addition to MB-339A trainers for the 61° Brigata Aerea at Lecce, this series included four **MB-339RM** (radiomisure) calibration aircraft delivered to 8° Gruppo Sorveglianza Elettronica of the 14° Stormo Radiomisure at Pratica de Mare from 16 February 1981, and fifteen **MB-339PAN**s (Pattuglia Acrobatica Nazionale) delivered to the Italian Air Force aerobatic team, the Frecce Tricolori, which began using the type on 27 April 1982. The PAN aircraft have the wingtip tanks deleted (to facilitate formation keeping) and a smoke generating system installed, but are otherwise similar to the standard MB-339A. At least two more MB-339As have since been converted to MB-339PAN standard to offset attrition. The last of 101 MB-339As for the Italian Air Force was delivered in 1987, and its pilots now gain their 'wings' after completing all phases of their advanced training on MB-339As. Except for the RM and PAN aircraft, all Italian Air Force MB-339As are camouflaged and are available for use as an emergency close air support force.

Ten MB-339As were delivered to the Argentine Navy in 1980, 16 to the Peruvian Air Force in 1981-82, 12 to the Royal Malaysian Air Force in 1983-84, two to Dubai in 1984, and 12 to Nigeria in 1985. In 1987 three more were delivered to Dubai, plus a batch to the Ghana Air Force. The higher powered **MB-339C** is described separately. Details of the MB-339B and single-seat MB-339K, of which no orders had been announced by early 1990, can be found in the 1989-90 *Jane's*. The following description applies to the MB-339A:

TYPE: Two-seat basic and advanced trainer and ground attack aircraft.

AIRFRAME: Structural design criteria based on MIL-A-8860A; 8g limit load factor in clean configuration. Cockpit designed for 40,000 pressurisation cycles. Service life requirement 12,000 flying hours and 24,000 landings in the training role. Entire structure specially treated to prevent corrosion.

WINGS: Cantilever low/mid-wing monoplane. Wing section NACA 64A-114 (mod) at centreline, NACA 64A-212 (mod) at tip. Leading-edge swept back 11° 18'. Sweepback at quarter-chord 8° 29'. All-metal stressed skin structure, with single main spar and auxiliary rear spar, built in two portions and bolted to fuselage. Skin stiffened by spanwise stringers, closely spaced ribs, and false ribs. Wingtip tanks permanently attached. Single fence on each wing at approx two-thirds span. Servo powered ailerons embody 'Irving' type aerodynamic balance provisions, and are statically balanced along their entire span. Balance tabs facilitate reversion to manual operation in the event of servo failure. Hydraulically actuated single-slotted flaps, operated by push/pull rods.

FUSELAGE: All-metal semi-monocoque structure, built in two main portions: forward (nose to engine mounting bulkhead), and rear (engine bulkhead to tailcone).

Aermacchi MB-339A of the Italian Air Force

Forward portion built of C section frames, four C section spars, longitudinal L section stringers, and skin panels. Rear section manufactured entirely from aluminium alloy except for firewall and most of tailcone, which are of stainless steel; four-bolt attachment to forward fuselage to facilitate access to engine. Hydraulically actuated, electrically controlled airbrake under centre of fuselage, just forward of CG.

TAIL UNIT: Cantilever all-metal structure, of similar construction to wings. Slightly sweptback vertical surfaces. Rudder and elevators are statically balanced, each having an electrically actuated dual-purpose balance and trim tab. Two auxiliary fins under rear fuselage.

LANDING GEAR: Hydraulically retractable tricycle type, with oleo-pneumatic shock absorbers; suitable for operation from semi-prepared runways. Nosewheel retracts forward, main units outward into wings. Hydraulically steerable nosewheel. Low-pressure mainwheel tubeless tyres size 545 × 175-10 (12 ply rating); nosewheel tubeless tyre size 380 × 150-4 (6 ply rating). Emergency extension system. Hydraulic disc brakes with anti-skid system.

POWER PLANT: One Rolls-Royce Viper Mk 632-43 turbojet, rated at 17.8 kN (4,000 lb st). Engines built in Italy under Rolls-Royce licence; final assembly by Piaggio. Fuel in two-cell rubber fuselage tank, capacity 781 litres (206 US gallons; 172 Imp gallons), and two integral wingtip tanks, combined capacity 632 litres (167 US gallons; 139 Imp gallons). Total internal capacity 1,413 litres (373 US gallons; 311 Imp gallons) usable. Single-point pressure refuelling receptacle in port side of fuselage, below wing trailing-edge. Gravity refuelling points on top of fuselage and each tip tank. Provision for two drop tanks, each of 325 litres (86 US gallons; 71.5 Imp gallons) usable capacity, on centre underwing stations. Anti-icing system for engine air intakes.

ACCOMMODATION: Crew of two in tandem, on Martin-Baker IT10F zero/zero ejection seats in pressurised cockpit. Rear seat elevated 32.5 cm (12¾ in). Rearview mirror for each occupant. Two-piece moulded transparent canopy, opening sideways to starboard.

SYSTEMS: Pressurisation system max differential 0.24 bars (3.5 lb/sq in). Bootstrap type air-conditioning system, which also provides air for windscreen and canopy demisting. Hydraulic system, pressure 172.5 bars (2,500 lb/sq in), for actuation of flaps, aileron servos, airbrake, landing gear, wheel brakes and nosewheel steering. Backup system for wheel brakes and emergency extension of landing gear. Main electrical DC power from one 28V 9kW engine driven starter/generator and one 28V 6kW secondary generator. Two 24V 22Ah nickel-cadmium batteries for engine starting. Fixed frequency 115/26V AC power from two 600VA single phase static inverters. External power receptacle. Low pressure demand type oxygen system, operating at 28 bars (400 lb/sq in).

AVIONICS AND EQUIPMENT: Typical avionics installation includes Collins AN/ARC-159(V)-2, or Magnavox AN/ARC-150(V), or Magnavox AN/ARC-164(V) UHF transceiver; Collins AN/ARC-186(V) VHF/AM and FM transceiver; Collins ICS-200 interphone; Collins AN/ARN-118(V) Tacan or Bendix/King KDM 706A DME; Collins 51RV-4B or Bendix/King RNA-34A VOR/ILS and MKI-3 marker beacon receiver; Collins DF-206 ADF; GEC Avionics AD-620C computerised area and dead reckoning navigation system; and Bendix/King AN/APX-100(V) or Italtel SIT 421A IFF. Standard instrumentation includes ARU-2B/A attitude director indicator, AQU-6/A HSI, Honeywell AS-339 attitude and heading reference system, AG-5 standby attitude indicator, and flight director system. Retractable landing light beneath port wing; taxying light on nosewheel leg.

ARMAMENT AND OPERATIONAL EQUIPMENT: Up to 2,040 kg (4,500 lb) of external stores can be carried on six underwing hardpoints, the inner four of which are stressed for loads of up to 454 kg (1,000 lb) each and the outer two for up to 340 kg (750 lb) each. Provisions are made, on the two inner stations, for the installation of two Macchi gun pods, each containing either a 30 mm DEFA 553 cannon with 120 rds, or a 12.7 mm AN/M-3 machine-gun with 350 rds. Other typical loads can include two Matra 550 Magic or AIM-9 Sidewinder air-to-air missiles on the two outer stations; four 1,000 lb or six 750 lb bombs; six SUU-11A/A 7.62 mm Minigun pods with 1,500 rds/pod; six Matra 155 launchers, each for eighteen 68 mm rockets; six Matra F-2 practice launchers, each for six 68 mm rockets; six LAU-68/A or LAU-32G launchers, each for seven 2.75 in rockets; six Aerea AL-25-50 or AL-18-50 launchers, each with twenty-five or eighteen 50 mm rockets respectively; six Aerea AL-12-80 launchers, each with twelve 81 mm rockets; four LAU-10/A launchers, each with four 5 in Zuni rockets; four Thomson-Brandt 100-4 launchers, each with four 100 mm Thomson-Brandt rockets; six Aerea BRD bomb/rocket dispensers; six Aermacchi 11B29-003 bomb/flare dispensers; six Thomson-Brandt 14-3-M2 adaptors, each with six 100 mm anti-runway bombs or 120 mm tactical support bombs; or two 325 litre (86 US gallon; 71.5 Imp gallon) drop tanks; or a photographic pod with four 70 mm Vinten cameras; or a single underwing Elettronica ECM pod, combined with a flare/chaff dispenser, onboard RHAW receiver and indicators. Provision for Aeritalia 8.105.924 fixed reflector sight or Saab RGS 2 gyroscopic gunsight; a gunsight can also be installed in rear cockpit, to enable instructor to evaluate manoeuvres performed by student pilot. All gunsights can be equipped with fully automatic Teledyne TSC 116-2 gun camera. Provision for towing type A-6B (1.83 × 9.14 m; 6 × 30 ft) aerial banner target; tow attachment point on inner surface of ventral airbrake.

DIMENSIONS, EXTERNAL:

Wing span over tip tanks	10.858 m (35 ft 7½ in)
Wing aspect ratio	6.1
Length overall	10.972 m (36 ft 0 in)
Height overall	3.994 m (13 ft 1¼ in)
Elevator span	4.08 m (13 ft 4¾ in)

Wheel track	2.483 m (8 ft 1¾ in)
Wheelbase	4.369 m (14 ft 4 in)
AREAS:	
Wings, gross	19.30 m² (207.74 sq ft)
Ailerons (total)	1.328 m² (14.29 sq ft)
Trailing-edge flaps (total)	2.21 m² (23.79 sq ft)
Airbrake	0.68 m² (7.32 sq ft)
Fin	2.37 m² (25.51 sq ft)
Rudder, incl tab	0.61 m² (6.57 sq ft)
Tailplane	3.38 m² (36.38 sq ft)
Elevators (total, incl tabs)	0.979 m² (10.54 sq ft)
WEIGHTS AND LOADING:	
Weight empty, equipped	3,125 kg (6,889 lb)
Basic operating weight empty	3,136 kg (6,913 lb)
Fuel load (internal, usable)	1,100 kg (2,425 lb)
T-O weight, clean	4,400 kg (9,700 lb)

Typical T-O weights with armament indicated:
A: four Mk 82 bombs and two drop tanks
  5,895 kg (13,000 lb)
B: six Mk 82 bombs 5,895 kg (13,000 lb)
C: two Macchi 30 mm gun pods, two LR-25-0 rocket launchers and two drop tanks 5,808 kg (12,805 lb)
D: four LR-25-0 launchers and two drop tanks
  5,642 kg (12,440 lb)
E: six LR-25-0 launchers 5,323 kg (11,735 lb)
Max T-O weight with external stores
  5,895 kg (13,000 lb)
Wing loading (50 per cent fuel)
  205 kg/m² (42.00 lb/sq ft)

PERFORMANCE (at clean T-O weight, ISA, except where indicated):
IAS limit/Mach limit
  Mach 0.85 (500 knots; 926 km/h; 575 mph)
Max level speed at S/L
  485 knots (898 km/h; 558 mph) IAS
Max level speed at 9,150 m (30,000 ft)
  Mach 0.77 (441 knots; 817 km/h; 508 mph)
Max speed for landing gear extension
  175 knots (324 km/h; 201 mph) IAS
T-O speed 100 knots (185 km/h; 115 mph)
Approach speed over 15 m (50 ft) obstacle
  98 knots (182 km/h; 113 mph) IAS
Landing speed 89 knots (165 km/h; 103 mph) IAS
Stalling speed 80 knots (149 km/h; 93 mph)
Max rate of climb at S/L 2,010 m (6,595 ft)/min
Time to 9,150 m (30,000 ft) 7 min 6 s
Service ceiling (30.5 m; 100 ft/min rate of climb)
  14,630 m (48,000 ft)
Min ground turning radius 8.45 m (27 ft 8¾ in)
T-O run at S/L: clean T-O weight 465 m (1,525 ft)
  max T-O weight 915 m (3,000 ft)
Landing run at S/L, ISA 415 m (1,362 ft)
Max range without drop tanks
  950 nm (1,760 km; 1,094 miles)
Max ferry range with two underwing drop tanks, 10% reserves 1,140 nm (2,110 km; 1,310 miles)
Max endurance without drop tanks 2 h 50 min
Max endurance at 7,620 m (25,000 ft) with two underwing drop tanks, 10% reserves 3 h 45 min
g limits +8/-4
PERFORMANCE (armed configuration, at T-O weights given earlier):
Radius of action, hi-lo-hi (no run-in or run-out):

A	320 nm (593 km; 368 miles)
B	212 nm (393 km; 244 miles)
C	275 nm (510 km; 317 miles)
D	305 nm (565 km; 351 miles)
E	165 nm (306 km; 190 miles)

Radius of action, lo-lo-lo (no run-in or run-out):

A	200 nm (371 km; 230 miles)
B	146 nm (271 km; 168 miles)
C	190 nm (352 km; 219 miles)
D	193 nm (358 km; 222 miles)
E	123 nm (228 km; 142 miles)

Aermacchi MB-339C, showing revised nose and vertical tail configuration *(Pilot Press)*

AERMACCHI MB-339C

This is an improved trainer/close air support version with a Viper 680 engine, featuring also a digital nav/attack system and other advanced avionics. In particular, it has an inertial platform, Doppler radar and radar altimeter for autonomous navigation; a nav/attack computer; laser rangefinder; and electronic self-protection systems. It also has enlarged wingtip tanks and a modified nose shape. It is intended for effective pilot training in modern mission management techniques. Design and development began in 1982-83. The prototype (I-AMDA) flew for the first time on 17 December 1985. The first of an initial batch of 20 production aircraft made a one-hour initial flight on 8 November 1988. This initial batch went to the Italian Air Force. Meanwhile, qualification of systems and weapons, including the AIM-9L Sidewinder and AGM-65D Maverick, was undertaken. In late 1989 it was announced that the Royal New Zealand Air Force was to purchase 18 MB-339Cs to replace Strikemasters.

The description of the MB-339A applies also to the MB-339C except for the following details:

POWER PLANT: One 19.57 kN (4,400 lb st) Rolls-Royce Viper Mk 680-43 turbojet. Fuselage fuel capacity as for MB-339A, but capacity of each integral tip tank increased to 500 litres (132 US gallons; 110 Imp gallons), giving total usable capacity of 1,781 litres (470 US gallons; 392 Imp gallons). Provision retained for two 325 litre (86 US gallon; 71.5 Imp gallon) drop tanks on centre underwing stations.

AVIONICS AND EQUIPMENT: Typical avionics installation includes Collins AN/ARN-118(V) type RT-1159/A Tacan or Bendix/King KDM 706A DME; Collins 51RV-4B VOR/ILS and MKI-3 marker beacon receiver; Collins ADF-6A ADF/LF; Collins DF-301E VHF/UHF ADF (optional); GEC Avionics AD-660 Doppler radar

First production Aermacchi MB-339C, equipped with Viper 680 engine and a digital nav/attack system

integrated with a Litton LR-80 inertial platform; GEC Avionics 620K navigation computer; Kaiser Sabre head-up display/weapons aiming computer; Aeritalia CRT multifunction display; Aeritalia/Honeywell HG7505 radar altimeter; FIAR P 0702 laser rangefinder; ELT-156 radar warning system; Logic stores management system; Bendix/King AN/APX-100 IFF; Astronautics ARU-50/A attitude director indicator; Astronautics AQU-13 HSI; Fairchild Weston video camera; HOTAS (hands on throttle and stick) controls;

Tracor AN/ALE-40 chaff/flare dispensers; and Elettronica ELT-555 active ECM pod.

ARMAMENT: As for MB-339A. Nav/attack system makes possible the employment of air-to-air infra-red missiles (AIM-9L and Matra Magic), AGM-65 Maverick air-to-ground missiles and Marte Mk II sea skimming anti-ship missiles.

DIMENSIONS, EXTERNAL: As for MB-339A except:
Wing span over tip tanks   11.22 m (36 ft 9¾ in)
Length overall   11.24 m (36 ft 10½ in)

AGUSTA

AGUSTA SpA

21017 Cascina Costa di Samarate (VA)
Telephone: 39 (331) 229111
Telex: 332569 AGUCA I
OFFICES:
Via Caldera 21, 20153 Milan
Telephone: 39 (2) 452751
Telex: 333280 AGUMI I
Fax: 39 (2) 48204701
Via Abruzzi 11, 00187 Rome
Telephone: 39 (6) 49801
Telex: 614398 AGURO I
Fax: 39 (6) 490309

CHAIRMAN AND CHIEF EXECUTIVE OFFICER:
Dott Roberto D'Alessandro

INTERNATIONAL CO-OPERATION: Ing Luigi Passini

MARKETING AND SALES: Dott Enrico Guerra

PRESS AND PUBLIC RELATIONS: Ing Francesco Fusco

PLANNING: Dott Roberto Leverone

AERONAUTICA BUSINESS UNIT: Ing Ferruccio Tommasi

LOGISTIC BUSINESS UNIT: Ing Michele Ferraioli

RESEARCH AND DEVELOPMENT BUSINESS UNIT:
Ing Bruno Lovera

AEROSPACE SYSTEM BUSINESS UNIT:
Ing Mario Barozzi

Formed originally in 1977, the Agusta Group (see 1980-81 *Jane's*) completely reorganised its structure from 1 January 1981 under a new holding company known as Agusta SpA. It became part of the Italian public holding agency EFIM, employing nearly 10,000 people in 12 factories in various parts of Italy.

The various domestic activities of Agusta are grouped under the location of the works, with the familiar names of Costruzioni Aeronautiche Giovanni Agusta, SIAI-Marchetti, Caproni Vizzola Costruzioni Aeronautiche and BredaNardi Costruzioni Aeronautiche no longer in use. In addition, Elicotteri Meridionali is a domestic affiliate and Agusta has four international affiliates in addition to its involvement with Sammi Agusta Aerospace of South Korea (which see). The various works and affiliates are as follows:

DOMESTIC WORKS
**Benevento Works
(ex-FOMB – Fonderie e Officine Meccaniche di Benevento SpA)**
Contrada Ponte Valentino - S.S. 90 bis, 82100 Benevento
Telephone: 39 (824) 53440/53441/53447
Telex: 710667
Fax: 39 (824) 53418
This works specialises in aircraft co-production and overhaul of helicopters and multi-engined aircraft.

**Brindisi Works
(ex-IAM – Industrie Aeronautiche Meridionali SpA)**
Contrada Santa Teresa Pinti, 72100 Brindisi
Telephone: 39 (831) 8911
Telex: 813360
Fax: 39 (831) 452659

**Cascina Costa Works
(ex-Costruzioni Aeronautiche Giovanni Agusta SpA)**
Via Giovanni Agusta 520, 21017 Cascina Costa di Samarate (VA)
Telephone: 39 (331) 229111
Telex: 332569 AGUCA I
Fax: 39 (331) 222525

**Monteprandone Works
(ex-BredaNardi Costruzioni Aeronautiche SpA)**
Casella Postale 108, San Benedetto del Trento (Ascoli Piceno), Monteprandone (AP)
Telephone: 39 (735) 801721
Telex: 560165 BRENAR I
Fax: 39 (735) 701927

**Rome Works
(ex-Ottico Meccanica Italiana SpA)**
Via della Vasca Navale 79/81, 00146 Rome
Telephone: 39 (6) 55421
Telex: 610137
Fax: 39 (6) 5593753

**Sesto Calende Works
(ex-SIAI – Marchetti SpA)**
Via Indipendenza 2, 21018 Sesto Calende (VA)
Telephone: 39 (331) 924421
Telex: 332601 SI AIA VI
Fax: 39 (331) 922525

**Somma Lombarda Works
(ex-Caproni Vizzola Costruzioni Aeronautiche SpA)**
Via Per Tornavento 15, 21019 Somma Lombardo
Telephone: 39 (331) 230826
Telex: 332554 CAVIZ I
Fax: 39 (331) 230622

**Tradate Works
(ex-Agusta Sistemi SpA)**
Via Isonzo 33, 21049 Tradate (VA)
Telephone: 39 (331) 815111
Telex: 350405
Fax: 39 (331) 843910

DOMESTIC AFFILIATE
Elicotteri Meridionali SpA
S.E.I. - Servizi Elicotteristici Italiani, Via Sicilia 43, 00187 Rome
Telephone: 39 (6) 49801
PRESIDENT: Dott Roberto D'Alessandro

INTERNATIONAL AFFILIATES
Agusta Aerospace Corporation
3050 Red Lion Road, Philadelphia, Pennsylvania 19114, USA
Telephone: 1 (215) 2811400
Telex: 6851181
Fax: 1 (215) 2810440
CHAIRMAN AND CHIEF EXECUTIVE OFFICER:
Ing Giuseppe Orsi
Agusta Aerospace Service SA
Avenue Louise 523, Brussels B-1050, Belgium
Telephone: 32 (2) 648585/6485515
Telex: 63349
GENERAL MANAGER: Dott Riccardo Baldini
Agusta Aviation Far East Pte Ltd
World Trade Center, 1 Maritime Square 08-01, 0409 Singapore
Telephone: 65 (273) 3100
Telex: 36126
GENERAL MANAGER: Dott Fulvio Maurogiovanni
OMI Corporation of America
1319 Powhatan Street, Alexandria, Virginia 22314, USA
Telephone: 1 (703) 5499191
Telex: 899141
CHAIRMAN: James F. Byrnes

CASCINA COSTA WORKS
The original Agusta company, established in 1907 by Giovanni Agusta, built many experimental and production aircraft before the Second World War. In 1952 Agusta acquired a licence to manufacture the Bell Model 47 helicopter, and the first Agusta built Model 47G made its initial flight on 22 May 1954.

In addition to the A 109A and A 129 of its own design, Agusta is currently producing under licence the Bell Models 206, 212 and 412, and the Sikorsky S-61A, SH-3H and HH-3F (S-61R). Agusta is now the sole production source of these Sikorsky aircraft. It has developed its own AS-61N1 short-fuselage derivative of the civil Sikorsky S-61N, produces under licence the Boeing CH-47C Chinook helicopter, and is collaborating with Westland Helicopters of the UK in developing the EH 101

three-turboshaft helicopter (see under EHI in the International section).

Other international programmes in which Agusta participates are the Eurofar tilt-rotor project, the JEH Tonal (derived from the A129) and the NH 90. Details of these also appear in the International section. The company also holds a 22 per cent share in FMA of Argentina.

AGUSTA A 109A Mk II (CIVIL VERSIONS)
The first of three A 109 flying prototypes flew for the first time on 4 August 1971. RAI and FAA certification for VFR operation was announced on 1 June 1975, and deliveries of the original A 109A production version started in early 1976. Certification for IFR single-pilot operation was obtained on 20 January 1977. Certification has also been granted in Australia, Brazil, Canada, France, West

Germany, Japan, Mexico, New Zealand, the Philippines, Sweden, Switzerland, the UK and Venezuela. Approximately 150 of this initial version, described in the 1981-82 *Jane's*, were built.

Deliveries of the uprated A 109A Mk II began in September 1981. This has an increase in transmission rating, a new tail rotor driveshaft, increased tail rotor blade life and reliability, new self-damping engine mounts, integral-design oil coolers and blowers, a structurally redesigned tailboom, higher-pressure hydraulic system, improved avionics and instrument layout, and a removable floor in the baggage compartment. It is also available in a utility version with less sophisticated interior and instrumentation. Under a 1983 agreement, Hellenic Aerospace Industries (see Greek section) has been producing major fuselage components for 77 Mk IIs.

In 1985 Agusta introduced a 'wide-body' version of the Mk II, with a more roomy and comfortable cabin created by modifying the shape of the underfloor fuel tanks and using bulged fuselage side panels similar to those of the medevac version. These changes do not affect either the basic structure or aerodynamic characteristics of the helicopter. The latest 'Plus' version features 335.6 kW (450 shp) Allison 250-C20R-1 engines, but with the same transmission ratings as for the C20B engines.

In late 1989 Agusta signed a contract with the Asian Helicopter Corporation of Japan for 65 A 109s, thought to be the largest civil helicopter contract ever. Another recent order has come from the Turkish Interior Ministry.

The following description applies to the standard A 109A Mk II, unless stated otherwise:

TYPE: Twin-engined general purpose helicopter.

ROTOR SYSTEM: Fully articulated four-blade single main rotor and port side two-blade semi-rigid delta-hinged tail rotor. Main rotor blades have an NACA 23011.3/13006 'droop snoot' aerofoil section, with thickness/chord ratios of 11.3 per cent at root and 6 per cent at tip, and are attached to hub by tension/torsion straps. They are of aluminium alloy bonded construction, with a Nomex core, have swept tips, stainless steel tip caps and leading-edge strips, and are protected against corrosion. A manual blade folding capability and rotor brake are optional. Tail rotor blades are of aluminium alloy, bonded at the trailing-edge, with a Nomex honeycomb core and stainless steel leading-edge strip.

ROTOR DRIVE: Main transmission assembly housed in fairing above passenger cabin, driving main rotor through a coupling gearbox and 90° two-stage (15.62:1) main reduction gearbox. Take-off drive from coupling gearbox drives tail rotor via an output shaft and tail rotor gearbox. Transmission ratings 552 kW (740 shp) for take-off and max continuous twin-engined operation, with max contingency rating of 607 kW (814 shp) for 6 s. Ratings for single-engined operation are 336 kW (450 shp) for take-off (5 min limit), 313 kW (420 shp) max continuous, and 336 kW (450 shp) max contingency for 10 s. Main rotor/engine rpm ratio 1:15.62; tail rotor/engine rpm ratio 1:2.80.

FUSELAGE AND TAIL UNIT: Pod and boom type, of aluminium alloy and honeycomb construction, built in four main sections: nose, cockpit, passenger cabin and tailboom. Sweptback vertical fins (above and below tailboom). Non-swept elevator, mid-mounted on tailboom forward of fins, is linked to collective pitch control.

LANDING GEAR: Retractable tricycle type, with oleo-pneumatic shock absorber in each unit. Single main-wheels and castoring (45° each side of centre), self-centring nosewheel. Hydraulic retraction, nosewheel forward, mainwheels upward into fuselage. Hydraulic emergency extension and locking. Magnaghi disc brakes on mainwheels. All tyres are of Kléber-Colombes tubeless type, and of same size (650 × 6) and pressure (5.9 bars; 85 lb/sq in). Tailskid under ventral fin. Emergency pop-out flotation gear and fixed snow skis optional.

POWER PLANT: Two Allison 250-C20B turboshafts (each 313 kW; 420 shp for 5 min for T-O, 298 kW; 400 shp max continuous power, 276 kW; 370 shp max cruise power, derated to 258 kW; 346 shp for twin-engine operation), mounted side by side in upper rear fuselage and separated from passenger cabin and from each other by firewalls. Two bladder fuel tanks in lower rear fuselage, combined capacity 560 litres (148 US gallons; 123 Imp gallons), of which 550 litres (145.3 US gallons; 121 Imp gallons) are usable. Refuelling point in each side of fuselage, near top of each tank. Oil capacity 7.7 litres (2.0 US gallons; 1.7 Imp gallons) for each engine and 12 litres (3.2 US gallons; 2.6 Imp gallons) for transmission. Provision for internal auxiliary tank containing up to 170 litres (44.9 US gallons; 37.4 Imp gallons) of fuel.

ACCOMMODATION: Crew of one or two on flight deck, with pilot seated on right. Dual controls optional. Main cabin seats up to six passengers on three forward or rearward facing seats in centre, plus three forward facing seats at rear. A seventh passenger can be carried in lieu of second crew member. Four/five-seat VIP layout available, with refreshment and music centre. Forward opening crew door and passenger door on each side. Large space at rear of cabin for up to 150 kg (331 lb) of baggage, with access via forward opening door on port side. Centre row of seats removable to permit use as freight transport. Medevac version can accommodate one stretcher installed crosswise (by replacing standard doors with bubble doors), and complete medical equipment including oxygen cylinders (enough for three hours' use), oxygen/air-oxygen respirator with flowmeter humidifier, ECG with monitoring equipment, and equipment for intensive care. A quick-change emergency medical service (EMS) unit is available which enables the standard transport configuration to be changed to air ambulance layout within a few minutes. The EMS configuration accommodates a pilot and three medical attendants, a longitudinally placed stretcher, and a cardio-circulatory and respiratory intensive care system. A second stretcher patient can be carried if necessary. In a cargo role, external freight can be transported on a CG hook. Sliding doors can be installed for rescue missions.

SYSTEMS: Two identical independent Magnaghi hydraulic systems, pressure 107 bars (1550 lb/sq in), supply dual

flight servo-controls and provide emergency power in the event of engine failure. A utility system connected to No. 2 servo-hydraulic system provides power to actuate landing gear, wheel and rotor braking, nosewheel locking, and emergency backup. 28V DC electrical system, using two 30V 150A engine driven starter/generators, and one 24V 13Ah nickel-cadmium battery (22Ah heavy duty battery on IFR version). Single phase AC power at 400Hz supplied by two 115/26V 250VA solid state static inverters. Third inverter as emergency backup on IFR version. External power receptacle. Engine anti-icing system, using engine bleed air.

AVIONICS: Standard instrumentation, plus Collins avionics for VFR or IFR operation, to customer's requirements, including VHF-20A VHF-AM com (dual in IFR version), AG-06 intercom, VIR-31A VOR/ILS with VOR/LOC, glideslope and marker beacon receiver, TDR-90 ATC transponder, ADF-60A and DME-40. Optional avionics include Honeywell AA-300 radio altimeter with linear glide-slope capture, Helcis II flight director and autotrim, AFCS, pilot's navigation instruments, co-pilot's flight and navigation instruments, EHSI, two- or three-axis autopilot, Bendix/FIAR RDR-1500 or Honeywell Primus 300SL weather radar, and Loran or Omega navigation system, depending on requirement.

EQUIPMENT: Depending upon mission, may include internal cargo platform, external cargo sling, externally mounted rescue hoist, first aid kit, one or two stretchers, Chadwick water bomber container for 208 or 584 litres (55 or 154.2 US gallons; 45.75 or 128.5 Imp gallons) of water or fire retardant, or equipment for exploration, thermal mapping, survey, or powerline control duties.

DIMENSIONS, EXTERNAL:

Main rotor diameter	11.00 m (36 ft 1 in)
Tail rotor diameter	2.03 m (6 ft 8 in)
Length overall, rotors turning	13.05 m (42 ft 9¾ in)
Fuselage: Length	10.706 m (35 ft 1½ in)
Max width (except wide-body)	1.44 m (4 ft 8½ in)
Height over tail fin	3.30 m (10 ft 10 in)
Elevator span	2.88 m (9 ft 5½ in)
Width over mainwheels	2.45 m (8 ft 0½ in)
Wheelbase	3.535 m (11 ft 7¼ in)
Passenger doors (each): Height	1.06 m (3 ft 5¾ in)
Width	1.15 m (3 ft 9¼ in)
Height to sill	0.65 m (2 ft 1½ in)
Baggage door (port, rear): Height	0.51 m (1 ft 8 in)
Width	1.00 m (3 ft 3¼ in)

DIMENSIONS, INTERNAL:

Cabin, excl flight deck: Length	1.63 m (5 ft 4¼ in)
Max width	1.32 m (4 ft 4 in)
Max height	1.28 m (4 ft 2½ in)
Volume	2.82 m³ (100 cu ft)
Baggage compartment volume	0.52 m³ (18.4 cu ft)

AREAS:

Main rotor blades (each)	1.84 m² (19.8 sq ft)
Tail rotor blades (each)	0.203 m² (2.185 sq ft)
Main rotor disc	95.03 m² (1022.9 sq ft)
Tail rotor disc	3.24 m² (34.87 sq ft)

WEIGHTS AND LOADINGS:

Basic weight empty, equipped:	
standard	1,418 kg (3,126 lb)
standard, 'Plus'	1,432 kg (3,157 lb)
offshore oil support (IFR)	1,604 kg (3,536 lb)
ambulance (IFR)	1,647 kg (3,631 lb)
firefighting	1,596 kg (3,518 lb)
Max external slung load	907 kg (2,000 lb)
Max baggage	150 kg (331 lb)
Typical T-O weight:	
offshore oil support (IFR)	2,596 kg (5,723 lb)
ambulance (IFR)	2,409 kg (5,311 lb)
Max certificated T-O weight	2,600 kg (5,732 lb)
Max disc loading	27.4 kg/m² (5.60 lb/sq ft)
Max power loading	4.15 kg/kW (6.82 lb/shp)

PERFORMANCE: (S/L, ISA, except where indicated. A: AUW of 2,250 kg; 4,960 lb, B: AUW of 2,450 kg; 5,400 lb, C: AUW of 2,600 kg; 5,732 lb, D: 'Plus' at AUW of 2,600 kg; 5,732 lb):

Never-exceed speed:	
A, B, C, D	168 knots (311 km/h; 193 mph)
Max cruising speed: A	154 knots (285 km/h; 177 mph)
B, C	150 knots (278 km/h; 172 mph)
Max cruising speed at 1,830 m (6,000 ft):	
D	152 knots (281 km/h; 175 mph)
Econ cruising speed:	
A, B, C	126 knots (233 km/h; 145 mph)
Max rate of climb at S/L: A	643 m (2,110 ft)/min
B	555 m (1,820 ft)/min
C	503 m (1,650 ft)/min
D	504 m (1,655 ft)/min
Rate of climb at S/L, one engine out:	
A	152 m (500 ft)/min
B	108 m (355 ft)/min
C	78 m (255 ft)/min
D	138 m (455 ft)/min
Service ceiling, 30.5 m (100 ft)/min rate of climb, at max	
continuous power: A, B, D	4,575 m (15,000 ft)
C	4,450 m (14,600 ft)
Service ceiling, one engine out, 30.5 m (100 ft)/min rate of	
climb, at max continuous power:	
C	1,675 m (5,500 ft)
D	2,530 m (8,300 ft)
Hovering ceiling IGE: A	3,750 m (12,300 ft)
B	2,985 m (9,800 ft)
C	2,410 m (7,900 ft)
D	3,800 m (12,465 ft)
Hovering ceiling OGE: A	2,880 m (9,450 ft)
B	2,072 m (6,800 ft)
C	1,493 m (4,900 ft)
D	2,600 m (8,530 ft)
Range with max standard fuel, no reserves:	
A	350 nm (648 km; 402 miles)
B	341 nm (631 km; 392 miles)
C	332 nm (615 km; 382 miles)
D	440 nm (815 km; 506 miles)
Endurance with max fuel, no reserves: A	3 h 12 min
B	3 h 2 min
C	2 h 57 min
D	4 h 35 min

Agusta A 109A Mk II general purpose helicopter in 'wide-body' configuration

Agusta A 109A Mk II twin-engined general purpose helicopter (Pilot Press)

Monaco-registered Agusta A 109C at Helitech '89 *(Kenneth Munson)*

AGUSTA A 109C and A 109 MAX

These FAA certificated versions of the A 109 were announced by the company's US subsidiary, Agusta Aerospace Corporation, at the beginning of 1989.

The **A 109C** has 'Plus' type 313/335.6 kW (420/450 shp) Allison 250-C20R-1 turboshafts, transmission rating increased from 552 kW (740 shp) to 589 kW (790 shp), new main rotor blades of composite construction and Wortmann section tail rotor blades, strengthened landing gear, and an increased max T-O weight of 2,720 kg (5,996 lb), permitting a 109 kg (240 lb) increase in payload. Four were ordered in 1989 by the Sultan of Johore, Malaysia.

The **A 109 Max** is an improved medevac variant, with a 3.96 m³ (140 cu ft) cabin volume able to accommodate two pilots, two stretcher cases and two sitting casualties or medical attendants. The new cabin layout has been engineered by Custom Aircraft Completions of Teterboro, New Jersey, and it can be entered by newly designed upward opening gull wing doors.

WEIGHTS (A 109C):
Weight empty, equipped	1,538 kg (3,390 lb)
Max T-O weight	2,720 kg (5,996 lb)

PERFORMANCE (A 109C):
Max cruising speed at 915 m (3,000 ft)	152 knots (282 km/h; 175 mph)
Service ceiling, one engine out	1,890 m (6,200 ft)
Hovering ceiling: IGE	3,350 m (11,000 ft)
OGE	2,400 m (7,900 ft)
Range with 700 litres (185 US gallons; 154 Imp gallons) of fuel	360 nm (667 km; 414 miles)
Endurance, fuel as above	4 h 44 min

AGUSTA A 109A Mk II (MILITARY, NAVAL and LAW ENFORCEMENT VERSIONS)

Several non-commercial versions of the A 109A have been developed by Agusta. In general, their configuration, structure and power plant are similar to those of the standard civil versions, although specially modified versions can be made available if required. 'Plus' versions with 335.6 kW (450 shp) Allison 250-C20R-1 engines are also available. Features of some or all military and naval versions include, as standard, dual controls and instrumentation; rotor brake; tail rotor control magnetic brake; sliding doors; environmental control system; emergency flotation gear; armoured seats; heavy duty battery; particle separator; external cargo hook; multi-purpose universal supports for external stores; rescue hoist; and high-load cargo floor. The naval versions, specially configured for shipboard compatibility, can be equipped with four-axis AFCS, radar altimeter, internal auxiliary fuel tanks, non-retractable landing gear, search radar, anchorage points for deck lashings, and an automatic navigation system.

In late 1988 Belgium ordered 28 in anti-armour and 18 in scout configurations under its Aéromobilité 1 programme to replace existing Aerospatiale Alouette II helicopters. Offset agreements were signed with Belgian manufacturing companies, which include A 109 assembly by Sabca. Deliveries are expected to take place between June 1991 and June 1993. The order includes supply of Saab HeliTOW systems and 500 TOW anti-armour missiles. Collins Government Avionics Division of Rockwell is supplying the avionics management system, ATHS, ARN-149 ADF, ARC-186 VHF transceiver and bus interface unit. Collins Defense Communications is supplying HF-9000 transceivers. Agusta also promoted the A 109 as a contender for the Canadian Forces' CFLH light helicopter programme, involving the procurement of about 80 helicopters in the mid-1990s, and has an agreement with Grumman to promote an Agusta helicopter as a contender for the US Army's 'adversary' helicopter programme.

The principal military, naval and other non-commercial versions were listed in some detail in the 1984-85 *Jane's*. The following is an abbreviated description:

Aerial scout. Can be armed with a flexibly mounted 7.62 mm or 12.7 mm machine-gun, with stabilised sight, plus two XM157 launchers (each with seven 2.75 in rockets). Normal crew of three.

Light attack against tanks and other hard-point targets. Has been demonstrated with Hughes M65 TOW system incorporating undernose telescopic sight unit, plus four or eight TOW missiles. Normal crew of two. Argentine Army has adapted its A 109As to carry Mathogo anti-tank missiles.

Light attack against soft-point targets. Various combinations of armament include a pintle mounted 7.62 mm machine-gun in each doorway; a flexible, remotely controlled externally mounted 7.62 mm gun; twin trainable, remotely controlled externally mounted 7.62 mm guns; two external machine-gun pods; or two gun pods and two rocket launchers. Normal crew of two. Suited to escort and area suppression.

Command and control. For target designation and direction of helicopter attack force. Can be armed with combination of rockets and flexible machine-guns, as described in preceding paragraph.

Utility. For up to seven troops; two stretcher patients and two medical attendants; externally mounted rescue hoist; or underfuselage hook for slung load.

Mirach. Version carrying two Mirach 100 RPVs for battlefield surveillance, reconnaissance, target acquisition, elint, ECM, attack on ground or naval targets, and enemy defence saturation or decoy.

ESM/ECM. Electronic warfare version, for military and naval use. Available with passive ESM only, plus weapon systems if required; and with passive ESM plus modularised active ECM (jamming), plus any required weapons. Provision for chaff dispenser to be mounted on tailboom.

Naval. Primary naval missions are anti-surface vessel, electronic warfare, standoff missile guidance, reconnaissance, and anti-submarine classification. Secondary capabilities for search and rescue, troop transportation, ambulance, flying crane, coastguard patrol, and inter-ship liaison duties. Configurations for electronic warfare and utility roles generally similar to those described in preceding 'Utility' and 'ESM/ECM' paragraphs. For the ASW role, specialised equipment includes MAD, one or two homing torpedoes and six marine markers. For the ASV role the naval A 109A carries a high performance long-range search radar with high discrimination in rough sea conditions. The surface attack is performed with air-to-surface wire-guided missiles. For the TG-2 (standoff missile guidance) mission, the helicopter is equipped with a special system to control and guide a ship-launched Otomat missile. For armed patrol, the naval A 109A is equipped with a search radar and armament to customer's requirements. The coastguard patrol configuration includes a search radar, a special installation for external high efficiency loudspeakers, and a searchlight.

Law enforcement and other patrol duties. For patrol (including armed patrol) and surveillance, traffic control, search and rescue, firefighting, and similar utility missions. Principal SAR equipment includes search radar, rescue hoist, stretcher/first aid kits, radar altimeter, skis or emergency flotation gear, AFCS, and flare/smoke grenades. For aerial patrol it can include 360° radar, automatic stability control system, external loudspeakers, FLIR, pollution monitoring equipment, system for spraying chemical retardants, and other items depending upon requirements of mission. A specific **coastal patrol** version is in service with the Italian Guardia di Finanza, offering all-weather maritime patrol capability. It has a stretched nose to accommodate the avionics and high-power searchlight, and is also fitted with light emergency floats, survival equipment and a loudspeaker housed in the baggage compartment. The cockpit features a compact instrument panel to improve visibility, with vertical scale engine instruments. Mission equipment includes an Omega LRN 85 navigation system, FIAR (Bendix) RDR 1500 360° scan search radar, and a Honeywell SPZ-7300 four-axis automatic flight control system with approach to hovering mode. The fully integrated avionics system enables the helicopter to patrol automatically an area along preset courses and automatically approach radar engaged targets. A cabin-mounted 7.62 mm machine-gun can be carried.

ROTOR DRIVE: As for civil A 109A Mk II, except for twin-engined max contingency rating of 638 kW (856 shp) and 5 min single-engined T-O rating of 313 kW (420 shp).

TYPICAL WEIGHTS (military Mk II):
Basic weight empty	1,418 kg (3,126 lb)
Weight empty, equipped: utility	1,560 kg (3,439 lb)
ESM/ECM	1,627 kg (3,587 lb)
ambulance	1,630 kg (3,594 lb)
scout, attack, air defence	1,650 kg (3,638 lb)
anti-tank	1,790 kg (3,946 lb)
Armament/equipment/payload:	
ambulance (1 medical attendant)	80 kg (176 lb)
air defence (8 missiles)	150 kg (331 lb)
anti-tank (8 missiles)	196 kg (432 lb)
ESM/ECM (radar warning, deception jammer, noise jammer, ESM equipment)	270 kg (595 lb)
scout (2 podded 12.7 mm and 2 pintle mounted 7.62 mm machine-guns)	287 kg (633 lb)
attack (2 podded 12.7 mm machine-guns and 14 rockets in pods)	344 kg (758 lb)
utility (7 equipped troops)	630 kg (1,389 lb)
T-O weight: ambulance	2,330 kg (5,136 lb)
air defence	2,500 kg (5,512 lb)
scout, attack, anti-tank, Mirach, ESM/ECM, utility (max T-O weight)	2,600 kg (5,732 lb)

PERFORMANCE (S/L, ISA, except where indicated. A: AUW of 2,250 kg; 4,960 lb, B: AUW of 2,450 kg; 5,400 lb, C: AUW of 2,600 kg; 5,732 lb, D: 'Plus' in light attack configuration at 2,720 kg, 5,995 lb AUW): As civil Mk II except:

Max cruising speed: A	155 knots (287 km/h; 178 mph)	
B	150 knots (278 km/h; 173 mph)	
C	147 knots (272 km/h; 169 mph)	
D	136 knots (252 km/h; 157 mph)	
Econ cruising speed: A	126 knots (233 km/h; 145 mph)	
B	125 knots (232 km/h; 144 mph)	
C	124 knots (230 km/h; 143 mph)	
Max rate of climb at S/L: A	640 m (2,100 ft)/min	
D	516 m (1,690 ft)/min	
Service ceiling, 30.5 m (100 ft)/min rate of climb, at max continuous power: A	5,485 m (18,000 ft)	
B, D	4,575 m (15,000 ft)	
C	4,450 m (14,600 ft)	

Range with max standard fuel, no reserves:
A	320 nm (593 km; 368 miles)
B	310 nm (574 km; 357 miles)
C	300 nm (556 km; 345 miles)

Agusta A 109 EOA of the Italian Army *(Ivo Sturzenegger)*

Range with max standard fuel, 10 min reserves:
Mirach   360 nm (667 km; 414 miles)
Range: D   360 nm (667 km; 414 miles)
Endurance with max standard fuel, no reserves:
A   3 h 43 min
B   3 h 30 min
C   3 h 15 min
D   3 h 50 min
Endurance with max standard fuel, 10 min reserves:
Mirach   4 h 30 min

AGUSTA A 109 EOA

Twenty-four examples of this light multi-role helicopter (LMH) version of the A 109 were ordered by the Italian Army as EOA (Elicottero d'Osservazione Avanzata) advanced observation helicopters. Deliveries were made in 1988 to the Aviazione Leggera dell'Esercito, to take over from fixed-wing SIAI-Marchetti SM 1019s.

The EOA has the lengthened nose and fixed, raised landing gear of the A 109-K (see following entry), but is powered by uprated Allison 250-C20R engines, offering better hot and high performance than the -C20Bs in the standard A 109A Mk II. Other features include sliding cabin doors, crashworthy fuel tanks, a wide range of armament options, and electronic warfare equipment. A description appeared in the 1989-90 *Jane's*.

AGUSTA A 109-K

This multi-role hot and high military variant of the A 109A Mk II is powered by two 538 kW (722 shp) Turbomeca Arriel 1K turboshafts (instead of the A 109's usual 313 kW; 420 shp Allisons). It flew for the first time in April 1983.

Designed for operation by a pilot and gunner in its primary combat role, the A 109-K has an uprated transmission, a new main rotor hub made of composites, elastomeric bearings, composites blades with a hard surface coating that is resistant to abrasion by sand and hard dust, a new tail rotor of Wortmann blade section, a longer nose to house additional avionics, and a taller and non-retractable high shock absorption wheeled landing gear.

The second prototype, which began flying in March 1984, was fully representative of the planned production version. Differences by comparison with the standard A 109A Mk II are as follows:

TYPE: Twin-engined multi-role helicopter.

ROTOR SYSTEM AND DRIVE: Composites main rotor blades and hub, with elastomeric bearings, and special blade surface coating, for greater corrosion/abrasion resistance. New tail rotor of slightly reduced diameter, with high-efficiency Wortmann aerofoil section and stainless steel skins. Optional rotor brake. Main transmission uprated to 671 kW (900 shp) for take-off and max continuous twin-engined operation. Ratings for single-engined operation are 492 kW (660 shp) for 2.5 minutes, and 373 kW (500 shp) max continuous.

FUSELAGE: Nose lengthened by 40 cm (15¾ in) and fitted with an upward hinged door on each side, for access to avionics. Provision for ECM or other sensors on nose.

LANDING GEAR: Non-retractable tricycle type, giving increased clearance between fuselage and ground. Changes restricted to replacement of nose leg actuator by a fixed strut, and replacement of each main leg actuator by a fixed strut and a V support frame.

POWER PLANT: Two Turbomeca Arriel 1K turboshafts, each rated at 540 kW (724 shp) for 2.5 minutes, 522 kW (700 shp) for take-off (5 minutes) and 436 kW (585 shp) max cruise power. Engine particle separator optional. Standard usable fuel capacity 550 litres (145 US gallons; 121 Imp gallons), with optional 150 litre (39.6 US gallon; 33 Imp gallon) auxiliary tanks. Optional closed circuit refuelling system and optional 200 litre (53 US gallon; 44 Imp gallon) ferry tanks in cabin. Self-sealing fuel tanks optional. Independent fuel and oil system for each engine.

ACCOMMODATION: Normal crew of two for combat missions, comprising pilot (on right) and gunner. Smaller instrument panel to improve forward view. Up to six passengers in cabin of utility version.

Agusta A 129 light anti-tank, attack and advanced scout helicopter *(Pilot Press)*

SYSTEMS: Two independent hydraulic and electrical systems. 28V DC electrical system supplied by two 160A starter/generators, with 13Ah nickel-cadmium battery and external power socket. Optional 22Ah or 27Ah battery. Two or three 250VA solid-state inverters optional. Optional high load three-phase AC power at 400Hz supplied by 6kVA 115V engine driven alternator and single-phase AC by a 250VA solid state inverter. Second alternator optional.

AVIONICS: Basic installation comprises dual UHF/VHF AM-FM, Collins AN/ARN-126 VOR/GS/ILS, Collins ADF-60, AG-06 intercom, SIT 421 IFF transponder, Honeywell three-axis AFCS and AN/ASN-75 nav compass system. Options include DME, Tacan, VLF Omega, weather radar and ELT system.

ARMAMENT AND OPERATIONAL EQUIPMENT (optional): Total of four stores attachments, two on each side of cabin, on outriggers. Typical loads include two 7.62 mm or 12.7 mm gun pods, 70 mm or 80 mm rocket launchers, or up to eight TOW anti-armour missiles (with roof mounted sight), Stinger air-to-air missiles, RPVs, plus a 7.62 or 12.7 mm side-firing gun in cabin. Chaff/flare dispenser, radar and laser warning systems, FLIR, gyrostabilised sight, night vision goggles, rescue hoist, searchlight and cargo platform among options.

DIMENSIONS, EXTERNAL:
Tail rotor diameter   2.00 m (6 ft 6¾ in)
Length of fuselage   11.106 m (36 ft 5¼ in)
AREA:
Tail rotor disc   3.143 m² (33.83 sq ft)
WEIGHTS AND LOADINGS:
Weight empty   1,592 kg (3,510 lb)
Max T-O weight   2,850 kg (6,283 lb)
Max disc loading   30.0 kg/m² (6.15 lb/sq ft)
Max power loading   2.64 kg/kW (4.34 lb/shp)
PERFORMANCE (at max T-O weight except where indicated):
Never-exceed speed   150 knots (278 km/h; 172 mph)
*Max level speed at S/L, clean:
ISA   138 knots (255 km/h; 159 mph)
ISA + 20°C   140 knots (259 km/h; 161 mph)
*Max cruising speed at S/L, at average weight, clean:
ISA   141 knots (261 km/h; 162 mph)
ISA + 20°C   144 knots (266 km/h; 166 mph)
**Econ cruising speed at S/L, at average weight, clean:
ISA   128 knots (237 km/h; 147 mph)
ISA + 20°C   131 knots (243 km/h; 151 mph)
Max rate of climb at S/L: ISA   530 m (1,740 ft)/min
ISA + 20°C   509 m (1,670 ft)/min

Rate of climb at S/L, one engine out:
ISA or ISA + 20°C   167 m (550 ft)/min
Service ceiling:
ISA or ISA + 20°C   6,100 m (20,000 ft)
Service ceiling, one engine out: ISA   2,770 m (9,100 ft)
ISA + 20°C   1,950 m (6,400 ft)
Hovering ceiling IGE at average weight, clean:
ISA   5,640 m (18,500 ft)
ISA + 20°C   4,970 m (16,300 ft)
Hovering ceiling OGE at average weight, clean:
ISA   3,350 m (11,000 ft)
ISA + 20°C   2,680 m (8,800 ft)
Max range at S/L, clean:
ISA   290 nm (537 km; 333 miles)
ISA + 20°C   284 nm (526 km; 326 miles)
*reduced by 9 knots (17 km/h; 11 mph) with two gun pods fitted
**reduced by 6 knots (11 km/h; 7 mph) with two gun pods fitted

AGUSTA A 109-KN

This is a naval variant of the A 109-K, intended for anti-ship, off-shore patrol, over the horizon targeting, electronic warfare and vertical replenishment roles. It uses the same type of engines and has similar performance, with only the rate of climb marginally increased.

AGUSTA A 129 MANGUSTA

The Italian Army first made known its requirements for a light anti-armour helicopter in 1972, and the selected A 129 design received Italian Army go-ahead in March 1978, undergoing several changes of configuration before reaching its final form in 1980. Detail design was completed on 30 November 1982. The first A 129 (MM 590/E.I. 901) made the official first flight on 15 September 1983, following two earlier unofficial flights of which the first took place on 11 September. First flights of the second and third prototypes took place on 1 July and 5 October 1984; the fourth was flown on 27 May 1985, and the fifth on 1 March 1986.

Initially, the A 129 was intended as a day/night anti-tank and fire support helicopter for the Italian Army. A scout version is also proposed. Besides TOW missiles, armament can include a chin-mounted gun turret, rockets and air-to-air missiles.

Sixty A 129s are being produced to equip two Italian Army Aviation operational squadrons, but early deliveries were delayed until April 1990, partly by the decision to fit the SAAB Emerson HeliTOW system to all the A 129s. A requirement exists for an additional 30 aircraft, plus reserves, to equip a third operational squadron.

A plan to equip the Dutch Army with an initial batch of Mangustas (20) has been shelved and no other foreign orders had been received by early 1990.

In an unrelated engine test programme, an A 129 powered by two Allison/Garrett LHTEC T800-LHT-800 turboshafts flew for the first time in October 1988.

TYPE: Light anti-tank, attack and advanced scout helicopter.

ROTOR SYSTEM: Fully articulated four-blade main rotor and two-blade semi-rigid delta-hinged tail rotor, each with elastomeric bearings and low-noise tips (various tip designs evaluated before production). Main rotor blades, which have a very low vibration level, each consist of a carbonfibre and Kevlar spar, Nomex honeycomb leading- and trailing-edge, stainless steel leading-edge abrasion strip, frangible tip, and skin of composite materials. They are designed to have a ballistic tolerance against hits from 12.7 mm ammunition, but are expected also to have considerable tolerance against 23 mm hits. The hub has the same ballistic tolerance; all mechanical linkages and moving parts are housed inside the rotor

Agusta A 109-K multi-role hot and high variant of the A 109A Mk II *(Avio Data)*

mast to eliminate foreign object damage, decrease icing problems, and reduce radar signature. There are no lubricated bearings in the rotor head. Tail rotor blades are also of composite materials, with a stainless steel leading-edge, and are tolerant to 12.7 mm hits.

ROTOR DRIVE: Transmission rating 969 kW (1,300 shp) (two engines), 704 kW (944 shp) for single-engined operation, with emergency rating of 759 kW (1,018 shp); power input into transmission is at 27,000 rpm. All driveshafts, components and couplings ballistically tolerant to 12.7 mm hits. Main transmission has integral independent oil cooling system; intermediate and tail rotor gearboxes are grease lubricated. Transmission and gearboxes are designed to continue to operate safely for at least 30 min without oil (45 min already demonstrated). Accessory gearbox forward of main transmission. In normal operation, accessories are driven by main gear train, but on ground they can be engaged by a pilot actuated clutch which connects No. 1 engine to the accessory section without engaging the rotors. Rotor brake fitted, to stop rotors quickly while the two engines run at ground idle, one driving the accessories.

WINGS: Cantilever mid mounted stub wings, built of composite materials, aft of rear cockpit in plane of main rotor mast.

FUSELAGE: Conventional semi-monocoque structure of aluminium alloy longerons and frames. Honeycomb panels in centre-fuselage and fuel tank areas. Composite materials, making up 45 per cent of total fuselage weight (excluding engine) and 16.1 per cent of total empty weight, are used for nosecone, tailboom, tail rotor pylon, engine nacelles, canopy frame and maintenance panels. Total wetted surface area of airframe (excl blades and hub) is 50 m² (538.2 sq ft), of which 35 m² (376.7 sq ft) (70 per cent) are of composite materials. Small and narrow frontal area. Rollover bulkhead in nose and robust A-shaped reinforced frame extending from lower fuselage to rotor hub, for crew protection; armour protection for vital areas of power plant. Overall infra-red-absorbing paint finish. Airframe has a ballistic tolerance against 12.7 mm armour-piercing ammunition, and meets the crashworthiness standards of MIL-STD-1290 (vertical velocity changes of up to 11.2 m (36.75 ft)/sec and longitudinal changes of up to 13.1 m (43 ft)/sec).

TAIL UNIT: Sweptback main fin, with tail rotor mounted near top on port side. Small underfin, serving also as mount for tailwheel. Tailplane mid-mounted on tailboom in line with fin leading-edge. All tail surfaces built of composite materials.

LANDING GEAR: Non-retractable tailwheel type, with single wheel on each unit. Hydraulic shock strut in each main unit. Gear designed to withstand hard landings at descent rates in excess of 10 m (32.8 ft)/s.

POWER PLANT: Two Rolls-Royce Gem 2 Mk 1004D turboshafts, each with a max continuous rating of 615 kW (825 shp) for normal twin-engined operation; intermediate contingency rating of 657 kW (881 shp) for 1 h; max contingency rating of 704 kW (944 shp) for 2½ min; and emergency rating (S/L, ISA) of 759 kW (1,018 shp) for 20 s. Production engines licence built in Italy by Piaggio. Fireproof engine compartment, with engines separated to improve survivability of one or other from enemy fire. Two separate fuel systems, with crossfeed capability; interchangeable self-sealing and crash resistant tanks, self-sealing lines, and digital fuel feed control. Tanks can be foam-filled for fire protection. Single-point pressure refuelling. Infra-red exhaust suppression system and low engine noise levels. Separate independent lubrication oil cooling system for each engine. Provision for auxiliary (self-ferry) fuel tanks on inboard underwing stations.

ACCOMMODATION: Pilot and co-pilot/gunner in separate cockpits in tandem. Elevated rear (pilot's) cockpit. External crew field of view exceeds MIL-STD-850B. Each cockpit has a flat plate low-glint canopy with upward hinged door panels on starboard side, blow-out side panel for exit in emergency, and armoured crashworthy seat. Landing gear design and crashworthy seats reduce impact from 50 g to 20 g in crash.

SYSTEMS: Hydraulic system includes three main circuits dedicated to flight controls and two independent circuits for rotor and wheel braking. Main system operates at pressure of 207 bars (3,000 lb/sq in) and is fed by three independent power groups, two integrated and driven mechanically by the main transmission, the third integrated and driven by the tail rotor gearbox. Dual actuators are provided for main and tail rotor flight controls. Hydraulic system flow rate 23.6 litres (6.2 US gallons; 5.2 Imp gallons)/min in each main group. Spring type reservoirs, pressurised at 0.39 bars (5.6 lb/sq in). Electrical system includes fly by wire backup for mechanical control system. Full automatic stabilisation equipment, integrated with computerised IMS central management system. Automatic fire extinguishing system.

AVIONICS AND OPERATIONAL EQUIPMENT: All main functions of helicopter are handled and monitored by a fully integrated digital multiplex system (IMS), which controls com, nav, flight director, autopilot, fly by wire, transmission and engine condition monitoring, fuel/hydraulic/electrical systems monitoring, aircraft per-

Agusta A 129 attack helicopter for the Italian Army, armed with TOW missiles and rocket launchers

formance, caution and warning systems, and rocket fire control. IMS is managed by two redundant central computers, each capable of operating system independently. They are backed by two interface units which pick up outputs from sensors and avionic equipment and transfer them, via redundant MIL-1553B databuses, to main computers for real-time processing. Processed information is presented to pilot and co-pilot/gunner on separate graphic/alphanumeric head-down multi-function displays (MFDs) with standard multi-function keyboards for easy access to information, including area navigation and synthetic waypoint map, weapons status and selection, radio tuning and mode selection, caution and warning, and display of aircraft performance; conventional instruments and dials are provided as backup. IMS computer can store up to 100 waypoints, or up to ten flight plans with ten waypoints each, and 100 pre-set frequencies for HF, VHF and UHF radio management. Navigation is controlled by navigation computer of IMS coupled to a Doppler radar and radar altimeter. Synthetic map presentation of waypoints, target areas and dangerous areas is shown on pilot's or co-pilot's MFD.

The A 129 has full day/night operational capability, with equipment designed to give both crew members a view outside helicopter irrespective of light conditions. A pilot's night vision system (HIRNS: helicopter infra-red night system) allows nap-of-the-earth (NOE) flight by night, a picture of world outside being generated by Honeywell mini-FLIR sensor mounted on a Ferranti steerable platform at nose of aircraft and presented to pilot through monocle of his Honeywell integrated helmet and display sighting system (IHADSS), to which it is slaved. Symbology containing information required for flight is superimposed onto image, giving a true head-up reference. Co-pilot/gunner is also equipped with IHADSS. The HeliTOW sight gives the co-pilot/gunner direct view optics, television and FLIR, plus a laser for ranging. The A 129 also has provision for a mast mounted sight (MMS). Active and passive self-protection systems (ECCM and ECM) standard on Italian Army A 129. Passive electronic warfare systems include radar and laser warning receivers and chaff/flare dispensers.

ARMAMENT: Four underwing attachments, inner pair stressed for loads of up to 300 kg (661 lb) each, outer pair (at wingtips) also for 300 kg each. All stations incorporate articulation which allows pylon to be elevated 2° and depressed 10° from armament datum line. They are aligned with the aircraft automatically, with no need for boresighting. Initial armament of up to eight TOW wire guided anti-tank missiles (two, three or four in pod suspended from each wingtip station), with

Saab/Emerson HeliTOW launch system and full TOW 2 capability; with these can be carried, on the inboard stations, either two 7.62, 12.7 or 20 mm gun pods, or two launchers each for seven air-to-surface rockets. For general attack missions, rocket launchers can be carried on all four stations (two nineteen-tube plus two seven-tube); Italian Army has specified SNIA-BPD 81 mm and 70 mm rockets. Alternatively, is able to carry six Hellfire anti-tank missiles (three beneath each wingtip); eight Hot missiles; AIM-9L Sidewinder, Matra Mistral, Javelin or Stinger air-to-air missiles for aerial combat; two gun pods plus two nineteen-tube rocket launchers; or grenade launchers. A chin turret for a 12.7 mm gun may be mounted under the nose for self defence.

DIMENSIONS, EXTERNAL:

Main rotor diameter	11.90 m (39 ft 0½ in)
Tail rotor diameter	2.24 m (7 ft 4¼ in)
Wing span	3.20 m (10 ft 6 in)
Width over TOW pods	3.60 m (11 ft 9¾ in)
Length overall, both rotors turning	14.29 m (46 ft 10½ in)
Fuselage: Length	12.275 m (40 ft 3¼ in)
Max width	0.95 m (3 ft 1½ in)
Height:	
over tail fin, tail rotor horizontal	2.65 m (8 ft 8¼ in)
tail rotor turning	3.315 m (10 ft 10½ in)
to top of rotor head	3.35 m (11 ft 0 in)
Tailplane span	3.00 m (9 ft 10 in)
Wheel track	2.20 m (7 ft 3½ in)
Wheelbase	6.955 m (22 ft 9¾ in)

AREAS:

Main rotor disc	111.2 m² (1,196.95 sq ft)
Tail rotor disc	3.94 m² (42.42 sq ft)

WEIGHTS AND LOADINGS:

Weight empty, equipped	2,529 kg (5,575 lb)
Max internal fuel load	750 kg (1,653 lb)
Max external weapons load	1,200 kg (2,645 lb)
Max T-O weight	4,100 kg (9,039 lb)
Max disc loading	33.3 kg/m² (6.8 lb/sq ft)
Max power loading	3.05 kg/kW (5.0 lb/shp)

PERFORMANCE:

At mission T-O weight of 3,700 kg (8,157 lb), at 2,000 m (6,560 ft), ISA + 20°C, except where indicated, the A 129 is designed to meet the following performance requirements:

Dash speed	170 knots (315 km/h; 196 mph)
Max level speed at S/L	140 knots (259 km/h; 161 mph)
Max rate of climb at S/L	655 m (2,150 ft)/min
Hovering ceiling: IGE	3,750 m (12,300 ft)
OGE	3,015 m (9,900 ft)

Basic 2 h 30 min mission profile with 8 TOW and 20 min fuel reserves:

Fly 54 nm (100 km; 62 miles) to battle area, mainly in

NOE mode, 90 min loiter (incl 45 min hovering), and return to base

Max endurance, no reserves	3 h
g limits	+ 3.5/–0.5

AGUSTA A 129 (DEVELOPED VERSIONS)

Four developed variants of the A 129 have been proposed by Agusta, which released first details at the 1985 Paris Air Show. They are intended to belong to the overall A 129 family, sharing major components such as the dynamic units and logistic support structure, but designed for specifically different roles. (The **scout** version of the A 129 is not included, as this is basically an adaptation of the anti-armour A 129, and can be so configured in the field.)

The first of the new variants, named **Tonal**, is described under the JEH heading in the International section. Second proposed version is a ship or shore based **naval** development for anti-shipping and maritime support roles, with nose mounted radar, Elettronica ESM antennae at nose and tail and at the tips of the stub wings, a chaff dispenser on the starboard side behind the tailplane, and an armament of two Marte Mk 2, four Sea Skua or other sea-skimming missiles in the anti-shipping role or Mavericks, TOWs or rocket pods for maritime support. It will be possible for this helicopter to undertake OTH (over the horizon) target acquisition for long-range missiles launched from ships. Equipped and take-off weights are expected to be 2,680 kg (5,908 lb) and 3,920 kg (8,642 lb) respectively, allowing a 3 hour mission at a search speed of 120 knots (222 km/h; 138 mph).

The third proposal is for the **LBH** light battlefield support version which would combine the Mangusta's rotor system, power plant and landing gear with an entirely new and larger fuselage having side by side crew seating and a cabin able to accommodate an 8/10 man assault squad, or six stretchers and two medical attendants. Provisions would be made for a chin mounted gun turret, a 272 kg (600 lb) capacity rescue hoist, side looking airborne radar, and gun or rocket pods. It is expected to operate in conjunction with the anti-armour and scout versions. If required to undertake a freight transport role, a 1,400 kg (3,086 lb) load could be carried using the cargo hook.

The fourth version is the **Utility**, based on the battlefield support version but in the 4-5 tonne class and able to carry two crew plus 12 passengers or other loads including six stretchers plus two medical assistants. On 10 August 1988 a 15-year agreement was signed between Agusta and FMA of Argentina for the joint development and construction of this helicopter, with Agusta responsible for the design, development and production of the drive system and other main systems, while the fuselage is the responsibility of FMA. Subsequently, FMA delegated this work to a consortium in which Agusta has a 49 per cent shareholding, Techint 10 per cent and Tecnologia Aeroespacial SA 41 per cent, which will assemble and sell the A 129U in Latin America. Sales forecast for the region is 200 out of the worldwide total of 600. The initial design stage has been completed, with detail design scheduled to last until October 1991. This would allow the three prototypes to be completed between April and July 1992, with testing to last until October 1993, when production aircraft should be available for delivery. Meanwhile, in 1989 AeroSpace Technologies of Australia (ASTA) negotiated to join Agusta and FMA on the A 129 Utility programme, with the intention of assisting in design, component manufacture and perhaps full assembly in Victoria. A memorandum of understanding was signed between Agusta and ASTA in December 1989.

The Utility is to be powered by two LHTEC CT 800 turboshaft engines, each rated at 986 kW (1,322 shp) for 10 minutes, 919 kW (1,233 shp) for 30 minutes, and 766 kW (1,027 shp) max continuous. One engine out rating is 1,031 kW (1,382 shp) for 2 minutes 30 seconds and 1,081 kW

Italian Police Agusta-Bell 212 utility helicopter, with 360° TV camera in spherical pod *(Avio Data)*

(1,450 shp) emergency. For single pilot IFR operation, three avionics configurations are available: conventional avionics and instrumentation with three-axis AFCS; com/nav function integrated through one cockpit management system; or a fully integrated management system.

The following details refer to the A 129 Utility:

WEIGHTS:

Weight empty	2,550 kg (5,621 lb)
Max T-O weight	4,850 kg (10,692 lb)

PERFORMANCE:

Max cruising speed	154 knots (285 km/h; 177 mph)
Hovering ceiling OGE	3,500 m (11,480 ft)
Max range, with auxiliary tanks	
	674 nm (1,250 km; 776 miles)
Endurance	3 h 20 min

AGUSTA-BELL 206B JETRANGER III

The JetRanger has been manufactured under licence from Bell since the end of 1967; deliveries began in 1972 of the Agusta-Bell 206B JetRanger II, and of the JetRanger III at the end of 1978. A description of the JetRanger III appears under the Bell entry in the Canadian section. Approx 1,000 JetRangers have been built by Agusta, and production was expected to continue at least until 1990.

AGUSTA-BELL 212

The Agusta-Bell 212 is a twin-engined utility transport helicopter generally similar to the Bell Model 212 Twin Two-Twelve described in the Canadian section.

Recent customers for the AB 212 have included the Italian Air Force, which ordered 35 equipped for the SAR role, and the Italian Police. Production is planned to continue until at least 1992.

The AB 212ASW naval version is described separately.

DIMENSIONS, EXTERNAL: As Bell Model 212 except:

Main rotor diameter	14.63 m (48 ft 0 in)
Length overall, rotors turning	17.40 m (57 ft 1 in)

AREA:

Main rotor disc	168.1 m² (1,809.5 sq ft)

WEIGHTS: As Bell Model 212 except:

Weight empty (standard)	2,630 kg (5,800 lb)

PERFORMANCE (at AUW of 4,536 kg; 10,000 lb, ISA):

Cruising speed at S/L	110 knots (204 km/h; 127 mph)
Max rate of climb at S/L	567 m (1,860 ft)/min
Service ceiling	5,180 m (17,000 ft)
Hovering ceiling: IGE	3,960 m (13,000 ft)
OGE	3,050 m (10,000 ft)
Max range at 1,525 m (5,000 ft) with standard fuel, no reserves:	
on two engines	267 nm (494 km; 307 miles)
on one engine	318 nm (589 km; 366 miles)

AGUSTA-BELL 212ASW

The AB 212ASW is an extensively modified version of the AB 212, intended primarily for anti-submarine search, classification and attack missions, and for attacks on surface vessels, while operating from the decks of small ships, but suitable also for search and rescue, electronic warfare, fire support, troop transport, liaison and utility roles. The current SAR version has such additional features as a hydraulically operated external hoist and a four-channel Honeywell autopilot. The 212ASW benefits from considerable naval operational experience gained with the single-engined AB 204AS, and can operate from the same small ship decks. More than 100 are in service with the Italian and other navies; the most recent customers have included the navies of Greece (12, including some in electronic warfare configuration), Iraq (5), Turkey (12 in both ASW and ASV configurations) and Venezuela (6).

Apart from local strengthening and the provision of deck mooring equipment, the airframe structure remains essentially similar to that of the commercial Model 212 and military UH-1N, described under the Bell entry in the Canadian section. Main differences from the civil Agusta-Bell 212 are as follows:

TYPE: Twin-engined anti-submarine and anti-surface-vessel helicopter.

POWER PLANT: One Pratt & Whitney Canada PT6T-6 Turbo Twin Pac, rated at 1,398 kW (1,875 shp). Protection against salt water corrosion. Provision for one internal or two external auxiliary fuel tanks.

ACCOMMODATION: Normal crew of three or four. Volume of cabin is 6.1 m³ (215 cu ft), with floor area of 5.0 m² (54 sq ft). With sonar installed, volume is reduced to 5.1 m³ (180 cu ft). Can accommodate two pilots and seven passengers; or two pilots, four stretcher patients and attendant. Single sliding door, with jettisonable emergency exit panel, on each side.

SYSTEMS: Standard duplicated hydraulic systems for flight controls, as in AB 212. The hydraulic system operates the automatic flight control system. Self-contained hydraulic system for operation of sonar, rescue hoist and other utilities. Electrical system capacity increased to cater for higher power demand (28V DC, and three phase 200/115V or single phase 26V AC at 400Hz); the two standard generators are integrated with a 20kVA alternator.

AVIONICS AND EQUIPMENT: Complete instrumentation for day and night sea operation in all weathers. Avionics installed are UHF transceiver, HF transceiver, and Agusta AG-03-M intercom, for communications; ADF, Tacan and homing UHF, for navigation assistance; radar altimeter, Doppler radar, ASW navigation computer, and automatic flight control system with General Electric SR-3 gyro platform. Honeywell four-axis autopilot with AATH (automatic approach to hover) mode for automatic navigation; IFF/SIF transponder; search radar and radar transponder; data link; and Bendix AN/AQS-13B/F sonar for ASW search.

ARMAMENT AND OPERATIONAL EQUIPMENT: Weapons may consist of two Motofides 244 AS or two Mk 44/46 homing torpedoes, or two Marte Mk 2 or Sea Skua type air-to-surface missiles. Rescue hoist, capacity 272 kg (600 lb), standard. Provisions for auxiliary installations such as a 2,270 kg (5,000 lb) capacity cargo sling, inflatable emergency pontoons, internal and external auxiliary fuel tanks, according to mission.

ASW MISSION: Basic sensor system for ASW search and attack is a Bendix AN/AQS-13B/F low-frequency variable depth sonar, with a max operating depth of 137 m (450 ft). Automatic navigation system permits positioning of helicopter over any desired dip point of a complex search pattern. Position of helicopter, computed by automatic navigation system, is integrated with sonar target information in radar tactical display where both surface and underwater tactical situations can be continuously monitored. Additional navigation and tactical information provided by UHF direction finding equipment, from an A/A mode-capable Tacan and a radar transponder. Automatic flight control system (AFCS) integrates basic automatic stabilisation equipment with signal output from radar altimeter, Doppler

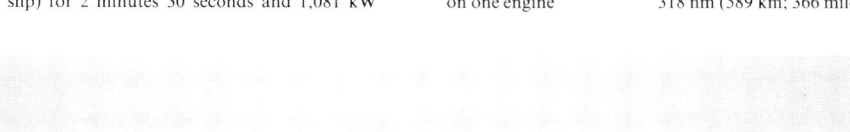

Mockup of the A 129 Utility passenger/cargo version of the Mangusta

radar, sonar cable angle signals, and outputs from dry cable transducer. Effectiveness of this system results in hands-off flight from cruise condition to sonar hover in all weathers and under rough sea conditions. Specially designed cockpit display shows pilots all flight parameters for each phase of ASW operation. Attack mission is carried out with two homing torpedoes, or with depth charges.

ASV MISSION: For this mission AB 212ASW carries a Ferranti Seaspray long-range search radar, with very efficient scanner design and installation possessing high discrimination in rough sea conditions. Provisions made to permit incorporation of future radar system developments. Automatic navigation systems and search radar are integrated to permit continuously updated picture of tactical situation. Provisions also incorporated for installation of the most advanced ECM systems (Selenia or Elettronica is system most commonly used). Surface attack is performed with air-to-surface missiles of the Marte Mk 2 or Sea Skua type.

STANDOFF MISSILE GUIDANCE MISSION: In this mission the AB 212ASW, with special equipment, can provide midcourse passive guidance for the ship launched Otomat 2 surface-to-surface missile. Equipment includes an SMA/APS series 360° search radar and a TG-2 real-time target data transmission system for guidance of the missile.

DIMENSIONS, EXTERNAL: As AB 212, except:
Max width: with torpedoes	3.95 m (12 ft 11½ in)
with missiles	4.17 m (13 ft 8¼ in)

WEIGHTS (A: ASW mission with Mk 46 torpedoes, B: ASV mission with AS.12 missiles, C: search and rescue mission; all at S/L, ISA):
Weight empty, equipped:	
A, B, C	3,420 kg (7,540 lb)
Crew of three: A, B, C	240 kg (529 lb)
Mission equipment:	
A (two Mk 46 torpedoes)	490 kg (1,080 lb)
B (AS.12 installation and XM-58 sight)	
	180 kg (396 lb)
C (rescue hoist)	40 kg (89 lb)
Full fuel (normal tanks)	1,021 kg (2,250 lb)
Auxiliary external tanks	32 kg (70 lb)
Auxiliary fuel	356 kg (785 lb)
Mission T-O weight: A	5,070 kg (11,176 lb)
B	4,973 kg (10,961 lb)
C	4,937 kg (10,883 lb)

PERFORMANCE (at max T-O weight except where indicated, ISA):
Never-exceed speed	130 knots (240 km/h; 150 mph)
Max level speed at S/L	106 knots (196 km/h; 122 mph)
Max cruising speed with armament	
	100 knots (185 km/h; 115 mph)
Max rate of climb at S/L: A	396 m (1,300 ft)/min
Rate of climb at S/L, one engine out:	
A	61 m (200 ft)/min
Hovering ceiling IGE: A	3,200 m (10,500 ft)
Hovering ceiling OGE:	
A at AUW of 4,763 kg (10,500 lb)	396 m (1,300 ft)

Search endurance (A) with 50% at 90 knots (167 km/h; 103 mph) cruise and 50% hovering OGE, 10% reserve fuel   3 h 12 min

Search range (B) with 10% reserve fuel
                                332 nm (615 km; 382 miles)

Endurance (B), no reserves   4 h 7 min
Endurance (C) at 90 knots (167 km/h; 103 mph) search speed   5 h 4 min
Max range with auxiliary tanks, 100 knots (185 km/h; 115 mph) cruise at S/L, 15% reserves
                                360 nm (667 km; 414 miles)

Max endurance with auxiliary tanks, no reserves
                                                          5 h

AGUSTA-BELL 412 SP and GRIFFON

The first Bell prototype of the Model 412 was flown for the first time in August 1979, and customer deliveries began in January 1981. Licence production by Agusta was initiated later that year, and civil versions for a variety of applications are now available from the Italian manufacturer. They include a dedicated version for offshore work equipped with pop-out inflatable pontoons, Bendix weather radar, a Spectrolab searchlight and special avionics. An EMS (emergency medical service) version has also been certificated. A description of the basic civil Model 412 SP can be found under the Bell entry in the Canadian section of this edition.

Agusta has also developed its own multi-purpose military version of the helicopter, known as the **Griffon**, for such applications as direct fire support, area suppression, scouting and reconnaissance, air defence, assault transport, combat equipment transport, and battlefield support. Special features include high-energy-absorbing landing gear, energy attenuating seats for crew and troops (the former also armour protected), and crash resistant self-sealing fuel tanks. Other survivability options can include passive (radar and laser warning, and missile detection) and active (ECM, radar jammer and decoy) systems, and a variety of ordnance can be carried. The Griffon is capable of performing medevac, tactical support, logistic transport, maritime surveillance, pollution monitoring, search and rescue, and patrol duties, and of being

Agusta-Bell 212ASW in the insignia of the Spanish Navy *(Ivo Sturzenegger)*

Agusta-Bell Griffon military helicopter, derived from the Bell Model 412 *(Pilot Press)*

used effectively against surface ships, tanks and other armoured vehicles.

A version for SAR, maritime surveillance and pollution monitoring has been developed for the Italian forces, equipped with an integrated 360° roof mounted search radar, FLIR, TV, four-axis autopilot and special navigation system. First deliveries were due in 1989.

A prototype of the Griffon was flown for the first time in August 1982. Deliveries began in January 1983, and 75 civil and military AB 412 SPs had been sold by 1 January 1988 (when the last updated figure was received). Customers in Italy include the Army, Carabinieri and Special Civil Protection fleet; others include the Zimbabwe Air Force (10), Ugandan Army, and Finnish coastguard (2). The Griffon differs from the standard civil Model 412 SP in the following respects:

TYPE: Multi-purpose military helicopter.

AIRFRAME: Reinforced impact-absorbing landing gear, and armour protection in selected areas.

POWER PLANT: One 1,342 kW (1,800 shp) Pratt & Whitney Canada PT6T-3B Turbo Twin Pac (single-engine ratings 764 kW; 1,025 shp for 2½ min and 723 kW; 970 shp for 30 min), as in civil Model 412. IR emission reduction devices optional. Fuel system and capacity as for Model 412 (1,250 litres; 330 US gallons; 275 Imp gallons). Single-point refuelling. Two 76 or 341 litre (20 or 90 US gallon; 16.7 or 75 Imp gallon) auxiliary fuel tanks optional.

ACCOMMODATION: One or two pilots on flight deck, on energy-absorbing, armour protected seats. Fourteen crash-attenuating troop seats in main cabin in personnel transport roles, six patients and two medical attendants in ambulance version, or up to 1,814 kg (4,000 lb) of cargo or other equipment. Space for 181 kg (400 lb) of baggage in tailboom. Total of 51 fittings in cabin floor for attachment of seats, stretchers, internal hoist or other special equipment.

SYSTEMS: Generally as for Bell 212/412. Electrical system supplied by two independent 30V 200A DC starter/generators (derated to 150A) and 34Ah nickel-cadmium

battery, with three 250VA single-phase solid state inverters or a 10kVA alternator for AC power.

AVIONICS AND EQUIPMENT: Typical avionics can include UHF/VHF (FM-AM) and HF secure voice com, ADF, VHF/UHF-DF, radar altimeter, IFF, DME, Tacan, VOR, navigation system, radar, Doppler radar, and four-axis AFCS. Optional avionics include AN/APR-39 radar warning receiver, laser warning receiver and pulse-Doppler radar missile detector system for passive warning of threats; active countermeasures options include AN/ALQ-144 ECM set, AN/ALQ-136 radar jammer, and chaff/flare dispenser. A 272 kg (600 lb) capacity external rescue hoist can be fitted for search and rescue mission, and an external hook for cargo, battlefield support and other duties. Other optional equipment includes auxiliary fuel tanks, emergency floats, rotor brake, heavy duty heater, heated windscreen, loudspeakers and searchlight, depending upon mission.

ARMAMENT: Wide variety of external weapon options for the Griffon includes a swivelling turret for a 12.7 mm gun, two 25 mm Oerlikon cannon, four or eight TOW anti-tank missiles, two launchers each with nineteen 2.75 in SNORA or twelve 81 mm rockets, 12.7 mm machine-guns (in pods or door mounted), four air-to-air or air defence suppression missiles, or, for attacking surface vessels, four Sea Skua or similar air-to-surface missiles.

WEIGHTS:
Weight empty, equipped (standard configuration)	
	2,841 kg (6,263 lb)
Max T-O weight	5,400 kg (11,905 lb)

PERFORMANCE (at max T-O weight, ISA):
Never-exceed speed at S/L	
	140 knots (259 km/h; 161 mph)
Cruising speed: at S/L	122 knots (226 km/h; 140 mph)
at 1,500 m (4,920 ft)	125 knots (232 km/h; 144 mph)
at 3,000 m (9,840 ft)	123 knots (228 km/h; 142 mph)
Max rate of climb at S/L	438 m (1,437 ft)/min
Rate of climb at S/L, one engine out	168 m (551 ft)/min

Agusta-Bell AB 412 SP operated by the Zimbabwe Air Force *(Avio Data)*

Service ceiling, 30.5 m (100 ft)/min climb rate
          5,180 m (17,000 ft)
Service ceiling, one engine out, 30.5 m (100 ft)/min climb
    rate   2,320 m (7,610 ft)
Hovering ceiling: IGE   1,250 m (4,100 ft)
    OGE   670 m (2,200 ft)
Range with max standard fuel at appropriate cruising
    speed (see above), no reserves:
    at S/L   354 nm (656 km; 407 miles)
    at 1,500 m (4,920 ft) 402 nm (745 km; 463 miles)
    at 3,000 m (9,840 ft) 434 nm (804 km; 500 miles)
Max endurance: at S/L   3 h 36 min
    at 1,500 m (4,920 ft)   4 h 12 min

AGUSTA-SIKORSKY AS-61 and ASH-3H

Agusta licence manufacture of the Sikorsky S-61 and SH-3D Sea King started in 1967, and deliveries of anti-submarine ASH-3Ds to the Italian Navy began in 1969. Additional orders have since been placed, both for the Italian armed forces and for other navies, including recently those of Brazil (four) and Argentina (four). Models currently in production are the utility **AS-61**, the **SH-3D/TS** (Trasporto Speciale) VIP transport, and the upgraded **SH-3H** multi-role naval version.

Apart from some local strengthening, uprated engines and an improved horizontal tail surface, the Agusta built airframe remains essentially similar to that of the Sikorsky built SH-3D/H (see 1982-83 *Jane's*), of which production has ended. The Agusta SH-3H is capable of operation in the roles of anti-submarine search, classification and strike; anti-surface-vessel (ASV); anti-surface-missile defence (ASMD); electronic warfare (EW); tactical troop lift; search and rescue (SAR); vertical replenishment; and casualty evacuation.

In mid-1987, an SH-3 became the first airborne testbed for the BAe/Bendix HELRAS long-range high resolution dipping sonar intended for naval versions of the Anglo-Italian EH 101 Sea King replacement helicopter.

The US Navy awarded Agusta a contract to develop and manufacture modification kits for some USN Sikorsky Sea Kings to bring them up to the latest SH-3H standard.

The following description applies to the ASH-3H:

TYPE: Twin-engined amphibious all-weather naval helicopter.

ROTOR SYSTEM: Five-blade main and tail rotors. All-metal fully articulated oil lubricated main rotor. Flanged cuffs on blades bolted to matching flanges on all-steel rotor head. Main rotor blades are interchangeable and are provided with an automatic folding system. Rotor brake standard. All-metal tail rotor.

ROTOR DRIVE: Both engines drive through freewheel units and rotor brake to main gearbox. Steel driveshafts. Tail rotor shaft driven through intermediate and tail gearboxes. Accessories driven by power take-off on tail rotor shaft. Main rotor/engine rpm ratio 1 : 93.43. Tail rotor/engine rpm ratio 1 : 16.7.

FUSELAGE: Single-step boat hull of all-metal semi-monocoque construction. Tail section folds to reduce stowage requirements.

TAIL SURFACE: Fixed strut braced stabiliser on starboard side of tail section.

LANDING GEAR: Amphibious. Land gear consists of two twin-wheel main units, which are retracted rearward hydraulically into stabilising floats, and non-retractable tailwheel. Oleo-pneumatic shock absorbers. Mainwheels and tubeless tyres size 6.50-10 type III, pressure 4.83 bars (70 lb/sq in). Tailwheel and tyre size 6.00-6. Hydraulic disc brakes. Boat hull and pop-out flotation bags in stabilising floats permit emergency operation from water.

POWER PLANT: Two 1,118 kW (1,500 shp) General Electric T58-GE-100 turboshafts, mounted side by side above the cabin. An optional anti-ice/sand shield can be provided. Fuel in underfloor bag tanks with a total capacity of 3,180 litres (840 US gallons; 699 Imp gallons). Internal auxiliary fuel tank may be fitted for long-range ferry purposes. Pressure and gravity refuelling points.

ACCOMMODATION: Crew of four in ASW role (pilot, co-pilot and two sonar operators); accommodation for up to 31 paratroops in troop lift role, 15 stretchers and a medical attendant in casualty evacuation configuration, and up to 25 survivors in SAR role. Dual controls. Crew door at rear of flight deck on port side. Large loading door at rear of cabin on starboard side.

SYSTEMS: Three main hydraulic systems. Primary and auxiliary systems operate main rotor control. Utility system for landing gear, winches and blade folding, pressure 207 bars (3,000 lb/sq in). Electrical system includes two 20kVA 200V three phase 400Hz engine driven generators, a 26V single phase AC supply fed from the aircraft's 22Ah nickel-cadmium battery through an inverter, and DC power provided as a secondary system from two 200A transformer-rectifier units.

ARMAMENT AND OPERATIONAL EQUIPMENT (ASW/ASV roles): As equipped for these roles the ASH-3H is a fully integrated all-weather weapons system, capable of operating independently of surface vessels, and has the following equipment and weapons to achieve this task: low-frequency 360° depth AQS-18/AQS-13F sonar; Doppler radar and ASW automatic navigation system; SMA/APS-707 radar with one or two transceivers, with chin radome for 360° coverage; radio altimeter; AFCS; marine markers and smoke floats; two or four homing torpedoes (A 244 AS, Mk 44 or Mk 46); or four depth charges. The AFCS provides three-axis stabilisation in pilot-controlled manoeuvres, attitude hold, heading hold and height hold in cruising flight; controlled transition manoeuvres to and from hover; automatic height control and plan position control in the hover; and trim facility. According to the threat, the Agusta SH-3H can be equipped with medium-range (four AS.12 air-to-surface wire-guided) missiles or long-range (two Marte Mk 2 or Exocet AM39/Harpoon type) anti-shipping missiles. The

SMA/APS-707 radar has been specially designed to operate in a dense electronic emission environment and has a special interface to draw out target data to feed the computer for the long-range missiles. Provisions are also incorporated for the installation of MAD and advanced EW systems.

OPERATIONAL EQUIPMENT (Search and rescue and transport roles): Search radar, and variable speed hydraulic rescue hoist of 272 kg (600 lb) capacity mounted above starboard side cargo door.

DIMENSIONS, EXTERNAL:

Main rotor diameter	18.90 m (62 ft 0 in)
Main rotor blade chord	0.46 m (1 ft 6¼ in)
Tail rotor diameter	3.23 m (10 ft 7 in)
Distance between rotor centres	11.10 m (36 ft 5 in)
Length overall, both rotors turning	21.91 m (71 ft 10.7 in)
Length of fuselage	16.69 m (54 ft 9 in)
Length, main rotor and tail pylon folded	14.40 m (47 ft 3 in)
Width (over sponsons), rotors folded	4.98 m (16 ft 4 in)
Height to top of rotor head	4.74 m (15 ft 6½ in)
Height overall, main rotor and tail pylon folded	4.93 m (16 ft 2 in)
Height overall, tail rotor turning	5.23 m (17 ft 2 in)
Wheel track	3.96 m (13 ft 0 in)
Wheelbase	7.18 m (23 ft 6½ in)
Crew door (fwd, port): Height	1.68 m (5 ft 6 in)
Width	0.91 m (3 ft 0 in)
Height to sill	1.14 m (3 ft 9 in)
Main cabin door (stbd): Height	1.52 m (5 ft 0 in)
Width	1.73 m (5 ft 8 in)
Height to sill	1.14 m (3 ft 9 in)

AREAS:

Main rotor blades (each)	4.14 m² (44.54 sq ft)
Tail rotor blades (each)	0.22 m² (2.38 sq ft)
Main rotor disc	280.5 m² (3,019 sq ft)
Tail rotor disc	8.20 m² (88.30 sq ft)
Stabiliser	1.86 m² (20.00 sq ft)

WEIGHTS:

Internal load capacity (cargo)	2,720 kg (6,000 lb)
Max external load capacity (with low response sling)	3,630 kg (8,000 lb)
Max T-O weight	9,525 kg (21,000 lb)

PERFORMANCE (at max T-O weight):

Never-exceed speed	144 knots (267 km/h; 165 mph)
Typical cruising speed	120 knots (222 km/h; 138 mph)
Max rate of climb at S/L	670 m (2,200 ft)/min
Service ceiling	3,720 m (12,200 ft)
Hovering ceiling: IGE	2,500 m (8,200 ft)
OGE	1,130 m (3,700 ft)
Range with 31 troops	314 nm (582 km; 362 miles)
Range with max standard fuel	630 nm (1,166 km; 725 miles)

AGUSTA-SIKORSKY AS-61N1 SILVER

Manufacture by Sikorsky of the S-61L and S-61N commercial helicopters ended in 1980, after completion of 13 of the former model and 123 of the latter. Production rights to the S-61N were acquired by Agusta, which developed a modified version, designated AS-61N1 Silver. Greater range and slightly less seating capacity than the standard S-61N account for the two principal differences in the AS-61N1. The fuselage is shortened by 1.27 m (4 ft 2 in), reducing maximum seating capacity from 30 to 28, and internal fuel capacity is increased to 3,482 litres (920 US gallons; 766 Imp gallons). The Silver is tailored primarily to carry 24 passengers over distances of up to 550 nm (1,019 km; 633 miles). Initially, the standard S-61N power plant of two 1,119 kW (1,500 shp) General Electric CT58-140-1/2 turboshafts is retained.

The prototype flew for the first time on 25 July 1984. Italian RAI certification was received in 1987 and FAA certification in 1988. The latest customer is the Sultan of Johore, Malaysia, for two.

DIMENSIONS, EXTERNAL:

Main rotor diameter	18.90 m (62 ft 0 in)
Length of fuselage	17.97 m (58 ft 11½ in)
Height over tail rotor	5.24 m (17 ft 2¼ in)
Width over sponsons	5.82 m (19 ft 1⅓ in)

DIMENSIONS, INTERNAL:

Cabin, excl flight deck: Length	8.26 m (27 ft 1⅛ in)
Baggage compartment volume	2.26 m³ (80 cu ft)

AREA:

Main rotor disc	280.5 m² (3,019 sq ft)

WEIGHTS:

Max useful load (offshore configuration)	3,560 kg (7,850 lb)
Max T-O weight: internal payload	9,525 kg (21,000 lb)
with slung load	10,205 kg (22,500 lb)

PERFORMANCE (A at average gross weight of 8,618 kg; 19,000 lb, B at 9,525 kg; 21,000 lb, C at 9,979 kg; 22,000 lb):

Never-exceed speed at S/L:

A	131 knots (242 km/h; 151 mph) IAS
B	115 knots (213 km/h; 132 mph) IAS
C	103 knots (191 km/h; 118 mph) IAS

Cruising speed at S/L:

A	121 knots (224 km/h; 139 mph) IAS

Max rate of climb at S/L, max continuous power:

A	396 m (1,300 ft)/min
B	320 m (1,050 ft)/min

Agusta-Sikorsky ASH-3H ASW helicopter of the Italian Navy *(Press Office Sturzenegger)*

Hovering ceiling IGE: A	2,135 m (7,000 ft)	
B	1,130 m (3,700 ft)	
C	335 m (1,100 ft)	

Range at S/L, with max fuel, incl 30 min reserves at cruising speed:

A	553 nm (1,025 km; 637 miles)	
B	526 nm (974 km; 605 miles)	

Agusta-Sikorsky AS-61N1 Silver (two General Electric CT58-140-1/2 turboshafts) *(Avio Data)*

AGUSTA-SIKORSKY AS-61R (HH-3F)

Agusta began production of this multi-purpose search and rescue helicopter in 1974, and deliveries began in 1976. The latest examples have updated avionics, which will be retrofitted to the original production series.

TYPE: Twin-engined amphibious helicopter.

ROTOR SYSTEM: Five-blade fully articulated main rotor of all-metal construction. Flanged cuffs on blades bolted to matching flanges on rotor head. Control by rotating and stationary swashplates. Blades do not fold. Rotor brake standard. Conventional tail rotor with five aluminium blades.

ROTOR DRIVE: Twin turbines drive through freewheeling units and rotor brake to main gearbox. Steel driveshafts. Tail rotor shaft driven through intermediate gearbox and tail gearbox. Main rotor/engine rpm ratio 1 : 93.43. Tail rotor/engine rpm ratio 1 : 16.7.

FUSELAGE: All-metal semi-monocoque structure of pod and boom type. Cabin of basic square section.

TAIL SURFACE: Strut braced horizontal stabiliser on starboard side of tail rotor pylon.

LANDING GEAR: Hydraulically retractable tricycle type, with twin wheels on each unit. Mainwheels retract forward into sponsons, each of which provides 2,176 kg (4,797 lb) of buoyancy and, with boat hull, permits amphibious operation. Oleo-pneumatic shock absorbers. All wheels and tyres tubeless Type III rib, size 22.1 × 6.50-10, pressure 6.55 bars (95 lb/sq in). Hydraulic disc brakes.

POWER PLANT: Two 1,118 kW (1,500 shp) General Electric T58-GE-100 turboshafts, mounted side by side above cabin, immediately forward of main transmission. Fuel in four bladder tanks beneath cabin floor, with total capacity of 4,225 litres (1,116 US gallons; 929 Imp gallons), of which 4,183 litres (1,105 US gallons; 920 Imp gallons) are usable. Provisions for removable internal auxiliary fuel tanks. Refuelling point on port side of fuselage. Total oil capacity 26.5 litres (7 US gallons; 5.8 Imp gallons).

ACCOMMODATION: Crew of two side by side on flight deck, with dual controls. Provision for flight engineer or attendant. Accommodation in SAR configuration for 10 passenger seats and six stretchers; utility version can accommodate up to 26 troops on foldable, safety belt-equipped seats, 15 stretchers plus two medical attendants, or cargo. Jettisonable sliding door on starboard side at front of cabin. Internal door between cabin and flight deck. Hydraulically operated rear loading ramp, in two hinged sections, giving opening with minimum width of 1.73 m (5 ft 8 in) and headroom of up to 2.21 m (7 ft 3 in). Ramp can be operated when helicopter is on the water. Reinforced (41 kg/m²; 200 lb/sq ft loading) cargo floor in utility version.

SYSTEMS: Primary and auxiliary hydraulic systems, pressure 103.5 bars (1,500 lb/sq in), for flying control servos. Utility hydraulic system, pressure 207 bars (3,000 lb/sq in), for landing gear, rear ramp and winches. Pneumatic system, pressure 207 bars (3,000 lb/sq in), for emergency blow-down landing gear extension. Electrical system includes 24V 22Ah battery, two 20kVA 115V AC generators and one 300A DC generator. APU standard.

EQUIPMENT: SAR version has comprehensive avionics suite for that role (including search/nav radar, Loran, FLIR and nav computer), plus 272 kg (600 lb) capacity rescue hoist, Nightsun searchlight, detachable rescue platform for use when afloat, auxiliary flotation system, loudhailer set, and sea anchor. Equipment for utility missions can include low response external cargo sling.

DIMENSIONS, EXTERNAL:

Main rotor diameter	18.90 m (62 ft 0 in)
Main rotor blade chord	0.46 m (1 ft 6¼ in)
Tail rotor diameter	3.15 m (10 ft 4 in)

Agusta-Sikorsky HH-3F (AS-61R) search and rescue helicopter of the Italian Air Force *(Ivo Sturzenegger)*

Distance between rotor centres	11.22 m (36 ft 10 in)
Length overall, excl radome	22.25 m (73 ft 0 in)
Length of fuselage	17.45 m (57 ft 3 in)
Width over landing gear	4.82 m (15 ft 10 in)
Height to top of rotor head	4.90 m (16 ft 1 in)
Height overall	5.51 m (18 ft 1 in)
Wheel track	4.06 m (13 ft 4 in)
Wheelbase	5.21 m (17 ft 1 in)
Cabin door (fwd, stbd): Height	1.65 m (5 ft 4¾ in)
Width	1.22 m (4 ft 0 in)
Height to sill	1.27 m (4 ft 2 in)
Rear ramp: Length	4.29 m (14 ft 1 in)
Width	1.85 m (6 ft 1 in)

DIMENSIONS, INTERNAL:

Cabin (excl flight deck): Length	7.89 m (25 ft 10½ in)
Max width	1.98 m (6 ft 6 in)
Max height	1.91 m (6 ft 3 in)
Floor area	approx 15.16 m² (168 sq ft)
Volume	approx 29.73 m³ (1,050 cu ft)

AREAS:

Main rotor blades (each)	3.71 m² (39.9 sq ft)
Tail rotor blades (each)	0.22 m² (2.35 sq ft)
Main rotor disc	280.5 m² (3,019 sq ft)
Tail rotor disc	7.80 m² (83.9 sq ft)
Stabiliser	2.51 m² (27.0 sq ft)

WEIGHTS:

Weight empty	6,010 kg (13,255 lb)
Max cargo payload: internal	2,270 kg (5,000 lb)
external	3,628 kg (8,000 lb)
Normal T-O weight	9,635 kg (21,247 lb)
Max T-O weight	10,000 kg (22,050 lb)

PERFORMANCE (at normal T-O weight except where indicated):

Max level speed at S/L:		
normal T-O weight	141 knots (261 km/h; 162 mph)	
max T-O weight	138 knots (255 km/h; 159 mph)	

Cruising speed at S/L, AUW of 9,072 kg (20,000 lb), ISA + 20°C:

for best range	130 knots (241 km/h; 150 mph)	
for best endurance	75 knots (139 km/h; 86 mph)	
Max rate of climb at S/L	408 m (1,340 ft)/min	
Service ceiling: normal T-O weight	3,385 m (11,100 ft)	
Hovering ceiling IGE	2,195 m (7,200 ft)	
Min ground turning radius	11.29 m (37 ft 0½ in)	
Runway LCN at max T-O weight	approx 4.75	

Typical mission profiles (ISA + 20°C):

SAR: Loiter for 5 h in search area 50 nm (92 km; 57 miles) from base, hover for 30 min to rescue survivors, return to base and land, 10% fuel remaining

Utility: Fly 240 nm (445 km; 276 miles) from base, pick up 24 fully equipped troops and return to base, landing with 272 kg (600 lb) of fuel remaining

Range with max standard fuel, no reserves
770 nm (1,427 km; 886 miles)
Endurance with max standard fuel, no reserves   8 h

MONTEPRANDONE WORKS

This branch of Agusta, formerly BredaNardi, continues to produce, under licence from their US manufacturers, the NH-300C and NH-500D and E light helicopters. Descriptions of the Model 500 series can be found under the McDonnell Douglas Helicopters heading in the US section of this edition, and of the Model 300C under the Schweizer heading. It is also licensed to manufacture, and to sell in central Europe, the McDonnell Douglas Model 530F.

Sales continue for agricultural work (mainly of the NH-300C) and training. In recent years they have included 20 NH-300s to the Greek Air Force flying school, and 50 NH-500Es to the Italian Air Force for training.

NH-300C built by Agusta's Monteprandone works
(Avio Data)

Agusta (SIAI-Marchetti) SF.260W flown by the *Team America* **demonstration team (uprated with 253.5 kW; 340 hp Textron Lycoming TIO-540 engine)** *(John Wegg)*

SESTO CALENDE WORKS

AERODROME AND MAIN WORKS: Vergiate (Varese)
OTHER WORKS: Sesto Calende (Varese) and Malpensa

Founded in 1915, SIAI-Marchetti produced a wide range of military and civil landplanes and flying-boats up to the end of the Second World War. Now known simply as the Sesto Calende works of Agusta, current products include piston, turboprop and turbofan powered trainers and the SF.600 utility transport. Since the 1970s it has been engaged in the co-production of licence built Boeing CH-47C, Bell 204/205/212/412, and Sikorsky S-61A, SH-3D/H and HH-3F helicopters.

On 6 October 1988 a memorandum of intent was signed with Grumman Aircraft Systems (a division of Grumman Corporation), covering the development phase of a collaborative programme aimed at submitting a version of the S.211 for the USAF/USN's Joint Primary Aircraft Training System (JPATS) requirement, to find an off the shelf replacement for the Cessna T-37 and Beechcraft T-34C. If selected, Grumman would be prime contractor, responsible for producing the aircraft and training system, consisting of syllabus definition, courseware, simulators and support. Agusta/Grumman also project possible joint sales through US foreign military sales and European-NATO Joint Jet Pilot Training (ENJJPT) programme opportunities.

The Sesto Calende works undertakes the overhaul and repair of various types of aircraft (notably the C-130 Hercules, DHC-5 Buffalo and Cessna Citation II). It participates in national or multi-national programmes, producing parts for the Aeritalia G222, Panavia Tornado, AMX, Airbus A310, Dassault Falcon 100 and Atlantique 2.

The works at Sesto Calende, Vergiate and Malpensa total 1,370,267 m² (14,749,416 sq ft) in area, of which 119,494 m² (1,286,221 sq ft) are covered, and employed nearly 2,000 people in 1990.

AGUSTA (SIAI-MARCHETTI) SF.260

The prototype for the SF.260 series, known as the F.250, was designed by Dott Ing Stelio Frati and built by Aviamilano. Flown for the first time on 15 July 1964, it was powered by a 186.5 kW (250 hp) Textron Lycoming engine and was certificated for aerobatic flying. A description appeared in the 1965-66 *Jane's*.

The version developed initially, for civil production, was manufactured, at first under licence from Aviamilano, by SIAI-Marchetti, and is designated SF.260. It received FAA type approval on 1 April 1966. Subsequently SIAI-Marchetti became the official holder of the type certificate and of all manufacturing rights in the SF.260.

Descriptions of the civil SF.260A and SF.260B can be found in the 1980-81 and earlier editions of *Jane's*, and of the SF.260C in the 1985-86 edition. Current models are as follows:

SF.260D. Improved and updated civil version, replacing SF.260C, with aerodynamic and structural improvements developed for military SF.260M. Certificated by RAI on 14 December 1985 and by FAA in October 1986.

SF.260M. Two/three-seat military trainer, developed from civil SF.260A and first flown on 10 October 1970. Introduced a number of important structural and aerodynamic improvements, many of which were subsequently applied to later models. Meets requirements for basic flying training; instrument flying; aerobatics, including deliberate spinning and recovery; night flying; navigation flying; and formation flying. Detailed customer list in 1984-85 and earlier editions of *Jane's*.

SF.260W Warrior. Trainer/tactical support version of SF.260M, first flown in May 1972. Two or four underwing pylons, for up to 300 kg (661 lb) of external stores, and cockpit stores selection panel. Able to undertake a wide variety of roles, including low-level strike; forward air control; forward air support; armed reconnaissance; and

liaison. Also meets same requirements as SF.260M for use as a trainer. Customers as listed in 1984-85 and earlier *Jane's*. One aircraft (described in 1980-81 and earlier editions) completed as **SF.260SW Sea Warrior** surveillance/SAR/supply version.

SF.260TP. Turboprop powered development. Described separately.

By early 1990 more than 800 SF.260s of all models had been delivered to civil operators and to 24 air forces worldwide, and production of the piston engined models was being stepped up.

Two major new orders for SF.260Ds were announced in March 1990. The Fox 51 Company of Texas is to buy 60, the first seven of which will be used by Doss Aviation for the pre-selection of US military pilots. The Turkish Air Force ordered 40 SF.260Ds for military training with an agreement for co-production by the TAI aerospace manufacturing group.

The following description is generally applicable to all piston engined models unless otherwise stated:

TYPE: Two/three-seat fully aerobatic military light aircraft.

WINGS: Cantilever low-wing monoplane. Wing section NACA 64₁-212 (modified) at root, NACA 64₁-210 (modified) at tip. Dihedral 6° 20′ from roots (5° on SF.260D). Incidence 2° 45′ at root, 0° at tip. No sweepback. All-metal light alloy safe-life structure, with single main spar and auxiliary rear spar, built in two portions bolted together at centreline and attached to fuselage by six bolts. Press-formed ribs. Skin butt joined and flush riveted. Differentially operating Frise ailerons, and electrically actuated single-slotted flaps. Flaps operated by torque tube and mechanical linkage, ailerons by pushrods and cables. Servo tab in each aileron.

FUSELAGE: Semi-monocoque safe-life structure of light alloy frames, stringers and flush riveted skin; glassfibre front panel of engine cowling and detachable glassfibre tailcone.

TAIL UNIT: Cantilever light alloy safe-life structure, with sweptback vertical surfaces, fixed incidence tailplane and one-piece elevator. Rudder and elevator operated by cables. Controllable trim tab in starboard half of elevator; ground adjustable tab on rudder.

LANDING GEAR: Electrically retractable tricycle type, with manual emergency actuation. Inward retracting main gear, of trailing arm type, and rearward retracting nose unit, each embodying Magnaghi oleo-pneumatic shock absorber (type 2/22028 in main units). Each welded steel tube main leg is hinged to the main and rear spars. Nose unit is of leg and fork type, with coaxial shock absorber and torque strut. Cleveland P/N 3080A mainwheels, with size 6.00-6 tube and tyre (6-ply rating), pressure 2.45 bars (35.5 lb/sq in). Cleveland P/N 40-77A nosewheel, with size 5.00-5 tube and tyre (6-ply rating), pressure 1.96 bars (28.4 lb/sq in). Cleveland P/N 3000-500 independent hydraulic single-disc brake and parking brake on each mainwheel. Nosewheel steering (20° to left or right) is operated directly by the rudder pedals, to which it is linked by pushrods. Up-lock secures main gear in retracted position during flight; anti-retraction system prevents main gear from retracting whenever strut is compressed by weight of aircraft.

POWER PLANT: One 194 kW (260 hp) Textron Lycoming O-540-E4A5 flat-six engine, driving a Hartzell HC-C2YK-1BF/8477-8R two-blade constant-speed metal propeller with spinner. AEIO-540-D4A5 engine available optionally. Fuel in two light alloy tanks in wings, capacity of each 49.5 litres (13.1 US gallons; 10.9 Imp gallons); and two permanent wingtip tanks, capacity of each 72 litres (19 US gallons; 15.85 Imp gallons). Total internal fuel capacity 243 litres (64.2 US gallons; 53.5 Imp gallons), of which 235 litres (62.1 US gallons; 51.7 Imp gallons) are usable. Individual refuelling point on top of each tank. In addition, SF.260W may be fitted with two 80 litre (21.1

US gallon; 17.5 Imp gallon) auxiliary tanks on underwing pylons. Oil capacity (all models) 11.4 litres (3 US gallons; 2.5 Imp gallons).

ACCOMMODATION (SF.260D): Three seats in enclosed cockpit, two side by side in front, one at rear. Two children with a combined weight not exceeding 113 kg (250 lb) may occupy rear seat. One-piece fully transparent rearward sliding Plexiglas canopy, with rubber cord canopy release. Baggage compartment, capacity 40 kg (88 lb), behind rear seat. Cabin carpeted, heated and ventilated; walls thermally insulated and soundproofed by a glassfibre lining. Slots at base of windscreen admit air for windscreen defrosting.

ACCOMMODATION (SF.260M; W similar): Side by side front seats (for instructor and pupil in SF.260M), with third seat centrally at rear. Front seats individually adjustable fore and aft, with forward folding backs and provision for back type parachute packs. Dual controls standard. All three seats equipped with lap belts and shoulder harnesses. Baggage compartment aft of rear seat. Upper portion of canopy tinted. Emergency canopy release handle for each front seat occupant. Steel tube windscreen frame for protection in the event of an overturn.

SYSTEMS (SF.260M; other models generally similar): Hydraulic equipment for mainwheel brakes only. No pneumatic system. 24V DC electrical system of single-conductor negative earth type, including 70A Prestolite engine mounted alternator/rectifier and 24V 24Ah Varley battery, for engine starting, flap and landing gear actuation, fuel booster pumps, electronics and lighting. Sealed battery compartment in rear of fuselage on port side. Connection of an external power source automatically disconnects the battery. Heating system for carburettor air intake. Emergency electrical system for extending landing gear if normal electrical actuation fails; provision for mechanical extension in the event of total electrical failure. Cabin heating, and windscreen de-icing and demisting, by heat exchanger using engine exhaust air. Additional manually controlled warm air outlets for general cabin heating. Oxygen system optional.

AVIONICS AND EQUIPMENT (SF.260M; W generally similar): Basic instrumentation and military equipment to customer's requirements. Blind-flying instrumentation and communications equipment optional: typical selection includes dual Collins 20B VHF com; Collins VIR-31A VHF nav; Collins ADF-60A; Collins TDR-90 ATC transponder; Collins PN-101 compass; ID-90-000 RMI; and Gemelli AG04-1 intercom. Landing light in nose, below spinner. Instrument panel can be slid rearward to provide access to rear of instruments.

ARMAMENT (SF.260W): Two or four underwing hardpoints, able to carry external stores on NATO standard pylons up to a maximum of 300 kg (661 lb) when flown as a single-seater. Typical alternative loads can include one or two SIAI gun pods, each with one or two 7.62 mm FN machine-guns and 500 rds; two Aerea AL-8-70 launchers each with eight 2.75 in rockets; two LAU-32 launchers each with seven 2.75 in rockets; two Aerea AL-18-50 launchers each with eighteen 2 in rockets; two Aerea AL-8-68 launchers each with eight 68 mm rockets; two Aerea AL-6-80 launchers each with six 81 mm rockets; two LUU-2/B parachute flares; two SAMP EU 32 125 kg general purpose bombs or EU 13 120 kg fragmentation bombs; two SAMP EU 70 50 kg general purpose bombs; Mk 76 11 kg practice bombs; two cartridge throwers for 70 mm multi-purpose cartridges, F 725 flares, or F 130 smoke cartridges; one or two photo-reconnaissance pods with two 70 mm automatic cameras; two supply containers; or two 80 litre (21.1 US gallon; 17.5 Imp gallon) auxiliary fuel tanks.

DIMENSIONS, EXTERNAL:

Wing span over tip tanks	8.35 m (27 ft 4¾ in)
Wing chord: at root	1.60 m (5 ft 3 in)
mean aerodynamic	1.325 m (4 ft 4¼ in)
at tip	0.784 m (2 ft 6⅞ in)
Wing aspect ratio (excl tip tanks)	6.3
Wing taper ratio	2.2
Length overall	7.10 m (23 ft 3½ in)
Fuselage: Max width	1.10 m (3 ft 7¼ in)
Max depth	1.042 m (3 ft 5 in)
Height overall	2.41 m (7 ft 11 in)
Elevator span	3.01 m (9 ft 10½ in)
Wheel track	2.274 m (7 ft 5½ in)
Wheelbase	1.66 m (5 ft 5¼ in)
Propeller diameter	1.93 m (6 ft 4 in)
Propeller ground clearance	0.32 m (1 ft 0½ in)

DIMENSIONS, INTERNAL:

Cabin: Length	1.66 m (5 ft 5¼ in)
Max width	1.00 m (3 ft 3¼ in)
Height (seat cushion to canopy)	0.98 m (3 ft 2½ in)
Volume	1.50 m³ (53 cu ft)
Baggage compartment volume	0.18 m³ (6.36 cu ft)

AREAS:

Wings, gross	10.10 m² (108.70 sq ft)
Ailerons (total, incl tabs)	0.762 m² (8.20 sq ft)
Trailing-edge flaps (total)	1.18 m² (12.70 sq ft)
Fin	0.76 m² (8.18 sq ft)
Dorsal fin	0.16 m² (1.72 sq ft)
Rudder, incl tab	0.60 m² (6.46 sq ft)

Tailplane	1.46 m² (15.70 sq ft)
Elevator, incl tab	0.96 m² (10.30 sq ft)

WEIGHTS AND LOADINGS:

Manufacturer's basic weight empty:	
M	755 kg (1,664 lb)
W	770 kg (1,697 lb)
Weight empty, equipped: D	755 kg (1,664 lb)
M	815 kg (1,797 lb)
W	830 kg (1,830 lb)
Fuel:	
in-wing and wingtip tanks (all versions)	169 kg (372.5 lb)
underwing tanks (W only)	114 kg (251.5 lb)
Typical mission weights:	
M, trainer (clean)	1,140 kg (2,513 lb)
W, two 47 kg (103.5 lb) machine-gun pods and full internal fuel	1,163 kg (2,564 lb)
W, one Alkan 500B cartridge thrower, one two-camera reconnaissance pod and full internal fuel	1,182 kg (2,605 lb)
W, trainer with 94 kg (207 lb) external stores	1,249 kg (2,753 lb)
W, self-ferry with two 80 litre (21.1 US gallon; 17.5 Imp gallon) underwing tanks	1,285 kg (2,833 lb)
W, two 125 kg bombs and 150 kg (331 lb) internal fuel	1,300 kg (2,866 lb)
W, two AL-8-70 rocket launchers and 160 kg (353 lb) internal fuel	1,300 kg (2,866 lb)
Max T-O weight: D, M, Aerobatic	1,100 kg (2,425 lb)
D, Utility	1,100 kg (2,425 lb)
M, Utility	1,200 kg (2,645 lb)
W, max permitted	1,300 kg (2,866 lb)
Max wing loading: D	109 kg/m² (22.4 lb/sq ft)
M	119 kg/m² (24.4 lb/sq ft)
W	129 kg/m² (26.4 lb/sq ft)
Max power loading: D	5.68 kg/kW (9.33 lb/hp)
M	6.19 kg/kW (10.17 lb/hp)
W	6.70 kg/kW (11.01 lb/hp)

PERFORMANCE (C at AUW of 1,102 kg; 2,430 lb, M at AUW of 1,200 kg; 2,645 lb, W at 1,300 kg; 2,866 lb, except where indicated):

Never-exceed speed:	
D, M	235 knots (436 km/h; 271 mph)
Max level speed at S/L:	
D	187 knots (347 km/h; 215 mph)
M	180 knots (333 km/h; 207 mph)
W	165 knots (305 km/h; 190 mph)
Max cruising speed (75% power):	
D at 3,050 m (10,000 ft)	178 knots (330 km/h; 205 mph)
M at 1,500 m (4,925 ft)	162 knots (300 km/h; 186 mph)
W at 1,500 m (4,925 ft)	152 knots (281 km/h; 175 mph)
Stalling speed, flaps and landing gear up:	
M	74 knots (137 km/h; 86 mph)
W	88 knots (163 km/h; 102 mph)
Stalling speed, flaps and landing gear down:	
D	60 knots (111 km/h; 70 mph)
M	68 knots (126 km/h; 79 mph)
W	72 knots (134 km/h; 83 mph)
Max rate of climb at S/L: D	546 m (1,791 ft)/min
M	457 m (1,500 ft)/min
W	381 m (1,250 ft)/min
Time to 1,500 m (4,925 ft): M	4 min
W	6 min 20 s
Time to 2,300 m (7,550 ft): M	6 min 50 s
W	10 min 20 s
Time to 3,000 m (9,850 ft): M	10 min
W	18 min 40 s
Service ceiling: D	5,790 m (19,000 ft)
M	4,665 m (15,300 ft)
W	4,480 m (14,700 ft)
T-O run at S/L: D	480 m (1,575 ft)
M	384 m (1,260 ft)
T-O to 15 m (50 ft) at S/L: M	606 m (1,988 ft)
W	825 m (2,707 ft)
Landing from 15 m (50 ft) at S/L: D	445 m (1,460 ft)
M	539 m (1,768 ft)
W	645 m (2,116 ft)
Landing run at S/L: D, M	345 m (1,132 ft)

Operational radius:
W, 6 h 25 min single-seat armed patrol mission at 1,163 kg (2,564 lb) AUW, incl 5 h 35 min over operating area, 20 kg (44 lb) fuel reserves
50 nm (92 km; 57 miles)
W, 3 h 38 min single-seat strike mission, incl two 5 min loiters over separate en-route target areas, 20 kg (44 lb) fuel reserves 250 nm (463 km; 287 miles)
W, 4 h 54 min single-seat strike mission, incl 5 min over target area, 20 kg (44 lb) fuel reserves
300 nm (556 km; 345 miles)
W, 4 h 30 min single-seat photo-reconnaissance mission at 1,182 kg (2,605 lb) AUW, incl three 1 h loiters over separate en-route operating areas, 20 kg (44 lb) fuel reserves 150 nm (278 km; 172 miles)
W, 6 h 3 min two-seat self-ferry mission with two 80 litre (21.1 US gallon; 17.5 Imp gallon) underwing tanks, at 1,285 kg (2,833 lb) AUW, 30 kg (66 lb) fuel reserves 926 nm (1,716 km; 1,066 miles)

Agusta (SIAI-Marchetti) SF.260TP with gun pods *(Avio Data)*

Agusta (SIAI-Marchetti) SF.260TP turboprop trainer, with additional side view (centre) of piston engined SF.260M *(Pilot Press)*

Range with max fuel:	
D (two-seat)	805 nm (1,490 km; 925 miles)
M (two-seat)	890 nm (1,650 km; 1,025 miles)
g limits (M):	
at max Aerobatic T-O weight	+6/−3
at max Utility T-O weight without external load	+4.4/−2.2

AGUSTA (SIAI-MARCHETTI) SF.260TP

First flown in July 1980, the SF.260TP is a turboprop powered development of the SF.260M/W, the airframe remaining virtually unchanged aft of the firewall except for substitution of an inset rudder trim tab and provision of an automatic fuel feed system.

More than 60 SF.260TPs have been ordered by military customers.

AIRFRAME: As SF.260M/W, except for increased overall length and provision of trim tab in rudder.

POWER PLANT: One Allison 250-B17D turboprop, flat rated at 261 kW (350 shp) and driving a Hartzell HC-B3TF-7A/T10173-25R three-blade constant-speed fully-feathering and reversible-pitch propeller with spinner. Fuel capacity as for SF.260M/W; automatic fuel feed system. Oil capacity 7 litres (1.8 US gallons; 1.5 Imp gallons).

ACCOMMODATION, SYSTEMS, AVIONICS AND EQUIPMENT: Generally as for SF.260.

DIMENSIONS, EXTERNAL AND INTERNAL, AND AREAS:

As for SF.260 except:	
Length overall	7.40 m (24 ft 3¼ in)

WEIGHTS AND LOADINGS: As for SF.260M/W except:

Weight empty, equipped	750 kg (1,654 lb)
Max power loading: trainer	4.60 kg/kW (7.56 lb/shp)
Warrior	4.98 kg/kW (8.19 lb/shp)

PERFORMANCE (at trainer Utility T-O weight of 1,200 kg; 2,645 lb, ISA):

Never-exceed speed	236 knots (437 km/h; 271 mph)
Max level speed at 3,050 m (10,000 ft)	228 knots (422 km/h; 262 mph)
Max cruising speed at 2,440 m (8,000 ft)	216 knots (400 km/h; 248 mph)
Econ cruising speed at 4,575 m (15,000 ft)	170 knots (315 km/h; 195 mph)
Stalling speed at S/L, flaps down, power off	68 knots (126 km/h; 79 mph)
Max rate of climb at S/L	660 m (2,065 ft)/min
Service ceiling	7,500 m (24,600 ft)
T-O run	298 m (978 ft)
T-O to 15 m (50 ft)	467 m (1,532 ft)
Landing from 15 m (50 ft)	533 m (1,749 ft)
Landing run, without reverse pitch	307 m (1,007 ft)
Range at 4,575 m (15,000 ft) with max fuel, 30 min reserves	512 nm (949 km; 589 miles)

AGUSTA (SIAI-MARCHETTI) S.211

This lightweight, low-cost basic trainer and light attack aircraft was first revealed in the form of a model at the Paris Air Show in May/June 1977. Two flying prototypes were built initially, and the first of these (I-SITF) made its initial flight on 10 April 1981.

Deliveries of production S.211s began in November 1984. Customers include the air forces of the Philippines (18), Singapore (30) and Haiti (4). The first six S.211s for Singapore were delivered in component knocked-down form for reassembly; subsequent aircraft were built by SAMCO, a subsidiary of Singapore Aerospace (SA, which see). The Philippine order, signed in 1988, also covered an option for a further 18 aircraft, with final assembly of 14 of the initial 18 undertaken by Philippine Aerospace Development Corporation (which see). The first S.211 for the Philippines was delivered in September 1989. Nine of the aircraft are to be operated by the 100th Training Wing at Fernando Air Base, Lipa City, Laguna. Of the other nine, some will be used by the 5th Fighter Wing at Basa AB, Luzon, for training and the remainder will operate in a ground support role from Mactan AB, Cebu.

In partnership with Grumman Aircraft Systems, a version of the S.211 is to be submitted for the USAF/USN's JPATS competition (see introduction).

Features of the S.211 are its safe stalling and spinning characteristics, and the very low airframe weight, made possible by the fact that some 61 per cent of the external surfaces are made from composite materials.

In order to improve the S.211's operational capabilities a special nav/attack version, equipped with an OMI/Litton lightweight head-up display and Omega navigation computer, is under development. Joint development, with SA, of a lengthened version of the S.211 was announced at the Paris Air Show in June 1987. An enhanced version of the S.211 with a 14.2 kN (3,190 lb st) JT15D engine is also under development, offering also an increased fuel capacity.

The following description applies to the standard production S.211:

TYPE: Two-seat basic trainer and light attack aircraft.

WINGS: Cantilever shoulder-wing monoplane, with supercritical section developed by computer with the assistance of the US universities of New York and Kansas. Thickness/chord ratio 15 per cent at root, 13 per cent at tip. Incidence 2° 13′ at root, –1° 17′ at tip. Anhedral 2° from roots. Sweepback 15° 30′ at quarter-chord. Two-spar metal torsion box structure, forming integral fuel tank; attached to fuselage by four bolts. Upper and lower skins each formed by two one-piece panels joined along centreline and to the spars. Hydraulically actuated ailerons, with electric trim, and large area electrically actuated Fowler flaps, on trailing-edges.

FUSELAGE: Conventional metal and glassfibre semi-monocoque structure. Hydraulically actuated airbrake under centre-fuselage. Equipment bay in nose. Large quick-disconnect panel at rear, for rapid engine access or removal.

TAIL UNIT: Cantilever metal structure. Sweptback fin; horn balanced rudder with electrically operated trim tab; electrically actuated variable incidence tailplane has sweptback leading-edge. Horn balanced elevators, with servo tab.

LANDING GEAR: Hydraulically retractable tricycle type, of Messier-Bugatti/Magnaghi design. Oleo-pneumatic shock absorber in each unit. All units retract forward into fuselage (main units turning through 90° to lie flat in undersides of engine air intake trunks). Nosewheel steerable 18° left and right. Mainwheels size 6.50-8; nosewheel size 5.00-5 with water deflecting tyre. Designed for sink rate of 4 m (13 ft)/s. Wheel brakes actuated hydraulically, independently of main hydraulic system. Provision for emergency free-fall extension.

POWER PLANT: One 11.13 kN (2,500 lb st) Pratt & Whitney Canada JT15D-4C non-afterburning turbofan, with electronic fuel control, mounted in rear of fuselage; lateral intake each side of fuselage, with splitter plate. Fuel in 650 litre (171.5 US gallon; 143 Imp gallon) integral wing tank and 150 litre (39.5 US gallon; 33 Imp gallon) fuselage tank; total capacity 800 litres (211 US gallons; 176 Imp gallons). Single gravity refuelling point in top surface of starboard wing. Electric fuel pump for engine starting and emergency use. Fuel and oil systems permit inverted flight. Provision for two 270 litre (71.3 US gallon; 59.4 Imp gallon) drop tanks on inboard underwing stores points. Oil capacity 10 kg (22 lb).

ACCOMMODATION: Seats for two persons in tandem in pressurised and air-conditioned cockpit under one-piece framed canopy opening sideways to starboard: pupil in front, instructor on rear seat elevated 28 cm (11 in). Internal transparent screen between seats. Martin-Baker Mk 10 lightweight zero/zero ejection seats for both occupants.

SYSTEMS: Environmental control system for cockpit pressurisation and air-conditioning, using engine bleed air for heating, freon vapour for cooling. Max pressure differential 0.24 bars (3.5 lb/sq in). Hydraulic system, pressure 207 bars (3,000 lb/sq in), for actuation of airbrake, landing gear, freon compressor and aileron boost, and independent actuation of wheel brakes. Primary electrical system is 28V DC, using an engine driven starter/generator; nickel-cadmium battery; two static inverters supply AC power for instruments and avionics. External power receptacle in port side of lower fuselage aft of wing. Demand type main oxygen system, at 124 bars (1,800 lb/sq in) pressure, sufficient to supply both occupants for 4 hours, plus bottles for emergency oxygen supply.

AVIONICS AND EQUIPMENT: Standard avionics fit includes two V/UHF com, ADF, VOR/ILS and DME or Tacan, IFF or ATC, ICS, AHRS, HSI and AI, with full dual controls and handover. Provision for dual gyro stabilised gunsight system with miniaturised video recording or film camera. Additional provisions for R/Nav, radar altimeter, Doppler radar, head-up display, radar warning system and ECM.

ARMAMENT: Four underwing hardpoints, stressed for loads of up to 330 kg (727.5 lb) inboard, 165 kg (364 lb) outboard; max external load 660 kg (1,455 lb). Typical loads can include four single- or twin-gun 7.62 mm machine-gun pods, four 12.7 mm gun pods, or (inboard only) two 20 mm gun pods; four AL-18-50 (18 × 50 mm), Matra F2 (6 × 68 mm), LAU-32 (7 × 2.75 in), or AL-6-80 (6 × 81 mm) rocket launchers, or (inboard only) two Matra 155 (18 × 68 mm), SNORA RWK-020 (12 × 81 mm) or 100 mm rocket launchers; four bombs or practice bombs of up to 150 kg size, or (inboard only) two bombs or napalm containers of up to 300 kg; four 74 mm cartridge throwers; or (inboard only) two photo-reconnaissance pods each with four cameras and infra-red linescan; or (inboard only) two 270 litre (71.3 US gallon; 59.4 Imp gallon) auxiliary fuel tanks. Ferranti ISIS D-211 optical weapon aiming system optional (fitted in aircraft for Haiti).

DIMENSIONS, EXTERNAL:

Wing span	8.43 m (27 ft 8 in)
Wing chord: at root	2.151 m (7 ft 0¾ in)
mean aerodynamic	1.646 m (5 ft 4¾ in)
at tip	1.00 m (3 ft 3¼ in)
Wing aspect ratio	5.1
Length overall	9.31 m (30 ft 6½ in)
Height overall	3.80 m (12 ft 5½ in)

Agusta (SIAI-Marchetti) S.211 of the Republic of Singapore Air Force *(Ivo Sturzenegger)*

Agusta (SIAI-Marchetti) S.211 basic trainer and light attack aircraft *(Pilot Press)*

Tailplane span	3.96 m (13 ft 0 in)
Wheel track	2.29 m (7 ft 6 in)
Wheelbase	4.02 m (13 ft 2¼ in)
AREAS:	
Wings, gross	12.60 m² (135.63 sq ft)
Airbrake	0.42 m² (4.52 sq ft)
Vertical tail surfaces (total)	2.01 m² (21.64 sq ft)
Horizontal tail surfaces (total)	3.378 m² (36.36 sq ft)
WEIGHTS:	
Weight empty, equipped	1,850 kg (4,078 lb)
Max usable fuel: internal	622 kg (1,371 lb)
external	390 kg (860 lb)
Max T-O weight: trainer, clean	2,750 kg (6,063 lb)
armed version	3,150 kg (6,944 lb)
PERFORMANCE (at T-O weight of 2,500 kg; 5,511 lb except where indicated):	
Never-exceed speed	
Mach 0.80 (400 knots; 740 km/h; 460 mph EAS)	
Max cruising speed at 7,620 m (25,000 ft)	
	360 knots (667 km/h; 414 mph)
Rotation speed	90 knots (167 km/h; 104 mph)
Stalling speed, flaps down	74 knots (138 km/h; 86 mph)
Max rate of climb at S/L	1,280 m (4,200 ft)/min
Time to 6,100 m (20,000 ft)	6 min 12 s
Service ceiling	12,200 m (40,000 ft)
T-O run (S/L, ISA)	390 m (1,280 ft)
T-O to 15 m (50 ft)	512 m (1,680 ft)
Landing from 15 m (50 ft)	705 m (2,313 ft)
Landing run (S/L, ISA)	361 m (1,185 ft)
Min air turning radius at S/L	less than 305 m (1,000 ft)

Typical attack radius with four rocket launchers, AUW of 3,150 kg (6,944 lb):
hi-lo-hi, out and back at 265 knots (491 km/h; 305 mph) at 9,150 m (30,000 ft), 2 h 50 min mission (incl 5 min over target), 60 kg (132 lb) of fuel remaining
300 nm (556 km; 345 miles)
lo-lo-lo, out and back at 250 knots (463 km/h; 288 mph) at less than 305 m (1,000 ft), 1 h 5 min mission (incl 5 min over target), 60 kg (132 lb) of fuel remaining
125 nm (231 km; 144 miles)
Max range on internal fuel, 30 min reserves
900 nm (1,668 km; 1,036 miles)
Ferry range (AUW of 3,150 kg; 6,944 lb, max internal and external fuel) at 270 knots (500 km/h; 311 mph) at 9,150 m (30,000 ft), 90 kg (198 lb) of fuel remaining
1,340 nm (2,483 km; 1,543 miles)

Endurance, 30 min reserves	3 h 50 min
Sustained g limit at 4,575 m (15,000 ft)	3.4
g limits:	+6/–3 clean
	+5/–2.5 with external stores

AGUSTA (SIAI-MARCHETTI) SF.600TP CANGURO (KANGAROO)

The prototype F.600 Canguro (I-CANG), built by General Avia and then powered by 261 kW (350 hp) Textron Lycoming TIO-540-J flat-six piston engines, made its first flight on 30 December 1978. This aircraft was described under the General Avia heading in the 1979-80 *Jane's*.

The basic production aircraft was offered initially with Allison 250-B17C turboprops and non-retractable landing gear; major options included retractable landing gear and a swing-tail fuselage. The current standard power plant is two 335 kW (450 shp) Allison 250-B17F engines. The aircraft can be adapted for a variety of roles which include passenger/troop or cargo transport, paratroop transport, air ambulance, maritime surveillance, electronic intelligence, and agricultural duties. The retractable gear version is considered especially suitable for a maritime surveillance role, equipped with an underfuselage radar system, or FLIR and/or SLAR.

Certification by the RAI was received in the Spring of 1987 in accordance with FAR Pt 23. The initial production batch totalled nine aircraft, and the first three of these, for the Rome based air taxi operator Sun Line, were delivered in April 1988. They were used for air taxi operations to Corsica, Elba and Sardinia. The Canguro is to be produced in South Korea by a newly formed company known as Sammi Agusta Aerospace. Inaugurated on 22 May 1989, this Italo-South Korean company is a joint venture by Gruppo Agusta and Sammi Corporation, one of the major engineering industrial groups in South Korea. It has been established to build the SF.600 Canguro and to market this aircraft in the Pacific basin area.

A new, modern 400,000 m² (4.3 million sq ft) aeronautical facility is to be built, which will have a workforce of about 400 people. In addition to Canguro production, the new company is intended to be responsible for the marketing and, eventually, local manufacture of the whole range of Agusta fixed-wing aircraft and helicopters. In January 1990 a Canguro completed a 10,800 km (20,000 km; 12,425 mile) staged flight from Italy to South Korea.

TYPE: Twin-turboprop passenger, cargo, ambulance and general utility transport.

WINGS: Cantilever high-wing monoplane. Wing section NASA GAW-1, with 17 per cent thickness/chord ratio.

Agusta (SIAI-Marchetti) SF.600TP in standard form with non-retractable landing gear

tail unit, and electric de-icing of propellers, are optional.

AVIONICS: Wide range of IFR com/nav avionics available, to customer's requirements. Typical installation includes VHF, UHF and HF com, ADF, VOR/LOC/ILS, DME and ATC transponder. Options include Omega nav system, weather radar, three-axis autopilot and flight director.

EQUIPMENT: Can be equipped for target towing, with floor mounted winch, 2,000 m (6,560 ft) of cable, electric power unit (100A/28V DC), and miss-distance indicator system; with undertail hook for towing one or more gliders; with one or two Wild or Zeiss type photogrammetric automatic cameras (plus additional avionics at customer's option); with equipment for in-flight inspection and calibration of ground radio/navigation aids; or with appropriate sensors and radar warning receiver. Other specialised applications include agricultural duties (single underfuselage tank, plus bubble type and additional lower windows in pilot's door, windscreen and nose-gear wire cutters, ceiling mounted airscoop, and anti-corrosion paint finish). The maritime surveillance version can be equipped with nose mounted search and navigation radar, underfuselage side/down-looking surveillance radar, belly mounted panoramic camera and forward looking oblique camera, FLIR or low light level TV camera under fuselage, Omega-VLF area navigation system, advanced compass system, periscopic sextant, bubble side windows for observers, and a searchlight.

Basic Agusta (SIAI-Marchetti) SF.600TP, with additional side view (centre) of version with retractable landing gear *(Pilot Press)*

DIMENSIONS, EXTERNAL:

Wing span	15.00 m (49 ft 2½ in)
Wing chord, constant	1.60 m (5 ft 3 in)
Wing aspect ratio	9.4
Length overall	12.15 m (39 ft 10½ in)
Height overall	4.60 m (15 ft 1 in)
Tailplane span	5.89 m (19 ft 4 in)
Wheel track	2.40 m (7 ft 10½ in)
Wheelbase	4.88 m (16 ft 0 in)
Propeller diameter	2.29 m (7 ft 6 in)
Crew door (fwd, port): Height	1.14 m (3 ft 9 in)
Width	0.86 m (2 ft 10 in)
Height to sill	0.90 m (2 ft 11½ in)
Cargo door (rear, port):	
Height	1.13 m (3 ft 8½ in)
Width	1.49 m (4 ft 10¾ in)
Height to sill	0.90 m (2 ft 11½ in)

DIMENSIONS, INTERNAL:

Cabin, excl flight deck: Length	5.05 m (16 ft 6¾ in)
Width	1.23 m (4 ft 0½ in)
Height	1.27 m (4 ft 2 in)
Floor area	6.0 m² (64.6 sq ft)
Volume	7.90 m³ (279 cu ft)

AREAS:

Wings, gross	24.00 m² (258.3 sq ft)
Fin	1.69 m² (18.19 sq ft)
Rudder	1.35 m² (14.53 sq ft)
Tailplane	3.68 m² (39.61 sq ft)
Elevators (total)	2.76 m² (29.71 sq ft)

WEIGHTS AND LOADINGS:

Weight empty (standard utility version)	
	1,875 kg (4,133 lb)
Max T-O weight	3,400 kg (7,495 lb)
Max cargo floor loading	400 kg/m² (81.93 lb/sq ft)
Max wing loading	141.7 kg/m² (29.0 lb/sq ft)
Max power loading	5.07 kg/kW (8.33 lb/shp)

PERFORMANCE (at max T-O weight, ISA):

Max cruising speed at 1,525 m (5,000 ft)	
	165 knots (306 km/h; 190 mph)
Cruising speed (75% power) at 3,050 m (10,000 ft)	
	155 knots (287 km/h; 178 mph)
Stalling speed, flaps down	59 knots (109 km/h; 68 mph)
Max rate of climb at S/L	451 m (1,480 ft)/min
Rate of climb at S/L, one engine out	152 m (500 ft)/min
Service ceiling	7,315 m (24,000 ft)
Service ceiling, one engine out	3,050 m (10,000 ft)
T-O run	287 m (940 ft)
T-O to 15 m (50 ft)	408 m (1,340 ft)
Landing from 15 m (50 ft):	
without propeller reversal	479 m (1,570 ft)
with propeller reversal	396 m (1,300 ft)
Landing run: without propeller reversal	280 m (920 ft)
with propeller reversal	204 m (670 ft)
Range at 3,050 m (10,000 ft), 10% reserves:	
with max payload	324 nm (600 km; 372 miles)
with max fuel and 500 kg (1,102 lb) payload	
	853 nm (1,580 km; 981 miles)

Dihedral 2°. Incidence (constant) 1° 30′. All-metal riveted structure in aluminium alloy, with stressed skin. Centre-section has main spar and two auxiliary spars; outboard of engines, wings have two spars. All-metal ailerons and electrically operated double-slotted flaps. Electrically operated trim tab in port aileron.

FUSELAGE: Aluminium alloy semi-monocoque structure of frames, stringers, bulkheads and stressed skin. Swing-tail rear fuselage available optionally.

TAIL UNIT: Cantilever all-metal stressed skin structure. Trim tabs in rudder (actuated mechanically) and each elevator (electrically/mechanically operated). Small dorsal fin.

LANDING GEAR: Choice of retractable or non-retractable tricycle gear, of trailing arm type, with oleo-pneumatic shock absorber in each unit. Twin-wheel main units, mounted on small stub-wings attached to fuselage floor; single steerable nose unit. Mainwheels and tyres size 7.00-6, pressure 2.90 bars (42 lb/sq in); nosewheel and tyre size 6.00-6. Hydraulic disc brakes on main units.

POWER PLANT: Two 335 kW (450 shp) Allison 250-B17F turboprops in current production version, each driving a Hartzell three-blade constant-speed fully-feathering reversible-pitch propeller. Fuel in four identical outer-wing tanks, total capacity 1,100 litres (290.6 US gallons; 242 Imp gallons). Self-sealing tanks optional on military versions. Provision for underwing tanks, total capacity 600 litres (158.5 US gallons; 132 Imp gallons). Oil capacity 11.4 litres (3.0 US gallons; 2.5 Imp gallons).

ACCOMMODATION: Pilot and co-pilot or passenger on flight deck. Dual controls standard. Cabin accommodates up to nine passengers at 100 cm (40 in) seat pitch (2-2-2-2-1); six passengers in VIP version, with reclining seats, folding tables, bar and toilet; or 10 paratroops on inward facing seats; or two stretcher patients and two medical attendants; or freight. Baggage compartment at rear of cabin in standard passenger version; in centre of cabin, opposite toilet, in VIP version; rear compartment used to store folding passenger seats when converted for cargo use. Forward door on port side for crew. Wider, sliding door at rear on port side for passenger and freight loading and paratroop dropping, with smaller emergency door opposite this on starboard side. Cargo version can accept three 1.30 × 1.15 × 1.07 m (51 × 45 × 42 in) containers, or two of size 2.20 × 1.15 × 1.07 m (87 × 45 × 42 in).

SYSTEMS: Standard cabin heating/defrosting system uses engine bleed air; ventilation is provided by ram air; freon air-conditioning system optional. Primary electrical system is 28V DC, powered by two 150A engine driven starter/generators, with a 24V 22Ah nickel-cadmium battery for independent engine starting and emergencies. AC power, 115V at 400Hz, is provided when required by a static inverter. Pneumatic de-icing system for wings and

SOMMA LOMBARDA WORKS

The Caproni company, formed in 1910, was the oldest Italian aircraft manufacturer before its name was dropped by the Agusta Group, which had acquired a 100 per cent shareholding in Caproni Vizzola in 1983. Its works at Vizzola Ticino have approx 30,000 m² (322,917 sq ft) of covered space, and are equipped to manufacture complete structural subassemblies for helicopters and medium-sized fixed-wing aircraft. The Somma Lombarda works also produces ground support equipment for General Electric T64/CT64, J79, J85 and CF6 and Turbo Union RB199 turbojet and turbofan engines.

AGUSTA (CAPRONI VIZZOLA) C22J VENTURA

The C22J is a two-seat lightweight training and pleasure/sport aircraft, developed as a private venture. A prototype (I-CAVJ), powered by 1.0 kN (220 lb st) TRS 18-046 engines, made its first flight on 21 July 1980.

Intended primarily for student pilot screening, basic and proficiency training, the C22J is also suitable for ECM evaluation, ground and air navaid calibration, ecological survey and high-speed liaison. It can be converted easily for photographic survey duties, or for use as an RPV.

The first pre-series C22J (I-GIAC) made its initial flight

on 17 February 1983, and differs from the prototype in having shorter span wings, with tip tanks, and more powerful TRS 18-1 engines. RAI certification is to FAR Pt 23 standards.

The following description applies to the intended production version:

TYPE: Two-seat basic training aircraft.

WINGS: Cantilever shoulder-wing monoplane. Constant chord wings, of Wortmann FX-67K-170 section. Dihedral 2°. Incidence 1° 9′. No sweepback. Single-spar structure, built as two panels and joined on centreline, with aluminium alloy skin and extruded leading-edge.

Electrically actuated trailing-edge plain flaps can be set in any position throughout their full range of movement. Flaps operate in conjunction with aluminium alloy airbrakes/spoilers, of which there is one in upper surface of each wing, forward of flap. Airbrakes are opened manually, but move with flaps to provide balanced control. Aerodynamically balanced ailerons operate differentially and are drooped to provide additional flap area. All movable surfaces of extruded aluminium alloy, operated by push/pull rods. No tabs.

FUSELAGE: Tadpole shaped structure, designed as a laminar lifting body. Primary load-bearing keel and wing spar pickup cross-structure is of light alloy, inside moulded glassfibre shell. NACA type flush engine air inlet of glassfibre in top of fuselage, aft of cockpits. Tailboom is of light alloy.

TAIL UNIT: Cantilever T tail, with light alloy stressed skin tailplane. Full span balanced elevator is a chemically milled extrusion, and has spring trim, actuated by Industria electrical system located in fin. All-metal two-spar stressed skin fin, bolted to tailboom. All control surfaces operated by push/pull rods. No tabs. Rudder pedals adjustable in flight.

LANDING GEAR: Retractable tricycle type, actuated electrically with manual backup. All units retract forward into fuselage. Cantilever sprung main legs, of glassfibre epoxy; rubber-in-torsion shock absorption on nose unit. Cleveland mainwheels, with Goodyear size 5.00-5 tyres (6 ply rating), pressure 3.0 bars (43.5 lb/sq in). Test nosewheel, with Dunlop tyre, size 260 × 85 mm (4 ply rating), pressure 5.0 bars (72.5 lb/sq in). Cleveland independent hydraulic disc brakes on mainwheels. Steerable nosewheel, linked to rudder pedals. Safety lock for up and down positions. Electrical warning system.

POWER PLANT: Two Microturbo TRS 18-1 turbojets, each rated at 1.47 kN (330 lb st) for take-off and 1.28 kN (288 lb st) max continuous, mounted side by side in fuselage aft of cockpits. Integral fuel tank in each wing leading-edge, combined capacity 290 litres (76.6 US gallons; 64 Imp gallons), and two 70 litre (18.5 US gallon; 15.5 Imp gallon) wingtip tanks. Total fuel capacity 430 litres (113.6 US gallons; 95 Imp gallons). Fuel system incorporates fuselage collector tank which permits inverted flight. Refuelling point at each wingtip. Provision for two 112 litre (29.6 US gallon; 24.5 Imp gallon) underwing drop tanks. Oil capacity 0.8 litre (1.7 US pints; 1.4 Imp pints).

ACCOMMODATION: Seats for two persons side by side under jettisonable canopy hinged at rear and opening upward. Seats are semi-supine. Dual controls on production version. Single instrument panel and centre console, eliminating need for dual instruments and avionics. Cockpit heated, ventilated and demisted.

SYSTEMS: Hydraulic system for mainwheel brakes only. No pneumatic system. Electrical system is 28V DC, incorporating two Microturbo 1.3kW starter/generators and a 24V 18Ah lead-acid battery. Cockpit ventilation and demisting by heat exchangers on jetpipes. Demand type low-pressure oxygen system, capacity 6.7 litres (0.24 cu ft), for each occupant.

Agusta (Caproni Vizzola) C22J Ventura, equipped as standard with wingtip tanks

AVIONICS AND EQUIPMENT: Avionics bay in top of fuselage, aft of cockpits. Collins Micro Line nav/com radio, Pro Line flight director, navigation, landing and anti-collision lights, standard.

ARMAMENT: Provision for two standard NATO underwing pylons, for a wide range of stores for gunnery/weapon training, photographic reconnaissance and target towing missions. Typical loads can include one drop tank and one three-camera pod; two drop tanks; two 7.62 mm gun pods and 500 rds of ammunition; two Simpres AL-18-50 pods with eighteen 2 in rockets; four SAMP EU70 50 kg general purpose bombs; four Mk 70 11 kg or M38-A2 50 kg practice bombs; or two Dornier DATS 1 50 kg towed targets.

DIMENSIONS, EXTERNAL:

Wing span	9.20 m (30 ft 2¼ in)
Wing chord, constant	0.90 m (2 ft 11½ in)
Wing aspect ratio	11.1
Length overall	6.26 m (20 ft 6½ in)
Fuselage: Max width	1.228 m (4 ft 0½ in)
Height overall	1.88 m (6 ft 2 in)
Tailplane span	2.66 m (8 ft 8¾ in)
Wheel track	1.81 m (5 ft 11¼ in)
Wheelbase	1.81 m (5 ft 11¼ in)

AREAS:

Wings, gross	7.65 m² (82.35 sq ft)
Ailerons (total)	0.718 m² (7.73 sq ft)
Trailing-edge flaps (total)	0.824 m² (8.87 sq ft)
Airbrakes/spoilers (total)	0.572 m² (6.16 sq ft)
Fin	0.808 m² (8.70 sq ft)
Rudder	0.225 m² (2.42 sq ft)
Tailplane	1.40 m² (15.07 sq ft)
Elevator	0.338 m² (3.64 sq ft)

WEIGHTS AND LOADING:

Weight empty	738 kg (1,627 lb)
Max internal fuel	360 kg (794 lb)
Max external stores	250 kg (551 lb)
Max T-O and landing weight	1,255 kg (2,767 lb)
Max wing loading	164.0 kg/m² (33.59 lb/sq ft)

PERFORMANCE (at max T-O weight):

Max permissible diving speed	325 knots (602 km/h; 374 mph)
Max operating speed	305 knots (565 km/h; 351 mph)
Max cruising speed at S/L	260 knots (482 km/h; 299 mph)
Max design manoeuvring speed	228 knots (422 km/h; 262 mph)
Max diving speed with airbrakes fully deployed	214 knots (396 km/h; 246 mph)
Econ cruising speed at 3,050 m (10,000 ft)	175 knots (324 km/h; 202 mph)
Max speed for landing gear extension	140 knots (259 km/h; 161 mph)
Stalling speed, flaps down, power off	74 knots (137 km/h; 85 mph) EAS
Max rate of climb at S/L	600 m (1,970 ft)/min
Rate of climb at S/L, one engine out	177 m (580 ft)/min
Time to climb to 5,000 m (16,400 ft)	10 min
Max operating altitude	7,620 m (25,000 ft)
Service ceiling	10,000 m (32,800 ft)
Service ceiling, one engine out	5,500 m (18,045 ft)
T-O run at S/L, ISA, zero wind	650 m (2,133 ft)
T-O to 15 m (50 ft), conditions as above	880 m (2,887 ft)
T-O to 15 m (50 ft) at 1,500 m (4,920 ft), ISA, zero wind	1,000 m (3,280 ft)
Max range with wingtip tanks	700 nm (1,296 km; 805 miles)
Max endurance	3 h
g limits	+7/−3.5

ELICOTTERI MERIDIONALI SpA

This company was formed with assistance from Agusta and began to operate in October 1967. It remains affiliated to Agusta. In 1968 EM (Elicotteri Meridionali SpA) acquired rights to the co-production, marketing and servicing of the Boeing CH-47C Chinook transport helicopter for customers in Italy and certain foreign countries. Italian production of the CH-47C airframe is undertaken by the Sesto Calende works.

EM, whose works occupy a total area of more than 300,000 m² (3,229,170 sq ft), participates in the manufacturing programmes for the Agusta A 109A Mk II and A 129, Agusta-Bell 206B and 212, and Agusta-Sikorsky SH-3H helicopters. It has complete facilities for overhaul, repair and field assistance. EM is the designated overhaul organisation for all types of Italian Army helicopter, and is also distributor in Italy for Allison 250 turboshaft engines.

A new factory, completed in August 1983 at Anagni, has a total area of 218,000 m² (2,346,550 sq ft), including 18,000 m² (193,750 sq ft) of covered space, devoted to production of composite materials, especially rotor blades and other structures for helicopters.

Italian built Boeing CH-47C Plus with T55-L-712E engines, advanced transmission, composite rotor blades and a 50,000 lb take-off weight *(Avio Data)*

EM (BOEING) CH-47C CHINOOK

Italian manufacture of the CH-47C began in the Spring of 1970, initially to meet an order for Italian Army Aviation. Later customers are detailed in the 1989-90 *Jane's*.

EM also produced a further 10 aircraft, designated **CH-47C Plus**, for operation by the Italian Army on behalf of the Civil Protection Agency. Simultaneously with this additional production, an upgrading programme was begun, to fit the earlier aircraft with new Textron Lycoming T55-L-712E engines, composite rotor blades and a more advanced transmission system. Max T-O weight is increased to 22,680 kg (50,000 lb).

Agusta developed, jointly with Hosp Ital SpA (a division of Cogefar) of Milan, an **ESFC** (emergency surgery flying centre) version of the Chinook for use as a mobile hospital. Details of the ESFC can be found in the 1983-84 *Jane's*. One was delivered to the Italian Army in 1987.

The Italian Army's entire fleet of Chinooks is being overhauled at the rate of three a year by EM, which redelivered the first of 23 then-operational aircraft in March 1986. These aircraft are used for a wide range of duties, one important role being that of firefighting, in which configuration they can be equipped with a 5,000 litre (1,321 US gallon; 1,100 Imp gallon) metal tank for retardant.

AVIOLIGHT

AVIOLIGHT SRL

Via delle Industrie, San Sebastiano al Vesuvio, 80040
Naples
Telephone: 39 (81) 771011
Telex: 720373
Fax: 39 (81) 716367
PRESIDENT: Prof Ing Luigi Pascale
GENERAL MANAGER: Raffaele Veneruso

This company was formed on 29 February 1988 by
Partenavia (which see), Avio Interiors of Latina, and the
Naples based company Tecnam owned by the Pascale
brothers. Its initial function has been to undertake
production of the (originally Partenavia) P.86 Mosquito.

Aviolight has since also assumed responsibility for
development and support of other existing single-engined
Partenavia aircraft, enabling the latter company to
concentrate entirely on its twin-engined range.

AVIOLIGHT P.86 MOSQUITO

Powered by an Italian KFM 112M flat-four engine of
44.7 kW (60 hp), the prototype of this lightweight
two-seater was built by Partenavia and flew for the first time
on 27 April 1986. Production Mosquitos, to which the
detailed description applies, have a more powerful engine,
and conform with FAR Pt 23 Utility category standards.
An initial series of 100 is being produced for the Aero Club
d'Italia.

TYPE: Two-seat light aircraft.
WINGS: High-wing monoplane, with single streamline
section bracing strut each side. Constant chord non-swept
wings, of NACA 63A-416 (modified) section, with 1° 30′
dihedral and 3° incidence. Two-spar torsion box
structure of 2024-T3 aluminium alloy, with trailing-edge
split flaps and plain ailerons. No tabs.
FUSELAGE: Semi-monocoque forward fuselage and tubular
tailboom, all of aluminium alloy.
TAIL UNIT: Cantilever all-metal stressed skin structure of
2024-T3 aluminium alloy, with front and rear channel
section spars. Fixed incidence tailplane, mounted above
tailboom on short pylon. Endplate fins and rudders. No
rudder tabs; trim tab in centre of elevator.
LANDING GEAR: Non-retractable tricycle type, with Partenavia leaf spring shock absorption. McCreary wheel size
5.00-5, and tyre size 360 × 120-165 mm (5 ply), on each
unit; tyre pressures 1.72 bars (25 lb/sq in) on main gear,
1.03 bars (15 lb/sq in) on nose unit. Cleveland 30-18
brakes.
POWER PLANT: One 56 kW (75 hp) Limbach L 2000 flat-four
engine, driving a Hoffmann two-blade fixed-pitch
propeller with spinner. Single integral fuel tank in wings,
capacity 70 litres (18.5 US gallons; 15.4 Imp gallons).
Refuelling point in inboard section of starboard wing. Oil
capacity 2.5 litres (0.66 US gallon; 0.55 Imp gallon).
ACCOMMODATION: Side by side seats for pilot and one
passenger, with baggage space behind seats. Upward
opening door, with window, on each side of cabin. Cabin
ventilated via ram air intake in wing leading-edge.
AVIONICS: Bendix/King or Collins VHF com/nav radio,
ADF and ATC transponder at customer's option.

DIMENSIONS, EXTERNAL:
Wing span	10.00 m (32 ft 9¾ in)
Wing chord, constant	1.25 m (4 ft 1¼ in)
Wing aspect ratio	8.0
Length overall	6.775 m (22 ft 2¾ in)
Fuselage: Max width	1.22 m (4 ft 0 in)
Height overall	1.923 m (6 ft 3¾ in)
Tailplane span	2.80 m (9 ft 2¼ in)
Wheel track	2.00 m (6 ft 6¾ in)
Wheelbase	1.567 m (5 ft 1½ in)
Propeller diameter	1.65 m (5 ft 5 in)
Propeller ground clearance	0.325 m (1 ft 0¾ in)
Cabin doors (each): Height	0.90 m (2 ft 11½ in)
Max width	0.60 m (1 ft 11½ in)
Height to sill	0.975 m (3 ft 2½ in)

DIMENSIONS, INTERNAL:
Cabin: Length	0.90 m (2 ft 11½ in)
Max width	1.00 m (3 ft 3¼ in)

First prototype P.86 Mosquito two-seat light aircraft, as originally flown with KFM engine

Max height	1.00 m (3 ft 3¼ in)
Floor area	0.86 m² (9.26 sq ft)
Volume	0.82 m³ (28.96 cu ft)
Baggage compartment: Volume	0.42 m³ (14.83 cu ft)

AREAS:
Wings, gross	12.50 m² (135.2 sq ft)
Ailerons (total)	1.028 m² (11.07 sq ft)
Rudders (total)	0.61 m² (6.57 sq ft)
Tailplane	1.34 m² (14.42 sq ft)
Elevator	0.80 m² (8.61 sq ft)

WEIGHTS AND LOADINGS:
Basic weight empty	320 kg (705 lb)
Max fuel weight	50 kg (110 lb)
Max T-O and landing weight	540 kg (1,190 lb)
Max wing loading	43.2 kg/m² (8.85 lb/sq ft)
Max power loading	9.66 kg/kW (15.87 lb/hp)

PERFORMANCE (estimated, at max T-O weight):
Never-exceed speed	150 knots (278 km/h; 172 mph)
Max level speed at S/L	97 knots (180 km/h; 112 mph)
Max cruising speed at S/L	86 knots (160 km/h; 99 mph)
Econ cruising speed at S/L	80 knots (148 km/h; 92 mph)
Stalling speed: flaps up	41 knots (76 km/h; 47 mph)
flaps down	36 knots (67 km/h; 42 mph)
Max rate of climb at S/L	235 m (770 ft)/min
Service ceiling	3,995 m (13,100 ft)
T-O run	149 m (490 ft)
T-O to 15 m (50 ft)	311 m (1,020 ft)
Landing from 15 m (50 ft)	120 m (395 ft)
Range with max fuel at econ cruising speed, allowances for start, taxi, T-O and 30 min reserves	340 nm (630 km; 391 miles)

AVIOLIGHT (PARTENAVIA) P.66D DELTA

Having assumed responsibility for Partenavia's single-
engined aircraft, Aviolight is putting into production a new
version of the P.66, last described in the 1984-85 edition of
Jane's. As an initial step, the company fitted a 119 kW (160
hp) Textron Lycoming O-320-D2A piston engine in a P.66B
Oscar (I-AVLT), which has also been given P.66T Charlie
Trainer type upturned wingtips. In this form, the aircraft
was first flown in September 1988.

The production version is designated P.66D Delta and
features a full IFR instrument panel. Compared to
the previous Oscar model, the Delta has lower fuel
consumption, better hot and high performance, and
requires less frequent maintenance. Its airframe conforms
to FAR Pt 23 requirements.

The following details apply to the prototype:
TYPE: Two/three-seat light monoplane.
WINGS: Braced high-wing monoplane with single streamline
section bracing strut each side. Wing section NACA
63A₃-515. Dihedral 1° 30′. Incidence at root 1° 40′. No
sweepback. Stressed skin two-spar torsion box structure
of aluminium alloy, with one-piece GFRP moulded
leading-edges. Ailerons and electrically operated slotted
trailing-edge flaps of similar construction to wings. No
tabs. Upturned wingtips.
FUSELAGE: Forward portion, to rear of cabin, has a welded
steel tube basic structure to which are attached light alloy
skin panels. Rear fuselage is of conventional light alloy
stressed skin construction.
TAIL UNIT: Cantilever stressed skin metal torsion box
structure with sweptback vertical surfaces. All-moving
tailplane in two symmetrical halves joined by steel
cross-tube. Geared trim tab.
LANDING GEAR: Non-retractable tricycle type, with steerable
nosewheel. Cantilever spring steel main legs. Oleo-
pneumatic nosewheel shock absorber. Van Sickle wheels
(size 40-77B nose, 40-86B main) and McCreary tyres (size
5.00-5 five-ply on nosewheel, 6.00-6 six-ply on main
units). Cleveland type 30-18 hydraulic disc brakes.

DIMENSIONS, EXTERNAL:
Wing span	9.99 m (32 ft 9¼ in)
Wing chord, constant	1.36 m (4 ft 5½ in)
Wing aspect ratio	7.43
Length overall	6.98 m (22 ft 10¾ in)
Height overall	2.77 m (9 ft 1 in)
Wheel track	2.10 m (6 ft 10½ in)
Wheelbase	1.51 m (4 ft 11½ in)
Doors (each): Height	0.96 m (3 ft 2 in)
Width	0.62 m (2 ft 0½ in)
Height to sill	0.69 m (2 ft 3 in)

DIMENSIONS, INTERNAL:
Cabin: Max length	2.20 m (7 ft 2½ in)
Max width	0.90 m (2 ft 11½ in)
Max height	1.30 m (4 ft 3 in)
Floor area	2.0 m² (21.53 sq ft)
Volume	2.5 m³ (88.29 cu ft)
Baggage space, aft of seats	0.3 m³ (10.59 cu ft)

AREAS:
Wings, gross	13.40 m² (144.2 sq ft)
Ailerons (total)	0.90 m² (9.69 sq ft)
Trailing-edge flaps (total)	1.00 m² (10.76 sq ft)
Fin	0.70 m² (7.53 sq ft)
Rudder	0.50 m² (5.38 sq ft)
Tailplane, incl tab	2.10 m² (22.60 sq ft)

WEIGHTS (prototype):
Weight empty	640 kg (1,411 lb)
Max T-O weight	930 kg (2,050 lb)

PERFORMANCE (prototype):
Max level speed at S/L	132 knots (245 km/h; 152 mph)
Max cruising speed (75% power) at 1,800 m (5,900 ft)	124 knots (230 km/h; 143 mph)
Stalling speed: flaps up	53 knots (99 km/h; 61 mph)
flaps down	47 knots (87 km/h; 54 mph)
Service ceiling	4,500 m (14,765 ft)
T-O run	220 m (722 ft)
T-O to 15 m (50 ft)	440 m (1,444 ft)
Landing run	210 m (689 ft)
Max endurance	more than 5 h

GENERAL AVIA

GENERAL AVIA COSTRUZIONI AERONAUTICHE SRL

Via Trieste 22-24, 20096 Pioltello, Milan
Telephone: 39 (2) 92 66 774
Fax: 39 (2) 92 16 03 95
TECHNICAL DIRECTOR: Dott Ing Stelio Frati
TECHNICAL: Dott Ing Giancarlo Monti
PUBLIC RELATIONS: Carla Bielli

Dott Ing Stelio Frati is well known for the many
successful light aircraft which, as a freelance designer, he
has developed since 1950. These have included the Procaer
F15 Picchio; the F.250, now manufactured by Agusta as the
SF.260; and the F.20 Pegaso, described in the 1981-82
Jane's. General Avia developed and built the prototype of
the Canguro transport aircraft described under the
Agusta heading in this section. In 1983 it developed for
SIAI-Marchetti a retractable landing gear version of the
Canguro. In the following year it started construction of the
F.1300 Jet Squalus, which was financed by Promavia of
Belgium (which see).

In 1988, as a private venture, General Avia began
manufacturing the fuselage of a 19-passenger twin-turbofan
commuter transport, known as the F.3500 Sparviero. The
entry for the Sparviero that appeared in the 1985-86 *Jane's*
has been reprinted for this edition, in anticipation of further
progress on the aircraft.

GENERAL AVIA F.20 TP CONDOR

The Condor is a four-seat turboprop powered aircraft
intended for both military applications as weapon training,
long-range maritime surveillance, search and rescue,
anti-armour, and ground attack. It can be equipped with
two stores pylons under each wing, the outer one on each
side being capable of carrying a 300 litre (79.25 US gallon;
66 Imp gallon) auxiliary fuel tank.

The prototype (I-GEAC) flew for the first time on 7 May
1983, and shortly afterwards was granted a special
airworthiness certificate. The programme for full certification has been delayed in order to give priority to the
Promavia Jet Squalus programme (see Belgian section). A
full description can be found in the 1987-88 *Jane's.*

GENERAL AVIA F.22 PINGUINO (PENGUIN)

On 13 June 1989 the first prototype F.22 Pinguino
(I-GEAD) flying club trainer flew for the first time from the
airport at Orio al Serio (Bergamo), where work is now based
(*tel:* 39 35 31 15 90). Details apply to this aircraft. A second
prototype has a 119 kW (160 hp) Textron Lycoming engine
and a retractable landing gear. This is known simply as the
F.22.

TYPE: Side by side two-seat primary trainer.
WINGS: All-metal cantilever low-wing monoplane, built in
one piece with single spar. Electrically actuated flaps.
FUSELAGE: All-metal semi-monocoque structure.
TAIL UNIT: Cantilever all-metal structure with swept fin and
rudder. Trim tab on elevator.

LANDING GEAR: First prototype has non-retractable tricycle type, with steerable nosewheel. Oleo shock absorbers. Faired main legs.

POWER PLANT: One 86.5 kW (116 hp) Textron Lycoming O-235-2NC flat-four engine, driving a two-blade wooden propeller with large spinner. 119 kW (160 hp) O-320-D2A optional, but installed in second prototype. Fuel capacity 135 litres (35.7 US gallons; 29.7 Imp gallons).

ACCOMMODATION: Two seats side by side under a sliding canopy.

AVIONICS: Bendix/King Silver Crown nav/com, ADF, audio console and transponder.

DIMENSIONS, EXTERNAL:

Wing span	8.50 m (27 ft 10¾ in)
Wing chord: at root	1.589 m (5 ft 2½ in)
at tip	0.876 m (2 ft 10½ in)
Wing aspect ratio	6.69
Length overall	7.30 m (23 ft 11½ in)
Height overall	2.84 m (9 ft 3¾ in)
Tailplane span	3.00 m (9 ft 10 in)
Wheel track	2.90 m (9 ft 6¼ in)
Wheelbase	1.86 m (6 ft 1¼ in)
Propeller diameter	1.78 m (5 ft 10 in)

AREAS:

Wings, gross	10.82 m² (116.25 sq ft)
Fin	0.738 m² (7.94 sq ft)
Rudder	0.505 m² (5.44 sq ft)
Tailplane	1.24 m² (13.35 sq ft)
Elevator, incl tab	1.02 m² (10.98 sq ft)

WEIGHTS AND LOADINGS:

Weight empty, equipped	520 kg (1,146 lb)
Max T-O weight: Aerobatic	750 kg (1,653 lb)
Utility	800 kg (1,764 lb)
Max wing loading: Aerobatic	69.4 kg/m² (14.22 lb/sq ft)
Utility	74.1 kg/m² (15.17 lb/sq ft)
Max power loading: Utility	9.25 kg/kW (15.21 lb/hp)

PERFORMANCE (86.5 kW; 116 hp engine):

Max level speed at S/L	129 knots (240 km/h; 149 mph)
Cruising speed at 1,830 m (6,000 ft)	119 knots (220 km/h; 137 mph)
Stalling speed, flaps down	49 knots (90 km/h; 56 mph)
Max rate of climb at S/L	258 m (845 ft)/min
Service ceiling	4,270 m (14,000 ft)
T-O run	240 m (790 ft)

Model of the General Avia F.3500 Sparviero commuter transport

First General Avia F.22 Pinguino *(Editoriale Domus-Volare)*

Landing run	160 m (525 ft)
Max range, no reserves	539 nm (1,000 km; 621 miles)

GENERAL AVIA F.3500 SPARVIERO (HAWK)

Design of this twin-turbofan commuter transport began in 1983; its general appearance is shown in an accompanying illustration. The possibility of a manufacturing partnership was explored in 1985 but the project was subsequently halted while work continued on other programmes. However, in 1988 construction of a fuselage began.

The Sparviero will be of conventional aluminium alloy construction, with flush riveted skin. The retractable landing gear will be actuated hydraulically, with a steerable nosewheel. Accommodation in the pressurised fuselage will be for a flight crew of two plus up to 19 passengers and a galley unit; intended max pressure differential is 0.32 bars (4.6 lb/sq in).

POWER PLANT: Two 13.34 kN (3,000 lb st) Pratt & Whitney Canada JT15D-5 turbofan engines, in underwing pods. Fuel capacity 3,500 litres (924.6 US gallons; 770 Imp gallons).

DIMENSIONS, EXTERNAL:

Wing span	19.40 m (63 ft 7¾ in)
Wing aspect ratio	10.04
Length overall	15.20 m (49 ft 10½ in)
Height overall	5.60 m (18 ft 4½ in)
Tailplane span	6.40 m (21 ft 0 in)

DIMENSIONS, INTERNAL:

Cabin: Length	6.60 m (21 ft 8 in)
Max width	1.80 m (5 ft 10¾ in)
Max height	1.80 m (5 ft 10¾ in)

AREA:

Wings, gross	37.50 m² (403.65 sq ft)

WEIGHTS AND LOADINGS (estimated):

Weight empty, equipped	4,800 kg (10,582 lb)
Max T-O weight	8,500 kg (18,740 lb)
Max wing loading	226.6 kg/m² (46.43 lb/sq ft)
Max power loading	318.6 kg/kN (3.12 lb/lb st)

PERFORMANCE (estimated, at max T-O weight):

Max level speed at 3,050 m (10,000 ft)	350 knots (648 km/h; 402 mph)
Max cruising speed at 4,575 m (15,000 ft)	315 knots (583 km/h; 362 mph)
Econ cruising speed at 6,100 m (20,000 ft)	280 knots (518 km/h; 322 mph)
Stalling speed, flaps down	70 knots (130 km/h; 81 mph)
Max rate of climb at S/L	762 m (2,500 ft)/min
Rate of climb at S/L, one engine out	228 m (750 ft)/min
Service ceiling	10,670 m (35,000 ft)
Service ceiling, one engine out	5,485 m (18,000 ft)
T-O run	390 m (1,280 ft)
Landing run	365 m (1,198 ft)
Range: max payload	430 nm (796 km; 495 miles)
max fuel	970 nm (1,796 km; 1,116 miles)

GLASFASER
GLASFASER ITALIANA SRL
Via Delle Ghiaie 3, 24030 Valbrembo (Bergamo)
Telephone: 39 (35) 612617

This company, which has specialised in the construction and repair of glassfibre sailplanes, has constructed the prototype of an aerobatic competition aircraft known as the **T-30 Katana**. Test flying was expected to start in January 1990.

Designed by Pietro Terzi, the Katana is powered by a 224 kW (300 hp) Textron Lycoming engine. The fuselage has a glassfibre skin over a metal structure, and the wings are also of metal. Three had been ordered by early 1990.

PARTENAVIA
PARTENAVIA COSTRUZIONI AERONAUTICHE SpA
Via Giovanni Pascoli 7, 80026 Casoria (Naples)
Telephone: 39 (81) 5502111
Telex: 720199 PARTNA I
PRESIDENT: Gen Fulvio Ristori
GENERAL MANAGER AND EXECUTIVE DIRECTOR: Ing Carlo Rosini
TECHNICAL MANAGER: Ing C. A. D'Amato
PRESS RELATIONS: Mrs F. Ridolfi

This company was founded in 1957 and has since built a series of light aircraft designed by its founder, Prof Ing Luigi Pascale. It came under the control of Aeritalia in July 1981 and is now part of that Group.

Since 1974 Partenavia has occupied a 12,000 m² (129,165 sq ft) facility on Capodichino Airport, Naples, where it is concentrating on production of the P.68C and P.68C-TC twin-engined seven-seat light aircraft, a derivative known as the Observer, and the turboprop powered Viator. Development and support of its single-engined designs is now the responsibility of Aviolight (which see).

PARTENAVIA P.68

The original P.68, designed by Prof Ing Luigi Pascale in 1968, was described in the 1975-76 *Jane's*. From it was developed the P.68B Victor twin-engined light transport, which entered production in the Spring of 1974. Details of the P.68B, P.68C-R, P.68 floatplane/amphibian and P.68R can be found in the 1980-81 and earlier editions of *Jane's*.

The following versions are currently in production:

P.68C. Improved version of P.68B, with lengthened nose, increased fuel capacity, and several internal changes. Detailed description applies primarily to this version (also known formerly as the Victor), which superseded the P.68B (1979-80 *Jane's*) in late 1979.

P.68C-TC. Similar to P.68C, but powered currently by Textron Lycoming TIO-360-A1C6D turbocharged engines with fuel injection. Certificated in June 1980. In production. Available as landplane or with twin amphibious floats. (Latter version first flown from land and water on 26 and 27 June 1985 respectively.)

P.68 Observer. Special observation version; described separately.

By the beginning of 1990 Partenavia had delivered approx 400 aircraft of the P.68 series, most of them for export to operators in more than 20 countries.

TYPE: Six/seven-seat light transport and trainer.

WINGS: Cantilever high-wing monoplane. Wing section NACA 63-3₁515. Dihedral 1°. Incidence 1° 30′. No sweepback. Stressed skin two-spar torsion box structure of aluminium alloy. All-metal ailerons and electrically operated single-slotted trailing-edge flaps. Hoerner GFRP wingtips. No tabs.

FUSELAGE: Conventional all-metal semi-monocoque structure of frames and longerons, with four main longerons and stressed skin covering. Fuselage/wing intersection mainly of GFRP.

TAIL UNIT: Cantilever stressed skin metal structure. All-moving tailplane, in two symmetrical halves joined by steel cross-tube and of constant chord except for increase at leading-edge roots. Balance tab in tailplane trailing-edge, over 80 per cent of span. Sweptback fin and rudder, with small dorsal fin. Trim tab in rudder.

LANDING GEAR: Non-retractable tricycle type, with steerable nosewheel. Cantilever spring steel main legs. Oleopneumatic shock absorber on nosewheel. Cleveland

Partenavia P.68C-TC six/seven-seat light aircraft (*Avio Data*)

Partenavia P.68C, with additional side view (centre) of P.68C-TC (*Pilot Press*)

mainwheels, type 40-96, with Pirelli eight-ply tyres size 6.00-6. Goodyear six-ply nosewheel tyre, size 5.00-5. Cleveland type 30-61 hydraulic disc brakes. Parking brake. Streamline wheel fairings standard. C-TC version available optionally with De Vore PK twin-float gear having retractable ground wheels.

POWER PLANT (P.68C): Two 149 kW (200 hp) Textron Lycoming IO-360-A1B6 flat-four engines, each driving a Hartzell HC-C2YK-2C/C-7666A-4 two-blade constant-speed fully-feathering propeller with spinner. Integral fuel tank in each wing, total capacity 538 litres (142 US gallons; 118 Imp gallons), of which 520 litres (137 US gallons; 114 Imp gallons) are usable. Refuelling point above each wing. Oil capacity 15 litres (4 US gallons; 3.3 Imp gallons).

ACCOMMODATION: Seating for seven persons in cabin, including pilot, in two rows of two seats and a rear bench seat for three persons. A club seating arrangement is available optionally, having the two middle seats facing rearward with a folding table between them and the bench seat. Front seats are of the adjustable sliding type. Access to all seats via large forward opening car type door on port side at front of cabin. Up to 181 kg (400 lb) of baggage can be carried in compartment aft of rear bench seat. Access to baggage compartment from inside cabin, or via large forward hinged door on starboard side at rear, which serves also as emergency exit. Two stretchers or other loads can be carried when all passenger seats are removed. Dual controls, cabin heating, ventilation and soundproofing standard.

SYSTEMS: Electrical power supplied by two 24V 70A alternators and a 24V 17Ah battery. No hydraulic system. Goodrich pneumatic de-icing system optional.

AVIONICS AND EQUIPMENT (P.68C): Wide range of Collins Micro Line or Bendix/King Silver Crown avionics, and Edo-Aire Mitchell Century III autopilot, to customer's requirements. Provision for SunAir ASB 100 HF radio. Standard equipment includes airspeed indicator, gyro horizon, directional gyro, two cylinder head temperature gauges, clock, exhaust gas temperature gauge, outside air temperature gauge, rate of climb indicator, sensitive altimeter, electric turn rate indicator, inertia reel shoulder harness for pilot and co-pilot, stall warning system, four upholstered seats with back pockets, and one bench seat with folding back (with safety belts on all seats), cabin fire extinguisher, six individual fresh air outlets and six floor warm air vents, windscreen defrosters, cabin soundproofing, annunciator panel warning lights, two map lights, individual reading lights, individual instru-

ment panel floodlights with rheostat, anti-collision strobe light, two landing/taxying lights, navigation lights, anti-static kit, external power receptacle, oil coolers with thermostatic control, quick drain fuel and oil valves, and towbar. Optional equipment includes Janitrol 45,000 BTU combustion heater, wing and tail pneumatic de-icing system, electrothermal propeller de-icing system, 0.46 × 0.58 m (18 × 23 in) floor panel for photogrammetric camera, including periscope sight hatch, second airspeed indicator, second gyro horizon, chronometer, second altimeter, pilot's and co-pilot's vertically adjustable seats, alcohol windscreen de-icing, heated stall warning indicator, all-leather interior, forced ventilation blower, ice light and second oil cooler.

DIMENSIONS, EXTERNAL:

Wing span	12.00 m (39 ft 4½ in)
Wing chord (constant)	1.55 m (5 ft 1 in)
Wing aspect ratio	7.7
Length overall	9.55 m (31 ft 4 in)
Height overall	3.40 m (11 ft 1¾ in)
Tailplane span	3.90 m (12 ft 9½ in)
Wheel track	2.40 m (7 ft 10½ in)
Wheelbase	3.50 m (11 ft 5¾ in)
Propeller diameter	1.88 m (6 ft 2 in)
Distance between propeller centres	4.10 m (13 ft 5½ in)
Baggage door, stbd: Height	0.80 m (2 ft 7½ in)
Width	0.80 m (2 ft 7½ in)

DIMENSIONS, INTERNAL:

Cabin: Length	3.58 m (11 ft 9 in)
Max width	1.16 m (3 ft 9½ in)
Max height	1.20 m (3 ft 11¼ in)
Baggage space	0.56 m³ (20 cu ft)

AREAS:

Wings, gross	18.60 m² (200.2 sq ft)
Ailerons (total)	1.79 m² (19.27 sq ft)
Trailing-edge flaps (total)	2.37 m² (25.51 sq ft)
Fin	1.59 m² (17.11 sq ft)
Rudder, incl tab	0.44 m² (4.74 sq ft)
Tailplane, incl tab	4.41 m² (47.47 sq ft)

WEIGHTS AND LOADINGS:

Weight empty: C	1230 kg (2,711 lb)
C-TC	1,300 kg (2,866 lb)
*Max T-O weight: C, C-TC	1,990 kg (4,387 lb)
Max landing weight: C, C-TC	1,890 kg (4,166 lb)
Max wing loading: C, C-TC	107 kg/m² (21.9 lb/sq ft)
Max power loading: C	6.68 kg/kW (10.97 lb/hp)
C-TC	6.36 kg/kW (10.45 lb/hp)

*C-TC amphibian 317 kg (700 lb) heavier

PERFORMANCE (at max T-O weight):

Max level speed:

C at S/L	174 knots (322 km/h; 200 mph)
C-TC at 5,335 m (17,500 ft)	195 knots (361 km/h; 224 mph)

Max cruising speed (75% power):

C at 2,290 m (7,500 ft)	166 knots (307 km/h; 191 mph)
C-TC at 6,100 m (20,000 ft)	183 knots (339 km/h; 211 mph)
C-TC at 3,660 m (12,000 ft)	172 knots (318 km/h; 198 mph)

Cruising speed (65% power):

C at 3,350 m (11,000 ft)	161 knots (298 km/h; 185 mph)
C-TC at 3,050 m (10,000 ft)	158 knots (293 km/h; 182 mph)

Cruising speed (55% power):

C at 3,660 m (12,000 ft)	150 knots (278 km/h; 173 mph)
C-TC at 3,050 m (10,000 ft)	147 knots (272 km/h; 169 mph)

Stalling speed, flaps up: C, C-TC	65 knots (120 km/h; 75 mph)
Stalling speed, flaps down: C, C-TC	58 knots (106 km/h; 66 mph)
Max rate of climb at S/L: C	457 m (1,500 ft)/min
C-TC	472 m (1,550 ft)/min

Rate of climb at S/L, one engine out:

C	82 m (270 ft)/min
C-TC	88 m (290 ft)/min
Service ceiling: C	5,850 m (19,200 ft)
C-TC	7,620 m (25,000 ft)
Service ceiling, one engine out: C	2,100 m (6,900 ft)
C-TC	4,420 m (14,500 ft)
T-O run: C, C-TC	230 m (755 ft)
T-O to 15 m (50 ft): C	396 m (1,300 ft)
C-TC	385 m (1,263 ft)
Landing from 15 m (50 ft): C, C-TC	488 m (1,600 ft)
Landing run: C, C-TC	215 m (705 ft)
Accelerate/stop distance: C	473 m (1,550 ft)
C-TC	510 m (1,673 ft)

Optimum cruising range (C), 45 min reserves:

75% power at 2,290 m (7,500 ft)	1,050 nm (1,945 km; 1,209 miles)
65% power at 3,350 m (11,000 ft)	1,140 nm (2,112 km; 1,312 miles)
55% power at 3,660 m (12,000 ft)	1,210 nm (2,242 km; 1,393 miles)

Optimum cruising range (C-TC) at 3,660 m (12,000 ft), 45 min reserves:

75% power	775 nm (1,436 km; 892 miles)
65% power	940 nm (1,742 km; 1,082 miles)
55% power	1,020 nm (1,890 km; 1,175 miles)

Range with max fuel (C-TC):

65% power at 6,400 m (21,000 ft)	1,100 nm (2,037 km; 1,266 miles)

PARTENAVIA P.68 OBSERVER

Developed originally in collaboration with Sportavia-Pützer of West Germany, the Observer has a forward and downward view for the crew equal to that of a helicopter. The Plexiglas nose, cockpit and associated structure were designed by Sportavia-Pützer; the prototype (D-GERD) was constructed at that company's Dahlemer-Binz factory, and first flew on 20 February 1976.

With its good low-speed handling characteristics, the Observer is considered to be capable of performing many roles allocated normally to helicopters. It is intended particularly for patrol and observation operations.

The first Partenavia built Observer was flown in the Spring of 1980, and certification was obtained in June of that year. Improvements were made subsequently to the flight deck and instrument panel. By the beginning of 1988 a total of 34 Observers had been ordered, for customers in Africa, Australia, western Europe, and North and South America. Twelve of these were for the Italian Police, delivered in 1988. No more recent sales figure was received.

An accompanying illustration shows the **Observer 2**, which features upturned wingtips, 100 litres (26.4 US gallons; 22 Imp gallons) of extra fuel in the wet wings, and larger tyres. Optional avionics and equipment for both versions include nose-mounted weather radar or an Electronique Aerospatiale ATAL television surveillance system.

DIMENSIONS, EXTERNAL: As P.68C except:

Length overall	9.35 m (30 ft 8 in)
Wheelbase	3.80 m (12 ft 5½ in)

WEIGHTS AND LOADINGS:

Weight empty	1,280 kg (2,822 lb)
Max T-O weight	1,960 kg (4,321 lb)
Max wing loading	105.3 kg/m² (21.58 lb/sq ft)
Max power loading	6.58 kg/kW (10.80 lb/hp)

PERFORMANCE (at max T-O weight):

Max level speed at S/L	174 knots (322 km/h; 200 mph)

Cruising speed:

75% power at 2,285 m (7,500 ft)	165 knots (306 km/h; 190 mph)
65% power at 3,350 m (11,000 ft)	160 knots (296 km/h; 184 mph)

55% power at 3,660 m (12,000 ft)	
	149 knots (276 km/h; 171 mph)
Stalling speed: flaps up	64 knots (118 km/h; 74 mph)
flaps down	56 knots (101 km/h; 64 mph)
Max rate of climb at S/L	488 m (1,600 ft)/min
Rate of climb at S/L, one engine out	98 m (320 ft)/min
Service ceiling	6,100 m (20,000 ft)
Service ceiling, one engine out	2,375 m (7,800 ft)
T-O run	229 m (750 ft)
T-O to 15 m (50 ft)	387 m (1,270 ft)
Landing from 15 m (50 ft)	479 m (1,570 ft)
Landing run	210 m (690 ft)
Accelerate/stop distance	473 m (1,550 ft)
Optimum cruising range, 45 min reserves:	
75% power at 2,285 m (7,500 ft)	
	1,060 nm (1,964 km; 1,220 miles)
65% power at 3,350 m (11,000 ft)	
	1,140 nm (2,112 km; 1,312 miles)
55% power at 3,660 m (12,000 ft)	
	1,200 nm (2,224 km; 1,382 miles)

PARTENAVIA AP 68TP-600 VIATOR
(WAYFARER)

The first retractable landing gear version of the Spartacus (I-RAIZ, c/n 6) made its initial flight in early July 1984. It was followed on 29 March 1985 by a prototype of the Viator (I-RAIL, previously known as the Spartacus 10), which has a longer fuselage than the fixed-gear AP 68TP-300, seating two additional passengers.

Twelve Viators had been ordered by early 1989 (when the last updated figure was received), of which the first three delivered went to Aeritalia for photogrammetric and other duties, Transavio, and a customer in Sierra Leone. The next three were for British, Italian and African customers.

Reports suggest that headroom in the forward section of the cabin has since been increased by 15 cm (6 in), a port door added to the flight deck, the instrument panel made larger, and options extended to include camera hatches in the floor for survey duties. Future plans include the development of a larger rear door for parachuting.

The description applies to the Viator in early production form, unless stated otherwise:

TYPE: Twin-turboprop general purpose transport.

WINGS: As described for P.68C Victor. Trim tab in starboard aileron. Goodrich pneumatic boot de-icing of leading-edges optional.

FUSELAGE: Similar to P.68C, but slightly longer.

TAIL UNIT: Vertical surfaces similar to P.68C, but of increased chord. Fixed incidence tailplane with separate elevators; geared tab in port elevator. Pneumatic boot de-icing of leading-edges.

LANDING GEAR: Retractable tricycle type, with electrically controlled hydraulic actuation. Oleo-pneumatic shock absorber in each unit. Nosewheel retracts forward, mainwheels inward into fuselage fairing. Cleveland wheels, sizes 40-77B (nose) and 40-163EA (main), with McCreary 8-ply tyres, sizes 6.50-8 (main) and 6.00-6 (nose). Mainwheel tyre pressure 4.83 bars (70 lb/sq in). Cleveland disc brakes. No anti-skid units.

POWER PLANT: Two Allison 250-B17C turboprops, each flat rated at 244.5 kW (328 shp) for T-O and max continuous operation. Hartzell HC-B3TF-7A/T10173B-21R three-blade constant-speed fully-feathering reversible-pitch metal propellers with spinners. Fuel in two 380 litre (100.4 US gallon; 83.6 Imp gallon) tanks in wings and a 40 litre (10.6 US gallon; 8.8 Imp gallon) tank in each engine nacelle. Total capacity 840 litres (222 US gallons; 185 Imp gallons). Two 100 litre (26.4 US gallon; 22 Imp gallon) underwing tanks optional. Refuelling point at each wingtip. Oil capacity 11.4 litres (3.0 US gallons; 2.5 Imp gallons) per engine.

ACCOMMODATION: Standard club seating for pilot and nine passengers, in five rows of two seats (second and fourth rows rearward facing). Forward opening door on starboard side of flight deck, and for second/third row passengers on port side at centre of cabin. (Latest examples also have port side flight deck door.) Double door (starboard, rear) provides access for rear seat passengers, and to 181 kg (400 lb) capacity baggage compartment aft of rear seats, and serves also as an emergency exit. With all passenger seats removed and special kits installed, up to 12 parachutists, or two stretcher patients plus two medical attendants, can be carried in cabin. Dual controls, and cabin heating, ventilation and soundproofing, are standard. Hot air for cabin heating and windscreen de-icing is provided by heat exchangers installed on both turbine cases.

SYSTEMS: Primary electrical power supplied by two 150A 28V DC starter/generators and two voltage regulators. In the event of primary electrical failure, power is supplied by a 24V 29Ah lead-acid battery (self-sufficient for engine starting), and an inverter for 115/26V AC power. Electric de-icing of engine air intakes, propellers, pitot and stall detector; and pneumatic boot de-icing of wing leading-edges, are standard. Oxygen system optional.

AVIONICS: Bendix/King Silver Crown IFR package standard. Typical installations include HF com, DME, weather radar (Honeywell or Bendix), autopilot, and Narco ELT.

DIMENSIONS, EXTERNAL:

Wing span	12.00 m (39 ft 4½ in)

Partenavia P.68 Observer 2 featuring upturned wingtips to improve low-speed handling characteristics

Partenavia Viator (two Allison 250-B17C turboprops)

Partenavia Viator 10-seat twin-turboprop light transport *(Pilot Press)*

Wing chord, constant	1.55 m (5 ft 1 in)
Wing aspect ratio	7.7
Length overall	10.85 m (35 ft 7¼ in)
Fuselage: Length	9.66 m (31 ft 8¼ in)
Max width	1.20 m (3 ft 11¼ in)
Height overall	3.64 m (11 ft 11¼ in)
Tailplane span	4.01 m (13 ft 2 in)
Wheel track	2.167 m (7 ft 1¼ in)
Wheelbase	3.51 m (11 ft 6¼ in)
Propeller diameter	2.03 m (6 ft 8 in)
Propeller ground clearance	0.725 m (2 ft 4½ in)
Distance between propeller centres	
	4.03 m (13 ft 2¾ in)
Passenger door (port): Height	1.03 m (3 ft 4½ in)
Width	0.80 m (2 ft 7½ in)
Height to sill	0.79 m (2 ft 7 in)

Passenger/emergency door (stbd):	
Height (mean)	0.91 m (2 ft 11½ in)
Width	1.10 m (3 ft 7¼ in)
Height to sill	0.79 m (2 ft 7 in)
DIMENSIONS, INTERNAL:	
Cabin, excl flight deck and baggage compartment:	
Length	3.60 m (11 ft 9¾ in)
Max width	1.12 m (3 ft 8 in)
Max height	1.20 m (3 ft 11¼ in)
Floor area	4.00 m² (43.06 sq ft)
Volume	4.70 m³ (165.98 cu ft)
Baggage compartment volume	0.65 m³ (22.95 cu ft)
AREAS:	
Wings, gross	18.60 m² (200.2 sq ft)
Ailerons (total)	1.76 m² (18.94 sq ft)

Trailing-edge flaps (total)	2.42 m² (26.05 sq ft)
Fin	2.90 m² (31.22 sq ft)
Rudder, incl tab	1.64 m² (17.65 sq ft)
Tailplane	3.76 m² (40.47 sq ft)
Elevators (total)	1.30 m² (13.99 sq ft)

WEIGHTS AND LOADINGS:

Basic weight empty	1,640 kg (3,615 lb)
Max fuel load (usable)	680 kg (1,499 lb)
Max payload	910 kg (2,006 lb)
Max T-O and landing weight	2,850 kg (6,283 lb)
Max ramp weight	2,875 kg (6,338 lb)
Max zero-fuel weight	2,550 kg (5,622 lb)
Max wing loading	153.23 kg/m² (31.38 lb/sq ft)
Max power loading	5.83 kg/kW (9.58 lb/shp)

PERFORMANCE (at max T-O weight):

Max operating speed	
	200 knots (370 km/h; 230 mph) IAS
Max level and max cruising speed at 3,660 m (12,000 ft)	
	220 knots (408 km/h; 253 mph)
Econ cruising speed at 3,660 m (12,000 ft)	
	170 knots (315 km/h; 196 mph)
Stalling speed, power off:	
flaps up	81 knots (151 km/h; 94 mph)
flaps down	70 knots (130 km/h; 81 mph)
Max rate of climb at S/L	589 m (1,932 ft)/min
Rate of climb at S/L, one engine out	131 m (430 ft)/min
Max operating altitude	7,620 m (25,000 ft)
Service ceiling, one engine out	3,355 m (11,000 ft)

T-O run	275 m (900 ft)
T-O to 15 m (50 ft)	460 m (1,510 ft)
Landing from 15 m (50 ft)	500 m (1,640 ft)
Landing run	250 m (820 ft)
Min ground turning radius	10.36 m (34 ft 0 in)
Range at long-range power, allowances for start, taxi, take-off, descent, and 45 min reserves:	
with max payload	445 nm (824 km; 512 miles)
with max fuel	860 nm (1,594 km; 990 miles)

PIAGGIO
INDUSTRIE AERONAUTICHE E MECCANICHE RINALDO PIAGGIO SpA

Via Cibrario 4, 16154 Genova Sestri, Genoa
Telephone: 39 (10) 60041
Telex: 270695 AERPIA I
Fax: 39 (10) 603378
HEADQUARTERS: Genova Sestri
FACTORIES: Genova Sestri, Finale Ligure (SV), and Wichita, Kansas, USA
BRANCH OFFICE: Via A. Gramsci 34, Rome
OTHER WORKS: Genova Sestri
CHAIRMAN AND MANAGING DIRECTOR:
   Dott Rinaldo Piaggio
GENERAL MANAGER: Dott Ing Giulio C. Valdonio
DIRECTOR OF INTERNATIONAL PROGRAMMES:
   Dott Ing Bruno Mori
DIRECTOR, AIRCRAFT DIVISION: Dott Ing Piero Selvaggi
DIRECTOR, COMMERCIAL: Commander G. B. Pizzinato

The original Piaggio company began the construction of aeroplanes in its Genova Sestri plant in 1916, and later in the Finale Ligure works. The present company was formed on 29 February 1964, and has since operated as an independent concern. It employs about 2,000 people in three production divisions and in Italy has a total covered works area (Genova Sestri and Finale Ligure) of approx 120,000 m² (1,291,670 sq ft). In the USA, the Wichita factory of approximately 10,000 m² (107,640 sq ft) is dedicated to the construction of Avanti fuselages. In addition to aircraft of its own design, Piaggio is producing components for the Aeritalia G222, Panavia Tornado and AMX. Aeritalia (which see) acquired a 31 per cent holding in Piaggio in 1988.

The activities of the Aero-Engine Division are described in the appropriate section of this edition.

PIAGGIO P.180 AVANTI

Active development of this new corporate aircraft was started by Piaggio in 1982. Gates Learjet became a partner in 1983, but withdrew for economic reasons on 13 January 1986. All of Gates' tooling, together with the forward fuselages of the first three development aircraft (two flying prototypes and one for static tests), were transferred to Piaggio.

Construction began in late 1984, and the first Avanti (I-PJAV) made its first flight on 23 September 1986. The second aircraft (I-PJAR) first flew on 14 May 1987. RAI certification was awarded on 7 March 1990. Piaggio is building two initial production batches of 12 and 18 aircraft, using subassemblies produced both in the USA by Piaggio Aviation and in Italy. Final assembly is at Genova. The first production Avanti first flew on 29 January 1990, and FAA (FAR 23) certification was expected in May/June 1990.

Major design features are the adoption of a 'three lifting surfaces' concept, to reduce cruise drag and fuel consumption, and placement of the engines aft of the rear pressure bulkhead to minimise engine noise levels in the cabin. Primary lifting surface is the main wing, which is situated just above the mid position (to avoid drag-inducing bulges in the circular-section fuselage) and, by virtue of the pusher engine installation, has no propeller induced vortexes impinging on the leading-edge. The second lifting surface is the horizontal T tailplane and elevators, which provide orthodox control from a conventional location. The third is the foreplane, which not only assists the main wing in supporting the aircraft but allows the latter to be reduced in size, thereby also reducing cruise drag and fuel consumption. In assembly, fuselage skins are stretch-formed in unusually large panels to minimise seams, maintaining precise contour tolerances to ten one-thousandths of an inch. Structural members are then shaped to conform exactly to the skin, rather than the conventional reverse.

While most of the Avanti is of conventional metal construction, the nosecone, tailcone, tail unit, engine nacelles, foreplanes, wing outboard flaps and landing gear doors are built of composite materials: graphite/epoxy (carbonfibre) in areas of high stress and glassfibre or Kevlar/epoxy elsewhere. These parts of the airframe—48 components in all, representing about 18 per cent of the aircraft's operating weight empty—are manufactured under subcontract (main parts by Sikorsky Aircraft and Edo). The wings and rear fuselage sections are Italian built; front fuselage sections are constructed in the USA.

Piaggio P.180 Avanti prototype with new fin, but original sectioned windscreen

TYPE: Twin-turboprop corporate transport.
WINGS: Cantilever non-swept mid-wing monoplane, tapered on leading- and trailing-edges. Piaggio PE 1491 G (modified) section at root, PE 1332 G section at tip; thickness/chord ratio 13 per cent. Dihedral 2° from roots. Incidence 0°. Sweep 0° at 15 per cent chord. Integrally machined skins and spars of aluminium alloy; main spar forms an integral fail-safe structural unit with rear pressure bulkhead and main landing gear. Trailing-edge flaps (outboard of engine nacelles) are made in composites. Flaps are actuated electrically, as is trim tab in starboard aileron. Hot air anti-icing of outboard leading-edges.
FOREPLANE: All-composite fail-safe fixed incidence (+3°) foreplane at tip of nose, with 5° anhedral, fitted with electrically actuated all-composite single-slotted auxiliary trailing-edge flaps. Piaggio PE 1300 GN4 aerofoil section, thickness/chord ratio 13 per cent, and 0° sweep at 50 per cent chord. Electric anti-icing of leading-edges. Auxiliary flaps do not control the aircraft in pitch, but are coupled with the main wing flaps and deflect with them to offset changes in trim.
FUSELAGE: Circular-section pressurised fail-safe structure of mainly metal construction (machined aluminium alloy), with rear pressure bulkhead in line with wing main spar. Nosecone, tailcone, baggage door and landing gear doors are built of composite materials. Two composite ventral fins under tailcone.
TAIL UNIT: All-sweptback, all-composite T tail, with variable incidence, 5° anhedral tailplane and balanced elevators and rudder. Trim tab in rudder. No tail unit anti-icing.
LANDING GEAR: Dowty Aerospace hydraulically retractable tricycle type, with single-wheel main units and steerable, twin-wheel nose unit. Main units retract rearward into sides of fuselage; nose unit retracts forward. Dowty hydraulic shock absorbers. Tyre sizes 6.50-10 (main) and 5.00-4 (nose). Multi-disc carbon brakes.
POWER PLANT: Two 1,107 kW (1,485 shp) Pratt & Whitney Canada PT6A-66 turboprops, flat rated at 634 kW (850 shp) and mounted above the wing in an all-composite nacelle and driving a counter-rotating Hartzell five-blade constant-speed fully-feathering reversible-pitch pusher propeller with metal spinner. Propeller blades de-iced by engine exhaust. Fuel in two fuselage tanks totalling 680 litres (180 US gallons; 149.5 Imp gallons) and two 460 litre (121.5 US gallon; 101 Imp gallon) wing tanks; total fuel capacity 1,600 litres (423 US gallons; 352 Imp gallons). Optional single pressure refuelling point in lower centre-fuselage. Gravity refuelling point in upper part of fuselage.
ACCOMMODATION: Crew of one or two on flight deck; certificated for single pilot operation. Seating in main cabin for up to nine passengers, with galley, fully enclosed

toilet and coat storage area. Club passenger seats are armchair type, which can be reclined, tracked and swivelled, and locked at any angle. Foldaway tables can be extended between facing club seats. Two-piece wraparound windscreen. Rectangular cabin windows, including one emergency exit at front on starboard side. Indirect lighting behind each window ring, plus individual overhead lights. Airstair door at front on port side. Baggage compartment aft of rear pressure bulkhead, with door immediately aft of wing on port side. Entire cabin area pressurised and air-conditioned.
SYSTEMS: AiResearch bleed air environmental control system, with max pressure differential of 0.62 bars (9.0 lb/sq in). Single hydraulic system driven by electric motor, with handpump for emergency backup, for landing gear extension only. Electrical system powered by two starter/generators and a 25V 38Ah nickel-cadmium battery. 0.62 m³ (22 cu ft) oxygen system. Hot air anti-icing of main wing outer leading-edges; electric anti-icing for foreplane and windscreen; rubber boot for engine air intake, coupled with dynamic particle separator.
AVIONICS AND EQUIPMENT: Standard Collins EFIS (three CRTs), Collins VHF com/nav equipment, Collins WXR-840 weather radar, Collins dual transponder TDR-90, Collins single DME and ADF system, Collins radio altimeter, Collins primary and secondary compass systems, Aeronetics dual RMI, Collins APS-65A digital autopilot systems, JET dual vertical gyro, and Collins electronic air data system.

DIMENSIONS, EXTERNAL:

Wing span	14.03 m (46 ft 0½ in)
Foreplane span	3.38 m (11 ft 1 in)
Wing chord: at root	1.82 m (5 ft 11¾ in)
at tip	0.62 m (2 ft 0½ in)
Foreplane chord: at root	0.79 m (2 ft 7 in)
at tip	0.55 m (1 ft 9⅔ in)
Wing aspect ratio	12.30
Foreplane aspect ratio	5.05
Length overall	14.41 m (47 ft 3½ in)
Fuselage: Length	12.53 m (41 ft 1¼ in)
Max width	1.95 m (6 ft 4¾ in)
Height overall	3.94 m (12 ft 11 in)
Tailplane span	4.25 m (13 ft 11½ in)
Wheel track	2.84 m (9 ft 4 in)
Wheelbase	5.79 m (19 ft 0 in)
Propeller diameter	2.16 m (7 ft 1 in)
Propeller ground clearance	0.80 m (2 ft 7½ in)
Distance between propeller centres	4.13 m (13 ft 6½ in)
Passenger door (fwd, port): Height	1.35 m (4 ft 5 in)
Width	0.61 m (2 ft 0 in)
Height to sill	0.58 m (1 ft 10¾ in)

Baggage door (rear, port): Height	0.60 m (1 ft 11¾ in)
Width	0.70 m (2 ft 3½ in)
Height to sill	1.38 m (4 ft 6½ in)
Emergency exit (stbd): Height	0.67 m (2 ft 2¼ in)
Width	0.48 m (1 ft 7 in)

DIMENSIONS, INTERNAL:

Passenger cabin: Length	4.45 m (14 ft 7¼ in)
Max width	1.85 m (6 ft 0¾ in)
Max height	1.75 m (5 ft 9 in)
Volume	10.62 m³ (375.0 cu ft)
Baggage compartment: Floor length	1.70 m (2 ft 3½ in)
Max length	2.10 m (6 ft 10¾ in)
Volume	1.25 m³ (44.14 cu ft)

AREAS:

Wings, gross	16.00 m² (172.22 sq ft)
Ailerons (total, incl tab)	0.66 m² (7.10 sq ft)
Trailing-edge flaps (total)	1.60 m² (17.23 sq ft)
Foreplane	2.25 m² (24.22 sq ft)
Foreplane flaps (total)	0.58 m² (6.30 sq ft)
Fin	4.73 m² (50.91 sq ft)
Rudder, incl tab	1.05 m² (11.30 sq ft)
Tailplane	3.83 m² (41.23 sq ft)
Elevators (total, incl tabs)	1.24 m² (13.35 sq ft)

WEIGHTS AND LOADINGS:

Weight empty, equipped	3,266 kg (7,200 lb)
Operating weight empty, one pilot	3,343 kg (7,370 lb)
Max fuel load	1,291 kg (2,846 lb)
Max payload	966 kg (2,129 lb)
Payload with max fuel	310 kg (683 lb)
Max T-O weight	4,903 kg (10,810 lb)
Max ramp weight	4,944 kg (10,900 lb)
Max landing weight	4,658 kg (10,270 lb)
Max zero-fuel weight	4,309 kg (9,500 lb)
Max wing loading	306.44 kg/m² (62.76 lb/sq ft)
Max power loading	3.87 kg/kW (6.36 lb/shp)

PERFORMANCE (preliminary, pre-certification, at max T-O weight except where indicated):

Max operating Mach number	0.7
Max operating speed	280 knots (519 km/h; 322 mph) IAS
Max level speed at 8,535 m (28,000 ft)	400 knots (740 km/h; 460 mph)
Stalling speed, at max landing weight:	
flaps up	105 knots (194 km/h; 121 mph) CAS
flaps down	90 knots (167 km/h; 104 mph) CAS
Max rate of climb at S/L	945 m (3,100 ft)/min
Rate of climb at S/L, one engine out	290 m (950 ft)/min
Service ceiling	12,495 m (41,000 ft)
Service ceiling, one engine out	9,600 m (31,500 ft)
T-O to 15 m (50 ft)	844 m (2,770 ft)
Landing from 15 m (50 ft) at max landing weight	710 m (2,330 ft)
Range at 11,890 m (39,000 ft):	
IFR reserves	1,500 nm (2,780 km; 1,727 miles)
VFR reserves	1,820 nm (3,372 km; 2,095 miles)

PIAGGIO P.166-DL3SEM

The P.166 has been produced in several basic versions, of which the original piston engined P.166 was described in the 1963-64 Jane's; the P.166M, P.166B Portofino and P.166C in the 1971-72 Jane's; the P.166S in the 1974-75 Jane's; and the P.166-DL2 in the 1978-79 Jane's.

Current version is the turboprop powered P.166-DL3, which flew for the first time on 3 July 1976 and received FAA and RAI certification in 1978. It can be configured and equipped for a wide variety of duties, including executive transport (EXC); transport and dropping of up to 10 paratroops (PAR); air ambulance for two stretchers and two medical attendants (AMB); multi-engine aircrew training (MTR); light tactical transport (LTT); armed military counter-insurgency, field support, and search and rescue (AML); maritime reconnaissance (MAR); environmental control and geophysical survey (ECS); aerial

Piaggio P.180 Avanti corporate transport, production configuration (*Pilot Press*)

photogrammetry (APH); and aerial firefighting (AFF). Piaggio is currently completing a batch of 12 P.166-DL3SEM maritime and ecological patrol aircraft for the Italian Ministry of Merchant Marine. They are equipped for a variety of surveillance, reconnaissance and search and rescue duties. Deliveries were expected to be completed by June 1990. Additional orders total 10 for the Italian Guardia di Finanza (Border Guard).

TYPE: Twin-turboprop light transport.

WINGS: Shoulder gull-wing cantilever monoplane. NACA 230 wing section. Dihedral 21° 30′ on inner portion, 2° 30′ on outer wings. Incidence 2° 43′ at root. Sweepback 7° 30′ at quarter-chord. Aluminium alloy flush riveted torsion box structure, with single main spar and auxiliary rear spar. All-metal slotted ailerons, with geared and trim tab in starboard aileron. All-metal hydraulically actuated slotted flaps. Rubber boot leading-edge de-icing optional.

FUSELAGE: Aluminium alloy flush riveted semi-monocoque structure of frames and I section extruded stringers: no longerons.

TAIL UNIT: Cantilever aluminium alloy structure, with flush riveted smooth skin on fixed surfaces and beaded skin on control surfaces. Rudder and elevators statically and dynamically balanced. Geared and trim tabs in elevators; trim tab in rudder. Rubber boot leading-edge de-icing of fin and tailplane optional.

LANDING GEAR: Retractable tricycle type. Magnaghi oleo-pneumatic shock absorbers in all units. Hydraulic actuation. Nosewheel retracts rearward, main units upward. Goodyear 24 × 7.7 mainwheels with size 8.50-10 tyres, pressure 3.79 bars (55 lb/sq in). Goodyear steerable and self-centring nosewheel with size 6.00-6 tyre, pressure 2.90 bars (42 lb/sq in). Goodyear or Magnaghi hydraulic brakes.

POWER PLANT: Two Textron Lycoming LTP 101-700 turboprops, each flat rated at 447.5 kW (600 shp) and driving a Hartzell HC-B3DL/LT10282-9.5 three-blade constant-speed fully-feathering metal pusher propeller. Fuel in two 212 litre (56 US gallon; 46.5 Imp gallon) outer-wing main tanks, two 323 litre (85.3 US gallon; 71 Imp gallon) wingtip tanks, and a 116 litre (30.6 US gallon; 25.5 Imp gallon) fuselage collector tank; total standard internal fuel capacity 1,186 litres (313.3 US

gallons; 260.9 Imp gallons). Auxiliary fuel system available optionally, comprising a 232 litre (61.3 US gallon; 51 Imp gallon) fuselage tank, transfer pump and controls; with this installed, total usable fuel capacity is increased to 1,418 litres (374.6 US gallons; 312 Imp gallons). Gravity refuelling points in each main tank and tip tank. Provision for two 177 or 284 litre (46.8 or 75 US gallon; 39 or 62.5 Imp gallon) underwing drop tanks. Air intakes and propeller blades de-iced by engine exhaust.

ACCOMMODATION: Crew of two on raised flight deck, with dual controls. Aft of flight deck, accommodation consists of a passenger cabin, utility compartment and baggage compartment. Access to flight deck is via passenger/cargo double door on port side, forward of wing, or via individual crew door on each side of flight deck. External access to baggage compartment via port side door aft of wing. Passenger cabin extends from rear of flight deck to bulkhead at wing main spar; fitting of passenger carrying, cargo or other interiors is facilitated by two continuous rails on cabin floor, permitting considerable flexibility in standard or customised interior layouts. Standard seating for eight passengers, with individual lighting, ventilation and oxygen controls. Flight deck can be separated from passenger cabin by a screen. Door in bulkhead at rear of cabin provides access to utility compartment, in which can be fitted a toilet, bar, or mission equipment for various roles. Entire accommodation is heated, ventilated and soundproofed. Emergency exit forward of wing on starboard side. Windscreen hot-air demisting standard. Windscreen wipers, washers and methanol spray de-icing optional.

SYSTEMS: Hydraulic system, pressure 127 bars (1,840 lb/sq in), for landing gear, flap and brake actuation, nosewheel steering and lock, and (on APH version) actuation of ventral door. Handpump for emergency extension of landing gear. Standard electrical system is 28V DC, supplied by two engine driven starter/generators and a nickel-cadmium battery. External power receptacle. Static or rotary inverters, to supply AC power for avionics and instruments, available optionally. Oxygen system.

AVIONICS AND EQUIPMENT (DL3SEM): UHF-AM, VHF-AM, VHF-FM, encrypted HF and HF/SSB com radios; navigation system includes ANI-7000 Loran-C, Sierra AN/ARN-136A Tacan, Collins VOR-31A VOR/ILS, Collins MC-103 radio compass, direction finder, IFF transponder and radar altimeter. Search and surveillance equipment includes FIAR/Bendix RDR 1500 360° radar with dual CRT colour displays; MSP-Daedalus AA 2000 infra-red/ultraviolet linescanning system; 2500 A FLIR system; two 70 mm Vinten 618 aerial cameras (one vertical, one side-looking); and a 3 million candlepower ORC Locator II searchlight under the port wing.

AVIONICS AND EQUIPMENT (general): Standard avionics packages available to individual customer's requirements: minimum recommended package includes two VHF com, two VHF nav (VOR/ILS), ADF, ATC transponder, compass system and intercom. Optional avionics include radar, autopilot, navigation system and synthesiser type HF radio. Quickly interchangeable individual seats of various types, bench seat, divan or stretchers for EXC, PAR, AMB, MTR and LTT versions; strengthened floor in LTT. Four underwing pylons standard on AML, for ordnance, supply containers and auxiliary fuel tanks. Four pylons and integrated search/detection/identification/plotting and reporting system on MAR. Magnetometer, multiscanner, multiple-head camera and associated equipment in ECS version. Two cameras, associated equipment, and ventral

Piaggio P.166-DL3SEM used by the Italian Ministry of Merchant Marine

sliding doors in APH, with option for four underwing pylons. Internal removable water/extinguisher container and rapid charge/discharge system for AFF.

DIMENSIONS, EXTERNAL:

Wing span: without tip tanks	13.51 m (44 ft 4 in)
with tip tanks	14.69 m (48 ft 2½ in)
Wing chord: at root	2.40 m (7 ft 10½ in)
at tip	1.15 m (3 ft 9¼ in)
Wing aspect ratio	7.3
Length overall	11.88 m (39 ft 0 in)
Height overall	5.00 m (16 ft 5 in)
Tailplane span	5.10 m (16 ft 9 in)
Wheel track	2.66 m (8 ft 9 in)
Wheelbase	4.71 m (15 ft 5½ in)
Propeller diameter	2.36 m (7 ft 9 in)
Cabin door: Height	1.38 m (4 ft 6 in)
Width	1.28 m (4 ft 2 in)

DIMENSIONS, INTERNAL:

Cabin, incl flight deck: Length	3.20 m (10 ft 6 in)
Max width	1.57 m (5 ft 2 in)
Max height	1.76 m (5 ft 9 in)
Floor area	5.14 m² (55.3 sq ft)
Volume	6.63 m³ (234.1 cu ft)

Utility compartment: Length	0.65 m (2 ft 1½ in)
Max width	1.52 m (5 ft 0 in)
Max height	1.70 m (5 ft 7 in)
Volume	2.27 m³ (80.2 cu ft)
Baggage compartment volume	1.80 m³ (63.6 cu ft)

AREAS:

Wings, gross	26.56 m² (285.9 sq ft)
Ailerons (total)	1.95 m² (21.00 sq ft)
Trailing-edge flaps (total)	2.38 m² (25.60 sq ft)
Fin	1.62 m² (17.44 sq ft)
Rudder, incl tab	1.23 m² (13.24 sq ft)
Tailplane	3.50 m² (37.67 sq ft)
Elevators, incl tabs	1.29 m² (13.88 sq ft)

WEIGHTS AND LOADINGS:

Weight empty, equipped	2,688 kg (5,926 lb)
Max fuel	1,036 kg (2,284 lb)
Max payload	1,092 kg (2,407 lb)
Max T-O weight	4,300 kg (9,480 lb)
Max ramp weight	4,320 kg (9,524 lb)
Max zero-fuel weight	3,800 kg (8,377 lb)
Max landing weight	4,085 kg (9,006 lb)
Max wing loading	162 kg/m² (33.2 lb/sq ft)
Max power loading	4.81 kg/kW (7.9 lb/shp)

PERFORMANCE (at max T-O weight except where indicated):

Never-exceed speed
220 knots (407 km/h; 253 mph) CAS
Max level and max cruising speed at 3,050 m (10,000 ft)
215 knots (400 km/h; 248 mph)
Econ cruising speed at 3,660 m (12,000 ft)
162 knots (300 km/h; 186 mph)
Stalling speed:
flaps and landing gear up
86 knots (160 km/h; 99 mph) CAS
flaps and landing gear down
75 knots (139 km/h; 87 mph) CAS

Max rate of climb at S/L	573 m (1,880 ft)/min
Rate of climb at S/L, one engine out	140 m (460 ft)/min
Max operating altitude	7,315 m (24,000 ft)
Service ceiling, one engine out	3,170 m (10,400 ft)
T-O to 15 m (50 ft)	610 m (2,000 ft)

Landing from 15 m (50 ft) at max landing weight
487 m (1,600 ft)
Range, VFR:

with max payload	750 nm (1,390 km; 863 miles)
with max fuel	1,150 nm (2,131 km; 1,324 miles)

JAPAN

FUJI

FUJI HEAVY INDUSTRIES LTD (Fuji Jukogyo Kabushiki Kaisha)

Subaru Building, 7-2, 1-chome, Nishi-shinjuku, Shinjuku-ku, Tokyo 160
Telephone: 81 (3) 347 2525
Telex: 0 232 2268 FUJI J
Fax: 81 (3) 347 2588
PRESIDENT: Toshihiro Tajima
UTSUNOMIYA MANUFACTURING DIVISION: 1-11, Yonan 1-chome, Utsunomiya, Tochigi 320
Telephone: 81 (286) 58 1111

Aircraft Division

GENERAL MANAGERS:
Yasumasa Honda (Managing Director)
Koichiro Shimmen (Commercial Business)
Masayuki Hara (Marketing and Sales, Defence Programmes)

Utsunomiya Manufacturing Division

GENERAL MANAGERS:
Akitoshi Nagao (Managing Director, and General Manager of Aircraft Plant)
Takeshi Makino (Director and General Manager, Aircraft Engineering Division)

Fuji Heavy Industries, established on 15 July 1953, is a successor to the Nakajima aircraft company, which was established in 1917 and built 25,935 aircraft up to the end of the Second World War.

The present Utsunomiya Manufacturing Division (Aircraft and Rolling Stock Plants) occupies a site of 510,094 m² (5,490,600 sq ft) including a floor area of 188,490 m² (2,028,887 sq ft) and in early 1990 employed 3,257 people.

Details of Fuji production of the Cessna L-19E Bird Dog, Beechcraft Mentor, and several modified versions of the Mentor designated LM-1 Nikko, LM-2, KM, KM-2, KM-2B and TL-1, have appeared in previous editions of *Jane's*. The KM-2Kai, a turboprop version of the KM-2, is described in this entry.

Fuji is currently producing the Bell Model 205 and AH-1S HueyCobra helicopters, as described in this entry. It is building wing main assemblies for JMSDF Lockheed P-3C Orions (see Kawasaki entry); main landing gear doors and some titanium airframe parts for Japanese built McDonnell Douglas F-15J fighters (see Mitsubishi entry); and wings, tailplanes and canopies for the Kawasaki T-4 jet trainer (which see). Commercial aircraft components are produced for the Boeing 747 (spoilers, inboard and outboard ailerons), Boeing 757 (outboard trailing-edge flaps), Boeing 767 (wing/body fairings and main landing gear doors), McDonnell Douglas MD-11 (outboard ailerons) and Fokker 50 (rudder and elevators). Those for the 767 and MD-11 are designed by Fuji, and manufactured from advanced composite materials.

FUJI KM-2Kai

JMSDF designation: T-5

In 1984 Fuji refitted a company owned KM-2 with an Allison 250-B17D turboprop in place of the Textron Lycoming IGSO-480 piston engine. Designated KM-2D, it made its first flight on 28 June 1984, and was described in the 1988-89 *Jane's*. JCAB certification (Aerobatic and Utility categories) was gained on 14 February 1985.

In March 1987 Fuji received an initial JMSDF contract to replace the current fleet of 31 KM-2s with a further developed variant of the KM-2D, designated KM-2Kai, which has additional changes to the cabin structure and equipment. First flight of a production KM-2Kai was made on 27 April 1988, and deliveries began in August 1988 under the JMSDF designation T-5. Eight T-5s had been ordered by March 1990.

First production Fuji KM-2Kai (T-5) for the JMSDF

The following description applies to the T-5:

TYPE: Two/four-seat primary trainer.

WINGS: Cantilever low-wing monoplane. All-metal light alloy structure, with tapered, non-swept wings of NACA 23016.5 section at root, NACA 23012 at tip. Dihedral 6° from roots. Incidence 4° at root, 1° at tip. Plain ailerons and single-slotted flaps, of light alloy, on trailing-edges. Anti-servo tab in each aileron, port tab being controllable for trim.

FUSELAGE: Conventional light alloy semi-monocoque structure.

TAIL UNIT: Cantilever light alloy structure, with sweptback vertical and non-swept horizontal surfaces. Fixed incidence tailplane; balanced elevators and rudder. Controllable tab in each elevator; anti-servo tab in rudder.

LANDING GEAR: Electrically retractable tricycle type, with emergency manual control. Oleo-pneumatic shock absorber in each unit. Main units retract inward into wings, nose unit rearward into fuselage. Single Cleveland wheel and Goodyear tyre on each main unit, size 6.50-8 (6 ply); Goodyear nosewheel and tyre, size 5.00-5 (4 ply). Nose unit is steerable ±16°. Cleveland single-disc hydraulic brakes.

POWER PLANT: One Allison 250-B17D turboprop, flat rated at 261 kW (350 shp), driving a Hartzell HC-B3TF-7A/T10173-18 three-blade constant-speed fully-feathering propeller with spinner. Two bladder type fuel tanks in each wing, one of 94.6 litres (25 US gallons; 20.8 Imp gallons) capacity and one of 87 litres (23 US gallons; 19.2 Imp gallons); total capacity 363 litres (96 US gallons; 80 Imp gallons). Gravity refuelling point in top surface of each wing. Oil capacity 9.5 litres (2.5 US gallons; 2.1 Imp gallons).

ACCOMMODATION: Enclosed cabin seating two persons side by side, with dual controls (Aerobatic version), or four persons in pairs in Utility version. Rearward sliding canopy. Accommodation heated and ventilated.

SYSTEMS: Hydraulic system for brakes only. Electrical system includes a 30V 150A starter/generator, two 160VA static inverters, and a 24Ah battery for engine starting and emergency.

AVIONICS AND EQUIPMENT: Standard items include UHF and VHF radio, intercom, ADF, Tacan, SIF, and IFR training hood.

DIMENSIONS, EXTERNAL:

Wing span	10.04 m (32 ft 11¼ in)

Wing chord: at root	2.13 m (6 ft 11¾ in)
at tip	1.07 m (3 ft 6¼ in)
Wing aspect ratio	6.11
Length overall	8.44 m (27 ft 8¼ in)
Height overall	2.96 m (9 ft 8½ in)
Elevator span	3.71 m (12 ft 2 in)
Wheel track	2.92 m (9 ft 7 in)
Wheelbase	2.27 m (7 ft 5½ in)
Propeller diameter	2.12 m (6 ft 11½ in)
Propeller ground clearance	0.37 m (1 ft 2½ in)

DIMENSIONS, INTERNAL:

Cabin: Length	2.90 m (9 ft 6¼ in)
Max width	1.27 m (4 ft 2 in)
Max height	1.33 m (4 ft 4½ in)

AREAS:

Wings, gross	16.50 m² (177.6 sq ft)
Ailerons (total, incl tabs)	1.09 m² (11.73 sq ft)
Trailing-edge flaps (total)	1.98 m² (21.31 sq ft)
Fin, incl dorsal fin	1.28 m² (13.78 sq ft)
Rudder, incl tab	0.66 m² (7.10 sq ft)
Tailplane	3.46 m² (37.24 sq ft)
Elevators (total, incl tabs)	1.39 m² (14.96 sq ft)

WEIGHTS AND LOADINGS (A: Aerobatic, U: Utility):

Weight empty: A, U	1,082 kg (2,385 lb)
Max fuel weight: A, U	644 kg (1,420 lb)
Max T-O weight: A	1,585 kg (3.494 lb)
U	1,805 kg (3,979 lb)
Max wing loading: A	96.06 kg/m² (19.67 lb/sq ft)
U	109.39 kg/m² (22.40 lb/sq ft)
Max power loading: A	6.07 kg/kW (9.98 lb/shp)
U	6.92 kg/kW (11.37 lb/shp)

PERFORMANCE (at max Aerobatic T-O weight except where indicated):

Never-exceed speed 223 knots (413 km/h; 256 mph) EAS	
Max level speed at 2,440 m (8,000 ft)	
	193 knots (357 km/h; 222 mph)
Econ cruising speed at 2,440 m (8,000 ft)	
	155 knots (287 km/h; 178 mph)
Stalling speed, flaps and landing gear down, power off	
	56 knots (104 km/h; 65 mph)
Max rate of climb at S/L	518 m (1,700 ft)/min
Service ceiling	7,620 m (25,000 ft)
Min ground turning radius	7.38 m (24 ft 2½ in)
T-O run	302 m (990 ft)
T-O to 15 m (50 ft)	430 m (1,410 ft)
Landing from 15 m (50 ft)	515 m (1,690 ft)
Landing run	174 m (570 ft)
Range with max payload (Utility version), MIL-C-5011A reserves	510 nm (945 km; 587 miles)

FUJI-BELL UH-1H and Advanced Model 205A-1
Japanese designation: HU-1H

Fuji is manufacturing Bell UH-1H helicopters under sublicence from Mitsui and Co Ltd, Bell's Japanese licensee, following the completion of 34 commercial 204Bs between 1962 and 1973 and 20 of the higher powered Model 204B-2 (1989-90 and earlier *Jane's*) from 1974-87.

Following the delivery of 90 HU-1Bs (Japanese military version of the 204B) to the Japan Ground Self-Defence Force by early 1973, Fuji production continued with the UH-1H (military version of the Bell 205 and known in Japan as the HU-1H), of which the first example flew for the first time on 17 July 1973; 125 had been ordered for the JGSDF by March 1990, and a further eight were approved in the FY 1990 budget.

The Fuji-Bell HU-1H has the same airframe and dynamic components as the Bell built UH-1H but has a longer tail rotor and Kawasaki built Textron Lycoming T53 engine. Fuji is now the sole producer of this helicopter, US production having ended during the past year.

Bell, in conjunction with Fuji, has developed an upgrade programme for the Bell 205 which, when modified, is known as the **Advanced Model 205A-1**. A prototype (N19AL) made its first flight from Bell's Experimental Flight Research Center at Arlington, Texas, on 23 April 1988. Modifications include replacement of the standard main rotor blades with the extended chord, tapered tip blades of the UH-1N/Model 212 series (see Canadian section); installation of a 1,342 kW (1,800 shp) Textron Lycoming T53-L-703 turboshaft and the 962 kW (1,290 shp) rated transmission of the Bell Model 212, and incorporation of Bell's liquid inertial vibration eliminator (LIVE) system, which uses heavy non-viscous fluid (mercury) isolators between the transmission and fuselage to reduce rotor vibration by a claimed 80 per cent. The reduction in vibration improves crew and passenger comfort and increases the Advanced 205A-1's maximum cruising speed to 130 knots (241 km/h; 150 mph) and combat dash speed to 140 knots (259 km/h; 161 mph). The prototype Model 205A-1 was demonstrated to US Army officials at the Army Aviation Center, Fort Rucker, Alabama, and the Army Aviation Systems Command at St Louis, Missouri, in the Summer of 1988, and made a demonstration tour of Japan, the Far East and Southeast Asia during 1989.

The following details apply to the standard Fuji-Bell HU-1H:

TYPE: Single-engined general purpose helicopter.
ROTOR SYSTEM: Two-blade semi-rigid main rotor. Interchangeable blades, built up of extruded aluminium spars

Prototype Bell Advanced Model 205A-1, developed jointly with Fuji of Japan

and laminates, now being replaced by new composite blades, with unidirectional glassfibre roving spar, afterbody of glassfibre skin over a Nomex honeycomb core, unidirectional glassfibre roving trailing-edge, and a polyurethane leading-edge abrasion strip. A stainless steel sheath under this strip on the outboard portion of the blade reinforces the inertia weight attachment and enhances tree cutting capability. Stabilising bar above and at right angles to main rotor blades. Underslung feathering axis head. Two-blade all-metal tail rotor of honeycomb construction. Blades do not fold.

ROTOR DRIVE: Shaft drive to both main and tail rotors. Transmission rating 820 kW (1,100 shp). Main rotor rpm 294-324.

FUSELAGE: Conventional all-metal semi-monocoque structure.

TAIL SURFACE: Small synchronised elevator on rear fuselage is connected to the cyclic control to increase allowable CG travel.

LANDING GEAR: Tubular skid type. Lock-on ground handling wheels and inflated nylon float bags available.

POWER PLANT: One 1,044 kW (1,400 shp) Kawasaki built Textron Lycoming T53-K-13B turboshaft, mounted aft of the transmission on top of the fuselage and enclosed in cowlings. Five interconnected rubber fuel cells, total capacity 844 litres (223 US gallons; 186 Imp gallons), of which 799 litres (211 US gallons; 176 Imp gallons) are usable. Overload fuel capacity of 1,935 litres (511 US gallons; 425 Imp gallons) usable, obtained by installation of kit comprising two 568 litre (150 US gallon; 125 Imp gallon) internal auxiliary fuel tanks interconnected with the basic fuel system.

ACCOMMODATION: Pilot and 11-14 troops, or six litters and a medical attendant, or 1,759 kg (3,880 lb) of freight. Crew doors open forward and are jettisonable. Two doors on each side of cargo compartment; front door is hinged to open forward and is removable, rear door slides aft. Forced air ventilation system.

AVIONICS AND EQUIPMENT: FM, UHF, VHF radio sets, IFF transponder, Gyromatic compass system, direction finder set, VOR receiver and intercom standard. Optional nav/com systems. Standard equipment includes bleed air heater and defroster, comprehensive range of engine and flight instruments, power plant fire detection system, 30V 300A DC starter/generator, navigation, landing and anti-collision lights, controllable searchlight, hydraulically boosted controls. Optional equipment includes external cargo hook, auxiliary fuel tanks, rescue hoist, 150,000 BTU muff heater.

DIMENSIONS, EXTERNAL:

Main rotor diameter	14.63 m (48 ft 0 in)
Tail rotor diameter	2.59 m (8 ft 6 in)
Main rotor blade chord	0.53 m (1 ft 9 in)
Tail rotor blade chord	0.213 m (8.4 in)

Length:

overall (main rotor fore and aft)	17.62 m (57 ft 9⅝ in)
fuselage	12.77 m (41 ft 10¾ in)

Height:

overall, tail rotor turning (excl fin tip antenna)	4.41 m (14 ft 5½ in)
to top of main rotor head	3.60 m (11 ft 9¾ in)
Stabiliser span	2.84 m (9 ft 4 in)
Width over skids	2.91 m (9 ft 6½ in)

DIMENSIONS, INTERNAL:

Cabin: Max width	2.34 m (7 ft 8 in)
Max height	1.25 m (4 ft 1¼ in)
Volume (excl flight deck)	approx 6.23 m³ (220 cu ft)

AREAS:

Main rotor disc	168.11 m² (1,809.56 sq ft)
Tail rotor disc	5.27 m² (56.7 sq ft)

WEIGHTS AND LOADINGS:

Weight empty, equipped	2,390 kg (5,270 lb)
Max T-O and landing weight	4,309 kg (9,500 lb)
Max disc loading	25.6 kg/m² (5.25 lb/sq ft)
Max power loading	4.13 kg/kW (6.78 lb/shp)

PERFORMANCE (at max T-O weight):

Max level and max cruising speed	110 knots (204 km/h; 127 mph)
Max rate of climb at S/L	488 m (1,600 ft)/min
Service ceiling	3,840 m (12,600 ft)
Hovering ceiling: IGE	4,145 m (13,600 ft)
OGE	335 m (1,100 ft)
Range at S/L	252 nm (467 km; 290 miles)

FUJI-BELL AH-1S

In FY 1982 Fuji was selected as prime contractor for a licence manufacturing programme for Bell AH-1S HueyCobra anti-armour helicopters for the JGSDF; these correspond to the US Army AH-1F version. Kawasaki is delivering the T53-K-703 engines for these aircraft. The JGSDF had previously purchased two Bell built AH-1S in 1977 and 1978 for operational evaluation.

The first Fuji built AH-1S made its initial flight on 2 July 1984. Current JGSDF plans are to purchase 88 AH-1S. These will equip five anti-tank helicopter squadrons, with a surplus to be used for attrition replacements and aircraft for training. Orders have so far been placed for 62 aircraft, of which 54 were due to be delivered by the end of March 1990. The first squadron is based at Obihiro on Hokkaido, and the second at Hachinohe.

Fuji built AH-1S HueyCobra for the JGSDF

ISHIDA
THE ISHIDA CORPORATION
116 Myoken-cho, Showa-ku, Nagoya 466
Telephone: 81 (52) 782 4332
Fax: 81 (52) 781 6407
Texas Technical Center:
DMAV Inc, 2205 West Division, Unit C-5, Arlington,
   Texas 76013, USA
Telephone: 1 (817) 265 8843
Fax: 1 (817) 274 1379
CHIEF OF AERODYNAMICS: J. David Kocurek

ISHIDA TW-68
The TW-68 is being developed as a tilt-wing shuttle
aircraft for civil corporate, commuter, freight and SAR
operations. It is entirely Japanese funded, up to and
including first flight of a prototype, and has been designed
by DMAV Inc (Dual Mode Air Vehicle), a US company
whose workforce includes a number of former Bell
employees.

Design features include a small, hydraulically driven
ducted fan in the upper horizontal tail surface, to provide
pitch attitude control during hovering in the absence of
propeller cyclic pitch control; and differentially operated
flaperons, acting in the propeller slipstream, for yaw and
roll control. Wind tunnel testing has been completed, and a
full-scale mockup was under construction at DMAV in
early 1990. Four prototypes are to be built in the USA; first
flight is anticipated in mid-1993.

General appearance of the TW-68 is shown in an
accompanying artist's impression. Principal data are:
POWER PLANT: Two 1,640 kW (2,200 shp) class turboshaft
engines, driving five-blade propellers.
ACCOMMODATION: Flight crew of two. Cabin seating for nine
(corporate), 14 (commuter) or a maximum of 16
passengers, or equivalent freight or other payload.
DIMENSIONS, EXTERNAL:

Wing span	10.97 m (36 ft 0 in)
Wing chord, constant	2.16 m (7 ft 1 in)

Artist's impression of the Ishida TW-68 tilt-wing transport aircraft. Canard surfaces have been deleted from the original design

Wing aspect ratio	5.08	AREA:	
Distance between propeller centres		Wings, gross	23.69 m² (255.0 sq ft)
	7.53 m (24 ft 8½ in)	WEIGHTS:	
Length overall	12.00 m (39 ft 4½ in)	Max T-O weight: VTOL	5670 kg (12 500 lb)
Fuselage: Max width	1.78 m (5 ft 10 in)	STOL	7484 kg (16 500 lb)
Height overall	4.08 m (13 ft 4¾ in)	PERFORMANCE (estimated):	
Propeller diameter	5.08 m (16 ft 8 in)	Max level speed	350 knots (648 km/h; 403 mph)
DIMENSIONS, INTERNAL:		Max cruising speed	268 knots (496 km/h; 308 mph)
Cabin: Length	4.82 m (15 ft 10 in)	Best range speed	187 knots (346 km/h; 215 mph)
Max width	1.63 m (5 ft 4 in)	Best endurance speed	170 knots (315 km/h; 196 mph)
Max height	1.60 m (5 ft 3 in)		

KAWASAKI
KAWASAKI JUKOGYO KABUSHIKI KAISHA (Kawasaki Heavy Industries Ltd)
1-18 Nakamachi-Dori, 2-chome, Chuo-ku, Kobe
TOKYO AND AEROSPACE GROUP OFFICE: World Trade Center
Building, 4-1, Hamamatsu-cho 2-chome, Minato-ku,
Tokyo
Telephone: 81 (3) 435 2111
Telex: 242-4371 KAWAJU J
PRESIDENT: Hiroshi Ohba
Aerospace Group
EXECUTIVE MANAGING DIRECTOR AND GROUP SENIOR GENERAL
   MANAGER:
Kanji Sonoda
WORKS: Gifu and Akashi

Kawasaki Aircraft Co amalgamated with Kawasaki
Dockyard Co and Kawasaki Rolling Stock Mfg Co to form
Kawasaki Heavy Industries Ltd on 1 April 1969. The
Aerospace Group employs some 5,400 people. Kawasaki
has a 25 per cent holding in Nippi (which see).

In addition to extensive overhaul work, Kawasaki has
built many US aircraft under licence since 1955, as detailed
in earlier *Jane's*. From the Lockheed P2V-7 (P-2H)
Neptune it developed the P-2J anti-submarine aircraft (see
1978-79 *Jane's*), two of which were later converted to UP-2J
configuration with equipment for target towing, ECM
training and drone launch operations, and two others as
UP-2J(E) electronic intelligence (elint) aircraft, equipped
with HLR-105 and HLR-106 systems. Two of these four
aircraft still serve with No. 81 Squadron (31st Fleet Air
Wing) at Iwakuni.

Lockheed P-3C Orion for the JMSDF, assembled by Kawasaki

Kawasaki is producing, as prime contractor, the T-4
intermediate jet trainer to succeed the Lockheed T-33A and
Fuji T-1. The company has developed, jointly with MBB of
West Germany, the BK 117 twin-engined multi-purpose
helicopter described in the International section. Kawasaki
has exclusive rights to produce and develop the former
Boeing 107 Model II helicopter. McDonnell Douglas MD
500 series light helicopters are being manufactured under a
licence agreement concluded in October 1967. By 1 April
1990 a total of 160 KV107 series helicopters had been
delivered, and 286 MD 500s to government and commercial
operators in Japan. The company is now co-producing
Boeing CH-47 Chinooks for the Japanese armed forces.

Kawasaki is a subcontractor to Mitsubishi (which see) for
rear fuselages, wings and tail units of the McDonnell
Douglas F-15J and DJ Eagles being licence built in Japan; is
subcontracted to build forward and mid fuselage sections,
and wing ribs, for the Boeing 767 jet transport; and has been
nominated by the JASDF as prime contractor for
maintenance and support of its Grumman E-2C Hawkeye
AEW and Lockheed C-130 Hercules transport aircraft.

Kawasaki is prime contractor for fabrication and
assembly of engines for the Bell AH-1S gunship helicopters
built in Japan by Fuji. Its aero engine activities are described
in the appropriate section of this edition.

KAWASAKI (LOCKHEED) P-3C ORION
Kawasaki is prime contractor for licence production of
the Lockheed P-3C/Update II Orion, 100 of which are to be
purchased by the JMSDF. Of these, 88 had been ordered up
to and including FY 1989; a further eight were approved for

FY 1990. The first three (US built) P-3Cs were handed over
to the JMSDF in April 1981. The next four were assembled
by Kawasaki from knocked-down assemblies; the first of
these made its initial flight on 17 March 1982, and was
delivered on 26 May that year to Fleet Squadron 51 at
Atsugi Air Base. The remaining 81 are being built almost
entirely in Japan, and 60 had been delivered by 31 March
1990. Two squadrons, each with 10 aircraft, are based
at Atsugi. The third and fourth P-3C squadrons, at
Hachinohe, were equipped in 1985-86, a fifth at Shimofusa
in 1987 and a sixth at Kanoya in 1989. Two aircraft, ordered
in FYs 1987 and 1988, are equipped as EP-3 electronic
surveillance versions. Kawasaki is responsible for building
P-3C centre-fuselages, and for final assembly and flight
testing. Participants in the programme include Fuji,
Mitsubishi, Nippi and Shin Meiwa for the airframe, and
IHI for the engines.

For possible future procurement, Kawasaki has proposed
a number of variants to the Japan Defence Agency
including an improved ASW version, ocean surveillance
version, electronic warfare trainer, a military transport and
a systems testbed.

KAWASAKI T-4
Kawasaki was named by the Japan Defence Agency on 4
September 1981 as the prime contractor to develop a new
intermediate trainer to replace Lockheed T-33As and Fuji
T-1A/Bs in service with the JASDF. The designation XT-4
was allocated officially to the type during its development.

Current plans call for procurement of about 200
production T-4s, for pilot training, liaison and other duties.
Funding was approved in the FY 1983 and 1984 defence
budgets to procure four flying prototypes. A total of 91
production aircraft had been ordered up to and including
FY 1990.

The T-4 is based on Kawasaki's KA-851 design, by an
engineering team led by Mr Kohki Isozaki. Mitsubishi
(centre fuselage and engine air intakes) and Fuji (rear
fuselage, wings and tail unit) each have a 30 per cent share in
the production programme. Kawasaki, as prime contractor,
builds the forward fuselage, and is responsible for final
assembly and flight test.

The T-4 was required to have high subsonic manoeuvrability, and to be able to carry external loads under the
wings and fuselage. Basic design studies were completed in
October 1982, and prototype construction began in April
1984. The first XT-4 (56-5601) made its first flight on 29 July
1985, and all four prototypes were delivered between
December 1985 and July 1986, preceded by static and
fatigue test aircraft. Production began in FY 1986, and the
first T-4 made its initial flight on 28 June 1988. Deliveries
started on 20 September 1988, and the first 15 aircraft are in
service with the 31st Flying Training Squadron of the
JASDF's 1st Air Wing at Hamamatsu, near Tokyo; the
33rd and 35th FTS were due to receive T-4s during 1990. An
enhanced capability version has been proposed to the Japan
Defence Agency as a possible replacement for the
Mitsubishi T-2.

TYPE: Tandem two-seat intermediate jet trainer and liaison aircraft.

WINGS: Cantilever mid-wing monoplane. Supercritical aerofoil section, with thickness/chord ratios of 10.3 per cent (root) and 7.3 per cent (tip). Anhedral 7° from roots. Incidence 0°. Sweepback at quarter-chord 27° 30'. Extended chord on outer panels, giving a 'dog-tooth' leading-edge. Main structure of aluminium alloy, with slow crack growth characteristics. Double-slotted trailing-edge flaps of aluminium alloy with AFRP trailing-edges. Ailerons of plain hinged type, made of CFRP and fitted with Teijin hydraulically powered actuators. No tabs.

FUSELAGE: Conventional semi-monocoque structure (frames and longerons), mainly of aluminium alloy with minimum use of titanium in critical areas. Slow crack growth characteristics. CFRP airbrake on each side at rear.

TAIL UNIT: Cantilever structure, with sweepback on all surfaces. Fin and rudder are made of CFRP; all-moving anhedral tailplane is of aluminium alloy except for CFRP trailing-edge. Rudder and tailplane powered hydraulically via Mitsubishi servo actuators.

LANDING GEAR: Hydraulically retractable tricycle type, with Sumitomo oleo-pneumatic shock absorber in each unit. Single-wheel main units retract forward and inward; steerable nosewheel retracts forward. Bendix (Kayaba) mainwheels, tyre size 22 × 5.5-13.8, pressure 19.31 bars (280 lb/sq in); Bendix (Kayaba) nosewheel, tyre size 18 × 4.4-11.6, pressure 12.76 bars (185 lb/sq in). Bendix (Kayaba) carbon brakes and Hydro-Aire (Sumitomo) anti-skid units on mainwheels.

POWER PLANT: Two 16.37 kN (3,680 lb st) Ishikawajima-Harima F3-IHI-30 turbofans, mounted side by side in centre-fuselage. Internal fuel in two 401.25 litre (106 US gallon; 88.3 Imp gallon) wing tanks and two Japanese built Goodyear rubber bag tanks in fuselage, one of 776 litres (205 US gallons; 170.7 Imp gallons) and one of 662.5 litres (175 US gallons; 145.7 Imp gallons). Total internal capacity 2,241 litres (592 US gallons; 493 Imp gallons). Single pressure refuelling point in outer wall of port engine air intake. Provision to carry one 450 litre (119 US gallon; 99 Imp gallon) Shin Meiwa drop tank on each underwing pylon. Oil capacity 5 litres (1.3 US gallons; 1.1 Imp gallons).

ACCOMMODATION: Crew of two in tandem in pressurised and air-conditioned cockpit with wraparound windscreen and one-piece sideways (to starboard) opening canopy. Dual controls standard; rear (instructor's) seat elevated 27 cm (10.6 in). UPC (Stencel) SHIS-3J ejection seats and Teledyne McCormick Selph canopy severance system, licence built by Daicel Chemical Industries. Baggage compartment in centre of fuselage, with external access via door on port side.

SYSTEMS: Shimadzu bootstrap type air-conditioning and pressurisation system (max differential 0.28 bars; 4.0 lb/sq in). Two independent hydraulic systems (one each for flight controls and utilities), each operating at 207 bars (3,000 lb/sq in) and each with separate air/fluid reservoir pressurised at 3.45 bars (50 lb/sq in). Flow rate of each hydraulic system 45 litres (12 US gallons; 10 Imp gallons)/min. No pneumatic system. Electrical system powered by two 9kW Shinko engine driven starter/generators. Tokyo Aircraft Instruments onboard oxygen generating system.

AVIONICS AND EQUIPMENT: Mitsubishi Electric J/ARC-53 UHF com, Nagano JRC J/AIC-103 intercom, Nippon Electric J/ARN-66 Tacan, Toyo Communication (Teledyne Electronics) J/APX-106 SIF, Japan Aviation Electronics (Honeywell) J/ASN-3 AHRS, Tokyo Keiki (Honeywell) J/ASK-1 air data computer, Shimadzu (Kaiser) J/AVQ-1 HUD, and Tokyo Aircraft Instrument J/ASH-3 VGH recorder.

ARMAMENT: No built-in armament. Two Nippi pylons under each wing for carriage of drop tanks (see Power Plant paragraph); one Nippi pylon under fuselage, on which can be carried target towing equipment, an ECM/chaff dispenser or an air sampling pod.

DIMENSIONS, EXTERNAL:
Wing span	9.94 m (32 ft 7½ in)
Wing chord: at root	3.11 m (10 ft 2½ in)
at tip	1.12 m (3 ft 8 in)
Wing aspect ratio	4.7
Length overall	13.00 m (42 ft 8 in)
Length of fuselage	11.96 m (39 ft 3 in)
Height overall	4.60 m (15 ft 1¼ in)
Tailplane span	4.40 m (14 ft 5¼ in)
Wheel track	3.20 m (10 ft 6 in)
Wheelbase	5.10 m (16 ft 9 in)

DIMENSIONS, INTERNAL:
Cockpit: Length	3.20 m (10 ft 6 in)
Max width	0.69 m (2 ft 3 in)
Max height	1.40 m (4 ft 7¼ in)

AREAS:
Wings, gross	21.00 m² (226.05 sq ft)
Ailerons (total)	1.51 m² (16.25 sq ft)
Trailing-edge flaps (total)	2.93 m² (31.54 sq ft)
Fin	3.78 m² (40.69 sq ft)
Rudder	0.91 m² (9.80 sq ft)
Tailplane	6.04 m² (65.02 sq ft)

WEIGHTS:
Weight empty	3,700 kg (8,157 lb)

Kawasaki T-4 twin-turbofan intermediate trainers of the Japan Air Self-Defence Force

Kawasaki T-4 trainer (two Ishikawajima-Harima F3-IHI-30 turbofans) *(Pilot Press)*

T-O weight, clean	5,500 kg (12,125 lb)
Max design T-O weight	7,500 kg (16,535 lb)

PERFORMANCE (in clean configuration. A: at weight of 4,700 kg; 10,361 lb with 50% fuel; B: at T-O weight of 5,500 kg; 12,125 lb):
Max level speed: A	Mach 0.9
Max level speed at S/L:	
A	560 knots (1,038 km/h; 645 mph)
Cruising speed: B	Mach 0.75
Stalling speed: A	90 knots (167 km/h; 104 mph)
Max rate of climb at S/L: B	3,050 m (10,000 ft)/min
Service ceiling: B	15,240 m (50,000 ft)
T-O run, 35°C: B	549 m (1,800 ft)
Landing run: A	670 m (2,200 ft)
Min ground turning radius	9.45 m (31 ft 0 in)
Range (B) at Mach 0.75 cruising speed:	
internal fuel only	700 nm (1,297 km; 806 miles)
with two 450 litre drop tanks	
	900 nm (1,668 km; 1,036 miles)
g limits	+7.33/-3

KAWASAKI KV107IIA

Kawasaki has exclusive rights to manufacture and sell the Boeing 107 Model II helicopter. The first KV107 to be produced by Kawasaki under this licence agreement flew for the first time in May 1962, and FAA type approval for this initial version was granted in November 1965. Details of the initial production KV107II models have been given in the 1984-85 and earlier editions of *Jane's*. Production of the KV107IIA was reportedly due to end in Spring 1990, after delivery of the last four A-5s to the JASDF.

The KV107IIA, introduced in 1968, has uprated turboshafts for improved performance during VTOL and in hot and high conditions. A prototype, converted from a standard KV107II-2, first flew on 3 April 1968. Type approval was granted by the JCAB on 26 September 1968 and by the FAA on 15 January 1969.

Since then, several versions of the KV107IIA have been produced, including the **A-2** (three built), **A-3** (seven for MCM: mine countermeasures duties with the JMSDF), **A-4** (18 as tactical transports for the JGSDF), **A-17** (one for Japanese Metropolitan Police), and a series of special missions **A-SM-1/-2/-3/-4** versions (16 in all) for Saudi Arabia. Details of these, which remain available, can be found in the 1987-88 and earlier editions of *Jane's*. Production in recent years has centred on the following version:

KV107IIA-5. Long-range search and rescue helicopter for JASDF. Total of 35 delivered by early 1990; four more due for delivery by March 1990. Extended-range fuel tank each side of fuselage, making total capacity 3,785 litres (1,000 US gallons; 833 Imp gallons). Extensive nav/com equipment, four searchlights, domed observation window and rescue hoist. Thirty-one have a Kawasaki/Boeing automatic flight control system.

A total of 160 KV107IIs and IIAs (all versions) had been delivered by 31 March 1990. The description which follows applies to the commercial KV107IIA-2, except where indicated:

TYPE: Twin-engined transport helicopter.

AIRFRAME: As described in 1989-90 *Jane's*.

POWER PLANT: Two 1,044 kW (1,400 shp) General Electric CT58-140-1 or Ishikawajima-Harima CT58-IHI-140-1 turboshafts (max continuous rating 932 kW; 1,250 shp), mounted side by side at base of rear rotor pylon. Fuel tanks in sponsons, capacity 1,324 litres (350 US gallons; 291 Imp gallons) standard. Extended range fuel tank on each side of fuselage of KV107IIA-4/5, increasing total capacity to 3,785 litres (1,000 US gallons; 833 Imp gallons). Other versions have provision for 632 litre (167 US gallon; 139 Imp gallon) auxiliary tank or 3,929 litre (1,038 US gallon; 864 Imp gallon) extended range tank in cabin.

ACCOMMODATION: Standard accommodation for two pilots, cabin attendant and 25 passengers in airliner version. Seats in eight rows, in pairs on port side and single seats on starboard side (two pairs at rear of cabin) with central aisle. Airliner fitted with parcel rack and a rollout baggage container, with capacity of approximately 680 kg (1,500 lb), located in underside of rear fuselage. Ramp of utility model is power operated on the ground or in flight and can be removed or left open to permit carriage of extra-long cargo.

AVIONICS AND EQUIPMENT: Standard avionics include stability augmentation system (SAS) and automatic speed trim system (AST). Optional avionics include automatic stabilisation equipment (ASE); automatic flight control system (AFCS); Doppler radar; radio altimeter; HF, VHF and UHF radio; ADF; VOR/ILS; Tacan; compass system; attitude director indicator system; and intercom system.

DIMENSIONS, EXTERNAL:

Rotor diameter (each)	15.24 m (50 ft 0 in)
Length overall, both rotors turning	25.40 m (83 ft 4 in)
Length of fuselage	13.59 m (44 ft 7 in)
Height to top of rear rotor head	5.13 m (16 ft 10 in)
Wheel track (c/l of shock struts)	3.94 m (12 ft 11 in)
Wheelbase	7.59 m (24 ft 11 in)

WEIGHTS:

Weight empty, equipped	5,250 kg (11,576 lb)
Max payload (at 8,618 kg; 19,000 lb T-O and landing weight)	3,172 kg (6,993 lb)
Fuel weight:	
standard sponson tanks	1,032 kg (2,275 lb)
auxiliary tank	493 kg (1,087 lb)
extended range tank	3,061 kg (6,748 lb)
Max T-O and landing weight	8,618 kg (19,000 lb)
	or 9,706 kg (21,400 lb)

PERFORMANCE (KV107IIA-2 at 8,618 kg; 19,000 lb AUW):

Never-exceed speed	146 knots (270 km/h; 168 mph)
Max level speed at S/L, normal rated power	137 knots (254 km/h; 158 mph)
Cruising speed at 1,525 m (5,000 ft)	130 knots (241 km/h; 150 mph)
Max rate of climb at S/L	625 m (2,050 ft)/min
Max vertical rate of climb at S/L	381 m (1,250 ft)/min
Service ceiling	5,180 m (17,000 ft)
Service ceiling, one engine out	1,740 m (5,700 ft)
Hovering ceiling: IGE	3,565 m (11,700 ft)
OGE	2,680 m (8,800 ft)
T-O to 15 m (50 ft)	131 m (430 ft)
Landing from 15 m (50 ft), one engine out	84 m (275 ft)
Range: standard fuel	192 nm (357 km; 222 miles)
max fuel	592 nm (1,097 km; 682 miles)

KAWASAKI (BOEING) CH-47 CHINOOK
JASDF/JGSDF designation: CH-47J

The FY 1984 defence budget approved the purchase of three Boeing CH-47 Chinook helicopters: two for the JGSDF and one for the JASDF, which have eventual requirements for 39 and 15 respectively. The first two aircraft, delivered in Spring 1986, were US built, the third was delivered in CKD (component knocked down) form for assembly in Japan. Kawasaki has been granted a licence for local manufacture of Chinooks ordered for the Japanese services; the Japanese version is generally similar to the CH-47D, and is designated CH-47J. The first CH-47Js for the JGSDF and JASDF were delivered in late 1986, and deliveries totalled 13 and seven respectively by 31 March 1990. The FY 1989 and 1990 budgets provided for 10 more for the JGSDF and four for the JASDF.

KAWASAKI (MCDONNELL DOUGLAS) MODEL 500D
JGSDF/JMSDF designation: OH-6D

The first Model 369D (500D) built by Kawasaki under licence from Hughes (now McDonnell Douglas) Helicopters was flown for the first time on 2 December 1977; JCAB Normal category certification was awarded on 20 April 1978. Nine Model 500Ds had been delivered for civil operation in Japan by March 1990. The JGSDF ordered 100 as OH-6Ds, all of which had been delivered by the end of March 1990; purchase of a further 11 approved for FY 1989 and 15 for FY 1990. The OH-6D was also selected by the JMSDF for the training role. Seven had been delivered by 31 March 1990; purchase of two more was approved in FY 1989.

Kawasaki KV107IIA-5 of the Japan Air Self-Defence Force

Kawasaki built Boeing CH-47J Chinook in JASDF camouflage *(Ivo Sturzenegger)*

Kawasaki (McDonnell Douglas) OH-6D light helicopter of the JGSDF *(Ivo Sturzenegger)*

MITSUBISHI
MITSUBISHI JUKOGYO KABUSHIKI KAISHA (Mitsubishi Heavy Industries Ltd)

5-1, Marunouchi 2-chome, Chiyoda-ku, Tokyo 100
Telephone: 81 (3) 212 3111
Telex: J22282 and J22443
NAGOYA AIRCRAFT WORKS: 10, Oye-cho, Minato-ku, Nagoya 455
PRESIDENT: Kentaro Aikawa
EXECUTIVE VICE-PRESIDENTS:
  Nobuichi Tsuruoka
  Yu Tashiro
  Takaaki Yamada (Managing Director, and General Manager of Aircraft and Special Vehicle Headquarters)
GENERAL MANAGER, AIRCRAFT DEPARTMENT:
  Tatsuji Tamaki

Mitsubishi began the production of aircraft in 1921, and manufactured 18,000 aircraft of approximately 100 different types prior to 1945, as well as 52,000 engines in the 1,000-2,500 hp range. The present Komaki South plant was built in 1952 and, together with the Oye and Komaki North plants, was later consolidated as Nagoya Aircraft Works, with a combined floor area of 552,463 m² (5,946,666 sq ft).

Mitsubishi was prime contractor for the T-2 supersonic trainer and F-1 close support combat aircraft for the JASDF, with Fuji, Nippi and Shin Meiwa as principal subcontractors. It is currently producing forward and rear fuselages for JMSDF Lockheed P-3C Orions, under subcontract to Kawasaki (which see). Other subcontract work includes manufacture of rear passenger cabin sections of the Boeing 767 jet transport. Part of this work is, in turn, subcontracted by Mitsubishi to Shin Meiwa. Mitsubishi also manufactures tailcones for the McDonnell Douglas DC-10 and MD-11, and wing trailing-edges for the MD-80 series of transports.

Mitsubishi's aero engine activities are described in the appropriate section of this edition.

MITSUBISHI F-4EJKai

In co-operation with Kawasaki as subcontractor, Mitsubishi was the JDA's prime contractor in producing F-4EJ Phantom tactical fighters for the JASDF, under licence from McDonnell Douglas Corporation. The last of 140 F-4EJs was delivered to the JASDF on 20 May 1981; Mitsubishi is engaged currently in a major programme to update F-4EJ equipment and weapon systems. The prototype F-4EJKai (07-8431) was first flown on 17 July 1984 and delivered on the following 13 December. It has a Westinghouse AN/APG-66J fire control system, advanced avionics which include a Litton LN-39 INS, head-up display, and J/APR-4Kai radar warning receiver, lookdown/shootdown capability with AIM-7E/F Sparrows or AIM-9P/L Sidewinders, and can carry two ASM-1 anti-shipping missiles. Current plans are to convert 100 of the JASDF's 125 remaining F-4EJs to F-4EJKai configuration and another 17 to RF-4EJ reconnaissance-fighters. Work has begun on an initial batch of 45 F-4EJKai conversions, of which the first five were due to be redelivered to the JASDF by the end of March 1990. Some of the upgraded aircraft are now expected to be allocated to close air support rather than interceptor duties.

Mitsubishi Electric is in charge of the RF-4EJ conversion programme, which will utilise a development by its Melco subsidiary of an elint pod derived from the Thomson-CSF Astac system fitted to French Air Force Mirage F1-CRs. Conversion will also include a converter and new computer to render the digital pods compatible with the F-4's analog systems, and a TRT radar altimeter.

MITSUBISHI (MCDONNELL DOUGLAS) F-15J and F-15DJ EAGLE

The Japan Defence Agency plans to procure a total of 187 McDonnell Douglas F-15 Eagles, including 14 US built aircraft (two single-seat F-15Js and 12 two-seat F-15DJs). The two US built F-15Js were followed by eight assembled in Japan from US supplied knocked-down assemblies. First aircraft of the latter batch flew on 26 August 1981 and was delivered on 11 December that year. A total of 157 F-15J/DJs had been funded up to FY 1989, and a further 10 were approved in FY 1990. Approx 100 had been delivered by the Spring of 1988.

First JASDF F-15 squadron was No. 202 (5th Air Wing) at Nyutabaru, which was activated in December 1982 with 20 F-15J/DJs. Other units now equipped are No. 201 and No. 203 Squadron of the 2nd Air Wing at Chitose, Hokkaido; No. 204 (7th Air Wing, at Hyakuri); and Nos. 205 and 303 (6th Air Wing, Komatsu). Mitsubishi is building the forward and centre-fuselages, and is responsible for final assembly and flight testing. Participants in the programme include Fuji (landing gear doors), Kawasaki (wings and tail assembly), Nippi (pylons and missile launchers), Shin Meiwa (drop tanks), Sumitomo (landing gear), and IHI (engines). The J/ALQ-8 ECM and radar warning systems of all these aircraft are of Japanese design and manufacture.

MITSUBISHI FS-X

Under the programme title FS-X, the Japan Defence Agency examined a number of alternative options for a successor to the Mitsubishi F-1 close support fighter. Eventually, derivatives of the F-15 and F/A-18, and a proposal to develop a wholly indigenous Japanese design, were rejected in October 1987 in favour of a derivative of the General Dynamics F-16C Fighting Falcon. Initial airframe and radar design contracts were awarded by the JDA in March 1990.

The FS-X will be developed jointly by GD and a Japanese industry team headed by Mitsubishi as prime contractor. Other Japanese airframe companies involved will include Kawasaki and Fuji. The active phased-array radar, EW (ECM/ESM) mission computer and IRS will be developed using Japanese domestic technology. Japan will be totally responsible for the FS-X programme, including all funding, and will subcontract approx 40 per cent of the work to US companies.

The FS-X will have a new wing, of Japanese design and all-composites co-cured construction, with a greater area than that of the F-16, and a lengthened nose to accommodate the additional mission avionics. It will have a longer rear fuselage than the F-16, containing a 129 kN (29,000 lb st) class afterburning turbofan; ventral canard surfaces will flank the air intake duct. Candidate engines are the General Electric F110-GE-129 and Pratt & Whitney F100-PW-229. Armament is expected to include Mitsubishi AAM-3 air-to-air missiles and Mitsubishi XASM-2 air-to-ship missiles.

MITSUBISHI (SIKORSKY) S-61

Mitsubishi holds licence agreements to manufacture the Sikorsky S-61, S-61B (HSS-2/2A/2B) and S-61A helicopters. Between 1 April 1989 and 31 March 1990 Mitsubishi delivered 17 HSS-2Bs (for ASW) to the JMSDF. By the latter date it had delivered to the JMSDF, for ASW and rescue, 167 helicopters of the HSS-2 series and 17 S-61As, out of a total order for 185 HSS-2/2A/2B/S-61As. The final S-61A was approved in the FY 1988 budget and was due for delivery by May 1990.

MITSUBISHI (SIKORSKY) SH-60J and UH-60J

Detailed design work on this S-70B-3 developed version of the Sikorsky SH-60B Seahawk anti-submarine helicopter, to meet the specific requirements of the JMSDF, was funded under the FY 1983 budget. Japanese avionics and equipment, including ring laser gyro AHRS, data link, tactical data processing and automatic flight management systems, are integrated by the Technical Research and Development Institute of the Japan Defence Agency. The first of two prototype XSH-60Js, based on imported airframes, flew for the first time on 31 August 1987. These two aircraft are now undergoing evaluation by the 51st Air

Artist's impression of the Mitsubishi FS-X fighter derived from the General Dynamics F-16C

Mitsubishi built Sikorsky HSS-2Bs of the JMSDF *(Ivo Sturzenegger)*

Second prototype Mitsubishi (Sikorsky) XSH-60J anti-submarine helicopter

Unit of the JMSDF at Atsugi. The JMSDF has a requirement for 80-100 SH-60Js, the first 12 of which were funded in FY 1989 and a further 11 in FY 1990.

Mitsubishi is also prime contractor for the licence assembly of 40 Sikorsky UH-60J helicopters to be procured

for search and rescue duties with the JASDF. The first three UH-60Js were ordered in FY 1988 and were due to be delivered by 31 March 1990. Two more were funded in FY 1989, and another two in FY 1990. In addition, three UH-60Js for the JMSDF were funded in FY 1989.

NAL
NATIONAL AEROSPACE LABORATORY
7-44-1 Jindaijihigashi-machi, Chofu City, Tokyo 182
Telephone: 81 (422) 47 5911
DIRECTOR-GENERAL: Hideo Nagasu
DEPUTY DIRECTOR-GENERAL: Dr Kazuyuki Takeuchi

The National Aerospace Laboratory (NAL) is a government establishment responsible for research and development in the field of aeronautical and space sciences. Since 1962 it has extended its activity in the field of V/STOL techniques.

NAL ASUKA
The Asuka was a large experimental STOL transport aircraft developed by the NAL. It first flew on 28 October 1985 and completed its test programme during 1989. The

aircraft was based upon the airframe of the Kawasaki C-1 tactical transport, with the two Pratt & Whitney JT8D engines replaced by four MITI/NAL FJR710/600S high bypass ratio turbofans, installed above and far ahead of the wing leading-edges in nacelles with upper surface blowing (USB); wing leading-edge and aileron boundary layer control systems; inboard flaps replaced by USB flaps; structural strengthening of the fuselage and landing gear; and a digital stability and control augmentation system.

Data obtained from the flight test programme will, it is hoped, enable NAL to develop, in co-operation with the Japanese aerospace industry, a commercial STOL transport aircraft able to operate from 800 m (2,625 ft) runways with 150 passengers. In its first STOL landing, on 23 March 1988, the prototype required a ground run of only 439 m (1,440 ft).

A full description of the Asuka, and a three-view drawing, were published in the 1986-87 *Jane's*, and a shortened version in the 1988-89 and 1989-90 editions.

NAL SPACEPLANE STUDIES
The NAL is assisting in the study programme for a possible future Japanese spaceplane, and has tunnel tested a number of alternative configurations since about 1982. In 1988 it received a Dornier 228-200 to be used for simulation of the final approach and landing phases of an eventual spaceplane. This aircraft is equipped with INS, GPS, and a special work station from which its flight characteristics can be changed and controlled by computers. An extensive system study on the single-stage-to-orbit (SSTO) aircraft has been carried out with the aid of computational fluid dynamics on the supercomputers. Researches on hypersonic air-breathing engines and lightweight high-temperature structures are also being conducted. Construction of a ramjet/scramjet engine test facility was initiated in April 1989 as a three-year plan, by partly remodelling an existing rocket engine high altitude test facility. Composite structure test facilities are also under construction for test and evaluation of advanced materials and structures.

NIPPI

NIHON HIKOKI KABUSHIKI KAISHA (Japan Aircraft Manufacturing Co Ltd)
3175 Showa-machi, Kanazawa-ku, Yokohama 236
Telephone: 81 (45) 773 5111
Telex: (3822) 267 NIPPI J
Fax: 81 (45) 771 1253
OTHER WORKS: Atsugi
PRESIDENT: Teruaki Yamada
EXECUTIVE MANAGING DIRECTOR:
Atsumasa Kubota (General Affairs and Public Relations)

Nippi's Yokohama plant has a floor area of 56,885 m² (612,325 sq ft) and employs about 1,000 persons. The Atsugi plant, which employs about 650 persons, has a floor area of 39,280 m² (422,820 sq ft). Kawasaki has a 25 per cent holding in Nippi.

The Yokohama plant manufactures wing in-spar ribs for the Boeing 767; elevators for the Boeing 757; components and assemblies for the Kawasaki built P-3C (engine nacelles) and T-4 (pylons) and Mitsubishi built F-15J (pylons and launchers); major dynamic components for the Kawasaki CH-47J; V-2500 engine ducts; shelters for

Mitsubishi built Patriot ground-to-air missiles; body structures for Japanese satellites; tail units for Japanese built rocket vehicles; and targets for the Japan Defence Agency.

The Atsugi plant is engaged chiefly in the overhaul, repair and maintenance of various types of aircraft and helicopters, including those of the Japan Defence Agency and Maritime Safety Agency, and carrier based aircraft of the US Navy.

SHIN MEIWA

SHIN MEIWA INDUSTRY CO LTD
Nippon Building, 6-2, Otemachi 2-chome, Chiyoda-ku, Tokyo 100
Telephone: 81 (3) 245 6611
Telex: 222 2431 SMIC T J
Fax: 81 (3) 245 6616
HEAD OFFICE: 1-5-25, Kosone-Cho, Nishinomiya-Shi, Hyogo-Ken
Telephone: 81 (798) 47 0331
Telex: 5644493
WORKS (AIRCRAFT DIVISION):
Konan and Tokushima
PRESIDENT: Shinji Tamagawa
EXECUTIVE MANAGING DIRECTOR, AND GENERAL MANAGER, AIRCRAFT DIVISION: Yukio Koya
SALES MANAGER AND PUBLIC RELATIONS:
Junpei Matsuo (Tokyo Office)

The former Kawanishi Aircraft Company became Shin Meiwa in 1949 and established itself as a major overhaul centre for Japanese and US military and commercial aircraft.

Shin Meiwa's principal activities concern overhaul work on flying-boats and amphibians. It manufactures drop tanks for the Kawasaki T-4 trainer, and in 1987 modified two Learjet 36As into U-36A naval fleet training support aircraft for the JMSDF.

Shin Meiwa also produces components for other aircraft, including underwing drop tanks for Mitsubishi built McDonnell Douglas F-15J Eagles; nose and tail cones, ailerons and trailing-edge flaps for the Kawasaki built Lockheed P-3C; wing and tail engine pylons for the McDonnell Douglas MD-11, under subcontract to Rohr Industries Inc; and components for the Boeing 767, under subcontract to Mitsubishi.

SHIN MEIWA SS-2A
JMSDF designation: US-1A

The **US-1** search and rescue amphibian first flew on 16 October 1974, and was described in the 1985-86 and earlier editions of *Jane's*.

The first US-1 was delivered on 5 March 1975, and 10 are now in service with No. 71 SAR Squadron of the JMSDF, based at Iwakuni and Atsugi. The last four of these aircraft are fitted with T64-IHI-10J turboprops, and are designated **US-1A**. The earlier aircraft were to be retrofitted with these engines. No other news of the US-1A has been received since 1986.

A full description of the US-1A can be found in the 1988-89 *Jane's*, with a shortened version in the 1989-90 edition.

JORDAN

JA

JORDAN AEROSPACE
c/o Jordan Technology Group, PO Box 5296, Amman
Telephone: 962 (6) 89160/2
Fax: 962 (6) 89161
PUBLIC RELATIONS MANAGER: Ms Rana Abu-Odeh

This company was established in 1989 to manufacture locally the Schweizer TH-330 helicopter and to market it in the Middle East and Africa. The company is owned jointly by Jordan Technology Group (50 per cent), Schweizer Aircraft Corporation (35 per cent) and the Cyprus based Aerospace Marketing Services (15 per cent). A description

of the Schweizer 330 can be found in the US section. Jordan Aerospace planned to produce 20 of these aircraft per year over an initial five-year period.

KOREA, SOUTH

DHI

DAEWOO HEAVY INDUSTRIES CO LTD
6 Mansok-dong, Tong-gu (PO Box 7955), Inchon 160
Telephone: 82 (32) 721011-16
Telex: 23301
MANAGING DIRECTOR, AEROSPACE PRODUCT DIVISION:
Hyo Sang Cho

Daewoo Heavy Industries began manufacturing aircraft components in 1985; current activities include producing components for the BAe Hawk jet trainer. More recent contracts are to manufacture main wings for the Lockheed P-7A maritime patrol aircraft and components for the Dornier 328 regional transport.

KA

KOREAN AIR
KAL Building, CPO Box 864, 41-3 Seosomun-Dong, Chung-Ku, Seoul
Telephone: 82 (2) 751 7114
Telex: KALHO K 27526
CHAIRMAN AND CHIEF EXECUTIVE OFFICER: C. H. Cho
PRESIDENT: C. K. Cho
Aerospace Division
Marine Center Building 18FL, 118-2-ka, Namdaemun-Ro, Chung-Ku, Seoul
Telephone: 82 (2) 771 66
Telex: KALHO K 27526 (SELDBKE)
Fax: 82 (2) 756 7929
SENIOR MANAGING VICE-PRESIDENT: Y. T. Shim
MANAGING VICE-PRESIDENT, MARKETING AND SALES:
J. K. Lee
Korean Institute of Aeronautical Technology (KIAT)
Address/telephone/telex/fax details as for Aerospace Division
RESEARCH ENGINEER: Chang Duk Hwang

Aerospace Division, one of several divisions of Korean Air, was established in 1976 to manufacture and develop aircraft. It is now a leading aircraft manufacturer in Korea. In early 1989 the Aerospace Division occupied a 64.75 ha (160 acre) site at Kim Hae, including a floor area of 130,065 m² (1.4 million sq ft), and had a workforce of about 1,800 people.

Since 1978, Korean Air has carried out the complete overhaul of Republic of Korea Air Force aircraft. Programmed depot maintenance of US military aircraft in the Pacific area, under US government contract, began in 1979 and has included structural repair of F-4 Phantom IIs, systems modifications for the F-16 Fighting Falcon, MSIP upgrading of the F-15 Eagle and overhaul of C-130 Hercules transports. KA plans a major expansion in its co-production and subcontract programmes, and began deliveries in April 1988 of wingtip extensions and flap track

fairings for the Boeing 747 and fuselage components for the McDonnell Douglas MD-11.

As a part of the Korean aircraft industry development programme from 1988, Korean Air is engaged in developing microlight aircraft (see Sport Aircraft section), the five-seat Chang-Gong 91 cabin monoplane, and a modified Model 520MK light helicopter, derived from the Model 500, in association with McDonnell Douglas. Also projected is a primary trainer for the Korean Air Force, designated KTX-1. This would have a 298 kW (400 shp) turboprop engine, max T-O weight of 1,542 kg (3,400 lb), a cruising speed of 200 knots (370 km/h; 230 mph) and range of 720 nm (1,334 km; 829 miles).

KA (KIAT) CHANG-GONG 91 (BLUE SKY 91)

The name Chang-Gong has been applied to a number of projects undertaken by the KIAT division of Korean Air, the first two of which (Chang-Gong I and II) were adaptations of foreign microlight designs. Chang-Gong III, which made its first flight in the Autumn of 1988, was an experimental two-seat light aircraft built mainly of composites and powered by two 17.9 kW (24 hp) German piston engines. It was partly funded by two private companies (glassfibre and aluminium manufacturers), and is described as having possibly some limited domestic applications. No further details of the Chang-Gong III were known at the time of going to press.

Following these three projects, and benefiting from the experience gained from them, KIAT is now building a more ambitious design, the five-seat Chang-Gong 91 cabin monoplane illustrated in an accompanying three-view drawing. Construction of the prototype began on 21 June 1988, and it is scheduled to fly for the first time in February 1992. The following description applies to this aircraft:
TYPE: Four/five-seat light aircraft.
WINGS: Cantilever low-wing monoplane, with constant NACA 63₂-415 section and slightly tapered trailing-edges. Dihedral 6° from roots. Incidence 2°. Sweepback 0° 52' 48" at quarter-chord. All-metal single-spar fail-safe wings, with all-composite Frise ailerons and single-slotted

flaps on trailing-edges. Control surfaces actuated mechanically. No tabs.
FUSELAGE: Light alloy semi-monocoque structure, with glassfibre cowling panels and tailcone.
TAIL UNIT: Cantilever all-composites structure, with swept-back vertical and non-swept horizontal surfaces. One-piece all-moving tailplane, with large central servo tab. Balanced rudder, with ground adjustable tab. Control surfaces actuated mechanically.
LANDING GEAR: Non-retractable tricycle type, with single wheel, oleo-pneumatic shock absorber and speed fairing on each unit. Nosewheel steerable ±35°.
POWER PLANT: One 149 kW (200 hp) Textron Lycoming IO-360-C1C6 flat-four engine, driving a two-blade constant-speed propeller with spinner. Four removable fuel tanks in wings, inboard pair each having a capacity of 87 litres (23 US gallons; 19.1 Imp gallons) and outboard pair 53 litres (14 US gallons; 11.7 Imp gallons) each. Total fuel capacity 280 litres (74 US gallons; 61.6 Imp gallons). Refuelling points in wing upper surfaces. Oil capacity 7.6 litres (2 US gallons; 1.7 Imp gallons).
ACCOMMODATION: Side by side seats in front for pilot and one passenger. Second pair of seats behind these, to rear of which is a fifth (child's) seat. Space for 45.4 kg (100 lb) of baggage behind rearmost seat. Front-hinged, outward opening door at front on starboard side, over wing, and at rear (aft of wing) on port side. Entire accommodation ventilated.
SYSTEMS: 14V DC electrical system powered by engine driven alternator. No air-conditioning, oxygen, hydraulic or pneumatic systems.
AVIONICS: Bendix/King KX 155/165 Silver Crown com/nav.
DIMENSIONS, EXTERNAL:

Wing span	10.52 m (34 ft 6 in)
Wing chord: at root	1.66 m (5 ft 5½ in)
at tip	1.20 m (3 ft 11¼ in)
Wing aspect ratio	7.44
Length overall	7.74 m (25 ft 4¾ in)
Length of fuselage	7.08 m (23 ft 3 in)
Height overall	2.53 m (8 ft 3½ in)

Tailplane span	3.35 m (11 ft 0 in)
Wheel track	2.59 m (8 ft 6 in)
Wheelbase	1.71 m (5 ft 7¼ in)
Propeller diameter	1.89 m (6 ft 2½ in)
Passenger door (fwd, stbd):	
Height	1.86 m (6 ft 1¼ in)
Width	0.91 m (3 ft 0 in)
Height to sill	0.91 m (3 ft 0 in)
Passenger door (rear, port):	
Height	1.71 m (5 ft 7¼ in)
Width	0.66 m (2 ft 2 in)
Height to sill	0.70 m (2 ft 3½ in)

DIMENSIONS, INTERNAL:

Cabin: Max length	3.05 m (10 ft 0 in)
Max width	1.22 m (4 ft 0 in)
Max height	1.86 m (6 ft 1¼ in)
Floor area	3.41 m² (36.7 sq ft)
Volume	2.24 m³ (79.0 cu ft)
Baggage compartment volume	0.34 m³ (12.0 cu ft)

AREAS:

Wings, gross	14.86 m² (160.0 sq ft)
Ailerons (total)	1.24 m² (13.37 sq ft)
Trailing-edge flaps (total)	1.82 m² (19.60 sq ft)
Fin, incl dorsal fin	0.72 m² (7.70 sq ft)
Rudder	0.52 m² (5.60 sq ft)
Tailplane, incl tab	1.11 m² (11.90 sq ft)

WEIGHTS AND LOADINGS:

Basic operating weight empty	680 kg (1,500 lb)
Max fuel weight	181 kg (400 lb)
Max T-O weight	1,225 kg (2,700 lb)
Max wing loading	82.39 kg/m² (16.87 lb/sq ft)
Max power loading	8.22 kg/kW (13.50 lb/hp)

PERFORMANCE (estimated, at max T-O weight):

Max level speed at S/L	142 knots (263 km/h; 163 mph)
Max cruising speed at 1,525 m (5,000 ft)	131 knots (242 km/h; 150 mph)
Econ cruising speed (65% power) at 2,135 m (7,000 ft)	125 knots (231 km/h; 143 mph)
Stalling speed at S/L, 40° flap, power off	51 knots (95 km/h; 59 mph)

Korean Air Chang-Gong 91 five-seat cabin monoplane (*Jane's/Mike Keep*)

Max rate of climb at S/L	306 m (1,005 ft)/min
Service ceiling	4,575 m (15,000 ft)
T-O run	189 m (618 ft)
T-O to 15 m (50 ft)	281 m (921 ft)
Landing from 15 m (50 ft)	196 m (643 ft)
Landing run	164 m (536 ft)
Range at 2,135 m (7,000 ft), 159 kg (350 lb) fuel, 65% power	813 nm (1,506 km; 936 miles)

KA (MCDONNELL DOUGLAS) MODELS 500, 520 and 530

Korean Air has manufactured the McDonnell Douglas (originally Hughes) Models 500D and 500MD under licence from the US manufacturer since 1976, as described in earlier editions of *Jane's*. A total of 307 of these two models had been delivered by 1 January 1989. A new offset agreement was signed in 1984, under which KA has supplied McDonnell Douglas Helicopter Co with major fuselage assemblies for the commercial Models 500E and 530F. More than 170 shipsets of these two models had been delivered to the USA by 1 January 1989. Descriptions of the 500E and 530F can be found in the US section. A modified version of the Model 520, designated **520MK**, is under development.

KBHC
KOREA BELL HELICOPTER COMPANY
8-161 Hyorim-Li, Sapkyo-up, Yesan-kun, Chungchong-Namdo
Telephone: 82 (361) 458 37 1991/5
Fax: 82 (361) 458 37 1996
DIRECTOR: Y. H. Kim

SEOUL OFFICE: 1460-10 Hanjong Building, Sucho-dong, Sucho-ku, Seoul
Telephone: 82 (2) 585 1661/3 and 1881
Telex: K 25622
Fax: 82 (2) 587 1881
KBHC is a joint venture corporation between Bell Helicopter Textron (see US section) and Korea Technologies Corporation (KTC), a subsidiary of United Industries International that has represented Bell Helicopter and other US companies in Korea for many years. KBHC is licensed to repair, overhaul and modify Bell types, and to manufacture some components. Facilities are located at Yesan, south of Seoul. Depot level inspection, maintenance, overhaul and repair of military and civil Bell helicopters operating in Korea and the Pacific Rim area began in April 1988.

SAAC
SAMMI AGUSTA AEROSPACE COMPANY LTD
53rd Floor, DLI 63 Building, 60 Yoido-dong, Yeong-deungpo-ku, Seoul
Telephone: 82 (2) 7800032
Telex: K 22392/3
Fax: 82 (2) 7802918

PRESIDENT: Sil Dong Kim
SENIOR VICE-PRESIDENT: O. I. Romiti (Agusta)

Inaugurated on 22 May 1989, this Italo-Korean company is a joint venture by the Agusta group and Sammi Corporation, one of the major engineering industrial groups in South Korea. It was established to build the Agusta (SIAI-Marchetti) SF.600 Canguro twin-engined light transport in Korea and to market this aircraft in the Pacific basin area.

A new, modern 400,000 m² (4.3 million sq ft) aeronautical facility is to be built, which will have a workforce of about 400 people. In addition to Canguro production, the new company is intended to be responsible for the marketing and, eventually, local manufacture of the whole range of Agusta fixed-wing aircraft and helicopters.

SSA
SAMSUNG AEROSPACE
US OFFICE: 14251 East Firestone Boulevard (Suite 200), La Mirada, California 90638, USA
Telephone: 1 (213) 802 2211
Telex: 212588
Fax: 1 (213) 802 3011
INFORMATION: Ryan Kunchul Koh
Bell Helicopter Textron and Samsung Aerospace are joined in an agreement for future production of medium helicopters in Korea. Samsung, selected in 1986 as prime contractor for the Korean government's KF-X (McDonnell Douglas F/A-18 Hornet) fighter aircraft production programme, has received approval also to enter the helicopter business. The agreement with Bell calls for SSA to produce major fuselage and tailboom assemblies for the Bell Models 212 and 412SP, descriptions of which can be found under the Bell heading in the Canadian section. Initial production began in May 1988 and will continue until 1992. Bell and SSA have facilities to build complete helicopters at SSA's manufacturing centres in Changwon and Sacheon. Plans call for 93 per cent local manufacture by the early 1990s.

The KF-X fighter programme calls for South Korea to purchase 12 F/A-18s off the shelf, assemble 36 more from kits supplied by McDonnell Douglas, and to co-produce at least another 72 under supervision from the US manufacturer. SSA will be lead contractor in the co-production programme, with Daewoo and Hanjin as principal subcontractors.

NETHERLANDS

FOKKER
NV KONINKLIJKE NEDERLANDSE VLIEGTUIGFABRIEK FOKKER
CORPORATE CENTRE: PO Box 12222, 1100 AE Amsterdam-Zuidoost
Telephone: 31 (20) 6056666
Telex: 11526 FMHS NL
Fax: 31 (20) 6057015
CHAIRMAN: Martin Kuilman

OPERATING COMPANIES:
Fokker Aircraft BV, PO Box 12222, 1100 AE Amsterdam-Zuidoost
Telephone: 31 (20) 6056666
Telex: 11526 FMHS NL
Fax: 31 (20) 6057015
PRESIDENT: M. van der Veen
EXECUTIVE VICE-PRESIDENT, MARKETING AND SALES: C. H. Biersma

Fokker Aircraft Services BV, PO Box 3, 4630 AA Hoogerheide
Fokker Space and Systems BV, PO Box 12222, 1100 AE Amsterdam-Zuidoost
Fokker Special Products BV, PO Box 59, 7900 AB Hoogeveen
Aircraft Financing and Trading BV, PO Box 12222, 1100 AE Amsterdam-Zuidoost
Avio-Diepen BV, PO Box 5952, 2280 HZ Rijswijk

Royal Netherlands Aircraft Factories NV Fokker, founded by Anthony Fokker in 1919, forms the main aircraft industry in the Netherlands, employing some 12,700 people in 1990. Under a new company structure which became effective on 1 January 1987, Fokker comprises a corporate centre and six operating companies.

Fokker has an important share in the European manufacturing programme for the General Dynamics F-16 fighter, being responsible for component production and assembly of F-16s for the Netherlands (214), Denmark (12) and Pakistan (6). Seventy-two F-16s for Norway were delivered between January 1980 and June 1984 (see earlier editions of *Jane's*). Deliveries to the RNethAF began in June 1979, following the first flight by a Dutch assembled F-16 (J-259) on 3 May 1979. Deliveries totalled 189 to the RNethAF by 1 January 1990, and 12 to the Royal Danish Air Force. Altogether, Fokker is producing 1,440 centre-fuselages, 1,377 wing moving surfaces, 1,054 main landing gear doors, 526 main landing gear legs, 292 horizontal stabilisers, 688 rudders and 673 fin leading-edges (for Fokker's own assembly line, as well as for a similar line in Belgium and for General Dynamics, which manufactures F-16s for the USAF and for 'third nation' sales). Fokker-built F-16s for the RNethAF are being fitted with brake-chute housings in an extended fin root fairing. The first new aircraft so fitted was delivered to No. 315 Squadron on 30 June 1987; older aircraft will be modified later.

Some 5,500 people are employed at the Schiphol plant, Amsterdam, which accommodates the Fokker 50 and 100

Fokker 50 twin-turboprop transport (two Pratt & Whitney Canada PW125B engines) in the insignia of Busy Bee — Air Executive of Norway

and F-16 assembly lines and test flying facilities, and builds wing moving surfaces for Airbus Industrie. Also at Schiphol are the design offices, spare parts stores, research and development department, numerically controlled milling department, metal bonding department, electronics division, space integration and test facilities and scientific and administrative computer facilities.

The Drechtsteden plant, formed by the integrated production facilities at Dordrecht and Papendrecht, employs approx 2,200 people. Most of these are engaged on detail production and component assembly for the Fokker 50 and 100, F-16, Airbus A300/A310 and Shorts 330/360 and Sherpa.

At Ypenburg the installation of F-16 centre-fuselages is carried out by a workforce of 800 people. Composite material components for the Fokker 50, Fokker 100, Shorts 330/360/Sherpa and Airbus A300/A310, and radomes and fairings for the Westland Lynx helicopter, are manufactured at Ypenburg. A new 30,000 m² (322,917 sq ft) composites plant at Ypenburg was due to become fully operational in May 1990.

Woensdrecht (Fokker Aircraft Services BV), which has a current workforce of about 900, specialises in maintenance, overhaul, repair and modification of civil and military aircraft. Component production for the Patriot missile began in mid-1985. Also at Woensdrecht the ELMO plant (Fokker Aircraft), with a workforce of approx 600, produces electrical and electronic systems and cable harnesses.

Hoogeveen (Fokker Special Products BV) is engaged in all activities relating to industrial products such as licence programmes, shelters, missile launchers, pylons and fuel tanks. It employs about 600 people.

FOKKER 50

On 24 November 1983, to mark the 25th anniversary in airline service of the F27 Friendship, Fokker announced follow-on developments of both the F27 and the F28 Fellowship, to be known respectively as the Fokker 50 and Fokker 100. Both aircraft build on successfully proven airframes, but with significant design and structural changes, allied to more efficient (and more fuel-efficient) power plants, increased use of composite materials, greater passenger comfort and convenience, advanced digital avionics, and improved airport handling characteristics. In consequence, more than 80 per cent of the component parts of the Fokker 50 are new or modified by comparison with those of the F27.

The two prototypes utilised modified F27 fuselages rather than the redesigned fuselage of the production aircraft. The first of them (PH-OSO) flew for the first time on 28 December 1985, and the second (PH-OSI) on 30 April 1986; the first production Fokker 50 (PH-DMO) flew on 13 February 1987, and JAR 25 certification was granted by the Dutch RLD on 15 May 1987. FAA type approval (FAR 25) was awarded on 16 February 1989.

Differences from the F27 include new-technology engines, in redesigned nacelles, with six-blade propellers; use of carbon, aramid and glassfibre composites in such areas as the wings, tailplane, fin, radome, engine nacelles and propellers; passenger door relocated at the front of the aircraft, and the large cargo door deleted; more windows in the passenger cabin; newly designed cabin interior; extensive interior noise reduction; all-new cockpit design; a twin-wheel nose landing gear; latest technology systems; dedicated door concept; pneumatic system replaced by a hydraulic system; and a cruising speed some 12 per cent higher than that of the F27. Seating range is 46-58, with 50 as standard, but the cabin offers considerable flexibility for other layouts, including ample accommodation for baggage and freight. Studies for a stretched 50-200 are continuing. The production programme is shared with Dassault (centre and rear fuselage sections), Fuji (rudder and elevators), Deutsche Airbus (wing trailing-edges/control surfaces,

tailcone and dorsal fin), Sabca (outer wing skins and wingtips), and Dowty (propellers and landing gear).

Firm orders for 120 Fokker 50s had been received by 31 March 1990. Deliveries (to DLT) began on 7 August 1987 and totalled 74 by 31 March 1990. Thirty-one Fokker 50s were scheduled to be built in 1990.

TYPE: Twin-turboprop short-haul transport.

WINGS: Cantilever high-wing monoplane. Wing section NACA 64_4-421 (modified) at root, NACA 64_2-415 (modified) at tip. Outer panels have 2° 30′ dihedral and 2° washout. Incidence 3° 30′. No sweepback. All-metal riveted and metal-bonded two-spar stressed skin primary structure, consisting of centre-section and two detachable outer wings. Detachable AFRP leading-edges with rubber boot de-icers. Trailing-edge skins are of composite material, supported by ribs of composite or metal construction. Single-slotted all-metal trailing-edge flaps (two segments per wing, divided by engine nacelle), operated by spindle/drive-nut. Flaps are actuated hydraulically, with electrical backup system, and are mechanically interconnected. Aileron structure is formed by bonded skin/stringer assemblies riveted to front, centre and rear spars and ribs, with leading-edges of composite material. Ailerons are actuated mechanically via cables. Each has an inboard spring tab and outboard geared/balance tab; starboard balance tab serves also as an electrically operated trim tab. Horn balance, known as Foklet, of metal reinforced composites, at each wingtip to increase lateral stability at low airspeeds.

FUSELAGE: All-metal stressed skin primary structure, built to fail-safe principles, with cylindrical portions metal bonded and conical part riveted. Pressurised between rear bulkhead of nosewheel compartment and circular pressure bulkhead aft of baggage compartment. Nosecone, fairings, nosewheel doors, access doors and cabin floor are of composite materials.

TAIL UNIT: Cantilever fin and fixed incidence tailplane of all-metal primary construction. Leading-edges are made of composites and have integral pneumatic de-icing boots; part of dorsal fin also of composite material. Elevators and rudder (both built by Fuji in Japan) are cable actuated. Elevators are mechanically interconnected, with trim tab in starboard elevator. Rudder is provided with a trim tab, geared balance tab and horn balance.

LANDING GEAR: Retractable tricycle type of Dowty manufacture, with twin wheels on all units. Main units are attached to wings, retracting rearward hydraulically into

rear extension of engine nacelle; nosewheels retract forward. Long-stroke oleo-pneumatic shock absorber in each unit (single-stage on nose unit, double-acting on main units). Goodyear wheels and tyres on all units. Standard main unit tyres are size 34 × 10.75-R16, with pressure of 5.86 bars (85 lb/sq in); size 34 × 10.75-16 tyres, pressure 5.52 bars (80 lb/sq in), are optional. Nosewheel tyres are size 24 × 7.7-10, with pressure of 3.10 bars (45 lb/sq in). Goodyear hydraulic brakes, incorporating anti-skid system. Hydraulic nosewheel steering (±73°); free-castoring angle of ±130° available for towing.

POWER PLANT: Two 1,864 kW (2,500 shp) Pratt & Whitney Canada PW125B turboprops, each driving a Dowty six-blade propeller with spinner. Propellers have all-composite blades and Beta control. Lucas Aerospace 8.2 kW (11 hp) electric motor for engine starting. Composite materials used in construction of engine air intakes and nacelle cowlings. Fuel in two integral tanks located between the two spars of the central spar box outboard of the engine nacelle, with total standard capacity of 5,136 litres (1,357 US gallons; 1,130 Imp gallons). Single-point pressure refuelling and overwing gravity points. Engine air intakes, propeller blades and spinners de-iced electrically.

ACCOMMODATION: Crew of two and observer seat on flight deck, plus one cabin attendant. Second attendant seat optional. Two cabin configurations available: basic configuration with four cabin doors (also serving as Type I emergency exits), accommodating 50 passengers at 81 cm (32 in) pitch; or optional configuration with two cabin doors (Type I emergency exits), two Type III emergency exits and a dedicated cargo door, accommodating 54 seats at 81 cm (32 in) pitch. Both configurations have a four-abreast layout with an aisle width of 46 cm (18 in) and overhead stowage bins. Toilet, stowage area, passenger door with integral airstair (port side) and service door (starboard side) are at front of cabin. Baggage/cargo compartment at rear of cabin, with cargo door on starboard side. Aft cabin wall in optional configuration is movable, to create different baggage/cargo compartment volumes. Basic configuration has a forward baggage/cargo compartment and rear galley with two doors (one service and one cargo). Optional configuration has galley at front of cabin. Both configurations have alternative layouts with seats for up to 58 passengers. Entire accommodation pressurised and air-conditioned. Windscreens anti-iced electrically, flight

Fokker 50 twin-turboprop short-haul transport, with additional side view of proposed stretched 50-200
(Pilot Press)

deck side windows and cabin windows demisted by hot air.

SYSTEMS: Hamilton Standard air-conditioning system. AiResearch digital cabin pressure control system. Max pressure differential 0.38 bars (5.46 lb/sq in). Hydraulic system, operating at 207 bars (3,000 lb/sq in) pressure via two engine driven Abex pumps, for landing gear actuation, brakes, nosewheel steering and flap drive. Pneumatic de-icing of wing, fin and tailplane leading-edges, using engine bleed air. Primary electrical system powered by a Sundstrand 30/40kVA integrated drive generator mounted on propeller gearbox of each engine, supplying 115/200V three-phase AC at 400Hz, with two 300A transformer-rectifiers and two 43Ah nickel-cadmium batteries for 28V DC power. Sundstrand/Turbomach T62T-46C APU optional. Configured for ground use, APU (combined with a Sundstrand 115V 20kVA oil-cooled generator, accessory controls and provisions) provides AC self-sufficiency during turnaround cycles, servicing and maintenance. APU also provides air supply for flight deck and cabin air-conditioning. Unit is fitted to fireproof bulkhead aft of wheel bay in starboard nacelle.

AVIONICS: Flight deck has dual Honeywell EDZ-806 electronic flight instrument system (EFIS) with CRT displays for primary flight and navigation information, and space provisions for a central multifunction display. Standard avionics include Honeywell SPZ-600 AFCS with Cat. I landing (Cat. II landing optional); Honeywell FZ-500 dual flight director systems; Bendix/King dual Series III VHF com, single Series III ADF and DME (latter including frequency hold facility), and Series III ATC transponder; Honeywell Primus P-650 weather radar with dual presentation on EFIS; dual Bendix/King Series III VHF nav with VOR/ILS/marker beacon receiver; TRT AHV-530A (ARINC 552A) radio altimeter with dual presentation on EFIS; dual Litton LTR 81.01 AHRS; Sundstrand Mk II GPWS (ARINC 549); Honeywell AZ-800 air data computer; Fairchild A100 (ARINC 557) cockpit voice recorder; Collins 346-2B (ARINC 560) PA system; Sundstrand 980-4100 DXUS (ARINC 573) flight data recorder, incl underwater locator beacon; and Teledyne Model 70-275 flight data acquisition unit. Full provisions for Cat. II landing on AFCS, single Collins 628T-2A HF com to ARINC 559A2 and second ADF; space provisions for second DME, second ATC transponder, VLF-Omega/King KNS 660 nav system, and Dorne & Margolin ELT.

DIMENSIONS, EXTERNAL:

Wing span	29.00 m (95 ft 1¾ in)
Wing chord: at root	3.464 m (11 ft 4½ in)
at tip	1.40 m (4 ft 7 in)
Wing aspect ratio	12.0
Length overall	25.247 m (82 ft 10 in)
Fuselage: Max width	2.70 m (8 ft 10¼ in)
Height overall (static)	8.317 m (27 ft 3½ in)
Tailplane span	9.746 m (31 ft 11¾ in)
Wheel track	7.20 m (23 ft 7½ in)
Wheelbase	9.70 m (31 ft 10 in)
Propeller diameter	3.66 m (12 ft 0 in)
Propeller ground clearance	1.162 m (3 ft 9¾ in)
Propeller/fuselage clearance	0.593 m (1 ft 11¼ in)
Passenger door (fwd, port): Height	1.78 m (5 ft 10 in)
Width	0.76 m (2 ft 6 in)
Service door (rear, port) and cargo door (fwd, stbd), each:	
Height	1.27 m (4 ft 2 in)
Width	0.61 m (2 ft 0 in)
Cargo door (rear, stbd): Height	1.27 m (4 ft 2 in)
Width	0.86 m (2 ft 9¾ in)

DIMENSIONS, INTERNAL:

Cabin, excl flight deck: Length	15.96 m (52 ft 4 in)
Width at floor	2.11 m (6 ft 11 in)
Max width	2.50 m (8 ft 2½ in)
Max height	1.96 m (6 ft 5¼ in)
Floor area (excl toilet)	30.2 m² (325.0 sq ft)
Baggage/cargo volume (standard commuter version):	
main compartments	7.38 m³ (260.6 cu ft)
wardrobe compartment	0.82 m³ (29.0 cu ft)
overhead bins	2.22 m³ (78.4 cu ft)

AREAS:

Wings, gross	70.0 m² (753.5 sq ft)
Ailerons (total)	3.66 m² (39.40 sq ft)
Trailing-edge flaps (total)	17.15 m² (184.60 sq ft)
Fin, incl dorsal fin	17.60 m² (189.44 sq ft)
Rudder, incl tab	3.17 m² (34.12 sq ft)
Tailplane	16.00 m² (172.22 sq ft)
Elevators (total, incl tab)	3.17 m² (34.12 sq ft)

WEIGHTS:

Typical operating weight empty	12,520 kg (27,602 lb)
Max fuel load	4,123 kg (9,090 lb)
Max payload	6,080 kg (13,404 lb)
Max ramp weight: standard	19,990 kg (44,070 lb)
optional	20,820 kg (45,900 lb)
Max T-O weight: standard	19,950 kg (43,982 lb)
optional	20,820 kg (45,900 lb)
Max landing weight: standard	19,500 kg (42,990 lb)
optional	19,730 kg (43,500 lb)
Max zero-fuel weight	18,600 kg (41,000 lb)

PERFORMANCE:

Max operating Mach number	0.507
Typical cruising speed	282 knots (522 km/h; 325 mph)

Typical climb speed
200 knots (370 km/h; 230 mph) CAS
Typical descent speed
227 knots (420 km/h; 261 mph) CAS

Max operating altitude	7,620 m (25,000 ft)
Service ceiling, one engine out, AUW of 18,250 kg (40,234 lb), ISA	4,110 m (13,485 ft)
Min ground turning radius	18.07 m (59 ft 3½ in)

Runway LCN (51 cm; 20 in flexible pavement), 34 × 10.75-R16 tyres at 5.86 bars (85 lb/sq in):

AUW of 19,050 kg (42,000 lb)	16.9
AUW of 20,820 kg (45,900 lb)	18.4

T-O field length at S/L, ISA, 15° flap:

standard MTOW	1,200 m (3,937 ft)
optional MTOW	1,355 m (4,450 ft)

Landing field length at S/L, ISA, 35° flap:

standard MLW	1,120 m (3,675 ft)
optional MLW	1,130 m (3,710 ft)

Range with 50 passengers and baggage, reserves for 45 min continued cruise at long-range schedule* and 87 nm (161 km; 100 mile) diversion:
at standard MTOW:
high-speed* procedure
1,109 nm (2,055 km; 1,277 miles)
min fuel procedure 1,216 nm (2,253 km; 1,400 miles)
at optional MTOW:
high speed* procedure
1,523 nm (2,822 km; 1,754 miles)
min fuel procedure
1,665 nm (3,085 km; 1,917 miles)

* *relevant speed and altitude details not received*

OPERATIONAL NOISE LEVELS:

T-O	79.4 EPNdB
Approach	96.7 EPNdB
Sideline	85.2 EPNdB

FOKKER 50-200

Fokker revealed at the Paris Air Show in June 1989 that it was actively pursuing with interested customers a stretched version of the Fokker 50. The Fokker 50-200 would have a 3.00 m (9 ft 10 in) plug inserted in the forward fuselage and a 1.50 m (4 ft 11 in) plug at the rear, enabling it to seat 68 passengers at the standard 81 cm (32 in) pitch or a maximum of 80 in high-density configuration, with a strengthened wing structure to accommodate the higher operating weights. Availability of the 50-200 would also depend upon delivery rate of its Pratt & Whitney Canada PW130 engines; at current rate, the first 50-200s would be ready for delivery in 1994, given a 1990 go-ahead.

FOKKER 50 MARITIME AND SURVEILLANCE VERSIONS

The following maritime and surveillance variants of the Fokker 50 are available. No orders had been announced at the time of going to press.

Maritime Mk 2. Basic unarmed maritime patrol version, for duties which include coastal surveillance, search and rescue, and environmental control. Crew of up to six persons.

Maritime Enforcer Mk 2. Similar to Maritime Mk 2, but equipped for armed surveillance, anti-submarine and anti-shipping warfare, with enhanced avionics and provisions for carrying external stores (armament chosen and installed by operator).

TYPE: Twin-turboprop maritime patrol aircraft.

WINGS, FUSELAGE AND TAIL UNIT: As described for Fokker 50, except that airframe is heavily treated with anti-corrosive measures.

LANDING GEAR: As described for Fokker 50, but with mainwheel tyre pressures of 5.52 bars (80 lb/sq in) standard, or 4.50 bars (65 lb/sq in) for low pressure tyres. Nosewheel tyre pressure increased to 3.80 bars (55 lb/sq in).

POWER PLANT: As for Fokker 50, plus additional centre-wing fuel tank of 2,310 litres (610 US gallons; 508 Imp gallons) capacity, and two 938 litre (248 US gallon; 206.5 Imp gallon) tanks on underwing pylons, giving overall total fuel capacity of 9,322 litres (2,463 US gallons; 2,051 Imp gallons). Methyl bromide fire extinguishing system, with flame detectors.

ACCOMMODATION: Crew of two on flight deck, with folding seat for third crew member if required. Main cabin of Maritime Mk 2 fitted out as tactical compartment (for two to four operators), containing advanced avionics, galley, toilet and crew rest area. Enforcer accommodates crew of seven including two pilots; tactical co-ordinator (Tacco) responsible for off-airways navigation and overall efforts of mission crew; acoustic sensor operator (ASO) to handle active and passive sonobuoys, acoustic receivers and processor display system; non-acoustic sensor operator (NASO) controlling search radar and electronic surveillance subsystem; and two observers. Bubble windows for observers at front of main cabin. Rear cabin door is openable in flight.

SYSTEMS: Generally as described for Fokker 50, except that oxygen system includes individual supply for each tactical crew member.

AVIONICS AND EQUIPMENT: Com/nav equipment comprises AN/ARC-190(V) HF transceivers, two Bendix/King VCS-40 VHF transceivers, Elmer SRT-561 VHF/UHF transceiver (three in Enforcer), interphone, crew address

system, two Litton LTN-92 inertial navigation systems, air data computer, Bendix/King DFS-43 radio compass, two TRT AHV-530 radio altimeters, Collins DF-301E VHF/UHF direction finder, two Bendix/King VNS-41 VOR/ILS/marker beacon receivers, Honeywell EDZ-806 EFIS, Teledyne AN/APX-101 IFF transponder, dual Honeywell SPZ-600 AFCS, weather radar, low altitude warning system, and Tacan.

OPERATIONAL EQUIPMENT: Both versions fitted with Litton AN/APS-140(V) 360° search radar in ventral radome. Additional mission equipment in Enforcer includes Teledyne AN/ASN-150 central tactical computer and display system, radar detection and display system, on-top position indicator/receiver, dual sonobuoy signal receivers, and CDC AN/UYS-503 sonobuoy processing system. Both passive and active sonobuoys are carried (up to 40 of SSQ-36, SSQ-41B or SSQ-47B type, up to 120 smaller buoys, or a mixture of both sizes), and launched from the internal stores area in the rear of the cabin. General Instrument AN/ALR-606(V)3 electronic surveillance and monitoring equipment to detect radar transmissions, which can be classified and recorded and their bearings transferred to the tactical display. Infra-red detection system (IRDS). MAD. A data link with available ground or shipborne systems can be provided.

ARMAMENT (Maritime Enforcer Mk 2): Fokker installs Alkan stores management system and provisions for armament; weapon mix and purchase is up to customer. Two 907 kg (2,000 lb) stores attachments on the fuselage and three under each wing (capacities 295 kg; 650 lb inboard, 680 kg; 1,500 lb in centre, and 113 kg; 250 lb outboard). Typical ASW armament can include two or four Mk 44, Mk 46, Sting Ray or A244/S torpedoes and/or depth bombs. For anti-shipping warfare, two AM39 Exocet, AGM-65F Maverick, AGM-84A Harpoon, Sea Skua, Sea Eagle or similar air-to-surface missiles can be carried. Auxiliary fuel tanks can be carried on the central underwing pylons.

DIMENSIONS: As for Fokker 50

WEIGHTS AND LOADINGS (A: Maritime Mk 2, B: Maritime Enforcer Mk 2):

Operating weight empty: A	13,314 kg (29,352 lb)
B (typical)	14,796 kg (32,620 lb)
Max fuel (incl pylon tanks): A	7,257 kg (16,000 lb)
B	7,511 kg (16,560 lb)
Normal T-O weight: both	20,820 kg (45,900 lb)
Max T-O weight: both	21,545 kg (47,500 lb)
Emergency overload T-O weight:	
B	22,680 kg (50,000 lb)
Max landing weight: both	19,730 kg (43,500 lb)
Max zero-fuel weight: both	18,144 kg (40,000 lb)
Max wing loading: both	291.6 kg/m² (59.75 lb/sq ft)
Max power loading: both	6.39 kg/kW (10.5 lb/shp)

PERFORMANCE (at normal T-O weight except where indicated):

Normal cruising speed	259 knots (480 km/h; 298 mph)
Typical search speed at 610 m (2,000 ft)	150 knots (277 km/h; 172 mph)
Service ceiling: both	7,620 m (25,000 ft)
Service ceiling, one engine out: A	3,565 m (11,700 ft)

Runway LCN (42 per cent tyre deflection) at 15,875 kg (35,000 lb) AUW: A:

rigid pavement, L 76.2 cm (30 in)	10.4
flexible pavement, h 25.4 cm (10 in)	11.4
flexible pavement, h 12.7 cm (5 in)	9.0

Runway LCN (42 per cent tyre deflection) at 20,410 kg (45,000 lb) AUW: A:

rigid pavement, L 76.2 cm (30 in)	16.0
flexible pavement, h 25.4 cm (10 in)	14.8
flexible pavement, h 12.7 cm (5 in)	12.0

Runway CBR, unpaved soil, h 25.4 cm (10 in), 3,000 passes: A:

AUW of 15,875 kg (35,000 lb)	6.2%
AUW of 20,410 kg (45,000 lb)	7.8%

T-O run at S/L, AUW of 21,320 kg (47,000 lb):

ISA	1,525 m (5,000 ft)
ISA + 20°C	1,700 m (5,575 ft)

Landing distance (unfactored, ISA at S/L), landing weight of 18,990 kg (41,866 lb)   762 m (2,500 ft)

Max radius of action with 1,814 kg (4,000 lb) mission load   1,200 nm (2,224 km; 1,382 miles)

Max range, no reserves
3,680 nm (6,820 km; 4,237 miles)

Max endurance, reserves for 30 min hold, 5% fuel remaining   14 h 42 min

FOKKER 100

Announced simultaneously with the Fokker 50, the Fokker 100 is derived from the F28 Mk 4000, which it superseded on the production line. It has a longer fuselage, extended and much redesigned wings, Rolls-Royce Tay turbofans, a completely new CRT flight deck and cabin interior, and extensively modernised systems. The first prototype (PH-MKH) made its initial flight on 30 November 1986, and a second (PH-MKC) joined the flight test and certification programme on 25 February 1987, followed by the first series production aircraft (for the Ivory Coast Government) on 25 September 1987.

The Fokker 100 complies with the Stage 3 noise requirements of FAR Pt 36, and RLD certification to JAR Pt 25 was received on 20 November 1987, followed by Cat.

Fokker 100 twin-turbofan short/medium-range transport in the insignia of USAir

III autoland certification in June 1988. The first aircraft for Swissair made its initial flight on 30 December 1987, and was delivered on 29 February 1988. FAA type approval was granted on 30 May 1989, and certification of a version with uprated Tay Mk 650 engines, flown for the first time on PH-MKH on 8 June 1988, was received on 1 July 1989. First delivery of this version, to USAir, took place on the same day. Other options in this version include a new passenger door, large cargo doors, upper deck avionics and a polished outer skin.

The Fokker 100 is being produced in collaboration with Deutsche Airbus (large fuselage sections and tail section) and Shorts (wings); Grumman is subcontractor for the engine nacelles and thrust reversers, and Dowty for the landing gear. An agreement for IPTN of Indonesia to supply milled components and wing and tail components was announced in June 1988.

By 31 March 1990 firm orders for 224 Fokker 100s had been placed, of which 41 had been delivered. Thirty-five Fokker 100s were due for completion during 1990.

TYPE: Twin-turbofan short/medium-haul transport.

WINGS: Cantilever low-wing monoplane. Fokker designed, advanced transonic wing sections, which offer substantially improved aerodynamic efficiency, especially at high speeds. Thickness/chord ratio up to 12.3 per cent on inner panels, 9.6 per cent at tip. Dihedral 2° 30′. Sweepback at quarter-chord 17° 24′. Light alloy torsion box structure, comprising two-spar centre-section (integral with fuselage) and two outer panels with two main spars and auxiliary front spar. Fail-safe construction. Lower skin of outer wings made of three planks. Taper rolled top skin. Forged ribs in centre-section, built-up ribs in outer panels. Light alloy leading-edges, with hot air de-icing. Irreversible hydraulically operated ailerons. In the third mode, both ailerons are driven manually via servo tabs. Hydraulically operated double-slotted Fowler flaps with electrical alternative extension. Five-panel, hydraulically operated lift dumpers in front of flaps on each wing. Flaps and ailerons are of carbonfibre, spoilers and aileron servo tabs of aluminium alloy.

FUSELAGE: Circular-section semi-monocoque light alloy fail-safe structure, made up of skin panels with bonded Z-stringers. Bonded double plates at door and window cutouts. Quickly detachable sandwich floor panels (carbonfibre and glassfibre with Nomex core). Hydraulically operated metal airbrakes form rear end of fuselage. AFRP wing/fuselage fairing panels.

TAIL UNIT: Cantilever light alloy T structure, with hydraulically actuated variable incidence tailplane. Third mode is electric operation. Hydraulically boosted elevators, with manual backup. Hydraulically operated rudders, with manual third mode. Fin constructed from honeycomb sandwich skin panels in conjunction with multiple spars; dorsal fin of aramid fibre. Light alloy elevator, carbonfibre rudder. Hot air de-icing of tailplane leading-edge.

LANDING GEAR: Hydraulically retractable tricycle type, with twin wheels on each unit. Main units retract inward into wing/body fairing; nosewheel retracts forward. Dowty shock absorber in each unit. Goodyear tyres, size H40 × 14-19 on main units (pressure 9.38 bars; 136 lb/sq in), size 24 × 7.7-10 (pressure 5.86 bars; 85 lb/sq in) on nose unit. Loral multiple-disc carbon brakes, with anti-skid system. Steerable nose unit (effective angle ±76°).

POWER PLANT: Two 61.6 kN (13,850 lb st) Rolls-Royce Tay Mk 620 turbofans initially, fitted with thrust reversers and pylon mounted on sides of rear fuselage. Nacelles manufactured from composite materials. Option in 1989 of 67.2 kN (15,100 lb st) Tay Mk 650 turbofans. Fuel in

4,840 litre (1,278.5 US gallon; 1,064.5 Imp gallon) main tank in each wing and 3,140 litre (829.5 US gallon; 691 Imp gallon) tank (seven flexible cells) in wing centre-section, giving total standard internal capacity of 12,820 litres (3,386.5 US gallons; 2,820 Imp gallons). Refuelling point under starboard wing, near wing/fuselage belly fairing. Oil capacity (two engines) 23 kg (51 lb).

ACCOMMODATION: Crew of two on flight deck; three cabin attendants. Standard accommodation for 107 passengers, in five-abreast seating (3+2) at 81 cm (32 in) pitch. Optional layouts include 12 first class seats (four-abreast) at 91 cm (36 in) pitch plus 85 economy class (five-abreast) at 32 in; 55 business class at 86 cm (34 in) plus 50 economy class, all five-abreast; or 122 tourist class passengers at 74 cm (29 in) pitch. Reduced galley and stowage space in 122 seat layout. Standard layout includes two galleys, two toilets, two wardrobes, two other stowage/wardrobe compartments, and carry-on baggage compartment. Outward opening passenger door at front of cabin on port side, with outward opening service/emergency door opposite on starboard side. Optional auxiliary service door on port side near rear galley. Two overwing emergency exits (inward opening plug type) each side. Two underfloor baggage/cargo holds (one forward of wing, one aft), with three downward opening doors on starboard side. Option for three identical enlarged, upward opening cargo doors and a moving belt loading system. Entire accommodation air-conditioned.

SYSTEMS: AiResearch air-conditioning and pressurisation system. Two fully independent hydraulic systems for actuation of flight control surfaces, landing gear, brakes and nosewheel steering. AiResearch pneumatic system. Sundstrand integrated drive generator electrical supply system. Oxygen system for flight crew and passengers. AiResearch thermal anti-icing system for wings and tail unit. Electric anti-icing of flight deck windows, pitot tubes, static vents, angle of attack vanes and ice detector probe. Garrett GTCP 36-150R APU.

AVIONICS: Standard avionics include dual VHF com (to ARINC 716), PA system (ARINC 715), audio management system, ATC transponder (ARINC 718), triple AHRS (ARINC 705), dual radio altimeters (ARINC 707), dual VOR with marker beacon receiver (ARINC 711), dual ILS (ARINC 710), dual ADF

Fokker 100 stretched development of the F28 (two Rolls-Royce Tay turbofans) *(Pilot Press)*

(ARINC 712), dual DME (ARINC 709), Collins EFIS electronic display systems: primary flight display (PFD) and navigation display (ND) for each pilot, and multi-function display system (MFDS), consisting of two CRTs on centre instrument panel. EFIS and MFDS display units are identical in size. Dual digital air data systems (ARINC 706) with computer driven instruments, weather radar (ARINC 708 on ND), dual advanced flight management systems (AFMS), and Collins digital automatic flight control and augmentation system (AFCAS) for Cat. IIIA automatic landing plus full flight regime autothrottle system. (Cat. IIIB autoland certification completed in 1988.) Optional avionics include single or dual HF com (ARINC 719), third VHF com, Selcal (ARINC 714), second ATC, third ILS, third radio altimeter, music reproducer, ACARS, aircraft integrated data system, and Cat. IIIB autoland capability.

DIMENSIONS, EXTERNAL:

Wing span	28.08 m (92 ft 1½ in)
Wing chord: at root	5.28 m (17 ft 4 in)
at tip	1.26 m (4 ft 1½ in)
Wing aspect ratio	8.4
Length overall	35.53 m (116 ft 6¾ in)
Fuselage: Length	32.50 m (106 ft 7½ in)
Max diameter	3.30 m (10 ft 10 in)
Height overall	8.50 m (27 ft 10½ in)
Tailplane span	10.04 m (32 ft 11½ in)
Wheel track (c/l of shock struts)	5.04 m (16 ft 6½ in)
Wheelbase	14.01 m (45 ft 11½ in)
Passenger door (fwd, port): Height	2.21 m (7 ft 3 in)
Width	0.86 m (2 ft 9¾ in)
Service door (fwd, stbd): Height	1.28 m (4 ft 2½ in)
Width	0.61 m (2 ft 0 in)
Cargo compartment doors (fwd and rear, stbd):	
Height (each)	0.95 m (3 ft 1½ in)
Width (each)	0.90 m (2 ft 11½ in)
Height to sill (MTOW):	
fwd door at front	1.31 m (4 ft 3½ in)
fwd door at rear	1.37 m (4 ft 6 in)
rear door	1.46 m (4 ft 9½ in)
Overwing emergency exits (four, each):	
Height	0.91 m (3 ft 0 in)
Width	0.51 m (1 ft 8 in)

DIMENSIONS, INTERNAL:

Cabin, excl flight deck: Length	21.19 m (69 ft 6¼ in)

Max length of seating area	18.80 m (61 ft 8¼ in)
Max width	3.10 m (10 ft 2 in)
Width at floor	2.90 m (9 ft 6¼ in)
Max height	2.01 m (6 ft 7¼ in)
Max floor area	58.48 m² (629.5 sq ft)
Max volume	107.58 m³ (3,799 cu ft)
Overhead stowage bins (total)	5.23 m³ (184.7 cu ft)
Additional baggage space (total)	3.17 m³ (112.0 cu ft)
Underfloor compartment volume:	
fwd	9.72 m³ (343.3 cu ft)
rear	7.36 m³ (260 cu ft)

AREAS:

Wings, gross	93.5 m² (1,006.4 sq ft)
Ailerons (total)	3.528 m² (37.98 sq ft)
Trailing-edge flaps (total)	17.00 m² (182.99 sq ft)
Lift dumpers (total)	5.27 m² (56.73 sq ft)
Rudder	2.30 m² (24.76 sq ft)
Elevators (total)	5.71 m² (61.46 sq ft)
Airbrakes (total)	1.81 m² (19.48 sq ft)

WEIGHTS (A: basic weights, Tay 620; B: optional weights, Tay 650):
Typical operating weight empty:

A	24,375 kg (53,738 lb)
B	24,541 kg (54,103 lb)
Max payload (weight-limited): A	12,365 kg (27,260 lb)
B	12,199 kg (26,894 lb)
Max ramp weight: A	43,320 kg (95,500 lb)
B	44,680 kg (98,500 lb)
Max T-O weight: A	43,090 kg (95,000 lb)
B	44,452 kg (98,000 lb)
Max landing weight: A, B	39,915 kg (88,000 lb)
Max zero-fuel weight: A, B	36,740 kg (81,000 lb)

PERFORMANCE (A and B as for Weights):

Max operating Mach number	0.77
Max operating speed at 7,375 m (24,200 ft)	
	452 knots (837 km/h; 520 mph)
Approach speed at max landing weight	
	129 knots (239 km/h; 149 mph)
Service ceiling	10,670 m (35,000 ft)

FAR T-O field length at S/L, ISA, at max T-O weight:

A	1,840 m (6,037 ft)
B	1,717 m (5,634 ft)
FAR landing field length at max landing weight (S/L, ISA): A, B	1,400 m (4,594 ft)

Range with 107 passengers and baggage:

A	1,340 nm (2,483 km; 1,543 miles)
B	1,595 nm (2,956 km; 1,836 miles)

OPERATIONAL NOISE LEVELS (FAR Pt 36 and ICAO Annex 16):

Flyover: A	83.4 EPNdB
B	81.8 EPNdB
Approach: A	93.4 EPNdB
B	93.0 EPNdB
Sideline: A	89.3 EPNdB
B	91.7 EPNdB

NEW ZEALAND

PAC

PACIFIC AEROSPACE CORPORATION LIMITED

Private Bag HN 3027, Hamilton Airport, Hamilton
Telephone: 64 (71) 436 144
Telex: NZ 21242 PACORP
Fax: 64 (71) 436 134
CHIEF EXECUTIVE: Andrew Hyde
ENGINEERING MANAGER: Ron Guest
SALES MANAGER: Bob Geer

The former New Zealand Aerospace Industries Ltd was reconstituted on 1 July 1982 as Pacific Aerospace Corporation Ltd. PAC maintains full spares support for the Airtrainer CT4A/CT4B, Fletcher FU24-954 series and the Cresco 600. It is continuing to market the Fletcher FU24-954, Cresco 600, and new CT4C/CR variants of the Airtrainer. A new civilian version of the CT4B military trainer is also being marketed. PAC carries out phase servicing of BAC 167 Strikemasters and Bell Iroquois helicopters of the RNZAF, and continues to manufacture installation kits for the RNZAF's Project Kahu A-4 Skyhawk upgrade programme (which see).

Shareholding in PAC changed in late 1989, and is currently divided between ASTA of Australia (75.1 per cent, previously held by Agricultural Holdings) and Lockheed Corporation of the USA (24.9 per cent).

PAC FLETCHER FU24-954

The US built FU24 prototype flew in July 1954, followed by the first production aircraft five months later, as recorded in earlier editions of *Jane's*. Type certification was granted on 22 July 1955. All manufacturing and sales rights were transferred to New Zealand in 1964, and by January 1990 a total of 292 Fletcher FU24 series aircraft had been completed, including 62 for export to Australia, Bangladesh, Dubai, Iraq, Pakistan, Thailand, Uruguay and the USA. A factory refurbishment/upgrade programme is also offered by PAC for earlier FU24 aircraft.

A full description of the current standard production version, the FU24-954, can be found in the 1985-86 *Jane's*. The following is an abbreviated version of that entry:
TYPE: Agricultural and general purpose aircraft.
AIRFRAME: See 1985-86 *Jane's*.
POWER PLANT: One 298 kW (400 hp) Textron Lycoming IO-720-A1A or A1B flat-eight engine, driving a Hartzell HC-C3YR-1R/847SR three-blade constant-speed metal propeller with spinner. Fuel tanks in wing leading-edges; total usable capacity 254 litres (67 US gallons; 55.8 Imp gallons) normal, 481 litres (127 US gallons; 105.75 Imp gallons) with optional long-range tanks.
ACCOMMODATION (agricultural models): Enclosed cockpit for pilot and one passenger on side by side seats under rearward sliding canopy. Tinted windscreen and canopy side windows. Cockpit reinforced for overturn/crash protection. Large port side cargo door. Optional features include cockpit heating, additional cargo floor area and dual controls.
ACCOMMODATION (utility models): Enclosed cabin for pilot and up to seven passengers or equivalent freight. Dual controls and cockpit heating optional. Rearward sliding hood over front two seats. Large passenger/cargo door on port side.
AGRICULTURAL EQUIPMENT: Glassfibre hopper aft of cockpit, capacity 1,211 litres (320 US gallons; 266 Imp gallons) of liquid, 1,066 kg (2,350 lb) of dry chemicals. Hopper outlets for spreading of solids (fertiliser, dry ice, poison bait etc). Transland Swathmaster for topdressing, seeding and high-volume spraying. Transland Boommaster for liquid spraying with booms, nozzles, fan driven pump etc for low- and high-volume spraying. Micronair spraying equipment with electrically or fan driven pump, varied control systems, side loading valve for liquids, and special adaptor plate for interchangeability of equipment.

PAC Fletcher FU24-954 (Textron Lycoming IO-720 engine)

OPTIONAL EQUIPMENT (all models): Full blind-flying instrumentation with ADF, VHF, VOR and DME. Full dual controls; dual mainwheels and brakes, wheel and leg fairings; long-range fuel tanks; cabin heating and air-conditioning systems; metric instrumentation.

DIMENSIONS, EXTERNAL:

Wing span	12.81 m (42 ft 0 in)
Length overall	9.70 m (31 ft 10 in)
Height overall	2.84 m (9 ft 4 in)
Wheel track	3.71 m (12 ft 2 in)
Wheelbase	2.28 m (7 ft 6 in)
Propeller diameter	2.18 m (7 ft 2 in)

DIMENSIONS, INTERNAL:

Cabin: Length	3.18 m (10 ft 5 in)
Max width	1.22 m (4 ft 0 in)
Max height	1.27 m (4 ft 2 in)
Floor area	3.87 m² (41.7 sq ft)
Volume aft of hopper	3.37 m³ (119.0 cu ft)
Hopper volume	1.22 m³ (43.0 cu ft)

AREA:

Wings, gross	27.31 m² (294.0 sq ft)

WEIGHTS AND LOADINGS:

Weight empty, equipped	1,188 kg (2,620 lb)
Max disposable load (Agricultural)	1,275 kg (2,810 lb)
Normal max T-O weight	2,204 kg (4,860 lb)
Max Agricultural T-O weight	2,463 kg (5,430 lb)
Max cabin floor loading	1,884.6 kg/m² (386 lb/sq ft)
Wing loading at Normal max T-O weight	
	80.71 kg/m² (16.53 lb/sq ft)
Power loading at Normal max T-O weight	
	7.39 kg/kW (12.15 lb/hp)

PERFORMANCE (at Normal max T-O weight):

Never-exceed speed	143 knots (265 km/h; 165 mph)
Max level speed at S/L	126 knots (233 km/h; 145 mph)
Max cruising speed (75% power)	
	113 knots (209 km/h; 130 mph)
Operating speed for spraying (75% power)	
	90-115 knots (167-212 km/h; 104-132 mph)
Stalling speed:	
flaps up	55 knots (102 km/h; 64 mph)
flaps down	49 knots (91 km/h; 57 mph)
Max rate of climb at S/L	280 m (920 ft)/min
Service ceiling	4,875 m (16,000 ft)
T-O run	244 m (800 ft)
T-O to 15 m (50 ft)	372 m (1,220 ft)
Landing from 15 m (50 ft)	390 m (1,280 ft)
Landing run	207 m (680 ft)
Swath width (agricultural models):	
oily	23 m (75 ft)
aqueous	21.3-24.4 m (70-80 ft)
dust	7.6-15.2 m (25-50 ft)
Range with max normal fuel, 45 min reserves	
	383 nm (709 km; 441 miles)

PAC CRESCO 08-600

Design of this turboprop development of the FU24 began in 1977, and the prototype (ZK-LTP) first flew on 28 February 1979. The Cresco has many components interchangeable with the FU24-954, and its name is Latin for 'I grow'. The first production Cresco was flown in early 1980, and the type entered service in January 1982. Five, all for domestic customers, were completed by April 1986. Current production in early 1990 included three for Bangladesh, one equipped for agricultural roles and the other two in utility configuration, with passenger conversion kits supplied.

Marketing and support are continuing for the agricultural/utility and counter-insurgency versions, and a variant powered by a P&WC PT6A-27 or -34AG turboprop is under consideration.

The description of the FU24-954 applies also to the current production Cresco, except in the following respects:
TYPE: Turboprop powered agricultural and general purpose aircraft.
AIRFRAME: See 1986-87 *Jane's*.
POWER PLANT: One Textron Lycoming LTP 101-700A-1A turboprop, flat rated at 447 kW (599 shp) and driving a Hartzell HC-B3TN-3D/T10282 three-blade constant-speed metal propeller with spinner. Four fuel tanks in wing centre-section, total capacity 545.5 litres (144 US gallons; 120 Imp gallons). Two refuelling points in upper surface of each wing. Oil capacity 5.5 litres (1.4 US gallons; 1.2 Imp gallons). Chin mounted engine air intake, fitted with Centrisep filter panel.
ACCOMMODATION: Pilot only, or crew of two side by side, under rearward sliding bulged cockpit hood. Tinted windscreen and canopy side panels standard. Dual controls available optionally. Large forward hinged door, with window, aft of wing on port side. Generous cargo space immediately aft of hopper. Alternatively, in utility/cargo version with hopper removed, seats can be fitted for up to six additional passengers or 12 parachutists. Cockpit ventilated; heating system optional.
SYSTEMS: See 1986-87 *Jane's*.
AVIONICS: See 1986-87 *Jane's*.
AGRICULTURAL EQUIPMENT: Generally similar to FU24-954, except for substantially larger hopper, increasing capacity to 1,779 litres (470 US gallons; 391 Imp gallons) of liquid or 1,860 kg (4,100 lb) of dry chemical. Range of dispersal systems available to customer's requirements, from ultra-high-volume solids dispersal to ultra-low-volume spray.
DIMENSIONS, EXTERNAL:

Wing span	12.81 m (42 ft 0 in)
Length overall	11.07 m (36 ft 4 in)
Height overall	3.63 m (11 ft 10¾ in)
Wheelbase	2.77 m (9 ft 1¼ in)

PAC Cresco 08-600 (Textron Lycoming LTP 101-700A-1A turboprop) in COIN configuration

Propeller diameter	2.59 m (8 ft 6 in)
Cargo door (port): Height	0.94 m (3 ft 1 in)
Width	0.94 m (3 ft 1 in)
Height to sill	0.91 m (3 ft 0 in)

DIMENSIONS, INTERNAL:
Cargo compartment volume (aft of hopper)

	3.40 m³ (120.0 cu ft)
Hopper volume	1.77 m³ (62.5 cu ft)

AREA:

Wings, gross	27.31 m² (294.0 sq ft)

WEIGHTS AND LOADINGS:

Weight empty, equipped	1,270 kg (2,800 lb)
Max disposable load (Agricultural, incl fuel)	
	1,828 kg (4,030 lb)
Max fuel load	435 kg (960 lb)
Max T-O weight: Normal	2,925 kg (6,450 lb)
Agricultural	3,175 kg (7,000 lb)
Max landing weight	2,925 kg (6,450 lb)

Wing loading:
at Normal max T-O weight

	107.12 kg/m² (21.94 lb/sq ft)

at Agricultural max T-O weight

	116.25 kg/m² (23.81 lb/sq ft)

Power loading:

at Normal max T-O weight	6.55 kg/kW (10.77 lb/shp)
at Agricultural max T-O weight	
	7.11 kg/kW (11.69 lb/shp)

PERFORMANCE (at max Normal T-O weight, ISA, except where indicated):

Never-exceed speed	177 knots (328 km/h; 204 mph)
Max level speed at S/L	148 knots (274 km/h; 170 mph)
Max cruising speed (75% power)	
	133 knots (246 km/h; 153 mph)
Stalling speed at 2,767 kg (6,100 lb) AUW, flaps down, power off	52 knots (97 km/h; 60 mph)
Max rate of climb at S/L	379 m (1,245 ft)/min
Absolute ceiling	5,485 m (18,000 ft)
T-O run	323 m (1,058 ft)
T-O to 15 m (50 ft)	436 m (1,430 ft)
Landing from 15 m (50 ft)	500 m (1,640 ft)
Range at 3,175 kg (7,000 lb) MTOGW with standard fuel, no reserves	460 nm (852 km; 529 miles)

PAC AIRTRAINER CT4B, C and CR

The CT4 Airtrainer was a New Zealand redesign of the Australian Victa Airtourer and first flew in prototype form on 23 February 1972. A total of 96 CT4 series aircraft was built before production ceased in 1977.

PAC is now offering three variants, as follows:

CT4B. With 157 kW (210 hp) Teledyne Continental IO-360-HB flat-six engine: production line reopened for manufacture of civil versions, with military variants to follow.

CT4C. With 313 kW (420 shp) Allison 250-B17-0 turboprop replacing the 157 kW (210 hp) Continental IO-360-H flat-six piston engine of the CT4A/B. Non-retractable landing gear. Overall length increased. Prototype due to fly in late 1990.

CT4CR. As CT4C, but with retractable landing gear. (Phase 2 of CT4C conversion: prototype proposed in late 1991.)

TYPE: Two/three-seat fully aerobatic light training aircraft.
WINGS: Cantilever low-wing monoplane. Wing section NACA 23012 (modified) at root, NACA 4412 (modified) at tip. Dihedral 6° 45′ at chord line. Incidence 3° at root, 0° at tip. Root chord increased by forward sweep of the inboard leading-edges. Single main spar light alloy stressed skin structure, with glassfibre wingtips that are detachable to permit optional wingtip fuel tanks to be fitted. Single-slotted electrically actuated flap and aerodynamically balanced bottom-hinged aileron on each trailing-edge, of light alloy construction with fluted skins. No tabs.
FUSELAGE: All-metal stressed skin semi-monocoque structure. Glassfibre engine cowling.
TAIL UNIT: Cantilever light alloy structure, with some aerodynamic balance. One-piece elevator, statically balanced. Ground adjustable tab on rudder. Rudder controlled by rod and cable linkage, elevator by rod and mechanical linkage. Electrically actuated trim control for rudder and elevator.
LANDING GEAR: Tricycle type, retractable on CT4CR, non-retractable on CT4B and C. Non-retractable gear has cantilever spring steel main legs, and steerable nosewheel carried on telescopic strut and oleo shock absorber. Main units fitted with Dunlop Australia wheels and tubeless tyres size 6.00-6; nosewheel fitted with tubeless tyre size 5.00-5. Dunlop Australia single-disc toe operated hydraulic brakes, with hand operated parking lock. Landing gear designed to shear before any excess impact loading is transmitted to wing, to minimise structural damage in the event of a crash landing.
POWER PLANT: As given in individual model listings. CT4B has a total standard fuel capacity of 204.5 litres (54 US gallons; 45 Imp gallons). Wingtip tanks, each of 77 litres (20.5 US gallons; 17 Imp gallons) capacity, available optionally.

ACCOMMODATION: Two seats side by side under hinged, fully transparent Perspex canopy. Space to rear for optional third seat or 52 kg (115 lb) of baggage or equipment. Dual controls standard.

DIMENSIONS, EXTERNAL (all versions, except where indicated):

Wing span	7.92 m (26 ft 0 in)
Wing chord: at root	2.17 m (7 ft 1¼ in)
at tip	0.98 m (3 ft 2½ in)
Wing aspect ratio	5.25
Length overall: B	7.06 m (23 ft 2 in)
C, CR	7.14 m (23 ft 5 in)
Height overall	2.59 m (8 ft 6 in)
Fuselage: Max width	1.12 m (3 ft 8 in)
Max depth	1.40 m (4 ft 7¼ in)
Tailplane span	3.61 m (11 ft 10 in)
Wheel track	2.97 m (9 ft 9 in)
Wheelbase	1.71 m (5 ft 7⅜ in)

DIMENSIONS, INTERNAL (all versions):

Cabin: Length	2.74 m (9 ft 0 in)
Max width	1.08 m (3 ft 6½ in)
Max height	1.35 m (4 ft 5 in)

AREAS (all versions):

Wings, gross	11.98 m² (129.0 sq ft)
Ailerons (total)	1.07 m² (11.56 sq ft)
Flaps (total)	2.10 m² (22.60 sq ft)
Fin	0.60 m² (6.43 sq ft)
Rudder, incl tab	0.58 m² (6.26 sq ft)
Tailplane	1.43 m² (15.40 sq ft)
Elevator	1.26 m² (13.60 sq ft)

WEIGHT:

Max T-O weight (all)	1,202 kg (2,650 lb)

PERFORMANCE (estimated: C and CR at AUW of 1,111 kg; 2,450 lb):

Max level speed at S/L:	
C	205 knots (380 km/h; 236 mph)
CR	234 knots (434 km/h; 269 mph)
Max level speed at 3,050 m (10,000 ft):	
C	208 knots (385 km/h; 239 mph)
CR	240 knots (445 km/h; 276 mph)
Max level speed at 6,100 m (20,000 ft):	
C	195 knots (361 km/h; 224 mph)
CR	228 knots (422 km/h; 262 mph)
Stalling speed at S/L:	
flaps up: C, CR	57 knots (106 km/h; 66 mph)
flaps down: C, CR	44 knots (82 km/h; 51 mph)
Max rate of climb at S/L, ISA:	
C	843 m (2,765 ft)/min
CR	930 m (3,050 ft)/min
Service ceiling: CR	9,900 m (32,500 ft)
Time to 6,100 m (20,000 ft): CR	10 min 9 s
T-O run at S/L, ISA:	
C, CR	117 m (384 ft)
T-O to 15 m (50 ft) at S/L, ISA:	
C, CR	206 m (675 ft)
Landing run: CR	160 m (525 ft)
Range with max fuel (75% power), ISA, no reserves:	
at S/L: C	464 nm (860 km; 534 miles)
CR	529 nm (980 km; 609 miles)
at 3,050 m (10,000 ft): C	624 nm (1,156 km; 718 miles)
CR	724 nm (1,342 km; 834 miles)

PAC Airtrainer CT4C turboprop conversion of the CT4 *(Jane's/Mike Keep)*

RNZAF
ROYAL NEW ZEALAND AIR FORCE
Air Staff, Defence Headquarters, Stout Street, Wellington C1

Telephone: 64 (4) 726 499

Telex: 3513 DEF COM NZ

KAHU PROJECT MANAGER: Gp Capt James Barclay

RNZAF A-4 SKYHAWK UPGRADE

Under the project name Kahu (Maori for 'Hawk'), the RNZAF's fleet of 22 A-4 Skyhawks (17 A-4s and five TA-4s) is being upgraded and refurbished. Manufacturing and installation of the upgrade kits are carried out by New Zealand subcontractors Pacific Aerospace Corporation (PAC, which see) and Safe Air respectively.

The Kahu programme calls for the Skyhawks to be upgraded for their existing roles and also to receive improved capability for maritime roles and self-defence. It involves wing spar replacement, and the integration of a new avionics suite, combined with the ability to carry Maverick or AIM-9L Sidewinder missiles and GBU-16 laser guided bombs, and improved ESM/ECM. Main ingredients of the avionics upgrade are a modified Westinghouse AN/APG-66(NZ) radar, with capability for maritime target tracking added; a Litton LN-93 inertial navigation system, using ring laser gyros; a Ferranti 4510 series wide-angle HUD with video camera, and two head-down displays; new digital flight control system; addition of a radar warning receiver and chaff/flare dispenser; and cockpit redesigned for HOTAS (hands on throttle and stick) operation. The aircraft are completely rewired for compatibility with a MIL-STD-1553B data bus, and have growth potential for the future use of FLIR and night vision goggles if required.

A TA-4K 'prototype' of the Kahu-standard aircraft (NZ6254) flew for the first time on 7 June 1988, followed by a single-seat upgraded A-4K (NZ6205) in August 1988.

Handover of the first Project Kahu A-4 took place on 6 July 1989, and six modernised 'production' aircraft had been delivered to RNZAF Base Ohakea by the end of January 1990. Eight more were then undergoing modernisation, and the remaining seven were due to begin modernisation later,

concurrent with delivery of the second batch. Expected completion date for the final aircraft was October 1990.
AVIONICS: Include Westinghouse AN/APG-66 (NZ) radar; Collins AN/ARC-182 VHF/UHF and AN/ARC-159 UHF standby radios, VIR-130 VOR/ILS with glideslope

and AN/ARN-118 Tacan; Smiths AN/APN-194 radar altimeter; Hazeltine AN/APX-72 IFF; General Instruments AN/ALR-66 (VE) radar warning receiver; Garrett digital air data computer; and Goodyear AN/ALE-39 chaff/flare dispenser.

NIGERIA

AIEP
AERONAUTICAL INDUSTRIAL ENGINEERING AND PROJECT MANAGEMENT CO LTD
General Aviation Service Centre, PO Box 5662, Old Kaduna Airport
Telephone: 234 (62) 217573
Telex: 71327 AIEP NG

Fax: 234 (62) 217325
MANAGING DIRECTOR: G Hübner

AIEP AIR BEETLE
AIEP, in which Dornier GmbH of West Germany has a 60 per cent holding, has completed a prototype of this ab initio trainer, which had completed over 280 hours' flying by early 1990. It is believed to have made its first flight in

1988. Powered by a 134 kW (180 hp) Textron Lycoming flat-four engine, the Air Beetle is a variant of the US Van's RV-6 homebuilt (see Sport Aircraft section), reportedly differing only in being fitted with toe operated brakes for both occupants. After certification, the Air Beetle was expected to enter production to supplement the Nigerian Air Force's BAe Bulldog trainers.

PAKISTAN

PAC
PAKISTAN AERONAUTICAL COMPLEX
Kamra, District Attock
WORKS: F-6 Rebuild Factory, Mirage Rebuild Factory, and Aircraft Manufacturing Factory (all at Kamra)
Telephone: 92 (51) 580260/5
Telex: 5601 PAC KAMRA PK
Fax: 92 (51) 584162
DIRECTOR GENERAL:
Air Vice-Marshal Farooq Umar
MANAGING DIRECTORS:
Air Cdre Abdul Wahid (AMF)
Air Cdre Akbar Mehdi (MRF)
Air Cdre Shaukat Ali Khan (F-6RF)

Located approximately midway between Islamabad and Peshawar, the Pakistan Aeronautical Complex is an organ of the Pakistan Ministry of Defence. It comprises three factories, as follows:

The **Aircraft Manufacturing Factory** (AMF) came into operation in mid-1981, as licence production centre for the Saab Safari/Supporter two/three-seat light aircraft, which has the Pakistani name Mushshak (Urdu for 'proficient'). Progressive assembly of the first 92 of these aircraft began in 1976 from semi-knocked-down and completely knocked-down kits, and it is now being manufactured at Kamra from raw materials. By early 1990 a total of 191 Mushshaks were in service with various units of the Pakistan Army and Air Force, with output continuing at the rate of 16 a year. In 1988 flight testing began with a more powerful 156.6 kW (210 hp) Teledyne Continental TIO-360-MB engine installed, resulting in a considerable increase in performance, and in 1989 this version received US certification to FAR Pt 23. At least 100 of the uprated version are said to be required.

Major facilities at the AMF include equipment to manufacture all GFRP components of the Mushshak. Engines, instruments, electrical equipment and radios are imported, but almost all other items are manufactured locally.

The AMF is collaborating with NAMC in China in developing a new jet trainer known as the **Karakorum 8**, described under the NAMC/PAC heading in the International section.

The **Mirage Rebuild Factory** (MRF), which began operating in 1978, can accomplish complete overhaul of Mirage III/5 aircraft, Atar 9C turbojets, and all associated aircraft components and engine accessories. It has a current capacity for overhauling 8-10 aircraft and more than 50 engines per year. It can overhaul and rebuild third country Mirage III/5s, engines, components and accessories. Since 1988 the MRF has also overhauled Mirage aircraft of the United Arab Emirates Air Force. The facility is being upgraded to undertake improved life core (ILC) modification and overhaul of Pratt & Whitney F100-PW-200/220E turbofans, together with their engine jet fuel starter, and will soon have a limited capability to service and overhaul F-16 aircraft components. The MRF has a site area of more than 810,000 m² (8,715,000 sq ft) and a workforce of nearly 2,000 trained engineers and technicians.

The **F-6 Rebuild Factory**, or F-6RF, was established in 1980 for the primary purpose of overhauling the Pakistan Air Force's Chinese Shenyang F-6 aircraft and their accessories. It is authorised to manufacture about 4,000 spares items for that aircraft, and also produces the 1,140 litre (301 US gallon; 250 Imp gallon) auxiliary fuel tanks fitted to the F-6. The F-6RF possesses modern technical facilities for various engineering processes such as surface treatment, heat treatment, forging, casting, non-destructive testing, and other machine tools required to manufacture items from raw materials. The F-6RF has now begun overhaul of Pakistan Air Force FT-5s, FT-6s and A-5Cs. In due course it is expected to assume responsibility for the rebuild of Chinese F/FT-7 aircraft in PAF service.

Pakistan Air Force Mushshak refitted with Teledyne Continental TIO-360-MB flat-six engine of 156.6 kW (210 hp)

PAC (AMF) MUSHSHAK
As noted in the AMF paragraphs above, 191 Mushshaks had been delivered to the Pakistan Army and Air Force by early 1990, in the approximate ratio of 2 to 1. The 156.6 kW (210 hp) uprated variant, first flown in June 1988, was certificated in February 1989, and all new-production aircraft are now to this standard. It was reported in 1989 that about 20 Mushshaks had been ordered by the United Arab Emirates Air Force, and requirements by other countries were being discussed.

The following description applies to the initial production version with 149 kW (200 hp) power plant; no data were received for the higher powered version.
TYPE: Two/three-seat training and observation light aircraft.
WINGS: Braced shoulder-wing monoplane with single strut each side. Thickness/chord ratio 10 per cent. Dihedral 1° 30'. All-metal structure, sweptforward 5° from roots. Mass balanced all-metal ailerons. Electrically operated all-metal plain sealed flaps. Servo tab in starboard aileron.
FUSELAGE: Metal box structure. Glassfibre tailcone, engine cowling panels and wing strut/landing gear attachment fairings.
TAIL UNIT: Cantilever metal structure comprising swept fin and rudder and one-piece mass balanced horizontal 'stabilator' with large anti-servo and trimming tab. Glassfibre fin tip. Trim tab in rudder.
LANDING GEAR: Non-retractable tricycle type. Cantilever composite spring main legs. Goodyear 6.00-6 mainwheels and 5.00-5 steerable nosewheel. Cleveland disc brakes on main units.
POWER PLANT: One 149 kW (200 hp) Textron Lycoming IO-360-A1B6 flat-four engine, driving a Hartzell HC-C2YK-4F/FC7666A-2 two-blade constant-speed metal propeller with spinner. Two integral wing fuel tanks, total capacity 190 litres (50.2 US gallons; 41.8 Imp gallons). Oil capacity 7.5 litres (2.0 US gallons; 1.6 Imp gallons). From 10-20 s inverted flight (limited by oil system) permitted.
ACCOMMODATION: Side by side adjustable seats, with provision for back type or seat type parachutes, for two persons beneath fully transparent upward hinged canopy. Dual controls standard. Space aft of seats for 100 kg (220 lb) of baggage (with external access on port side) or, optionally, a rearward facing third seat. Upward hinged door, with window, beneath wing on port side. Cabin heated and ventilated.
SYSTEM: 28V 50A DC electrical system.
AVIONICS AND EQUIPMENT: Provision for full blind-flying instrumentation and radio. Landing light in nose.

ARMAMENT: Provision for six underwing attachment points, the inner two stressed to carry up to 150 kg (330 lb) each and the outer four up to 100 kg (220 lb) each. Possible armament loads include two 7.62 mm machine-gun pods, two pods each with seven 75 mm air-to-surface rockets, four pods each with seven 68 mm rockets, eighteen 75 mm rockets, or six wire guided anti-tank missiles.

DIMENSIONS, EXTERNAL:
Wing span	8.85 m (29 ft 0½ in)
Wing chord (outer panels, constant)	1.36 m (4 ft 5½ in)
Length overall	7.00 m (22 ft 11½ in)
Height overall	2.60 m (8 ft 6½ in)
Tailplane span	2.80 m (9 ft 2¼ in)
Wheel track	2.30 m (7 ft 6½ in)
Wheelbase	1.59 m (5 ft 2¾ in)
Propeller diameter	1.88 m (6 ft 2 in)
Cabin door (port): Height	0.78 m (2 ft 6¾ in)
Width	0.52 m (1 ft 8½ in)

DIMENSIONS, INTERNAL:
Cabin: Max width	1.10 m (3 ft 7¼ in)
Max height (from seat cushion)	1.00 m (3 ft 3¼ in)

AREAS:
Wings, gross	11.90 m² (128.1 sq ft)
Ailerons (total)	0.98 m² (10.55 sq ft)
Flaps (total)	1.55 m² (16.68 sq ft)
Fin	0.77 m² (8.29 sq ft)
Rudder, incl tab	0.73 m² (7.86 sq ft)
Horizontal tail surfaces (total)	2.10 m² (22.6 sq ft)

WEIGHTS:
Weight empty, equipped	646 kg (1,424 lb)
Max T-O weight: Normal	1,200 kg (2,645 lb)
Utility	1,125 kg (2,480 lb)
Aerobatic	900 kg (1,984 lb)

PERFORMANCE (at max T-O weight, Utility category):
Never-exceed speed	197 knots (365 km/h; 227 mph)
Max level speed at S/L	127 knots (236 km/h; 146 mph)
Cruising speed	112 knots (208 km/h; 129 mph)
Stalling speed, flaps down, power off	58 knots (107 km/h; 67 mph)
Max rate of climb at S/L	246 m (807 ft)/min
Time to 1,830 m (6,000 ft)	9 min 18 s
Service ceiling	4,100 m (13,450 ft)
T-O run	205 m (673 ft)
T-O to 15 m (50 ft)	385 m (1,263 ft)
Landing from 15 m (50 ft)	390 m (1,280 ft)
Landing run	155 m (509 ft)
Max endurance (65% power) at S/L, 10% reserves	5 h 10 min
g limits:	+4.4/-1.76 Utility
	+6/-3 Aerobatic

PERU

INDAER PERU

INDUSTRIA AERONAUTICA DEL PERU SA

Chinchon 1070, Lima 27
Telephone: 51 (14) 42 0355
Telex: 20125 PE MINAR
Fax: 51 (14) 42 4953
PRESIDENT: Alfredo Arrisueno
GENERAL MANAGER: Fernando Carulla

An early entry for Indaer Peru, the nation's sole aircraft manufacturer, last appeared in the 1985-86 *Jane's*. At that time, financial constraints had compelled abandonment of plans to assemble, and eventually manufacture, MB-339A jet trainers under licence from Aermacchi of Italy.

After studying the Peruvian civil aircraft inventory and the country's needs for a specific type of aircraft, as well as the potential markets domestically and external, especially in developing countries, it was decided instead to undertake a more modest programme for a general aviation aircraft that would provide an alternative to both microlights and the more expensive light aircraft. This has resulted in the Chuspi and Urpi designs described in the following entries.

In addition, Indaer Peru has signed agreements with Aero Boero of Argentina (which see) to produce the AB 115 and AB 180 in Peru, and with Pilatus (see Swiss section) for production of the PC-6 Turbo-Porter.

INDAER PERU IAP-001 CHUSPI (MOSQUITO)

Design of the prototype Chuspi, Indaer Peru's first production aircraft, was based upon those of such popular aircraft as the Light Aircraft Avid Flyer, Denney Kitfox, HAPI Cygnet and Piper Cub. It began in late 1986, criteria including a light structure with high fatigue life; gentle stall and flight characteristics; STOL capability, with steep angle of climb; wing designed to achieve low stalling speed; exceptional outward/downward view; ease of flying and maintenance; ability to operate from unprepared fields, and to adapt to float gear; and an adequate service ceiling for operation over the Andes.

The prototype was built by Indaer with the collaboration of the Escuela de Oficiales y Suboficiales of the Peruvian Air Force. It was unveiled in July 1987 and made it first flight, in Peruvian Air Force insignia, in the following month. Conceived initially as a multi-purpose aircraft for such duties as sport flying, dual control basic trainer, and (with a Louisiana Agrilites ULV system) cropspraying, the Chuspi entered series production in January 1988, the first production aircraft making its initial flight in September of that year. By the following month, 20 had been ordered: 12 by the Ministry of Transportation and eight, for agricultural use, by private farmers. The first 10 Chuspis had been completed by the end of 1989, and 12 had been delivered by late January 1990.

TYPE: Two-seat sport aircraft.
WINGS: Braced high-wing monoplane, with streamline section V struts each side. Thickness/chord ratio 12 per cent. Dihedral 2° 30'. Incidence 2° 30' at root, 0° at fifth rib. Two aluminium spars, I-beam plywood ribs, covered with heat-shrunk Dacron. Glassfibre wingtips. Full span aluminium flaperons, hinged at centre of pressure. Wings can be folded for transportation and storage.
FUSELAGE: Rectangular section welded structure of 4130 chrome molybdenum steel tube, covered with Dacron. Two-piece engine cowling of pre-moulded glassfibre.
TAIL UNIT: Welded structure of 4130 chromoly steel tube, covered with heat-shrunk Dacron. Sweptback fin, integral with fuselage; wire braced, non-swept fixed incidence tailplane.
LANDING GEAR: Choice of tailwheel or tricycle type, both non-retractable, with 4130 steel tube mainwheel Vs and side axles. Tyre sizes 8.00-6 (main), 5.00-5 (nose); pressure (all three) 1.38 bars (20 lb/sq in). Mainwheel drum brakes. Can be adapted to glassfibre or Edo inflatable floats, or skis.

IAP-001 Chuspi demonstrating the use of ULV cropspraying equipment

POWER PLANT: One 48 kW (64 hp) Rotax 532 LC two-cylinder piston engine, with twin carburettors and electric starter, driving a two-blade fixed-pitch spinnered propeller via a 2.58:1 planetary reduction gear. Standard fuel capacity of 45.4 litres (12 US gallons; 10 Imp gallons) in tank in starboard wing; second, optional tank of same capacity in port wing. Gravity refuelling point for each tank in wing upper surface. Oil capacity 0.95 litre (0.25 US gallon; 0.21 Imp gallon).
ACCOMMODATION: Two seats side by side, in fully enclosed cabin protected by rollover cage. Upward opening window/door on each side. Cabin heater optional.
SYSTEMS AND AVIONICS: Electrical system. VHF transceiver optional.
DIMENSIONS, EXTERNAL:

Wing span	9.15 m (30 ft 0¼ in)
Wing chord, constant	1.07 m (3 ft 6 in)
Wing aspect ratio	7.23
Length overall	5.20 m (17 ft 0¾ in)
Fuselage: Max width	3.26 m (10 ft 8¼ in)
Max depth	3.83 m (12 ft 6¾ in)
Width, wings folded	2.40 m (7 ft 10½ in)
Height overall (tail up)	1.75 m (5 ft 9 in)
Tailplane span	2.36 m (7 ft 9 in)
Wheel track	1.53 m (5 ft 0¼ in)
Wheelbase: tricycle version	1.00 m (3 ft 3¼ in)
tailwheel version	3.80 m (12 ft 5½ in)
Propeller diameter	1.83 m (6 ft 0 in)
Propeller ground clearance:	
tricycle version	0.16 m (6⅜ in)
tailwheel version	0.44 m (1 ft 5½ in)

DIMENSIONS, INTERNAL:

Cabin: Length	1.23 m (4 ft 0½ in)
Max width	0.99 m (3 ft 3 in)
Max height	1.17 m (3 ft 10 in)
Floor area	0.41 m² (4.42 sq ft)
Volume	1.42 m³ (50.1 cu ft)

AREAS:

Wings, gross	11.58 m² (124.6 sq ft)
Flaperons (total)	1.40 m² (15.07 sq ft)
Fin	0.507 m² (5.46 sq ft)
Rudder	0.339 m² (3.65 sq ft)
Tailplane	0.893 m² (9.61 sq ft)
Elevators (total)	0.680 m² (7.32 sq ft)

WEIGHTS AND LOADINGS:

Weight empty	214 kg (472 lb)
Max fuel weight: 1 tank	80 kg (176.5 lb)
2 tanks	160 kg (353 lb)
Max T-O weight	409 kg (901 lb)
Max wing loading	35.32 kg/m² (7.23 lb/sq ft)
Max power loading	8.58 kg/kW (14.09 lb/hp)

PERFORMANCE (A: single-seat at 322 kg; 710 lb AUW; B: two-seat at 392 kg; 864 lb):

Never-exceed speed: A, B	96 knots (177 km/h; 110 mph)
Max cruising speed: A, B	69 knots (129 km/h; 80 mph)
Stalling speed: A	22 knots (40 km/h; 25 mph)
B	28 knots (51 km/h; 32 mph)
Max rate of climb at S/L: A	427 m (1,400 ft)/min
B	293 m (960 ft)/min
Service ceiling: A	6,700 m (22,000 ft)
B	4,880 m (16,000 ft)
T-O run: A	30 m (99 ft)
B	50 m (164 ft)
T-O to 15 m (50 ft): A	70 m (230 ft)
B	150 m (493 ft)
Landing from 15 m (50 ft): A	110 m (361 ft)
B	180 m (591 ft)
Landing run: A	70 m (230 ft)
B	93 m (305 ft)
Range with max optional fuel:	
A, B	238 nm (441 km; 274 miles)
g limits	+3.8 (+5.8 ultimate)

INDAER PERU IAP-002 AG-CHUSPI

Due to an increasing domestic and foreign demand for an economical cropspraying aircraft, Indaer began to redesign the Chuspi in July 1989 to fulfil such a requirement. A prototype began flight testing in November 1989. The test programme was due to be completed in March 1990, enabling series production to begin in May.

The Ag-Chuspi is equipped with an 18-nozzle ultra-low-volume (ULV) spraybar system (nine nozzles each wing). To reduce drag and improve manoeuvrability for operations in small fields surrounded by trees and mountains, it carries its chemical payload in modified in-wing tanks. The starboard wing contains a 30.3 litre (8 US gallon; 6.7 Imp gallon) fuel tank, sufficient to allow two hours of operation with an adequate reserve, plus a 22.7 litre (6 US gallon; 5 Imp gallon) chemical tank. The port wing has a 53 litre (14 US gallon; 11.7 Imp gallon) chemical tank, giving a total load of 75.7 litres (20 US gallons; 16.7 Imp gallons) of chemical. In addition, the Ag-Chuspi differs in being a single-seater, with cabin width reduced to 0.89 m (2 ft 11 in). With appropriate specialised equipment, the Ag-Chuspi can also be used for seeding or fishery farm feeding.

INDAER PERU IAP-003 URPI (DOVE)

The Urpi is a reinforced and stretched version of the Chuspi, with a 0.51 m (1 ft 8 in) longer fuselage, wider (1.07 m; 3 ft 6 in) and more comfortable two-seat cabin, and a 56 kW (75 hp) Revmaster VW engine. It is intended for basic training, sport and flying club use, and highway/traffic patrol. Design was completed in November 1989, and first flight was expected in March 1990, followed by the start of series production three months later.

Two views of the Indaer Peru Chuspi: prototype (left) with tricycle landing gear, and (right) in 'taildragger' configuration with mainwheel speed fairings

PHILIPPINES

PAC

PHILIPPINE AIRCRAFT COMPANY INC

RPMCI Hangar, Manila Domestic Airport, PO Box 7633, Airport Airmail Exchange, Pasay City 1300, Metro Manila
Telephone: 63 (2) 832 3375 and 832 3380
Telex: 66621 WPAC PN
Fax: 63 (2) 833 0605
PRESIDENT: Rolando P. Moscardon
EXECUTIVE VICE-PRESIDENT AND GENERAL MANAGER:
Col Manuel B. Camacho (Ret'd)

It was announced in November 1987 that PAC Inc had concluded an agreement with Denney Aerocraft of the USA (see Sport Aircraft section) to manufacture, market and support the latter company's Kitfox two-seat single-engined homebuilt aircraft in the Western Pacific area. PAC also manufactures some parts and components for other US companies.

PAC SKYFOX

Local production of the Denney Kitfox, as the PAC Skyfox, began in early 1988, and four had been completed by February 1989. An airframe description of the Kitfox can be found in the Sport Aircraft section; the following details apply to the PAC Skyfox:
POWER PLANT: One 48 kW (64 hp) Rotax 532 LC two-cylinder piston engine, with electric starter, driving a two-blade propeller. Fuel capacity (two wing tanks) 45.5 litres (12 US gallons; 10 Imp gallons).

DIMENSIONS, EXTERNAL:
Wing span	9.55 m (31 ft 4 in)
Wing chord, constant	1.29 m (4 ft 3 in)
Wing aspect ratio	7.65
Length overall	5.21 m (17 ft 1 in)
Length, wings folded	6.40 m (21 ft 0 in)
Width, wings folded	2.39 m (7 ft 10 in)
Height overall	1.70 m (5 ft 7 in)
Wheel track	1.45 m (4 ft 9 in)
Wheelbase	3.86 m (12 ft 8 in)

First example of the PAC Skyfox version of the Denney Kitfox *(Anglo Philippine Aviation)*

AREA:
Wings, gross	11.92 m² (128.3 sq ft)

WEIGHTS:
Weight empty	190.5 kg (420 lb)
Max T-O weight	431 kg (950 lb)

PERFORMANCE (A: single-seat at 123.5 kg; 600 lb AUW, B: two-seat at 175 kg; 850 lb):
Never-exceed speed, and max level speed at S/L:	
A, B	86 knots (160 km/h; 100 mph)
Max cruising speed (75% power) at S/L:	
A	78 knots (145 km/h; 90 mph)
B	74 knots (137 km/h; 85 mph)
Stalling speed, power off, flaps up:	
A	28 knots (52 km/h; 32 mph)
B	33 knots (62 km/h; 38 mph)
Stalling speed, power on, flaps down:	
A	22 knots (41 km/h; 25 mph)
B	27 knots (49 km/h; 30 mph)
Max rate of climb at S/L: A	488 m (1,600 ft)/min
B	396 m (1,300 ft)/min
Service ceiling (approx): A	6,100 m (20,000 ft)
B	4,880 m (16,000 ft)
T-O run: A	15-23 m (50-75 ft)
B	19-28 m (60-90 ft)
Landing run: A	31-37 m (100-120 ft)
B	37-46 m (120-150 ft)
Range at 65% power: A	252 nm (467 km; 290 miles)
B	221 nm (410 km; 255 miles)

PADC

PHILIPPINE AEROSPACE DEVELOPMENT CORPORATION

MIA Road, Pasay, Metro Manila
POSTAL ADDRESS: PO Box 7395, Airmail Distribution Center, NAIA, Pasay City 1300
Telephone: 63 (2) 832 27 41 to 50
Telex: 63883 PADC PN and 66019 PADC PN
Fax: 63 (2) 8179742
PRESIDENT: Oscar M. Alejandro
EXECUTIVE VICE-PRESIDENT: Jose L. Bustamante
MARKETING DIRECTOR: Antonio S. Duarte

SUBSIDIARY:
Philippine Helicopter Services Inc (PHSI) (maintenance and overhaul of BO 105 helicopters; overhaul and repair of MDHC (Hughes) helicopter rotor blades; and repair of Zahnradfabrik Friedrichshafen AG products).

PADC is a government owned corporation established in 1973 to undertake business and development projects in the aviation and aerospace industry in the Philippines. It is engaged in the manufacture and assembly of **BO 105** helicopters and **Islander** light transport aircraft, under licence agreements with MBB of West Germany and Pilatus Britten-Norman of the UK respectively. By early 1989,

PADC had assembled 44 BO 105s and 65 Islanders (including 22 Islanders for the Philippine Air Force), and had manufactured the GFRP components for both types of aircraft.

PADC is the appointed area service centre for the Islander, and for Piper aircraft, Bendix/King com/nav equipment, and Allison 250 series turboprops. It is also engaged in the repair and overhaul of Textron Lycoming and Continental piston engines; propeller repair and overhaul; aircraft hangarage, repair and customising; aircraft and aero engine related accessories sales; spare parts sales; and repair and maintenance of Fokker F27 aircraft.

UDRD

UNIVERSAL DYNAMICS RESEARCH AND DEVELOPMENT

Penthouse, Zeta II Building, 191 Salcedo Street, Legaspi Village, Makati, Metro Manila
Telephone: 63 (2) 876 493
Telex: 66497 DEFCO PN or 23708 DEFCON PH
PRESIDENT: Capt Panfilo V. Villaruel

UDRD DEFIANT 300

Design of this attractive tandem two-seat aircraft was started in the early 1980s by the President of UDRD. When the prototype (RP-X239) made its initial flight on 24 February 1988, it was claimed to be the first new aircraft of all-Philippine design for 35 years.

The Defiant 300 has tapered, non-swept wings of NACA 2418 (root) and 2412 (tip) section, with 5° dihedral and 2° incidence, and a semi-monocoque fuselage. Construction is largely of locally grown hardwoods. A number of local businesses assisted the project with sponsorship, and assistance was also given by the Philippine Aerospace and Sciences Foundation. Applications foreseen for the Defiant include training, sport flying, reconnaissance/surveillance, counter-insurgency and agricultural use, and it was hoped to initiate series production once the aircraft had been certificated.
POWER PLANT: One 224 kW (300 hp) Textron Lycoming IO-540-K1B5 flat-six engine, driving a two-blade Hartzell FC8477A-4 aluminium propeller with spinner.

DIMENSIONS, EXTERNAL:
Wing span	9.52 m (31 ft 2¾ in)
Wing chord: at root	1.86 m (6 ft 1¼ in)
at tip	1.07 m (3 ft 6 in)
mean aerodynamic	1.49 m (4 ft 10¾ in)
Wing aspect ratio	7.2
Length overall	8.54 m (28 ft 0¼ in)
Height overall	3.73 m (12 ft 3 in)

AREA:
Wings, gross	12.55 m² (135.1 sq ft)

WEIGHTS:
Weight empty	1,278 kg (2,817 lb)

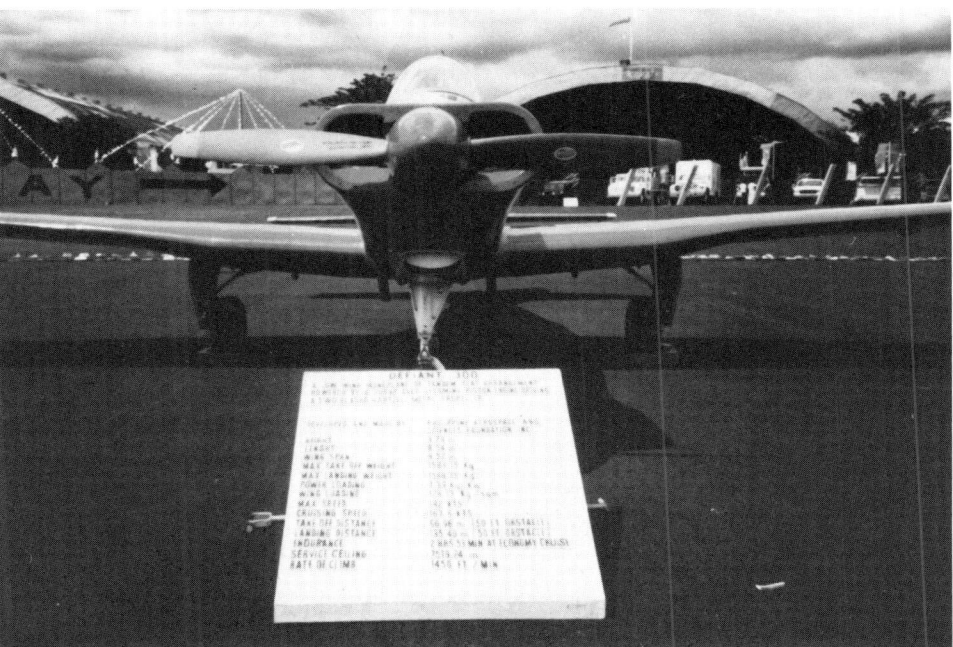

Prototype Universal Dynamics Defiant 300 two-seat sporting/training aircraft *(Anglo Philippine Aviation)*

Max T-O weight	1,583 kg (3,490 lb)
Max landing weight	1,568 kg (3,457 lb)

PERFORMANCE:
Max level speed	193 knots (357 km/h; 222 mph)
Econ cruising speed	167 knots (309 km/h; 192 mph)
Stalling speed: flaps up	81 knots (150 km/h; 93 mph)
flaps down	59 knots (110 km/h; 68 mph)
Unstick speed	85 knots (158 km/h; 98 mph)
Max rate of climb at S/L	470 m (1,540 ft)/min
Service ceiling	7,520 m (24,670 ft)
T-O run	395 m (1,294 ft)
Landing run	397 m (1,302 ft)
Max range	1,023 nm (1,896 km; 1,178 miles)

POLAND

PZL
ZRZESZENIE WYTWÓRCÓW SPRZETU LOTNICZEGO I SILNIKOWEGO PZL (Association of Aircraft and Engine Industry)
ul. Miodowa 5, 00-251 Warszawa
Telephone: 48 (22) 261441
Telex: 814281
PRESIDENT: Tadeusz Ryczaj
DIRECTOR: Ing Jan Stojanowicz, MSc

The manufacture of aircraft in Poland began in 1910. In 1928 an industrial syndicate was established, grouping the existing aircraft factories into the Panstwowe Zaklady Lotnicze (State Aviation Works) to produce aircraft to meet domestic and export needs. Since then the Polish aircraft industry has designed and built nearly 35,000 aircraft, helicopters and gliders of various types, as well as aero engines and equipment.

Until 1981 the aviation industry was organised under control of the ZPLS-PZL (Aircraft and Engine Industry Union). In 1982 (see earlier editions of this annual) its activities came under the control of the Bureau of Ministers Plenipotentiary for the Aircraft and Engine Industry, and it is currently organised as the Zrzeszenie Wytwórców

Sprzetu Lotniczego i Silnikowego PZL (Association of Aircraft and Engine Industry), managed by a council representing all factories which are members of the Association. Production plants within the Association are self-dependent.

Other members of the Association include the BTNU (Biuro Techniczne Nowych Uruchomień: Engineering Office for the Implementation of New Projects), and the PPT (Przedsiebiorstwo Projektowo-Technologiczne: Design and Production Methods Enterprise). The Instytut Lotnictwa (which see) is also a member of the Association.

The Polish aviation and diesel engine industry currently comprises 23 factories, scientific and development units, technical and commercial organisations, which between them employ about 90,000 qualified workers. Its work has a broad base which includes research, design, development, manufacture, foreign trade, agricultural aviation services, and technical support for its own products operated by other countries.

Production by the Polish aviation industry relies substantially on aircraft, engines and equipment of its own design, as well as on co-operation and co-production with leading foreign aircraft manufacturers in both the East and the West. These programmes currently include the

multi-purpose PZL-104 Wilga, the PZL-106 Kruk and M-18 Dromader agricultural aircraft; wing and tail component assembly for the Soviet Il-86 wide-bodied transport; the PZL-110 Koliber and M-20 Mewa light multi-purpose, training and sporting aircraft; local service transports such as the An-2 and An-28; the Mi-2, Kania, Sokól and SW-4 helicopters; sailplanes (see SZD entry in that section); piston, turbojet and turboprop engines (see PZL entries in the Aero Engines section); and aircraft military equipment, propellers, and ground equipment for agricultural aircraft and helicopters.

The export sales of all Polish aviation products are handled by:

Pezetel Foreign Trade Enterprise Ltd
Aleja Stanów Zjednoczonych 61, PO Box 6, 00-991 Warszawa 44
Telephone: 48 (22) 10 80 01
Telex: 814651 PZL PL
DIRECTOR AND GENERAL MANAGER:
Jerzy Krezlewicz, MA
MANAGER OF AVIATION DEPARTMENT: Kazimierz Niepsuj
MANAGER OF PUBLICITY DEPARTMENT:
Ing Wojciech Kowalczyk

IL
INSTYTUT LOTNICTWA (Aviation Institute)
Al. Krakowska 110/114, 02-256 Warszawa-Okecie
Telephone: 48 (22) 460011 and 460993
Telex: 813537
GENERAL MANAGER: Dr Ing Konrad Tott
CHIEF CONSULTANT FOR SCIENTIFIC AND TECHNICAL
CO-OPERATION: Dipl Eng Jerzy Grzegorzewski, MScEng

Founded in 1926, the Instytut Lotnictwa is directly subordinate to the Ministry of Heavy and Machine Building Industry and is responsible for all research and development work in the Polish aviation industry. It conducts scientific research, including the investigation of problems associated with low-speed and high-speed aerodynamics, static and fatigue tests, development and testing of aero engines, flight instruments, space science instrumentation, and other equipment, flight tests, and materials technology. It is also responsible for the construction of aircraft and aero engines, the latest such programme being the I-22 two-seat jet trainer.

PZL I-22 IRYD (IRIDIUM)
Pictures of this new jet trainer and light attack aircraft first appeared in a Polish television programme in October 1986, and it was identified by the designation I-22 a few weeks later, although the first prototype had made its first flight as long ago as 3 March 1985. Three further prototypes (first flights 26 June 1988, 13 May 1989 and 22 October 1989) have since been completed.

The I-22 was designed at the Instytut Lotnictwa by a team led by chief designer Dr Eng Alfred Baron. They were assisted by the Ośrodek Badawczo-Rozwojowy Sprzetu Komunikacyjnego (Communications Equipment Research and Development Centre) at Mielec, where the prototypes were built, and various other Polish aviation industry establishments.

Evidently intended as a successor to the PZL Mielec TS-11 Iskra, the I-22 has been designed to cover the full spectrum of pilot, navigation, air combat, reconnaissance and ground attack training, with day/night and bad-weather capability. This versatility, coupled with the ability to operate from unprepared airstrips and carry a useful variety of ordnance, enables the I-22 also to fulfil the role of light close support aircraft. To this end, the airframe is designed to be tolerant of battle damage, capable of quick and inexpensive repair, and is stressed to a standard that will permit later the use of more powerful engines (one designated K-15, rated at 14.7 kN; 3,305 lb st, is under development, as described in the Engines section) and the carriage of a greater weapons load, without jeopardising permissible load factors. Service life of the I-22 has been calculated on the basis of 2,500 flying hours or 10,000 take-offs and landings.

TYPE: Two-seat advanced jet trainer, reconnaissance and light close support aircraft.

WINGS: Cantilever high-wing monoplane, with 18° sweepback on leading-edges, non-swept trailing-edges, and 4° 30′ anhedral from roots. Two-spar all-metal stressed skin structure, built as one unit with centre and inboard portions forming integral fuel tanks. Laminar flow aerofoil section, with multi-stage geometric and aerodynamic twist. All-metal mass balanced ailerons, actuated by pushrods with hydraulic boost. All-metal single-slotted trailing-edge flaps deflect hydraulically (20° for take-off, 40° for landing), with auxiliary pneumatic system for emergency deflection in the event of hydraulic failure.

FUSELAGE: Conventional oval-section all-metal semi-monocoque structure of frames and longerons, with aluminium alloy skin. Door type airbrake on each side beneath centre-fuselage, actuated hydraulically.

Three-view drawing *(Pilot Press)* **and photograph of the third prototype** *(Lech Zielaskowski)* **of the PZL I-22 tandem-seat advanced trainer, reconnaissance and ground attack aircraft**

TAIL UNIT: Conventional all-metal structure, with sweepback on all surfaces. Curved fillet at base of fin. Variable incidence tailplane, mid-mounted on fuselage tailcone, is actuated hydraulically; will have slight anhedral on production version. Mass balanced elevators and rudder, actuated by pushrods. Ground adjustable tab on rudder.

LANDING GEAR: Retractable tricycle type, with single wheel and low pressure tubeless tyre on each unit. Hydraulic extension and retraction: nose unit retracts forward, main units upward into engine nacelles. Auxiliary pneumatic system for lowering gear in an emergency. Oleo-pneumatic shock absorber in each unit. Hydraulic disc brakes on mainwheels; auxiliary mainwheel parking brake serves also as emergency brake. Braking parachute in fuselage tailcone. Small tail bumper under rear of fuselage.

POWER PLANT: Two 10.79 kN (2,425 lb st) PZL Rzeszów SO-3W22 non-afterburning turbojets, pod mounted on lower sides of centre-fuselage. Fuel in three integral wing tanks (combined capacity 1,180 litres; 312 US gallons; 259.5 Imp gallons) and two fuselage tanks (combined capacity 1,360 litres; 359 US gallons; 299 Imp gallons), to give total internal capacity of 2,540 litres (671 US gallons; 558.5 Imp gallons). Provision for one 400 litre (106 US

gallon; 88 Imp gallon) auxiliary tank to be carried under each wing. Fuel system permits up to 30 s of inverted flight. Single-point pressure refuelling (at front of port engine nacelle), plus gravity filling point for each tank. Air intakes anti-iced by engine bleed air.

ACCOMMODATION: Pressurised, heated and air-conditioned cockpit, with tandem seating for pupil (in front) and instructor; rear seat elevated 400 mm (15¾ in). For solo flying, pilot occupies front seat. Back-type parachute, oxygen bottle and emergency pack for both occupants. Individual framed canopies, each hinged at rear and opening upward pneumatically. Rearview mirror in front cockpit. VS-1 rocket assisted ejection seats, fitted with canopy breakers, can be operated at zero altitude and at speeds down to 81 knots (150 km/h; 94 mph). Dual controls standard; front cockpit equipped for IFR flying. Windscreen anti-iced by electric heating, supplemented by alcohol spray. Remaining transparencies anti-iced and demisted by hot engine bleed air.

SYSTEMS: Cockpits pressurised and air-conditioned by engine bleed air. Air from air-conditioning system also used to pressurise crew's g suits. Main hydraulic system, nominal pressure 210 bars (3,045 lb/sq in), actuates landing gear extension and retraction, wing flaps, airbrakes, tailplane incidence, brake-chute deployment, differential braking of mainwheels, and parking/emergency brake. Auxiliary hydraulic system for aileron control boost. Pneumatic system comprises three separate circuits, each supplied by a nitrogen bottle pressurised at 150 bars (2,175 lb/sq in): one powers emergency extension of wing flaps for landing, one the emergency extension of the landing gear; the third is for canopy opening, closing and sealing, windscreen fluid de-icing system, and hydraulic reservoir pressurisation. All three bottles charged simultaneously through a common nozzle. Electrical system, powered by two 9kW DC starter/generators, supplies 115V single-phase AC (via two 1kVA static converters) and 36V three-phase AC (via 500VA electro-mechanical converters), both at 400Hz; two 24V batteries provide DC power in the event of a double failure. Each AC voltage is supplied by one main converter and one standby, the latter automatically assuming full load if a main converter fails. Engine fire detection and extinguishing system (two freon bottles in rear fuselage). Electronic control system for gun firing and weapon release.

AVIONICS AND EQUIPMENT: Avionics bays in nose and under floor of rear cockpit. Avionics include VHF and UHF multi-channel com radio; ADF; radar altimeter for low level flying; marker beacon receiver; ILS; IFF; and audio-visual radar warning system. Blind-flying instrumentation. Flight data recorder in dorsal fin fillet.

ARMAMENT: One 23 mm GSh-23L twin-barrel cannon in underfuselage pack, with up to 200 rds (50 rds normally carried for training missions), plus gyro gunsight and nose mounted gun camera. Four underwing attachments, each stressed for load of up to 500 kg (1,102 lb), for bombs, guided or unguided rockets, or (inboard stations only) auxiliary fuel tanks.

DIMENSIONS, EXTERNAL:
Wing span	9.60 m (31 ft 6 in)
Wing aspect ratio	4.6
Length overall	13.22 m (43 ft 4½ in)
Height overall	4.30 m (14 ft 1¼ in)
Wheel track	2.71 m (8 ft 10¾ in)
Wheelbase	4.90 m (16 ft 1 in)

AREAS:
Wings, gross	19.92 m² (214.4 sq ft)
Ailerons (total)	1.362 m² (14.66 sq ft)
Trailing-edge flaps (total)	3.36 m² (36.17 sq ft)
Airbrakes (total)	0.60 m² (6.46 sq ft)
Fin	2.72 m² (29.28 sq ft)
Rudder, incl tab	0.957 m² (10.30 sq ft)
Tailplane	3.14 m² (33.80 sq ft)
Elevators (total)	1.694 m² (18.23 sq ft)

WEIGHTS AND LOADINGS:
Operational weight empty	3,962 kg (8,735 lb)
Max fuel weight: internal	2,120 kg (4,674 lb)
external:	640 kg (1,411 lb)
Max external stores load	1,200 kg (2,645 lb)
Max T-O weight	7,493 kg (16,519 lb)
Max wing loading	376.15 kg/m² (77.08 lb/sq ft)
Max power loading	694.6 kg/kN (6.81 lb/lb st)

PERFORMANCE:
Max Mach number	0.85
Max level speed at S/L, ISA	494 knots (915 km/h; 568 mph)
Max cruising speed at altitude	499 knots (924 km/h; 574 mph)
Max rate of climb at S/L, ISA	2,220 m (7,283 ft)/min
Service ceiling	12,600 m (41,340 ft)
T-O run	770 m (2,525 ft)
T-O to 15 m (50 ft)	1,020 m (3,350 ft)
Landing from 15 m (50 ft)	950 m (3,115 ft)
Landing run	330 m (1,085 ft)
Range with max internal fuel	901 nm (1,670 km; 1,037 miles)
g limits (clean)	+8/-4

WSK-PZL MIELEC
WYTWÓRNIA SPRZETU KOMUNIKACYJ-NEGO-PZL MIELEC (Transport Equipment Manufacturing Centre, Mielec)

ul. Ludowego Wojska Polskiego 3, 39-300 Mielec
Telephone: 48/ Mielec 7010
Telex: 0632293 C WSK PL
GENERAL MANAGER: Ing Mieczyslaw Szymanski
COMMERCIAL DIRECTOR: Marian Krzemień, MSc

Largest and best equipped aircraft factory in Poland, the PZL factory at Mielec was founded in 1938, and had produced nearly 15,000 aircraft by 1 January 1990. In current production are the An-2 general utility biplane, the An-28 twin-turboprop light general purpose transport, the Dromader series of agricultural aircraft and the twin-engined M-20 Mewa executive and ambulance aircraft. In 1977 Mielec began to manufacture components, including fins, tailplanes, engine pylons, and wing slats and flaps, for the Ilyushin Il-86 Soviet wide-bodied transport. By 1 January 1990 Mielec had completed 241 shipsets of Il-86 components and eight sets for the Il-96.

PZL MIELEC (ANTONOV) An-2 ANTEK
NATO reporting name: Colt

The prototype of the An-2, designed to a specification of the Ministry of Agriculture and Forestry of the USSR, made its first flight on 31 August 1947. In 1948 the aircraft went into production in the USSR as the An-2, with a 746 kW (1,000 hp) ASh-62 engine.

By 1960, more than 5000 An-2s had been built in the Soviet Union, as fully described in previous editions of *Jane's*. Licence rights were granted to China, where the first locally produced An-2 was completed in December 1957, as the Yunshuji-5 or Y-5. Limited production continues in China.

Since 1960, apart from a few dozen Soviet built An-2Ms (1971-72 *Jane's*), continued production of the An-2 has been primarily the responsibility of PZL Mielec, the original licence arrangement providing for two basic versions: the An-2T transport and An-2R agricultural version. The first Polish built An-2 was flown on 23 October 1960. Mielec has since built more than 11,730 An-2s for domestic use and for export to the USSR (10,427), Bulgaria, Czechoslovakia, Egypt, France, the German Democratic Republic, Hungary, North Korea, Mongolia, Netherlands, Romania, Sudan, Tunisia and Yugoslavia. They include 7,777 An-2Rs. In 1989 AICSA of Colombia (which see) assembled two An-2s from kits supplied from PZL Mielec via Pezetel.

Polish built versions have different designations from those built in the USSR. They include the An-2 Geofiz; An-2LW; An-2P, PK, P-Photo and PR; An-2R; An-2S; An-2T, TD and TP. Further details of these can be found in the 1983-84 and earlier editions of *Jane's*.

The following details apply to the PZL Mielec An-2P:
TYPE: Single-engined general purpose biplane.
WINGS: Unequal span single-bay biplane. Wing section RPS 14 per cent (constant). Dihedral, both wings, approx 2° 48′. All-metal two-spar structure, fabric covered aft of front spar. I type interplane struts. Differential ailerons and full span automatic leading-edge slots on upper wings, slotted trailing-edge flaps on both upper and lower wings. Flaps operated electrically, ailerons mechanically by cables and push/pull rods. Electrically operated trim tab in port aileron.
FUSELAGE: All-metal stressed skin semi-monocoque structure of circular section forward of cabin, rectangular in the cabin section and oval in the tail section.
TAIL UNIT: Braced metal structure. Fin integral with rear fuselage. Fabric covered tailplane. Elevators and rudder operated mechanically by cables and push/pull rods. Electrically operated trim tab in rudder and port elevator.
LANDING GEAR: Non-retractable split axle type, with long stroke oleo shock absorbers. Mainwheel tyres size 800 × 260 mm, pressure 2.25 bars (32.7 lb/sq in). Pneumatic shoe brakes on main units. Fully castoring and self-centring PZL Krosno tailwheel, size 470 × 210, with electro-pneumatic lock. For rough field operation the oleo-pneumatic shock absorbers can be charged from a compressed air cylinder installed in the rear fuselage. Interchangeable ski landing gear available optionally.
POWER PLANT: One 746 kW (1,000 hp) PZL Kalisz ASz-62IR nine-cylinder radial aircooled engine, driving an AW-2 four-blade variable-pitch metal propeller. Six fuel tanks in upper wings, with total capacity of 1,200 litres (317 US gallons; 264 Imp gallons). Oil capacity 120 litres (31.7 US gallons; 26.4 Imp gallons).
ACCOMMODATION: Crew of two on flight deck, with access via passenger cabin. Standard accommodation for 12 passengers, in four rows of three with centre aisle. Two foldable seats for children in aisle between first and second rows, and infant's cradle at front of cabin on starboard side. Toilet at rear of cabin on starboard side. Overhead racks for up to 160 kg (352 lb) of baggage, with space for coats and additional 40 kg (88 lb) of baggage between rear pair of seats and toilet. Emergency exit on starboard side at rear. Walls of cabin are lined with glass-wool mats and inner facing of plywood to reduce internal noise level. Cabin floor is carpeted. Cabin heating and starboard windscreen de-icing by engine bleed air; port and centre windscreens are electrically de-iced. Cabin ventilation by ram air intakes on underside of top wings.
SYSTEMS: Compressed air cylinder, of 8 litres (0.28 cu ft) capacity, for pneumatic charging of shock absorbers and operation of tailwheel lock at 49 bars (711 lb/sq in) pressure and operation of mainwheel brakes at 9.80 bars (142 lb/sq in). Contents of cylinder are maintained by AK-50 P engine driven compressor, with AD-50 automatic relief device to prevent overpressure. DC electrical system is supplied with basic 27V power (and 36V or 115V where required) by an engine driven generator and a storage battery. CO_2 fire extinguishing system with automatic fire detector.
AVIONICS AND EQUIPMENT: Dual controls and blind-flying instrumentation standard. R-842 HF and RS-6102 or Baklan-5 VHF lightweight radio transceivers, RW-UM radio altimeter (A-037 from 1 April 1989), ARK-9 radio compass, MRP-56P marker beacon receiver, GIK-1 gyro compass, GPK-48 gyroscopic direction indicator and SPU-7 intercom.

Hungarian registered PZL Mielec (Antonov) An-2 with agricultural spraygear *(Paul Jackson)*

DIMENSIONS, EXTERNAL:
Wing span: upper	18.18 m (59 ft 7¾ in)
lower	14.24 m (46 ft 8½ in)
Wing chord (constant): upper	2.45 m (8 ft 0½ in)
lower	2.00 m (6 ft 6¾ in)
Wing aspect ratio: upper	7.6
lower	7.1
Wing gap	2.17 m (7 ft 1½ in)
Length overall: tail up	12.74 m (41 ft 9½ in)
tail down	12.40 m (40 ft 8¼ in)
Height overall: tail up	6.10 m (20 ft 0 in)
tail down	4.01 m (13 ft 2 in)
Tailplane span	7.20 m (23 ft 7½ in)
Wheel track	3.36 m (11 ft 0¼ in)
Wheelbase	8.19 m (26 ft 10½ in)
Propeller diameter	3.60 m (11 ft 9¾ in)
Propeller ground clearance	0.69 m (2 ft 3¼ in)
Cargo door (port): Mean height	1.55 m (5 ft 1 in)
Mean width	1.39 m (4 ft 6¾ in)
Emergency exit (stbd, rear): Height	0.65 m (2 ft 1½ in)
Width	0.51 m (1 ft 8 in)

DIMENSIONS, INTERNAL:
Cargo compartment: Length	4.10 m (13 ft 5½ in)
Max width	1.60 m (5 ft 3 in)
Max height	1.80 m (5 ft 11 in)

AREAS:
Wings, gross: upper	43.54 m² (468.7 sq ft)
lower	27.98 m² (301.2 sq ft)
Ailerons (total)	5.90 m² (63.5 sq ft)
Trailing-edge flaps (total)	9.60 m² (103 sq ft)
Fin	3.20 m² (34.4 sq ft)
Rudder, incl tab	2.65 m² (28.52 sq ft)
Tailplane	7.56 m² (81.4 sq ft)
Elevators (total, incl tab)	4.72 m² (50.81 sq ft)

WEIGHTS AND LOADINGS:
Weight empty	3,450 kg (7,605 lb)
Max fuel weight	900 kg (1,984 lb)
Max T-O weight	5,500 kg (12,125 lb)
Max landing weight	5,250 kg (11,574 lb)
Max zero-fuel weight	4,800 kg (10,582 lb)

Max wing loading	76.82 kg/m² (15.7 lb/sq ft)
Max power loading	7.38 kg/kW (12.13 lb/hp)

PERFORMANCE (at AUW of 5,250 kg; 11,574 lb):

Max level speed at 1,750 m (5,740 ft)	
	139 knots (258 km/h; 160 mph)
Econ cruising speed	100 knots (185 km/h; 115 mph)
Min flying speed	49 knots (90 km/h; 56 mph)
T-O speed	43 knots (80 km/h; 50 mph)
Landing speed	46 knots (85 km/h; 53 mph)
Max rate of climb at S/L	210 m (689 ft)/min
Service ceiling	4,400 m (14,425 ft)
Time to 4,400 m (14,425 ft)	30 min
T-O run: hard runway	150 m (492 ft)
grass	170 m (558 ft)
T-O to 15 m (50 ft): hard runway	475 m (1,558 ft)
grass	495 m (1,624 ft)
Landing from 15 m (50 ft): hard runway	427 m (1,401 ft)
grass	432 m (1,417 ft)
Landing run: hard runway	170 m (558 ft)
grass	185 m (607 ft)
Range at 1,000 m (3,280 ft) with 500 kg (1,102 lb) payload	485 nm (900 km; 560 miles)

PZL MIELEC (ANTONOV) An-28
NATO reporting name: Cash

The Antonov bureau developed the An-28 for service on Aeroflot's shortest routes, particularly those operated by An-2s into places relatively inaccessible to other fixed-wing types. It is suitable for carrying passengers, cargo and mail, for scientific expeditions, geological survey, forest fire patrol, air ambulance or rescue operations, and parachute training. The An-28 will not stall, even with the control column held in the extreme rearward position, because of the action of its automatic slots. If an engine fails, the upper surface spoiler forward of the aileron on the opposite wing is opened automatically; as a result, the wing bearing the dead engine drops only 12° in 5 s instead of the 30° that it would drop through loss of lift without the action of the Antonov patented spoiler. The fixed tailplane slat, also patented, improves handling during a high angle of attack climbout. Under icing conditions, if the normal anti-icing system fails, ice collects on the slat rather than the tailplane, to retain controllability.

The early history of this twin-turboprop light general purpose transport has been given in many previous editions of *Jane's*. Official Soviet flight testing was completed in 1972, and the production designation An-28 was allocated during 1973. The first pre-production An-28 (SSSR-19723) originally retained the same engines as the prototype, but in April 1975 (re-registered SSSR-19753) it flew for the first time with 716 kW (960 shp) Glushenkov TVD-10 turboprops, which are installed also in production An-28s. Series production was entrusted to PZL Mielec in 1978, and a temporary type certificate, under Soviet NLGS-2 regulations, was awarded on 4 October that year to the second Soviet built pre-production aircraft (originally SSSR-19754, later SSSR-48105).

Polish manufacture began with an initial batch of 15 aircraft, and 105 had been completed by January 1990. First flight by a Polish built An-28 (SSSR-28800) was made on 22 July 1984, and the following description applies to this version, which received its full Soviet type certificate on 7 February 1986:

TYPE: Twin-turboprop short-range passenger transport.

WINGS: Braced high-wing monoplane, with single streamline section bracing strut each side. Wing section TsAGI P-II-14 (thickness/chord ratio 14 per cent). Constant chord, non-swept no-dihedral centre-section, set at 4° incidence; tapered outer panels have 2° dihedral, negative incidence and 2° sweepback at quarter-chord. Conventional two-spar all-duralumin torsion box structure, with steel attachment fittings. Duralumin automatic leading-edge slats over full span of outer panels. Entire trailing-edges hinged, the single-slotted mass and aerodynamically balanced ailerons being designed to droop with the large, two-segment double-slotted flaps. Unpowered ailerons and hydraulically actuated flaps are of duralumin, with fabric and CFRP skins respectively;

Antonov An-28, built by PZL Mielec, in Polish Air Force insignia *(Jane's Soviet Intelligence Review)*

port aileron has a CFRP trim tab. Slab type spoiler, also of CFRP, forward of each aileron and each outer flap segment at 75 per cent chord. Thermal anti-icing of wing leading-edges by engine bleed air. Short stub-wing extends from each side of the lower fuselage, carrying the main landing gear unit and providing lower attachment for the wing bracing strut.

FUSELAGE: Conventional all-metal semi-monocoque non-pressurised structure. Underside of rear fuselage upswept and incorporating clamshell doors for passenger and cargo loading.

TAIL UNIT: Cantilever all-metal structure. Twin fins and rudders, mounted vertically on an inverted-aerofoil, no-dihedral fixed incidence tailplane. Conventional elevators. Fixed leading-edge slat under full span of tailplane leading-edge. Electrically actuated trim tab in each rudder and each elevator; main controls are unpowered. Thermal (engine bleed air) anti-icing of tailplane and fin leading-edges.

LANDING GEAR: Non-retractable tricycle type, with single Soviet built wheel and PZL oleo-pneumatic shock absorber on each unit. Main units have wide tread balloon tyres of Soviet manufacture, size 720 × 320 mm, pressure 3.5 bars (51 lb/sq in), and are mounted on small stub-wings which curve forward and downward at front to serve as mudguards. Steerable (± 50°) and self-centring nosewheel, with size 595 × 185 × 280 mm Stomil (Poland) tyre, pressure 3.5 bars (51 lb/sq in). Soviet multi-disc hydraulic brakes on main units, and Soviet inertial anti-skid units.

POWER PLANT: Two 716 kW (960 shp) PZL Rzeszów TVD-10B turboprops, each driving an AW-24AN three-blade automatic propeller with full feathering and reversible-pitch capability. Two centre-section and two outer-wing integral fuel tanks in wing spar boxes, with total capacity of 1,960 litres (518 US gallons; 431 Imp gallons). Refuelling point on each tank. Oil capacity 16 litres (4.2 US gallons; 3.5 Imp gallons) per engine. Air intakes lined with epoxy laminate and anti-iced by engine bleed air; propellers, spinners and pitot heads anti-iced electrically.

ACCOMMODATION: Pilot and co-pilot on flight deck, which has bulged side windows and electric anti-icing for windscreens, and is separated from main cabin by a bulkhead with connecting door. Dual controls standard. Jettisonable emergency door at front on each side. Standard cabin layout of passenger version has seats for 17 people, with six single seats on port side, one single seat and five double seats on starboard side of aisle, at 72 cm

(28 in) pitch. Aisle width 34.5 cm (13.5 in). Five passenger windows in each side of cabin. Seats fold back against walls when aircraft is operated as a freighter or in mixed passenger/cargo role, the seat attachments providing cargo tiedown points. Hoist of 500 kg (1,102 lb) capacity able to deposit cargo in forward part of cabin. Entire cabin heated, ventilated and soundproofed. Outward/downward opening clamshell double door, under upswept rear fuselage, for passenger and cargo loading. Emergency exit at rear of cabin on each side.

SYSTEMS: No air-conditioning, pressurisation or pneumatic systems. Hydraulic system for flap and spoiler actuation, mainwheel brakes and nosewheel steering, with emergency backup system for spoiler extension and mainwheel braking. Primary electrical system is three-phase AC, with two engine driven alternators providing 200/115V power for heating systems, engine vibration monitoring, fuel pump, radio, recorders, and instrument lights. Transformer-rectifiers on this system provide 36V AC power for pressure gauges, artificial horizon, navigation and recording equipment, and 27V DC for control systems and signalling, internal and external lighting, firefighting system, propeller pitch control and feathering, radio, and engine starting and monitoring systems. In emergency, 36V AC can be provided by a static inverter and 27V DC by two 25Ah batteries. Thermal (engine bleed air) anti-icing of outer-wing, fin and tailplane leading-edges. Electric anti-icing of flight deck windscreens, propellers, spinners and pitot heads. Oxygen system (for crew plus two passengers) optional. No APU.

AVIONICS: Standard avionics include Baklan-5 (USSR) VHF com radio, R-855UM (USSR) VHF emergency locator transmitter, ARK-15 radio compass, MRP-66 marker beacon receiver, RW-5 or A-037 radio altimeter, Grebien-1 navigation unit, BUR-1-2A flight recorder, and SGU-6 intercom. Blind-flying instrumentation standard.

DIMENSIONS, EXTERNAL:

Wing span	22.063 m (72 ft 4½ in)
Wing chord: at root	2.20 m (7 ft 2½ in)
mean aerodynamic	1.886 m (6 ft 2¼ in)
at tip	1.10 m (3 ft 7¼ in)
Wing aspect ratio	12.25
Length overall	13.10 m (42 ft 11¾ in)
Fuselage: Length	12.68 m (41 ft 7¼ in)
Max width	1.90 m (6 ft 2¾ in)
Max depth	2.14 m (7 ft 0¼ in)
Height overall	4.90 m (16 ft 1 in)
Tailplane span	5.14 m (16 ft 10¼ in)
Wheel track	3.405 m (11 ft 2 in)
Wheelbase	4.354 m (14 ft 3½ in)
Propeller diameter	2.80 m (9 ft 2¼ in)
Propeller ground clearance	1.25 m (4 ft 1¼ in)
Distance between propeller centres	5.20 m (17 ft 0¾ in)
Rear clamshell doors: Length	2.40 m (7 ft 10½ in)
Total width: at top	1.00 m (3 ft 3¼ in)
at sill	1.40 m (4 ft 7 in)
Emergency exits (rear, each): Height	0.91 m (3 ft 0 in)
Width	0.51 m (1 ft 8 in)

DIMENSIONS, INTERNAL:

Cabin, excl flight deck: Length	5.26 m (17 ft 3 in)
Max width	1.74 m (5 ft 8½ in)
Max height	1.60 m (5 ft 3 in)
Floor area	approx 7.5 m² (80.73 sq ft)
Volume	approx 14.0 m³ (494.4 cu ft)

AREAS:

Wings, gross	39.72 m² (427.5 sq ft)
Ailerons (total)	4.33 m² (46.61 sq ft)
Trailing-edge flaps (total)	7.986 m² (85.96 sq ft)
Spoilers (total)	1.667 m² (17.94 sq ft)
Fins (total)	10.00 m² (107.64 sq ft)

Antonov An-28 passenger light transport, produced in Poland by WSK-PZL Mielec *(Pilot Press)*

Rudders (total, incl tabs)	4.00 m² (43.06 sq ft)
Tailplane	8.85 m² (95.26 sq ft)
Elevators (total, incl tabs)	2.56 m² (27.56 sq ft)

WEIGHTS AND LOADINGS:

Weight empty, equipped	3,900 kg (8,598 lb)
Max fuel load	1,529 kg (3,371 lb)
Max payload	2,000 kg (4,409 lb)
Max T-O and landing weight	6,500 kg (14,330 lb)
Max zero-fuel weight	5,884 kg (12,972 lb)
Normal wing loading	153.5 kg/m² (31.5 lb/sq ft)
Max power loading	4.64 kg/kW (7.62 lb/shp)

PERFORMANCE (at max T-O weight):

Never-exceed speed	210 knots (390 km/h; 242 mph)
Max level and max cruising speed at 3,000 m (9,850 ft)	189 knots (350 km/h; 217 mph)
Econ cruising speed at 3,000 m (9,850 ft)	181 knots (335 km/h; 208 mph)
Lift-off speed	73 knots (135 km/h; 84 mph)
Approach speed	70 knots (130 km/h; 81 mph)
Landing speed, flaps down	76 knots (140 km/h; 87 mph)
Max rate of climb at S/L	500 m (1,640 ft)/min
Rate of climb at S/L, one engine out	210 m (689 ft)/min
Service ceiling	above 6,000 m (19,685 ft)
Min ground turning radius	16.00 m (52 ft 6 in)
T-O run	260 m (853 ft)
T-O to 10.7 m (35 ft)	360 m (1,180 ft)
Landing from 15 m (50 ft)	315 m (1,035 ft)
Landing run	170 m (558 ft)
Range:	
max payload, no reserves	302 nm (560 km; 348 miles)
max fuel and 1,000 kg (2,205 lb) payload, 30 min reserves	736 nm (1,365 km; 848 miles)
g limit	+3

PZL MIELEC M-18 DROMADER (DROMEDARY)

The Dromader agricultural aircraft was designed to meet the requirements of FAR Pt 23. Particular attention was paid to pilot safety, and all parts of the structure exposed to contact with chemicals are treated with polyurethane or epoxy enamels, or manufactured from stainless steel.

The prototype was first flown on 27 August 1976, and a second prototype flew on 2 October 1976. They were followed by ten pre-series aircraft, of which eight were used for operating trials. The Dromader has been certificated in Australia, Brazil, Canada, China, Czechoslovakia, France, the German Democratic Republic, Poland, the USA and Yugoslavia. Customers include operators in Australia, Brazil, Bulgaria, Canada, Chile, China, Cuba, Czechoslovakia, the German Democratic Republic, Greece (30 for firefighting), Hungary, Iran, Morocco, Nicaragua, Poland, Portugal, Spain, Swaziland, Trinidad, Turkey, the USA, Venezuela and Yugoslavia.

Series production began in 1979, and the following versions have been produced:

M-18. Initial single-seat agricultural version, last described in 1988-89 *Jane's*. Awarded Polish type certificate on 27 September 1978. Production ended in 1984.

M-18A. Two-seat agricultural version, introduced for operators requiring to transport a ground mechanic/loader to provisional airstrips. Entered production in 1984, following Polish supplementary type certification on 14 February that year. FAA type certificate for M-18 extended to M-18A in September 1987. In production.

M-18AS. Two-seat training version of M-18A, with smaller hopper to create space for instructor's cockpit aft of front seat. This rear cockpit installation is readily interchangeable with that of M-18A. First flight 21 March 1988. In production.

T45 Turbine Dromader. Turboprop version, powered by an 895 kW (1,200 shp) Pratt & Whitney Canada PT6A-45AG engine with Hartzell propeller. Under development by James Mills in co-operation with Melex USA Inc and described under Melex heading in US section.

In addition to the above, any M-18 can be converted to a

Polish built Antonov An-28 light general purpose transport (two PZL Rzeszów TVD-10B turboprops) *(Lech Zielaskowski)*

M-18 single-seat version of the Dromader agricultural aircraft *(R. J. Malachowski)*

firefighting role, a prototype in this configuration having been flown for the first time on 11 November 1978. An amphibious water bomber floatplane variant is under consideration.

A total of 550 Dromaders (all versions) had been built by 1 January 1990, of which 90 per cent were for export.

The following description applies to the current production M-18A, unless stated otherwise:

TYPE: Two-seat agricultural aircraft.

WINGS: Cantilever all-metal low-wing monoplane, of constant chord, with 1° 25' dihedral on centre-section and 6° on outer panels. Wing sections NACA 4416 at root, NACA 4412 at end of centre-section, and NACA 4412 on outer panels. Incidence 3°. Single steel capped duralumin spar. All-metal two-section trailing-edge slotted flaps, actuated hydraulically. All-metal slotted ailerons, mass and aerodynamically balanced, actuated by pushrods. Trim tab in each aileron.

FUSELAGE: All-metal structure. Main frame, of helium-arc welded chrome-molybdenum steel tube, oiled internally against corrosion. Duralumin side panels, detachable for airframe inspection and cleaning. Fixed stainless steel bottom covering.

TAIL UNIT: All-metal structure, with braced tailplane. Corrugated skin. Aerodynamically and mass balanced rudder and elevators. Elevator actuated by pushrods, rudder by cables. Trim tab on rudder and each elevator.

LANDING GEAR: Non-retractable tailwheel type. Oleopneumatic shock absorber in each unit. Main units have tyres size 800 × 260 mm, and are fitted with hydraulic disc brakes, parking brake and wire cutters. Fully castoring tailwheel, lockable for take-off and landing, with size 380 × 150 mm tyre.

POWER PLANT: One 746 kW (1,000 hp) PZL Kalisz ASz-62IR nine-cylinder radial aircooled supercharged engine, driving a PZL Warszawa AW-2-30 four-blade constant-speed aluminium propeller. Integral fuel tank in each outer wing panel, combined usable capacity 400 or 712 litres (105.7 or 188 US gallons; 88 or 156.6 Imp gallons). Gravity feed header tank in fuselage.

ACCOMMODATION: Single adjustable seat in fully enclosed, sealed and ventilated cockpit which is stressed to withstand 40g impact. Additional cabin located behind cockpit and separated from it by a wall. Latter is equipped with a rigid seat, with protective padding and safety belt, a port-side jettisonable door, windows (port and starboard), fire extinguisher, and ventilation valve. Communication with the pilot is provided via a window in the dividing wall, and by intercom. In M-18AS, standard hopper is replaced by a smaller one, permitting installation of a bolt-on instructor's cabin. Second cockpits of M-18A and M-18AS are quickly interchangeable. Glassfibre cockpit roof and rear fairing, latter with additional small window each side. Rear cockpit of M-18AS has more extensive glazing. Adjustable shoulder type safety harness. Adjustable rudder pedals. Quick-opening door on each side of front cockpit; port door jettisonable.

SYSTEMS: Hydraulic system, pressure 98-137 bars (1,421-1,987 lb/sq in), for flap actuation, disc brakes and dispersal system. Electrical system powered by 28.5V 100A generator, with 24V 25Ah nickel-cadmium battery and overvoltage protection relay.

AVIONICS AND EQUIPMENT: RS6102 (Polish built), Bendix/King KX 175B or KY 195B com transceiver, KI 201C nav receiver, VOR-OBS indicator, gyro compass, radio compass, stall warning, landing lights, taxi light and night working light optional. Navigation lights, cockpit light, instrument panel lights, and two rotating beacons standard. Built-in jacking and tiedown points in wings and rear fuselage; towing lugs on main landing gear. Cockpit fire extinguisher and first aid kit.

AGRICULTURAL AND OTHER EQUIPMENT: Glassfibre epoxy hopper, with stainless steel tube bracing, forward of

PZL Mielec M-18AS two-seat dual-control training version of the Dromader *(Andrzej Glass)*

cockpit; capacity (M-18A) 2,500 litres (660 US gallons; 550 Imp gallons) of liquid or 1,350 kg (2,976 lb) of dry chemical (1,850 kg; 4,078 lb under CAM 8 conditions). Smaller hopper in M-18AS. Deflector cable from cabin roof to fin. M-18 variants can be fitted optionally with several different types of agricultural and firefighting systems, as follows: spray system with 54/96 nozzles on spraybooms; dusting system with standard, large or extra large spreader; atomising system with six atomisers; water bombing installation; and fire-bombing installation with foaming agents. Aerial application roles can include seeding, fertilising, weed or pest control, defoliation, forest and bush firefighting, and patrol flights. Special wingtip lights permit agricultural flights at night, and the aircraft can operate in both temperate and tropical climates.

DIMENSIONS, EXTERNAL:

Wing span	17.70 m (58 ft 0¾ in)
Wing chord, constant	2.286 m (7 ft 6 in)
Wing aspect ratio	7.8
Length overall	9.47 m (31 ft 1 in)
Height over tail fin	3.70 m (12 ft 1¾ in)
Height overall (flying attitude)	4.60 m (15 ft 1 in)
Tailplane span	5.60 m (18 ft 4½ in)
Wheel track	3.48 m (11 ft 5 in)
Propeller diameter	3.30 m (10 ft 10 in)
Propeller ground clearance (tail up)	0.23 m (9 in)

AREAS:

Wings, gross	40.00 m² (430.5 sq ft)
Ailerons (total)	3.84 m² (41.33 sq ft)
Trailing-edge flaps (total)	5.69 m² (61.25 sq ft)
Vertical tail surfaces (total)	2.65 m² (28.5 sq ft)
Horizontal tail surfaces (total)	6.50 m² (70.0 sq ft)

WEIGHTS AND LOADINGS (M-18A):

Basic weight empty	2,690 kg (5,930 lb)
Weight empty, equipped	2,750-2,860 kg (6,063-6,305 lb)
Payload: FAR 23	1,050-1,350 kg (2,315-2,976 lb)
CAM 8	1,550-1,850 kg (3,417-4,078 lb)
Max T-O weight: FAR 23	4,200 kg (9,259 lb)
CAM 8	4,700 kg (10,362 lb)
Max landing weight	4,200 kg (9,259 lb)
Max wing loading (FAR 23)	105.0 kg/m² (21.51 lb/sq ft)
Max power loading (FAR 23)	5.63 kg/kW (9.26 lb/hp)

PERFORMANCE (M-18A at 4,200 kg; 9,259 lb T-O weight, ISA. A: without agricultural equipment; B: with spreader equipment):

Never-exceed speed: A	151 knots (280 km/h; 174 mph)
Max level speed: A	138 knots (256 km/h; 159 mph)
B	128 knots (237 km/h; 147 mph)
Cruising speed at S/L:	
A	110 knots (205 km/h; 127 mph)
B	102 knots (190 km/h; 118 mph)
Normal operating speed:	
A	124 knots (230 km/h; 143 mph)
B	108 knots (200 km/h; 124 mph)
Stalling speed, power off, flaps up:	
A, B	65 knots (119 km/h; 74 mph)
Stalling speed, power off, flaps down:	
A, B	59 knots (109 km/h; 68 mph)
Max rate of climb at S/L: A	414 m (1,360 ft)/min
B	340 m (1,115 ft)/min
Service ceiling: A	6,500 m (21,325 ft)
T-O run: A	180-200 m (590-656 ft)
B	210-245 m (689-805 ft)
Landing run: A, B	260-300 m (853-984 ft)

Max range, no reserves:

A, 400 litres (105.7 US gallons; 88 Imp gallons) fuel
291 nm (540 km; 335 miles)
A, 712 litres (188 US gallons; 156.6 Imp gallons) fuel
523 nm (970 km; 602 miles)

g limits: FAR 23	+3.4/−1.4
CAM 8	+3/−1.2

PZL MIELEC M-20 MEWA (GULL)

The M-20 Mewa six/seven-seat twin-engined aircraft is the Polish version of the Piper PA-34-200T Seneca II, developed under an agreement made with Piper Aircraft Corporation in 1977. It is designed for passenger transport, training, liaison and ambulance duties, and is certificated to FAR Pt 23. The Mewa can be operated from concrete runways or grass strips, and differs chiefly from the US built Seneca in being powered by Polish built PZL-F engines.

Adaptation of the PA-34-200T Seneca II airframe to accept this power plant occupied the first half of 1978, and the first Polish prototype made its initial flight on 25 July 1979. The Mewa has been produced in three versions, any of which can be configured for passenger carrying or as an air ambulance. Details of the M-20 00 (four built in 1979-80) and M-20 01 (five built in 1983-84) can be found in the 1987-88 and earlier *Jane's*.

Current production in 1990, for customers in Austria, West Germany, India and Turkey, was centred on a batch of 15 M-20 02 aircraft powered by Teledyne Continental TSIO/LTSIO-360-KB turbocharged engines.

The following details (except for performance) apply to the M-20 02 with Teledyne Continental engines:

PZL Mielec M-20 Mewa, a Polish version of the Piper PA-34-200T Seneca II

TYPE: Six/seven-seat executive and ambulance aircraft.

WINGS: Cantilever low-wing monoplane. NACA 65₂-415 section constant chord wings, with 7° dihedral from roots and 2° incidence. Leading-edges sweptforward at root. Safe-life stressed skin structure of aluminium alloy, including the Frise ailerons and single-slotted trailing-edge flaps. Optional pneumatic anti-icing of leading-edges.

FUSELAGE: Semi-monocoque safe-life structure of aluminium alloy.

TAIL UNIT: Cantilever type, of similar construction to wings, with sweptback vertical and non-swept horizontal surfaces. Rudder is aerodynamically and mass balanced, and fitted with an anti-servo tab. Slab type all-moving tailplane, with trim tab. Pneumatic anti-icing of fin and tailplane leading-edges optional.

LANDING GEAR: Hydraulically retractable tricycle type, with single wheel and oleo strut on each unit. Mainwheels retract inward into wings, nosewheel forward. Size 6.00-6 wheels on all three units, tyre pressures 3.79 bars (55 lb/sq in) on main units, 2.76 bars (40 lb/sq in) on nose unit. Emergency gravity extension. PZL Hydral disc brakes; parking brake.

POWER PLANT: Two 164 kW (220 hp) Teledyne Continental TSIO-360-KB turbocharged, counter-rotating flat-six engines, each driving a three-blade constant-speed propeller with spinner and (optionally) electric blade de-icing. Two 92.75 litre (24.5 US gallon; 20.4 Imp gallon) fuel tanks in each wing leading-edge; total standard fuel capacity 371 litres (98 US gallons; 81.6 Imp gallons). Optional auxiliary tank in each leading-edge can increase this total to 484.5 litres (128 US gallons; 106.6 Imp gallons). Oil capacity 10 litres (2.64 US gallons; 2.2 Imp gallons) per engine.

ACCOMMODATION: Passenger version seats one or two pilots plus five or four passengers, with optional seventh seat. Baggage space aft of rear seats. Ambulance version can carry one stretcher patient, two medical attendants and one other person in addition to the pilot. The stretcher rack replaces the right hand centre seat and, like the seat, can be quickly and easily removed. The rack has special guides which can be connected to the door threshold to facilitate stretcher loading; they can be folded back when the stretcher is on board and locked. There are hooks in the cabin ceiling for suspending a transfusion set, and the aircraft carries an oxygen installation for the patient. The doctor's seat (centre, left) has an earphone and microphone, enabling him to contact the ground for assistance if required, and there is a nurse's seat at the rear. A modified electrical system permits an incubator to be installed.

SYSTEMS: Two independent hydraulic systems, one operating at 154 bars (2,233 lb/sq in) for landing gear extension/retraction and the other at 103.5 bars (1,500 lb/sq in) for wheel braking. Electrical system powered by two 24V 55A alternators and a 24V 25Ah battery. Pneumatic wing and tail anti-icing system optional.

AVIONICS: Multi-channel VOR/LOC radio and blind-flying instrumentation standard. Radio rangefinder, radio marker, radio compass and three-axis autopilot optional. Polish ARL 1601 ADF, CG 121 slaved gyro, RS 6102 VHF com transceiver, MRP-66 marker transceiver and SSA-1 audio control panel.

DIMENSIONS, EXTERNAL:

Wing span	11.86 m (38 ft 11 in)
Wing chord: at root	1.88 m (6 ft 2 in)
at tip	1.60 m (5 ft 3 in)
Wing aspect ratio	7.3
Length overall	8.72 m (28 ft 7¼ in)
Height overall	3.02 m (9 ft 11 in)
Tailplane span	4.13 m (13 ft 6½ in)
Wheel track	3.37 m (11 ft 0¾ in)
Wheelbase	2.13 m (7 ft 0 in)
Propeller diameter	1.93 m (6 ft 4 in)

DIMENSIONS, INTERNAL:

Cabin: Length	3.17 m (10 ft 4¾ in)
Max width	1.24 m (4 ft 0¾ in)

Max height	1.07 m (3 ft 6¼ in)
Volume	5.53 m³ (195.3 cu ft)

AREAS:

Wings, gross	19.18 m² (206.5 sq ft)
Ailerons (total)	1.17 m² (12.59 sq ft)
Trailing-edge flaps (total)	1.94 m² (20.88 sq ft)
Fin	1.96 m² (21.10 sq ft)
Rudder	0.89 m² (9.58 sq ft)
Tailplane, incl tab	3.60 m² (38.75 sq ft)

WEIGHTS AND LOADINGS:

Weight empty (standard)	1,290 kg (2,844 lb)
Max T-O weight	2,070 kg (4,563 lb)
Max landing weight	1,970 kg (4,343 lb)
Max zero-fuel weight	1,810 kg (3,990 lb)
Max wing loading	107.9 kg/m² (22.10 lb/sq ft)
Max power loading	6.86 kg/kW (11.13 lb/hp)

PERFORMANCE (at max T-O weight, PZL-F engines):

Never-exceed speed	194 knots (360 km/h; 223 mph)
Max level speed at 1,500 m (4,920 ft)	148 knots (275 km/h; 171 mph)
Econ cruising speed at 1,500 m (4,920 ft)	140 knots (260 km/h; 162 mph)
Stalling speed, flaps down	59 knots (108 km/h; 68 mph)
Max rate of climb at S/L	384 m (1,260 ft)/min
Service ceiling	4,000 m (13,125 ft)
T-O to 15 m (50 ft)	460 m (1,510 ft)
Landing from 15 m (50 ft)	655 m (2,150 ft)

Range, 45 min reserves:

with max standard fuel 550 nm (1,020 km; 634 miles)
with max standard and auxiliary fuel
734 nm (1,360 km; 845 miles)

PZL MIELEC M-21 DROMADER MINI

This reduced capacity version of the Dromader was developed in response to a need expressed by many users of the M-18 for a smaller version, with a less powerful engine and reduced chemical load. Construction of two flying prototypes and static testing of the airframe started in August 1981, and the first prototype (SP-PDM) flew for the first time on 18 June 1982, powered by a PZL-3S engine. First flight of the same aircraft with a PZL-3SR engine was made on 20 October 1983. The second prototype, also with the -3SR engine, made its initial flight on 21 March 1985, gaining a provisional type certificate. Agricultural service trials were conducted in Yugoslavia during June-September 1986 and March-June 1987. Series production has not been undertaken.

Details and an illustration of the Dromader Mini can be found in the 1989-90 and earlier editions of *Jane's*.

PZL MIELEC M-24 DROMADER SUPER

The Dromader Super is the largest member of the Dromader family, but utilises the same rear fuselage, outer wings, landing gear, power plant and tail unit as the M-18A. Fuel capacity is increased to 1,400 litres (370 US gallons; 308 Imp gallons).

Five prototypes of the M-24 were built, including one for static testing. The first two, which flew for the first time on 14 July 1987 (SP-PFA) and 27 April 1988, were each powered by a 746 kW (1,000 hp) ASz-62IR engine; the next two, first flown on 14 October and 18 November 1988, each have a K9-AA engine (conversion of the ASz-62IR) rated at 860 kW (1,170 hp). Hopper capacity has been increased to 2,700 litres (713 US gallons; 594 Imp gallons) or 1,800 kg (3,968 lb), and other features include wings increased in span and having a new aerofoil section. Production has not yet begun. An M-24T turboprop version, with a P&WC PT6A-65AG engine, is also planned.

DIMENSIONS, EXTERNAL:

Wing span	19.90 m (65 ft 3½ in)
Wing aspect ratio	8.8
Length overall	10.80 m (35 ft 5¼ in)
Height overall: tail up	4.30 m (14 ft 1¼ in)
tail down	3.78 m (12 ft 4¾ in)
Wheelbase	7.40 m (24 ft 3½ in)
Propeller diameter	3.60 m (11 ft 9¾ in)

AREA:

Wings, gross	45.00 m² (484.4 sq ft)

WEIGHTS AND LOADINGS:

Weight empty	2,870 kg (6,327 lb)
Max fuel weight	1,010 kg (2,226 lb)
Max T-O and landing weight:	
Normal	5,000 kg (11,023 lb)
Max T-O weight: Restricted	5,500 kg (12,125 lb)
Max wing loading:	
Normal	111.1 kg/m² (22.75 lb/sq ft)
Restricted	122.2 kg/m² (25.03 lb/sq ft)
Max power loading, 746 kW (1,000 hp) engine:	
Normal	6.71 kg/kW (11.02 lb/hp)
Restricted	7.38 kg/kW (12.12 lb/hp)

PERFORMANCE (746 kW; 1,000 hp engine):

Max cruising speed	119 knots (220 km/h; 137 mph)
Stalling speed, flaps down	59 knots (110 km/h; 68 mph)
Max rate of climb at S/L: clean	300 m (984 ft)/min
with agricultural equipment	180 m (590 ft)/min
Service ceiling	4,000 m (13,125 ft)
T-O to 15 m (50 ft)	340 m (1,116 ft)
Landing from 15 m (50 ft)	470 m (1,542 ft)
Range: standard	971 nm (1,800 km; 1,118 miles)
self-ferry	1,888 nm (3,500 km; 2,175 miles)
g limits	+3.5/−1.4

PZL MIELEC M-26 ISKIERKA (LITTLE SPARK)

The Iskierka is a single-piston-engined aircraft, designed to FAR Pt 23 and intended for civil pilot training and pilot selection for military training. Selected parts and assemblies of the M-20 Mewa were used in the design of the wings, tail unit, landing gear, power plant, and electrical and power systems. Chief designer is Mr Krzysztof Piwek.

The Iskierka is being developed with two different engines, as the **M-26 00** with a PZL-F engine and **M-26 01** with a Textron Lycoming AEIO-540. The first prototype (SP-PIA), with a PZL-F, made its initial flight on 15 July 1986; first flight of the Textron Lycoming powered M-26 01 (SP-PIB) took place on 24 June 1987. Flight testing has been somewhat delayed, but was continuing in early 1990.

TYPE: Tandem two-seat training aircraft.

WINGS: Cantilever low-wing monoplane. NACA 65₂-415 section constant chord wings, with 7° dihedral from roots and 2° incidence. Sweptforward leading-edges at root. Safe-life stressed skin structure of aluminium alloy, including the Frise ailerons and single-slotted trailing-edge flaps. No spoilers, airbrakes or tabs.

FUSELAGE: Semi-monocoque safe-life structure of aluminium alloy.

TAIL UNIT: Conventional cantilever type, of similar construction to wings, with sweptback vertical and non-swept horizontal surfaces. Fixed incidence tailplane. Trim tab in starboard elevator.

LANDING GEAR: Retractable tricycle type, actuated hydraulically, with single wheel and oleo strut on each unit. Mainwheels retract inward into wings, nosewheel rearward. Size 6.00-6 wheels on all three units; tyre pressures 3.43 bars (50 lb/sq in) on main units, 2.16 bars (31 lb/sq in) on nose unit. PZL Hydral hydraulic disc brakes on mainwheels. Parking brake.

POWER PLANT (M-26 00): One 153 kW (205 hp) PZL-F 6A-350CA flat-six engine, driving a PZL Warszawa-Okecie US 142 three-blade constant-speed propeller with pointed spinner, or a two-blade Hartzell BHC-C2YF-2CKUF constant-speed propeller. One 92 litre (24.3 US gallon; 20.2 Imp gallon) fuel tank in each wing leading-edge, plus a 9 litre (2.4 US gallon; 2.0 Imp gallon) fuselage tank, to give total capacity of 193 litres (51 US gallons; 42.4 Imp gallons). Gravity fuelling point in top of each wing tank. Oil capacity 10 litres (2.6 US gallons; 2.2 Imp gallons).

Second prototype of the PZL Mielec M-24 Dromader Super agricultural aircraft (*Andrzej Glass*)

Mockup of the proposed M-24T turboprop version of the M-24 Dromader Super (*Andrzej Glass*)

POWER PLANT (M-26 01): One 224 kW (300 hp) Textron Lycoming AEIO-540-L1B5D flat-six engine, driving a Hoffmann HO-V123K-V/200AH-10 three-blade constant-speed propeller. Second tank in each wing. Total fuel capacity 377 litres (99.6 US gallons; 82.8 Imp gallons). Gravity fuelling point in top of each outer wing tank. Oil capacity 15 litres (4.0 US gallons; 3.3 Imp gallons).

ACCOMMODATION: Tandem seats for pupil (in front) and instructor, under framed canopy which opens sideways to starboard. Rear seat is elevated. Baggage compartment aft of rear seat. Both cockpits heated and ventilated.

SYSTEMS: Two independent hydraulic systems, one operating at 154 bars (2,233 lb/sq in) for landing gear extension/retraction and the other at 103 bars (1,494 lb/sq in) for wheel braking. DC electrical power supplied by a 24V alternator (50A in M-26 00, 100A in M-26 01) and a 25Ah battery.

AVIONICS AND EQUIPMENT: Polish made ARL 1601 ADF system, CG 121 slaved gyro system, RS 6102 VHF com transceiver, SSA-1 audio control panel, and ORS-2M marker beacon receiver standard. Landing light in port wing leading-edge.

DIMENSIONS, EXTERNAL:

Wing span	8.60 m (28 ft 2½ in)
Wing chord: at root	1.88 m (6 ft 2 in)
at tip	1.60 m (5 ft 3 in)
Wing aspect ratio	5.3
Length overall	8.30 m (27 ft 2¾ in)
Height overall	2.96 m (9 ft 8½ in)
Tailplane span	3.80 m (12 ft 5½ in)
Wheel track	2.93 m (9 ft 7¼ in)
Wheelbase	1.93 m (6 ft 4 in)
Propeller diameter	1.90 m (6 ft 2¾ in)

DIMENSIONS, INTERNAL:

Cockpits: Total length	2.91 m (9 ft 6½ in)
Max width	0.88 m (2 ft 10½ in)
Max height	1.30 m (4 ft 3¼ in)

AREAS:

Wings, gross	14.00 m² (150.7 sq ft)
Ailerons (total)	1.17 m² (12.59 sq ft)
Trailing-edge flaps (total)	1.06 m² (11.41 sq ft)
Fin	1.96 m² (21.10 sq ft)
Rudder	0.89 m² (9.58 sq ft)
Tailplane	3.30 m² (35.52 sq ft)
Elevators (total, incl tab)	1.15 m² (12.38 sq ft)

WEIGHTS AND LOADINGS (A: M-26 00, B: M-26 01):

Weight empty: A	850 kg (1,874 lb)
B	940 kg (2,072 lb)
Max fuel weight: A	139 kg (306 lb)
B	271 kg (597 lb)
Max T-O and landing weight: A	1,200 kg (2,645 lb)
B	1,400 kg (3,086 lb)
Max wing loading: A	85.7 kg/m² (17.56 lb/sq ft)
B	100.0 kg/m² (20.5 lb/sq ft)
Max power loading: A	7.86 kg/kW (12.91 lb/hp)
B	6.26 kg/kW (10.29 lb/hp)

PERFORMANCE (estimated, at max T-O weight, A and B as above):

Never-exceed speed:	
A, B	194 knots (360 km/h; 223 mph)
Max level speed at S/L:	
A	143 knots (265 km/h; 165 mph)
B	173 knots (320 km/h; 199 mph)

PZL Mielec M-26 Iskierka tandem two-seat primary trainer (*Pilot Press*)

Stalling speed, flaps down:

A	53 knots (98 km/h; 61 mph)
B	60 knots (110 km/h; 69 mph)

Max rate of climb at S/L: A		240 m (787 ft)/min
B		480 m (1,575 ft)/min
T-O to 15 m (50 ft): A		450 m (1,476 ft)
B		570 m (1,870 ft)
Landing from 15 m (50 ft): A		430 m (1,411 ft)
B		540 m (1,772 ft)

Range with max fuel, 30 min reserves:

A	507 nm (940 km; 584 miles)
B	874 nm (1,620 km; 1,006 miles)
g limits: A	+6/−3
B at 1,100 kg (2,425 lb) AUW	+7/−3.5
B at max T-O weight	+4/−1.72

**First prototype PZL Mielec M-26 00 Iskierka
(153 kW; 205 hp PZL-F 6A-350CA engine)**

WSK-PZL SWIDNIK
WYTWÓRNIA SPRZETU KOMUNIKACYJ-NEGO lm. ZYGMUNTA PULAWSKIEGO-PZL SWIDNIK (Zygmunt Pulawski Transport Equipment Manufacturing Centre, Swidnik)

ul. Przodowników Pracy 1, 21-045 Swidnik k/Lublina
Telephone: 48 (81) 12061, 12071, 13061 and 13071
Telex: 0642301 WSK PL
GENERAL MANAGER: Andrzej Zeh, MScEng
DIRECTOR OF RESEARCH AND DEVELOPMENT, AND CHIEF
 DESIGNER: Stanisław Kaminski, MScEng
SALES MANAGER: Jan Widz, MSc
PRESS RELATIONS: Jerzy Jurak, MSc

The factory at Swidnik was established in 1951 and was engaged initially in manufacturing components for the LiM-1 (MiG-15) jet fighter. In 1955, Swidnik began licence production of the Soviet designed Mi-1 helicopter, some 1,700 of which were built under the designation SM-1, followed by 450 examples of the Swidnik developed SM-2. A design office was formed at the factory to work on variants and developments of the basic SM-1 design and on original projects such as the SM-4 Latka.

In September 1957, the Swidnik works was named after the famous pre-war PZL designer Zygmunt Pulawski, and currently employs about 10,000 people. Production is concentrated at present on various developments of the Soviet designed Mil Mi-2 turbine powered helicopter, and manufacture of wing and tailplane slats for the PZL Mielec (Antonov) An-28.

Swidnik, together with other PZL factories at Mielec and Kalisz, is manufacturing components for the Soviet Ilyushin Il-86 wide-bodied airliner.

PZL SWIDNIK (MIL) Mi-2
NATO reporting name: Hoplite

The Mil Mi-2, first flown in September 1961, was designed in the USSR by the Mikhail L. Mil bureau. Development of the two prototypes continued in the USSR until the helicopter had completed its initial State trials programme. Then, in accordance with an agreement signed in January 1964, further development, production and marketing of the Mi-2 were assigned exclusively to the Polish aircraft industry, which flew its own first example of the Mi-2 on 4 November 1965.

Series production began in 1965, and Swidnik has since built more than 5,250 for various civil and military operators; the majority of these have been exported. Among the operators of the Mi-2 are the air forces of Bulgaria, Czechoslovakia, East Germany, Hungary, Iraq, North Korea, Libya, Poland (Mi-2CH, Mi-2T, Mi-2URN, Mi-2URP and Mi-2US and other variants), Syria and the USSR, and civil operators in European and various

PZL Swidnik (Mil) Mi-2T helicopter of the Polish Air Force *(Andrzej Glass)*

developing countries. Production of the Mi-2B (see separate entry) accounts for "a few per cent" of the overall total.

During the course of production the Mi-2 has undergone continuous improvement and upgrading, with versions for new applications being developed to meet specific customers' requirements. A full list of these can be found in the 1984-85 and earlier *Jane's*; the principal civil versions being produced in 1989 were as follows:
  (a) Convertible passenger/cargo transport;
  (b) Ambulance and rescue version (Mi-2R);
  (c) Agricultural version, for dusting or conventional and ultra-low-volume spraying. In service in Bulgaria, Czechoslovakia, Egypt, Iraq, Poland and USSR;
  (d) Freighter version, with external cargo sling and electric hoist;
  (e) Training version;
  (f) Aerial photography versions, able to carry photographic, photogrammetric, thermal imaging or TV cameras for oblique or vertical pictures.
The following armed military variants have been produced:
Mi-2URN. As Mi-2US, but with two Mars 2 launchers (each with 16 S-5 57 mm unguided rockets) instead of pylon mounted gun pods. PKV gunsight in cockpit for aiming of all weapons. In service since 1973.

Mi-2URP. Anti-tank version, with cabin-side outriggers for four 9M14M Malyutka (AT-3 'Sagger') wire-guided missiles. Four additional missiles carried in cargo compartment. In service since 1976; later version can carry four 9M32 Strela 2 missiles.

Mi-2US. Gunship version, equipped with 23 mm NS-23KM cannon on port side of fuselage, two 7.62 mm gun pods on each side pylon, and two other 7.62 mm PK type movable machine-guns in rear cabin.

The following details apply specifically to the basic Mi-2, except where indicated:

TYPE: Twin-turbine general purpose light helicopter.
ROTOR SYSTEM: Three-blade main rotor fitted with hydraulic blade vibration dampers. All-metal blades, of NACA 230-12M section. Flapping, drag and pitch hinges on each blade. Main rotor blades and those of two-blade tail rotor each consist of an extruded duralumin spar with bonded honeycomb trailing-edge pockets. Anti-flutter weights on leading-edges, balancing plates on trailing-edges. Hydraulic boosters for longitudinal, lateral and collective pitch controls. Coil spring counterbalance mechanism in main and tail rotor systems. Pitch change centrifugal loads on tail rotor carried by ribbon type steel torsion elements. Rotors do not fold. Electric blade de-icing system for main and tail rotors. Rotor brake fitted.
ROTOR DRIVE: Main rotor shaft driven via gearbox on each engine; three-stage WR-2 main gearbox, intermediate gearbox and tail rotor gearbox. Main rotor/engine rpm ratio 1 : 24.6; tail rotor/engine rpm ratio 1 : 4.16. Main gearbox provides drive for auxiliary systems and take-off for rotor brake. Freewheel units permit disengagement of a failed engine and also autorotation.
FUSELAGE: Conventional semi-monocoque structure of pod and boom type, made up of three main assemblies: the nose (including cockpit), central section, and tailboom. Construction is of sheet duralumin, bonded and spot welded or riveted to longerons and frames. Main load bearing joints are of steel alloy.
TAIL UNIT: Variable incidence horizontal stabiliser controlled by collective pitch lever.
LANDING GEAR: Non-retractable tricycle type, plus tailskid. Twin-wheel nose unit. Single wheel on each main unit. Oleo-pneumatic shock absorbers in all units, including tailskid. Main shock absorbers designed to cope with both normal operating loads and possible ground resonance. Mainwheel tyres size 600 × 180, pressure 4.41 bars (64 lb/sq in). Nosewheel tyres size 400 × 125, pressure 3.45 bars (50 lb/sq in). Pneumatic brakes on mainwheels. Metal ski landing gear optional.

Mi-2URN of the Polish Air Force, armed with a 23 mm cannon and twin pods of 57 mm rockets

POWER PLANT: Two 298 kW (400 shp) Polish built Isotov GTD-350 turboshafts, mounted side by side above cabin. Fuel in single rubber tank, capacity 600 litres (158.5 US gallons; 131 Imp gallons), under cabin floor. Provision for carrying a 238 litre (63 US gallon; 52.4 Imp gallon) external tank on each side of cabin. Refuelling point in starboard side of fuselage. Oil capacity 25 litres (6.6 US gallons; 5.4 Imp gallons). Engine air intake de-icing by engine bleed air.

ACCOMMODATION: Normal accommodation for one pilot on flight deck (port side). Seats for up to eight passengers in air-conditioned cabin, comprising back to back bench seats for three persons each, with two optional extra starboard side seats at the rear, one behind the other. All passenger seats are removable for carrying up to 700 kg (1,543 lb) of internal freight. Access to cabin via forward hinged doors on each side at front of cabin and aft on port side. Pilot's sliding window jettisonable in emergency. Ambulance version has accommodation for four stretchers and a medical attendant, or two stretchers and two sitting casualties. Side by side seats and dual controls in pilot training version. Cabin heating, ventilation and air-conditioning standard. Electric de-icing of windscreen.

SYSTEMS: Cabin heating, by engine bleed air, and ventilation; heat exchangers warm atmospheric air for ventilation system during cold weather. Hydraulic system, pressure 65 bars (940 lb/sq in), for cyclic and collective pitch control boosters. Hydraulic fluid flow rate 7.5 litres (1.98 US gallons; 1.65 Imp gallons)/min. Vented reservoir, with gravity feed. Pneumatic system, pressure 49 bars (710 lb/sq in), for mainwheel brakes. AC electrical system, with two STG-3 3kW engine driven starter/generators and 208V 16kVA three-phase alternator. 24V DC system, with two 28Ah lead-acid batteries.

AVIONICS AND EQUIPMENT: Standard equipment includes two transceivers (MF/HF), gyro compass, radio compass, radio altimeter, intercom system and blind-flying panel. Electrically operated wiper for pilot's windscreen. Fire extinguishing system, for engine bays and main gearbox compartment, is generally similar to, but simpler than, the freon system fitted to the Soviet Mil Mi-8, and can be actuated automatically or manually.

OPERATIONAL EQUIPMENT: Agricultural version carries a hopper on each side of the fuselage (total capacity 1,000 litres; 264 US gallons; 220 Imp gallons of liquid or 750 kg; 1,650 lb of dry chemical) and either a spraybar to the rear of the cabin on each side or a distributor for dry chemicals under each hopper. Swath width covered by the spraying version is 40-45 m (130-150 ft). As a search and rescue aircraft, an electric hoist, capacity 120 kg (264 lb), is fitted. In the freight role an underfuselage hook can be fitted for suspended loads of up to 800 kg (1,763 lb). Illustrations in the Polish press have shown a version equipped for laying smokescreens. Diesel oil from external tanks on each side of the cabin is injected into large-diameter pipes extending backward and downward from the upper part of the rotor pylon. These pipes do not touch the engine exhausts but are warmed sufficiently to convert the diesel oil into dense white smoke. Nose and tail warning radar fitted to some military versions.

ARMAMENT: Mi-2URN combat support and armed reconnaissance version of the Polish Air Force (see model listings) has a 23 mm and two 7.62 mm guns, plus a pylon mounted pod of sixteen 57 mm unguided rockets on each side of the fuselage; a five-gun variant (one fixed 23 mm on port side, two pylon mounted and two cabin mounted 7.62 mm) is designated Mi-2US. Polish Air Force Mi-2 URPs (see illustration in 1988-89 Jane's) can carry two 'Sagger' anti-tank missiles mounted on pylons on each side of the cabin.

DIMENSIONS, EXTERNAL:
Main rotor diameter	14.50 m (47 ft 6⅞ in)
Main rotor blade chord (constant, each)	
	0.40 m (1 ft 3¾ in)
Tail rotor diameter	2.70 m (8 ft 10¼ in)
Length overall, rotors turning	17.42 m (57 ft 2 in)
Length of fuselage	11.40 m (37 ft 4¾ in)
Height to top of rotor head	3.75 m (12 ft 3½ in)
Stabiliser span	1.85 m (6 ft 0¾ in)
Wheel track	3.05 m (10 ft 0 in)
Wheelbase	2.71 m (8 ft 10¾ in)
Tail rotor ground clearance	1.59 m (5 ft 2¾ in)
Cabin door (port, rear): Height	1.065 m (3 ft 5¾ in)
Width	1.115 m (3 ft 8 in)
Cabin door (stbd, front): Height	1.11 m (3 ft 7¾ in)
Width	0.75 m (2 ft 5½ in)
Cabin door (port, front): Height	1.11 m (3 ft 7¾ in)
Width	0.78 m (2 ft 6¾ in)

DIMENSIONS, INTERNAL:
Cabin:	
Length: incl flight deck	4.07 m (13 ft 4¼ in)
excl flight deck	2.27 m (7 ft 5½ in)
Mean width	1.20 m (3 ft 11¼ in)
Mean height	1.40 m (4 ft 7 in)

AREAS:
Main rotor blades (each)	2.40 m² (25.83 sq ft)
Tail rotor blades (each)	0.22 m² (2.37 sq ft)
Main rotor disc	166.4 m² (1,791.11 sq ft)
Tail rotor disc	5.73 m² (61.68 sq ft)
Horizontal stabiliser	0.70 m² (7.53 sq ft)

PZL Swidnik Kania Model 1 twin-turboshaft light helicopter *(Lech Zielaskowski)*

WEIGHTS AND LOADING:
Weight empty, equipped:	
passenger version	2,402 kg (5,295 lb)
cargo version	2,372 kg (5,229 lb)
ambulance version	2,410 kg (5,313 lb)
agricultural version	2,372 kg (5,229 lb)
Basic operating weight empty:	
single-pilot versions	2,365 kg (5,213 lb)
dual control version	2,424 kg (5,344 lb)
Max payload, excl pilot, oil and fuel	800 kg (1,763 lb)
Normal T-O weight (and max T-O weight of agricultural version)	3,550 kg (7,826 lb)
Max T-O weight (special versions)	3,700 kg (8,157 lb)
Max disc loading	22.4 kg/m² (4.6 lb/sq ft)

PERFORMANCE (at 3,550 kg; 7,826 lb T-O weight):
Never-exceed speed at 500 m (1,640 ft):	
agricultural version	84 knots (155 km/h; 96 mph)
other versions	113 knots (210 km/h; 130 mph)
Max cruising speed at 500 m (1,640 ft):	
agricultural version (without agricultural equipment)	102 knots (190 km/h; 118 mph)
other versions	108 knots (200 km/h; 124 mph)
Max level speed with agricultural equipment	84 knots (155 km/h; 96 mph)
Econ cruising speed at 500 m (1,640 ft):	
for max range	102 knots (190 km/h; 118 mph)
for max endurance	54 knots (100 km/h; 62 mph)
Max rate of climb at S/L	270 m (885 ft)/min
Time to 1,000 m (3,280 ft)	5 min 30 s
Time to 4,000 m (13,125 ft)	26 min
Service ceiling	4,000 m (13,125 ft)
Hovering ceiling: IGE	approx 2,000 m (6,560 ft)
OGE	approx 1,000 m (3,280 ft)
Min landing area	30 × 30 m (100 × 100 ft)
Range at 500 m (1,640 ft):	
max payload, 5% fuel reserves	91 nm (170 km; 105 miles)
max internal fuel, no reserves	237 nm (440 km; 273 miles)
max internal and auxiliary fuel, 30 min reserves	313 nm (580 km; 360 miles)
max internal and auxiliary fuel, no reserves	430 nm (797 km; 495 miles)
Endurance at 500 m (1,640 ft), no reserves:	
max internal fuel	2 h 45 min
max internal and auxiliary fuel	5 h
Endurance (agricultural version), 5% reserves:	
spraying	40 min
dusting	50 min

PZL SWIDNIK Mi-2B

The PZL Mi-2B differs from the Mi-2 in having a different electrical system and more modern navigation aids. It has been manufactured in the same versions (except agricultural) as the Mi-2, and has the same flight performance. Empty equipped weights are 2,300 kg (5,070 lb) for the passenger version and 2,293 kg (5,055 lb) for the cargo version; T-O weight remains unchanged at 3,550 kg (7,826 lb). Rotor blade de-icing is not available on the Mi-2B.

PZL SWIDNIK KANIA/KITTY HAWK

In collaboration with Allison in the USA, PZL Swidnik developed the Kania or Kitty Hawk, powered by two Allison 250-C20B turboshaft engines. Two examples were converted from Mi-2 airframes, and the first of these (SP-PSA) made its initial flight on 3 June 1979.

Polish certification of the Kania was carried out in two stages. The first took place in 1979-81 and resulted, on 1 October 1981, in a supplementary type certificate to that of the Mi-2. The second stage, concerning a considerably improved **Kania Model 1** version, was carried out during 1982-86 under the leadership of Stanisław I. Markisz. Improvements included, among others, redesigned cockpit and cabin layout, engine and flight controls, engine and transmission cowlings. On 21 February 1986 this version of the Kania was granted a separate type certificate as an FAR

Pt 29 (Transport Category B) day and night SVFR multi-purpose utility helicopter with Category A engine isolation. Three had been built by mid-1989.

The Kania Model 1 is offered in a number of versions and configurations. These include passenger transport (with standard, executive or customised interiors), cargo transport (internal or slung load), agricultural (LV and ULV spraying, spreading and dusting), medical evacuation, training, rescue, and aerial surveillance.

TYPE: Twin-turboshaft multi-purpose light helicopter.

ROTOR SYSTEM: Three-blade fully articulated main rotor and two-blade seesaw tail rotor. Glassfibre/epoxy blades on both rotors. Three hydraulic boosters for longitudinal, lateral and collective pitch control augmentation. Electric de-icing of main and tail rotor blades (incl icing and 'system out' warnings) optional.

ROTOR DRIVE: Transmission includes main rotor, intermediate and tail rotor gearboxes, each with individual lubrication system. Main gearbox equipped with freewheel units, oil cooling system, oil temperature and pressure gauges and switches, tacho-generator with low and high rpm warning, air compressor, and a spare power pad of 19.1 kW (25.6 shp) at 8,000 rpm. Steel engine driveshafts, each with two crowned tooth couplings. Tail rotor driveshaft of duralumin tube, with similar crowned tooth couplings and anti-friction bearings.

FUSELAGE AND TAIL UNIT: Conventional semi-monocoque fuselage and circular-section tailboom. Glassfibre/epoxy horizontal stabiliser at end of tailboom. Hoist and cargo sling attachment points standard.

LANDING GEAR: Non-retractable tricycle type, plus tailskid. Twin-wheel castoring and self-centring nose unit; single wheel on each main unit. Pneumatic brakes on mainwheels.

POWER PLANT: Two Allison 250-C20B turboshafts, mounted side by side above cabin; each rated at 313 kW (420 shp) for T-O, 30 min twin-engine emergency power and one engine out max continuous power, and 276 kW (370 shp) for normal cruise. Automatic and manual torque sharing control systems standard. Two separate fuel boost systems, each with fuel filter bypass switch, fuel pressure gauge and switch, connected by crossfeed. Standard usable fuel capacity of 600 litres (158.5 US gallons; 131 Imp gallons), with provision for additional 423 litres usable (111.75 US gallons; 93 Imp gallons) in optional auxiliary tanks. Fuel quantity gauge and fuel reserve warning. Two separate oil systems, each with oil cooling, temperature and pressure gauges, oil filter bypass pop-up and chip warning. Each engine equipped with starter/generator, engine fuel pump effective for cruise after both boost pumps out, N1 and N2 tacho-generators, TOT gauge and switch, start counter, and 'engine out' warning. Dual engine inlet anti-icing standard. Each engine compartment equipped with fire detection system and with automatic and manual fire extinguishing systems.

ACCOMMODATION: Pilot (port side), and co-pilot or passenger, on adjustable and removable front seats, each fitted with safety belt. Dual controls optional. Accommodation for up to eight more persons, on two three-person bench seats and a single or double seat at rear of cabin, all with safety belts. Seats removable for carriage of cargo (up to 1,200 kg; 2,645 lb), two or four stretchers plus medical attendants, agricultural or other specialised equipment. Access to cabin via jettisonable door on each side at front (port door of sliding type) and larger passenger/cargo door at rear on port side. Pilot's windscreen wiper standard, co-pilot's optional. Cargo and stretcher tiedown points in cabin floor. Cabin soundproofing and ventilation standard; heating, carpets, double pane windows, pilot's heated windscreen, all optional. Baggage compartment at rear of cabin. Cockpit and cabin lighting standard.

SYSTEMS: Hydraulic system, with pressure gauge and switch, standard. Compressed air system, with accumulator and system gauges, standard. Ventilation standard, with individually controllable fresh air outlets; Casey cabin heaters optional, with individual control of hot air flow and central control of overall cabin air temperature. DC electrical system based on two 28V 150A starter/ generators and a 25Ah nickel-cadmium battery, with ground power receptacle. Ground/battery power, battery overtemperature and 'generator out' warnings standard. A 16kVA AC generator and/or 115V 250A static inverter are optional; this AC system is equipped with AC generator and AC 115V warnings. Dual fire detection and extinguishing systems for engines standard.

AVIONICS AND EQUIPMENT: Primary instrumentation includes attitude, altitude, airspeed, turn and slip, and rate of climb indicators; magnetic compass and gyro compass; HSI; clock; VHF com transceiver; and full range of power plant and systems control, monitoring and warning instruments. Optional radio-navigation avionics include digital ADF, R/Nav (VOR 1), audio panel, VOR/LOC/glideslope converter, transponder with or without altitude encoder, marker beacon receiver, DME, second VHF com transceiver, VOR 2 receiver, HF com transceiver, and radar altimeter. Standard equipment includes dual anti-collision lights, navigation lights, portable fire extinguisher, tool kit and first aid kit. Fluorescent tube cabin lighting and/or individual lights optional.

OPERATIONAL EQUIPMENT: According to mission, the Kania can be equipped with an 800 kg (1,763 lb) capacity stabilised cargo sling; 120 kg (265 lb) capacity hoist (275 kg; 606 lb hoist under test in 1986); stretchers and casualty care equipment; or equipment for a variety of agricultural duties.

DIMENSIONS, EXTERNAL:
Main rotor diameter	14.558 m (47 ft 9¼ in)
Tail rotor diameter	2.70 m (8 ft 10¼ in)
Length overall, rotors turning	17.47 m (57 ft 3¾ in)
Length of fuselage	12.03 m (39 ft 5½ in)
Height to top of rotor head	3.75 m (12 ft 3½ in)
Stabiliser span	1.84 m (6 ft 0½ in)
Wheel track	3.05 m (10 ft 0 in)
Wheelbase	2.71 m (8 ft 10¾ in)

DIMENSIONS, INTERNAL:
Cabin: Length, incl flight deck	4.07 m (13 ft 4¼ in)
Max width	1.50 m (4 ft 11 in)
Max height	1.62 m (5 ft 3¾ in)
Floor area	5.68 m² (61.1 sq ft)
Volume	7.76 m³ (274.0 cu ft)
Baggage compartment volume	0.45 m³ (15.89 cu ft)

AREAS:
Main rotor disc	166.50 m² (1,792.2 sq ft)
Tail rotor disc	5.725 m² (61.6 sq ft)

WEIGHTS:
Basic weight empty	2,000 kg (4,409 lb)
Max load in cabin	1,200 kg (2,645 lb)
Max cargo sling load	800 kg (1,763 lb)
Max agricultural chemical load	1,000 kg (2,205 lb)
Max load in baggage compartment	100 kg (220 lb)
Normal T-O weight	3,350 kg (7,385 lb)
Max T-O weight	3,550 kg (7,826 lb)

PERFORMANCE (clean aircraft at S/L, ISA, zero wind, at normal T-O weight):
Max cruising speed	116 knots (215 km/h; 134 mph)
Econ cruising speed	102 knots (190 km/h; 118 mph)
Max rate of climb (T-O power)	525 m (1,725 ft)/min
Rate of climb, one engine out	61 m (200 ft)/min
Service ceiling	4,000 m (13,125 ft)
Hovering ceiling: IGE	2,500 m (8,200 ft)
OGE	1,375 m (4,510 ft)

Range at econ cruising speed:
standard fuel, 30 min reserves	232 nm (430 km; 267 miles)
standard fuel, no reserves	266 nm (493 km; 306 miles)
max fuel, 30 min reserves	432 nm (800 km; 497 miles)
max fuel, no reserves	466 nm (863 km; 536 miles)

PZL SWIDNIK W-3 SOKÓL (FALCON)

Development of this all-new Polish helicopter took place in the second half of the 1970s, and the first flight was made on 16 November 1979 by one of five prototypes, which subsequently underwent a wide range of tiedown tests. The remaining prototypes were completed embodying changes made as a result of these tests, the manufacturer's flight trials being resumed on 6 May 1982 by the second aircraft (SP-PSB). Certification trials with two other aircraft were carried out in a wide range of operating conditions, including heavy icing conditions and extreme temperatures of −60°C and +50°C. Certification to Soviet NLGW regulations has been completed. Larger than the Mi-2/ Kania, the Sokól accommodates a crew of two, and 12 passengers or a maximum 2,100 kg (4,630 lb) of internal cargo.

Eleven Sokóls had been built by mid-1989. A Soviet order for 35 was announced in early 1990.

TYPE: Twin-turboshaft medium weight multi-purpose helicopter.

ROTOR SYSTEM: Four-blade fully articulated main rotor and three-blade tail rotor. Main rotor has a pendular Salomon type vibration absorber, providing smooth flight and low vibration levels. Blades of both rotors constructed of laminated glassfibre impregnated with

PZL Swidnik W-3 Sokól in Polish Air Force insignia *(Ivo Sturzenegger)*

PZL Swidnik W-3 Sokól twin-turboshaft helicopter *(Pilot Press)*

epoxy resin. Main rotor blades have tapered tips. Three hydraulic boosters for longitudinal, lateral and collective pitch control of main rotor, and one booster for tail rotor control. Blade anti-icing by electrically heated elements. Rotor brake fitted.

ROTOR DRIVE: Transmission driven via main rotor, intermediate and tail rotor gearboxes. Tail rotor driveshaft of duralumin tube with splined couplings.

FUSELAGE AND TAIL UNIT: Light alloy semi-monocoque structure, with circular section semi-monocoque tailboom. Fin integral with tailboom structure and fitted with glassfibre trailing-edge panels. Horizontal stabiliser, under end of tailboom, has a single continuous spar, is built up of laminated glassfibre impregnated with epoxy resin, and is not interconnected with the main rotor control system.

LANDING GEAR: Non-retractable tricycle type, plus tailskid beneath tailboom. Twin-wheel castoring nose unit; single wheel on each main unit. Oleo-pneumatic shock absorber in each unit. Mainwheel tyres size 500 × 250 mm; nosewheel tyres size 400 × 150 mm. Pneumatic disc brakes on mainwheels. Metal ski landing gear optional.

POWER PLANT: Two PZL-10W turboshafts (Polish developed helicopter version of Glushenkov TVD-10), each with rating of 662 kW (888 shp) for T-O and 30 min OEI, and emergency ratings of 735 kW (986 shp) and 845.5 kW (1,134 shp) for 8 min and 2½ min OEI respectively. Particle separators on engine intakes, and inlet de-icing, are standard. Power plant is equipped with advanced electronic fuel control system for maintaining rotor speed at pilot-selected value amounting to ±5 per cent of normal rpm, and also for torque sharing as well as for supervising engine limits during start-up and normal or OEI operation. Engines and main rotor gearbox are mounted on a bed frame, eliminating any drive misalignment due to deformations of the fuselage structure. Bladder fuel tanks beneath cabin floor, with combined capacity of 1,700 litres (449 US gallons; 374 Imp gallons). Auxiliary tank, capacity 1,100 litres (290.5 US gallons; 242 Imp gallons), optional.

ACCOMMODATION: Pilot (port side), and co-pilot or flight engineer, side by side on flight deck, on adjustable seats with safety belts. Dual controls and dual flight instrumentation optional. Accommodation for 12 passengers in main cabin. Seats removable for carriage of internal cargo. Ambulance version will carry four stretcher cases and a medical attendant. Baggage space at rear of cabin. Door on each side of flight deck; large

sliding door for passenger and/or cargo loading on port side at forward end of cabin; second sliding door at rear of cabin on starboard side. Optically flat windscreens, improving view and enabling wipers to sweep a large area. Accommodation soundproofed, heated (by engine bleed air) and ventilated.

SYSTEMS: Two independent hydraulic systems, working pressure 90 bars (1,300 lb/sq in), for controlling main and tail rotors, unlocking collective pitch control lever, and feeding damper of directional steering system. Flow rate 11 litres (2.9 US gallons; 2.4 Imp gallons)/min in each system. Vented gravity feed reservoir, at atmospheric pressure. Pneumatic system for actuating hydraulic mainwheel brakes. Electrical system providing both AC and DC power. Fire detection/extinguishing system. Air-conditioning and oxygen systems optional. Neutral gas system optional, for inhibiting fuel vapour explosion.

AVIONICS AND EQUIPMENT: Standard IFR nav/com avionics permit adverse weather operation by day or night. Weather radar optional. Stability augmentation system standard. Cargo version equipped with 2,100 kg (4,630 lb) capacity external hook and 150 kg (331 lb) capacity rescue hoist; 300 kg (661 lb) capacity hoist to become available.

DIMENSIONS, EXTERNAL:
Main rotor diameter	15.70 m (51 ft 6 in)
Tail rotor diameter	3.03 m (9 ft 11¼ in)
Length overall, rotors turning	18.85 m (61 ft 10⅛ in)
Length of fuselage	14.21 m (46 ft 7½ in)
Height to top of rotor head	4.12 m (13 ft 6¼ in)
Stabiliser span	3.45 m (11 ft 3¾ in)
Wheel track	3.40 m (11 ft 2 in)
Wheelbase	3.55 m (11 ft 7¾ in)
Passenger/cargo doors:	
Height (each):	1.20 m (3 ft 11¼ in)
Width: port	0.95 m (3 ft 1½ in)
starboard	1.25 m (4 ft 1¼ in)

DIMENSIONS, INTERNAL:
Cabin: Length	3.20 m (10 ft 6 in)
Max width	1.55 m (5 ft 1 in)
Max height	1.40 m (4 ft 7 in)

AREAS:
Main rotor disc	193.6 m² (2,083.8 sq ft)
Tail rotor disc	7.21 m² (77.6 sq ft)

WEIGHTS:
Minimum basic weight empty	3,300 kg (7,275 lb)
Basic operating weight empty (multi-purpose versions)	3,630 kg (8,002 lb)

Max payload, internal or external	2,100 kg (4,630 lb)
Normal T-O weight	6,100 kg (13,448 lb)
Max T-O weight	6,400 kg (14,110 lb)

PERFORMANCE (at normal T-O weight at 500 m; 1,640 ft, ISA, except where indicated):

Never-exceed speed	145 knots (270 km/h; 167 mph)
Max level speed	138 knots (255 km/h; 158 mph)
Max cruising speed	127 knots (235 km/h; 146 mph)
Econ cruising speed	119 knots (220 km/h; 137 mph)
Max rate of climb at S/L	510 m (1,673 ft)/min

Rate of climb at S/L, one engine out:

at 30 min rating	30 m (100 ft)/min
at 8 min emergency rating	96 m (315 ft)/min
at 2½ min emergency rating	186 m (610 ft)/min

Service ceiling:

at normal T-O weight	5,100 m (16,725 ft)
at T-O weight below normal	up to 6,000 m (19,680 ft)

Service ceiling, one engine out:

at 30 min rating	500 m (1,640 ft)
at 8 min emergency rating	1,800 m (5,905 ft)
at 2½ min emergency rating	approx 2,300 m (7,545 ft)

Hovering ceiling: IGE   3,000 m (9,845 ft)
OGE   2,100 m (6,890 ft)

Range:

standard fuel, 5% reserves	367 nm (680 km; 422 miles)
standard fuel, no reserves	386 nm (715 km; 444 miles)
with auxiliary fuel, 5% reserves	626 nm (1,160 km; 721 miles)
with auxiliary fuel, no reserves	661 nm (1,225 km; 761 miles)

Endurance:

standard fuel, 5% reserves	3 h 50 min
standard fuel, no reserves	4 h 5 min
with auxiliary fuel, 5% reserves	6 h 41 min
with auxiliary fuel, no reserves	7 h 5 min

PZL SWIDNIK SW-4

Development of this 4/5-seat single-engined multipurpose light helicopter began in 1985. Its general appearance is shown in the accompanying illustrations.

POWER PLANT: On 298 kW (400 shp) PZL Rzeszów GTD-350 turboshaft.

DIMENSIONS, EXTERNAL:

Main rotor diameter	9.00 m (29 ft 6⅓ in)
Main rotor blade chord	0.318 m (1 ft 0½ in)
Tail rotor diameter	1.40 m (4 ft 7 in)
Tail rotor blade chord	0.20 m (7.9 in)

Length:

overall, both rotors turning	10.50 m (34 ft 5½ in)
fuselage	8.30 m (27 ft 2¾ in)
Height overall	2.75 m (9 ft 0¼ in)
Skid track	1.80 m (5 ft 11 in)

DIMENSIONS, INTERNAL:

Cabin: Length

Length	2.00 m (6 ft 6¾ in)
Max width	1.35 m (4 ft 5¼ in)
Max height	1.30 m (4 ft 3¼ in)

AREAS:

Main rotor disc	63.62 m² (684.8 sq ft)
Tail rotor disc	1.54 m² (16.57 sq ft)

Mockup of the PZL Swidnik SW-4 four/five-seat light helicopter *(Lech Zielaskowski)*

PZL Swidnik SW-4 (298 kW; 400 shp PZL Rzeszów GTD-350 engine) *(Pilot Press)*

WEIGHTS:

Weight empty	730 kg (1,609 lb)
Normal T-O weight	1,400 kg (3,086 lb)
Max T-O weight	1,500 kg (3,307 lb)

PERFORMANCE (estimated, at normal T-O weight):

Max level speed at 500 m (1,640 ft)
    129 knots (240 km/h; 149 mph)
Max cruising speed   119 knots (220 km/h; 137 mph)

Service ceiling	5,000 m (16,400 ft)
Hovering ceiling: IGE	3,000 m (9,850 ft)
OGE	2,000 m (6,560 ft)

Range:
with max payload and standard fuel, 5% reserves
    216 nm (400 km; 248 miles)
with auxiliary fuel tank   485 nm (900 km; 559 miles)

PZL WARSZAWA-OKECIE
PANSTWOWE ZAKŁADY LOTNICZE WARSZAWA-OKECIE (State Aviation Works, Warsaw-Okecie)

Aleja Krakowska 110/114, 00-971 Warsaw
Telephone: 48 (22) 460031/9 and 465061/9
Telex: 817735 and 814649
Fax: 48 (22) 465479
GENERAL MANAGER: Ryszard Leja, MSc
EXPORT MANAGER: Andrzej Jaworowski, Eng MSc

The Okecie factory, founded in 1928, is responsible for light aircraft development and production, and for the design and manufacture of associated agricultural equipment for its own aircraft and for those built at other factories in the Polish aviation industry. It has produced more than 3,500 aircraft since 1945.

PZL-104 WILGA (ORIOLE) 35 and 80

The PZL-104 Wilga is a light general purpose aircraft for a wide variety of general aviation and flying club duties. The prototype Wilga 1 flew for the first time on 24 April 1962. This aircraft, and other early models, were described in the 1968-69 *Jane's*.

Production of the improved Wilga 35 and Wilga 32 began in 1968, and both received a Polish type certificate on 31 March 1969; the Wilga 32 was described in the 1974-75 *Jane's*, and its Indonesian built modified version, the Lipnur Gelatik, in the 1975-76 edition.

The aircraft is currently manufactured in two basic versions: the **Wilga 35** (first flight 28 July 1967), which meets the requirements of British BCAR regulations, and the **Wilga 80** (first flown on 30 May 1979), which conforms to US FAR Pt 23 requirements. The latter has the carburettor air intake located further aft. Aeroclub versions (Wilga 35A and 80A) are fitted with a glider towing hook;

This version of the PZL-104 Wilga 35, with wingtip antennae, is described as being "for UHF retransmission"

Wilgas with agricultural equipment are designated 35R and 80R, and aircraft with twin Airtech (Canada) LAP-3000 floats are known as Wilga 35H and 80H.

Wilgas have been sold to customers in Australia, Austria, Belgium, Bulgaria, Canada, Cuba, Czechoslovakia, Denmark, Egypt, Finland, Germany (Democratic Republic), Germany (Federal Republic), Hungary, Indonesia, Italy, North Korea, Poland, Romania, Spain, Sweden, Switzer-land, Turkey, the UK, the USA, the USSR (379 by 15 January 1989), Venezuela and Yugoslavia.

Total sales of the Wilga (all versions) had reached 890 by 1 January 1990.

Currently under study in 1990 was the STOL multi-purpose **Wilga 35M**, a variant of the Wilga 35A with extended operational range. With a max T-O and landing weight of 1,300 kg (2,866 lb), it would be powered by a 260.5

kW (360 hp) M-14P nine-cylinder radial engine, driving (on the prototype) a W530TA-D35 two-blade constant-speed propeller or (on any production version) a PZL-144 propeller.

The following description applies to the Wilga 35 and 80, except where a specific version is indicated:

TYPE: Single-engined general purpose aircraft.

WINGS: Cantilever high-wing monoplane. Wing section NACA 2415. Dihedral 1°. All-metal single-spar structure, with leading-edge torsion box and beaded metal skin. Each wing attached to fuselage by three bolts, two at spar and one at forward fitting. All-metal aerodynamically and mass balanced slotted ailerons, with beaded metal skin. Ailerons can be drooped to supplement flaps during landing. Manually operated all-metal slotted flaps with beaded metal skin. Fixed metal slat on leading-edge along full span of wing and over fuselage. Tab on starboard aileron.

FUSELAGE: All-metal semi-monocoque structure in two portions, riveted together. Forward section incorporates main wing spar carry-through structure. Rear section is in the form of a tailcone. Beaded metal skin. Floor in cabin is of metal sandwich construction, with a paper honeycomb core, covered with foam rubber.

TAIL UNIT: Braced all-metal structure, with sweptback vertical surfaces. Stressed skin single-spar tailplane attached to fuselage by a single centre fitting and supported by a single aluminium alloy strut on each side. Stressed skin two-spar fin structure of semi-monocoque construction. Rudder and one-piece elevator are aerodynamically horn balanced and mass balanced. Trim tab at centre of elevator trailing-edge.

LANDING GEAR: Non-retractable tailwheel type. Semi-cantilever main legs, of rocker type, have oleo-pneumatic shock absorbers. Low-pressure tyres size 500 × 200 mm on mainwheels. Hydraulic brakes. Steerable tailwheel, tyre size 255 × 110 mm, carried on rocker frame with oleo-pneumatic shock absorber. Metal ski landing gear, and Airtech Canada LAP-3000 twin-float landing gear, optional.

POWER PLANT: One 194 kW (260 hp) PZL AI-14RA nine-cylinder supercharged radial aircooled engine (AI-14RA-KAF in Wilga 80), driving a PZL US-122000 two-blade constant-speed wooden propeller. Two removable fuel tanks in each wing, with total capacity of 195 litres (51.5 US gallons; 43 Imp gallons). Refuelling point on each side of fuselage, at junction with wing. For longer-range operation, an additional 90 litre (23.8 US gallon; 19.8 Imp gallon) fuel tank can be installed in place of the rear pair of seats. Oil capacity 16 litres (4.2 US gallons; 3.5 Imp gallons).

ACCOMMODATION: Passenger version accommodates pilot and three passengers, in pairs, with adjustable front seats. Baggage compartment aft of seats, capacity 35 kg (77 lb). Rear seats can be replaced by additional fuel tank for longer-range operation. Upward opening door on each side of cabin, jettisonable in emergency. In the parachute training version the starboard door is removed and replaced by two tubular uprights with a central connecting strap, and the starboard front seat is rearward facing. Jumps are facilitated by a step on the starboard side and by a parachute hitch. A controllable towing hook can be attached to the tail landing gear permitting the Wilga, in this role, to tow a single glider of up to 650 kg (1,433 lb) weight or two or three gliders with a combined weight of 1,125 kg (2,480 lb).

SYSTEMS: Hydraulic system pressure 39 bars (570 lb/sq in). Engine starting is effected pneumatically by a built-in system of 7 litres (0.25 cu ft) capacity with a pressure of 49 bars (710 lb/sq in). Electrical system powered by DC generator and 24V 10Ah battery.

AVIONICS AND EQUIPMENT: Standard avionics and equipment include VHF transceiver and blind-flying instrumentation. Optional avionics and equipment include RS-6102 (of Polish design), R-860 II, R860 IIM, Bendix/King KY 195 or other radio; and ARL-1601 VHF, ARK-9, Bendix/King KR 85 or AV-200 ADF, GB-1 gyro compass, K2-715 airspeed and altitude recorder, sun visors, exhaust silencer and windscreen wiper.

DIMENSIONS, EXTERNAL:
Wing span: 35	11.12 m (36 ft 5¾ in)
80	11.13 m (36 ft 6¼ in)
Wing chord (constant)	1.40 m (4 ft 7¼ in)
Wing aspect ratio	8.0
Length overall: 35	8.10 m (26 ft 6¾ in)
80	8.03 m (26 ft 4¼ in)
Height overall	2.96 m (9 ft 8½ in)
Tailplane span	3.70 m (12 ft 1¾ in)
Wheel track	2.75 m (9 ft 0¼ in)
Wheelbase	6.70 m (21 ft 11¾ in)
Propeller diameter	2.65 m (8 ft 8 in)
Passenger doors (each): Height	1.00 m (3 ft 3¼ in)
Width	1.50 m (4 ft 11 in)

DIMENSIONS, INTERNAL:
Cabin: Length	2.20 m (7 ft 2½ in)
Max width	1.20 m (3 ft 10 in)
Max height	1.50 m (4 ft 11 in)
Floor area	2.20 m² (23.8 sq ft)
Volume	2.40 m³ (85 cu ft)
Baggage compartment	0.50 m³ (17.5 cu ft)

AREAS:
Wings, gross	15.50 m² (166.8 sq ft)

Prototype PZL Warszawa-Okecie PZL-105M six-seat general utility aircraft *(R. J. Malachowski)*

Ailerons (total)	1.57 m² (16.90 sq ft)
Trailing-edge flaps (total)	1.97 m² (21.20 sq ft)
Fin	0.97 m² (10.44 sq ft)
Rudder	0.92 m² (9.90 sq ft)
Tailplane	3.16 m² (34.01 sq ft)
Elevator, incl tab	1.92 m² (20.67 sq ft)

WEIGHTS AND LOADINGS (Wilga 35A and 80):
Weight empty, equipped	870 kg (1,918 lb)
Max T-O and landing weight	1,300 kg (2,866 lb)
Max wing loading	83.9 kg/m² (17.18 lb/sq ft)
Max power loading	6.70 kg/kW (11.02 lb/hp)

PERFORMANCE (Wilga 35A, at max T-O weight):
Never-exceed speed	150 knots (279 km/h; 173 mph)
Max level speed	105 knots (194 km/h; 120 mph)
Cruising speed (75% power)	85 knots (157 km/h; 97 mph)
Cruising speed for max range	74 knots (137 km/h; 85 mph)
Stalling speed: flaps up	35 knots (65 km/h; 41 mph)
flaps down	30 knots (56 km/h; 35 mph)
Max rate of climb at S/L	276 m (905 ft)/min
Time to 1,000 m (3,280 ft)	3 min
Service ceiling	4,040 m (13,250 ft)
T-O run (grass)	121 m (397 ft)
Landing run	106 m (348 ft)
Range with max fuel, 30 min reserves	275 nm (510 km; 317 miles)

PZL-105 FLAMING (FLAMINGO)

Although referred to at first as the Wilga 88, the PZL-105 is an entirely new design, developed as a successor to the Wilga 35/80 series to meet the needs of operators requiring STOL characteristics combined with greater speed, range and payload capacity. The design team was led by Roman Czerwiński, under the direction of Andrzej Frydrychewicz. Three flying prototypes and a static test airframe are being built. First flight was made on 19 December 1989, and certification is anticipated in 1991.

Intended to maintain the versatility of the Wilga, the PZL-105 will have a choice of power plants (**PZL-105M** with M-14P engine and **PZL-105L** with an IO-720) and landing gears, and will be suitable for such duties as light passenger or cargo transport, sport flying and aero club use, glider towing, parachute training, air ambulance, patrol or geophysical survey, and agricultural use. It can operate from unprepared airstrips, and is to be certificated to FAR Pt 23 (Amendments 1-28) in the Normal category.

General appearance of the PZL-105 is shown in the accompanying illustrations.

TYPE: Single-engined general purpose aircraft.

WINGS: All-metal high-wing monoplane, with wing section similar to NASA GA(W)-1. Single bracing strut on each side. Single-slotted Fowler trailing-edge flaps and flaperons, actuated electrically. Glassfibre wingtips. Construction generally similar to that of Wilga.

FUSELAGE: Conventional all-metal semi-monocoque structure.

TAIL UNIT: All-metal structure comprising sweptback fin and rudder, with low-set unswept tailplane and elevators. Raked tips on fin and tailplane. Electrically actuated trim tab on port elevator; ground adjustable tab on rudder.

LANDING GEAR: Non-retractable type, with single mainwheels on cantilever self-sprung legs (glassfibre leaf springs) and a steerable tailwheel with oleo-pneumatic shock absorption. Low pressure tyres and hydraulic disc brakes on mainwheels. May also be fitted with floats, skis (with snow brakes) or wheel/skis.

POWER PLANT: Initial choice (PZL-105M) of one 268.5 kW (360 hp) Vedeneyev M-14P nine-cylinder aircooled radial engine, driving a W-530-TA-D35 two-blade constant-speed propeller. Provision for later use (PZL-105L) of 298 kW (400 hp) Textron Lycoming IO-720-A1B flat-eight engine and Hartzell propeller. Fuel in integral tanks in wings, total capacity 270 litres (71.3 US gallons; 59.4 Imp gallons).

ACCOMMODATION: Fully enclosed cabin, with seats for up to six persons (including pilot and optional second pilot) in three rows of two. Large door each side, with upward opening top half; downward opening lower halves incorporate steps. Dual controls optional. Cabin heated and ventilated.

DIMENSIONS, EXTERNAL:
Wing span	12.70 m (41 ft 8 in)
Wing aspect ratio	9.5
Length overall	8.60 m (28 ft 2½ in)
Height overall	2.80 m (9 ft 2¼ in)
Wheel track	3.10 m (10 ft 2 in)
Wheelbase	6.086 m (19 ft 11½ in)
Propeller diameter	2.40 m (7 ft 10½ in)
Cabin door: Height	1.10 m (3 ft 7¼ in)
Width	1.60 m (5 ft 3 in)

DIMENSIONS, INTERNAL:
Cabin: Length	2.80 m (9 ft 2¼ in)
Max width	1.10 m (3 ft 7¼ in)
Max height	1.20 m (3 ft 11¼ in)

AREAS:
Wings, gross	16.90 m² (181.9 sq ft)
Ailerons (total)	1.13 m² (12.16 sq ft)
Trailing-edge flaps (total)	1.95 m² (20.99 sq ft)

WEIGHTS AND LOADINGS:
Standard weight empty, equipped	1,100 kg (2,425 lb)
Max T-O weight	1,850 kg (4,078 lb)
Max wing loading	109.5 kg/m² (22.42 lb/sq ft)
Max power loading	6.89 kg/kW (11.32 lb/hp)

PERFORMANCE (estimated. A: at 1,250 kg; 2,756 lb AUW, B: at 1,650 kg; 3,637 lb, rest at max T-O weight):
Never-exceed speed	165 knots (306 km/h; 190 mph)
Max level speed	140 knots (260 km/h; 161 mph)
Max cruising speed (134 kW; 180 hp)	116 knots (216 km/h; 134 mph)
Econ cruising speed (107.5 kW; 144 hp)	102 knots (190 km/h; 118 mph)
Stalling speed: A	45 knots (83 km/h; 52 mph)
B	52 knots (95 km/h; 59 mph)
Max rate of climb at S/L: A	523 m (1,716 ft)/min
B	396 m (1,299 ft)/min
T-O run: A	42 m (138 ft)
B	111 m (365 ft)
T-O to 15 m (50 ft): A	117 m (384 ft)
B	218 m (716 ft)
Landing from 15 m (50 ft): A	168 m (552 ft)
B	201 m (660 ft)
Landing run: A	66 m (217 ft)
B	94 m (309 ft)
Range with max fuel:	
at max cruising speed	533 nm (989 km; 614 miles)
at econ cruising speed	625 nm (1,159 km; 720 miles)
g limits	+3.8/-1.52

PZL-106B KRUK (RAVEN)

The PZL-106 was designed in early 1972 by a team led by Andrzej Frydrychewicz. The first prototype (SP-PAS) flew for the first time on 17 April 1973, powered by a 298 kW (400 hp) Textron Lycoming IO-720 engine. It was followed in October of that year by a second Textron Lycoming engined prototype (SP-PBG) and, from October 1974, by four prototypes fitted with the 441 kW (592 hp) PZL-3S radial engine that powers the PZL-106A and B. Production versions also have a low-mounted tailplane instead of the earlier T tail, and a greater chemical load in a larger hopper. Manufacture of some 600 aircraft for the member countries of the CMEA (Council for Mutual Economic Aid) is anticipated. A total of more than 246 (all versions) had been built by 1 January 1990, including 144 PZL-106As produced between 1976-81. Details of the PZL-106A, and of the AR and AT prototypes, can be found in the 1985-86 and earlier editions of *Jane's.*

The following versions of the Kruk are the most recent:

PZL-106AS. To increase the performance of PZL-106A Kruks operated by Pezetel in Egypt and the Sudan, PZL Warszawa-Okecie adapted the design to take a 746 kW (1,000 hp) PZL (Shvetsov) ASz-62IR nine-cylinder radial engine instead of the standard 441 kW (592 hp) PZL-3S. The prototype of this version (SP-PBD) flew for the first time on 19 August 1981. First ten re-engined in 1982; 44

converted by early 1987. Hopper load reduced to 750 kg (1,653 lb) initially, due to heavier engine. Re-certificated in July 1983 for operation at higher (Restricted) max T-O weight of 3,600 kg (7,936 lb). New-production aircraft with this engine are to PZL-106BS standard (which see).

PZL-106B. Prototypes for improved series, having redesigned wings with a new aerofoil section, increased span and area, trailing-edge flaps, and shortened V bracing struts. First prototype (SP-PKW) flew for the first time on 15 May 1981. Two further prototypes made their first flights in July and September 1981. Weights and performance data in 1985-86 and earlier *Jane's*.

PZL-106BR. Version with geared PZL-3SR engine; first flown on 8 July 1983. Tested also with wingtip vanes (three at each tip). Total of 64 built by 1 January 1990.

PZL-106BS. The prototype (SP-PBK) of this uprated version of the Kruk, with a PZL (Shvetsov) ASz-62IR radial engine, flew for the first time on 8 March 1982. Total of 15 built by 1 January 1990. For Restricted category operation, with higher max T-O weight and increased load of chemical.

PZL-106BT Turbo-Kruk. Turboprop version; described separately.

The following description applies generally to the piston engined PZL-106B series, except where a specific version is indicated:

TYPE: Single-engined agricultural aircraft. Structure is corrosion resistant, and is additionally protected by an external finish of polyurethane enamel.

WINGS: Braced low-wing monoplane with upward cambered tips. NACA 2415 wing section throughout span. Dihedral 4° from roots. Incidence 6° 6'. Sweepback 1° at quarter-chord. All-metal two-spar duralumin structure, of constant chord. Metal and polyester fabric covering. Glassfibre wingtips, with upswept undersurfaces. Full span four-segment fixed leading-edge slats on each wing, of glassfibre sandwich construction with foam core. Slotted ailerons of duralumin, with polyester fabric covering. Trailing-edge flaps of similar construction. Ground adjustable tab on each aileron initially; aircraft from tenth production batch onward have electrically actuated trim tab in port aileron. Duralumin streamline section V bracing struts, with jury struts.

FUSELAGE: Welded steel tube structure, protected by several coats of polyurethane enamel and covered with quickly removable panels of light alloy and GFRP. Steel tube structure can be pressure tested for crack detection.

TAIL UNIT: Conventional duralumin structure, initially with single tailplane bracing strut each side; two struts each side from ninth production batch onward. Fixed surfaces metal covered; rudder and mass balanced elevators are polyester fabric covered. Trim tab in port elevator, automatic tab on rudder.

LANDING GEAR: Non-retractable tailwheel type, with oleo-pneumatic shock absorber in each unit. Mainwheels, with low-pressure tyres size 800 × 260 mm, each carried on side V and half-axle. Mainwheel tyre pressure 2.0 bars (29 lb/sq in). Pneumatically operated hydraulic disc brakes on mainwheels. Parking brake. Steerable tailwheel, with tubeless tyre size 350 × 135 mm, pressure 2.5 bars (36.25 lb/sq in).

POWER PLANT: *(PZL-106BR):* One 448 kW (600 hp) PZL-3SR seven-cylinder radial aircooled geared and supercharged engine, driving a PZL US-133000 four-blade constant-speed metal propeller. *(PZL-106BS):* One 746 kW (1,000 hp) PZL (Shvetsov) ASz-62IR nine-cylinder radial aircooled engine and AW-2-30 propeller. Fuel in two integral wing tanks, total capacity 560 litres (148 US gallons; 123 Imp gallons); can be increased to total of 950 litres (251 US gallons; 209 Imp gallons) by using hopper as auxiliary fuel tank. Gravity refuelling point on each wing; semi-pressurised refuelling point on starboard side of fuselage. Oil capacity 54 litres (14.3 US gallons; 11.9 Imp gallons) max in BR, 67 litres (17.7 US gallons; 14.7 Imp gallons) in BS. Carburettor air filter fitted.

ACCOMMODATION: Single vertically adjustable seat in enclosed, ventilated and heated cockpit with steel tube overturn structure. Provision for instructor's cockpit with basic dual controls, forward of main cockpit and offset to starboard, for training of pilots in agricultural duties. Optional rearward facing second seat (for mechanic) to rear. Jettisonable window/door on each side of cabin. Pilot's seat and seat belt designed to resist 40g impact.

SYSTEMS: Pneumatic system, rated at 49 bars (710 lb/sq in), for brakes and agricultural equipment. Electrical power, from 3kW 27.5V DC generator and 24V 15Ah battery, for engine starting, pneumatic system control, aircraft lights, instruments, VHF transceiver and semi-pressurised refuelling. Cockpit air-conditioning system optional.

EQUIPMENT: VHF com transceiver standard. Easily removable non-corroding (GFRP) hopper/tank, forward of cockpit, can carry more than 1,000 kg (2,205 lb) (see under 'Weights and Loadings' paragraph) of dry or liquid chemical, and has a maximum capacity of 1,400 litres (370 US gallons; 308 Imp gallons). Turnround time, with full load of chemical, is in the order of 28 s. The hopper has a quick-dump system that can release 1,000 kg of chemical in 5 s or less. A pneumatically operated

PZL-106BR Kruk single-seat agricultural aircraft *(Jane's/Mike Keep)*

intake for the loading of dry chemicals is optional. Distribution system for liquid chemical (jets or atomisers) is powered by a fan driven centrifugal pump. A precise and reliable dispersal system, with positive on/off action for dry chemicals, gives effective swath widths of 30-35 m (100-115 ft). For ferry purposes, hopper can be used to carry additional fuel instead of chemical. When the Kruk is converted into a two-seat trainer (see 'Accommodation' paragraph), standard hopper can be replaced easily by a special container with reduced capacity tank for liquid chemical. Steel cable cutter on windscreen and each mainwheel leg; steel deflector cable runs from top of windscreen cable cutter to tip of fin. Windscreen washer and wiper standard. Other equipment includes 720-channel ultra short wave transceiver (optional), artificial horizon, gyro compass, engine hour meter, clock, rearview mirror, second (mechanic's) seat (optional), cockpit air-conditioning (optional), cockpit heating and ventilation, landing light, anti-collision light, and night working lights (optional).

DIMENSIONS, EXTERNAL:
Wing span	14.90 m (48 ft 10½ in)
Wing chord, constant	2.16 m (7 ft 1 in)
Wing aspect ratio	6.9
Length overall: BR	9.25 m (30 ft 4½ in)
BS	9.34 m (30 ft 7¾ in)
Height overall	3.32 m (10 ft 10¾ in)
Tailplane span	5.77 m (18 ft 11¼ in)
Wheel track	3.10 m (10 ft 2¼ in)
Wheelbase	7.41 m (24 ft 3¾ in)
Propeller diameter: BR	3.10 m (10 ft 2 in)
BS	3.30 m (10 ft 10 in)
Propeller ground clearance (tail up)	0.39 m (1 ft 3¼ in)
Crew doors (each): Height	0.91 m (2 ft 11¾ in)
Width	1.06 m (3 ft 5¾ in)
Baggage door: Height	0.70 m (2 ft 3½ in)
Width	0.60 m (1 ft 11¾ in)

DIMENSIONS, INTERNAL:
Cabin: Length	1.37 m (4 ft 6 in)
Max width	1.25 m (4 ft 1¼ in)
Max height	1.30 m (4 ft 3¼ in)
Floor area	1.12 m² (12.05 sq ft)
Rear cockpit/baggage compartment:	
Length	1.40 m (4 ft 7 in)
Width	1.00 m (3 ft 3¼ in)
Depth	0.60 m (1 ft 11¾ in)

AREAS:
Wings, gross	31.69 m² (341.1 sq ft)

Ailerons (total)	4.34 m² (46.72 sq ft)
Trailing-edge flaps (total)	4.44 m² (47.79 sq ft)
Leading-edge slats (total)	4.25 m² (45.75 sq ft)
Fin	1.26 m² (13.56 sq ft)
Rudder, incl tab	1.62 m² (17.44 sq ft)
Tailplane	3.34 m² (35.95 sq ft)
Elevators, incl tab	4.22 m² (45.42 sq ft)

WEIGHTS AND LOADINGS:
Weight empty, equipped: BR	1,790 kg (3,946 lb)
BS	2,080 kg (4,585 lb)
Max chemical payload: BR	1,300 kg (2,866 lb)
BS	1,150 kg (2,535 lb)
Max T-O and landing weight: BR, BS	3,000 kg (6,614 lb)
BR (Restricted category)	3,450 kg (7,606 lb)
BS (Restricted category)	3,500 kg (7,716 lb)
Max wing loading (Restricted category):	
BR	108.86 kg/m² (22.30 lb/sq ft)
BS	110.44 kg/m² (22.62 lb/sq ft)
Max power loading (Restricted category):	
BR	7.70 kg/kW (12.68 lb/hp)
BS	4.69 kg/kW (7.72 lb/hp)

PERFORMANCE (at max T-O weight):
Never-exceed speed:	
BR, BS	145 knots (270 km/h; 167 mph)
Max level speed at S/L:	
BR, BS	116 knots (215 km/h; 134 mph)
Operating speed with max chemical load:	
BR	81-86 knots (150-160 km/h; 93-99 mph)
BS	86 knots (160 km/h; 99 mph)
Stalling speed at S/L:	
BR, BS	54 knots (100 km/h; 62 mph)
Max rate of climb at S/L (with agricultural equipment):	
BR	228 m (748 ft)/min
BS	372 m (1,220 ft)/min
T-O run (with agricultural equipment):	
BR	250 m (820 ft)
BS	120 m (394 ft)
Landing run (with agricultural equipment):	
BR, BS	200 m (656 ft)
Range with max standard fuel:	
BR, BS	485 nm (900 km; 559 miles)

PZL-106BT TURBO-KRUK

This turboprop version of the Kruk was flown for the first time (prototype SP-PAA) on 18 September 1985. It has increased wing sweep, a taller fin, and carries a larger load of chemical. A total of 11 production aircraft had been built

PZL-106BT Turbo-Kruk, first version of the Kruk with a Czechoslovak turboprop

by 1 January 1990, at which time the Turbo-Kruk was operating in Egypt, East Germany and Poland.

Differences from the piston engined Kruk are as follows:
AIRFRAME: Wing sweepback 6° at quarter-chord. Dihedral 6°. Taller fin.
POWER PLANT: One 544 kW (730 shp) Walter M 601 D turboprop, driving an Avia V 508 D three-blade propeller with spinner.

DIMENSIONS, EXTERNAL:
Wing span	15.00 m (49 ft 2½ in)
Wing chord, constant	2.16 m (7 ft 1 in)
Wing aspect ratio	7.1
Length overall	10.24 m (33 ft 7¼ in)
Height overall	3.82 m (12 ft 6½ in)
Propeller diameter	2.50 m (8 ft 2½ in)

AREAS:
Wings, gross	31.69 m² (341.1 sq ft)
Fin	1.82 m² (19.59 sq ft)

WEIGHTS AND LOADINGS:
Weight empty, equipped	1,680 kg (3,704 lb)
Max chemical payload	1,300 kg (2,866 lb)
Max T-O weight	3,500 kg (7,716 lb)
Max landing weight	3,000 kg (6,614 lb)
Max wing loading	110.44 kg/m² (22.62 lb/sq ft)
Max power loading	6.07 kg/kW (9.97 lb/shp)

PERFORMANCE (at max T-O weight):
Never-exceed speed	145 knots (270 km/h; 167 mph)
Max level speed at S/L:	
without agricultural equipment	135 knots (250 km/h; 155 mph)
with agricultural equipment	116 knots (215 km/h; 134 mph)
Operating speed with max chemical load	81-92 knots (150-170 km/h; 93-106 mph)
Stalling speed at S/L	49 knots (90 km/h; 56 mph)
Max rate of climb at S/L (with agricultural equipment)	360 m (1,180 ft)/min
T-O run (with agricultural equipment)	230 m (755 ft)
Landing run (with agricultural equipment)	130 m (427 ft)
Range with max standard fuel	485 nm (900 km; 559 miles)

PZL-140 GĄSIOR (GANDER)

The Gąsior, design of which was started in 1984, has been proposed as a specialised firefighting and cropspraying aircraft combining the qualities and several airframe parts of the PZL Mielec An-2 and Warszawa-Okecie PZL-106 Kruk.

If approved, the PZL-140 would combine the power plant, cabin module, rear fuselage, tailplane and tailwheel of the PZL-106BS, and the vertical tail of the PZL-106BT Turbo-Kruk, with the propeller and main landing gear of the An-2. Thus the only major new structure required would be the forward fuselage, which would form an integral tank or hopper for water, retardant or agricultural chemical. This would have two or four internal chambers with a total volume of 3.4 m³ (120.1 cu ft), permitting a max payload of 3,000 kg (6,614 lb) to be carried.

Versions of the PZL-140 with a new (895 kW; 1,200 hp) variant of the ASz-62 radial engine, or an 895 kW (1,200 shp) TVD-20 turboprop, have also been projected. General appearance of the aircraft is shown in an accompanying drawing. (See also Addenda.)

DIMENSIONS, EXTERNAL:
Wing span (lower)	14.67 m (48 ft 1½ in)
Length overall	10.72 m (35 ft 2 in)
Height overall	5.04 m (16 ft 6½ in)

AREA:
Wings, gross	60.5 m² (651.2 sq ft)

PZL-110 Koliber Series III, Polish built version of the Socata Rallye 100ST

WEIGHTS AND LOADINGS (746 kW; 1,000 hp ASz-62 engine):
Standard weight empty, equipped	2,340 kg (5,159 lb)
Max T-O weight: Normal category	5,250 kg (11,574 lb)
Restricted category	5,700 kg (12,566 lb)
Wing loading (Normal cat)	86.8 kg/m² (17.78 lb/sq ft)
Power loading (Normal cat)	7.04 kg/kW (11.57 lb/hp)

PERFORMANCE (estimated at max Normal T-O weight, 746 kW; 1,000 hp ASz-62):
Never-exceed speed	145 knots (270 km/h; 167 mph)
Normal operating speed	129 knots (240 km/h; 149 mph)
Stalling speed, power off:	
flaps up	59 knots (109 km/h; 68 mph)
flaps down	53 knots (98 km/h; 61 mph)
Max rate of climb at S/L	210 m (689 ft)/min
Service ceiling	3,600 m (11,800 ft)
T-O to 15 m (50 ft): grass	750 m (2,461 ft)
concrete	690 m (2,264 ft)
Landing from 15 m (50 ft): grass	410 m (1,346 ft)
concrete	660 m (2,166 ft)
Normal range, no reserves	270 nm (500 km; 310 miles)
Max ferry range, with fuel in hopper	1,888 nm (3,500 km; 2,175 miles)
g limits:	+3/−1 Restricted
	+3.26/−1.3 Normal

PZL-110 KOLIBER (HUMMING-BIRD)

Under this designation, PZL Warszawa-Okecie is producing under licence a two/four-seat version of the Socata Rallye 100 ST, the lowest powered model in the Rallye light aircraft family. The first PZL-110, modified to receive an 86.5 kW (116 hp) PZL-F (Franklin) engine, made its initial flight on 18 April 1978.

The first production PZL-110 was flown on 8 May 1979, and ten Series I aircraft were built during that year. A Polish type certificate was awarded on 24 August 1979.

Although suitable for touring and liaison duties, the Koliber is intended primarily for basic and refresher flying training. Series II production aircraft (built 1983-84) are approved for limited aerobatics, and are for use only by Polish aeroclubs. Twenty-five have been delivered to Polish aero clubs since 1984. Production of Series III (45 aircraft) was still awaiting availability of PZL-F 4A-235B31 engines in early 1990.

On 27 September 1988 PZL Warszawa-Okecie began flight testing a four-seat **Koliber-150** (SP-PHA), powered by a 112 kW (150 hp) Textron Lycoming O-320-E2A flat-four engine driving a Sensenich 74DM6-0-58 two-blade constant-speed propeller. This version was certificated in 1989 and is in production.

The following description applies to the Koliber-150:
TYPE: Four-seat light aircraft.
WINGS: Cantilever low-wing monoplane. Wing section NACA 63A416 (modified). Dihedral 7°. Incidence 4°. All-metal single-spar structure. Wide chord slotted ailerons. Full span automatic leading-edge slats. Long span electrically actuated trailing-edge slotted flaps. Ailerons and flaps have corrugated metal skin. Ground adjustable aileron tabs. No anti-icing.
FUSELAGE: All-metal semi-monocoque structure.
TAIL UNIT: Cantilever all-metal structure, with corrugated skin on mass balanced control surfaces. Fixed incidence tailplane. One controllable tab on elevator; ground adjustable tab on rudder.
LANDING GEAR: Non-retractable tricycle type, with oleo-pneumatic shock absorption. Castoring nosewheel. Hydraulic disc brakes.
POWER PLANT: One 112 kW (150 hp) Textron Lycoming O-320-E2A flat-four engine, driving a Sensenich 74DM6-0-58 two-blade constant-speed propeller. Fuel in two metal tanks in wings, with total capacity of 95 litres (25 US gallons; 20.9 Imp gallons). Refuelling points above wings. Oil capacity 6 litres (1.6 US gallons; 1.3 Imp gallons).
ACCOMMODATION: Two side by side seats, plus bench seat at rear, under large rearward sliding canopy. Dual controls. Heating and ventilation standard.
SYSTEMS AND EQUIPMENT: 12V electrical system, with 50A alternator and 30Ah battery. Equipment includes UHF transceiver, ADF, VOR, electrically powered gyro attitude indicator, turn and bank indicator, and directional gyro. Equipment for the training role includes pupil's window blinds for instrument training, front seat backrests suitable for use with back type parachutes, safety belts, and accelerometers.

DIMENSIONS, EXTERNAL:
Wing span	9.74 m (31 ft 11½ in)
Wing chord, constant	1.30 m (4 ft 3 in)
Wing aspect ratio	7.5
Length overall	7.30 m (23 ft 11½ in)
Height overall	2.80 m (9 ft 2¼ in)
Tailplane span	3.67 m (12 ft 0½ in)
Wheel track	2.01 m (6 ft 7¼ in)
Wheelbase	1.71 m (5 ft 7¼ in)
Propeller diameter	1.78 m (5 ft 10 in)

AREAS:
Wings, gross	12.66 m² (136.3 sq ft)
Ailerons (total)	1.56 m² (16.79 sq ft)
Trailing-edge flaps (total)	2.40 m² (25.83 sq ft)
Vertical tail surfaces (total)	1.74 m² (18.73 sq ft)
Horizontal tail surfaces (total)	3.48 m² (37.50 sq ft)

WEIGHTS AND LOADINGS:
Weight empty, equipped	548 kg (1,208 lb)
Max T-O weight: Utility	770 kg (1,697 lb)
Normal	850 kg (1,874 lb)
Max wing loading: Utility	60.82 kg/m² (12.46 lb/sq ft)
Normal	67.14 kg/m² (13.76 lb/sq ft)
Max power loading: Utility	8.90 kg/kW (14.63 lb/hp)
Normal	7.60 kg/kW (12.49 lb/hp)

PERFORMANCE (at 770 kg; 1,697 lb Utility max T-O weight):
Never-exceed speed	145 knots (270 km/h; 167 mph)
Max level speed at S/L	108 knots (200 km/h; 124 mph)
Max cruising speed at S/L	92 knots (170 km/h; 106 mph)
Stalling speed: flaps up	50 knots (92 km/h; 58 mph)
flaps down	45 knots (82 km/h; 51 mph)
Max rate of climb at S/L	252 m (827 ft)/min

The proposed PZL-140 Gąsior firefighting/agricultural biplane, with additional side view of the PZL-140T Gąsior Turbo (Jane's/Mike Keep)

Service ceiling	3,700 m (12,140 ft)
T-O run at S/L	146 m (479 ft)
T-O to 15 m (50 ft) at S/L	354 m (1,161 ft)
Landing from 15 m (50 ft) at S/L	290 m (952 ft)
Landing run at S/L	128 m (420 ft)
Range at 500 m (1,640 ft) with max fuel, no reserves	
	324 nm (600 km; 373 miles)

PZL-126 MRÓWKA (ANT)

Design of this very small agricultural aircraft, and of an innovatory new airborne spraying system, was initiated in the late 1970s by Dipl Eng Andrzej Słocinski of PZL Warszawa-Okecie, who remains in charge of the Mrówka programme today. Its propeller, rear fuselage and parts of the landing gear were built by students of the factory's training college. Preliminary design was completed in late 1982 and initial detail design work in the second quarter of 1983, but original plans for a first flight in 1985 were revised pending a reappraisal of the project. One reason for this was the unavailability at that time of production PZL-F (Franklin) engines; it was also felt that the proposed use of many components from other existing production Polish aircraft might not be as satisfactory as was thought, and that more effort should be expended in perfecting the new agricultural equipment. However, by the Autumn of 1985 the project was sufficiently advanced for a full size mockup to be built and exhibited at the Olsztyn agricultural aviation exhibition. Construction of three prototypes has now begun, and the first of these (SP-PMA) made its first flight on 20 April 1990.

As now configured, the PZL-126 design meets the requirements of FAR Pt 23 (USA) and BCAR Section K (UK). It can be dismantled quickly for long-distance transportation in the cabin of an An-2 biplane, or can be towed on its own landing gear by a light all-terrain vehicle. Landing gear is normally of tricycle type, with a 'taildragger' gear available optionally. Another option to be tested on the prototypes is a wing with full span flaps, airbrakes and spoilers, instead of the basic slotted flaps plus flaperons system. The dedicated agricultural spray system is in the form of vaned and pressurised wingtip pods of chemical, attached by quick-fastening locks to facilitate rapid replacement of empty pods by full ones. (These are replaced by extended wingtips on prototype, as illustrated, increasing span by 1.00 m; 3 ft 3.4 in.) A special retractable device for spreading biological agents is installed in the fuselage underside aft of the cockpit. Further details of individual dispersal systems are given in the 'Equipment' paragraph.

The primary use intended for the Mrówka is as an economical small aircraft for use on farms and smallholdings, but it is considered suitable also for patrol and liaison missions (eg for detecting/controlling forest fires, identification of diseased vegetation, and monitoring areas of polluted land and water).

TYPE: Single-seat light agricultural and ecological support aircraft.

WINGS: Cantilever low-wing monoplane, of constant chord and NASA GA(W)-1 wing section. Single-spar metal structure, with trailing-edge single-slotted flaps inboard and flaperons outboard. Some components of glassfibre/epoxy construction. Alternative wings with full span flaps, airbrakes and spoilers also to be tested.

FUSELAGE: Conventional metal semi-monocoque structure, built in two portions. Some elements constructed of glassfibre/epoxy composite material.

TAIL UNIT: Cantilever all-metal structure, comprising rectangular fin and rudder and low-set tailplane with one-piece elevator. Trim tab on starboard half of elevator; ground adjustable tab on rudder.

LANDING GEAR: Non-retractable tricycle gear standard. Cantilever self-sprung mainwheel legs; shock absorber in nosewheel unit. Size 350 × 135 mm tyres on all three

First prototype PZL-126 Mrówka experimental agricultural aircraft (R. J. Malachowski)

wheels, pressure 1.23 bars (17.8 lb/sq in) on main units and 0.78 bar (11.3 lb/sq in) on nose unit. Mainwheels fitted with differential hydraulic disc brakes. Tailwheel configuration optional.

POWER PLANT: One 44.7 kW (60 hp) PZL-F 2A-120-C1 flat-twin engine, driving a two-blade fixed-pitch wooden propeller with spinner. (Interchangeable propellers for agricultural flying or patrol mission.) Integral fuel tanks in wing torsion box. Fuel capacity 70 litres (18.5 US gallons; 15.4 Imp gallons).

ACCOMMODATION: Single adjustable seat under one-piece moulded canopy, opening sideways to starboard. Seat and canopy taken from SZD-51 Junior sailplane.

SYSTEMS: Hydraulic system for mainwheel brakes only; 12V DC electrical system.

AVIONICS: VFR instrumentation standard, plus 720-channel UHF com and 10-channel radio telephone.

EQUIPMENT: Dedicated system for spraying with low volume liquid chemicals (pyrethroids) consists of a 25 litre (6.6 US gallon; 5.5 Imp gallon) pod at each wingtip. Spraying is controlled electrically by a push-button on the throttle lever and effected by dispersing the liquid under pressure via an atomiser at the rear of each pod. An area of 25 ha (61.8 acres) can be covered with one pair of full pods. Biological agents, such as the eggs of the Trichogramma wasp, are carried in capsules in a paper tape wound on a reel which is housed in the lower fuselage behind the cockpit and extended through an openable hatch in the floor. One spreader holds a 3 kg (6.6 lb) package of eggs, on four reels, and at a drop rate of four capsules every 50 m (164 ft) can cover an area of 800 ha (1,977 acres) on a single loading. Like the spray system, the spreader's actuation is electrical, by means of a push-button on the throttle lever. Other equipment can include cameras and first aid appliances.

*DIMENSIONS, EXTERNAL:

Wing span	6.00 m (19 ft 8¼ in)
Length overall	4.66 m (15 ft 3½ in)
Height overall	2.53 m (8 ft 3¾ in)

WEIGHT:

Max T-O and landing weight	420 kg (926 lb)

PERFORMANCE:

Operating speed:	75 knots (140 km/h; 87 mph)

*Further details in Addenda

PZL-130 ORLIK (SPOTTED EAGLET)

Initial proposals for the PZL-130 were prepared in 1980, and detail design began in the Autumn of 1981 under the leadership of Mr Andrzej Frydrychewicz. Prototype construction started in the Spring of 1983. Two prototypes began flight testing in 1984: SP-PCA (c/n 002) on 12 October and SP-PCC (004) on 29 December, followed by SP-PCB on 12 January 1985; a static test aircraft was also completed. The Orlik was designed and built to FAR Pt 23 standards and was certificated in two categories (Utility and Aerobatic) in early 1988. Construction of two pre-production aircraft started in 1986: the first, powered by a 246 kW (330 hp) Vedeneyev M-14Pm engine, made its initial flight on 19 February 1988, and the second, with a PZL Kalisz K8-AA engine, on 19 March 1988. Both were test flown by the Polish Air Force in 1989, resulting in a decision to continue instead with development of the turboprop version, described separately. A full description of the piston engined Orlik can be found in the 1989-90 Jane's.

PZL-130T TURBO ORLIK

This turboprop version of the Orlik, intended for home and export markets, was designed in 1985 by Mr Andrzej Frydrychewicz, the chief designer of PZL Warszawa-Okecie, initially in collaboration with the Canadian company Airtech Canada (which see). In January 1986 work began to convert the third PZL-130 (SP-PCC) to take a Pratt & Whitney Canada PT6A-25A engine. Changes were made to the landing gear, internal systems (including replacement of the two pneumatic systems by a single hydraulic system), avionics and instrumentation. The dorsal fin was also enlarged. This aircraft made its first flight as the Turbo Orlik prototype on 13 July 1986, and received a provisional type certificate under FAR Pt 23 in January 1987, but later that month the aircraft and both occupants were lost. Airtech Canada is no longer involved in the programme.

Three further development aircraft have been completed, the first of them (c/n 007) being powered by a Motorlet Walter M 601 E engine and flying for the first time on 12 January 1989. The second PT6A-25A engined aircraft (c/n 008) was completed by December 1989, and was about to begin flight testing in the Spring of 1990. Of the first production batch of ten, five will go to the Polish Air Force.

The following description applies to the PT6A engined prototypes:

TYPE: Tandem two-seat primary, basic and multi-purpose trainer.

WINGS: Cantilever low-wing monoplane. Wing section NACA 64,215 (modified). Dihedral 5° from roots. Incidence 0° at root, −3° at tip. One-piece all-metal (light alloy) multi-spar box structure. Torsion box, stiffened by riveted omega formers, forms integral fuel tanks. Trailing-edge skin panels are stiffened by L formers, electrically spot welded. Tapered planform, with raked tips of glassfibre/epoxy. Leading-edges are detachable. All-metal constant chord three-position single-slotted trailing-edge flaps, actuated electrically. Frise differential ailerons are also all-metal and of constant chord, aerodynamically and mass balanced, and actuated mechanically via pushrods and torque tube in fuselage. Electrically actuated trim tab on port aileron. Provision for anti-icing system in leading-edges.

FUSELAGE: All-metal (light alloy) unpressurised semi-monocoque structure, with skin panels stiffened by electrically spot welded L formers.

TAIL UNIT: Cantilever light alloy structure, with sweptback vertical and non-swept horizontal surfaces. Fin integral with rear fuselage. Curved dorsal fin; shallow ventral strake under fuselage tailcone. One-piece two-spar fixed incidence tailplane. Elevators aerodynamically and mass

PZL-126 Mrówka agricultural and general purpose light aircraft (Jane's/Mike Keep)

Pre-production Turbo Orlik with Walter M 601 E turboprop

PZL Warszawa-Okecie Turbo Orlik tandem-seat trainer (PT6A-25A turboprop) *(Pilot Press)*

AVIONICS: Bendix/King VHF and UHF com, intercom and ADF.

ARMAMENT: Four underwing hardpoints, stressed for 200 kg (441 lb) each inboard, 160 kg (353 lb) each outboard.

DIMENSIONS, EXTERNAL:

Wing span	8.00 m (26 ft 3 in)
Wing chord: at root	2.00 m (6 ft 6¾ in)
mean aerodynamic	1.62 m (5 ft 3¾ in)
Wing aspect ratio	5.2
Length overall	8.68 m (28 ft 5¾ in)
Fuselage: Max width	0.90 m (2 ft 11½ in)
Height overall	3.53 m (11 ft 7 in)
Tailplane span	3.50 m (11 ft 5¾ in)
Wheel track	3.10 m (10 ft 2 in)
Wheelbase	2.22 m (7 ft 3½ in)
Propeller diameter	2.29 m (7 ft 6 in)

DIMENSIONS, INTERNAL:

Cockpits: Length	2.95 m (9 ft 8¼ in)
Baggage compartment volume	0.17 m³ (6.0 cu ft)

AREAS:

Wings, gross	12.28 m² (132.2 sq ft)
Ailerons (total, incl tab)	1.38 m² (14.85 sq ft)
Trailing-edge flaps (total)	1.37 m² (14.75 sq ft)
Fin, incl dorsal fin	1.20 m² (12.92 sq ft)
Rudder, incl tab	0.65 m² (6.97 sq ft)
Tailplane	1.81 m² (19.48 sq ft)
Elevators (total, incl tab)	0.94 m² (10.12 sq ft)

DESIGN WEIGHTS AND LOADINGS (A: Aerobatic, U: Utility):

Weight empty, equipped, standard	1,150 kg (2,535 lb)
Max usable fuel (internal)	366 kg (807 lb)
Max T-O and landing weight: A	1,580 kg (3,483 lb)
U (no stores)	1,750 kg (3,858 lb)
U (with external stores)	2,155 kg (4,751 lb)
Max wing loading: A	128.66 kg/m² (26.35 lb/sq ft)
U (no stores)	142.51 kg/m² (29.19 lb/sq ft)
U (with external stores)	175.49 kg/m² (35.94 lb/sq ft)
Max power loading: A	3.85 kg/kW (6.33 lb/shp)
U (no stores)	4.27 kg/kW (7.01 lb/shp)
U (with external stores)	5.26 kg/kW (8.64 lb/shp)

DESIGN PERFORMANCE (at max Aerobatic T-O weight except where indicated):

Max permissible diving speed	302 knots (560 km/h; 347 mph)
Max level speed at 4,575 m (15,000 ft)	269 knots (499 km/h; 310 mph)
Max cruising speed at S/L	236 knots (438 km/h; 272 mph)
Stalling speed, power off:	
flaps up, landing gear down	78 knots (144 km/h; 90 mph)
flaps and landing gear down:	
A	63 knots (115 km/h; 72 mph)
U (no stores)	66 knots (122 km/h; 76 mph)
U (with external stores)	73 knots (135 km/h; 84 mph)
Max rate of climb at S/L	954 m (3,130 ft)/min
Service ceiling	10,060 m (33,000 ft)
T-O run	250 m (821 ft)
T-O to 15 m (50 ft)	410 m (1,345 ft)
Landing from 15 m (50 ft)	570 m (1,870 ft)
Landing run	370 m (1,214 ft)

Range with max internal fuel, AUW of 1,600 kg (3,527 lb):

U at 248 knots (460 km/h; 286 mph)	603 nm (1,117 km; 694 miles)
U at 140 knots (260 km/h; 161 mph)	694 nm (1,287 km; 800 miles)

Endurance with max internal fuel, AUW as above:

U at 248 knots (460 km/h; 286 mph)	2 h 26 min
U at 140 knots (260 km/h; 161 mph)	4 h 57 min

Range with max internal and external fuel, AUW of 1,977 kg (4,358 lb):

U at 245 knots (454 km/h; 282 mph)	1,166 nm (2,161 km; 1,343 miles)
U at 147 knots (272 km/h; 169 mph)	1,198 nm (2,220 km; 1,397 miles)

Endurance with max internal and external fuel, AUW as above:

U at 245 knots (454 km/h; 282 mph)	4 h 46 min
U at 147 knots (272 km/h; 169 mph)	8 h 10 min
g limits	+6/–3 at Aerobatic T-O weight
	+4.4/–1.76 at max T-O weight

balanced, controlled by rods and cables; electrically actuated trim tab on port elevator. Aerodynamically and mass balanced rudder, also with electrically actuated trim tab, is cable controlled.

LANDING GEAR: Hydraulically retractable tricycle type, all three units retracting into fuselage (mainwheels inward, nosewheel rearward). PZL Warszawa-Okecie oleopneumatic shock absorber in each unit (nosewheel on semi-fork with shimmy damper and centring device). Low pressure tubeless tyres (2.0 bars; 29 lb/sq in in all three), size 500 × 200 mm (main) and 400 × 140 mm (nose). Differential disc brakes, operated hydraulically. Parking brake. No anti-skid units.

POWER PLANT: One 410 kW (550 shp) Pratt & Whitney Canada PT6A-25A turboprop, driving a Hartzell HC-B3TN-3B/T10173K-11R three-blade constant-speed metal propeller with feathering and reverse pitch. Propeller blades de-iced electrically. Four integral fuel tanks (two of 110 litres; 29 US gallons; 24.2 Imp gallons and two of 100 litres; 26.5 US gallons; 22.0 Imp gallons capacity) in wing torsion box, plus a 9 litre (2.5 US gallon; 2.0 Imp gallon) collector tank in fuselage; total usable internal fuel capacity 420 litres (111 US gallons; 92.4 Imp gallons). Overwing refuelling point for each wing tank.

Fuel and oil systems adapted for aerobatics, including up to 30 s of inverted flight. Electrically adjustable exhaust flaps for engine cooling air. Provision for two 150 litre (39.6 US gallon; 33 Imp gallon) auxiliary tanks on underwing stations.

ACCOMMODATION: Tandem seating for pupil and instructor under one-piece canopy, which opens sideways to starboard. Rear (instructor's) seat slightly elevated. Both seats are adjustable electrically, can accommodate back type and seat type parachutes, and are fitted with seat belts/harnesses. Full dual controls standard; rudder pedals are adjustable (three positions). Windscreen and canopy frames are of glassfibre/epoxy; windscreen is removable, canopy jettisonable. Cockpits heated (electric heater with blower) and ventilated. Baggage compartment aft of rear seat.

SYSTEMS: Hydraulic system for landing gear actuation. Electrical power (115V/400Hz) supplied by 6kW Lear Siegler starter/generator and two 24V 15Ah nickel-cadmium batteries, with three-phase 36V/400Hz AC converters. External DC power socket. Oxygen bottles and crew masks. Provision for anti-icing of wing leading-edges.

PORTUGAL

OGMA
OFICINAS GERAIS DE MATERIAL AERONÁUTICO (General Aeronautical Material Workshops)
2615 Alverca
Telephone: 351 (1) 258 1803
Telex: 14479 OGMA P
Fax: 351 (1) 258 1288
DIRECTOR:
Lt-Gen Eng Rui do Carmo da Conceição Espadinha
DEPUTY DIRECTOR AND COMMERCIAL MANAGER:
Maj-Gen A. Leitão
PRODUCTION MANAGER: Col C. A. Silva Lopes

OGMA, founded in 1918, is the department of the Portuguese Air Force responsible for maintenance and repair, at depot level, of its aircraft, avionics, engines, ground communications and radar equipment, and can undertake similar work for civil or military national or foreign customers. OGMA has a total covered area of 116,000 m² (1,248,612 sq ft), and a workforce of approx 2,500 people.

Under a contract signed in 1959, OGMA undertakes IRAN, refurbishing and rehabilitation, periodic inspection and emergency maintenance and crash repair of US Air Force and US Navy aircraft. For Aerospatiale of France, OGMA has manufactured main and tail rotor structures for

the SA 315B Lama and some components for other helicopters. As indicated in the French section, it is undertaking licence assembly of 17 of the 18 Aerospatiale Epsilon trainers ordered by the Portuguese Air Force.

OGMA's engine repair and maintenance facility, with a covered area of 28,000 m² (301,390 sq ft), overhauls military and commercial turbojets and turbofans (up to 146.8 kN; 33,000 lb st), and turboprop and turboshaft engines of up to 5,667 kW (7,600 shp). In addition to two fully computerised test cells, this facility is equipped with plasma spray, two vacuum furnaces, complete cleaning and electroplating facilities, non-destructive testing, shot-peening and other specific equipment. Besides work for the Portuguese Air

Force, OGMA also overhauls, under contract, Artouste III and Turmo IV turboshaft engines for Turbomeca of France; and, as a maintenance/overhaul centre for Allison, T56 engines and gearboxes for the USAF and other customers.

OGMA performs major maintenance on C-130/L-100

Hercules transport aircraft as a Lockheed Service Center, and on Alouette III, Puma and Ecureuil helicopters as an Aerospatiale Station-Service.

The Avionics Division has premises covering an area of approx 6,400 m² (68,900 sq ft), fully equipped to the latest demands in the field of maintenance for new generation

avionics, communications systems, test equipment and calibration laboratories. OGMA is licensed by Litton Systems of Canada to carry out level 2 and 2A maintenance on LTN-72 INS equipment, and is currently doing work for that company.

ROMANIA

CNIAR

CENTRUL NATIONAL AL INDUSTRIEI AERONAUTICE ROMÂNE (National Centre of the Romanian Aeronautical Industry)

39 Bulevardul Aerogarii, Sector 1, Bucharest
Telephone: 40 (0) 5027 14
Telex: 11648 AEROM
DIRECTOR GENERAL: Dipl Eng Ion Petroaica
COMMERCIAL DIRECTOR: Dipl Eng Vasile Racovitan

Romania has had a tradition of aviation since the earliest days of flying, dating from the first monoplane built in France in early 1906 by the Romanian engineer Traian Vuia. Since then the Romanian aircraft industry (IAR) has produced some 90 different types of landplane, including helicopters (of which 80 were Romanian designed), and about 40 different types of sailplane. The foundations for

the present industry were laid at Brasov in 1926, and details of its history from then until the late 1960s can be found in the 1983-84 and earlier editions of *Jane's*.

The industry was reorganised in 1968, and its activities are now undertaken, within the Ministry of Machine Building Industry, by the CNIAR. The two main aircraft factories are the ICA at Brasov and IAv Bucuresti. The latter was enlarged in the late 1970s to cater for the Rombac 1-11 manufacturing programme. A third factory, IAv Bacau, builds the Soviet Yak-52 under licence. Romanian versions of the SOKO/CNIAR Orao/IAR-93 (see International section) are manufactured at IAv Craiova, which is also producing the indigenous IAR-99 Soim jet trainer. Viper 632 and 633 engines for the IAR-93, Spey 512-14DW engines for the Rombac 1-11, and Turmo IV CA engines for the IAR-330 (Puma) helicopter, are built by the Turbomecanica Enterprise in Bucharest. Aerofina Buch-

arest is a dedicated factory for avionics and airborne equipment; forgings and castings for the aviation industry are manufactured at IMRA (Intreprinderea Metalurgica Romana Pentru Aeronautica), also in Bucharest.

Exports and imports of aircraft and aero engines are the responsibility of Tehnoimportexport (see next entry); avionics and electronic equipment sales are dealt with by Electronum and Electroexportimport. Aeronautical research and development are undertaken by INCREST (formerly IMFCA), the Aerospace Research and Design Institute at Bucharest. INCREST also designs and manufactures aerospace equipment, including anti-skid brakes, engine stands, fuel monitoring equipment, intercoms and various aviation raw materials. The flight test centre is the CIIAR (Centrul de încercari in zbor) at Craiova.

TEHNOIMPORTEXPORT

TEHNOIMPORTEXPORT FOREIGN TRADE COMPANY

2-Street Doamnei (PO Box 110), Bucharest
Telephone: 40 (0) 164570
Telex: 10254 TEHIER

DEPUTY DIRECTOR: Dipl Eng Dumitru Stănescu
INFORMATION: E. M. Preda (Dept 21)

Tehnoimportexport is the sole foreign trade organisation in Romania representing the aircraft industry.

IAv BACAU

INTREPRINDEREA DE AVIOANE BACAU (Bacau Aircraft Enterprise)

Bacau
DIRECTOR GENERAL: Dipl Eng Eugen Pascariu

This factory, originally an aircraft repair centre known as URA (later IRA), manufactures hydraulic, pneumatic, air-conditioning, fuel system and landing gear components for the Rombac 1-11 jet transport and the IAR-93 close support fighter. It is building under licence the Soviet Yakovlev Yak-52 two-seat trainer.

IAv BACAU (YAKOVLEV) Yak-52

Announced in late 1978, the Yak-52 is a tandem-cockpit variant of the Yak-50, with unchanged span and length, but with a semi-retractable tricycle landing gear to reduce damage in a wheels-up landing. It is a replacement for the Yak-18, and made its first flight less than a year after design was started. Production was entrusted to the Romanian aircraft industry, under the Comecon (Council for Mutual Economic Assistance) programme.

Manufacture began at Bacau in 1979, and the aircraft is in series production; it does not have an IAR designation number. IAv Bacau delivered its 1,000th Yak-52 in 1987, and production was continuing in 1988.
TYPE: Tandem two-seat piston engined primary trainer.
WINGS: Cantilever low-wing monoplane of single-spar stressed skin all-metal construction. Clark YN wing section, with thickness/chord ratio of 14.5 per cent at root, 9 per cent at tip. Dihedral 2° from roots. Incidence 2°. No sweepback: each wing comprises a single straight-tapered panel, attached directly to the side of the fuselage. Fabric covered slotted ailerons. Light alloy

Yakovlev Yak-52 primary trainer, of which more than 1,000 have been built in Romania by IAv Bacau

trailing-edge split flaps. Ground adjustable tab on each aileron.
FUSELAGE: Conventional light alloy semi-monocoque structure.
TAIL UNIT: Cantilever light alloy structure. Fin and fixed incidence tailplane metal covered; control surfaces fabric covered. Horn balanced rudder, with ground adjustable tab. Mass balanced elevators. Controllable tab in port elevator.
LANDING GEAR: Semi-retractable tricycle type, with single wheel on each unit. Pneumatic actuation, nosewheel retracting rearward, main units forward. All three wheels

remain fully exposed to airflow, against the undersurface of the fuselage and wings respectively, to offer greater safety in the event of a wheels-up emergency landing. Oleo-pneumatic shock absorbers. Mainwheel tyre size 500 × 150; nosewheel tyre size 400 × 150. Tyre pressure (all units) 3.0 bars (43 lb/sq in). Pneumatic brakes. Skis can be fitted in place of wheels for Winter operations, permissible at temperatures down to –42°C.
POWER PLANT: One 268 kW (360 hp) Vedeneyev M-14P nine-cylinder aircooled radial, driving a two-blade variable-pitch propeller type V-530TA-D35, without spinner. Louvres in front of cowling to regulate cooling. Two-part cowling, split on horizontal centreline. Two fuel tanks, in wingroots forward of spar, each with capacity of 61 litres (16.1 US gallons; 13.5 Imp gallons). Collector tank in fuselage of 5.5 litres (1.45 US gallons; 1.25 Imp gallons) capacity supplies engine during inverted flight. Total internal fuel capacity 122 litres (32.2 US gallons; 27 Imp gallons). Oil capacity 22.5 litres (5.9 US gallons; 5 Imp gallons).
ACCOMMODATION: Tandem seats for pupil and instructor (at rear) under long 'glasshouse' canopy, with separate rearward sliding hood over each seat. Seats and dual flying controls are adjustable. Sides of cockpit have a soft synthetic lining. Heating and ventilation standard.
SYSTEMS: No hydraulic system. Independent main and emergency pneumatic systems, pressure 50 bars (725 lb/sq in), for flap actuation, landing gear actuation, engine starting, and wheel brake control. Pneumatic systems supplied by two compressed air bottles, mounted behind rear seat and recharged in flight by an AK-50T compressor. GSR-3000M 28.5V engine driven generator and (in port wing) 25V Varley battery for DC electric power; two static inverters in fuselage for 36V AC power at 400Hz.
AVIONICS AND EQUIPMENT: Dual engine and flying instruments. Equipment includes GMK-1A gyro compass,

Yakovlev Yak-52 tandem two-seat primary trainer *(Pilot Press)*

ARK-15M automatic radio compass, Baklan-5 VHF com and SPU-9 intercom. Oxygen system optional.

DIMENSIONS, EXTERNAL:

Wing span	9.30 m (30 ft 6¼ in)
Wing chord: at root	1.997 m (6 ft 6¾ in)
at tip	1.082 m (3 ft 6½ in)
Wing aspect ratio	5.8
Length overall	7.745 m (25 ft 5 in)
Fuselage: Max width	0.90 m (2 ft 11½ in)
Height overall	2.70 m (8 ft 10¼ in)
Tailplane span	3.16 m (10 ft 4½ in)
Wheel track	2.715 m (8 ft 10¾ in)
Wheelbase	1.86 m (6 ft 1¼ in)
Propeller diameter	2.40 m (7 ft 10½ in)
Propeller ground clearance	0.36 m (1 ft 2¼ in)

DIMENSIONS, INTERNAL:

Cockpit: Max width	0.736 m (2 ft 5 in)
Max height	1.12 m (3 ft 8 in)

AREAS:

Wings, gross	15.00 m² (161.5 sq ft)
Ailerons (total)	1.98 m² (21.31 sq ft)
Trailing-edge flaps (total)	1.03 m² (11.09 sq ft)
Fin	0.609 m² (6.55 sq ft)
Rudder	0.871 m² (9.37 sq ft)
Tailplane	1.325 m² (14.26 sq ft)
Elevators (total, incl tab)	1.535 m² (16.52 sq ft)

WEIGHTS AND LOADINGS:

Weight empty	1,000 kg (2,205 lb)
Max fuel load	100 kg (220 lb)
Max T-O weight	1,290 kg (2,844 lb)
Max wing loading	86.0 kg/m² (17.61 lb/sq ft)
Max power loading	4.80 kg/kW (7.90 lb/hp)

PERFORMANCE:

Never-exceed speed	194 knots (360 km/h; 223 mph)
Max level speed at 500 m (1,640 ft)	
	162 knots (300 km/h; 186 mph)
Max cruising speed at 1,000 m (3,280 ft)	
	145 knots (270 km/h; 167 mph)
Econ cruising speed at 1,000 m (3,280 ft)	
	102 knots (190 km/h; 118 mph)
Stalling speed: flaps up	60 knots (110 km/h; 69 mph)
flaps down:	
power on	54-57 knots (100-105 km/h; 62-66 mph)
engine idling	46-49 knots (85-90 km/h; 53-56 mph)
Max rate of climb at S/L	420 m (1,378 ft)/min
Service ceiling: without oxygen	4,000 m (13,125 ft)
with oxygen	6,000 m (19,685 ft)
Min ground turning radius	6.22 m (20 ft 5 in)
T-O run	170 m (558 ft)
Landing run	300 m (984 ft)
Range with max fuel	297 nm (550 km; 341 miles)
Endurance with max fuel	2 h 50 min
g limits	+7/−5

IAv BUCURESTI

INTREPRINDEREA DE AVIOANE BUCURESTI (Bucharest Aircraft Enterprise)

44 Bulevardul Ficusului, Baneasa Airport, Bucharest
Telephone: 40 (0) 336260
DIRECTOR GENERAL: Dipl Eng Teodor Zanfirescu
CHIEF ENGINEER: Dipl Eng Mirica Dimitrescu

IAv Bucuresti's predecessor, IRMA, was formed in 1959 from part of the former URMV-3 at Brasov (see 1979-80 and earlier editions of *Jane's*). The present title was adopted in 1980. The factory is currently responsible for manufacture of the BAe One-Eleven (components and complete aircraft) and the Pilatus Britten-Norman Islander. It specialises in the repair and overhaul of various large and small aircraft; is agent and repair centre for Textron Lycoming engines; and manufactures aircraft equipment.

IAv BUCURESTI ROMBAC 1-11 (BAe ONE-ELEVEN)

IAv Bucuresti is the Romanian prime contractor for the licence manufacture of BAe One-Eleven twin-turbofan transports, under the Romanian designation Rombac 1-11. A corresponding programme provides for Romanian manufacture of the Rolls-Royce Spey engines. Details of British production of the One-Eleven can be found in the 1974-75 and 1981-82 *Jane's*.

Industrial transfer to the Romanian aircraft industry, preceded in 1981-82 by delivery of a BAe built Srs 487 freighter and two Srs 525/1s, was completed in 1986. The first flight by a Romanian assembled Srs 560 (YR-BRA) was made on 18 September 1982, and this aircraft entered service with Tarom in January 1983. Of the initial batch of 22 to be built in Romania, six had been completed by 1 January 1987, the last time an update was received; four more were due for completion by the end of that year.

Romanian versions are designated as follows:

Series 495. Combines standard fuselage and accommodation of British built Series 400 with wings and power plant of Series 560 and a modified landing gear system, using low-pressure tyres, to permit operation from secondary low-strength runways with poorer grade surfaces. Two on order in 1987.

Series 560. Derived from British built Series 300/400, this version has a lengthened fuselage (2.54 m; 100 in fwd of wing, 1.57 m; 62 in aft) which accommodates up to 109 passengers in main cabin. Wingtip extensions increase span by 1.52 m (5 ft). Main landing gear strengthened and heavier wing planks used to cater for increased AUW.

The following description applies to the Series 495 and 560:

TYPE: Twin-turbofan short/medium-range transport.

WINGS: Cantilever low-wing monoplane. Modified NACA cambered wing section. Thickness/chord ratio 12½ per cent at root, 11 per cent at tip. Dihedral 2°. Incidence 2° 30′. Sweepback 20° at quarter-chord. All-metal structure of copper based aluminium alloy, built on fail-safe principles. Three-shear-web torsion box with integrally machined skin/stringer panels. Ailerons of Redux bonded light alloy honeycomb, manually operated through servo tabs. Port servo tab used for trimming. Hydraulically operated light alloy Fowler flaps. Light alloy spoiler/airbrakes on upper surface of wing, operated hydraulically. Hydraulically actuated lift dumpers, inboard of spoilers. Flaps on Series 495 have a glassfibre coating. Thermal de-icing of wing leading-edges with engine bleed air.

FUSELAGE: Conventional circular-section all-metal fail-safe structure with continuous frames and stringers. Skin made from copper based aluminium alloy.

TAIL UNIT: Cantilever all-metal fail-safe structure, with variable incidence T tailplane, controlled through duplicated hydraulic units. Fin integral with rear fuselage. Elevators and rudder actuated hydraulically through tandem jacks. Leading-edges of fin and tailplane de-iced by engine bleed air.

LANDING GEAR: Retractable tricycle type, with twin wheels on each unit. Hydraulic retraction, nose unit forward, main units inward. Oleo-pneumatic shock absorbers. Hydraulic nosewheel steering. Wheels have tubeless tyres, 5-plate heavy duty hydraulic disc brakes, and anti-skid units. Mainwheel tyres size 40 × 12 on Srs 560, pressure 11.03 bars (160 lb/sq in); size 44 × 16 on Srs 495, pressure 5.72 bars (83 lb/sq in). Nosewheel tyres size 24 × 7.25 on Srs 560, pressure 7.58 bars (110 lb/sq in); size 24 × 7.7 on Srs 495, pressure 7.24 bars (105 lb/sq in).

POWER PLANT: Two Rolls-Royce Spey Mk 512-14DW turbofans, each rated at 55.8 kN (12,550 lb st), pod-mounted on sides of rear fuselage. Fuel in integral wing tanks with usable capacity of 10,160 litres (2,684 US gallons; 2,235 Imp gallons) and centre-section tank of 3,968 litres (1,048 US gallons; 873 Imp gallons) usable capacity; total usable fuel 14,129 litres (3,732 US gallons; 3,108 Imp gallons). Executive versions can be fitted with auxiliary fuel tanks of up to 5,791 litres (1,530 US gallons; 1,274 Imp gallons) usable capacity. Pressure refuelling point in fuselage forward of wing on starboard side. Provision for gravity refuelling. Oil capacity (total engine oil) 13.66 litres (3.6 US gallons; 3 Imp gallons) per engine. Engine hush kits standard.

ACCOMMODATION (Srs 495): Crew of two on flight deck and up to 89 passengers in main cabin. Single class or mixed class layout, with movable divider bulkhead to permit any first/tourist ratio. Typical mixed class layout has 16 first class (four abreast) and 49 tourist (five abreast) seats. Galley units normally at front on starboard side. Coat space available on port side aft of flight deck. Ventral entrance with hydraulically operated airstair. Forward passenger door on port side incorporates optional power operated airstair. Galley service door forward on starboard side. Overwing emergency exit on each side. Two baggage and freight holds under floor, fore and aft of wings, with doors on starboard side. Upward opening forward freight door available at customer's option. Entire accommodation air-conditioned.

ACCOMMODATION (Srs 560): Crew of two on flight deck and up to 109 passengers in main cabin. Two overwing emergency exits on each side. One toilet on each side of cabin at rear. Otherwise generally similar to Srs 495.

SYSTEMS: Fully duplicated air-conditioning and pressurisation systems. Air bled from engine compressors through heat exchangers. Max pressure differential 0.52 bars (7.5 lb/sq in). Hydraulic system, pressure 207 bars (3,000 lb/sq in), operates flaps, spoilers, rudder, elevators, tailplane, landing gear, brakes, nosewheel steering, ventral and forward airstairs and windscreen wipers. No pneumatic system. Electrical system utilises two 30kVA AC generators, driven by constant speed drive and starter units, plus a similar generator mounted on the APU and shaft driven. Gas turbine APU in tailcone to provide ground electric power, air-conditioning and engine starting, also some system checkout capability. APU is run during take-off to eliminate performance penalty of bleeding engine air for cabin air-conditioning.

AVIONICS AND EQUIPMENT: Communications and navigation avionics generally to customers' requirements. Typical installation includes dual VHF com to ARINC 546, dual VHF nav to ARINC 547A, including glideslope receivers, marker beacon receiver, flight/service interphone system, ADF, ATC transponder to ARINC 532D, DME, weather radar. Compass system and flight director system (dual) also installed. Autopilot system. Provision on the Srs 560 for additional equipment, including automatic throttle control, for low weather minima operation.

DIMENSIONS, EXTERNAL:

Wing span	28.50 m (93 ft 6 in)
Wing chord: at root	5.00 m (16 ft 5 in)
at tip	1.61 m (5 ft 5 in)
Wing aspect ratio	8.5
Length overall: Srs 495	28.50 m (93 ft 6 in)
Srs 560	32.61 m (107 ft 0 in)
Length of fuselage: Srs 495	25.55 m (83 ft 10 in)
Srs 560	29.67 m (97 ft 4 in)
Height overall	7.47 m (24 ft 6 in)
Tailplane span	8.99 m (29 ft 6 in)
Wheel track	4.34 m (14 ft 3 in)
Wheelbase: Srs 495	10.08 m (33 ft 1 in)
Srs 560	12.62 m (41 ft 5 in)

Passenger door (fwd, port): Height	1.73 m (5 ft 8 in)
Width	0.84 m (2 ft 9 in)
Height to sill	2.08 m (6 ft 10 in)
Ventral entrance, bulkhead door:	
Height	1.83 m (6 ft 0 in)
Width	0.66 m (2 ft 2 in)
Height to sill	2.08 m (6 ft 10 in)
Freight door (fwd, starboard):	
Height (projected)	0.79 m (2 ft 7 in)
Width	0.91 m (3 ft 0 in)
Height to sill	1.04 m (3 ft 5 in)
Freight door (rear, starboard):	
Height (projected)	0.71 m (2 ft 4 in)
Width	0.91 m (3 ft 0 in)
Height to sill	1.17 m (3 ft 10 in)
Freight door, main deck (optional, fwd, Srs 495):	
Height	1.85 m (6 ft 1 in)
Width	3.05 m (10 ft 0 in)
Galley service door (fwd, starboard):	
Height (projected)	1.22 m (4 ft 0 in)
Width	0.69 m (2 ft 3 in)
Height to sill	2.08 m (6 ft 10 in)

DIMENSIONS, INTERNAL (Srs 495):

Cabin, excl flight deck: Length	17.32 m (56 ft 10 in)
Max width	3.15 m (10 ft 4 in)
Max height	1.98 m (6 ft 6 in)
Floor area	approx 47.4 m² (510 sq ft)
Freight hold: fwd	10.02 m³ (354 cu ft)
rear	4.42 m³ (156 cu ft)

DIMENSIONS, INTERNAL (Srs 560):

Cabin, excl flight deck: Length	21.44 m (70 ft 4 in)
Total floor area	approx 59.5 m² (640 sq ft)
Freight holds (total volume)	19.45 m³ (687 cu ft)

AREAS (Srs 495, 560):

Wings, gross	95.78 m² (1,031.0 sq ft)
Ailerons (total)	2.86 m² (30.8 sq ft)
Flaps (total)	16.26 m² (175.0 sq ft)
Spoilers (total)	2.30 m² (24.8 sq ft)
Vertical tail surfaces (total)	10.91 m² (117.4 sq ft)
Rudder, incl tab	3.05 m² (32.8 sq ft)
Horizontal tail surfaces (total)	23.97 m² (258.0 sq ft)
Elevators, incl tab	6.54 m² (70.4 sq ft)

WEIGHTS AND LOADINGS:

Operating weight empty, typical:	
Srs 495 (89 seats)	23,286 kg (51,339 lb)
Srs 560 (109 seats)	25,267 kg (55,704 lb)
Max payload, typical: Srs 495	10,733 kg (23,661 lb)
Srs 560	11,474 kg (25,296 lb)
Max T-O weight:	
Srs 495: standard	41,730 kg (92,000 lb)
optional	44,680 kg (98,500 lb)
Srs 560: standard	45,200 kg (99,650 lb)
optional	47,400 kg (104,500 lb)
Max ramp weight:	
Srs 495: standard	41,955 kg (92,500 lb)
optional	44,905 kg (99,000 lb)
Srs 560: standard	45,450 kg (100,200 lb)
optional	47,625 kg (105,000 lb)
Max landing weight:	
Srs 495: standard	38,100 kg (84,000 lb)
optional	39,465 kg (87,000 lb)
Srs 560	39,465 kg (87,000 lb)
Max zero-fuel weight:	
Srs 495: standard	33,110 kg (73,000 lb)
optional	34,020 kg (75,000 lb)
Srs 560	36,740 kg (81,000 lb)
Max wing loading: Srs 495	466.3 kg/m² (95.5 lb/sq ft)
Srs 560	495.1 kg/m² (101.4 lb/sq ft)
Max power loading: Srs 495	400.2 kg/kN (3.92 lb/lb st)
Srs 560	424.5 kg/kN (4.16 lb/lb st)

PERFORMANCE (at standard max T-O weights):

Design diving speed (S/L)	
	410 knots (760 km/h; 472 mph) EAS
Max level and max cruising speed at 6,400 m (21,000 ft)	
	470 knots (870 km/h; 541 mph)
Econ cruising speed at 10,670 m (35,000 ft)	
	410 knots (760 km/h; 472 mph)
Stalling speed (landing flap setting, at standard max landing weight):	
Srs 495	98 knots (182 km/h; 113 mph) EAS
Srs 560	100 knots (186 km/h; 115 mph) EAS

Romanian assembled Rombac 1-11-561RC of Ryanair (two Rolls-Royce Spey Mk 512-14DW turbofans) *(Paul R. Duffy)*

Rate of climb at S/L at 300 knots (555 km/h; 345 mph)
EAS: Srs 495   786 m (2,580 ft)/min
Srs 560   722 m (2,370 ft)/min
Max cruising height   10,670 m (35,000 ft)
Min ground turning radius (to outer wingtip):
Srs 495   15.24 m (50 ft 0 in)
Srs 560   17.07 m (56 ft 0 in)
Runway LCN, rigid pavement (l 30): Srs 495   32
Srs 560   53
T-O run at S/L, ISA: Srs 495   1,676 m (5,500 ft)
Srs 560   1,981 m (6,500 ft)
Balanced T-O to 10.7 m (35 ft) at S/L, ISA:
Srs 495   1,798 m (5,900 ft)
Srs 560   2,225 m (7,300 ft)

Landing distance (BCAR) at S/L, ISA, at standard max
landing weight: Srs 495   1,440 m (4,725 ft)
Srs 560   1,455 m (4,775 ft)
Max still air range, ISA, with reserves for 200 nm (370
km; 230 mile) diversion and 45 min hold:
Srs 495   1,933 nm (3,582 km; 2,226 miles)
Srs 560   1,897 nm (3,515 km; 2,184 miles)
Still air range with typical capacity payload, ISA, reserves
as above:
Srs 495 at 44,680 kg (98,500 lb)
1,454 nm (2,694 km; 1,674 miles)
Srs 560 at 47,400 kg (104,500 lb)
1,327 nm (2,459 km; 1,528 miles)
Srs 495 executive aircraft with additional 5,602 litres

(1,479 US gallons; 1,232 Imp gallons) fuel and ten
passengers   2,875 nm (5,325 km; 3,308 miles)

IAv BUCURESTI (PILATUS BRITTEN-NORMAN) ISLANDER

The Pilatus Britten-Norman Islander (see UK section)
has been manufactured under licence in Romania, originally
by IRMA, for many years. The first Romanian built
example flew for the first time at Baneasa Airport,
Bucharest, on 4 August 1969, and the initial commitment to
build 215 Islanders was completed in 1976. A total of more
than 480 had been delivered to Pilatus Britten-Norman by
mid-May 1990, and was expected to reach 500 by the end of
the year.

IAv CRAIOVA
INTREPRINDEREA DE AVIOANE CRAIOVA (Craiova Aircraft Enterprise)

Str. Aeroport 1, R-1100 Craiova
Telephone: 40 (41) 24170
Telex: 41290 COCO R
DIRECTOR GENERAL: Dipl Eng Dumitru Geantă

This factory is responsible for Romanian manufacture of
the IAR-93 close support and ground attack aircraft and
operational trainer described under the SOKO/CNIAR
heading in the International section. Craiova's latest
product is the IAR-99 Soim jet trainer.

IAR-99 SOIM (HAWK)

The existence of this new Romanian designed advanced
jet trainer/light ground attack aircraft first became known
during the 1983 Paris Air Show. It was designed by the
Institutul de Aviatie at Bucharest and built at Craiova,
and is powered by a version of the non-afterburning
Rolls-Royce Viper Mk 632 turbojet installed in the
IAR-93A.

Three prototypes were built, of which 002 was used for
structural testing. First flight, by 001, was made on 21
December 1985. An initial batch of seven IAR-99s was
delivered to the Romanian Air Force, starting in 1987.

TYPE: Tandem two-seat advanced jet trainer and light
ground attack aircraft.

WINGS: Cantilever low-wing monoplane, with 3° dihedral
from roots. Wing section NACA 64₁A-214 (mod) at
centreline, NACA 64₁A-212 (mod) at tip. Sweepback at

Production IAR-99 Soim (Rolls-Royce Viper Mk 632 turbojet) in Romanian Air Force markings

quarter-chord 6° 35'. Incidence 1°. Each wing has
two-spar all-metal structure, with machined skin panels
forming integral fuel tanks; attached to fuselage by four
bolts. All-metal single-slotted flaps, actuated by a single
hydraulic jack. Flaps retract gradually when airspeed
reaches 162 knots (300 km/h; 186 mph). Aluminium
honeycomb ailerons, actuated by hydraulic servojacks,
are statically balanced along entire span. Electrically

operated servo tab in port aileron. Flaps deflect 20° for
take-off, 40° for landing; ailerons deflect 15° up or down.
FUSELAGE: Conventional all-metal semi-monocoque structure, of oval cross-section, consisting of frames, stringers,
spars, skin panels, and honeycomb panels for fuel tank
compartments. Main (forward and centre) fuselage
joined to rear fuselage by four bolts. Two hydraulically
actuated airbrakes under rear fuselage.
TAIL UNIT: Cantilever metal structure. Tapered horizontal
surfaces (one-piece tailplane and two horn balanced
elevators. Sweptback vertical fin, with dorsal fairing and
statically balanced rudder. Aluminium honeycomb
rudder and elevators, actuated manually via push/pull
rods. Electrically operated trim tabs in each elevator and
rudder. Elevators deflect 20° up, 10° down; rudder 25° to
right and left.
LANDING GEAR: Retractable tricycle type, with single wheel
and oleo-pneumatic shock absorber on each unit.
Mainwheels retract inward, nosewheel forward, all
wheels being fully enclosed by doors when retracted.
Landing light in port wingroot leading-edge. Mainwheels
fitted with tubeless tyres, size 552 × 164-10, pressure 7.5
bars (108.8 lb/sq in), and hydraulic disc brakes with
anti-skid system. Nosewheel has tubeless tyre size 445 ×
150-6, pressure 4.0 bars (58.0 lb/sq in).
POWER PLANT: One Rolls-Royce Viper Mk 632-41 M
turbojet, rated at 17.79 kN (4,000 lb st). Fuel in two
flexible bag tanks in centre-fuselage, capacity 900 litres
(238 US gallons; 198 Imp gallons), and four integral
tanks between wing spars, combined capacity 470 litres
(124 US gallons; 103 Imp gallons). Total internal fuel
capacity 1,370 litres (362 US gallons; 301 Imp gallons).
Gravity refuelling point on top of fuselage. Provision for
two drop tanks, each of 225 litres (59.5 US gallons;
49.5 Imp gallons) capacity. Max internal/external fuel
capacity 1,820 litres (481 US gallons; 400 Imp gallons).

Romania's new advanced jet trainer, the IAR-99 Soim *(Pilot Press)*

ACCOMMODATION: Crew of two in tandem, on zero/zero ejection seats in pressurised and air-conditioned cockpit. Rear seat elevated 35 cm (13.8 in). Dual controls standard. One-piece canopy with internal screen (trainer), or (in ground attack version) individual canopies, all opening sideways to starboard.

SYSTEMS: Engine compressor bleed air for pressurisation, air-conditioning, anti-*g* suit and windscreen anti-icing system, and to pressurise fuel tanks. Hydraulic system, operating at pressure of 206 bars (2,990 lb/sq in), for actuation of landing gear and doors, flaps, airbrakes, ailerons and mainwheel brakes. Emergency hydraulic system for operation of landing gear, doors, flaps and wheel brakes. Main electrical system, supplied by 9kW 28V DC generator, with nickel-cadmium battery, ensures operation of main systems, in case of emergency, and engine starting. Two static inverters, total output 1,500VA, supply two secondary networks: 115V/400Hz and 26V/400Hz. Oxygen system for two crew for 2 h 30 min.

AVIONICS AND EQUIPMENT: Standard avionics include radio communication, crew intercom, radar altimeter, marker beacon receiver, IFF, ADF, gyro platform and flight recorder.

ARMAMENT: Removable ventral gun pod containing 23 mm GSh-23 gun with 200 rds. Gun/rocket firing and weapon release controls, including electrically controlled AA-1F gyroscopic gunsight and AFCT-1 gun camera, in front cockpit only. Four underwing hardpoints stressed for loads of 250 kg (551 lb) each. Typical underwing stores can include four 250 kg bombs; four triple carriers for three 50 kg bombs (or two 100 kg and one 50 kg bombs); four L 16-57 launchers each containing sixteen 57 mm air-to-surface rockets; four L 32-42 launchers each containing thirty-two 42 mm air-to-surface rockets; infra-red air-to-air missiles (outer pylons only); two 7.62 mm machine-gun pods with 800 rds/pod (inboard pylons only); and auxiliary fuel tanks (see under 'Power Plant') on the inboard pylons.

DIMENSIONS, EXTERNAL:

Wing span	10.16 m (33 ft 4 in)
Wing chord: at root	2.305 m (7 ft 6¾ in)
at tip	1.30 m (4 ft 3¼ in)
Wing aspect ratio	5.52
Length overall	11.009 m (36 ft 1½ in)
Height overall	3.898 m (12 ft 9½ in)
Tailplane span	4.12 m (13 ft 6¼ in)
Wheel track	2.69 m (8 ft 10 in)
Wheelbase	4.38 m (14 ft 4½ in)

AREAS:

Wings, gross	18.71 m² (201.4 sq ft)
Ailerons (total)	1.567 m² (16.87 sq ft)
Flaps (total)	2.54 m² (27.34 sq ft)
Fin, incl dorsal fin	1.919 m² (20.66 sq ft)
Rudder	0.629 m² (6.77 sq ft)
Tailplane	3.123 m² (33.62 sq ft)
Elevators (total)	1.248 m² (13.43 sq ft)

WEIGHTS AND LOADINGS:

Basic weight empty	3,364 kg (7,416 lb)
Max fuel weight: internal	1,100 kg (2,425 lb)
external	360 kg (794 lb)
Max T-O weight: trainer	4,630 kg (10,207 lb)
ground attack	5,860 kg (12,919 lb)
Max wing loading: trainer	247.5 kg/m² (50.69 lb/sq ft)
ground attack	313.2 kg/m² (64.15 lb/sq ft)
Max power loading: trainer	260.2 kg/kN (2.55 lb/lb st)
ground attack	329.6 kg/kN (3.23 lb/lb st)

PERFORMANCE:

Never-exceed speed	Mach 0.76
Max level speed at S/L	458 knots (850 km/h; 528 mph)
Max rate of climb at S/L	2,100 m (6,890 ft)/min
Service ceiling	12,900 m (42,325 ft)
Min air turning radius	330 m (1,083 ft)
T-O run: trainer	450 m (1,477 ft)
ground attack	960 m (3,150 ft)
T-O to 15 m (50 ft): trainer	750 m (2,461 ft)
ground attack	1,250 m (4,101 ft)
Landing from 15 m (50 ft): trainer	740 m (2,428 ft)
ground attack	870 m (2,855 ft)
Landing run: trainer	550 m (1,805 ft)
ground attack	670 m (2,199 ft)
Max endurance with internal fuel: trainer	2 h 42 min
ground attack	1 h 46 min
Max range with internal fuel:	
trainer	608 nm (1,128 km; 701 miles)
ground attack	522 nm (967 km; 601 miles)

ICA
INTREPRINDEREA DE CONSTRUCTII AERONAUTICE (Aeronautical Construction Enterprise)
Casuta Postala 198, 2200 Brasov
Telephone: 40 (21) 92114037
Telex: 61 266

ICA, created in 1968, continues the work begun in 1926 by IAR-Brasov and undertaken in 1950-59 as URMV-3 Brasov. Today, it manufactures most types of Romanian designed light aircraft, plus Puma helicopters under licence from Aerospatiale of France (as the IAR-330); is undertaking the series manufacture of Ka-126 helicopters; and produces the IS-28/29 series of Romanian sailplanes and motor gliders. It also produces aircraft components and equipment.

ICA IAR-825TP TRIUMF
The IAR-825TP turboprop powered tandem-seat aircraft was developed to FAR Pt 23 standards as a multi-role trainer for the Romanian Air Force. The prototype (YR-IGB) flew for the first time on 12 June 1982, with a 507 kW (680 shp) P&WC PT6A-15AG engine. Series production with a more powerful (559 kW; 750 shp) PT6A-25C engine was originally planned to begin in 1986, but apparently did not do so. ICA stated in early 1989 that the programme had "recently been reconsidered", and that a modified aircraft was expected to fly in December 1989. However, no details of any changes have yet been received.

In its original form, the IAR-825 had some features in common with the IAR-823 (1988-89 *Jane's*), utilising essentially the same aerofoil section for the wings, which have metal skinned flaps and ailerons, larger capacity integral fuel tanks, and are strengthened for the carriage of practice weapons in the armament training role. They are interchangeable with those of the IAR-823. Fuselage, landing gear and tail unit are of new design.

The following details apply to the prototype:
TYPE: Turboprop powered military trainer.
WINGS: Cantilever low-wing monoplane. Wing section NACA 23012 (modified). Dihedral 7° from roots. Incidence 3° at root, 1° at tip. Conventional all-metal structure, with single main spar and rear auxiliary spar; three-point attachment to fuselage. Riveted spars, ribs and skin of corrosion-proof aluminium alloy. Leading-edges riveted, and sealed to ribs and main spar to form main torsion box and integral fuel tanks. Electrically actuated all-metal single-slotted flaps and all-metal Frise slotted ailerons. Ground adjustable tab on each aileron.
FUSELAGE: Conventional metal semi-monocoque structure. Small bumper under tailcone.
TAIL UNIT: Cantilever metal structure. Two-spar duralumin covered sweptback fin and non-swept tailplane; horn balanced rudder and elevators. Electrically actuated automatic trim tab in each elevator; controllable tab in rudder.
LANDING GEAR: Retractable tricycle type, with steerable nosewheel. Electric retraction, main units inward, nose unit rearward. Emergency manual actuation. Oleo-pneumatic shock absorbers. Mainwheel tyres size 500 × 180 mm, nosewheel tyre 450 × 150 mm. Independent hydraulic mainwheel brakes. Shimmy damper on nose unit.
POWER PLANT: One 507 kW (680 shp) Pratt & Whitney Canada PT6A-15AG turboprop, driving a Hartzell HC-B3TN-3/T10173-13R three-blade constant-speed reversible-pitch metal propeller. Wings incorporate four

Prototype of the ICA Brasov IAR-825TP Triumf tandem-seat military trainer

integral fuel tanks. Two streamlined auxiliary tanks above wingtips optional.
ACCOMMODATION: Seats for two persons in tandem, under one-piece framed canopy which opens sideways to starboard. Dual controls standard.

DIMENSIONS, EXTERNAL:

Wing span, excl tip tanks	10.00 m (32 ft 9¾ in)
Wing aspect ratio	6.7
Length overall	8.99 m (29 ft 6 in)
Height overall	3.20 m (10 ft 6 in)
Wheel track	2.45 m (8 ft 0½ in)

DIMENSIONS, INTERNAL:

Cockpit: Max length	2.60 m (8 ft 6½ in)
Max width	0.87 m (2 ft 10¼ in)

AREA:

Wings, gross	15.00 m² (161.5 sq ft)

WEIGHTS (A: Aerobatic, U: Utility category):

Weight empty	1,250 kg (2,756 lb)
Max T-O weight: A	1,700 kg (3,748 lb)
U	2,300 kg (5,070 lb)

PERFORMANCE (at Aerobatic max T-O weight, PT6A-15AG engine):

Never-exceed speed	296 knots (550 km/h; 341 mph)
Max level speed at S/L	226 knots (420 km/h; 261 mph)
Max cruising speed at S/L	
	210 knots (390 km/h; 242 mph)
Stalling speed, flaps down, power off	
	57 knots (105 km/h; 66 mph)
Max rate of climb at S/L	960 m (3,150 ft)/min
Service ceiling	9,000 m (29,525 ft)
T-O to 15 m (50 ft)	250 m (820 ft)
Landing from 15 m (50 ft)	300 m (985 ft)
Range with max fuel, 30 min reserves	
	647 nm (1,200 km; 745 miles)
Endurance, conditions as above	3 h
g limits	+6/−3

ICA IAR-831 PELICAN
The Pelican, the prototype of which (YR-IGA) made its first public appearance at the 1983 Paris Air Show, is essentially a combination of the IAR-825TP airframe with the 216 kW (290 hp) Textron Lycoming flat-six engine of the IAR-823. A certification flight test programme was continuing in early 1989.
TYPE: Two-seat light aircraft.
AIRFRAME: Generally as described for IAR-825TP, except for changes necessitated by different engine installation.
POWER PLANT: One 216 kW (290 hp) Textron Lycoming IO-540-G1D5 flat-six engine, driving a Hartzell HC-92 WK-1D/W two-blade constant-speed metal propeller with spinner. Fuel in four integral tanks in wings.
ACCOMMODATION: As described for IAR-825TP.
DIMENSIONS, EXTERNAL AND INTERNAL:
As for IAR-825TP

WEIGHTS AND LOADINGS (A: Aerobatic category, U: Utility):

Weight empty	950 kg (2,094 lb)
Max T-O weight: A	1,200 kg (2,645 lb)
U	1,500 kg (3,307 lb)
Max wing loading: A	80.0 kg/m² (16.39 lb/sq ft)
U	100.0 kg/m² (20.48 lb/sq ft)
Max power loading: A	5.56 kg/kW (9.12 lb/hp)
U	6.94 kg/kW (11.40 lb/hp)

PERFORMANCE (at Aerobatic max T-O weight except where indicated):

Never-exceed speed	270 knots (500 km/h; 310 mph)
Max level speed	172 knots (320 km/h; 199 mph)
Max cruising speed, 75% power at S/L	
	159 knots (295 km/h; 183 mph)
Stalling speed, flaps up	60 knots (110 km/h; 69 mph)
Max rate of climb at S/L	420 m (1,380 ft)/min
Service ceiling	5,600 m (18,375 ft)
T-O to 15 m (50 ft)	300 m (984 ft)
Landing from 15 m (50 ft)	250 m (820 ft)
Range with max fuel	701 nm (1,300 km; 807 miles)
g limits:	+6/−3 Aerobatic
	+3.8/−1.9 Utility

ICA (AEROSPATIALE) IAR-330L PUMA
An agreement for licence production of the Aerospatiale AS 330 Puma in Romania was concluded in 1977, an initial quantity of 100 being involved. A total of 145 had been completed by early 1989, most of them reportedly for the Romanian Air Force. Production is continuing.

IAR-831 prototype two-seat light aircraft

ICA built IAR-330L Puma helicopter in Romanian Air Force camouflage

ICA (Kamov) Ka-126 (537 kW; 720 shp Koptchenko TV-O-100 turboshaft) *(John Fricker)*

ICA (KAMOV) Ka-126
NATO reporting name: Hoodlum-B

Work on a turboshaft version of the Kamov Ka-26 (see Soviet section of 1989-90 and earlier *Jane's*) began in 1981, and a photograph published in that year depicted an early mockup apparently identical to the piston engined version except for the substitution of a very small (and still unidentified), closely cowled turboshaft on each side of the cabin roof. A photograph of this version appeared in the 1986-87 *Jane's*.

Subsequently, it was decided to adopt a single turboshaft, installed above the cabin. A ground test vehicle was completed in early 1986, and a prototype Ka-126 (SSSR-01963, illustrated in the 1988-89 *Jane's*) flew for the first time later that year. This was followed by four pre-production aircraft, the first of which made its initial flight in the USSR in May 1988; first flight by a Romanian built Ka-126 took place on 31 December 1988.

It had been announced in 1985 that conversion of Ka-26s to Ka-126 standard would be undertaken in Romania, but in fact the Ka-126 is in series production as a new-build aircraft. The first Romanian production aircraft was flown for the first time on 14 February 1989. Updated equipment includes new low-volume spraygear and pellet dispensing system designed in Hungary, and low-cost nav/com radio.

Compared with the Ka-26, the Ka-126 has a significant increase in payload, endurance and range capability and the ability for greater year-round utilisation. It can also hover with full load at 1,000 m (3,280 ft), whereas the Ka-26 can do so only at sea level.

A version with twin Allison 250-C20B turboshafts is being developed, with first flight expected in the second half of 1991. The following description applies to the current production Ka-126:

TYPE: Twin-turboshaft general purpose light helicopter.

ROTOR SYSTEM AND DRIVE: Contra-rotating coaxial three-blade rotor system, with hydraulic dampers fitted to each rotor head and rotor shafts inclined forward. Blades, made of glass-textolyte (plastics) materials, have advanced aerofoil section, are interchangeable, and are equipped with an anti-icing system. Energy storage system (two contra-rotating flywheels running at 30,000 rpm) are connected to shaft between engine and transmission. Depending on how pilot manages collective lever, this stored energy can keep helicopter flying for up to 40 s after engine failure.

FUSELAGE: Small extensively glazed crew cabin forward of rotor mast, and two tapered cylindrical plastics tailbooms.

TAIL UNIT: Tailplane mounted at extremity of tailbooms; twin endplate fins and rudders, toed inward at 15°.

LANDING GEAR: Non-retractable four-wheel landing gear. Main units, at rear, carried by stub wings. All four units embody oleo-pneumatic shock absorbers. Forward wheels of castoring type, not fitted with brakes. Rear wheels fitted with pneumatically operated brakes. Provision for large inflatable pontoons, across front of aircraft forward of nosewheels and under each mainwheel unit.

POWER PLANT: One 537 kW (720 shp) Koptchenko TV-O-100 turboshaft, installed centrally in streamline fairing above cabin. Fuel capacity 750 litres (198 US gallons; 165 Imp gallons).

ACCOMMODATION: Fully enclosed cabin, with door on each side, fitted out normally for operation by single pilot; second seat and dual controls optional. Cabin warmed and demisted by air from combustion heater, which also heats passenger compartment when fitted. Air filter on nose of agricultural version. The space aft of the cabin, between the main landing gear units and under the rotor transmission, is able to accommodate a variety of interchangeable payloads. For agricultural work, a chemical hopper (capacity 1,000 litres; 264 US gallons; 220 Imp gallons) and dust spreader or spraybars are fitted in this position, on the aircraft's centre of gravity. This equipment is quickly removable and can be replaced by a cargo/passenger pod accommodating four or six persons, with provision for a seventh passenger beside the pilot; or two stretcher patients, two seated casualties and a medical attendant in ambulance role. Alternatively, aircraft can be operated with either an open platform for hauling freight or a hook for slinging bulky loads at the end of a cable or in a cargo net.

SYSTEMS: Powered controls, actuated by single hydraulic system, with manual override in case of system failure. Anti-icing system for rotor blades and windscreen is activated automatically by radioisotope ice warning device and utilises an alcohol glycerine mixture.

AVIONICS: The flying and navigation equipment is adequate for all-weather operation, by day and night. VHF and HF radio are fitted, together with a radio compass and radio altimeter.

DIMENSIONS, EXTERNAL:

Rotor diameter (each)	13.00 m (42 ft 7¾ in)
Length of fuselage	7.75 m (25 ft 5 in)
Height to top of rotor head	4.15 m (13 ft 7½ in)
Span over tail unit (rudder trailing-edges)	
	3.224 m (10 ft 7 in)
Wheel track: mainwheels	2.56 m (8 ft 4¾ in)
nosewheels	0.90 m (2 ft 11½ in)
Wheelbase	3.479 m (11 ft 5 in)

DIMENSIONS, INTERNAL:

Passenger pod: Max length	2.04 m (6 ft 8¼ in)
Max width	1.28 m (4 ft 2½ in)
Max height	1.40 m (4 ft 7 in)

WEIGHTS:

Max payload	1,000 kg (2,205 lb)
Max T-O weight	3,250 kg (7,165 lb)

PERFORMANCE:

Max level speed	97 knots (180 km/h; 112 mph)
Cruising speed	81 knots (150 km/h; 93 mph)
Service ceiling	3,800 m (12,470 ft)
Hovering ceiling OGE	1,000 m (3,280 ft)
Max range	351 nm (650 km; 404 miles)
Endurance	4 h 30 min

Kamov Ka-126 single-turboshaft helicopter, being produced in Romania by ICA Brasov
(Pilot Press)

SINGAPORE

SA

SINGAPORE AEROSPACE PTE LTD

540 Airport Road, Paya Lebar, Singapore 1953
Telephone: 65 287 1111
Telex: RS 55851 SAERO
Fax: 65 280 9713
PRESIDENT: Quek Poh Huat
VICE-PRESIDENT MARKETING: Michael Ng
MARKETING EXECUTIVE: Suzanna Chia

Singapore Aerospace group (previously known as Singapore Aircraft Industries) consists of five subsidiaries, as follows:

Singapore Aerospace Engineering Pte Ltd,
Seletar West Camp, Singapore 2879
Telephone: 65 481 5955
Telex: RS 25507 SAMAIR
Fax: 65 482 0245
VICE-PRESIDENT/GENERAL MANAGER: Richard Liao

Maintenance, modification, repair and servicing of civil and military aircraft and helicopters. Authorised service centre for Bell Helicopter Textron and Aerospatiale (Super Puma).

Singapore Aerospace Systems Pte Ltd,
505A Airport Road, Paya Lebar, Singapore 1953
Telephone: 65 287 2222
Telex: RS 55851 SAERO
Fax: 65 284 4414
VICE-PRESIDENT/GENERAL MANAGER: Foo Hee Liat

Service, maintenance, overhaul and repair of civil and military aircraft components and equipment. Authorised service centre for Hydraulic Research Textron, Allied Signal (Bendix/King), Rockwell Collins, J.E.T., Lucas Aerospace, Ferranti, Sextant Avionique, Teledyne, ECE, Thomson-CSF, Astronautics, TRT, Superflexit, Kollsman, Revue Thommen and Aerospatiale.

Singapore Aerospace Engines Pte Ltd,
501 Airport Road, Paya Lebar, Singapore 1953
Telephone: 65 285 1111
Telex: RS 33268 SAENG
Fax: 65 282 3010
VICE-PRESIDENT/GENERAL MANAGER: Chong Kok Pan

Overhaul and repair of Pratt & Whitney JT8D and JT15D, Rolls-Royce Avon Mk 207, Curtiss-Wright J65, Allison T56/501, General Electric J85 and Textron Lycoming T53 aero engines.

Singapore Aerospace Manufacturing Pte Ltd,
503 Airport Road, Paya Lebar, Singapore 1953
Telephone: 65 284 6255
Telex: RS 38216 SAMPL
Fax: 65 288 0965 and 284 2704
VICE-PRESIDENT/GENERAL MANAGER: Goh Chin Khee

Manufacture of aircraft structure and aero engine components, external stores and composite structures.

Singapore Aerospace Supplies Pte Ltd,
540 Airport Road, Paya Lebar, Singapore 1953
Telephone: 65 287 2033
Telex: RS 51158 SASUPP
Fax: 65 284 1167 and 280 6179
GENERAL MANAGER: Wong Peng Hock

Stocks and supplies a wide range of parts and components for civil and military aircraft, and is the material support specialist for Singapore Aerospace.

The Singapore Aerospace group was formed (as Singapore Aircraft Industries Pte Ltd) in early 1982 as a government owned industrial group under control of the Ministry of Defence's Sheng-Li Holding Company Pte Ltd. It has a combined workforce of more than 2,600.

Major programmes have included rebuilding, refurbishing and A-4 to TA-4 conversion of Skyhawk aircraft for the RSAF and other air forces, and depot level maintenance, overhaul, repair and refurbishment of many types of aircraft including the C-130 Hercules, F-5E/F Tiger II, Hunter, Strikemaster and several models of Bell and Aerospatiale helicopters. The work started at Seletar, but a new 15,000 m² (161,450 sq ft) factory at Paya Lebar was opened in October 1983.

SA's subsidiaries have a substantial capability in the fields of aircraft and engine overhaul, maintenance and repair, component and equipment manufacture for civil and military aircraft and aero engines, external stores equipment and defence avionics.

In 1985, SA began assembly of 30 SIAI-Marchetti S.211 jet trainers (which see) for the RSAF. It also assembled 17 of the 22 Super Pumas ordered by the RSAF, and is a participant in the P120L helicopter programme described in the International section.

SA A-4S-1 SUPER SKYHAWK

In 1986, SA completed the re-engining of two McDonnell Douglas A-4S Skyhawks with General Electric F404-GE-100D non-afterburning turbofans. The engine increases dash speed by 15 per cent, but gives much greater improvement in acceleration, turn-rate and take-off. Grumman and GE helped with the redesign work.

This Phase I conversion is being applied to 52 RSAF A-4S and TA-4S and 25 aircraft had been modified by early 1990. Two other testbed aircraft were to complete a year's development flying for the Phase II avionics upgrade with Ferranti 4150 head-up display, new head-down display and Litton LN-93 laser inertial navigation system.

The RSAF was in 1989 discussing acquisition of 14 additional F404 engines and about 20 stored A-4 airframes in order to produce another 10 A-4S-1s, apparently to make good attrition.

SA conversion of an A-4S to A-4S-1 Super Skyhawk configuration

The following description applies to the A-4S-1, except where stated.
TYPE: Single-seat attack aircraft.
AIRFRAME: As described in 1989-90 *Jane's*.
POWER PLANT: One 48.04 kN (10,800 lb st) General Electric F404-GE-100D non-afterburning turbofan, with air intake each side of fuselage aft of cockpit. Internal fuel in integral wing tanks (combined capacity 2,142.5 litres; 566 US gallons; 471.3 Imp gallons) and self-sealing fuselage tank aft of cockpit (870.5 litres; 230 US gallons; 191.5 Imp gallons), giving total capacity of 3,013 litres (796 US gallons; 662.8 Imp gallons). One 1,136 or 1,514 litre (300 or 400 US gallon; 250 or 333 Imp gallon) drop tank can be carried on the underfuselage stores rack, and a 568 or 1,136 litre (150 or 300 US gallon; 125 or 250 Imp gallon) drop tank on each inboard underwing rack. Single-point refuelling receptacle in rear of engine compartment; all tanks have provisions for both pressure and gravity refuelling. When used as a tanker for other aircraft, fuel from the wing tanks and underwing drop tanks (but not that in the fuselage tank) can be transferred to the receiving aircraft via a refuelling store carried on the underfuselage centreline rack. This store contains a 1,136 litre (300 US gallon; 250 Imp gallon) fuel cell, a constant-speed ram air turbine driven hydraulic pump, a hydraulically operated hose reel and 18.3 m (60 ft) of hose with a drogue. It can transfer fuel to the receiver aircraft at approx 681 litres (180 US gallons; 150 Imp gallons)/min.
ACCOMMODATION: Pilot only, on Douglas Escapac zero/zero lightweight ejection seat, under one-piece canopy hinged at rear and opening upward. (Two Escapac seats in tandem, under elongated canopy, for instructor and pupil in TA-4S-1). Bullet resistant windscreen. Cockpit(s) pressurised and air-conditioned.
SYSTEMS: As listed in 1989-90 *Jane's*.
AVIONICS AND EQUIPMENT: The main Phase II upgrade is listed in the introductory copy.
ARMAMENT: Two 20 mm Mk 12 cannon in wingroots. Five external stores points (one on underfuselage centreline and two under each wing) for wide variety of bombs,

rockets, gun pods, missiles and (except on outboard pair) drop tanks.

DIMENSIONS, EXTERNAL:

Wing span	8.38 m (27 ft 6 in)
Length overall	12.72 m (41 ft 8⅝ in)
Height overall	4.57 m (14 ft 11⅞ in)
Wheel track	2.37 m (7 ft 9½ in)
Wheelbase	3.64 m (11 ft 11⅛ in)

AREA:

Wings, gross	24.14 m² (259.82 sq ft)

WEIGHTS AND LOADING:

Operating weight empty	4,649 kg (10,250 lb)
Max fuel weight: internal	2,364 kg (5,213 lb)
external (one 400 and two 300 US gallon tanks)	2,961 kg (6,529 lb)

Max T-O weight	10,206 kg (22,500 lb)
Max landing weight	7,257 kg (16,000 lb)
Max zero-fuel weight	7,841 kg (17,287 lb)
Max wing loading	422.8 kg/m² (86.6 lb/sq ft)
Thrust/weight ratio	0.48

PERFORMANCE (at max T-O weight except where indicated):

Never-exceed speed at S/L	628 knots (1,163 km/h; 723 mph)
Max level speed at S/L	609 knots (1,128 km/h; 701 mph)
Max cruising speed at 9,145 m (30,000 ft)	445 knots (825 km/h; 512 mph)
Econ cruising speed at 10,670 m (35,000 ft)	424 knots (786 km/h; 488 mph)
Stalling speed at S/L	133 knots (247 km/h; 154 mph)
Max rate of climb at S/L	3,326 m (10,913 ft)/min

Combat ceiling	12,200 m (40,000 ft)
Min ground turning radius	3.76 m (12 ft 4 in)
T-O run	1,220 m (4,000 ft)
T-O to 15 m (50 ft)	1,768 m (5,800 ft)
Landing from 15 m (50 ft) at max landing weight	1,590 m (5,215 ft)
Landing run at max landing weight	1,372 m (4,500 ft)
Range, 113 kg (250 lb) fuel reserve:	
with max payload	625 nm (1,158 km; 720 miles)
with max internal/external fuel	2,046 nm (3,791 km; 2,356 miles)

SOUTH AFRICA

ATLAS
ATLAS AIRCRAFT CORPORATION OF SOUTH AFRICA (PTY) LIMITED

PO Box 11, Atlas Road, 1620 Kempton Park, Transvaal
Telephone: 27 (11) 927 9111
Telex: 724403
Fax: 27 (11) 395 1103
GENERAL MANAGER: G. W. Ward

Atlas Aircraft Corporation, which was founded in 1963, was hard hit early in 1990 by South African defence cuts, which forced it to cancel 11 big programmes and stretch out another 49. It had become the 11th arms exporter in the world. Atlas has good manufacturing, design and development facilities for airframes, engines, missiles and avionics. It developed the Cheetah version of the Mirage III and the Rooivalk gunship helicopter as well as the V3B and V3C missiles and many weapons installations.

ATLAS CAVA

It is now officially stated that Atlas is developing a new fighter/ground attack aircraft designated Cava for the South African Air Force to enter service during the mid/late 1990s. The SAAF has stated that the Cava will be based on the Mirage III/Cheetah design and powered more probably by one, but possibly two licence built Snecma Atar 9K-50 engines. The aircraft will be newly built rather than modified from existing in-service airframes. The Mirage III wing adapted for the Cheetah will be further developed and fly by wire might be added. Cava will have the latest avionics available in South Africa, a newly modernised version of the Cheetah nav/attack system, which is already giving the SAAF its first accurate long toss and first-pass laydown capability.

Cava is to replace early Mirage IIIs as well as the small, but essential force of Buccaneers, the eight Canberras that have already been retired, and eventually the South African Mirage F1s. The path of developing an existing design was chosen because South Africa has neither the technological nor financial resources, and now no longer the operational necessity to develop a completely new aircraft or its engine. The settlements in Angola and Namibia have given the SAAF a pause in which to prepare future policy and decide on equipment level.

Armament for the Cava could include the V3B or its emerging replacement V3C dogfight missile, conventional bombs or the South African smart bomb. The home avionics industry has developed effective ECM equipment for the Mirage F1, but a modern medium-range air-to-air missile is becoming necessary.

ATLAS CHEETAH

The Cheetah is a redesigned, upgraded version of the South African Air Force Mirage III, externally similar to the Israeli Kfir, but ostensibly modified independently by Atlas Aircraft. The Cheetah's existence was revealed in July 1985 and it became operational in Summer 1987.

About 15 Mirage III-EZ, four III-RZ and four III-R2Z single-seaters can be converted to Cheetah EZs, but they will probably equip only No. 5 Squadron at Louis Trichardt base. All existing South African Mirage IIIs are powered by 60.8 kN (13,670 lb st) Snecma Atar 9Cs, except for the four Mirage III-R2Zs, which have 70.6 kN (15,873 lb st) Atar 9K-50s for which Atlas has had the manufacturing licence since the mid-1970s.

The mixture of Mirage III-CZs, two-seat III-BZ trainers and reconnaissance III-RZ/R2Zs in service with No. 2 Squadron at Hoedspruit are not considered worth converting, having been in SAAF service since 1963. They will be replaced by the Cava.

The first Cheetahs were two-seat DZs, some of which are certainly intended for No. 85 Combat Flying School at Pietersburg, but a second crewman is probably also envisaged for operational flying. The single-seat Cheetah has only a small nose-mounted ranging radar and no cooling-air intake or cable ducts connecting the nose with the centre fuselage equipment bay. The lateral strakes are mounted much closer to the nose. The two-seater is obviously more elaborately equipped and could be intended as a pathfinder for the single-seaters. The SAAF has 16

Single-seat Cheetah EZ developed by Atlas from the Mirage III

Atlas Cheetah DZ two-seat combat trainer, a redesigned and upgraded Mirage III *(Jane's/Mike Keep)*

III-BZ, -DZ and D2Z two-seaters, which could be converted.

Conversion to Cheetah involves replacement of about 50 per cent of the airframe, fitting of the Atar 9K-50 engine and new avionics. Aerodynamic changes include two small strakes ahead of the cockpit, fixed canards aft of the intakes, short fences replacing the slot fences on the wing, large dog-tooth outboard leading-edge extensions and possibly rephased control surfaces. The strakes probably smooth the airflow past the canopy and onto the fin at high angles of attack to ward off yaw departures. All these should greatly improve turning performance, though to nothing like the level of today's agile fighters.

The radome of the two-seater DZ is large enough to contain a basic lookdown search-and-track radar. The undernose fairing just aft of the pitot boom contains two radar warning antennae and a large cooling-air intake, suggesting powerful avionics with high heat output. The long lateral fairings further aft cover cable harnesses passing from the nose to the centre fuselage, skirting the pressure cabin, as on earlier Mirage III two-seaters.

The former rocket motor fairing under the tail of both versions is replaced by an enlarged fairing probably containing ECM equipment. There is an indication of a radar altimeter to assist in low flying. There is an Elbit head-up display, a helmet-mounted sight, possibly of South African design, and an Elbit nav/attack system probably including an inertial system for navigation and weapon delivery.

Weapons include two 30 mm DEFA cannon in the wing-roots and AIM-9 Sidewinder and Matra R.550 Magic that are now probably being replaced by Armscor V3B and

then V3C Kukri missiles. Matra R.530 medium-range missiles may still be in service. The South African AS.30 air-to-surface missiles might have been upgraded with laser guidance to form the basis, with a designator pod, of the unspecified South African smart weapon used to destroy the bridge at Cuito Cuanavale in 1988. The Cheetah has been seen loaded with eight 500 lb bombs, two underwing drop tanks and two V3B self-defence missiles.

ATLAS XH-2 ROOIVALK (KESTREL)

Development begun in 1981 finally resulted in the public rollout on 15 January 1990 of the XH-2 Rooivalk gunship escort helicopter based on the Aerospatiale SA 330 Puma, of which South Africa acquired about 50 some years ago. Stages in development included the XH-1 Alpha based on the Alouette III, which appeared in 1984 and was flying in 1985, and the XTP-1 Puma-based experimental test platform, which appeared in 1986 and was used for weapons and system development. The development of the XH-2 itself led to the SAAF began in 1984.

Unfortunately, the virtual cessation of armed conflict around South Africa's borders and the consequent major reductions in armed forces and equipment have left the XH-2 without a customer and Atlas has no alternative but to look for exports.

The XH-2 is based on the dynamics of the French SA 330 Puma, with the notable exception that the engines have had to be moved aft to leave a full field of view for the pilot in the rear seat. The rear drives from the Turmo engines are therefore probably taken up by a transverse combining gearbox to enter the main transmission through the former tail rotor drive coupling. The extensive mechanical modifications required for this new layout explain the South African claim to be capable of designing and manufacturing helicopter transmissions, which they would otherwise have to obtain from France or Romania.

The intakes are shielded from dust by adapted Puma particle separator assemblies. No self-protection system, such as cooled exhaust, IR jammer, flare/chaff dispensers or radar warning systems can be seen in early photographs. The tricycle landing gear of the Puma is replaced in the XH-2 by a high-absorption main undercarriage forward and a tailwheel behind the ventral fin.

Although the XH-2 is a gunship rather than an anti-tank helicopter, armament includes air-to-surface missiles, probably a South African weapon already used in Angola and possibly laser guided. The four-tube missile pods suggest that the front apertures may be intended to be covered by doors to shield the missile sensor heads before lock-on. Other weapons include pods of South African 68 mm unguided rockets, single V3-series air-to-air missiles on the tips of the pylons and the turreted GAF-1 20 mm cannon first fitted to the experimental XH-1 Alpha. Both crewmen have a helmet mounted sight, probably a version of the sight developed for the V3 series and additionally adapted for the gun. The chin mounted optical turret seems unlikely to have direct-view optics, but is claimed to be stabilised and to contain FLIR with automatic tracking. There is a head-up display, almost certainly located in the rear cockpit to help the pilot aim the unguided rockets.

Only basic data have been released so far, as follows:

BASIC DATA:

Main rotor diameter	15.08 m (49 ft 5¾ in)	
Length overall	16.65 m (54 ft 7½ in)	
Max T-O weight	over 8,000 kg (17,637 lb)	

Max cruising speed over 145 knots (269 km/h; 167 mph)
Max range, with 30 min reserves
400 nm (741 km; 460 miles)

XH-2 Rooivalk gunship derived from the Aerospatiale SA 330 Puma by Atlas

SPAIN

AISA
AERONAUTICA INDUSTRIAL SA

Cuatros Vientos (Carretera del Aeroclub), Apartado 27094, Madrid 28044

Telephone: 34 (1) 208 13 40

Telex: E 49872 MADRID

Fax: 34 (1) 208 39 58

PRESIDENT: J. A. Pérez-Nievas
GENERAL MANAGER: Carlos Herraiz
DESIGN MANAGER: Rafael Moreno
PRESS RELATIONS: Enrique Gutierrez

This company was founded in 1923, assuming its present title in 1934. Its design office has, since the Second World War, been responsible for several liaison, training and sporting aircraft for the Spanish Air Force and aeroclub flying schools. The Cuatros Vientos factory has a covered area of 9,580 m² (103,118 sq ft) and employs about 200 people.

AISA repairs and overhauls US aircraft, in particular the Beechcraft B55 Barons and F33 Bonanzas operated by the Spanish Air Force and the National School of Aeronautics. It also repairs and overhauls Bell 47, 204, 205, 206 and 212, and Boeing CH-47, helicopters for the Spanish Army, Navy and Air Force and civilian operators. As a subcontractor to

Messier-Bugatti, it is producing landing gear shock absorbers and hydraulic actuators for the Dassault Mirage F1, 2000 and Falcon series, Dassault/Dornier Alpha Jet, and other European aviation programmes. Under subcontract to CASA, it produces structural components for the C-212 Aviocar and Airbus transports; and, in offset programmes, helicopter structures and hydraulic components for Aerospatiale and Agusta. AISA modernises Spanish Air Force Mirage IIIs, and is also involved in the Eurofighter EFA programme. AISA is preparing the Spanish Army's nine CH-47Cs for conversion by Boeing to CH-47Ds.

CASA
CONSTRUCCIONES AERONAUTICAS SA

Rey Francisco 4, Apartado 193, 28008 Madrid

Telephone: 34 (1) 247 25 00

Telex: 27418 CASA E

Fax: 34 (1) 248 88 85

WORKS: Getafe, Ajalvir, Tablada, San Pablo, San Fernando and Cádiz

PRESIDENT AND CHAIRMAN OF THE BOARD:
Javier Alvarez Vara
MANAGING DIRECTOR: Luis Escudero
PUBLIC RELATIONS AND PRESS MANAGER:
José de Sanmillán

CASA was founded in 1923 and is now owned 85 per cent by the Spanish state holding company INI, 11 per cent by MBB, 0.66 per cent by Dassault and the rest by other minority shareholders. After hard years during the mid-1980s, the company broke even in 1989 and its prospects are now strong. The former 13 per cent holding by Northrop was acquired by INI, but it is reported that INI would be prepared to reduce its holding to 25 per cent to let another European company take a stake in CASA.

In 1989, CASA formed Industria de Turbopropulsores (ITP) to make parts for and assemble turbojet engines, including the EJ100 for the European Fighter Aircraft, the F404 for the F-18, possibly the R-R Pegasus for Spanish Matadors (Harriers) and the eventual engine for the CASA AX. A second company, Compania Espanola de Sistemas Aeronauticas (CESA) was formed with a 40 per cent holding by Lucas Aerospace. The CASA space division has been greatly expanded and a largely automated composites manufacturing plant has been set up at Iliescas, near Toledo.

The largest of CASA's present programmes is its 4.2 per cent share in Airbus (see International section). It makes horizontal tail surfaces, landing gear doors, wing ribs and skins, leading and trailing edges and passenger doors for the A300/310/320, many of them in composites. Similar work will be done for the A330/340.

Second-largest programme is CASA's share in the European Fighter Aircraft (EFA), also detailed in the International section. CASA is active in all four of EFA's joint teams for avionics, control systems, flight management system and structure. The last-named includes sharing the

starboard wing with BAe and the rear fuselage with Aeritalia. CASA is responsible for integration and software creation of the EFA communication subsystem.

In October 1989, CASA won the competition to design, stress, test and manufacture the entire wing of the Saab 2000 turboprop commuter. CASA will use the same advanced metal bonding technique as used for the Saab 340, but more composites will be included. The Saab 2000 should fly early in 1992 and be certificated and delivered in 1993.

Early in 1990, CASA had preliminary talks with Ilyushin about developing and marketing a westernised version of the 60-passenger Il-114 turboprop commuter, possibly with western engines. In exchange, the CN-235 might be sold in the USSR.

CASA has designed and is manufacturing the tailplane of the McDonnell Douglas MD-11 and makes outer flaps for the Boeing 757.

With Agusta, Westland and Fokker, CASA is a member of the Joint European Helicopter (JEH) consortium (see International section). The company is also in the European Future Large Aircraft Group, formerly called FIMA when it included Lockheed (see International section).

CASA is in the team of Spanish companies led by Ceselsa that will update 18 single-seat and five two-seat Mirage IIIs for the Spanish Air Force. Retrofits will include in-flight refuelling and pressure ground refuelling. The company has also made an offer to update Spanish Lockheed P-3s with the assistance of Boeing, Inisel, Sainco and other Spanish companies.

In past years, CASA has made centre-fuselages for Dassault Mirage F1s and components for McDonnell Douglas F/A-18s, both for the Spanish Air Force. It has assembled 57 MBB BO 105s for the Spanish Army and 24 plus 32 armed BO 105s for Iraq, plus 19 more for Spanish government agencies and two BK 117s for ICONA. It assembled 12 of the 18 AS532B₁ Super Pumas for the Spanish Army and installed Thorn EMI Searchwater AEW radars in three Spanish Navy Sikorsky SH-3Ds. CASA manufactures tail components for the Sikorsky S-70 and would assemble and test S-70s purchased for the Spanish armed forces. CASA has also assembled 40 Enaer T-35C Pillans for the Spanish Air Force under the designation E.26 Tamiz.

For many years, CASA has been maintaining and

modernising US Air Force and Navy aircraft and helicopters. The main current types are the McDonnell Douglas F-15 and F-4.

CASA's own aircraft programmes include the C-212 Aviocar and the C-101 Aviojet. The CN-235 is shared with IPTN under Airtech (see International section) and CASA is looking for a partner to produce the new AX operational trainer.

A decision may be taken in 1990 on a 60/65-passenger commuter airliner, possibly a derivative of the CN-235, although IPTN is planning its own development of this type. But CASA is also actively studying a 100-passenger commuter designated AK-100 (see International section) in association with Aerospatiale and Aeritalia. A prefeasibility study had been launched at the end of 1988. The resultant consortium would be independent of the Aerospatiale-Aeritalia ATR company.

CASA has seven factories covering 275,000 m² (2,960,075 sq ft) and employs about 10,700 people.

AIRTECH (CASA-IPTN) CN-235
Details of this twin-turboprop transport aircraft can be found in the International section.

CASA AX
In January 1990, after years of preliminary planning by CASA, the Spanish government gave CASA a Ptas 90 million ($829,000) contract for a three-year pre-feasibility study for an AX advanced trainer and close support aircraft. This would be followed in 1994 by a two-year definition phase and the aircraft should be operational in about 1998.

CASA has been looking for partners in the AX programme both in Europe and the USA.

The AX would incorporate a large part of the systems technology developed for EFA. CASA believes there will be a need for a trainer to introduce pilots to the systems they will meet in operational aircraft. The engine would be a non-afterburning version of either the EJ200 or the F404. The necessity for transonic performance had not been decided at the time of going to press.

CASA C-212 SERIES 300 AVIOCAR
The original C-212-5 Series 100 Aviocar (1981-82 and earlier *Jane's*), of which 135 examples (including ten

development aircraft) were built by CASA and 29 under licence by Nurtanio (IPTN) in Indonesia, was followed in 1979 by the improved Srs 200 with more powerful TPE331-10 engines and increased max T-O weight. Details of the latter version can be found in the 1987-88 *Jane's*. The standard model is now the Series 300, which was certificated in December 1987. Military variants are designated **C-212-M**.

The C-212 is certificated under FAR Pt 25, can be operated under FAR Pt 121 and Pt 135 conditions, and is well within the noise requirements of FAR Pt 36. By January 1990 total sales of the Aviocar (all versions) had reached 434 (207 civil and 227 military), of which more than 400 had been delivered by CASA and IPTN, with production continuing. This total includes 13 Series 300 C-212-Ms for the air forces of Angola (four), Panama (three), France (five), Bolivia (one) and at least six civil Series 300s. CASA has agreed in principle to let Fairchild manufacture the C-212 in the USA if the US Air Force adopts it as a light transport.

Maritime patrol and elint/ECM versions of the Aviocar are described separately, as is the re-engined **C-212P**. The following description applies to the Series 300 transport and equivalent C-212-M.

TYPE: Twin-turboprop STOL utility transport.

WINGS: Cantilever high-wing monoplane. Wing section NACA 65_3-218. Incidence 2° 30′. No dihedral or sweepback on main wings, but wingtips have 45° dihedral. All-metal light alloy fail-safe structure. Light alloy ailerons and double-slotted trailing-edge flaps. Trim tab in port aileron. Pneumatic de-icing of leading-edges (rubber boots and engine bleed air).

FUSELAGE: Semi-monocoque non-pressurised fail-safe structure of light alloy construction. New nose section, compared with Srs 200, providing additional volume for baggage (civil) or avionics (special mission versions).

TAIL UNIT: Cantilever two-spar all-metal structure, with dorsal fin. Fixed incidence tailplane, mid mounted on rear of fuselage. Trim tab in rudder and each elevator. Pneumatic de-icing of leading-edges (rubber boots and engine bleed air).

LANDING GEAR: Non-retractable tricycle type, with single mainwheels and single steerable nosewheel. CASA oleo-pneumatic shock absorbers. Goodyear wheels and tyres, main units size 11.00-12 Type III (10-ply rating), nose unit size 24-7.7 Type VII (8-ply rating). Tyre pressure 3.86 bars (56 lb/sq in) on main units, 3.72 bars (54 lb/sq in) on nose unit. Goodyear hydraulic disc brakes on mainwheels. No brake cooling. Anti-skid system optional.

POWER PLANT: Two Garrett TPE331-10R-513C turboprops, each flat rated at 671 kW (900 shp) and equipped with an automatic power reserve (APR) system providing 690 kW (925 shp) in the event of one engine failing during take-off. Dowty Aerospace R-334/4-82-F/13 four-blade constant-speed fully-feathering reversible-pitch propellers. Fuel in four integral wing tanks, with total capacity of 2,040 litres (539 US gallons; 449 Imp gallons), of which 2,000 litres (528 US gallons; 440 Imp gallons) are usable. Gravity refuelling point above each tank. Single pressure refuelling point in starboard wing leading-edge. Additional fuel can be carried in one 1,000 litre or two 750 litre (264 or 198 US gallon; 220 or 165 Imp gallon) optional ferry tanks inside cabin, and/or two 500 litre (132 US gallon; 110 Imp gallon) auxiliary underwing tanks. Oil capacity 4.5 litres (1.2 US gallons; 1.0 Imp gallon) per engine.

ACCOMMODATION: Crew of two on flight deck; cabin attendant in civil version. For troop transport role, main cabin can be fitted with 25 inward facing seats along cabin walls, to accommodate 24 paratroops with an instructor/jumpmaster; or seats for 25 fully equipped troops. As an ambulance, cabin is normally equipped to carry 12 stretcher patients and four medical attendants.

CASA C-212-300M Aviocar of the Fuerza Aérea Panameña

As a freighter, up to 2,700 kg (5,952 lb) of cargo can be carried in main cabin, including two LD1, LD727/DC-8 or three LD3 containers, or light vehicles. Cargo system, which is certificated to FAR Pt 25, includes roller loading/unloading system and 9g barrier net. Photographic version is equipped with two Wild RC-10A vertical cameras and a darkroom. Navigation training version has individual desks/consoles for instructor and five pupils, in two rows, with appropriate instrument installations. Civil passenger transport version has standard seating for up to 26 persons in mainly three-abreast layout at 72 cm (28.5 in) pitch, with provision for quick change to all-cargo or mixed passenger/cargo interior. Toilet, galley and 400 kg (882 lb) capacity baggage compartment standard, plus additional 150 kg (330 lb) in nose bay. VIP transport version can be furnished to customer's requirements. Forward and outward opening door on port side immediately aft of flight deck; forward/outward opening passenger door on port side aft of wing; inward opening emergency exit opposite each door on starboard side. Additional emergency exit in roof of forward main cabin. A two-section underfuselage loading ramp/door aft of main cabin is openable in flight for discharge of paratroops or cargo, and can be fitted with optional external wheels for door protection during ground manoeuvring. Interior of rear loading door can be used for additional baggage stowage in civil version. Entire accommodation heated and ventilated; air-conditioning optional.

SYSTEMS: Freon cycle or (on special mission versions) engine bleed air air-conditioning system optional. Hydraulic system, operating at a service pressure of 138 bars (2,000 lb/sq in), provides power via an electric pump to actuate mainwheel brakes, flaps, nosewheel steering and rear cargo ramp/door. Handpump for standby hydraulic power in case of electrical failure or other emergency. Electrical system is supplied by two 9kW starter/generators, three batteries and three static converters. Pneumatic boot de-icing of wing and tail unit leading-edges; electric de-icing of propellers and windscreens. Oxygen system for crew (incl cabin attendant); two portable oxygen cylinders for passenger supply. Engine and cabin fire protection systems.

AVIONICS AND EQUIPMENT: Standard avionics include Collins VHF com, VOR/ILS, ADF, DME, ATC transponder, radio altimeter, intercom (with Gables control) and PA system; Bendix/King directional gyro; Honeywell AFCS and flight director; Collins ADF; and Bendix weather radar. Blind-flying instrumentation standard. Optional avionics include second Collins ADF and transponder; Collins HF and UHF com; Global Omega nav; Honeywell weather radar; Martech emergency radio beacon; and Fairchild flight data and cockpit voice recorders.

ARMAMENT (military versions, optional): Two machine-gun pods or two rocket launchers, or one launcher and one gun pod, on hardpoints on fuselage sides (capacity 250 kg; 551 lb each).

DIMENSIONS, EXTERNAL:

Wing span	20.28 m (66 ft 6½ in)
Wing chord: at root	2.50 m (8 ft 2½ in)
at tip	1.25 m (4 ft 1¼ in)
Wing aspect ratio	10.0
Length overall	16.15 m (52 ft 11¾ in)
Fuselage: Max width	2.30 m (7 ft 6½ in)
Height overall	6.60 m (21 ft 7¾ in)
Tailplane span	8.40 m (27 ft 6¾ in)
Wheel track	3.10 m (10 ft 2 in)
Wheelbase	5.55 m (18 ft 2½ in)
Propeller diameter	2.74 m (9 ft 0 in)
Propeller ground clearance (min)	1.32 m (4 ft 4 in)
Distance between propeller centres	5.30 m (17 ft 4¾ in)
Passenger door (port, rear):	
Max height	1.58 m (5 ft 2¼ in)
Max width	0.70 m (2 ft 3½ in)
Crew and servicing door (port, fwd):	
Max height	1.10 m (3 ft 7¼ in)
Max width	0.58 m (1 ft 10¾ in)
Rear loading door: Max length	3.66 m (12 ft 0 in)
Max width	1.70 m (5 ft 7 in)
Max height	1.80 m (5 ft 11 in)
Emergency exit (stbd, fwd): Height	1.10 m (3 ft 7¼ in)
Width	0.58 m (1 ft 10¾ in)
Emergency exit (stbd, rear): Height	0.94 m (3 ft 1 in)
Width	0.55 m (1 ft 9¾ in)

CASA C-212 Series 300 Aviocar, the current standard production version *(Pilot Press)*

DIMENSIONS, INTERNAL:
Cabin (excl flight deck and rear loading door):
Length: passenger version	7.22 m (23 ft 8¼ in)
cargo/military	6.50 m (21 ft 4 in)
Max width	2.10 m (6 ft 10¾ in)
Max height	1.80 m (5 ft 11 in)
Floor area: passenger	13.51 m² (145.4 sq ft)
cargo/military	12.21 m² (131.4 sq ft)
Volume: passenger	23.7 m³ (837 cu ft)
cargo/military	21.3 m³ (752 cu ft)

Cabin: volume incl flight deck and rear loading door
	27.0 m³ (953.5 cu ft)
Baggage compartment volume	3.6 m³ (127 cu ft)

AREAS:
Wings, gross	41.0 m² (441.33 sq ft)
Ailerons (total, incl tab)	3.75 m² (40.36 sq ft)
Trailing-edge flaps (total)	7.47 m² (80.41 sq ft)
Fin, incl dorsal fin	6.27 m² (67.49 sq ft)
Rudder, incl tab	2.05 m² (22.07 sq ft)
Tailplane	12.57 m² (135.31 sq ft)
Elevators (total, incl tabs)	3.56 m² (38.32 sq ft)

WEIGHTS AND LOADINGS:
Manufacturer's weight empty	3,780 kg (8,333 lb)
Weight empty, equipped (cargo)	4,400 kg (9,700 lb)
Max payload: cargo	2,700 kg (5,952 lb)
military	2,820 kg (6,217 lb)
Max fuel: standard	1,600 kg (3,527 lb)
with underwing auxiliary tanks	2,400 kg (5,291 lb)
Max T-O weight: standard	7,700 kg (16,975 lb)
military version	8,000 kg (17,637 lb)
Max ramp weight	7,750 kg (17,085 lb)
Max landing weight	7,450 kg (16,424 lb)
Max zero-fuel weight	7,100 kg (15,653 lb)
Max cabin floor loading	732 kg/m² (150 lb/sq ft)
Max wing loading: standard	187.8 kg/m² (38.46 lb/sq ft)
Max power loading: standard	5.74 kg/kW (9.43 lb/shp)

PERFORMANCE (at max T-O weight. A: passenger version, B: freighter, C: military version at 8,000 kg; 17,637 lb MTOGW):
Max operating speed (VMO):
A, B, C	200 knots (370 km/h; 230 mph)

Max cruising speed at 3,050 m (10,000 ft):
A, B, C	191 knots (354 km/h; 220 mph)

Econ cruising speed at 3,050 m (10,000 ft):
A, B, C	162 knots (300 km/h; 186 mph)

Stalling speed in T-O configuration:
A, B, C	78 knots (145 km/h; 90 mph)

Max rate of climb at S/L: A, B, C	497 m (1,630 ft)/min

Rate of climb at S/L, one engine out:
A, B, C	95 m (312 ft)/min

Service ceiling: A, B, C
	7,925 m (26,000 ft)

Service ceiling, one engine out:
A, B, C	3,380 m (11,100 ft)
FAR T-O distance: A, B	817 m (2,680 ft)
FAR landing distance: A, B	866 m (2,840 ft)

MIL-7700C T-O distance to 15 m (50 ft):
C	610 m (2,000 ft)

MIL-7700C landing distance from 15 m (50 ft):
C	462 m (1,516 ft)
MIL-7700C landing run: C	285 m (935 ft)

Required runway length for STOL operation:
C	384 m (1,260 ft)

Range (civil operation, IFR reserves):
with 25 passengers, at max cruising speed
	237 nm (440 km; 273 miles)

with 1,713 kg (3,776 lb) payload
	773 nm (1,433 km; 890 miles)

Range (military operation):
with max payload	450 nm (835 km; 519 miles)

with max standard fuel and 2,120 kg (4,674 lb) payload
	907 nm (1,682 km; 1,045 miles)

with max standard and auxiliary fuel and 1,192 kg (2,628 lb) payload
	1,446 nm (2,680 km; 1,665 miles)

Maritime patrol Series 300 Aviocars in the insignia of the Argentine coastguard (Prefectura Naval)

ACCOMMODATION (ASW version): Pilot and co-pilot on flight deck, with OTPI and additional central console for radar repeater; controls for radio navigation, Doppler, DME, ADF, UHF/DF, Omega and VOR/ILS; weapons delivery controls; and intervalometer for rockets. Avionics rack on port side, aft of pilot, for com/nav equipment; second rack on starboard side, aft of co-pilot, contains avionics for mission equipment (radar, sonobuoys, MAD and ESM). Immediately aft of the latter rack, along the starboard side of the cabin, are three control consoles for the mission crew members. The first console has the radar control and display, ESM control and display, and intercom switch control. The second has the tactical display and control, MAD recorder and control, and intercom switch (ICS). The rearmost of the three incorporates intercom switch, sonobuoy receiver control unit, acoustic control panel, and acoustic control and display units.

ACCOMMODATION (maritime patrol version): Pilot and co-pilot on flight deck, with central console for radar repeater; control for radio navigation, Doppler, DME, ADF, UHF/DF, Omega, VOR/ILS and searchlight. Avionics rack on port side, aft of pilot, for com/nav and radar equipment. On starboard side of cabin is a console for the radar operator that incorporates radar PPI and ICS controls. Posts for two observers at rear of cabin.

AVIONICS: Communications equipment includes one HF and two VHF transceivers, single UHF, and interphone. Navigation equipment includes automatic flight control system, flight director, VOR/ILS (including VOR/LOC), glideslope and marker beacon receiver, DME, ADF, UHF/DF, radar altimeter, VLF/Omega, autopilot and compass.

OPERATIONAL EQUIPMENT (ASW version): Underfuselage search radar with 360° scan, electronic support measures (ESM), sonobuoy processing system (SPS), OTPI, MAD, tactical processing system (TPS), IFF/SIF transponder, sonobuoy and smoke marker launcher, torpedoes, rockets and other weapons.

OPERATIONAL EQUIPMENT (maritime patrol version): Nose mounted AN/APS-128 100kW search radar with 270° scan, searchlight, FLIR (optional), smoke markers and camera.

ARMAMENT: Includes option to carry torpedoes such as Mk 46 and Sting Ray, and air-to-surface missiles such as Sea Skua and AS 15TT.

CASA C-212 AVIOCAR (ELINT/ECM VERSION)

A version of the Aviocar for electronic intelligence and electronic countermeasures duties entered development in 1981. At least six (all Series 200s) have been ordered by undisclosed customers, and two C-212s previously delivered to the Portuguese Air Force have been modified retrospectively for elint/ECM duties. This version is also available for the Series 300.

The elint/ECM version carries equipment for automatic signal interception, classification and identification in dense signal environments, data from which enable a map to be drawn plotting the position and characteristics of hostile radars. Emitters for the jamming part of the mission are also carried.

CASA C-212P AVIOCAR

No orders had been received by early 1990 for the C-212P Aviocar, a Series 300 powered by 820 kW (1,100 shp) P&WC PT6A-65 engines to improve hot and high performance. The C-212P was certificated in Spain in 1989.

CASA C-101 AVIOJET

Spanish Air Force designation: E.25 Mirlo (Blackbird)
Chilean Air Force designations: T-36 and A-36 Halcón

The first of four prototypes of this basic and advanced military jet trainer made its initial flight on 27 June 1977. MBB (West Germany) and Northrop (USA) collaborated in the design.

The first Spanish production aircraft flew in 1979. Export versions have been equipped for ground attack, either for training or combat.

In 1990, CASA began an 18-month modernisation of the C-101 weapon system for training or, as in Jordan and Chile, for front-line use. The system will include a Ferranti head-up display and a prototype was due to fly by the end of 1990.

The following versions have been built:

C-101EB. Initial production trainer version for Spanish Air Force, with 15.57 kN (3,500 lb st) TFE731-2-2J engine. Total of 88 delivered originally from 17 March 1980 (later increased to 92); now in service with one squadron of the Academia General del Aire at San Javier, two squadrons of the Grupo de Escuelas (41st Air Group) at Matacán, and

CASA C-212 AVIOCAR (ASW and MARITIME PATROL VERSIONS)
Swedish Navy designation: Tp89

For service with the Spanish Air Force, and for several foreign countries, CASA has developed versions of the C-212 equipped for anti-submarine and maritime patrol duties. Nine Srs 100/200s were ordered by the Spanish Air Force for SAR duties, three by the Spanish Ministry of Finance, one ASW version by the Swedish Navy, two for maritime patrol (with a SLAR and IR/UV search equipment) by the Swedish coastguard, eight for maritime patrol by the Venezuelan Navy, 10 for maritime patrol by the Mexican Navy, two by Sudan and one by the Uruguayan Air Force. All these versions are available also for the Series 300. Argentina's Prefectura Naval ordered five Series 300s. The Portuguese have ordered three CASA C-212s to be equipped with a Swedish Space Corporation system with SLAR, FLIR, IR/UV scanner, cameras, consoles, recorders and air-ground links for offshore patrol.

TYPE: Twin-turboprop ASW and maritime patrol aircraft.
AIRFRAME: Generally similar to standard C-212 except for addition of nose radome and various external antennae.
POWER PLANT: As for standard C-212. Auxiliary fuel tanks, total capacity 1,400 litres (370 US gallons; 308 Imp gallons).

CASA C-101CC Aviojet light attack aircraft *(Pilot Press)*

the Patrulla Aguila (Eagle Patrol) display team of the Spanish Air Force, which has seven aircraft. Described in 1983-84 *Jane's*.

C-101 BB. Armed export version, with 16.46 kN (3,700 lb st) TFE731-3-1J engine, in service with air forces of Chile (14 **BB-02**) and Honduras (four **BB-03**, similar except for avionics). All BB-02s except first four were assembled under licence in Chile (see ENAER entry in Chilean section). Known as **T-36 Halcón** (Hawk) in Chilean service.

C-101 CC. Light attack version, with more powerful TFE731-5-1J engine (normal rating 19.13 kN; 4,300 lb st, military power reserve (MPR) rating 20.91 kN; 4,700 lb st), and other modifications. First of two prototypes flown on 16 November 1983. Twenty-three **CC-02** ordered by Chile, of which 22 for assembly and partial manufacture by ENAER as **A-36 Halcón** (deliveries still in progress in 1990), and 16 **CC-04** delivered in 1987-88 to Royal Jordanian Air Force. These two operators hold options for a total of 14 more.

C-101 DD. Enhanced training version, announced in 1984 and flown for the first time on 20 May 1985. Additional avionics include Ferranti head-up display, weapon aiming computer and inertial platform, and GEC Sensors AD 6601 Doppler velocity sensor. Power plant as for C-101CC. No orders announced up to Spring 1990.

The following description applies to the standard C-101CC except where indicated:

TYPE: Tandem two-seat basic and advanced trainer and light tactical aircraft.

WINGS: Cantilever low-wing monoplane. Norcasa 15 symmetrical wing section, thickness/chord ratio 15 per cent. Dihedral 5°. Incidence 1°. Sweepback at quarter-chord 1° 53′. All-metal (aluminium alloy) three-spar fail-safe stressed-skin structure, with six-bolt attachment to fuselage. Plain ailerons and slotted trailing-edge flaps, of glassfibre/honeycomb sandwich construction. Flap track guides of titanium. Ailerons actuated hydraulically, with electrically actuated artificial spring feel and manual backup. Ground adjustable tab on port aileron.

FUSELAGE: All-metal semi-monocoque fail-safe structure. Hydraulically operated aluminium honeycomb airbrake under centre of fuselage.

TAIL UNIT: Cantilever all-metal structure, with electrically actuated variable incidence tailplane. Aluminium honeycomb rudder and elevators, actuated manually via push/pull rods. Electrically actuated trim tab in rudder. Twin ventral strakes under jetpipe on armed versions.

LANDING GEAR: Hydraulically retractable tricycle type, with single wheel and oleo-pneumatic shock absorber on each unit. Forward retracting Dowty Aerospace nose unit, with non-steerable nosewheel and chined tubeless tyre size 457 × 146 (18 × 5.75-8). Inward retracting mainwheels with tubeless tyres size 622 × 216 (24.5 × 8.5-10) and hydraulically actuated multi-disc brakes.

POWER PLANT: One Garrett TFE731 non-afterburning turbofan (see model listings for details), with lateral intake on each side of fuselage abreast of second cockpit. Fuel in one 1,155 litre (305 US gallon; 254 Imp gallon) fuselage bag tank, one 575 litre (152 US gallon; 126.5 Imp gallon) integral tank in wing centre-section, and two outer wing integral tanks, each of 342 litres (90.4 US gallons; 75.25 Imp gallons). Total internal fuel capacity 1,730 litres (457 US gallons; 380.5 Imp gallons) normal, 2,414 litres (637.8 US gallons; 531 Imp gallons) maximum, of which 1,667 litres (440 US gallons; 367 Imp gallons) and 2,337 litres (617 US gallons; 514 Imp gallons), respectively, are usable. Fuel system permits up to 30 s of inverted flight. Pressure refuelling point beneath port air intake; gravity fuelling point for each tank. No provision for external fuel tanks. Oil capacity 8.5 litres (2.2 US gallons; 1.8 Imp gallons).

ACCOMMODATION: Crew of two in tandem, on Martin-Baker Mk 10L zero/zero ejection seats, under individual canopies which open sideways to starboard and are separated by internal screen. Rear (instructor's) seat elevated 32.5 cm (12¾ in). Cockpit pressurised and air-conditioned by engine bleed air. Dual controls standard.

SYSTEMS: Hamilton Standard three-wheel bootstrap type air-conditioning and pressurisation system, differential 0.28 bars (4.07 lb/sq in), using engine bleed air. Single hydraulic system, pressure 207 bars (3,000 lb/sq in), for landing gear, ailerons, flaps, airbrake, anti-skid units and wheel brakes. Backup system comprising compressed nitrogen bottle for landing gear extension and accumulator for aileron boosters and emergency braking. Pneumatic system for air-conditioning, pressurisation and canopy seal. Electrical system includes 28V 9kW DC starter/generator, two 700VA static inverters for 115/26V single phase AC power, and two 24V 23Ah nickel-cadmium batteries for emergency DC power and engine starting. High pressure gaseous oxygen system.

AVIONICS AND EQUIPMENT: C-101EB and BB as listed in earlier *Jane's*. Standard C-101CC equipped with Magnavox AN/ARC-164 UHF com, Collins 21B VHF com, Collins VIR-31A VOR/ILS, Collins DME-40, Collins ADF-60, Andrea AN/AIC-18 interphone, Teledyne/CASA AN/APX-101 IFF/SIF, Dorne and Margolin DMELT 8.1 ELT, Honeywell ZC-222 flight director, Honeywell AS-339 gyro platform, ADI-500C,

CASA C-101CC-04 Aviojet of the Royal Jordanian Air Force *(Ivo Sturzenegger)*

RD-550A HSI, Avimo RGS2 gunsight (front and rear cockpit), and CASA SCAR-81 armament control system. Wide range of alternative avionics and equipment available for export versions, including a Maverick pod, and (in the DD), a Ferranti FD 4513 head-up display and weapon aiming computer, Litton LN-39 inertial platform, Aeritalia mission computer, all linked by MIL-1553 digital bus, FIAR P 0702 laser ranger, HOTAS controls, General Instrument AN/ALR-66 radar warning receiver, GEC Sensors AD 6601-12 Doppler velocity sensor, Aeritalia radar altimeter, Collins AN/ARC-182(V) UHF/VHF-AM/FM com, Ferranti FD 5000 video camera, Vinten Vicon 78 chaff and flare dispenser and Ferranti FD2062 rear seat monitor.

ARMAMENT AND OPERATIONAL EQUIPMENT: Large bay below rear cockpit suitable for quick-change packages, including a 30 mm DEFA 553 cannon pod with 130 rds, a twin 12.7 mm Browning M3 machine-gun pod with 220 rds/gun, reconnaissance camera, ECM package or laser designator. Six underwing hardpoints, capacities 500 kg (1,102 lb) inboard, 375 kg (827 lb) centre and 250 kg (551 lb) outboard; total external stores load 2,250 kg (4,960 lb). Typical armament can include one 30 mm cannon with up to 130 rds, or two 12.7 mm guns, in the fuselage; and four LAU-10 pods of 5 in rockets, six 250 kg BR250 bombs, four LAU-3/A rocket launchers, four 125 kg BR125 bombs and two LAU-3/A launchers, two AGM-65 Maverick missiles, or two AIM-9L Sidewinders or Matra Magic.

DIMENSIONS, EXTERNAL:

Wing span	10.60 m (34 ft 9⅜ in)
Wing chord: at c/l	2.36 m (7 ft 9 in)
at tip	1.41 m (4 ft 7½ in)
Wing aspect ratio	5.6
Length overall	12.50 m (41 ft 0 in)
Height overall	4.25 m (13 ft 11¼ in)
Tailplane span	4.32 m (14 ft 2 in)
Wheel track (c/l of shock struts)	3.18 m (10 ft 5¼ in)
Wheelbase	4.77 m (15 ft 7¾ in)

AREAS:

Wings, gross	20.00 m² (215.3 sq ft)
Ailerons (total)	1.18 m² (12.70 sq ft)
Trailing-edge flaps (total)	2.50 m² (26.91 sq ft)
Fin	2.10 m² (22.60 sq ft)
Rudder	1.10 m² (11.84 sq ft)
Tailplane	3.44 m² (37.03 sq ft)
Elevators	1.00 m² (10.76 sq ft)

WEIGHTS AND LOADINGS:

Weight empty, equipped	3,500 kg (7,716 lb)
Max fuel weight: usable	1,822 kg (4,017 lb)
total	1,882 kg (4,149 lb)
Max external stores load	2,250 kg (4,960 lb)
T-O weight:	
trainer, clean: BB, CC	4,570 kg (10,075 lb)
DD	4,600 kg (10,141 lb)
ground attack: BB	5,600 kg (12,345 lb)
CC, DD	6,300 kg (13,890 lb)
Max landing weight:	
3.66 m (12 ft)/s sink rate	4,700 kg (10,361 lb)
3.05 m (10 ft)/s sink rate	5,800 kg (12,787 lb)
Wing loading:	
trainer, clean: BB, CC	228.5 kg/m² (46.80 lb/sq ft)
DD	230.0 kg/m² (47.11 lb/sq ft)
ground attack: BB	280.0 kg/m² (57.35 lb/sq ft)
CC, DD	315.0 kg/m² (64.52 lb/sq ft)
Power loading:	
trainer, clean: BB	277.9 kg/kN (2.72 lb/lb st)
CC (normal)	239.1 kg/kN (2.34 lb/lb st)
CC (with MPR)	218.7 kg/kN (2.14 lb/lb st)
DD (normal)	240.7 kg/kN (2.36 lb/lb st)
DD (with MPR)	220.2 kg/kN (2.16 lb/lb st)

ground attack: BB	340.8 kg/kN (3.34 lb/lb st)
CC, DD (normal)	329.6 kg/kN (3.23 lb/lb st)
CC, DD (with MPR)	301.0 kg/kN (2.95 lb/lb st)

PERFORMANCE (C-101BB at 4,400 kg; 9,700 lb AUW, C-101CC and DD at 4,500 kg; 9,921 lb):

Max limiting Mach No. (all)	Mach 0.80
Never-exceed speed (all)	
	450 knots (834 km/h; 518 mph) IAS
Max level speed at S/L:	
BB	373 knots (691 km/h; 430 mph)
CC	415 knots (769 km/h; 478 mph)
Max level speed at height:	
BB at 7,620 m (25,000 ft)	
	430 knots (797 km/h; 495 mph)
CC and DD at 6,100 m (20,000 ft)	
	435 knots (806 km/h; 501 mph)
CC and DD at 4,575 m (15,000 ft) with MPR	
	450 knots (834 km/h; 518 mph)
Econ cruising speed at 9,145 m (30,000 ft) (all)	
	Mach 0.60 (354 knots; 656 km/h; 407 mph)
Unstick speed (all)	115 knots (213 km/h; 132 mph)
Touchdown speed (all)	95 knots (176 km/h; 109 mph)
Stalling speed (all):	
flaps up	99 knots (183 km/h; 114 mph) IAS
flaps down	88 knots (164 km/h; 102 mph) IAS
Max rate of climb at S/L: BB	1,152 m (3,780 ft)/min
CC and DD (normal)	1,494 m (4,900 ft)/min
CC and DD (with MPR)	1,859 m (6,100 ft)/min
Time to 7,620 m (25,000 ft): BB	8 min 30 s
CC, DD	6 min 30 s
Service ceiling: BB	12,200 m (40,000 ft)
CC, DD	12,800 m (42,000 ft)
T-O run: BB	630 m (2,065 ft)
CC, DD	560 m (1,835 ft)
T-O to 15 m (50 ft): BB	850 m (2,790 ft)
CC, DD	750 m (2,460 ft)
Landing from 15 m (50 ft) (all)	800 m (2,625 ft)
Landing run (all)	480 m (1,575 ft)

Typical interdiction radius (lo-lo-lo) with four 250 kg bombs and 30 mm gun:
CC and DD, 3 min over target, 30 min reserves
280 nm (519 km; 322 miles)

Typical close air support radius (lo-lo-lo):
CC and DD with four 19 × 2.75 in rocket launchers and 30 mm gun, 50 min loiter over battle area, 8 min over target, 30 min reserves
200 nm (370 km; 230 miles)
CC and DD, load as above plus two 125 kg bombs, 30 min loiter, 10 min attack (MPR thrust) and 7% reserves
170 nm (315 km; 196 miles)
CC and DD with two Maverick missiles and 30 mm gun, 8 min over target, 30 min reserves
325 nm (602 km; 374 miles)

Typical ECM radius:
BB and CC, 3 h 15 min loiter over target, 30 min reserves
330 nm (611 km; 380 miles)

Typical photo-reconnaissance radius (hi-lo-hi):
BB and CC, 30 min reserves
520 nm (964 km; 599 miles)

Armed patrol, no underwing stores, 100 nm (185 km; 115 mile) transit from base to patrol area:
BB, CC and DD with one 30 mm or two 12.7 mm guns, 45 min reserves
3 h 30 min at 200 knots (370 km/h; 230 mph) at S/L

Ferry range (all), 30 min reserves
2,000 nm (3,706 km; 2,303 miles)

Typical training mission endurance (all):
two 1 h 10 min general handling missions, incl aerobatics, with 20 min reserves after second mission

Max endurance (all)	7 h
g limits (all):	
at 4,800 kg (10,582 lb) AUW	+7.5/-3.9
at 6,300 kg (13,890 lb) AUW	+5.5/-1

SWEDEN

FFV

FFV AEROTECH
S-73281 Arboga
Telephone: 46 (589) 800
Telex: 732 46 FFVA S

FFV AEROTECH BA-14 STARLING
The BA-14 Starling two-seat light aircraft, built primarily from composites, first flew on 25 August 1988, and a second was to fly during 1990. It was designed by Mr Björn Andreasson and is a joint venture by Malmo Forsknings & Innovations AB (MFI) and FFV Aerotech. Following certification to FAR Pt 23 standards, the Starling was to be marketed in basic two-seat touring and training form, with optional instrumentation and radio for IFR training, and optional 119 kW (160 hp) engine driving a constant-speed propeller; as a reconnaissance aircraft carrying cameras, video equipment and other special sensors; as a light transport with optional stretcher installation; and as an agricultural sprayplane, with a chemical hopper behind the cockpit, and sprayers with atomisers under the wings.

TYPE: Two-seat multi-purpose light aircraft.

WINGS: Shoulder-wing monoplane, with single bracing strut each side. No dihedral. Sweepforward 3°. GFRP composite construction; spar caps reinforced with carbonfibre pultruded bars. Welded steel tube wing carry-through structure. Detachable wingtips. Conventional ailerons. Junkers type auxiliary aerofoil flaps aft of wing trailing-edge.

FUSELAGE: Semi-monocoque pod and boom structure of GFRP composites. Downward hinged hatch for access to baggage/freight compartment in upswept portion of centre-fuselage.

TAIL UNIT: V tail comprising fixed surfaces with large horn balance control surfaces, of sheet metal construction. Small ventral fin carrying tailskid.

Prototype of the FFV BA-14 Starling two-seat light aircraft

LANDING GEAR: Non-retractable tricycle type. Mainwheels carried on an arched GFRP leafspring.

POWER PLANT: One 85.75 kW (115 hp) Textron Lycoming O-235 flat-four engine standard, driving a two-blade fixed-pitch propeller. A 119 kW (160 hp) Textron Lycoming O-320 engine is optional for Utility and Normal category operation, standard for Restricted category operation. Welded steel tube engine mounting.

ACCOMMODATION: Two persons side by side under large one-piece transparent canopy. Baggage compartment aft of seats. All flying controls operated through pushrods. Safety harness standard for both occupants.

DIMENSIONS, EXTERNAL:

Wing span	11.38 m (37 ft 4 in)
Length overall	6.56 m (21 ft 6¼ in)
Height overall	2.70 m (8 ft 10¼ in)
Wheel track	2.26 m (7 ft 5 in)
Wheelbase	1.65 m (5 ft 5 in)

WEIGHTS (U, Utility category; N, Normal category; R, Restricted category):

Weight empty: U, N		480 kg (1,059 lb)
R		505 kg (1,114 lb)
Standard fuel		60 kg (132 lb)
Max T-O weight: U		710 kg (1,565 lb)
N		815 kg (1,796 lb)
R		950 kg (2,094 lb)

PERFORMANCE (estimated):

Max level speed at S/L:		
U		130 knots (240 km/h; 150 mph)
N		125 knots (231 km/h; 144 mph)
R		150 knots (278 km/h; 172 mph)
Max rate of climb at S/L: U		213 m (700 ft)/min
N		183 m (600 ft)/min
R		274 m (900 ft)/min
T-O to 15 m (50 ft): U		330 m (1,083 ft)
N		425 m (1,395 ft)
R		390 m (1,280 ft)

SAAB-SCANIA

SAAB-SCANIA AKTIEBOLAG
S-581 88 Linköping
Telephone: 46 (13) 18 00 00
Telex: 50040 SAABLG S
Fax: 46 (13) 18 18 02
PRESIDENT: Georg Karnsund
EXECUTIVE VICE-PRESIDENT: Bertil Krook
Saab Aircraft Division
Telephone: 46 (13) 18 00 00
GENERAL MANAGER: Christer Skogsborg
DIRECTOR OF COMMERCIAL AIRCRAFT SECTOR:
Tomy Hjorth
DIRECTOR OF MILITARY AIRCRAFT SECTOR:
Tomy Ivarsson
PUBLIC AFFAIRS MANAGER: Rolf Erichs
WORKS: Linköping, Malmö, Ödeshog, Norrköping and Kramfors
SAAB 340 MARKETING:
Saab Aircraft International Ltd, Leworth House, 14-16 Sheet Street, Windsor, Berkshire SL4 1BG, England
Telephone: 44 (753) 859991
Telex: 847 815 SFIWIN G
Fax: 44 (753) 858884
PRESIDENT: Jeffrey Marsh
PUBLIC RELATIONS AND PROMOTIONAL SERVICES:
Mike Savage
Saab Aircraft of America Inc, 200 Fairbrook Drive, Herndon, Virginia 22070, USA
PRESIDENT: Ove Dahlén
PUBLIC RELATIONS: Ron Sherman
Telephone: 1 (703) 478 9720
Fax: 1 (703) 478 9727

The original Svenska Aeroplan AB was founded at Trollhättan in 1937 for the production of military aircraft. In 1939 this company was amalgamated with the Aircraft Division (ASJA) of the Svenska Järnvägsverkstäderna rolling stock factory in Linköping, where the main aerospace factory is now located. The company's name was changed to Saab Aktiebolag in May 1965. During 1968 Saab merged with Scania-Vabis, to strengthen the two companies' position in automotive products. Malmö Flygindustri (MFI) was acquired in the same year.

Saab-Scania has more than 50,000 employees, organised in three operating divisions and one major subsidiary (Saab-Scania Combitech). Of these, nearly 6,500 are employed by the Saab Aircraft Division, including 5,500 at Linköping.

Saab-Scania's current aerospace activities include production of the JA 37 Viggen and Saab 340B, and development of the Saab JAS 39 Gripen and Saab 2000. Since 1949 the company has delivered more than 2,000 military jet aircraft and more than 1,500 piston engined aircraft. Since 1962, it has had a dealership for McDonnell Douglas (Hughes) helicopters in Scandinavia and Finland. Since 1978, it has manufactured inboard wing flaps and vanes for the McDonnell Douglas MD-80 series, and now also produces composite spoilers for the MD-82/83; it is currently manufacturing tailplanes, elevators, rudders,

ailerons and spoilers for the British Aerospace 146. A 25,000 m² (269,100 sq ft) factory at Linköping, for final assembly of the Saab 340, was completed in July 1982; an extension to this facility, to accommodate also the wing and tail unit production, was inaugurated on 26 June 1986.

In the electronics field, current production items include computer systems, autopilots, fire control and bombing systems for piloted aircraft, and electronics for guided missiles. Spaceborne computers, electro-optical fire control systems and field artillery computer systems are also under development and in production.

SAAB 340B
Swedish Air Force designation: Tp100
First details of the 340, then called Saab-Fairchild SF 340, were announced in January 1980 and the go-ahead on joint design, development, manufacture and marketing was given in September 1980. Saab took complete control of the programme in November 1985 and Fairchild continued as a subcontractor until 1987, when SF was dropped from the designation.

SF 340 (SE-ISF) made the first flight on 26 January 1983. The fourth (first production) 340A (SE-E04) flew on 5 March 1984. Ten European nations and the USA took part in the certification process to JAR 25, resulting in Swedish certification in May 1984 and virtually simultaneous certification by the other countries in June.

The 340A first went into service, with Crossair, in June 1984 and the first in the USA entered service in August that year. The first corporate 340A was delivered in November 1985. From mid-1985, engine power was increased from

1,215 kW (1,630 shp) to 1,294 kW (1,735 shp) and propeller diameter was increased. Earlier aircraft were retrofitted. An improved cabin with new lining and larger overhead bins, plus improved fittings, was introduced in mid-1988. It was designed and fitted by Metair Aircraft of the UK and met the FAA fire-resistance standards that were to become mandatory in August 1990.

The 340B hot and high version was announced in late 1987 and replaced the 340A on the production line from c/n 160. It was certificated on 3 July 1989 and the first aircraft was delivered to Crossair in September 1989. The 340B is powered by General Electric CT7-9B turboprops with automatic power reserve (APR). Tailplane span is extended, operating weights increased and range with maximum payload improved.

By April 1990, firm orders for the 340A and B totalled 310, of which more than half were for US customers and the rest for Europe, Australia, South East Asia and South America. More than 100 were ordered during 1989 and AMR Eagle, a subsidiary of American Airlines, placed a single order for 50 with an option for 50 more. A total of 177 340As and 340Bs had been delivered by April 1990.

Full details of the Saab 340A were given in the 1989-90 *Jane's*.

TYPE: Twin-turboprop regional transport aircraft.

WINGS: Cantilever low-wing monoplane. Basic wing section NASA MS(1)-0313 with thickness/chord ratios of 16 and 12 per cent at root and tip respectively. Dihedral 7° from roots. Incidence 2° at root. Sweepback 3° 36' at quarter-chord. Tapered two-spar wings embodying fail-safe principles. Stringers and skins of 2024/7075 aluminium alloy. Wingroot/fuselage fairings of Kevlar

Saab 340B airliner (two General Electric CT7-9B turboprops) *(Pilot Press)*

Swedish Air Force Tp 100 (Saab 340B) of the Swedish government VIP flight

sandwich. Hydraulically actuated single-slotted trailing-edge flaps with aluminium alloy spars, honeycomb panels faced with aluminium sheet, and leading/trailing-edges of Kevlar. Ailerons have Kevlar skins and glassfibre leading-edges. Electrically operated geared/trim tab in each aileron. Pneumatic boot de-icing of leading-edges.

FUSELAGE: Conventional fail-safe/safe-life semi-monocoque pressurised metal structure, of circular cross-section. Built in three portions: nose (incl flight deck), passenger compartment, and tail section (incorporating baggage compartment). All doors of aluminium honeycomb. Nosecone of Kevlar; cabin floor of carbonfibre sandwich.

TAIL UNIT: Cantilever structure, with sweptback vertical and non-swept horizontal surfaces, the latter having marked dihedral. Fin integral with fuselage. Construction similar to that of wings, with tailplane and fin of aluminium honeycomb. Rudder and elevators have Kevlar skins and glassfibre leading-edges. Geared/trim tab in each elevator; spring/trim tab in rudder. Pneumatic boot de-icing of fin and tailplane leading-edges.

LANDING GEAR: Retractable tricycle type, of AP Precision Hydraulics design and manufacture, with twin Goodyear wheels and oleo-pneumatic shock absorber on each unit. Hydraulic actuation. All units retract forward, main units into engine nacelles. Mainwheel doors of Kevlar sandwich. Hydraulically steerable nose unit (60° to both left and right), with shimmy damper. Mainwheel tyres size 24 × 7.7-10, pressure 6.89 bars (100 lb/sq in); nosewheel tyres size 18 × 6.0-6, pressure 3.79 bars (55 lb/sq in). Independent Goodyear carbon hydraulic disc brakes on main units, with anti-skid control.

POWER PLANT: Two General Electric CT7-9B turboprops, each rated at 1,305 kW (1,750 shp) for normal T-O and 1,394 kW (1,870 shp) with automatic power reserve. Dowty (Hamilton Standard optional) four-blade slow-turning constant-speed propellers, with full autofeathering and reverse pitch capability, each with spinner and glassfibre/polyurethane foam/carbonfibre moulded blades. Fuel in integral tank in each outer wing; total capacity 3,220 litres (850.5 US gallons; 708 Imp gallons). Single-point pressure refuelling inlet in starboard outer wing panel. Overwing gravity refuelling point in each wing.

ACCOMMODATION: Two pilots and provision for observer on flight deck; attendant's seat (forward, port) in passenger cabin. Main cabin accommodates up to 37 passengers, in 12 rows of three, with aisle, and rearward facing seat on starboard side at front. The rearward facing seat can be replaced by an optional galley module or baggage/wardrobe module; the two modules can replace both seats. Seat pitch 76 cm (30 in). Standard provision for galley, wardrobe or storage module on port side at front of cabin, regardless of installations on starboard side. Movable bulkhead aft of last row of seats. Toilet at front or rear of cabin. Aircraft can be converted quickly to various passenger/freight combinations (eg, 15 passengers and 1,814 kg; 4,000 lb of cargo). A corporate/executive version and a quick-change (QC: from all-passenger to all-freight) version are also available. Passenger door (plug type) at front of cabin on port side, with separate airstair. Type II emergency exit opposite this on starboard side, and over wing on each side. Overhead crew escape hatch in flight deck roof. Baggage space under each passenger seat; overhead storage bins. Main baggage/cargo compartment aft of passenger cabin, with large plug type door on port side. Entire accommodation pressurised, including baggage compartment.

SYSTEMS: Hamilton Standard environmental control system (max pressure differential 0.48 bars; 7.0 lb/sq in) maintains a S/L cabin environment up to an altitude of 3,660 m (12,000 ft) and a 1,525 m (5,000 ft) environment up to the max cruising altitude of 7,620 m (25,000 ft). Single on-demand hydraulic system, operating between 138 and 207 bars (2,000-3,000 lb/sq in), for actuation of landing gear, wheel and propeller braking, nosewheel steering and wing flaps. System is powered by single 28V DC electric motor driven pump, rated delivery 9.5 litres (2.5 US gallons; 2.1 Imp gallons)/min. Self-pressurising main reservoir with 5.08 litres (0.18 cu ft) capacity, operating at pressure of 1.79-2.69 bars (26-39 lb/sq in). Hydraulic backup via four accumulators and pilot operated handpump, working via an emergency reservoir of 2.5 litres (0.09 cu ft) capacity. Electrical power supplied by two 28V 400A DC engine driven starter/generators, each connected to a separate busbar. Variable frequency 115/200V for heating circuits provided by two 26kVA AC generators; single-phase 115V and 26V AC at 400Hz for avionics provided by static inverters. Two 27Ah nickel-cadmium batteries for ground power and engine starting; standby 5Ah lead-acid battery for emergency use. External power receptacle. Pneumatic boot de-icing of wing and tail unit leading-edges, using engine bleed air. Flight deck windows have electric anti-icing and electrically driven windscreen wipers. Electric anti-icing is provided also for engine air intakes, propellers and pitot heads. Demisting by means of air-conditioning system. Plug-in connections for oxygen masks. Kidde engine fire detection system. Duncan/Garrett GTCP 36-150W APU kit certificated for installation as optional extra, to provide standby and emergency electrical power, main engine starting assistance, ground pre-heating and pre-cooling, and other power support functions.

AVIONICS AND EQUIPMENT: Standard avionics include all equipment required for FAR 121 operations. Aircraft is equipped with Bendix/King Gold Crown III or Collins Pro Line II com/nav radios, and a Collins integrated digital flight guidance and autopilot system (FGAS) consisting of attitude and heading reference units, electronic (CRT) flight display units, fail-passive autopilot/flight director system, colour weather radar, air data system with servo instruments, and radio altimeter. Lucas Aerospace electroluminescent flight deck instrument panel array. Dowty Aerospace microprocessor-based flight deck central warning system. Rosemount pitot static tubes, total temperature sensors and stall warning system. Provision for additional avionics to customer's requirements. Landing light in each wing leading-edge.

DIMENSIONS, EXTERNAL:
Wing span	21.44 m (70 ft 4 in)
Wing aspect ratio	11.0
Length overall	19.73 m (64 ft 8¾ in)
Fuselage: Max diameter	2.31 m (7 ft 7 in)
Height overall	6.86 m (22 ft 6 in)
Tailplane span	9.25 m (30 ft 4¼ in)
Wheel track	6.71 m (22 ft 0 in)
Wheelbase	7.14 m (23 ft 5 in)
Propeller diameter	3.35 m (11 ft 0 in)
Propeller ground clearance	0.58 m (1 ft 11 in)
Passenger door: Height	1.60 m (5 ft 3 in)
Width	0.69 m (2 ft 3¼ in)
Height to sill	1.63 m (5 ft 4 in)
Cargo door: Height	1.30 m (4 ft 3 in)
Width	1.35 m (4 ft 5 in)
Height to sill	1.68 m (5 ft 6 in)
Emergency exit (fwd, stbd): Height	1.32 m (4 ft 4 in)
Width	0.51 m (1 ft 8 in)
Emergency exits (overwing, each):	
Height	0.91 m (3 ft 0 in)
Width	0.51 m (1 ft 8 in)

DIMENSIONS, INTERNAL:
Cabin, excl flight deck, incl toilet and galley:	
Length	10.39 m (34 ft 1 in)
Max width	2.16 m (7 ft 1 in)
Width at floor	1.70 m (5 ft 7 in)

Max height	1.83 m (6 ft 0 in)
Volume	33.4 m³ (1,179.5 cu ft)
Baggage/cargo compartment volume	
	6.8 m³ (240.0 cu ft)

AREAS:
Wings, gross	41.81 m² (450.0 sq ft)
Ailerons (total)	2.12 m² (22.84 sq ft)
Trailing-edge flaps (total)	8.07 m² (86.84 sq ft)
Fin (incl dorsal fin)	10.53 m² (113.38 sq ft)
Rudder (incl tab)	2.76 m² (29.71 sq ft)
Tailplane	14.57 m² (156.83 sq ft)
Elevators (total, incl tabs)	3.29 m² (35.40 sq ft)

WEIGHTS AND LOADINGS:
Typical operating weight empty	8,035 kg (17,715 lb)
Max payload (weight limited)	3,758 kg (8,285 lb)
Max fuel load	2,581 kg (5,690 lb)
Max ramp weight	13,063 kg (28,800 lb)
Max T-O weight	12,927 kg (28,500 lb)
Max landing weight	12,700 kg (28,000 lb)
Max zero-fuel weight	11,793 kg (26,000 lb)
Max wing loading	309.1 kg/m² (63.33 lb/sq ft)
Max power loading	4.64 kg/kW (7.62 lb/shp)

PERFORMANCE (at MTOW, ISA, except where indicated):
Max operating speed (VMO)	
	250 knots (463 km/h; 288 mph)
Max operating Mach No. (MMO)	0.5
Max cruising speed:	
at 4,575 m (15,000 ft)	282 knots (522 km/h; 325 mph)
at 6,100 m (20,000 ft)	280 knots (519 km/h; 322 mph)
Best range cruising speed at 7,620 m (25,000 ft)	
	252 knots (467 km/h; 290 mph)
Stalling speed: flaps up	106 knots (197 km/h; 123 mph)
T-O flap	95 knots (176 km/h; 110 mph)
approach flap	92 knots (171 km/h; 106 mph)
landing flap	88 knots (164 km/h; 102 mph)
Max rate of climb at S/L	625 m (2,050 ft)/min
Rate of climb at S/L, one engine out	160 m (525 ft)/min
Service ceiling: standard	7,620 m (25,000 ft)
optional	9,450 m (31,000 ft)
Service ceiling, one engine out (net)	3,445 m (11,300 ft)
FAR Pt 25 required T-O field length:	
at S/L	1,325 m (4,347 ft)
at S/L, ISA + 15°C	1,430 m (4,692 ft)
at 1,525 m (5,000 ft)	1,660 m (5,447 ft)
at 1,525 m (5,000 ft), ISA + 15°C	2,025 m (6,644 ft)
FAR Pt 25 required landing field length (at MLW):	
at S/L	1,050 m (3,445 ft)
at 1,525 m (5,000 ft)	1,180 m (3,872 ft)
Min ground turning radius	15.85 m (52 ft 0 in)
Runway LCN: flexible pavement	8
rigid pavement	10
Range with 35 passengers and baggage, reserves for 45 min hold at 1,525 m (5,000 ft) and 100 nm (185 km; 115 mile) diversion:	
at max cruising speed	820 nm (1,520 km; 945 miles)
at long-range cruising speed	
	975 nm (1,807 km; 1,123 miles)
Range with 30 passengers, reserves as above:	
at max cruising speed	
	1,095 nm (2,030 km; 1,261 miles)
at long-range cruising speed	
	1,310 nm (2,427 km; 1,509 miles)

OPERATIONAL NOISE LEVELS (FAR Pt 36, Appendix C):
T-O (with cutback)	78.0 EPNdB
Sideline	86.4 EPNdB
Approach	91.6 EPNdB

SAAB 2000

This programme was launched on 15 December 1988 with the simultaneous order for 25, plus options for 25, from Crossair. The first metal was cut in February 1990 and first flight is planned for mid-1992, with deliveries following in the second half of 1993. By April 1990, the Crossair order had been followed by Salair (five plus five), Northwest

Artist's impression of the Saab 2000 in the colours of launch customer Crossair

General arrangement of the Saab 2000 *(Pilot Press)*

Airlink (Express Airlines) (10), AMR Eagle (options for 50), Business Express (options for 10), Brit Air (options for four), Salenia AB (three plus three), Hazelton Airlines (options for two) and one unannounced. Orders and options totalled 135 during the first year alone.

The 2000 retains the fuselage cross-section, flight deck and many of the systems of the 340, but has a capacity for up to 50 passengers. For the 2000, the 340 wing is scaled up with 15 per cent more span and 33 per cent more area, but the same advanced aerofoil. The engine nacelles are located further away from the fuselage. Saab is aiming at a cruising speed of 360 knots (667 km/h; 414 mph) and announced a memorandum of understanding with General Motors in July 1989 to adopt the Allison Gas Turbine Division GMA 2100A turboprop based on the T406 turboshaft from the Bell/Boeing V-22 Osprey. Maximum output is 3,393 kW (4,550 shp) to FAR Pt 33 and JAR, but it will be flat rated to 2,722 kW (3,650 shp) for take-off.

It is intended that the 2000 should be able to climb to 20,000 ft in 11 minutes and cruise at altitudes between 5,485 m and 9,450 m (18,000 ft and 31,000 ft), equalling jet speeds over short to medium-length stages, but retaining turboprop block fuel consumption. Economic range will be between 100 nm (185 km; 115 miles) and 1,000 nm (1,850 km; 1,150 miles) and cabin noise level will be 10 dB below that of the 340.

In late 1989, the Swedish government agreed to provide Saab with a loan of between $163 million and $187 million to cover development of the 2000 between 1989 and 1994, to be repaid by royalties from the 31st aircraft onwards until the year 2009. Saab has agreed to retain a high proportion of Saab 2000 work in Sweden.

Saab plans to extend its airliner manufacturing plant at Linköping by 15,000 m² (161,445 sq ft) and a number of major risk-sharing subcontractors have been recruited in addition to Allison. It was announced in November 1989 that Dowty is to supply to Allison a slow turning, high performance propeller with six swept blades. It includes a hydraulic control, hydraulic pump with mechanical overspeed protection, de-icing and an electric feathering pump. Propeller control is electric and integrated with the

full authority digital engine control to allow single lever engine control. Dowty and Allison are already collaborating on a propeller for another T406 power plant.

In October 1989, CASA took on the design, stressing, testing and manufacture of the entire wing including movable surfaces and part of the engine nacelles. It will also equip, install and test the main undercarriage. The first wing is to be delivered to Linköping in late 1991. Wing geometry and basic structure were defined by Saab. The contract is worth $500,000, half of it funded by the Andalusian government in whose region much of the work will be concentrated.

Also in October 1989, Valmet signed to produce the fin, rudder, tailplane and elevators of the 2000 and take part in development. The production work will be done by its Flygplansfabriken division, with Advanced Composites Oy (ADCO) as a subcontractor for metal bonding. Flygplansfabriken will invest $8.4 million and ADCO $5.3 million. Total value of the agreement is $69.8 million.

In January 1990, Westland received an order worth £40 million to produce the rear fuselage section of the 2000.

Hamilton Standard is to provide the environmental control system, incorporating the Recircair technique to economise on engine bleed. Saab selected the Collins Pro Line 4 integrated avionics systems including autopilot, flight management and avionics maintenance system, all controlled from the integrated avionics processing system. Pro Line 4 also includes Collins com/nav/pulse and radio tuning units, digital air data and attitude heading reference, and solid-state weather radar. Options include TCAS, the actual flight management system, and turbulence weather radar. Electronic flight instruments include the primary flight display and navigation display and engine indication and crew alerting system with checklist mode.

The following data were current in April 1990:

POWER PLANT: Two Allison GMA 2100A turboprops, each flat rated at 2,722 kW (3,650 shp). Dowty six-blade, slow turning, constant-speed propellers with full autofeathering and reverse pitch. Fuel in integral tank in each outer wing; total capacity 5,185 litres (1,370 US gallons; 1,140 Imp gallons). Single point pressure refuelling inlet in

starboard outer wing panel. Overwing gravity refuelling point in each wing.

ACCOMMODATION: Flight crew of three or four, including cabin attendant(s). Standard accommodation for 50 passengers in three-abreast seating with single aisle. Overhead baggage bins on starboard side. Range of galley options and locations, to customer's requirements. Toilet can be located at either end of cabin. Other passenger service options include wardrobe and stowage areas. Main cargo compartment aft of passenger cabin. Provision for additional, smaller cargo area at front of cabin on starboard side. Entire accommodation pressurised at 0.48 bars (7.0 lb/sq in). Main airstair door at front on port side, with smaller cargo door opposite. Main cargo door at rear on port side, with service door/emergency door on opposite side. Type III emergency exit over wing on each side.

DIMENSIONS, EXTERNAL:

Wing span	24.76 m (81 ft 2¾ in)
Wing aspect ratio	11.0
Length overall	27.03 m (88 ft 8¼ in)
Fuselage: Max diameter	2.31 m (7 ft 7 in)
Height overall	7.73 m (25 ft 4 in)
Wheel track	8.23 m (27 ft 0 in)
Wheelbase	10.97 m (36 ft 0 in)
Propeller diameter	3.81 m (12 ft 6 in)
Passenger door: Height	1.60 m (5 ft 3 in)
Width	0.69 m (2 ft 3 in)
Height to sill	1.63 m (5 ft 4 in)
Cargo door (rear compartment, port):	
Height	1.30 m (4 ft 3 in)
Width	1.35 m (4 ft 5 in)
Height to sill	1.68 m (5 ft 6 in)
Stowage compartment door (fwd, stbd):	
Height	1.12 m (3 ft 8 in)
Width	0.51 m (1 ft 8 in)
Emergency exit/Service door (rear, stbd):	
Height	1.22 m (4 ft 0 in)
Width	0.61 m (2 ft 0 in)
Emergency exits (overwing, each):	
Height	0.91 m (3 ft 0 in)
Width	0.51 m (1 ft 8 in)

DIMENSIONS, INTERNAL:

Cabin, excl flight deck, incl toilet and galley:	
Length	16.70 m (54 ft 9½ in)
Max width	2.16 m (7 ft 1 in)
Width at floor	1.70 m (5 ft 7 in)
Max height	1.83 m (6 ft 0 in)
Volume	52.7 m³ (1,860.0 cu ft)
Baggage/cargo compartment:	
Volume	10.2 m³ (360.0 cu ft)

AREA:

Wings, gross	55.74 m² (600.0 sq ft)

WEIGHTS AND LOADINGS:

Typical operating weight empty	12,700 kg (28,000 lb)
Max payload (weight limited)	5,896 kg (13,000 lb)
Max fuel load	4,155 kg (9,160 lb)
Max ramp weight	21,455 kg (47,300 lb)
Max T-O weight	21,320 kg (47,000 lb)
Max landing weight	20,410 kg (45,000 lb)
Max zero-fuel weight	18,600 kg (41,000 lb)
Max wing loading	382.3 kg/m² (78.33 lb/sq ft)
Max power loading	3.92 kg/kW (6.44 lb/shp)

PERFORMANCE (at MTOW, ISA, except where indicated):

Max operating speed (V$_{MO}$)	
below 3,050 m (10,000 ft)	
	250 knots (463 km/h; 288 mph)
above 3,050 m (10,000 ft)	
	270 knots (500 km/h; 311 mph)
Max operating Mach No. (M$_{MO}$) (under review)	0.62
Max cruising speed:	
at 7,620 m (25,000 ft)	366 knots (678 km/h; 421 mph)
at 9,450 m (31,000 ft)	355 knots (658 km/h; 409 mph)
Best range cruising speed at 9,450 m (31,000 ft)	
	300 knots (556 km/h; 345 mph)
Max rate of climb at S/L	707 m (2,320 ft)/min
Rate of climb at S/L, one engine out	183 m (600 ft)/min
Time to 6,100 m (20,000 ft)	10 min
Service ceiling	9,450 m (31,000 ft)
Service ceiling, one engine out (net)	6,220 m (20,400 ft)
FAR Pt 25 required T-O field length:	
at S/L	1,485 m (4,875 ft)
at S/L, ISA +15°C	1,610 m (5,280 ft)
at 1,525 m (5,000 ft)	1,835 m (6,020 ft)
at 1,525 m (5,000 ft), ISA +15°C	1,990 m (6,530 ft)
FAR Pt 25 required landing field length (at MLW):	
at S/L	1,310 m (4,300 ft)
at 1,525 m (5,000 ft)	1,440 m (4,725 ft)
Min ground turning radius	18.85 m (61 ft 10 in)
Runway LCN (paved runways)	max 15
Range with 50 passengers and baggage, reserves for 45 min hold at 1,525 m (5,000 ft) and 100 nm (185 km; 115 mile) diversion:	
at max cruising speed	
	1,345 nm (2,492 km; 1,550 miles)

SAAB JAS 39 GRIPEN (GRIFFIN)

The Swedish government approved funding for project definition and initial development of this Viggen replacement in June 1980. Known as the JAS 39 (Jakt/Attack/Spaning: fighter/attack/reconnaissance), it is a multi-role combat aircraft to replace, successively, the AJ/SH/SF/JA 37 versions of the Viggen and all remaining Swedish Air Force J 35 Drakens. A similar financial commitment was made by Industri Gruppen JAS, a Swedish aerospace industry group formed in 1980 by Saab-Scania, Volvo Flygmotor, Ericsson Radio Systems and FFV Aerotech.

On 3 June 1981 the group submitted to the Swedish Defence Materiel Administration (FMV) its initial proposals for an aircraft to meet the JAS requirement. Power plant is a modified version of the General Electric F404 afterburning turbofan offering higher thrust and having a strengthened front fan to meet Swedish bird strike requirements. The engine was developed and is produced, as the RM12, by Volvo Flygmotor.

The Gripen has cropped delta wings and close-coupled all-moving foreplanes and some 30 per cent is manufactured from CFRP, permitting weight savings of up to 25 per cent and enabling the normal T-O weight to be kept down to approx 8,000 kg (17,635 lb). Like the Viggen, the JAS 39 will be adapted to the specific Swedish defence profile, using 800 m (2,625 ft) V-90 airstrips and similar lengths of ordinary roads as air bases. It will require only simple maintenance, with turnround service handled mainly by conscripts.

The FMV evaluated the Swedish industry proposals against aircraft from other countries, and recommended adoption of the Saab design. The programme approved by the Swedish government on 6 May 1982 covers the development and procurement of 140 aircraft in two batches by the year 2000, and a contract for the first 30 was signed on 30 June 1982. The Swedish parliament should decide on a third production batch, of an improved version designated JAS 39C, in 1996. Overall programme go-ahead was confirmed in the Spring of 1983, and prototype construction began in 1984. The ultimate requirement is for 21 to 23 squadrons totalling 340-350 aircraft. Gripen deliveries will start in early 1993. A design study of a two-seat JAS 39B tactical trainer was authorised in July 1989, and some of the first 140 Gripens may be two-seaters. The JAS 39B has a 0.5 m (1 ft 7¾ in) fuselage plug. Development of the two-seater took on new interest late in 1989 when Saab offered a modified JAS 39B design to the US Air Force as a two-seat reconnaissance and attack trainer.

Five prototypes of the Gripen are being built, the first of which was rolled out on 26 April 1987 and made its first flight on 9 December 1988. This aircraft was lost on 2 February 1989, without major injury to its pilot, when it crashed while landing in gusty conditions after its sixth test flight, prompting considerable modification of the fly-by-wire system software. The first flight of the second prototype was made on 4 May 1990. The four remaining prototypes will now be joined by a Viggen for radar testing, and the first production Gripen. Further delays were caused in 1990 by a problem of slow acceleration of the GE-Volvo RM12 engine. The first three and a half sets of carbonfibre wings were manufactured for Saab by British Aerospace, but for all subsequent aircraft Saab is responsible for all CFRP components including the wings, canards, fin, and major (eg engine and landing gear) doors.

The following description applies to the single-seat prototypes:

TYPE: Single-seat all-weather, all-altitude fighter, attack and reconnaissance aircraft.

AIRFRAME: Close-coupled canard configuration, with 30 per cent CFRP composites in its fail-safe construction. Cropped delta main wings, mid-mounted on fuselage; leading-edge flaps with dog-tooth; inboard and outboard elevons on trailing-edges. Sweptback all-moving foreplanes, mounted on upper sides of engine air intake trunks. Leading-edge sweepback approx 43° on canards, 45° on main wings. No horizontal tail surfaces. Airbrakes on rear of fuselage. AP Precision Hydraulics retractable tricycle landing gear, single mainwheels retracting hydraulically forward into fuselage; steerable twin-wheel nose unit retracts rearward. Goodyear wheels, tyres, carbon disc brakes and anti-skid units. Nosewheel braking. Entire gear designed for high rate of sink.

POWER PLANT: One General Electric/Volvo Flygmotor

RM12 (F404-400) turbofan, rated initially at approx 54 kN (12,140 lb st) dry and 80.5 kN (18,100 lb st) with afterburning. Near-rectangular intakes, each with splitter plate. Fuel in self-sealing main tank and collector tank in fuselage. Active control of CG location provided by Intertechnique fuel management system.

ACCOMMODATION: Pilot only, on Martin-Baker S10LS zero/zero ejection seat under teardrop canopy. Hinged canopy and one-piece windscreen by Lucas Aerospace.

SYSTEMS: BAe environmental control system for cockpit air-conditioning, pressurisation and avionics cooling. Hughes-Treitler heat exchanger. Two main Dowty hydraulic systems and one auxiliary system, with Abex pumps. Sundstrand main electrical power generating system (40kVA constant speed, constant frequency at 400Hz) comprises an integrated drive generator, generator control unit and current transformer assembly. Lear Astronics triplex digital fly by wire flight control system, with Moog electrically signalled servo-valves for primary flight control actuators, Lucas Aerospace rotary actuators ('geared hinges') for leading-edge flaps, and Saab Combitech aircraft motion sensors and throttle actuator subsystem. Single-channel analog backup system in the event of main FBW system failure. Lucas Aerospace auxiliary and emergency power system, comprising a gearbox mounted turbine, hydraulic pump and a 10kVA AC generator, to provide emergency electric and hydraulic power in the event of an engine or main generator failure. In emergency role, the turbine is driven by engine bleed or APU air; if this is not available the stored energy mode, using pressurised oxygen and methanol, is selected automatically. Microturbo TGA 15 APU and DA 15 air turbine starter for engine starting, cooling air and standby electric power.

AVIONICS: Bofors Aerotronics AMR 345 VHF/UHF-AM/FM com transceiver. Honeywell laser inertial navigation system. Ericsson EP-17 electronic display system in cockpit, using one Hughes Aircraft wide-angle head-up display with a Ferranti FD 5040 video camera, for weapon aiming, and three interchangeable Ericsson head-down CRT displays, plus a minimum of conventional analog instruments for backup purposes only. The head-up display, using advanced diffraction optics, combines symbology and video images. Left hand (flight data) head-down display normally replaces all conventional flight instruments. Central display shows a computer generated map of the area surrounding the aircraft with tactical information superimposed. Right hand CRT is a multi-sensor display showing information on targets acquired by the video camera, radar and FLIR. An Ericsson SDS 80 computing system, incorporating more than 30 microcomputers, controls the aircraft's central air data computer, radar, electronic displays, fuel management, hydraulic, environmental control and other systems, and allows for multi-mode use and flexibility for further development. A BAe three-axis strapdown gyro-magnetic unit provides standby attitude and heading information.

OPERATIONAL EQUIPMENT: Ericsson/Ferranti PS-05/A multi-mode pulse-Doppler target search and acquisition (lookdown/shootdown) system, comprising a nose mounted radar of 1kW output and (depending on mission) a pod mounted forward-looking infra-red sensor or a laser rangefinder pod. For fighter missions, this system provides fast target acquisition at long range; search and multi-target track-while-scan; quick scanning and lock-on at short ranges; and automatic fire control for missiles and cannon. In the attack and reconnaissance roles its operating functions are search against sea and ground targets; ground and sea target track-while-scan; mapping, with normal and high resolution; fire control for missiles and other attack weapons; and obstacle avoidance and navigation. The FLIR pod, carried externally under the starboard engine air intake trunk, forward of the wing leading-edge, is used for attack and reconnaissance missions at night, providing a heat picture of the target on the right hand head-down CRT. A radar warning receiver fairing is mounted near the tip of the fin. The JAS 39 will also carry advanced ECM, both built-in and externally.

ARMAMENT: Internally mounted 27 mm Mauser BK27 automatic cannon in fuselage and dogfight missiles on the wingtips. Five other external hardpoints (two under each wing and one on the centreline). These stations can carry short and medium range air-to-air missiles such as RB71 (Sky Flash), RB74 (AIM-9L Sidewinder) or AMRAAM; air-to-surface missiles such as Maverick; anti-shipping missiles such as Saab RBS 15F; conventional or retarded bombs; or air-to-surface rockets. MBB is contracted to develop for the Gripen a submunitions dispenser based on its MDS that can glide towards its target before releasing its bomblets on command. The Swedish Defence Materiel Administration (FMV) has proposed developing a glide bomb known as TSA (Tungt Styrt Attackvapen; heavy guided attack weapon), with a warhead weighing several hundred kg, for attacking large targets such as bridges. There will be a series of mission pods.

DIMENSIONS, EXTERNAL (approx):

Wing span	8.00 m (26 ft 3 in)
Length overall	14.10 m (46 ft 3 in)
Height overall	4.70 m (15 ft 5 in)
Wheel track	2.60 m (8 ft 6½ in)
Wheelbase	5.30 m (17 ft 4¾ in)

WEIGHT:

Design max T-O weight	approx 8,000 kg (17,635 lb)

PERFORMANCE:

Max level speed	supersonic at all altitudes
T-O and landing strip length	approx 800 m (2,625 ft)
g limit	+9

SAAB JA 37 VIGGEN (THUNDERBOLT)

The Saab 37 Viggen multi-mission combat aircraft has been produced to fulfil the primary roles of attack, interception, reconnaissance and training. Its STOL characteristics enable it to operate from narrow runways of about 500 m (1,640 ft) length. By early 1988 Viggens (all versions) equipped 15 of the planned total of 17 Swedish Air Force squadrons.

The first of seven prototypes flew for the first time on 8 February 1967, and by April 1969 all six single-seat prototypes were flying. The seventh was the prototype for the two-seat Sk37 operational trainer.

Production deliveries of the AJ 37, SF 37, SH 37 and Sk37 versions totalled 180. Details of these, and of the Saab 37X proposed export version, can be found in the 1980-81 and earlier editions of *Jane's*. The following version was to continue in production until Spring 1990:

JA 37. Single-seat interceptor, with more powerful Volvo Flygmotor RM8B engine. Improved performance, and secondary capability for attack missions. Four elevon hydraulic actuators under each wing, instead of three as on other versions, and a modified, taller tail fin similar to that of the Sk37. Total of 149 ordered, to re-equip eight Draken fighter squadrons of the Swedish Air Force: two squadrons each of Wings F4, F16 and F21, and one each of F13 and F17. First flight by a production JA 37 (c/n 301) was made on 4 November 1977. Deliveries, to the second squadron of

First prototype of the Saab JAS 39 Gripen multi-role air defence and attack aircraft

Saab JAS 39 Gripen multi-role combat aircraft for the Swedish Air Force (*Pilot Press*)

Saab JA 37 Viggens of the Swedish Air Force in current blue-grey finish

Saab JA 37 Viggen single-seat interceptor *(Pilot Press)*

F13 Wing at Norrköping, began in 1979, and the 100th JA 37 was delivered on 20 August 1985. More than 130 had been delivered by 1 January 1990. Improvements added since the JA 37's entry into service include new generation AIM-9L Sidewinder missiles, effective also against head-on targets, and an aircraft-to-aircraft communications system known as fighter link which makes possible efficient liaison between aircraft, even at night and in IMC conditions, regardless of their relative positions.

TYPE: Single-seat all-weather multi-purpose combat aircraft.

WINGS: Tandem arrangement of delta foreplane, with trailing-edge flaps, and a rear mounted delta main wing with two-section hydraulically actuated powered elevons on each trailing-edge. Main wing has compound sweep on leading-edge plus dog-tooth extensions on outer panels. Extensive use of metal bonded honeycomb panels for wing control surfaces, foreplane flaps and main landing gear doors.

FUSELAGE: Conventional structure, using light metal forgings, heat resistant plastics bonding, titanium and metal bonded honeycomb. Four plate type airbrakes round rear fuselage.

TAIL UNIT: Vertical surfaces only, main fin and powered rudder supplemented by a small ventral fin. The main fin can be folded downward to port. More than 20 fins for JA 37s made of composite materials, to gain experience in preparation for the JAS 39 programme.

LANDING GEAR: Retractable tricycle type of Saab origin, built by Motala Verkstad and designed for a max rate of sink of 5 m (16.4 ft)/s. Power steerable twin-wheel nose unit retracts forward. Each main unit has two wheels in tandem and retracts inward into main wing and fuselage.

Main oleos shorten during retraction. Nosewheel tyres size 18 × 5.5, pressure 10.7 bars (155 lb/sq in). Mainwheel tyres size 26 × 6.6, pressure 14.8 bars (215 lb/sq in). Goodyear wheels and brakes. Dunlop anti-skid system.

POWER PLANT: One Volvo Flygmotor RM8B (supersonic development of the Pratt & Whitney JT8D-22) turbofan, fitted with a Swedish developed afterburner and thrust

reverser. This engine is rated at 72.1 kN (16,203 lb st) dry and 125 kN (28,108 lb st) with afterburning. Thrust reverser doors are actuated automatically by compression of the oleo as the nose gear strikes the runway. The ejector is normally kept open at subsonic speeds to reduce fuselage base drag and closes at supersonic speeds. Fuel is contained in one tank in each wing, a saddle tank over the engine, one tank in each side of the fuselage, and one aft of the cockpit. Electric pumps deliver fuel to the engine from the central fuselage tank, which is kept filled continuously from the peripheral tanks. Pressure refuelling point beneath starboard wing. Provision for jettisonable external tank on centreline pylon.

ACCOMMODATION: Pilot only, on Saab-Scania fully adjustable rocket assisted zero/zero ejection seat beneath rearward hinged clamshell canopy. Cockpit pressurisation, heating and air-conditioning by engine bleed air. Birdproof windscreen.

SYSTEMS: Two independent hydraulic systems, each of 207 bars (3,000 lb/sq in) pressure, each with engine driven pump; auxiliary electrically operated emergency pump. Three-phase AC electrical system supplies 210/115V 400Hz power via a Westinghouse 75kVA liquid-cooled brushless generator, which also provides 28V DC power via 24V nickel-cadmium batteries and rectifier. Emergency standby power from 6kVA ram air turbo-generator. External power receptacle on port side of fuselage. Graviner fire detection system.

AVIONICS AND FLIGHT EQUIPMENT: Total of about 50 avionics units, with a total weight of approx 600 kg (1,323 lb). Automatic speed control system, Smiths electronic head-up display, Bofors Aerotronics aircraft attitude instruments, radio and fighter link equipment, Singer-Kearfott SKC-2037 central digital computer, Garrett LD-5 digital air data computer, Singer-Kearfott KT-70L inertial measuring equipment, Honeywell/Saab-Scania SA07 digital automatic flight control system, Honeywell radar altimeter, Decca Doppler Type 72 navigation equipment, SATT radar warning system, Ericsson radar display system and electronic countermeasures, and AIL Tactical Instrument Landing System (TILS). Most avionics equipment is connected to the central digital computer, which is programmed to check out and monitor these systems both on the ground and during flight. Ram air cooling for avionics compartment.

ARMAMENT AND OPERATIONAL EQUIPMENT: Permanent underbelly pack, offset to port side of centreline, containing one 30 mm Oerlikon KCA long-range cannon with 150 rounds, a muzzle velocity of 1,050 m (3,445 ft)/s, a rate of fire of 1,350 rds/min, and a projectile weight of 0.36 kg (0.79 lb). Improved fire control equipment. This gun installation permits retention of the three underfuselage stores attachment points, in addition to the four underwing hardpoints. Advanced target search and acquisition system, based on a high performance long-range Ericsson PS-46/A pulse-Doppler radar which is resistant to variations of weather, altitude, clutter and ECM. Armament can include two BAe Sky Flash (Swedish designation RB71) and six AIM-9L Sidewinder (RB74) air-to-air missiles. For air-to-surface attack, a total of twenty-four 135 mm rockets can be carried in four pods.

DIMENSIONS, EXTERNAL:

Main wing span	10.60 m (34 ft 9¼ in)
Main wing aspect ratio	2.4
Foreplane span	5.45 m (17 ft 10½ in)
Length overall (incl probe)	16.40 m (53 ft 9¾ in)
Length of fuselage	15.58 m (51 ft 1½ in)
Height overall	5.90 m (19 ft 4¼ in)
Height overall, main fin folded	4.00 m (13 ft 1½ in)
Wheel track	4.76 m (15 ft 7½ in)
Wheelbase (c/l of shock absorbers)	5.69 m (18 ft 8 in)

AREAS:

Main wings, gross	46.00 m² (495.1 sq ft)
Foreplanes, outside fuselage	6.20 m² (66.74 sq ft)

Saab 35OE (modified J 35 D) Draken for the Austrian Air Force

WEIGHTS (approx):

T-O weight: clean	15,000 kg (33,070 lb)
with normal armament	17,000 kg (37,478 lb)

PERFORMANCE:

Max level speed: at high altitude	above Mach 2
at 100 m (300 ft)	Mach 1.2
Approach speed	approx 119 knots (220 km/h; 137 mph)
Time to 10,000 m (32,800 ft) from brakes off, with afterburning	less than 1 min 40 s
T-O run	approx 400 m (1,310 ft)
Landing run	approx 500 m (1,640 ft)
Required landing field length:	
conventional landing	1,000 m (3,280 ft)
no-flare landing	500 m (1,640 ft)
Tactical radius with external armament:	
hi-lo-hi	over 540 nm (1,000 km; 620 miles)
lo-lo-lo	over 270 nm (500 km; 310 miles)

SAAB 35 DRAKEN (DRAGON)

Under the revised designation **J 35J** (previously J 35F Mod or J 35F-Ny: new), 50 or more J 35F Draken fighters of F10 Wing of the Swedish Air Force, based near Ängelholm in southern Sweden, are being updated to extend their service life until the end of the 1990s, when they will be replaced by the JAS 39 Gripen. Saab Aircraft Division is responsible for modification and redelivery, with FFV Aerotech as subcontractor.

Two additional inboard underwing pylons are fitted, allowing four tanks and two air-to-air missiles, or four missiles and two tanks. Operation of the automatic gun and weapons electronics are changed, radar and IFF improved, infra-red missile target seeker upgraded, altitude warning system added, and instruments improved.

F10 Wing will be the only unit operating this version of the Draken. Redeliveries were to be completed in 1990.

The Austrian Air Force received 24 Saab 35OEs, modified from J 35Ds, between 1987 and 1989.

The J 35D and F were last described fully in the 1969-70 *Jane's*.

SAAB 105

Saab is to complete a life extension programme on 140 Saab 105 trainer/light attack aircraft (Swedish Air Force Sk60) in 1991. The Saab 105 is also entered, as the **Saab 2060**, in the competition for the US Joint Primary Aircraft Training System (JPATS), for which a new engine and avionics would be fitted. No US partner had been announced at the time of going to press.

SWITZERLAND

DÄTWYLER

MDC MAX DÄTWYLER AG

Flugplatz, CH-3368 Bleienbach-Langenthal
Telephone: 41 (63) 283 111
Telex: 982626 MDC CH
Fax: 41 (63) 232 429
PRESIDENT OF THE BOARD: Max Dätwyler

Dätwyler has specialised for many years in the repair and modification of light aircraft. It has also manufactured components for the Pilatus Porter/Turbo-Porter STOL transport aircraft and B4-PC11 sailplane, and for the Dassault Mercure jet transport, and this work continues. Its latest design is the MD-3 Swiss Trainer.

DÄTWYLER MD-3 SWISS TRAINER

The MD-3-160 prototype (HB-HOH) made its first flight, with Mr Dätwyler at the controls, on 12 August 1983. The second prototype was to be completed in Spring 1990 and FAR 23 certification was expected in late 1990. A full description and illustration of the prototype can be found in the 1988-89 *Jane's*.

FFA

FFA FLUGZEUGWERKE ALTENRHEIN AG

CH-9423 Altenrhein
Telephone: 41 (71) 43 01 11
Telex: 88 29 06 FFA CH
Fax: 41 (71) 42 11 54
PRESIDENT: Charles Brönimann
CHIEF ENGINEER: Hansjörg Candrian
DIRECTOR OF SALES AND MARKETING: Alex Quaite

This company had its origin in AG für Dornier Flugzeuge, the Swiss branch of the West German Dornier company. In 1948 it became an entirely Swiss company named FFA (Flug-und Fahrzeugwerke AG). In January 1987 the complete aviation activity was sold to the Justus Dornier group in Zurich, and the present company name took effect on 1 June 1987.

Current activities, besides production of the AS 202 Bravo, consist of subcontracting for various aircraft manufacturers throughout the world, and licence production of components for Swiss built Northrop F-5E/F Tiger IIs. Overhaul, servicing and maintenance for the Swiss Air Force and for general aviation are also done at Altenrhein. FFA has 350 employees, approximately two-thirds of whom are engaged in aviation activities. Details of the FFA-2000 Eurotrainer are now given under the FFT heading in the German section.

FFA AS 202/18A BRAVO

Following an agreement concluded with SIAI-Marchetti of Italy, FFA undertook production of the AS 202 Bravo light trainer and sporting aircraft.

The Swiss assembled AS 202/15 prototype (HB-HEA) flew for the first time on 7 March 1969. The Italian built second prototype flew on 7 May 1969. The third aircraft (HB-HEC) made its first flight on 16 June 1969, and the first production aircraft on 22 December 1971. The AS 202/15 (34 built: 1981-82 *Jane's*) and AS 202/26A (prototype only: 1985-86 and earlier editions) are no longer available.

The following version remained available in 1989:

AS 202/18A. Two/three-seat aerobatic version. First flew (HB-HEY) on 22 August 1974. Swiss certification granted on 12 December 1975; FAA certification awarded on 17 December 1976. Deliveries totalled 180 by early 1990, in Switzerland and to foreign customers as listed in the 1987-88 and earlier *Jane's*. A second pair of Bravos (A4s) was delivered to Oman during 1989. Variants include the A2 (higher max T-O/landing weight, extended canopy, electric trim), A3 (as A2 but with mechanical trim and 24V electrical system) and A4 (as A2 but with CAA approved special instrumentation). The 11 AS 202/18A4s for the BAe Flying College are known by the name **Wren**.

The following description applies to the AS 202/18A:

TYPE: Two/three-seat light aircraft.

WINGS: Cantilever low-wing monoplane. Wing section NACA 63₂618 (modified) at centreline, 63₂415 at tip. Thickness/chord ratio 17.63 per cent at root, 15 per cent at tip. Dihedral 5° 43' from roots. Incidence 3°. Sweepback at quarter-chord 0° 40'. Conventional aluminium single-spar fail-safe structure, with riveted honeycomb laminate skin. Aluminium single-slotted flaps and single-slotted ailerons. Ground adjustable tab on each aileron.

FUSELAGE: Conventional aluminium semi-monocoque fail-safe structure, with engine cowling and several fairings of glassfibre.

TAIL UNIT: Cantilever aluminium single-spar structure with sweptback vertical surfaces. Rudder mass balanced, with provision for anti-collision beacon. Fixed incidence tailplane. Two-piece elevator with full span electrically

One of the two FFA AS 202/18A4s delivered to Oman during 1989

actuated trim tab on starboard half. Electrically actuated tab in rudder of current 202/18A4.

LANDING GEAR: Non-retractable tricycle type, with steerable nosewheel. Rubber cushioned shock absorber struts of SIAI-Marchetti design. Mainwheel tyres size 6.00-6; nosewheel tyre size 5.00-5. Tyre pressure (all units) 2.41 bars (35 lb/sq in). Independent hydraulically operated disc brake on each mainwheel.

POWER PLANT: One 134 kW (180 hp) Textron Lycoming AEIO-360-B1F flat-four engine, driving a Hartzell HC-C2YK-1BF/F7666A-2 two-blade constant-speed propeller with spinner. Hoffmann three-blade propeller optional. Two wing leading-edge rubber fuel tanks with total capacity of 170 litres (44.9 US gallons; 37.4 Imp gallons). Refuelling point above each wing. Starboard tank has additional flexible fuel intake for aerobatics. Christen 801 fully aerobatic oil system, capacity 7.6 litres (2 US gallons; 1.6 Imp gallons).

ACCOMMODATION: Seats for two persons side by side, in Aerobatic versions, under rearward sliding jettisonable transparent canopy. Space at rear in Utility versions for a third seat or 100 kg (220 lb) of baggage. Dual controls, cabin ventilation and heating standard.

SYSTEMS: Hydraulic system for brake actuation. One 12V 60A engine driven alternator (24V in A3) and one 25Ah battery provide electrical power for engine starting, lighting, instruments, communications and navigation installations. 28V electrical system optional.

AVIONICS AND EQUIPMENT: Provision for VHF radio, VOR, ADF, Nav-O-Matic 200A autopilot, blind-flying instrumentation or other special equipment at customer's option. Clutch and release mechanism for glider towing optional.

DIMENSIONS, EXTERNAL:

Wing span	9.75 m (31 ft 11¾ in)
Wing chord: at root	1.88 m (6 ft 2 in)
at tip	1.16 m (3 ft 9½ in)
Wing aspect ratio	6.5
Length overall	7.50 m (24 ft 7¼ in)
Length of fuselage	7.15 m (23 ft 5½ in)
Height overall	2.81 m (9 ft 2¾ in)
Tailplane span	3.67 m (12 ft 0½ in)
Wheel track	2.25 m (7 ft 4½ in)
Wheelbase	1.78 m (5 ft 10 in)
Propeller diameter	1.88 m (6 ft 2 in)
Propeller ground clearance	0.31 m (1 ft 0¼ in)

DIMENSIONS, INTERNAL:

Cabin: Max length	2.15 m (7 ft 0½ in)
Max width	1.00 m (3 ft 4 in)
Max height	1.10 m (3 ft 7¼ in)
Floor area	2.15 m² (23.14 sq ft)

AREAS:

Wings, gross	13.86 m² (149.2 sq ft)
Ailerons (total)	1.09 m² (11.7 sq ft)
Trailing-edge flaps (total)	1.49 m² (16.04 sq ft)
Fin	0.45 m² (4.84 sq ft)
Rudder, incl tab	0.94 m² (10.12 sq ft)
Tailplane	1.88 m² (20.24 sq ft)
Elevators, incl tab	0.76 m² (8.18 sq ft)

WEIGHTS AND LOADINGS:

Weight empty, equipped	710 kg (1,565 lb)
Max useful load (incl fuel): Aerobatic	177 kg (390 lb)
Utility	248 kg (546 lb)
Max T-O and landing weight:	
Aerobatic: A/A1	950 kg (2,094 lb)
A2/A3	980 kg (2,160 lb)
A4	1,010 kg (2,226 lb)
Utility: current 18A models	1,080 kg (2,380 lb)
Max wing loading: Utility	75.8 kg/m² (15.52 lb/sq ft)
Max power loading: Utility	7.84 kg/kW (12.86 lb/hp)

PERFORMANCE (Utility category at max T-O weight):

Never-exceed speed	173 knots (320 km/h; 199 mph)
Max level speed at S/L	130 knots (241 km/h; 150 mph)
Max cruising speed (75% power) at 2,440 m (8,000 ft)	122 knots (226 km/h; 141 mph)
Econ cruising speed (55% power) at 3,050 m (10,000 ft)	109 knots (203 km/h; 126 mph)
Stalling speed, engine idling:	
flaps up	62 knots (115 km/h; 71 mph)
flaps down	49 knots (90 km/h; 56 mph)
Max rate of climb at S/L	244 m (800 ft)/min
Service ceiling	5,180 m (17,000 ft)
T-O run at S/L	215 m (705 ft)
T-O to 15 m (50 ft) at S/L	415 m (1,360 ft)
Landing from 15 m (50 ft)	465 m (1,525 ft)
Landing run	210 m (690 ft)
Range with max fuel, no reserves	615 nm (1,140 km; 707 miles)
Max endurance	5 h 30 min
g limits	+6/−3

PILATUS
PILATUS FLUGZEUGWERKE AG
CH-6370 Stans

Telephone: 41 (41) 63 61 11

Telex: 866202 PIL CH

Fax: 41 (41) 613351

CHAIRMAN AND GENERAL MANAGER: W. Gubler
DIRECTOR OF PROGRAMMES: D. C. Klöckner
DIRECTOR OF MARKETING AND SALES: U. Wenger
DIRECTOR OF PRODUCTION: W. Zbinden

Pilatus Flugzeugwerke AG was formed in December 1939; details of its early history can be found in previous editions of *Jane's*. It is part of the Oerlikon-Bührle Group. Current products are the PC-6 Turbo-Porter, the PC-7 Turbo-Trainer and PC-9. The PC-12 is being developed.

On 24 January 1979 Pilatus purchased the assets of Britten-Norman (Bembridge) Ltd of the UK, which has operated since then under the name Pilatus Britten-Norman Ltd (which see) as a subsidiary of Pilatus Aircraft Ltd.

PILATUS PC-6 TURBO-PORTER
US Army designation: UV-20A Chiricahua

The PC-6 is a single-engined multi-purpose utility aircraft, with STOL characteristics permitting operation from unprepared strips under harsh environmental and terrain conditions. It can be converted rapidly from a freighter to a passenger transport, and adapted for a great number of missions, including supply dropping, search and rescue, ambulance, aerial survey and photography, parachuting, cropspraying, water bombing, rainmaking and glider or target towing. The PC-6 can operate from soft ground, snow, glacier or water.

The first piston engined prototype made its first flight on 4 May 1959, and details of piston engined production models can be found in contemporary editions of *Jane's*. The early PC-6/A, A1, A2, B, B1, B2 and C2-H2 Turbo-Porters, with various turboprop power plants, were last described in the 1974-75 edition, and the B2-H2 in editions up to and including 1986-87. The B1 and B2 can be fitted with an air inlet filter for operation in desert conditions and for agricultural applications.

Current version since 1985 is the **PC-6/B2-H4**, in which for CAR.3 operations (commercial operations with fare paying passengers) the maximum take-off weight is increased by 600 kg (1,323 lb), resulting in a payload increase of up to 570 kg (1,257 lb) compared with previous models. This was achieved by improving the aerodynamic efficiency of the wings with new tip fairings, enlarging the dorsal fin, installing uprated mainwheel shock absorbers and a new tailwheel assembly, and a slight strengthening of the airframe. While the H4 modification can be retrofitted to all existing PC-6/B2-H2 models equipped with electrically operated longitudinal trim, all new-production Porters since mid-1985 have been of the H4 version.

About 480 PC-6 aircraft, of all models, have been delivered (including US licence manufacture), and are operating in more than 50 countries. Military operators include the air forces of Angola, Argentina, Australia, Austria, Bolivia, Burma, Chad, Dubai, Ecuador, Iran, Oman, Peru, Sudan, Switzerland and Thailand, and the US Army.

Approx 40 Turbo-Porters (all H2 or earlier series) have been completed in agricultural configuration: these are in service in Indonesia, Sudan, Switzerland, Thailand and Zaïre. For liquid spraying, a stainless steel tank (capacity 1,330 litres; 351.5 US gallons; 292.5 Imp gallons) is installed behind the two front seats, and 46- or 62-nozzle spraybooms are fitted beneath the wings. In this configuration the aircraft can cover a swath width of 45 m (148 ft). An ultra-low-volume system, using four to six atomisers or two to six Micronairs, is also available, permitting increase in swath width up to 400 m (1,310 ft).

For dusting with granulated materials, the lower part of the standard tank can be replaced by a discharge and dispersal door permitting coverage of a swath width of up to 20 m (66 ft). A Transland spreader can be fitted for dust application (swath up to 30 m; 100 ft). Effective swath width of these versions is 13-40 m (43-131 ft), the optimum being approx 20 m (66 ft).

Both versions are fitted with small doors in the fuselage sides, giving access to the tank/hopper for servicing, removal or replenishment, and two single seats or a bench seat for three persons can be installed aft of the tank. Optional items include an engine air intake screen and a loading door for chemical in the top of the fuselage.

The structural description which follows is applicable to the standard B2-H4 version:

TYPE: Single-engined STOL utility transport.
WINGS: Braced high-wing monoplane, with single streamline-section bracing strut each side. Wing section NACA 64-514 (constant). Dihedral 1°; incidence 2°; single-spar all-metal structure, with span-increasing tip fairings. Entire trailing-edge hinged, inner sections consisting of electrically operated all-metal double-slotted flaps and outer sections of all-metal single-slotted ailerons. No airbrakes or de-icing equipment.
FUSELAGE: All-metal semi-monocoque structure.
TAIL UNIT: Cantilever all-metal structure. Variable incidence tailplane. Flettner tabs on elevator. Enlarged dorsal fin.

Pilatus PC-6 Turbo-Porter delivered to the Dubai Air Force

LANDING GEAR: Non-retractable tailwheel type. Oleo shock absorbers of Pilatus design in all units. Steerable/lockable tailwheel. Goodyear Type II mainwheels and GA 284 tyres size 24 × 7 or 7.50 × 10 (pressure 2.21 bars; 32 lb/sq in); oversize Goodyear Type III wheels and tyres optional, size 11.0 × 12, pressure 0.88 bars (12.8 lb/sq in). Goodyear tailwheel with size 5.00-4 tyre. Goodyear disc brakes. Pilatus wheel/ski gear optional.
POWER PLANT: One 507 kW (680 shp) Pratt & Whitney Canada PT6A-27 turboprop (flat rated at 410 kW; 550 shp at S/L), driving a Hartzell HC-B3TN-3D/T-10178 C or CH, or T10173 C or CH constant-speed fully-feathering reversible-pitch propeller with Beta mode control. Standard fuel in integral wing tanks, usable capacity 644 litres (170 US gallons; 142 Imp gallons). Two underwing auxiliary tanks, each of 245 litres (65 US gallons; 54 Imp gallons), available optionally. Oil capacity 12.5 litres (3.3 US gallons; 2.75 Imp gallons).
ACCOMMODATION: Cabin has pilot's seat forward on port side, with one passenger seat alongside, and is normally fitted with six quickly removable seats, in pairs, to the rear of these for additional passengers. Up to 11 persons, including the pilot, can be carried in 2-3-3-3 high density layout; or up to ten parachutists, who can be dropped from heights of up to 7,620 m (25,000 ft); or two stretchers plus three attendants in ambulance configuration. Floor is level, flush with door sill, and is provided with seat rails. Forward opening door beside each front seat. Large rearward sliding door on starboard side of main cabin. Port side sliding door optional. Double doors, without central pillar, on port side. Hatch in floor 0.58 × 0.90 m (1 ft 10¾ in × 2 ft 11½ in), openable from inside cabin, for aerial camera or for supply dropping. Hatch in cabin rear wall 0.50 × 0.80 m (1 ft 7 in × 2 ft 7 in) permits stowage of six passenger seats or accommodation of freight items up to 5.0 m (16 ft 5 in) in length. Walls lined with lightweight soundproofing and heat insulation material. Adjustable heating and ventilation systems provided. Dual controls optional.
SYSTEMS: Cabin heated by engine bleed air. Scott 8,500 oxygen system optional. 200A 30V starter/generator and 24V 34Ah (optionally 40Ah) nickel-cadmium battery.
EQUIPMENT: Generally to customer's requirements, but can include stretchers for ambulance role, aerial photography and survey gear, agricultural equipment (see earlier paragraphs) or an 800 litre (211 US gallon; 176 Imp gallon) water tank in cabin, with quick release system, for firefighting role. The 1,330 litre agricultural tank can also be used in the firebombing role.

DIMENSIONS, EXTERNAL:
Wing span	15.87 m (52 ft 0¾ in)
Wing chord, constant	1.90 m (6 ft 3 in)
Wing aspect ratio	8.4
Length overall	11.00 m (36 ft 1 in)
Height overall (tail down)	3.20 m (10 ft 6 in)
Elevator span	5.12 m (16 ft 9½ in)

Wheel track	3.00 m (9 ft 10 in)
Wheelbase	7.87 m (25 ft 10 in)
Propeller diameter	2.56 m (8 ft 5 in)
Cabin double door (port) and sliding door (starboard):	
Max height	1.04 m (3 ft 5 in)
Width	1.58 m (5 ft 2¼ in)

DIMENSIONS, INTERNAL:
Cabin, from back of pilot's seat to rear wall:	
Length	2.30 m (7 ft 6½ in)
Max width	1.16 m (3 ft 9½ in)
Max height (at front)	1.28 m (4 ft 2½ in)
Height at rear wall	1.18 m (3 ft 10½ in)
Floor area	2.67 m² (28.6 sq ft)
Volume	3.28 m³ (107 cu ft)

AREAS:
Wings, gross	30.15 m² (324.5 sq ft)
Ailerons (total)	3.83 m² (41.2 sq ft)
Flaps (total)	3.76 m² (40.5 sq ft)
Fin	1.70 m² (18.3 sq ft)
Rudder, incl tab	0.96 m² (10.3 sq ft)
Tailplane	4.03 m² (43.4 sq ft)
Elevator, incl tab	2.11 m² (22.7 sq ft)

WEIGHTS AND LOADINGS:
Weight empty, equipped	1,270 kg (2,800 lb)
Max fuel weight: internal	508 kg (1,120 lb)
underwing	392 kg (864 lb)
Max payload:	
with reduced internal fuel	1,130 kg (2,491 lb)
with max internal fuel	1,062 kg (2,341 lb)
with max internal and underwing fuel	
	571 kg (1,259 lb)
Max T-O weight, Normal (CAR 3):	
wheels (standard)	2,800 kg (6,173 lb)
skis	2,600 kg (5,732 lb)
Max landing weight: wheels	2,660 kg (5,864 lb)
skis	2,600 kg (5,732 lb)
Max cabin floor loading	488 kg/m² (100 lb/sq ft)
Max wing loading (Normal):	
wheels	92.87 kg/m² (19.03 lb/sq ft)
skis	86.23 kg/m² (17.67 lb/sq ft)
Max power loading (Normal):	
wheels	6.83 kg/kW (11.22 lb/shp)
skis	5.13 kg/kW (8.43 lb/shp)

PERFORMANCE (at max T-O weight, ISA, Normal category):
Never-exceed speed 151 knots (280 km/h; 174 mph) IAS	
Econ cruising speed at 3,050 m (10,000 ft)	
	115 knots (213 km/h; 132 mph)
Stalling speed, power off, flaps down	
	52 knots (96 km/h; 60 mph)
Max rate of climb at S/L	287 m (941 ft)/min
Max operating altitude	7,620 m (25,000 ft)
T-O run at S/L	197 m (646 ft)
Landing run at S/L	127 m (417 ft)
Max range at 115 knots (213 km/h; 132 mph) at 3,050 m (10,000 ft), no reserves:	
with max payload	394 nm (730 km; 453 miles)

Pilatus PC-6/B2-H4 Turbo-Porter, the standard version since 1985 (*Pilot Press*)

with max internal fuel   500 nm (926 km; 576 miles)
with max internal and underwing fuel
                870 nm (1,612 km; 1,002 miles)
g limits   +3.72/−1.5

PILATUS PC-7 TURBO-TRAINER
Swiss Air Force designation: PC-7/CH

The PC-7 Turbo-Trainer is a fully aerobatic two-seat training aircraft, powered by a 410 kW (550 shp) Pratt & Whitney Canada PT6A-25A turboprop. It can be used for basic, transition and aerobatic training and, with suitable equipment installed, for IFR and tactical training. It received FAA certification to FAR Pt 23 on 12 August 1983, and also meets the requirements of a selected group of US military specifications (Trainer category). As a single-seater, it is flown from the front seat. The PC-7 also holds type certificates in the Aerobatic and Utility categories from the Swiss Federal Office for Civil Aviation (5 December 1978/6 April 1979) and the French DGAC (16 May 1983).

The first production PC-7 was flown on 18 August 1978, and deliveries began in December of that year. Sales totalled over 400 by 1 May 1990. Customers include the air forces of Abu Dhabi (24), Angola (18), Austria (16), Bolivia (36), Burma (17), Chile (10 for Navy), Guatemala (12), Iran (35), Iraq (52), Malaysia (44), Mexico (75), Netherlands (10), Switzerland (40) and undisclosed countries; other customers include CIPRA of France (2), Swissair (1), Contraves (1) and three US private owners (1 each). From the 1987 air show season the French Patrouille Martini formation display team has flown three PC-7s, equipped with smoke generator pods.

The PC-7 is available with new, lightweight Mk CH 15A ejection seats developed in collaboration with Martin-Baker. These offer safe escape for both occupants at speeds between 60 knots on the runway and 300 knots in the air (111-556 km/h; 69-345 mph), and at altitudes up to 6,700 m (22,000 ft).

TYPE: Single-engined single/two-seat training aircraft.

WINGS: Cantilever low-wing monoplane. Wing section NACA 64$_7$A-415 at root, NACA 64$_1$A-612 at tip. Dihedral 7^6 on outer panels. Sweepback 1° at quarter-chord. One-piece all-metal single-spar structure, with auxiliary spar, ribs and stringer-reinforced skin. Constant chord centre-section and tapered outer panels. Alclad aluminium alloy (2022 or 2024) skin, reinforced by stringers. Some fairings of GFRP. Mass balanced ailerons; trailing-edge split flaps, extending under fuselage. Flaps actuated electrically, ailerons mechanically by pushrods. Trim tab in port aileron.

FUSELAGE: All-metal semi-monocoque structure, with stringers, bulkheads and aluminium alloy skin. Some fairings of GFRP.

TAIL UNIT: Cantilever all-metal structure, of similar construction to wings. Dorsal fin; small ventral fin under tailcone. Forward strakes ahead of leading-edges of tailplane. Trim tab in starboard half of elevator; anti-servo tab in rudder. All control surfaces mass balanced and cable operated.

LANDING GEAR: Electrically actuated retractable tricycle type, with emergency manual extension. Mainwheels retract inward, nosewheel rearward. Oleo-pneumatic shock absorber in each unit. Castoring nosewheel, with shimmy dampers. Goodrich mainwheels and tyres, size 6.50-8, pressure 4.5 bars (65 lb/sq in). Goodrich nosewheel and tyre, size 6.00-6, pressure 2.75 bars (40 lb/sq in). No mainwheel doors. Goodrich hydraulic disc brakes on mainwheels. Parking brake.

POWER PLANT: One 485 kW (650 shp) Pratt & Whitney Canada PT6A-25A turboprop, flat rated at 410 kW (550 shp at S/L), driving a Hartzell HC-B3TN-2/T10173C-8 three-blade constant-speed fully-feathering propeller with spinner. Fuel in integral tanks in outer wing leading-edges, total usable capacity 474 litres (125 US gallons; 104 Imp gallons). Overwing refuelling point on each tank. Engine oil system permits up to 30 s of inverted flight. Provision for two 152 or 240 litre (40 or 63.5 US gallon; 33.5 or 52.75 Imp gallon) underwing drop tanks. Oil capacity 16 litres (4.2 US gallons; 3.5 Imp gallons).

ACCOMMODATION: Adjustable seats for two persons in tandem (instructor at rear), beneath rearward sliding jettisonable Plexiglas canopy. Martin-Baker Mk CH 15A lightweight ejection seats available optionally. Dual controls standard. Cockpits ventilated and heated by engine bleed air, which can also be used for windscreen de-icing. Space for 25 kg (55 lb) of baggage aft of seats, with external access.

SYSTEMS: Freon air-conditioning and oxygen systems standard. Hydraulic system for mainwheel brakes only. No pneumatic system. 28V DC operational electrical system, incorporating Lear Siegler 30V 200A starter/generator and Marathon 36Ah or 42Ah nickel-cadmium battery; two static inverters for AC power supply. Ground power receptacle in port side of rear fuselage. Goodrich propeller electric de-icing system optional.

AVIONICS AND EQUIPMENT: Basic flight and navigation instrumentation in both cockpits, except for magnetic compass (front cockpit only). Additional nav and com equipment to customer's requirements. Other optional equipment includes instrument flying hood to screen

Pilatus PC-7 Turbo-Trainer of the Royal Netherlands Air Force

Pilatus PC-7 Turbo-Trainer (Pratt & Whitney Canada PT6A-25A turboprop) *(Pilot Press)*

pupil from rear cockpit during IFR training. Landing/taxying light standard on each mainwheel leg.

DIMENSIONS, EXTERNAL:

Wing span	10.40 m (34 ft 1 in)
Wing chord: mean aerodynamic	1.64 m (5 ft 5 in)
mean geometric	1.60 m (5 ft 3 in)
Wing aspect ratio	6.5
Length overall	9.78 m (32 ft 1 in)
Height overall	3.21 m (10 ft 6 in)
Tailplane span	3.40 m (11 ft 2 in)
Wheel track	2.60 m (8 ft 6 in)
Wheelbase	2.32 m (7 ft 7 in)
Propeller diameter	2.36 m (7 ft 9 in)

AREAS:

Wings, gross	16.60 m² (179.0 sq ft)
Ailerons (total)	1.621 m² (17.45 sq ft)
Trailing-edge flaps (total)	2.035 m² (21.90 sq ft)
Fin, incl dorsal fin	1.062 m² (11.43 sq ft)
Rudder, incl tab	0.959 m² (10.32 sq ft)
Tailplane	1.783 m² (19.19 sq ft)
Elevators, incl tab	1.395 m² (15.02 sq ft)

WEIGHTS AND LOADINGS:

Basic weight empty	1,330 kg (2,932 lb)
Max T-O weight: Aerobatic	1,900 kg (4,188 lb)
Utility	2,700 kg (5,952 lb)
Max ramp weight: Utility	2,711 kg (5,976 lb)
Max landing weight:	
Aerobatic (military specification)	1,804 kg (3,977 lb)
Aerobatic (FAR Pt 23)	1,900 kg (4,188 lb)
Utility	2,565 kg (5,655 lb)
Max zero-fuel weight	1,664 kg (3,668 lb)
Max wing loading:	
Aerobatic	114.5 kg/m² (23.44 lb/sq ft)
Utility	162.7 kg/m² (33.31 lb/sq ft)
Max power loading:	
Aerobatic	4.63 kg/kW (7.61 lb/shp)
Utility	6.59 kg/kW (10.82 lb/shp)

PERFORMANCE (at max T-O weight, ISA, except where indicated. A: Aerobatic category, B: Utility category):

Never-exceed speed:		
A, B		270 knots (500 km/h; 310 mph) EAS
Max operating speed:		
A, B		270 knots (500 km/h; 310 mph) EAS
Max cruising speed at 6,100 m (20,000 ft):		
A		222 knots (412 km/h; 256 mph)
B		196 knots (364 km/h; 226 mph)
Econ cruising speed at 6,100 m (20,000 ft):		
A		171 knots (317 km/h; 197 mph)
B		165 knots (305 km/h; 190 mph)

Manoeuvring speed:		
A		175 knots (325 km/h; 202 mph) EAS
B		181 knots (335 km/h; 208 mph) EAS
Max speed with flaps and landing gear down:		
A, B		135 knots (250 km/h; 155 mph) EAS
Stalling speed, flaps and landing gear up, power off:		
A		71 knots (131 km/h; 82 mph) EAS
B		83 knots (154 km/h; 96 mph) EAS
Stalling speed, flaps and landing gear down, power off:		
A		64 knots (119 km/h; 74 mph) EAS
B		74 knots (138 km/h; 86 mph) EAS
Max rate of climb at S/L: A		655 m (2,150 ft)/min
B		364 m (1,195 ft)/min
Time to 5,000 m (16,400 ft): A		9 min
B		17 min
Max operating altitude		7,620 m (25,000 ft)
Service ceiling: A		10,060 m (33,000 ft)
B		7,925 m (26,000 ft)
T-O run at S/L: A		240 m (787 ft)
B		780 m (2,560 ft)
T-O to 15 m (50 ft) at S/L: A		400 m (1,312 ft)
B		1,180 m (3,870 ft)
Landing from 15 m (50 ft) at S/L at max landing weight:		
A		510 m (1,675 ft)
B		800 m (2,625 ft)
Landing run at S/L at max landing weight:		
A		295 m (968 ft)
B		505 m (1,655 ft)
Max range at cruise power at 5,000 m (16,400 ft), 5% fuel plus 20 min reserves:		
A		647 nm (1,200 km; 745 miles)
B		1,420 nm (2,630 km; 1,634 miles)
Endurance at 6,100 m (20,000 ft), with reserves:		
A, at max speed		3 h 0 min
A, for max range		4 h 22 min
B, at max speed		2 h 36 min
B, for max range		3 h 45 min
g limits: A		+6/−3
B		+4.5/−2.25

PILATUS PC-9

Design of the PC-9, as an advanced, high performance turboprop trainer suitable for all aspects from basic through to advanced flying, began in May 1982. Despite an external similarity to the PC-7, it has only about 10 per cent structural commonality with that aircraft, differences including a more powerful engine, stepped tandem cockpits with ejection seats, a ventral airbrake, modified wing profiles and tips, new ailerons, a longer dorsal fin,

First Australian Pilatus PC-9 single/two-seat trainer

Pilatus PC-9 basic/advanced trainer (Pratt & Whitney Canada PT6A-62 turboprop) *(Pilot Press)*

mainwheel doors, and larger wheels with high pressure tyres. The PC-9 complies with FAR Pt 23 (Amendments 1-28), plus special conditions as specified by the Swiss Federal Office for Civil Aviation, in both the Aerobatic and Utility categories, and also complies with selected parts of US military specifications.

Flight testing of major components, and aerodynamic optimisation of the new design, were completed during 1982-83 on a PC-7 technology demonstration aircraft, and were followed by two pre-production PC-9s (HB-HPA, first flight 7 May 1984, and HB-HPB, first flown on 20 July 1984). The second of these was more fully representative of the production version. Aerobatic certification was obtained on 19 September 1985. Sales now total about 140.

First customer for the PC-9 was the Union of Burma Air Force, which ordered four. It was followed by the Royal Saudi Air Force, which ordered 30 on 26 September 1985. The first of these was handed over to the RSAF on 15 December 1986, and all have now been delivered. On 16 December 1985 the Australian Defence Minister announced his government's decision to order PC-9s for the RAAF, and a contract for 67 aircraft, to be co-produced by Hawker de Havilland and ASTA, was signed on 10 July 1986. The Australian version is designated **PC-9/A**. For the Australian order, Pilatus supplied two complete aircraft in 1987; these were followed by six in kit form (first kit delivered 27 February 1987), and major components for a further 11; the remaining 48 are being built by HDH and ASTA. The two Swiss built aircraft, and the first two assembled in Australia, were handed over to the RAAF on 14 December 1987.

TYPE: Single/two-seat training aircraft.

WINGS: Cantilever low-wing monoplane. Wing section PIL15M825 at root, PIL12M850 at tip. Dihedral 7° from centre-section. Incidence 1° at root, washout −2° at tip. Sweepback 1° at quarter-chord. One-piece all-metal single-spar primary structure with auxiliary spar, ribs, and stringer-reinforced skin. Constant chord centre-section and tapered outer panels. Alclad aluminium alloy (2024) skin; some fairings of GFRP. Mass balanced plain ailerons; trailing-edge split flaps extending under fuselage with plate type airbrake at centre. Flaps and airbrake actuated hydraulically, ailerons mechanically by push-rods. Aileron trim is by an electrically actuated, movable centring spring on the control column.

FUSELAGE: All-metal semi-monocoque structure with stringers, bulkheads and aluminium alloy skin. Some fairings of GFRP.

TAIL UNIT: Cantilever all-metal structure with mass balanced cable operated rudder and elevator. Trim tab in starboard half of elevator, and trim/anti-balance tab in rudder, both mass balanced and electrically actuated.

LANDING GEAR: Retractable tricycle type, with hydraulic actuation in both normal and emergency modes. Mainwheels retract inward into wing centre-section, nosewheel rearward; all units enclosed by doors when retracted. Oleo-pneumatic shock absorber in each leg unit. Hydraulically actuated nosewheel steering. Goodrich wheels and tyres, with Goodrich multi-piston hydraulic disc brakes on mainwheels. RAAF version has low pressure tyres for grass field operation. Parking brake.

POWER PLANT: One 857 kW (1,150 shp) Pratt & Whitney Canada PT6A-62 turboprop, flat rated at 708 kW (950 shp), driving a Hartzell HC-D4N-ZA/09512A four-blade constant-speed fully-feathering propeller with spinner. Single lever engine control. Fuel in two integral tanks in wing leading-edges, total usable capacity 535 litres (141.3 US gallons; 117.7 Imp gallons). Overwing refuelling point on each side. Fuel system includes a 12 litre (3.2 US gallon; 2.6 Imp gallon) aerobatics tank in fuselage, forward of front cockpit, which permits up to 60 s of inverted flight. Provision for two 154 or 248 litre (40.7 or 65.5 US gallon; 33.9 or 54.5 Imp gallon) drop tanks on the centre underwing attachment points. Total oil capacity 16 litres (4.2 US gallons; 3.5 Imp gallons).

ACCOMMODATION: Two Martin-Baker Mk CH 11A adjustable ejection seats, each with integrated personal survival pack and fighter-standard pilot equipment. Stepped tandem arrangement with rear seat elevated 15 cm (6.3 in). Seats operable, through canopy, at zero height and speeds down to 60 knots (112 km/h; 70 mph). Anti-*g* system optional. One-piece acrylic Perspex windscreen; one-piece framed canopy, incorporating rollover bar, opens sideways to starboard. Dual controls standard. Cockpit heating, ventilation and canopy demisting standard. Space for 25 kg (55 lb) of baggage aft of seats, with external access.

SYSTEMS: AiResearch environmental control system, using air cycle and engine bleed air, for cockpit heating/ ventilation and canopy demisting. Fairey Systems hydraulic system, pressure 207 bars (3,000 lb/sq in), for actuation of landing gear, mainwheel doors, nosewheel steering, flaps and airbrake; system max flow rate 18.8 litres (4.97 US gallons; 4.14 Imp gallons)/min. Bootstrap oil/oil reservoir, pressurised at 3.45-207 bars (50-3,000 lb/sq in). Oil/nitrogen accumulator, also charged to 207 bars (3,000 lb/sq in), provides emergency hydraulic power for flaps and landing gear. Primary electrical system (28V DC operational, 24V nominal) powered by a Lear Siegler 30V 200A starter/generator and a 24V 40Ah battery; two static inverters supply 115/26V AC power at 400Hz. Ground power receptacle provided. Electric anti-icing of pitot tube, static ports and AOA transmitter standard; electric de-icing of propeller blades optional. Diluter demand oxygen system, selected and controlled individually from a panel in each cockpit.

AVIONICS AND EQUIPMENT: Both cockpits fully instrumented to standard customer specifications, with Kratos computer operated instrument system (COINS). RAAF aircraft have Bendix/King EFIS (see below) as standard. Single or dual system VHF, UHF and/or HF to customer's requirements. Audio integrating system controls audio services from com, nav and interphone systems. Customer-specified equipment provides flight environmental, attitude and direction data, and ground-transmitted position determining information. Retractable 250W landing/taxying light in each main landing gear leg bay. Optional equipment includes Bendix/King CRT displays (electronic ADI and HSI, standard on PC-9/A), J.E.T. head-up displays, encoding altimeter, emergency locator transmitter and underwing drop tanks.

DIMENSIONS, EXTERNAL:

Wing span	10.124 m (33 ft 2½ in)
Wing chord: mean aerodynamic	1.65 m (5 ft 5 in)
mean geometric	1.61 m (5 ft 3½ in)
Wing aspect ratio	6.3
Length overall	10.175 m (33 ft 4¾ in)
Height overall	3.26 m (10 ft 8⅓ in)
Wheel track	2.54 m (8 ft 4 in)
Propeller diameter	2.44 m (8 ft 0 in)

AREAS:

Wings, gross	16.29 m² (175.3 sq ft)
Ailerons (total)	1.57 m² (16.90 sq ft)
Trailing-edge flaps (total)	1.77 m² (19.05 sq ft)
Airbrake	0.30 m² (3.23 sq ft)
Fin	0.86 m² (9.26 sq ft)
Rudder, incl tab	0.90 m² (9.69 sq ft)
Tailplane	1.80 m² (19.38 sq ft)
Elevator, incl tab	1.60 m² (17.22 sq ft)

WEIGHTS AND LOADINGS (A: Aerobatic, U: Utility):

Basic weight empty	1,685 kg (3,715 lb)
Max T-O weight: A	2,250 kg (4,960 lb)
U	3,200 kg (7,055 lb)
Max ramp weight: A	2,260 kg (4,982 lb)
U	3,210 kg (7,077 lb)
Max landing weight: A	2,250 kg (4,960 lb)
U	3,100 kg (6,834 lb)
Max zero-fuel weight: A	1,900 kg (4,188 lb)
Max wing loading: A	138.1 kg/m² (28.3 lb/sq ft)
U	196.4 kg/m² (40.2 lb/sq ft)
Max power loading: A	3.18 kg/kW (5.22 lb/shp)
U	4.52 kg/kW (7.42 lb/shp)

PERFORMANCE (at appropriate max T-O weight, ISA, propeller speed 2,000 rpm):

Max permissible diving speed: A, U
Mach 0.73 (360 knots; 667 km/h; 414 mph EAS)
Max operating speed: A, U
Mach 0.68 (320 knots; 593 km/h; 368 mph EAS)
Max level speed:
A at S/L 270 knots (500 km/h; 311 mph)
A at 6,100 m (20,000 ft)
300 knots (556 km/h; 345 mph)
Manoeuvring speed:
A 210 knots (389 km/h; 242 mph) EAS
U 200 knots (370 km/h; 230 mph) EAS
Max speed with flaps and/or landing gear down:
A and U 150 knots (278 km/h; 172 mph) EAS
Stalling speed, engine idling:
A, flaps and landing gear up
79 knots (147 km/h; 91 mph) EAS
U, flaps and landing gear down
93 knots (172 km/h; 107 mph) EAS

A, flaps and landing gear down
        70 knots (130 km/h; 81 mph) EAS
U, flaps and landing gear down
        86 knots (159 km/h; 99 mph) EAS

Max rate of climb at S/L: A	1,250 m (4,100 ft)/min
Time to 4,575 m (15,000 ft): A	4 min 30 s
Max operating altitude	7,620 m (25,000 ft)
Service ceiling	12,200 m (40,000 ft)
T-O run at S/L: A	227 m (745 ft)
T-O to 15 m (50 ft) at S/L: A	372 m (1,220 ft)
Landing from 15 m (50 ft) at S/L: A	538 m (1,765 ft)

Landing run at S/L:
    A (normal braking action)   417 m (1,368 ft)
Max range at cruise power at 7,620 m (25,000 ft), 5% fuel
    plus 20 min reserves   887 nm (1,642 km; 1,020 miles)
Endurance (typical mission power settings)
    2 sorties of 1 h duration plus 20 min reserves

g limits: A	+7/−3.5
U	+4.5/−2.25

Artist's impression of the Pilatus PC-12 pressurised light transport

PILATUS PC-12

Pilatus announced its plan to develop a single-turboprop, pressurised, fast utility aircraft at the NBAA Show in October 1989, when it had already completed 60 per cent of full-scale engineering development. The company was looking for risk-sharing partners in the programme, but was still continuing alone during early 1990, intending to fly the first of two prototypes in December 1990 and gain FAR Part 23 Amendment 36 certification in early 1992. The power plant is the specially developed P&WC PT6A-67B flat rated to 895 kW (1,200 shp) up to about 4,572 m (15,000 ft).

In terms of capacity, speed and economy, the PC-12 represents strong competition for the stretched Federal Express Cessna 208B Caravan I freighter and the Beech King Air 200 business aircraft, respectively in its **PC-12F** freighter and **PC-12P** passenger versions. Other possible missions include medevac, surveillance, border patrol, training and parachuting. About 60 per cent of sales are expected to come from North America.

The maximum cruising speed of 268 knots (497 km/h; 309 mph) at up to 25,000 ft (7,620 m), the required stalling speed of 61 knots (113 km/h; 71 mph) and the expected short-field performance are produced by the high aspect ratio, tapered wing with an aerofoil derived from the NASA GAWA-1 and fitted with Fowler flaps extending over 67 per cent of the span.

The T tail keeps the tailplane clear of propeller slipstream and wing wake and easily compensates for the very wide CG range. It also avoids contact with loading vehicles. There is a large freight door aft, to port, and a separate airstair passenger door forward of the wing. The PC-12 will be cleared for single-pilot operation in IFR and have full de-icing on wings, tail, windscreen, propeller and engine intake. A three-axis autopilot and Bendix/King Gold Crown EFIS-based avionics will be standard.

TYPE: Single-turboprop, pressurised utility/business transport.

WINGS: Conventional two-spar all metal structure with internal fuel tankage. Aerofoil derived from NASA GAWA-1. Dihedral from roots. Fowler flaps over 67 per cent of trailing-edge. CG range 25 to 46 per cent MAC at 4,000 kg (8,818 lb).

FUSELAGE: Oval section with flat floor from bulkhead behind flight deck to aft end of rear freight door.

TAIL UNIT: T tail with pivoting tailplane for trimming. Fin and rudder extend below rear fuselage. Rudder has trim tab.

LANDING GEAR: Hydraulically retractable tricycle type, with single low pressure mainwheels and single nosewheel. Propeller ground clearance maintained with nose leg compressed and nosewheel tyre flat. Main legs retract inward into wings and nose leg rearward under flight deck.

POWER PLANT: One 1,327 kW (1,780 shp) P&WC PT6A-67B turboprop, flat rated to 895 kW (1,200 shp) for T-O; 746 kW (1,000 shp) for climb and cruise. Hartzell four-blade composite propeller turning at 1,700 rpm. Usable fuel 1,514 litres (400 US gallons; 333 Imp gallons) in wings. Single-point pressure refuelling optional.

ACCOMMODATION: Two-seat flight deck: aircraft to be approved for single pilot, but dual controls and second flight instrument panel optional. Forward airstair passenger door and upward opening rear freight door standard. Pressurised to 0.38 bars (5.5 lb/sq in) differential giving 2,440 m (8,000 ft) cabin altitude at 7,620 m (25,000 ft). Limit of nine passengers under FAR 23 or business layout for six with toilet.

SYSTEMS: No firm details given at time of going to press except that de-icing includes pneumatic boots on wings and tail, electric protection for windscreen and propeller and engine bleed air for engine intake.

AVIONICS: Three-axis autopilot and Bendix/King EFIS-based IFR package as standard equipment.

DIMENSIONS, EXTERNAL:

Wing span	13.78 m (45 ft 2½ in)
Wing aspect ratio	8.4
Length overall	13.954 m (45 ft 9½ in)
Tailplane span	5.15 m (16 ft 10¾ in)
Wheel track	4.53 m (14 ft 10½ in)
Wheelbase	3.48 m (11 ft 5 in)
Propeller diameter	2.67 m (8 ft 9 in)
Passenger door: Height	1.34 m (4 ft 4¾ in)
Width	0.62 m (2 ft 0½ in)
Cargo door: Height	1.36 m (4 ft 5½ in)
Width	1.32 m (4 ft 4 in)

DIMENSIONS, INTERNAL (PC-12F except where indicated):

Cabin: Length, excl flight deck	5.16 m (16 ft 11 in)
Max width	1.51 m (4 ft 11½ in)
Floor width	1.26 m (4 ft 1½ in)
Height	1.45 m (4 ft 9 in)
Usable cargo volume	9.24 m³ (326.3 cu ft)
Baggage compartment (PC-12P)	1.12 m³ (39.5 cu ft)

WEIGHTS:

Weight empty: PC-12F	2,183 kg (4,813 lb)
PC-12P	2,386 kg (5,260 lb)
Max payload: PC-12F	1,400 kg (3,086 lb)
PC-12P	1,150 kg (2,535 lb)
Max ramp weight	4,020 kg (8,862 lb)
Max T-O weight	4,000 kg (8,818 lb)
Max landing weight	3,800 kg (8,377 lb)
Max zero fuel weight	3,700 kg (8,157 lb)

PERFORMANCE (estimated):

Max cruising speed at 7,620 m (25,000 ft)	268 knots (497 km/h; 309 mph)
Stalling speed, landing configuration	61 knots (113 km/h; 71 mph)
Max operating altitude	7,620 m (25,000 ft)
Max rate of climb at S/L	625 m (2,050 ft)/min
T-O to 15 m (50 ft)	595 m (1,952 ft)
Landing from 15 m (50 ft)	490 m (1,608 ft)
Max IFR range, 45 min reserves	1,600 nm (2,965 km; 1,842 miles)

Pilatus PC-12 pressurised light utility and business transport *(Pilot Press)*

SWISS FEDERAL AIRCRAFT FACTORY (F+W)

EIDGENÖSSISCHES FLUGZEUGWERK— FABRIQUE FÉDÉRALE D'AVIONS— FABBRICA FEDERALE DI AEROPLANI

CH-6032 Emmen

Telephone: 41 (41) 59 41 11

Telex: 868 505 FWE CH

Fax: 41 (41) 55 25 88

MANAGING DIRECTOR: Hansjürg Kobelt

F+W is the Swiss government's official aircraft establishment for research, development, production, maintenance and modification of military aircraft and guided missile systems. It employs about 800 people in its works at Emmen, which cover 140,000 m² (1,506,946 sq ft). Research and development are divided among four departments: aerodynamics and thermodynamics, with appropriate test facilities which include four wind tunnels for speeds of up to Mach 4-5, test cells for piston engines and turbojets (with or without afterburners), all equipped with computerised data acquisition and processing; structural and systems engineering for aircraft, helicopters and space hardware, with a speciality in fatigue analysis and testing of entire aircraft structures; electronics and missile systems, covering all system aspects of aircraft and helicopter avionics, missiles and RPVs; and prototype fabrication, flight test, instrumentation, and system and environmental testing.

The production department covers the whole field of production capabilities, from mechanical and sheet metal parts to composite parts and subassemblies (including leading-edge slats for the McDonnell Douglas MD-80 series and wingtips for the Airbus A320); electronics, electrical, electro-mechanical and electro-optical subassemblies; final assembly of missiles, missile systems, aircraft and helicopters. Recent major activities have included licence manufacture of aircraft, helicopters and missile systems, and fabrication of all shrouds for the Ariane and Titan 3 space launchers. Nineteen of the 20 BAe Hawk Mk 66s ordered for the Swiss Air Force are being assembled by F+W.

F+W is general contractor for full licence production of the MDAC Dragon missile, completed a similar programme for the Rapier missile in 1987, began one for the TOW anti-tank missile in 1986 and one for the Stinger anti-aircraft missile in 1989. Missiles are assembled and tested at F+W and delivered to the Swiss government.

F+W conducts wind tunnel tests for foreign aircraft manufacturers, ground transportation developers and users, and for the building industry. It develops and integrates internal stores and performs other modification work on military aircraft, including, currently, adding canard surfaces to Swiss Air Force Mirages. Subsonic wind tunnel tests have been made, and appropriate models built, of the Hermès spacecraft.

F+W proprietary products include a low-level dispenser bombing system and acoustic systems for failure and flight envelope warning; all-electronic linear angle of attack and g indicators; scoring indicators for air-to-air or ground-to-air shooting, with a microcomputer based ground station; multi-component strain gauge balances for testing purposes, covering forces from a few hundred grammes to several tons; water separators for aircraft conditioning; and POHWARO hot water rockets. (Details of these rockets can be found in the 1977-78 *Jane's*.) Co-operative development led to the Farner KZD 85 target drone described in the RPVs & Targets section of the 1987-88 *Jane's*, and F+W has since developed the air vehicle and catapult launcher of a new reconnaissance/aerial survey mini-RPV system known as the Ranger. Services are also offered for environmental testing, especially on F+W's own designed and proven test installation for high-shock long-duration tests.

F+W MIRAGE IMPROVEMENT PROGRAMME

The Swiss government approved funding in 1985 to retrofit Swiss Air Force Mirage IIIs. There are 30 III-S, 18 III-RS, two III-BS and two III-DS. Main items are a fixed canard and strake on each side of the nose. These improve manoeuvrability and increase stability in yaw near the upper limit of the flight envelope.

Other improvements include new audible warning and visual angle of attack monitoring systems, to alert the pilot when approaching limits of the flight envelope;

BAe Hawk Mk 66, of which 19 are being assembled by F + W at Emmen in 1990-91

Martin-Baker Mk 6 zero/zero ejection seats in place of the present Mk 4 seats; addition of infra-red and passive/active ECM; provision of more powerful VHF radios; wing refurbishing; ability to carry two underwing 500 litre (132 US gallon; 110 Imp gallon) drop tanks and a 730 litre (193

US gallon; 160.5 Imp gallon) centreline tank; mounting of improved blast deflectors for the two internal guns, to allow firing at high angles of attack; and a new camouflage paint scheme. The retrofit programme is to continue into the 1990s.

TAIWAN

AIDC

AERO INDUSTRY DEVELOPMENT CENTER

PO Box 90008-10, Taichung, Taiwan 40722
Telephone: 886 (4) 2523051 and 2523052
Telex: 51140 AIDC
OTHER WORKS: Kang-Shan
DIRECTOR: Dr Hsichun M. Hua
DEPUTY DIRECTORS:
    Dr Shih-sen Wang (Research and Engineering)
    Y. L. Chang (Manufacturing)

The AIDC was established on 1 March 1969 as a successor to the Bureau of Aircraft Industry (BAI), which was formed in 1946 in Nanjing and moved to Taiwan in 1948. AIDC now employs more than 5,000 people, and is a subsidiary of the Chung Shan Institute of Science and Technology.

Between 1969 and 1976, the AIDC produced in Taiwan 118 Bell UH-1H (Bell Model 205) helicopters under licence for the Chinese Nationalist Army. From 1968 to 1974 it built a PL-1A prototype and 55 PL-1B Chienshou trainers (1975-76 *Jane's*), based on the US Pazmany PL-1, for the Nationalist Air Force. From 1974 to 1986 the AIDC was engaged in licence building 248 Northrop F-5E Tiger II tactical fighters (see 1986-87 *Jane's*) and 36 two-seat F-5Fs for the Chinese Nationalist Air Force.

The AIDC designed and produced the T-CH-1 turboprop basic trainer for the Chinese Nationalist Air Force (see 1981-82 *Jane's*). More recently, it has developed and produced the AT-3 twin-turbofan trainer, and completed several prototypes of the Ching-Kuo, an indigenously designed jet fighter.

AIDC CHING-KUO

Taiwan's IDF (indigenous defensive fighter) programme is devoted to the development of an air superiority fighter intended primarily to replace about 100 F/TF-104G Starfighters of the Chinese Nationalist Air Force in the middle to late 1990s. The need for an indigenous programme followed the US government's embargo on the sale to Taiwan of the Northrop F-20 Tigershark or any comparably advanced fighter. The same restrictions did not apply, however, to US technical assistance, and since May 1982, when the concept of an indigenous type was initiated, several US aerospace companies have collaborated with the AIDC in developing its own aircraft to meet the requirement.

Under the collective project name An Hsiang (Safe Flight), four subsidiary programmes were undertaken, including one named Tien Chien (Sky Sword) to develop the aircraft's primary missile armament. The airframe design was developed, with the collaboration of General Dynamics, under the title Ying Yang (Soaring Eagle), while the Yun Han (Cloud Man) programme involved the Chung Shan Institute of Science and Technology, of which AIDC is a subsidiary, working with Garrett Turbine Engine Co to develop an afterburning version of the latter's TFE731 turbofan engine. The avionics for the aircraft are being acquired and integrated under the leadership of Smiths Industries Aerospace Group Inc under the codename Tien Lei (Sky Thunder). In 1988, the aircraft itself was named after the late President of Taiwan, Chiang Ching-Kuo.

Four prototypes of the Ching-Kuo have reportedly been authorised, and the first of these (77-8001) was rolled out on 10 December 1988. It made its first flight on 28 May 1989, but was seriously damaged during take-off for a demonstration on 29 October 1989. At least one more prototype had already flown by that date. The CNAF is

First prototype AIDC Ching-Kuo indigenous defensive fighter. Three were flying in mid 1990

AIDC Ching-Kuo fighter (two Garrett TFE1042-7 turbo-fans) *(Pilot Press)*

believed to have an eventual requirement for about 250-300 of these aircraft, to replace some of its Northrop F-5E/Fs as well as its F-104s; a proportion of these may be of a two-seat version, able to serve both as an operational trainer and in an anti-shipping role. Subject to successful completion of flight testing, production of the Ching-Kuo was intended to begin in 1990.

TYPE: Single-seat air defence fighter.

AIRFRAME: Shoulder-wing monoplane, of blended wing/body design. Moderately sweptback wings, extended forward at wingroot leading-edges; sweptback fin and rudder; fuselage mounted all-moving tailplane. Wings have full span flaperons and leading-edge manoeuvring flaps. Prototypes are of metal construction, but possibility of later introduction of composites has been suggested.

LANDING GEAR: Retractable tricycle type of Menasco design, with single wheel and oleo-pneumatic shock absorber on each unit. Nose unit retracts forward, main units inward/upward into engine air intake trunks.

POWER PLANT: Two Garrett TFE1042-7 turbofans side by side in rear fuselage, each developing 21.44 kN (4,820 lb st) dry and 37.10 kN (8,340 lb st) with afterburning. Elliptical air intakes, with splitter plates, mounted low on centre-fuselage beneath wingroot extensions.

ACCOMMODATION: Pilot only, on Martin-Baker Mk 12 zero/zero ejection seat. One-piece bubble canopy, hinged at rear and opening upward. Cockpit pressurised and air-conditioned.

SYSTEMS: AiResearch environmental control system. GEC Astronics fly by wire control system. Westinghouse variable-speed constant-frequency electrical power generating system.

AVIONICS AND EQUIPMENT: Golden Dragon 53 (GD-53) multi-mode pulse-Doppler radar, a modified version of the GE Aerospace AN/APG-67 (V) incorporating also some elements of the Westinghouse AN/APG-66, has a range of approx 81 nm (150 km; 93 miles), capability for air and sea search, and lookdown/shootdown capability. Litton (LN-39?) inertial navigation system. Bendix/King cockpit displays (three multi-function and one head-up). Sidestick controller.

ARMAMENT: One 20 mm M61A Vulcan cannon in starboard side of fuselage, beneath extended wingroot leading-edge. Photo-Sonics gun camera. Six attachment points for external stores: two under fuselage, one under each wing and one at each wingtip. Prototype at rollout shown with four Sky Sword I short-range infra-red homing air-to-air missiles (two underwing and two at wingtips). Other combinations may include two medium-range Sky Sword II air-to-air missiles under fuselage in addition to four Sky Sword Is; or three Hsiung Feng II anti-shipping missiles (under wings and fuselage) plus two wingtip Sky Sword Is. In attack role, underwing and underfuselage hardpoints could be occupied by Maverick (or similar) missiles, single or cluster bombs, or rocket pods.

DIMENSIONS, WEIGHTS AND PERFORMANCE:
No details yet available, but believed to be similar dimensionally to General Dynamics F-16 and capable of max level speed of about Mach 1.2.

AIDC AT-3

In July 1975, AIDC was awarded a contract to design and develop prototypes of a new basic and advanced military jet training aircraft, designated XAT-3. Construction of two prototypes (0801 and 0802) began in January 1978, and these flew for the first time on 16 September 1980 and 30 October 1981 respectively. Following receipt of a contract for 60 production aircraft, AIDC began the manufacture of these, under the CAF designation AT-3, in March 1982. The first production aircraft (0803) made its initial flight on 6 February 1984. Deliveries began in the following month, and 56 had been delivered by the beginning of 1989.

According to 1988 press reports, the AT-3 has the CNAF name Tsu-Chiang; and a single-seat A-3 version named Lui-Meng is now also in production. The single-seater was said to have a max external stores load of 2,721 kg (6,000 lb), including Sidewinder air-to-air missiles on wingtip launch rails, and to be intended for both ground attack and maritime strike roles.

In 1989, two AT-3s were being upgraded to give them a close air support combat capability. Lear Siegler International is prime contractor for this programme, which includes installation of a Westinghouse APG-66 radar and fire control system. Both aircraft were flying early in 1990, but no decision on modifying the remaining AT-3s had been announced.

The following description applies to the standard production AT-3:

TYPE: Tandem two-seat twin-turbofan military trainer.

WINGS: Cantilever low-wing monoplane of supercritical section. Thickness/chord ratio 10 per cent. Dihedral 0° 46′. Incidence 1° 30′. Sweepback at quarter-chord 7° 20′. One-piece carry-through wing, with a machined torsion box, attached to fuselage by six bolts. Multi-spar light alloy structure, with heavy plate machined skin. Hydraulically powered light alloy honeycomb sealed-gap ailerons. Electrically operated light alloy single-slotted trailing-edge flaps. No anti-icing system.

FUSELAGE: Light alloy semi-monocoque basic structure, with steel, magnesium and graphite/epoxy used in certain areas. Built in three sections: forward fuselage, including cockpit; centre fuselage, including nacelles; and rear fuselage, including vertical and horizontal tail assembly. Two electrically controlled hydraulically actuated airbrakes, of laminated graphite/epoxy construction, mounted on fuselage undersurface forward of mainwheel wells. Fail-safe structure in pressurised cockpit section.

TAIL UNIT: Cantilever all-metal structure, integral with rear fuselage. One-piece all-moving tailplane; incidence varied by tandem hydraulic actuator. Dual hydraulic actuators for rudder, with yaw stability augmentation. No trim tabs.

LANDING GEAR: Hydraulically retractable tricycle type, with single wheel on each unit. Main units retract inward into fuselage, nosewheel forward. Oleo-pneumatic shock absorber in each unit. Two-position extending nose leg increases static angle of attack by 3° 30′, to reduce T-O run, and is shortened automatically during retraction. Emergency extension by gravity. Mainwheels and tyres size 24 × 8.00-13, pressure 8.96 bars (130 lb/sq in). Hydraulically steerable nose unit, with wheel and tyre size 18 × 6.50-8, pressure 5.51 bars (80 lb/sq in). All-metal multi-disc brakes.

POWER PLANT: Two Garrett TFE731-2-2L non-afterburning turbofans (each 15.57 kN; 3,500 lb st), installed in nacelle on each side of fuselage. Inclined ram air intakes, each with splitter plate, abreast of rear cockpit. Engine starting

by onboard battery or ground power. All fuel carried in fuselage, in two equal-size rubber impregnated nylon bladder tanks, with combined capacity of 1,630 litres (430.6 US gallons; 358.5 Imp gallons). Two independent fuel systems, one for each engine, with crossfeed to allow fuel from either or both systems to be fed to either or both engines. Pressure fuelling point forward of, and below, port air intake for internal and external tanks. A 568 litre (150 US gallon; 125 Imp gallon) auxiliary drop tank can be carried on each inboard underwing pylon. Oil capacity 5.7 litres (1.5 US gallons; 1.25 Imp gallons) total, 1.9 litres (0.5 US gallon; 0.42 Imp gallon) usable. Fire warning and extinguishing systems for each engine bay.

ACCOMMODATION: Crew of two in tandem on zero/zero ejection (through canopy) seats, under individual manually operated canopies which open sideways to starboard. Crew separated by internal windscreen. Independent miniature detonation cord (MDC) system to break each canopy for ground and in-flight emergency egress. MDC can be operated from outside cockpit on ground. Rear seat elevated 30 cm (12 in). Dual controls standard.

SYSTEMS: AiResearch bootstrap air cycle environmental control system, for cockpit air-conditioning and pressurisation (max differential 0.34 bars; 5 lb/sq in), canopy seal, demisting, and pressurisation of g suits, hydraulic reservoirs and external fuel tanks. Two independent hydraulic systems, pressure 207 bars (3,000 lb/sq in), with engine driven pumps (flow rate 34.4 litres; 9.09 US gallons; 7.57 Imp gallons/min). Air type reservoir, pressurised at 2.41 bars (35 lb/sq in). Flight control hydraulic system provides power only for operation of primary flying control surfaces. Utility system serves primary flying control surfaces, landing gear, landing gear doors, airbrakes, wheel brakes, nosewheel steering, and stability augmentation system. Primary electrical power supplied by two 28V 12kW DC starter/generators, one on each engine. One 40Ah nickel-cadmium battery for engine starting. Two static inverters supply AC power at 400Hz. External DC power socket on starboard side of centre fuselage. Hydraulic and electrical systems can be sustained by either engine. Liquid oxygen system, capacity 5 litres (1.3 US gallons; 1.1 Imp gallons), for crew.

AVIONICS AND EQUIPMENT: Most radio and nav equipment located in large avionics bays in forward fuselage. Standard avionics include UHF com, intercom, IFF/SIF, Tacan, panel mounted VOR/ILS/marker beacon indicator, attitude and heading reference system and angle of attack system, plus full blind-flying instrumentation. Wide range of optional avionics available.

ARMAMENT AND OPERATIONAL EQUIPMENT: Manually adjustable gunsight and camera in forward cockpit, for armament training. Large weapons bay beneath rear cockpit can house variety of stores, including quick-change semi-recessed machine-gun packs. Disposable weapons can be carried on a centreline pylon (stressed for 907 kg; 2,000 lb load), two inboard underwing pylons (each 635 kg; 1,400 lb and capable of accepting triple ejector racks), two outboard underwing pylons (each 272 kg; 600 lb), and wingtip launch rails (each of 91 kg; 200 lb capacity), subject to a max external stores load of 2,721

AIDC AT-3 tandem two-seat trainers (two Garrett TFE731 turbofans)

kg (6,000 lb). Weapons that can be carried include GP, SE, cluster and fire bombs; SUU-25A/A, -25C/A and -25E/A flare dispensers; LAU-3/A, -3A/A, -3B/A, -10/A, -10A/A, -60/A, -68A/A and -68B/A rocket launchers; wingtip infra-red air-to-air missiles; and rocket pods, practice bombs, and bomb or rocket training dispensers. The aircraft can also be equipped with an A/A37U-15TTS aerial target system, carried on the centreline and outboard pylons.

DIMENSIONS, EXTERNAL:

Wing span	10.46 m (34 ft 3¾ in)
Wing chord: at root	2.80 m (9 ft 2¼ in)
at tip	1.40 m (4 ft 7 in)
Wing aspect ratio	5.0
Length overall, incl nose probe	12.90 m (42 ft 4 in)
Height overall	4.36 m (14 ft 3¾ in)
Tailplane span	4.83 m (15 ft 10¼ in)
Wheel track	3.96 m (13 ft 0 in)
Wheelbase	5.49 m (18 ft 0 in)

AREAS:

Wings, gross	21.93 m² (236.05 sq ft)
Ailerons (total)	1.33 m² (14.32 sq ft)
Trailing-edge flaps (total)	2.53 m² (27.23 sq ft)
Fin	3.45 m² (37.14 sq ft)
Rudder	1.15 m² (12.38 sq ft)
Tailplane	5.02 m² (54.04 sq ft)

WEIGHTS AND LOADINGS:

Weight empty, equipped	3,855 kg (8,500 lb)
Max fuel: internal	1,270 kg (2,800 lb)
external	884 kg (1,950 lb)
Max external stores load	2,721 kg (6,000 lb)
Normal T-O weight:	
trainer, 'clean'	5,216 kg (11,500 lb)
Max T-O weight with external stores	
	7,938 kg (17,500 lb)
Max landing weight	7,360 kg (16,225 lb)
Max wing loading	362 kg/m² (74.14 lb/sq ft)
Max power loading	254.9 kg/kN (2.5 lb/lb st)

PERFORMANCE (at max T-O weight):

Max limiting Mach No.	1.05
Max level speed:	
at S/L	485 knots (898 km/h; 558 mph)
at 11,000 m (36,000 ft)	
	Mach 0.85 (488 knots; 904 km/h; 562 mph)
Max cruising speed at 11,000 m (36,000 ft)	
	Mach 0.83 (476 knots; 882 km/h; 548 mph)
Stalling speed:	
flaps and landing gear up	
	100 knots (185 km/h; 115 mph)
flaps and landing gear down	
	90 knots (167 km/h; 104 mph)
Max rate of climb at S/L	3,078 m (10,100 ft)/min
Service ceiling	14,625 m (48,000 ft)
T-O run	458 m (1,500 ft)
T-O to 15 m (50 ft)	671 m (2,200 ft)
Landing from 15 m (50 ft)	945 m (3,100 ft)
Landing run	671 m (2,200 ft)
Range with max internal fuel	
	1,230 nm (2,279 km; 1,416 miles)
Endurance with max internal fuel	3 h 12 min

THAILAND

IAC

INTERNATIONAL AIRCRAFT COMPANY LTD

DIRECTOR: Danai Phasatanan

At the beginning of 1988 IAC sought Thai government financial support to assemble the US RotorWay Exec two-seat light helicopter (which see) at the factory of the

Siam International Co. It had already imported five Execs in CKD kit form, and two of them were delivered to the Thai Police Aviation Division.

IAC then developed a modified two-seat helicopter, known as the **E-Tan** (Wasp), based on the Exec. Powered by an aircooled 119 kW (160 hp) flat-four engine, the E-Tan was ground tested at Chulalongkorn University, Bangkok,

before making its first flight in early 1989. It was certificated in Thailand in early 1990. Ultimate production capacity is 10 a month. The RotorWay name is no longer used. Performance estimates include a cruising speed of 108 knots (200 km/h; 124 mph), S/L climb rate of 396 m (1,300 ft)/min, service ceiling of 3,960 m (13,000 ft), and max range of 234 nm (435 km; 270 miles).

RTAF (SWDC)
ROYAL THAI AIR FORCE (Science and Weapon Systems Development Centre)
Office of Aeronautical Engineering, Don Muang Air Base, Praholyothin Road, Bangkok 10220
Telephone: 66 (2) 531 1824 or 241 2885
DIRECTOR OF SWDC: Air Marshal Prasert Ratanakan
CHIEF DESIGNER: Gp Capt Preecha Wannabhoom

The Office of Aeronautical Engineering was set up in 1975, and has been responsible for all subsequent design activity. Its most ambitious product to date, the RTAF-5 turboprop trainer and FAC aircraft, was designed and built entirely in Thailand and made its first flight on 5 October 1984. A full description appeared in the 1986-87 and earlier editions.

RTAF (RFB) FANTRAINER 400 and 600
In 1984, the RTAF ordered 31 Fantrainer 400s and 16 Fantrainer 600s from RFB. One of each was delivered complete fitted with composite wings. The bare fuselages of another 15 Fantrainer 600s were delivered to Thailand and fitted there with composite wings bought from RFB. These 16 machines are established in service at the training base at Kampensaeng for RTAF pilot training, each aircraft flying an average of 50 hours per month. The RTAF was considering eliminating the intermediate training stage with Cessna T-37s before converting onto Northrop F-5s.

Production of the 400s began in 1986 with the design and manufacture of metal wings interchangeable with the German composite wings. The composite wing is 89 kg (196 lb) lighter. Incorporating centre fuselages sent from Germany, eight Fantrainer 400s had been completed by the end of 1989 and delivered to the RTAF for training flying instructors. Another 12 were to be assembled during 1990 and the final 11 during 1991, all with metal wings. The

RTAF metal winged Fantrainer 600 prototype

RTAF had not ordered composite replacement wings by April 1990. Neither was the additional batch of 15 armed Fantrainer 600s ordered. All Thai Fantrainers have the Yankee rocket-assisted escape system.

Three Fantrainer prototypes remain in Germany, two 600s and one 400, and one of them was chartered by Lufthansa for pilot training.

The description of the Fantrainer in the German section applies also to the RTAF aircraft, except as follows:
WINGS: Cantilever mid-wing monoplane. All-metal stressed skin structure, with two-spar wing box forming integral fuel tank in each wing. Wings are bolted to each other at centre-section and attached to fuselage by two barrel pins on main spar and two shear bolts on rear spar. Corrugated skins at wingroots, over mainwheel bays.

WEIGHTS:

Weight empty: 400	1,275 kg (2,811 lb)
600	1,325 kg (2,921 lb)
Max internal fuel: 400, 600	365 kg (805 lb)
Max T-O weight:	
400, Aerobatic	1,600 kg (3,527 lb)
400, Utility	1,820 kg (4,012 lb)
600, Aerobatic	1,650 kg (3,637 lb)
600, Utility	1,870 kg (4,122 lb)

PERFORMANCE (600 prototype at Utility max T-O weight):

Never-exceed speed	220 knots (408 km/h; 253 mph)
Cruising speed (70% power) at 915 m (3,000 ft)	
	186 knots (345 km/h; 214 mph)
Stalling speed, 60° flap	82 knots (152 km/h; 95 mph)
Rate of climb at 610 m (2,000 ft)	579 m (1,900 ft)/min

TURKEY

KOC HOLDING
Istanbul

Through its Geneva-based Koc trading company Kofisa Trading SA, Koc Holdings formally agreed with Agusta to form a joint company in Turkey to promote the public and private aerospace sectors. Primary objective would be to start a Turkish helicopter industry, possibly providing the A 129 Mangusta or a licensed Bell 412A with uprated transmission designed to compete with the Sikorsky UH-60. In spite of the agreement, the 40 Agusta/SIAI-Marchetti SF-260Ds ordered for the Turkish Air Force in March 1990 are to be assembled by TAI.

TAI
TUSAŞ AEROSPACE INDUSTRIES INC (TUSAŞ Havacilik ve Uzay Sanayi A.Ş.)
PO Box 18, 06690 Kavaklidere, Ankara
Telephone: 90 (4) 3242140
Telex: 44640 TAI TR
Fax: 90 (4) 3244807
MANAGING DIRECTOR: J. R. Jones
F-16 PROGRAMME DIRECTOR: Kaya Ergenç

TAI is a majority owned Turkish company made up of Turkish (51 per cent) and American (49 per cent) partners and was formed on 15 May 1984. The major percentage shareholders are Turkish Aerospace Industries Inc (49) and General Dynamics (42); other shareholders are General Electric (7), the Turkish Armed Forces Foundation (1.9) and the Turkish Air League (0.1).

Two of the management positions are currently filled by General Dynamics executives and within a year these posts will be taken over by Turks. The objectives of the company are to construct an aircraft facility capable of manufacturing modern weapon systems, helicopters and aerospace vehicles, modernise aircraft, perform research and development work in the field of aerospace and finally to design, develop and manufacture total weapon systems for the Turkish armed forces.

TAI is under contract to General Dynamics to assemble and deliver 152 of the 160 F-16C and D aircraft ordered by the Turkish Air Force (the Peace Onyx programme), and to fabricate and assemble rear and centre fuselages and wings of F-16 aircraft for the US Air Force. The first F-16C was delivered to the Turkish Air Force on 30 November 1987. By the end of 1989, 35 aircraft had been delivered, a further 15 were on the assembly line or in flight status, and all work was continuing ahead of schedule. The aircraft produced at TAI facilities meet all the specifications and quality standards of the US Air Force.

TAI facilities cover an area of 2.3 million m² (24,754,900 sq ft) with a factory floor area of over 100,000 m² (1,076,300 sq ft), consisting of production facilities, administrative building and housing and social facilities including 800 apartments, medical centre, school and shopping centre. The production facilities include fabrication and assembly, chemical processing, paint shops, fuel calibration and flight operations buildings and are equipped with high-technology machinery and equipment capable of producing and assembling modern aircraft.

The manufacturing and assembly building covers 62,500 m² (672,687 sq ft) under one roof. The fabrication area includes a numerical control machining centre, complete forming capability including bladder press, detail fabrication shops, harness manufacture, hydraulic tubing and one of the largest chemical processing and chemical milling buildings of its kind. TAI also has one of the most up-to-date computer capabilities in the world.

TAI assembled General Dynamics F-16Cs over the Tusas factory

The company had more than 1,800 employees by the end of 1989 and this figure was to expand to 2,000 in 1990. There is a modern training centre for electrical, hydraulic, airframe, avionics and other aircraft-related skills. General Dynamics had trained 346 Turkish employees at its Fort Worth Division, and another 742 have been trained in the TAI Training Centre in Mürted.

Research and development activities have already begun. The company is involved in preliminary work on design and development of unmanned air vehicles and also participates in the development of the Future Large Aircraft (Euroflag) with six other European nations.

UNION OF SOVIET SOCIALIST REPUBLICS

ANTONOV
OLEG K. ANTONOV DESIGN BUREAU

Kiev 252062
Telephone: 7 (-) 442 6124
GENERAL DESIGNER: Pyotr Vasilyevich Balabuyev
DEPUTY CHIEF DESIGNER: Anatoli G. Bulanenko
ASSISTANT CHIEF DESIGNER: Ye. D. Goloborodjko
DIRECTOR GENERAL, KIEV WORKS: A. M. Malachine

This design bureau, based at Kiev, is named after its founder, Oleg Konstantinovich Antonov who, after establishing his reputation with a series of successful glider and sailplane designs, became one of the Soviet Union's leading designers of transport aircraft, particularly those types intended for short field operation. He died on 4 April 1984, at the age of 78.

Aircraft in current production at Kiev are the An-32 and An-124. Manufacture of the An-72/74 series is centred at Kharkov. Wings for the An-124 are built in Tashkent and airlifted to Kiev for final assembly. The very large An-225 is expected to be built at Kiev, where the prototype was assembled and first flown. The small An-2 and An-28 are manufactured in Poland by PZL Mielec.

ANTONOV An-2
NATO reporting name: Colt

Following manufacture of the An-2M specialised agricultural version of this large single-engined biplane, in the mid-sixties, production of the An-2 came to an end at Kiev in the Soviet Union. Details of the various versions that were built can be found in the 1971-72 *Jane's*.

Several versions of the An-2 continued in production under licence in Poland in 1989 (see WSK-PZL Mielec entry). Others have been built at Harbin and Shijiazhuang, in China (see SAP entry), under the Chinese designation Y-5.

ANTONOV An-3

It was first reported in the Spring of 1972 that the Antonov design bureau was engaged on design studies for a turboprop development of the An-2 biplane (see WSK-PZL Mielec in Polish section). Designated An-3, the aircraft was intended specifically for agricultural duties and was then expected to compete with the Polish turbofan engined WSK-Mielec M-15 as the next generation agricultural aircraft for use throughout the countries of eastern Europe and the Soviet Union.

At the 1979 Paris Air Show, Mr Oleg Antonov emphasised his continued interest in agricultural aircraft, and confirmed that a prototype of the the An-3 had been produced by retrofitting an An-2 with a 706 kW (946 shp) Glushenkov TVD-10 turboprop, driving a slow turning large-diameter three-blade propeller optimised for an aircraft operating speed of 75-97 knots (140-180 km/h; 87-112 mph). He added that an important feature was the ability of the turboprop to ensure adequate cockpit air-conditioning, with clean air at 18-20°C, during operation in ambient temperatures of 40-45°C.

A photograph of the An-3 prototype (SSSR-30576) under test was released to the East European press in 1979 and was reproduced in the 1982-83 and previous editions of *Jane's*. The production standard aircraft shown in an accompanying illustration differs externally from the standard An-2 in having a longer and slimmer nose, housing initially a 1,081 kW (1,450 shp) Glushenkov TVD-20 turboprop, and with short plugs inserted immediately fore and aft of the wings to lengthen the fuselage. The cockpit is further forward, and is sealed and air-conditioned. Instrumentation, electrical and fuel systems are all new, and the former multi-panelled starboard cockpit windows are replaced by a single large blister window. When equipped for agricultural duties, access to the cockpit is via a small door on the port side. When the aircraft is to be used only for transport duties, this door is omitted and access is via the main cabin door and through the airtight door leading from the cabin to the flight deck.

The An-3 can be equipped for either dusting or spraying. The chemical spraytank has a capacity of 2,200 litres (581 US gallons; 484 Imp gallons), representing an increase of more than 50 per cent over that of the An-2; the cost of spraying each hectare of land is reduced by 25 to 30 per cent. A total of 1,200 litres (317 US gallons; 264 Imp gallons) of fuel is carried in six tanks in the upper wings.

State trials of the An-3 were conducted with renewed urgency in 1982-83, under the project leadership of Mr V. J. Zadrozhnyi, following rejection of the M-15 in the Soviet Union. Although plans were announced for the large-scale conversion of An-2s to An-3 standard, there has been no evidence of their implementation. Instead, it became known in 1988 that a new turboprop had been developed for the An-3 in the shape of the 1,140 kW (1,528 shp) Glushenkov TVD-1500.

Six payload-to-height records were set by an An-3 in 1985. On 12 December, piloted by Vladimir Lysenko, it lifted a record 2,583 kg (5,694 lb) to 2,000 m and set two further Class C1f records by climbing to 6,100 m (20,013 ft) with a payload of 2,000 kg, qualifying also for the record with 1,000 kg. On the following day, piloted by Sergei Gorbik, it lifted 2,375 kg (5,236 lb) to 2,000 m and set two further Class C1e records for 1,000 and 2,000 kg lifted to 6,150 m (20,177 ft).

Antonov An-3 agricultural biplane (Glushenkov TVD-20 turboprop) *(Robert Senkowski)*

Antonov An-3 turboprop agricultural aircraft, with original flight deck side windows *(Pilot Press)*

Antonov An-12BP ('Cub') four-turboprop general purpose military transport aircraft *(Pilot Press)*

DIMENSIONS, EXTERNAL: As for An-2, except:
Length overall	14.33 m (47 ft 0 in)

WEIGHT:
Max T-O weight	5,800 kg (12,787 lb)

PERFORMANCE:
Normal cruising speed	97 knots (180 km/h; 112 mph)
Rate of climb at S/L with max payload	240 m (785 ft)/min

ANTONOV An-12
NATO reporting name: Cub

More than 900 An-12 medium-range freighters were built for military and civil use before production ended in the Soviet Union in 1973. Versions continuing in service with the Soviet air forces, and identified by NATO reporting names, are as follows:

Electronic intelligence version of the Antonov An-12 known to NATO as 'Cub-B', with investigating F-104G of Royal Norwegian Air Force

Cub. Entered service as standard Soviet paratroop and freight transport in 1959. Replacement with Il-76s began in 1974, and fewer than 150 'Cubs', designated **An-12BP** in the USSR, now equip Military Transport Aviation (VTA) units located primarily along the southern and far eastern periphery of the Soviet Union. Up to 200 more serve in Soviet air armies and air forces of military districts and groups of forces. Another 120 An-12s are operated nominally by Aeroflot, forming an immediately available reserve military transport force. 'Cub' has a tail gunner's position. In the commercial production version, first demonstrated at the 1965 Paris Air Show, the turret is replaced by a streamline fairing.

China is building, at the Hanzhong factory of the Shaanxi Aircraft Company, its own version of the An-12BP. Known as the **SAC Y-8**, this is listed in the Chinese section, together with a specialised maritime surveillance version designated **Y-8MPA**.

Cub-A. Electronic intelligence (elint) version. Generally similar to basic 'Cub' but with blade aerials on front fuselage, aft of flight deck, and other changes.

Cub-B. Conversion of 'Cub' transport for elint duties with Soviet Naval Air Force. Examples photographed over international waters by the crews of Swedish and Norwegian combat aircraft each had two additional radomes under the forward and centre fuselage, plus other antennae. About 10 produced.

Cub-C. ECM variant carrying several tons of electrical generation, distribution and control gear in cabin, and palletised jammers for at least five wavebands faired into belly, plus ECM dispensers. Glazed nose and undernose radar of transport retained. An ogival 'solid' fuselage tailcone, housing electronic equipment, is fitted in place of the usual gun position.

Cub-D. ECM variant. Equipment differs from that of 'Cub-C', to handle different active countermeasures duties. About 20 'Cub-C and D' aircraft are believed to serve with the Soviet Navy.

The following abbreviated details apply to the standard Soviet built military An-12BP transport. A full description can be found in the 1979-80 *Jane's*.

TYPE: Four-engined cargo transport.

POWER PLANT: Four 2,942 kW (3,945 ehp) Ivchenko AI-20K turboprops, driving AV-68 four-blade reversible-pitch propellers. All fuel in 22 bag tanks in wings, total normal capacity 13,900 litres (3,672 US gallons; 3,058 Imp gallons). Max capacity 18,100 litres (4,781 US gallons; 3,981 Imp gallons).

ACCOMMODATION: Pilot and co-pilot side by side on flight deck. Engineer's station on starboard side, behind co-pilot. Radio operator in well behind pilot, facing outward. Navigator in glazed nose compartment. Rear gunner in tail turret. Crew door on port side forward of wing. No integral rear loading ramp. Access to freight hold via large door under upswept rear fuselage, comprising two longitudinal halves which can be hinged upward inside cabin to provide access for direct loading of freight from trucks. Undersurface of fuselage aft of this door is formed by a further, rear-hinged, door which retracts upward into fuselage to facilitate loading and unloading. Equipped to carry 90 troops or 60 paratroops, all of whom can be despatched in under one minute, with rear door panels folded upward.

ARMAMENT: Two 23 mm NR-23 guns in tail turret.

DIMENSIONS, EXTERNAL:

Wing span	38.00 m (124 ft 8 in)
Wing chord (mean)	3.452 m (11 ft 4 in)
Wing aspect ratio	11.85
Length overall	33.10 m (108 ft 7¼ in)
Height overall	10.53 m (34 ft 6½ in)
Tailplane span	12.20 m (40 ft 0¼ in)
Wheel track	5.42 m (17 ft 9½ in)
Wheelbase	10.82 m (35 ft 6 in)
Propeller diameter	4.50 m (14 ft 9 in)
Rear loading hatch: Length	7.70 m (25 ft 3 in)
Width	2.95 m (9 ft 8 in)

DIMENSIONS, INTERNAL:

Cargo hold: Length	13.50 m (44 ft 3½ in)
Max width	3.50 m (11 ft 5¾ in)
Max height	2.60 m (8 ft 6¼ in)
Volume	97.2 m³ (3,432.6 cu ft)

AREA:

Wings, gross	121.70 m² (1,310 sq ft)

WEIGHTS:

Weight empty	28,000 kg (61,730 lb)
Max payload	20,000 kg (44,090 lb)
Normal T-O weight	55,100 kg (121,475 lb)
Max T-O weight	61,000 kg (134,480 lb)

PERFORMANCE:

Max level speed	419 knots (777 km/h; 482 mph)
Max cruising speed	361 knots (670 km/h; 416 mph)
Min flying speed	88 knots (163 km/h; 101 mph)
Landing speed	108 knots (200 km/h; 124 mph)
Max rate of climb at S/L	600 m (1,970 ft)/min
Service ceiling	10,200 m (33,500 ft)
T-O run	700 m (2,300 ft)
Landing run	500 m (1,640 ft)
Range:	
with max payload	1,942 nm (3,600 km; 2,236 miles)
with max fuel	3,075 nm (5,700 km; 3,540 miles)

ANTONOV An-22 ANTHEUS
NATO reporting name: Cock

The prototype of this very large transport aircraft flew for the first time on 27 February 1965. About 45 production An-22s remain available to the Soviet air forces and Aeroflot, which uses the aircraft primarily for military support duties. Deliveries were completed during 1974. A structural description can be found in the 1982-83 and earlier editions.

One An-22 has been adapted to deliver the wings of production An-124 transports non-stop over the 1,693 nm (3,136 km; 1,949 mile) route from the Valery Chkalov plant in Tashkent, where they are built, to the assembly plant in Kiev. Each 23 tonne port or starboard wing is carried on a mount above the centre-section, in such a way that flexing of the An-22 in flight is not transmitted to the An-124 wing structure. Addition of a small central tail fin was the only modification needed to preserve the handling qualities of the An-22 when carrying a wing in this manner.

TYPE: Long-range heavy turboprop transport.

POWER PLANT: Four 11,185 kW (15,000 shp) Kuznetsov NK-12MA turboprops, each driving a pair of four-blade contra-rotating propellers.

ACCOMMODATION: Crew of five or six. Navigator's station in nose. Cabin for 28-29 passengers aft of flight deck, separated from main cabin by bulkhead containing two doors. Uninterrupted main cabin, with reinforced titanium floor, tiedown fittings and rear loading ramp. When ramp lowers, a large door which forms the underside of the rear fuselage retracts upward inside fuselage to permit easy loading of tall vehicles. Rails in roof of cabin for four travelling gantries continue rearward on underside of this door. Two winches, used in conjunction with the gantries, each have a capacity of 2,500 kg (5,500 lb). Door in each landing gear fairing, forward of wheels, for crew and passengers.

DIMENSIONS, EXTERNAL:

Wing span	64.40 m (211 ft 4 in)
Length overall	approx 57.92 m (190 ft 0 in)
Height overall	12.53 m (41 ft 1½ in)
Propeller diameter	6.20 m (20 ft 4 in)

DIMENSIONS, INTERNAL:

Main cabin: Length	33.0 m (108 ft 3 in)
Max width	4.4 m (14 ft 5 in)
Max height	4.4 m (14 ft 5 in)

AREA:

Wings, gross	345 m² (3,713 sq ft)

ECM version of the Antonov An-12 ('Cub-C'), operated temporarily in Egyptian Air Force insignia

Antonov An-22 Antheus long-range heavy transport aircraft (four Kuznetsov NK-12MA turboprops) *(P.J. Cooper)*

WEIGHTS:
Weight empty, equipped	114,000 kg (251,325 lb)
Max payload	80,000 kg (176,350 lb)
Max fuel	43,000 kg (94,800 lb)
Max T-O weight	250,000 kg (551,160 lb)

PERFORMANCE:
Max level speed	399 knots (740 km/h; 460 mph)
T-O run	1,300 m (4,260 ft)
Landing run	800 m (2,620 ft)
Range with max fuel and 45,000 kg (99,200 lb) payload	5,905 nm (10,950 km; 6,800 miles)
Range with max payload	2,692 nm (5,000 km; 3,100 miles)

ANTONOV An-24
NATO reporting name: Coke

Production of the An-24 in the Soviet Union ended in 1978, after about 1,100 had been delivered. A version known as the **Y7-100** (which see) continues in production at Xian in China.

ANTONOV An-26
NATO reporting name: Curl

First displayed in public at the 1969 Paris Air Show, the An-26 is generally similar to the earlier An-24RT specialised freighter, with an auxiliary turbojet in the starboard engine nacelle, but has more powerful AI-24T turboprop engines and a completely redesigned rear fuselage of the 'beaver-tail' type. This embodies Oleg Antonov's special type of loading ramp, which forms the underside of the rear fuselage when retracted, in the usual way, but can be slid forward under the rear of the cabin to facilitate direct loading, or when the cargo is to be airdropped.

There are two versions:

An-26. Original version, with electrically/manually operated conveyor built in flush with cabin floor to facilitate movement of freight.

An-26B. Improved version, announced in 1981. Equipped to carry three standard freight pallets, each 2.44 m (8 ft) long, 1.46 m (4 ft 9½ in) wide and 1.60 m (5 ft 3 in) high, with a total weight of 5,500 kg (12,125 lb). Rollgangs on floor, mechanism to move the pallets, and moorings, enable two men to load and unload all three pallets in 30 min. Rollgangs can be stowed against sides of cabin.

Although intended primarily for cargo carrying, the An-26 can be adapted easily for passenger, ambulance or paratroop transport duties. More than 1,000 were built before the An-26 was superseded in production by the An-32, including exports to at least 27 Warsaw Pact and other foreign air forces. Examples operated by Angolan government forces are reported to have been used for bombing missions, and one of the Mozambique An-26s has been photographed with a bomb rack on the fuselage below each wingroot trailing-edge. Aeroflot has more than 200, which are available to supplement the military An-26s assigned to air commands in Soviet regiments and squadrons. Others have been supplied to Aerocaribbean of Cuba, Aeronica of Nicaragua, Air Mongol, Alyemda of the People's Democratic Republic of Yemen, Ariana Afghan Airlines, CAAC of China, Cubana, LAM of Mozambique, Syrianair and Tarom of Romania. Details of the derivative **Y-7H-500** built by Xian Aircraft Company can be found in the Chinese section.

TYPE: Twin-turboprop pressurised short-haul transport.

WINGS: Cantilever high-wing monoplane, with 2° anhedral on outer panels. Incidence 3°. Sweepback at quarter-chord on outer panels 6° 50′; at leading-edge 9° 41′. Conventional all-metal two-spar structure, with ribs and stringers, built in five sections: centre-section, two inner wings and two detachable outer wings. Wing skin is attached by electrical spot welding. Mass balanced servo compensated ailerons, with large trim tabs of glassfibre construction. Hydraulically operated, tracked and slotted

Antonov An-22 Antheus long-range heavy transport aircraft *(Pilot Press)*

Antonov An-26 twin-turboprop short-haul transport *(Pilot Press)*

TsAGI flaps along entire wing trailing-edges inboard of unpowered ailerons; single-slotted flaps on centre-section, double-slotted outboard of nacelles. Servo tab and electrically operated trim tab in each aileron. Bleed-air thermal de-icing system.

FUSELAGE: Semi-monocoque aluminium alloy structure in front, centre and rear portions, of bonded/welded construction. Skin on lower portion of fuselage is made of 'bimetal' (duralumin-titanium) sheet for protection during operations from unpaved airfields. Blister on each side forward of rear loading ramp, carrying tracks to enable ramp to slide forward under fuselage.

TAIL UNIT: Cantilever all-metal structure, with large dorsal fin, ventral fin strake on each side of rear ramp. 9°

dihedral on tailplane. All controls manually operated. Manually operated trim tab in each elevator. Electrically operated combined trim/servo tab in rudder. All leading-edges incorporate bleed-air thermal de-icing system.

LANDING GEAR: Hydraulically retractable tricycle type, with twin wheels on each unit. Emergency extension by gravity. All units retract forward. Shock absorbers of oleo-nitrogen type on main units; nitrogen-pneumatic type on nose unit. Mainwheel tyres size 1,050 × 400, pressure 5.9 bars (85 lb/sq in). Nosewheel tyres size 700 × 250, pressure 3.9 bars (57 lb/sq in). Mainwheels fitted with hydraulic disc brakes and anti-skid units. Nosewheels can be steered hydraulically through 45°

Antonov An-26 of Aerocaribbean. Note open intake for auxiliary turbojet on starboard nacelle *(Paul Duffy)*

each side while taxying and are controllable through ±10° during take-off and landing.

POWER PLANT: Two 2,103 kW (2,820 ehp) Ivchenko AI-24VT turboprops, each driving a four-blade constant-speed fully-feathering propeller. Electric de-icing system for propeller blades and hubs; hot air system for engine air intakes. One 7.85 kN (1,765 lb st) RU 19A-300 auxiliary turbojet in starboard nacelle for use, as required, at take-off, during climb and in level flight, and for self-contained starting of main engines. Two independent but interconnected fuel systems, with 5,500 kg (12,125 lb) of fuel, contained in integral tanks in inner wings and ten bag tanks in centre-section. Pressure refuelling socket in starboard engine nacelle. Gravity fuelling point above each tank area. Carbon dioxide inert gas system to create fireproof condition inside fuel tanks.

ACCOMMODATION: Basic crew of five (pilot, co-pilot, radio operator, flight engineer and navigator), with station at rear of cabin on starboard side for loading supervisor or load dispatcher. Optional domed observation window for navigator on port side of flight deck. Electric de-icing system for windscreens. Toilet on port side aft of flight deck; crew door, small galley and oxygen bottle stowage on starboard side. Emergency escape hatch in door immediately aft of flight deck. Large downward hinged rear ramp/door, hinged to an anchorage mounted on tracks running forward under the blister fairings. This enables ramp/door to slide forward under fuselage for direct loading on to cabin floor or for airdropping of freight. When doing so, its rear is supported by the pivoted swinging arm on each side which also raises and lowers door in the alternative fixed-hinge mode. Door can be locked in any intermediate position. Electrically powered mobile winch, capacity 2,000 kg (4,409 lb), hoists crates through rear entrance and runs on a rail in the cabin ceiling to position payload in cabin. Electrically and manually operated conveyor, capacity 4,500 kg (9,920 lb), built-in flush with cabin floor of original An-26, facilitates loading and airdropping of freight. An-26B has removable rollgangs, mechanism for moving pallets inside hold, and moorings (see introductory notes). Both versions can accommodate a variety of motor vehicles, including GAZ-69 and UAZ-469 military vehicles, or cargo items up to 1.50 m (59 in) high by 2.10 m (82.6 in) wide. Height of rear edge of cargo door surround above the cabin floor is 1.50 m (4 ft 11 in). Cabin is pressurised and air-conditioned, and can be fitted with a row of tip-up seats along each wall to accommodate a total of 38 to 40 persons. Conversion to troop transport role, or to an ambulance for 24 stretcher patients and a medical attendant, takes 20 to 30 min in the field.

SYSTEMS: Air-conditioning system uses hot air tapped from the 10th compressor stage of each engine, with a heat exchanger and turbocooler in each nacelle. Cabin pressure differential 0.29 bars (4.27 lb/sq in). Main and emergency hydraulic systems, pressure 151.7 bars (2,200 lb/sq in), for landing gear retraction, nosewheel steering, flaps, brakes, windscreen wipers, propeller feathering and operation of cargo ramp and emergency escape doors. Handpump to operate doors only and build up pressure in main system. Electrical system includes two 27V DC starter/generators on engines, a standby generator on the auxiliary turbojet, and three storage batteries for emergency use. Two engine driven alternators provide 115V 400Hz single-phase AC supply, with standby inverter. Basic source of 36V 400Hz three-phase AC supply is two inverters, with standby transformer. Permanent oxygen system for pilot, installed equipment for other crew members and three portable bottles for personnel in cargo hold.

AVIONICS AND EQUIPMENT: Standard com/nav avionics comprise two VHF transceivers, HF, intercom, two ADF, radio altimeter, glidepath receiver, glideslope receiver, marker beacon receiver, weather/navigation radar, directional gyro and flight recorder. Optional equipment includes a flight director system, astrocompass and autopilot. Standard operational equipment includes parachute static line attachments and retraction devices, tiedowns, jack to support ramp sill, flight deck curtains, sun visors and windscreen wipers. Optional items include OPB-1R sight for pinpoint dropping of freight, medical equipment, and liquid heating system.

DIMENSIONS, EXTERNAL:

Wing span	29.20 m (95 ft 9½ in)
Wing aspect ratio	11.7
Length overall	23.80 m (78 ft 1 in)
Height overall	8.575 m (28 ft 1½ in)
Width of fuselage	2.90 m (9 ft 6 in)
Depth of fuselage	2.50 m (8 ft 2½ in)
Tailplane span	9.973 m (32 ft 8¾ in)
Wheel track (c/l shock struts)	7.90 m (25 ft 11 in)
Wheelbase	7.651 m (25 ft 1¼ in)
Propeller diameter	3.90 m (12 ft 9½ in)
Propeller ground clearance	1.227 m (4 ft 0¼ in)
Crew door (stbd, front): Height	1.40 m (4 ft 7 in)
Width	0.60 m (1 ft 11¾ in)
Height to sill	1.47 m (4 ft 9¾ in)
Loading hatch (rear): Length	3.40 m (11 ft 1¾ in)
Width at front	2.40 m (7 ft 10½ in)
Width at rear	2.00 m (6 ft 6¾ in)
Height to sill	1.47 m (4 ft 9¾ in)
Height to top edge of hatchway	3.014 m (9 ft 10¾ in)
Emergency exit (in floor at front):	
Length	1.02 m (3 ft 4¼ in)
Width	0.70 m (2 ft 3½ in)
Emergency exit (top): Diameter	0.65 m (2 ft 1½ in)
Emergency exits (one each side of hold):	
Height	0.60 m (1 ft 11¾ in)
Width	0.50 m (1 ft 7½ in)

DIMENSIONS, INTERNAL:

Cargo hold: Length of floor	11.50 m (37 ft 8¾ in)
Width of floor	2.40 m (7 ft 10½ in)
Max height	1.91 m (6 ft 3 in)

AREAS:

Wings, gross	74.98 m² (807.1 sq ft)
Vertical tail surfaces (total, incl dorsal fin)	15.85 m² (170.61 sq ft)
Horizontal tail surfaces (total)	19.83 m² (213.45 sq ft)

WEIGHTS:

Weight empty	15,020 kg (33,113 lb)
Normal payload	4,500 kg (9,920 lb)
Max payload	5,500 kg (12,125 lb)
Normal T-O and landing weight	23,000 kg (50,706 lb)
Max T-O and landing weight	24,000 kg (52,911 lb)

PERFORMANCE (at normal T-O weight):

Cruising speed at 6,000 m (19,685 ft)	237 knots (440 km/h; 273 mph)
T-O speed	108 knots (200 km/h; 124 mph) CAS
Landing speed	102 knots (190 km/h; 118 mph) CAS
Max rate of climb at S/L	480 m (1,575 ft)/min
Service ceiling	7,500 m (24,600 ft)
T-O run, on concrete	780 m (2,559 ft)
T-O to 15 m (50 ft)	1,240 m (4,068 ft)
Landing from 15 m (50 ft)	1,740 m (5,709 ft)
Landing run, on concrete	730 m (2,395 ft)
Min ground turning radius	22.3 m (73 ft 2 in)
Range, no reserves:	
with max payload	594 nm (1,100 km; 683 miles)
with max fuel	1,376 nm (2,550 km; 1,584 miles)

ANTONOV An-28
NATO reporting name: Cash

An-28 production takes place at the WSK-PZL Mielec works in Poland (see Polish section).

ANTONOV An-30
NATO reporting name: Clank

The An-30 aerial survey aeroplane was developed from the An-24RT and An-26 twin-turboprop transports, to which it is generally similar. The major modifications are made to the nose, which is extensively glazed to give the navigator a wide field of view, and to the flight deck, which is raised to provide access to the navigator's compartment. There are fewer windows in the main cabin, which contains a darkroom and film storage cupboard, as well as survey cameras and a control desk. Other amenities include a toilet, buffet and crew rest area with armchairs and couches. All accommodation is pressurised and air-conditioned.

Photography can be automatic or semi-automatic if required, but two photographer/surveyors are normally carried, in addition to a flight crew of five (pilot, co-pilot, flight engineer, radio operator and navigator). Details of equipment available for map-making and other air survey duties can be found in previous editions of this yearbook.

The power plant comprises two 2,103 kW (2,820 ehp) Ivchenko AI-24VT turboprops, with water injection, each driving an AV-72T four-blade constant-speed fully-feathering and reversible-pitch propeller. Main engines are supplemented by a 7.85 kN (1,765 lb st) RU 19A-300 auxiliary turbojet in the rear of the starboard engine nacelle. The latter is used for engine starting, and for take-off, climb and cruise power in the event of failure of one of the primary engines. Max fuel capacity is 6,200 litres (1,638 US gallons; 1,364 Imp gallons).

The An-30 can be converted into a transport aircraft by placing cover plates over the camera apertures. It retains the standard An-24 cabin door, on the port side of the fuselage at the rear, together with the standard forward freight compartment door on the starboard side and the load hoisting/conveying system.

A version designated **An-30M** 'Sky Cleaner' is shown in accompanying illustrations. Inside the main cabin, instead of the usual photographic equipment, it carries eight modular containers of granular carbon dioxide. This can be seeded into clouds to induce precipitation over arable land, increase snow cover or fight forest fires. It can also protect a specific area, such as a large city, against excessive precipitation, by causing it to be distributed in surrounding regions. An externally mounted pod on each side of the centre-fuselage houses six multiple dispensers (similar to military IRCM flare dispensers) for meteorological cartridges that are fired into the clouds. Capacity of each chemical modular container is 130 kg (286 lb). Rate of

Meteorological cartridge dispenser on An-30M

discharge of the carbon dioxide granules is 0.8-6 kg (1.75-13.25 lb)/min. Number of cartridges carried is 384. This version of the An-30 has a chin radome, as do some standard An-30 survey aircraft.

DIMENSIONS, EXTERNAL:

Wing span	29.20 m (95 ft 9½ in)
Wing aspect ratio	11.4
Length overall	24.26 m (79 ft 7 in)
Height overall	8.32 m (27 ft 3½ in)
Tailplane span	9.09 m (29 ft 10 in)
Fuselage, nominal diameter	2.90 m (9 ft 6¼ in)
Wheel track (c/l of oleos)	7.90 m (25 ft 11 in)
Wheelbase	7.65 m (25 ft 1¼ in)
Propeller diameter	3.90 m (12 ft 9½ in)
Propeller ground clearance	1.20 m (3 ft 11¼ in)

AREAS:

Wings, gross	74.98 m² (807.1 sq ft)
Vertical tail surfaces (total, incl dorsal fin)	
	15.85 m² (170.61 sq ft)
Horizontal tail surfaces (total)	17.23 m² (185.46 sq ft)

WEIGHTS:

Basic operating weight	15,590 kg (34,370 lb)
Weight of aerial photography equipment	
	650 kg (1,433 lb)
Max T-O and landing weight	23,000 kg (50,706 lb)

PERFORMANCE:

Max level speed	291 knots (540 km/h; 335 mph)
Cruising speed at 6,000 m (19,685 ft)	
	232 knots (430 km/h; 267 mph)
Landing speed	95 knots (175 km/h; 109 mph)
Service ceiling:	
with APU operating	8,300 m (27,230 ft)
without APU	7,300 m (23,950 ft)
T-O run on concrete	710 m (2,330 ft)
Landing run on concrete	670 m (2,198 ft)
Range with max fuel, no reserves	
	1,420 nm (2,630 km; 1,634 miles)

ANTONOV An-32
NATO reporting name: Cline
Indian Air Force name: Sutlej

This pressurised short/medium-range transport is a developed version of the An-26, with a generally similar airframe, except for having triple-slotted trailing-edge flaps outboard of the nacelles, automatic leading-edge slats, much enlarged ventral fins and a full span slotted tailplane. Improvements have also been made to the landing gear retraction mechanism, the de-icing and air conditioning systems, the electrical system and engine starting. In all, about 40 per cent of the subsystems, installations and units have been changed.

Two versions were offered initially, differing only in the type of Ivchenko AI-20 turboprop fitted, as listed in the 1988-89 and earlier editions of Jane's. All production An-32s have been delivered with AI-20D Series 5 engines, each rated at 3,812 kW (5,112 ehp).

The large increase in power compared with the An-26 is intended specifically to improve take-off performance, service ceiling and payload under 'hot and high' conditions. Thus, the An-32 is able to operate from airfields 4,000-4,500m (13,125-14,750 ft) above sea level in an ambient temperature of ISA + 25°C, and can transport 3 tonnes of freight over a 594 nm (1,100 km; 683 mile) stage length, with fuel reserves. The overwing location of the engines requires nacelles of considerable depth, as the main landing gear units continue to retract into the underwing portions.

Antonov An-30M 'Sky Cleaner' weather modification aircraft

Low pressure tyres (of the same sizes as those on the An-26) permit operation from unpaved strips. Maximum tyre pressure is 3.9 bars (57 lb/sq in) on the nosewheels and 5.9 bars (85 lb/sq in) on the mainwheels. All shock absorbers are of the oleo-nitrogen type. The high position of the engines reduces the possibility of stone or debris ingestion. A TG-16M APU, housed in the rear of the starboard landing gear fairing, helps to make the An-32 independent of ground servicing equipment by providing onboard engine starting capability at airfields up to 4,500 m (14,750 ft) above sea level.

A rear loading hatch and forward-sliding ramp/door, similar to those of the An-26, are retained, as well as a winch and a hoist with increased capacity of 3,000 kg (6,615 lb), to facilitate handling of the maximum payload of more than 6 tonnes of freight on 12 pallets. Cargo or vehicles can be airdropped by parachute, including extraction of large loads by drag parachute, with the aid of removable roller conveyors and guide rails on the floor of the hold. The air-conditioned and pressurised accommodation enables alternative payloads to include 50 passengers or 42 parachutists and a jumpmaster, on a row of tip-up seats along each cabin wall, or 24 stretcher patients and up to three medical personnel; the normal crew of three comprises pilot, co-pilot and navigator, with provision for a flight engineer.

The prototype An-32 was exhibited at the 1977 Paris Air Show. India began taking delivery of 123 (named **Sutlej** after a Punjabi river) in 1984. Peru has 15, which have been seen with four racks for bombs, two on each side of the fuselage below the wings; and a number of An-32s were acquired by Afghanistan. Other orders are understood to have been received from Cape Verde, Nicaragua (two for Aeronica), Sao Tome and Principe, and Tanzania. Much of the current production of 40 An-32s per year is for the Soviet armed forces.

In addition to the basic transport versions of the An-32, specially equipped variants are available for a variety of duties, including firefighting, fisheries surveillance, agricultural work, and air ambulance use, complete with operating theatre.

Antonov An-32 short/medium-range transport (two Ivchenko AI-20D turboprops) *(Pilot Press)*

Antonov An-32 in landing configuration *(Aviation Magazine International/Jacques Marmain)*

DIMENSIONS, EXTERNAL:
As for An-26, except:

Length overall	23.78 m (78 ft 0¼ in)
Height overall	8.75 m (28 ft 8½ in)
Tailplane span	10.23 m (33 ft 6¾ in)
Propeller diameter	4.70 m (15 ft 5 in)
Propeller ground clearance	1.55 m (5 ft 1 in)

DIMENSIONS, INTERNAL:

Cargo hold: Length	15.68 m (51 ft 5¼ in)
Max width	2.78 m (9 ft 1¼ in)
Max height	1.84 m (6 ft 0½ in)
Volume	66.0 m³ (2,330 cu ft)

AREAS:

Wings, gross	74.98 m² (807.1 sq ft)
Ailerons (total)	6.12 m² (65.88 sq ft)
Flaps (total)	15.00 m² (161.46 sq ft)
Vertical tail surfaces (total, incl dorsal fin)	17.22 m² (185.36 sq ft)
Horizontal tail surfaces (total)	20.30 m² (218.5 sq ft)

WEIGHTS:

Weight empty	16,800 kg (37,038 lb)
Weight empty, equipped	17,308 kg (38,158 lb)
Max payload	6,700 kg (14,770 lb)
Max fuel	5,445 kg (12,004 lb)
Max fuel with max payload	2,267 kg (4,998 lb)
Max ramp weight	27,250 kg (60,075 lb)
Max T-O weight	27,000 kg (59,525 lb)
Max landing weight	25,000 kg (55,115 lb)

PERFORMANCE:

Max cruising speed	286 knots (530 km/h; 329 mph)
Econ cruising speed	254 knots (470 km/h; 292 mph)
Landing speed	100 knots (185 km/h; 115 mph)
Optimum cruising height	8,000 m (26,250 ft)
Service ceiling	9,400 m (30,840 ft)
Service ceiling, one engine out	4,800 m (15,750 ft)
T-O run on concrete	760 m (2,495 ft)
T-O to 15 m (50 ft)	1,200 m (3,940 ft)
Landing run	470 m (1,542 ft)
Range, with 45 min reserves:	
with max payload	464 nm (860 km; 534 miles)
with 5,500 kg (12,125 lb) payload	1,080 nm (2,000 km; 1,243 miles)

ANTONOV An-70

According to *Isvestia*, in its issue for 20 December 1988, an aircraft designated An-70 is under development to replace some of the remaining An-12s of the Soviet air forces. It was intended to enter production in 1988, but manufacture has been deferred until 1995.

ANTONOV An-72 and An-74
NATO reporting name: Coaler

Two prototypes of the An-72 twin-turbofan STOL transport were built, plus a third airframe for static testing. Photographs of one of these aircraft (SSSR-19774) were released by the Soviet Tass news agency shortly after the first flight of an An-72 on 22 December 1977. Details and photographs of the prototypes (NATO 'Coaler-A') have appeared in previous editions of *Jane's*. Together with eight pre-series aircraft, they were built at Kiev. Manufacture was then transferred to a plant in Kharkov.

In its current series production form, the An-72 has an extended wing span, lengthened fuselage and other refinements. It is available in several forms, including a specialised version for operation in polar regions which has the designation An-74. All have the same basic airframe and are built on the same assembly line at the rate of 20 aircraft a year. Versions identified by early 1990 are as follows:

An-72A ('Coaler-C'). Light STOL transport for military and civil operation. Crew of two on flight deck. Conventional landing gear, with twin-wheel nose unit and two wheels in tandem on each main unit. D-36 turbofans fitted initially will be superseded eventually by more powerful Lotarev D-436s.

An-72AT ('Coaler-C'). Cargo carrying version of An-72A, equipped to accommodate international standard containers.

An-72S ('Coaler-C'). Executive transport version, with cabin divided by bulkheads into three separate compartments. Forward compartment comprises toilets, a wardrobe and galley for hot and cold meals. The central compartment serves as both a working area and a place to relax. On the right side are a small table, a sofa for three persons, a wardrobe and a baggage space. The sofa and wardrobe can be replaced by three pairs of armchair seats. Opposite is the working area, with a table, two pivoting armchairs and an intercom. The rear compartment contains 12 pairs of armchairs. Provision is made for adapting the interior to carry a light vehicle, freight, 38 persons on seats along the sidewalls and in the centre of the cabin, or eight stretcher patients in a casualty evacuation role.

An-74 ('Coaler-B'). Specialised version for operation in the Arctic and Antarctic, with flight crew of five, more advanced navigation aids including inertial navigation system, provision for wheel/ski landing gear and much increased fuel capacity. Airframe identical with that of An-72A, except for having two observation blister windows at the rear of the flight deck and at the front of the main cabin on the port side, and a larger nose radome that does not follow curve of fuselage undersurface. Production of about 100 An-74s anticipated.

Absence of observation windows identifies the Antonov An-72 *(Jane's Defence Weekly/Paul Beaver)*

Antonov An-74 ('Coaler-B') STOL transport, with scrap view of 'Madcap' rotodome *(Pilot Press)*

It is expected that the An-72/74 series will develop into a 'family' of different types at least as diverse as the earlier An-24/26/30/32. Already, examples have been seen in military camouflage. An AEW&C version is flying and has been given the NATO reporting name 'Madcap' (see separate entry).

Design features of the An-72A make it uniquely suited to its primary role, as a STOL replacement for the turboprop An-26, with the emphasis on freight carrying. Its low pressure tyres and multi-wheel landing gear enable it to operate from unprepared airfields, or from surfaces covered with ice or snow; and the high-set engines avoid problems caused by foreign object ingestion. The exhaust efflux is ejected over the upper surface of the wing and down over very large multi-slotted flaps. By taking advantage of the so-called 'Coanda effect', which causes the airflow to 'attach to' the extended flaps, a considerable increase in lift can be achieved. The An-72A has a ramp/door of the kind fitted to the An-26, which can be hinged down conventionally to allow wheeled or tracked vehicles to be driven into the hold or, alternatively, can slide forward under the fuselage to permit direct loading from a truck.

Particular care was taken to ensure easy handling in the air. The An-72A's Doppler based automatic navigation system, linked to an onboard computer, is pre-programmed before take-off on a push-button panel to the right of the large cockpit map display. Failure warning panels above the windscreen display red lights for critical failures, yellow lights for non-critical failures, to minimise the time that needs to be spent on monitoring instruments and equipment.

First details of the An-74 were given in February 1984, when the Soviet newspaper *Pravda* referred to it as a new transport intended for operation in the Arctic and Antarctic regions. The report stated that, unlike the Il-18D turboprop transports used to carry men and equipment between Leningrad and the Antarctic base of Molodejnaya, the An-74 can have a wheel/ski landing gear for operation on snow and ice landing strips. It was described as an all-weather aircraft, equipped with the latest available radio navigation aids, and with de-icing equipment on the wings, tail unit and engine air intakes. In the Polar regions, its duties include assistance in setting up scientific stations on Arctic ice floes, airdropping supplies to motorised trans-Antarctic expeditions, and reconnaissance to observe changes in the icefields. First demonstration of its capabilities was given on 14 March 1986, when an An-74

touched down alongside the Arctic drifting research station Severny Polious 27 (North Pole 27) and pulled up within 300 m (985 ft), to lift to safety 27 men whose 900 m (2,950 ft) runway had been split into two sections as the icefield broke up.

The following details apply to both the An-72A and An-74 as described in publicity brochures from Aviaexport:

TYPE: Twin-turbofan light STOL transport.

WINGS: Cantilever high-wing monoplane, with 17° sweepback on leading-edge. Straight trailing-edge on inner panels. Tapered outer panels have modest trailing-edge sweepback. Multi-spar structure. Short constant chord centre-section, without dihedral or anhedral, mounted above fuselage to avoid encroaching on internal space. Approx 10° anhedral on outer panels. Wing upper surface blowing requires engines to be mounted above and forward of wings, to exhaust over upper surface. Aft of nacelles, wing skin, spoilers and flaps made of titanium. Hydraulically actuated full span leading-edge flaps outboard of nacelles, embodying thermal anti-icing. Wide span trailing-edge flaps, double-slotted in exhaust efflux, triple-slotted between nacelles and outer wing panels. Normal T-O flap setting 25-30°; max deflection 60°. Four-section spoilers forward of triple-slotted flaps on each side; two outer sections on each side raised before landing, remainder opened automatically on touchdown by sensors actuated by weight on main landing gear. Conventional mechanically actuated ailerons inset on outer wing panels. Two tabs in port aileron, one in starboard aileron.

FUSELAGE: Conventional all-metal semi-monocoque structure of circular cross-section. Underside of upswept rear fuselage formed by ramp/door, which can hinge downward conventionally or slide forward under fuselage to permit direct loading of hold from truck. Underfuselage fairing panel aft of ramp drops and moves backward slightly to release ramp.

TAIL UNIT: Cantilever all-metal T tail, with wide chord sweptback vertical surfaces and fixed-incidence tailplane. Double-hinged rudder, with tab in lower portion of two-section aft panel. During normal flight only the lower rear segment is used. Both rear segments are used during low-speed flight. The forward segment is actuated automatically to offset thrust asymmetry. Tailplane leading-edge sweep slightly greater than that of wings, with straight trailing-edge on horn balanced and mechanically actuated, aerodynamically balanced elev-

Antonov An-74 ('Coaler-B') twin-turbofan STOL transport *(Paul Jackson)*

ators. Two tabs in each elevator. Inverted leading-edge slat on tailplane linked to wing flaps. Leading-edges of fin and tailplane, including slat, are de-iced by engine bleed air. Tapered fairing forward of fin/tailplane junction, blending into large ogival rear fairing.

LANDING GEAR: Hydraulically retractable tricycle type, made primarily of titanium. Twin wheels on rearward retracting steerable nose unit. Each main unit comprises two trailing-arm legs in tandem, each with a single wheel, retracting inward through 90° so that wheels lie horizontally in bottom of large fairings, outside fuselage pressure cell. Oleo-pneumatic shock absorber in each unit. Low pressure tyres, size 720 × 310 on nosewheels, 1,050 × 400 on mainwheels. Hydraulic disc brakes. Telescopic strut is hinged downward, from rear of each side fairing, to support fuselage during direct loading of hold with ramp/door under fuselage.

POWER PLANT: Current versions have two Lotarev D-36 high bypass ratio turbofans, each rated at 63.74 kN (14,330 lb st). These will be superseded by two Lotarev D-436 turbofans, each rated at 73.6 kN (16,550 lb st). Integral fuel tanks between spars of outer wings. Thrust reversers standard.

ACCOMMODATION: Pilot and co-pilot/navigator side by side on roomy flight deck of An-72, plus a flight engineer, with provision for a fourth person; pilot, co-pilot, navigator, radio operator and flight engineer in An-74. Heated windows. Two windscreen wipers. Flight deck and cabin pressurised and air-conditioned. Main cabin designed primarily for freight, including four UAK-2.5 containers or four PAV-2.5 pallets each weighing 2,500 kg (5,511 lb); but An-72 has folding seats for 68 passengers along side walls and on removable central seats. It can carry 57 parachutists, and has provision for 24 stretcher patients, 12 seated casualties and an attendant in ambulance configuration. An-74 is able to carry eight mission staff in combi role, in two rows of seats, with tables, and with two bunks installed, one on each side of cabin aft of seats. Bulged observation windows on port side for navigator and hydrologist. Provision for wardrobe and galley. Movable bulkhead between passenger and freight compartments, with provision for up to 1,500 kg (3,307 lb) of freight in rear compartment. Large downward hinged and forward sliding rear ramp/door for loading trucks and tracked vehicles, and for direct loading of hold from trucks, as described under An-26 entry. It is openable in flight, enabling freight loads of up to 7,500 kg (16,535 lb), with a maximum of 2,500 kg (5,511 lb) per individual item, to be airdropped by parachute extraction system. Removable mobile winch, capacity 2,500 kg (5,511 lb), assists loading of containers up to 1.90 × 2.44 × 1.46 m (6 ft 3 in × 8 ft × 4 ft 9½ in) in size, pallets 1.90 × 2.42 × 1.46 m (6 ft 3 in × 7 ft 11 in × 4 ft 9½ in) in size, and other bulky items. Cargo straps and nets are stowed in lockers on each side of hold when not in use. Provision for building roller conveyors into floor. Main crew and passenger door at front of cabin on port side. Small emergency exit and servicing door at rear of cabin on starboard side.

SYSTEMS: Air-conditioning system provides comfortable environment to altitude of 10,000 m (32,800 ft), with independent temperature control in flight deck and main cabin areas. It can be used to refrigerate main cabin when perishable goods are carried. Hydraulic system for actuating landing gear, flaps, ailerons, variable incidence tailplane and ramp. Electrical system powers auxiliary systems, flight deck equipment, lighting and mobile hoist. Thermal de-icing system for leading-edges of wings and tail unit, engine air intakes and cockpit windows.

Mr Gorbachev's visit to the Antonov OKB produced the first illustration of an AEW&C version of the An-74 (background), known to NATO as 'Madcap'

An-74 after touchdown, with thrust reversers erected and flaps extended
(Paul Jackson)

AVIONICS AND EQUIPMENT: HF com, VHF com/nav, ADF. Large radome over navigation/weather radar in nose. Doppler based automatic navigation system, with map display on flight deck. 'Odd Rods' IFF standard. An-74 has enhanced avionics, including INS. Provision for APU in starboard landing gear fairing. This can be used to heat the cabin; and, under cold ambient conditions, servicing personnel can gain access to major electric, hydraulic and air-conditioning components without stepping outside.

DIMENSIONS, EXTERNAL:
Wing span	31.89 m (104 ft 7½ in)
Length overall	28.07 m (92 ft 1¼ in)
Fuselage: Max diameter	3.10 m (10 ft 2 in)
Height overall	8.65 m (28 ft 4½ in)
Wheel track	4.15 m (13 ft 7½ in)
Wheelbase	8.12 m (26 ft 7¾ in)

Rear loading door: Length	7.10 m (23 ft 3½ in)
Width	2.40 m (7 ft 10½ in)

DIMENSIONS, INTERNAL:
Cabin: Length	10.50 m (34 ft 5¼ in)
Width at floor level	2.15 m (7 ft 0½ in)
Height	2.20 m (7 ft 2½ in)

AREA:
Wings, gross	98.62 m² (1,062 sq ft)

WEIGHTS (D-36 engines):
Max payload: normal	10,000 kg (22,045 lb)

Max T-O weight:
from 1,800 m (5,905 ft) runway	34,500 kg (76,060 lb)
from 1,500 m (4,920 ft) runway	33,000 kg (72,750 lb)
from 1,000 m (3,280 ft) runway	27,500 kg (60,625 lb)

PERFORMANCE (An-72A with D-36 engines. A: at T-O weight of 33,000 kg; 72,750 lb, B: at T-O weight of 27,500 kg; 60,625 lb on 1,000 m; 3,280 ft unprepared runway):

Antonov An-124 heavy freight transport, with landing gear extended *(P. J. Cooper)*

Max level speed at 10,000 m (32,800 ft):
A	380 knots (705 km/h; 438 mph)

Cruising speed at 10,000 m (32,800 ft):
A, B	297-324 knots (550-600 km/h; 342-373 mph)

Approach speed: A   97 knots (180 km/h; 112 mph)
Service ceiling: A   10,700 m (35,100 ft)
B   11,800 m (38,715 ft)
Service ceiling, one engine out: A   5,100 m (16,730 ft)
B   6,800 m (22,300 ft)
T-O run: A   930 m (3,052 ft)
B   620 m (2,035 ft)
T-O to 10.7 m (35 ft): A   1,170 m (3,840 ft)
B   830 m (2,725 ft)
Landing run: A   465 m (1,525 ft)
B   420 m (1,380 ft)
Range, with 45 min reserves:
A with max payload   430 nm (800 km; 497 miles)
A with 7,500 kg (16,535 lb) payload
1,080 nm (2,000 km; 1,240 miles)
A with max fuel   2,590 nm (4,800 km; 2,980 miles)
B with 5,000 kg (11,020 lb) payload
430 nm (800 km; 497 miles)
B with max fuel   1,760 nm (3,250 km; 2,020 miles)
PERFORMANCE (An-74 with D-36 engines):
Generally as for An-72A, except:
Range, with 2 hour reserves:
with max payload   620 nm (1,150 km; 715 miles)
with 1,500 kg (3,307 lb) payload
2,265 nm (4,200 km; 2,610 miles)

ANTONOV An-74 VARIANT
NATO reporting name: Madcap

A photograph taken during a visit to the Antonov OKB by Mr Gorbachev shows, in the background, the much modified tail of an An-74 bearing the serial number SSSR-780151. This has a large, sweptforward fin and rudder, at the top of which is mounted an AEW&C rotodome (see illustration on page 237). It can be assumed that this aircraft bears the same relationship to the Ilyushin 'Mainstay' as does the Grumman E-2C Hawkeye to the Boeing E-3 Sentry, with similar potential for export to selected customers. Development is at an early stage, with a few aircraft completed and much work required to produce a satisfactory avionics suite. It has been suggested by Rear Admiral Thomas Brooks, US Director of Naval Intelligence, that 'Madcap' might be intended for operation from the Soviet Navy's new aircraft carriers of the 'Tbilisi' class.

ANTONOV An-124
NATO reporting name: Condor

The prototype An-124 (SSSR-680125) was flown for the first time on 26 December 1982 by the Antonov bureau's chief test pilot, Vladimir Terski. He also commanded the second prototype (SSSR-82002 *Ruslan*, named after the giant hero of Russian folklore immortalised by Pushkin) when it was exhibited in public for the first time at the Paris Air Show in May/June 1985. The number of aircraft flown had increased to 20 (including two prototypes) by 1989. Operational flying is said to have started in January 1986 when units of a US/Canadian Euclid 154 tonne dumper truck were transported for use by Yakut diamond miners. Deliveries to VTA's heavy-lift military units, to replace the An-22, began in 1987.

Except for having a low mounted tailplane, the general configuration of the An-124 is similar to that of its US counterpart, the Lockheed C-5 Galaxy. It has an upward hinged visor type nose, and rear fuselage ramp/door, for simultaneous front and rear loading/unloading. Advanced features include a 100 per cent fly by wire control system, titanium floor throughout the main hold, and 5,500 kg (12,125 lb) of composites, making up more than 1,500 m² (16,150 sq ft) of its surface area and giving a weight saving of

Nose of the An-124 opens upward around the flight deck *(Anna T. Hogg)*

more than 2,000 kg (4,410 lb). The 24-wheel landing gear enables the An-124 to operate from unprepared fields, hard packed snow and ice covered swampland. Steerable nose- and mainwheels enable it to turn on a 45 m (148 ft) wide runway. Payloads range from the largest Soviet main battle tanks to complete missile systems, Siberian oil well equipment and earth movers.

Manufacture and assembly of the An-124 are centred in Antonov's headquarters works at Kiev. The wings are built in Tashkent, from where each port or starboard wing is ferried in one piece to Kiev above the fuselage of a specially adapted An-22 transport aircraft.

On 26 July 1985, an An-124 lifted a payload of 171,219 kg (377,473 lb) to a height of 10,750 m (35,269 ft). This exceeded by 53 per cent the previous official record for maximum payload lifted to 2,000 m, set by a Lockheed C-5A Galaxy, and also qualified for 20 other FAI approved records with payloads from 75,000 to 170,000 kg.

On 6-7 May 1987, a closed circuit distance record was set by an An-124 which covered a distance of 10,880.625 nm (20,150.921 km; 12,521.201 miles) in a time of 25 h 30 min, landing with a small amount of fuel remaining in its tanks. The route was from Moscow to Astrakhan, Tashkent, Lake Baikal, Petropavlovsk, Chukot Peninsula, Murmansk, Zhdanov and back to Moscow.

TYPE: Long-range heavy-lift freight transport.

WINGS: Cantilever shoulder-wing monoplane, of super-critical section, with anhedral. Sweepback approx 35° on inboard leading-edge, 32° over most of span. Conventional light alloy construction, with one-piece root-to-tip upper surface extruded skin panel on each wing. Strip of carbonfibre skin panels on undersurface forward of trailing-edge control surfaces. Glassfibre wingtips. Each wing has two-section aileron, three-section single-slotted Fowler flaps, and six-section full-span leading-edge flaps. Small slot in outer part of

two inner flap segments on each side, to optimise aerodynamics. Front and rear portions of each flap guide fairing made of glassfibre; centre portion of carbonfibre. Eight spoilers on upper surface of each wing, forward of trailing-edge flaps. No fences, vortex generators or tabs. All moving surfaces hydraulically operated, with hydraulic flutter dampers on ailerons. Bleed air anti-icing of wing leading-edges.

FUSELAGE: Conventional semi-monocoque light alloy structure of basic double-bubble form. Hard chine between sides and shallow-section bottom surface. Central frames each made up of four large forgings. Visor type nose door and rear ramp/door described under 'Accommodation' heading. Fairings over intersection of fuselage lobes, in line with wing, from rear of flight deck to plane of fin leading-edge, made primarily of glassfibre with central, and lower underwing, portions of carbonfibre. Other carbonfibre components include nose and main landing gear doors, some service doors, and clamshell doors aft of rear loading ramp. Glassfibre components include most of bottom skin panels forming underfuselage blister fairing between main landing gear legs, plus nosecone and tailcone. All control runs and other services are channelled along roof of fuselage.

TAIL UNIT: Cantilever all-metal structure, except for glassfibre tips of fixed incidence tailplane and strip of carbonfibre skin panels forward of each control surface. Rudder and each elevator in two sections, without tabs. Control surfaces hydraulically operated, with hydraulic flutter dampers. Electro-impulse de-icing of fin and tailplane leading-edges.

LANDING GEAR: Hydraulically retractable nosewheel type. Nose gear comprises two independent forward retracting and steerable twin-wheel units, side by side. Each main gear comprises five independent inward retracting twin-wheel units, of which the front two units on each side are steerable. Each mainwheel bogie is enclosed by separate upper and lower doors when retracted. Nosewheel doors and lower mainwheel doors close when gear is extended. All wheel doors are of carbonfibre. Main gear bogies can be retracted individually for repair or wheel change. Mainwheel tyres size 1,270 × 510. Nosewheel tyres size 1,120 × 450. Aircraft can 'kneel', by retracting nosewheels and settling on two extendable 'feet', giving floor of hold a 3.5° slope to assist loading and unloading. Rear of cargo hold can be lowered by compressing main gear oleos. Carbon brakes are normally toe operated, via rudder pedals. For severe braking, pedals are depressed by both toes and heels.

POWER PLANT: Four Lotarev D-18T turbofans, each rated at 229.5 kN (51,590 lb st). Thrust reversers standard. Engine cowlings of glassfibre; pylons have carbonfibre skin at rear end. All fuel in ten integral tanks in wings.

ACCOMMODATION: All crew and passenger accommodation on upper deck; freight and/or vehicles on lower deck. Flight crew of six, in pairs, on flight deck, with place for loadmaster in lobby area. Pilot and co-pilot on fully adjustable seats, which rotate for improved access. Two flight engineers, on wall-facing seats on starboard side, have complete control of master fuel cocks, detailed systems instruments, and digital integrated data system with CRT monitor. Behind pilot are the navigator and communications specialist, also on wall-facing seats. Between flight deck and wing carry-through structure, on port side, are toilets, washing facilities, galley, equipment compartment, and two cabins for total of up to six relief crew, with table and facing bench seats convertible into bunks. Aft of wing carry-through is a passenger cabin for up to 88 persons. Hatches in upper deck provide access to the wing and tail unit for maintenance in places where workstands may not be available. Flight deck and passenger cabin are each accessible from cargo hold by means of an hydraulically folding ladder, operated

Antonov An-124 (four Lotarev D-18T turbofans) *(Pilot Press)*

automatically with manual override. Rearward sliding and jettisonable window on each side of flight deck. Primary access to flight deck via airstair door, with ladder extension, forward of wing on port side. Smaller door forward of this and slightly higher. Door from main hold aft of wing on starboard side. Upper deck doors at rear of flight deck on starboard side and at rear of passenger cabin on each side. Emergency exit from upper deck aft of wing on each side. Hydraulically operated visor type upward hinged nose takes 7 min to open fully, with simultaneous extension of folding nose loading ramp. When open, nose is steadied by reinforcing arms against wind gusts. No hydraulic, electrical or other system lines are broken when nose is open. Radar wiring passes through hollow tube in hinge. Hydraulically operated rear loading doors take 3 min to open, with simultaneous extension of three-part folding ramp. This can be locked in intermediate position for direct loading from truck or loading galley. Aft of ramp, centre panel of fuselage undersurface hinges upward; clamshell door to each side opens downward. Completely unobstructed lower deck freight hold has titanium floor, attached 'mobilely' to lower fuselage structure to accommodate changes of temperature, with rollgangs and retractable attachments for cargo tiedowns. A narrow catwalk along each sidewall facilitates access to, and mobility past, loaded freight. No personnel are carried on lower deck in flight, because of low pressurisation of hold. Two electric travelling cranes in roof of hold, each with two lifting points, offer total lifting capacity of 20,000 kg (44,100 lb). Two winches can each pull a 3,000 kg (6,614 lb) load.

SYSTEMS: Entire interior of aircraft is pressurised and air-conditioned. Max pressure differential 0.55 bars (7.8 lb/sq in) on upper deck, 0.25 bars (3.55 lb/sq in) on lower deck. Four independent hydraulic systems. Quadruple redundant fly by wire flight control system, with mechanical emergency fifth channel to hydraulic control servos. Special secondary bus electrical system. Landing lights under nose and at front of each main landing gear fairing. APU in rear of each landing gear fairing is used for engine starting, and can be operated in the air or on the ground to open loading doors for airdrop from rear or normal ground loading/unloading, as well as for supplying electrical, hydraulic and air-conditioning systems.

AVIONICS AND EQUIPMENT: Comprehensive but conventional flight deck equipment, including automatic flight control system control panel at top of glareshield, weather radar screen and moving map display forward of throttle and thrust reverse levers on centre console. No electronic flight displays. Dual attitude indicator/flight director and HSIs, and vertical tape engine instruments. Two dielectric areas of nose visor enclose forward looking weather radar and downward looking ground mapping/navigation radar. Hemispherical dielectric fairing above centre fuselage for satellite navigation receiver. Quadruple INS, plus Loran and Omega. Small two-face mirror, of V form, enables pilots to adjust their seating position until their eyes are reflected in the appropriate mirror, which ensures an optimum field of view from the flight deck.

DIMENSIONS, EXTERNAL:
Wing span	73.30 m (240 ft 5¾ in)
Length overall	69.10 m (226 ft 8½ in)
Height overall	20.78 m (68 ft 2¼ in)

DIMENSIONS, INTERNAL:
Cargo hold: Length	36.0 m (118 ft 1¼ in)
Max width	6.4 m (21 ft 0 in)
Max height	4.4 m (14 ft 5¼ in)

AREA:
Wings, gross	628.0 m² (6,760.0 sq ft)

WEIGHTS:
Max payload	150,000 kg (330,693 lb)

Max fuel		230,000 kg (507,063 lb)
Max T-O weight		405,000 kg (892,872 lb)

PERFORMANCE:
Max cruising speed		467 knots (865 km/h; 537 mph)
Normal cruising speed at 10,000-12,000 m (32,800-39,370 ft)		
		432-459 knots (800-850 km/h; 497-528 mph)
Approach speed		
		124-140 knots (230-260 km/h; 143-162 mph)
T-O balanced field length at max T-O weight		
		3,000 m (9,850 ft)
Landing run at max landing weight		800 m (2,625 ft)
Range:		
with max payload		2,430 nm (4,500 km; 2,795 miles)
with max fuel		8,900 nm (16,500 km; 10,250 miles)

OPERATIONAL NOISE LEVELS:
Stated to meet ICAO requirements

ANTONOV An-225 MRIYA
NATO reporting name: Cossack

The An-225 Mriya (Dream) is the first aircraft built to fly at a gross weight exceeding one million pounds. There was need for an aircraft large enough to carry on its back a Soviet space shuttle orbiter. Initially, a modified Myasishchev M-4 bomber (NATO 'Bison-C'), designated VM-T, was used to fly orbiters such as *Buran* and components of their Energiya rocket launch vehicles into Baikonur Cosmodrome. This was not entirely satisfactory, as the VM-T can lift only 40 tonnes in this way, whereas *Buran* has an empty weight of 70 tonnes. So it was not possible for the VM-T to ferry on its back a complete orbiter.

In mid-1985 the Antonov OKB was entrusted with the task of producing an aircraft large enough to carry not only a ready-to-launch orbiter but major portions of the Energiya and the kind of heavy engineering structures that the Soviet Union's oil, gas, chemical and electrical power generating industries frequently need to transport into remote and inhospitable regions of the USSR. It already had experience of piggyback external cargo operations, having ferried individual port and starboard wings for its

An-124 freighters from the manufacturing centre at Tashkent to the Kiev assembly plant routinely for years on the back of a modified An-22 heavy freighter.

The Antonov designers used the An-124 as the basis for the An-225. They stretched the fuselage and wings of what was then the world's largest production aircraft, to increase by approximately 50 per cent the An-124's maximum take-off weight of 405 tonnes and payload of 150 tonnes. The basic cabin cross-section, with a height of 4.4 m (14 ft 5¼ in) and width of 6.4 m (21 ft 0 in), was unchanged. So was the type of turbofan selected to power the new aircraft. The number of engines was simply increased from four to six. Similarly, the main landing gear was uprated from five pairs of wheels on each side of the fuselage to seven pairs. The tail was redesigned, with twin fins and rudders that would avoid airflow problems associated with piggyback loads.

The prototype An-225 (SSSR-480182) made a 75 min first flight on 21 December 1988, only three weeks after its unveiling at Kiev. On that occasion it took off from what the *Tass* news agency described as "a 1,000 m (3,280 ft) runway". In service, the An-225 is intended to operate from airports with a 3,500 m (11,500 ft) runway when carrying its maximum payload.

The An-225 has a visor type upward hinged nose door identical with that of the An-124 but no rear ramp/door. A rear loading/unloading capability is not necessary for the primary tasks of the An-225. Elimination of the rear door facilitated design and saved considerable structural weight.

An aircraft with the load carrying capability of the An-225 has potential military applications. Missile systems too large to be transported speedily over long distances in any other way could be flown to an operational site as easily as a shuttle orbiter can be piggybacked to Baikonur. This would require a sizeable fleet of An-225s, whereas only one more aircraft has yet been funded. If further examples are needed, it should be possible to provide them, without major industrial or economic problems, thanks to commonality of design with the An-124.

On 22 March 1989, the prototype An-225 set a total of 106 world and class records during a 3½ hour flight from Kiev. Taking off at a weight of 508,200 kg (1,120,370 lb), with a payload of 156,300 kg (344,576 lb), it flew around a 2,000 km closed circuit via Vitebsk and Leningrad at an average speed of 438.75 knots (813.09 km/h; 505.24 mph), achieving a maximum altitude of 12,340 m (40,485 ft) en route. The first flight carrying *Buran* was made on 13 May 1989, from Baikonur.

TYPE: Six-engined heavy transport.

WINGS: Cantilever shoulder-wing monoplane, of supercritical section. Basically standard An-124 wings, with anhedral, attached outboard of new centre-section. Sweepback 35° on inboard leading-edge, 32° over outer half of span. Conventional light alloy construction, with one-piece upper surface extruded skin panel outboard of centre-section on each wing. Glassfibre wingtips. Each wing has two-section aileron, three-section single-slotted Fowler flaps on outer panels and single section on centre-section, and six-section leading-edge flaps on outer panels only. Eight airbrakes (inboard) and eight spoilers (outboard) on upper surface of each wing and centre-section forward of trailing-edge flaps. No fences, vortex generators or tabs. All moving surfaces hydraulically operated.

FUSELAGE: Conventional semi-monocoque light alloy structure of basic double-bubble form. Hard chine between sides and shallow-section bottom surface. Visor type nose door described under 'Accommodation' heading. Fairings over intersection of fuselage lobes, in line with wing, from rear of flight deck to position forward of

Antonov An-225 Mriya (NATO 'Cossack') six-turbofan heavy freight transport *(Pilot Press)*

Antonov An-225 carrying *Buran* space shuttle at 1989 Paris Air Show (*J. M. G. Gradidge*)

tailplane, made of glassfibre and carbonfibre. Other carbonfibre components include nose and main landing gear doors, and some service doors. Glassfibre components include most of bottom skin panels forming underfuselage blister fairing between main landing gear legs, plus nosecone and tailcone. All control runs and other services are channelled along roof of fuselage.

TAIL UNIT: Twin fins and two-section rudders, toed inward, at the tips of a dihedral tailplane. Three-section elevator on each side. Conical fairing aft of each tailplane tip. Control surfaces hydraulically operated.

LANDING GEAR: Hydraulically retractable nosewheel type. Nose gear comprises two independent forward retracting and steerable twin-wheel units, side by side. Each main gear comprises seven independent inward retracting twin-wheel units, with tyres size 1,270 × 510. Rear four pairs of wheels on each side are steerable. Each mainwheel bogie is enclosed by separate upper and lower doors when retracted. Nosewheel doors and lower mainwheel doors close when gear is extended. Aircraft can 'kneel', by retracting nosewheels and settling on two extendable 'feet', giving floor a slope to assist loading and unloading.

POWER PLANT: Six Lotarev D-18T turbofans, each rated at 229.5 kN (51,590 lb st) and each fitted with thrust reverser. Engine cowlings of glassfibre. All fuel in integral

tanks in wings, including additional tanks in new centre-section. Max capacity estimated at well over 300,000 kg (661,375 lb).

ACCOMMODATION: Flight crew of six, in pairs, on flight deck, with place for loadmaster in lobby area. Pilot and co-pilot on fully adjustable seats that rotate for improved access. Two flight engineers, on wall-facing seats on starboard side. Navigator and communications specialist behind pilot, also on wall-facing seats. Rest area for relief crew slightly larger than that of An-124. Cabin for 60–70 persons above hold aft of wing carry-through. Primary access to flight deck via airstair door, with ladder extension, forward of wing on port side. Door to main hold aft of wing on starboard side. Hydraulically operated visor type upward hinged nose takes 7 min to open fully, with simultaneous extension of folding nose loading ramp. Completely unobstructed lower deck freight hold, 43.0 m (141 ft) long, has titanium floor, attached 'mobilely' to lower fuselage structure to accommodate changes of temperature, with rollgangs and retractable attachments for cargo tiedowns. Interior can be heated with warm air from a perforated tube above the floor on each side of hold. Internal loads can include vehicles, ground test and field maintenance equipment required by external loads. Two longitudinal mounting beams for external loads above wing centre-

section. Small blister fairings forward of beams and forward of tailplane cover load attachments.

AVIONICS AND EQUIPMENT: Generally similar to An-124, with comprehensive but conventional flight deck equipment including automatic flight control system and moving map display; no electronic flight displays. Two dielectric areas of nose visor enclose forward looking weather radar and downward looking ground mapping/navigation radar. Quadruple INS, plus Loran and Omega.

DIMENSIONS, EXTERNAL:
Wing span	88.40 m (290 ft 0 in)
Length overall	84.00 m (275 ft 7 in)
Height overall	18.10 m (59 ft 4¾ in)
Tailplane span	32.65 m (107 ft 1½ in)

WEIGHTS:
Max payload, internal or external
  250,000 kg (551,150 lb)
Max T-O weight   600,000 kg (1,322,750 lb)

PERFORMANCE (estimated):
Cruising speed
  378-458 knots (700-850 km/h; 435-528 mph)
Min turning radius about nosewheels   50 m (165 ft)
T-O run, carrying *Buran* 2,500–2,800 m (8,200–9,185 ft)
Range with 200,000 kg (440,900 lb) internal payload
  2,425 nm (4,500 km; 2,795 miles)

BERIEV

GENERAL DESIGNER: Alexander K. Konstantinov

This design bureau is named after Georgi Mikhailovich Beriev, whose death at the age of 77 was reported in July 1979. Based at Taganrog, in the northeast corner of the Sea of Azov, it has been the centre for all Soviet seaplane development since 1945.

BERIEV Be-12 (M-12) TCHAIKA (SEAGULL)
NATO reporting name: Mail

This twin-turboprop medium-range anti-submarine and maritime reconnaissance amphibian flew for the first time in 1960. Production started in 1964, and Be-12s have since formed standard equipment at coastal air bases of the Soviet Northern and Black Sea Fleets, for anti-submarine and surveillance duties out to some 200 nm (370 km; 230 miles) from shore. Of an estimated total of 100 built, about 75 remain in Soviet service.

TYPE: Twin-turboprop anti-submarine and maritime patrol amphibian.

WINGS: Cantilever high-wing monoplane of sharply cranked configuration to raise propellers clear of water. Unswept constant chord centre-section; tapered outer panels. All-metal two-spar structure. Hydraulically boosted ailerons actuated by pushrods. Two electrically operated tabs in each aileron. Hydraulically actuated trailing-edge flaps in two sections on each wing, from aileron to centre-section (passing under engine) and on centre-section.

Beriev Be-12 Tchaika twin-turboprop maritime reconnaissance amphibian (*Pilot Press*)

Beriev Be-12 Tchaika anti-submarine and maritime patrol amphibian flying-boat of the Soviet Naval Air Force *(Swedish Air Force via FLYGvapenNYTT)*

FUSELAGE: Single-step all-metal semi-monocoque hull of high length to beam ratio. Two long strakes, one above the other, on each side of front fuselage to prevent spray from enveloping the propellers at take-off.

TAIL UNIT: All-metal structure. Considerable dihedral on two-spar tailplane, which has two endplate fins and horn balanced rudders at tips. Control surfaces actuated by pushrods, with hydraulic boost. Electrically operated trim tab in each elevator and each rudder.

LANDING GEAR: Hydraulically retractable tailwheel type, comprising single-wheel main units which retract upward through 180° to lie flush within sides of hull, and a rearward retracting steerable tailwheel. Oleo-pneumatic mainwheel shock absorbers. Except for top of each mainwheel, all units are fully enclosed by doors when retracted. Non-retractable wingtip floats.

POWER PLANT: Two Ivchenko AI-20M turboprops, each rated at 3,124 kW (4,190 ehp) and driving an AV-68I four-blade variable-pitch propeller. Metal cowlings open downward in halves, permitting their use as servicing platforms. Fuel tanks, between spars in wings and in fuselage, with total capacity of approx 11,000 litres (2,905 US gallons; 2,420 Imp gallons).

ACCOMMODATION: Crew of five on flight deck. Glazed navigation and observation station in nose. Astrodome observation station in top of rear fuselage. Side hatches in rear fuselage permit loading while afloat.

SYSTEMS: Hydraulic system actuates flaps and landing gear. Two engine driven generators power 28V DC electrical system.

AVIONICS AND EQUIPMENT: No details available of com/nav systems or IFF. Radome above nose glazing. MAD (magnetic anomaly detection) 'sting' extends rearward from tail. APU exhausts through aperture in port side of rear fuselage.

ARMAMENT: Internal weapons bay in bottom of hull aft of step. One large and one smaller external stores pylon under each outer wing panel, for torpedoes, depth charges, mines and other stores.

DIMENSIONS, EXTERNAL:
Wing span	29.71 m (97 ft 5¾ in)
Wing aspect ratio	8.4
Length overall	30.17 m (99 ft 0 in)
Height overall	7.00 m (22 ft 11½ in)
Propeller diameter	4.85 m (16 ft 0 in)

AREA:
Wings, gross	105 m² (1,130 sq ft)

WEIGHTS:
Max operational load	10,000 kg (22,045 lb)
Max T-O weight	31,000 kg (68,345 lb)

PERFORMANCE:
Max level speed	328 knots (608 km/h; 378 mph)
Normal operating speed	172 knots (320 km/h; 199 mph)
Rate of climb at S/L	912 m (2,990 ft)/min
Service ceiling	11,280 m (37,000 ft)
Range with max fuel	4,050 nm (7,500 km; 4,660 miles)

BERIEV A-40 ALBATROSS

In a statement in Spring 1988, Rear Adm William O. Studeman, former US director of naval intelligence, said that the Soviet Union was developing a seaplane, with the provisional Western designation 'Tag-D', which had a possible ASW/surveillance/minelaying role. No details were given, but the designation implied that it had been photographed by a US reconnaissance satellite at Taganrog, where the Beriev OKB is centred. No clues were given to the 'Tag-A, B and C' types that must have been identified earlier.

Tag-D was identified as the A-40 Albatross amphibian when the prototype made its first public appearance in the Aviation Day flypast at Tushino Airport, Moscow, on 20 August 1989. The commentator described it as an aircraft for search and rescue, designed under the leadership of Mr A. Konstantinov. A feature in the 6 August issue of *Krasnaya Zvezda* stated that the A-40 will be confined to SAR missions near the coast, and that the next task

confronting its designers is to produce a similar aircraft capable of operating anywhere in the Pacific.

A stores bay, 6.10 m (20 ft) long, in the bottom of the hull, aft of the step, the large nose radar, unidentified hemispherical fairings at the rear of the large pods that house the main landing gear under the wingroots, cylindrical containers (possibly ESM) above the wingtip floats, an in-flight refuelling noseprobe and other items

Beriev A-40 Albatross multi-role amphibian, photographed on Aviation Day 1989 *(Quadrant/Flight)*

Beriev A-40 Albatross twin-turbofan amphibian *(Pilot Press)*

Another view of the twin-turbofan A-40 Albatross amphibian showing the Soloviev D-30KPV turbofans *(AP/Viktor Yurchenko)*

suggest that Adm Studeman's role assessment could also have been correct. However, Mr Konstantinov has suggested that production of the A-40 may no longer be considered necessary.

A second prototype of the A-40 is reported to have been completed in 1989.

TYPE: Twin-turbofan multi-role amphibian.

WINGS: Cantilever high-wing monoplane of relatively high aspect ratio. Sweepback approx 27° on leading-edge, from root. Full-span leading-edge flaps. Long-span two-section area-increasing flaps and aileron occupy full span of each trailing-edge.

FUSELAGE: Single-step hull of high length to beam ratio. Strake on each side of nose and on each side of double-chine planing bottom forward of step. Water

rudder at rear of hull. Large underwing pod on each side of hull, faired into wingroot.

TAIL UNIT: T tail, with all surfaces swept back. Large dorsal fin.

LANDING GEAR: Retractable tricycle type. Main units retract into large underwing pods, aft of wing trailing-edge. Non-retractable stabilising float pylon-mounted under each wingtip.

POWER PLANT: Two Soloviev D-30KPV turbofans (each 117.7 kN; 26,455 lb st), pylon-mounted above fuselage, aft of wings. Flight refuelling probe above nose.

ACCOMMODATION: Conventional flight deck, with door to rear of this on port side. Three circular cabin windows between door and wingroot fairing, probably on each side. Rescue team with power boats, liferafts and other

specialised equipment can be carried, and there is room for up to 60 survivors, who enter the aircraft via hatches in the side of the hull with the aid of mechanised ramps.

EQUIPMENT: In SAR version, onboard equipment to combat hypothermia is available, together with resuscitation and surgical equipment and medicines. Electro-optical sensors and searchlights to detect shipwreck survivors by day or night.

DIMENSIONS, EXTERNAL:
Wing span	41.8 m (137 ft 1½ in)
Length overall, excl noseprobe	43.0 m (141 ft 0 in)
Max depth of hull forward of wing	4.0 m (13 ft 2 in)
Tailplane span	12.0 m (39 ft 4 in)

ILYUSHIN

DESIGN BUREAU HEADQUARTERS: Moscow Central Airport, Khodinka, Moscow

GENERAL DESIGNER: Genrikh V. Novozhilov

This design bureau is named after its former leader, Sergei Vladimirovich Ilyushin, who died on 9 February 1977 at the age of 83. Aircraft designed by Ilyushin and still in service include the Il-14 piston engined light transport and four-turboprop Il-18 transport, of which details have been given in earlier editions of *Jane's*, and the Il-28 twin-jet bomber, produced also in China (see 1986-87 edition). More recent types from the Ilyushin bureau are as follows:

ILYUSHIN Il-20
NATO reporting name: Coot-A

The prototype of the basic Il-18 four-turboprop airliner flew for the first time on 4 July 1957 and production models entered service with Aeroflot in 1959. Production exceeded 700 aircraft, of which more than 100 were exported for use by commercial airlines; a few were delivered for military and government use, usually as VIP transports. Those still in civilian and military use include former passenger carrying Il-18s converted into freighters for Aeroflot by Factory 402 at Moscow/Bykovo. Modifications include installation of a freight door 3.50 m (11 ft 6 in) wide in the rear fuselage and a strengthened cabin floor.

An anti-submarine derivative, the **Il-38** (NATO reporting name 'May'), is in service and is described separately. Another military variant of the Il-18, seen for the first time in 1978, is the **Il-20** elint/reconnaissance aircraft, known to NATO as **Coot-A** and shown in accompanying illustrations. In this case, the airframe appears to be basically unchanged by comparison with the transport. It carries under its fuselage a container about 10.25 m long and 1.15 m deep (33 ft 7½ in × 3 ft 9 in), which is assumed to house side looking radar. There is a further container, about 4.4 m long and 0.88 m deep (14 ft 5 in × 2 ft 10½ in), on each side of the forward fuselage, containing a door over a camera or other sensor. Numerous other antennae and blisters can be seen, about eight of them on the undersurface

Ilyushin Il-20 (NATO 'Coot-A') elint/reconnaissance development of the Il-18 airliner *(Pilot Press)*

of the centre and rear fuselage, with two large plates projecting above the forward fuselage. A brief reference to a further variant of the Il-18, designated **Il-22**, appears after this entry.

A detailed description of the commercial airliner versions of the Il-18 can be found in the 1979-80 and earlier editions of *Jane's*. The following abbreviated details of the Il-18D are retained as an indication of likely features of the military Il-20:

POWER PLANT: Four 3,169 kW (4,250 ehp) Ivchenko AI-20M turboprops, each driving an AV-68I four-blade reversible-pitch propeller. Ten flexible fuel tanks in inboard panel of each wing and integral tank in outboard panel, with a total capacity of 23,700 litres (6,261 US gallons; 5,213 Imp gallons). Some Il-18 airliners have additional bag tanks in centre-section, giving a total capacity of 30,000 litres (7,925 US gallons; 6,600 Imp gallons).

Ilyushin Il-20 (NATO 'Coot-A') electronic intelligence (elint) and reconnaissance aircraft *(Swedish Air Force, via FLYGvapenNYTT)*

DIMENSIONS, EXTERNAL:

Wing span	37.42 m (122 ft 9¼ in)
Wing chord: at root	5.61 m (18 ft 5 in)
at tip	1.87 m (6 ft 2 in)
Wing aspect ratio	10
Length overall	35.9 m (117 ft 9 in)
Height overall	10.17 m (33 ft 4 in)
Tailplane span	11.80 m (38 ft 8½ in)
Wheel track	9.00 m (29 ft 6 in)
Wheelbase	12.78 m (41 ft 10 in)
Propeller diameter	4.50 m (14 ft 9 in)
Cabin doors (each): Height	1.40 m (4 ft 7 in)
Width	0.76 m (2 ft 6 in)
Height to sill	2.90 m (9 ft 6 in)

DIMENSIONS, INTERNAL:

Flight deck: Volume	9.36 m³ (330 cu ft)
Cabin, excl flight deck:	
Length	approx 24.0 m (79 ft 0 in)
Max width	3.23 m (10 ft 7 in)
Max height	2.00 m (6 ft 6¾ in)
Volume	238 m³ (8,405 cu ft)

AREA:

Wings, gross	140 m² (1,507 sq ft)

WEIGHTS (Il-18D airliner):

Max payload	13,500 kg (29,750 lb)
Max T-O weight	64,000 kg (141,100 lb)

PERFORMANCE (Il-18D airliner, at max T-O weight):

Max cruising speed	364 knots (675 km/h; 419 mph)
Econ cruising speed	337 knots (625 km/h; 388 mph)
Operating height	8,000-10,000 m (26,250-32,800 ft)
T-O run	1,300 m (4,265 ft)
Landing run	850 m (2,790 ft)
Range, 1 h reserves:	
with max fuel	3,508 nm (6,500 km; 4,040 miles)
with max payload	1,997 nm (3,700 km; 2,300 miles)

ILYUSHIN Il-22
NATO reporting name: Coot-B

A substantial number of Il-22 airborne command post adaptations of the Il-18 transport is operational with Soviet air forces. No details are available, but it would be logical to expect a variety of external fairings and antennae. NATO reporting name for these aircraft is 'Coot-B'.

ILYUSHIN Il-38
NATO reporting name: May

The airframe of this intermediate-range shore-based anti-submarine/maritime patrol aircraft was developed from that of the Il-18 airliner in the same way that the US Navy's P-3 Orion was based on the Lockheed Electra transport. The fuselage is lengthened, and the complete wing assembly is much farther forward than on the Il-18, to cater for the effect on the CG position of internal equipment and stores.

Il-38s of the Soviet Naval Air Force are encountered over the Baltic and North Atlantic. A treaty of friendship and co-operation signed with the People's Democratic Republic of Yemen permits patrols over the Red Sea, Gulf of Aden, Arabian Sea and Indian Ocean from a base in that country. Other Il-38s have been deployed periodically to Libya and Syria.

In 1975, the Indian Navy ordered an initial batch of three refurbished ex-Soviet Navy Il-38s, which equip INAS 315 at Dabolim, Goa. About 59 are believed to be operational with Soviet naval units.

TYPE: Four-turboprop maritime patrol aircraft.

WINGS: Cantilever low-wing monoplane. Dihedral 3° from roots. Mean thickness/chord ratio 14 per cent. All-metal structure. Three spars in centre-section, two in outer wings. All-metal ailerons are mass and aerodynamically balanced, and fitted with electrically actuated trim tabs. Flying controls cable actuated. Hydraulically actuated double-slotted flaps. Electro-thermal de-icing.

FUSELAGE: Circular-section all-metal semi-monocoque structure of fail-safe type, with ripstop doublers around window cutouts, door frames and the more heavily loaded skin panels.

TAIL UNIT: Cantilever all-metal structure. Electrically actuated trim tabs in rudder and elevators. Additional spring tab in rudder. Flying controls cable actuated and power assisted. Electro-thermal de-icing.

LANDING GEAR: Retractable tricycle type, strengthened by comparison with that of Il-18. Hydraulic actuation. Four-wheel bogie main units, with 930 mm × 305 mm tyres and hydraulic brakes. Steerable (45° each way) twin nosewheel unit, with 700 mm × 250 mm tyres. Hydraulic brakes and nosewheel steering. Pneumatic emergency braking.

POWER PLANT: Four Ivchenko AI-20M turboprops, each rated at 3,169 kW (4,250 shp), driving AV-68I four-blade reversible-pitch metal propellers. Multiple bag type fuel tanks in centre-section and in inboard panel of each wing, and integral tank in outboard panel, with a total capacity of 30,000 litres (7,925 US gallons; 6,600 Imp gallons). Pressure fuelling through four international standard connections in inner nacelles. Provision for overwing

fuelling. Oil capacity 58.5 litres (15.45 US gallons; 12.85 Imp gallons) per engine. Engines started electrically.

ACCOMMODATION: Pilot and co-pilot side by side on flight deck, with dual controls; flight engineer to rear. Number of operational crew believed to be nine, but unconfirmed. Flight deck is separated from main cabin by a pressure bulkhead to reduce hazards following sudden decompression of either. Main cabin has few windows and contains search equipment, electronic equipment and crew stations appropriate to role. Door is on starboard side at rear of cabin (location of Il-18 service door).

SYSTEMS: Cabin pressurised to max differential of 0.49 bars (7.1 lb/sq in). Electrical system includes eight engine driven generators for 28V DC and 115V 400Hz AC supply. Hydraulic system, pressure 207 bars (3,000 lb/sq in), for landing gear retraction, nosewheel steering, brakes, elevator and rudder actuators, flaps, weapon bay doors and radar antennae.

AVIONICS AND EQUIPMENT: Navigation/weather radar in nose. Search radar in undernose radome. MAD tail 'sting'. Automatic navigation equipment, radio compasses and radio altimeter probably similar to those of Il-18.

ARMAMENT: Two weapons/stores bays forward and aft of wing carry-through structure on most aircraft, to accommodate a variety of attack weapons and sonobuoys.

DIMENSIONS, EXTERNAL:
As listed under Il-20 entry, except:

Length overall	39.60 m (129 ft 10 in)
Height overall	10.17 m (33 ft 4 in)

Ilyushin Il-38 anti-submarine/maritime patrol derivative of the Il-18 airliner *(Pilot Press)*

Ilyushin Il-38 (four Ivchenko AI-20M turboprops) over the Mediterranean, escorted by an RAF Hawk in 63 Squadron markings *(Royal Air Force)*

WEIGHTS:
Weight empty   36,000 kg (79,367 lb)
Max T-O weight   63,500 kg (140,000 lb)
PERFORMANCE:
Max level speed at 6,400 m (21,000 ft)
                390 knots (722 km/h; 448 mph)
Max cruising speed at 8,230 m (27,000 ft)
                330 knots (611 km/h; 380 mph)
Patrol speed at 600 m (2,000 ft)
                216 knots (400 km/h; 248 mph)
Min flying speed   103 knots (190 km/h; 118 mph)
T-O run   1,300 m (4,265 ft)
Landing run with propeller reversal   850 m (2,790 ft)
Range with max fuel   3,887 nm (7,200 km; 4,473 miles)
Patrol endurance with max fuel   12 h

ILYUSHIN Il-62
NATO reporting name: Classic

Brief details of the early history of this rear-engined four-turbofan long-range airliner can be found in the 1982-83 *Jane's*. Structural and specification details of the Il-62/62M/62MK series of production aircraft are contained in the 1989-90 and previous editions.

ILYUSHIN Il-76
NATO reporting name: Candid
Indian Air Force name: Gajaraj

Towards the end of the 1960s, the Ilyushin design bureau, under the leadership of Mr G. V. Novozhilov, began design of a heavy transport to replace the turboprop An-12. Nominal task for the aircraft was to transport 40 tonnes of freight for a distance of 2,700 nm (5,000 km; 3,100 miles) in less than six hours. It had to be capable of operation from short unprepared airstrips, in the most difficult weather conditions experienced in Siberia, the north of the Soviet Union and the Far East, while being much simpler to service and able to fly much faster than the An-12.

A prototype of this transport, known as the Il-76 (SSSR-86712), flew for the first time on 25 March 1971 and series production began in 1975. Subsequent operation in the most difficult weather and ground conditions of Central and Eastern Siberia revealed operating costs more than 25 per cent lower per tonne/km than for the An-12. This suggested that the Il-76 would be competitive with river transport, even during Summer months.

It was clear from the start that the Il-76 had considerable potential as a military transport. Evaluation by the Soviet Air Force had reached an advanced stage by 1974, when an official film depicted Il-76s with twin-gun rear turrets in use as vehicles for Soviet airborne troops, presumably with a development squadron.

Since that time, development of the Il-76 has continued, and the following major production versions can now be identified:

Il-76 (Candid-A). Initial basic production version.

Il-76T (Candid-A). Developed version, with additional fuel tankage in wing centre-section, above fuselage, and heavier payload. No armament.

Il-76M (Candid-B). As Il-76T, but for military use, with rear gun turret containing two twin-barrel 23 mm GSh-23L guns, and small ECM fairings between centre windows at front of navigator's compartment, on each side of front fuselage, and on each side of rear fuselage. Packs of ninety-six 50 mm IRCM (infra-red countermeasures) flares in landing gear fairings and/or on sides of rear fuselage of Soviet aircraft operating into combat areas. Turret and ECM not always fitted on export Il-76Ms. Up to 140 troops or 125 paratroops can be carried as an alternative to freight.

Il-76TD (Candid-A). Unarmed version, generally similar to Il-76T. First identified in November 1982, when an example registered SSSR-76467 passed through Shannon Airport in Ireland. Fully operational from July 1983, this version has Soloviev D-30KP-1 engines which maintain full power up to ISA + 23°C against ISA + 15°C for earlier models. Max T-O weight and payload are increased. An increase of 10,000 kg (22,046 lb) in max fuel capacity provides an increase of 648 nm (1,200 km; 745 miles) in range with max fuel.

One Il-76TD has been equipped to transport members of Soviet Antarctic expeditions between Maputo in Mozambique and Molodozhnaya Station in Antarctica. The hold has been soundproofed and contains seats, a buffet kitchen, toilet and working facilities. Baggage is carried in containers. On its first proving flight from Moscow, via Leningrad, Larnaca, Djibouti and Maputo to Molodozhnaya and Novolazarevskaya stations, this aircraft carried 94 passengers and 14,000 kg (30,865 lb) of scientific equipment and other cargo. The final stage from Maputo was flown on 25 February 1986, replacing the Il-18D used on the service for five years.

Il-76MD (Candid-B). Military version, generally similar to Il-76M but with same improvements as Il-76TD.

By Spring 1990, about 450 military Il-76s and Il-76M/MDs had been delivered to first-line squadrons of the Soviet Transport Aviation force, as An-12 replacements, from the assembly plant at Tashkent. Other customers for the military version include the air forces of Algeria, Iraq, Czechoslovakia and Poland. India has 24, which are known by the Indian Air Force name of **Gajaraj.**

India is reported to be considering the conversion of some of its standard Il-76s for AEW duties. A specialised AEW&C version of the Il-76, known to NATO as 'Mainstay', is described separately, as is the Il-78 flight refuelling tanker version known as 'Midas'. Iraq has operated locally modified Il-76s in a tanker role since the mid-1980s, and has developed an AEW&C version, named **Adnan 1**, which resembles 'Mainstay' but is said to embody a locally manufactured ground radar in its rotodome. Adnan 1, named after a former Iraqi defence Minister, supersedes the Baghdad 1, described and illustrated in the 1989-90 *Jane's*. (*See Iraqi section.*)

Aeroflot has more than 120 Il-76s, including Il-76Ts and Il-76Ms, which form an immediately available military reserve. At least 85 civil and military Il-76s have been exported. Of these, Iraqi Airways has received a total of about 33 Il-76Ts and Il-76Ms (one has been shot down), which are operated on behalf of the military services; Jamahiriya Libyan Arab Airlines has 21 Il-76Ts and Il-76Ms; Syrianair has two Il-76Ms and two Il-76Ts. The guns are removed from the rear turret of Il-76Ms in airline service, and the first of at least two Il-76MDs delivered to Cubana, in November 1984, had no tail turret.

In specialised roles, Il-76s have served as a testbed for the power plant of the Il-86 and the Lotarev D-236 propfan, and as aircraft in which Soviet cosmonauts have been able to experience several tens of seconds of weightlessness during training. The engine testbed has the designation **Il-76LL** and is available for flight test work on a commercial contract basis, from the Soviet Flight Research Institute. Engines of up to 245 kN (55,100 lb st) can be installed in place of the aircraft's normal port inner D-30KP.

Production was continuing at the rate of more than 50 aircraft a year in 1989. The following description applies to the Il-76T:

TYPE: Four-turbofan medium/long-range freight transport.
WINGS: Cantilever monoplane, mounted above fuselage to leave interior unobstructed, and with constant anhedral from junction with centre-section on each side. Sweepback 25° at quarter-chord. Thickness/chord ratio 13 per cent at root, 10 per cent at tip. All-metal five-piece structure, comprising centre-section, two inner panels carrying engines, and two outer panels. Leading-edge sweepback constant. Trailing-edge sweep increases outboard of joint between each inner and outer panel. Multi-spar fail-safe construction. Centre-section integral with fuselage. Mass balanced ailerons, with balance/trim tabs. Two-section triple-slotted flaps over approx 75 per cent of each semi-span, from wingroot to inboard edge of aileron. Eight upper surface spoilers forward of flaps on each wing, four on each inner and outer wing panel. Leading-edge slats over almost entire span, two on each inner panel, three on each outer panel.
FUSELAGE: All-metal semi-monocoque fail-safe structure of basically circular section. Underside of upswept rear fuselage made up of two outward hinged clamshell doors, upward hinged panel between these doors, and downward hinged loading ramp.
TAIL UNIT: Cantilever all-metal structure, with variable incidence T tailplane. All surfaces sweptback. All control surfaces aerodynamically balanced. Tabs in rudder and each elevator.

Ilyushin Il-76MD four-turbofan heavy freight carrying transport, with added scrap view (centre right) of Il-78 tanker *(Pilot Press)*

Ilyushin II-76TD freight transport (four Soloviev D-30KP-1 turbofans) in Aeroflot insignia *(P. J. Cooper)*

LANDING GEAR: Hydraulically retractable tricycle type, designed for operation from prepared and unprepared runways. Steerable nose unit made up of two pairs of wheels, side by side, with central oleo. Main gear on each side is made up of two units in tandem, each unit with four wheels on a single axle. Low-pressure tyres size 1,300 × 480 on mainwheels, 1,100 × 330 on nosewheels. Nosewheels retract forward. Main units retract inward into two large ventral fairings under fuselage, with an additional large fairing on each side of lower fuselage over actuating gear. During retraction mainwheel axles rotate around leg, so that wheels stow with axles parallel to fuselage axis (ie: wheels remain vertical but at 90° to direction of flight). All doors on wheel wells close when gear is down, to prevent fouling of legs by snow, ice, mud, etc. Oleo-pneumatic shock absorbers. Tyre pressure can be varied in flight from 2.5 to 5 bars (36-73 lb/sq in) to suit different landing strip conditions. Hydraulic brakes on mainwheels.

POWER PLANT: Four Soloviev D-30KP turbofans, each rated at 117.7 kN (26,455 lb st), in individual underwing pods. Each pod is carried on a large forward-inclined pylon and is fitted with a clamshell thrust reverser. Integral fuel tanks between spars of inner and outer wing panels. Total fuel capacity reported to be 81,830 litres (21,617 US gallons; 18,000 Imp gallons).

ACCOMMODATION: Crew of seven, including two freight handlers. Conventional side by side seating for pilot and co-pilot on spacious flight deck. Station for navigator below flight deck in glazed nose. Crew door on port side of nose. Forward hinged main cabin door on each side of fuselage forward of wing. Two windows on each side of hold serve as emergency exits. Hold has reinforced floor of titanium alloys, with folding roller conveyors, and is loaded via rear ramp. Entire accommodation is pressurised, and advanced mechanical handling systems are provided for containerised and other freight, which can include standard ISO containers, each 12 m (39 ft 4½ in) long, building machinery, heavy crawlers and mobile cranes. Typical loads include six containers measuring either 2.99 × 2.44 × 2.44 m (9 ft 9¾ in × 8 ft × 8 ft) or 2.99 × 2.44 × 1.90 m (9 ft 9¾ in × 8 ft × 6 ft 2¾ in) and with loaded weights of 5,670 kg (12,500 lb) or 5,000 kg (11,025 lb) respectively; or twelve containers measuring 1.46 × 2.44 × 1.90 m (4 ft 9¼ in × 8 ft × 6 ft 2¾ in) and each weighing 2,500 kg (5,511 lb) loaded; or six pallets measuring 2.99 × 2.44 m (9 ft 9¾ in × 8 ft) and each weighing 5,670 kg (12,500 lb); or twelve pallets measuring 1.46 × 2.44 m (4 ft 9¼ in × 8 ft) and each weighing 2,500 kg (5,511 lb). Folding seats along sidewalls in central portion of hold. Quick configuration changes can be made by the use of modules, each able to accommodate 30 passengers in four-abreast seating, litter patients and medical attendants, or cargo. Three such modules can be carried, each approx 6.10 m (20 ft) long, 2.44 m (8 ft) wide and 2.44 m (8 ft) high. They are loaded through the rear doors by means of two overhead travelling cranes, and are secured to the cabin floor with cargo restraints. Two winches at front of hold, each with capacity of 3,000 kg (6,615 lb). Cranes embody total of four hoists, each with capacity of 2,500 kg (5,511 lb). Ramp can be used as additional hoist, with capacity of up to 30,000 kg (66,140 lb) to facilitate loading of large vehicles and those with caterpillar tracks. Pilot's and co-pilot's windscreens can each be fitted with two wipers, top and bottom.

SYSTEMS: Flight deck only, or entire interior, can be pressurised; max differential 0.50 bars (7.25 lb/sq in). Hydraulic system includes servo motors and motors to drive the flaps, slats, landing gear and its doors, ramp, rear fuselage clamshell doors and load hoists. Flying control boosters are supplied by electric pumps and are independent of the central hydraulic supply. Manual control is possible after booster failure. Electrical system includes engine driven generators, auxiliary generators driven by an APU, DC converters and batteries. It powers the pumps for the flying control system boosters, radio and avionics, and lighting systems.

AVIONICS AND EQUIPMENT: Full equipment for all-weather operation by day and night, including a computer for automatic flight control and automatic landing approach. Weather radar in nose; navigation and ground mapping radar in undernose radome. APU in port side landing gear fairing for engine starting and to supply all aircraft systems on ground, making aircraft independent of ground facilities.

DIMENSIONS, EXTERNAL:
Wing span	50.50 m (165 ft 8 in)
Wing aspect ratio	8.5
Length overall	46.59 m (152 ft 10¼ in)
Fuselage: Max diameter	4.80 m (15 ft 9 in)
Height overall	14.76 m (48 ft 5 in)
Rear loading aperture: Width	3.40 m (11 ft 1¾ in)
Height	3.45 m (11 ft 4 in)

DIMENSIONS, INTERNAL:
Cabin: Length: excl ramp	20.00 m (65 ft 7½ in)
incl ramp	24.50 m (80 ft 4½ in)
Width	3.40 m (11 ft 1¾ in)
Height	3.46 m (11 ft 4¼ in)
Volume	235.3 m³ (8,310 cu ft)

AREA:
Wings, gross	300.0 m² (3,229.2 sq ft)

WEIGHTS AND LOADINGS (A: Il-76T, B: Il-76TD):
Max payload: A	40,000 kg (88,185 lb)
B	48,000 kg (105,820 lb)
Max T-O weight: A	170,000 kg (374,785 lb)
B	190,000 kg (418,875 lb)
Permissible axle load (vehicles):	
A	7,500-11,000 kg (16,535-24,250 lb)

Permissible floor loading:
A	1,450-3,100 kg/m² (297-635 lb/sq ft)
Max wing loading: A	566.7 kg/m² (116.05 lb/sq ft)
B	633.3 kg/m² (129.72 lb/sq ft)
Max power loading: A	361.1 kg/kN (3.54 lb/lb st)
B	403.6 kg/kN (3.95 lb/lb st)

PERFORMANCE (Il-76T):
Max level speed	459 knots (850 km/h; 528 mph)
Cruising speed	405-432 knots (750-800 km/h; 466-497 mph)
T-O speed	114 knots (210 km/h; 131 mph)
Approach and landing speed	119-130 knots (220-240 km/h; 137-149 mph)
Normal cruising height	9,000-12,000 m (29,500-39,370 ft)
Absolute ceiling	approx 15,500 m (50,850 ft)
T-O run	850 m (2,790 ft)
Landing run	450 m (1,475 ft)
Nominal range with 40,000 kg (88,185 lb) payload	2,700 nm (5,000 km; 3,100 miles)
Max range, with reserves	3,617 nm (6,700 km; 4,163 miles)

ILYUSHIN Il-76 (AEW&C)
NATO reporting name: Mainstay

Development of this AEW&C (airborne early warning and control) version of the Il-76 began in the 1970s as a replacement for the Tu-126s operated by the Soviet Voyska PVO home defence force and tactical air forces. Known to NATO as 'Mainstay', it has a conventionally located rotating 'saucer' radome, lengthened fuselage forward of the wings, a flight refuelling probe, a new IFF system and comprehensive ECM equipment. The normal glazing around a navigator's station in the nose is replaced by non-transparent fairings. There is an intake, presumably for avionics cooling, at the front of the dorsal fin; and the rear gun turret of the military Il-76M has been deleted.

AEW&C version of Ilyushin Il-76, known to NATO as 'Mainstay' *(Pilot Press)*

'Mainstays' provide Soviet forces with the capability to detect and track aircraft and cruise missiles flying at low altitude over land and water and could be used to help direct fighter operations over European and Asian battlefields as well as to enhance air surveillance and defence of the USSR. About 12 had been deployed, mostly to the Soviet north-western TVD (theatre of military operations), by early 1990, and a production rate of five aircraft a year is expected. They are intended to operate primarily with the Soviet air forces' MiG-29, MiG-31 and Sukhoi Su-27 counter-air fighters. A Soviet designation of **A-50** has been reported but not confirmed.

ILYUSHIN Il-78
NATO reporting name: Midas
In the mid-1970s the Ilyushin OKB began development of the Il-78 probe-and-drogue flight refuelling tanker version of the Il-76MD. Known to NATO as 'Midas', it is replacing the modified Myasishchev M-4 ('Bison') aircraft that have served previously in this role. The first operational 'Midas' entered service in 1987, in support of both tactical and strategic combat aircraft. Generally similar to the Il-76M transport, it is a three-point tanker, with refuelling pods of the same type under the outer wings and on the port side of the rear fuselage. Rear turret retained as flight refuelling observation station, without guns.

ILYUSHIN Il-86
NATO reporting name: Camber
The early history of this four-turbofan wide-bodied passenger transport was outlined in the 1982-83 and previous editions of *Jane's*. Construction of two prototypes was started in 1974. On 22 December 1976, piloted by Hero of the Soviet Union A. Kuznetsov, the first of these (SSSR-86000) made a first flight of about 40 min after taking off in 1,700 m (5,575 ft) from a 1,820 m (5,970 ft) runway at the old Moscow Central Airport of Khodinka, where the Ilyushin Bureau has its headquarters, to the official flight test centre.

Aircraft SSSR-86002, which flew for the first time at Voronezh on 24 October 1977, was described as the first production Il-86. Aeroflot took delivery of its first Il-86 (SSSR-86004) on 24 September 1979, and scheduled services began on 26 December 1980. First international service operated by Il-86 was Moscow-East Berlin, from 3 July 1981. It is intended to produce a total of more than 100 Il-86s by 1995, of which about 65 are believed to have entered service by the beginning of 1989. To remedy deficiencies in designed performance, the prototype of a new version with Soloviev PS-90A (D-90) high bypass ratio turbofans, each rated at approximately 157 kN (35,300 lb st), was scheduled to fly for the first time in 1990.

For production aircraft, wing slats, pylons to carry the engine pods, the tail fin and tailplane are being manufactured in Poland by PZL Mielec. Final assembly is centred at Voronezh. The airframe is believed to be designed for 40,000 flying hours or 20,000 landings.

The following description applies to the initial production Il-86:

TYPE: Four-turbofan wide-bodied passenger transport.

WINGS: Cantilever monoplane of all-metal construction (fixed surfaces made at Voronezh). Wings mounted in low/mid position on fuselage. Dihedral from roots. Sweepback 35° at quarter-chord. Three spars in inner wings, two in each outer panel. Large double-slotted trailing-edge flaps, in two sections along entire span of each wing inboard of aileron. Multi-section spoilers and airbrakes in top surface, forward of all four flap sections. Full span leading-edge slats, with small cutaway to clear each inboard engine pylon. Shallow fence on top surface in line with each pylon.

FUSELAGE: Conventional semi-monocoque light alloy pressurised structure of circular cross section. Floors of main and lower decks of honeycomb and carbonfibre reinforced plastics.

TAIL UNIT: Conventional sweptback cantilever structure, with tailplane dihedral. Variable incidence tailplane. Each control surface in two sections.

LANDING GEAR: Retractable four-unit type. Forward retracting steerable twin-wheel nose unit, and three four-wheel bogie main units. Two of the latter retract inward into the wingroot fairings; the third unit is mounted centrally under the fuselage, slightly forward of the others, and retracts forward. (Main landing gear made at Kuybyshev.) Mainwheel tyres size 1,300 × 480; nosewheel tyres size 1,120 × 450.

POWER PLANT: Four Kuznetsov NK-86 turbofans, each rated at 127.5 kN (28,660 lb st), mounted on pylons forward of wing leading-edges. Engines fitted with combined thrust reversers/noise attenuators. Integral fuel tanks in wings, capacity 70,000-80,000 litres (18,492-21,133 US gallons; 15,398-17,597 Imp gallons).

ACCOMMODATION: Standard flight crew comprises two pilots and a flight engineer, with provision for a navigator if required. Flight engineer's seat normally faces to starboard, aft of co-pilot, but can pivot to central forward-facing position to enable the engineer to operate the throttles. Upper deck, on which all seats are located, is divided into three separate cabins by wardrobes, a serving area connected by elevator to the lower deck galley, and cabin staff accommodation, with a total of eight toilets at front (2) and rear (6) of the aircraft. Cabins feature unusually large windows, indirect lighting in walls and in ceiling panels, and enclosed baggage lockers at top of side walls. Preponderance of metal and natural fibre materials rather than plastics throughout cabins to enhance safety in an emergency. Up to 350 passengers in basic nine-abreast seating throughout, with two aisles, each 55 cm (21.6 in) wide. Suggested mixed class alternative layout provides for 28 passengers six-abreast in the front cabin, and 206 passengers eight-abreast in the other two cabins. Passengers enter via three airstair doors (made in Kharkov), which hinge down from the port side of the lower deck. One of these doors is forward of the wing; the others are aft of the wing. Four further doors at upper deck level on each side, for emergency use (using dual inflatable escape slides) and for use at airports where the utilisation of high level boarding steps or bridges is preferred. Coats and hand baggage are stowed on the lower deck before passengers climb one of three fixed staircases to the main deck. (A version of the Il-86 is available without the lower deck airstair doors and staircases, reducing operating weight empty by 3,000 kg; 6,610 lb and permitting installation of 25 more seats on upper deck.) Cargo holds on the lower deck are designed to accommodate heavy or registered baggage and freight in 8 standard LD3 containers, or 16 LD3 containers if some of the carry-on baggage racks are omitted. Access is via upward hinged doors forward of the starboard wingroot leading-edge and at the side of the rear hold. Containers can be loaded and unloaded by means of a self-propelled truck with built-in roller conveyor. Films can be shown in flight, and there is a choice of 12 tape recorded audio programmes. A bar-buffet can be provided on the lower deck in place of the baggage and freight accommodation in the forward vestibule.

SYSTEMS: Four completely self-contained hydraulic systems, each operated by one of the engines, for actuation of flying control surfaces, tailplane variable incidence, spoilers, airbrakes, slats, flaps, landing gear, nosewheel steering, wheel brakes, anti-skid system, and upper level doors when passenger gangways are used. No provision for manual operation of primary flying control surfaces after failure of powered systems. All hot pipelines of air-conditioning system, and all fuel supply lines, outside pressure cell. Primary 200/155V 400Hz AC electrical system, powered by four 40kVA engine driven generators. Secondary 36V three-phase AC and 27V DC systems. Five accumulators and static transformer. Smoke detection system, with sensors in baggage, freight and equipment stowage areas. Pulse generating de-icing system consuming 500 times less energy than a conventional hot air or electrical system. APU in tailcone.

AVIONICS: All avionics equipment located within pressurised part of fuselage. Flight control and nav systems provide for automatic climb to the selected height, control of the rate of climb and automatic descent, and permit automatic landing in ICAO Cat IIIA conditions. Pre-programmable Doppler nav system with readout display screen on flight deck, on which microfilmed maps

'Mainstay', the AEW&C version of the Il-76 (*333 Squadron, Royal Norwegian Air Force*)

Ilyushin Il-78 (NATO 'Midas') with only the fuselage-side refuelling pod fitted, photographed during a tanking mission with a 'Bear' bomber north of Finnmark, northern Norway (*Royal Norwegian Air Force*)

Ilyushin Il-86 four-turbofan wide-bodied passenger transport (*Pilot Press*)

Ilyushin Il-86 wide-bodied transport (four Kuznetsov NK-86 turbofans) in Aeroflot markings *(Anton Wettstein)*

can be projected. Position of aircraft is indicated by cursor, driven by system computer. Nav system is updated automatically by inputs from VOR or VOR/DME radio beacons.

DIMENSIONS, EXTERNAL:

Wing span	48.06 m (157 ft 8¼ in)
Length overall	59.54 m (195 ft 4 in)
Fuselage: Length	56.10 m (184 ft 0¾ in)
Max diameter	6.08 m (19 ft 11½ in)
Height overall	15.81 m (51 ft 10½ in)
Tailplane span	20.57 m (67 ft 6 in)
Wheel track (c/l of outer shock struts)	
	11.15 m (36 ft 7 in)
Wheelbase	21.34 m (70 ft 0 in)

DIMENSIONS, INTERNAL:

Main cabins: Height	2.61 m (8 ft 7 in)
Max width	approx 5.70 m (18 ft 8½ in)

AREA:

Wings, gross	320 m² (3,444 sq ft)

WEIGHTS:

Max payload	42,000 kg (92,600 lb)
Max fuel	86,000 kg (189,600 lb)
Max T-O weight (dependent on size and type of runway)	190,000-208,000 kg (418,875-458,560 lb)
Max landing weight	175,000 kg (385,800 lb)

PERFORMANCE (designed):

Normal cruising speed at 9,000-11,000 m (30,000-36,000 ft) 486-512 knots (900-950 km/h; 559-590 mph)

Approach speed
130-141 knots (240-260 km/h; 149-162 mph)

Field length for T-O and landing
2,300-2,600 m (7,550-8,530 ft)

* Range: with 40,000 kg (88,185 lb) payload
1,944 nm (3,600 km; 2,235 miles)
* with max fuel 2,480 nm (4,600 km; 2,858 miles)
* *Reports suggest that these design ranges are not being achieved. The East German airline Interflug quotes a max range of 1,350 nm (2,500 km; 1,550 miles) in its sales literature.*

ILYUSHIN Il-96-300 and Il-96-350

Although the 300-seat **Il-96-300** bears a superficial resemblance to the Il-86, it is a new design. Advanced structural materials, including a new high-purity aluminium alloy, and state of the art technology are intended to make practicable a service life of 60,000 hours and 12,000 landings. Use of four Soloviev PS-90A high bypass ratio turbofans is expected to overcome the kind of performance deficiencies experienced with the Il-86, notably in terms of range.

The first of five Il-96-300 prototypes (SSSR-96000) was flown from the aerodrome of Khodinka, near Moscow, headquarters of the Ilyushin OKB, on 28 September 1988. The second followed on 28 November 1989, with the third scheduled to fly for the first time in May 1990. The other two prototypes are being used for static and fatigue testing.

It was planned originally to complete a total of 1,200 flights, representing 1,800 flying hours, before certification in late 1990. These totals are being reduced to 750 flights and 1,200 hours, because of certain areas of commonality with the Il-86. By February 1990, the first prototype had logged nearly 280 hours in 250 flights, the second prototype had flown four times.

A 350-seat version, designated **Il-96-350**, is scheduled to fly for the first time in 1993. Intended for high capacity medium-range operation, it will have a 3.0 m (9 ft 10 in) plug inserted in the fuselage forward of the wing and a 2.5 m (8 ft 2½ in) plug aft of the wing, enabling passenger seating to be increased to 350 at 81 cm (32 in) pitch or 400 at 75.5 cm (29.8 in) pitch. The power plant will be unchanged. Range with max payload will be approx 3,775 nm (7,000 km; 4,350 miles).

It is intended to manufacture 60-70 production Il-96s at Voronezh during the period of the Soviet 1990-95 five-year plan. Most will go to Aeroflot, which has already ordered more than 100, but CSA of Czechoslovakia has stated its intention to operate Il-96s. As with the Il-86, some components of the Il-96 are being manufactured by PZL Mielec in Poland.

The following details refer to the basic Il-96-300:

TYPE: Four-turbofan wide-bodied passenger transport.

WINGS: Cantilever low/mid-wing monoplane of all-metal construction (except for flaps), with winglets. Dihedral from roots. Supercritical section, with sweepback of 30° at quarter-chord. Three spars in inner wings, two in each outer panel. Seven machined skin panels, three top surface and four bottom, with integral stiffeners, on each wing. Full-span leading-edge slats in seven sections on each wing, with small cutaways to clear engine pylons. Entire trailing-edge of each wing occupied by, successively, a double-slotted inboard flap, a small inboard aileron, two-section single-slotted flaps, and the outboard aileron, which is used only as a gust damper and to smooth out buffeting. Flaps are made of composites. Three airbrakes forward of each inboard flap. Six spoilers forward of outer flaps; inboard pair supplement ailerons, others operate as both airbrakes and supplementary ailerons. All flying controls operated by triplex fly by wire system, with manual reversion.

FUSELAGE: Conventional semi-monocoque light alloy pressurised structure of circular cross-section. Floors of main deck and underfloor holds of honeycomb and CFRP.

TAIL UNIT: Conventional sweptback cantilever structure, with tailplane dihedral. Sweepback at quarter-chord 37° 30' on tailplane, 45° on fin. Variable incidence tailplane. Leading- and trailing-edges of fin and tailplane made of composites. Each control surface in two sections. No tabs.

LANDING GEAR: Retractable four-unit type. Forward retracting steerable twin-wheel nose unit, and three four-wheel bogie main units. Two of the latter retract inward into the wingroot/fuselage fairings; the third unit is mounted centrally under the fuselage, to the rear of the others, and retracts forward after the bogie has itself pivoted upward 20°. Oleo-pneumatic shock absorbers.

Nosewheel tyres size 1,260 × 460; mainwheel tyres size 1,300 × 480. Tyre pressure (all) 11.65 bars (169 lb/sq in).

POWER PLANT: Four Soloviev PS-90A turbofans, each rated at 156.9 kN (35,275 lb st), mounted on pylons forward of wing leading-edges. Thrust reversal standard. Integral fuel tanks in wings and fuselage centre-section, total capacity 152,620 litres (40,318 US gallons; 33,572 Imp gallons). APU in tailcone.

ACCOMMODATION: Crew of three on flight deck, comprising pilot, co-pilot and flight engineer, plus two seats for supplementary crew or an observer. Ten or 12 cabin staff. Basic all-tourist configuration has two cabins for 66 and 234 passengers respectively, nine-abreast at 87 cm (34.25 in) seat pitch, separated by a buffet counter, video stowage and lifts from the galley on the lower deck. The two aisles are each 55 cm (21.65 in) wide. There are two toilets and a wardrobe at the front, six more toilets, a rack for cabin staff's belongings and seats for cabin staff at the rear. Seats recline, and are provided with individual tables, ventilation, earphones and attendant call button. Indirect lighting is standard. The 235-seat mixed class version has a front cabin for 22 first class passengers, six-abreast in pairs, at 102 cm (40 in) seat pitch and with aisles 75.5 cm (29.7 in) wide; a centre cabin with 40 business class seats, eight-abreast at 90 cm (35.4 in) seat pitch and with aisles 56.5 cm (22.25 in) wide; and a rear cabin for 173 tourist class passengers, basically nine-abreast at 87 cm (34.25 in) seat pitch, with an aisle width of 55 cm (21.65 in). Unlike the Il-86, the passenger cabin is entered through three doors on the port side of the upper deck, at the front and rear and forward of the wings. Opposite each door, on the starboard side, is an emergency exit door. The lower deck houses a front cargo compartment for six ABK-1.5 (LD3) containers or igloo pallets, a central compartment aft of the wing for ten ABK-1.5 containers or pallets, and a tapering compartment for general cargo at the rear. Three doors on the starboard side provide separate access to each compartment. The galley and lifts are located between the front cargo compartment and the wing, with a separate door aft of the door to the front cargo compartment.

AVIONICS AND EQUIPMENT: On the flight deck, conventional standby instruments are retained, but primary flight information is presented on dual twin-screen colour

Ilyushin Il-96-300 four-turbofan long-range transport *(Pilot Press)*

Prototype Ilyushin Il-96-300 (four Soloviev PS-90A turbofans), which flew for the first time on 28 September 1988

CRTs, fed by triplex INS, a satellite-based and Omega navigation system and other sensors. Triplex flight control and flight management systems, together with a head-up display, permit fully automatic en-route control and operations in ICAO Cat IIIA minima. Duplex engine and systems monitoring and failure warning systems feed in-flight information to both the flight engineer's station and monitors on the ground. Autothrottle is based on IAS, without angle of attack protection. Another electronic system provides real-time automatic weight and CG situation data.

DIMENSIONS, EXTERNAL:

Wing span	57.66 m (189 ft 2 in)
Wing aspect ratio	9.5
Length overall	55.35 m (181 ft 7¼ in)
Fuselage: Length	51.15 m (167 ft 9¾ in)
Diameter	6.08 m (19 ft 11½ in)
Height overall	17.57 m (57 ft 7¾ in)
Tailplane span	20.57 m (67 ft 6 in)
Wheel track	10.40 m (34 ft 1½ in)
Wheelbase	20.065 m (65 ft 10 in)
Passenger doors (three): Height	1.83 m (6 ft 0 in)
Width	1.07 m (3 ft 6 in)
Height to sill: No. 1 and 2	4.54 m (14 ft 10¾ in)
No. 3	4.80 m (15 ft 9 in)
Emergency exit doors (three):	
Height	1.825 m (5 ft 11¾ in)
Width	1.07 m (3 ft 6 in)
Cargo compartment doors (front and centre):	
Height	1.825 m (5 ft 11¾ in)
Width	1.78 m (5 ft 10 in)
Height to sill: front	2.34 m (7 ft 8¼ in)
centre	2.48 m (8 ft 1¾ in)
Cargo compartment door (rear):	
Height	1.38 m (4 ft 6¼ in)
Width	0.972 m (3 ft 2¼ in)
Height to sill	2.74 m (9 ft 0 in)
Galley door: Height	1.20 m (3 ft 11¼ in)
Width	0.80 m (2 ft 7½ in)

DIMENSIONS, INTERNAL:

Cabins, excl flight deck:

Height	2.60 m (8 ft 6¼ in)
Max width	approx 5.70 m (18 ft 8½ in)
Volume	350 m³ (12,360 cu ft)
Cargo hold volume: front	37.10 m³ (1,310 cu ft)
centre	63.80 m³ (2,253 cu ft)
rear	15.00 m³ (530 cu ft)

AREAS:

Wings, gross	391.6 m² (4,215 sq ft)
Vertical tail surfaces (total)	61.0 m² (656.6 sq ft)
Horizontal tail surfaces (total)	96.5 m² (1,038.75 sq ft)

WEIGHTS:

Basic operating weight	117,000 kg (257,940 lb)
Max payload	40,000 kg (88,185 lb)
Max T-O weight	216,000 kg (476,200 lb)
Max landing weight	175,000 kg (385,810 lb)
Max zero-fuel weight	157,000 kg (346,120 lb)

PERFORMANCE (estimated):

Normal cruising speed at 10,100-12,100 m (33,135-39,700 ft)

	459-486 knots (850-900 km/h; 528-559 mph)
Approach speed	140 knots (260 km/h; 162 mph)
Balanced T-O runway length	2,600 m (8,530 ft)
Balanced landing runway length	1,980 m (6,500 ft)

Range, with UASA reserves:

with max payload	4,050 nm (7,500 km; 4,660 miles)
with 30,000 kg (66,140 lb) payload	4,860 nm (9,000 km; 5,590 miles)
with 15,000 kg (33,070 lb) payload	5,940 nm (11,000 km; 6,835 miles)

OPERATIONAL NOISE LEVELS:

Il-96-300 is designed to conform with ICAO Chapter 3 Annex 16 noise requirements

ILYUSHIN Il-96 (Twin-engined version)

The Ilyushin OKB is studying a twin-engined version of the Il-96, powered by Lotarev D-18 turbofans, each rated at between 275 and 314 kN (61,750-70,500 lb st), or equivalent Western turbofans. Like the West European Airbus A330 and A340, the twin-engined and four-engined variants of the Il-96 would use substantially the same wings.

ILYUSHIN Il-114

The Il-114 is the smallest of the new generation of Soviet transport aircraft that is being designed and built for introduction into service during the next decade. Intended to replace aircraft in the class of the An-24, it is being developed for short-haul and feeder services from both paved and grass surfaces. About 10 per cent of the airframe by weight is made of composites and equipment is to the latest standards for ICAO Cat I and II operations. The initial specification calls for 60 seats, but this total could be increased by rearrangement of the interior, and the fuselage

could be lengthened to seat 70/75 persons if required. Service life is intended to be 30,000 hours and 30,000 landings.

The general characteristics of the Il-114 were finalised in 1986, and the prototype (SSSR-54000) flew for the first time at the Zhukovsky flight test centre on 29 March 1990. Using up to three assembly lines, it is planned to manufacture some 500 production aircraft during the period of the Soviet 1990-95 five-year plan, with deliveries to begin in 1992. Parts of the wings will be manufactured in Romania, other portions of the airframe in Poland and Romania, and the tail unit in Bulgaria. Poland will be involved in production of the power plant. Final assembly will be under Ilyushin management in a plant at Tashkent.

TYPE: Twin-turboprop short-range passenger and freight transport.

WINGS: Cantilever low-wing monoplane, built in three sections. Slight dihedral on centre-section; much increased dihedral on outer panels. All-metal two-spar structure of aluminium-lithium, with basic torsion box formed by spars and skins with riveted stringers. Removable leading-edge on outer panels with electric de-icing. Double-slotted trailing-edge flaps, inboard and outboard of engine nacelle, and ailerons, over full span. Servo tab and trim tab in each aileron. Two airbrakes (inboard) and spoiler (outboard) forward of flaps on each wing. Purpose of spoilers is to supplement ailerons differentially for roll control after an engine failure during take-off.

FUSELAGE: Conventional aluminium alloy semi-monocoque structure of circular section, built as five major subassemblies.

TAIL UNIT: Conventional cantilever metal structure, with sweptback vertical surfaces. Elevators and rudder operated manually through pushrods. Trim and servo tabs in rudder; trim tab in each elevator. Leading-edges of fin and tailplane de-iced electrically.

LANDING GEAR: Retractable tricycle type, with twin wheels on each unit, manufactured by WSK-PZL Krosno. All units retract forward hydraulically, with emergency extension by gravity. Oleo-pneumatic shock absorber in each unit. Tyres size 620 × 80 on nosewheels, 880 × 305 on mainwheels. Nosewheels steerable ±55°. Disc brakes on mainwheels. All wheel doors remain closed except during retraction or extension of the landing gear.

POWER PLANT: Two 1,766 kW (2,368 shp) Isotov TV7-117 turboprops, each driving a six-blade CB-34 carbonfibre-reinforced composites propeller with spinner. Fuel in integral tanks in wings, total capacity 8,125 litres (2,146 US gallons; 1,787 Imp gallons). APU in tailcone.

ACCOMMODATION: Flight crew of two, plus stewardess. Emergency exit window on each side of flight deck. Four-abreast seats for 60 passengers in main cabin, at 75 cm (29.5 in) seat pitch, with central aisle 45 cm (17.72 in) wide. Airstair type passenger door at front of cabin on port side, further door at rear on port side, both opening outward. Galley, cloakroom and toilet at rear, with emergency escape slide by service door on starboard side. Type III emergency exit over each wing. Service doors at front and rear of cabin on starboard side. Baggage compartments forward of cabin on starboard side and to rear of cabin. Optional large carry-on baggage shelves in lobby by main door at front of cabin.

SYSTEMS: Dual redundant pressurisation and air-conditioning system using engine bleed air from both engines. Two independent hydraulic systems, pressure 207 bars (3,000 lb/sq in), for landing gear actuation, wheel brakes, nosewheel steering and flaps. Three-phase 115/220V 400Hz AC electrical system powered by 40kW alternator on each engine. Secondary 24V DC system. Electro-thermal anti-icing system for propeller blades and windscreen. Engine air intakes de-iced by hot air.

AVIONICS: Digital avionics for automatic or manual control by day or night, including automatic approach and landing in limiting weather conditions (ICAO Cat I and II). Two CRTs for each pilot for flight and navigation

Ilyushin Il-114 (two Isotov TV7-117 turboprops) *(Jane's/Mike Keep)*

Prototype Ilyushin Il-114 twin-turboprop airliner, first flown on 29 March 1990

information. Centrally mounted CRT for engine and systems data.

DIMENSIONS, EXTERNAL:

Wing span	30.00 m (98 ft 5¼ in)
Length overall	26.31 m (86 ft 4 in)
Diameter of fuselage	2.86 m (9 ft 4½ in)
Height overall	9.32 m (30 ft 7 in)
Tailplane span	11.10 m (36 ft 5 in)
Wheel track	8.40 m (27 ft 6½ in)
Wheelbase	9.13 m (29 ft 11½ in)
Propeller diameter	3.60 m (11 ft 9¾ in)
Propeller ground clearance	0.62 m (2 ft 0½ in)
Propeller fuselage clearance	0.97 m (3 ft 2¼ in)
Passenger doors (each): Height	1.70 m (5 ft 7 in)
Width	0.90 m (2 ft 11¼ in)

Service door (front): Height	1.30 m (4 ft 3¼ in)
Width	0.96 m (3 ft 1¾ in)
Service door (rear): Height	1.38 m (4 ft 6¼ in)
Width	0.61 m (2 ft 0 in)
Emergency exit (each): Height	0.91 m (2 ft 11¾ in)
Width	0.51 m (1 ft 8 in)

DIMENSIONS, INTERNAL:

Length between pressure bulkheads	22.24 m (72 ft 11½ in)
Cabin: Max height	1.92 m (6 ft 3½ in)

WEIGHTS:

Operating weight empty	13,700 kg (30,200 lb)
Max payload	6,000 kg (13,227 lb)
Max fuel	6,500 kg (14,330 lb)
Max T-O weight	21,000 kg (46,300 lb)

PERFORMANCE (estimated):

Nominal cruising speed	270 knots (500 km/h; 310 mph)
Approach speed	100 knots (185 km/h; 115 mph)
Optimum cruising height	8,100 m (26,575 ft)
T-O run: paved	1,200 m (3,940 ft)
unpaved	1,400 m (4,600 ft)
Landing run: paved or unpaved	1,300 m (4,265 ft)

Range, with reserves:
with 5,400 kg (11,905 lb) payload
540 nm (1,000 km; 621 miles)
with 3,600 kg (7,935 lb) payload
1,538 nm (2,850 km; 1,770 miles)
with 1,500 kg (3,300 lb) payload
2,590 nm (4,800 km; 2,980 miles)

KAMOV

GENERAL DESIGNER: Sergei V. Mikheyev
DEPUTY GENERAL DESIGNER: Veniamin Kasjanikov

Formed in 1947, this design bureau continues the work of Nikolai I. Kamov, a leading designer of rotating wing aircraft from the late 1920s, who died on 24 November 1973, aged 71.

All current Kamov production helicopters have coaxial contra-rotating rotors, but the Ka-118 and V-62, now being developed, will each have a single main rotor. The bureau's general designer has stated that the OKB studies continuously the merits of other configurations including, but only on paper, tilt-rotor types such as the American Bell/Boeing Osprey.

KAMOV Ka-25
NATO reporting name: Hormone

The prototype of this military helicopter took part in the Soviet Aviation Day flypast over Tushino Airport, Moscow, in July 1961. About 460 production Ka-25s were built in 1966-75, of which about 100 remain operational with the Soviet Navy. Others are in first-line service in India, Syria, Vietnam and Yugoslavia.

Three versions are identified by NATO reporting names:

Hormone-A. Basic ship-based anti-submarine version, operated from a variety of Soviet Navy ships, including missile frigates, cruisers, the helicopter carriers *Moskva* and *Leningrad*, and carrier/cruisers of the 'Kiev' class. A major shortcoming is said to be lack of night and all-weather sonar dipping capability. Being replaced progressively by Ka-27 ('Helix-A').

Hormone-B. Special electronics variant, able to provide over-the-horizon target acquisition for cruise missiles launched from ships. These include SS-N-3B (NATO 'Shaddock') missiles launched from 'Kresta I' cruisers; SS-N-12 ('Sandbox') missiles from 'Kiev' class carrier/cruisers and 'Slava' class cruisers; SS-N-19 missiles from the battle cruisers *Kirov* and *Frunze*; and SS-N-22 missiles from destroyers of the 'Sovremenny' class. 'Kiev' and 'Kirov' class ships can each carry three 'Hormone-Bs', the other classes one each. Larger undernose radome with more spherical undersurface than that of 'Hormone-A'. Cylindrical radome under rear of cabin. Data link equipment.

Hormone-C. Utility and search and rescue model, generally similar to 'Hormone-A' but with inessential operational equipment and weapons removed. This version sometimes has a yagi aerial mounted on the nose.

A full description of the Ka-25 can be found in previous editions of *Jane's*. An abbreviated entry follows:

POWER PLANT: Two 671 kW (900 shp) Glushenkov GTD-3F turboshafts, mounted side by side above cabin, forward of rotor driveshaft, on early aircraft. Later aircraft have 738 kW (990 shp) GTD-3BM turboshafts. Independent fuel supply to each engine. Provision for carrying external fuel tank on each side of cabin.

ACCOMMODATION: Pilot and co-pilot side by side on flight deck, with rearward sliding door on each side. Entry to main cabin is via a rearward sliding door to rear of main landing gear on port side. Cabin accommodates two or three systems operators in ASW role, but is large enough to contain 12 folding seats for passengers.

AVIONICS AND EQUIPMENT: Equipment available for all versions includes autopilot, navigational system, radio compass, radio communications, lighting system for all-weather operation by day or night, and hoist mounted above cabin door. IFF antennae (NATO 'Odd Rods') above nose and alongside central tail fin. Dipping sonar housed in compartment at rear of main cabin, immediately forward of tailboom, and search radar in an undernose radome (diameter 1.25 m; 4 ft 1 in) on

anti-submarine version, which can have a canister of sonobuoys mounted externally aft of the starboard main landing gear. Most aircraft have a cylindrical housing for ESM above the tailboom, with a shallow blister fairing to the rear of the cylindrical housing. Provision for a camera pod on port side of cabin.

ARMAMENT: Doors under the fuselage of some aircraft enclose a weapons bay for two 450 mm (18 in) ASW torpedoes, nuclear depth charges and other stores.

DIMENSIONS, EXTERNAL:

Rotor diameter (each)	15.74 m (51 ft 7¾ in)
Length of fuselage	9.75 m (32 ft 0 in)
Height to top of rotor head	5.37 m (17 ft 7½ in)
Width over tail-fins	3.76 m (12 ft 4 in)
Wheel track: front	1.41 m (4 ft 7½ in)
rear	3.52 m (11 ft 6½ in)
Cabin door: Height	1.10 m (3 ft 7¼ in)
Width	1.20 m (3 ft 11¼ in)

Kamov Ka-25 ('Hormone-A') anti-submarine helicopter of the Soviet Navy *(Piotr Butowski)*

DIMENSIONS, INTERNAL:

Cabin, excl flight deck:	
Length	3.95 m (12 ft 11½ in)
Max width	1.50 m (4 ft 11 in)
Max height	1.25 m (4 ft 1¼ in)

WEIGHTS:

Weight empty	4,765 kg (10,505 lb)
Max T-O weight	7,500 kg (16,535 lb)

PERFORMANCE:

Max level speed	113 knots (209 km/h; 130 mph)
Normal cruising speed	104 knots (193 km/h; 120 mph)
Service ceiling	3,350 m (11,000 ft)
Range, with reserves:	
with standard fuel	217 nm (400 km; 250 miles)
with external tanks	351 nm (650 km; 405 miles)

KAMOV Ka-26
NATO reporting name: Hoodlum-A

The Ka-26 (NATO 'Hoodlum-A') first flew in proto-type form in 1965 and entered service as an agricultural aircraft in the Soviet Union in 1970, being used primarily over orchards and vineyards. It is used widely on Aeroflot's air ambulance services and is suitable for many other applications, including cargo and passenger transport, aerial survey, forest firefighting, mineral prospecting, pipeline construction, laying transmission lines, and a number of military duties, including search and rescue (for detailed descriptions of variants see 1986-87 and earlier editions).

In total, 850 Ka-26s were built. They were delivered for civilian service in 15 countries; military operators include the air forces of Bulgaria and Hungary. ICA Brasov (see Romanian section) is building a turbine powered development known as the Ka-126 ('Hoodlum-B').

Abbreviated details of the Ka-26 follow. A full description can be found in the 1987-88 and previous editions of *Jane's*.

TYPE: Twin-engined general purpose light helicopter.

POWER PLANT: Two 242.5 kW (325 hp) Vedeneyev M-14V-26 aircooled radial piston engines, mounted in pods on short stub wings at top of fuselage.

ACCOMMODATION: Fully enclosed cabin, with door on each side, fitted out normally for operation by single pilot; second seat and dual controls optional. Cabin warmed and demisted by air from combustion heater, which also heats passenger compartment when fitted. Air filter on nose of agricultural version. The space aft of the cabin, between the main landing gear units and under the rotor transmission, is able to accommodate a variety of interchangeable payloads. For agricultural work, a chemical hopper (capacity 900 kg; 1,985 lb) and dust spreader or spraybars are fitted in this position, on the aircraft's centre of gravity. This equipment is quickly removable and can be replaced by a cargo/passenger pod accommodating four or six persons, with provision for a seventh passenger beside the pilot; or two stretcher patients, two seated casualties and a medical attendant in ambulance role. Alternatively, the Ka-26 can be operated with either an open platform for hauling freight or a hook for slinging bulky loads at the end of a cable or in a cargo net.

DIMENSIONS, EXTERNAL:

Rotor diameter (each)	13.00 m (42 ft 8 in)
Vertical separation between rotors	1.17 m (3 ft 10 in)
Length of fuselage	7.75 m (25 ft 5 in)
Height overall	4.05 m (13 ft 3½ in)
Width over engine pods	3.64 m (11 ft 11½ in)
Width over agricultural spraybars	11.20 m (36 ft 9 in)
Tailplane span	4.60 m (15 ft 1 in)
Wheel track: mainwheels	2.42 m (7 ft 11½ in)
nosewheels	0.90 m (2 ft 11½ in)

Kamov Ka-26 jet control testbed helicopter *(courtesy of Helicopter International)*

Wheelbase	3.48 m (11 ft 5 in)
Passenger pod door: Height	1.40 m (4 ft 7 in)
Width	1.25 m (4 ft 1¼ in)

DIMENSIONS, INTERNAL:

Passenger pod:	
Length, floor level	1.83 m (6 ft 0 in)
Width, floor level	1.25 m (4 ft 1¼ in)
Headroom	1.40 m (4 ft 7 in)

WEIGHTS:

Operating weight, empty: stripped	1,950 kg (4,300 lb)
cargo/platform	2,085 kg (4,597 lb)
cargo/hook	2,050 kg (4,519 lb)
passenger	2,100 kg (4,630 lb)
agricultural	2,216 kg (4,885 lb)
Fuel weight: transport	360 kg (794 lb)
other versions	100 kg (220 lb)
Payload: transport	900 kg (1,985 lb)
agricultural duster	1,065 kg (2,348 lb)
agricultural sprayer	900 kg (1,985 lb)
with cargo platform	1,065 kg (2,348 lb)
flying crane	1,100 kg (2,425 lb)
Normal T-O weight: transport	3,076 kg (6,780 lb)
agricultural	2,980 kg (6,570 lb)
Max T-O weight: all versions	3,250 kg (7,165 lb)

PERFORMANCE (at max T-O weight):

Max level speed	91 knots (170 km/h; 105 mph)
Max cruising speed	81 knots (150 km/h; 93 mph)
Econ cruising speed	49-59 knots (90-110 km/h; 56-68 mph)
Agricultural operating speed range	16-62 knots (30-115 km/h; 19-71 mph)
Service ceiling	3,000 m (9,840 ft)
Service ceiling, one engine out	500 m (1,640 ft)
Hovering ceiling at AUW of 3,000 kg (6,615 lb):	
IGE	1,300 m (4,265 ft)
OGE	800 m (2,625 ft)

Range with 7 passengers, 30 min fuel reserves	215 nm (400 km; 248 miles)
Max range with auxiliary tanks	647 nm (1,200 km; 745 miles)
Endurance at econ cruising speed	3 h 42 min

KAMOV Ka-26 JET CONTROL TESTBED

Since 1974, the Kamov OKB has conducted an extensive programme of research and flight testing of an anti-torque jet thruster control system similar to that developed by McDonnell Douglas Helicopters of the USA under the trade name NOTAR (NO TAil Rotor). Following initial testbench and wind tunnel experiments, the system was installed in a Ka-26 helicopter. The normal tailboom and tail unit were replaced by a tubular boom housing a fan and system of jet nozzles, of which various types were tested.

Two pilots were carried by the Ka-26 testbed. The pilot in the left-hand seat flew the helicopter by means of the standard co-axial rotor directional control system. Before the research phase of each flight, he trimmed the aircraft by rudder input and then handed over control to the right-seat pilot, whose rudder pedals controlled the jet thruster system.

Results showed that Kamov's jet system has control capabilities comparable with those provided by a tail rotor, while reducing danger for ground personnel, eliminating the hazard of tail rotor contact with natural or man-made objects on the ground during operations in restricted areas, and offering other advantages of the kind claimed for the NOTAR system. In consequence, Kamov is now developing a helicopter designated Ka-118 (which see) to utilise its jet thruster control system commercially.

KAMOV Ka-27
NATO reporting name: Helix-A, B and D

Ka-27 is the Soviet designation for military versions of the helicopter known as the Ka-32 in its civil forms. The basic airframe, power plant, systems and equipment of the Ka-27 and Ka-32 are identical. Furnishings, avionics and mission equipment vary according to role.

Design of the Ka-27/Ka-32 was started in 1969; the prototype flew for the first time in December 1974. First reference to the military version appeared in the 1981 document on *Soviet Military Power* published by the US Department of Defense, which referred to "Hormone variant" helicopters that could be carried in a telescoping hangar on the new 'Sovremenny' class of Soviet guided missile destroyers, for ASW missions. Photographs of such helicopters were released to the technical press after two of them had been seen on the stern platform of the *Udaloy*, first of a new class of Soviet ASW guided missile destroyers, during exercises in the Baltic in September 1981. The US Department of Defense referred to the ASW helicopter as Ka-27 in 1982. At least 16 were observed on board the 'Kiev' class carrier/cruiser *Novorossiysk* during its maiden deployment in 1983, since when the replacement of 'Hormone-As' with Ka-27s has continued.

Versions identified by unclassified NATO reporting names are:

Helix-A. Basic ASW helicopter, with probable crew of three. Operational since 1982. Equipment includes undernose 360° search radar, a ventral weapons bay for torpedoes and other stores, internal stowage for sonobuoys, IFF (NATO 'Odd Rods'), colour coded identification flares, radar warning antennae on nose and above tailplane, directional ESM radomes above rear of engine bay fairing

Kamov Ka-26 with passenger cabin in Aeroflot service *(Jane's Defence Weekly/Paul Beaver)*

and at tip of tailcone, rectangular container on each side of bottom centre fuselage for emergency flotation bags, dipping sonar compartment behind clamshell doors at rear of fuselage, and Doppler box under tailboom. More than 90 in Soviet Naval Aviation service. Eighteen ordered for Indian Navy. (See also separate entry on **Ka-28**.)

'Helix-A' follows closely the configuration of 'Hormone' but has a longer and more capacious fuselage pod, no central tail fin, and different undernose radome. The overall dimensions of the two aircraft are generally similar, enabling 'Helix' to be stowed on board ship in hangars and via deck lifts built for its predecessor.

Helix-B (**Ka-27B** = Boyevoya, combat). Sea-based combat version to replace 'Hormone-B'. Assigned initially to the Northern and Pacific Fleets in 1985, and photographed on board the *Ivan Rogov* in the Mediterranean in 1987. Primary functions are the transport of seaborne assault troops, delivery of precision-guided weapons and target designation. Panels around nose, and undernose fairings, for sensors and specialised equipment. Two pylons on each side of cabin for rocket packs and other stores. About 30 in service.

Helix-B (**Ka-29TB**). See Ka-29 entry.

Helix-C. Civil versions. See Ka-32 entry.

Helix-D (**Ka-27PS**). Search and rescue and plane guard helicopter, first seen on the *Novorossiysk*. Basically similar to 'Helix-A' but some operational equipment deleted. Features include an external fuel tank on each side of the cabin, as on the civil Ka-32 'Helix-C', and a winch beside the port cabin door.

The general description of the Ka-32 (which see) applies also to the Ka-27.

KAMOV Ka-28

First identified publicly at an air show in Yugoslavia in May 1988, the Ka-28 is an export version of the Ka-27 ('Helix-A') ASW helicopter. An accompanying placard described the power plant as two 1,618 kW (2,170 shp) TV3-117BK turboshafts. A total of 3,680 kg (8,113 lb) of fuel was stated to be carried in 12 tanks.

The Ka-28 appears to be outwardly identical to the Ka-27. Its max level speed was quoted as 135 knots (250 km/h; 155 mph) at an AUW of 10,700 kg (23,590 lb), with a max cruising speed of 124-129 knots (230-240 km/h; 143-149 mph) and max rate of climb of 750 m (2,460 ft)/min at S/L. It was said to be effective against submarines cruising at up to 40 knots (75 km/h; 47 mph), at a depth of 500 m (1,640 ft), out to 108 nm (200 km; 124 miles) from its base, by day and night.

KAMOV Ka-29

Among aircraft seen in public for the first time at the Frunze (Khodinka) air show in Moscow, in August 1989, was a version of the Ka-27 series identified as the Ka-29TB (Transportno-Boyevoya, combat transport). Known to NATO as 'Helix-B', it is a development of the Ka-27B, which has the same reporting name. The main cabin door, on the port side aft of the landing gear, is divided horizontally into two sections, opening upward and downward, to facilitate rapid exit. Three flat-plate glazings replace the two-piece curved windscreen of the Ka-27. Beneath them, the shallow-curved nose is made up of panels over operational equipment that includes an internally mounted gun. Sensor pods under the nose appear to be similar to the electro-optics and RF missile guidance pods of the Mi-24 'Hind'. Four wing pylons are standard, as on the Ka-27B, for AT-6 (NATO 'Spiral') air-to-surface missiles and 57 mm or 80 mm rocket packs. Operational equipment includes an ESM 'flower pot' above the rear engine bay fairing, an infra-red jammer (NATO 'Hot Brick') at the extreme rear of the same fairing, a Doppler

Ka-29TB (NATO 'Helix-B') combat transport helicopter *(Jane's Defence Weekly/Paul Beaver)*

Kamov Ka-29TB combat transport helicopter *(Jane's/Mike Keep)*

box under the tailboom, radar warning receivers and 'Odd Rods' IFF. The flight deck and engine bay are heavily armoured.

DIMENSIONS, EXTERNAL:
Rotor diameter (each)	16.40 m (53 ft 9½ in)
Blade length, aerofoil section (each)	5.45 m (17 ft 10½ in)
Blade chord	0.48 m (1 ft 7 in)
Vertical separation of rotors	1.40 m (4 ft 7 in)
Length overall, excl noseprobe and rotors	11.50 m (37 ft 8¾ in)
Width between centrelines of outboard pylons	5.65 m (18 ft 6½ in)
Width over tail fins and centred rudders	3.65 m (12 ft 0 in)
Width of flight deck	2.20 m (7 ft 2 in)
Mainwheel track	3.50 m (11 ft 6 in)
Nosewheel track	1.40 m (4 ft 7 in)
Wheelbase	3.00 m (9 ft 10 in)

WEIGHT:
Max T-O weight	12,000 kg (26,455 lb)

PERFORMANCE:
Max level speed	143 knots (265 km/h; 165 mph)
Max range	270 nm (500 km; 310 miles)

KAMOV Ka-32
NATO reporting name: Helix-C

The Ka-32 was identified officially when the first prototype (SSSR-04173) was exhibited in public with other Soviet and Polish aircraft at Minsk Airport, in late 1981, during the fourth CMEA scientific/technical conference on the use of aircraft in the national economy. As expected, it proved to be a demilitarised counterpart to the Ka-27 (NATO 'Helix-A') naval helicopter already observed on the Soviet ASW guided missile destroyer *Udaloy*, and was given the NATO reporting name **Helix-C**. Major applications of the civil Ka-32 shown at Minsk were said to be for construction/assembly and flying crane duties, and it carried a truck as a slung load during the flying display. It was claimed to be able to lift up to 5,000 kg (11,023 lb) as an external slung load, and to have a range of 100 nm (185 km; 115 miles) with such a load.

A detailed appraisal of the Ka-32 became possible in June 1985, when a prototype of the utility version (SSSR-31000), converted from an ASW Ka-27, was exhibited at the Paris Air Show. Its designer explained that there are two civil versions:

Kamov Ka-28 anti-submarine helicopter (NATO 'Helix-A') in Yugoslav service *(Ivo Sturzenegger)*

Kamov Ka-32S ('Helix-C') under automatic control, with no crew on flight deck

Kamov Ka-32T ('Helix-C') utility helicopter (two Isotov TV3-117V turboshafts) *(Pilot Press)*

Ka-32T. As displayed in Paris. Basic transport and flying crane, with limited avionics. Duties include transport of internal and external freight, and passengers, along airways and over local routes.

Ka-32S (maritime). Equipped with more comprehensive avionics, including undernose radar, for operation to full IMC standards from icebreakers in adverse weather conditions and over terrain devoid of landmarks. Duties include ice patrol, guidance of ships through icefields, unloading and loading ships (up to 30 tonnes an hour, 360 tonnes a day), support of offshore drilling rigs, and maritime search and rescue.

According to Mr Mikheyev, the Ka-32 was conceived as a completely autonomous 'compact truck', able to stow in much the same space as the Ka-25 with its rotors folded, despite its much greater power and capability, and able to operate independently of ground support equipment. Titanium and composite materials are used extensively throughout the airframe, with particular emphasis on resistance to corrosion. Special attention was also paid to ease of handling, with a single pilot. Yaw control is by differential collective pitch applied through the rudder pedals. A 'mix' in the collective control system maintains constant total rotor thrust during turns, to reduce the pilot's workload when landing on a pitching deck, and to simplify transition into hover and landing. The twin rudders are intended mainly to improve control in autorotation, but are effective in co-ordinating turns in normal cruising flight. Being a 'workhorse' the helicopter is not designed for negative g loading.

Flight can be maintained on one engine at maximum take-off weight. The effectiveness of the automatic control system is illustrated by an accompanying photograph of a Ka-32S in flight. Both crew doors are open, to show that there is nobody on the flight deck; the crew can be seen in the rear doorway of the main cabin.

Several dozen Ka-32s were in service with Aeroflot by early 1989. Export customers include Interflug of East Germany, which has ordered three for delivery in 1990-91.

The description which follows applies specifically to the Ka-32T displayed at the 1985 Paris Air Show, but is generally applicable also to the Ka-32S and the military Ka-27/28/29 series:

TYPE: Twin-turbine utility helicopter.

ROTOR SYSTEM: Two fully articulated three-blade coaxial contra-rotating rotors. Blades of all-composites construction, with carbonfibre and glassfibre main spars, pockets (13 per blade) of a material similar to Kevlar, and a filler similar to Nomex. As in all Soviet helicopters, blades have a non-symmetrical aerofoil section. Each blade is fitted with a ground adjustable tab. The three lower blades each carry an adjustable vibration damper, comprising two dependent weights, mounted on the root section, and there are further vibration dampers in the fuselage. Tip light on each blade of upper rotor. Blades fold manually outboard of all control mechanisms, to a folded width within the track of the main landing gear. Electrothermal de-icing of the entire profiled portion of each blade, operating at all times when engines are

running. Heat generated by rotor head prevents icing of droop stops. Main rotor hub is 50 per cent titanium/50 per cent steel. Rotor brake standard.

FUSELAGE: Conventional all-metal semi-monocoque structure of pod and boom type, making extensive use of titanium for primary components. Tailcone of composites material. Lower fuselage sealed for flotation.

TAIL UNIT: Braced structure, comprising fixed incidence tailplane, elevators, twin endplate fins and rudders, with aluminium alloy structure and composite skins. Single bracing strut under each side of tailplane. Fins toe inward approx 25°. Fixed leading-edge slat on each fin prevents airflow over fin stalling in crosswinds or at high yaw angles.

LANDING GEAR: Four-wheel type. Oleo-pneumatic shock absorbers. Nosewheels are smaller than mainwheels and of castoring type. Rear legs are pivoted on some versions, to retract upward about their wishbone supports so that the wheels can be moved to a position where they offer least interference to emissions from the undernose radar. Mainwheel tyres size 600 × 180. Nosewheel tyres size 400 × 150.

POWER PLANT: Two 1,660 kW (2,225 shp) Isotov TV3-117V turboshafts, with automatic synchronisation system, mounted side by side above cabin, forward of rotor driveshaft. Main gearbox brake standard. Oil cooler fan aft of gearbox. Electrothermal intake anti-icing. Cowlings hinge downward for use as maintenance platforms. All standard fuel in tanks under cabin floor and inside container on each side of centre fuselage. Provision for auxiliary tanks in cabin. Refuelling point behind small forward hinged door on port side, where bottom of tailboom meets rear of cabin. APU in rear of engine bay fairing on starboard side, for engine starting and to power all essential hydraulic and electrical services on the ground, eliminating need for GPU.

ACCOMMODATION: Pilot and navigator side by side on large air-conditioned flight deck, in fully adjustable seats. Rearward sliding jettisonable door with blister window on each side. Seat behind navigator, on starboard side, for observer, loadmaster or rescue hoist operator. Electric windscreen anti-icing. Direct access to cabin from flight deck. Heated and ventilated main cabin can accommodate freight or 16 passengers, on three folding seats at rear, six along port sidewall and seven along starboard sidewall. Lifejackets under seats. Fittings to carry stretchers. No provisions for toilet or galley. Pyramid structure can be fitted on floor beneath rotor driveshaft to prevent swinging of external cargo sling loads. Rearward sliding door aft of main landing gear on port side, with steps below. Emergency exit door opposite. Door to avionics compartment on port side of tailboom.

SYSTEMS: Dual hydraulically powered flight control systems without manual reversion. Spring stick trim.

AVIONICS AND EQUIPMENT: Include electro-mechanical flight director controlled from autopilot panel, Doppler hover indicator, two HSI and air data computer. Autopilot is capable of providing automatic approach and hover at a height of 25 m (82 ft) over landing area, on predetermined course, using Doppler. Radar altimeter. Doppler box under tailboom. Doors at rear of fuel tank bay provide access to small compartment for auxiliary fuel, or liferafts which eject during descent in emergency, by command from flight deck. Container on each side of fuselage, under external fuel containers, for emergency flotation bags, deployed by water contact (not fitted to prototype shown in Paris). Rescue hoist, capacity 300 kg (661 lb), can be installed between top of door opening and landing gear. Optional external load sling, with automatic release and integral load weighing and stabilisation systems. Equipment on prototype (not necessarily standard on

Provisional three-view of Kamov 'Hokum' *(Pilot Press)*

production Ka-32s) included IFF, two radar warning antennae above tailplane, and two ESM radomes above rear fuselage and tail.

DIMENSIONS, EXTERNAL:
Rotor diameter (each)	15.90 m (52 ft 2 in)
Length overall: excl rotors	11.30 m (37 ft 1 in)
rotors folded	12.25 m (40 ft 2¼ in)
Width, rotors folded	4.00 m (13 ft 1½ in)
Height to top of rotor head	5.40 m (17 ft 8½ in)
Wheel track: mainwheels	3.50 m (11 ft 6 in)
nosewheels	1.40 m (4 ft 7 in)
Wheelbase	3.02 m (9 ft 11 in)
Cabin door: Height	approx 1.20 m (3 ft 11¼ in)
Width	approx 1.20 m (3 ft 11¼ in)

DIMENSIONS, INTERNAL:
Cabin: Length	4.52 m (14 ft 10 in)
Max width	1.30 m (4 ft 3 in)
Max height	1.32 m (4 ft 4 in)

WEIGHTS:
Max payload: internal	4,000 kg (8,818 lb)
external	5,000 kg (11,023 lb)
Normal T-O weight	11,000 kg (24,250 lb)
Max flight weight with slung load	12,600 kg (27,775 lb)

PERFORMANCE (at AUW of 11,000 kg; 24,250 lb):
Max level speed	135 knots (250 km/h; 155 mph)
Max cruising speed	124 knots (230 km/h; 143 mph)
Service ceiling at normal T-O weight	6,000 m (19,685 ft)
Hovering ceiling OGE	3,500 m (11,480 ft)
Range with max fuel	432 nm (800 km; 497 miles)
Endurance with max fuel	4 h 30 min

KAMOV Ka-118

Mr Sergei V. Mikheyev announced at the Helicopter Association International Convention in Dallas, on 4 February 1990, that the Kamov OKB intends to develop a light helicopter embodying the jet thruster control system flight tested on a Ka-26 testbed (which see). Designated Ka-118, the new aircraft will break with Kamov tradition by utilising a single four-blade rotor, with swept tips. Its general configuration is shown in an accompanying three-view drawing.

The Ka-118 is intended primarily as a five-seat business transport. The type of power plant to be installed had not been decided in early 1990. A single 530 kW (710 shp) Koptchenko TV-O-100 turboshaft is being considered, as are alternative proposals for one or two engines of Allison, Pratt & Whitney Canada, Rolls-Royce and Turbomeca design. The composite rotor blades have been developed by Mr Vyacheslov Savin, who was responsible earlier for the new blades of the Ka-126.

The following specification details refer to the Ka-118 powered by a single TV-O-100 engine:

WEIGHTS (estimated):
Max payload: internal	800 kg (1,765 lb)
external	1,000 kg (2,205 lb)
Normal T-O weight	1,950 kg (4,300 lb)
Max T-O weight: internal load	2,150 kg (4,740 lb)
slung load	2,250 kg (4,960 lb)

PERFORMANCE (estimated):
Max level speed	162 knots (300 km/h; 186 mph)
Max cruising speed	145 knots (270 km/h; 168 mph)
Max rate of climb at S/L	660 m (2,165 ft)/min
Service ceiling	6,150 m (20,175 ft)
Hovering ceiling IGE	3,000 m (9,850 ft)
Range with max standard fuel	512 nm (950 km; 590 miles)
Range with auxiliary tanks	810 nm (1,500 km; 932 miles)

Provisional three-view drawing of Kamov Ka-118 five-seat helicopter *(Pilot Press)*

KAMOV Ka-126
NATO reporting name: Hoodlum-B

Responsibility for manufacture of the turbine powered Ka-126 has been allocated to ICA Brasov (see Romanian section).

KAMOV Ka-136 (Ka-34?)
NATO reporting name: Hokum

It became known in Summer 1984 that the Kamov bureau had begun flight testing a new combat helicopter that has the NATO reporting name 'Hokum'. Various designations have been suggested for it in the Western press. A design bureau designation of Ka-136 and service designation of Ka-34 appear most likely but have not been confirmed in any way.

The accompanying photograph, first published in the US Department of Defense's *Soviet Military Power* document, is the only one that had become available by Spring 1990. 'Hokum' can be seen to have coaxial contra-rotating and widely separated three-blade rotors, with swept blade tips; a streamlined fuselage with a tapered nose like that of a jet attack aircraft, with pitot, transducer to provide data for a fire control computer, and undernose sensor pack; and a retractable landing gear.

DoD states that this helicopter has not been observed carrying anti-tank guided weapons. Its primary armament of unguided rocket packs, air-to-air missiles and a rapid-fire gun suggest its suitability for employment as a low-level helicopter intercept system by day and night and in adverse weather conditions. Other combat roles could include "countering enemy attacks, preparing for and executing counter-offensives, and supporting combined-arms offensives into an opponent's territory". This last application would make 'Hokum' eminently suitable as an escort for amphibious assault Ka-29TB 'Helix-Bs' based on Soviet Navy aircraft carriers, and it is worth bearing in mind that Kamov military helicopters have always been produced for mainly maritime use.

Unlike other combat helicopters, 'Hokum's' crew of two appear to be seated side by side. Its power plant is believed to comprise two Isotov TV3-117VK turboshafts, each rated at 1,640 kW (2,200 shp). Survivability is enhanced by use of infra-red suppressors, infra-red decoy dispensers and armour.

In 1990, 'Hokum' was still at the development stage, with only prototypes involved in flight and structural testing. The DoD expects it to enter service in the near future.

DIMENSIONS, EXTERNAL:
Rotor diameter (each)	14.0 m (45 ft 10 in)
Length overall, excl nose probe and gun	13.5 m (44 ft 3½ in)
Height overall	5.4 m (17 ft 8 in)

WEIGHT (estimated):
Max T-O weight	7,500 kg (16,500 lb)

PERFORMANCE (estimated):
Max level speed	189 knots (350 km/h; 217 mph)
Combat radius	135 nm (250 km; 155 miles)

KAMOV Ka-226

Announced at the 1990 HAI Convention in Dallas, the Ka-226 is a refined development of the Ka-126 utility and agricultural helicopter, powered by two Allison 250-C20B turboshafts manufactured in the USA. The engines, each rated at 313 kW (420 shp), are mounted side by side aft of the rotor mast, in the same position as the single turboshaft of the Ka-126, with individual drive-shafts to the modified rotor gearbox. Standard fuel capacity is 870 litres (230 US gallons; 191 Imp gallons). Changes to the shape of the nose, twin tail fins and rudders, and passenger pod are evident in the accompanying photograph of a model. The passenger cabin has much larger windows than that of the Ka-26/126, and remains interchangeable with other payload modules including agricultural systems having a hopper capacity of 1,000 litres (264 US gallons; 220 Imp gallons). A new rotor system, interchangeable with the standard co-axial system, will be made available later. Cockpit instrumentation and avionics will be to customers' choice. Standard accommodation will be for one pilot and seven passengers.

The prototype Ka-226 was expected to fly before the end of 1990. FAA certification will be sought, to make the helicopter acceptable to an international export market. Delivery of production Allison engines is scheduled to begin in late 1991, with an anticipated requirement for up to 600 engines over the next 10 years. Ka-226 manufacture will be centred in the USSR.

DIMENSIONS, EXTERNAL:
Rotor diameter (each)	13.00 m (42 ft 7¾ in)
Length overall, excl rotors	8.10 m (26 ft 7 in)
Width over stub-wings	3.22 m (10 ft 6¾ in)
Height to top of rotor head	4.15 m (13 ft 7½ in)
Wheel track: nosewheels	0.90 m (2 ft 11½ in)
mainwheels	2.56 m (8 ft 4¾ in)
Wheelbase	3.48 m (11 ft 5 in)
Passenger pod: Length	2.04 m (6 ft 8¼ in)
Width	1.28 m (4 ft 2¼ in)
Depth	1.40 m (4 ft 7¼ in)

WEIGHTS:
Max payload	1,000 kg (2,205 lb)
Normal T-O weight	3,100 kg (6,835 lb)
Max T-O weight	3,250 kg (7,165 lb)

PERFORMANCE (estimated):
Max level speed	110 knots (205 km/h; 127 mph)
Max cruising speed	100 knots (185 km/h; 115 mph)
Service ceiling	5,250 m (17,225 ft)
Hovering ceiling IGE	1,950 m (6,400 ft)
Range with max fuel	324 nm (600 km; 373 miles)
Endurance with max fuel	4 h 30 min

Kamov 'Hokum' combat helicopter *(US Department of Defense)*

Artist's impression of the Kamov V-62 medium-size utility helicopter

Model of Kamov Ka-226 (two Allison 250-C20B turboshafts) *(John Fricker)*

KAMOV V-62

Like the Ka-118, the V-62 medium helicopter departs from the Kamov tradition in having a single main rotor. Its configuration resembles closely that of Western helicopters such as the Aerospatiale Dauphin, with a fan-in-fin similar to the latter's fenestron. Between 50 and 55 per cent of its structure will be made of composites.

The general appearance of the V-62 is shown in an accompanying illustration. Few details are yet available, except that it will accommodate 12-14 passengers and will be powered by two 970 kW (1,300 shp) TVD-1500 turboshafts supplied by the Novikov (Ribinsk) OKB.

Construction of a prototype V-62 had begun in early 1990. Primary purpose of the helicopter will be to replace Mi-2s, Mi-4s and Ka-26s in the Soviet economy, but export sales are anticipated.

WEIGHT:
Max T-O weight   5,500-6,000 kg (12,125-13,225 lb)
PERFORMANCE (estimated):
Normal cruising speed   151 knots (280 km/h; 174 mph)

Kamov Ka-226, a refined development of the Ka-126 utility helicopter *(Jane's/Mike Keep)*

MiG

MIKOYAN OKB

6 Leningradskoye Highway, PO Box 125171, Moscow
Telephone: (Velikov) 7 (95) 158 2452
  (Waldenberg) 7 (95) 417 0504
GENERAL DESIGNER IN CHARGE OF BUREAU:
  Rostislav A. Belyakov
DEPUTY GENERAL DESIGNER: Mikhail Waldenburg

Colonel-General Artem I. Mikoyan, who died on 9 December 1970 at the age of 65, was head of the design bureau responsible for the MiG series of fighter aircraft from 1940. With Mikhail I. Gurevich (1893-1976), a mathematician, he collaborated in the design of the first really modern Soviet jet fighter, the MiG-15, which began to enter squadron service in numbers in 1949.

The MiG-17, a progressive development of the MiG-15, was first observed in Soviet squadrons in 1953 or 1954, and was followed into service by the supersonic MiG-19, which appeared in 1955 and was manufactured also in large numbers in China (see earlier editions of *Jane's*).

All available details follow of aircraft designed subsequently by the Mikoyan bureau that are currently in service, in production or known to be under development:

MIKOYAN MiG-21
NATO reporting names: Fishbed and Mongol

MiG-21s and Chinese-built variants continue to be flown by more than 40 air forces worldwide, but replacement with later fighters has left fewer than 500 in first-line units of the Soviet tactical air forces, including 60 of the reconnaissance models known to NATO as 'Fishbed-H'. Early MiG-21F/PF/PFM variants (NATO 'Fishbed-C/D/F') still serve with various Warsaw Pact and Soviet-supplied air forces; details of their individual features can be found in the 1985-86 and earlier editions of *Jane's*. The major versions currently deployed with Soviet air forces of the military districts (MDs) and groups of forces, and variants of these basic versions, are as follows:

MiG-21PFMA (Fishbed-J). Multi-role version with Tumansky R-11F2S-300 turbojet, rated at 38.25 kN (8,598 lb st) dry and 60.8 kN (13,668 lb) with afterburning, improved radar (NATO 'Jay Bird'), and four underwing pylons instead of two. Deepened dorsal spine fairing above fuselage. Two outboard pylons carry either fuel tanks or radar-homing AA-2C 'Atoll' missiles to supplement infra-red AA-2/2Ds (K-13As) on inboard pylons and GSh-23 twin-barrel 23 mm gun. Zero-speed, zero-altitude ejection seat.

MiG-21 MF ('Fishbed-J') of the Polish Air Force *(Lech Zielaskowski)*

Mikoyan MiG-21 SMB ('Fishbed-K') single-seat multi-role fighter *(Pilot Press)*

MiG-21R (Fishbed-H). Tactical reconnaissance version, basically similar to MiG-21PFMA. Equipment includes an external pod for forward facing or oblique cameras, or elint sensors, on fuselage centreline pylon. Suppressed ECM antenna at mid-point on dorsal spine and optional radar warning receivers in wingtip fairings.

MiG-21MF (Fishbed-J). Generally similar to MiG-21PFMA but with a Tumansky R-13-300 turbojet, lighter in weight and with higher performance ratings. Gun gas deflector beneath each suction relief door forward of wingroot. Entered service with Soviet air forces in 1969.

MiG-21M. Export variant of MiG-21MF. Generally similar to MiG-21PFMA, but with R-11F2S-300 engine. Superseded MiG-21FL on Hindustan Aeronautics production line in India, with IAF designation Type 96. First Indian built MiG-21M handed over officially to IAF on 14 February 1973; HAL production ended 1981.

MiG-21RF (Fishbed-H). Tactical reconnaissance version of MiG-21MF. Equipment as for MiG-21R.

MiG-21SMB (Fishbed-K). Similar to MiG-21MF, but deep dorsal spine extends rearward as far as brake parachute housing, to provide maximum fuel tankage and optimum aerodynamic form. Deliveries reported to have begun in 1971.

MiG-21bis (Fishbed-L). Third generation multi-role air combat/ground attack version. Tumansky R-25-300 turbojet, rated at 73.6 kN (16,535 lb st) with afterburning, updated avionics and generally improved construction standards. Wider and deeper dorsal fairing than that of MiG-21MF. Max fuel capacity of seven internal self-sealing tanks increased to 2,900 litres (766 US gallons; 638 Imp gallons).

MiG-21bis (Fishbed-N). Advanced version of 'Fishbed-L' with further improved avionics, indicated by 'Swift Rod' ILS antennae under nose and on fin tip. Empty weight reported to be 6,000 kg (13,225 lb), clean T-O weight 8,500 kg (18,740 lb). Rate of climb at AUW of 6,800 kg (15,000 lb), with 50% fuel and two 'Atoll' missiles, is 17,700 m (58,000 ft)/min. Carries two radar homing AA-2C 'Atolls' outboard and two 'Aphids' inboard, or four 'Aphids'. Produced also by HAL in India from 1980 to 1987.

MiG-21U (Mongol). Two-seat training versions. Initial version, 'Mongol-A', is generally similar to the MiG-21F but has two cockpits in tandem with sideways hinged (to starboard) double canopy, larger mainwheels and tyres of MiG-21PF, one-piece forward airbrake, and pitot boom repositioned above intake. Cannon armament is deleted. Later models, 'Mongol-B', have the broader-chord vertical tail surfaces and under-rudder brake parachute housing of the later operational variants, with a deeper dorsal spine and no dorsal fin fillet.

MiG-21US (Mongol-B). Similar to later MiG-21U but with provision for SPS flap-blowing, and retractable periscope for instructor in rear seat. Max internal fuel capacity 2,400 litres (634 US gallons; 528 Imp gallons).

MiG-21UM (Mongol-B). Two-seat trainer counterpart of MiG-21MF with R-13 turbojet and four underwing stores pylons.

In addition to these Soviet developed versions, the Chinese aircraft industry (which see) is producing fighters based on the MiG-21, under the designation **J-7/F-7**.

The following details refer to the MiG-21MF ('Fishbed-J'):

TYPE: Single-seat multi-role fighter.

WINGS: Cantilever mid-wing monoplane of clipped delta planform, with 2° anhedral from roots. TsAGI section; thickness/chord ratio 5 per cent at root, 4.2 per cent at tip. No leading-edge camber. Sweepback on leading-edges 57°. Small pointed fairing on each side of fuselage forward of wingroot leading-edge. Small boundary layer

MiG-21bis ('Fishbed-N') armed with two AA-2C 'Atolls' outboard and two AA-8 'Aphids' inboard

fence above each wing near tip. All-metal structure, with two primary spars and one auxiliary spar. Inset ailerons, hydraulically boosted. Large 'blown' plain trailing-edge flaps, actuated hydraulically.

FUSELAGE: Circular section all-metal semi-monocoque structure. Ram air intake in nose, with three-position movable centrebody. Forward hinged door in top of nose gives access to avionics. Large dorsal spine fairing along top of fuselage from canopy to fin, housing control pushrods, avionics, single-point refuelling cap and fuel tank. Forward hinged door type airbrake on each side of underfuselage below wing leading-edge. A further forward hinged airbrake under fuselage forward of ventral fin. All airbrakes actuated hydraulically. Blister fairings above and below wing on each side to accommodate mainwheels when retracted.

TAIL UNIT: Cantilever all-metal structure, with all surfaces sharply swept. Conventional fin and hydraulically boosted rudder. Hydraulically boosted one-piece all-moving horizontal surface, mass balanced at tips, with two gearing ratios for use at varying combinations of altitude and airspeed. Tailplane trim switch on control column. No trim tabs. Single large ventral fin.

LANDING GEAR: Hydraulically retractable tricycle type, with single wheel on each unit; all units housed in fuselage when retracted. Forward retracting non-steerable nosewheel unit, tyre size 500 × 180; inward retracting mainwheels which turn to stow vertically inside fuselage. Size 800 × 200 tyres on mainwheels, inflated to approximately 7.93 bars (115 lb/sq in), ruling out normal operation from grass runways. Pneumatic disc brakes on all three wheels, supplied from compressed air bottles. Steering by differential mainwheel braking. Wheel doors remain open when legs are extended. Brake parachute housed inside acorn fairing at base of rudder.

POWER PLANT: One Tumansky R-13-300 turbojet, rated at 41.55 kN (9,340 lb st) dry and 64.73 kN (14,550 lb st) with afterburning. Fuel tanks in fuselage, and two integral tanks in each wing, with total capacity of 2,600 litres (687 US gallons; 572 Imp gallons), of which approx 1,800 litres (475 US gallons; 396 Imp gallons) are usable within CG limits at low speed. Provision for carrying one finned external fuel tank, capacity 490 litres (130 US gallons; 108 Imp gallons) or 800 litres (211 US gallons; 176 Imp gallons), on underfuselage pylon and two 490 litre drop

tanks on outboard underwing pylons. Two jettisonable solid propellant JATO rockets can be fitted under rear fuselage, aft of wheel doors.

ACCOMMODATION: Pilot only, on zero/zero ejection seat with spring loaded arm at top which ensures that seat cannot be operated unless hood is closed. Canopy is sideways hinged, to starboard, and is surmounted by a small rearview mirror. Flat bulletproof windscreen. Cabin air-conditioned. Armour plating forward and aft of cockpit.

SYSTEMS: Duplicated hydraulic system, supplied by engine driven pump, with backup by battery powered electric pump, and emergency electric tailplane trim and manual operation of flying controls. Autostabilisation in pitch and roll only.

AVIONICS AND EQUIPMENT: Search and track radar (NATO 'Jay Bird') in intake centrebody, with search range of 10.8 nm (20 km; 12.5 miles). Other standard avionics include VOR, ARK automatic radio-compass, IFF and Sirena 3 radar warning system with an indicator marked in 45° sectors in front of and behind the aircraft. Gyro gunsight maintains precision up to 2.75 g. Automatic ranging can be fed into gunsight. Full blind-flying instrumentation, with attitude and heading indicators driven by remote central gyro platform.

ARMAMENT: One twin-barrel 23 mm GSh-23 gun, with 200 rounds, in belly pack. Four underwing pylons for weapons or drop tanks. Typical loads for interceptor role include two AA-2/2D (K-13A) 'Atoll' air-to-air missiles on inner pylons and two radar homing AA-2C 'Atolls' or two UV-16-57 rocket packs (each sixteen 57 mm rockets) on outer pylons; or two drop tanks and two AA-2/2D or AA-2C 'Atolls'. Typical loads for ground attack role are four UV-16-57 rocket packs; two 500 kg and two 250 kg bombs; or four 240 mm S-24 air-to-surface rockets.

DIMENSIONS, EXTERNAL (MiG-21MF):

Wing span	7.15 m (23 ft 5½ in)
Length, incl pitot boom	15.76 m (51 ft 8½ in)
Fuselage length, intake lip to jetpipe nozzle	12.30 m (40 ft 4¼ in)
Height overall	4.00 m (14 ft 9 in)
Tailplane span	3.70 m (12 ft 8 in)
Wheel track	2.69 m (8 ft 10 in)
Wheelbase	4.81 m (15 ft 9½ in)

AREA:

Wings, gross	23.0 m² (247.0 sq ft)

WEIGHTS (MiG-21MF):

Weight empty	5,843 kg (12,882 lb)
T-O weight:	
with four K-13A missiles	8,200 kg (18,078 lb)
with two K-13A missiles and two 490 litre (130 US gallon; 108 Imp gallon) drop tanks	8,950 kg (19,730 lb)
with two K-13As and three drop tanks	9,400 kg (20,725 lb)
Max T-O weight	9,800 kg (21,605 lb)

PERFORMANCE (MiG-21MF):

Max level speed above 11,000 m (36,000 ft)	Mach 2.05 (1,175 knots; 2,175 km/h; 1,353 mph)
Max level speed at low altitude	Mach 1.06 (701 knots; 1,300 km/h; 807 mph)
Landing speed	146 knots (270 km/h; 168 mph)
Design ceiling	18,000 m (59,050 ft)
Practical ceiling	about 15,250 m (50,000 ft)
T-O run at normal AUW	800 m (2,625 ft)
Landing run	550 m (1,805 ft)
Combat radius (hi-lo-hi):	
with four 250 kg bombs, internal fuel	200 nm (370 km; 230 miles)
with two 250 kg bombs and drop tanks	400 nm (740 km; 460 miles)
Range, internal fuel only	593 nm (1,100 km; 683 miles)
Ferry range, with three external tanks	971 nm (1,800 km; 1,118 miles)

Top to bottom: Side views of the 'Flogger-B', 'Flogger-C' and 'Flogger-E' variants of the MiG-23 series
(Pilot Press)

PERFORMANCE (MiG-21US, clean):

Max level speed above 12,200 m (40,000 ft)		
	Mach 2.02 (1,159 knots; 2,150 km/h; 1,335 mph)	
Max level speed at S/L		
	Mach 1.06 (701 knots; 1,300 km/h; 807 mph)	
Max rate of climb at S/L	6,400 m (21,000 ft)/min	
Rate of climb at 11,000 m (36,000 ft)		
	3,050 m (10,000 ft)/min	
Time to 1,500 m (4,920 ft)	20 s	
Turn rate at 4,575 m (15,000 ft):		
instantaneous (Mach 0.5)	11.1°/s	
instantaneous (Mach 0.9)	13.4°/s	
sustained (Mach 0.9)	7.5°/s	
T-O run	700 m (2,297 ft)	

UPGRADED MiG-21

The Soviet Union has offered to India, and possibly to other countries, an uprated version of the MiG-21. Based on the MiG-21bis, the new aircraft would embody advanced wing technology, an R-33D turbofan of the kind fitted to the MiG-29, increased fuel capacity, multi-mode radar, state of the art avionics including a flight management system and head-up display, and combat flaps.

MIKOYAN MiG-23
NATO reporting names: Flogger-A, B, C, E, F, G, H and K

The Ye-231 (or Ye-23IG) prototype of this variable geometry (izmenyaemaya geometriya; IG) air combat fighter was displayed in public for the first time on 9 July 1967, during the Aviation Day flypast at Domodedovo Airport, Moscow, soon after its first flight. Pre-series aircraft were delivered to the Soviet Air Force in 1970, followed by initial series production MiG-23 interceptors in 1973. Subsequently, the MiG-23 and related MiG-27 superseded the MiG-21 progressively as primary equipment of the Soviet tactical air forces and Voyska PVO home defence interceptor force. MiG-23s are flown by all of the Warsaw Pact air forces, and have been exported to 12 other air forces. Production ended in the mid-1980s.

US press reports suggest that former Egyptian operated MiG-23s are being flown by the US Air Force from an air base in the western USA, alongside MiG-21s, for realistic air-to-air combat training of USAF and allied pilots. At least four others were presented to China in a technology transfer deal.

There have been 12 versions of the MiG-23:

MiG-23 (Flogger-A). Ye-23IG prototype shown at Domodedovo on 9 July 1967. One Lyulka AL-7F-1 afterburning turbojet, rated at 98.1 kN (22,046 lb st). Illustrated in 1973-74 and preceding editions of *Jane's*.

MiG-23S (Flogger-A). Pre-production version, with AL-7F-1 engine. S in designation denoted Sapphir radar.

MiG-23SM (Flogger-A). As MiG-23S, but with four APU-13 pylons for external stores added under engine air intake ducts and fixed inboard wing panels.

MiG-23UB. Tandem two-seat training counterpart of MiG-23S.

MiG-23M (Flogger-B). First series production version. Single-seat air combat fighter with Tumansky R-27 turbojet, rated at 68.65 kN (15,430 lb st) dry and 100.0 kN (22,485 lb st) with afterburning. Wings moved forward about 61 cm (2 ft) to compensate for lighter engine, increasing gap between wing and tailplane. Length of rear fuselage reduced; size of dorsal fin increased; wing chord increased on movable panels, giving large dogtooth.

MiG-23MF (Flogger-B). Improved version of MiG-23M, with more powerful R-29 engine and uprated equipment, including J band radar (NATO 'High Lark'), Sirena-3 radar warning system, Doppler, and a small infra-red search/track pod under the cockpit. The first Soviet aircraft with a demonstrated ability to track and engage targets flying below its own altitude. Standard version for Soviet air forces from about 1975, and for other Warsaw Pact air forces from 1978.

MiG-23B (NATO 'Flogger-F') of the Iraqi Air Force with added Dassault type flight refuelling probe forward of windscreen. Such a system has not yet been observed on MiGs of the Soviet Air Force (*Jane's Defence Weekly/Tony Banks*)

MiG-23UM (Flogger-C). Tandem two-seat version suitable for both operational training and combat use. Individual canopy over each seat. Rear seat slightly higher than forward seat, with retractable periscopic sight for occupant. Dorsal spine fairing of increased depth aft of rear canopy. Otherwise identical to MiG-23M with R-27 turbojet. Supplied to Soviet and Warsaw Pact air forces and those of other countries, including Angola, Cuba, Egypt, India and Libya.

MiG-23MS (Flogger-E). Export version of 'Flogger-B', equipped to a lower standard. Smaller radar (NATO 'Jay Bird': search range 15 nm; 29 km; 18 miles, tracking range 10 nm; 19 km; 12 miles) in shorter nose radome. No infra-red sensor or Doppler navigation equipment. Armed with 'Atoll' missiles and GSh-23 gun. In service in Angola, Algeria, Cuba, Iraq, North Korea and Libya. Some used by Soviet air forces.

MiG-23B (Flogger-F). Export single-seat fighter-bomber. Has the nose shape, laser rangefinder, raised seat, cockpit external armour plate and larger, low pressure tyres of Soviet air forces' MiG-27 ('Flogger-D'), but retains the power plant, variable geometry intakes and GSh-23 twin-barrel gun of the MiG-23MF interceptor. Provision for AS-7 'Kerry' missiles. Supplied to Algeria, Cuba, Egypt, Ethiopia, Iraq, Libya, Syria and Vietnam.

MiG-23ML (Flogger-G). Lightened version (L of designation = logkiy; light), first identified when six aircraft from Kubinka air base made goodwill visits to Finland and France in Summer 1978. Basically similar to MiG-23MF, but with a Tumansky R-35F-300 afterburning turbojet. Rear fuselage fuel tank removed. Much smaller dorsal fin. Modified nosewheel leg. The radar is lighter in weight, and the undernose sensor pod on some aircraft is of new design. Standard Soviet operational variant, also exported to Czechoslovakia, the German Democratic Republic and Syria.

MiG-23BN (Flogger-H). As 'Flogger-F' but with small fairing for radar warning receiver added on each side at bottom of fuselage, immediately forward of nosewheel doors. Operated by Bulgarian, Czechoslovak and Polish air forces. Total of 80 delivered to Indian Air Force in 1980-82 to re-equip Nos. 10, 220 and 221 Squadrons. Has also been used by Soviet air forces.

MiG-23MLD (Flogger-K). D added to designation stands for dorabotannyy (modified). Development of 'Flogger-G', identified by dogtooth notch at junction of wing glove leading-edge and intake trunk on each side, to generate vortices to improve stability in yaw at high angles of attack. This compensates for use of smaller ventral folding fin and small 'Flogger-G' type dorsal fin. New IFF antenna forward of windscreen. AA-11 (NATO 'Archer') close-range air-to-air missiles on fuselage pylons. Pivoting weapon pylons under outer wings.

About 900 'Flogger-B/G/K' interceptors serve with the Soviet strategic air defence interceptor force, and a further 900 in tactical air force regiments.

MiG-23ML 'Flogger-G' single-seat variable geometry fighter of the Czechoslovak Air Force (*Letectvi + Kosmonautika/Václav Jukl*)

The two-seat MiG-23UM, identical to the early MiG-23M except for second cockpit

'Flogger-K' version of the MiG-23 interceptor (*Pilot Press*)

The following description refers specifically to the single-seat MiG-23ML ('Flogger-G') as supplied to the Soviet air forces:

TYPE: Single-seat variable geometry air combat fighter.

WINGS: Cantilever shoulder-wing monoplane of conventional light alloy construction, with front and rear main spars and auxiliary centre spar. Sweepback of main panels variable in flight or on the ground by manual control, at 16°, 45° or 72°. Two hydraulic wing sweep motors driven separately by main and control booster systems. If one system fails, wing sweep system remains effective at 50 per cent normal angular velocity. Extended chord (dogtooth) on outer panels visible when wings are swept. Fixed triangular inboard panels, with leading-edges swept at 72°. Welded steel pivot box carry-through structure. Full span hydraulically actuated trailing-edge single-slotted flaps, each in three sections, permitting independent actuation of outboard sections when wings are fully swept. No ailerons. Two-section hydraulically actuated upper surface spoilers/lift dumpers, forward of mid and inner flap sections on each side, operate differentially in conjunction with horizontal tail surfaces (except when disengaged at 72° sweep), and collectively for improved runway adherence and braking after touchdown. Hydraulically actuated leading-edge flap on outboard two-thirds of each main (variable geometry) panel, coupled to trailing-edge flaps.

FUSELAGE: Conventional semi-monocoque structure of basic circular section; flattened on each side of cockpit, forward of lateral air intake trunks which blend into circular shape of rear fuselage. Large flat splitter plate, with boundary layer bleeds, forms inboard face of each intake. Two small rectangular suction relief doors in each trunk, under inboard wing leading-edge. Perforations under rear fuselage, aft of mainwheel bays, are pressure relief vents. Four hydraulically actuated door type airbrakes, mounted two on each side of rear fuselage above and below horizontal tail surface. Rear fuselage detachable between wing and tailplane for engine servicing.

TAIL UNIT: Hydraulically actuated all-moving horizontal surfaces, swept back at 57° on leading-edge, operate both differentially and symmetrically to provide aileron and elevator function respectively. Conventional fin, swept back at 65° on leading-edge, with inset rudder. Fin and forward portion of each horizontal surface of conventional light alloy construction with spars and ribs. Rudder and rear of each horizontal surface have honeycomb core. Ground adjustable tab on each horizontal surface at inboard trailing-edge. Large ventral fin in two portions. Lower portion is hinged to fold to starboard when landing gear is extended, to increase ground clearance.

LANDING GEAR: Hydraulically retractable tricycle type, with single wheel on each main unit and steerable twin-wheel nose unit. Main units retract inward into rear of air intake trunks. Main fairings to enclose these units are attached to legs. Small inboard fairing for each wheel bay hinged to fuselage belly. Nose unit, fitted with small mudguard over each wheel, retracts rearward. Mainwheels fitted with brakes and anti-skid units. Brake parachute, area 21m² (226 sq ft), in cylindrical fairing at base of rudder with split conic doors.

POWER PLANT: One Tumansky R-35F-300 turbojet, rated at up to 127.5 kN (28,660 lb st) with max afterburning in aircraft for Soviet Air Force. Water injection system, capacity 28 litres (7.4 US gallons; 6.15 Imp gallons). Four fuel tanks in fuselage, aft of cockpit, and two in wings. Max internal fuel capacity 5,750 litres (1,519 US gallons; 1,265 Imp gallons). Variable geometry air intakes and variable nozzle. Provision for carrying jettisonable external fuel tank, capacity 800 litres (211 US gallons; 176 Imp gallons), on underfuselage centreline pylon, and two more under fixed wing panels. Two additional external tanks of same capacity may be carried on non-swivelling pylons under outer wings for ferry flights, with wings in fully forward position. Attachment for assisted take-off rocket on each side of fuselage aft of landing gear.

ACCOMMODATION: Pilot only, on zero/zero ejection seat in air-conditioned and pressurised cockpit, under small hydraulically actuated rearward hinged canopy. Bullet-proof windscreen. Small electrically heated rearview mirror on top of canopy.

AVIONICS AND EQUIPMENT: J band multi-mode radar (NATO 'High Lark 2': search range 46 nm; 85 km; 53 miles, tracking range 29 nm; 54 km; 34 miles) behind dielectric nosecone. No radar scope; instead, picture is projected onto head-up display. RSBN-6S ILS, with antennae (NATO 'Swift Rod') under radome and at tip of fin trailing-edge; suppressed UHF antennae form top of fin and forward fixed portion of ventral fin; yaw vane above fuselage aft of radome; angle of attack sensor on port side. SRO-2 (NATO 'Odd Rods') IFF antenna immediately forward of windscreen. Soviet Air Force version. Sirena-3 antennae in horns at inboard leading-edge of each outer wing and below ILS antenna on fin. Retractable landing/taxying light under each engine air intake.

MiG-27 ('Flogger-D') of Soviet Air Force (by courtesy of Flieger Revue)

ARMAMENT: One 23 mm GSh-23L twin-barrel gun in fuselage belly pack, with large flash eliminator around muzzles. One pylon under centre-fuselage, one under each engine air intake duct, and one under each fixed inboard wing panel, for air-to-air missiles, bombs, rocket packs or other external stores. Use of twin launchers under air intake ducts permits carriage of four R-60 ('Aphid') missiles, plus two R-23 ('Apex') on underwing pylons.

DIMENSIONS, EXTERNAL:

Wing span: fully spread	13.965 m (45 ft 10 in)
fully swept	7.779 m (25 ft 6¼ in)
Length overall: excl nose probe	15.88 m (52 ft 1¼ in)
incl nose probe	16.71 m (54 ft 10 in)
Height overall	4.82 m (15 ft 9¾ in)

AREA:

Wings, gross: spread	37.3 m² (401.5 sq ft)
swept	34.2 m² (368.1 sq ft)

WEIGHTS:

Weight empty	10,200 kg (22,485 lb)
Max external weapon load	3,000 kg (6,615 lb)
T-O weight	14,800-17,800 kg (32,625-39,250 lb)

PERFORMANCE:

Max level speed: at height, with weapons	Mach 2.35
at S/L	Mach 1.15
Max rate of climb at S/L	14,400 m (47,250 ft)/min
Service ceiling	18,000 m (59,055 ft)
T-O run	500 m (1,640 ft)
Landing run	750 m (2,460 ft)
Combat radius:	
with six air-to-air missiles	620 nm (1,150 km; 715 miles)
with 2,000 kg (4,410 lb) of bombs	378 nm (700 km; 435 miles)
Range:	
with max internal fuel	810 nm (1,500 km; 932 miles)
with external tanks	1,375 nm (2,550 km; 1,584 miles)
g limit	+8.5

MIKOYAN MiG-27
NATO reporting names: Flogger-D and J
Indian Air Force name: Bahadur (Valiant)

Although the single-seat variable-geometry ground attack aircraft known to NATO as 'Flogger-D/J' have many airframe features in common with the MiG-23, they differ in important respects and are designated MiG-27. Their use of fixed air intakes and a two-position (on/off) afterburner nozzle is consistent with the primary requirement of transonic speed at low altitude. Two versions are operational in Soviet tactical air force regiments:

MiG-27 (Flogger-D). Initial version for Soviet tactical air forces, introduced in second half of the 1970s. Forward portion of fuselage completely redesigned by comparison with interceptor versions of MiG-23. Instead of having an ogival radome, 'Flogger-D' nose is sharply tapered in side elevation, with a radar ranging antenna and a small sloping window covering a laser rangefinder. KN-23 inertial navigation system. Doppler navigation radar in nose. Additional armour on flat sides of cockpit. Seat and canopy raised to improve view from cockpit. Wider, low-pressure mainwheel tyres. Six-barrel 23 mm Gatling type underbelly gun replaces GSh-23 of interceptor. Bomb/JATO rack under each side of rear fuselage in addition to five pylons for external stores, including tactical nuclear weapons and the air-to-surface missiles known to NATO as AS-7 'Kerry', AS-10 'Karen', AS-12 'Kegler' and AS-14 'Kedge'. Typical external load comprises six 500 kg bombs and two 800 litre (211 US gallon; 176 Imp gallon) jettisonable fuel tanks. Bullet shape antenna above each glove pylon, associated with missile guidance. Radar warning receiver blister on each side of front fuselage, ahead of nosewheel bay.

MiG-27M (Flogger-J). Identified in 1981. Wider nose, with lip at top, over window for laser rangefinder, and blister fairing with rectangular window for laser target designator below. Enhanced electro-optical sensors, probably with rearward laser designation capability for laser guided bomb delivery. Blade antenna for IFF on each side of undersurface aft of designator fairing. RSBN ILS

Nose of MiG-27M 'Flogger-J'
(Jane's Defence Weekly/Paul Beaver)

IRCM flare container on rear fuselage of MiG-27
(Jane's Defence Weekly/Paul Beaver)

antenna on port side of nose. Bullet shape antennae above wingroot glove pylons and external armour on sides of cockpit deleted. Wingroot leading-edge extensions added (see illustrations). Armament includes two gun pods on underwing pylons, with gun barrels that can be depressed for attacking ground targets. Container for IR countermeasures flares, in form of short fence, can be mounted on fuselage to each side of dorsal fin. MiG-27M export version is being built under licence by HAL in India as the Bahadur (Valiant) (see Indian section).

About 830 'Flogger-Ds' and 'Js' are deployed with the Soviet tactical air forces (with which they operated in Afghanistan), plus at least one squadron with the East German Air Force. The somewhat similar aircraft known to NATO as 'Flogger-F and H' are members of the MiG-23 series, with variable geometry intakes and a GSh-23 twin-barrel gun, although having the nose shape, raised seat and larger, low pressure tyres of 'Flogger-D'. Both versions have been operated by Soviet units; but the 'F' and 'H' are basically export counterparts of 'Flogger-D', with lower standards of equipment and performance, and are described under the MiG-23 entry. Production of the 'F' and 'H' was completed in the mid-1980s.

The following data apply to the MiG-27M 'Flogger-J':

POWER PLANT: Generally similar to MiG-23MF, but R-29B-300 engine rated at 78.45 kN (17,635 lb st) dry and 112.8 kN (25,350 lb st) with max afterburning.

DIMENSIONS, EXTERNAL: As MiG-23, plus:

Length overall	17.10 m (56 ft 1¼ in)
Tailplane span	5.75 m (18 ft 10¼ in)

AREA:

Horizontal tail surfaces	6.88 m² (74.06 sq ft)

WEIGHTS:

Weight empty	10,700 kg (23,590 lb)
Max external load	4,500 kg (9,920 lb)
Max T-O weight	18,100-20,700 kg (39,900-45,635 lb)

PERFORMANCE:

Max level speed: at height	Mach 1.77
at S/L	Mach 1.1
Max rate of climb at S/L	12,000 m (39,370 ft)/min
Service ceiling	14,000 m (45,900 ft)
T-O run	800 m (2,625 ft)
Landing run	950 m (3,120 ft)

Comparison of this photograph of a MiG-27M 'Flogger-J' with that of a 'Flogger-D' shows the restyled nose, absence of bullet shape antennae on the wing gloves, addition of wingroot leading-edge extensions and depressed barrel of gun in port underwing pod

First illustration of what could be a 'Foxbat-F' defence suppression version of the MiG-25 (copied from *Krasnaya Zvezda*)

MiG-27M ('Flogger-J') single-seat ground attack aircraft *(Pilot Press)*

Combat radius, with underbelly fuel tank, four 500 kg
  bombs and two 'Atoll' missiles, lo-lo-lo
  210 nm (390 km; 240 miles)
Range with max internal fuel
  944 nm (1,750 km; 1,087 miles)
Max ferry range with three external tanks
  1,350 nm (2,500 km; 1,550 miles)
g limit +7.0

MIKOYAN MiG-25
NATO reporting name: Foxbat

Still the fastest combat aircraft identified in squadron service, and holder of the absolute height record for aeroplanes, the MiG-25 was designed nearly 30 years ago to counter the threat of the B-70 Mach 3 strategic bomber then under development for the US Air Force. Its early history has been described in previous editions of *Jane's*. Emphasis was placed on high-speed, high-altitude capability and a radar/missile fit that would permit attack over a considerable range; manoeuvrability was less important. Despite the subsequent NATO switch to low-level operations, about 400 MiG-25s continue to equip the Soviet strategic interceptor force; a further 50 interceptors and 120 reconnaissance MiG-25s serve with the tactical air forces. Others fly in the national markings of Algeria, India, Iraq, Libya and Syria. Production was completed in the mid-1980s. Six versions have been identified:

MiG-25 (Foxbat-A). Basic interceptor, designed to attack high-flying targets, with large radar (NATO 'Fox Fire') in nose and armed with four air-to-air missiles on underwing attachments. Powered by two 110 kN (24,700 lb st) Tumansky R-15 turbojets. Production cut back in 1977-78, reflecting new emphasis on interception of low flying targets. Most 'Foxbat-As' in service in the Soviet Union, and some operated by the Libyan Arab Air Force, have been converted to 'Foxbat-E' standard. 'Foxbat-As' remain operational in Algeria, Iraq and Syria.

MiG-25R (Foxbat-B). Basic reconnaissance version, with five camera windows and various flush dielectric panels aft of very small dielectric nosecap for radar. Equipment believed to include Doppler navigation system and side looking airborne radar (SLAR). Powered by two 110 kN (24,700 lb st) Tumansky R-15BD-300 turbojets. No armament. Slightly reduced span. Wing leading-edge sweep constant from root to tip. Operated by Soviet tactical air forces, and in Algeria, India, Libya and Syria.

MiG-25U (Foxbat-C). Trainer, of which first photographs were published towards the end of 1975. Generally

similar to operational versions, but with redesigned nose section, containing separate cockpit with individual canopy, forward of standard cockpit and at a lower level. No search radar or reconnaissance sensors in nose. In service with air forces of Soviet Union and India (two).

MiG-25R (Foxbat-D). Generally similar to 'Foxbat-B', but with larger SLAR (side looking airborne radar)

dielectric panel, further aft on side of nose, and no cameras. Operated by Soviet Air Force and in Libya.

MiG-25M (Foxbat-E). Converted 'Foxbat-A' with changes to radar and equipment to provide limited lookdown/shootdown capability comparable with that of 'Flogger-B'. Undernose sensor pod. Engines uprated to 137.3 kN (30,865 lb st). Developed via aircraft known as the **Ye-266M**, which set three time-to-height records in 1975 and also holds the absolute height record of 37,650 m (123,524 ft).

MiG-25 (Foxbat-F). First illustrated in the Soviet press in 1986, this 'Wild Weasel' type of defence suppression aircraft carries AS-11 (NATO 'Kilter') anti-radiation missiles to attack surface-to-air missile sites over long stand-off ranges. Airframe generally similar to 'Foxbat' interceptors, but with dielectric panel aft of radome on port side (possibly both sides) of front fuselage. Entered service in 1988.

The following description applies to the MiG-25 ('Foxbat-A') interceptor except where indicated:
TYPE: Single-seat interceptor.
WINGS: Cantilever high-wing monoplane. Anhedral 4° from roots. Sweepback on leading-edge approx 40° inboard, 38° outboard of each outer missile attachment. Sweepback at quarter-chord 32°. Wing structure basically of arc-welded nickel steel, with titanium leading-edge. Upper surface fence in line with each inboard weapon attachment; shorter shallow fence in line with each outer attachment. Long anti-flutter body (max diameter 30 cm; 11.8 in) at each wingtip, housing avionics. Light alloy aileron at centre of each semi-span, with simple light alloy

The reconnaissance version of the MiG-25 known to NATO as 'Foxbat-B' in service with the Libyan Arab Air Force. Note the camera-carrying nose and dielectric panel *(US Navy)*

MiG-25M ('Foxbat-E') interceptor of the Libyan Arab Air Force, armed with 'Acrid' and 'Aphid' air-to-air missiles *(US Navy)*

flap on inboard 37 per cent of trailing-edge. No other movable wing surfaces.

FUSELAGE: Basic fuselage is quite slim, but is blended into the rectangular air intake trunks, which have wedge inlets. Inner walls of intakes are curved at top and do not run parallel with outer walls; a hinged panel forms the lower lip of each intake, enabling intake area to be varied electronically. Airbrake beneath jetpipes, between ventral fins. Structure mainly of arc-welded nickel steel.

TAIL UNIT: Cantilever structure comprising twin outward canted fins with inset rudders, and all-moving horizontal surfaces. All surfaces sweptback (tailplane 50°, fins 60°), without tabs. Main structures of arc-welded nickel steel, with titanium leading-edges and light alloy rear sections. Two outward canted ventral fins, with retractable sprung tailskids. Large areas of each main and ventral fin form flush antennae.

LANDING GEAR: Retractable tricycle type. Single wheel, with high pressure tyre of 1.20 m (47.25 in) diameter, on each forward retracting main unit. Wheel stows vertically between air intake duct and outer skin of each trunk. Twin-wheel forward retracting nose unit. Twin brake-chutes in fairing above and between jet nozzles.

POWER PLANT: Two Tumansky R-15BD-300 single-shaft turbojets, each rated at 110 kN (24,700 lb st) with afterburning. Water-methanol injection standard. Fuel in two structural tanks in fuselage, between cockpit and engine bay, in saddle tanks around intake ducts, and integral tank in each wing, filling almost the entire volume inboard of outer fence. Total fuel capacity approx 14,000 kg (30,865 lb) or 17,410 litres (4,600 US gallons; 3,830 Imp gallons).

ACCOMMODATION: Pilot only, on KM-1 zero-height, 80 knot (150 km/h; 93 mph) ejection seat similar to that fitted to some versions of MiG-21. Canopy hinged to open sideways, to starboard.

AVIONICS AND EQUIPMENT: Main fire control radar (NATO 'Fox Fire': range believed to be 45 nm; 85 km; 52 miles) in nose, forward of avionics compartment housing navigation radar. SRZO-2 (NATO 'Odd Rods') IFF and SOD-57M ATC/SIF, with antennae in starboard fin tip. Sirena-3 360° radar warning system with receivers in centre of each wingtip anti-flutter body and starboard fin tip. Unidentified ECCM, decoys and jammers. RSB-70/RPS HF, RSIU-5 VHF, R-831 UHF communications equipment, SP-50 (NATO 'Swift Rod') ILS, MRP-56P marker beacon receiver and ARK-15 radio compass. Retractable landing light under front of each intake trunk.

ARMAMENT: Air-to-air missiles on four underwing attachments. These may comprise one infra-red and one radar homing example of the missile known to NATO as 'Acrid' under each wing. Alternatively, one 'Apex' and a pair of 'Archers' or 'Aphids' can be carried under each wing. Backup optical weapon sight.

DIMENSIONS, EXTERNAL:
Wing span: 'Foxbat-A'	13.95 m (45 ft 9 in)
'Foxbat-B'	13.40 m (44 ft 0 in)
Wing aspect ratio: 'Foxbat-A'	3.4
Length overall	23.82 m (78 ft 1¾ in)
Length of fuselage	19.40 m (63 ft 7¾ in)
Height overall	6.10 m (20 ft 0¼ in)

AREA:
Wings, gross: 'Foxbat-A'	56.83 m² (611.7 sq ft)

WEIGHTS (estimated):
Basic operating weight, empty:	
'Foxbat-A'	at least 20,000 kg (44,100 lb)
'Foxbat-B'	19,600 kg (43,200 lb)
Normal T-O weight	36,000 kg (79,365 lb)
Max T-O weight: 'Foxbat-A'	37,425 kg (82,500 lb)
'Foxbat-B'	41,000 kg (90,385 lb)

PERFORMANCE ('Foxbat-A' estimated):
Never-exceed combat speed:	
all versions	Mach 2.82
Max level speed at low altitude: 'Foxbat-A', with four	
'Acrid' missiles and 50% fuel	Mach 0.85
'Foxbat-B'	Mach 0.98

This photograph shows clearly the tandem cockpits in the nose of the MiG-25U ('Foxbat-C')

Mikoyan MiG-25M single-seat fighter (NATO 'Foxbat-E'), with scrap view of front fuselage of two-seat MiG-25U *(Pilot Press)*

Landing speed:	
'Foxbat-A'	146 knots (270 km/h; 168 mph)
Max rate of climb at S/L:	
'Foxbat-A'	12,480 m (40,950 ft)/min
Time to 11,000 m (36,000 ft) with afterburning:	
'Foxbat-A'	2 min 30 s
Service ceiling: 'Foxbat-A'	24,400 m (80,000 ft)
'Foxbat-B, D'	23,000 m (75,450 ft)
T-O run: 'Foxbat-A'	1,380 m (4,525 ft)
'Foxbat-B'	1,250 m (4,100 ft)
Landing run: 'Foxbat-A'	2,180 m (7,150 ft)
'Foxbat-B'	800 m (2,625 ft)
Normal operational radius:	
'Foxbat-A'	610 nm (1,130 km; 700 miles)
Max combat radius, econ power:	
'Foxbat-A'	780 nm (1,450 km; 900 miles)
Range with max fuel:	
'Foxbat-B'	863 nm (1,600 km; 994 miles)
g limit	+5

MIKOYAN MiG-29
NATO reporting name: Fulcrum
Indian Air Force name: Baaz (Eagle)

Operational in its basic single-seat land-based form since early 1985, the MiG-29 is a twin-engined combat aircraft comparable in size to the US F/A-18 Hornet. About seven per cent of its airframe, by weight, is made of composites. Its large pulse Doppler lookdown/shootdown radar is limited to search-while-scan rather than track-while-scan, but is supplemented by a laser rangefinder and an infra-red search/track sensor, mounted inside a transparent dome in front of the windscreen, offset to starboard. Operating in conjunction with a helmet-mounted aiming device, these enable the MiG-29 to approach its target without emitting any detectable radar or radio signals. Its sustained turn rate is much improved over earlier Soviet fighters, and thrust-to-weight ratio is better than 1. Supermanoeuvrability and post-stall behaviour were tested during development, and simulated combats have taken place in the post-stall region. Following early modifications, the MiG-29 will not enter a flat spin, is reluctant to enter a normal spin, and will recover as soon as the controls have been released.

Although operated primarily as a single-seat counter-air fighter, the MiG-29 has a full dual-role air combat/attack capability. Academician Rostislav A. Belyakov, general designer of the Mikoyan OKB, has referred to its "substantial growth potential". A combat-capable two-seat version has been in production and service for several years. Modified carrier-based and fly by wire versions have flown, and the full list of MiG-29 variants identified to date is as follows:

Fulcrum-A. Basic land-based single-seat version, of which three variants may be identified as follows:

1. The original single-seat production version, with two ventral tail fins similar to those of the Sukhoi Su-27. (Illustrated in 1987-88 *Jane's*.)

2. First version displayed in public, when a detachment of six from Kubinka air base made a goodwill visit to Finland on 1 July 1986. Instead of ventral fins, this variant has its dorsal fins extended forward as what appear to be simple overwing fences but are packed with infra-red countermeasures flares.

3. Differs from second variant in having extended-chord rudders.

Fulcrum-B (MiG-29UB). Combat trainer with second seat in front of the normal cockpit, under a continuous canopy. Nose radar replaced by radar rangefinder. Periscope above canopy. Underwing stores pylons retained.

Fulcrum-C. Basically similar to 'Fulcrum-A' variant 3, but with more deeply curved top to fuselage aft of the cockpit, containing extensive equipment. This may have been transferred from inside the lower fuselage to provide room for additional fuel.

Fulcrum-D. Used for ski-jump take-off and deck landing trials on board the Soviet Navy carrier *Tbilisi* in late 1989. Basically similar to 'Fulcrum-A' with original narrow-chord rudders. Upward folding outer wing panels,

MiG-29 ('Fulcrum-A', later series) single-seat counter-air fighter, with added side view (top) of MiG-29UB ('Fulcrum-B') two-seat combat trainer *(Pilot Press)*

with bulged tips, probably for ESM equipment. No intake foreign-object-damage doors required for carrier operation, permitting deletion of overwing louvres and internal ducting in lightweight aluminium-lithium alloy centre-section, and providing much increased integral fuel tankage (2,550 litres; 674 US gallons; 561 Imp gallons in centre-section). In-flight refuelling capability. Strengthened landing gear. Arrester hook. No flare dispenser 'fences' forward of dorsal fins. Different IRST. Expected to form standard close-range air defence/attack force on *Tbilisi* and its sister ships.

FBW Fulcrum. An experimental MiG-29, with fly by wire controls, was flown for the first time by Mikoyan chief test pilot Valery Menitsky in late 1989. Features include a different tailplane, a slightly changed wing position, and modifications to change the centre of gravity. Claimed to be more comfortable to fly, with increased permissible angle of attack, better manoeuvrability and improved cruise efficiency.

Production is centred at a factory in Moscow. More than 500 MiG-29s are operational with air forces of the Soviet military districts and groups of forces stationed in East Germany, Hungary, and in the Soviet Union west of the Urals. Export deliveries of an initial quantity of 50 MiG-29s ordered by India (42 single-seat, eight two-seat) had been completed by mid-1987, and have been followed by 20 more. Others have been delivered to Cuba, Czechoslovakia, East Germany, Iraq, North Korea, Poland, Syria and Yugoslavia. Deliveries to Afghanistan were reported to be imminent in early 1990.

There is nothing to suggest that the Soviet Union is yet equipping this counter-air fighter to refuel in flight. Also, although the MiG-29 has a high-set cockpit, giving its pilot a reasonable forward view over the sloping nose, he lacks the all-round field of view offered to the pilots of western fighters such as the F-15 and F-16 through 360° low-sill canopies. Nor can the bulky head-up display, IR sensor, and large wing leading-edge extensions be helpful in this respect. Flying control surfaces are actuated hydraulically rather than by a fly by wire system.

Comparison of the general configurations of the MiG-29 'Fulcrum' and much larger Su-27 'Flanker' shows that the two designs are strikingly similar in most respects, even in such detail as current tail fin location, the manner in which the mainwheels retract into the wingroots, and the use of hinged doors that shield the underslung engine air intakes against ingestion of stones, snow, slush, ice and foreign objects during take-off and landing on the kind of runways used by Warsaw Pact front-line air forces, especially in Winter. On the land-based MiG-29, when the intake trunks are closed, engine air is taken in through a series of lateral louvres in the upper surface of the aircraft's deep wingroot leading-edge extensions.

At the 1989 Paris Air Show, Mr Belyakov stated that he hoped to exhibit an uprated version of the MiG-29 with CRT cockpit displays replacing conventional instruments at the next show in 1991. The aircraft will probably also embody fly by wire controls. These and other technologies were not available in proven form in the Soviet Union when the MiG-29 design was frozen in the 1970s.

The following description refers specifically to the later production land-based 'Fulcrum-A', but is generally applicable to other versions, except as already noted:

TYPE: All-weather counter-air fighter, with attack capability.

WINGS: Cantilever low-wing monoplane. Leading-edge sweepback approx 42° on outer wings, with very large ogival root extensions. Anhedral approx 2°. Computer controlled leading-edge manoeuvring flaps over full span except for tips. Plain flap and aileron, both of carbonfibre honeycomb construction, on trailing-edge of each wing. Manually adjustable trim tab on trailing-edge of each aileron. All control surfaces are hydraulically actuated.

FUSELAGE: Semi-monocoque all-metal structure, sharply tapered and downswept aft of flat-sided cockpit area, with ogival dielectric nosecone. Hydraulically actuated forward-hinged airbrakes above and below rear fuselage between jetpipes. Small vortex generator on each side of nose probe helps to overcome tendency to aileron reversal effects at angles of attack above 25° experienced in flight testing.

TAIL UNIT: Cantilever structure, comprising twin fins, small inset rudders, and all-moving horizontal surfaces, all carried on slim booms alongside engine nacelles. Interconnect allows rudders to augment roll rate. Vertical surfaces, constructed of carbonfibre honeycomb, swept back at approx 40° and canted outward at 7°, each with dorsal fin that extends forward as an overwing housing for IRCM flares and chaff. About 65 per cent of horizontal surfaces is of conventional aluminium alloy construction, remainder of carbonfibre, with leading-edge sweepback of approx 50°. No tabs. All control surfaces hydraulically actuated. Mechanical yaw stability augmentation system.

LANDING GEAR: Retractable tricycle type, with single wheel on each main unit and twin nosewheels. Mainwheels retract forward into wingroots, turning through 90° to lie flat above leg. Nosewheels, on trailing-link oleo, retract rearward between engine air intakes. Hydraulic retraction and extension, with mechanical emergency release. Mainwheel tyre size 770 × 200; nosewheel tyre size 530 × 100. Steel brakes. Mudguard to rear of nosewheels.

Container for cruciform brake-chute recessed in centre of boat-tail between engine nozzles.

POWER PLANT: Two Isotov RD-33 turbofans, each rated at 50 kN (11,240 lb st) dry and 81.4 kN (18,300 lb st) with afterburning. Engine ducts are canted at approx 9° and have wedge intakes, sweptback at approx 35°, under wingroot leading-edge extensions. Multi-segment ramp system, including top-hinged forward door inside each intake that closes the duct while the aircraft is taking off

or landing, to prevent ingestion of foreign objects, ice or snow. Air is then fed to each engine through louvres in top of wingroot leading-edge extension and gap above top lip of intake. Integral fuel tanks in inboard portion of each wing and in fuselage between wings; total capacity 4,365 litres (1,153 US gallons; 960 Imp gallons). Attachment for a non-conformal external fuel tank under fuselage, between ducts, and another under each wing. Single-point pressure refuelling through receptacle in

MiG-29UB ('Fulcrum-B') two-seat combat trainer of the Indian Air Force *(courtesy Air International)*

MiG-29 'Fulcrum-D' on the deck of the carrier/cruiser *Tbilisi*

Naval version of MiG-29 with folding wings, arrester hook and enlarged wingtips *(Jane's/Mike Keep)*

port wheel well. Overwing receptacles for manual fuelling. Airscoop for APU above rear fuselage on port side.

ACCOMMODATION: Pilot only, on K-36D zero/zero ejection seat, under rearward hinged transparent blister canopy in high-set cockpit. Sharply inclined one-piece curved windscreen. Three internal mirrors provide rearward view.

SYSTEM: Hydraulically actuated flying controls. No fly by wire system.

AVIONICS: HO-193 coherent pulse Doppler engagement radar (NATO 'Slot Back'; detection range 54 nm; 100 km; 62 miles); infra-red search/track sensor forward of windscreen (protected by removable fairing on non-operational flights) collimated with laser rangefinder; inertial navigation system; SRZO-2 (NATO 'Odd Rods') IFF; Sirena-3 360° radar warning system, with sensors on wingroot extensions, wingtips and port fin. Two SO-69 ECM antennae under conformal dielectric fairings in leading-edge of each wingroot extension; head-up display; and helmet-mounted target designation system for off-axis aiming of air-to-air missiles.

ARMAMENT AND OPERATIONAL EQUIPMENT: Six medium-range radar homing R-27 (AA-10; NATO 'Alamo-A') and/or close-range R-73 (AA-11; 'Archer') air-to-air missiles, on three pylons under each wing. Provision for carrying AA-9 ('Amos') and R-60 (AA-8; 'Aphid') missiles. Able to carry bombs and 57 mm, 80 mm and 240 mm rockets in attack role. One 30 mm gun in port wingroot leading-edge extension.

DIMENSIONS, EXTERNAL:

Wing span	11.36 m (37 ft 3¼ in)
Wing chord: on centreline	5.60 m (18 ft 4½ in)
at tip	1.27 m (4 ft 2 in)
Length overall, incl nose probe	17.32 m (56 ft 10 in)
Height overall	4.73 m (15 ft 6¼ in)
Tailplane span	7.78 m (25 ft 6¼ in)
Wheel track	3.10 m (10 ft 2 in)
Wheelbase	3.67 m (12 ft 0½ in)

AREA:

Wings, gross	35.20 m² (378.9 sq ft)

WEIGHTS (approx):

Operating weight empty	8,175 kg (18,025 lb)
Normal T-O weight (interceptor)	15,000 kg (33,065 lb)
Max T-O weight	18,000 kg (39,700 lb)

PERFORMANCE:

Max level speed: at height	
	Mach 2.3 (1,320 knots; 2,440 km/h; 1,520 mph)
at S/L	Mach 1.06 (700 knots; 1,300 km/h; 805 mph)
Max rate of climb at S/L	19,800 m (65,000 ft)/min
Service ceiling	17,000 m (56,000 ft)
T-O run	240 m (790 ft)
Landing run	600 m (1,970 ft)
Max range	approx 1,130 nm (2,100 km; 1,300 miles)

MIKOYAN MiG-31
NATO reporting name: Foxhound

Evidence that the Mikoyan design team was developing an improved interceptor based on the MiG-25 (NATO 'Foxbat') came first from Lt Viktor Belyenko, the Soviet pilot who defected to Japan in a 'Foxbat-A' in September 1976. He said that the airframe of the new fighter was strengthened to permit supersonic flight at low altitude; more powerful engines were fitted, each giving 137.3 kN (30,865 lb st) with afterburning; the avionics were improved; and fuselage mountings had been added to enable the aircraft to carry six air-to-air missiles.

In mid-1982 it became known that NATO had allocated the reporting name 'Foxhound' to what the technical press referred to as 'Super Foxbat' and which was subsequently

Left to right: 'Aphid', 'Archer' and 'Alamo-A' missiles on a MiG-29 of the Soviet Air Force *(Piotr Butowski)*

MiG-29 (NATO 'Fulcrum-A') of the Czechoslovak Air Force *(Letectvi + Kosmonautika/Václav Jukl)*

identified as the MiG-31. A three-view was displayed publicly for the first time in September of the following year, during briefings at the annual AFA Convention in Washington, DC, enabling the aircraft to be illustrated in the Addenda to the 1983-84 *Jane's*. The drawing showed significant new features, including tandem seating for a two-man crew, much enlarged engine air intakes, rearward extension of the jet nozzles, and wingroot leading-edge extensions on wings that were little changed in size and shape from those of the MiG-25. Its general accuracy was confirmed in the Autumn of 1985 when the pilot of an F-16 of the Royal Norwegian Air Force intercepted and photographed a MiG-31 off the coast of eastern Finnmark in northern Norway.

The MiG-31's large pulse-Doppler radar is said to embody technology found in the Hughes AN/APG-65 digital radar fitted in the US Navy's F/A-18 Hornet, providing true lookdown/shootdown and multiple target engagement capability for the first time in a Soviet

interceptor. Other equipment includes active countermeasures dispensers, and an infra-red search/track sensor.

Delivery of MiG-31s to Voyska PVO air defence regiments had begun by early 1983, and more than 160 are now operational, deployed from the Arkhangelsk area near the USSR's western borders to Dolinsk on Sakhalin Island, north of Japan. Production is centred at the Gorkiy airframe plant. Although the MiG-31 is not required to operate at the extremely high speeds attainable by the MiG-25, it appears that the latter aircraft's arc-welded nickel steel structure has been retained. A switch to light alloy construction would have required extensive redesign of such well proven features as the basic wing structure, as well as major manufacturing changes.

TYPE: Two-seat all-weather interceptor.

WINGS: Cantilever high-wing monoplane. Anhedral 4° from roots. Sweepback on leading-edge approx 40°, at quarter-chord 32°, with small sharply-swept wingroot extensions. Upper surface fence in line with each inboard weapon pylon. Aileron and flap on each wing, of greater span than those of MiG-25. No wingtip fairings or mountings.

FUSELAGE: Basic fuselage is slim, but is blended into wide rectangular air intake trunks, which have wedge inlets. Inner wall of each inlet is curved and does not run parallel with outer wall. Hinged panel forms lower lip of each inlet, and there is a large door towards the forward part of each top surface.

TAIL UNIT: Twin outward canted fins, with inset rudders, and all-moving one-piece horizontal surfaces. All surfaces sharply sweptback, without tabs. Two outward canted ventral fins. Large areas of each main and ventral fin form flush antennae. Aerodynamic fairings between base of each fin and engine duct, extending well forward of leading-edge.

LANDING GEAR: Retractable tricycle type. Staggered twin wheels on each main unit, retracting forward into air intake trunk. Rearward retracting twin nosewheel unit with mudguard.

POWER PLANT: Two Tumansky turbojets, each reportedly rated at 137.3 kN (30,865 lb st) with afterburning. Fuel tankage probably similar to that of MiG-25, which has two structural tanks in fuselage, between cockpit and engine bay, saddle tanks around intake ducts, and integral tank in each wing, filling almost the entire volume inboard of outer stores pylon, with total capacity of approx 17,410 litres (4,600 US gallons; 3,830 Imp gallons). Provision for two large external fuel tanks on outer underwing pylons.

MiG-31 all-weather interceptor, with periscope raised above rear cockpit

ACCOMMODATION: Pilot and weapon systems operator in tandem. Canopy has only limited side glazing for rear cockpit and blends into shallow dorsal spine fairing which extends to forward edge of jet nozzles.

AVIONICS AND EQUIPMENT: Main fire control radar of pulse-Doppler lookdown/shootdown type in nose, with reported search range of 165 nm (305 km; 190 miles) and tracking range of 145 nm (270 km; 167 miles). Infra-red sensor in bottom of front fuselage. Radar warning receivers, active IR and electronic countermeasures.

ARMAMENT: Aircraft seen to date each had four AA-9 (NATO 'Amos') semi-active radar homing long-range air-to-air missiles in pairs under fuselage, and twin mounts for AA-8 ('Aphid') air-to-air missiles on one large pylon under each wing. These pylons plus outer underwing pylons (not yet observed) can probably increase the number of AA-9s carried by MiG-31 to reported total of eight. An integral large-calibre gun appears to be mounted on the starboard side of the lower fuselage, adjacent to the main landing gear.

DIMENSIONS, EXTERNAL (estimated):
Wing span   14.00 m (45 ft 11¼ in)
Length of fuselage, nosecone tip to end of jetpipe
    21.50 m (70 ft 6½ in)

WEIGHTS (estimated):
Weight empty   21,825 kg (48,115 lb)
Max T-O weight   41,150 kg (90,725 lb)

PERFORMANCE (estimated):
Max level speed at height   Mach 2.4
    (1,375 knots; 2,550 km/h; 1,585 mph)
Max combat radius   1,135 nm (2,100 km; 1,305 miles)

This MiG-31 has underbelly AA-9 ('Amos') and underwing AA-8 ('Aphid') missiles
(US Department of Defense)

MiG-31 (NATO 'Foxhound') all-weather interceptor *(Pilot Press)*

MIL

2 Sokolnichyesky Val, Moscow 107113
Telephone: 7 (95) 264 3791
GENERAL DESIGNER IN CHARGE OF BUREAU:
    Marat N. Tishchenko
CHIEF DESIGNER: Alexei Ivanov
DEPUTY CHIEF DESIGNER: Mark V. Vineberg

Mikhail L. Mil was connected with Soviet gyroplane and helicopter development from at least 1930 until his death on 31 January 1970. His original Mi-l, which was designed in 1949, first flown in 1950 and introduced into squadron service in 1951, was the first helicopter to enter series production in the Soviet Union. Current products of the design bureau named after him are as follows:

MIL Mi-2 (V-2)
NATO reporting name: Hoplite
Built exclusively in Poland and described under Polish aircraft industry entry for WSK-PZL Swidnik. About 675 serve with Soviet military ground forces.

MIL Mi-6
NATO reporting name: Hook
Announced in the Autumn of 1957, the Mi-6 was then the world's largest helicopter. From it were developed the Mi-10 and Mi-10K flying crane helicopters, and its dynamic components were used in duplicated form on the V-12 (Mi-12) of 1967, which remains the largest helicopter yet flown anywhere in the world.

Five Mi-6s are reported to have been built for development testing, followed by an initial pre-series of 30 and subsequent manufacture of more than 800 for military and civil use. About 450 serve currently with Soviet ground forces. Others serve with the Algerian, Iraqi, Peruvian and Vietnamese air forces and the Peruvian Army air force. A full structural description can be found in the 1983-84 and previous editions of *Jane's*.

TYPE: Heavy transport helicopter.

POWER PLANT: Two 4,101 kW (5,500 shp) Soloviev D-25V (TV-2BM) turboshafts, mounted side by side above cabin, forward of main rotor shaft. Eleven internal fuel tanks, with total capacity of 6,315 kg (13,922 lb), and two external tanks, on each side of cabin, with total capacity of 3,490 kg (7,695 lb). Provision for two additional ferry tanks inside cabin, with total capacity of 3,490 kg (7,695 lb).

ACCOMMODATION: Crew of five, consisting of two pilots, navigator, flight engineer and radio operator. Four jettisonable doors and overhead hatch on flight deck.

Electro-thermal anti-icing system for glazing of flight deck and navigator's compartment. Equipped normally for cargo operation, with easily removable tip-up seats along side walls. When these seats are supplemented by additional seats installed in centre of cabin, 65-90 passengers can be carried, with cargo or baggage in the aisles. Normal military seating is for 70 combat equipped troops. As an air ambulance, 41 stretcher cases and two medical attendants on tip-up seats can be carried. One of attendant's stations is provided with intercom to flight deck, and provision is made for portable oxygen installations for the patients. Cabin floor is stressed for loadings of 2,000 kg/m² (410 lb/sq ft), with provision for cargo tiedown rings. Rear clamshell doors and ramps are operated hydraulically. Standard equipment includes an electric winch of 800 kg (1,765 lb) capacity and pulley block system. Central hatch in cabin floor for cargo sling system for bulky loads. Three jettisonable doors, fore and aft of main landing gear on port side and aft of landing gear on starboard side.

AVIONICS AND EQUIPMENT: Standard equipment includes VHF and HF communications radio, intercom, radio altimeter, radio compass, three-channel autopilot, marker beacon receiver, directional gyro and full all-weather instrumentation.

ARMAMENT: Some military Mi-6s are fitted with a 12.7 mm machine-gun in the fuselage nose.

DIMENSIONS, EXTERNAL:
Main rotor diameter   35.00 m (114 ft 10 in)
Tail rotor diameter   6.30 m (20 ft 8 in)
Length overall, rotors turning   41.74 m (136 ft 11½ in)
Length of fuselage, excl nose gun and tail rotor
    33.18 m (108 ft 10½ in)
Height overall   9.86 m (32 ft 4 in)
Wing span   15.30 m (50 ft 2½ in)
Wheel track   7.50 m (24 ft 7¼ in)
Wheelbase   9.09 m (29 ft 9¾ in)
Rear loading doors: Height   2.70 m (8 ft 10¼ in)
    Width   2.65 m (8 ft 8¼ in)
Passenger doors:
    Height: front door   1.70 m (5 ft 7 in)
      rear doors   1.61 m (5 ft 3½ in)
    Width   0.80 m (2 ft 7½ in)
    Sill height: front door   1.40 m (4 ft 7¼ in)
      rear doors   1.30 m (4 ft 3¼ in)
Central hatch in floor
    1.44 m (4 ft 9 in) × 1.93 m (6 ft 4 in)

DIMENSIONS, INTERNAL:
Cabin: Length   12.00 m (39 ft 4½ in)
    Max width   2.65 m (8 ft 8¼ in)

Mil Mi-8 ('Hip-C') military helicopter of the Hungarian Air Force. This differs from the commercial versions in having circular cabin windows, and weapon carriers on outriggers *(Peter J. Bish)*

Mil Mi-6 heavy general purpose helicopter (two Soloviev D-25V turboshafts) of the Soviet air forces *(Ivo Sturzenegger)*

Max height: at front	2.01 m (6 ft 7 in)
at rear	2.50 m (8 ft 2½ in)
Cabin volume	80 m³ (2,825 cu ft)

WEIGHTS:

Weight empty	27,240 kg (60,055 lb)
Max internal payload	12,000 kg (26,450 lb)
Max slung cargo	8,000 kg (17,637 lb)
Fuel load: internal	6,315 kg (13,922 lb)
with external tanks	9,805 kg (21,617 lb)
Max T-O weight with slung cargo at altitudes under	
1,000m (3,280 ft)	38,400 kg (84,657 lb)
Normal T-O weight	40,500 kg (89,285 lb)
Max T-O weight for VTO	42,500 kg (93,700 lb)

PERFORMANCE (at max T-O weight for VTO):

Max level speed	162 knots (300 km/h; 186 mph)
Max cruising speed	135 knots (250 km/h; 155 mph)
Service ceiling	4,500 m (14,750 ft)
Range with 8,000 kg (17,637 lb) payload	
	334 nm (620 km; 385 miles)
Range with external tanks and 4,500 kg (9,920 lb) payload	540 nm (1,000 km; 621 miles)
Max ferry range (tanks in cabin)	
	781 nm (1,450 km; 900 miles)

MIL Mi-8 (V-8)
NATO reporting name: Hip

Shown in public for the first time during the 1961 Soviet Aviation Day display, the original Mi-8 prototype (NATO **Hip-A**) had a single 2,013 kW (2,700 shp) Soloviev turboshaft and four-blade main rotor. When fitted with the five-blade rotor that became standard on subsequent aircraft, it was redesignated **Hip-B**. The second prototype, which flew for the first time on 17 September 1962, introduced the now-standard Isotov twin-turbine power plant and became **Hip-C** to NATO in both civil and military forms.

There are three civil transport versions, identified by large square cabin windows, as follows:

Mi-8. Passenger version, with standard seating for 28-32 persons in main cabin.

Mi-8T. General utility version, equipped normally to carry internal or external freight, but able to accommodate 24 tip-up passenger seats along the cabin walls.

Mi-8 Salon. De luxe version. Main cabin is furnished normally for eleven passengers, with an eight-place couch facing inward on the port side, and two chairs and a swivelling seat on the starboard side. There is a table on the starboard side. An air-to-ground radio telephone and removable ventilation fans are standard equipment. Forward of the main cabin is a compartment for a hostess, with buffet and crew wardrobe. Aft of the main cabin are a toilet (port) and passenger wardrobe (starboard), to each side of the entrance. An alternative nine-passenger layout is available. The Mi-8 Salon has a max T-O weight of 10,400 kg (22,928 lb) and range of 205 nm (380 km; 236 miles) with 30 min fuel reserve. In other respects it is similar to the standard Mi-8.

Military versions, with small circular cabin windows, are identified by the following NATO reporting names:

Hip-C. Standard equipment of Soviet army support forces. Twin-rack for stores on each side of cabin, able to carry total of 128 × 57 mm rockets in four packs, or other weapons. More than 1,500 in service with Soviet ground forces. Some uprated to Mi-17 standard, as **Mi-8T** and **Mi-8TB**, identified by port-side tail rotor.

Hip-D. For airborne communications role. Generally similar to 'Hip-C' but with canisters of rectangular section on outer stores racks and added antennae above forward part of tailboom.

'Hip-C' military version of Mil Mi-8 twin-turbine helicopter, with additional side view (bottom) of commercial version *(Pilot Press)*

Hip-E. Improved version of 'Hip-C'. One flexibly mounted 12.7 mm machine-gun in nose. Triple stores rack on each side of cabin, able to carry up to 192 rockets in six suspended packs, plus four 'Swatter' anti-tank missiles (semi-automatic command to line of sight) on rails above racks. About 250 in service with Soviet ground forces. Some uprated to Mi-17 standard, as **Mi-8TBK**, identified by port-side tail rotor.

Hip-F. Export counterpart of 'Hip-E'. Missile armament changed to six 'Saggers' (manual command to line of sight).

Hip-G. Airborne communications version with rearward inclined 'hockey stick' antennae projecting from rear of cabin and from undersurface of tailboom, aft of box for Doppler radar.

Hip-H. See separate entry on Mi-17.

Hip-J. Additional small boxes on each side of fuselage, fore and aft of main landing gear legs, identify this ECM version.

Hip-K. Communications jamming ECM version with large antenna array on each side of cabin, of the kind seen previously on the Mi-4 ('Hound-C'). No Doppler radar box under tailboom. Some uprated to Mi-17 standard, identified by port-side tail rotor.

More than 10,000 Soviet built Mi-8s and uprated Mi-17s (described separately) have been delivered for military and civil use from two plants in Kazan and Ulan Ude. Component production of the Mi-8 has also taken place at Harbin in China. An estimated total of 2,400 Mi-8s and Mi-17s support Soviet armies in the field. Many others are

operated by Soviet air forces, and military Mi-8s have been supplied to at least 39 other air forces, as listed in previous editions of *Jane's*.

Production is now concentrated on versions of the uprated Mi-17, except for the commercial Salon and export variants which remain available.

TYPE: Twin-engined transport helicopter.

ROTOR SYSTEM: Five-blade main rotor and three-blade starboard-side tail rotor. Transmission comprises a type VR-8 two-stage planetary main reduction gearbox giving main rotor shaft/engine rpm ratio of 0.016 : 1, intermediate and tail gearboxes, main rotor brake and drives off the main gearbox for the tail rotor, fan, AC generator, hydraulic pumps and tachometer generators. Main rotor shaft inclined forward at 4° 30′ from vertical. All-metal main rotor blades of basic NACA 230 section; solidity 0.0777. Each main blade is made up of an extruded light alloy spar carrying the blade root fitting, 21 trailing-edge pockets and the blade tip. Pockets are honeycomb filled. Main rotor blades are fitted with balance tabs, embody a spar failure warning system, and are interchangeable. Their drag and flapping hinges are a few inches apart, and they are carried on a machined spider. Control system utilises irreversible hydraulic boosters. Main rotor collective pitch control is interlocked to throttle controls. All-metal tail rotor blades, each made up of a spar and honeycomb filled trailing-edge. Automatically controlled electro-thermal de-icing system on all blades. In an emergency, the rotor

'Hip-K' communications jamming variant of the Mi-8

'Hip-D' has additional antennae as well as the canisters to which reference is made in the accompanying copy. It has an airborne communications role

'Hip-J' ECM variant of the Mi-8

blades of the Mi-8 and intermediate and tail gearboxes are interchangeable with those of the piston-engined Mi-4, although this prevents use of the de-icing system.

FUSELAGE: Conventional all-metal semi-monocoque structure of pod and boom type.

TAIL UNIT: Tail rotor support acts as small vertical stabiliser. Horizontal stabiliser near end of tailboom.

LANDING GEAR: Non-retractable tricycle type, with steerable twin-wheel nose unit, which is locked in flight, and single wheel on each main unit. All units embody oleo-pneumatic (gas) shock absorbers. Mainwheel tyres size 865 × 280; nosewheel tyres size 595 × 185. Pneumatic brakes on mainwheels. Pneumatic system can also recharge tyres in the field, using air stored in main landing gear struts. Optional mainwheel fairings.

POWER PLANT: Two 1,267 kW (1,700 shp) Isotov TV2-117A turboshafts (1,454 kW; 1,950 shp TV3-117MTs in Mi-8T/TB/TBK). Main rotor speed governed automatically, with manual override. Single flexible internal fuel tank, capacity 445 litres (117.5 US gallons; 98 Imp gallons), and two external tanks, one each side of cabin, with capacity of 745 litres (197 US gallons; 164 Imp gallons) in the port tank and 680 litres (179.5 US gallons; 149.5 Imp gallons) in the starboard tank. Total standard fuel capacity 1,870 litres (494 US gallons; 411.5 Imp gallons). Provision for carrying one or two additional ferry tanks in cabin, raising max total capacity to 3,700 litres (977 US gallons; 814 Imp gallons). Fairing over starboard external tank houses optional cabin air-conditioning equipment at front. Engine cowling side panels form maintenance platforms when open, with access via hatch on flight deck. Engine air intake de-icing standard. Total oil capacity 60 kg (132 lb).

ACCOMMODATION: Two pilots side by side on flight deck, with provision for a flight engineer's station. Windscreen de-icing standard. Basic passenger version is furnished with 28 four-abreast track mounted tip-up seats at a pitch of 72-75 cm (28-29.5 in), with a centre aisle 32 cm (12.5 in) wide, a wardrobe and baggage compartment; or 32 seats without wardrobe. Seats and bulkheads of basic version are quickly removable for cargo carrying. Mi-8T and standard military versions have cargo tiedown rings in floor, a winch of 200 kg (440 lb) capacity and pulley block system to facilitate the loading of heavy freight, an external cargo sling system (capacity 3,000 kg; 6,614 lb), and 24 tip-up seats along the side walls of the cabin. All versions can be converted for air ambulance duties, with accommodation for 12 stretchers and a tip-up seat for a medical attendant. The large windows on each side of the flight deck slide rearward. The sliding, jettisonable main passenger door is at the front of the cabin on the port side. An electrically operated rescue hoist (capacity 150 kg; 330 lb) can be installed at this doorway. The rear of the cabin is made up of clamshell freight loading doors, which are

Infra-red suppressor and flare dispensers on Mi-8MT (*Jane's Defence Weekly/Paul Beaver*)

smaller on the commercial versions, with a downward hinged passenger airstair door inset centrally at the rear. Hook-on ramps are used for vehicle loading.

SYSTEMS: Standard heating system can be replaced by full air-conditioning system. Two independent hydraulic systems, each with own pump; operating pressure 44-64 bars (640-925 lb/sq in). DC electrical supply from two 27V 18kW starter/generators and six 28Ah storage batteries. AC supply for de-icing system and some radio equipment supplied by 208/115/36/7.5V 400Hz generator, with 36V three-phase standby system. Provision for oxygen system for crew and, in ambulance version, for patients. Freon fire extinguishing system in power plant bays and service fuel tank compartments, actuated automatically or manually. Two portable fire extinguishers for use in cabin.

AVIONICS AND EQUIPMENT: Standard equipment includes a type R-842 HF transceiver with frequency range of 2 to 8MHz and range of up to 540 nm (1,000 km; 620 miles), type R-860 VHF transceiver operating on 118 to 135.9MHz over ranges of up to 54 nm (100 km; 62 miles), intercom, radio telephone, type ARK-9 automatic radio compass, type RV-3 radio altimeter with 'dangerous height' warning, and four-axis autopilot to give yaw, roll and pitch stabilisation under any flight conditions, stabilisation of altitude in level flight or hover, and stabilisation of pre-set flying speed, navigation equipment

and instrumentation for all-weather flying by day and night, including two gyro horizons, two airspeed indicators, two main rotor speed indicators, turn indicator, two altimeters, two rate of climb indicators, magnetic compass, radio altimeter, radio compass and astrocompass for Polar flying. Doppler radar in box under forward part of tailboom. Military versions can be fitted with external flight deck armour, an infra-red suppressor above forward end of tailboom and flare dispensers above rear cabin window on each side.

ARMAMENT: See individual model descriptions of military versions.

DIMENSIONS, EXTERNAL:

Main rotor diameter	21.29 m (69 ft 10¼ in)
Tail rotor diameter	3.91 m (12 ft 9⅞ in)
Distance between rotor centres	12.65 m (41 ft 6 in)
Length overall, rotors turning	25.24 m (82 ft 9¾ in)
Length of fuselage, excl tail rotor	18.17 m (59 ft 7⅜ in)
Width of fuselage	2.50 m (8 ft 2½ in)
Height overall	5.65 m (18 ft 6½ in)
Wheel track	4.50 m (14 ft 9 in)
Wheelbase	4.26 m (13 ft 11¾ in)
Fwd passenger door: Height	1.41 m (4 ft 7¼ in)
Width	0.82 m (2 ft 8¼ in)
Rear passenger door: Height	1.70 m (5 ft 7 in)
Width	0.84 m (2 ft 9 in)
Rear cargo door: Height	1.82 m (5 ft 11½ in)
Width	2.34 m (7 ft 8¼ in)

DIMENSIONS, INTERNAL:

Passenger cabin: Length	6.36 m (20 ft 10¼ in)
Width	2.34 m (7 ft 8¼ in)
Height	1.80 m (5 ft 10¾ in)
Cargo hold (freighter):	
Length at floor	5.34 m (17 ft 6¼ in)
Width	2.34 m (7 ft 8¼ in)
Height	1.80 m (5 ft 10¾ in)
Volume	approx 23 m³ (812 cu ft)

AREAS:

Main rotor disc	356 m² (3,832 sq ft)
Tail rotor disc	12 m² (129.2 sq ft)

WEIGHTS:

Weight empty:	
civil passenger version	6,799 kg (14,990 lb)
civil cargo version	6,624 kg (14,603 lb)
military versions (typical)	7,260 kg (16,007 lb)
Max payload: internal	4,000 kg (8,820 lb)
external	3,000 kg (6,614 lb)
Fuel: standard tanks	1,450 kg (3,197 lb)
with 2 auxiliary tanks	2,870 kg (6,327 lb)
Normal T-O weight	11,100 kg (24,470 lb)
T-O weight with 28 passengers, each with 15 kg (33 lb) of baggage	11,570 kg (25,508 lb)
T-O weight with 2,500 kg (5,510 lb) of slung cargo	11,428 kg (25,195 lb)
Max T-O weight for VTO	12,000 kg (26,455 lb)

PERFORMANCE (civil Mi-8):

Max level speed at 1,000 m (3,280 ft):	
normal AUW	140 knots (260 km/h; 161 mph)
Max level speed at S/L:	
normal AUW	135 knots (250 km/h; 155 mph)
max AUW	124 knots (230 km/h; 142 mph)
with 2,500 kg (5,510 lb) of slung cargo	97 knots (180 km/h; 112 mph)
Max cruising speed:	
normal AUW	122 knots (225 km/h; 140 mph)
max AUW	97 knots (180 km/h; 112 mph)
Service ceiling	4,500 m (14,760 ft)
Hovering ceiling at normal AUW:	
IGE	1,900 m (6,235 ft)
OGE	800 m (2,625 ft)
Ranges:	
cargo version at 1,000 m (3,280 ft), with standard fuel, 5% reserves:	
normal AUW	251 nm (465 km; 289 miles)
max AUW	240 nm (445 km; 276 miles)
with 28 passengers at 1,000 m (3,280 ft), with 20 min fuel reserves	270 nm (500 km; 311 miles)
ferry range of cargo version, with auxiliary fuel, 5% reserves	647 nm (1,200 km; 745 miles)

PERFORMANCE (Mi-8MT):

Max cruising speed	129 knots (240 km/h; 149 mph)
Service ceiling	3,980 m (13,050 ft)
Range with max fuel, 5% reserves	
	267 nm (495 km; 307 miles)

Mil Mi-10K (NATO 'Harke-B') preparing to lift a 10-tonne sheet steel drum to the top of a tower at the Sinarski pipe works in Kamensk-Uralskii *(Tass)*

MIL Mi-10 and Mi-10K
NATO reporting name: Harke

There have been two versions of this flying crane development of the Mi-6:

Harke-A. This original version, designated **Mi-10** or **V-10**, was demonstrated at the 1961 Soviet Aviation Day display at Tushino, having flown for the first time in the previous year. Above the line of the cabin windows the Mi-6 and Mi-10 were almost identical, but the depth of the fuselage was reduced considerably on the Mi-10, and the tailboom was deepened so that the flattened undersurface ran unbroken to the tail. The Mi-10 also lacked the fixed wings of the Mi-6, and was fitted with a tall long-stroke quadricycle landing gear, with wheel track exceeding 6.0 m (19 ft 8 in) and clearance under the fuselage of 3.75 m (12 ft 3½ in) with the aircraft fully loaded. This enabled the Mi-10 to taxi over a load it was to carry and to accommodate loads as bulky as a prefabricated building.

Harke-B. This developed version, known as the **Mi-10K**, was displayed in public for the first time, in Moscow, on 26 March 1966. It embodied a number of important design changes, most apparent of which were a reduction in the height of the landing gear and a more slender tail rotor support structure.

The Mi-10K can be operated by a crew of only two pilots. This is made possible by provision of an additional cockpit gondola under the front fuselage, with full flying controls and a rearward facing seat. By occupying this seat, one of the pilots can control the aircraft in hovering flight and, at the same time, have an unrestricted view of cargo loading, unloading and hoisting, which are also under his control.

In the Mi-10K, the maximum slung payload was initially 11,000 kg (24,250 lb) but was expected to be increased to 14,000 kg (30,865 lb) by using Soloviev D-25VF turboshafts, uprated to 4,847 kW (6,500 shp) each.

A detailed description of the original Mi-10 can be found in the 1982-83 and earlier editions of *Jane's*. A total of about 55 of both versions had been delivered by 1977, when production was resumed briefly, at a modest rate, after a six-year break. Most production helicopters are thought to be Mi-10Ks, to which the following data apply. A more extensive description can be found in the 1983-84 and previous editions of *Jane's*.

TYPE: Heavy flying-crane helicopter.

POWER PLANT: Two 4,101 kW (5,500 shp) Soloviev D-25V turboshafts in early production aircraft, mounted side by side above cabin, forward of main rotor driveshaft. Fuel capacity, in standard internal and two external tanks, on sides of cabin, 9,000 litres (2,377 US gallons; 1,980 Imp gallons). Provision for ferry tanks in cabin.

ACCOMMODATION: Two pilots on flight deck, which has bulged side windows to provide an improved downward view. Flight deck is heated and ventilated and has provision for oxygen equipment. Additional cockpit gondola under front fuselage (see introductory notes). Crew door is immediately aft of flight deck on port side. Main cabin can be used for freight and/or passengers, 28 tip-up seats being installed along the side walls. Freight is loaded into this cabin through a door on the starboard side, aft of the rear landing gear struts, with the aid of a boom and 200 kg (440 lb) capacity electric winch. External sling gear standard, with hatch in the cabin floor, directly beneath main rotor shaft.

DIMENSIONS, EXTERNAL:

Main rotor diameter	35.00 m (114 ft 10 in)
Tail rotor diameter	6.30 m (20 ft 8 in)
Length overall, rotors turning	41.89 m (137 ft 5½ in)
Length of fuselage	32.86 m (107 ft 9¾ in)
Height overall	7.80 m (25 ft 7 in)
Wheel track (c/l of shock struts)	5.00 m (16 ft 4¾ in)
Wheelbase	8.74 m (28 ft 8 in)
Freight loading door: Height	1.56 m (5 ft 1½ in)
Width	1.26 m (4 ft 1½ in)
Height to sill	1.82 m (5 ft 11½ in)
Cabin floor hatch: Diameter	1.00 m (3 ft 3¼ in)

DIMENSIONS, INTERNAL:

Cabin: Length	14.04 m (46 ft 0¾ in)
Width	2.50 m (8 ft 2½ in)
Height	1.68 m (5 ft 6 in)
Volume	approx 60 m³ (2,120 cu ft)

WEIGHTS:

Weight empty	24,680 kg (54,410 lb)
Max fuel load with ferry tanks in cabin	
	8,670 kg (19,114 lb)
Max T-O weight with slung cargo	38,000 kg (83,775 lb)

PERFORMANCE:

Cruising speed, empty	135 knots (250 km/h; 155 mph)
Max cruising speed with slung load	
	109 knots (202 km/h; 125 mph)
Service ceiling	3,000 m (9,850 ft)
Ferry range with auxiliary fuel	
	428 nm (795 km; 494 miles)

MIL Mi-14 (V-14)
NATO reporting name: Haze

The Mi-14 shore-based amphibious helicopter flew for the first time in 1973. Overall dimensions, power plant and dynamic components are generally similar to those of the Mi-17, reflecting parallel development from the Mi-8 airframe. New features include a boat hull on the fuselage, a sponson carrying an inflatable flotation bag on each side at the rear, and a small float under the tailboom, to confer a degree of amphibious capability. The fully retractable landing gear comprises two forward-retracting single-wheel nose units and two rearward retracting twin-wheel main units. There is a Doppler radar box under the forward part of the tailboom.

Three versions may be identified by NATO reporting names, as follows:

Haze-A (Mi-14PL). Basic ASW version, with crew of four. Operational anti-submarine equipment can be seen to include a large undernose radome, a retractable sonar unit housed in the starboard rear of the planing bottom, forward of what appear to be two sonobuoy or signal flare chutes, and a towed magnetic anomaly detection (MAD) bird stowed against the rear of the fuselage pod. Weapons include torpedoes and depth charges, carried in an enclosed bay in the bottom of the hull.

Haze-B (Mi-14BT). Mine countermeasures version, with fuselage strake and pod on starboard side of cabin, and no MAD. Two additional equipment boxes under the tailboom, to each side of the Doppler container. In service with Soviet, East German and Polish Navies.

Haze-C (Mi-14PS). Search and rescue version in service in Soviet Union and Poland. Fuselage strake and

Mil Mi-14PL anti-submarine helicopter ('Haze-A') in East German service
(by courtesy of Flieger Revue)

Mil Mi-14PL (V-14) ASW helicopter (NATO 'Haze-A') *(Pilot Press)*

The Mi-14PS search and rescue helicopter ('Haze-C') in Polish service (*courtesy of Helicopter International*)

Mil Mi-17 ('Hip-H') of the Czechoslovak Air Force (*Letectvi + Kosmonautika/Václav Jukl*)

shorter nacelles, the air intakes extending forward only to the mid-point of the door on the port side at the front of the cabin. Also new is the small orifice on each side forward of the jetpipe. Take-off rating of each of the two Isotov TV3-117MT turboshafts is 1,454 kW (1,950 shp), which offers a considerable improvement in performance compared with the Mi-8. Correct rotor speed is maintained automatically by a system that also synchronises the output of the two engines. Should one engine stop, the output of the other is increased automatically to a contingency rating of 1,640 kW (2,200 shp), enabling the flight to continue. An APU is carried to start the turboshafts pneumatically, and the engine air intakes are fitted with deflectors to prevent the ingestion of sand, dust or foreign objects at unprepared landing sites.

Cabin configuration and payloads are unchanged by comparison with the Mi-8; but the civilian Mi-17 is described by Aviaexport as essentially a cargo carrying helicopter, with secondary passenger transport role.

A further uprated version, designated **Mi-17-1VA**, was shown for the first time at the 1989 Paris Air Show. The example displayed (SSSR-95043) was said to have been produced for the Soviet Ministry of Health as a flying hospital equipped to the highest practicable standards for a relatively small helicopter. Its special interior, using equipment developed in Hungary, had provision for three stretchers, an operating table, extensive surgical and medical equipment, and accommodation for a doctor/surgeon and three nursing attendants. Installation of more powerful TV3-117VM engines, each rated at 1,678 kW (2,250 shp), provides improved rates of climb and hovering ceilings. Otherwise, weights and performance are generally unchanged.

The following data apply to the basic Mi-17:

DIMENSIONS, EXTERNAL AND INTERNAL:
As for Mi-8, except:

Distance between rotor centres	12.661 m (41 ft 6½ in)
Length overall, rotors turning	25.352 m (83 ft 2 in)
Length of fuselage, excl tail rotor	18.424 m (60 ft 5⅜ in)
Height to top of main rotor head	4.755 m (15 ft 7¼ in)
Wheel track	4.510 m (14 ft 9½ in)
Wheelbase	4.281 m (14 ft 0½ in)

WEIGHTS:

Weight empty, equipped	7,100 kg (15,653 lb)
Max payload: internal	4,000 kg (8,820 lb)
external, on sling	3,000 kg (6,614 lb)
Normal T-O weight	11,100 kg (24,470 lb)
Max T-O weight	13,000 kg (28,660 lb)

PERFORMANCE (A at normal T-O weight; B at max T-O weight):

Max level speed: B	135 knots (250 km/h; 155 mph)
Max cruising speed: B	129 knots (240 km/h; 149 mph)
Service ceiling: A	5,000 m (16,400 ft)
B	3,600 m (11,800 ft)
Hovering ceiling OGE: A	1,760 m (5,775 ft)
Range with max standard fuel, 5% reserves:	
A	267 nm (495 km; 307 miles)
B	251 nm (465 km; 289 miles)
Range with auxiliary fuel:	
A	513 nm (950 km; 590 miles)

pod as on 'Haze-B'. Double-width sliding door at front of cabin on port side, with retractable rescue hoist. Searchlight on each side of nose.

Of at least 230 Mi-14s built, 10 have been exported to Bulgaria, 14 to Cuba, 12 to Libya, at least five to Poland, six to Romania, eight to the German Democratic Republic, 12 to Syria, and unknown quantities to North Korea and Yugoslavia. Production continues.

DIMENSIONS, EXTERNAL:

Main rotor diameter	21.29 m (69 ft 10¼ in)
Length overall, rotors turning	25.30 m (83 ft 0 in)
Height overall	6.93 m (22 ft 9 in)

WEIGHT:

Max T-O weight	14,000 kg (30,865 lb)

PERFORMANCE:

Max level speed	124 knots (230 km/h; 143 mph)
Max cruising speed	116 knots (215 km/h; 133 mph)
Normal cruising speed	110 knots (205 km/h; 127 mph)
Service ceiling	3,500 m (11,500 ft)
Range with max fuel	612 nm (1,135 km; 705 miles)
Endurance with max fuel	5 h 56 min

MIL Mi-17
NATO reporting name: Hip-H

First displayed in public at the 1981 Paris Air Show, the basic **Mi-17** combines the airframe of the Mi-8 with the uprated power plant that is used also in the Mi-14 and Mi-24. It is available in both military and civil forms, and is known to NATO as 'Hip-H'. Many are operational side by side with Mi-8s in the Soviet armed forces, and have seen service in Afghanistan and Central America. They have the same armament options as the older aircraft, supplemented by 23 mm GSh-23 gun packs, and the military versions often have external armour plate on the sides of the cockpit, an ASO-2 chaff/flare dispenser under the tailboom and 'Hot Brick' IR jammer at the forward end of the tailboom.

Export deliveries include 16 to Cuba in 1983, and others subsequently to Angola, India, North Korea, Nicaragua, Papua New Guinea, Peru and Poland. Mi-8s can be updated to Mi-17 standard, and many of those in Soviet service have been converted in this way (see Mi-8 entry).

The general description of the Mi-8 applies also to the Mi-17, except that the tail rotor is on the port side of the vertical stabiliser. The change of power plant is identified by

MIL Mi-24
NATO reporting name: Hind

Details of the early history of the Mi-24 can be found in the 1989-90 and previous editions of *Jane's*. It was designed originally as a heavily armed assault transport for a squad of troops (a capability that is retained in all versions). As a result, it lacks the slim silhouette that is optimum for a gunship; but progressive changes to the airframe, power plant, operational equipment and weapons, and the

Mi-17 military general purpose helicopter, with external stores carriers (*Pilot Press*)

'Hind-G' version of Mi-24 with 'clutching hand' wingtip fittings *(copied from Soviet Military Review)*

Mil Mi-24P gunship, known to NATO as 'Hind-F' *(Jane's/Mike Keep)*

addition of infra-red jammers, exhaust suppressors and flare dispensers as a result of combat experience, plus increased armour, have maintained the aircraft's effectiveness through a succession of variants, as follows:

Hind-A. Initial series production version, observed in service in East Germany in Spring 1974. Assault helicopter, with crew of three, comprising pilot, co-pilot/gunner and ground engineer, and places for up to eight fully equipped troops in main cabin. Access to flight deck via large rearward sliding blistered transparent panel which forms the aft flight deck window on the port side, and a large upward hinged window forward of this. Auxiliary wings, with considerable anhedral, carry total of four underwing pylons for rocket pods, special bombs, or other stores, and rails for four AT-2 (NATO 'Swatter') anti-tank missiles under endplate pylons at wingtips. One 12.7 mm single-barrel DShK machine-gun in nose, slaved to undernose sighting system. Camera at top of port inner underwing pylon. Anti-torque rotor, originally on starboard side of offset tail pylon, repositioned to port side when original TV2-117 engines were replaced by TV3-117s on later and converted aircraft.

Hind-B. Similar to 'Hind-A' except that auxiliary wings have neither anhedral nor dihedral, and carry only the two inboard weapon stations on each side. This version preceded 'Hind-A' but was not built in large numbers.

Hind-C. Training version. Generally similar to late model 'Hind-A' but without nose gun and undernose blister fairing, and no missile rails at wingtips.

Hind-D (Mi-24D). First observed in 1977. Basically similar to late model 'Hind-A', with TV3-117 engines and tail rotor on port side, but with completely new and heavily armoured accommodation for weapon operator and pilot, in tandem, forward of the engine inlets and above the fuselage floor for primary gunship role. Flight mechanic carried in main cabin. Transport capability retained. Undernose Gatling type 12.7 mm machine-gun in a turret provides air-to-air as well as air-to-surface capability. Extended nosewheel leg to increase ground clearance of sensor pack; nosewheels semi-exposed when retracted. Weapons, equipment and other details listed in aircraft

structural description. Export models, including those for Afghanistan, Cuba and India, are designated **Mi-25**.

Hind-E (Mi-24W). As 'Hind-D', but with modified wingtip launchers and four underwing pylons for a total of up to 12 AT-6 (NATO 'Spiral') radio guided tube-launched anti-tank missiles in pairs, and enlarged undernose missile guidance pod on port side, with fixed searchlight to rear. AA-8 ('Aphid') air-to-air missiles can be carried on underwing pylons. HUD for pilot, replacing former reflector gunsight. Export models are designated **Mi-35**.

Hind-F (Mi-24P = pushka; cannon). First shown in service with Soviet forces in photographs published in 1982. Generally similar to 'Hind-E' but with the nose gun turret replaced by a GSh-30-2 twin-barrel 30 mm gun (with 750 rds) mounted inside a semi-cylindrical pack on the starboard side of the fuselage, and the bottom of the nose smoothly faired above and forward of sensors. Export models are designated **Mi-35P**.

Hind-G. First identified at Chernobyl, after the accident at a nuclear power station, this version lacks the usual undernose electro-optical and RF guidance packs for anti-tank missiles. Instead of wingtip weapon attachments, it has 'clutching hand' mechanisms, associated with NBC (nuclear/biological/chemical) warfare, on lengthened pylons. Other features include a lozenge shape housing with cylindrical insert under the port side of the cabin, a bubble window on the starboard side, and a plate of triangular shape mounted in the tailskid. Small numbers of 'Hind-Gs' are deployed individually throughout the Soviet ground forces.

Deliveries of all models are known to exceed 2,300, from plants in Arsenyev and Rostov, but production is now reducing from a long-maintained rate of more than 15 a month. Most of the 1,250 deployed with Soviet armies equip approximately 20 helicopter attack regiments of Mi-8/17s and Mi-24s. Other operators include the air forces of Afghanistan, Algeria, Angola, Bulgaria, Cuba, Czechoslovakia, East Germany, Hungary, India, Iraq, Libya, Mozambique, North Korea, Nicaragua, Peru, Poland, Vietnam and South Yemen. Used operationally in Chad, Nicaragua, Ceylon, Angola, Afghanistan and in the Gulf

War (where at least one Iranian F-4 Phantom fell victim to a 'Spiral' anti-tank missile fired from a 'Hind'), they have accumulated unrivalled combat experience.

The following details apply to the 'Hind-D' gunship version:

TYPE: Gunship helicopter, with transport capability.

ROTOR SYSTEM: Dynamic components developed from those of Mi-8. Five-blade constant-chord main rotor, of NACA 230 blade section, and three-blade tail rotor; latter on port side of offset tail fin. Main rotor blades, with titanium spars, glassfibre skin and honeycomb core, on forged and machined steel head, with conventional flapping, drag and pitch change articulation. Blade spars nitrogen pressurised for crack detection. Hydraulic lead/lag dampers. Balance tab and electric leading-edge de-icing on each blade. Main rotor brake standard. Aluminium alloy tail rotor blades.

FUSELAGE: Conventional all-metal semi-monocoque structure of pod and boom type. Forward portion, above shallow floor structure, embodies 8 mm hardened steel integral side armour.

AUXILIARY WINGS: All-metal cantilever shoulder wings of tapered planform, with about 16° anhedral and 20° incidence. No movable surfaces. Wings contribute about 25 per cent of total lift in cruising flight.

TAIL UNIT: Swept fin, offset at 3°, serves also as tail rotor pylon. Variable incidence horizontal stabiliser at base of fin.

LANDING GEAR: Tricycle type, with rearward retracting steerable twin-wheel nose unit, and single-wheel main units with oleo-pneumatic shock absorbers and low pressure tyres. Main units retract rearward and inward into the aft end of the fuselage pod, turning through 90° to stow almost vertically, discwise to the longitudinal axis of the fuselage, under prominent blister fairings. Tubular tripod skid assembly, with shock strut, protects tail rotor in a tail-down take-off or landing.

POWER PLANT: Two Isotov TV3-117 turboshafts, each with max rating of 1,640 kW (2,200 shp), mounted side by side above the cabin, with their output shafts driving rearward to the main rotor shaft through a combining gearbox. 8 mm hardened steel armour protection for engines. Main fuel tank in fuselage to rear of cabin, with bag tanks under cabin floor. Internal fuel capacity of 1,500 kg (3,307 lb) can be supplemented by 1,000 kg (2,205 lb) auxiliary tank in cabin. Provision for carrying (instead of auxiliary tank) up to four external fuel tanks, each with capacity of 500 litres (132 US gallons; 110 Imp gallons), on two inner pylons under each wing. Optional deflectors and separators for foreign objects and dust in air intakes; and infra-red suppression exhaust mixer boxes over exhaust ducts. APU mounted transversely inside fairing aft of rotor head.

ACCOMMODATION: Pilot (at rear) and weapon operator on armoured seats in tandem cockpits under individual canopies. Dual flying controls, with retractable pedals in front cockpit. Flight mechanic on jump-seat in narrow passage between flight deck and main cabin. Front canopy hinged to open sideways, to starboard; footstep under starboard side of fuselage for access to pilot's rearward hinged door. Rear seat raised to give pilot an unobstructed forward view. Anti-fragment shield between cockpits. Main cabin can accommodate eight persons on folding seats, or four stretchers. At front of passenger cabin on each side is a door, divided horizontally into two sections which are hinged to open upward and downward respectively, with integral step on lower portion. Optically flat bulletproof glass windscreen, with wiper, for each crew member. Cockpits heated and ventilated.

SYSTEMS: Dual electrical system, with three generators. Stability augmentation system. Electro-thermal de-icing system for main and tail rotor blades. Cabin heating and ventilation systems.

AVIONICS AND EQUIPMENT: Include VHF and UHF radio, autopilot, radar altimeter, blind-flying instrumentation, and ADF navigation system with Doppler-fed mechanical map display. Retractable landing/taxiing light under nose. Navigation lights. Anti-collision light above tailboom. Air data sensor boom forward of top starboard corner of bulletproof windscreen at extreme nose. Undernose pods for electro-optics and RF missile guidance. Gun camera on port wingtip. Colour-coded identification flare system. Many small antennae and blisters, including IFF (NATO 'Odd Rods') and radar warning antennae on each side of front fuselage and on trailing-edge of tail rotor pylon. Infra-red jammer in 'flower pot' container above forward end of tailboom; decoy flare dispenser under tailboom forward of tailskid assembly initially; later triple racks (total of 192 flares) on sides of centre-fuselage.

ARMAMENT: One remotely controlled four-barrel Gatling type 12.7 mm machine-gun in undernose turret, slaved to undernose sighting system. Rails for four AT-2 'Swatter' anti-tank missiles under endplate pylons at wingtips. Four underwing pylons for UV-32-57 rocket pods (each thirty-two S-5 type 57 mm rockets), pods each containing twenty 80 mm rockets, UPK-23 pods each containing a GSh-23 twin-barrel 23 mm gun, up to 1,500 kg (3,300 lb) of chemical or conventional bombs, PFM-1 mine dispensers, or other stores. Helicopter can be landed to install reload weapons carried in cabin. PKV reflector gunsight for pilot. Provisions for firing AK-47 guns from cabin windows.

DIMENSIONS, EXTERNAL:

Main rotor diameter	17.30 m (56 ft 9 in)
Tail rotor diameter	3.90 m (12 ft 9½ in)
Length overall:	
excl rotors and gun	17.50 m (57 ft 5 in)
rotors turning	21.50 m (70 ft 6½ in)
Height overall: rotors turning	6.50 m (21 ft 4 in)

WEIGHTS (Mi-24P):

Weight empty	8,200 kg (18,078 lb)
Max external stores	2,400 kg (5,290 lb)
Normal T-O weight	12,000 kg (26,455 lb)

PERFORMANCE (Mi-24P):

Max level speed	172 knots (320 km/h; 199 mph)
Max cruising speed	159 knots (295 km/h; 183 mph)
Econ cruising speed	117 knots (217 km/h; 135 mph)
Max rate of climb at S/L	750 m (2,460 ft)/min
Service ceiling	4,500 m (14,750 ft)
Hovering ceiling OGE	2,200 m (7,200 ft)
Combat radius:	
with max military load	86 nm (160 km; 99 miles)
with two external fuel tanks	
	121 nm (224 km; 139 miles)
with four external fuel tanks	
	155 nm (288 km; 179 miles)
Range:	
standard internal fuel	243 nm (450 km; 280 miles)
with auxiliary tank in cabin	
	431 nm (800 km; 497 miles)

Mil Mi-35P export version of 'Hind-F' helicopter gunship *(Kenneth Munson)*

MIL Mi-25
NATO reporting name: Hind-D

Some export variants of the Mi-24 ('Hind-D'), including those for Angola, India and Peru, are designated Mi-25. Such a change presumably signifies different equipment standards.

MIL Mi-26
NATO reporting name: Halo

Design of the Mi-26 heavy lift helicopter began in the early 1970s to meet the requirement for an aircraft of greater capability than the Mi-6 and Mi-10, for day and night operation in all weathers. Except for the four-engined twin-rotor Mi-12 (see 1977-78 *Jane's*), which did not progress beyond prototype testing, it is the heaviest helicopter yet flown anywhere in the world. Its rotor diameter is smaller than that of the Mi-6 and Mi-10, but this is offset by the fact that the Mi-26 is the first helicopter to operate successfully with an eight-blade main rotor.

It has obvious military applications, with a payload and cargo hold very similar in size to those of a Lockheed C-130 Hercules. To meet also Soviet Ministry of Civil Aviation requirements, for operation in Siberia and northern swamp and tundra areas of the USSR, emphasis had to be placed on reliability, especially when operating into unprepared landing sites. According to Mr Marat Tishchenko, General Designer in charge of the Mil Bureau, this (plus, no doubt, the need to ensure torsional stiffness) explains why the main rotor blades have conventional steel spars.

Use of titanium for the rotor hub helped the Mil Bureau to meet the official requirement of an empty weight only 50 per cent of the aircraft's maximum permissible take-off weight. A further contribution to weight saving resulted from the decision to design the main gearbox in-house. The end product offers an impressive power to weight ratio, despite the need to absorb an unprecedented input from two Lotarev D-136 turboshafts. Nor does the Mi-26 need auxiliary wings, like the Mi-6, to achieve its required payload/range performance.

The prototype Mi-26 flew for the first time on 14 December 1977. The example shown at the 1981 Paris Air Show (SSSR-06141) was stated to be one of several prototypes or pre-production examples then flying. In-field evaluation, probably with a single air force development squadron, began in early 1983 and the Mi-26 was fully operational by 1985. More than 50 are in service. The first export order, for ten, was placed by India, and the first two of these were delivered in June 1986.

During three days in February 1982, the Mi-26 set five world helicopter payload-to-height records, exceeding records established previously by the Sikorsky CH-54B Skycrane and Mil Mi-12. On 2 February, piloted by G. P. Karapetyan, it lifted a 10,000 kg payload to 6,400 m (20,997 ft). On 3 February, piloted by G. V. Alfeurov, it lifted a payload of 25,000 kg to 4,100 m (13,451 ft), and lifted a total mass of 56,768.8 kg (125,153.8 lb) to a height of 2,000 m. On 4 February, it lifted a payload of 15,000 kg to 5,600 m (18,373 ft), piloted by S. V. Petrov; and 20,000 kg to 4,600 m (15,092 ft), piloted by A. P. Kholoupov.

An uprated version of the Mi-26 is under development, with more powerful engines, all-composites rotor blades, and a maximum payload of 22,000 kg (48,500 lb). The following details apply to the current version:

TYPE: Twin-turboshaft heavy transport helicopter.

ROTOR SYSTEM: Eight-blade constant-chord main rotor, with flapping and drag hinges, droop stops and hydraulic drag dampers; no elastomeric bearings or hinges. Five-blade constant-chord tail rotor, mounted on starboard side of tail fin. Each main rotor blade consists of a one-piece

Mil Mi-26 in Soviet military colours *(Jane's Defence Weekly/Paul Beaver)*

Mil Mi-26, first helicopter to operate successfully with an eight-blade main rotor *(Pilot Press)*

Mil Mi-26 heavy lift helicopter (two Lotarev D-136 turboshafts) in Soviet military service

tubular steel spar and 26 glassfibre aerofoil shape full chord pockets, 'Nomex'-filled with ribs and stiffeners and non-removable titanium leading-edge abrasion strip. Blades have moderate twist, taper in thickness towards tip, and are attached to small forged titanium head of unconventional design. Ground adjustable tab on trailing-edge of each blade. Hydraulically powered cyclic and collective pitch controls actuated by small parallel jacks, with redundant autopilot and stability augmentation system inputs. Tail rotor blades made of glassfibre, attached to forged titanium head. Leading-edge of main and tail rotor blades heated electrically for anti-icing. Main rotor rpm 132.

ROTOR DRIVE: Conventional transmission. Tail rotor shaft runs inside roof of cabin. Main gearbox type VR-26, rated at 14,914 kW (20,000 hp), is fan cooled, with air intake above rear of engine cowlings.

FUSELAGE: Conventional all-metal riveted semi-monocoque structure of pod and boom type, with clamshell rear loading doors and ramp. Flattened undersurface to tailboom. Engine bay made of titanium for fire protection.

TAIL UNIT: Sweptback vertical stabiliser, carrying tail rotor, profiled to produce sideways lift. Ground adjustable variable incidence horizontal stabiliser mounted on leading-edge of vertical stabiliser, a short distance above the tailboom. Both components are of all-metal construction.

LANDING GEAR: Non-retractable tricycle type, with twin wheels on each unit. Steerable nosewheels. Mainwheel tyres size 1,120 × 450. Retractable tailskid at end of tailboom to permit unrestricted approach to rear cargo doors. Length of main legs can be adjusted hydraulically to facilitate loading through rear doors and to permit landing on varying surfaces. A device on the main gear indicates take-off weight to flight engineer at lift-off, on panel on shelf to rear of his seat.

POWER PLANT: Two 8,380 kW (11,240 shp) Lotarev D-136 free-turbine turboshafts, mounted side by side above cabin, forward of main rotor driveshaft. Air intakes are fitted with particle separators to prevent foreign object ingestion, and have both electrical and bleed air anti-icing systems. Above and behind is a central oil cooler intake. There is a system for synchronising the output of the engines and maintaining constant rotor rpm. If one engine fails, output of the other is increased to maximum power automatically. Independent fuel system for each engine. Fuel in eight underfloor rubber tanks, feeding into two header tanks above engines, which permit gravity feed for a period in emergencies. Max fuel capacity 12,000 litres (3,170 US gallons; 2,640 Imp gallons). Two large panels on each side of main rotor mast fairing, aft of engine exhaust outlet, hinge downward as work platforms.

ACCOMMODATION: Crew of five on flight deck, consisting of pilot (on port side) and co-pilot side by side, with navigator's seat between pilots, and seats for flight engineer and loadmaster to rear. Four-seat passenger compartment aft of flight deck. Loads that can be accommodated in hold include two airborne infantry combat vehicles and a standard 20,000 kg (44,100 lb) ISO container. About 20 tip-up seats along each side wall of hold. Max military seating for about 85 combat equipped troops. Heated windscreen, with wipers. Four large blistered side windows on flight deck. Forward pair swing open slightly outward and rearward. Downward hinged doors, with integral airstairs, at front of hold on port side, and on each side of hold aft of main landing gear units. Hold is loaded via a downward hinged lower door, with integral folding ramp, and two clamshell upper doors which form rear wall of hold when closed. Doors are

opened and closed hydraulically, with backup handpump for emergency use. Two electric hoists on overhead rails, each with capacity of 2,500 kg (5,511 lb), enable loads to be transported along cabin. Winch for hauling loads, capacity 500 kg (1,100 lb). Roller conveyor in floor and load lashing points throughout hold. Flight deck and hold fully air-conditioned.

SYSTEMS: Two hydraulic systems, operating pressure 207 bars (3,000 lb/sq in). (Much higher pressure than usual for Soviet helicopters, reflected by small size of jacks for rotor head controls.) 28V DC electrical system. APU under flight deck, with intake louvres (forming fuselage skin when closed) and exhaust on starboard side, for engine starting and to supply hydraulic, electrical and air-conditioning systems on ground. Only flight deck pressurised. Four-axis autostabilisation.

AVIONICS AND EQUIPMENT: All items necessary for day and night operations in all weathers are standard, including weather radar in the hinged (to starboard) nosecone, Doppler, map display, HSI, and automatic hover system. Com/nav equipment generally similar to that of Yak-42. Hatch for load sling in bottom of fuselage, in line with main rotor shaft, enabling sling cable to be attached to internal winching gear. Closed circuit TV cameras to observe slung payloads. Operational equipment on military version includes infra-red jammers and suppressors, infra-red decoy dispensers and colour-coded identification flare system.

DIMENSIONS, EXTERNAL:
Main rotor diameter	32.00 m (105 ft 0 in)
Tail rotor diameter	7.61 m (24 ft 11½ in)
Length overall, rotors turning	40.025 m (131 ft 3¾ in)
Length of fuselage, excl tail rotor	33.727 m (110 ft 8 in)
Height to top of rotor head	8.145 m (26 ft 8¾ in)
Width over mainwheels	8.15 m (26 ft 9 in)
Wheel track	7.17 m (23 ft 6¼ in)
Wheelbase	8.95 m (29 ft 4½ in)

DIMENSIONS, INTERNAL:
Freight hold:
Length: ramp trailed	15.00 m (49 ft 2½ in)
excl ramp	12.00 m (39 ft 4¼ in)
Width	3.25 m (10 ft 8 in)
Height	2.95-3.17 m (9 ft 8 in to 10 ft 4¾ in)
Volume	121 m³ (4,273 cu ft)

AREAS:
Main rotor disc	804.25 m² (8,657 sq ft)
Tail rotor disc	45.48 m² (489.6 sq ft)

WEIGHTS AND LOADINGS:
Weight empty	28,200 kg (62,170 lb)
Max payload, internal or external	20,000 kg (44,090 lb)
Normal T-O weight	49,500 kg (109,125 lb)
Max T-O weight	56,000 kg (123,450 lb)
Max rotor disc loading	69.6 kg/m² (14.26 lb/sq ft)
Max power loading	3.34 kg/kW (5.49 lb/shp)

PERFORMANCE:
Max level speed	159 knots (295 km/h; 183 mph)
Normal cruising speed	137 knots (255 km/h; 158 mph)
Service ceiling	4,600 m (15,100 ft)
Hovering ceiling OGE, ISA	1,800 m (5,900 ft)
Range with max internal fuel at max T-O weight, 5% reserves	432 nm (800 km; 497 miles)

MIL Mi-28
NATO reporting name: Havoc

Design of the Mi-28 twin-engined combat helicopter was started in 1980, and the first prototype flew for the first time on 10 November 1982. Development was 90 per cent complete by June 1989, and a production contract had been signed to achieve IOC by 1991-92. The three prototypes used for development testing were all fitted originally with a three-blade tail rotor. By the time the third example was carried to the 1989 Paris Air Show on board an Antonov An-22 freight transport, this had been changed for a four-blade 'scissors' type tail rotor, superficially similar to that of the McDonnell Douglas AH-64 Apache. However, there are important differences between the two rotors. That of the Mi-28 comprises two independent two-blade rotors on the same shaft, known in the USA as a Δ_3 (delta 3) rotor. The resultant flapping freedom relieves loads in flight. In parallel, the agility of the Mi-28 has been enhanced by doubling the hinge offset of the main rotor blades by comparison with those of the Mi-24.

Great emphasis has been placed on survivability. The crew compartments are protected by titanium and composite armour, as well as armoured glass windows. The more vital structural elements are shielded by the less vital ones. Both engines cannot be knocked out by a single hit. All vital units and parts are redundant and widely

Mil Mi-28 combat helicopter (two Isotov TV3-117 turboshafts) *(Jane's/Mike Keep)*

separated. The multiple fuel tanks in the centre fuselage are enclosed in a composites second skin, outside the metal skin of the fuselage, and the designers claim that no explosion, fire or fuel leakage will occur if the tanks are hit by a bullet or shell fragment.

Energy absorbing seats and landing gear would protect the crew in a crash landing with a descent rate of 15 m (50 ft)/s. The crew doors are rearward hinged, to open quickly and remain open in an emergency. Parachutes are mandatory for all Soviet military helicopter aircrew, and if the crew of an Mi-28 had to take to their parachutes an emergency system would blast away the doors and stub wings, although there is no provision for rotor separation. This action would also inflate a bladder beneath each door sill, so that as the crew jumped they would bounce off the bladders to clear the wheels of the main landing gear.

A door on the port side, aft of the stub wing, provides access to a compartment containing some of the avionics. This compartment is large enough to permit the combat rescue of two persons on the ground, although it lacks windows, heating and ventilation.

A handcrank, inserted in the end of each stub wing, enables stores weighing up to 500 kg (1,100 lb) to be winched on to the pylons without the need for hoists or other ground equipment. The Mi-28's current 30 mm gun is identical with that used on Soviet Army ground vehicles and uses the same ammunition. Jamming is averted by attaching the twin ammunition boxes to each side of the gun mounting, so that they turn to each side, elevate and depress with the gun.

Members of the Mil OKB have stated that versions of the Mi-28 are under development for naval amphibious assault support, night attack and air-to-air missions.

TYPE: Twin-engined combat helicopter.
ROTOR SYSTEM: Five-blade main rotor; two independent two-blade tail rotors set as a narrow X (35°/145°) on same shaft. Main rotor blades have very cambered high-lift section, with sweptback tip leading-edge. Full-span tab on trailing-edge of each blade. Blade structure comprises a numerically controlled, spirally wound glassfibre D-spar and blade pockets of a Kevlar-like material with Nomex-like honeycomb core. Titanium erosion strip on blade leading-edge. Each blade has a single elastomeric root bearing, mechanical droop stop and hydraulic drag damper. Glassfibre tail rotor blades also have elastomeric bearings for flapping. Rotor brake lever on starboard side of cockpit. Main and tail blades are electrically de-iced. Probes for low airspeed sensing system in main rotor blade tips.
ROTOR DRIVE: Strong and simple machined titanium rotor head with automatic grease lubrication. Power output shafts from engines drive main gearbox from each side. Tail rotor gearbox, at base of tail pylon, driven conventionally by aluminium alloy shaft inside composite duct on top of tailboom. Transmission capable of running without oil for 20-30 minutes. Main rotor rpm 242.
WINGS: Cantilever mid-mounted wings of low aspect ratio, with sweptback leading-edge. Each wing has a light alloy primary box structure, with leading- and trailing-edges of composites. No movable surfaces. Tiedown in each wingtip.
FUSELAGE: Basically a conventional light alloy semi-monocoque structure, with titanium armour around cockpits and vulnerable areas. Access door of composites aft of wing on port side.

Mil Mi-28 (NATO 'Havoc') combat helicopter at 1989 Paris Air Show (*Paul Jackson*)

TAIL UNIT: Sweptback fin has light alloy primary box structure, with composites leading- and trailing-edges. Braced two-position horizontal stabiliser of composites construction, at tip on port side, is linked to the collective.
LANDING GEAR: Non-retractable tailwheel type, with single wheel on each unit. Mainwheel tyres size 720 × 320, pressure 5.4 bars (78 lb/sq in). Castoring tailwheel with tyre size 480 × 200.
POWER PLANT: Two Isotov TV3-117 turboshafts, each rated at 1,640 kW (2,200 shp), in pod mounted above each wingroot. Three jetpipes inside downward deflected composites nozzle fairing on each side of third prototype shown in Paris. Upward deflecting type also tested. Ivchenko AI-9V APU in rear of main pylon structure supplies compressed air for engine starting and to drive a small turbine for pre-flight ground checks. Deflectors for dust and foreign objects forward of air intakes. Air intakes de-iced by engine bleed air. Internal fuel capacity approx 1,900 litres (502 US gallons; 418 Imp gallons). Provision for four external fuel tanks on underwing pylons. APU to rear of main rotor gearbox.
ACCOMMODATION: Co-pilot/gunner in front cockpit; pilot behind, on elevated seat. Flat non-glint tinted transparencies of armoured glass. Flying controls for pilot only.
SYSTEMS: Cockpits air-conditioned and pressurised by engine bleed air. Duplicated hydraulic systems, pressure 152 bars (2,200 lb/sq in). 200V AC electrical system supplied by two generators on accessory section of main gearbox, ensuring continued supply during autorotation. Low airspeed system standard, giving speed and drift via blade-tip pitot tubes at −7 to +42 km/h (−3.7 to +22 knots; −4.3 to +26 mph).
AVIONICS AND EQUIPMENT: Conventional IFR instrumentation, with autostabilisation, autohover, and hover/heading hold lock in attack mode. Standard UHF/VHF nav/com. Pilot has head-up display. Radio for missile guidance in nose radome. Radar warning receivers fitted. Small IFF fairing on each side of nose and tail. Two slots, one above the other on port side of tailboom, for colour-coded identification flares. Three pairs of rectangular formation keeping lights in top of tailboom

and one further pair in top of main rotor pylon fairing. Daylight optical weapons sight and laser ranger/designator in double-glazed nose turret above gun, with which it rotates through ±110°. Wiper on outer glass which protects inner optically-flat panel. Cylindrical container on each side of this turret for FLIR and low light level TV night vision systems (not fitted to aircraft in Paris). Aircraft designed for use with night vision goggles.
ARMAMENT AND OPERATIONAL EQUIPMENT: One Type 2A42 30 mm turret mounted gun (with 300 rds) at nose, able to rotate ±110°, elevate 13° and depress 45°. Rates of fire 900 rds/min air-to-air, 300 rds/min air-to-ground. (A new specially designed gun is under development.) Two pylons under each stub wing, each with capacity of 480 kg (1058 lb), typically for a total of 16 improved AT-6 (NATO 'Spiral') radio guided tube-launched anti-tank missiles and two UV-20 pods of twenty 57 mm or 80 mm rockets. Missiles can be launched only from the front cockpit; rockets and gun can be fired from both cockpits. Radio guidance equipment for missiles in small radome on nose. Undernose pod encloses optical sighting system and laser rangefinder. Housing on each side of nose for low light level TV and FLIR night combat systems. Infra-red suppressors and infra-red decoy dispensers fitted.

DIMENSIONS, EXTERNAL:
Main rotor diameter	17.20 m (56 ft 5 in)
Tail rotor diameter	3.84 m (12 ft 7¼ in)
Length overall, excl rotors	16.85 m (55 ft 3½ in)
Width over stub wings	4.87 m (16 ft 0 in)
Height overall	4.81 m (15 ft 9½ in)

WEIGHTS:
Weight empty	7,000 kg (15,430 lb)
Max T-O weight	11,400 kg (25,130 lb)

PERFORMANCE (estimated):
Max level speed	164 knots (305 km/h; 189 mph)
Max cruising speed	143 knots (265 km/h; 165 mph)
Service ceiling	5,800 m (19,025 ft)
Hovering ceiling OGE	3,600 m (11,800 ft)
Range with max fuel	253 nm (470 km; 292 miles)
Endurance with max fuel	2 h 0 min
g limits	+3/−0.5

MIL Mi-34
NATO reporting name: Hermit

Exhibited in public for the first time at the 1987 Paris Air Show, the Mi-34 (NATO 'Hermit') is a lightweight two/four-seat helicopter intended primarily for pilot training and international competition flying. Like the Polish PZL Swidnik SW-4, it is offered as a replacement for DOSAAF's veteran Mi-1 helicopter trainers; but, whereas the SW-4 is turboshaft powered, the Mi-34 has a Vedeneyev piston engine of the same basic type as that fitted in DOSAAF's current family of Yakovlev fixed-wing training aircraft and Kamov Ka-26 helicopters. Other applications for which the Mi-34 is suited include light utility, observation and liaison duties, and border patrol.

Two prototypes and a structure test airframe had been completed by mid-1987. The first flight took place in 1986 and an Mi-34 became subsequently the first Soviet helicopter to perform a normal loop and a roll. A decision on whether or not the Mi-34 will be produced under the next five-year plan was scheduled to be made in 1988-89. If ordered, manufacture is likely to be centred at WSK-PZL Swidnik in Poland.

TYPE: Light general purpose helicopter.
ROTOR SYSTEM: Semi-articulated four-blade main rotor, with flapping and cyclic pitch hinges but with natural flexing in the lead/lag plane. Blades are made of glassfibre with carbonfibre reinforcement, and are attached by flexible steel straps to a head similar to that of the McDonnell Douglas (Hughes) MD 500. Two-blade tail rotor of similar composites construction, on starboard side of tailboom. Mechanical flight controls, with no hydraulic boost.

Close-up of nose of third prototype of the Mil Mi-28 (*Brian M. Service*)

FUSELAGE: Simple riveted light alloy structure of pod and boom configuration.
TAIL UNIT: Sweptback fin, mid-mounted on port side of tailcone, with small constant chord unswept T tailplane.
LANDING GEAR: Conventional non-retractable skids on arched support tubes. Small tailskid to protect tail rotor.
POWER PLANT: One 242 kW (325 hp) Vedeneyev M-14V-26 nine-cylinder radial aircooled engine mounted sideways in the centre-fuselage. Fuel consumption 45 kg (99 lb)/hour.
ACCOMMODATION: Normally one or two pilots, side by side, in enclosed cabin, with optional dual controls. Rear of cabin contains low bench seat, available for two passengers and offering a flat floor for cargo carrying. Forward hinged door on each side of flight deck and on each side of rear cabin.

DIMENSIONS, EXTERNAL:
Main rotor diameter	10.00 m (32 ft 9¾ in)
Tail rotor diameter	1.48 m (4 ft 10¼ in)
Length of fuselage	8.71 m (28 ft 7 in)
Width of fuselage	1.42 m (4 ft 8 in)
Skid track	2.06 m (6 ft 9¼ in)

WEIGHTS:
Fuel weight	120 kg (265 lb)

T-O weight, training and aerobatic missions:
Normal	1,260 kg (2,777 lb)
Max	1,350 kg (2,976 lb)

PERFORMANCE (at T-O weight of 1,260 kg; 2,777 lb, except where indicated):
Max level speed	118 knots (220 km/h; 136 mph)
Max cruising speed	97 knots (180 km/h; 112 mph)
Normal cruising speed	86 knots (160 km/h; 99 mph)
Max speed rearward	70 knots (130 km/h; 80 mph)
Service ceiling	4,500 m (14,765 ft)
Hovering ceiling	1,500 m (4,920 ft)

Range at max T-O weight with 160 kg (352 lb) payload 194 nm (360 km; 223 miles)
g limits at AUW of 1,020 kg (2,249 lb) and speeds of 27-81 knots (50-150 km/h; 31-93 mph) +3/-0

TWIN-TURBINE DEVELOPMENT OF MIL Mi-34
The Mil OKB has requested international co-operation in developing a twin-turbine helicopter based on the Mi-34. No details are available, except that the projected aircraft would embody the dynamic systems of the Mi-34 and would have a T-O weight of 1,500-1,700 kg (3,300-3,750 lb).

MIL Mi-35
This is an export version of the Mi-24 'Hind-E'.

MIL Mi-38
The Mi-38 is a medium transport helicopter that the Mil OKB is developing as a replacement for the Mi-8/17 series. Shown in model form at the 1989 Paris Air Show, it was said by General Designer Marat N. Tishchenko to be at the mockup stage at that time, with a first flight scheduled for 1992-93 and production planned to start in 1996. Design will be to FAR Pt 29 standards, for day/night operation over a temperature range of –60°C to +50°C. Western engines could be installed in place of the standard Soviet turboshafts if requested by foreign customers.
TYPE: Twin-turbine multi-role helicopter.
ROTOR SYSTEM: Five-blade main rotor of composites construction, with considerable non-linear twist and swept tips. Hydraulic drag dampers. Elastomeric bearings. Single lubrication point, at driveshaft. Two independent two-blade tail rotors, set as narrow X on same shaft, with blades of composites construction and elastomeric bearings. Electric blade de-icing.
FUSELAGE: Conventional pod and boom configuration with clamshell loading doors at rear of main cabin and large passenger/freight door at front on port side. Hatch in cabin floor, under main rotor driveshaft location, for tactical or emergency airdrop of cargo and for slung cargo cable attachment. Windows for survey cameras could also occupy this position.
TAIL UNIT: Sweptback fin, small ventral fin, and stabiliser at bottom of tailcone.
LANDING GEAR: Retractable tricycle type. Nose gear retracts forward under floor of flight deck. Main units retract into housings on sides of the cabin. Low-pressure tyres. Optional pontoons for emergency use in overwater missions.
POWER PLANT: Two TV7-117V turboshafts, each flat rated at 1,715 kW (2,300 shp) for T-O, developed at V. Ya. Klimov bureau in Leningrad. Single-engine output of 2,610 kW (3,500 shp) available for safe T-O after failure of one engine. Power plant mounted above cabin, to rear of main reduction gear, with air intakes and filters in sides of cowling. Forward part of cowling houses VD-100 APU, hydraulic, air-conditioning, electrical and other system components. Bag fuel tanks beneath floor of main cabin. Liquid petroleum gas fuel planned as alternative to aviation kerosene.
ACCOMMODATION: Crew of two on flight deck, separated from main cabin by compartment for majority of avionics. Single-pilot operation possible for cargo missions. Lightweight seats for up to 32 passengers as alternative to unobstructed hold for 5,000 kg (11,020 lb) of freight. Ambulance and air survey versions are

Prototype of the Mil Mi-34 (Vedeneyev M-14V-26 engine) (*Piotr Butowski*)

Mil Mi-34 two/four-seat training and competition helicopter (*Pilot Press*)

Mil Mi-38 medium transport helicopter to replace the Mi-8/17 (*Pilot Press*)

planned. Provision for hoist over side freight door, remotely controlled hydraulically actuated rear cargo ramp, powered hoist on overhead rails in cabin, and roller conveyor system in cabin floor and ramp.
SYSTEMS: Air-conditioning by compressor bleed air, or APU on the ground, maintains a temperature of not more than 25°C on flight deck in outside temperature of 40°C, and not less than 15°C on flight deck and in main cabin in outside temperature of –50°C. Three independent hydraulic systems, any one of which is able to maintain control of the helicopter in an emergency. Fly by wire flight control system, with manual backup. Electrical system has three independent AC generators, two batteries, and transformer/rectifiers for DC supply. Independent fuel system for each engine, with automatic cross-feed.
AVIONICS: Five colour CRTs on flight deck for use in flight and by servicing personnel on the ground. Pre-set flight

control system allows full autopilot, autohover and automatic landing. Equipment monitoring, failure warning and damage control system. Avionics controlled by large central computer, linked also to automatic navigation system with Doppler, ILS, satellite navigation system, weather/navigation radar, autostabilisation system and automatic radio compass. Closed-circuit TV for monitoring cargo loading and slung loads. Other options include sensors for weighing and CG positioning of cargo in cabin, and for checking the weight of slung loads.

DIMENSIONS, EXTERNAL:
Main rotor diameter	21.23 m (69 ft 8 in)
Forward freight door: Width	1.50 m (4 ft 11 in)
Height	1.70 m (5 ft 7 in)

Floor hatch: Length		1.15 m (3 ft 9¼ in)
Width		0.75 m (2 ft 5½ in)
DIMENSIONS, INTERNAL:		
Main cabin: Length		6.70 m (22 ft 0 in)
Width		1.85 m (6 ft 0¾ in)
Height		2.20 m (7 ft 2½ in)
WEIGHTS (provisional):		
Normal T-O weight		13,460 kg (29,672 lb)
Max T-O weight		14,500 kg (31,965 lb)
PERFORMANCE (estimated):		
Max level speed		
	151-156 knots (280-290 km/h; 174-180 mph)	
Cruising speed		
	143-148 knots (265-275 km/h; 165-171 mph)	

Service ceiling	6,500 m (21,325 ft)
Hovering ceiling OGE	2,500 m (8,200 ft)
Range, 30 min reserves:	
with 5,000 kg (11,020 lb) payload	
	175 nm (325 km; 202 miles)
with 3,500 kg (7,715 lb) payload and standard fuel	
	430 nm (800 km; 497 miles)
with 1,800 kg (3,965 lb) payload and auxiliary fuel	
	700 nm (1,300 km; 808 miles)

MYASISHCHEV

This design bureau was formed in 1951, under the leadership of Professor Vladimir Mikhailovich Myasishchev, who died on 14 October 1978, at the age of 76. It is now known as the Experimentalnyy Mashinostroitelnyy Zavod 'Serp i Molot' imeni V. Myasishcheva (V. Myasishchev Experimental Machine Factory 'Hammer and Sickle').

MYASISHCHEV M-4
NATO reporting name: Bison
It is doubtful if any of the M-4 strategic bombers and maritime reconnaissance aircraft described in previous editions of *Jane's* remain operational, but those examples modified into probe-and-drogue refuelling tankers for the 'Backfire/Bear/Blinder' attack force will continue in service until sufficient Il-78s (NATO 'Midas') are available to replace them entirely. About 40 are thought to remain.

The M-4 is powered by four Mikulin AM-3D turbojets, each rated at 85.3 kN (19,180 lb st).

DIMENSIONS, EXTERNAL (basic 'Bison-A' strategic bomber):
Wing span	50.48 m (165 ft 7½ in)
Length overall	47.20 m (154 ft 10 in)
Tailplane span	15.00 m (49 ft 2½ in)

WEIGHT (basic 'Bison-A' strategic bomber):
Max T-O weight	158,750 kg (350,000 lb)

PERFORMANCE (basic 'Bison-A' strategic bomber, estimated):
Max level speed at 11,000 m (36,000 ft)
538 knots (998 km/h; 620 mph)
Service ceiling 13,700 m (45,000 ft)
Max unrefuelled combat radius
3,025 nm (5,600 km; 3,480 miles)
Range at 450 knots (835 km/h; 520 mph) with more than 5,450 kg (12,000 lb) of bombs
4,320 nm (8,000 km; 4,970 miles)

MYASISHCHEV VM-T ATLANT
The VM-T (SSSR-01502) is an M-4 bomber that has been adapted to carry on its back outsize loads such as the *Buran* space shuttle orbiter and large components of the Energiya rocket launch vehicle. Most apparent modification involved replacement of the standard sweptback vertical tail surfaces by twin endplate fins and rudders of rectangular shape.

Maximum payload of the VM-T is 40 metric tons, requiring the removal of *Buran's* orbital manoeuvring system engines, tail fin and other components before it could be transported. The later Antonov An-225 can carry a complete space shuttle orbiter.

MYASISHCHEV M-17
NATO reporting name: Mystic
This Soviet counterpart to the US Air Force's Lockheed U-2/TR-1 high-altitude reconnaissance aircraft was first reported in 1982, after a prototype had been observed at Ramenskoye flight test centre and allocated the US provisional designation 'Ram-M'. It is believed that the first two prototypes were single-engined, the third twin-engined.

According to Soviet press reports, this aircraft was designed by the Myasishchev OKB. An official designation of M-17 has been quoted; NATO allocated the reporting name 'Mystic'. To what extent the type has been used for military purposes is unknown. All references by the Soviet media have described civilian research missions, including a church-sponsored flight from Moscow at Christmas 1989 to investigate the possibility of holes in the ozone layer. This would explain why inscriptions on the airframe of one of the single-engined examples (SSSR-17401) have included (in English) 'Global Ozone Reserve will guarantee you high profits', 'Aeromonitoring flying laboratory', and (in Russian) 'Merry Christmas'. Another example (SSSR-17103), shown in an accompanying illustration, is now included in the outdoor exhibition of historic aeroplanes at Monino. If an aircraft of this type is still perceived as necessary for military purposes, it is likely that the twin-engined version would be built.

The general configuration of the M-17 is shown in the illustrations. It is a single-seater, with a large compartment in the lower part of its fuselage pod for cameras and other sensors. The long-span, high aspect ratio wings can be assumed to give it the same kind of powered sailplane performance as the U-2 series. The type of engine fitted was unknown in Spring 1990.

Myasishchev VM-T Atlant, an M-4 bomber adapted to carry loads in canisters or sections of the Energiya launch vehicle *(Quadrant/Flight)*

Myasishchev M-17, in single-engined form, photographed at Monino in 1990 *(Nigel Eastaway)*

Myasishchev M-17 high-altitude reconnaissance and environmental research aircraft *(Jane's/Mike Keep)*

TYPE: Single-seat high-altitude reconnaissance aircraft.
WINGS: Cantilever high-wing monoplane of high aspect ratio. Constant sweepback on leading-edge. Unswept trailing-edge on outer wings; increased chord on inner wings, with no sweep between tailbooms. Constant anhedral from roots. Aileron, with tab, and three-section flaps extend over most of trailing-edge of each wing.
FUSELAGE: Long fuselage pod, with side air ducts for engine, which is mounted at rear of pod.
TAIL UNIT: Twin fins and rudders, with bridging horizontal surfaces at tips, carried on two slender tailbooms. Conventional rudders and elevators, with tabs. Long and shallow ventral strake under rear of each tailboom.
LANDING GEAR: Retractable tricycle type, with twin wheels on each unit. All units retract rearward, mainwheels into tailbooms.
ACCOMMODATION: Single seat under rearward hinged canopy.
DIMENSIONS, EXTERNAL (Single-engined; approx):

Wing span	40.75 m (133 ft 6½ in)
Length overall	21.25 m (69 ft 6½ in)
Height overall	5.25 m (17 ft 3 in)
Wheel track	6.66 m (21 ft 10 in)
Wheelbase	5.65 m (18 ft 4 in)

Single-engined prototype of Myasishchev M-17 'Mystic' (*Piotr Butowski*)

SUKHOI

23A Polikarpov St, Moscow 125284
Telephone: 7 (95) 945 6525
GENERAL DESIGNER OF SUKHOI BUREAU:
Mikhail Petrovich Simonov
DEPUTY GENERAL DESIGNER:
Konstantin Marbaschev
PROJECT DESIGNER, Su-25: Vladimir P. Babak
DEPUTY CHIEF DESIGNER: Nikolai Fedorovich Nikitin

This design bureau is named after Pavel Osipovich Sukhoi, who headed it from 1953 until his death in September 1975. It remains one of the two primary Soviet centres for fighter and attack aircraft development, and is widening its activities to include civilian aircraft, in some cases with Western partners.

A memorandum of understanding, initiated in partnership with Gulfstream Aerospace of the USA, concerns "the feasibility of a joint venture in the development, manufacture and marketing of a business type supersonic aircraft".

Another memorandum of understanding between Sukhoi and Dassault Aviation of France concerns the joint development of a conventional subsonic business jet.

SUKHOI Su-15
NATO reporting name: Flagon

Details of the initial versions of this twin-jet delta-wing interceptor can be found in the 1983-84 and previous editions of *Jane's*. The number of late-model Su-15s remaining in Soviet home defence units is believed to be about 400, in three versions, as follows:

Flagon-E. Single-seat interceptor. Longer-span wings than those of earlier 'Flagon-A, C and D', with compound sweep. Tumansky R-13F-300 turbojets, each rated at 64.73 kN (14,550 lb st), and additional fuel, giving increased speed and range. Uprated avionics (NATO 'Twin Scan' replacing 'Skip Spin' radar). Major production version, operational since second half of 1973.

Flagon-F. Last known production version. Ogival nose radome instead of conical type of earlier variants. Generally similar to 'Flagon-E', but with different engines.

Flagon-G. Two-seat training version of 'Flagon-F',

'Flagon-F' twin-jet interceptor, armed with 'Anab' missiles and gun pods (*Swedish Coast Guard/Air Patrol*)

with probable combat capability. Individual rearward hinged canopy over each seat. Periscope fitted above rear canopy for enhanced forward view. Overall length unchanged.

The following details apply to 'Flagon-F':

TYPE: Single-seat twin-jet all-weather interceptor.
WINGS: Cantilever mid-wing monoplane. Basic wings are of simple delta form, similar to those of earlier Su-11, but with new and extended outer panels. Sweepback 60° on inner wings, 47° on outer panels. No dihedral or anhedral. All-metal structure. Single boundary layer fence above each wing at approx 70 per cent span. Large-chord plain flap extends from inboard end of aileron to fuselage on each side.
FUSELAGE: Cockpit section is basically circular with large ogival dielectric nosecone. Centre-fuselage is faired into rectangular section air intake ducts. Two door type airbrakes at top and bottom on each side of rear fuselage, forward of tailplane.
TAIL UNIT: Cantilever all-metal structure, with 60° leading-edge sweepback on all surfaces. All-moving tailplane,

with anhedral, mounted slightly below mid position and fitted with anti-flutter bodies near tips. Conventional rudder. No trim tabs.
LANDING GEAR: Tricycle type, with single wheel on each main unit and twin nosewheels, all on levered-suspension legs. Mainwheels retract inward into wings and intake ducts; nosewheels retract forward, with blistered doors. Nosewheels steerable. Container for brake-chute between base of rudder and tailpipe.
POWER PLANT: Two turbojets, with variable area nozzles, mounted side by side in rear fuselage. These are reported to be Tumansky R-25s, each rated at 92.5 kN (20,795 lb st) with afterburning. Ram air intakes, with variable ramps on splitter plates, embodying vertical slots for boundary layer control. Blow-in auxiliary inlets between main intake and wing leading-edge in side of each duct. Fuel tanks in centre-fuselage and wings.
ACCOMMODATION: Single zero/zero ejection seat in enclosed cockpit, with rearward sliding blister canopy. Rearview mirror above canopy of some aircraft.
ARMAMENT: Two pylons for external stores under each wing. Normal armament comprises one radar homing and one infra-red homing air-to-air missile (NATO 'Anab') on outboard pylons, and an infra-red homing close-range missile ('Aphid') on each inboard pylon. Side by side pylons under centre-fuselage for weapons, including GSh-23L 23 mm gun pods, or external fuel tanks.
AVIONICS AND EQUIPMENT: Large I-band radar (NATO 'Twin Scan') in nose, SOD-57M ATC/SIF nav system, SRO-2 (NATO 'Odd Rods') IFF, Sirena-3 radar warning system.
DIMENSIONS, EXTERNAL (estimated):

Wing span	9.15 m (30 ft 0 in)
Length overall	21.33 m (70 ft 0 in)
Height overall	5.10 m (16 ft 8½ in)

WEIGHTS (estimated):

Weight empty	11,000 kg (24,250 lb)
Max T-O weight	18,000 kg (39,680 lb)

PERFORMANCE (estimated):

Max level speed above 11,000 m (36,000 ft) with external stores	Mach 2.1
Time to 11,000 m (36,000 ft)	2 min 30 s
Service ceiling	20,000 m (65,600 ft)
Combat radius	538 nm (998 km; 620 miles)

Sukhoi Su-15 ('Flagon-F') single-seat twin-jet all-weather interceptor, with additional side elevations of 'Flagon-E' (top) and 'Flagon-G' (bottom) (*Pilot Press*)

Armament of Su-17M-4 can comprise four underwing rocket packs, two underfuselage rocket packs and two AA-8 'Aphid' missiles *(Jane's Defence Weekly/Paul Beaver)*

Su-17M-4 ('Fitter-K'), latest single-seat version of the variable geometry 'Fitter' series *(Pilot Press)*

SUKHOI Su-17, Su-20 and Su-22
NATO reporting names: Fitter-C, D, E, F, G, H, J and K

The early history of this variable geometry fighter series, developed from the sweptwing Su-7 (NATO 'Fitter-A'), has been described in previous editions of *Jane's*. About 1,060 are deployed currently by Soviet tactical air forces, 75 more by Soviet Naval Aviation units assigned to anti-shipping strike and amphibious support roles in the Baltic Sea area, and a further Naval unit of indeterminate size in the Pacific theatre. All aircraft of this type in Soviet service are designated Su-17. Differences between the various current versions are as follows:

Su-17 (S-32, Fitter-C). Basic single-seat attack aircraft for Soviet tactical air forces, with Lyulka AL-21F-3 turbojet and eight stores pylons. Manual wing sweep control. Additional wing fence on fixed centre-section each side. Curved dorsal fin between tail fin and dorsal spine fairing. Operational since 1971, in relatively small numbers. Serves also with Soviet Navy and, as **Su-20** (S-32MK), with air forces of Algeria, Czechoslovakia, Egypt, Iraq and Poland.

Su-17M (S-32M, Fitter-D). Generally similar to 'Fitter-C', but forward fuselage lengthened by 0.38 m (15 in) and drooped 3° to improve pilot's view while keeping intake face vertical. Added undernose electronics pod for Doppler navigation radar. Laser rangefinder in intake centrebody.

Su-17U (U-32, Fitter-E). Tandem two-seat trainer for Soviet air forces. Generally similar to 'Fitter-D', but without electronics pod. Deepened dorsal spine fairing, almost certainly to provide additional fuel tankage. Port wingroot gun deleted.

Su-17UM (Fitter-G). Two-seat trainer variant of 'Fitter-H', with combat capability. Deepened dorsal spine fairing and drooped front fuselage like 'Fitter-E'. Taller vertical tail surfaces. Shallow ventral fin (removable). Starboard gun only. Laser rangefinder fitted in intake centrebody.

Su-17M-1/M-2 (Fitter-H). Improved single-seater for Soviet air forces. Basically as 'Fitter-D', but with wide and deep dorsal fairing aft of canopy, like 'Fitter-E/G'. Doppler navigation radar fitted internally in deepened undersurface of nose. Taller fin like 'Fitter-G'. Removable ventral fin. Retains both wingroot guns. About 165 'Fitter-H/Ks' are equipped for tactical reconnaissance

duties, carrying typically a centreline sensor pod, an active ECM pod under the port wing fixed centre-section, and two underwing fuel tanks. Forty supplied to Hungary.

Su-17M-4 (Fitter-K). Latest single-seat version for Soviet air forces, identified in 1984, still with AL-21F-3 engine. Dorsal fin embodies small cooling air intake at front. Additional pylon for AA-8 ('Aphid') air-to-air missile between each pair of underwing pylons.

Late versions of the variable-geometry 'Fitter' exported to Afghanistan, Angola, North Korea, Libya, Peru, Syria, Vietnam, and North and South Yemen were seen to have a more bulged rear fuselage, now known to house a Tumansky R-29BS-300 turbojet, as fitted in the MiG-27, with rearranged external air ducts, and a shorter plain metal shroud terminating the rear fuselage. This change of power plant, and/or variations in equipment standard, is covered by the following changes to the Soviet type designation:

Su-22U (Fitter-E). As Su-17U, but with Tumansky engine.

Su-22 (Fitter-F). Export counterpart of 'Fitter-D', with slightly modified undernose electronics pod.

Tumansky R-29B turbojet, rated at 112.8 kN (25,350 lb st) with afterburning. Gun in each wingroot. Weapons include 'Atoll' air-to-air missiles. Aircraft supplied to Peru had Sirena-2 limited coverage radar warning receiver and virtually no navigation aids. Some basic US-supplied avionics fitted subsequently.

Su-22 (Fitter-G). Export counterpart of Su-17 'Fitter-G', with R-29B engine.

Su-22M-2 (Fitter-J). Generally similar to 'Fitter-H' but with Tumansky engine. Internal fuel tankage 6,270 litres (1,656 US gallons; 1,379 Imp gallons). More angular dorsal fin. 'Atoll' air-to-air missiles. Supplied to Libya and Peru.

Su-22M-4 (Fitter-K). Similar to Soviet Air Force 'Fitter-K', for Czechoslovakia, East Germany and Poland.

Production of the variable geometry 'Fitter' series has been reduced drastically in recent years. The following description applies to the Su-17 ('Fitter-C') except where indicated:

TYPE: Single-seat ground attack fighter.

WINGS: Cantilever mid-wing monoplane, with wide span fixed centre-section and three-position manually operated variable geometry outer panels, with min sweep angle of 28°, intermediate angle of 45° and max sweep angle of approx 62°. Slight sweepback on trailing-edge of area-increasing centre-section flaps. Outboard of these flaps, centre-section trailing-edge is swept to align with trailing-edge of outer panels when they are fully swept. Full span leading-edge slats on movable panels. Trailing-edge of each movable panel made up of a slotted flap, operable only when the wings are spread, and a slotted aileron operable at all times. Large main fence on each side, at junction of fixed and movable panels, is square-cut at front and incorporates attachments for external stores. Shorter fence above centre-section on each side, inboard of main fence.

FUSELAGE: Conventional all-metal semi-monocoque structure of circular section. Large dorsal spine fairing along top of fuselage, from canopy to fin. Ram air intake in nose, with variable shock-cone centrebody. Four door type airbrakes, at top and bottom on each side of rear fuselage, forward of tailplane. Pitot on port side of nose; transducer to provide pitch and yaw data for fire control computer and antennae on starboard side.

TAIL UNIT: Cantilever all-metal structure, with sweepback on all surfaces. All-moving horizontal surfaces, with anti-flutter body projecting forward on each side near tip. Conventional rudder. No tabs.

LANDING GEAR: Retractable tricycle type, with single wheel on each unit. Nosewheel retracts forward, requiring blistered door to enclose it. Main units retract inward into centre-section. Container for single cruciform brake-chute between base of rudder and tailpipe.

POWER PLANT: One Lyulka AL-21F-3 turbojet, rated at 76.5 kN (17,200 lb st) dry and 110 kN (24,700 lb st) with afterburning. Fuel capacity increased to 4,550 litres (1,202 US gallons; 1,000 Imp gallons) by added tankage in dorsal spine fairing. Provision for carrying up to four 800 litre (211 US gallon; 176 Imp gallon) drop tanks on outboard wing pylons and under fuselage. When underfuselage tanks are carried, only the two inboard wing pylons may be used for ordnance, to a total weight of 1,000 kg (2,204 lb). Two solid propellant rocket units can be attached to rear fuselage to shorten T-O run.

ACCOMMODATION: Pilot only, on ejection seat, under rearward hinged transparent canopy. Rearview mirror above canopy. HUD standard.

AVIONICS AND EQUIPMENT: SRD-5M (NATO 'High Fix') I-band ranging radar in intake centrebody; ASP-5ND fire control system; Sirena-3 radar warning system providing 360° coverage, with antennae in slim cylindrical housing above brake-chute container and in each centre-section leading-edge, between fences; SRO-2M IFF; SOD-57M ATC/SIF, with transponder housing beneath brake-chute container; SP-50 ILS, RSB-70 HF and RSIU-5/R-831 UHF/VHF.

Sukhoi Su-22M-4 ('Fitter-K') of Czechoslovak Air Force, with four flare/chaff dispensers visible beside its dorsal spine *(Letectvi + Kosmonautika/Václav Jukl)*

ARMAMENT: Two 30 mm NR-30 guns, each with 70 rds, in wingroot leading-edges. Total of nine weapon pylons (one on centreline, two tandem pairs under fuselage, one under each centre-section leading-edge, one under each main wing fence) for more than 3,175 kg (7,000 lb) of bombs, including nuclear weapons, rocket pods, 23 mm gun pods and guided missiles such as the air-to-surface AS-7 (NATO 'Kerry'), AS-9 ('Kyle') and AS-10 ('Karen').

DIMENSIONS, EXTERNAL:

Wing span: fully spread	13.80 m (45 ft 3 in)
fully swept	10.00 m (32 ft 10 in)
Wing aspect ratio: fully spread	4.8
fully swept	2.7
Length overall, incl probes	18.75 m (61 ft 6¼ in)
Fuselage length	15.40 m (50 ft 6¼ in)
Height overall	5.00 m (16 ft 5 in)

AREAS (estimated):

Wings, gross: fully spread	40.0 m² (430.0 sq ft)
fully swept	37.0 m² (398.0 sq ft)

WEIGHTS (Su-17M-4):

Max external stores	4,250 kg (9,370 lb)
Normal T-O weight	16,400 kg (36,155 lb)
Max T-O weight	19,500 kg (42,990 lb)

PERFORMANCE (Su-17M-4):

Max level speed: at height	Mach 2.09
at S/L	Mach 1.14
	755 knots (1,400 km/h; 870 mph)
Service ceiling	15,200 m (49,865 ft)
T-O run	900 m (2,955 ft)
Landing run	950 m (3,120 ft)
Range with max fuel:	
at high altitude	1,240 nm (2,300 km; 1,430 miles)
at low altitude	755 nm (1,400 km; 870 miles)

SUKHOI Su-24
NATO reporting name: Fencer

Design of this variable geometry attack aircraft was started in 1965 by Yevgeniy A. Ivanov, who had succeeded Pavel Sukhoi as director of the Sukhoi OKB. An early prototype, known as the T-60 and illustrated in the 1989-90 *Jane's*, had delta wings with downswept tips. The T-61 was similar, but with four auxiliary booster motors mounted vertically in the fuselage for improved take-off performance. The prototype of the variable geometry version chosen for series production, designated T-62, flew for the first time in 1969-70. Early production aircraft had the official designation Su-19. By 1981, when deliveries had reached the rate of 60-70 a year, this had been changed to Su-24 for improved versions.

In early 1990, more than 500 were assigned to strategic missions in four of the five Soviet continental TVDs

Sukhoi Su-24 ('Fencer-C') two-seat attack aircraft *(Swedish Air Force)*

(theatres of military operations). By consolidating all USSR-based Su-24s into VGK (Supreme High Command) subordinate air armies in this way, their responsiveness and ability to meet theatre demands are both enhanced. The strike components of the Legnica and Vinnitsa air armies consist almost exclusively of Su-24s. About 300 other Su-24s equip tactical deep-interdiction units of the air forces of military districts and groups of forces, and at least one squadron serves with the Baltic Fleet air force for maritime reconnaissance. In addition, 15 have been supplied to Libya, and 12 have been ordered by Syria.

The ability of the Su-24 to deliver a wide range of air-to-surface missiles provides defence suppression and some hard-target kill potential. A specially developed long-range navigation system and electro-optical weapons systems enable it to penetrate hostile airspace at night or in poor weather with great precision and then deliver ordnance within 55 m (180 ft) of the target. An already-impressive combat radius was increased in the 1980s by the addition of an in-flight refuelling probe, and provision for carrying buddy refuelling tanks – a move which necessitated development of a similar probe for the Su-27s that escort Su-24s on combat missions.

Five versions can be identified by NATO reporting names:

Fencer-A. Identifiable by rectangular rear fuselage box enclosing jet nozzles.

Fencer-B. Rear fuselage box around jet nozzles has deeply dished bottom skin between nozzles. Larger brake-chute housing.

Fencer-C. Introduced in 1981. Important equipment changes. Multiple fitting on nose instead of former simple

probe. Triangular fairing forward of each fixed wingroot, on side of air intake (presumably housing ECM equipment of the kind seen on the fuselage sides, forward of the nosewheel doors, of ground attack MiG-23/27 'Floggers') and also on each side of fin, near tip.

Fencer-D. Introduced in 1983, with added probe-and-drogue flight refuelling capability. Slightly longer nose (approx 0.75 m; 2 ft 6 in) forward of windscreen; chord of lower part of tail fin extended, giving kinked leading-edge; large overwing fences integral with extended wingroot glove pylons, probably for AS-14 (NATO 'Kedge') missiles in class of US Maverick; undernose aerials deleted; blister, probably for electro-optical sensor, added aft of nosewheel bay; and single long noseprobe. Soviet designation **Su-24MK**.

Fencer-E. About 65 of these maritime reconnaissance variants of 'Fencer-D', retaining the ability to carry air-to-surface missiles, are operational with tactical air force and naval units. Deliveries to the Baltic Fleet, to replace Tu-16s, began in Summer 1985.

In addition, an electronic jamming/sigint/reconnaissance version, to replace the 'Brewer-E' model of the Yak-28, was undergoing systems development in 1988.

The following details apply specifically to 'Fencer-C' but are generally applicable to all versions:

TYPE: Two-seat variable geometry attack aircraft.

WINGS: Cantilever shoulder-wing monoplane, each wing comprising a triangular fixed glove box and three-position pivoted outer panel of all-metal construction. Slight anhedral from roots. Leading-edge sweepback on outer panels estimated at 16° fully forward, and 68° fully swept, with an intermediate sweep angle of 45°. Full span leading-edge slats; aileron and two-section double-slotted trailing-edge flaps on each outer panel. Differential spoilers forward of flaps for roll control at low speeds and for use as lift dumpers on landing.

FUSELAGE: Conventional all-metal semi-monocoque structure of slab-sided rectangular section, with integral engine air intake trunks. Splitter plate and outer lip of each intake are inclined slightly downward. Variable intake ramps. Airbrake under each side of centre-fuselage, curved to follow shape of underbelly fairing.

TAIL UNIT: Cantilever all-metal structure, comprising single fin with 30° sweptback inset rudder, and all-moving 50° sweptback horizontal surfaces which operate together for pitch control and differentially for roll control, assisted by use of the wing spoilers when the wings are not fully swept. Two slightly splayed ventral fins, one each side of fuselage undersurface.

LANDING GEAR: Retractable tricycle type, with twin wheels on each unit. Main units retract forward and inward into air intake duct fairings; nose unit retracts rearward. Trailing link type of shock absorbers in main units and low pressure tyres for operation from semi-prepared fields. Mudguard on nosewheels.

POWER PLANT: Two Lyulka AL-21F-3A turbojets, each rated at 110 kN (24,700 lb st) with afterburning. Internal fuel capacity, estimated at 13,000 litres (3,434 US gallons; 2,860 Imp gallons), can be supplemented by four 1,250 litre (330 US gallon; 275 Imp gallon) external tanks on wing and glove pylons.

ACCOMMODATION: Crew of two (pilot and weapon systems officer) side by side in ejection capsule. Cockpit width 1.65 m (5 ft 5 in). Jettisonable canopy, hinged to open upward and rearward.

AVIONICS: Latest photographs show a small avionics pod at top of engine air intake duct on each side, immediately aft of lip, and on each side of fin. These pods appear similar to those immediately forward of the nosewheel bay of ground attack versions of the MiG-23/27.

ARMAMENT: Eight pylons under fuselage, each wingroot glove and outer wings for guided and unguided air-to-surface weapons, including nuclear weapons, missiles such as AS-7 (NATO 'Kerry'), AS-10 ('Karen'), AS-11 ('Kilter'), AS-12 ('Kegler'), AS-13 ('Kingbolt') and AS-14 ('Kedge'), rockets of 57 mm to 370 mm calibre, bombs (typically 36 × 100 kg FAB-100), 23 mm gun pods or external fuel tanks. Two pivoting underwing pylons were the first of their kind observed on a Soviet aircraft. No internal weapons bay. One six-barrel 30 mm Gatling type gun inside fairing on starboard side of fuselage undersurface. Unidentified fairing on other side.

Sukhoi Su-24 ('Fencer-D') with wings fully spread and landing gear extended *(US Department of Defense)*

Sukhoi Su-24 ('Fencer-D') variable geometry attack aircraft *(Jane's/Mike Keep)*

DIMENSIONS, EXTERNAL:

Wing span: spread	17.63 m (57 ft 10 in)
swept	10.36 m (34 ft 0 in)
Length overall, incl probe	24.53 m (80 ft 5¾ in)
Height overall	4.97 m (16 ft 3¾ in)
Wheel track	3.70 m (12 ft 1½ in)

AREA:

Wings, gross	42.00 m² (452 sq ft)

WEIGHTS (Su-24MK):

Weight empty, equipped	19,000 kg (41,885 lb)
Max external stores	8,000 kg (17,635 lb)
Normal T-O weight	36,000 kg (79,365 lb)
Max T-O weight	39,700 kg (87,520 lb)

PERFORMANCE (Su-24MK):

Max speed, clean: at height	Mach 2.18
at S/L	Mach 1.15
Service ceiling	17,500 m (57,400 ft)
T-O run	1,300 m (4,265 ft)
Landing run	950 m (3,120 ft)
Combat radius:	
lo-lo-lo	over 174 nm (322 km; 200 miles)
lo-lo-hi with 2,500 kg (5,500 lb) of weapons	515 nm (950 km; 590 miles)
hi-lo-hi, with 3,000 kg (6,615 lb) of weapons and two external tanks	565 nm (1,050 km; 650 miles)

Two-seat Su-25UB ('Frogfoot-B') in service with the Czechoslovak Air Force
(Letectvi + Kosmonautika/Václav Jukl)

SUKHOI Su-25 and Su-28
NATO reporting name: Frogfoot

When first observed by satellite at Ramenskoye flight test centre in 1977, this Soviet counterpart to the US Air Force's A-10 Thunderbolt II single-seat attack aircraft was given the provisional US designation Ram-J. The prototype, powered by two 25.5 kN (5,732 lb st) non-afterburning versions of the Tumansky RD-9 turbojet, had been flown for the first time on 22 February 1975 by Vladimir Ilyushin. Production began in 1978, with more powerful Tumansky R-95 engines (each 39.2 kN; 8,818 lb st). The NATO reporting name 'Frogfoot' was released in 1982, after a trials unit, followed by a single squadron of 12 aircraft, had been sent to Afghanistan to support Soviet ground forces fighting in mountain terrain, and the Su-25 attained full operational capability in 1984. The emphasis during operational use in Afghanistan is said to have been on techniques for co-ordinating low level close support by fixed-wing aircraft and Mi-24 helicopter gunships. More than 300 Su-25s, the latest examples with upgraded R-195 turbojets, have been delivered from the Tbilisi airframe plant, to Soviet tactical units and the air forces of Afghanistan, Bulgaria, Czechoslovakia, Hungary and Iraq. Of these, 23 were lost by Soviet air force units in Afghanistan. A maritime version is expected to serve on the *Tbilisi* and other large Soviet Navy carriers.

Mr Vladimir P. Babak, chief designer responsible for the Su-25, gave details of the aircraft's design philosophy and characteristics during the 1989 Paris Air Show. The major requirement of survivability led to features which account for 7.5 per cent of the normal T-O weight. As well as the all-welded cockpit of titanium armour, the Su-25 has pushrods rather than cables to actuate its control surfaces, duplicated in the case of the elevators. Main load-bearing members are damage-resistant. The engines are widely separated in stainless steel bays, and the fuel tanks are filled with reticulated foam for fire protection. Numerous IRCM flare dispensers are calculated to protect the aircraft during eight attack runs.

Serviceability is enhanced by a maintenance system that can be packaged into four pods for carriage on the Su-25's weapon pylons. These take care of everything from onboard systems checks to environmental protection, ground electrical power supply for engine starting and other purposes, and pressure refuelling from all likely sources of supply in a front-line area.

Sukhoi Su-25 ('Frogfoot-A') in lightly armed training configuration *(US Department of Defense)*

Versions of the Su-25 identified to date are as follows:

Su-25K (Frogfoot-A). Basic single-seat close support version to which detailed description applies. Accuracy of laser guidance system is claimed to place bombs within 5 m (16 ft) of a target over a stand-off range of 10.7 nm (20 km; 12.5 miles). Current plans envisage an increase of max weapons load to 6,400 kg (14,100 lb).

Su-25UB (Frogfoot-B). Tandem two-seat operational conversion and weapons training version of which photographs first became available in Spring 1989. Rear seat considerably higher than front seat, giving marked hump-back appearance. Separate hinged portion of continuous framed canopy over each cockpit. Taller tail fin, increasing overall height to 5.20 m (17 ft 0¾ in). New 'shark's fin' IFF antenna forward of windscreen instead of 'Odd Rods'. Weapon pylons and gun retained. With

arrester hook beneath rear fuselage has been used for deck landing training on dummy flight deck marked out on runway at Saki naval airfield, and on deck of carrier *Tbilisi*. In service with Soviet and Czechoslovak Air Forces.

Su-25UT (Frogfoot-B). Generally similar to Su-25UB but without arrester hook. Prototype only, but under consideration as advanced trainer for Soviet air forces and DOSAAF. First flown on 6 August 1985.

Su-28. Export model of 'Frogfoot-B'. Length overall 15.36 m (50 ft 4¾ in).

TYPE: Single-seat close support aircraft.

WINGS: Cantilever shoulder-wing monoplane. Anhedral from roots. Approx 20° sweepback. Three-spar structure. Entire trailing-edge occupied by hydraulically actuated ailerons, with manual backup, and double-slotted two-section flaps. Multiple tabs in each aileron. Full span leading-edge slats in two segments on each wing. Extended chord leading-edge 'dogtooth' on outer 50 per cent of each wing. Pods at wingtips each split at rear to form airbrakes which project above and below wing when extended, like those of Grumman A-6 Intruder. Retractable landing light in base of each pod, aft of dielectric nosecap for ECM. Small landing light glareshield under each pod.

FUSELAGE: Conventional all-metal semi-monocoque structure, with 24 mm (0.94 in) welded titanium armoured cockpit. Pitot on port side of nose; transducer to provide data for fire control computer on starboard side.

TAIL UNIT: Conventional cantilever all-metal structure. Variable incidence tailplane, with slight dihedral. Manually operated elevators and two-section inset rudder. Upper rudder section operated through sensor vanes and transducers on starboard nose pitot and automatic electro-mechanical yaw damping system. Tabs in lower rudder segment and each elevator.

LANDING GEAR: Hydraulically retractable tricycle type. Mainwheels retract to lie horizontally in bottom of engine air intake trunks. Single wheel with low-pressure tyre on each levered suspension unit. Oleo-pneumatic shock absorber on each unit. Mudguard on forward retracting steerable nosewheel. Mainwheel tyres size 840 × 360; nosewheel tyre size 660 × 200. Brakes on mainwheels. Twin cruciform brake-chutes housed in tailcone.

Sukhoi Su-28 (Su-25UB), with added side elevation (centre right) of Su-25K *(Pilot Press)*

POWER PLANT: Two non-afterburning Tumansky R-195 turbojets in long nacelles at wingroots, each rated at 44.18 kN (9,921 lb st). Engines can operate on any fuel likely to be found in a combat area, including MT petrol and diesel oil. Fuel tanks in fuselage between cockpit and wing front spar, and between rear spar and fin leading-edge, and in wing centre-section. Provision for external fuel tank on each inboard underwing pylon.

ACCOMMODATION: Single K-36D zero/zero ejection seat under sideways hinged (to starboard) canopy, with small rearview mirror on top. Flat bulletproof windscreen. Folding ladder for access to cockpit built into port side of fuselage.

SYSTEM: 28V DC electrical system, supplied by two engine-driven generators.

AVIONICS: SRO-2 (NATO 'Odd Rods') IFF antennae forward of windscreen and under tail. Sirena-3 radar warning system antenna above fuselage tailcone.

ARMAMENT AND OPERATIONAL EQUIPMENT: One twin-barrel 30 mm gun with rate of fire of 3,000 rds/min in bottom of front fuselage on port side, with 250 rds (sufficient for a one second burst during each of five attacks). Eight large pylons under wings for 4,400 kg (9,700 lb) of air-to-ground weapons, including 57 mm to 370 mm rockets, laser guided rocket-boosted 350 kg, 490 kg and 670 kg bombs, 500 kg incendiary, anti-personnel and chemical cluster bombs, and pods each containing a 23 mm GSh-23 gun with twin barrels that can pivot downward for attacking ground targets, and 260 rds. Two small outboard pylons for AA-2D 'Atoll' or AA-8 'Aphid' air-to-air self-defence missiles. Laser rangefinder and target designator under flat sloping window in nose. Chaff/flare dispensers (total of 256 flares) carried above root of tailplane and above rear of engine ducts. Strike camera in top of nosecone.

DIMENSIONS, EXTERNAL (Su-25K):

Wing span	14.36 m (47 ft 1½ in)
Length overall	15.53 m (50 ft 11½ in)
Height	4.80 m (15 ft 9 in)

AREA:

Wings, gross	33.7 m² (362.75 sq ft)

WEIGHTS:

Weight empty	9,500 kg (20,950 lb)
Max T-O weight	14,600-17,600 kg (32,187-38,800 lb)

PERFORMANCE:

Max level speed at S/L	Mach 0.8
	(526 knots; 975 km/h; 606 mph)
Max attack speed, airbrakes open	
	372 knots (690 km/h; 428 mph)
Landing speed (typical)	108 knots (200 km/h; 124 mph)
Service ceiling	7,000 m (22,965 ft)
T-O run: typical	600 m (1,970 ft)
with max weapon load from unpaved surface	
	under 1,200 m (3,935 ft)
Landing run: normal	600 m (1,970 ft)
with brake-chutes	400 m (1,312 ft)

Range with 4,400 kg (9,700 lb) weapon load and two external tanks:

at S/L	405 nm (750 km; 466 miles)
at height	675 nm (1,250 km; 776 miles)
g limits: with 1,500 kg (3,306 lb) of weapons	+6.5
with 4,400 kg (9,700 lb) of weapons	+5.2

SUKHOI Su-26M

Among Soviet aircraft that participated in the World Aerobatic Championships in Hungary, in August 1984, were two examples of the hitherto unknown Sukhoi Su-26, which had flown for the first time in June of that year. Brief details of this initial version can be found in the 1985-86 *Jane's*. The three examples that gained both the men's and women's team prizes at the 1986 World Aerobatic Championships in the UK (c/n 06, 07 and 08) were modified Su-26Ms, identified by a sharp-cornered (rather than rounded) rudder and reduced fuselage side glazing. The following description applies to the current production Su-26M:

TYPE: Single-seat aerobatic competition aircraft.

Sukhoi Su-25K ('Frogfoot-A') combat aircraft of the Czechoslovak Air Force
(Letectvi + Kosmonautika/Václav Jukl)

WINGS: Cantilever mid-wing monoplane of tapered planform. Specially developed symmetrical wing section, variable along span; slightly concave in region of ailerons to increase their effectiveness; leading-edge somewhat sharper than usual to make aircraft more responsive to control surface movement. Thickness/chord ratio 18 per cent at root, 12 per cent at tip. No dihedral, incidence or sweep at quarter-chord. One-piece two-spar all-composites structure, without ribs, covered with three-lamination glassfibre/epoxy (GFRP). Foam filled front box spar with carbonfibre reinforced plastics (CFRP) booms and wound glassfibre webs. Channel section rear spar of CFRP. Outer 67 per cent of each wing trailing-edge formed by plain aileron with CFRP box spar, GFRP skin and foam filling. Each aileron, actuated by pushrods, has ground adjustable tab on trailing-edge and two suspended triangular balance tabs. No flaps.

FUSELAGE: Oval-section, with basic welded truss structure of VNS-2 high strength stainless steel tubing. Lower nose section of truss removable to facilitate detachment of wings. Three-lamination GFRP skin panels, with duralumin reinforcement, are all quickly removable for access to interior. Light alloy engine cowlings.

TAIL UNIT: Conventional cantilever fin and tailplane of similar construction to wings. Horn balanced rudder and elevators of similar construction to ailerons and each with ground adjustable tab. Elevators actuated by pushrods, rudder by cable.

LANDING GEAR: Non-retractable tailwheel type. Arched cantilever mainwheel legs of titanium alloy. Mainwheels size 350 × 135 mm, with hydraulic disc brakes. Steerable tailwheel, on titanium spring, connected to rudder.

POWER PLANT: One 268 kW (360 hp) Vedeneyev M-14P nine-cylinder radial engine, driving a three-blade Gerd Mühlbauer variable-pitch metal propeller. Optional V-530TA-D35 two-blade variable-pitch propeller. Steel tube engine mounting. Fuel tank in fuselage forward of front spar; capacity 60 litres (16 US gallons; 13 Imp gallons). External tank, capacity 140 litres (37 US gallons; 31 Imp gallons), can be added for ferry flights. Oil capacity 22.6 litres (6 US gallons; 5 Imp gallons). Fuel and oil systems adapted for inverted flight.

ACCOMMODATION: One-piece pilot's seat of GFRP, inclined at 45° and designed for use with PLP-60 back-pack parachute. Rearward hinged jettisonable canopy. Safety harness anchored to fuselage structure.

SYSTEM: Electrical system of 24/28V, with 3kW generator, batteries and external supply socket.

AVIONICS: Briz VHF radio.

DIMENSIONS, EXTERNAL:

Wing span	7.80 m (25 ft 7 in)
Wing chord: at root	1.95 m (6 ft 4¾ in)
at tip	1.10 m (3 ft 7¼ in)
Wing aspect ratio	5.6
Length overall	6.83 m (22 ft 4¾ in)
Height overall	2.20 m (7 ft 2¾ in)
Tailplane span	2.95 m (9 ft 8¼ in)
Wheel track	2.20 m (7 ft 2½ in)
Wheelbase	5.05 m (16 ft 6¾ in)
Propeller diameter	2.40 m (7 ft 10½ in)

AREAS:

Wings, gross	11.90 m² (128.0 sq ft)
Ailerons (total)	1.18 m² (12.70 sq ft)
Fin	0.34 m² (3.66 sq ft)
Rudder	0.89 m² (9.58 sq ft)
Tailplane	1.10 m² (11.84 sq ft)
Elevators (total)	1.53 m² (16.47 sq ft)

WEIGHTS:

Normal competition T-O weight	720 kg (1,587 lb)
Max T-O weight	800 kg (1,764 lb)

PERFORMANCE:

Never-exceed speed	243 knots (450 km/h; 280 mph)
Max level speed	189 knots (350 km/h; 217 mph)
Normal cruising speed	140 knots (260 km/h; 161 mph)
T-O speed	65 knots (120 km/h; 75 mph)
Landing speed	62 knots (115 km/h; 72 mph)
Stalling speed	60 knots (110 km/h; 69 mph)
Max rate of climb at S/L	1,080 m (3,540 ft)/min
Service ceiling	4,000 m (13,125 ft)
Rate of roll	more than 360°/s
T-O run	250 m (820 ft)
Landing run	350 m (1,150 ft)
Ferry range at 1,000 m (3,280 ft)	
	432 nm (800 km; 497 miles)
g limits	+12/-10

SUKHOI Su-27
NATO reporting name: Flanker

The Su-27 was developed specifically for all-weather air-to-air combat, under the project designation T-10, and this remains its sole operational role. It is inherently unstable and is controlled by a four-channel analog fly by wire flight control system with no mechanical backup. Development was not easy, and two pilots lost their lives before major airframe redesign resulted in the production configuration. Manufacture is centred in a plant at Komsomolsk, Khabarovsk Territory. More than 100 were in service with the Soviet strategic air defence forces in early 1990, including units based in the Kola Peninsula and in the Far East of the USSR, as replacements for older types such as the Yak-28P, Su-15 and Tu-28P/128. Operating in conjunction with the AEW&C 'Mainstay', they have been particularly active in simulated interceptions of NATO aircraft over the Barents Sea. All fighter components of the Legnica and Vinnitsa air armies are re-equipping with Su-27s, which have sufficient range to escort Su-24 'Fencer' deep-penetration strike missions against the UK and western Europe. Lookdown/shootdown weapon systems and beyond-visual-range air-to-air missiles provide formidable potential against low-flying aircraft and cruise missiles.

Versions identified to date by NATO reporting names are as follows:

Flanker-A. Prototypes, the first of which was flown on 20 May 1977 by Major Vladimir Ilyushin, then Sukhoi's chief test pilot. Curved wingtips, rearward retracting nosewheel, and tail fins mounted centrally above the engine housings (see illustrations in 1985-86 *Jane's*).

Flanker-B. Single-seat land-based production version, with square wingtips carrying launchers for air-to-air missiles, tail fins located outboard of engine housings, extended tailcone, forward retracting nosewheel and other

Sukhoi Su-26M aerobatic competition aircraft *(Brian M. Service)*

Two views of Su-27 'Flanker-B variant 2' approaching to land on carrier *Tbilisi*

changes. First flown 20 April 1981. Standard equipment in Soviet air forces. Deliveries to the air force of Afghanistan were reported to be imminent in Spring 1990.

Flanker-B variant 2. Version for ramp-assisted operation from Soviet Navy carriers, first mentioned by Rear Adm William O. Studeman, USN, in Spring 1988. Basically similar to land-based 'Flanker-B' but with movable foreplanes, first tested on experimental Su-27 designated Model 1024. Folding outer wing panels, strengthened landing gear with twin-wheel nose unit, added arrester hook, flight refuelling capability. Long tailcone of land-based version deleted, to prevent tailscrapes during take-off and landing. Able to carry buddy flight refuelling pod on centreline pylon. Carrier approach speed 130 knots (240 km/h; 150 mph).

Flanker-C (Su-27UB). Tandem two-seat trainer version of 'Flanker-B', with full combat capability. Taller fin, increasing overall height to 6.357 m (20 ft 10¼ in).

No composites, but many titanium components, are used in the currently operational airframe; new versions of the Su-27, now under development, will embody composites. Similarly, the present 1970s style cockpit instrumentation and conventional control column are being superseded by four CRTs and side-stick controller. Evaluation of vectoring nozzles has been completed on the experimental foreplane-equipped Model 1024. Sukhoi's General Designer, Mr Mikhail Simonov, confirmed at the 1989 Paris Air Show that trials had been conducted with a retractable flight refuelling probe fitted forward of the cockpit on the port side of two aircraft, one of them a two-seater, with which an endurance of up to 16 hours was demonstrated. One of the aircraft flew non-stop some 7,550 nm (14,000 km; 8,700 miles) from Moscow to the Pacific coast of the USSR and back. Compatibility was proved with an Il-78 tanker and an Su-24 fitted with a buddy refuelling pack.

Model 1024 experimental version of Su-27 with foreplanes *(Piotr Butowski)*

A specially prepared Su-27, known as the P-42, held four time-to-height records in early 1990, including a climb to 12,000 m (39,370 ft) in 55.542 seconds.

The following details apply to the standard 'Flanker-B':

TYPE: Single-seat all-weather counter-air fighter.

WINGS: Cantilever mid-wing monoplane. Basic wing sweepback 42° on leading-edge, with long and smoothly curved leading-edge root extensions. Anhedral approx 2° 30′. Comparatively conventional all-metal two-spar structure. No ailerons. Full-span leading-edge flaps and plain half-span inboard flaperons are controlled manually for take-off and landing, computer controlled in flight.

FUSELAGE: Semi-monocoque all-metal structure of basically circular section, sloping down sharply aft of canopy. Cockpit high-set behind drooped nose. Large ogival dielectric nosecone. Long rectangular blast panel forward of gun on starboard side, above wingroot extension. Large forward hinged door type airbrake in top of centre-fuselage.

TAIL UNIT: Cantilever structure, comprising uncanted twin fins and rudders, mounted on narrow decks outboard of engine housings, and one-piece differential/collective tailerons, all sharply sweptback. Tailerons operate in conjunction with flaperons and rudders for pitch and roll control. The flight control system limits g loading to +9 and normally limits angle of attack to 30-35°. However, the angle of attack limiter can be overruled manually for certain flight manoeuvres. Fins have extensions beneath decks to form parallel but widely separated ventral fins.

LANDING GEAR: Retractable tricycle type, with single wheel on each unit. Mainwheels retract forward into wingroots. Nosewheel, with mudguard, also retracts forward. Mainwheel tyres size 1030 × 350, pressure 12.25-15.7 bars (178-227 lb/sq in); nosewheel tyre size 680 × 260, pressure 9.3 bars (135 lb/sq in). Brake-chute housed in fuselage tailcone.

POWER PLANT: Two Lyulka AL-31F turbofans, each rated at 123.85 kN (27,557 lb st) with afterburning. Large auxiliary air intake louvres in bottom of each three-ramp engine duct near primary wedge intake. Two rows of small vertical louvres in each side wall of wedge, and others in top face. Fine-grille screen hinges up from bottom of each duct to shield engine from foreign object ingestion during take-off and landing.

ACCOMMODATION: Pilot only, on K-36MD zero/zero ejection seat, under large rearward opening transparent blister canopy, with low sill. Helmet mounted target designation system.

AVIONICS AND EQUIPMENT: Track-while-scan coherent pulse Doppler radar (antenna diameter approx 1.0 m; 3 ft 4 in) with reported search range of 130 nm (240 km; 150 miles) and tracking range of 100 nm (185 km; 115 miles). Infra-red search/track (IRST) sensor in transparent housing forward of windscreen. Sirena-3 (or later) 360° radar warning receivers, outboard of each bottom air intake lip and at tail. Integrated fire control system enables the radar, IRST and laser rangefinder to be slaved to the pilot's helmet mounted target designator and displayed on the wide-angle HUD.

ARMAMENT: One 30 mm gun in starboard wingroot extension, with 149 rds. Up to ten air-to-air missiles, on tandem pylons under fuselage between engine ducts,

Sukhoi Su-27UB 'Flanker-C' two-seat combat trainer *(Brian M. Service)*

Sukhoi Su-27, with added side elevation (bottom) of two-seat Su-27UB *(Pilot Press)*

beneath each duct, under each centre-wing and outer-wing, and at each wingtip. Aircraft illustrated at top right has two short-burn semi-active radar homing AA-10A missiles (NATO 'Alamo-A') in tandem under fuselage; two short-burn infra-red homing AA-10B ('Alamo-B') missiles on the centre-wing pylons; and a long-burn semi-active radar homing AA-10C ('Alamo-C') beneath each engine duct. The four outer pylons are unoccupied, but are able to carry either AA-11 ('Archer') or AA-8 ('Aphid') close-range infra-red missiles. AA-9 ('Amos') missiles optional in place of AA-10s. Chaff/flare dispensers at top of fuselage between engine nacelles.

DIMENSIONS, EXTERNAL ('Flanker-B'):

Wing span	14.70 m (48 ft 2¾ in)
Length overall, excl nose probe	21.935 m (71 ft 11½ in)
Height overall	5.932 m (19 ft 5½ in)
Fuselage: Max width	1.50 m (4 ft 11 in)
Tailplane span	9.90 m (32 ft 6 in)
Distance between fin tips	4.30 m (14 ft 1¼ in)
Wheel track	4.33 m (14 ft 2½ in)
Wheelbase	5.88 m (19 ft 3½ in)

WEIGHTS (B, 'Flanker-B'; C, 'Flanker-C'):

Max T-O weight: B	22,000-30,000 kg (48,500-66,135 lb)
C	22,500 kg (49,600 lb)

PERFORMANCE:

Max level speed:	
at height: B, C	Mach 2.35
	(1,345 knots; 2,500 km/h; 1,550 mph)
at S/L: B, C	Mach 1.1
	(725 knots; 1,345 km/h; 835 mph)
Service ceiling: B, C	18,000 m (59,055 ft)
T-O run: B	500 m (1,640 ft)
C	550 m (1,805 ft)
Landing run: B	600 m (1,970 ft)
C	650 m (2,135 ft)
Combat radius: B	810 nm (1,500 km; 930 miles)
Range with max fuel:	
B	over 2,160 nm (4,000 km; 2,485 miles)
C	1,620 nm (3,000 km; 1,865 miles)
g limit (operational): B, C	+9

SUKHOI S-21

This 8/10-seat supersonic business aircraft is the subject of a joint feasibility study by Sukhoi and Gulfstream Aerospace of the USA. Further details can be found in the International section of this edition.

SUKHOI S-51

In early 1990 the Sukhoi OKB was at the initial design stage of a 50/65-seat supersonic transport designated S-51, the initial letter of this designation referring to General Designer Mikhail Simonov. The airframe has been described as a scaled-up version of the S-21. Its variable-cycle power plant, in which Rolls-Royce of the UK is involved, is intended to make possible a range of 5,000 nm (9,265 km; 5,755 miles) at Mach 2 at a height of 18,000 m (59,000 ft).

SUKHOI S-80

First new civilian aircraft of Sukhoi design to be completed, under the Soviet industry's konversiya programme, is likely to be this multi-role STOL transport, of which models were first exhibited at the 1989 Paris Air Show. The prototype is scheduled to fly in 1992. Available details follow:

TYPE: Twin-turboprop multi-purpose STOL transport.

WINGS: Cantilever high-wing configuration, with tandem wings. The larger rear wing has anhedral on the outer panels, and winglets.

FUSELAGE: Pod type fuselage, suspended from both wings.

TAIL UNIT: Twin sweptback fins and rudders carried on two tailbooms that extend rearward from the engine nacelles and connect both wings. T tailplane bridges tips of tail fins.

LANDING GEAR: Retractable tricycle type, with single wheel on each unit. Mainwheels retract into sponsons, on each side of the cabin at the rear. Nosewheel retracts forward.

POWER PLANT: Two turboprops of approx 820 kW (1,100 shp), each driving a five-blade constant-speed propeller.

ACCOMMODATION: Two seats on flight deck. According to role, main cabin can have seats for 21 passengers or be equipped for air ambulance, freight transport or special civilian and military tasks including air photography. Door at centre of cabin, on port side. Rear loading doors and ramp.

DIMENSION:

Span of rear wing	15.80 m (51 ft 10 in)

WEIGHT:

Max T-O weight	6,300 kg (13,890 lb)

PERFORMANCE (estimated):

Max level speed	324 knots (600 km/h; 372 mph)
Nominal cruising speed	243 knots (450 km/h; 280 mph)
Service ceiling	10,000 m (32,800 ft)
T-O run	525 m (1,725 ft)
Landing run	985 m (3,235 ft)
Range with max fuel	1,940 nm (3,600 km; 2,237 miles)

Sukhoi Su-27 'Flanker-B' photographed from a P-3B of No. 333 Squadron, Royal Norwegian Air Force

Sukhoi Su-27UB 'Flanker-C' has taller fins to compensate for raised rear cockpit (Brian M. Service)

Model of Sukhoi S-80 in air ambulance form (John Fricker)

Provisional three-view of Sukhoi OKB's S-80 twin-turboprop utility transport (Pilot Press)

TUPOLEV

GENERAL DESIGNER IN CHARGE OF BUREAU:
  Dr Alexei Andreyevich Tupolev
DEPUTY CHIEF OF BUREAU: Andrei Kandolov
CHIEF DESIGNER, COMMERCIAL AIRCRAFT:
  Lev Aronovich Lanovski
CHIEF DESIGNERS:
  Dmitry S. Markov
  L. L. Selyakov

Andrei Tupolev, born in 1888, was a leading figure in the Central Aero-Hydrodynamic Institute (TsAGI) in Moscow from the time when it was founded, in 1929, until his death on 23 December 1972. Current chief designers of the bureau which bears his name include his son, Dr Alexei A. Tupolev.

TUPOLEV Tu-16
NATO reporting name: Badger

The prototype of the basic intermediate-range bomber version of this aircraft (NATO 'Badger-A'), which had the Tupolev design bureau designation Tu-88, was flown for the first time by N. Rybko in Winter 1951-52. It entered series production as the Tu-16 in 1953, and made its first major public appearance on 1 May 1954. About 2,000 Tu-16s were eventually delivered to the medium-range bomber force and to Soviet Naval Aviation, in various forms. An estimated 220 remain operational, mostly with the Smolensk and Irkutsk air armies, equipped to carry both nuclear and conventional weapons. Many of those replaced by Tu-26s have been modified to serve with the force of 20 Tu-16 in-flight refuelling tankers and 135 of various versions equipped for ECM duties and strategic reconnaissance in support of the attack units. Soviet Naval Aviation has about 100 attack models of 'Badger', plus 70 tankers and up to 80 reconnaissance and ECM models.

Current versions of the Tu-16 are known by the following NATO reporting names:

Badger-A (Tu-16A). Basic strategic jet bomber, able to carry nuclear or conventional free-fall weapons. Glazed nose, with small undernose radome. Defensive armament of seven 23 mm guns. Some equipped as flight refuelling tankers, using a unique wingtip-to-wingtip transfer technique to refuel other Tu-16s, or a probe-and-drogue system to refuel Tu-22s. Operational with Chinese Air Force and Navy; production continues in China under the designation Xian **H-6** (see Chinese section).

Badger-C (Tu-16K-10). Anti-shipping version, first seen at 1961 Soviet Aviation Day display. Mikoyan K-10 air-to-surface winged missile (NATO 'Kipper') carried in recess under fuselage (**Badger-C Mod** carries 'Kingfish' on underwing pylons). Wide nose radome (NATO 'Puff Ball'), in place of glazing and nose gun of 'Badger-A'. No provision for free-fall bombs. About 100 operational with Soviet Northern, Baltic, Black Sea and Pacific Fleets.

Badger-D (Tu-16R). Maritime/electronic reconnaissance version. Nose similar to that of 'Badger-C'. Larger undernose radome; three radomes in tandem under weapons bay.

Badger-E. Photographic and electronic reconnaissance version. Similar to 'Badger-A' but with cameras in bomb bay and two additional radomes under fuselage, larger one aft.

Badger-F (Tu-16R). Basically similar to 'Badger-E' but with electronic intelligence pod on a pylon under each wing. No radomes under centre-fuselage.

Badger-G. Converted from 'Badger-B'. Generally similar to 'Badger-A', but with underwing pylons for two rocket-powered air-to-surface missiles (NATO 'Kelt') which can be carried over a range greater than 1,735 nm (3,220 km; 2,000 miles). Free-fall bombing capability retained. Majority serve with anti-shipping squadrons of Soviet Naval Air Force. Some transferred to Iraq.

'Badger-J' ECM jamming version of Tu-16PP *(Swedish Air Force)*

Tupolev Tu-16R, in the form known to NATO as 'Badger-F', with additional side view (bottom) of Tu-16R 'Badger-D' *(Pilot Press)*

A Soviet Navy Tu-16, probably a 'Badger-G', has been illustrated with an ECM nose thimble of the kind seen beneath the in-flight refuelling probe of 'Bear-G'. It can be assumed that it also carries further pods like those of 'Bear-G' on its centre or rear fuselage.

Badger-G modified. Specially equipped to carry 'Kingfish' air-to-surface missile under each wing; first observed in mid-1981. Large radome, presumably associated with missile operation, under centre-fuselage, replacing chin radome. Device mounted externally on glazed nose might help to ensure correct attitude of Tu-16 during missile launch. Operational with Soviet Northern, Black Sea and Pacific Fleets.

Badger-H (Tu-16PP). Stand-off or escort ECM aircraft, with primary function of chaff dispensing to protect missile carrying strike force. The dispensers, with a total capacity of up to 9,075 kg (20,000 lb) of chaff, are located in the weapons bay area. Hatch aft of weapons bay. Two teardrop radomes, fore and aft of weapons bay. Two blade antennae aft of weapons bay. Glazed nose and chin radome.

Badger-J (Tu-16PP). Specialised ECM jamming/elint aircraft to protect strike force, with some equipment located in a canoe shape radome protruding from inside the weapons bay and surrounded by heat exchangers and exhaust ports. Anti-radar noise jammers operate in A to I bands inclusive. Glazed nose as 'Badger-A'. Some aircraft (as illustrated) have large flat-plate antennae at wingtips.

Badger-K (Tu-16R). Electronic reconnaissance variant, with nose as 'Badger-A'. Two teardrop radomes, inside and forward of weapons bay; four small pods on centreline in front of rear radome.

Maritime reconnaissance versions of 'Badger' make regular flights over units of the US Navy and other NATO naval forces at sea in the Atlantic, Pacific and elsewhere. They also make electronic intelligence (elint) sorties around the coastlines of NATO and other countries. Strike, tanker and ECM variants of 'Badger' have been deployed to a base at Cam Ranh Bay, the former US Navy base in Vietnam; but at least eight of them returned to the Soviet Union in December 1989 and do not appear to have been replaced.

TYPE: Twin-jet medium bomber and maritime reconnaissance/attack aircraft.

AS-6 'Kingfish' air-to-surface missile beneath wing pylon of Tu-16 'Badger-G modified' *(Piotr Butowski)*

Tupolev Tu-16R ('Badger-D') maritime/electronic reconnaissance aircraft *(Royal Navy)*

WINGS: Cantilever high mid-wing monoplane, with 3° anhedral, 1° incidence and with 35° of leading-edge sweep on outer panels; 41° sweep on inboard panels. PR-1-10S-9 wing section; thickness/chord ratio 15.7 per cent. Two-spar light alloy structure, with two fences on each wing. Entiree trailing-edge made up of slotted flaps (max deflection 35°) and mass balanced ailerons, each with trim tab. Heavy engine nacelles form root fairings. Versions equipped for in-flight refuelling have modified wingtips (see illustration of 'Badger-J').

FUSELAGE: All-metal semi-monocoque structure of oval cross-section, made in five sections. The nose section houses the navigator's pressure cabin with double-glazed nose panels in a magnesium alloy frame, the pilots' pressure cabin, the forward gunner's cabin, and radar equipment. The second and fourth sections house the aircraft's fuel tanks, with the weapon compartment between them; the tail section contains a pressure cabin for the radio operator and rear gunner. Skin panels made of 3 mm light alloy sheet.

TAIL UNIT: Cantilever all-metal structure, with 42° leading-edge sweepback on all surfaces. Tailplane incidence –1° 30′. Trim tabs in rudder and each elevator.

LANDING GEAR: Hydraulically retractable tricycle type. Twin-wheel nose unit retracts rearward. Main four-wheel bogies retract into housings projecting beyond the wing trailing-edge. Mainwheel tyre size 1100 × 330; nosewheel tyre size 900 × 275.

POWER PLANT: Early Tu-16s have two Mikulin AM-3A turbojets, each rated at 85.21 kN (19,155 lb st) at sea level. Later aircraft fitted with RD-3M-500 (AM-3M) turbojets, each rated at 93.05 kN (20,920 lb st). Engines semi-recessed into sides of fuselage. Divided air intake ducts: main duct passes through wing torque box between spars; secondary duct passes under wing to feed into primary airflow in front of engine. Engines separated from wings and fuselage by firewalls. Jetpipes inclined outward 3° to shield fuselage from effects of exhaust gases. Fuel in wing and fuselage tanks, with total capacity of approx 43,750 litres (11,558 US gallons; 9,624 Imp gallons). Provision for underwing auxiliary fuel tanks and for flight refuelling. Tu-16 tankers trail hose from starboard wingtip; receiving equipment is in port wingtip extension.

ACCOMMODATION: Normal crew of six, with two pilots side by side on flight deck. Navigator, on seat with armoured sides and base, in glazed nose of all versions except 'Badger-C and D'. Manned tail position plus lateral observation blisters in rear fuselage under tailplane. Entry via two hatches in bottom of fuselage, in front and rear structural sections.

AVIONICS AND EQUIPMENT: Radio and radar aids include R-807 and R-808 HF and RSIU-3M VHF R/T equipment, as well as IFF, an ARK-5 radio compass, radio altimeter and Sirena-2 radar warning receivers. Other equipment differs according to role.

ARMAMENT: Forward dorsal and rear ventral barbettes each containing two 23 mm NR-23 guns. Two similar guns in tail position controlled by an automatic gun ranging radar set. Seventh, fixed, gun on starboard side of nose of versions with nose glazing. Bomb load of up to 9,000 kg (19,800 lb) delivered from weapons bay 6.5 m (21 ft) long in standard bomber, under control of navigator. Naval versions can carry air-to-surface winged standoff missiles.

DIMENSIONS, EXTERNAL ('Badger-G'):

Wing span	32.99 m (108 ft 3 in)
Length overall	34.80 m (114 ft 2 in)
Height overall	10.36 m (34 ft 0 in)
Basic diameter of fuselage	2.50 m (8 ft 2½ in)
Tailplane span	11.75 m (38 ft 6½ in)
Wheel track	9.775 m (32 ft 0¾ in)
Wheelbase	10.91 m (35 ft 9½ in)

AREAS:

Wings, gross	164.65 m² (1,772.3 sq ft)
Ailerons (total)	14.77 m² (159.0 sq ft)
Flaps (total)	25.17 m² (270.9 sq ft)
Vertical tail surfaces	23.30 m² (250.8 sq ft)
Horizontal tail surfaces	34.45 m² (370.8 sq ft)

WEIGHTS ('Badger-G'):

Weight empty, equipped	37,200 kg (82,000 lb)
Normal T-O weight	75,000 kg (165,350 lb)

PERFORMANCE ('Badger-G', at max T-O weight):
Max level speed at 6,000 m (19,700 ft)
535 knots (992 km/h; 616 mph)
Service ceiling 12,300 m (40,350 ft)
Range with 3,790 kg (8,360 lb) bomb load
3,200 nm (5,925 km; 3,680 miles)
Max unrefuelled combat radius
1,700 nm (3,150 km; 1,955 miles)

TUPOLEV Tu-95 and Tu-142
NATO reporting name: Bear

Although the first prototype of Andrei Tupolev's large four-turboprop 'Bear' was flown in the Summer of 1954, most of the 160 'Bears' now flying with the Soviet air armies are of the upgraded 'Bear-G' or new-production 'Bear-H' missile-carrying versions. In its *Soviet Military Power* document, the US Department of Defense warned that 'Bear-H' and the new 'Blackjack' give the Soviet air forces the capability to attack the USA with hundreds of difficult-to-detect, hard-target-kill AS-15 'Kent' cruise missiles. Similarly, most of the 80 Soviet Naval Aviation 'Bears' are of the 'F' model, which differs so greatly from earlier versions that its designation was changed from **Tu-95** to **Tu-142**. High performance is not the only factor that has kept this aircraft in continuous production for 35 years, to balance attrition and introduce new versions. Equally important has been its ability to accommodate extensive avionics and the largest air-to-surface missiles and radars yet carried by combat aircraft.

'Bears' deployed regularly to staging bases in Cuba and Angola are capable of covering the North and South Atlantic from the Mediterranean approaches westward to the US east coast, and southward to the Cape of Good Hope. They are encountered off the US east coast during transits between Murmansk and Cuba, and during elint missions from Cuba. 'Bear-Hs' from Dolon air base in the central USSR carry out simulated attack and training missions against the USA and Canada. Other 'Bears', including missile armed 'Gs', have been reassigned to a theatre role, and conduct regular combat training exercises against naval and land targets in the northern Pacific region. Eight 'Bears' were stationed at Cam Ranh in

Vietnam; but five of them returned to the Soviet Union in December 1989 and do not appear to have been replaced.

Versions identified by NATO reporting names are as follows:

Bear-A (Tu-95). Basic Tu-95 strategic bomber, first shown in Aviation Day display at Tushino in July 1955. Internal stowage for two nuclear or a variety of conventional free-fall weapons. Fitted with chin radar, and defensive armament comprising three pairs of 23 mm cannon in remotely controlled rear dorsal and ventral barbettes and manned tail turret. Two glazed blisters on rear fuselage, under tailplane, are used for sighting by the gunner controlling all these weapons. The dorsal and ventral barbettes can also be controlled from a station aft of the flight deck. Max range with 11,340 kg (25,000 lb) bomb load is 8,000 nm (14,800 km; 9,200 miles). Few remain in service.

Bear-B (Tu-95K). First seen in 1961 Aviation Day flypast. Generally similar to 'Bear-A' but able to carry a large air-to-surface aeroplane type missile (NATO reporting name 'Kangaroo') under fuselage, with associated radar (NATO 'Crown Drum') in wide undernose radome, replacing the original glazing. Defensive armament retained. A few 'Bear-Bs' operate in maritime reconnaissance role, with flight refuelling nose-probe, an elint blister fairing on the starboard side of the rear fuselage, and a reconnaissance camera mounted to photograph obliquely downward through a port below and forward of this blister. Some carry a pointed canister under each wing, for air sampling.

Bear-C (Tu-95KM). Third Tu-95 strike version, able to carry 'Kangaroo'; first observed near NATO naval forces in September 1964. Generally similar to 'Bear-B' but with an elint blister fairing on *both* sides of rear fuselage, and a camera on each side. Refuelling probe standard. Has been observed with a faired tailcone housing special equipment, like that first seen on a 'Bear-D' and illustrated on a 'Bear-G'.

Bear-D. Identified in August 1967, this maritime reconnaissance version of the Tu-95 has a glazed nose, an undernose radar (NATO 'Short Horn'), a large underbelly radome for I band surface search radar (NATO 'Big Bulge'), an elint fairing on each side of the rear fuselage like 'Bear-C', a nose refuelling probe, and a variety of blisters and antennae, including a streamlined fairing on each tailplane tip. The housing for I band tail warning radar (NATO 'Box Tail') above the tail turret is much larger than on previous versions. Tasks include pinpointing of maritime targets for missile launch crews on board ships and aircraft which are themselves too distant to ensure precise missile aiming and guidance. 'Bear-D' carries no offensive

Top to bottom: Tu-95 'Bear-D', Tu-142 'Bear-F' Mod 1, Tu-142M 'Bear-F' Mod 4, Tu-95 'Bear-G'
(Pilot Press)

'Bear-J' version of Tupolev Tu-142, which maintains communications between Soviet national command authorities and the Soviet Navy's nuclear submarines, over long ranges. The ventral pod for the VLF trailing-wire antenna is under the centre-fuselage in the weapon bay area (*US Air Force*)

'Bear-G' has two large pylons under the wingroots on which to carry 'Kitchen' missiles (*UK Ministry of Defence*)

Deep flight deck glazing and new undernose antennae are features of the 'Bear-H' cruise missile carrier (*UK Ministry of Defence*)

weapons. About 15 operational, probably converted from 'Bear-As'.

A 'Bear-D' was the first version seen, in 1978, with the normal tail turret and associated radome replaced by a faired tailcone housing special equipment. A similar tail is fitted to 'Bear-G'.

Bear-E. Reconnaissance version of Tu-95, converted from 'Bear-A', with refuelling probe and rear fuselage elint fairings as on 'Bear-C'. Six camera windows in bomb bay, in pairs in line with the wing flaps, with a seventh window to the rear on the starboard side. Few only.

Bear-F (Tu-142). Anti-submarine aircraft. First of the Tu-142 series of extensively redesigned 'Bears', with more highly cambered wings, double-slotted flaps, longer fuselage forward of the wings and rudder of increased chord. Longer pressure cabin provides space for improved galley facilities and for a relief crew on long missions. Deployed initially by the Soviet Naval air force in 1970, since when several variants have been seen. Re-entered production in the mid-1980s. Originally, 'Bear-F' had enlarged and lengthened fairings aft of its inboard engine nacelles, and undernose radar. The main underfuselage J band radar housing is considerably farther forward than on 'Bear-D' and smaller in size; there are no large blister fairings under and on the sides of the rear fuselage; and the nosewheel doors are bulged prominently, suggesting the use of larger or low pressure tyres. 'Bear-F' has two stores bays for sonobuoys, torpedoes and nuclear depth charges in its rear

fuselage, one of them replacing the usual rear ventral gun turret and leaving the tail turret as the sole defensive gun position. The variants of 'Bear-F' are identified as follows:

Mod 1: As original 'Bear-F' but reverted to standard size nacelles. Chin mounted J band radar deleted. Fewer protrusions.

Mod 2 (Tu-142M): Fuselage nose lengthened by 23 cm (9 in) and roof of flight deck raised. Angle of refuelling probe lowered by 4°.

Mod 3: MAD boom added to fin tip. Fairings at tips of tailplane deleted. Rear stores bay lengthened and made less wide.

Mod 4: Chin radar reinstated. Self-protection ECM thimble radome on nose, plus other fairings. Observation blister on each side of rear fuselage deleted. Entered service with the air force of the Soviet Northern Fleet in 1985.

Most of approximately 65 'Bear-Fs' in Soviet service are to Mod 3 or Mod 4 standard.

In 1988-89, Indian Navy Squadron INAS 312 took delivery of eight 'Bear-Fs' for maritime reconnaissance from its base in Goa.

Bear-G (Tu-95). Generally similar to 'Bear-B/C' but reconfigured for elint missions and to carry two AS-4 ('Kitchen') supersonic air-to-surface missiles instead of one AS-3 ('Kangaroo'), on a large pylon under each wingroot. Features include a large new undernose radome (NATO 'Down Beat'), an ECM thimble under the in-flight refuelling probe, a streamlined ECM pod on each side at the

bottom of both the centre and rear fuselage, and a 'solid' tailcone, containing special equipment, similar in shape to that on some 'Bear-Ds'. Ventral gun turret provides sole defensive armament. More than 45 in service with the Irkutsk air army.

Bear-H (Tu-142K). Latest production version, based on the Tu-142 type airframe of 'Bear-F' but with a shorter fuselage, of the same length as 'Bear-B/C'. Equipped to carry up to 10 long-range cruise missiles, including the AS-15 (NATO 'Kent') and, probably, the AS-19 in the early 1990s. Aircraft observed up to mid-1988 had only an internal (rotary?) launcher for six of these ALCMs, but pylon mountings for two more can be attached under each wingroot. Built at Kuybyshev, 'Bear-H' achieved initial operational capability in 1984 and more than 70 had been built by Summer 1989. Features include a larger and deeper radome built into the nose and a small fin-tip fairing. There are no elint blister fairings on the sides of the rear fuselage and the ventral gun turret is deleted. Some aircraft have only a single twin-barrel gun, instead of the usual pair, in the tail turret.

Bear-J. Identified in 1986, this is the Soviet equivalent of the US Navy's E-6A and EC-130Q Tacamo aircraft, equipped with VLF communications avionics to maintain an on-station/all-ocean link between national command authorities and nuclear missile armed submarines under most operating conditions. Large ventral pod for VLF trailing-wire antenna under centre-fuselage in weapons bay

A 'Bear-F' Mod 3 seen over the Pacific in late 1988 shows the MAD sting on the fin and linear antenna above the fuselage adjacent to the wingroot. Soviet naval aviation has an air regiment of 'Bear-Fs' in the Pacific augmented by II-38 'Mays'.

The Tu-95 'Bear-G' is a reconfigured 'Bear-B or C' equipped to carry 'Kitchen' missiles *(UK Ministry of Defence)*

area. Undernose fairing as on 'Bear-F Mod 4'. Fin-tip pod with trailing-edge of the kind seen on some 'Bear-Hs'. Satcom dome aft of flight deck canopy. Operational in comparatively small numbers with the Soviet Northern and Pacific Fleets, it appears to use a modified Tu-142 'Bear-F' airframe.

The following structural description applies to the Tu-95 series:

TYPE: Four-turboprop long-range bomber and maritime reconnaissance aircraft.

WINGS: Cantilever mid-wing monoplane. Slight anhedral. Sweepback 37° at quarter-chord on inner panels, 35° at quarter-chord on outer panels. All-metal structure, with four spars in inboard panels, three spars outboard. All-metal three-segment hydraulically powered ailerons and two-segment area-increasing flaps on each wing. Trim tab in each inboard aileron segment. Spoilers in top surface of wing forward of inboard end of ailerons. Three boundary layer fences on top surface of each wing. Thermal anti-icing system in leading-edges.

FUSELAGE: All-metal semi-monocoque structure of circular section, containing three pressurised compartments. Those forward and aft of the weapons bay are linked by a crawlway tunnel. The tail gunner's compartment is not accessible from the other compartments.

TAIL UNIT: Cantilever all-metal structure, with sweepback on all surfaces. Adjustable tailplane incidence. Hydraulically powered rudder and elevators. Trim tabs in rudder and each elevator. Thermal anti-icing system in tailplane leading-edge.

LANDING GEAR: Hydraulically retractable tricycle type. Main units consist of four-wheel bogies, with tyres of approx 1.50 m (5 ft) diameter and hydraulic internal expanding brakes. Twin wheels on nose unit. All units retract rearward, main units into nacelles built on to wing trailing-edge. Retractable tail bumper consisting of two small wheels. Braking parachute may be used to reduce landing run.

POWER PLANT: Four Kuznetsov NK-12MV turboprops, each with max rating of 11,033 kW (14,795 ehp) and driving eight-blade contra-rotating reversible-pitch Type

The version of the Tupolev Tu-142 known to NATO as 'Bear-H' *(Pilot Press)*

AV-60N propellers. Fuel in wing tanks, with normal capacity of 95,000 litres (25,100 US gallons; 20,900 Imp gallons). Flight refuelling probe above nose of most current operational aircraft.

ACCOMMODATION AND ARMAMENT: See notes applicable to individual versions and under 'Fuselage'.

OPERATIONAL EQUIPMENT ('Bear-D'): Large I band radar (NATO 'Big Bulge') in blister fairing under centre-fuselage, for reconnaissance and to provide data on potential targets for anti-shipping aircraft or surface vessels. In latter mode, PPI presentation is data linked to missile launch station. Four-PRF range J band circular

and sector scan navigation radar (NATO 'Short Horn'). I band tail warning radar (originally NATO 'Bee Hind'; later 'Box Tail') in housing at base of rudder. SRO-2 IFF (NATO 'Odd Rods'), A-321 ADF, A-322Z Doppler radar, A-325Z/321B Tacan/DME and ILS. Two remotely controlled chaff/flare dispensers.

DIMENSIONS, EXTERNAL ('Bear-F', approx):
Wing span	51.10 m (167 ft 8 in)
Length overall	49.50 m (162 ft 5 in)
Height overall	12.12 m (39 ft 9 in)

WEIGHT ('Bear-F', estimated):
Max T-O weight	188,000 kg (414,470 lb)

The Tu-126 airborne early warning and control system aircraft, known to NATO as 'Moss'

PERFORMANCE:
 Max level speed at 7,620 m (25,000 ft)
  Mach 0.82 (500 knots; 925 km/h; 575 mph)
 Over-target speed at 12,500 m (41,000 ft)
  Mach 0.78 (450 knots; 833 km/h; 518 mph)
 Nominal cruising speed 384 knots (711 km/h; 442 mph)
 Max unrefuelled combat radius
  4,475 nm (8,285 km; 5,150 miles)

TUPOLEV Tu-126
NATO reporting name: Moss

An officially released Soviet documentary film, shown in the West in 1968, included sequences depicting a military version of the Tu-114 four-turboprop transport (see 1972-73 *Jane's*), carrying above its fuselage a rotating 'saucer' type early warning radar (NATO 'Flap Jack') with a diameter of about 11 m (36 ft). This was a logical development, as the Tu-114 had a fuselage of larger diameter than the military Tu-95, and could accommodate more easily the extensive avionic equipment and crew of 12 required by what was soon confirmed as the Soviet air forces' first generation airborne early warning and control system aircraft, with the designation Tu-126. It proved to have also wings similar to those of the Tu-114, with extended chord trailing-edge flaps, rather than the 'straight' trailing-edge of the Tu-95. The interior of the fuselage is fully air-conditioned. Few cabin windows are installed.

The general appearance of the Tu-126, which has the NATO reporting name 'Moss', is shown in the accompanying illustrations. It can be seen to have a flight refuelling nose-probe, ventral tail fin and numerous additional antennae and blisters for electronic equipment, including streamlined fairings and associated dielectric panels on the sides of the rear fuselage as on the Tu-95 'Bear-C/D'. The power plant comprises four 11,033 kW (14,795 ehp) Kuznetsov NK-12MV turboprops. Wing fuel tanks have a capacity of 60,800 kg (134,040 lb).

The Tu-126 was intended to work in conjunction with contemporary interceptors. After locating incoming low-level strike aircraft, it would ideally direct towards them fighters armed with 'snapdown' air-to-air missiles able to be fired from a cruising height of 6,100 m (20,000 ft) or higher. It had a further, obvious application in assisting strike aircraft to elude enemy interceptors picked up by its radar. However, the Tu-126 is said, by US defence experts, to have demonstrated some effectiveness in overwater exercises but to be ineffective over land.

About six Tu-126s remain operational with the Soviet air defence forces, pending complete replacement of 'Moss' by the far more effective Il-76 derivative known to NATO as 'Mainstay'.

DIMENSIONS, EXTERNAL:
Wing span	51.20 m (168 ft 0 in)
Wing aspect ratio	8.42
Length overall	55.20 m (181 ft 1 in)
Fuselage diameter	3.70 m (12 ft 1½ in)
Height overall	16.05 m (52 ft 8 in)
Wheel track	13.70 m (44 ft 11½ in)
Propeller diameter	5.60 m (18 ft 4½ in)

AREA:
Wings, gross	311.1 m² (3,349 sq ft)

WEIGHT (estimated):
Max T-O weight	170,000 kg (374,785 lb)

PERFORMANCE:
Max level speed	459 knots (850 km/h; 528 mph)
Normal operating speed	351 knots (650 km/h; 404 mph)
Max range without flight refuelling	6,775 nm (12,550 km; 7,800 miles)

TUPOLEV Tu-22
NATO reporting name: Blinder

First shown publicly in the 1961 Aviation Day flypast over Moscow, the Tu-22 was the first operational Soviet bomber capable of supersonic performance for short periods. Of the ten examples which took part in that display, only one carried visible weapons, in the form of an air-to-surface missile (NATO reporting name 'Kitchen'), some 11 m (36 ft) long, semi-submerged in the underside of its fuselage. This aircraft had also a wider nose radome.

A total of 22 Tu-22s took part in the 1967 display at Domodedovo. Most carried 'Kitchen' missiles; all had a partially retractable nose refuelling probe and the wide radome seen on the single missile-armed aircraft in 1961.

About 250 Tu-22s were built, in four versions, as follows:

Blinder-A. Basic reconnaissance bomber, with fuselage weapons bay for free-fall nuclear and conventional bombs. 'Blinder-A' entered limited service.

Blinder-B. Generally similar to 'Blinder-A' but equipped to carry air-to-surface nuclear missile (NATO reporting name 'Kitchen') recessed in weapons bay. Larger radar and partially retractable flight refuelling probe on nose.

Tupolev Tu-22 twin-jet supersonic bomber ('Blinder-A') *(Pilot Press)*

Tupolev Tu-22 photographed from an investigating interceptor of the Swedish Air Force *(via FLYGvapenNYTT)*

'Backfire-B' version of the Tupolev Tu-26 with wings spread, photographed from an interceptor of the Swedish Air Force
(via FLYGvapenNYTT)

Blinder-C. Maritime reconnaissance version, with six camera windows in weapons bay doors. Flight refuelling probe like 'Blinder-B'. Modifications to nosecone, dielectric panels, etc. on some aircraft indicate an electronic intelligence role or equipment for electronic counter-measures (ECM) duties.

Blinder-D. Training version. Cockpit for instructor in raised position aft of standard flight deck, with stepped-up canopy. In service in the Soviet Union and Libya.

About 75 'Blinder-As' and 'Blinder-Bs' remain operational alongside Tu-16s in medium-range units of the Smolensk and Irkutsk air armies. Most are used now for support roles, such as ECM jamming and reconnaissance. The Soviet Naval Air Force has about 30 bombers and 20 equipped for maritime reconnaissance and ECM duties, based mainly in the southern Ukraine and Estonia to protect sea approaches to the USSR. The Libyan and Iraqi Air Forces each have a few Tu-22s.

The following details apply to 'Blinder-A and B' but are generally applicable to all versions except as noted under model descriptions:

TYPE: Twin-jet supersonic bomber and maritime patrol aircraft.

WINGS: Cantilever mid-wing monoplane. Constant slight anhedral from roots. Sweepback approx 45° on leading-edge outboard of fence and 50° inboard of fence, increasing to acute sweep at roots. Conventional all-metal structure. Fully powered two-section ailerons, with tab in each inboard section. Flaps inboard and outboard of wheel pod on each wing trailing-edge.

FUSELAGE: All-metal semi-monocoque structure of circular section, with area rule 'waisting' at wingroots.

TAIL UNIT: Cantilever all-metal structure, with sweepback on all surfaces. Fully powered all-moving horizontal surfaces at bottom of fuselage. Aerodynamically balanced rudder, with inset tab.

LANDING GEAR: Retractable tricycle type. Wide track four-wheel bogie main units retract rearward into pods built on to wing trailing-edges. Oleo-pneumatic shock absorbers. Main legs designed to swing rearward for additional cushioning during taxying and landing on rough runways. Twin-wheel nose unit retracts rearward. Small retractable skid to protect rear fuselage in tail-down landing or take-off. Twin brake-chutes standard.

POWER PLANT: Two Koliesov VD-7 turbojets, each rated at 137.5 kN (30,900 lb st) with afterburning, mounted in pods above rear fuselage, on each side of tail fin. Lip of each intake is in the form of a ring which can be translated forward by jacks for take-off. Air entering ram intake is then supplemented by air ingested through annular slot between ring and main body of pod. Jetpipes have convergent-divergent nozzle inside outer fairing. Semi-retractable flight refuelling probe on nose of 'Blinder-B', with triangular guard underneath to prevent drogue damaging nosecone.

ACCOMMODATION: Crew of three in tandem. Row of windows in bottom of fuselage, aft of nose radome, at navigator/systems operator's station. Pilot has upward ejection seat; other crew members have downward ejection seats.

ARMAMENT AND OPERATIONAL EQUIPMENT: Weapons bay in centre-fuselage, with double-fold doors on 'Blinder-A'. Special doors with panels shaped to accommodate recessed 'Kitchen' missile on 'Blinder-B'. Single 23 mm NR-23 gun in radar directed tail turret, beneath 'Bee Hind' tail warning radar antenna. Radar in nose. Chaff/flare countermeasures dispensers and bombing assessment cameras carried in rear of wheel pods of some aircraft.

DIMENSIONS, EXTERNAL (estimated):
Wing span	23.75 m (78 ft 0 in)
Length overall	40.53 m (132 ft 11½ in)
Height overall	10.67 m (35 ft 0 in)

WEIGHT (estimated):
Max T-O weight	83,900 kg (185,000 lb)

PERFORMANCE (estimated):
Max level speed at 12,200 m (40,000 ft)
Mach 1.4 (800 knots; 1,480 km/h; 920 mph)
Service ceiling 18,300 m (60,000 ft)
Max unrefuelled combat radius
1,295 nm (2,400 km; 1,490 miles)

TUPOLEV Tu-26 (Tu-22M)
NATO reporting name: Backfire

NATO first acknowledged the existence of a Soviet variable geometry medium bomber in the Autumn of 1969. A prototype was observed in July 1970, on the ground near the manufacturing plant at Kazan in western Russia, and was confirmed subsequently as a twin-engined design by the Tupolev Bureau. At least two prototypes were built, and flight testing is believed to have started in 1971. Up to 12 pre-production models followed, for development testing, weapons trials and evaluation, by the beginning of 1973. The Soviet press continues to refer to the type as the **Tu-22M**, but the current designation is believed to be **Tu-26**. The NATO reporting name allocated to the aircraft is 'Backfire'.

Three versions of the Tu-26/Tu-22M have been identified by NATO reporting names:

Backfire-A. Initial version. Slightly inclined lateral air intakes, with large splitter plates. Large pods on the wing trailing-edges were believed until recently to house the main landing gear when retracted; but it is now known that the mainwheels always retracted into the fuselage in the same way as those on later versions of the bomber. 'Backfire-A' is thought to have equipped only one squadron.

Backfire-B. Initial series production version, with increased wing span and wing trailing-edge pods eliminated except for shallow underwing fairings, no longer protruding beyond the trailing-edge. 'Backfire-Bs' are seen usually with

the standard flight refuelling nose probe removed, although the housing remains, in the form of a long fairing. This is assumed to stress Soviet assertions that the aircraft are intended for peripheral/theatre operations rather than long-range strategic use, and are therefore exempt from restrictions that would have been imposed on intercontinental bombers by the SALT 2 treaty had it been ratified. Initial armament was normally a single 'Kitchen' missile semi-recessed under fuselage. Current aircraft have a rack for a 'Kitchen' under each fixed wing centre-section panel, although fuselage mount is retained. External stores racks seen frequently under engine air intake trunks. Two GSh-23 twin-barrel 23 mm guns in tail mounting, initially beneath ogival radome, later with drum-shape radome of larger diameter.

Backfire-C. This advanced production version, with wedge type engine air intakes, is operational in large numbers, in both long-range bomber and maritime roles, having entered service with the Black Sea Fleet air force in 1985. Upturned nosecone with small pod at tip. No visible flight refuelling probe. Single GSh-23 twin-barrel 23 mm gun, with barrels one above the other, in aerodynamically improved tail mounting, beneath large drum-shape radome.

'Backfires' are capable of performing nuclear strike, conventional attack and anti-ship missions, their low-level penetration features making them more survivable than earlier Soviet bombers. More than 350 were in service in early 1990, deployed primarily against NATO in Europe and over the Atlantic, with about one-third of the force in the far east of the Soviet Union. Demonstrated in-flight refuelling capability would enable them to be used against the continental US if sufficient tankers were available. With the 1988 assignment of 'Backfire-Cs' to the Northern Fleet Air Force, the four Soviet fleets are now equipped with a total of 160 Tu-26s.

It is expected that the 'Backfire' strategic/maritime force will be maintained eventually at a total of at least 400 aircraft. Production appears to be limited to the average rate of 30 aircraft a year that was specified by the unratified SALT 2 agreement. 'Backfires' have been used for development launches of new generation Soviet cruise

Tupolev Tu-26 (NATO 'Backfire-B') bomber and maritime reconnaissance/attack aircraft, with additional side view (bottom) of 'Backfire-C' *(Pilot Press)*

Wedge type air intakes and missile racks under the fixed wing panels are features of 'Backfire-C'

missiles, but are not expected to become designated AS-15 carriers.

The following details refer specifically to 'Backfire-B':

TYPE: Twin-engined medium bomber and maritime reconnaissance/attack aircraft.

WINGS: Cantilever low/mid-wing monoplane, made up of a large span fixed centre-section and two variable geometry outer panels. No anhedral or dihedral, but wing section is so thin that considerable flexing of the outer panels takes place in flight. Leading-edge fence towards tip of centre-section on each side. Each outer wing panel is fitted with a full span leading-edge slat, aileron, and three-section slotted trailing-edge flaps aft of spoilers/lift dumpers. Wing sweep is believed to be variable from fully spread (20°) to fully swept (65°).

FUSELAGE: Forward of wings, fuselage is basically circular with large ogival dielectric nosecone. Centre-fuselage is faired into rectangular section air intake trunks, each fitted with a large splitter plate and assumed to embody complex variable geometry ramps. No external area rule 'waisting' of these trunks.

TAIL UNIT: Cantilever structure, with sweepback on all surfaces. All-moving horizontal surfaces; conventional inset rudder.

LANDING GEAR: Retractable tricycle type. Each mainwheel bogie comprises three unequally spaced pairs of wheels in tandem, which pivot inward from the vestigial fairing under the centre-section into the bottom of the fuselage.

POWER PLANT: Two turbofans with afterburners, mounted side by side in the rear fuselage. Reported to be uprated versions of the Kuznetsov NK-144 engines (each 196.1 kN; 44,090 lb st) that were developed for Tupolev's Tu-144 supersonic transport. Fuel tankage is believed to include integral tanks in the entire fixed portion of the wings and much of the centre-fuselage above the weapon bay. Removable flight refuelling nose probe; after one observed refuelling, a 'Backfire' prototype remained airborne for a further 10 h.

ACCOMMODATION: Pilot and co-pilot side by side on flight deck, under upward opening gull-wing doors hinged on centreline. Two crew members further aft, as indicated by position of windows between flight deck and air intakes.

AVIONICS AND EQUIPMENT: Large bombing and navigation radar (NATO 'Down Beat') inside dielectric nosecone. Radar (NATO 'Bee Hind') for tail turret, above guns. Fairing with flat glazed front panel under front fuselage is believed to be for a video camera to provide visual assistance for weapon aiming.

ARMAMENT: Primary armament of two 'Kitchen' air-to-surface missiles, carried under the fixed centre-section panel of each wing, or a single 'Kitchen' semi-recessed in the underside of the centre-fuselage. Multiple racks for twelve 500 kg bombs sometimes fitted under air intake trunks. Alternative weapon loads include up to 12,000 kg (26,450 lb) of conventional bombs, carried internally. US reports have suggested that the Soviet Union is developing decoy missiles to assist penetration of advanced defence systems, in addition to very advanced ECM and ECCM. Two GSh-23 twin-barrel 23 mm guns, with barrels side by side horizontally, in radar directed tail mounting.

DIMENSIONS, EXTERNAL (estimated):

Wing span: fully spread	34.30 m (112 ft 6½ in)
fully swept	23.40 m (76 ft 9¼ in)
Length overall	39.60 m (129 ft 11 in)
Height overall	10.80 m (35 ft 5¼ in)

WEIGHTS:

Nominal weapon load	12,000 kg (26,450 lb)
Max T-O weight	130,000 kg (286,600 lb)

PERFORMANCE (estimated):

Max level speed: at high altitude	Mach 2.0
at low altitude	Mach 0.9
Max unrefuelled combat radius	
	2,160 nm (4,000 km; 2,485 miles)

TUPOLEV Tu-160
NATO reporting name: Blackjack

First photographs of the Tupolev variable geometry strategic bomber known to NATO as 'Blackjack' became available officially after former US Defense Secretary Frank Carlucci was invited to inspect an example at Kubinka air base, near Moscow, on 2 August 1988. It had been assumed earlier that 'Blackjack' was intended for a high altitude standoff role, armed with AS-15 (NATO 'Kent') air-launched cruise missiles that have a range of 1,620 nm (3,000 km; 1,850 miles) carrying a 200 kT nuclear warhead. However, Mr Carlucci was told by Colonel-General Boris F. Korolkov that it also carries short-range attack missiles (AS-16, NATO 'Kickback') similar to the US Air Force's SRAMs. The purpose of such weapons is defence suppression along the path of a bomber making a low altitude penetration to attack primary targets with free-fall nuclear bombs or missiles. So, it must be deduced that 'Blackjack' was designed for both subsonic

cruise/supersonic dash at around Mach 2 at 18,300 m (60,000 ft) and transonic penetration at low altitude.

Designed under the leadership of Mr V. I. Bliznuk, 'Blackjack' is about 20 per cent longer than the US Air Force's B-1B, with a greater unrefuelled combat radius and much higher supersonic speed. It is in no way a simple scale-up of 'Backfire'. Common features include low mounted variable geometry wings and a massive dorsal fin; but 'Blackjack's' horizontal tail surfaces are mounted high, near the intersection of the dorsal fin and all-moving main fin. The very long and sharply swept fixed root panel of each wing, and the engine installation, appear to resemble those of the long-retired Tu-144 supersonic airliner rather than 'Backfire'.

The Soviet Union is expected to build a production series of at least 100 'Blackjacks' in a complex that has been added to the huge Kazan airframe plant. More than 15 had been completed by August 1989, when a single example was flown at low altitude over Tushino Airport during the Aviation Day flypast. The commentator confirmed the official designation Tu-160 that was reported in the 1989-90 *Jane's*. The first operational squadron was formed in 1988 at Dolon air base in the central USSR (from where 'Bear-H' bombers currently conduct training missions against North America).

TYPE: Four-engined strategic bomber.

WINGS: Cantilever low-wing monoplane, made up of a large-span fixed centre-section and two variable geometry outer panels. Sweep of outer panels is selected manually, from 20° fully spread to 65° fully swept. Full-span leading-edge flaps. Long-span double-slotted trailing-edge flap and inset drooping aileron on each wing. When wings are fully swept, small inboard portion of each trailing-edge flap hinges upward and extends above wing.

Provisional three-view drawing of Tupolev Tu-160 strategic bomber (NATO 'Blackjack') *(Pilot Press)*

Tupolev Tu-160 strategic bomber, known to NATO as 'Blackjack' *(Piotr Butowski)*

FUSELAGE: Slim and shallow structure, blended with wingroots and shaped for maximum hostile radar signal deflection. Slightly upturned dielectric nosecone.

TAIL UNIT: One-piece all-moving upper fin pivots on the fixed lower portion some distance above the all-moving horizontal surfaces. Conical fairing aft of trailing-edge of fin/tailplane intersection.

LANDING GEAR: Twin nosewheels retract rearward. Main gear comprises two bogies, each with three pairs of wheels. Two forward pairs of wheels on each bogie are farther apart than the rear pairs. Retraction is very like that on Tu-154 airliner. As each leg pivots rearward, the bogie rotates through 90° around the axis of the centre pair of wheels, to lie parallel with the retracted leg. Gear retracts into the thickest part of the wing, between the fuselage and inboard engine on each side; so track is relatively small.

POWER PLANT: Four Type 'P' turbofans, each rated at 245 kN (55,115 lb st) with afterburning. Provision for in-flight refuelling assumed.

ACCOMMODATION: Four crew members in pairs, on individual ejection seats. One window on each side of flight deck can be moved inward and rearward for ventilation on ground. Flying controls use fighter type sticks rather than yokes or wheels. Crew enter via nosewheel bay.

AVIONICS: Radar in nose is claimed to provide terrain following capability. Fairing with flat glazed front panel, under forward fuselage, for video camera to provide visual assistance for weapon aiming. No head-up display. Single CRT for caution and warning data. Vertical tape engine instrumentation on centre console.

ARMAMENT: Internal stowage for up to 16,330 kg (36,000 lb) of free-fall bombs, short-range attack missiles or ALCMs. A rotary launcher can be installed in each of the two 10 m (33 ft) long weapon bays, carrying 12 AS-16 SRAMs or six ALCMs, currently AS-15s, to be superseded by supersonic AS-19s.

DIMENSIONS, EXTERNAL:

Wing span: fully spread	55.70 m (182 ft 9 in)
fully swept	33.75 m (110 ft)
Length overall	54.00 m (177 ft)
Height overall	12.80 m (42 ft)

WEIGHTS:

Max weapon load	16,330 kg (36,000 lb)
Max T-O weight	275,000 kg (606,260 lb)

PERFORMANCE:

Max level speed at high altitude	approx Mach 1.88
Max unrefuelled combat radius	
	3,940 nm (7,300 km; 4,535 miles)

TUPOLEV Tu-154M
NATO reporting name: Careless

The basic three-engined **Tu-154**, announced in the Spring of 1966, was developed to replace the Tu-104, Il-18 and An-10 transport aircraft on Aeroflot's medium/long stage lengths of up to 3,240 nm (6,000 km; 3,725 miles). The first of six prototype and pre-production models flew for the first time on 4 October 1968. Regular passenger services began on 9 February 1972.

The Tu-154 was superseded in production successively by the **Tu-154A**, **Tu-154B** and **Tu-154B-2**, with uprated

turbofans and many other refinements. Production of all four versions exceeded 600, of which more than 500 were delivered to Aeroflot and a total of 90 others to Balkan Bulgarian Airlines, Cubana, Malév and Tarom. Full descriptions of these aircraft can be found in the 1985-86 and previous editions of *Jane's*.

Following the development of the Tu-154B-2, the Tupolev Bureau decided that further improvement of the type would be impossible without more radical changes to the basic airframe and a switch to more modern engines. This led to development of the **Tu-154M**.

As the first step, a standard production Tu-154B-2 (SSSR-85317) was returned to the factory, where the original Kuznetsov NK-8-2U turbofans were removed. Soloviev D-30KU turbofans, as used on the Il-62M, were installed in their place, with the thrust rating of each engine (designated D-30KU-154-II in production form) reduced. The engine nacelles mounted on each side of the rear fuselage were developments of those fitted to the Il-62M, with the same type of clamshell thrust reverser on the engines they carried. To accommodate the centre engine, the TA-92 APU had to be transferred from its former position over the tail nozzle to the fuselage, and the air intake had to be enlarged. Flight testing began in 1982.

In its new configuration, as the prototype Tu-154M, SSSR-85317 had a redesigned tailplane; the slats were made smaller and the area of the spoilers was increased. The original three-crew flight deck and cabin layout for 169 passengers were retained, but the production Tu-154M offers alternative configurations for up to 180 economy class passengers. An executive version is available; and it is

Tupolev Tu-160 at Kubinka, awaiting inspection by former US Defense Secretary Frank Carlucci

Tupolev Tu-154M medium-range airliner (three Soloviev D-30KU-154-II turbofans) in service with CSA Czechoslovak Airlines
(Letectvi + Kosmonautika/Václav Jukl)

possible to remove all seats and utilise any version of the aircraft to carry light freight.

Production is centred in Kuybyshev, from where Aeroflot took delivery of its first two Tu-154Ms on 27 December 1984. Other customers include Aeronica of Nicaragua, Ariana Afghan Airlines (2), Balkan Bulgarian Airlines, CAAC of China, Chosonminhan Korean Airlines, Cubana, Libyan Arab Airlines (3), LOT Polish Airlines (10) and Syrianair (4). CSA of Czechoslovakia is taking delivery of seven. The Tu-154M is designed for a service life of 30,000 hours and 15,000 landings over a 15 year period.

TYPE: Three-turbofan medium-range transport aircraft.

WINGS: Cantilever low-wing monoplane. Sweepback 35° at quarter-chord. Anhedral on outer panels. Geometric twist along span. Conventional all-metal riveted three-spar structure, centre spar extending to just outboard of inner edge of aileron in each wing. Hydraulically actuated ailerons, double-slotted flaps and four-section spoilers forward of flaps on each wing. Electrically actuated slats on outer 80 per cent of each wing leading-edge. Tab in each aileron. Hot air anti-icing of wing leading-edge. Slats electrically heated.

FUSELAGE: Conventional all-metal semi-monocoque fail-safe structure of circular section. Single pressure cell, containing flight deck and two cabins separated by service compartments.

TAIL UNIT: Cantilever all-metal structure, with electrically actuated variable incidence T tailplane. Rudder and elevators of honeycomb sandwich construction. Sweepback of 40° at quarter-chord on horizontal surfaces, 45° on leading-edge of vertical surfaces. Control surfaces hydraulically actuated by irreversible servo controls. Tab in each elevator. Leading-edges of fin and tailplane and engine air intake anti-iced by hot air.

LANDING GEAR: Retractable tricycle type. Hydraulic actuation. Main units retract rearward into fairings on wing trailing-edge. Each consists of a bogie made up of three pairs of wheels in tandem. Rearward retracting anti-shimmy twin-wheel nose unit, steerable through ±63°. Disc brakes and anti-skid units on mainwheels.

POWER PLANT: Three Soloviev D-30KU-154-II turbofans, each rated at 104 kN (23,380 lb st), one in pod on each side of rear fuselage and one inside extreme rear of fuselage. Two lateral engines fitted with clamshell thrust reversers. Integral fuel tanks in wings: four tanks in centre-section and two in outer wings. For reasons of trim, all fuel is fed to a collector tank in the centre-section and thence to engines. Single-point refuelling. APU in rear fuselage.

ACCOMMODATION: Crew of three on flight deck, comprising two pilots and flight engineer, with provisions for navigator and five cabin staff. Alternative configurations for 180 economy class passengers, 164 tourist class with hot meal service, or 154 tourist/economy plus a separate first class cabin seating 8 to 24 persons. Mainly six-abreast seating with centre aisle. Washable non-flammable materials used for all interior furnishing. Fully enclosed luggage containers. Toilet, galley and wardrobe installations to customer's requirements. Executive and light cargo configurations available. Passenger doors are forward of the front cabin and between cabins on port side, with emergency and service doors opposite. All four doors open outward. Six emergency exits: two overwing and one immediately forward of engine nacelle on each side. Two pressurised baggage holds under floor of cabin, with two inward opening doors. Smaller unpressurised hold under rear of cabin.

SYSTEMS: Air-conditioning system pressure differential 0.58 bars (8.4 lb/sq in). Three independent hydraulic systems, working pressure 207 bars (3,000 lb/sq in), powered by engine driven pumps. Nos. 2 and 3 systems each have additional electric backup pump. Systems actuate landing gear retraction and extension, nosewheel steering, and operation of ailerons, rudder, elevators, flaps and spoilers. Three-phase 200/115V 400Hz AC electrical system supplied by three 40kVA alternators. Additional 36V 400Hz AC and 27V DC systems and four storage batteries. Engine fire extinguishing system in each nacelle. Smoke detectors in baggage holds.

AVIONICS: Avionics meet ICAO standards for Cat II weather minima and include updated navigation system with triplex INS. Automatic flight control system operates throughout flight except during take-off to 400 m (1,312 ft) and landing from 30 m (100 ft). Automatic go-round and automatic speed control provided by autothrottle down to 10 m (33 ft) on landing. Weather radar, transponder, Doppler, dual HF and VHF com and emergency VHF, cockpit voice recorder and GPWS standard.

DIMENSIONS, EXTERNAL:
Wing span	37.55 m (123 ft 2½ in)
Length overall	47.90 m (157 ft 1¾ in)
Height overall	11.40 m (37 ft 4¾ in)
Diameter of fuselage	3.80 m (12 ft 5½ in)
Tailplane span	13.40 m (43 ft 11½ in)
Wheel track	11.50 m (37 ft 9 in)
Wheelbase	18.92 m (62 ft 1 in)
Passenger doors (each): Height	1.73 m (5 ft 7 in)
Width	0.80 m (2 ft 7½ in)
Height to sill	3.10 m (10 ft 2 in)
Servicing door: Height	1.28 m (4 ft 2½ in)
Width	0.61 m (2 ft 0 in)
Emergency door: Height	1.28 m (4 ft 2½ in)
Width	0.64 m (2 ft 1¼ in)
Emergency exits (each): Height	0.90 m (2 ft 11½ in)
Width	0.48 m (1 ft 7 in)
Main baggage hold doors (each):	
Height	1.20 m (3 ft 11¼ in)
Width	1.35 m (4 ft 5 in)
Height to sill	1.80 m (5 ft 11 in)
Rear (unpressurised) hold:	
Height	0.90 m (2 ft 11½ in)
Width	1.10 m (3 ft 7¼ in)
Height to sill	2.20 m (7 ft 2½ in)

DIMENSIONS, INTERNAL:
Cabin: Width	3.58 m (11 ft 9 in)
Height	2.02 m (6 ft 7½ in)
Volume	163.2 m³ (5,763 cu ft)
Main baggage holds: front	21.5 m³ (759 cu ft)
rear	16.5 m³ (582 cu ft)
Rear underfloor hold	5.0 m³ (176 cu ft)

AREAS:
Wings, gross	201.45 m² (2,169 sq ft)
Horizontal tail surfaces	42.20 m² (454.24 sq ft)

WEIGHTS:
Basic operating weight empty	55,300 kg (121,915 lb)
Max payload	18,000 kg (39,680 lb)
Max fuel	39,750 kg (87,633 lb)
Max T-O weight	100,000 kg (220,460 lb)
Max landing weight	80,000 kg (176,366 lb)
Max zero-fuel weight	74,000 kg (163,140 lb)

PERFORMANCE:
Max cruising speed	513 knots (950 km/h; 590 mph)
Max cruising height	11,900 m (39,000 ft)
Balanced field length for T-O and landing	
	2,500 m (8,200 ft)

Range:
with max payload	2,100 nm (3,900 km; 2,425 miles)
with max fuel and 5,450 kg (12,015 lb) payload	
	3,563 nm (6,600 km; 4,100 miles)

TUPOLEV Tu-154C

This freight carrying version of the Tu-154 was announced in the Autumn of 1982. It is being offered primarily as a conversion of the Tu-154B, with an unobstructed cargo volume of 72 m³ (2,542 cu ft) in the main cabin. A freight door 2.80 m (9 ft 2¼ in) wide and 1.87 m (6 ft 1½ in) high is installed in the port side of the cabin, forward of the wing, with a ball mat inside and roller tracks the full length of the floor of the cabin. Typical loads include nine standard international pallets measuring 2.24 × 2.74 m (88 × 108 in), plus additional freight in the standard underfloor baggage holds which have a volume of 38 m³ (1,341 cu ft). Nominal range of the Tu-154C, with 20,000 kg (44,100 lb) of cargo, is 1,565 nm (2,900 km; 1,800 miles).

TUPOLEV Tu-155

The first flight of an aeroplane fuelled with liquid hydrogen was made by the Tu-155 (SSSR-85035) on 15 April 1988. As can be seen in an illustration opposite, the

Tupolev Tu-154M medium-range three-turbofan transport aircraft *(Pilot Press)*

Prototype of the twin-turbofan Tupolev Tu-204, under development to replace the Tu-154 *(Air Portraits)*

This photograph of the tail of the Tu-155 testbed shows external fuel ducting for the NK-88 centre engine *(Tass)*

Tupolev Tu-204 medium-range transport (two Soloviev PS-90A turbofans) *(Jane's/Mike Keep)*

Tu-155 is basically a Tu-154 three-turbofan transport that has been converted into a testbed for evaluating the viability of cryogenic fuels. The standard centre engine has been replaced by a Kuznetsov NK-88, probably based on the NK-8 turbofans fitted to early Tu-154A/Bs. A large tank to cater for the greatly increased fuel mass is installed in the rear of the cabin. Ducting visible on the starboard side of the rear fuselage is assumed to pipe the cryogenic fuel from this tank to the centre engine.

More than 30 special systems had to be developed to ensure safe storage and handling of the fuel. In particular, refrigeration and insulation systems were essential to maintain the fuel at extremely low temperature, calling for new materials and special vacuum-tight welding techniques.

In addition to liquid hydrogen, the NK-88 engine is designed to operate on liquefied natural gas, and the Tu-155 was equipped for its NK-88 engine to run on methane when it was flown to the 9th Congrès sur le Gaz Naturel at Nice in the Autumn of 1989. General Designer Nikolai Kuznetsov reported that Soviet government funding of the programme has been denied, and proposals to modify further Tu-154s for intensive airline-type testing had been shelved in early 1990.

The long-term advantage of liquid hydrogen is that it can, in theory, be produced in unlimited quantities from water, although current production costs are high. Also, it is claimed to offer major reductions in the harmful ecological effects of aircraft on the atmosphere. Reserves of natural gas worldwide are estimated as adequate for 60 to 70 years of use as a primary fuel.

TUPOLEV Tu-204

It was announced in 1983 that the Tupolev Bureau was developing a new medium-range transport aircraft, designated Tu-204, to replace the Tu-154. Preliminary details became available in Spring 1985 and the programme was finalised in 1986. The first prototype (SSSR-64001) was flown for the first time on 2 January 1989 by Tupolev's chief

test pilot, A. Talavkine, and it was hoped to achieve basic certification before the end of 1990, followed by icing and cold weather certification in early 1991. Aeroflot has expressed a requirement for up to 500 Tu-204s. Production is centred in a plant at Ulianovsk.

The basic **Tu-204** is designed to carry 190-214 passengers. It can be flown by a two-person crew, but Aeroflot required accommodation for a flight engineer and there is provision for a fourth seat for an instructor or observer. Control is fly by wire, with analog reversion, and the decision to use conventional yokes followed evaluation of an alternative sidestick on a Tu-154 testbed. The flight deck compares with current Western practice, including a dual EFIS with six colour CRT displays, and a triplex automatic approach and landing system is standard, permitting operation in ICAO Cat IIIA minima. About 18 per cent of the airframe structure by weight is made of composites.

In addition to the basic version described in detail in this entry, Dr Alexei A. Tupolev announced at the 1989 Paris Air Show that the Tu-204 will be made available in two increased-weight forms.

A first option, designated **TU-204-100**, increases the max T-O weight to 99,500 kg (219,355 lb) and max payload to 24,000 kg (52,910 lb), offering a range of 2,860 nm (5,300 km; 3,293 miles) with full tanks and all seats occupied.

The second option, designated **TU-204-200**, increases the max T-O weight to 107,900 kg (237,875 lb) and max fuel load to 32,400 kg (71,428 lb), making possible a max range of 3,875 nm (7,180 km; 4,460 miles).

Of the six prototypes, No. 2 was scheduled to fly in Spring 1990, followed by No. 3 in June and No. 4 in August. Two are being used for structural and fatigue testing. Production is planned at the rate of 80 to 90 aircraft per year. The Tu-204 is designed for a service life of 45,000 flight hours and 20,000 landings or 20 years. Turnaround time between flights is targeted at 50 minutes, with a maximum of 2 h 50 min for an engine change and 33 min for replacement of a wheel and brake.

TYPE: Twin-turbofan medium-range transport.

WINGS: Cantilever low/mid-wing monoplane, with dihedral from roots and sweepback of 28°. Supercritical wing section, with thickness/chord ratio of 14 per cent at the root, 9-10 per cent at the tip, and negative twist. Three-piece two-spar torsion-box structure, with winglets. Metal structure, covered partly with carbonfibre. Each wing trailing-edge carries two-section double-slotted flaps. Two-section upper-surface airbrakes forward of each centre-section flap; five-section spoilers forward of each outer flap. Inset aileron outboard of flaps on each wing. Four-section leading-edge slats over full span. Carbonfibre skin on spoilers, airbrakes and flaps. Glassfibre wingroot fairings. No tabs.

FUSELAGE: Semi-monocoque pressurised structure of oval section. Conventional all-metal construction, utilising aluminium-lithium and titanium. Composites used only for nose radome and some access panels.

TAIL UNIT: Conventional configuration, with sweepback on all surfaces. Extensive use of composites, particularly for the leading-edges of the fixed surfaces and for the elevators and rudder. The torsion box of the fin forms an integral fuel tank which is used for automatic trimming of the CG in flight.

LANDING GEAR: Hydraulically retractable tricycle type. Electro-hydraulically steerable twin-wheel nose unit (±10° via rudder pedals; ±70° by electric steering control). Nosewheels retract forward; four-wheel bogie main units retract inward into wing/fuselage fairings. Carbon disc brakes, electrically controlled. Tyre size 1,070 × 390 mm on mainwheels, 840 × 290 mm on nosewheels.

POWER PLANT: Two Soloviev PS-90A turbofans, each rated at 156.9 kN (35,275 lb st), mounted underwing in composite cowlings. Fuel in six integral tanks in wings and one in tail fin, total capacity 30,000 litres (7,925 US gallons; 6,600 Imp gallons).

ACCOMMODATION: Can be operated by pilot and co-pilot, but Aeroflot has specified requirement for a flight engineer.

Provision for fourth seat. Three basic single-aisle passenger arrangements: (1) 190 seats, with 12 seats four-abreast in first class cabin at front at pitch of 99 cm (39 in), 35 business class seats six-abreast at pitch of 99 cm (39 in) in centre cabin, and 143 tourist class seats six-abreast at pitch of 81 cm (32 in) at rear; (2) 196 seats, with 12 seats four-abreast at pitch of 99 cm (39 in) in first class cabin at front and 184 six-abreast tourist class seats at pitch of 81 cm (32 in) at rear; (3) 214 seats, all six-abreast at tourist class pitch of 81 cm (32 in). All configurations have an office, a wardrobe and a toilet immediately aft of the flight deck, and two more toilets, a large buffet/office and a wardrobe at the rear of the passenger accommodation. Overhead stowage for hand baggage. Passenger doors at front and rear of cabin on port side, with service doors opposite. Type I emergency exit doors fore and aft of wing on each side. Inflatable slide for emergency use at each of the eight doors. Two underfloor baggage/freight holds: forward hold able to accommodate five type 2AK-0.7 or 2AK-0.4 containers; rear hold accommodates seven containers.

SYSTEMS: Triplex fly by wire digital control system, with triplex analog backup. Three independent hydraulic systems, pressure 207 bars (3,000 lb/sq in). Ailerons, elevators, rudder, spoilers and airbrakes are operated by all three systems; flaps, leading-edge slats, brakes and nosewheel steering are operated by two systems; landing gear retraction and extension are effected by all three systems. Electrical power supplied by two 200/115V 400Hz AC generators and a 27V DC system. Type TA-12-60 APU in tailcone.

AVIONICS: EFIS equipment comprises two colour CRTs for flight and navigation information for each pilot, plus two central CRTs for engine and systems data. Other equipment includes an automatic flight control system, VHF and HF radio, intercom, VOR, DME, inertial navigation system and satellite navigation system.

DIMENSIONS, EXTERNAL:

Wing span	42.00 m (137 ft 9½ in)
Length overall	46.22 m (151 ft 7¾ in)
Fuselage cross-section	
	3.80 m × 4.10 m (12 ft 5½ in × 13 ft 5½ in)
Height overall	13.88 m (45 ft 6½ in)
Tailplane span	15.00 m (49 ft 2½ in)
Wheel track	7.82 m (25 ft 8 in)
Wheelbase	17.00 m (55 ft 9¼ in)
Passenger doors (each): Height	1.85 m (6 ft 0¾ in)
Width	0.84 m (2 ft 9 in)
Service doors (each): Height	1.60 m (5 ft 3 in)
Width	0.65 m (2 ft 1½ in)
Emergency exit doors (each): Height	1.442 m (4 ft 8¾ in)
Width	0.61 m (2 ft 0 in)
Baggage holds: Height to sill	2.71 m (8 ft 10¾ in)

DIMENSIONS, INTERNAL:

Cabin, excl flight deck: Length	30.18 m (99 ft 0 in)
Max width	3.57 m (11 ft 8½ in)
Max height	2.15 m (7 ft 0½ in)
Fwd cargo hold: Height	1.162 m (3 ft 9¾ in)
Volume	11.00 m³ (388 cu ft)
Rear cargo hold: Height	1.162 m (3 ft 9¾ in)
Volume	15.4 m³ (544 cu ft)

AREA:

Wings, gross	184.17 m² (1,982.5 sq ft)

WEIGHTS:

Operational weight empty	56,500 kg (124,560 lb)
Max payload	21,000 kg (46,300 lb)
Max baggage/freight: fwd hold	3,625 kg (7,990 lb)
rear hold	5,075 kg (11,190 lb)

Provisional three-view drawing of the turbofan powered Tupolev Tu-334, with additional side elevation (bottom) of version with propfan engines *(Pilot Press)*

Max fuel	24,000 kg (52,910 lb)
Max ramp weight	93,850 kg (206,900 lb)
Max T-O weight	93,500 kg (206,125 lb)
Max landing weight	86,000 kg (189,595 lb)
Max zero-fuel weight	77,500 kg (170,855 lb)
Max wing loading	507.7 kg/m² (104.0 lb/sq ft)
Max power loading	298.0 kg/kN (2.92 lb/lb st)

PERFORMANCE (estimated, at max T-O weight):

Cruising speed at 10,650-12,200 m (34,950-40,000 ft)	
	437-458 knots (810-850 km/h; 503-528 mph)
T-O speed	145 knots (269 km/h; 167 mph)
Approach speed	132 knots (245 km/h; 152 mph)
Time to cruising height after T-O	22-25 min
T-O run	1,230 m (4,035 ft)
T-O run, one engine out	2,030 m (6,660 ft)
Balanced T-O field length (30°C)	2,500 m (8,200 ft)
Balanced landing field length	2,130 m (6,990 ft)
Landing run	850 m (2,800 ft)
Range at Mach 0.78 at 11,000 m (36,100 ft) with max fuel and payload of 19,000 kg (41,887 lb), representing 196 passengers	2,077 nm (3,850 km; 2,392 miles)

TUPOLEV Tu-334

The Tupolev design bureau is developing a new twin-engined medium-range aircraft designated Tu-334, to replace Tu-134s on some Aeroflot routes. In order to meet the airline's requirement for such an aircraft to enter service during 1993, the Tu-334 will embody features of the Tu-204. In particular the basic wing configurations of the two designs have much in common, and the flight decks are expected to be identical in layout.

In its initial form, as described in this entry, the Tu-334 will be powered by two rear-mounted Lotarev D-436T turbofans. Later, it is expected to progress to two new D-27 propfan engines developed by the ZMKB (formerly Lotarev OKB). As shown in an accompanying illustration, the fuselage will be lengthened at that time, to an overall length of 36.90 m (121 ft 0¾ in), to increase capacity to

104/126 passengers. The turbofan powered prototype Tu-334 is expected to fly in mid-1992.

TYPE: Twin-turbofan medium-range airliner.

WINGS: Cantilever low/mid-wing monoplane. Supercritical section, with winglets. Four-section leading-edge slats over full span of each wing. Two-section trailing-edge flaps; inner section probably double-slotted, outer section single-slotted. Two airbrakes forward of each inner flap; four spoilers forward of each outer flap. Ailerons and other flying controls almost certainly operated by a fly by wire control system.

FUSELAGE: Conventional semi-monocoque pressurised structure, generally similar to that of Tu-204, with same cross-section but shorter.

TAIL UNIT: Cantilever T tail with sweepback on all surfaces.

LANDING GEAR: Retractable tricycle type, with twin wheels on each unit. Main units retract inward into wing/fuselage fairings. Trailing-link mainwheel legs.

POWER PLANT: Two Lotarev D-436T turbofans, each rated at 73.6 kN (16,550 lb st).

ACCOMMODATION: Basic seating for up to 102 passengers, six-abreast at seat pitch of 81 cm (32 in), with centre aisle. Two galleys, two toilets and a service compartment. Doors at front and rear of cabin on port side, with service doors opposite.

DIMENSIONS, EXTERNAL:

Wing span	29.10 m (95 ft 5¾ in)
Length overall	33.20 m (108 ft 11 in)
Height overall	8.40 m (27 ft 6½ in)

WEIGHT:

Max T-O weight	39,500 kg (87,080 lb)

PERFORMANCE (estimated):

Nominal cruising speed	442 knots (820 km/h; 510 mph)
Range: with 11,000 kg (24,250 lb) payload	
	645 nm (1,200 km; 745 miles)
with 5,500 kg (12,125 lb) payload	
	2,155 nm (4,000 km; 2,485 miles)

YAKOVLEV

GENERAL DESIGNER IN CHARGE OF BUREAU:
Sergei Yakovlev

The late Alexander Yakovlev was one of the most versatile Soviet designers, and products of his design bureau ranged from transonic long-range fighters to the Yak-24 tandem-rotor helicopter, an operational VTOL carrier based fighter and a variety of training and transport aircraft.

YAKOVLEV Yak-28
NATO reporting names: Brewer, Firebar and Maestro

First seen in considerable numbers in the 1961 Soviet Aviation Day flypast were three successors to the Yak-25/27 series (see 1971-72 *Jane's*), described by the commentator as supersonic multi-purpose aircraft and identified subsequently by the designation Yak-28. Brief details of the two-seat tactical attack versions known to NATO as 'Brewer-A, B and C' can be found in earlier editions of *Jane's*. Versions still operational are as follows:

Brewer-D. Reconnaissance version, with cameras or other sensors, including side looking airborne radar, in bomb bay. Two-seater, with pilot under blister canopy and navigator in glazed nose. Blister radome under fuselage forward of wings.

Brewer-E. First Soviet operational ECM escort aircraft, deployed in 1970. Active ECM pack built into bomb bay, from which it projects in cylindrical form. No

Yak-28P ('Firebar') fitted with original short radome and carrying two 'Anab' missiles *(Flug Revue)*

radome under front fuselage, but many additional antennae and fairings. Attachment under each outer wing, outboard of external fuel tank, for a rocket pod, chaff dispenser or anti-radiation missile.

US official sources estimate that about 125 'Brewer-Ds and Es' remain in service for tactical reconnaissance and ECM, and 40 for strategic ECM.

Firebar. Tandem two-seat all-weather fighter. No internal weapons bay. Armament comprises one 'Anab' air-to-air missile under each wing. Identified as **Yak-28P** (Perekhvatchik; interceptor), the suffix 'P' indicating that the design had been *adapted* for the fighter role. Longer dielectric nosecone fitted retrospectively on many Yak-28Ps in squadron service does not indicate any increase in radar capability or aircraft performance. About 60 Yak-28P 'Firebars' continue to operate with the Soviet Voyska PVO home defence interceptor force.

Maestro (Yak-28U). Trainer version of 'Firebar'. Normal cockpit layout replaced by two individual single-seat cockpits in tandem, each with its own canopy. Front canopy sideways hinged to starboard; rear canopy rearward sliding.

The airframe of the Yak-28 has been described in previous editions of *Jane's*. The following details apply specifically to the Yak-28P:

POWER PLANT: Two afterburning turbojets, related to Tumansky R-11 fitted to some versions of MiG-21, with rating of 58.4 kN (13,120 lb st). A pointed external fuel tank can be carried under the leading-edge of each wing, outboard of the engine nacelle.

ACCOMMODATION: Crew of two in tandem on ejection seats in pressurised cabin under long rearward sliding transparent blister canopy.

ARMAMENT: Two pylons under each outer wing. Normal armament comprises two air-to-air missiles (NATO 'Anab'), with alternative infra-red or semi-active radar homing heads.

DIMENSIONS, EXTERNAL (estimated):

Wing span	12.95 m (42 ft 6 in)
Length overall:	
Yak-28P (long nose)	23.00 m (75 ft 5½ in)
Height overall	3.95 m (12 ft 11½ in)

WEIGHT (estimated):

Max T-O weight: Yak-28P	20,000 kg (44,000 lb)

PERFORMANCE (Yak-28P, estimated):

Max level speed at 10,670 m (35,000 ft)	
Mach 1.88 (1,080 knots; 2,000 km/h; 1,240 mph)	
Cruising speed	496 knots (920 km/h; 571 mph)
Service ceiling	16,750 m (55,000 ft)
Max combat radius	500 nm (925 km; 575 miles)

YAKOVLEV Yak-36MP/Yak-38
NATO reporting name: Forger

Known originally as the **Yak-36MP** (Morskoy Palubnyi: maritime carrier-borne), the **Yak-38** is the V/STOL combat aircraft deployed by a Soviet Navy development squadron on the *Kiev*, the first of its class of four 40,000 ton carrier/cruisers to put to sea in 1976, and subsequently on its sister ships, the *Minsk*, *Novorossiysk* and *Baku*. Experimental operation from specially configured Ro/Ro ships has also been reported. The Yak-38 remains the only operational jet combat aircraft that shares the V/STOL capability of the Harrier, but requires three engines, rather than one, to make this possible. Two versions have been observed, as follows:

Forger-A. Basic single-seat combat aircraft, utilising a mixture of vectored thrust and direct jet lift. Prototype was completed in 1971 and production began in 1975. Twelve appear to be operational on each ship, in addition to 'Forger-Bs' and about 19 Kamov Ka-25 or Ka-27

Version of the Yak-28 known to NATO as 'Brewer-D' *(Flug Revue)*

anti-submarine and missile targeting helicopters. Primary roles assumed to be reconnaissance, strikes against small ships, and fleet defence against shadowing maritime reconnaissance aircraft.

Forger-B. Two-seat trainer, of which two are deployed on each carrier/cruiser. Second cockpit forward of normal cockpit, with ejection seat at a lower level, under a continuous transparent canopy. To compensate for the longer nose, a plug is inserted in the fuselage aft of the wing, lengthening the constant-section portion without requiring modification of the tapering rear fuselage assembly. In other respects this version appears to be identical to 'Forger-A', but has no ranging radar or weapon pylons.

Observers of deck flying by 'Forger-As' report that the aircraft appear to be extremely stable during take-off and landing. Initially, take-off was always made vertically, with the vectored thrust nozzles up to 10° forward of vertical. This was followed by a smooth conversion about 5 to 6 m (15-20 ft) above the deck, achieved by lowering the aircraft's nose about 5° below the horizon and maintaining this attitude until the aircraft had accelerated to 30-40 knots (55-75 km/h; 35-46 mph). At this speed, a 5° nose-up attitude was assumed, and the accelerating transition was continued by vectoring aft the nozzles of the propulsion engine.

This VTO technique has been superseded by a STOL type of take-off, with a short forward run, made possible by an automatic control system which ensures "that the lift engines are brought into use, and the thrust vectoring rear nozzles rotated, at the optimum point in the take-off run". STOL take-off can be assumed to offer improved payload/range capability.

Landing procedure begins with a gradual descent from far astern, with the last 400 m (1,300 ft) flown essentially level, about 30 m (100 ft) above the water. The aircraft crosses the ship's stern with about a 5 knot (10 km/h; 6 mph) closure rate, 10-14 m (35-45 ft) above the flight deck, then flares gently to a hover and descends vertically. Precise landings are ensured by the automatic control system, perhaps in association with laser devices lining each side of the rear deck.

Development has been continuous throughout the period since the Yak-38 was first seen on the *Kiev*. Some early 'Forger-As' lacked the now standard auxiliary intake doors aft of each engine air intake. A fence has been added on each side of the hinged door above the liftjets, extending back to a station in line with the wingroot leading-edge, presumably to prevent ingestion of reflected exhaust efflux. Production is thought to have totalled some 75 aircraft by October 1986; the rate is said to have been reduced drastically since then.

The following description applies to the single-seat 'Forger-A':

TYPE: Ship based V/STOL combat aircraft.

WINGS: Cantilever mid-wing monoplane, of very small area. Thickness/chord ratio estimated at 6 per cent or less. Constant anhedral from roots. Sweepback on leading-edge approx 45°. Conventional light alloy structure. Each wing comprises two all-metal panels of approx equal span, of which the outer panel folds vertically upward for stowage on board ship. Inboard panel has unswept trailing-edge, occupied by a large single-slotted Fowler flap. Outer panel has a slightly sweptback trailing-edge, occupied almost entirely by an aileron with setback hinges and inset trim tab. No leading-edge flaps or slats. Jet reaction control valve with upper and lower slots in each wingtip.

FUSELAGE: Conventional semi-monocoque light alloy structure of oval cross-section. Integral engine air intake ducts, with boundary layer splitter plates and downward inclined lips forward of rear edge of transparent cockpit canopy. Row of small blow-in auxiliary intake doors a short distance aft of each intake. Rearward hinged door over liftjets, immediately aft of canopy, with 16 spring loaded louvres. Location of corresponding side-hinged underfuselage doors conforms with forward tilt of lift engines. Positions of these doors are controlled automatically during take-off and landing as part of control system. Fence on each side of door above liftjets. Small fence aft of each door beneath liftjets. Yaw reaction control nozzle to each side of small tailcone. No reaction control system in nose.

TAIL UNIT: Conventional light alloy structure, with sweepback on all surfaces and considerable tailplane anhedral. Rudder and each elevator have setback hinges and trim tab. Air intake at front of long duct extending forward from base of fin, to cool avionics bay in rear fuselage.

LANDING GEAR: Retractable tricycle type. Single wheel on each unit, with legs of trailing link type with oleo-pneumatic shock absorption. Nose unit retracts rearward, main units forward into fuselage. Small bumper under upward curving rear fuselage.

POWER PLANT: Primary power plant is a Tumansky R-27V-300 turbojet (68 kN; 15,300 lb st), mounted in the centre-fuselage and exhausting through a single pair of hydraulically actuated vectoring side nozzles aft of the wings. No afterburner is fitted. Two Koliesov/Rybinsk RD-36-35FVR liftjets (each approx 30 kN; 6,725 lb st) in tandem immediately aft of cockpit, inclined forward at 13° from vertical, exhausting downward, and used also to adjust pitch and trim. Fuel tanks in fuselage, forward and aft of main engine. Drop tanks, each estimated to have capacity of 600 litres (158 US gallons; 132 Imp gallons), can be carried on underwing pylons.

ACCOMMODATION: Pilot only, on zero-speed/zero-height ejection seat, under sideways hinged (to starboard) transparent canopy. Electronic system ejects pilot automatically if aircraft height and descent rate are

The two-seat training version of the Yak-38 ('Forger-B')

Yakovlev Yak-38 single-seat V/STOL carrier based combat aircraft (NATO 'Forger-A') *(Jane's/Mike Keep)*

Yakovlev Yak-42 short/medium-range transport (three Lotarev D-36 turbofans)

sensed to indicate an emergency. Armoured glass windscreen.

AVIONICS: Ranging radar in nose. IFF (NATO 'Odd Rods') antennae forward of windscreen. Other avionics in rear fuselage. Fully automatic control system for use during take-off and landing, to ensure synchronisation of engine functioning, aerodynamic control operation, jet reaction nozzle operation, stabilisation and guidance.

ARMAMENT: No installed armament. Two pylons under fixed panel of each wing for 2,600-3,600 kg (5,730-7,935 lb) of external stores, including gun pods each containing a 23 mm twin-barrel GSh-23 cannon, rocket packs, bombs weighing up to 500 kg each, short-range air-to-surface missiles (NATO 'Kerry'), armour-piercing anti-ship missiles, air-to-air missiles ('Aphid') and auxiliary fuel tanks.

DIMENSIONS, EXTERNAL (estimated):

Wing span	7.32 m (24 ft 0 in)
Width, wings folded	4.88 m (16 ft 0 in)
Length overall: 'Forger-A'	15.50 m (50 ft 10¼ in)
'Forger-B'	17.68 m (58 ft 0 in)
Height overall	4.37 m (14 ft 4 in)
Tailplane span	3.81 m (12 ft 6 in)
Wheel track	2.90 m (9 ft 6 in)
Wheelbase	5.50 m (18 ft 0 in)

AREA (estimated):

Wings, gross	18.5 m² (199 sq ft)

WEIGHTS (estimated):

Basic operating weight, incl pilot(s):

'Forger-A'	7,485 kg (16,500 lb)
'Forger-B'	8,390 kg (18,500 lb)
Max T-O weight	11,700 kg (25,795 lb)

PERFORMANCE ('Forger-A', estimated, at max T-O weight):

Max level speed at height

Mach 0.95 (545 knots; 1,009 km/h; 627 mph)

Max level speed at S/L

Mach 0.8 (528 knots; 978 km/h; 608 mph)

Max rate of climb at S/L	4,500 m (14,750 ft)/min
Service ceiling	12,000 m (39,375 ft)

Combat radius:

with air-to-air missiles and external tanks, 75 min on station 100 nm (185 km; 115 miles)

with max weapons, lo-lo-lo

130 nm (240 km; 150 miles)

with max weapons, hi-lo-hi

200 nm (370 km; 230 miles)

YAKOVLEV Yak-41

The existence of this second-generation Yakovlev V/STOL fighter/attack aircraft was revealed by Rear Admiral William O. Studeman, USN, in Spring 1988. Its general configuration is shown in an accompanying DoD artist's impression of a Yak-41 on the deck of the Soviet Navy carrier *Tbilisi*. In fact, this aircraft had not yet carried out ship trials by early 1990, and there is no certainty that it will be based on the new class of 65,000 ton carriers. It may supersede Yak-38s on the smaller carrier/cruisers of the 'Kiev' class.

The artist's impression is based on initial overhead satellite photography, and gives no suggestion of the engine configuration. A press report has suggested that the Yak-41 is powered by a single vectored-thrust turbofan, designed under the leadership of Eng Khachaturov, on the lines of the Harrier's Rolls-Royce Pegasus. However, a liftjet/vectored-thrust multi-engine power plant similar to that of the Yak-38 seems equally likely. Evolutionary changes by comparison with the Yak-38 include a refined airframe configuration with twin tail fins, a nose radar with lookdown/shootdown capability, and supersonic performance.

YAKOVLEV Yak-42
NATO reporting name: Clobber

On the basis of experience with the Yak-40, the Yakovlev Design Bureau developed for Aeroflot this larger civil airliner with a similar three-engined layout. The basic design objectives were simple construction, reliability in

Artist's impression of Yak-41 on deck of carrier *Tbilisi (US Department of Defense)*

Yakovlev Yak-38 (NATO 'Forger-A') V/STOL combat aircraft on the carrier/cruiser *Novorossiysk.* **Note the underwing gun and rocket pods** *(Royal Navy)*

operation, economy, and the ability to operate in remote areas with widely differing climatic conditions. Up to 2,000 aircraft in this category were needed, for use particularly on feederline services extending north and south from the main east-west trans-Siberian trunk routes.

Three prototypes of the Yak-42 were ordered initially. The first of these (SSSR-1974) flew for the first time on 7

March 1975, with a wing sweepback of 11°, and was furnished as a 100-passenger local service version with carry-on baggage and coat stowage fore and aft of the cabin. The second prototype (SSSR-1975) had 23° of wing sweep, and cabin windows which extended further forward and rearward on each side, indicating that it was representative of the 120-seat version with three more rows of seats and no carry-on baggage areas. The third prototype (SSSR-1976; re-registered subsequently as SSSR-42303) differed from the second only in detail, having hot air de-icing on the tail surfaces as well as the wings; fairing discs over the mainwheels and longer leg fairings to improve airflow over the doorless main landing gear when retracted; and movement further forward of the overwing emergency exits.

It was made known that a decision on the degree of wing sweep to be standardised for production aircraft would be taken after simultaneous evaluation of the prototypes, in terms of high speed cruise, economy and low speed handling characteristics. The 23° wing showed itself superior, and aircraft No. SSSR-42303, exhibited at the 1977 Paris Salon, was generally typical of the first series of production Yak-42s, built at Smolensk to replace some Tu-134s in Aeroflot service. Further changes introduced on production aircraft include the use of four-wheel main landing gear bogies instead of the twin-wheel units fitted to the prototypes.

The Yak-42 entered scheduled passenger service with Aeroflot in late 1980, operating first over the Moscow-Krasnodar route. Seventy had been built by Spring 1990. Other customers include China and Indian Airlines, which announced an order for two in Autumn 1989.

Design is in accordance with airworthiness standards of the Soviet civil authorities and US FAR 25 requirements. Special care was taken during design to ensure that the D-36 engines conform with national and international limits on smoke and noise; and the Yak-42 is intended to operate in temperatures ranging from −50°C to +50°C. An APU is standard, for engine starting and ground services, making the aircraft independent of airport equipment.

The following details refer to the Yak-42 in its current production form. Wing span is increased by 48 cm (1 ft 7 in) and max T-O weight by 500 kg (1,102 lb) by comparison with early aircraft.

TYPE: Three-turbofan short/medium-range passenger transport.

WINGS: Cantilever low-wing monoplane, consisting of a centre-section and two outer panels. No dihedral or anhedral. Sweepback 23° at quarter-chord. All-metal two-spar torsion box structure. Two-section aileron on each wing, with servo tab on inner section and trim tab on outer section. Two-section single-slotted trailing-edge flaps on each wing. Three-section spoilers forward of outer flaps. Full span leading-edge flaps. Ailerons and flaps actuated hydraulically.

FUSELAGE: All-metal riveted, bonded and welded semi-monocoque structure, of basic circular section, blending into an oval section rear fuselage.

TAIL UNIT: Cantilever all-metal T tail structure, with sweepback on all surfaces. One-piece tailplane; incidence variable from 4° upward to 8° downward. Trim tab in each elevator. Trim tab and spring servo tab in rudder. Control surfaces actuated hydraulically.

LANDING GEAR: Hydraulically retractable tricycle heavy-duty type. Four-wheel bogie main units retract inward into flattened fuselage undersurface. Twin nosewheels retract forward. Hydraulic backup system for extension only. Emergency extension by gravity. Oleo-nitrogen shock absorbers. Steerable nose unit of levered suspension type. Low pressure tyres; size 930 × 305 on nosewheels. Hydraulic disc brakes on mainwheels. Nosewheel brakes to stop wheel rotation after take-off.

POWER PLANT: Three Lotarev D-36 three-shaft turbofans, each rated at 63.74 kN (14,330 lb st). Centre engine, mounted inside rear fuselage, has S-duct air intake. Outboard engines are mounted in pod on each side of rear fuselage. No thrust reversers. Integral fuel tanks between spars in wings, capacity approx 23,175 litres (6,120 US gallons; 5,100 Imp gallons). APU standard, for engine starting, and for power and air-conditioning supply on ground and, if necessary, in flight.

ACCOMMODATION: Crew of two side by side on flight deck, with provision for flight engineer if required, and two or three cabin attendants. Single passenger cabin, with total of 120 seats in six-abreast rows, at pitch of 75 cm (29.5 in), with centre aisle, 45 cm (17.7 in) wide, in high-density configuration. Alternative 104-passenger (96 tourist, 8 first class) local service configuration, with carry-on baggage and coat stowage compartments fore and aft of cabin. Main airstair door hinges down from undersurface of rear fuselage. Second door forward of cabin on port side, with integral airstairs. Service door opposite. Galley and crew coat stowage between flight deck and front vestibule. Passenger coat stowage and toilet between vestibule and cabin. Second coat stowage and toilet at rear of cabin. Two underfloor holds for cargo, mail and

Yakovlev Yak-42 three-turbofan short/medium-range passenger transport *(Pilot Press)*

baggage in nets or standard containers, loaded through a door on the starboard side, forward of wing. Chain-drive handling system for containers built into cabin floor. Forward hold accommodates six containers, each with capacity of 2.2 m³ (77.7 cu ft); rear hold takes three similar containers. Provision for convertible passenger/cargo interior, with enlarged loading door on port side of front fuselage. Two emergency exits overwing on each side. All passenger and crew accommodation pressurised and air-conditioned, and furnished with non-flammable materials.

AVIONICS AND EQUIPMENT: Flight and navigation equipment for operation by day and night under adverse weather conditions, with landings on concrete or unpaved runways in ICAO Category II weather minima down to 40 m (131 ft) visibility at 300 m (985 ft). Type SAU-42 automatic flight control system and area navigation system standard.

DIMENSIONS, EXTERNAL:

Wing span	34.88 m (114 ft 5¼ in)
Wing aspect ratio	8.11
Length overall	36.38 m (119 ft 4¼ in)
Fuselage diameter	3.80 m (12 ft 5½ in)
Height overall	9.83 m (32 ft 3 in)
Tailplane span	10.80 m (35 ft 5 in)
Wheel track	5.63 m (18 ft 5¾ in)
Wheelbase	14.78 m (48 ft 6 in)
Passenger door (fwd):	
Height	1.81 m (5 ft 11¼ in)
Width	0.83 m (2 ft 8½ in)
Passenger entrance (rear): Height	1.78 m (5 ft 10 in)
Width	0.81 m (2 ft 7¾ in)
Cargo door (convertible version):	
Height	2.025 m (6 ft 7¾ in)
Width	3.23 m (10 ft 7 in)
Baggage/cargo hold door: Height	1.35 m (4 ft 5 in)
Width	1.145 m (3 ft 9 in)
Height to sill	1.45 m (4 ft 9 in)

DIMENSIONS, INTERNAL:

Cabin: Length	19.89 m (65 ft 3 in)
Max width	3.60 m (11 ft 9¾ in)
Max height	2.08 m (6 ft 9¾ in)
Forward baggage compartment volume (100-seater)	
	19.8 m³ (700 cu ft)
Rear baggage compartment volume (100-seater)	
	9.5 m³ (335 cu ft)

AREAS:

Wings, gross	150 m² (1,615 sq ft)
Vertical tail surfaces (total)	23.29 m² (250.7 sq ft)
Horizontal tail surfaces (total)	27.60 m² (297.1 sq ft)

WEIGHTS:

Weight empty, equipped:	
104 seats	34,555 kg (76,180 lb)
120 seats	34,580 kg (76,236 lb)
Max payload	12,800 kg (28,220 lb)
Max fuel	18,500 kg (40,785 lb)
Max T-O weight	56,500 kg (124,560 lb)
Max landing weight	50,500 kg (111,333 lb)

PERFORMANCE:

Max cruising speed at 7,620 m (25,000 ft)	
	437 knots (810 km/h; 503 mph)
Econ cruising speed	400 knots (740 km/h; 460 mph)
T-O speed	119 knots (220 km/h; 137 mph) IAS
Approach speed	114 knots (210 km/h; 131 mph) IAS
Max cruising height	9,600 m (31,500 ft)
T-O balanced field length	2,200 m (7,220 ft)
Landing from 15 m (50 ft)	1,100 m (3,610 ft)

Range at econ cruising speed, with 3,000 kg (6,615 lb) fuel reserves:

with max payload	702 nm (1,300 km; 807 miles)
with 120 passengers (10,800 kg; 23,810 lb payload)	
	1,025 nm (1,900 km; 1,180 miles)
with 104 passengers (9,360 kg; 20,635 lb payload)	
	1,240 nm (2,300 km; 1,430 miles)
with max fuel	2,105 nm (3,900 km; 2,423 miles)

YAKOVLEV Yak-42M

This is a stretched version of the Yak-42, in which the fuselage is lengthened by 4.50 m (14 ft 9 in), to accommodate 156 to 168 passengers. The original D-36 engines are replaced by three Lotarev D-436 turbofans, each rated at 73.6 kN (16,550 lb st), with thrust reversers. The wings have a supercritical section, increased sweepback (25°), double-slotted flaps and winglets. Fly by wire flight controls and a five-tube EFIS are standard. Navigation equipment is also upgraded. First flight is expected in 1992. Aeroflot plans to buy 200.

DIMENSIONS, EXTERNAL:

Wing span	36.25 m (118 ft 11¼ in)
Wing aspect ratio	10.5

WEIGHT:

Max T-O weight	66,000 kg (145,505 lb)

PERFORMANCE (estimated):

Max cruising speed	448 knots (830 km/h; 515 mph)
Long-range cruising speed	
	432 knots (800 km/h; 497 mph)
Balanced T-O field length:	
at 62,000 kg (136,685 lb) AUW	1,800 m (5,900 ft)
at max T-O weight	2,300 m (7,550 ft)
Range:	
with 14,800 kg (32,625 lb) payload (156 passengers)	
	1,350 nm (2,500 km; 1,550 miles)
with 10,000 kg (22,050 lb) payload	
	2,025 nm (3,750 km; 2,330 miles)
Range with max fuel, with reserves	
	2,160 nm (4,000 km; 2,485 miles)

YAKOVLEV Yak-52

Production of this tandem two-seat piston engined primary trainer was entrusted to the Romanian aircraft industry (which see).

YAKOVLEV Yak-55/56/57

See Addenda.

AIRCRAFT OF UNKNOWN DESIGN

ASF. The ASF (air superiority fighter) is an offensive counter-air fighter that the Soviet Union is believed to be developing for initial operational capability in the late 1990s. Its manoeuvring capabilities will be significantly greater than those of the MiG-29 and Su-27.

CAF. The Soviet Union is developing in parallel with the ASF a new defensive counter-air fighter (CAF) with comparable manoeuvring capabilities. First flight is expected to take place by the mid-1990s, to permit an IOC before the end of the decade.

SOVIET AEROSPACECRAFT

SOVIET SPACE SHUTTLE

The Soviet space shuttle completed its first orbital mission successfully on 15 November 1988, in unmanned form. The orbiter, known as *Buran* (Snowstorm), was launched by an Energiya heavy-lift rocket vehicle from Baikonur Cosmodrome at 8 am local time. After two orbits, it was recovered 3 h 25 min later in a fully automatic landing on a runway 4,575 m (15,000 ft) long and 85 m (277 ft) wide, some 12 km (7.5 miles) from the launch pad.

Although the Soviet shuttle resembles its US counterpart superficially, there are significant differences. In particular, the four liquid oxygen/liquid hydrogen main engines are installed in the core component of Energiya instead of in the orbiter; and the four strap-on boosters run on oxygen/kerosene liquid propellants. Total thrust of the core component's four engines is about 5,783 kN (1,300,000 lb st). Each strap-on booster develops 7,117 kN (1,600,000 lb st). This configuration enables Energiya to be used as the launch vehicle for a variety of other payloads, as well as for shuttle missions. Thus, the Soviet Union has two vehicles rather than one, with the option of using Energiya by itself for payloads too large to be accommodated in the orbiter's payload bay.

The *Buran* orbiter flown on the first mission has a wing area and payload bay identical in size to those of the US orbiters. The wing is farther forward, to compensate for the absence of main engines in the rear fuselage, and the nosewheels are farther aft. The two-deck crew accommodation is slightly larger, with a volume of 70 m³ (2,472 cu ft), enabling up to ten cosmonauts to be carried on future manned flights, expected to begin in 1992. Four orbiters are being built under the current programme, for use in space station assembly missions, and for launching, retrieving and repairing satellites in orbit. Maximum payload is expected to be 30,400 kg (67,000 lb).

Buran weighed about 101,600 kg (224,000 lb) at lift-off in November 1988, but orbiters weighing up to 106,600 kg (235,000 lb) could be launched by the current configuration of Energiya. Total weight of the entire shuttle vehicle at lift-off was about 2,435,800 kg (5,370,000 lb). Its total thrust in vacuo built up to about 39,590 kN (8,900,000 lb) by the time the strap-on boosters separated. The four core engines continued running until a velocity of more than 7,620 m (25,000 ft)/s had been attained, eight minutes into the mission, at a height of 100 km (62 miles). Core separation

Buran **space shuttle orbiter on its Energiya launch rocket at Baikonur Cosmodrome** *(Tass)*

was effected by firing *Buran's* reaction control system thrusters. Orbital velocity was then achieved by firing *Buran's* two rear-mounted orbital manoeuvring system engines as it climbed to a height of about 160 km (100 miles). A second firing of these engines, 45 min into the mission, established *Buran* in a 250 km (155 mile) circular orbit, at an inclination of 51.6°.

Off the coast of Chile, over the Pacific, 2 h 20 min after lift-off, the orbiter was turned tail-first, so that its orbital manoeuvring system engines could be retrofired to initiate re-entry. Temperatures on some areas of the 40° nose-up airframe reached 1,535°C (2,800°F) during re-entry into the

atmosphere at Mach 25, when the orbiter was protected by 38,000 ceramic tiles. After a smooth touchdown on the runway at 183 knots (340 km/h; 211 mph), three cruciform braking parachutes were deployed to slow the orbiter.

DIMENSIONS, EXTERNAL (*Buran*):

Wing span	24.00 m (78 ft 9 in)
Length overall	36.40 m (119 ft 5 in)

DIMENSIONS, INTERNAL (*Buran*):

Payload bay: Length	18.30 m (60 ft 0 in)
Max width	4.60 m (15 ft 1 in)

AREA:

Wings, gross	250 m² (2,691 sq ft)

UNITED KINGDOM

BAe
BRITISH AEROSPACE PLC

HEADQUARTERS: 11 Strand, London WC2N 5JT
Telephone: 44 (71) 930 1020
Telex: 919221
Fax: 44 (71) 839 4774
CHAIRMAN: Professor Roland Smith, BA, MSc, PhD (Econ)
CHIEF EXECUTIVE: Richard Evans, CBE
DEPUTY CHIEF EXECUTIVE, ENGINEERING:
  I. R. Yates, CBE, BEng, FEng, FRAeS, FIMechE
DIRECTOR OF PUBLIC AFFAIRS: Jeremy Wooding
MANAGER, MEDIA RELATIONS: Irene Dodgson

The history of British Aerospace has been recorded in detail in previous editions of *Jane's*. The group, employing 130,000 people in the UK and overseas, changed its management structure early in 1989 by devolving responsi-

bility for business operations to its divisions and subsidiary companies. The Military Aircraft, Commercial Aircraft, Space Systems and Dynamics Divisions, with Royal Ordnance PLC and Rover Group (Holdings) PLC, became subsidiary companies. Another subsidiary, BAe Enterprises Ltd, operates the British Aerospace Flying College at Prestwick; Aerostructures Hamble Ltd; British Aerospace Simulation Ltd; British Aerospace Australia Ltd; and Steinheil Optronik GmbH.

British Aerospace has further overseas subsidiaries, including Arkansas Modification Centre, Little Rock, Arkansas, USA; British Aerospace Inc; British Scandinavian Aviation AB; and Ballast Nedam BV; as well as the following additional UK subsidiaries: British Aerospace (Insurance) Ltd, British Aerospace (Insurance Brokers) Ltd, and British Aerospace (Pension Fund Trustees) Ltd.

Associated companies include SEPECAT (formed in May 1966 by BAC and Breguet Aviation to control development and production of the Jaguar tactical strike fighter and trainer), Panavia Aircraft GmbH (see International section), Eurofighter Jagdflugzeug GmbH (see International section), British Aerospace (Holdings) Inc (formed to group all aerospace, defence and automotive interests in North America), and Arab-British Dynamics Co (inaugurated in 1977 by BAC Guided Weapons Division and the Egyptian government to manufacture the Swingfire missile in Egypt).

British Aerospace is a 20 per cent partner in the Airbus Industrie international consortium, and is a partner in Euromissile Dynamics Group (EMDG), formed with MBB and Aerospatiale for the development and production of anti-tank missiles.

BRITISH AEROSPACE (COMMERCIAL AIRCRAFT) LTD

HATFIELD: Hatfield, Hertfordshire AL10 9TL
Telephone: 44 (707) 262345
Telex: 22411
CIVIL MARKETING OPERATIONS CENTRE: PO Box 81, Hatfield, Hertfordshire AL10 9PL
Telephone: 44 (707) 268123
Telex: 826 876
Fax: 44 (707) 261696
BRISTOL: Filton House, Bristol BS99 7AR
Telephone: 44 (272) 693831
Telex: 44163
CHADDERTON: Chadderton Works, Greengate, Middleton, Manchester M24 1SA
Telephone: 44 (61) 681 2020
Telex: 667015
CHESTER: Broughton, near Chester, Clwyd CH4 0DR
Telephone: 44 (244) 535333
Telex: 61201
PRESTWICK: Prestwick Airport, Ayrshire KA9 2RW
Telephone: 44 (292) 79888
Telex: 77432

WOODFORD: Woodford Aerodrome, Chester Road, Woodford, Cheshire CK7 1QR
Telephone: 44 (61) 439 5050
Telex: 668939/667545
CHAIRMAN: S. Gillibrand, MSc, CEng, FRAeS
MANAGING DIRECTOR: R. M. McKinlay
TECHNICAL DIRECTOR: J. B. Scott-Wilson, MA, FRAeS
SENIOR VICE-PRESIDENT, MARKETING DEVELOPMENT:
  Denis Little
HEAD OF PUBLIC AFFAIRS: I. Woodward
DIRECTOR, PUBLIC RELATIONS AND PUBLICITY:
  David A. Dorman
PUBLIC RELATIONS MANAGER, HATFIELD: M. V. Brown
PUBLIC RELATIONS OFFICER, CHESTER: Ms K. Roden
PUBLIC RELATIONS MANAGER, PRESTWICK: Ms C. Lang
PUBLIC RELATIONS MANAGER, AIRBUS DIVISION: H. Berry
PUBLIC RELATIONS MANAGER, MANCHESTER: H. Holmes
PUBLIC RELATIONS MANAGER, FILTON: Mrs P. Telling
PUBLIC RELATIONS MANAGER, CORPORATE AIRCRAFT DIVISION:
  A. Piper

BAe Commercial Aircraft, centred at Hatfield, is subdivided into three profit-accountable sections: Airbus Division at Filton and Chester; Airlines Division at

Hatfield, Prestwick, Woodford and Chadderton; and Corporate Aircraft Division, also at Chester. It is responsible for design, development, production, marketing and support of the BAe 146 regional jet airliner, the BAe 125 business jet, the Jetstream Super 31 airliner, corporate and executive aircraft, the Jetstream 41 airliner and the Advanced Turboprop (ATP) transport. The company is also responsible for the Rombac 1-11 licence manufacturing programme with Romania; design, development and production of wings for all European Airbus transport aircraft (more than 40 sets delivered in 1988); VC10 conversion to the air to air refuelling role for the Royal Air Force; and F-111 maintenance under USAF contract. The company also supplies civil aircraft design, development, research, support, modification and refurbishing services. All marketing, sales and support activities are centred at the Civil Marketing Operations Centre at Hatfield. In 1989, BAe received record orders for 182 civil aircraft of five types.

BRITISH AEROSPACE (MILITARY AIRCRAFT) LTD

BROUGH: Brough, North Humberside HU15 1EQ
Telephone: 44 (482) 667121
Telex: 52634 BAEBRO G
DUNSFOLD: Dunsfold Aerodrome, Godalming, Surrey, GU8 4BS
Telephone: 44 (483) 272121
Telex: 859475 BAEDUN G
KINGSTON: Richmond Road, Kingston upon Thames, Surrey KT2 5QS
Telephone: 44 (81) 784 4700
Telex: 23726 BAEKIN G
Fax: 44 (81) 784 4801
PRESTON: Strand Road, Preston, Lancashire PR1 8UD
Telephone: 44 (772) 54722
Telex: 67616 BAEP G
SAMLESBURY: Samlesbury, Balderstone, Lancashire BB2 7LF
Telephone: 44 (25 481) 2371
Telex: 63435 BAES G

WARTON: Warton Aerodrome, Preston, Lancashire PR4 1AX
Telephone: 44 (772) 633333
Telex: 67627 BAEWAA G
CHAIRMAN: S. Gillibrand, MSc, SEng, FRAes
MANAGING DIRECTOR: J. P. Weston, MA(Eng)
TECHNICAL DIRECTOR: D. Gardner, BTech, DLC, CEng, FRAeS
VICE-PRESIDENT PUBLIC AFFAIRS: (BAe Defence Companies, Kingston): R. Gardner
HEAD OF PUBLIC AFFAIRS: David Mason
PUBLIC RELATIONS MANAGER, BROUGH: E. Barker
PUBLIC RELATIONS MANAGER, KINGSTON: J. Godden
PUBLIC RELATIONS MANAGER, WARTON: D. M. Kamiya

The year 1989 saw the expansion of BAe (Military Aircraft) Ltd at its new headquarters, Warton, and the establishment of departments at other Military Aircraft sites.

Main activities of this company include the development, in partnership with West Germany, Italy and Spain, of the European Fighter Aircraft (EFA); design and development

of the Experimental Aircraft Programme (EAP) technology demonstrator; design, development, production and support, with MBB and Aeritalia, of the Panavia Tornado; design, development, production and support of the V/STOL Harrier and Sea Harrier and, with McDonnell Douglas, of the AV-8B/GR. Mk 5/7 Harrier for the USMC and RAF, respectively, and the T-45A Goshawk for the US Navy; design, development, production and support of the Hawk attack/advanced jet trainer and Hawk 200 single-seat lightweight fighter.

In addition to major contracts for the update of RAF Phantom and Buccaneer aircraft, the company undertakes conversion programmes for the Canberra light bomber and target facilities aircraft, and makes major contributions to the BAe 146 and the Airbus family of airliners. Full product support services are provided for earlier aircraft still in service throughout the world.

The company offers a wide range of defence support services and additionally offers overseas and specialist training facilities covering a wide range of technical and management courses.

BRITISH AEROSPACE (DYNAMICS) LTD

CHAIRMAN: R. H. Evans, CBE
MANAGING DIRECTOR: N. V. Barber, BA, MSc, FRAeS
  Formed on 1 January 1989, BAE (Dynamics) Ltd

incorporates the former Air Weapons Division (Hatfield and Lostock); Army Weapons Division (Stevenage); and Naval and Electronic Systems Division (Bristol, Bracknell, Plymouth and Weymouth). The separate components were

first grouped together on 1 January 1988, and for that year only were known collectively as BAe Dynamics Division. Details of missiles and weapon systems will be found in the appropriate *Jane's* yearbooks.

BRITISH AEROSPACE (SPACE SYSTEMS) LTD

STEVENAGE: Argyle Way, Stevenage, Hertfordshire SG1 2AS
Telephone: 44 (438) 313456
Telex: 82130/82197

BRISTOL: PO Box No. 5, Filton, Bristol BS12 7QW
Telephone: 44 (272) 693831
Telex: 449452
CHAIRMAN: Admiral Sir Raymond Lygo, KCB, RN (Retd)
MANAGING DIRECTOR: J. A. Holt, MSc, BSc, CEng, MRAeS
PUBLIC RELATIONS MANAGER: J. Humby
  The Space and Communications Division is responsible

for the Skynet 4 UK military communications satellite programme, civil communications satellites, and pallets for the US Space Shuttle, as described in *Jane's Spaceflight Directory*. The Division is also responsible for development of the unmanned re-usable single-stage Hotol space transport, of which brief details are given in this section of *All the World's Aircraft*.

BAe JETSTREAM SUPER 31

Development of this current version of the Jetstream was launched by British Aerospace on 5 December 1978. A development aircraft (G-JSSD), converted from a Jetstream 1 built by Handley Page, flew for the first time on 28 March 1980. Full production go-ahead was given in January 1982, and the first production Jetstream 31 (G-TALL) made its first flight on 18 March 1982. On 29 June 1982 the Jetstream 31 was certificated to BCAR Section D in the UK. US certification under SFAR 41C followed on 30 November 1982. German (LBA) certification was gained in July 1983, Australian (DoA) certification in February 1984, Swedish (BCA) in December 1984, Dutch (RLD) in January 1985 and Canadian (DoT) in May 1987. First deliveries, to

customers in Germany and the UK, took place in December 1982, and the 200th delivery was made on 3 October 1988.

British Aerospace announced the Jetstream Super 31 at the 1987 Paris Air Show. This current production version provides significant improvements in performance and passenger comfort, and wider flexibility for regional and interline operations. These benefits derive from introduction of more powerful Garrett TPE331-12 turboprops, flat rated to give 760 kW (1,020 shp) at temperatures up to 25°C. The new power plant gives an 8 per cent power improvement at temperatures up to 20°C and, resulting from the flat rated characteristics, as much as 18 per cent power improvement at high altitude.

The Super 31 has a 400 kg (882 lb) increase in max T-O

weight and a 200 kg (441 lb) increase in zero-fuel weight. Internal changes include sidewash lighting; re-contoured furnishing panels giving 76 mm (3 in) increased width at head height; increased floor width and sunken aisle width; and window panels designed for reduced noise and vibration.

The first Jetstream Super 31 (also the 200th Jetstream built) was certificated on 7 October 1988 in the FAA's 19-seat Commuter category, formulated under FAR Pts 23-24. It was also certificated by the CAA on 6 September 1988 under the International Public Transport Category of BCAR Section D. First order, for 15 by Wings West of the USA, was announced on 13 October 1987, and 11 customers had 90 Super 31s on order by March 1990. At

BAe Jetstream Super 31 light transport of USAir Express

BAe Jetstream 31 twin-turboprop commuter/executive light transport *(Pilot Press)*

that time total orders for Jetstream 31s and Super 31s stood at 310, deliveries having totalled 15 and 32 respectively in 1989.

The following versions have been announced:

Airliner. Designed to carry 18/19 passengers. Able to operate up to 680 nm (1,260 km; 783 miles) stage length, without refuelling, with 18 passengers, baggage and full IFR reserves.

Corporate. Executive version, designed for eight to ten passengers, and able to carry nine passengers and baggage for 1,050 nm (1,945 km; 1,208 miles) with full IFR reserves. Typical interior has six fully reclining and swivelling chairs, a three-place divan, galley for hot and cold meal service, cocktail cabinet, wardrobe and washroom/toilet.

Executive Shuttle. Intended for the large company, shuttling its personnel between factories, or for the business charter market. With typical layout for 12 passengers, this version has a range of 1,050 nm (1,945 km; 1,208 miles) with full IFR reserves.

Special Role. Intended for various specialist applications such as military communications, casualty evacuation, multi-engine training, cargo operations, airfield calibration, resources survey and protection. A patrol version, designated **Jetstream 31EZ**, is available for operation in exclusive economic zones (ie offshore patrol and surveillance), with underbelly 360° scan radar, increased fuel, observation windows and searchlight. Two Jetstream 31 aircraft, specially equipped with Tornado IDS

avionics, were delivered to the Royal Saudi Air Force in November 1987 for navigator training.

A quick change (QC) facility allows conversion from 18-seat to 12/10-seat layouts in just a few hours. An underfuselage baggage pod, of 4.62 m (15 ft 2 in) external, and 3.21 m (10 ft 6½ in) internal length, provides stowage for an extra six cases and additional soft luggage. Penalties of pod fitment are a 3-4 knot (6-7.5 km/h; 3.5-4.5 mph) reduction in TAS at the cruise and a 1.5 per cent reduction in specific air range. A water methanol injection system has been developed for hot and high conditions, and the Super Jetstream 31 has been cleared for use from unsealed runways.

By the end of October 1989 the Jetstream 31 and Super 31 fleet had completed 1.28 million flying hours in 1.59 million flights.

TYPE: Commuter/executive light transport.

WINGS: Cantilever low-wing monoplane. Wing section NACA 63A418 at root, NACA 63A412 at tip. Dihedral 7° from roots. Incidence 2° at root, 0° at tip. Sweepback 0° 34′ at quarter-chord. Aluminium alloy fail-safe structure of front, main and rear spars, with chordwise ribs. Wing skins chemically etched and reinforced with bonded spanwise stringers. Aluminium alloy manually operated Frise ailerons. Hydraulically operated aluminium alloy double-slotted flaps. No slats or leading-edge flaps. Trim tab in each aileron. Goodrich rubber boot de-icing system for leading-edges.

FUSELAGE: Conventional aluminium alloy semi-monocoque fail-safe structure, with chemically milled skin panels. Nose and tail sections unpressurised.

TAIL UNIT: Cantilever two-spar aluminium alloy structure. Fixed incidence tailplane. Manually operated control surfaces. Trim tabs in rudder and each elevator. Goodrich rubber boot de-icing system for leading-edges.

LANDING GEAR: Retractable tricycle type, with nosewheel steering ($\pm$45°). Hydraulic retraction, mainwheels inward into wings, twin nosewheels forward. British Aerospace oleo-pneumatic shock absorbers in all units. Dunlop wheels and tyres: mainwheel tyres size 28 × 9.00-12, pressure 5.72 bars (83 lb/sq in); nosewheel tyres size 6.00-6, pressure 2.90 bars (42 lb/sq in). Anti-skid units.

POWER PLANT: Two 760 kW (1,020 shp) Garrett TPE331-12UAR turboprops, each driving a Dowty Aerospace four-blade variable- and reversible-pitch fully-feathering metal propeller. Fuel in integral tank in each wing, total capacity 1,850 litres (489 US gallons; 407 Imp gallons). Refuelling point on top of each outer wing. Automatic power reserve (APR) and water methanol injection optional.

ACCOMMODATION: Two seats side by side on flight deck, with provision for dual controls, though aircraft can be approved (subject to local regulations) for single pilot operation. Main cabin can be furnished in commuter layout for up to 19 passengers at 76/79 cm (30/31 in) pitch, or with executive interior for 8/10 passengers, but optional layouts are available, including a QC (quick change) option enabling an operator to change from an 18-seat layout to 12-seat executive configuration in around 1¼ hours. Downward opening passenger door, with integral airstairs, at rear of cabin on port side. Emergency exit over wing on each side. Baggage compartment in rear of cabin, aft of main door. Entire accommodation pressurised, heated, ventilated and air-conditioned. Toilet standard; galley and bar optional. Jetstream completion is by Field Aircraft at East Midlands Airport, Castle Donington, UK.

SYSTEMS: Air-conditioning system with cabin pressurisation at max differential of 0.38 bars (5.5 lb/sq in), providing a 2,440 m (8,000 ft) cabin altitude at 7,620 m (25,000 ft). Single hydraulic system, pressure 138 bars (2,000 lb/sq in), with two engine driven pumps, each capable of supplying 20.7 litres (5.46 US gallons; 4.55 Imp gallons)/min. One pump is capable of supplying all hydraulic systems. Combined air/oil reservoir, pressurised to 1.24 bars (18 lb/sq in), for main and emergency supply, for actuation of flaps, landing gear, brakes and nosewheel steering. APU optional.

AVIONICS: Standard Airliner avionics by Collins include dual VHF-22A com transceivers with CTL-22 controls; dual VIR-32 nav receivers with VOR/ILS/marker beacons and CTL-32 controls; dual RMI-36 radio magnetic indicators; ADF-60A with CTL-62 controller; DME-42 with IND-42C indicator; TDR-90 transponder with CTL-92 controller; WXR-270 colour weather radar with IND-270 display unit; dual Honeywell RD-450 horizontal situation indicators; dual Honeywell C-14 compass systems; dual Racal B692 communications control and public address system and six cabin loudspeakers. Optional Enhanced Specification avionics package adds Honeywell SPZ-500 automatic flight control system; dual Honeywell RD-550 horizontal situation indicators (replacing RD-450s); Collins DCP-270 information display control panel; Honeywell AL-245 altitude alert controller; dual Honeywell VG-14A vertical gyro subsystems, and toilet loudspeaker, to above. Standard flight deck equipment includes dual Honeywell GH-14 gyro horizons; dual Kollsman MAAS 39948 airspeed indicators, A.32069 vertical speed indicators and B.45152 encoding altimeters; dual Davtron M811B digital clocks/stopwatches; Aerospace Optics 84-207-1 flight director mode indicator, dual Aerospace Optics 99-230 marker beacon lights; SFENA H.301 standby artificial horizons, and Sangamo Weston S149-1-169 OAT gauge. Enhanced Specification adds or substitutes Honeywell AD-550C attitude director indicator, BA-141 encoding altitimeter, VS-200 vertical speed indicator and PC-500 autopilot controller to above.

DIMENSIONS, EXTERNAL:

Wing span	15.85 m (52 ft 0 in)
Wing chord: at root	2.19 m (7 ft 2½ in)
at tip	0.80 m (2 ft 7¼ in)
Wing aspect ratio	9.95
Length overall	14.37 m (47 ft 1½ in)
Length of fuselage	13.40 m (43 ft 11½ in)
Height overall	5.38 m (17 ft 8 in)
Fuselage: Max diameter	1.98 m (6 ft 6 in)
Tailplane span	6.60 m (21 ft 8 in)
Wheel track	5.94 m (19 ft 6 in)
Wheelbase	4.60 m (15 ft 1 in)
Propeller diameter	2.69 m (8 ft 10 in)
Passenger door: Height	1.42 m (4 ft 8 in)
Width	0.86 m (2 ft 10 in)
Emergency exits: Height	0.91 m (3 ft 0 in)
Width	0.56 m (1 ft 10 in)

DIMENSIONS, INTERNAL:

Cabin, excl flight deck: Length	7.39 m (24 ft 3 in)
Max width	1.85 m (6 ft 1 in)
Max height	1.80 m (5 ft 11 in)
Floor area	8.35 m² (90 sq ft)
Volume (trimmed aircraft)	16.99 m³ (600 cu ft)
Baggage compartment volume:	
Airliner	2.13-2.74 m³ (75.2-96.7 cu ft)
Corporate	1.34-1.48 m³ (47.2-52.2 cu ft)
Baggage pod (optional)	1.39 m³ (49 cu ft)

AREAS:

Wings, gross	25.20 m² (271.3 sq ft)
Ailerons, aft of hinge line (total)	1.52 m² (16.4 sq ft)
Trailing-edge flaps (total)	3.25 m² (35.0 sq ft)
Vertical tail surfaces (total)	7.72 m² (83.1 sq ft)
Horizontal tail surfaces (total)	7.80 m² (84.0 sq ft)

WEIGHTS AND LOADINGS:

Operating weight empty	4,578 kg (10,092 lb)
Baggage pod weight	59 kg (130 lb)
Max fuel	1,372 kg (3,024 lb)
Max payload	1,805 kg (3,980 lb)
Max capacity of baggage pod	197 kg (435 lb)
Max T-O weight	7,350 kg (16,204 lb)
Max ramp weight	7,400 kg (16,314 lb)
Max landing weight	7,080 kg (15,609 lb)
Max zero-fuel weight	6,500 kg (14,330 lb)
Max wing loading	291.6 kg/m² (59.72 lb/sq ft)
Max power loading	4.84 kg/kW (7.94 lb/shp)

PERFORMANCE (at max T-O weight, except where stated):

Max cruising speed at 4,570 m (15,000 ft)	
	264 knots (489 km/h; 304 mph)
Econ cruising speed at 7,620 m (25,000 ft)	
	244 knots (452 km/h; 281 mph)
Stalling speed, flaps down	86 knots (159 km/h; 99 mph)
Max rate of climb at S/L	683 m (2,240 ft)/min
Rate of climb at S/L, one engine out	137 m (450 ft)/min
Certificated ceiling	7,620 m (25,000 ft)
Service ceiling, one engine out	3,660 m (12,000 ft)
Min ground turning radius about nosewheel	
	6.50 m (21 ft 4 in)
T-O field length: BCAR Section D	1,440 m (4,724 ft)
T-O to 15 m (50 ft): SFAR 41C	975 m (3,200 ft)
Landing field length, at max landing weight:	
BCAR Section D	1,235 m (4,052 ft)
SFAR 41C/FAR 135	1,165 m (3,820 ft)
Accelerate/stop distance:	
SFAR 41C	1,362 m (4,470 ft)
Range with IFR reserves	
19 passengers	700 nm (1,296 km; 805 miles)
18 passengers, flight attendant and galley	
	600 nm (1,111 km; 690 miles)

BAe JETSTREAM 41

On 24 May 1989 British Aerospace announced development of this new version of the Jetstream. A full-scale cabin mockup was displayed at the 1989 Paris Air Show. The Jetstream 41 retains the same fuselage cross-section as the Super 31, but is 4.8 m (16 ft 0 in) longer, allowing it to seat up to 29 passengers in three-abreast configuration. Passenger entry is via an airstair door in the port forward

The 27/29-passenger BAe Jetstream 41 commuter airliner *(Pilot Press)*

fuselage. The wing is mounted lower on the fuselage so that the main spar no longer obstructs the cabin aisle, and a rearward-extended wingroot fairing encloses additional baggage space, replacing the Super 31's optional baggage pod. Other changes include increased wing span providing additional fuel capacity, twin wheels on main landing gear legs retracting forward, a V windscreen, duplicated control runs, and floor-mounted control columns replacing the control yokes of the smaller model.

British Aerospace's risk sharing partners in the programme are Field Aircraft Ltd of the UK, which is responsible for Jetstream completions, and Pilatus Flugzeugwerke AG of Switzerland, which will be responsible for manufacturing tail assemblies and ailerons. Gulfstream Aerospace Technologies of Oklahoma has been awarded a contract to produce 200 wing sets for the Jetstream 41, for delivery between 1990 and 2000. ML Slingsby Group will produce large composites components for the aircraft.

First flight of the Jetstream 41 is anticipated in early Summer 1991, with customer deliveries beginning in Autumn 1992 following certification to FAR/JAR 25 standards. A production rate of 35 aircraft per year is planned by the mid to late 1990s. By March 1990 British Aerospace had received a firm order for 10 Jetstream 41s from Pan Am Express, and held letters of intent or options on a further 100, including 50 options for American Eagle.

The description of the Jetstream Super 31 applies also to the Series 41 except as follows:
WINGS: Incidence 2.5°.
LANDING GEAR: Dunlop wheels and tyres: twin mainwheels on each leg, size 22 × 6.75, pressures 8.27 bars (120 lb/sq in); twin nosewheels, size 17 × 6.00, pressure 2.9 bars (42 lb/sq in). Dunlop three-rotor steel brakes; anti-skid standard. Steerable nosewheels, maximum steering angle 45°.
POWER PLANT: Two 1,118 kW (1,500 shp) Garrett TPE331-14HR(GR) flat rated turboprops, handed, each driving a five-blade constant-speed feathering McCauley metal propeller. Usable fuel capacity 3,273 litres (865 US gallons; 720 Imp gallons).
ACCOMMODATION: Flight crew of two; one attendant seated centrally at rear of cabin; and up to 29 passengers seated three-abreast at min seat pitch of 76.2 cm (30 in). Externally serviced toilet at rear on left side. Optional galley in 27-seat layout. Entrance door with integral airstair at front of cabin on port side. Emergency exit door over wing on each side and at rear of cabin on starboard side. Stowage for carry-on baggage in forward cabin on right side, coat stowage at forward and rear of cabin. Main baggage hold at rear of cabin, volume 4.81m³ (170 cu ft), with external door; additional baggage stowage in ventral wingroot fairing, volume 0.99 m³ (35 cu ft).
SYSTEMS: Normalair-Garrett air-conditioning system with cabin pressurisation at max differential 0.39 bars (5.7 lb/sq in).
AVIONICS: Honeywell Primus II four-tube EFIS standard. Dual nav/com with VOR/ILS/markers; ADF; DME; dual transponders; flight director; and weather radar standard. Five-tube EFIS and autopilot optional.

DIMENSIONS, EXTERNAL:

Wing span	18.29 m (60 ft 0 in)
Wing chord: at root	2.70 m (8 ft 10½ in)
at tip	0.71 m (2 ft 4 in)
Wing aspect ratio	10.3
Length overall	19.25 m (63 ft 2 in)
Height	5.74 m (18 ft 10 in)
Tailplane span	6.68 m (21 ft 11 in)
Wheel track	6.10 m (20 ft 0 in)
Wheelbase	7.32 m (24 ft 0 in)
Propeller diameter	2.84 m (9 ft 4 in)
Propeller ground clearance	0.46 m (1 ft 6 in)
Passenger door: Height	1.42 m (4 ft 8 in)
Width	0.74 m (2 ft 5 in)
Height to sill	1.24 m (4 ft 1 in)
Baggage door: Height	1.22 m (4 ft 0 in)
Width	1.35 m (4 ft 5 in)
Height to sill	1.68 m (5 ft 6 in)
Emergency exits, over wing: Height	0.99 m (3 ft 3 in)
Width	0.51 m (1 ft 8 in)
Emergency exits, rear: Height	1.22 m (4 ft 0 in)
Width	0.51 m (1 ft 8 in)

DIMENSIONS, INTERNAL:

Cabin: Length	9.55 m (31 ft 4 in)
Max width	1.85 m (6 ft 1 in)
Height	1.78 m (5 ft 10 in)
Volume	29.45 m³ (1,040 cu ft)

AREAS:

Wings, gross	32.59 m² (350.8 sq ft)
Ailerons (total)	1.94 m² (20.90 sq ft)
Trailing-edge flaps (total)	5.28 m² (56.8 sq ft)
Spoilers (total)	0.91 m² (9.78 sq ft)
Rudder, incl tab	2.03 m² (21.87 sq ft)
Tailplane	8.58 m² (92.35 sq ft)
Elevators, incl tabs	2.43 m² (26.18 sq ft)

WEIGHTS AND LOADINGS:

Weight empty	6,143 kg (13,544 lb)
Max fuel weight	2,495 kg (5,500 lb)
Max T-O weight	10,150 kg (22,377 lb)
Max ramp weight	10,200 kg (22,487 lb)
Max zero-fuel weight	9,000 kg (19,842 lb)
Max landing weight	9,850 kg (21,715 lb)
Max wing loading	311.5 kg/m² (63.8 lb/sq ft)
Max power loading	4.54 kg/kW (7.46 lb/shp)

PERFORMANCE (estimated, at max T-O weight, ISA, except where indicated):

Never-exceed speed:	
to 5,300 m (17,400 ft)	
	315 knots (583 km/h; 362 mph) CAS
above 5,300 m (17,400 ft)	Mach 0.65
	295 knots (547 km/h; 340 mph)
Max cruising speed at 6,100 m (20,000 ft)	
	292 knots (541 km/h; 336 mph)
Econ cruising speed at 6,100 m (20,000 ft)	
	260 knots (482 km/h; 299 mph)
Max rate of climb at S/L	670 m (2,200 ft)/min
Service ceiling	7,925 m (26,000 ft)
Service ceiling, one engine out	4,575 m (15,000 ft)
Min ground turning radius, based on nosewheel	
	10.67 m (35 ft 0 in)
T-O run	1,525 m (5,000 ft)
Landing run	1,280 m (4,200 ft)
Range with 29 passengers, IFR reserves	
	590 nm (1,093 km; 679 miles)

BAe 125 SERIES 800

US Air Force designation: C-29A

The prototype (G-BKTF) of this advanced version of the BAe 125 made a 3 h 8 min first flight on 26 May 1983, during which it climbed to its max operating altitude of 13,100 m (43,000 ft). Like the earlier turbojet and turbofan powered versions of the 125, of which a total of 573 were sold, it is primarily a twin-engined business aircraft but can be used in a wide variety of other civil and military roles, including communications, air ambulance, airways inspection and airline crew training. The **Series 800A** is built for the North American market, **Series 800B** for the rest of the world. Type certification was obtained on 4 May 1984 and the Certificate of Airworthiness, Public Transport

C-29A C-FIN version of the BAe 125 Series 800 for the US Air Force

BAe 125 Series 800 (two Garrett TFE731-5R-1H turbofans) *(Pilot Press)*

Category, on 30 May 1984. FAA certification followed on 7 June 1984.

By March 1990, Series 800 sales totalled 183; and 763 BAe 125s of all models had been ordered by operators in 40 countries. Recent deliveries include (on 24 April 1990) the first of six for the USAF equipped with LTV Sierra flight inspection equipment, to perform its combat flight inspection and navigation (C-FIN) mission, as replacements for its CT-39A and C-140A calibration fleet based at Scott AFB with the 1866th FCS. The USAF designation of these aircraft is **C-29A**. In August 1989 the Japan Air Self Defence Force ordered three for its flight inspection (FC-X) requirement. These aircraft will also be equipped by LTV's Sierra Research Division in Buffalo, New York. First delivery is scheduled for December 1992. British Aerospace delivered 30 Series 800s in 1989.

Airframe improvements compared with the Series 700 include a curved windscreen, sequenced nosewheel doors, extended fin leading-edge, larger ventral fuel tank, and an increased wing span which reduces induced drag, improves aerodynamic efficiency and accommodates additional fuel. The outboard 3.05 m (10 ft) of each wing was redesigned.

Garrett TFE731-5R-1H turbofans are fitted to improve airfield/climb performance and to increase both maximum speed and range. The interior was also redesigned. Increased headroom was achieved by relocating oxygen dropout units to the sidewall panels. Increased width resulted from sculpturing the sidewall panels around the fuselage frames, giving an extra 12.2 cm (4.8 in) at shoulder height. The flight deck incorporates a Collins EFIS-85 five-tube electronic flight instrument system, with a centrally-mounted multi-function display which can show flight plans and checklists.

TYPE: Twin-turbofan business transport aircraft.

WINGS: Cantilever low-wing monoplane. BAe wing sections. Thickness/chord ratio 14 per cent at root, 8.35 per cent at tip. Dihedral 2°. Incidence 2° 5′ 42″ at root, −3° 5′ 49″ at tip. Sweepback 20° at quarter-chord. Wings built in one piece and dished to pass under fuselage, to which they are attached by four vertical links, a side link and a drag spigot. All-metal two-spar fail-safe structure, with partial centre spar of approx two-thirds span, sealed to form integral fuel tankage which is divided into two compartments by centreline rib. Skins are single-piece units on each of the upper and lower semi-spans. Detachable leading-edges. Mass balanced ailerons, operated manually by cable linkage. Each aileron has a servo action geared tab; port tab trimmed manually via screwjack. Large four-position double-slotted flaps, actuated hydraulically via a screwjack on each flap. Mechanically operated hydraulic cutout prevents asym-

metric operation of the flaps. Airbrakes above and below each wing, forming part of flap shrouds, provide lift dumping facility during landing, and have interconnected controls to prevent asymmetric operation. TKS liquid system, using porous stainless steel leading-edge panels, for de-icing or anti-icing.

FUSELAGE: All-metal semi-monocoque fail-safe structure, making extensive use of Redux bonding. Constant circular cross-section over much of its length.

TAIL UNIT: Cantilever all-metal structure, with fixed incidence tailplane mounted on fin. Small fairings on tailplane undersurface to eliminate turbulence around elevator hinge cutouts. Extended dorsal fin, enclosing air-conditioning intake duct. Control surfaces operated manually via cable linkage. Geared tabs in rudder and each elevator. TKS liquid de-icing or anti-icing of tailplane leading-edges.

LANDING GEAR: Retractable tricycle type, with twin wheels on each unit. Hydraulic retraction; nosewheels forward, mainwheels inward into wings. Oleo-pneumatic shock absorbers. Fully castoring nose unit, steerable ±45°. Dunlop mainwheels and 12-ply tubeless tyres, size 23 × 7-12. Dunlop nosewheels and 6-ply tubeless tyres, size 18 × 4.25-10. Dunlop triple-disc hydraulic brakes with Maxaret anti-skid units on all mainwheels.

POWER PLANT: Two 19.13 kN (4,300 lb st) Garrett TFE731-5R-1H turbofans, pod mounted on sides of rear fuselage, in pods designed and manufactured by Grumman Aerospace. Optional thrust reversers developed by Dee Howard Company. Engine intake anti-icing by engine bleed air. Integral fuel tanks in wings, with combined capacity of 4,820 litres (1,273 US gallons; 1,060

Imp gallons). Rear underfuselage tank of 854 litres (226 US gallons; 188 Imp gallons) capacity, giving total capacity of 5,674 litres (1,499 US gallons; 1,248 Imp gallons). Single pressure refuelling point at rear of ventral tank. Overwing refuelling point near each wingtip.

ACCOMMODATION: Crew of two on flight deck, which is fully soundproofed, insulated and air-conditioned. Dual controls standard. Seat for third crew member. Standard executive layout has forward and rear baggage compartments, forward galley, wardrobe and toilet at rear. Individual recessed lights, air louvres and oxygen masks above each passenger position. Cabin styling offers the operator a choice of interchangeable furnishing units to suit individual requirements, with up to 14 seats. The wide seats swivel through 180°, are adjustable fore, aft and sideways, and can be reclined and used as a bed. Primary configuration from mid-1987 is an open plan layout, with the traditional club four seating moved to the rear of the cabin, the partial bulkhead at the front removed and the galley relocated behind the enlarged forward baggage area. Accommodation in the forward cabin comprises two individual swivelling chairs and a three-place settee. Outward opening door at front on port side, with integral airstairs. Emergency exit over wing on starboard side. Electric windscreen anti-icing. Optional heated baggage pannier in place of the rear underfuselage fuel tank.

SYSTEMS: AiResearch air-conditioning and pressurisation system. Max cabin differential 0.59 bars (8.55 lb/sq in). Oxygen system standard, with dropout masks for passengers. Hydraulic system, pressure 186-207 bars (2,700-3,000 lb/sq in), for operation of landing gear, mainwheel doors, flaps, spoilers, nosewheel steering, mainwheel brakes and anti-skid units. Two accumulators, pressurised by engine bleed air, one for main system pressure, the other providing emergency hydraulic power for wheel brakes in case of main system failure. Independent auxiliary system for lowering landing gear and flaps in the event of a main system failure. DC electrical system utilises two 30V 12kW engine driven starter/generators and two 24V 23Ah nickel-cadmium batteries. A 24V 4Ah battery provides separate power for standby instruments. AC electrical system includes two 1.25kVA static inverters, providing 115V 400Hz single-phase supplies, one 250VA standby static inverter for avionics, and two engine driven 208V 7.4kVA frequency-wild alternators for windscreen anti-icing. Ground power receptacle on starboard side at rear of fuselage for 28V external DC supply. Turbomach T-62T-40C8D-1 auxiliary power unit. Engine ice protection system supplied by engine bleed air. Graviner triple FD Firewire fire warning system and two BCF engine fire extinguishers. Stall warning system indicates approach to the stall, and an identification system operates a stick pusher to initiate a nose down pitching movement if the approach to the stall exceeds a predetermined rate.

AVIONICS AND EQUIPMENT: Digital avionics have been introduced and received FAA Cat II certification in 1987. Standard avionics include dual Collins VHF-22A com transceivers, Collins 628T-3 HF com transceiver, dual Collins VIR-32 VHF nav receivers with marker beacon indicator, dual Collins ADF-60B, dual Collins AHS-85 attitude and heading reference systems, dual Collins DME-42 DME, dual Collins TDR-90 ATC transponders, Collins WXR-300 weather radar, dual Collins ADS-82 air data systems, Collins APS-85 autopilot, dual Collins EFIS-85B-2 electronic flight instrument systems, Collins ALT-55B radio altimeter, Baker M1045 audio system, Global GNS-1000 flight management system, Pioneer KE-8300 stereo tape and FM/AM radio. In 1988 Royal Air Force BAe 125s of earlier series were fitted with an infra-red jammer in an extended tailcone to deflect heat seeking missiles.

DIMENSIONS, EXTERNAL:

Wing span	15.66 m (51 ft 4½ in)
Wing chord (mean)	2.29 m (7 ft 6¼ in)
Wing aspect ratio	7.06
Length overall	15.60 m (51 ft 2 in)
Height overall	5.36 m (17 ft 7 in)
Fuselage: Max diameter	1.93 m (6 ft 4 in)
Tailplane span	6.10 m (20 ft 0 in)
Wheel track (c/l of shock absorbers)	2.79 m (9 ft 2 in)

BAe 125 Series 800 delivered to Ferranti in 1989

Wheelbase	6.41 m (21 ft 0½ in)
Passenger door (fwd, port):	
Height	1.30 m (4 ft 3 in)
Width	0.69 m (2 ft 3 in)
Height to sill	1.07 m (3 ft 6 in)
Emergency exit (overwing, stbd):	
Height	0.91 m (3 ft 0 in)
Width	0.51 m (1 ft 8 in)

DIMENSIONS, INTERNAL:

Cabin (excl flight deck): Length	6.50 m (21 ft 4 in)
Max width	1.83 m (6 ft 0 in)
Max height	1.75 m (5 ft 9 in)
Floor area	5.11 m² (55.0 sq ft)
Volume	17.10 m³ (604.0 cu ft)
Baggage compartments:	
forward	0.74 m³ (26.0 cu ft)
rear	0.74 m³ (26.0 cu ft)
pannier (optional)	0.79 m³ (28.0 cu ft)

AREAS:

Wings, gross	34.75 m² (374 sq ft)
Ailerons (total)	2.05 m² (22.1 sq ft)
Airbrakes: upper (total)	0.74 m² (8.0 sq ft)
lower (total)	0.46 m² (5.0 sq ft)
Trailing-edge flaps (total)	4.83 m² (52.0 sq ft)
Fin (excl dorsal fin)	6.43 m² (69.2 sq ft)
Rudder	1.32 m² (14.2 sq ft)
Horizontal tail surfaces (total)	9.29 m² (100.0 sq ft)

WEIGHTS AND LOADING:

Basic weight empty	6,676 kg (14,720 lb)
Typical operating weight empty	6,858 kg (15,120 lb)
Max payload	1,306 kg (2,880 lb)
Max ramp weight	12,480 kg (27,520 lb)
Max T-O weight	12,430 kg (27,400 lb)
Max zero-fuel weight	8,164 kg (18,000 lb)
Max landing weight	10,590 kg (23,350 lb)
Max wing loading	357.69 kg/m² (73.26 lb/sq ft)

PERFORMANCE:

Never-exceed speed	Mach 0.87
Max level speed and max cruising speed at 8,840 m	
(29,000 ft)	456 knots (845 km/h; 525 mph)
Econ cruising speed at 11,900-13,100 m (39,000-43,000 ft)	400 knots (741 km/h; 461 mph)
Stalling speed in landing configuration at typical landing	
weight	92 knots (170 km/h; 106 mph)
Max rate of climb at S/L	945 m (3,100 ft)/min
Time to 10,670 m (35,000 ft)	19 min
Service ceiling	13,100 m (43,000 ft)
Min ground turning radius about nosewheel	
	9.14 m (30 ft 0 in)
T-O balanced field length at max T-O weight	
	1,713 m (5,620 ft)
Landing from 15 m (50 ft) at typical landing weight	
(6 passengers and baggage)	1,372 m (4,500 ft)
Range:	
with max payload	2,870 nm (5,318 km; 3,305 miles)
with max fuel, NBAA VFR reserves	
	3,000 nm (5,560 km; 3,454 miles)

BAe 1000

In 1988 British Aerospace began development of a proposed long-range, larger cabin variant of the BAe 125, then provisionally designated Series 900. Because of the substantial structural and systems changes involved, including modifications to meet the latest FAR and JAR certification requirements, it was decided that the aircraft would differ sufficiently from the original concept to justify an entirely new designation, and the BAe 1000 was launched at the National Business Aircraft Association Convention in Atlanta, Georgia, in October 1989.

Compared with the BAe 125 Series 800, which will remain in parallel production, the BAe 1000 features a fuselage stretch of 0.84 m (2 ft 9 in), achieved with a 0.46 m (1 ft 6 in) plug forward of, and a 0.38 m (1 ft 3 in) plug aft of the wing centre-section, and incorporating an additional cabin window on each side. Other changes include 23.13 kN (5,200 lb st) Pratt & Whitney Canada PW305 turbofans with thrust reversers as standard; a fuel tank in an extended forward wing fairing, capacity 614 litres (162 US gallons; 135 Imp gallons), and ventral tank capacity increased by 136 litres (36 US gallons; 30 Imp gallons); new lightweight systems, re-styled cabin interior with increased headroom, improved modular galley facilities, an external baggage hatch, and Honeywell SPZ8000 digital avionics. It will offer a 21 per cent increase in range and 15 per cent improvement in field performance over the Series 800.

First flight of the BAe 1000 was expected during the first half of 1990, with certification anticipated a year later and first customer deliveries expected shortly thereafter. Launch customers for the aircraft were J.C. Bamford Excavators Ltd (two) and The Yeates Group (one) in the UK, and in the USA United Technologies, which has ordered three plus an additional aircraft for its subsidiary Pratt & Whitney Canada. Aravco Ltd, a business jet charter operator based at London-Heathrow Airport, has also ordered two BAe 1000s. British Aerospace held orders for more than 10 aircraft in March 1990.

TYPE: Twin-turbofan business transport aircraft.

WINGS: Cantilever low-wing monoplane. BAe wing sections. Thickness/chord ratio 14 per cent at root, 8.35 per cent at tip. Dihedral 2°. Incidence 2° 5′ 42″ at root, −3° 5′ 49″ at tip. Sweepback 20° at quarter-chord. Wings built in one

Artist's impression of British Aerospace 1000 twin turbofan business aircraft

BAe 1000 stretched development of BAe 125 family (two P&WC PW305 turbofans) *(Pilot Press)*

piece and dished to pass under fuselage, to which they are attached by four vertical links, a side link and a drag spigot. All-metal two-spar fail-safe structure, with partial centre spar of approximately two-thirds span, sealed to form integral fuel tankage which is divided into two compartments by centreline rib. Skins are single-piece units on each of the upper and lower semi-spans. Detachable leading-edges. Mass balanced ailerons, operated manually by cable linkage. Each aileron has a servo action geared tab; port tab trimmed manually via screwjack. Large four-position double-slotted flaps, activated hydraulically via screwjack on each flap. Mechanically operated hydraulic cutout prevents asymmetric operation of the flaps. Airbrakes above and below each wing, forming part of the flap shrouds, provide lift dump facility during landing, and have interconnected controls to prevent asymmetric operation. TKS liquid de-icing and anti-icing system, using porous stainless steel leading-edge panels inboard, laser drilled titanium panels outboard. Underwing vortilon fitted to each wing in lieu of the upper wing fence on the Series 800.

FUSELAGE: All-metal semi-monocoque fail-safe structure, making extensive use of Redux bonding. Constant circular cross-section over much of its length. Intermediate fuselage frames fitted to meet the latest FAR/JAR certification requirements. Secondary rear pressure bulkhead forming the forward bulkhead of the rear baggage area (with baggage access door) permits maximum altitude certification to 13,100 m (43,000 ft) in the USA. Push-in/slide-up plug-type exterior baggage access door (63.5 × 35.5 cm; 25 × 14 in) on port side, forward of engine pod, interlocked to prevent engine start-up if open.

TAIL UNIT: Cantilever all-metal structure, with fixed-incidence tailplane mounted on fin. Small fairings on tailplane undersurface to eliminate turbulence around elevator hinge cutouts. Extended dorsal fin, enclosing air-conditioning intake duct. Control surfaces operated manually via cable linkage. Split elevator circuit with

normally locked break-out strut which splits automatically in the event of a control jam. Geared tabs in rudder and each elevator. TKS liquid de-icing or anti-icing of tailplane leading-edges.

LANDING GEAR: Retractable tricycle type, with twin wheels on each unit. Hydraulic retraction, nosewheels forward, mainwheels inward into wings. Oleo-pneumatic shock absorbers. Fully castoring nose unit, steerable ±45°. Dunlop mainwheels and 12-ply tubeless tyres, size 23 × 7.12. Dunlop nosewheels and 6-ply tubeless tyres, size 18 × 4.25-10. Dunlop triple-disc hydraulic brakes with Maxaret anti-skid units on all mainwheels.

POWER PLANT: Two 23.13 kN (5,200 lb st) Pratt and Whitney Canada PW305 turbofans on sides of rear fuselage, in pods designed and manufactured by Rohr Aerospace. Rohr target-type thrust reversers fitted as standard. Engine intake anti-icing by engine bleed air. Integral fuel tanks in wings, with combined capacity of 4,800 litres (1,268 US gallons; 1,056 Imp gallons). Rear underfuselage ventral tank of 1,014 litres (268 US gallons; 223 Imp gallons) capacity and forward under-fuselage ventral tank forming wingroot fairing, capacity 586 litres (155 US gallons; 129 Imp gallons), giving total capacity of 6,400 litres (1,691 US gallons; 1,408 Imp gallons). Single pressure refuelling point at rear of aft ventral tank. Overwing refuelling point near each wingtip.

ACCOMMODATION: Crew of two on flight deck, which is soundproofed, insulated and air-conditioned. Dual controls standard. Seat for third crew member. Standard executive layout has rear baggage compartment with forward wardrobe, forward galley comprising sink unit on port side, cooking and food stowage including fridge on starboard side, airliner style toilet at rear. Individual recessed lights, air louvres above each passenger position. Oxygen drop-out masks in headliner. Cabin styling offers the operator a choice of interchangeable furnishing units to suit individual requirements, with up to 15 seats. The extra wide seats swivel through 360°, are adjustable fore, aft and sideways, and can be reclined and used as a bed. Standard seating for eight, with club four seating at the front of the cabin, a three-place settee on the port side, and single seat on the starboard side with an entertainment/bar unit behind, including video and compact disc player. Outward opening door at front on port side, with integral airstairs. Emergency exit over wing on starboard side.

SYSTEMS: AiResearch three-wheel turbine air-conditioning and pressurisation system. Maximum cabin differential 0.59 bars (8.55 lb/sq in). Oxygen system standard, with drop-out masks for passengers. Hydraulic system, pressure 186-207 bars (2,700-3,000 lb/sq in), for operation of landing gear, mainwheel doors, flaps, spoilers, nosewheel steering, mainwheel brakes, anti-skid units and thrust reversers. Three accumulators, pressurised by engine bleed air, are for emergency hydraulic power for wheel brakes in case of main system failure. Independent auxiliary system for lowering landing gear and flaps in the event of a main system failure. DC electrical system utilises two 30V 12kW (restricted to 9kW) engine driven starter/generators and two 26V 43Ah nickel-cadmium batteries. A 24V 5Ah battery provides separate power for standby instruments. The AC system is deleted on the BAe 1000, those instruments requiring AC having their own dedicated inverter. Two engine driven 208V 7.4kVA frequency-wild alternators for windscreen anti-icing can also provide DC power through a standby transformer rectifier unit in emergency. Ground power receptacle on starboard side at rear of fuselage for 28V external DC supply. Turbomach T-62T-40C8D-1 APU standard. Engine ice protection system supplied by engine bleed air. Electric windscreen anti-icing. Graviner triple FD Firewire fire warning system and two BCF engine fire extinguishers standard. Stall warning system indicates approach to the stall, and an identification system operates a stick pusher to initiate a nose down pitching movement if the approach to the stall exceeds a predetermined rate.

AVIONICS AND EQUIPMENT: Standard Honeywell SPZ8000 avionics fit, includes dual EDZ-818 electronic flight instrument system; dual DFZ-800 automatic flight control system; dual SRZ-850 integrated radio/audio system; dual ADZ-810 air data system; dual Laseref III inertial reference system; DG-1086 global positioning system; dual FMZ-900 flight management system with colour display units; Primus 870 weather radar; AA-300 radio altimeter; or dual HF com; Motorola N1335B Selcal, and LSZ-850 lightning detection system.

DIMENSIONS, EXTERNAL:
Wing span	15.66 m (51 ft 4½ in)
Wing chord (mean)	2.29 m (7 ft 6¼ in)
Wing aspect ratio	7.06
Length overall	16.42 m (53 ft 10½ in)
Height overall	5.21 m (17 ft 1 in)
Fuselage: Max diameter	1.93 m (6 ft 4 in)
Tailplane span	6.10 m (20 ft 0 in)
Wheel track (c/l of shock absorbers)	2.79 m (9 ft 2 in)
Wheelbase	6.91 m (22 ft 8 in)
Passenger door: Height	1.30 m (4 ft 3 in)
Width	0.69 m (2 ft 3 in)
Height to sill	1.07 m (3 ft 6 in)
Baggage door: Height	0.64 m (2 ft 1 in)
Width	0.36 m (1 ft 2 in)
Emergency exit (overwing, stbd):	
Height	0.91 m (3 ft 0 in)
Width	0.51 m (1 ft 8 in)

DIMENSIONS, INTERNAL:
Cabin (excl flight deck): Length	7.44 m (24 ft 5 in)
Max width	1.83 m (6 ft 0 in)
Max height	1.75 m (5 ft 9 in)
Floor area	5.85 m² (62.95 sq ft)
Volume	approx 19.26 m³ (680.0 cu ft)
Baggage compartments, volume:	
rear (main)	1.47 m³ (52.0 cu ft)
forward (wardrobe)	0.28 m³ (10.0 cu ft)
optional (wardrobe extension)	0.28 m³ (10.0 cu ft)

AREAS:
Wings, gross	34.75 m² (374.0 sq ft)
Ailerons (total)	2.05 m² (22.1 sq ft)
Airbrakes (total): upper	0.74 m² (8.0 sq ft)
lower	0.46 m² (5.0 sq ft)
Trailing-edge flaps (total)	4.83 m² (52.0 sq ft)
Fin (excl dorsal fin)	6.43 m² (69.2 sq ft)
Rudder	1.32 m² (14.2 sq ft)
Horizontal tail surfaces (total)	9.29 m² (100.0 sq ft)

WEIGHTS AND LOADING:
Weight empty	7,629 kg (16,820 lb)
Typical operating weight empty	7,824 kg (17,250 lb)
Max payload	1,156 kg (2,550 lb)
Max T-O weight	14,060 kg (31,000 lb)
Max ramp weight	14,105 kg (31,100 lb)
Max zero-fuel weight	8,980 kg (19,800 lb)
Max landing weight	11,340 kg (25,000 lb)
Max wing loading	405.97 kg/m² (25,000 lb/sq ft)

PERFORMANCE (estimated, at max T-O weight, ISA, except where indicated):
Never-exceed speed	Mach 0.87
Max level and max cruising speed at 8,840 m (29,000 ft)	
	468 knots (867 km/h; 539 mph)
Econ cruising speed at 11,890-13,100 m (39,000-43,000 ft)	
	402 knots (745 km/h; 463 mph)

Stalling speed in landing configuration at typical landing weight   89 knots (165 km/h; 103 mph)
Time to 10,670 m (35,000 ft)	22 min
Service ceiling	13,100 m (43,000 ft)
T-O balanced field length	1,830 m (6,000 ft)
Landing from 15 m (50 ft) at typical landing weight (6 passengers and baggage)	1,280 m (4,200 ft)
Range:	
with max payload	3,440 nm (6,375 km; 3,961 miles)
with max fuel, NBAA VFR reserves	3,635 nm (6,736 km; 4,185 miles)

BAe ATP

British Aerospace announced its intention to develop an advanced turboprop (ATP) regional transport aircraft, to succeed the Super 748, on 1 March 1984. The prototype ATP (G-MATP) flew for the first time on 6 August 1986. A second aircraft (G-BMYM) followed on 20 February 1987, in the markings of the first domestic customer, British Midland Airways. Certification, under the European Joint Airworthiness Regulations (JAR 25), was achieved in March 1988 after 1,290 hours of flying with three aircraft. Revenue-earning services (with British Midland) began on 9 May 1988. By March 1990 orders had been placed by Airlines of Britain (British Midland, Loganair and Manx Airlines) for eight (plus two options), Bangladesh Biman (three), British Airways (eight + eight), SATA of Portugal (three), Air Wisconsin (14 + six), and LAR of Portugal (three + one). Avline Trading Corporation of Toronto, Canada, has an option on five ATPs. Deliveries in 1989 totalled 11 aircraft, and hours flown to end of December 1989 were approaching 30,000.

The ATP retains the same cabin cross-section as the Super 748 but has a longer fuselage. Standard accommodation is for 64 passengers at a seat pitch of 79 cm (31 in), but various layouts are available for 60 to 72 passengers. There are separate forward and rear passenger doors, with integral airstairs at the forward door, and separate forward and rear baggage doors. The sill height of the forward passenger door allows the ATP to use jetways at regional airports. Sound measurements taken during take-off and landing have shown the ATP to be between 2 and 7 EPNdB quieter than any other airliner in its class.

Several military variants of the ATP have been proposed by BAe, as described in previous editions of *Jane's*.

TYPE: Twin-turboprop regional transport aircraft.

WINGS: Cantilever low-wing monoplane, with dihedral from centre-section. All-metal two-spar fail-safe structure, generally similar to that of BAe 748. Wing spars do not intrude into passenger cabin. Horn balanced ailerons; Fowler trailing-edge flaps (manufactured by HAI, Greece); geared tab in each aileron. Pneumatic boot de-icing of leading-edges outboard of engine nacelles.

FUSELAGE: All-metal circular section semi-monocoque fail-safe structure, generally similar to BAe 748 but lengthened by 5.03 m (16 ft 6 in).

TAIL UNIT: Cantilever all-metal structure, with slightly swept vertical and non-swept horizontal surfaces. Power assisted rudder. Trim tab in each elevator; trim and spring tabs in rudder. Pneumatic boot de-icing of fin and tailplane leading-edges.

LANDING GEAR: Retractable tricycle type, of Dowty design, with twin-wheel main units and twin-wheel steerable (±47°) nose unit. All units retract forward, main units into bottom of engine nacelles. Oleo-pneumatic shock absorbers. Mainwheels fitted with 34 × 11.75-14 tubeless tyres. Nosewheels fitted with 22 × 6.75-10 tubeless tyres. Mainwheels have fusible plugs operating at 199°C. All wheels have 'roll on rim' capability. Dunlop carbon brakes and Maxaret anti-skid units on mainwheels. Inner and outer brakes on each leg supplied from two hydraulically independent systems via engine driven pump or standby DC pump.

POWER PLANT: Two 1,978 kW (2,653 shp) Pratt & Whitney Canada PW126A turboprops. Max continuous rating 1,781 kW (2,388 shp). BAe/Hamilton Standard slow-turning propellers, each having six blades of advanced aerodynamic profile and lightweight composite construction. Max thrust in reverse pitch 2,948 kg (6,500 lb). Fuel in two integral wing tanks, with combined usable capacity of 6,364 litres (1,681 US gallons; 1,400 Imp gallons). Single pressure refuelling point under starboard

British Aerospace ATP of Manx Airlines

Three-view drawing of the twin-turboprop BAe ATP transport (*Pilot Press*)

BAe ATP regional transport aircraft (two Pratt & Whitney Canada PW126 turboprops) in the livery of Loganair

outer wing. Max fuel transfer rate 636 litres (168 US gallons; 140 Imp gallons)/min.

ACCOMMODATION: Crew of two on flight deck; two cabin attendants. Main cabin has standard pressurised accommodation for 64 passengers, at seat pitch of 79 cm (31 in), in four abreast layout with central aisle. Alternative layouts provide 60 to 72 seats. Galley at rear of cabin on starboard side, toilet forward on port side. Separate passenger doors at front (with airstairs) and rear of cabin on port side. Compartment for carry-on baggage on port side of cabin, forward of front row of seats. Two baggage/freight compartments, one forward on starboard side and one aft of main cabin, both with external access. Overhead lockers above passenger seats. Forward cabin bulkhead can be moved on seat rails to permit flexibility for multi-sector or mixed passenger/cargo operations.

SYSTEMS: Hamilton Standard environmental control system with twin ECS packs offering sub-zero delivery temperature capability. Automatic pressurisation system, giving altitude equivalent to 2,440 m (8,000 ft) at 7,620 m (25,000 ft). Pressure differential 0.38 bars (5.5 lb/sq in). Each engine drives an Abex variable delivery hydraulic pump providing hydraulic power at a regulated pressure of 169 bars (2,450 lb/sq in) for landing gear actuation, nosewheel steering, brakes and airstairs. Auxiliary hydraulic power is supplied from a separate DC pump and reservoir for emergency operation of the landing gear and brakes. The system also provides hydraulic pressure for servicing when the engines are not running. Main system has a flow rate of 41 litres (11 US gallons; 9 Imp gallons)/min controlled to 169 bars (2,450 lb/sq in); emergency system has a flow rate of 2.25 litres (0.6 US gallon; 0.5 Imp gallon)/min controlled to 145 bars (2,100 lb/sq in). Air/oil reservoirs pressurised to 1.25 bars (18 lb/sq in). Electrical power provided by Lucas 200V 30/45kVA variable frequency alternators, mounted on each engine. 28V DC subsystem from either two TRUs or two 35Ah nickel-cadmium batteries. Second subsystem provides 1.5kVA 200/115V constant frequency power from two static inverters. Garrett Model GTCP36-150 APU for air-conditioning on the ground, and electrical power for battery charging, engine starting assist and other tasks.

AVIONICS AND EQUIPMENT: Digital avionics system using ARINC 429 data transmission, Smiths SDS-201 four-tube EFIS, Bendix King avionics. Twin VHF com, twin VHF nav, scanning DME with additional frequency under R/Nav control, ADF, ATC transponder, CVR, FDR and digital GPWS. Bendix RDS-86 colour weather radar, with checklist facility, can display weather on EFIS nav display. Built-in test and recording facility. Dual AFCS, each with Litton LTR 81-01 AHRS and Smiths digital DADS, for Cat II ILS capability. Options include second DME, second ADF, second transponder, R/Nav, MLS and single HF.

DIMENSIONS, EXTERNAL:

Wing span	30.63 m (100 ft 6 in)
Length overall	26.00 m (85 ft 4 in)
Height overall	7.14 m (23 ft 5 in)
Wheel track	8.46 m (27 ft 9 in)
Wheelbase	9.70 m (31 ft 9¾ in)
Propeller diameter	4.19 m (13 ft 9 in)
Propeller/fuselage clearance	0.80 m (2 ft 7½ in)
Passenger door (each): Height	1.73 m (5 ft 8 in)
Width	0.71 m (2 ft 4 in)
Height to sill: fwd door	1.96 m (6 ft 5 in)
rear door	1.71 m (5 ft 7½ in)

Model of the proposed BAe 132 ASW/ASV maritime variant of the ATP *(Paul Jackson)*

DIMENSIONS, INTERNAL:

Cabin: Length	19.20 m (63 ft 0 in)
Max width	2.50 m (8 ft 2⅝ in)
Max height	1.93 m (6 ft 4 in)
Volume	75.1 m³ (2,652 cu ft)
Baggage/freight compartment volume (64 seats):	
forward hold	4.39 m³ (155 cu ft)
rear hold	5.10 m³ (180 cu ft)
carry-on stowage	6.60 m³ (233 cu ft)
overhead lockers (max)	3.11 m³ (110 cu ft)

WEIGHTS:

Operating weight empty: JAR	14,193 kg (31,290 lb)
FAR	14,247 kg (31,410 lb)
Max fuel	5,080 kg (11,200 lb)
Max payload: JAR	6,990 kg (15,410 lb)
FAR	6,935 kg (15,290 lb)
Max ramp weight	22,997 kg (50,700 lb)
Max T-O weight	22,930 kg (50,550 lb)
Max landing weight	22,250 kg (49,050 lb)
Max zero-fuel weight	21,228 kg (46,800 lb)

PERFORMANCE:

Cruising speed for 150 nm (278 km; 173 mile) sector, ISA: high speed at 3,960 m (13,000 ft)

266 knots (493 km/h; 306 mph)

econ cruise at 5,485 m (18,000 ft)

236 knots (437 km/h; 272 mph)

Min ground turning radius about nosewheel

9.75 m (32 ft 0 in)

T-O field length:

at max T-O weight
1,463 m (4,800 ft)

for 150 nm (278 km; 173 mile) sector, 64 passengers, reserves for 100 nm (185 km; 115 mile) diversion, plus 45 min hold at 3,050 m (10,000 ft)

1,143 m (3,750 ft)

Landing field length at max landing weight

1,128 m (3,700 ft)

Range, with reserves for 100 nm (185 km; 115 mile) diversion and 45 min hold at 3,050 m (10,000 ft):

with max payload	575 nm (1,065 km; 662 miles)
with 64 passengers (5,806 kg; 12,800 lb)	
	985 nm (1,825 km; 1,134 miles)
with max fuel and 3,778 kg (8,330 lb) payload	
	1,860 nm (3,444 km; 2,140 miles)
Ferry range	2,198 nm (4,070 km; 2,529 miles)

OPERATIONAL NOISE LEVELS (BCAR Section N):

T-O	79.5 EPNdB
Approach	95.8 EPNdB
Sideline	82.7 EPNdB

BAe 132

British Aerospace has released brief details of this proposed anti-submarine-warfare/anti-surface-vessel-warfare (ASW/ASVW) variant of the ATP which can be configured to meet a variety of customer requirements. A 360° scan maritime reconnaissance radar can be mounted beneath the forward fuselage, with provision for internally or externally mounted magnetic anomaly detector (MAD); six stores hardpoints, two under each wing and two below the fuselage at the centre-section for the carriage of torpedoes, air-to-surface missiles, depth charges, bombs and mines. A total of 59 sonobuoys could be launched singly through a pressurised launcher or in patterns of up to six through a rotary launcher. A typical internal configuration would provide accommodation for three systems operators, a crew rest area with three bunks, a wardroom, toilet, stowage for sonic equipment and sonobuoy racks, 14-man dinghy and a 43 cm (1 ft 5 in) diameter rear launch chute.

BAe 146

RAF designation: BAe 146 CC. Mk 2

In August 1973, the former Hawker Siddeley Aviation announced that it was to produce with government support a four-turbofan quiet operating transport aircraft known as the HS 146. Within a few months economic problems in the UK halted this programme, but research and design continued on a limited basis. With the absorption of Hawker Siddeley Aviation into British Aerospace in April 1977, BAe continued to provide limited funding to allow the manufacture of assembly jigs, systems test rigs, and continuing design and wind tunnel testing. On 10 July 1978, the British Aerospace Board's decision to give the

BAe 146s in the insignia of Druk-Air of Bhutan (Series 100) and TNT/Malév of Hungary (200-QT)

146 programme a full go-ahead was approved by the government.

Production of what is now known as the BAe 146 is undertaken in several BAe factories, including Brough (fin and flaps), Filton (centre fuselage), Manchester (rear fuselage), Hamble (flap track fairings), and Prestwick (engine pylons). Hatfield builds the front fuselage and flight deck, and initially was responsible for all final assembly and flight testing. Under risk sharing agreements, Textron Aerostructures (USA) manufactures wings for the BAe 146, and Saab-Scania (Sweden) the tailplanes and all movable control surfaces.

In March 1987 British Aerospace announced that production of the BAe 146 was to be increased to 40 aircraft a year by 1990. To help achieve this increase, a second final assembly line for the aircraft has been established at the BAe factory at Woodford, near Manchester. Woodford manufactured four BAe 146s in 1988 and 10 in 1989, with a progressive build-up planned thereafter for a total of 100 over six years. The first of these (c/n 2106) flew on 16 May 1988.

In December 1989 Field Aircraft Ltd of East Midlands Airport was appointed as an approved maintenance, overhaul and completion centre for BAe 146s.

The following versions of the BAe 146 are available:

Series 100. Designed to operate from short or semi-prepared airstrips with minimal ground facilities, with a normal seating capacity of 82-93. Rollout of the Series 100 prototype (G-SSSH) took place on 20 May 1981, and first flight was made on 3 September 1981. Type certification was obtained on 4 February 1983 and Transport category CAA certification of the Series 100 was obtained on 20 May 1983, with the first delivery, to Dan-Air, on 21 May 1983, and first scheduled operation on 27 May. Thicker skin on centre fuselage of later production aircraft will permit increased T-O weight if required.

Series 200. Seating capacity of 82-112. Fuselage lengthened by five frame pitches (2.39 m; 7 ft 10 in). Increased maximum T-O weight and zero-fuel weight. Underfloor cargo volume increased by 35 per cent. The first Series 200 (G-WISC) flew on 1 August 1982 and received type certification on 4 February 1983. The first production Series 200 (N601AW) was delivered to Air Wisconsin in June 1983, and operated its first scheduled service on 27 June, following receipt of FAA certification of Series 100 and 200.

Series 300. Development of the Series 100, with length increased by inserting a forward fuselage plug of 2.46 m (8 ft 1 in) and rear plug of 2.34 m (7 ft 8 in). This enables 103 passengers to be carried five-abreast at 79 cm (31 in) pitch, with wardrobe and galley space. High-density seating enables 128 passengers to be carried six-abreast at 74 cm (29 in) pitch, subject to incorporation of Type III emergency exits in the centre fuselage. Wings and power plant unchanged. Thicker skin on centre-fuselage permits increased T-O weight of 44,225 kg (97,500 lb). Aerodynamic prototype (G-LUXE) was produced by conversion of the original Series 100 prototype (G-SSSH) and was flown for the first time in its new form on 1 May 1987. First production Series 300 (c/n 3120, N611AW) flew in June 1988, was certificated on 6 September and delivered on 28 December of that year to launch customer (May 1987) Air Wisconsin. The first few Series 300s have a max T-O weight of 43,090 kg (95,000 lb); max landing weight of 37,648 kg (83,000 lb); and max zero-fuel weight of 35,153 kg (77,500 lb).

146-QT Quiet Trader. Freighter versions of any series. Cabin volume allows the 146-200 freighter to carry six standard 2.74 × 2.24 m (108 × 88 in) pallets, with space for an extra half pallet, or up to nine standard LD3 containers. Minor modifications to the standard floor make possible a maximum freight payload of 11,827 kg (26,075 lb), and the floor stressing permits a maximum individual pallet load of 2,721 kg (6,000 lb). The additional capacity of the Series 300-QT will enable payloads of up to 12,490 kg (27,535 lb) to be carried.

The first freighter conversion, a Series 200 aircraft (N146FT), was undertaken in the USA by Hayes International Corporation (now Pemco Aeroplex), which was responsible for the design, manufacture and installation of the door, the freight handling equipment, internal structure reinforcements and furnishings. After conversion this aircraft (then N146QT) was purchased by TNT International Aviation Services, the Australian-origin transportation group, and, (re-registered G-TNTA) entered service on 5 May 1987. In June 1987 TNT and BAe reached agreements covering a long term commitment for the acquisition of up to 72 BAe 146-QTs over the following five years. A substantial number of these will be used for the TNT freight network; the balance of the aircraft will be available for sale or lease through Ansett Worldwide Aviation Services. Firm orders by TNT had increased to 23 by March 1990. By that date 11 Series 200-QTs had been delivered to TNT in Europe and two in Australia for use by Ansett Air Freight. The first of 10 Series 300-QTs ordered by TNT was delivered to Malmo Aviation of Sweden at the end of 1989.

146-QC Convertible. In August 1988, BAe announced a quick-change convertible passenger/freighter version of the 146 Series 200-QT and 300-QT. A prototype was displayed at the 1989 Paris Air Show and was subsequently sold to Ansett New Zealand in December 1989 after two

months of service trials. The 200-QC Convertible has a gross payload in freighter configuration of 10,039 kg (22,132 lb) and a range with standard tankage of 1,045 nm (1,936 km; 1,203 miles). For passenger transport 85 (five-abreast) may be carried up to 1,289 nm (2,388 km; 1,484 miles). Comparable data for the 300-QC Convertible are 10,887 kg (24,002 lb) up to 1,087 nm (2,014 km; 1,251 miles); and 96 passengers up to 1,233 nm (2,285 km; 1,420 miles). The first UK customer for the Series 200-QC is Princess Air of Southend, which was due to take delivery of a single aircraft in mid-1990.

Statesman. British Aerospace offers Statesman executive versions of all Series. The cabin area available allows flexibility of interior design. Staterooms, staff quarters, additional galley and wardrobe space can be provided. The initial BAe 146 Statesman was delivered in April 1986 as the first of two BAe 146 CC.Mk 2s for The Queen's Flight of the RAF. An additional aircraft was ordered for The Queen's Flight on 4 October 1989, and had been delivered for fitting out by the end of the year.

By 14 May 1990 orders totalled 29 Series 100s, 88 Series 200s, 38 Series 300s, 13 Series 200-QTs, 2 Series 200-QCs, 10 Series 300-QTs and six unidentified, or 186 in all, of which 147 had been delivered, including 36 in 1989. By that time the fleet had amassed more than 830,000 flying hours in one million flights.

In March 1990 a BAe 146-200 operated by LAN-Chile became the first commercial jet airliner to operate into Antarctica when it operated a route-proving service from Punte Arenas to the Chilean Air Force base at Teniente Marsh on King George Island. LAN-Chile's two Series 200s are equipped with a gravel runway all terrain protection kit and serve nine Chilean cities from the capital, Santiago.

The following description applies to the commercial Series 100, 200 and 300, except where indicated otherwise:

BAe 146 Series 200, with additional side view (centre) of Series 100 *(Pilot Press)*

BAe 146 Series 300 four-turbofan transport in the colours of Ansett New Zealand

TYPE: Four-turbofan short-range transport aircraft.

WINGS: Cantilever high-wing monoplane. British Aerospace high lift aerofoil section. Thickness/chord ratio 15.3 per cent adjacent to fuselage, 12.2 per cent at tip. Anhedral 3° at trailing-edge. Incidence 3° 6' at fuselage side, 0° at tip. Sweepback 15° at quarter-chord. All-metal fail-safe structure of light alloy with machined skins, integrally machined spars and ribs. Single-section hydraulically actuated tabbed Fowler flaps of light alloy, spanning 78 per cent of each wing trailing-edge, with Dowty actuators. Mechanically actuated balanced ailerons. Hydraulically operated roll spoiler outboard of three lift dumpers on each wing. Trim and servo tab in each aileron. No leading-edge lift devices. Hot air anti-icing of leading-edges.

FUSELAGE: All-metal fail-safe pressurised semi-monocoque structure. Strengthened centre section developed initially for the Series 300 will be standard on all future 146-100s. Flight deck and tailcone areas free of stringers. Remainder of structure has top hat stringers bonded to skins above keel area. Z section stringers wet assembled with bonding agent and riveted to skin in keel area. Chemically etched skins of light alloy. Petal airbrakes form tailcone when closed.

TAIL UNIT: Cantilever sweptback T tail, of all-metal construction. Chemically etched light alloy skins bonded to top hat section stringers. Fixed incidence tailplane. Manually operated balanced elevators, each with trim and servo tab. Powered rudder. Hot air anti-icing of tailplane leading-edges.

LANDING GEAR: Hydraulically retractable tricycle type, of Dowty design, with twin Dunlop wheels on each unit. Main units retract inward into fairings on fuselage sides; steerable (±70°) nose unit retracts forward. Oleo-pneumatic shock absorbers with wheels mounted on trailing axle. Simple telescopic nosewheel strut. Mainwheel tyres size 12.50-16 Type III, pressure (Series 100) 8.42 bars (122 lb/sq in). Nosewheel tyres size 7.50-10 Type III, pressure (Series 100) 7.80 bars (113 lb/sq in). Low pressure tyres optional. Dunlop multi-disc carbon brakes operated by duplicated hydraulic systems. Anti-skid units in both primary and secondary brake systems.

POWER PLANT: Four Textron Lycoming ALF 502R-5 turbofans, each rated at 31.0 kN (6970 lb st), installed in pylon mounted underwing pods. No reverse thrust. Fuel in two integral wing tanks and integral centre-section tank (the latter with a vented and drained sealing diaphragm above passenger cabin), having a combined usable capacity of 11,728 litres (3,098 US gallons; 2,580 Imp gallons). Optional auxiliary tanks in wingroot fairings, with combined capacity of 1,173 litres (310 US gallons; 258 Imp gallons), giving total capacity of 12,901 litres (3,408 US gallons; 2,838 Imp gallons). Single-point pressure refuelling, with coupling situated in starboard wing outboard of outer engine.

ACCOMMODATION: Crew of two pilots on flight deck, and two or three cabin staff. Optional observer's seat. Series 100 has accommodation in main cabin for 82 passengers with six-abreast seating at 84 cm (33 in) pitch, and up to 93 seats six-abreast at 74 cm (29 in) pitch. Series 200 has max capacity for 112 passengers with six-abreast seating at 74 cm (29 in) pitch. Series 300 has standard accommodation for 103 passengers, with five-abreast seating at 79 cm (31 in) pitch, and max seating for 128 passengers. All seating layouts have two toilets and a forward galley as standard. Series 300 has wardrobe at front of cabin on starboard

side. One outward opening passenger door forward and one aft on port side of cabin. Built-in airstairs optional. Servicing doors, one forward and one aft, on starboard side of cabin. Freight and baggage holds under cabin floor. All accommodation air-conditioned. Windscreen electrical anti-icing and demisting standard. Rain repellent system optional.

SYSTEMS: BAe/Normalair-Garrett cabin air-conditioning and pressurisation system, using engine bleed air. Electro-pneumatic pressurisation control with discharge valves at fore and aft of cabin. Max differential 0.47 bars (6.75 lb/sq in), giving 2,440 m (8,000 ft) equivalent altitude at 9,450 m (31,000 ft). Hydraulic system, duplicated for essential services, for landing gear, flaps, rudder, roll and lift spoilers, airbrakes, nosewheel steering, brakes and auxiliary fuel pumps; pressure 207 bars (3,000 lb/sq in). Electrical system powered by two 40kVA integrated-drive alternators to feed 115/200V 3-phase 400Hz primary systems. 28V DC power supplied by transformer-rectifier in each channel. Hydraulically powered emergency electrical power unit. Garrett GTCP 36-150 APU (36-100 in early aircraft) for ground air-conditioning and electrical power generation. High pressure gaseous oxygen system, pressure 124 bars (1,800 lb/sq in). Stall warning and identification system, comprising stick shaker (warning) and stick force (identification) elements, providing soft and hard corrective stick forces at the approach of stall conditions. Series 100: stick force soft with flaps up; Series 200: force soft above 185 knots (343 km/h; 213 mph) regardless of configuration.

AVIONICS: Smiths SEP 10 automatic flight control and flight guidance system incorporates a simplex Cat I autopilot with a flight director display and separate attitude reference for each pilot. Addition of extra equipment and wiring permits coupled approaches to Cat II minima. Standard ARINC interface with radio nav system allows choice of radio equipment. Basic avionics include dual VHF com, audio system, passenger address system,

cockpit voice recorder, dual compass systems, dual ADIs with separate attitude reference driven by single computer, marker beacon receiver, weather radar, dual radio altimeters, ground proximity warning system, dual DME, dual ATC transponders, dual VHF nav and dual ADF. Dowty-UEL flight deck warning system. Optional avionics include third VHF com, area navigation system, Selcal, tape reproducer, and single or dual HF com. Honeywell EFIS with Smiths LED engine instrument display incorporated as standard from Summer 1990, although electro-mechanical instruments continue to be available as customer option. Development under way of a digital flight deck incorporating Honeywell SPZ 1000 system to provide Cat III instrument landing capability.

DIMENSIONS, EXTERNAL:

Wing span, excl static dischargers	26.21 m (86 ft 0 in)
Note: Static discharger extends 6.3 cm (2½ in) from each wingtip	
Wing aspect ratio	8.97
Wing chord: at root	2.75 m (9 ft 0 in)
at tip	0.91 m (3 ft 0 in)
Length overall: Series 100	26.20 m (85 ft 11½ in)
Series 200	28.60 m (93 ft 10 in)
Series 300	30.99 m (101 ft 8¼ in)
Note: Static dischargers on elevator extend length of all series by 18.4 cm (7¼ in)	
Height overall: Series 100	8.61 m (28 ft 3 in)
Series 200	8.59 m (28 ft 2 in)
Fuselage max diameter	3.56 m (11 ft 8 in)
Tailplane span	11.09 m (36 ft 5 in)
Wheel track	4.72 m (15 ft 6 in)
Wheelbase: Series 100	10.09 m (33 ft 1½ in)
Series 200	11.20 m (36 ft 9 in)
Series 300	12.52 m (41 ft 1 in)
Passenger doors (port, fwd and rear):	
Height	1.83 m (6 ft 0 in)
Width	0.85 m (2 ft 9½ in)
Height to sill: fwd	1.88 m (6 ft 2 in)
rear	1.98 m (6 ft 6 in)

BAe 146 Series 300, the stretched version of this regional transport *(Pilot Press)*

BAe 146-QC convertible passenger/freighter

Servicing doors (stbd, fwd and rear):
Height	1.47 m (4 ft 10 in)
Width	0.85 m (2 ft 9½ in)
Height to sill: fwd	1.88 m (6 ft 2 in)
rear	1.98 m (6 ft 6 in)

Underfloor freight hold door (stbd, fwd):
Height	1.09 m (3 ft 7 in)
Width	1.35 m (4 ft 5 in)
Height to sill	0.78 m (2 ft 7 in)

Underfloor freight hold door (stbd, rear):
Height	1.04 m (3 ft 5 in)
Width	0.91 m (3 ft 0 in)
Height to sill	0.90 m (2 ft 11½ in)

Freight door (Freighter versions):
Height	1.93 m (6 ft 4 in)
Width: Series 100	2.92 m (9 ft 7 in)
Series 200	3.33 m (10 ft 11 in)
Height to sill	1.93 m (6 ft 4 in)

DIMENSIONS, INTERNAL:
Cabin (excl flight deck, incl galley and toilets):
Length: Series 100	15.42 m (50 ft 7 in)
Series 200	17.81 m (58 ft 5 in)
Series 300	20.20 m (66 ft 3¼ in)
Max width	3.42 m (11 ft 2½ in)
Max height	2.02 m (6 ft 7½ in)

Freight cabin, Series 200-QT:
Cargo floor: Length	16.08 m (52 ft 9 in)
Width	3.23 m (10 ft 7 in)
Volume: pallets/igloos	60.3 m³ (2,145 cu ft)
LD3 containers	42.66 m³ (1,422 cu ft)

Baggage/freight holds, underfloor:
Series 100	13.7 m³ (479 cu ft)
Series 200	18.3 m³ (645 cu ft)
Series 300	22.99 m³ (812 cu ft)

AREAS:
Wings, gross	77.30 m² (832 sq ft)
Ailerons (total)	3.62 m² (39 sq ft)
Trailing-edge flaps (total)	19.51 m² (210 sq ft)
Spoilers (total)	10.03 m² (108 sq ft)
Fin	15.51 m² (167 sq ft)
Rudder	5.30 m² (57 sq ft)
Tailplane	15.61 m² (168 sq ft)
Elevators, incl tabs	10.03 m² (108 sq ft)

WEIGHTS AND LOADINGS:
Operating weight empty:
Series 100	23,288 kg (51,342 lb)
Series 200	23,882 kg (52,651 lb)
Series 200-QT	22,310 kg (49,185 lb)
Series 300	24,878 kg (54,848 lb)
Series 300-QT	23,126 kg (50,985 lb)

Max payload: Series 100
	7,783 kg (17,158 lb)
Series 200	10,138 kg (22,350 lb)
Series 200-QT	11,709 kg (25,815 lb)
Series 300	10,728 kg (23,652 lb)
Series 300-QT	12,707 kg (28,015 lb)

Max fuel weight:
All series: standard	9,362 kg (20,640 lb)
optional	10,298 kg (22,704 lb)

Max T-O weight: Series 100
	38,102 kg (84,000 lb)
Series 200	42,184 kg (93,000 lb)
Series 300	44,225 kg (97,500 lb)

Max ramp weight: Series 100
	38,329 kg (84,500 lb)
Series 200	42,410 kg (93,500 lb)
Series 300	44,452 kg (98,000 lb)

Max zero-fuel weight: Series 100
	31,071 kg (68,500 lb)
Series 200	34,019 kg (75,000 lb)
Series 300	35,607 kg (78,500 lb)

Max landing weight: Series 100
	35,153 kg (77,500 lb)
Series 200	36,741 kg (81,000 lb)
Series 300	38,328 kg (84,500 lb)

Max wing loading:
Series 100	493.0 kg/m² (101.0 lb/sq ft)
Series 200	545.7 kg/m² (111.8 lb/sq ft)
Series 300	572.2 kg/m² (117.2 lb/sq ft)

Max power loading:
Series 100, standard	307.3 kg/kN (3.01 lb/lb st)
Series 200	340.2 kg/kN (3.34 lb/lb st)
Series 300	358.5 kg/kN (3.52 lb/lb st)

PERFORMANCE (at max standard T-O weight, except where indicated):
Max operating Mach No.	0.73

Max operating speed:
Series 100	300 knots (555 km/h; 345 mph) CAS
Series 200, 300	295 knots (546 km/h; 339 mph) CAS

Cruising speed at 8,840 m (29,000 ft) for 300 nm (556 km; 345 mile) sector:
Series 100/200:
high-speed	414 knots (767 km/h; 477 mph)
long-range	361 knots (669 km/h; 416 mph)

Series 300:
high-speed	426 knots (789 km/h; 491 mph)
long-range	377 knots (699 km/h; 434 mph)

Stalling speed, 30° flap:
Series 100	97 knots (180 km/h; 112 mph) EAS
Series 200, 300	102 knots (189 km/h; 118 mph) EAS

Stalling speed, 33° flap, at max landing weight:
Series 100	89 knots (165 km/h; 103 mph) EAS
Series 200, 300	92 knots (170 km/h; 106 mph) EAS

Min ground turning radius about nosewheels:
Series 100	11.53 m (37 ft 10 in)
Series 200	12.55 m (41 ft 2 in)
Series 300	13.97 m (45 ft 10 in)

T-O to 10.7 m (35 ft), S/L, ISA:
Series 100	1,219 m (4,000 ft)
Series 200, 300	1,509 m (4,950 ft)

FAR landing distance from 15 m (50 ft), S/L, ISA, at max landing weight: Series 100
	1,067 m (3,500 ft)
Series 200	1,103 m (3,620 ft)
Series 300	1,228 m (4,030 ft)

Range with standard fuel:
Series 100	1,620 nm (3,002 km; 1,865 miles)
Series 200	1,570 nm (2,909 km; 1,808 miles)
Series 300	1,520 nm (2,817 km; 1,750 miles)

Range with max payload:
Series 100	880 nm (1,631 km; 1,013 miles)
Series 200	1,130 nm (2,094 km; 1,301 miles)
Series 200-QT	1,150 nm (2,131 km; 1,324 miles)
Series 300	1,040 nm (1,927 km; 1,197 miles)

OPERATIONAL NOISE LEVELS (FAR Pt 36-12, certificated):
T-O: Series 100	81.8 EPNdB
Series 200	85.2 EPNdB
Series 300	86.8 EPNdB
Approach: Series 100	95.6 EPNdB
Series 200	95.8 EPNdB
Series 300	96.1 EPNdB
Sideline: Series 100	87.7 EPNdB
Series 200	87.3 EPNdB
Series 300	86.9 EPNdB

BAe 146 MILITARY VARIANTS

During the 1987 Paris Air Show, BAe announced brief details of the following military developments of the BAe 146, either of which may be fitted with an in-flight refuelling probe above the flight deck:

BAe 146M (Military Rear Loader). Projected development, with large hydraulically operated rear loading ramp/doors allied to lowered main deck floor, capable of accepting larger and heavier payloads. The main landing gear would be redesigned to a tandem configuration housed in fuselage sponsons.

BAe 146STA (Sideloading Tactical Airlifter). A derivative of the BAe 146-QT. A prototype (G-BSTA) was converted in the USA by Pemco Aeroplex from the second 146 built (a Series 100, c/n 1002) and made its first flight on 8 August 1988. Following display at Farnborough, it embarked upon a sales tour of the Far East and Australasia. The aircraft has the large, port-side freight door of the 146-200QT, an air-openable (outwards and forwards) parachuting door immediately behind the freight door (one each side in production version); and a flight refuelling probe. Similar conversions of Series 200/300 aircraft are offered.

Several types of mission are envisaged for the 146STA:

Paratrooping and supply dropping. Sixty fully-equipped paratroops may be deposited at a radius of 810 nm (1,501 km; 932 miles) on a hi-lo-hi mission; lo phase for 50 nm (92 km; 58 miles) each side of DZ. Standard 1.37 m x 1.22 m (54 in x 48 in) airdrop containers carried in re-supply role.

Troop transport. Maximum of 80 personnel; or 60 personnel over 1,660 nm (3,076 km; 1,911 miles) range.

Casualty evacuation. Radius of action, 780 nm (1,445 km; 898 miles) outbound with supplies and returning with 18 stretchers, 26 seated wounded and four attendants.

Freight transport. Floor loading, 976 kg/m² (200 lb/sq ft) throughout cargo hold. Self-contained loading ramp, with removable roller conveyor and ball-mat system. Five pallet positions stressed to 1,814 kg (4,000 lb), plus one to 3,175 kg (7,000 lb); net palletised payload 9,412 kg (20,750 lb).

Aerial tanker. Optional role. Two wingtip hose-drum pods. Disposable load of 11,340 kg (25,000 lb) of fuel at 200 nm (370 km; 230 miles) radius.

Search and Rescue. Optional role. Weather radar switched to surveillance mode. Typically 12 dinghies (32 persons each) airdropped through parachuting door. Loiter on station: 4.4 hours at 200 nm (370 km; 230 miles) from base.

Data for the 146-100STA are as for the civilian variant, except:
POWER PLANT: Four Textron Lycoming ALF 502R-MR turbofans. Fuel capacity 12,810 litres (3,384 US gallons; 2,818 Imp gallons).

DIMENSIONS, EXTERNAL:
Freight door: Height	1.93 m (6 ft 4 in)
Width	3.33 m (10 ft 11 in)

DIMENSIONS, INTERNAL:
Cabin: Unobstructed length	13.39 m (43 ft 11 in)
Width	3.33 m (10 ft 11 in)

Freight hold, underfloor:
Volume	13.54 m³ (478.0 cu ft)

WEIGHTS:
Max payload	10,319 kg (22,750 lb)

BAe 146STA Sideloading Tactical Airlifter in low-visibility camouflage

The first (UK assembled) BAe Hawk T. Mk 66 for Switzerland escorted by a DH Vampire Trainer of the type it will supplant

Max T-O weight	42,184 kg (93,000 lb)
Max zero-fuel weight	33,565 kg (74,000 lb)
Max landing weight	37,684 kg (83,000 lb)
PERFORMANCE (at max T-O weight):	
Three-engine ceiling	8,840 m (29,000 ft)
T-O to 15 m (50 ft)	1,174 m (3,850 ft)

BAe HAWK (TWO-SEAT VERSIONS)
RAF designations: Hawk T. Mks 1 and 1A
US Navy designation: T-45A Goshawk

Early history of the HS P1182 Hawk fully aerobatic basic/advanced jet trainer and light attack aircraft appeared in the 1989-90 edition of *Jane's*. The first-generation Hawk remains in production, but marketing emphasis is now on the more advanced Srs 100 and single-seat Srs 200 (described separately). Hawk design leadership transferred from Kingston to Brough in 1988, and final assembly and flight-test from Dunsfold to Warton in 1989. Versions are:

Hawk T. Mk 1. Basic two-seater for RAF flying and weapon training. Adour 151-01 (-02 in Red Arrows aircraft) non-afterburning turbofan, rated at 23.13 kN (5,200 lb st). Two dry underwing hardpoints. Underbelly 30 mm gun pack. Three-position flaps. Simple weapon sight in aircraft of Nos. 1 and 2 Tactical Weapons Units. Unarmed versions serve No. 4 FTS and the Central Flying School. Following basic Jet Provost or Tucano stage, future RAF fast-jet pilots fly 75 hours at No. 4 FTS and 54 hours' weapons and tactical training with one of TWUs. Total 176 delivered, of which 151 remained in January 1990, including conversions to Mk 1A. In 1992, Hawks will be introduced to the navigator training syllabus at No. 6 FTS, Finningley.

Hawk T. Mk 1A. Under a contract of January 1983, 88 Hawks of Nos. 1/2 TWUs and the Red Arrows were wired for carriage of an AIM-9L Sidewinder air-to-air missile on the inboard wing pylons and optional activation of the previously unused outer-wing hardpoints. The last conversion was re-delivered on 30 May 1986. A force of 72 Hawk T. Mk 1As is declared to NATO for point defence and participation in the RAF's Mixed Fighter Force, in which they would accompany radar-equipped Phantoms and Tornado ADVs on medium-range air defence sorties.

A two-part programme of wing replacement for the majority of RAF Hawks began in 1989, involving an initial 85 aircraft which are being modified by BAe. Work on a further 59 aircraft will be put out to tender, for completion by the mid-1990s.

Hawk 50 series. Initial export version, with Adour 851 turbofan, rated at 23.75 kN (5,340 lb st). Max operating weight increased by 30 per cent; disposable load by 70 per cent; range by 30 per cent. Revised tailcone shape to improve directional stability at high speed. Larger nose equipment bay. Two additional weapon pylons underwing. All four wing stations configured for single or twin store carriage; each pylon cleared to carry 515 kg (1,135 lb). Wet inboard pylons for 455 litre (120 US gallon; 100 Imp gallon) fuel tanks. Improved nav/com. Improved cockpit, with angle of attack indication, fully aerobatic twin gyro AHRS, slim seat head boxes and weapon control panel. Optional brake-chute. Suitable for ground attack in day VMC, and armed reconnaissance with camera/sensor pod. Sold to Finland (50 **Mk 51** to replace Fouga Magisters. Construction of components for 46 aircraft, and final assembly, undertaken in Finland by Valmet); Kenya (12 **Mk 52**); and Indonesia (20 **Mk 53** ground attack/trainers). Deliveries between December 1980 and October 1985.

Hawk 60 series. Development of the 50 series with Adour 861 turbofan, rated at 25.35 kN (5,700 lb st). Wing changes, including leading-edge devices and four-position

British Aerospace Hawk 60 series two-seat jet trainer, with additional side view (bottom) of
Hawk 100 series (*Pilot Press*)

flaps to improve lift capability. Low-friction nose leg, strengthened wheels and tyres, and adaptive anti-skid system. Drop tanks of 592 or 864 litre (156 or 228 US gallon; 130 or 190 Imp gallon) capacity. Provision for Sidewinder or Magic air-to-air missiles. Max operating weight increased by further 17 per cent compared with Mk 50 series, disposable load by 33 per cent and range by 30 per cent. Improved field performance, acceleration, rate of climb and turn rate. Sold to Zimbabwe (eight **Mk 60**), Dubai (nine **Mk 61**), Abu Dhabi (16 **Mk 63**), Kuwait (12 **Mk 64**), Saudi Arabia (30 **Mk 65**), Switzerland (20 **Mk 66**) and South Korea (20 ordered in 1990). Deliveries complete, apart from Swiss and Korean contracts. First Mk 66 (U-1251) flew on 7 April 1989 (final Hawk assembled at Dunsfold); delivered to Switzerland 8 November 1989, and accepted by SwAF 31 January 1990. Remaining 19 being assembled from BAe components by F + W at Emmen from early 1990.

T-45A Goshawk. The US Navy's requirement is for 302 Hawks, designated T-45A Goshawk. Further details can be found under the McDonnell Douglas/BAe entry in the International section.

Hawk 100 series. To exploit the Hawk's five-pylon capability for carrying external stores, BAe announced this enhanced ground attack development of the 60 series in mid-1982. Still basically a two-seater, but likely to carry only a pilot on combat missions, the 100 series will be powered by a 26.0 kN (5,845 lb st) Adour Mk 871 engine. It will have a MIL-STD-1553B databus integrating Singer Kearfott SKN 2416 inertial navigation unit of the type used on the F-16, an advanced Smiths Industries head-up display/weapon aiming computer (HUD/WAC), and new air data sensor package, with optional laser ranging and FLIR; improved weapons management system allowing pre-selection during flight and displaying weapon status; manual or automatic weapon release; passive warning radar; HOTAS (hands on throttle and stick) controls; full colour multi-purpose CRT display in each cockpit; and provision for carrying an ECM pod.

Max external load is identical to the 60 series at 3,084 kg (6,800 lb). T-O run reduced by typically 15 per cent; lo-lo-lo

combat radius is 129 nm (239 km; 148 miles) with four 1,000 lb bombs and gun pod; or 111 nm (205 km; 128 miles) with eight 500 lb bombs and gun pod. In a combat air patrol mission the Hawk 100 will be able to loiter at low level for 2¾ hours on station, 100 nm (185 km; 115 miles) from base, armed with two Sidewinder type missiles, a 30 mm gun pod and two 864 litre (228 US gallon; 190 Imp gallon) external tanks. Like the Hawk Series 200 (described separately), the 100 series aircraft is fitted with a combat wing incorporating a fixed leading-edge droop for increased lift and manoeuvrability in the Mach 0.3-0.7 regime, full-width flap vanes, manually selected combat flap and fuselage-mounted smurfs (side-mounted unit horizontal root tail fin) ahead of the leading-edge of the tailplane. An aerodynamic prototype of the 100 series (converted from company demonstrator G-HAWK/ZA101) flew on 21 October 1987, featuring an extended nose with forward-facing optical flats for the FLIR and laser rangefinder. This aircraft was due to begin trials of wingtip Sidewinder AAM rails at Warton in 1990.

Hawk 200 series. Single-seat multi-role combat version. Described separately.

Delivery of the first Swiss Hawk in November 1989 brought to 335 the number of two-seat Hawks assembled in Europe. Orders and commitments by February 1990 totalled 689, comprising 176 T. Mk 1/1As, 82 Srs 50s, 95 Srs 60s, 302 T-45As, two demonstrators (including a definitive Srs 100 to fly in 1991) and 12 Srs 100s ordered by Abu Dhabi in 1989. Three Srs 200 demonstrators have also been ordered. Contracts nearing signature in 1990 were with Brunei (16 Srs 100s), South Korea (100 Srs 100/200), Oman (20 Srs 60/100/200s) and Saudi Arabia (60 Srs 100/200s). Aircraft for Abu Dhabi, Brunei, South Korea and Saudi Arabia will have wingtip-mounted missile rails. Negotiations for the sale to Iraq of 50-70 Srs 100/200s were terminated in 1989 on UK Government instructions.

The following description applies to current UK production Hawks for export:

TYPE: Two-seat basic and advanced jet trainer, with capability for air defence and ground attack roles.

WINGS: Cantilever low-wing monoplane. Thickness/chord ratio 10.9 per cent at root, 9 per cent at tip. Dihedral 2°.

Sweepback 26° on leading-edge, 21° 30′ at quarter-chord. One-piece aluminium alloy wing, with six-bolt attachment to fuselage, employing a machined spars-and-skin torsion box (two main spars, auxiliary spar, ribs and machined skins with integral stringers), the greater part of which forms an integral fuel tank. Hydraulically activated double-slotted flaps. Outboard 300 mm (12 in) of flap vanes deleted by comparison with prototype aircraft. Ailerons, operated by AP Precision Hydraulics tandem actuators, are of honeycomb-filled aluminium alloy. No tabs. Small fence, of composites material, on leading-edge of each wing, at approximately two-thirds span. (Series 100: see Hawk 200 entry.)

FUSELAGE: Conventional aluminium alloy structure of frames and stringers, cut out to accept the one-piece wing. Large airbrake under rear fuselage, aft of wing.

TAIL UNIT: Cantilever all-metal structure, with sweepback on all surfaces. One-piece all-moving power operated (via push/pull rods) anhedral tailplane, with AP Precision Hydraulics tandem hydraulic actuators. Manually operated rudder, with electrically actuated trim tab. Two small ventral fins. Series 100 additionally fitted with smurfs (see Hawk 200 entry).

LANDING GEAR: Wide track hydraulically retractable tricycle type, with single wheel on each unit. AP Precision Hydraulics oleos and jacks. Main units retract inward into wing, ahead of front spar; castoring nosewheel retracts forward. Dunlop mainwheels, brakes and tyres size 6.50-10, pressure 9.86 bars (143 lb/sq in). Nosewheel and tyre size 4.4-16, pressure 8.27 bars (120 lb/sq in). Tail bumper fairing under rear fuselage. Anti-skid wheel brakes. Tail braking parachute, diameter 2.64 m (8 ft 8in), on Mks 52/53 and all 60 series aircraft.

POWER PLANT: One Rolls-Royce Turboméca Adour non-afterburning turbofan, as described under individual series entries. Air intake on each side of fuselage, forward of wing leading-edge. Engine starting by Microturbo integral gas turbine starter. Fuel in one fuselage bag tank of 868 litres (229 US gallons; 191 Imp gallons) capacity and integral wing tank of 836 litres (221 US gallons; 184 Imp gallons) capacity; total fuel capacity 1,704 litres (450 US gallons; 375 Imp gallons). Pressure refuelling point near front of port engine air intake trunk; gravity point on top of fuselage. Provision for carrying one 455, 592 or 864 litre (120, 156 or 228 US gallon; 100, 130 or 190 Imp gallon) drop tank on each inboard underwing pylon, according to series.

ACCOMMODATION: Crew of two in tandem under one-piece fully transparent acrylic canopy, opening sideways to starboard. Fixed front windscreen and separate internal windscreen in front of rear cockpit. Improved front windscreen fitted retrospectively to RAF Hawks, able to withstand a 1 kg (2.2 lb) bird at 528 knots (978 km/h; 607 mph). Rear seat elevated. Martin-Baker Mk 10B zero/zero rocket assisted ejection seats, with MDC (miniature detonating cord) system to break canopy before seats eject. The MDC can also be operated from outside the cockpit for ground rescue. Dual controls standard. Entire accommodation pressurised, heated and air-conditioned.

SYSTEMS: BAe cockpit air-conditioning and pressurisation systems, using engine bleed air. Two hydraulic systems; flow rate: System 1, 36.4 litres (9.6 US gallons; 8 Imp gallons)/min; System 2, 22.7 litres (6 US gallons; 5 Imp gallons)/min. Systems pressure 207 bars (3,000 lb/sq in), for actuation of control jacks, flaps, airbrake, landing gear and anti-skid wheel brakes. Compressed nitrogen accumulators provide emergency power for flaps and landing gear at a pressure of 2.75 to 5.5 bars (40 to 80 lb/sq in). Hydraulic accumulator for emergency operation of wheel brakes. Pop-up Dowty ram air turbine in upper rear fuselage provides emergency hydraulic power for flying controls in the event of an engine or No. 2 pump failure. No pneumatic system. DC electrical power from single brushless generator, with two static inverters to provide AC power and two batteries for standby power. Gaseous oxygen system for crew.

AVIONICS AND EQUIPMENT: The RAF standard of flight instruments includes Ferranti gyros and inverter, two Honeywell RAI-4 4 in remote attitude indicators and a magnetic detector unit, and Louis Newmark compass system. Radio and navigation equipment includes Sylvania UHF and VHF, Cossor CAT.7,000 Tacan, Cossor ILS with CILS.75/76 localiser/glideslope receiver and marker receiver, and IFF/SSR (Cossor 2720 Mk 10A IFF in aircraft for Finland).

ARMAMENT AND OPERATIONAL EQUIPMENT: Ferranti F.195 weapon sight and camera recorder in each cockpit of about 90 RAF and all 50 and 60 series aircraft. (Saab RGS2 sighting system in aircraft for Finland.) Underfuselage centreline mounted 30 mm Aden Mk 4 cannon with 120 rounds (VKT 12.7 mm machine-gun beneath Finnish aircraft), and two or four hardpoints underwing, according to series. Provision for pylon in place of the ventral gun pack. In RAF training roles the normal max external load is about 680 kg (1,500 lb), but the uprated Hawk has demonstrated its ability to carry a total external load of 3,084 kg (6,800 lb). Typical weapon loadings on 60 series include a 30 mm or 12.7 mm centreline gun pod and four packs each containing eighteen 68 mm rockets; a centreline reconnaissance pod

BAe's original two-seat Hawk demonstrator, modified to the aerodynamic shape of the Hawk 100 series

and four packs each containing twelve 81 mm rockets; seven 1,000 lb free fall or retarded bombs; four launchers each containing four 100 mm rockets; nine 250 lb or 250 kg bombs; thirty-six 80 lb runway denial or tactical strike bombs; five 600 lb cluster bombs; four Sidewinder/Magic air-to-air missiles; four CBLS 100/200 carriers each containing four practice bombs and four rockets; or two 592 litre (156 US gallon; 130 Imp gallon) drop tanks and two Maverick air-to-surface missiles. Vinten reconnaissance pod available for centre pylon. A configuration demonstrated at the 1983 Paris Air Show included a Sea Eagle anti-ship missile on the centreline pylon, plus two Sidewinder missiles and two 864 litre (228 US gallon; 190 Imp gallon) drop tanks underwing.

DIMENSIONS, EXTERNAL:

Wing span: normal	9.39 m (30 ft 9¾ in)
incl tip Sidewinders	9.94 m (32 ft 7⅜ in)
Wing chord: at root	2.65 m (8 ft 8¼ in)
at tip	0.90 m (2 ft 11½ in)
Wing aspect ratio	5.3
Length overall: excl probe:	
Mk 1, 50 and 60 series	11.17 m (36 ft 7¾ in)
100 series	11.68 m (38 ft 4 in)
incl probe	11.86 m (38 ft 11 in)
Height overall:	
Mk 1, 50 and 60 series	3.99 m (13 ft 1¼ in)
100 series	4.16 m (13 ft 8 in)
Tailplane span	4.39 m (14 ft 4¾ in)
Wheel track	3.47 m (11 ft 5 in)

AREAS:

Wings, gross	16.69 m² (179.6 sq ft)
Ailerons (total)	1.05 m² (11.30 sq ft)
Trailing-edge flaps (total)	2.50 m² (26.91 sq ft)
Airbrake	0.53 m² (5.70 sq ft)
Fin: Mk 1, 50 and 60 series	2.51 m² (27.02 sq ft)
100 series	2.61 m² (28.10 sq ft)
Rudder, incl tab	0.58 m² (6.24 sq ft)
Tailplane	4.33 m² (46.61 sq ft)

WEIGHTS:

Weight empty: 60 series	3,750 kg (8,267 lb)
100 series	3,970 kg (8,752 lb)
T-O weight:	
60 series trainer, clean	5,150 kg (11,350 lb)
Max T-O weight: T. Mk 1	5,700 kg (12,566 lb)
50 series	7,350 kg (16,200 lb)
60, 100 series	8,500 kg (18,739 lb)
Max landing weight: T. Mk 1	4,649 kg (10,250 lb)
60 series	7,650 kg (16,865 lb)

PERFORMANCE:

Max speed in dive at height	575 knots (1,065 km/h; 661 mph)
Max Mach number in dive	1.2

Max level speed:	
50 series	535 knots (990 km/h; 615 mph)
60, 100 series	560 knots (1,037 km/h; 644 mph)
Max level speed Mach number	0.88
Max rate of climb at S/L	3,600 m (11,800 ft)/min
Time to 9,145 m (30,000 ft), clean	6 min 6 s
Service ceiling	15,250 m (50,000 ft)
T-O run	550 m (1,800 ft)
Landing run: Series 60	518 m (1,700 ft)
Series 100	524 m (1,720 ft)
Combat radius:	
with 2,268 kg (5,000 lb) weapon load	538 nm (998 km; 620 miles)
with 908 kg (2,000 lb) weapon load	781 nm (1,448 km; 900 miles)
Ferry range, clean	1,313 nm (2,433 km; 1,510 miles)
Ferry range, 60 series, with two 864 litre (228 US gallon; 190 Imp gallon) drop tanks	2,200 nm (4,075 km; 2,530 miles)
Endurance, 100 nm (185 km; 115 miles) from base	approx 4 h
g limits	+8/−4

BAe HAWK 200 SERIES (SINGLE-SEATER)

On 20 June 1984, British Aerospace announced its intention to build as a private venture a demonstrator single-seat combat version of the Hawk, and this aircraft (ZG200) flew for the first time on 19 May 1986. It was lost, through no aircraft fault, on 2 July 1986, and was replaced by the first pre-production Hawk 200 (ZH200), which flew for the first time on 24 April 1987. A third demonstrator, with full 200 series avionics and systems, including a Westinghouse APG-66H radar, is due to fly in 1991.

Except for its taller fin and modified wing leading-edge, the Hawk 200 is virtually identical with the current production two-seater aft of the cockpit, giving 80 per cent airframe commonality. The avionics fit, which is similar to that of the Hawk 100 series, enables a radar, or FLIR and laser rangefinder, to be carried. Built-in twin-cannon armament frees the centreline pylon for other stores, including a 592 litre (156 US gallon; 130 Imp gallon) external fuel tank. Each of the four underwing pylons is capable of carrying 907 kg (2,000 lb), within the max external load of 3,493 kg (7,700 lb). The Hawk 200 is intended to take advantage of new, miniaturised, low-cost avionics and intelligent weapons now available. The wide range of missions that such equipment permits includes:

Airspace denial. Carrying two Sidewinder type missiles and two 864 litre (228 US gallon; 190 Imp gallon) drop tanks, the Hawk 200 could loiter for 3 hours on station at low level, 100 nm (185 km; 115 miles) from base; or for one hour on station 550 nm (1,018 km; 633 miles) from base. Max intercept radius is 720 nm (1,333 km; 828 miles).

The single-seat British Aerospace Hawk 200 series with nose-mounted radar (*Pilot Press*)

BAe pre-production Hawk 200 single-seat multi-role combat aircraft

Optional wingtip missile rail increases possible weapon load to six Sidewinder type AAMs.

Close air support. Five 1,000 lb and four 500 lb bombs could be delivered with precision up to 104 nm (192 km; 120 miles) from base in a lo-lo mission.

Battlefield interdiction. In a hi-lo-hi operation, the Hawk 200 has a radius of action of 510 nm (945 km; 587 miles), with a 1,360 kg (3,000 lb) military load.

Long-range photo reconnaissance. A wide area of search is made possible by the mission range of 1,723 nm (3,190 km; 1,982 miles) offered by two external tanks, carried with a pod containing cameras and infra-red linescan. A rapid role change could then permit follow-up attack by the same aircraft. Lo-lo radius by day or night is 510 nm (945 km; 586 miles).

Long-range deployment. Ferry range with two 864 litre (228 US gallon; 190 Imp gallon) and one 592 litre (156 US gallon; 130 Imp gallon) external tanks is 1,950 nm (3,610 km; 2,244 miles), unrefuelled and with 864 litre tanks retained. Reserves would allow 10 min over destination at 150 m (500 ft).

Anti-shipping strike. Armed with a Sea Eagle sea skimming anti-ship missile, and carrying two 864 litre (228 US gallon; 190 Imp gallon) tanks, the Hawk 200 could attack a ship 666 nm (1,234 km; 767 miles) from base, and return with 10 per cent fuel reserves. This puts ships in a wide area of the North Atlantic within range of the Hawk from shore bases. Weapon release could be beyond the target's radar envelope.

Three standards of equipment are envisaged, depending on the customer's mission requirements, as follows:

Day operation. The most simple equipment fit would comprise a gyro stabilised attack sight and attitude heading reference system, with navigation by radio aids. Navigation and weapon aiming capabilities could be extended by adding an inertial navigation system, head-up display and weapon aiming computer. Other options are HOTAS controls, laser rangefinder, IFF, radar warning receiver.

Night operation. With a FLIR and laser rangefinder mounted in a modified nosecone, the Hawk 200 could carry out precision ground attacks and tactical reconnaissance by day and night.

All-weather operation. Installation of the Westinghouse APG-66H advanced multi-mode radar adds all-weather target acquisition and navigational fixing capabilities. Weapons like the anti-shipping Sea Eagle and air-to-air Sky Flash could also be employed.

Interest in the Hawk 200 has been expressed by existing Hawk operators. In July 1988, Saudi Arabia signed an MoU covering a second batch of some 60 Hawks, a substantial proportion of which will be Series 200s fitted with APG-66H radar.

Changes by comparison with the two-seat Hawk are as follows:

TYPE: Single-seat multi-role combat aircraft.
WINGS: Same as for 100 series. Generally similar to Hawk two-seater except: revised fixed leading-edge droop enhances lift and manoeuvrability in the Mach 0.3-0.7 flight regime; manually-selected combat flap (less than ¼-flap setting) available below 350 knots (649 km/h; 403 mph) IAS allows in excess of 5g to be sustained at 300 knots (556 km/h; 345 mph) at sea level. Full-width flap vanes reinstated; detail modifications to wing dressing compared with 60 series. Optional wingtip rails for AIM-9 Sidewinder, or other air-to-air missiles, can be retrofitted.

FUSELAGE: Modified to single-seat configuration. Unchanged design concept and criteria.
TAIL UNIT: Hawk 100 and 200 fitted with smurfs (side-mounted unit horizontal root tail fin), this being a strake ahead of each tailplane to restore control authority at high angles of attack.
LANDING GEAR: Mainwheel tyres size 559 × 165-279, pressure 16.2 bars (235 lb/sq in). Nosewheel tyre size 457 × 140-203, pressure 7.24 bars (105 lb/sq in). Optional single Tornado-type nosewheel for increased T-O weight.
POWER PLANT: One Rolls-Royce Turbomeca Adour Mk 871 non-afterburning turbofan, with uninstalled rating of 26.0 kN (5,845 lb st).
ACCOMMODATION: Pilot only, on Martin-Baker Type 10L ejection seat, under side-hinged (to starboard) canopy.
SYSTEMS: Fairey Hydraulics yaw control system added, comprising rudder actuator and servo control system, incorporating an autostabiliser computer. Ferranti multi-function display in cockpit. Lucas Aerospace artificial feel system.
ARMAMENT: One or two internally mounted 25 mm Aden guns (with 100 rds each) beneath cockpit floor. Ferranti ISIS sight or Smiths head-up display optional. Chaff/flare dispenser (Vinten Vicon 78 Srs 300 or equivalent) at base of fin. All weapon pylons cleared for 8g manoeuvres with 500 kg (1,102 lb) loads.
DIMENSIONS, EXTERNAL:
As Hawk two-seater, except:

Length overall	11.38 m (37 ft 4 in)
Height overall	4.16 m (13 ft 8 in)
Wheelbase	3.298 m (10 ft 10 in)

AREAS:
As Hawk two-seater, except:

Fin	2.61 m² (28.10 sq ft)

WEIGHTS:

Weight empty	4,128 kg (9,100 lb)
Max fuel: internal	1,360 kg (3,000 lb)
internal plus three drop tanks	3,210 kg (7,080 lb)
Max weapon load	3,500 kg (7,700 lb)
Max T-O weight	9,101 kg (20,065 lb)

PERFORMANCE (estimated; no external stores or role equipment unless stated):

Never-exceed speed at height	
	Mach 1.2 (575 knots; 1,065 km/h; 661 mph)
Max level speed at S/L	
	560 knots (1,037 km/h; 644 mph)
Max cruising speed at S/L	
	550 knots (1,019 km/h; 633 mph)
Econ cruising speed at 12,500 m (41,000 ft)	
	430 knots (796 km/h; 495 mph)
Stalling speed, flaps down	
	106 knots (197 km/h; 122 mph) IAS
Max rate of climb at S/L	3,508 m (11,510 ft)/min
Service ceiling	15,250 m (50,000 ft)
Runway LCN: flexible pavement	15
rigid pavement	10
T-O run with max weapon load	1,585 m (5,200 ft)
T-O to 15 m (50 ft) with max weapon load	
	2,134 m (7,000 ft)
Landing from 15 m (50 ft) at landing weight of 4,550 kg	
(10,030 lb): with brake-chute	854 m (2,800 ft)
without brake-chute	1,250 m (4,100 ft)
Radius of action, hi-hi with one Sea Eagle anti-ship	
missile and two 864 litre (228 US gallon; 190 Imp	
gallon) drop tanks	311 nm (576 km; 358 miles)
Range:	
with internal fuel only	482 nm (892 km; 554 miles)
with internal fuel plus three drop tanks	
	1,950 nm (3,610 km; 2,244 miles)
g limits	+8/-4

BAe HARRIER
RAF designations: Harrier GR. Mk 3 and T. Mk 4/4A
Spanish Navy designation: VA.1 Matador (AV-8S and TAV-8S)

The Harrier was the world's first operational fixed-wing V/STOL strike fighter. It has now been supplanted in production by the AV-8B Harrier II/Harrier GR. Mk 5 (see International section: McDonnell Douglas/BAe), except for limited manufacture as a two-seat compatible trainer for the Sea Harrier. The Mk 50, Mk 54, and Mk 55 of the Spanish Navy continue in service, but surplus RAF Harrier GR.Mk 3s were withdrawn from the RAF beginning in 1988, some having been offered to Chile. All US Marine Corps AV-8As and TAV-8As have retired. Fuller details appeared in the 1989-90 and earlier editions of *Jane's*. Principal variants are currently:

Harrier T. Mk 4, 4A and 6, and Harrier T. Mk 4N and 8N. Two-seat trainer versions. The Mk 4A lacks an LRMTS nose. One T. Mk 4A (XZ455) was funded by the Royal Navy, but operated until recently by the RAF. Genuine Royal Navy two-seaters are designated Harrier T. Mk 4N; three were delivered, of which one was lost in 1985. Two-seat Harrier production for the UK thus 31, including prototypes. Following a February 1990 order for two-seat Harrier IIs (see International section), plans were abandoned to convert some RAF T. Mk 4s to T. Mk 6 standard, with night vision equipment for training pilots of GR. Mk 7s fitted with FLIR sensors. Other RAF trainers are to be transferred to the RN. Approval is awaited for some naval Harrier trainers to be fitted with cockpits representative of the Sea Harrier FRS. Mk 2 (but without radar) and re-designated T. Mk 8N.

BAe Sea Harrier FRS. Mk 1 with alternative inventories of Sidewinders, tanks, bombs, flares, practice bomb carriers and cannon *(Paul Jackson)*

BAe Sea Harrier FRS. Mk 2 aerodynamic prototype carrying four AMRAAM missiles

Two dual-control Harriers are employed in test programmes, including XW175 at RAE Bedford as the Vectored-thrust Advanced Aircraft Control (VAAC) Harrier (see 1987-88 *Jane's*: Cranfield entry). In 1987, XW267 joined the 'Nightbird' night vision equipment development programme at RAE Farnborough, fitted with FLIR and a compatible Ferranti Defence Systems nav/attack avionics suite in the front cockpit including an FD 4512 HUD/WAC; an upgraded digital INS; a projected map display; high-resolution, head-down raster display (both cockpits) and video recording facilities. In 1988, this aircraft entered service with the RAF's Strike/Attack Operational Evaluation Unit at Boscombe Down, operating in conjunction with Harrier GR. Mk 5s.

Harrier T. Mk 60. Two-seat operational trainer version for Indian Navy. T. Mk 4A configuration, but with complete Sea Harrier avionics except for Blue Fox radar. Four ordered. Deliveries to India began in March 1984, the third aircraft following in 1990.

Sea Harrier FRS. Mks 1, 2 and 51. Versions for Royal Navy and Indian Navy. Described separately.

Technical details as for Sea Harrier, except:

TYPE: V/STOL close support and reconnaissance aircraft.

LANDING GEAR: T. Mk 4 tyre pressures 6.90 bars (100 lb/sq in) on nose unit, 6.55 bars (95 lb/sq in) on main and outrigger units.

POWER PLANT: One Rolls-Royce Pegasus Mk 103 vectored thrust turbofan (95.6 kN; 21,500 lb st).

ACCOMMODATION: Crew of two (Mk 4) on Martin-Baker Mk 9D zero/zero rocket ejection seats.

AVIONICS AND EQUIPMENT: Plessey U/VHF, Ultra standby UHF, GEC Avionics AD 2770 Tacan and Cossor IFF, Ferranti FE 541 inertial navigation and attack system (INAS), with Honeywell C2G compass, Smiths electronic head-up display of flight information, and air data computer. Marconi ARI.18223 radar warning receiver. Ferranti Type 106 laser ranger and marked target seeker (LRMTS) retrofitted to some two-seat RAF Harriers.

DIMENSIONS, EXTERNAL:
Wing span	7.70 m (25 ft 3 in)
Length overall:	
two-seat (laser nose)	17.50 m (57 ft 5 in)
Height overall: two-seat	4.17 m (13 ft 8 in)
Tailplane span	4.24 m (13 ft 11 in)
Outrigger wheel track	6.76 m (22 ft 2 in)
Wheelbase, nosewheel to mainwheels	
	approx 3.45 m (11 ft 4 in)

AREAS:
Wings, gross	18.68 m² (201.1 sq ft)
Fin (excl ventral fin): two-seat	3.57 m² (38.4 sq ft)
Rudder, incl tab	0.49 m² (5.3 sq ft)
Tailplane	4.41 m² (47.5 sq ft)

WEIGHTS:
Weight empty (pilot/s plus four pylons; no guns):
T. Mk 4	6,693 kg (14,755 lb)
T. Mk 4A	6,568 kg (14,480 lb)
Internal fuel	2,295 kg (5,060 lb)
Max T-O weight: two-seat	11,880 kg (26,200 lb)

PERFORMANCE (single-seat):
Max level speed at S/L	635 knots (1,176 km/h; 730 mph)
Max Mach number in a dive at height	1.3
Time to 12,200 m (40,000 ft) from vertical T-O	
	2 min 23 s
Service ceiling	15,600 m (51,200 ft)
T-O run: with 2,270 kg (5,000 lb) payload at max T-O weight	approx 305 m (1,000 ft)
Range: hi-lo-hi with 1,995 kg (4,400 lb) payload	
	360 nm (666 km; 414 miles)
lo-lo with 1,995 kg (4,400 lb) payload	
	200 nm (370 km; 230 miles)
Ferry range	1,850 nm (3,425 km; 2,129 miles)
Range with one in-flight refuelling	
	more than 3,000 nm (5,560 km; 3,455 miles)

Endurance:
combat air patrol 100 nm (185 km; 115 miles) from base	1 h 30 min
with one in-flight refuelling	more than 7 h
g limits	+7.8/−4.2

BAe SEA HARRIER
RN designation: FRS. Mk 1/2
Indian Navy designation: FRS. Mk 51

On 15 May 1975, the British government announced its decision to proceed with full development of a maritime version of the Harrier, subsequently designated **Sea Harrier FRS. Mk 1**. The first Sea Harrier to fly (XZ450) made its first flight on 20 August 1978, and the first for the Royal Navy (XZ451) was handed over on 18 June 1979. The first Sea Harrier ship trials were carried out on board HMS *Hermes* during November 1979.

The initial Royal Navy order was for three development aircraft (XZ438-440). Successive production orders for 21, 10, 14 and 9 had taken the total to 57 by September 1984. All were built as Mk 1s, the last completed in June 1988. A contract for a further 10 in Mk 2 configuration (which see) was placed in March 1990. The Naval Intensive Flying Trials Unit for the Sea Harrier (No. 700A Squadron) was commissioned at RNAS Yeovilton on 19 September 1979. It became subsequently the normally shore based No. 899 HQ squadron, with eight aircraft. Front line units, each previously with five aircraft, but increased to eight from 1988, are Nos. 800 and 801 Squadrons, able to operate from the anti-submarine cruisers HMS *Invincible, Illustrious* and *Ark Royal.* Six similar Sea Harriers, designated **FRS. Mk**

51, ordered by the Indian Navy are in service with No. 300 (White Tiger) Squadron and operate from INS *Vikrant*, having been handed over from January 1983 and delivered (after training of pilots in the UK) from December 1983. Three standard, non-navalised T. Mk 4N two-seaters were delivered to the Royal Navy for land based training, and two T. Mk 60s to the Indian Navy. In November 1985 the Indian Government ordered 10 additional FRS. Mk 51 Sea Harriers and one more T. Mk 60 two-seat trainer. A letter of intent to purchase seven more FRS. Mk 51s and one Mk 60 was issued in September 1986, to equip the former HMS *Hermes* which was transferred to the Indian Navy as the INS *Viraat*. Deliveries of the second batch began in late 1989.

Following proposals by Lt Cdr D. R. Taylor, RN, tests were carried out successfully in 1977 with a ski-jump launching ramp designed to boost the short take-off performance of vectored thrust aircraft. This technique makes possible substantial benefits in Harrier operation both at sea and ashore, and is a feature of Royal Navy ships in which Sea Harriers are based. A 7° ski-jump ramp was originally fitted to HMS *Invincible* and HMS *Illustrious*; that in HMS *Ark Royal* was, and remains, more steeply angled, at 12°, which permits an increase of 1,135 kg (2,500 lb) in launch weight for the same T-O run, or a 50-60 per cent reduction in T-O run for the same weight. The two earlier ships are being modified to have 13° ramps and a complement of eight Sea Harriers. The first conversion, of HMS *Invincible*, was completed in January 1989.

Major changes compared with the Harriers in service with the RAF, Spanish Navy and US Marine Corps comprise the elimination of magnesium components, introduction of a raised cockpit, revised operational avionics, and installation of multi-mode Ferranti radar in a redesigned nose that folds to port for carrier stowage. Known by the name Blue Fox, this radar is a derivative of the frequency agile Seaspray radar fitted in the Royal Navy Lynx helicopter, but embodies changes to suit its different role, with air-to-air intercept and air-to-surface modes of operation.

The Royal Navy's Sea Harrier FRS. Mk 1 has a Rolls-Royce Pegasus 104 vectored thrust turbofan, with the same rating as the Pegasus 103 fitted to current RAF Harriers. Pegasus 104 incorporates additional anti-corrosion features and has the capability to generate more electrical power.

The Sea Harrier FRS. Mk 1 was intended to operate at approximately the same weights as the GR. Mk 3, and to lift a full military load with a 152 m (500 ft) flat deck run into an overdeck wind of 30 knots (55.5 km/h; 34.5 mph). It was first used operationally during the Falkland Islands campaign in 1982, from HMS *Hermes* and *Invincible*, when a total of 28 Sea Harriers flew 2,376 sorties. They destroyed 22 enemy aircraft in air-to-air combat without loss. Four Sea Harriers were lost in accidents and two to ground fire.

In January 1985 the UK Ministry of Defence awarded a contract to BAe for the project definition phase of a mid-life update of Royal Navy Sea Harriers. The upgraded Sea Harriers are designated **FRS. Mk 2**, and have a Pegasus 106 engine with similar rating to the 104.

The first of two development Mk 2s, an aerodynamic prototype converted at Dunsfold from Mk 1 ZA195, first flew on 19 September 1988 and was followed by XZ439 on 8 March 1989. A contract for conversion of Mk 1s to Mk 2 standard was signed by the UK MoD on 7 December 1988 and is believed to cover all 42 aircraft then extant although three have subsequently been lost. These will be modified at Kingston from October 1990 onward and re-delivered between 1991 and 1994, augmenting new-build Mk 2s.

Externally, the Mk 2 differs from the Mk 1 in having role change wingtip extensions that increase the span by 40.6 cm (1 ft 4 in); a less pointed nose radome; a longer rear fuselage, resulting from insertion of a 35 cm (1 ft 1¾ in) plug aft of the wing trailing-edge; and revisions of the antennae and external stores.

Installation of Ferranti Blue Vixen pulse-Doppler radar, instead of the original Blue Fox, gives the Sea Harrier FRS. Mk 2 all-weather lookdown/shootdown capability, with inherent track-while-scan, multiple target engagement, greatly increased missile launch range, enhanced surface target acquisition, and improved ECCM performance. In addition to the wide range of weapons with which the current operational Sea Harrier is compatible, the FRS. Mk 2 will be equipped to carry the air-to-air AIM-120 AMRAAM, on Dowty/Frazer-Nash launch rails compatible with the AIM-9L Sidewinder. The new launcher was first tested by a live AIM-9L release from an FRS. Mk 1 on 2 November 1988, and an accompanying illustration shows ZA195 fitted with four AMRAAMs, as first flown on 30 March 1989. Missile trials will begin in the USA (on XZ439) in 1991.

Airborne testing of the Blue Vixen radar began in an RAE BAe One-Eleven (ZF433) which completed its 114 hour/121 sortie programme in November 1987. Development work was transferred to an RAE BAe 125 (XW930) which first flew on 26 August 1988 with an A version radar. A second 125-600B (ZF130) has been fitted with a full FRS. Mk 2 weapon system, including a representative cockpit in the co-pilot's position and a Sidewinder acquisition round on an underwing pylon. The aircraft first flew at Woodford on 20 May 1988 and began

BAe Sea Harrier FRS. Mk 2 V/STOL fighter, reconnaissance and strike aircraft *(Pilot Press)*

development flying from Dunsfold in December 1988, but was not fitted with Blue Vixen (a B version) until September 1989. A B series Blue Vixen first flew in a Sea Harrier (XZ439) in early 1990.

Improved systems are built around a MIL-1553B databus. This uses a dual redundant data highway, allowing computerised time sharing of information processed in the databus control and interface unit.

Re-design of the cockpit includes a new HUD and dual multi-purpose head-down displays, but the proposed JTIDS terminal will not be fitted (except as a possible retrofit) following cancellation by the US Navy of the originally proposed equipment. All time-critical weapon systems controls are positioned on the up-front control panel, or on the throttle and stick.

Operational efficiency is improved by the ergonomic integration of additional switches as part of the control column and throttle handle functions. HOTAS (hands on throttle and stick) controls provide simultaneous control of the aircraft, radar and weapons systems without the need to operate separate controls and switches.

The following description applies to the Sea Harrier FRS. Mk 1:

TYPE: V/STOL fighter, reconnaissance and strike aircraft.

WINGS: Cantilever shoulder-wing monoplane. Wing section of BAe (HS) design. Thickness/chord ratio 10 per cent at root, 5 per cent at tip. Anhedral 12°. Incidence 1° 45′. Sweepback at quarter-chord 34°. One-piece aluminium alloy three-spar safe-life structure with integrally machined skins, manufactured by Brough factory of BAe, with six-point attachment to fuselage. Plain ailerons and flaps, of bonded aluminium alloy honeycomb construction. Ailerons irreversibly operated by Fairey tandem hydraulic jacks. Jet reaction control valve built into front of each outrigger wheel fairing. Entire wing unit removable to provide access to engine. Revised inboard one-third of FRS. Mk 2's wing incorporates additional fence, kinked leading edge, re-positioning of dog-tooth fillet closer to fuselage, and reduction of over-wing vortex-generators from 12 to 11. Fitment of AIM-120 AMRAAM missiles on outer wing pylons requires addition of 20.3 cm (8 in) extensions to each wingtip for aerodynamic reasons. For ferrying, 67.3 cm (2 ft 2½ in) extensions are available.

FUSELAGE: Conventional semi-monocoque safe-life structure of frames and stringers, mainly of aluminium alloy, but with titanium skins at rear and some titanium adjacent to engine and in other special areas. Access to power plant through top of fuselage, ahead of wing. Jet reaction control valves in nose and tailcone. Large forward hinged airbrake under fuselage, aft of mainwheel well. FRS. Mk 2 has nose structure slightly deepened and stiffened, plus new rear fuselage, increased in length by 35 cm (1 ft 1¾ in).

TAIL UNIT: One-piece variable incidence tailplane, with 15° of anhedral, irreversibly operated by Fairey tandem hydraulic jack. Rudder and trailing-edge of tailplane are of bonded aluminium honeycomb construction. Rudder is operated manually. Trim tab in rudder. Ventral fin under rear fuselage. Fin tip carries suppressed VHF aerial.

LANDING GEAR: Retractable bicycle type of Dowty Aerospace manufacture, permitting operation from rough unprepared surfaces of CBR as low as 3 to 5 per cent. Hydraulic actuation, with nitrogen bottle for emergency extension of landing gear. Single steerable nosewheel retracts forward, twin coupled mainwheels rearward, into fuselage. Small outrigger units retract rearward into fairings slightly inboard of wingtips. Nosewheel leg is of levered suspension Liquid Spring type. Dowty telescopic oleo-pneumatic main and outrigger gear. Dunlop wheels and tyres, size 26.00 × 8.75-11 (nose unit), 27.00 × 7.74-13 (main units) and 13.50 × 6.4 (outriggers). Dunlop multi-disc brakes and Dunlop-Hytrol adaptive anti-skid system.

POWER PLANT: One Rolls-Royce Pegasus Mk 104 or (FRS. Mk 2) Mk 106 vectored thrust turbofan (95.6 kN; 21,500 lb st), with four exhaust nozzles of the two-vane cascade type, rotatable through 98.5° from fully aft position. Engine bleed air from HP compressor used for jet reaction control system and to power duplicated air motor for nozzle actuation. The low drag intake cowls each have eight automatic suction relief doors aft of the leading-edge to improve intake efficiency by providing extra air for the engine at low forward or zero speeds. A 227 litre (60 US gallon; 50 Imp gallon) tank supplies demineralised water for thrust restoration in high ambient temperatures for STO, VTO and vertical landings. Fuel in five integral tanks in fuselage and two in wings, with total capacity of approx 2,865 litres (757 US gallons; 630 Imp gallons). This can be supplemented by two 455 litre (120 US gallon; 100 Imp gallon) jettisonable combat tanks, or two 864 litre (228 US gallon; 190 Imp gallon) tanks, or two 1,500 litre (396 US gallon; 330 Imp gallon) ferry tanks on the inboard wing pylons. Ground refuelling point in port rear nozzle fairing. Provision for in-flight refuelling probe above the port intake cowl.

ACCOMMODATION: Pilot only, on Martin-Baker Mk 10H zero/zero rocket ejection seat which operates through the miniature detonating cord equipped canopy of the pressurised, heated and air-conditioned cockpit. Sea Harrier seat raised 28 cm (11 in) compared with Harrier.

Manually operated rearward sliding canopy. Birdproof windscreen, with hydraulically actuated wiper. Windscreen washing system.

SYSTEMS: Three-axis limited authority autostabiliser for V/STOL flight. Pressurisation system of BAe design, with Normalair-Garrett and Delaney Gallay major components; max pressure differential 0.24 bars (3.5 lb/sq in). Two hydraulic systems; flow rate: System 1, 36 litres (9.6 US gallons; 8 Imp gallons)/min; System 2, 23 litres (6 US gallons; 5 Imp gallons)/min. Systems, pressure 207 bars (3,000 lb/sq in), actuate Fairey flying control and general services and a retractable ram air turbine inside top of rear fuselage, driving a small hydraulic pump for emergency power. Turbine deleted from FRS. Mk 2. Hydraulic reservoirs nitrogen pressurised at 2.75 to 5.5 bars (40 to 80 lb/sq in). AC electrical system with transformer-rectifiers to provide required DC supply. Two 15kVA generators. Two 28V 25Ah batteries, one of which energises a 24V motor to start Lucas gas turbine starter/APU. This unit drives a 6kVA auxiliary alternator for ground readiness servicing and standby. Normalair-Garrett liquid oxygen system of 4.5 litres (1.2 US gallons; 1 Imp gallon) capacity. Bootstrap cooling unit for equipment bay, with intake at base of dorsal fin. Autopilot function on Fairey Hydraulics, giving throughput to aileron and tailplane power controls as well as to three-axis autostabs. British Oxygen liquid oxygen system of 4.5 litres (1.2 US gallons; 1 Imp gallon) capacity in Royal Navy aircraft; those for Indian Navy have gaseous oxygen system. Lucas Mk 2 GTS/APU.

AVIONICS AND EQUIPMENT: Nose mounted Ferranti Blue Fox multi-mode radar, with TV raster daylight viewing tube which conveys flight information, as well as radar data, to pilot. New and larger Smiths electronic head-up display and 20,000 word digital weapon aiming computer. Autopilot, radar altimeter and Decca Doppler 72 radar. Ferranti self aligning attitude and heading reference platform and digital navigation computer. Radio navaids include UHF homing, GEC Avionics AD 2770 Tacan with offset facility and I band transponder. Radio com by multi-channel Plessey PTR 377 U/VHF, with VHF standby via D 403M transceiver. Passive electronic surveillance and warning of external radar illumination by receiver with forward and rear hemisphere antennae in fin and tailcone respectively.

ARMAMENT AND OPERATIONAL EQUIPMENT: Optically flat panel in nose, on port side, for F.95 oblique camera, which is carried as standard. A cockpit voice recorder with in-flight playback facility supplements the reconnaissance cameras, and facilitates rapid debriefing and mission evaluation. No built-in armament. Combat load is carried on four underwing and one underfuselage pylons, all with ML ejector release units. The inboard wing points and the fuselage point are stressed for loads of up to 910 kg (2,000 lb) each, and the outboard underwing pair for loads of up to 295 kg (650 lb) each; the two strake fairings under the fuselage can each be replaced by a 30 mm Aden gun pod and ammunition or, on FRS. Mk 2, by two AIM-120 AMRAAMs. The aircraft is cleared for operations with a maximum external load exceeding 2,270 kg (5,000 lb), and has flown with a weapon load of 3,630 kg (8,000 lb). FRS. Mk 2 outboard pylons re-stressed to 454 kg (1,000 lb). It is able to carry 30 mm guns, bombs, rockets and flares of UK and US designs. Alternative stores loads of RN Sea Harriers include a WE177 nuclear bomb; free-fall (467 kg; 1,030 lb) and parachute-retarded (508 kg; 1,120 lb) bombs; Lepus flares; and ML CBLS 100 carriers for Portsmouth Aviation 3 kg and 14 kg practice bombs. Four AIM-9 Sidewinder missiles are carried on the outboard underwing pylons (Matra Magic instead of Sidewinder on Indian Navy aircraft), and there is provision for two air-to-surface missiles of Sea Eagle or Harpoon type. FRS. Mk 2 accommodates up to four AIM-120 AMRAAMs, or two AIM-120s and four AIM-9L Sidewinders. BAe ALARM anti-radiation missile may replace AIM-120.

DIMENSIONS, EXTERNAL: As GR. Mk 3 except:

Wing span: FRS. Mk 1	7.70 m (25 ft 3 in)
FRS. Mk 2 (optional)	8.31 m (27 ft 3 in)
Length overall: FRS. Mk 1	14.50 m (47 ft 7 in)
FRS. Mk 2	14.10 m (46 ft 3 in)
Length overall, nose folded:	
FRS. Mk 1	12.73 m (41 ft 9 in)
FRS. Mk 2	13.16 m (43 ft 2 in)
Height overall	3.71 m (12 ft 2 in)

WEIGHTS (FRS. Mk 1):

Operating weight empty	6,374 kg (14,052 lb)
Max fuel: internal	2,295 kg (5,060 lb)
external	2,404 kg (5,300 lb)
Max weapon load: STO	3,630 kg (8,000 lb)
VTO	2,270 kg (5,000 lb)
Max T-O weight	11,880 kg (26,200 lb)

PERFORMANCE (FRS. Mk 1):

Max Mach No. at high altitude	1.25
Max level speed at low altitude	
above 640 knots (1,185 km/h; 736 mph) EAS	
Typical cruising speed:	
high altitude, for well over 1 h on internal fuel	
above Mach 0.8	
low altitude	

350-450 knots (650-833 km/h; 404-518 mph), with rapid acceleration to
600 knots (1,110 km/h; 690 mph)
STO run at max T-O weight, without ski-jump
approx 305 m (1,000 ft)
Time from alarm to 30 nm (55 km; 35 miles) combat area under 6 min
High altitude intercept radius, with 3 min combat and reserves for VL 400 nm (750 km; 460 miles)
Strike radius 250 nm (463 km; 288 miles)
g limits +7.8/−4.2

COMBAT PROFILES (FRS. Mk 2, from carrier fitted with a 12° ski-jump ramp, at ISA + 15°C and with a 20 knot; 37km/h; 23 mph wind over the deck):

Combat air patrol: Up to 1½ hours on station at a radius of 100 nm (185 km; 115 miles), carrying four AMRAAMs, or two AMRAAMs and two 30 mm guns, plus two 864 litre (228 US gallon; 190 Imp gallon) combat drop tanks. Deck T-O run: 137 m (450 ft).

Reconnaissance: Low level cover of 130,000 nm² (446,465 km²; 172,380 sq miles) at a radius of 525 nm (970 km; 600 miles) from the carrier, with outward and return flights at medium/high level, carrying two 30 mm guns and two 864 litre (228 US gallon; 190 Imp gallon) combat drop tanks. Overall flight time 1 h 45 min.

Surface attack (hi-lo-hi): Radius of action to missile launch 200 nm (370 km; 230 miles), carrying two Sea Eagle missiles and two 30 mm guns.

Take-off deck run for the above missions is 137 m, 107 m and 92 m (450 ft, 350 ft and 300 ft) respectively, with vertical landing.

Interception: A typical deck-launched interception could be performed against a Mach 0.9 target at a radius of 116 nm (215 km; 133 miles), or a Mach 1.3 target at 95 nm (175 km; 109 miles), after initial radar detection of the approaching target at a range of 230 nm (425 km; 265 miles), with the Sea Harrier at 2 min alert status, carrying two AMRAAM missiles.

BAe EAP

British Aerospace exhibited at the 1982 Farnborough Air Show, and again at the 1983 Paris Air Show, a full scale mockup of what was then known as the Agile Combat Aircraft (ACA). It represented the result of several years of private venture research and development by BAe, with industry support from Rolls-Royce, Dowty, Ferranti, Lucas, GEC Avionics and Smiths Industries, at a total estimated cost of £25 million by mid-1983. MBB of Germany and Aeritalia of Italy had also contributed to the project.

No government support for the ACA was forthcoming but, at the 1982 Farnborough show, the UK government announced that it would make a financial contribution to an experimental aircraft programme (EAP) technology demonstrator based on the ACA design. The aims of the programme were to bring together a specific range of new and advanced technologies being developed by BAe and other aerospace manufacturers in Europe.

On 26 May 1983, BAe announced that a contract had been signed with the Ministry of Defence for the design, development and construction of a single demonstrator aircraft which would be used to prove advanced technological features, including advanced aerodynamics; active control technology for unstable aircraft; a digital databus system; advanced electronic cockpit; and advanced structural design including the extensive use of carbonfibre composites.

The EAP demonstrator was funded by the UK Ministry of Defence, BAe, its industrial partners and equipment suppliers in Britain, Italy and West Germany. The co-bonded wings were designed and manufactured by BAe and Aeritalia.

With the UK committed to participation in the international programme for a European fighter aircraft (Eurofighter, see International section), the relevance of the EAP is that it is designed to represent a weapon system that would meet a generally similar requirement. During its first flight, on 8 August 1986, the EAP demonstrator (ZF534) accelerated to Mach 1.1 at 9,150 m (30,000 ft). It made public appearances at the Farnborough Air Show in 1986 and, following installation of new flight controls and an anti-spin parachute, at the Paris Air Show in 1987. By the end of 1989, the EAP had completed 209 flights (155 hours) and expanded the flight envelope to above Mach 1.6 (650 knots; 1,200 km/h; 750 mph CAS).

EAP is currently engaged on development work contributing directly to the EFA programme. This has so far included a comprehensive flight loads survey, a demonstration of the EFA airbrake configuration and trials to validate the lightning strike and EMC protection measures intended for EFA. Further work will include the development of flight control concepts and the evaluation of a variety of avionic and general system enhancements. A continuing programme of research in support of EFA and of a more general nature is envisaged for the future.

TYPE: Advanced technology demonstrator aircraft.

WINGS: Main wing aerofoil section varies from root to tip. Multi-spar carbonfibre composite co-bonded construction. Spars bonded to bottom skin; top skin bolted to spar flanges. Foreplanes of carbonfibre composite construction. Aerodynamic configuration provides high

BAe EAP advanced technology demonstrator photographed during trials of spine-mounted airbrake

Three-view drawing of BAe EAP demonstrator *(Pilot Press)*

negative stability. The aluminium alloy leading-edge flaps and aluminium/lithium alloy skinned trailing-edge flight surfaces, and the foreplanes, are operated by a GEC Avionics computer controlled active control system, using quadruplex full authority digital fly by wire technology developed in the Jaguar ACT programme. Liebherr/Magnaghi/Dowty Aerospace actuators on the foreplanes, rudder and inboard/outboard flaperon control surfaces are operated via a pilot's stick sensor assembly (PSSA) which uses spring damping and viscous loading to give the required stick resistance, to allow full and accurate movement of the stick in relation to aircraft speed and attitude. No reversionary mechanical or electrical signalling to flight control actuators.

FUSELAGE: Front fuselage is of semi-monocoque construction, with light alloy structure and carbonfibre composites side skins, cockpit floor and some belly skins. Engine air inlet duct of conventional aluminium alloy construction. Hinged forward lower lip. Centre and rear fuselage of conventional metal construction, using Tornado technology and components. Centre keel member of superplastic formed/diffusion bonded titanium, with a conventionally fabricated titanium structure, to save weight and space.

TAIL UNIT: Cantilever all-metal structure, consisting of single sweptback two-spar fin and rudder, essentially the same as those fitted to the Tornado.

LANDING GEAR: Hydraulically operated tricycle type, with single wheel on each unit. Rearward retracting steerable nose unit. Operation of the forward retracting Dowty main landing gear involves rotary movement about the leg of each wheel during retraction and lowering, to facilitate compact stowage and positive locking when the gear is fully down. Carbonfibre wheel brakes. Brake parachute housed between rudder and jet nozzle.

POWER PLANT: Two Turbo-Union RB199-34R Mk 104D turbofans, as fitted to the Tornado F. Mk 3, but with thrust reversers removed, rated in the 40.0 kN (9,000 lb st) class dry and 75.5 kN (17,000 lb st) class with afterburning. Installed in rear fuselage with downward opening doors for servicing and engine change. Lucas DECU 500 full authority digital engine control system, developed in conjunction with Rolls-Royce. Fuel is carried integrally in the wings and in 14 tanks in the fuselage.

ACCOMMODATION: Pilot only, on specially-developed Martin-Baker Mk 10LX zero/zero ejection seat, in pressurised cockpit embodying advanced processor-controlled avionics and utilities management and control

systems designed to reduce substantially the pilot's workload. Equipment includes three colour multifunction display CRTs supplied by Smiths Industries, and an advanced GEC Avionics head-up display embodying holographic optics, and an additional raster (TV-like) display for night flying. Processor-controlled cockpit lighting system adjusts lighting levels automatically throughout ambient lighting spectrum.

SYSTEMS: Environmental control system utilises engine bleed air piped inside fuselage spine fairing to a precooler and intercooler in systems/avionics bay aft of cockpit. Hot air is mixed with cold ram air taken in above engine intake splitter plate. Exhaust is ejected through duct above wingroot on each side of fuselage. Hydraulic system for actuating flying control surfaces and airbrakes, landing gear retraction and extension, nosewheel steering, anti-skid braking and air intake lip actuation. Lucas/Rotax secondary power system, with electric starter/generators. Liquid oxygen system. Comprehensive fire detection and extinguishing systems.

AVIONICS AND EQUIPMENT: Racal Acoustics RA 800 series digital audio control system (IDACS). GEC Avionics AD 3400 VHF/UHF multimode radio. GEC Avionics AD 2780 Tacan system. GEC Avionics television sensor in cockpit records what the pilot sees during flight. Ferranti FIN 1070 inertial navigation system and BAe SCR 300E flight data recorder. Major avionics units mounted in an innovative avionics equipment module in

the front fuselage behind the cockpit. Information supplied to VDO cockpit multi-function displays by 1553B databus highways, replacing great lengths of multicored conventional wiring.

DIMENSIONS, EXTERNAL:
Wing span	11.77 m (38 ft 7 in)
Wing chord at root	8.79 m (28 ft 0 in)
Wing aspect ratio	2.4
Foreplane span	4.45 m (14 ft 7¼ in)
Length overall, incl nose probe	17.72 m (58 ft 1⅝ in)
Length of fuselage	14.45 m (47 ft 5 in)
Height overall	5.70 m (18 ft 8⅜ in)
Wheel track	2.94 m (9 ft 7¾ in)
Wheelbase	4.21 m (13 ft 9¾ in)

AREAS:
Wings, gross	51.66 m² (556.1 sq ft)
Foreplanes, gross	3.81 m² (40.9 sq ft)
Trailing-edge flaps, total	4.98 m² (53.6 sq ft)
Leading-edge flaps, total	2.42 m² (26.0 sq ft)
Fin	8.25 m² (88.8 sq ft)
Rudder	1.59 m² (17.1 sq ft)

WEIGHTS (approx):
Weight empty	10,000 kg (22,050 lb)
Fuel	4,535 kg (10,000 lb)
Max T-O weight, clean	14,515 kg (32,000 lb)

PERFORMANCE:
Max speed at height	Mach 2.0 +

EUROFIGHTER (EFA)

Details of this military aircraft programme, in which British Aerospace is participating with companies from West Germany, Italy and Spain, can be found in the International section.

BAe (HS) BUCCANEER UPDATE

It was announced in February 1985 that British Aerospace had been appointed prime contractor for a programme to update Buccaneer S. 2Bs in service with the Royal Air Force, to improve the avionics, armaments and electronic countermeasures to meet Air Staff Requirement 1012.

A major element of the programme is the installation of a Ferranti FIN 1063 inertial navigation system. This is a derivative of the FIN 1064 which equips RAF SEPECAT Jaguars, minus the weapon aiming system. Ferranti is also updating the Airpass III (Blue Parrot) attack radar, and has added an interface between radar and INS. Marconi Defence Systems has raised the ARI.18228 radar warning system to Guardian Series 200 standard with a new cockpit display and forward facing C-D band antennae in wing leading-edge bullet fairings (augmenting original E-J band receivers in tailplane root fairing). Plessey radios and improved Louis Newmark automatic flight control system. Provision for crew's AR5 NBC respirator system. Twin Tracor AN/ALE-40 flare dispenser installation in lower rear fuselage; single chaff-dispensing ALE-40 scabbed to inside of outboard wing pylons.

Forty-two S. Mk 2B aircraft have been updated for further service in the maritime role from a total of 44 Mk 2Bs and four non-missile-carrying Mk 2As in current RAF service. (A further seven UK Buccaneers are used for trials.) Primary weapon is the BAe Sea Eagle anti-ship missile with which No. 208 Squadron was equipped in 1986, followed by No. 12 Squadron early in 1990. The Buccaneer S. Mk 2B has an equipped empty weight of 14,968 kg (33,000 lb) and max permitted speed of 580 knots (1,075 km/h; 668 mph) at wave-top height.

Updating has been undertaken by BAe at Woodford. Ten were re-delivered in 1987, 12 in 1988 and 17 in 1989, the first modified aircraft being XV350. The last aircraft (XX885) was returned to the RAF on 23 February 1990.

ARMAMENT: Strike: one WE177 nuclear bomb. Anti-ship attack: four BAe Sea Eagle missiles on underwing pylons, plus 11,024 litres (2,910 US gallons; 2,425 Imp gallons) of internal fuel (integral, weapons bay and weapons bay door tanks). Alternatively, four Matra AS.37 Martel anti-radiation missiles. (BAe AJ.167 TV-Martel withdrawn early 1990.) Target designator: underwing equipment of Westinghouse AN/AVQ-23E Pave Spike

Buccaneer S. Mk 2B at operational height, armed with four BAe Sea Eagle missiles *(Paul Jackson)*

designator pod, Westinghouse AN/ALQ-i0l(V)-10 jamming pod, AIM-9G Sidewinder self-defence missile and single fuel tank, plus optional four 508 kg (1,120 lb) retarded bombs in weapons bay. LGB: up to four 549 kg (1,210 lb) AN/CPU-123B Paveway guided bombs. Buddy tanker: one FRL Mk 20C or 20E hose pod. Training: Hunting CBLS 100 Mk 3 carrier and Portsmouth Aviation 3 kg and 14 kg practice bombs.

F-111

In 1978, BAe's Filton plant began undertaking depot level maintenance on General Dynamics F-111 strike aircraft based in the UK with the USAF's 20th TFW (F-111E) and 48th TFW (F-111F). A second five-year contract, covering approximately 150 F-111s, was agreed with the USAF on 1 October 1988, this also including structural fatigue testing and avionics modifications as applied to US-based F-111s.

V-22 OSPREY

BAe and Bell/Boeing concluded an MoU in 1987 covering examination by the British company of the latter's V-22 tilt-rotor aircraft in both military and civilian applications within the European NATO area. In 1989, Aeritalia and Dornier reached agreement with BAe to pursue the prospects of the V-22 tilt-rotor aircraft in collaborative tri-national projects.

PHANTOM

British Aerospace has a contract to design and manufacture new outer wings for the RAF's fleet of McDonnell Douglas Phantom aircraft. The work is being undertaken mainly by its Military Aircraft Company at Brough, the design authority for UK Phantoms, with some of the activity at BAe Hamble; 75 sets have been ordered.

The requirement was to design an outer wing to a new structural standard, which embodies accumulated knowledge gained from many years of structural support of the Phantom aircraft and test data from the full scale fatigue test specimen. The need to re-wing the aircraft arises from an escalation of problems with the current outer wings, resulting basically from the loads experienced during realistic operational training manoeuvres. Delivery of the new outer wings began in 1988 and forms a major element in a plan to extend the service life of the Phantom well into the 1990s, the operating units being Nos. 56 and 74 Squadrons at Wattisham; Nos. 19 and 92 at Wildenrath, West Germany; and No. 1345 Flight in the Falkland Islands. Installation is the responsibility of the Engineering Wing at RAF St Athan.

In 1989, Ferranti Defence Systems was commissioned by the MoD to study a possible cockpit update for RAF Phantoms, to be implemented in the event of further delays with the European Fighter Aircraft.

E-3D SENTRY AEW. Mk 1

BAe and Field Aviation Services were selected by Boeing in 1988 to perform installation and check-out (I&CO) duties on the seven E-3 AEW aircraft purchased for the RAF. The companies will be responsible for reception of the aircraft, installation and checking of some equipment, and maintenance in the pre-delivery phase between arrival in the UK and hand-over to the RAF. Most work will be undertaken at RAF Waddington, where the first Sentry AEW. Mk 1 was due in June 1990. Following I&CO (assisted by a Boeing team on only this one aircraft) the Sentry will be handed over to No. 8 Squadron at Waddington in January 1991.

BAe (BAC/VICKERS) VC10 C. Mk 1(K), K. Mk 2, 3 and 4 TANKERS

In addition to operating 13 of its original 14 VC10 C. Mk 1 transports, delivered in 1966-68 to No. 10 Squadron, the RAF has received tanker variants converted from former airline aircraft in the form of five **VC10 K. Mk 2s** (from July 1983) and four **Super VC10 K. Mk 3s** (from

Wind tunnel model of latest configuration of HOTOL aerospacecraft

February 1985) for No. 101 Squadron. Modification work was undertaken by BAe at Filton, the final aircraft flying on 9 August 1985, and involved installing an internal Flight Refuelling Mk 17B hose-and-drum unit (HDU), plus wing-mounted FR Mk 32/2800 HDUs. The basic VC10 and Super VC10 were last described fully in the 1969-70 *Jane's* under the British Aircraft Corporation entry, and specific tanker modifications in the 1987-88 edition.

Fourteen British Airways Super VC10s were bought by the RAF in 1981, plus a Gulf Air VC10 in 1982. After instructional disposals and scrapping, six Super VC10s remained in storage at Abingdon in 1988 as candidates for tanker conversion.

Early in 1990, BAe (Civil Aircraft) Ltd at Manchester was awarded a two-part contract to modify 13 aircraft to tankers. The first part, satisfying Air Staff Requirement 415, covers five of the Abingdon Super VC10s which will be modified to **K. Mk 4** standard with a Mk 17B HDU in the fuselage and two Mk 32 underwing pods. Work will be undertaken at Filton after the aircraft have been returned to airworthy condition for the ferry flight. Also included are general refurbishment and installation of military avionics (including air-to-air Tacan) and closed-circuit TV. JTIDS terminals will be installed at a later stage for relay of information between ground stations and AEW and interceptor aircraft. In the second programme, meeting ASR416, eight of No. 10 Squadron's transport aircraft will be given a secondary tanker capability with only the two underwing Mk 32 pods (plus Tacan and TV), becoming **C. Mk 1(K)**s. Conversion has been subcontracted to FR Aviation at Bournemouth, from where the first aircraft will be returned to the RAF in Spring 1992. An option is held on similar re-work of the remaining five Mk 1s. Unlike earlier programmes, neither Mk 1(K) nor Mk 4 conversions will involve installation of additional fuel tanks.

Details of previous modifications include:

WEIGHTS:

Max T-O weight: K. Mk 2	142,000 kg (313,056 lb)	
K. Mk 3	151,900 kg (334,882 lb)	
Theoretical max fuel weight*:		
K. Mk 2	78,170 kg (172,335 lb)	
K. Mk 3	83,420 kg (183,909 lb)	
Practical max fuel weight:		
K. Mk 2	74,000 kg (163,142 lb)	
K. Mk 3	80,000 kg (176,370 lb)	

* Max T-O weight exceeded when all tanks full.

BAe HOTOL

HOTOL (horizontal take-off and landing) is the name of a space transport study undertaken by the British Aerospace divisions at Warton and Brough (Military Aircraft), Stevenage (Space) and Filton (Commercial Aircraft) in conjunction with Rolls-Royce. The initial objective was a re-usable unmanned launch vehicle able to carry satellites into orbit for one-fifth the cost of current procedures. Later versions were expected to carry personnel into orbit to service space stations or other objects in low Earth orbits.

In February 1986 the British National Space Centre of the Department of Trade announced that it had allocated £375,000 to initiate a two-year proof of concept study costing £3 million. The initial funds covered the first six months of the study, in 1987; an equal amount was made available by industry. From October 1987, the study was maintained by additional BAe funds, but the British government announced in July 1988 that it would provide no further funding and the future of the programme is uncertain.

HOTOL would take off and land like a conventional aircraft. Novel features include a laser guided trolley for take-off, which would be left behind in the interests of weight saving. Landing would be on a relatively lightweight gear carried on board. This arrangement was adopted because the take-off weight would be about five times the landing weight. The key to the HOTOL concept is a revolutionary hybrid power plant under study by Rolls-Royce. Known as the RB545 Swallow, this would act as an air-breathing turbofan in the atmosphere, and as an oxygen/hydrogen rocket in space. Speed at transition from air-breathing to rocket power would be Mach 5 at 26,000 m (85,000 ft). Initial rig tests of critical components of the engine were conducted in 1986. However, in December 1988, the UK MoD declared the RB545's technology to be secret for the foreseeable future, thereby complicating the task of finding commercial backers to replace the withdrawn government funding.

Detail design is at an early stage, but BAe states that re-entry heat protection would be by a metal skin and not by tiles of the kind used on the US Space Shuttle. Titanium would be used on the upper surfaces.

DIMENSIONS (provisional):

Wing span	28.34 m (93 ft 0 in)
Length overall	62.97 m (206 ft 7¼ in)
Height overall	12.83 m (42 ft 1⅛ in)

WEIGHTS (provisional):

T-O weight	250,000 kg (551,155 lb)
Landing weight	47,500 kg (104,719 lb)

PERFORMANCE (provisional):

Payload into 300 km (162 mile) equatorial Earth orbit	8,000 kg (17,635 lb)
T-O speed	278 knots (515 km/h; 320 mph)
Landing speed	150 knots (278 km/h; 173 mph)
Landing run: dry runway	1,145 m (3,750 ft)
wet runway	1,500 m (4,925 ft)

BAF

BRITISH AIR FERRIES

Viscount House, Southend Airport, Essex SS2 6YL
Telephone: 44 (702) 354435
Telex: 995687 and 995576
Fax: 44 (702) 331914
CHIEF EXECUTIVE: I. M. Herman
COMMERCIAL DIRECTOR: M. B. Kay
FLIGHT OPERATIONS DIRECTOR: Capt W. J. Woodhouse

The engineering division of lease and charter airline BAF is licensed by the Civil Aviation Authority and British Aerospace to undertake life-extension modifications on the Vickers/BAC Viscount, 15 of which are operated under contract by the company on passenger and night freight services.

BAC VISCOUNT LIFE EXTENSION

By the end of 1988, five of BAF's 74-seat Viscount Series 800s had completed a comprehensive overhaul programme, the requirements of which, including rib and fuselage reconditioning, were formulated in a joint study with BAe.

BAC/Vickers Viscount Series 806 re-lifed by BAF for service into the 21st century

The aircraft are now certificated by the CAA for a further 15 years of service or 75,000 flights. Of 447 Viscounts built in 1948-64, approximately 60 remain airworthy and eligible for a similar re-work.

BROOKLANDS

BROOKLANDS AIRCRAFT COMPANY LIMITED
(Subsidiary of Brooklands Aerospace Group PLC)

Old Sarum Airfield, Salisbury, Wiltshire SP4 6BJ
Telephone: 44 (722) 21812
Telex: 47106 AERODS
Fax: 44 (722) 337100
CHAIRMAN: Alan Curtis
COMMERCIAL DIRECTOR: Andy Richardson

The original company responsible for the Optica programme, Edgley Aircraft Ltd, was formed in 1974 to design, build and market a specialised observation aircraft that would combine the all-round field of view of a helicopter with the lower operating costs of a fixed-wing aircraft. Fuel consumption of the Optica is claimed to be 16-24 per cent of that for a comparable light turbine helicopter, and operating costs (fixed and direct for 500 hours per year) 31 per cent.

Production of the Optica started in 1983 in the company's 6,505 m² (70,000 sq ft) premises at Old Sarum Airfield. The first production aircraft (c/n 003, G-BLFC) was rolled out and first flew on 4 August 1984. CAA type certification was granted on 8 February 1985 for day VFR flying and was extended to night and IFR clearance in time for the delivery of the first customer's aircraft in April 1985.

The company encountered financial difficulties, and a new firm, Optica Industries Ltd, re-started production in January 1986. Its plan to produce 46 aircraft in 1987 was disrupted by a severe fire on 16 January 1987, which destroyed the aircraft hangar and most of the completed aircraft inside.

Following the fire, on 14 April 1987, the company was renamed Brooklands Aircraft Company Ltd. The aircraft was renamed Optica Scout and is referred to as the Scout in the UK market. Excluding a prototype, a demonstrator, nine destroyed before delivery and a static test airframe, six Opticas had been delivered to customers by late 1989.

In March 1990 the company was placed under administration and a buyer was being sought.

Brooklands Optica Scout slow flying observation aircraft in representative Scoutmaster configuration *(J.M.G. Gradidge)*

Brooklands Optica Scout (Textron Lycoming IO-540 engine) *(Pilot Press)*

BROOKLANDS OPTICA SCOUT Mk II and SCOUTMASTER

First flown on 14 December 1979, the **Optica** is a three-seat observation aircraft, designed particularly for pipeline and powerline inspection; forestry and coastal patrol; police duties; frontier patrol; aerial photography; film, TV and press reporting; and touring. The cabin configuration is designed to give the best possible all-round view. Power plant is a ducted propulsor unit, offering very low levels of vibration and exceptional quietness, both within the cabin and from the ground. A low wing loading, pre-set inboard flaps and a low stalling speed facilitate continuous en-route flight at low speeds. Generous flap area provides good field performance from both hard and soft strips. Stability increases at low speeds.

An electronic surveillance version known as the **Scoutmaster** was revealed in mockup form in 1988. Development of this version, and possibly also a turbine powered Optica, is a joint venture with ASTA of Australia. Two versions of the Scoutmaster are offered: Scoutmaster I is the basic model, with Bendix/King Silver Crown avionics for IFR operation and a FLIR 2000G thermal imaging system. Scoutmaster II has comprehensive Gold Crown IFR nav/com, including radar altimeter and autopilot, Omega/VLF nav and Bendix RDR-1400C search radar in addition to the FLIR 2000G.

TYPE: Three-seat slow flying observation aircraft; stressed to BCAR Section K (non-aerobatic category) and FAR Pt 23 (Normal category).

WINGS: Cantilever mid-wing monoplane. Wing section NASA GA(W)-1; thickness/chord ratio 17 per cent. Dihedral 3° on outer panels. Incidence 0°. Constant chord single-spar non-swept wings of L72 duralumin stressed skin construction. Wingtips of GFRP. Fowler trailing-edge flaps (29 per cent of total wing chord) inboard and outboard of tailbooms. Electrically actuated outboard flaps can be set at angles up to 50° for landing; inboard flaps set permanently at 10°, giving the effect of a slotted wing, for continuous low speed flying. Bottom hinged, mass balanced slotted ailerons outboard of outer flaps, operated by pushrods. No spoilers or airbrakes.

CABIN: 'Insect eye' shaped structure, built of aluminium alloy with ICI Perspex windows, optionally tinted. Outward visibility approximately 270° in vertical plane and 340° in horizontal plane. Cabin attached to fan shroud and rest of airframe by six stators of steel tube and aluminium alloy shear web construction. Steel tube and aluminium alloy nose beam supports cabin floor. Horizontal window frame member just above floor level, together with nosewheel box, is designed to withstand 9g impact. Tinted windows optional. Two movable 7.5 kg (16.5 lb) ballast weights may be positioned on the nose beam. Two lamps are also mounted in the nose beam, one as a landing lamp, the other as a taxi/standby landing lamp.

TAIL UNIT: Twin-tailboom configuration, basically of aluminium alloy stressed skin tubular construction.

Limited GFRP content in non-load-bearing areas, including fin/tailplane fillets. Tailboom pick-up points at extremities of wing centre-section. Angular, inward canted fins and balanced rudders. Fixed incidence tailplane, with elevator, bridging space between tops of fins. Inset trim tab in elevator trailing-edge; no rudder tabs. Two movable 9 kg (20 lb) ballast weights may be positioned, one in each fin.

LANDING GEAR: Non-retractable tricycle type, with steerable nosewheel offset to port. Mainwheel legs embody rubber in compression shock absorption. Nosewheel shock absorption by bungee rubber in tension. Single wheel on each unit, tyre sizes 6.00-6 (main) and 5.00-5 (nose). Hydraulic disc brakes on mainwheels. Parking brake. Nosewheel mudguard of GFRP.

POWER PLANT: Ducted propulsor unit, with engine and fan forming a power pod separate from the main shroud. Pod is attached to fan shroud with four Lord rubber mountings, and supported by four stators of steel channel and aluminium alloy shear web construction, with steel tube engine bearers. Some fairings of GFRP. Five-blade Hydulignum fixed-pitch fan, driven by a 194 kW (260 hp) Textron Lycoming IO-540-V4A5D flat-six engine, mounted in a duct downstream of the fan. Fuel tank of 128 litres (33.8 US gallons; 28 Imp gallons) capacity in each wing leading-edge, immediately outboard of tailbooms and forward of wing spar. Tanks are of full wing section, but are designed not to be stressed by wing bending and torsion. Total usable fuel capacity 250 litres (66 US gallons; 55 Imp gallons). Refuelling point in upper surface of each wing. Oil capacity 7.6 litres (2.0 US gallons; 1.7 Imp gallons).

ACCOMMODATION: Cabin designed to accommodate up to three persons side by side on fore and aft adjustable seats, with either single- or two-pilot operation (left hand and centre seats). Dual controls standard. Baggage space aft of seats. Single elliptical door on each side, hinged at front and opening forward. Can be flown with doors removed. Cabin heated, by hot air from engine, and ventilated. A Janitrol combustion heater is offered as an extra.

SYSTEMS: Hydraulics for mainwheel brakes only. Electrical system (24V) includes engine driven alternator and storage battery for engine starting and actuation of flaps.

AVIONICS AND EQUIPMENT: Standard nav/com avionics by Bendix/King (Silver Crown). Alternative avionics could be provided. Special equipment which has been tested successfully includes FLIR, Barr & Stroud IR18 Mk II and an air-to-ground video relay. Other equipment such as GEC Avionics TICM II, searchlights and loudspeakers is being assessed.

DIMENSIONS, EXTERNAL:

Wing span	12.00 m (39 ft 4 in)
Wing chord: basic, constant	1.32 m (4 ft 4 in)
over 10° fixed flaps	1.45 m (4 ft 9 in)
Wing aspect ratio	9.1
Length overall	8.15 m (26 ft 9 in)
Height over fan shroud (excl aerial)	1.98 m (6 ft 6 in)
Diameter of fan shroud	1.68 m (5 ft 6 in)
Diameter of fan	1.22 m (4 ft 0 in)
Shroud ground clearance	0.25 m (10 in)
Height over tailplane	2.31 m (7 ft 7 in)
Tailplane span:	
c/l of tailbooms	3.40 m (11 ft 2 in)
intersection fin chord	2.60 m (8 ft 6½ in)
Wheel track	3.40 m (11 ft 2 in)
Wheelbase	2.73 m (9 ft 0 in)
Doors (each): Long axis	1.35 m (4 ft 5 in)
Short axis	0.96 m (3 ft 1¾ in)
Height to sill	0.51 m (1 ft 8 in)

DIMENSIONS, INTERNAL:

Cabin: Length	2.44 m (8 ft 0 in)
Max width (to door Perspex)	1.68 m (5 ft 6 in)
Max height	1.35 m (4 ft 5 in)
Floor area	0.72 m² (7.75 sq ft)

AREAS:

Wings, gross	15.84 m² (170.5 sq ft)
Ailerons (total)	1.55 m² (16.68 sq ft)
Trailing-edge flaps:	
inboard (total)	0.61 m² (6.57 sq ft)
outboard (total)	1.59 m² (17.12 sq ft)
Fins (total)	1.98 m² (21.31 sq ft)
Rudders (total)	1.10 m² (11.84 sq ft)
Tailplane	1.62 m² (17.44 sq ft)
Elevator, incl tab	1.26 m² (13.56 sq ft)

WEIGHTS AND LOADINGS (A, Scout; B, Scoutmaster I; C, Scoutmaster II):

Weight empty, equipped: A	948 kg (2,090 lb)
B	1,050 kg (2,315 lb)
C	1,180 kg (2,600 lb)
Max cabin load: A	231 kg (510 lb)
Crew (pilot/observer): B, C	154 kg (340 lb)
Fuel: B	111 kg (245 lb)
C	206 kg (454 lb)

Max T-O weight: A, B	1,315 kg (2,900 lb)
C	1,540 kg (3,395 lb)
Max wing loading: A, B	83.0 kg/m² (17.0 lb/sq ft)
C	97.2 kg/m² (19.9 lb/sq ft)
Max power loading: A, B	6.78 kg/kW (11.2 lb/hp)
C	7.94 kg/kW (13.1 lb/hp)

PERFORMANCE (Scout, at max T-O weight, forward limit CG):

Never-exceed speed	140 knots (259 km/h; 161 mph)
Max level speed	115 knots (213 km/h; 132 mph)
Cruising speed:	
50% power	86 knots (159 km/h; 99 mph)
70% power	103 knots (191 km/h; 119 mph)
Loiter speed (40% power)	70 knots (130 km/h; 81 mph)
Stalling speed, outboard flaps up	
	58 knots (108 km/h; 67 mph)

Max rate of climb at S/L	247 m (810 ft)/min
Service ceiling	4,275 m (14,000 ft)
T-O run	330 m (1,082 ft)
T-O to 15 m (50 ft)	472 m (1,548 ft)
Landing from 15 m (50 ft)	555 m (1,820 ft)
Landing run	278 m (912 ft)
Range with max fuel (45 min reserves):	
at 110 knots (204 km/h; 127 mph)	
	370 nm (685 km; 426 miles)
at 70 knots (130 km/h; 81 mph)	
	570 nm (1,056 km; 656 miles)
Endurance (45 min reserves):	
at 110 knots (204 km/h; 127 mph)	2 h 45 min
at 70 knots (130 km/h; 81 mph)	8 h
g limits	+3.8/-1.5

PERFORMANCE (B, Scoutmaster I; C, Scoutmaster II, at max T-O weight):

Operating speed range:

B	70-113 knots (130-210 km/h; 80-130 mph)
C	75-118 knots (139-218 km/h; 86-136 mph)

Max rate of climb at S/L:

B	244 m (800 ft)/min
C	216 m (710 ft)/min

Range (with IFR fuel reserves):

B	200 nm (370 km; 230 miles)
C	400 nm (740 km; 460 miles)

CMC

CHICHESTER-MILES CONSULTANTS LTD

West House, The Old Rectory, Ayot St Lawrence, Welwyn, Hertfordshire AL6 9BT
Telephone: 44 (438) 820341
CHAIRMAN: Ian Chichester-Miles

CMC LEOPARD

Mr Ian Chichester-Miles, formerly Chief Research Engineer of British Aerospace Aircraft Division at Hatfield, Hertfordshire, established Chichester-Miles Consultants to develop a high performance light business jet. Design of the four-seat Leopard started in January 1981 and was sufficiently advanced for a mockup to be completed in early 1982. Detail design and construction of a prototype by Designability Ltd of Dilton Marsh, Wiltshire, began in July 1982, under contract to CMC. First flight of this aircraft (G-BKRL) took place on 12 December 1988 at RAE Bedford. It has lower-powered engines, and lacks the full pressurisation/air-conditioning system, advanced avionics and instrumentation of the planned production aircraft. By November 1989 the prototype had made 10 flights investigating basic handling qualities at speeds approaching 190 knots (352 km/h; 219 mph) IAS. New tailplanes incorporating a TKS liquid anti-icing system were subsequently installed prior to resumption of flight testing aimed at expanding the airspeed, altitude and centre of gravity envelopes.

Design of the second Leopard prototype (002) began in April 1989. Slingsby Aviation (which see) is to manufacture the fuselage and wings of this aircraft in collaboration with Designability Ltd, both under contract to CMC. Leopard 002 is expected to be completed in September 1991. Apart from reprofiling of nose contours to accommodate EFIS avionics, and substitution of oleo-pneumatic main landing gear legs for the current rubber-in-compression units, the aircraft will be identical to the prototype. It will fly initially powered by early flight demonstration versions of the Noel Penny NPT 754 turbofans which will power production aircraft, pending engine certification.

TYPE: Four-seat light business aircraft.
WINGS: Cantilever mid-wing monoplane. ARA designed wing section and 3D profiles combining laminar flow and supercritical wing technology. Thickness/chord ratio 14 per cent at root, 11 per cent at tip. Sweepback at quarter-chord 25°. Two-spar structure, primarily of GFRP, with some carbonfibre reinforcement. Full span electrically actuated trailing-edge plain flaps of carbonfibre, with deflections of ±45° for high drag landing and air-braking/lift dumping. No ailerons or spoilers. Production aircraft to have TKS liquid de-icing and decontamination system in leading-edge.
FUSELAGE: Built in three sections: unpressurised nose section accommodating avionics and nosewheel gear when retracted, pressurised cabin section (production aircraft only), and unpressurised rear section providing a baggage bay, with fuel tanks below and equipment bays to rear. Basic monocoque structure, primarily of GFRP with some carbonfibre reinforcement; fore and aft cabin bulkheads, engine and tailplane axle frames moulded in. Pressure cabin section divided approximately along aircraft horizontal datum, with upper section formed by electrically actuated upward opening canopy hinged at windscreen leading-edge. Multiple latches around canopy lower edge. Bonded-in acrylic side windows carry pressurisation tension. Nose opens for access to avionics.
TAIL UNIT: All-moving fin and tailplane of all-composites construction. Sternpost projects to bottom of rear fuselage. Low-set tailplane in two independent sections, each mounted on a steel axle projecting from side of rear fuselage. Tailplane sections are operated collectively for control in pitch and differentially for roll control. Fin and tailplane sections each have a carbonfibre geared anti-servo tab, adjustable for trim. Anti-icing as for wings.
LANDING GEAR: Electrically retractable tricycle type, main units retracting inward into wingroot wells, nosewheels forward. Well closure doors linked mechanically to landing gear units. Gravity extension assisted by bias springs and aerodynamic drag. Long stroke shock absorber in each unit, using synthetic elastomers in

compression. Main units, each with single Cleveland wheel, size 500 × 5, have tyres size 11 × 4, pressure 4.82 bars (70 lb/sq in) on prototype, 7.24 bars (105 lb/sq in) on production aircraft. Twin-wheel nose unit has wheels size 400 × 3 and tyres size 8.5 × 2.75 in, pressure 2.75 bars (40 lb/sq in) on prototype, 3.8 bars (55 lb/sq in) on production aircraft. Hydraulic disc brakes. Parking brake. New, oleo-pneumatic main landing gear is being designed for production aircraft.
POWER PLANT: Prototype 001 has two Noel Penny Turbines NPT 301-3A turbojets each of nominal 1.33 kN (300 lb st) rating. Production aircraft will have two low-bypass Noel Penny Turbines NPT 754 turbofans, each of 3.34 kN (750 lb st). Each engine in nacelle, mounted on crossbeam located in rear fuselage. Nacelles of composite construction, with stainless steel firewalls and liquid de-icing system for leading-edges of production aircraft. Fuel tanks in fuselage, below baggage bay. Prototype has total fuel capacity of 455 litres (120 US gallons; 100 Imp gallons). Production aircraft will have maximum capacity of 591 litres (156 US gallons; 130 Imp gallons). Refuelling point on upper surface of fuselage, near base of fin.
ACCOMMODATION: Cabin seats four, in two pairs, on semi-reclining (35°) seats beneath upward opening jettisonable canopy. Options include dual controls, and accommodation for pilot, stretcher and attendant in medevac role. Unpressurised baggage bay aft of cabin, capacity 54 kg (120 lb), with external door in upper surface of fuselage.
SYSTEMS (production aircraft): Air-conditioning and pressurisation (max differential 0.66 bars: 9.6 lb/sq in) by engine bleed air, with simple Normalair-Garrett air cycle

cold air/dehumidifier unit. Electrical system powered by dual engine driven 3kVA starter/generators. Hydraulic system for brakes only.
AVIONICS AND EQUIPMENT (production aircraft): Full nav/com and storm-avoidance systems. Bendix/King avionics, mounted in nose bay, supply EADI and EHSI information to two CRTs in pilot's instrument panel. CRT displays can be transferred in the failure mode. Reduced scale electromechanical standby flight instruments. All avionics systems fully integrated with digital autopilot.

DIMENSIONS, EXTERNAL:

Wing span	7.16 m (23 ft 6 in)
Wing chord: at root	1.14 m (3 ft 9 in)
at tip	0.36 m (1 ft 2 in)
Wing aspect ratio	8.78
Length overall	7.52 m (24 ft 8 in)
Height overall	2.06 m (6 ft 9 in)
Height to canopy sill	0.76 m (2 ft 6 in)
Tailplane span	3.91 m (12 ft 10 in)
Wheel track	3.45 m (11 ft 4 in)
Wheelbase	3.20 m (10 ft 6 in)

DIMENSIONS, INTERNAL:

Cabin: Length	2.74 m (9 ft 0 in)
Max width	1.14 m (3 ft 9 in)
Max height	0.94 m (3 ft 1 in)
Baggage bay volume	0.40 m³ (14 cu ft)

AREAS:

Wings, gross	5.85 m² (62.9 sq ft)
Trailing-edge flaps (total)	1.24 m² (13.3 sq ft)
Fin	0.86 m² (9.3 sq ft)
Tailplane (incl tabs)	2.14 m² (23.0 sq ft)

Prototype of CMC Leopard business jet *(B. J. Cunnington/CMC)*

CMC Leopard prototype (two Noel Penny Turbines NPT 301-3A turbojets) *(Pilot Press)*

WEIGHTS AND LOADINGS (A: prototype, B: production aircraft, estimated):

Weight empty, equipped: B		862 kg (1,900 lb)
Max fuel weight: A		367 kg (810 lb)
B		476 kg (1,050 lb)
Max T-O weight: A		1,156 kg (2,550 lb)
B		1,701 kg (3,750 lb)
Max zero-fuel weight: A		1,043 kg (2,300 lb)
B		1,224 kg (2,700 lb)
Max landing weight: A		1,156 kg (2,550 lb)
B		1,497 kg (3,300 lb)
Max wing loading: A		197.7 kg/m² (40.5 lb/sq ft)
B		291.0 kg/m² (59.6 lb/sq ft)

PERFORMANCE (production aircraft, estimated, ISA):

Never-exceed speed		Mach 0.81
	(300 knots; 556 km/h; 345 mph) EAS	
Max level speed at 9,450 m (31,000 ft)		
	469 knots (869 km/h; 540 mph)	
Max and econ cruising speed at 15,545 m (51,000 ft)		
	434 knots (804 km/h; 500 mph)	
Stalling speed, full flap, at AUW of 1,406 kg (3,100 lb)		
	82 knots (152 km/h; 95 mph)	
Max rate of climb at S/L	1,660 m (5,450 ft)/min	
Rate of climb at S/L, one engine out		
	685 m (2,250 ft)/min	

Service ceiling	16,765 m (55,000 ft)
Service ceiling, one engine out	9,145 m (30,000 ft)
T-O to 15 m (50 ft)	727 m (2,385 ft)
T-O balanced field length	838 m (2,750 ft)
Landing from 15 m (50 ft) at AUW of 1,406 kg (3,100 lb)	747 m (2,450 ft)
Landing factored field length	823 m (2,700 ft)
Range with max fuel and max payload, with reserves	1,500 nm (2,775 km; 1,725 miles)

CRANFIELD
CRANFIELD INSTITUTE OF TECHNOLOGY, COLLEGE OF AERONAUTICS
Cranfield, Bedfordshire MK43 0AL
Telephone: 44 (234) 750111
Telex: 825072 C ITECH G
Fax: 44 (234) 751181
HEAD OF COLLEGE AND PROFESSOR OF AIRCRAFT DESIGN, DIRECTOR OF PROJECTS: Prof D. Howe
CHIEF DESIGNER: J. H. Webb
HEAD OF FLIGHT SYSTEMS AND MEASUREMENT LABORATORIES: D. A. Williams

The College of Aeronautics is a fully CAA and MoD(PE) approved design and manufacturing organisation based on the Cranfield Institute of Technology airfield. In support of aircraft and systems manufacturers, governments and research bodies, it undertakes a variety of aeronautical and high technology tasks ranging from feasibility studies to the design, manufacture, installation and certification of aircraft modifications. Recent work has included the VAAC Harrier and ASTRA Hawk for MoD (last described fully in the 1987-88 *Jane's*); design of the paratroop door for British Aerospace's BAe 146STA conversion; installation of atmospheric sampling equipment in a College of

Aeronautics Jetstream for National Power; and collaboration with Civil Aviation Authority for UK certification of the Canadair Challenger 601-3A business jet for which the College developed changes to the avionics, stall warning, instrumentation, crew oxygen and engine generator systems, structural modifications to the lower fuselage, an APU installation, and passenger door pressurisation venting.

CRANFIELD AERONAUTICAL SERVICES LIMITED
Cranfield Institute of Technology, Cranfield, Bedfordshire MK43 0AL
Telephone: 44 (234) 752746
Fax: 44 (234) 751181

CHAIRMAN: Prof D. Howe
Cranfield Aeronautical Services is the commercial arm of the Cranfield Institute of Technology, College of Aeronautics, for which it undertakes production work. Recent projects have included a water bomber conversion of a BAe 748 turboprop airliner (see 1987-88 *Jane's*) and

range-extension modifications for the BAC One-Eleven (see 1988-89 *Jane's*).

CROPLEASE
CROPLEASE PLC
Vicarage House, 58-60 Kensington Church Street, London W8 4DB
Telephone: 44 (71) 376 0448
Fax: 44 (71) 376 0340
CHAIRMAN: Richard Cox-Johnson
MANAGING DIRECTOR: Andrew McKinnon
CHIEF DESIGNER: Desmond Norman, CBE

Following the entry into receivership of the Norman Aeroplane Company Ltd in October 1988, design, manufacturing and marketing rights to the NAC 6 Fieldmaster aircraft were acquired by Mr Andrew McKinnon of the Irish-based leasing company Croplease Ltd. Croplease PLC was formed in April 1989 and acquired rights to the Fieldmaster and the business of Croplease Ltd.

CROPLEASE NAC 6 FIELDMASTER
The NAC 6 Fieldmaster was designed by Mr Desmond Norman, with financial support from the UK National Research Development Corporation, specifically for agricultural, firefighting and oil pollution control work. Representing an entirely new approach to the design of agricultural aircraft, it has a titanium chemical hopper which is an integral part of the fuselage structure, its outer surface being contoured to serve as the skin of that fuselage section. The power plant is mounted on the front of this hopper, the aft fuselage to its rear, and the wings are attached directly to each side of the hopper's base. The cockpit, in the rear fuselage, is protected by a strong rollover structure, and is large enough to accommodate a second seat in tandem. Removable dual controls are available, to simplify flight training and checkout procedures. The wing is fitted with wide span auxiliary aerofoil trailing-edge flaps, embodying a liquid spray dispersal system that discharges directly into the downwash of the flaps, and so ensures that the spray droplets achieve the best possible crop penetration.

The prototype Fieldmaster (G-NRDC), built by the Norman Aeroplane Company, made its first flight at Sandown, Isle of Wight, on 17 December 1981, and by March 1986 had flown 300 hours during flight testing, demonstrations and in-service spraying trials by an agricultural operator. The first production Fieldmaster (G-NACL) flew on 29 March 1987, and certification was received on 27 April.

In July 1987, the first two production Fieldmasters began a season of fire patrol flights and water bombing sorties in the Maritime Alps under contract to France Aviation. Turnround time between firefighting sorties averaged 3 min. These two aircraft were included in five purchased by Croplease Ltd of Shannon, Ireland.

Production of the Fieldmaster has re-started using components manufactured by UTVA in Yugoslavia.

On 28 November 1989 the first production Fieldmaster (G-NACL), in Firemaster configuration, made its first flight with a 917 kW (1,230 shp) PT6A-65AG turboprop driving a five-blade Hartzell propeller. This power plant will be available as an option on the Fieldmaster 65.

TYPE: Two-seat large capacity agricultural aircraft.

Photograph and three-view drawing *(Pilot Press)* **of Croplease NAC 6 Fieldmaster agricultural aircraft (Pratt & Whitney Canada PT6A-34AG turboprop)**

WINGS: Low-wing monoplane, with an overwing streamline section bracing strut each side. Wing section NACA 23012, modified on inner panels, where forward extension of leading-edge reduces thickness/chord ratio to 8.6 per cent at wingroot. Dihedral 4° 15′. Incidence 4° 30′. Conventional all-metal structure with full corrosion proofing. Electrically actuated wide span auxiliary aerofoil trailing-edge flaps, which incorporate plumbing for 24 standard spray nozzles on each wing. Micronair spray system (total 12 nozzles) optional. The ailerons are also of auxiliary aerofoil type. Servo tab in starboard

aileron, linked mechanically to rudder pedals, ensuring some bank with rudder movement.

FUSELAGE: Forward fuselage comprises structural titanium hopper with capacity of 2,032 kg (4,480 lb) dry, or 2,366 litres (625 US gallons; 520 Imp gallons) of liquid chemicals, and incorporating large door, vent system, inspection windows, and light. Firefighting modifications include additional 53 litre (14 US gallon; 11.6 Imp gallon) tank for Moussant fire retardant, which is mixed with water before release. Rear fuselage, attached to the rear of this hopper, is of semi-monocoque light alloy construction, fully corrosion proofed, and with easy access for cleaning and maintenance.

TAIL UNIT: Braced conventional structure of light alloy. Fixed incidence tailplane. Trim tab in port elevator. Servo tab in rudder controlled by stick movement, so that tab is moved automatically with bank.

LANDING GEAR: Non-retractable tricycle type, with single wheel on each unit. Nosewheel has alternative steerable or castoring facility. Main units of levered suspension type. Nosewheel tyre size 7.00-8, pressure 3.45 bars (50 lb/sq in); mainwheels have tubed tyres, diameter 736 mm (29 in), pressure 3.79 bars (55 lb/sq in). Cleveland hydraulic disc brakes. Landing gear incorporates wire cutters.

POWER PLANT: One 559 kW (750 shp) Pratt & Whitney Canada PT6A-34AG turboprop, driving a Hartzell type HC-B3TN-3/T10282+4 three-blade fully-feathering reversible-pitch metal propeller with spinner. Four integral fuel tanks, two per wing. Main tanks, each of 757 litres (200 US gallons; 166.5 Imp gallons), inboard; ferry tanks, each of 734 litres (194 US gallons; 161.5 Imp gallons), outboard. Total fuel capacity 1,490 litres (394 US gallons; 328 Imp gallons). Oil capacity 13 litres (3.5 US gallons; 2.9 Imp gallons). Engine air intake has a Centrisep filtration system.

ACCOMMODATION: Standard accommodation for pilot only, on fully adjustable seat in an enclosed cockpit, with rollover protective structure. Rear trainee/passenger seat optional. Dual controls optional, those for pupil easily removable. Crew safety helmets with headsets optional. Baggage space in fuselage. Sideways hinged door on each side. Birdproof armoured glass windscreen, two-speed

windscreen wiper and windscreen wash system optional. Accommodation ventilated; air-conditioning and heating system optional. Wirecutters forward of windscreen, and cable deflecting wire from top of windscreen to tip of fin.

SYSTEMS: Electrical system includes 24V 200A starter/generator. Hydraulic system for brakes only. Central warning system standard.

AVIONICS AND EQUIPMENT: Intercom standard. Avionics, and IFR instrument package, to customer requirements. Standard equipment includes an external power socket. Optional equipment includes airframe and engine hour meter; instrument lighting, navigation lights, fin and wingtip strobe lights; two forward looking retractable work lights, each 765,000 candlepower; automatic flagman installation; firefighting dump door and water scoop (see introductory copy); Transland gatebox, high volume spreader, quick disconnect flange kit, and side loading system; and Micronair installation, with flowmeter and rpm indicator.

DIMENSIONS, EXTERNAL:
Wing span	16.23 m (53 ft 3 in)
Wing chord (excl flaps): at root	2.01 m (6 ft 7¼ in)
at tip	1.45 m (4 ft 9 in)
Wing aspect ratio	7.96
Length overall	11.02 m (36 ft 2 in)
Height overall	4.12 m (13 ft 6 in)
Wheel track	5.28 m (17 ft 4 in)
Wheelbase	3.35 m (11 ft 0 in)
Propeller diameter	2.69 m (8 ft 10 in)

DIMENSION, INTERNAL:
Hopper volume	2.36 m³ (83 cu ft)

AREA:
Wings, gross	33.25 m² (358.0 sq ft)

WEIGHTS AND LOADINGS:
Standard empty weight	2,266 kg (4,995 lb)
Max T-O and landing weight:	
BCAR Public Transport Category	3,855 kg (8,500 lb)
UK CAA AN 90	4,535 kg (10,000 lb)
Max zero-fuel weight	3,855 kg (8,500 lb)
Max wing loading (AN 90)	136.37 kg/m² (27.93 lb/sq ft)
Max power loading (AN 90)	8.11 kg/kW (13.33 lb/shp)

PERFORMANCE (clean, with main landing gear fairings installed, at max Public Transport Category T-O weight, S/L, ISA, except where indicated):
Never-exceed speed	172 knots (318 km/h; 198 mph)
Max level speed:	
at S/L	143 knots (265 km/h; 165 mph)
at 1,830 m (6,000 ft)	147 knots (272 km/h; 169 mph)
Design manoeuvring speed	
	126 knots (233 km/h; 145 mph)
Stalling speed: flaps up	70 knots (129 km/h; 81 mph)
flaps down (30°)	60 knots (111 km/h; 69 mph)
Max rate of climb at S/L	293 m (960 ft)/min
Service ceiling	5,550 m (18,200 ft)
T-O run	419 m (1,375 ft)
T-O to 15 m (50 ft)	625 m (2,050 ft)
Landing from 15 m (50 ft)	472 m (1,550 ft)
Landing run at typical landing weight of 2,720 kg (6,000 lb), with propeller reversal	152 m (500 ft)
Range at 3,050 m (10,000 ft) with two crew, 454 kg (1,000 lb) of equipment and max fuel, no reserves	
	1,000 nm (1,853 km; 1,150 miles)
g limits	+3.4/-1.7

ISLAND

ISLAND AIRCRAFT LTD
(Subsidiary of Taurus Aviation Ltd)

Isle of Wight Airport, Sandown, Isle of Wight PO36 9PJ
Telephone: 44 (983) 406124
Telex: 86267 ARV SAN G
Fax: 44 (983) 405903
CHAIRMAN: C. Passmore
MANAGING DIRECTOR: C. Wald
CHIEF DESIGNER: J. N. Morton, BA

Island Aircraft (formerly ARV Aviation) was formed in 1984 to design and produce the two-seat Super2 light aircraft, powered by a British aero-engine developed by Hewland Engineering Ltd. The objective was to produce an aircraft with both low initial and very low maintenance costs, leading to relatively low costs per flying hour. The ability to operate from European grass strips was also an important objective. Use is made of superplastically formed aluminium alloy pressings to save weight and to reduce manufacturing costs. The Super2 is designed to British Civil Aviation Airworthiness Requirements, Section K, and FAR Pt 23.

ISLAND AIRCRAFT ARV-1 SUPER2

The prototype Super2 (G-OARV) flew for the first time on 11 March 1985, piloted by Mr Hugh Kendall, and was followed by two further trials/demonstrator aircraft. Before certification was obtained, in July 1986, the first five production aircraft were supplied in kit form, 65 per cent complete, for completion by homebuilders under the auspices of the Popular Flying Association. Subsequent deliveries, of completed aircraft, began with G-BMSJ (c/n 010) which went to the Airbourne School of Flying at Sandown, Isle of Wight. Planned production of eight aircraft per month by the end of 1987 was thwarted by power plant and financial problems, manufacture being temporarily suspended until these were rectified. Following a management buyout, production was resumed in 1988, but was substantially reduced again in the Spring of 1989 while negotiations were in hand to raise additional capital and to seek an alternative manufacturing site, with the aim of producing 100 aircraft per year by 1992.

The Super2 made its North American debut at the 1989 Experimental Aircraft Association Convention at Oshkosh, Wisconsin, at which time Island Aircraft was said to be negotiating with several US manufacturers for possible licence production of the aircraft in the United States.

TYPE: Two-seat light cabin monoplane.

WINGS: Braced shoulder-wing monoplane with single streamline bracing strut each side. Wing section NACA 2415 (modified). Single-spar wing, of aluminium alloy construction, cold bonded and flush riveted, is swept forward 5° 6′ to optimise the CG and the structural merits of a single uncompromised main bulkhead carrying the wings, bracing struts, controls, seats, fuel tank and main landing gear. Mass balanced ailerons operated by torque tube through leading-edge of manually operated plain flaps. Wings readily detachable for road transportation by light trailer.

FUSELAGE: Rear fuselage of aluminium alloy construction, cold bonded and flush riveted, with single curvature skinning. Forward of the main bulkhead the structure is conventional double beam carrying the firewall, nose landing gear and engine. Between the firewall and the main bulkhead, the fuselage is skinned by four panels,

Photograph *(Air Photo Supply)* **and three-view drawing** *(Pilot Press)* **of the Island Aircraft ARV-1 Super2 two-seat monoplane (Hewland Engineering AE 75 engine)**

superplastically formed in Supral 220/150 aluminium alloy.

TAIL UNIT: Conventional aluminium alloy structure, cold bonded and flush riveted, with three-spar fixed surfaces and single-spar mass balanced control surfaces. Trim tab on elevator.

LANDING GEAR: Non-retractable tricycle type. Cantilever main legs of tapered steel leaf spring. All three wheels size 3.50 × 6.0, with tyres size 13 × 4.00-6, pressure 1.72 bars (25 lb/sq in). Hydraulic disc brakes. Nose leg of leading link design, with rubber in tension springing, with damping by an adjustable Spax gas filled shock absorber. Wheels and brakes made by Island Aircraft.

POWER PLANT: One 57.4 kW (77 hp) Hewland Engineering AE 75 three-cylinder, 750 cc liquid cooled inline

two-stroke engine, driving a two-blade, fixed-pitch Hoffmann propeller through 2.7:1 reduction gearing. Electronically variable ignition timing. Serck aluminium radiator in recessed duct in rear fuselage. Normal fuel capacity 50 litres (13.2 US gallons; 11 Imp gallons) in single fuselage tank. Optional fuel capacity 68 litres (18 US gallons; 15 Imp gallons). Refuelling point in top of fuselage.

ACCOMMODATION: Enclosed cabin seating two side by side. The shoulder location of the wing with forward sweep, the low panel line and the close cowling of the small engine combine to provide an optimum view from the cabin, particularly in turns. Seats are adjustable for height, and fold to reveal baggage compartment. Additional storage space under the seats. Rearward hinged canopy is one-piece Perspex moulding with GFRP frame. Dual controls standard.

SYSTEMS: Wheel disc brakes operated hydraulically. Electrical system includes 11A or 15A alternator.

AVIONICS AND EQUIPMENT: Standard equipment includes three basic flight instruments plus engine instruments. Optional vacuum instruments driven by dual venturis mounted under the front fuselage. Radio equipment to customers' requirements.

DIMENSIONS, EXTERNAL:

Wing span	8.69 m (28 ft 6 in)
Width, wings folded	2.54 m (8 ft 4 in)
Wing aspect ratio	8.8
Length overall	5.49 m (18 ft 0 in)
Height overall	2.31 m (7 ft 7 in)
Tailplane span	2.54 m (8 ft 4 in)
Wheel track	1.83 m (6 ft 0 in)
Wheelbase	1.74 m (5 ft 8½ in)

Propeller diameter	1.60 m (5 ft 3 in)
Propeller ground clearance	0.23 m (9 in)

DIMENSIONS, INTERNAL:

Cabin: Length	1.27 m (4 ft 2 in)
Max width	0.99 m (3 ft 3 in)
Max height	1.09 m (3 ft 7 in)

AREAS:

Wings, gross	8.59 m² (92.5 sq ft)
Ailerons (total)	0.60 m² (6.5 sq ft)
Trailing-edge flaps (total)	0.89 m² (9.6 sq ft)
Fin	0.59 m² (6.4 sq ft)
Rudder	0.26 m² (2.8 sq ft)
Tailplane	1.23 m² (13.2 sq ft)
Elevators, incl tab	0.55 m² (5.9 sq ft)

WEIGHTS AND LOADINGS:

Weight empty, equipped	313 kg (690 lb)
Normal fuel weight	37 kg (80 lb)

Max T-O and landing weight: normal		499 kg (1,100 lb)
optional		528 kg (1,165 lb)
Max wing loading		58.35 kg/m² (11.95 lb/sq ft)
Max power loading		9.20 kg/kW (15.13 lb/hp)

PERFORMANCE (at max T-O weight):

Never-exceed speed	126 knots (232 km/h; 149 mph)
Max level speed	97 knots (180 km/h; 112 mph)
Max cruising speed	90 knots (167 km/h; 104 mph)
Econ cruising speed	80 knots (148 km/h; 92 mph)
Stalling speed, power off:	
flaps up	54 knots (99 km/h; 62 mph)
flaps down	48 knots (88 km/h; 55 mph)
Rate of climb at S/L	189 m (620 ft)/min
T-O to 15 m (50 ft)	712 m (2,336 ft)
Landing from 15 m (50 ft)	470 m (1,540 ft)
Range: normal fuel	270 nm (500 km; 311 miles)
optional fuel	370 nm (685 km; 426 miles)

MARSHALL
MARSHALL OF CAMBRIDGE (ENGINEERING) LTD (Aircraft Division)

Airport Works, Cambridge CB5 8RX
Telephone: 44 (223) 61133
Telex: 81208
Fax: 44 (223) 321032
CHAIRMAN: M. J. Marshall, DL
ENGINEERING DIRECTOR/CHIEF DESIGNER: R. E. Ward
SALES MANAGER: G. McA. Bacon
PUBLIC RELATIONS MANAGER: C. J. Buisseret

The Aircraft Division of this company (known as Marshalls Flying School Ltd until 1962) has specialised for many years in the modification, overhaul and repair of aircraft, including the design and installation of interior furnishing for executive transports and of avionics fits up to and including the complete outfitting of aircraft for calibration and electronic countermeasures roles.

In 1966, Marshall was appointed the designated centre for Royal Air Force Hercules transport aircraft, and in 1973 the company completed the conversion of an RAF Hercules C. Mk 1 to W. Mk 2 configuration, as detailed in the 1979-80 and earlier editions of *Jane's*. It has since undertaken the conversion of Hercules into flight refuelling tanker/receivers, and the lengthening of RAF Hercules C. Mk 1 transports to C. Mk 3 standard. The last of 29 C. Mk 3 conversions undertaken by Marshall was completed on 25 November 1985, as described in the 1987-88 and earlier editions of *Jane's*. Marshall now has a major contract to convert ex-airline TriStars into flight refuelling tankers and freighters for the RAF.

HERCULES C. Mk 1K TANKER and HERCULES C. Mk 1P/3P RECEIVER AIRCRAFT

Six Royal Air Force Lockheed Hercules C. Mk 1 aircraft have been converted by Marshall into flight refuelling tanker/receivers by fitting a Mk 17 hose drum unit (HDU) on the cargo compartment ramp, a drogue deployment box on the outside of the cargo bay door, four long-range fuel tanks in the cabin, and an in-flight refuelling probe over the flight deck. Modified in this way, each aircraft retains the availability of a pressurised cargo compartment for normal flight, but depressurises when operating with the drogue deployed. The first converted aircraft, designated Hercules **C. Mk 1K**, first flew on 8 June 1982 and became operational with No. 1312 Flight from Ascension Island in early August 1982. Total of five Mk 1s have been further modified by Marshall with a pod under each wingtip, containing 'Orange Blossom' ESM (equivalent to Racal MIR-2 'Orange Crop') equipment.

Sixteen RAF Hercules C. Mk 1 aircraft were fitted in 1982 with a probe to provide an in-flight refuelling capability, and are designated **C. Mk 1P**. During the Falklands campaign, one of them remained in the air for 28h on an operational mission, creating what was then a record for duration of flight in a Hercules. The RAF subsequently decided that all C. Mk 1 and C. Mk 3 Hercules would be equipped with probes, and the first **C. Mk 3P** (XV214) was returned to RAF Lyneham in February 1986, after conversion. Modification of the RAF's 31 Mk 1 and 30 Mk 3 Hercules was completed in 1989.

In 1987, some RAF Hercules began receiving Loral AN/ALQ-157 IR jamming equipment and chaff/flare dispensers on each side of the rear fuselage, and a contract was placed with General Instrument for AN/ALR-66 radar warning receivers. At the same time, 20 Hercules C. Mk 3s were equipped with a shallow underfuselage radome for Sierra Research AN/APN-169B station-keeping equipment to permit formation parachute-dropping in all weathers.

MARSHALL (LOCKHEED) TRISTAR TANKER CONVERSION

To meet a growing Royal Air Force requirement for flight refuelling tanker support, Marshall of Cambridge is converting to this role six Lockheed L-1011-500 TriStar transport aircraft purchased from British Airways in 1982 and is bidding for similar work on three more purchased from Pan Am in 1984. Work started in 1983 and the converted aircraft have been given the following RAF designations:

Lockheed Hercules C. Mk 1P equipped with wingtip pods for Racal 'Orange Blossom' ESM *(Paul Jackson)*

Lockheed TriStar KC. Mk 1 with freight door added by Marshall of Cambridge

TriStar K. Mk 1. Two interim (ZD950 and 953) and two full (ZD951 and 949) conversions to tanker/passenger standard, each with twin Flight Refuelling Mk 17T in-flight refuelling hose drum units (HDUs) and a total of seven fuel tanks in the fore and aft baggage compartments, to provide an additional 45,386 kg (100,060 lb) of fuel, giving a total aircraft fuel capacity of 142,111 kg (313,300 lb). The hose drum units deliver this fuel at a rate of 1,814 kg (4,000 lb)/min at 3.45 bars (50 lb/sq in). A flight refuelling probe is installed above the forward fuselage to provide a receiver capability. Closed circuit TV enables the crew to monitor all in-flight refuelling operations. The first K. Mk 1 (ZD950) flew on 9 July 1985. Its max T-O weight is increased to 244,940 kg (540,000 lb) and it received CA Release to Service on 1 December 1988. ZD953 was the first to re-join the RAF after conversion, on 25 March 1986, followed by ZD951 and 949 by mid-July of the same year. ZD950/953 further modified, as described below.

TriStar KC. Mk 1. Two aircraft (ZD948 and 952) converted to tanker/freighter role from civilian standard; further two (ZD950 and 953) from interim K. Mk 1. In addition to embodiment of the fuel system modifications, this requires the installation of a 2.64 m × 3.56 m (104 in × 140 in) cargo door on the port side, forward of the wing leading-edge, together with a cargo handling system. The passenger floor is strengthened to provide for high density loadings. In these aircraft all items carried on the cabin floor will be mounted on pallets. Thus, passengers can be carried when seat equipped pallets are fitted. ZD948 was re-delivered to the RAF on 9 December 1988 followed by ZD952 on 30 March 1989 and ZD953 on 18 December 1989. ZD950 due Winter 1990-91.

TriStar C. Mk 2(K). Three ex-Pan Am aircraft (ZE704-706), for planned conversion to the tanker/passenger role by the early 1990s. Two (ZE704 and 705) operated initially for trooping flights in airline standard accommodation; third stored at Cambridge. They were originally due to be similar to the K. Mk 1, apart from a fuel capacity reduced by 4,535 kg (10,000 lb) because of slight constructional differences between Pan Am and BA airframes. Designation to have been K. Mk 2. However, the MoD re-defined the Mk 2 specification to delete extra fuel tanks and fuselage-mounted HDUs. These aircraft will therefore have normal tankage of 96,724 kg (213,240 lb) and underwing refuelling pods only. Marshall has completed a design study to fit FRL Mk 32B pods to K. Mk 1, KC. Mk 1 and C. Mk 2(K) aircraft, and was expecting authorisation to begin modification of the first Mk 2 aircraft in early 1990. Mk 32 pods are capable of delivering fuel at a rate of 1,134 kg (2,500 lb)/min at 3.45 bars (50 lb/sq in) simultaneously from each pod. General Instrument AN/ALR-66 radar warning receivers will be fitted to RAF TriStars. All nine TriStars are assigned to No. 216 Squadron at RAF Brize Norton.

MARSHALL (LOCKHEED) TRISTAR MODIFICATION

Marshall is undertaking a variety of modification packages for civil TriStar operators. Following successful completion of the Sunset III package for British Airways which included major structural modification and outfitting, Marshall has also carried out max T-O weight increase modifications, Ageing Aircraft inspection/rectification programmes, and can offer freight door modification and additional fuel capacity modifications to civil operators.

NAC

THE NORMAN AEROPLANE COMPANY LTD (IN RECEIVERSHIP)

Mr N. D. Norman founded this company, as NDN Aircraft Ltd, in 1976. The company name was changed to The Norman Aeroplane Company in 1985, simultaneously with a transfer of its manufacturing centre to Wales.

Financial problems resulted in NAC calling in a receiver, Price Waterhouse, in July 1988. Subsequently, rights to the Fieldmaster agricultural and firefighting aircraft were sold to Andrew Mackinnon of Croplease Ltd (which see) in October 1988.

Details and a photograph of the NAC1 Freelance four-seat utility aircraft may be found in the 1989-90 edition of *Jane's*. No purchaser seems to have emerged to take over production of this aircraft. Technical data of the Firecracker turboprop trainer last appeared in the 1988-89 *Jane's* and historical background in the 1984-85 edition. The aircraft was not in production when NAC appointed a receiver.

NASH

NASH AIRCRAFT LTD (a subsidiary of Kinetrol Ltd)

Trading Estate, Farnham, Surrey GU9 9NU
Telephone: 44 (252) 723688
Telex: 858567
DIRECTORS:
  A. R. B. Nash (Managing)
  Roy G. Procter
  R. C. Nash

Mr Alan Nash acquired a controlling interest in Procter Aircraft Associates Ltd in early 1978, as a result of which the company was renamed Nash Aircraft Ltd in 1980. Its principal current activity is the development and manufacture of the Petrel two-seat light aircraft.

NASH PETREL

The company prototype of the Petrel (G-AXSF) made its first flight on 8 November 1980. In initial glider towing trials, it towed Vega, Mini-Nimbus and Nimbus sailplanes to a height of 610 m (2,000 ft) in under 4 min. During 1982 the original Textron Lycoming O-320-D2A engine was replaced by a 134 kW (180 hp) Textron Lycoming O-360-A3A, to optimise aircraft performance in the glider towing and pilot training roles. During 1983 a new high tailplane was designed and fitted, to improve stability and spin recovery. In 1984 upswept tips were fitted to the wings to improve handling.

Early in 1985 cuffs were fitted to the wing leading-edge, extending from 50 per cent span to the tips. These have now been removed, on attainment of the desired handling qualities. Work has proceeded towards achievement of a high production standard for the aircraft. The prototype has been fitted with a Hoffmann four-blade wooden propeller (replacing the original Sensenich two-blade metal unit) with the attendant advantages of quietness and improved glider-towing performance.

A pre-production batch of five Petrels is under construction. These will have either an O-320 or O-360 engine according to individual customer requirements.
TYPE: Two-seat light aircraft.
WINGS: Cantilever low-wing monoplane. Wing section NACA 3415. Dihedral 5° on outer panels. No sweepback or washout. All-metal constant chord structure, built in three sections: centre-section, integral with fuselage, to which outer panels are each attached with three bolts. Single main spar at 30 per cent chord and lightweight auxiliary spar at 66 per cent chord. Multiple ribs, with no spanwise stiffeners. All-metal NACA slotted flaps and Frise ailerons on outer panels. Flaps are operated

Company owned prototype of the Nash Petrel two-seat light aircraft

manually by pushrod and torque tube; ailerons are operated by pushrods.
FUSELAGE: All-metal structure. Four longeron basic structure, with flat sides and bottom and single-curvature top decking. Integral wing centre-section forms seat and main landing gear attachment structure.
TAIL UNIT: Cantilever all-metal structure. Fixed incidence tailplane. Manually operated tab in starboard elevator. Tab on rudder. Control surfaces mass balanced. Rudder operated by cables; elevators by pushrods.
LANDING GEAR: Non-retractable tricycle type. Nose unit consists of a telescopic strut with elastomeric shock absorption, carrying a Goodyear 5.00-6 wheel, and is steerable from the rudder pedals. Main gear is of cantilever steel leaf spring type, with Goodyear 6.00-6 wheels and hydraulic disc brakes. Tyre pressure (all) 1.72 bars (25 lb/sq in).
POWER PLANT: One 134 kW (180 hp) Textron Lycoming O-360-A3A flat-four engine, driving a Hoffmann four-blade fixed-pitch wooden propeller with spinner. Provision for alternative engines of 88-134 kW (118-180 hp). Removable fuel tanks in wing centre-section leading-edges, capacity 104.5 litres (27.6 US gallons; 23 Imp gallons).
ACCOMMODATION: Two persons side by side, on seats with individually adjustable backs. One-piece rearward sliding

bubble canopy. Dual controls standard. Baggage space aft of seats.
EQUIPMENT: Starter, generator and basic instrumentation. Radio, navigation and other equipment to customer's requirements.
DIMENSIONS, EXTERNAL:

Wing span	9.04 m (29 ft 8 in)
Wing chord, constant	1.37 m (4 ft 6 in)
Wing aspect ratio	6.3
Length overall	6.22 m (20 ft 5 in)
Height overall	2.23 m (7 ft 4 in)
Tailplane span	3.35 m (11 ft 0 in)
Wheel track	2.24 m (7 ft 4 in)
Wheelbase	1.52 m (5 ft 0 in)

AREA:

Wings, gross	13.00 m² (140.0 sq ft)

WEIGHTS:

Weight empty	544 kg (1,200 lb)
Max T-O weight	794 kg (1,750 lb)

PERFORMANCE (at max T-O weight):

Max level speed	115 knots (213 km/h; 132 mph)
Cruising speed	90 knots (167 km/h; 104 mph)
Stalling speed: flaps up	46 knots (86 km/h; 53 mph)
flaps down	40 knots (74 km/h; 46 mph)
Max rate of climb at S/L	350 m (1,150 ft)/min

OPERATION ABILITY
OPERATION ABILITY LTD

The Meadows, Firgrove Road, Whitehill, Bordon, Hampshire GU35 9DY
Telephone: 44 (4203) 5062
CHAIRMAN AND MANAGING DIRECTOR: Philip Scott

Mr Philip Scott, who is 85 per cent paralysed, formed Operation Ability with the objective of enabling himself to obtain a Private Pilot's Licence. Although he has lost the use of his legs, body, hands and much of his arms, Mr Scott became the first tetraplegic to have passed a CAA medical examination accepting him as 'fit to learn'.

The venture began in 1984 and, initially, a special design, the Cranfield A3, was prepared to meet the requirement. However, the foreseen high cost led to adoption of an alternative approach involving modifications to an Aérodis G802 Orion (see Sport Aircraft section: France) including conversion to jet power. In 1990, Mr Scott was talking to other companies which might wish to produce the Spur in Britain.

Operation Ability has since acquired a former Luftwaffe Focke-Wulf-Piaggio P.149D four-seat trainer aircraft (G-BRKD). A special hoist has been constructed by Watson and Haigh of Andover to enable Mr Scott to enter

and exit the cockpit, and work began in early 1990 on modifications which will enable him to fly the aircraft. These include provision of a hydraulic or electric servo actuator for rudder operation using either direct control or inputs from a yaw damper; conversion of the flap system from manual to hydraulic operation; new brake system; emergency backup system for lowering of the landing gear; and modifications to enable Mr Scott to operate all other cockpit equipment and avionics. A Racal Danac navigation computer donated to the Spur project by Racal Avionics Limited will be installed in the P149-D. The programme is sponsored by more than 50 firms and numerous individuals.

ORCA
ORCA AIRCRAFT LTD

Bodmin Airfield, Bodmin, Cornwall, PL30 4BU
Design and construction of the prototype SAH-1 two-seat light aircraft was undertaken by Trago Mills Ltd (Aircraft Division). The company was CAA approved for light aircraft design, development, manufacture and testing, and retained as design consultant Mr Frank H. Robertson, who has held engineering and senior design appointments with Vought Corporation in the USA, and with Miles, Saunders-Roe and Shorts in the UK.

In August 1988, key staff at Trago's Aircraft Division were joined by Mr Norman Whale, as principal financial backer, in a buy-out of the company. The revised organisation was renamed Orca Aircraft to reflect the Latin translation of the word whale. This company was placed under administration during the Summer of 1989, since when no further news has been received.

ORCA SAH-1

Design of the SAH-1 started in October 1977, and construction of a prototype began in January 1978. Both design and construction are to full CAA and FAR Pt 23

Orca SAH-1 side by side two-seat light aircraft *(Paul Jackson)*

Orca SAH-1 (88 kW; 118 hp Textron Lycoming O-235-L2A) *(Pilot Press)*

standards. The first flight of the prototype (G-SAHI) was made on 23 August 1983 and a full Certificate of Airworthiness, Public Transport Category, was obtained on 12 December 1985.

In the Summer of 1990 Brooklands Aircraft Company announced that it had entered into an agreement with designer Sydney Holloway to manufacture and market the aircraft as the SHB-1 Venture, but following Brooklands' financial difficulties this proposal has been abandoned.

In addition to the basic SAH-1, with O-235 engine, a more powerful version was projected, with a 119 kW (160 hp) Textron Lycoming AEIO-320-DB flat-four engine driving a constant-speed propeller.

TYPE: Two-seat fully aerobatic light aircraft.
WINGS: Cantilever low-wing monoplane. Wing section NACA 2413.6 (constant). Dihedral 5° from roots. Incidence 3° at root, 1° at tip. Tapered, non-swept aluminium alloy wings, with L65 spar booms and L72 sheet skins, stabilised with PVC foam. Trailing-edge single-slotted flaps and slotted ailerons of similar construction.

FUSELAGE: Aluminium alloy stressed skin structure, with radiused corners, incorporating centre-section spars.
TAIL UNIT: Aluminium alloy cantilever structure, stabilised with PVC foam. Constant chord tailplane, attached to fuselage, with horn balanced elevators; full span trim tab in starboard elevator. Sweptback fin and horn balanced rudder. Ventral fin.
LANDING GEAR: Non-retractable tricycle type, with single wheel on each unit. Oleo-pneumatic shock absorber in nosewheel leg; spring steel main legs. Cleveland mainwheels and tyres size 6.00-6, pressure 1.24 bars (18.0 lb/sq in). Nosewheel and tyre size 5.00-5, pressure 1.03 bars (15 lb/sq in). Cleveland hydraulic brakes.
POWER PLANT: One 88 kW (118 hp) Textron Lycoming O-235-L2A flat-four engine, driving a two-blade fixed-pitch propeller with spinner. Integral fuel tank in each wing leading-edge, total capacity 114 litres (30 US gallons; 25 Imp gallons). Refuelling point in upper surface of each wing. Oil capacity 5.7 litres (1.5 US gallons; 1.25 Imp gallons).
ACCOMMODATION: Two seats side by side under rearward

sliding bubble canopy. Baggage space aft of seats. Cockpit heated and ventilated.
SYSTEM: 60A engine driven alternator.
AVIONICS AND EQUIPMENT: Blind-flying instrumentation standard. Radio to customer's specification.

DIMENSIONS, EXTERNAL:
Wing span	9.36 m (30 ft 8⅜ in)
Wing chord: at root	1.515 m (4 ft 11⅔ in)
at tip	0.81 m (2 ft 8 in)
Wing aspect ratio	7.5
Length overall	6.58 m (21 ft 7¼ in)
Height overall	2.32 m (7 ft 7½ in)
Tailplane span	2.74 m (9 ft 0 in)
Wheel track	2.40 m (7 ft 10½ in)
Wheelbase	1.46 m (4 ft 9.6 in)
Propeller diameter	1.68 m (5 ft 6 in)
Propeller ground clearance	0.30 m (12 in)

DIMENSIONS, INTERNAL:
Cockpit: Length	1.52 m (5 ft 0 in)
Max width	1.21 m (3 ft 11½ in)
Baggage space	0.4 m³ (14.0 cu ft)

AREAS:
Wings, gross	11.15 m² (120.0 sq ft)
Ailerons (total)	0.89 m² (9.6 sq ft)
Trailing-edge flaps (total)	1.30 m² (14.0 sq ft)
Fin	0.96 m² (10.3 sq ft)
Rudder	0.63 m² (6.8 sq ft)
Tailplane	1.11 m² (12.0 sq ft)
Elevators, incl tab	0.93 m² (10.0 sq ft)

WEIGHTS AND LOADINGS:
Weight empty, equipped	499 kg (1,100 lb)
Max fuel load	85 kg (188 lb)
Max T-O weight	794 kg (1,750 lb)
Max wing loading	71.19 kg/m² (14.58 lb/sq ft)
Max power loading	9.02 kg/kW (14.83 lb/hp)

PERFORMANCE (at max T-O weight):
Never-exceed speed	164 knots (304 km/h; 188 mph) EAS
Max level speed at S/L	122 knots (226 km/h; 140 mph)
Max cruising speed, 75% power at S/L	110 knots (204 km/h; 127 mph)
Econ cruising speed, 50% power at S/L	93 knots (172 km/h; 107 mph)
Stalling speed:	
flaps up	54 knots (100 km/h; 63 mph) EAS
flaps down	47 knots (88 km/h; 55 mph) EAS
Max rate of climb at S/L	279 m (915 ft)/min
Service ceiling	5,000 m (16,400 ft)
T-O to 15 m (50 ft)	392 m (1,285 ft)
Landing from 15 m (50 ft)	290 m (953 ft)
Range with max fuel, 13.6 litres (3.6 US gallons; 3 Imp gallons) reserves at 78 knots (145 km/h; 90 mph) at 1,525 m (5,000 ft)	620 nm (1,149 km; 714 miles)

PILATUS BRITTEN-NORMAN
PILATUS BRITTEN-NORMAN LTD
(Subsidiary of Oerlikon-Bührle Holding Ltd)

The Airport, Bembridge, Isle of Wight PO35 5PR
Telephone: 44 (983) 872511
Telex: 86277 PBNBEM G
Fax: 44 (983) 873246
MANAGING DIRECTOR: Dr E. Haefliger
TECHNICAL DIRECTOR: R. Wilson
MARKETING DIRECTOR: A. Stansfeld
MARKETING SERVICES MANAGER: Richard M. Blake

In 1979 Pilatus Aircraft Ltd of Switzerland acquired all assets of Britten-Norman (Bembridge) Ltd, including the facilities on the Isle of Wight and the former Fairey SA Islander/Trislander production hardware at Gosselies in Belgium.

The previous history of this company can be found in the 1978-79 and earlier editions of *Jane's*. It produces the Islander transport aircraft in a variety of forms; the Islander is manufactured in Romania by IAv Bucuresti (which see), and more than 480 had been delivered to Pilatus Britten-Norman from that source by mid-May 1990. The last Trislander produced by Pilatus Britten-Norman was delivered to the Botswana Defence Force in September 1984.

PILATUS BRITTEN-NORMAN BN-2B ISLANDER

Detail design of the Islander began in April 1964 and construction of the prototype (G-ATCT) was started in September of the same year. It flew for the first time on 13 June 1965, powered by two 157 kW (210 hp) Rolls-Royce Continental IO-360-B engines and with wings of 13.72 m (45 ft) span. Subsequently, the prototype was re-engined with more powerful Textron Lycoming O-540 engines, with which it flew for the first time on 17 December 1965. The wing span was also increased by 1.22 m (4 ft) to bring the prototype to initial production standard.

The production prototype BN-2 Islander (G-ATWU) flew for the first time on 20 August 1966. The Islander received its domestic C of A on 10 August 1967 and an FAA type certificate on 19 December 1967.

Deliveries of Islanders began in August 1967, and various

Pilatus Britten-Norman BN-2B-26 Islander operated by Loganair

models, including military Defenders, have been supplied to operators in approx 120 countries. By December 1989 deliveries totalled 1,123, including 12 supplied to customers in 1989. Recent deliveries included a BN-2B for the West German operator Luftverkehr Friesland, which has used Islanders on its services to the Friesian Islands for 15 years.

Initial production Islanders were designated **BN-2**. Those built as standard from 1 June 1969 had the designation **BN-2A**, as described in the 1977-78 *Jane's*. The current standard piston engined model, from 1978, is the **BN-2B** Islander, which has a higher max landing weight and improved interior design. It is available with a choice of two piston engine power plants and either standard fuel tanks or standard tanks plus optional tanks in wingtips. Features, compared with the BN-2A (which is still available to order), include a range of passenger seats and covers, more robust door locks, improved door seals and stainless steel sills, redesigned fresh air system to improve ventilation

in hot and humid climates, smaller diameter propellers to decrease cabin noise, and redesigned flight deck and instrument panel. The two basic versions are designated **BN-2B-26** (with O-540 engines) and **BN-2B-20** (with IO-540s); BN-2B-27 and BN-2B-21 versions are no longer available, but improved tanks in wingtips are available as options to the basic BN-2B-26 and BN-2B-20 aircraft. The **BN-2T Turbine Islander**, powered by two Allison 250-B17C turboprops, and the military **Defender** and variants, are described separately.

A series of modification kits is available as standard or as an option for new production aircraft, and can also be supplied to operators in the field for retrospective fitting to existing aircraft. An extended nose, incorporating 0.62 m³ (22 cu ft) of additional baggage space, was introduced as an optional feature in 1972.

A Rajay turbocharging installation was developed in the United States by Jonas Aircraft, the New York based distributors for Pilatus Britten-Norman aircraft. The Rajay installation is a bolt-on unit, which can be fitted on to standard 194 kW (260 hp) engines.

The following description applies to the standard piston engined versions of the BN-2B:

TYPE: Twin-engined feederline transport.

WINGS: Cantilever high-wing monoplane. NACA 23012 constant wing section. No dihedral. Incidence 2°. No sweepback. Conventional riveted two-spar torsion box structure in one piece, using L72 aluminium-clad aluminium alloys. Flared-up wingtips of Britten-Norman design. Integral fuel tanks in wingtips optional. Slotted ailerons and single-slotted flaps of metal construction. Flaps operated electrically, ailerons by pushrods and cables. Ground adjustable tab on starboard aileron. BTR-Goodrich pneumatic de-icing boots optional.

FUSELAGE: Conventional riveted four-longeron semi-monocoque structure of pressed frames and stringers and metal skin, using L72 aluminium clad aluminium alloys.

TAIL UNIT: Cantilever two-spar structure, with pressed ribs and metal skin, using L72 aluminium-clad aluminium alloys. Fixed incidence tailplane and mass balanced elevator. Rudder and elevator are actuated by pushrods and cables. Trim tabs in rudder and elevator. Pneumatic de-icing of tailplane and fin optional.

LANDING GEAR: Non-retractable tricycle type, with twin wheels on each main unit and single steerable nosewheel. Cantilever main legs mounted aft of rear spar. All three legs fitted with oleo-pneumatic shock absorbers. All five wheels and tyres size 16 × 7-7, supplied by Goodyear. Tyre pressure: main 2.41 bars (35 lb/sq in); nose 2.00 bars (29 lb/sq in). Foot operated aircooled Cleveland hydraulic brakes on main units. Parking brake. Wheel/ski gear available optionally.

POWER PLANT: Two Textron Lycoming flat-six engines, each driving a Hartzell HC-C2YK-2B or -2C two-blade constant-speed feathering metal propeller. Propeller synchronisers optional. Standard power plant is the 194 kW (260 hp) O-540-E4C5, but the 224 kW (300 hp) IO-540-K1B5 can be fitted at customer's option. Optional Rajay turbocharging installation on 194 kW (260 hp) engines, to improve high altitude performance. Integral fuel tank between spars in each wing, outboard of engine. Total fuel capacity (standard) 518 litres (137 US gallons; 114 Imp gallons). Usable fuel 492 litres (130 US gallons; 108 Imp gallons). With optional fuel tanks in wingtips, total capacity is increased to 855 litres (226 US gallons; 188 Imp gallons). Additional pylon mounted underwing auxiliary tanks, each of 227 litres (60 US gallons; 50 Imp gallons) capacity, available optionally. Refuelling point in upper surface of wing above each internal tank. Total oil capacity 22.75 litres (6 US gallons; 5 Imp gallons).

ACCOMMODATION: Up to 10 persons, including pilot, on side by side front seats and four bench seats. No aisle. Seat backs fold forward. Access to all seats via three forward opening doors, forward of wing and at rear of cabin on port side and forward of wing on starboard side. Baggage compartment at rear of cabin, with port side loading door in standard versions. Exit in emergency by removing door windows. Special executive layouts available. Can be operated as freighter, carrying more than a ton of cargo; in this configuration the passenger seats can be stored in the rear baggage bay. In ambulance role, up to three stretchers and two attendants can be accommodated. Other layouts possible, including photographic and geophysical survey, parachutist transport or trainer (with accommodation for up to eight parachutists and a dispatcher), firefighting, public health spraying and crop spraying.

SYSTEMS: Southwind cabin heater standard. 45,000 BTU Stewart Warner combustion unit, with circulating fan, provides hot air for distribution at floor level outlets and at windscreen demisting slots. Fresh air, boosted by propeller slipstream, is ducted to each seating position for on-ground ventilation. Electrical DC power, for instruments, lighting and radio, from two engine driven 24V 50A self-rectifying alternators and a controller to main busbar and circuit breaker assembly. Emergency busbar is supplied by a 24V 17Ah heavy duty lead-acid battery in the event of a twin alternator failure. Ground power receptacle provided. Optional electric de-icing of propellers and windscreen, and pneumatic de-icing of wing and tail unit leading-edges. Intercom system, including second headset, and passenger address system are standard. Oxygen system available optionally for all versions.

AVIONICS AND EQUIPMENT: Standard items include blind-flying instrumentation, autopilot, dual flying controls and brake system, and a wide range of VHF and HF communications and navigation equipment.

DIMENSIONS, EXTERNAL:

Wing span	14.94 m (49 ft 0 in)
Wing chord (constant)	2.03 m (6 ft 8 in)
Wing aspect ratio	7.4
Length	10.86 m (35 ft 7¾ in)
Fuselage: Max width	1.21 m (3 ft 11½ in)
Max depth	1.46 m (4 ft 9¾ in)
Height overall	4.18 m (13 ft 8¾ in)
Tailplane span	4.67 m (15 ft 4 in)
Wheel track (c/l of shock absorbers)	3.61 m (11 ft 10 in)

Wheelbase	3.99 m (13 ft 1¼ in)
Propeller diameter	1.98 m (6 ft 6 in)
Cabin door (front, port):	
Height	1.10 m (3 ft 7½ in)
Width: top	0.64 m (2 ft 1¼ in)
Height to sill	0.59 m (1 ft 11¼ in)
Cabin door (front, starboard):	
Height	1.10 m (3 ft 7½ in)
Max width	0.86 m (2 ft 10 in)
Height to sill	0.57 m (1 ft 10½ in)
Cabin door (rear, port): Height	1.09 m (3 ft 7 in)
Width: top	0.635 m (2 ft 1 in)
bottom	1.19 m (3 ft 11 in)
Height to sill	0.52 m (1 ft 8½ in)
Baggage door (rear, port): Height	0.69 m (2 ft 3 in)

DIMENSIONS, INTERNAL:

Passenger cabin, aft of pilot's seat:	
Length	3.05 m (10 ft 0 in)
Max width	1.09 m (3 ft 7 in)
Max height	1.27 m (4 ft 2 in)
Floor area	2.97 m² (32 sq ft)
Volume	3.68 m³ (130 cu ft)
Baggage space aft of passenger cabin	1.39 m³ (49 cu ft)
Freight capacity:	
aft of pilot's seat, incl rear cabin baggage space	4.70 m³ (166 cu ft)
with four bench seats folded into rear cabin baggage space	3.68 m³ (130 cu ft)

AREAS:

Wings, gross	30.19 m² (325.0 sq ft)
Ailerons (total)	2.38 m² (25.6 sq ft)
Flaps (total)	3.62 m² (39.0 sq ft)
Fin	3.41 m² (36.64 sq ft)
Rudder, incl tab	1.60 m² (17.2 sq ft)
Tailplane	6.78 m² (73.0 sq ft)
Elevator, incl tabs	3.08 m² (33.16 sq ft)

WEIGHTS AND LOADINGS (A: 194 kW; 260 hp engines, B: 224 kW; 300 hp engines):

Weight empty, equipped (without avionics):	
A	1,866 kg (4,114 lb)
B	1,925 kg (4,244 lb)
Max payload: A	929 kg (2,048 lb)
B	870 kg (1,918 lb)
Payload with max fuel: A	692 kg (1,526 lb)
B	633 kg (1,396 lb)
Max fuel weight: standard: A, B	354 kg (780 lb)
with optional tanks in wingtips: A, B	585 kg (1,290 lb)
Max T-O and landing weight: A, B	2,993 kg (6,600 lb)
Max zero-fuel weight (BCAR):	
A, B	2,855 kg (6,300 lb)
Max wing loading: A, B	99.1 kg/m² (20.3 lb/sq ft)
Max floor loading, without cargo panels:	
A, B	586 kg/m² (120 lb/sq ft)
Max power loading: A	7.71 kg/kW (12.7 lb/hp)
B	6.68 kg/kW (11.0 lb/hp)

PERFORMANCE (at max T-O weight. A and B as above):

Never-exceed speed:	
A, B	183 knots (339 km/h; 211 mph) IAS
Max level speed at S/L:	
A	148 knots (274 km/h; 170 mph)
B	151 knots (280 km/h; 173 mph)
Max cruising speed (75% power) at 2,135 m (7,000 ft):	
A	139 knots (257 km/h; 160 mph)
B	142 knots (264 km/h; 164 mph)
Cruising speed (67% power) at 2,750 m (9,000 ft):	
A	134 knots (248 km/h; 154 mph)
B	137 knots (254 km/h; 158 mph)
Cruising speed (59% power) at 3,660 m (12,000 ft):	
A	130 knots (241 km/h; 150 mph)
B	132 knots (245 km/h; 152 mph)
Stalling speed:	
flaps up: A, B	50 knots (92 km/h; 57 mph) IAS
flaps down: A, B	40 knots (74 km/h; 46 mph) IAS
Max rate of climb at S/L: A	262 m (860 ft)/min
B	344 m (1,130 ft)/min
Rate of climb at S/L, one engine out:	
A	44 m (145 ft)/min
B	60 m (198 ft)/min
Absolute ceiling: A	4,145 m (13,600 ft)
B	6,005 m (19,700 ft)
Service ceiling: A	3,445 m (11,300 ft)
B	5,240 m (17,200 ft)
Service ceiling, one engine out: A	1,525 m (5,000 ft)
B	1,980 m (6,500 ft)
Min ground turning radius	9.45 m (31 ft 0 in)
T-O run at S/L, zero wind, hard runway:	
A	278 m (913 ft)
B	264 m (866 ft)
T-O run at 1,525 m (5,000 ft): A	396 m (1,299 ft)
B	372 m (1,221 ft)
T-O to 15 m (50 ft) at S/L, zero wind, hard runway:	
A	371 m (1,218 ft)
B	352 m (1,155 ft)
T-O to 15 m (50 ft) at 1,525 m (5,000 ft):	
A	528 m (1,732 ft)
B	496 m (1,628 ft)
Landing from 15 m (50 ft) at S/L, zero wind, hard runway: A, B	299 m (980 ft)
Landing from 15 m (50 ft) at 1,525 m (5,000 ft):	
A, B	357 m (1,170 ft)

Landing run at 1,525 m (5,000 ft): A, B	171 m (560 ft)
Landing run at S/L, zero wind, hard runway:	
A, B	140 m (460 ft)
Range at 75% power at 2,135 m (7,000 ft):	
A, standard fuel	622 nm (1,153 km; 717 miles)
A, with optional tanks	1,023 nm (1,896 km; 1,178 miles)
B, standard fuel	555 nm (1,028 km; 639 miles)
B, with optional tanks	920 nm (1,704 km; 1,059 miles)
Range at 67% power at 2,750 m (9,000 ft):	
A, standard fuel	713 nm (1,322 km; 822 miles)
A, with optional tanks	1,159 nm (2,147 km; 1,334 miles)
B, standard fuel	577 nm (1,070 km; 665 miles)
B, with optional tanks	975 nm (1,807 km; 1,123 miles)
Range at 59% power at 3,660 m (12,000 ft):	
A, standard fuel	755 nm (1,400 km; 870 miles)
A, with optional tanks	1,216 nm (2,253 km; 1,400 miles)
B, standard fuel	613 nm (1,136 km; 706 miles)
B, with optional tanks	1,061 nm (1,965 km; 1,221 miles)

PILATUS BRITTEN-NORMAN DEFENDER

The Defender is a variant of the civil Islander which can be adapted for a wide variety of government and military roles such as search and rescue, internal security, long-range patrol, forward air control, troop transport, logistic support and casualty evacuation. It is available with the same choices of wing configuration as the current civil versions and can be equipped with a wide range of sophisticated avionics, including nose mounted weather radar, providing the aircraft with a marine search capability. For an electronic warfare role, equipment can range from a simple radar warning receiver to a comprehensive passive electronic intelligence gathering system, ESM, and ECM coupled to the ESM to provide radar jamming or defensive chaff/IR flare dispensing. Other optional equipment includes four NATO standard underwing pylons for a variety of external stores, the inboard pair each carrying up to 340 kg (750 lb) and the outboard pair up to 159 kg (350 lb).

Typical underwing loads include twin 7.62 mm machine-guns in pod packs, 250 lb or 500 lb GP bombs, Matra rocket packs, SURA rocket clusters, wire guided missiles, 5 in reconnaissance flares, anti-personnel grenades, smoke bombs, marker bombs and 227 litre (60 US gallon; 50 Imp gallon) drop tanks.

Internal capacity for passengers, stretcher cases or cargo is the same as that of the civil Islander.

Britten-Norman Defenders/Islanders have been delivered to the Abu Dhabi Defence Force, Belgian Army, Belize Defence Force, Botswana Defence Force, British Army Parachute Association, Ciskei Defence Force, Ghana Air Force, Guyana Defence Force, Haitian Air Corps, Indonesian Army, Jamaica Defence Force, Malagasy Air Force, Presidential Flight of the Mexican Air Force, Royal Hong Kong Auxiliary Air Force, Panamanian Air Force, Somali Aeronautical Corps, Sultan of Oman's Air Force, Suriname Air Force, Mauritania Islamic Defence Force, the Seychelles Ministry of Agriculture and Fisheries, the Malawi Army Air Wing, Venezuelan Army Air Regiment, Zaïre Air Force, Zimbabwe Air Force and the Rwanda Air Force. Those operated by Ciskei, Haiti, Indonesia, Iraq, Somalia, Venezuela, Zaïre, Zimbabwe, Israel and Qatar are military Islanders, and are not equipped to carry offensive weapons; those which serve with the Cyprus National Guard, Indian Navy and Philippine Navy are Maritime Islanders.

The description given for the BN-2B Islander applies also to the Defender, except as follows:

POWER PLANT: Two 224 kW (300 hp) Textron Lycoming IO-540-K1B5 flat-six engines standard.

AVIONICS: Typical installation comprises 720 channel VHF nav/com transceivers with VOR/LOC and VOR/ILS, ADF, marker beacon receiver, transponder, HF com transceiver, weather radar and full autopilot. Optional equipment includes RWR, ESM and ECM.

PILATUS BRITTEN-NORMAN MARITIME DEFENDER

Generally similar to the Defender, the Maritime Defender differs by having a modified nose with a larger (Bendix RDR-1400) search radar, capable of detecting a 100 m² (1,076 sq ft) target in sea state 4-5 at a range of 36 nm (67 km; 41.5 miles). Scanning 60° on each side of the flight path, the radar provides a search width of 60 nm (111 km; 69 miles) at optimum altitude. The interior layout provides for pilot and co-pilot, a radar operator at a mid-cabin position on the starboard side, and two observers in the rear of the cabin, one aft of the radar operator, and one adjacent to a window on the port side.

Intended for coastal patrol, fishery and oil rig protection duties, as well as search and rescue support, the Maritime Defender is suitable for all-weather operation, by day or night, and carries the equipment necessary to fulfil such roles. This can include compass/HSI, horizon gyro (radar stabilisation), autopilot, ground mapping and weather radar, VLF/Omega, radio altimeter, dual VHF com, dual VHF nav/ILS, VHF marine band com, ADF, transponder,

DME, encoding altimeter and SSB HF com. Specialised equipment includes a searchlight installation and hand held camera; the four underwing pylons can be used to carry a loudspeaker pod, flares, parachute dinghy packs and a variety of weapons.

The description of the Defender applies also to the Maritime Defender, except that overall length is increased to 11.07 m (36 ft 3¾ in).

PILATUS BRITTEN-NORMAN BN-2T TURBINE ISLANDER and DEFENDER

On 2 August 1980 the prototype (G-BPBN) was flown of the BN-2T Turbine Islander, powered by two Allison 250-B17C turboprops. These enable the BN-2T to use available low cost jet fuel instead of scarce and costly Avgas, and offer a particularly low operating noise level.

British CAA certification of the Turbine Islander was received at the end of May 1981; FAR Pt 23 US type approval was granted on 15 July 1982. Full icing clearance to FAR Pt 25 was granted on 23 July 1984. The first production aircraft was delivered during December 1981. Thirty-seven aircraft had been delivered by December 1989.

The Turbine Islander is available for the same range of applications as the piston engined Islander, including a military version described separately.

The description of the BN-2B Islander applies also to the BN-2T, except as follows:

TYPE: Twin-turboprop feederline transport.

FUSELAGE: Generally as for BN-2B.

POWER PLANT: Two 298 kW (400 shp) Allison 250-B17C turboprops, flat rated at 238.5 kW (320 shp), and each driving a Hartzell three-blade constant-speed fully-feathering metal propeller. Usable fuel 814 litres (215 US gallons; 179 Imp gallons). Pylon mounted underwing tanks, each of 227 litres (60 US gallons; 50 Imp gallons) capacity, are available optionally for special purposes. Total oil capacity 5.7 litres (1.5 US gallons; 1.25 Imp gallons).

ACCOMMODATION: Generally as for BN-2B. In ambulance role can accommodate, in addition to the pilot, a single stretcher, one medical attendant, and five seated occupants; or two stretchers, one attendant, and three passengers; or three stretchers, two attendants, and one passenger. Other possible layouts include photographic and geophysical survey; parachutist transport or trainer (with accommodation for up to eight parachutists and a dispatcher); and pest control or other agricultural spraying. Maritime Turbine Islander/Defender versions available for fishery protection, coastguard patrol, pollution survey, search and rescue, and similar applications. Offered as an option is an in-flight sliding parachute door.

AVIONICS AND EQUIPMENT: Standard avionics and equipment generally similar to BN-2B. Other equipment, according to mission, includes fixed tail sting or towed bird magnetometer, spectrometer, or electromagnetic detection/analysis equipment (geophysical survey); one or two cameras, navigation sights, and appropriate avionics (photographic survey); 188.7 litre (50 US gallon; 41.5 Imp gallon) Micronair underwing spraypods complete with pump and rotary atomiser (pest control/agricultural spraying versions); radar, VLF/Omega nav system, radar altimeter, marine band and VHF transceivers, dinghies, survival equipment, and special crew accommodation (maritime versions).

DIMENSIONS, EXTERNAL:
As for BN-2B, except

Length overall: standard nose	10.87 m (35 ft 7¾ in)
weather radar nose	11.07 m (36 ft 3¾ in)
Propeller diameter	2.03 m (6 ft 8 in)

WEIGHTS:

Weight empty, equipped	1,832 kg (4,040 lb)
Payload with max fuel	608 kg (1,340 lb)
Max T-O weight	3,175 kg (7,000 lb)
Max landing weight	3,084 kg (6,800 lb)
Max zero-fuel weight	2,994 kg (6,600 lb)

PERFORMANCE (standard aircraft and Turbine Defender, at max T-O weight, ISA, except where indicated):

Max cruising speed:		
at 3,050 m (10,000 ft)	170 knots (315 km/h; 196 mph)	
at S/L	154 knots (285 km/h; 177 mph)	
Cruising speed, 72% power:		
at 3,050 m (10,000 ft)	150 knots (278 km/h; 173 mph)	
at 1,525 m (5,000 ft)	143 knots (265 km/h; 165 mph)	
Stalling speed, power off:		
flaps up	52 knots (97 km/h; 60 mph) IAS	
flaps down	45 knots (84 km/h; 52 mph) IAS	
Max rate of climb at S/L	320 m (1,050 ft)/min	
Rate of climb at S/L, one engine out	66 m (215 ft)/min	
Service ceiling	over 7,620 m (25,000 ft)	
Absolute ceiling, one engine out	over 3,050 m (10,000 ft)	
T-O run	255 m (837 ft)	
T-O to 15 m (50 ft)	381 m (1,250 ft)	
Landing from 15 m (50 ft)	339 m (1,110 ft)	
Landing run	231 m (757 ft)	
Range (IFR) with max fuel, reserves for 45 min hold plus 10%	590 nm (1,093 km; 679 miles)	
Range (VFR) with max fuel, no reserves	728 nm (1,349 km; 838 miles)	

Pilatus Britten-Norman BN-2T Turbine Islander with Micronair underwing spray system

Pilatus Britten-Norman BN-2T Turbine Islander *(Pilot Press)*

Pilatus Britten-Norman Islander AL. Mk 1 of the British Army Air Corps

PILATUS BRITTEN-NORMAN ASTOR DEFENDER

ASTOR (Airborne STand-off Radar) is the current acronym for a British Ministry of Defence programme which is seeking to fulfil a requirement for an airborne surveillance radar to provide an overall picture of a battle area. It is intended to operate in conjunction with a battlefield reconnaissance RPV called Phoenix, which would be sent in to obtain a closer look at any area or target shown by the ASTOR aircraft to be deserving of more detailed examination.

Two platforms are being evaluated for ASTOR, the high-level option being represented by a BAC/English Electric Canberra. The more versatile BN-2T Defender could be selected for production systems if it proves able to acquire sufficient data from medium heights. Radar trials have included GEC equipment in the Canberra and Ferranti equipment in the Defender, and a modified Thorn EMI Searchwater has been flying in the Canberra testbed since 1982. Up to 12 ASTOR platforms are required.

Pilatus Britten-Norman began work on an ASTOR (then CASTOR) Turbine Defender testbed (G-DLRA, c/n 2140; now ZG989) on 5 March 1984, and the converted aircraft made its first flight on 12 May, with the flat-bottomed undernose radome (designed to receive Ferranti radar) containing ballast only. This installation significantly altered the Defender's nose shape, but was considered the best location to provide optimum lookdown capability for the scanner. To provide ground clearance for the radar in this position, the nosewheel leg was lengthened by 30.5 cm (12 in) and a Trislander main landing gear fitted. Despite the ungainly appearance, flight tests demonstrated adequate performance and virtually unaltered handling characteristics.

In 1988, G-DLRA was fitted with a modified version of the Thorn EMI Skymaster radar and adopted the same nose profile as the AEW Defender (which see). Tests of its suitability as the low level ASTOR platform were continuing in 1989-90. Flown at altitudes up to 3,050 m (10,000 ft), these involved the new, electrically-driven

DIMENSIONS, EXTERNAL:	
Wing span	14.94 m (49 ft 0 in)
Wing aspect ratio	7.4
Length overall	12.37 m (40 ft 7¼ in)
Propeller diameter	2.03 m (6 ft 8 in)
WEIGHT:	
Design max T-O weight	3,630 kg (8,000 lb)

Pilatus Britten-Norman BN-2T Internal Security Defender of the Netherlands National Police

Pilatus Britten-Norman AEW Defender with radome for nose-mounted Thorn EMI Skymaster radar

Pilatus Britten-Norman AEW Defender, a Turbine Islander development with Skymaster surveillance radar *(Pilot Press)*

PILATUS BRITTEN-NORMAN SPECIAL ROLE BN-2T TURBINE ISLANDERS AND DEFENDERS

Army Air Corps designation: Islander AL. Mk 1

To complement the Maritime Defender (which was first offered in piston-engined form, as described earlier), several special-role adaptions of the BN-2T are now available or under development:

ASW/ASV Maritime Defender. This aircraft may be equipped to varying standards, to the customer's specification. Equipment can include a 360° radar and a FLIR. Four underwing hardpoints can be used to carry four Sea Skua missiles, ESM pods, survival packs, rockets, gun pods or other stores. A crew of three is normal, with room for a trainee.

The UK Ministry of Defence purchased Pilatus Britten-Norman's former Turbine Defender demonstrator (G-OPBN) in 1986, for use by the Royal Navy's Directorate-General of Underwater Weapons torpedo trials unit as ZF573.

ELINT Defender. In a programme jointly funded with Racal Radar Defence Systems Ltd, PBN has developed the Turbine Defender as an economically viable electronic warfare platform, and in 1989 a BN-2T (G-DEMO) was fitted with a Racal Kestrel lightweight EW avionics suite to serve as an ELINT Defender demonstrator.

The Kestrel system provides the ability to compile a comprehensive library of electronic intelligence which can be constantly updated. Kestrel is able to offer total radar band coverage with instant onboard analysis and/or data recording for ground replay and analysis, and allows the ELINT Defender to be used either in a peacetime strategic intelligence role or for tactical elint in an active environment. One equipment operator is carried in addition to the flight crew.

Underwing pods are an integral part of the Defender's elint system. Each carries two outward-facing antenna units for the Kestrel system; a further two are mounted on opposite sides of the tail fin. A precision navigation system, such as Omega or an INS, is standard. In a typical mission, the ELINT Defender could remain on task at 87 nm (161 km; 100 miles) from base for four hours.

Internal Security Defender. In 1988, PBN received orders for border patrol and internal security versions of the Defender from the Rijkspolitie (Netherlands National Police) and UK Army Air Corps. Optical, thermal imaging and other types of camera equipment may be carried internally or on the wing stations. Armament options include guns, rockets and bombs underwing. The Dutch aircraft are equipped with a comprehensive Collins avionics fit, Bendix RDR 1400C radar, blister windows, an in-flight-openable rear cabin door for a camera and infra-red sensor platform, Racal R-NAV2, and external points for long-range auxiliary fuel tanks. UK AAC Defenders have the Racal Avionics R-NAV2 navigation management system, Doppler 91 velocity sensor and Mk 32 Airborne Decca Navigator receiver.

Delivery of two aircraft to the Rijkspolitie was effected in 1988, and five **Islander AL. Mk 1s** were supplied to the AAC in February and March 1989 as replacements for DHC-2 Beavers used for security duties in Northern Ireland. These aircraft have additional, unspecified equipment, possibly including a Gepard Sensor Technologies Systems FLIR pod (see Addenda/Switzerland) on an underwing pylon for night surveillance operations. They became operational in May 1989 with 1 Flight at Aldergrove; two more are on order.

AEW Defender. To meet the need for a lightweight high performance AEW system, Pilatus Britten-Norman and Thorn EMI Electronics collaborated on a private venture basis to install the Thorn EMI Skymaster multi-mode radar into a Pilatus Britten-Norman Defender airframe (G-TEMI), and so create the AEW Defender. As the illustration shows, the nose radome of the AEW Defender is deeper, more bulbous and less angular than that of the original ASTOR aircraft, to house the Skymaster radar. In an AEW role this long-range radar, using pulse Doppler processing, can acquire and track automatically large numbers of targets flying at all altitudes against a land or sea background. For maritime reconnaissance (MR) the operator selects a non-coherent, frequency agile mode of operation, optimising the radar for the detection of small surface targets in high sea states out to the radar horizon.

The Defender's STOL performance enables it to be operated from forward unprepared strips, and in the air the aircraft's low radar cross section aids survivability. The **AEW/MR Defender** is fitted with a second console to increase operational flexibility and target handling capacity. An air-to-air and air-to-ground data link, ESM, IFF and navigation equipment may be fully integrated with the radar display and control system.

Production AEW Defenders will differ from standard aircraft in having an increase in wing span and all-up

antenna and additional signal processing techniques intended to provide the required quality of detection and azimuth resolution of slow moving targets against a ground clutter background. It was also equipped with a data link during 1989 to evaluate the system's interoperability with JSTARS.

Designed to meet UK General and Air Staff Requirement 3956, and to provide primary intelligence information in the immediate battle zone and beyond, while operating well within friendly territory, Skymaster has full 360° scan, and offers a wide area of coverage against moving and fixed targets. The associated transmitter, receiver and processing equipment are housed in the fuselage of the Islander, which is flown and operated by a two-man crew. Data acquired is processed and transmitted automatically, via an airborne link, to one or more ground stations.

The description of the standard BN-2T Turbine Islander applies also to the ASTOR Defender, except as follows:

TYPE: Twin-turboprop experimental battlefield surveillance aircraft.

FUSELAGE: Modified nose, as described in introductory paragraphs.

LANDING GEAR: Modified BN-2A Mk III Trislander main landing gear. Longer nosewheel leg to provide adequate ground clearance for radome. Main landing gear tyre size 6.50 × 8, pressure 2.4 bars (35 lb/sq in).

SYSTEMS AND AVIONICS: Multi-mode radar installed in nose, as described in introductory paragraphs. Other systems and avionics generally as described for Islander/Turbine Islander.

weight, plus additional fuel. Performance of the standard Defender will be restored by installation of higher-powered engines.

Defender 4000. Airframe and engine improvements developed for the AEW variant are now offered in a general purpose military variant designated Defender 4000. The new wing has the potential to lift 4,536 kg (10,000 lb), but 3,855 kg (8,500 lb) is currently considered adequate for military roles. At this latter weight, and with maximum internal fuel 50 per cent greater than the standard aircraft, the Defender 4000 has twice the carrying capacity of the earlier BN-2s.

The following description refers to the AEW Defender and Defender 4000 with increased span:

FUSELAGE, TAIL UNIT, LANDING GEAR: Similar to ASTOR Defender.

POWER PLANT: Two Allison 250-B17F turboprop engines, flat rated at 279.6 kW (375 shp). Usable internal fuel capacity 912 kg (2,010 lb).

SYSTEMS AND AVIONICS: As for Islander/Turbine Islander, except Thorn EMI Skymaster I-band, frequency-agile AEW radar antenna in extended nose, providing pulse Doppler AEW lookdown, pulse AEW lookup, pulse maritime surveillance and pulse navigation weather warning modes. INS or similar precision navigation equipment. Operator's console (35 cm; 14 in display screen, plus two touch-sensitive control surfaces) in centre fuselage; second console optional. Radar transmit-

Pilatus Britten-Norman ELINT Defender demonstrator with Racal Kestrel EW system

ter, accumulators, equipment conditioning and transmitter conditioning systems all in rear fuselage.

DIMENSIONS, EXTERNAL:
Wing span — 16.15 m (53 ft 0 in)
Length overall — 12.37 m (40 ft 7¼ in)

WEIGHT:
Max T-O weight — 3,855 kg (8,500 lb)

PERFORMANCE:
Cruising speed — 170 knots (315 km/h; 196 mph)

SHORTS
SHORT BROTHERS PLC

PO Box 241, Airport Road, Belfast BT3 9DZ, Northern Ireland
Telephone: 44 (232) 458444
Telex: 74688
Fax: 44 (232) 723974
OTHER FACTORIES: Newtownards, Castlereagh, Belfast (3), Dunmurry, Newtownabbey
LONDON OFFICE: Glen House, Stag Place, Victoria, London SW1E 5AG
Telephone: 44 (71) 828 9838
CHAIRMAN: Laurent Beaudoin
MANAGING DIRECTOR: R. W. R. McNulty, BA, BComm, CA
DEPUTY MANAGING DIRECTOR AND HEAD OF COMMERCIAL DIVISION: A. F. C. Roberts, OBE
HEAD OF MILITARY DIVISION: K. Brundle
HEAD OF DEFENCE SYSTEMS: C. R. Raith-Brown
HEAD OF AEROSTRUCTURES DIVISION: I. Heaton
HEAD OF MANUFACTURING DIVISION: G. Crawford
HEAD OF PUBLIC AFFAIRS: R. J. Gordon

Short Brothers were first established, as aeronauts, in 1898, and in 1901 they began the manufacture of balloons at Hove, Sussex. Works were later established in London, first at premises off Tottenham Court Road and, in 1906, at Battersea. In March 1909 Shorts opened the United Kingdom's first purpose built aircraft factory at Shellbeach, Isle of Sheppey. (The Short No. 1 had been ordered by F. T. McClean in January 1909.) The contract placed with Shorts by the Wright brothers in March 1909, for six Flyers, was the first aircraft series production contract to be placed in the world. The main aircraft works moved to Eastchurch in 1909-10, and to Rochester in 1913-14.

In June 1936 Short Brothers, in collaboration with Harland & Wolff Ltd, formed a new company known as Short & Harland Ltd to build aircraft in Belfast, and in 1947 activities were concentrated in Belfast under the name Short Bros & Harland Ltd. The name Short Brothers Ltd was re-adopted on 1 June 1977.

Up to early 1989, the UK government owned, directly or indirectly, 100 per cent of the issued shareholding. It was announced on 7 June 1989 that Bombardier of Canada had been successful in its bid to purchase Shorts. The acquisition was formally concluded on 4 October 1989. The company remains as a single entity, and retains its guided missile and UAV interests.

The company's current products include the 30-passenger Shorts 330 and 36/39-passenger Shorts 360-300 commuter airliners, in use throughout the world for passenger, freight and miscellaneous operations, and the C-23 Sherpa light military freighter. The earlier Skyvan STOL light transport has been discontinued. Following the take-over by Bombardier, Shorts is responsible for design, tooling and manufacture of the Canadair Regional Jet centre fuselage and plugs, plus other components, including flaps, ailerons, spoilerons and inboard spoilers. Deliveries were to start in July 1990.

Important collaborative agreements between Shorts and Embraer of Brazil were announced in May 1984. As a first step, Shorts is marketing and manufacturing under licence a modified version of the EMB-312 Tucano turboprop basic trainer, which was selected in March 1985 as the replacement for the Royal Air Force's Jet Provosts. The Shorts Tucano is being manufactured in the company's Shorlac (Short Light Aircraft Company) facility at the former Royal Naval Air Station Sydenham, Belfast.

The last of the refurbished Canberra PR. Mk 9s was delivered to the UK MoD in December 1989. Shorts remains a modification agency for the aircraft.

Short Brothers (Dunmurry) Ltd and SRC Composites

Shorts 330 transport aircraft on lease to the US Army Missile Range at Kwajalein Atoll, Marshall Islands

Ltd, which was acquired in October 1989, are becoming the centre for Shorts composites manufacture, including components for the 360, Sherpa, Boeing (various), Fokker 100, BAe 146, Shorts Tucano and Canberra.

Internationally, Shorts is collaborating as a risk sharing partner with Fokker in development and production of the Fokker 100, with responsibility for the wings, 25 sets of which were produced in 1989.

Shorts has produced all the main landing gear doors for the Boeing 747 and inboard trailing-edge flaps for the 757 (respectively 551 and 300 by March 1990) and received a follow-on order worth £75 million for further such components at a higher delivery rate in March 1990.

Shorts is also quality approved subcontractor to many major US and UK aerospace companies. Conversely, production of the wings for the Shorts 330/360 is undertaken jointly by CATIC of China and Fokker of the Netherlands.

During 1967, Shorts began the design and manufacture of pods for Rolls-Royce jet engines. It is currently podding RB211 engines for the Boeing 747, 757 and 767, and had produced pods for 1,340 RB211s by June 1989. Those produced for the 757 from mid-1983 utilise carbonfibre for the outer skin barrel of the nose cowl, offering a 25 per cent weight saving compared with aluminium alloy. The company also produces pods for the Textron Lycoming ALF 502 turbofans of the British Aerospace 146, and was responsible for the design and manufacture of the first flight test pod for the PW2037 turbofan chosen to power some Boeing 757s.

In September 1984 Shorts and Rohr Industries of the USA joined forces to offer a nacelle system for the advanced V2500 turbofan being developed by International Aero Engines AG for 150-seat jetliners; and in January 1985 it was announced that the Shorts/Rohr team had been selected to produce the pods for V2500 engines selected for the Airbus Industrie A320. Assembly of the pods began in 1987.

In addition to its activities in the field of piloted aircraft, Shorts is engaged in development and production of missiles and supersonic target drones, and production to

UK Ministry of Defence contract of the Skeet target drone. An agreement with McDonnell Douglas Helicopters of the USA covers adaptation of the Shorts Starstreak surface-to-air missile for airborne launch from the AH-64 Apache helicopter. Launch trials are expected to begin in late 1991.

The company's Flying Services Division operates maintenance units and airfields for various civil and military organisations, and flies and maintains aircraft and target drones for the Ministry of Defence. Short Brothers Air Services Limited, a subsidiary company, operates targets for the Ministry of Defence and provides a service for overseas countries.

SHORTS 330

The Shorts 330 is a 30-passenger twin-turboprop transport aircraft derived from the smaller Skyvan STOL utility transport, and retaining many of the latter type's well proven characteristics, including the large cabin cross-section. The first prototype (G-BSBH) flew for the first time on 22 August 1974. Eight years earlier, the first order for the 330 was placed by Command Airways of Poughkeepsie, New York, for three aircraft. CAA certification to full Transport Category requirements was granted on 18 February 1976; this was followed on 18 June 1976 by US FAR Pt 25 and Pt 36 approval, and subsequently by approvals from the Canadian Dept of Transport, the West German LBA and the Australian Dept of Transport. The 330 conforms with CAB Pt 298 (US) and meets the noise requirements of FAR Pt 36 by a substantial margin. Initial deliveries began in June 1976; first to enter service, on 24 August 1976, was a Time Air 330.

By the beginning of 1990 orders and options for all variants of the 330 (including 330-UTT and Sherpa) totalled 179 aircraft. None was built in 1989.

The first 26 Shorts 330s are powered by 875 kW (1,173 shp) PT6A-45A engines; the next 40 have PT6A-45B engines. Subsequent aircraft have more powerful PT6A-45R engines and a number of items as standard which were available only as options on the original version.

Shorts 330 twin-turboprop commuter and utility transport, with added side view (bottom) of Sherpa
(Pilot Press)

Three versions of the 330 are available:

330-200. Standard passenger version, as described in detail.

330-UTT. Military utility tactical transport version. Described separately.

Sherpa. Freighter version of 330-200, from which it differs mainly in having a ramp type full width rear loading door. In service with US Air Force and Army under designation C-23A. Described separately.

In addition, the US Army leases six ex-airline 330s, including four modified to military standards by Field Aircraft Services of Calgary, Alberta, for operation in the Kwajalein area of the Pacific.

The following description applies to the standard 330-200 passenger version:

TYPE: Twin-turboprop transport aircraft.

WINGS: Braced high-wing monoplane, of all-metal safe-life construction, built in three sections. Wing sections NACA 63A series (modified). Thickness/chord ratio 18 per cent at root, 14 per cent on outer panels. Dihedral 3° on outer panels. Centre-section, integral with top of centre-fuselage, has taper on leading- and trailing-edges, and is a two-spar single-cell box structure of light alloy with conventional skin and stringers. The strut braced outer panels, which are pin jointed to the centre-section, are reinforced Skyvan constant chord units, built of light alloy, and each consists of a two-cell box having wing skins made up of a smooth outer skin bonded to a corrugated inner skin. All-metal single-slotted ailerons. Geared trim tabs in ailerons. All-metal single-slotted flaps, each in three sections. Primary control surfaces are rod actuated. Optional Goodrich pneumatic boot de-icing of leading-edges.

FUSELAGE: Light alloy structure, built in two main portions: nose (including flight deck, nosewheel bay and forward baggage compartment); and the centre (including main wing spar attachment frames and lower transverse beams which carry the main landing gear and associated fairings) and rear portion (including aft baggage compartment and tail unit attachment frames). The nose and rear underfuselage are of conventional skin/stringer design. The remainder is composed of a smooth outer skin bonded to a corrugated inner skin and stabilised by frames.

TAIL UNIT: Cantilever all-metal two-spar structure with twin fins and rudders, basically similar to that of the Skyvan. Fixed incidence tailplane, with reinforced leading-edge. Full span elevator, aerodynamically balanced by set-back hinges. Rudders each have an unshielded horn aerodynamic balance. Primary control surfaces are rod actuated. Geared trim tabs in elevator and starboard rudder (port rudder, trim only). Optional Goodrich pneumatic boot de-icing of leading-edges.

LANDING GEAR: Menasco retractable tricycle type, with single wheel on each unit. Main units carried on short sponsons, into which the wheels retract hydraulically. Oleo-pneumatic shock absorbers. Nosewheel is steerable ±50°. Mainwheel tyre size 34 × 10.75-16; nosewheel tyre size 9-6. Normal tyre pressures: main units 5.45 bars (79 lb/sq in), nose unit 3.79 bars (55 lb/sq in).

POWER PLANT: Two 893 kW (1,198 shp) Pratt & Whitney Canada PT6A-45R turboprops, each driving a Hartzell five-blade constant-speed fully-feathering metal low-speed propeller. Fuel tanks in wing centre-section/fuselage fairing; total usable capacity increased from original 2,182 litres (576 US gallons; 480 Imp gallons) to 2,546 litres (672.5 US gallons; 560 Imp gallons) in January 1985. Normal cross-feed provisions to allow for pump failure. Single pressure refuelling point in starboard landing gear fairing, backed by three gravity refuelling points in fuselage spine.

ACCOMMODATION: Crew of two on flight deck, plus cabin attendant. Dual controls standard. Standard seating for 30 passengers, in ten rows of three at 76 cm (30 in) pitch, with wide aisle. Seat rails fitted to facilitate changes in configuration. Galley, toilet and cabin attendant's seat at rear. Large overhead baggage lockers. Entire accommo-

dation soundproofed and air-conditioned. Baggage compartments in nose (1.27 m³; 45 cu ft) and to rear of cabin (2.83 m³; 100 cu ft), each with external access and capable of holding a combined total of 500 kg (1,100 lb) of baggage. Passenger door is at rear of cabin on port side. Passenger version has two emergency exits on the starboard side, two on the port side (including passenger door) and one in the flight deck roof. Mixed traffic version has full access to these emergency exits. For mixed passenger/freight operation a partition divides the cabin into a rear passenger area (typically for 18 persons) and a forward cargo compartment, the latter being loaded through a large port side door, capable of admitting ATA 'D' type containers. In all-cargo configuration the cabin can accommodate up to seven 'D' type containers, with ample space around them for additional freight. Cabin floor is flat throughout its length, and is designed to support loadings of 181 kg (400 lb) per foot run at 610.3 kg/m² (125 lb/sq ft). Locally reinforced areas of higher strength are also provided. Seat rails can be used as cargo lashing points. Freight loading is facilitated by the low level cabin floor.

SYSTEMS: Hamilton Standard air-conditioning system, using engine bleed air. Hydraulic system of 207 bars (3,000 lb/sq in), supplied by engine driven pumps, operates landing gear, nosewheel steering, flaps and brakes (at half pressure) and includes emergency accumulators. Air/oil reservoir pressurised to 1.72 bars (25 lb/sq in) at 20°C. Main electrical system, for general services, is 28V DC and is of the split busbar type with cross-coupling for essential services. Lucas 28V 250A DC starter/generator for engine starting and aircraft services, with separate 1.5kW 200V AC output for windscreen anti-icing and demisting. Special AC sources of 115V and 26V available at 400Hz for certain instruments, avionics and fuel booster pumps. Anti-icing standard for engine intake ducts, inlet lips and propellers. Optional de-icing of wing and tailplane leading-edges.

AVIONICS AND EQUIPMENT: Passenger safety equipment standard. Wide range of radio and navigation equipment available to customer's requirements. Typical standard avionics comprise duplicated VHF communications and navigation systems, two glideslope/marker beacon receivers, two ILS repeaters, two radio magnetic indicators, one ADF, one transponder, one DME, PA system and weather radar. Flight data recorder and voice recorder available as standard options.

DIMENSIONS, EXTERNAL:

Wing span	22.76 m (74 ft 8 in)
Wing chord (standard mean)	1.85 m (6 ft 0.7 in)
Length overall	17.69 m (58 ft 0½ in)
Width of fuselage	2.24 m (7 ft 4 in)
Height overall	4.95 m (16 ft 3 in)
Tailplane span	5.68 m (18 ft 7¾ in)
Wheel track	4.24 m (13 ft 10⅞ in)
Wheelbase	6.15 m (20 ft 2 in)
Propeller diameter	2.82 m (9 ft 3 in)
Propeller ground clearance	1.83 m (6 ft 0 in)
Cabin floor: Height above ground	0.94 m (3 ft 1 in)
Passenger door (port, rear):	
Height	1.57 m (5 ft 2 in)
Width	0.71 m (2 ft 4 in)
Height to sill	0.94 m (3 ft 1 in)
Cargo door (port, forward):	
Height	1.68 m (5 ft 6 in)
Width	1.42 m (4 ft 8 in)
Height to sill	0.94 m (3 ft 1 in)

DIMENSIONS, INTERNAL:

Cabin: Max length, incl toilet	9.47 m (31 ft 1 in)
Max width	1.93 m (6 ft 4 in)
Max height	1.93 m (6 ft 4 in)
Floor area	18.77 m² (202 sq ft)
Volume (all-cargo)	34.83 m³ (1,230 cu ft)
Baggage compartments volume (total usable)	
	4.11 m³ (145 cu ft)
Cabin overhead lockers (total)	1.13 m³ (40 cu ft)

AREAS:

Wings, gross	42.1 m² (453.0 sq ft)
Ailerons (total, aft of hinges)	2.55 m² (27.5 sq ft)
Trailing-edge flaps (total)	7.74 m² (83.3 sq ft)
Fins (total)	8.65 m² (93.1 sq ft)
Rudders (total, aft of hinges)	2.24 m² (24.1 sq ft)
Tailplane (total)	7.77 m² (83.6 sq ft)
Elevator (total, aft of hinges)	2.55 m² (27.4 sq ft)

WEIGHTS AND LOADINGS:

Weight empty, equipped (incl crew of three):	
330-200 for 30 passengers	6,680 kg (14,727 lb)
Fuel	2,032 kg (4,480 lb)
Max payload for normal max T-O weight:	
30 passengers and baggage	2,653 kg (5,850 lb)
cargo	3,400 kg (7,500 lb)
Max T-O weight	10,387 kg (22,900 lb)
Max landing weight	10,251 kg (22,600 lb)
Max wing loading	246.8 kg/m² (50.55 lb/sq ft)
Max power loading	5.81 kg/kW (9.56 lb/shp)

PERFORMANCE (at max T-O weight, ISA at S/L, except where indicated):

Max cruising speed at 3,050 m (10,000 ft), AUW of 9,525 kg (21,000 lb)	190 knots (352 km/h; 218 mph)
Econ cruising speed at 3,050 m (10,000 ft), AUW of 9,525 kg (21,000 lb)	160 knots (296 km/h; 184 mph)
Stalling speed, flaps and landing gear up	90 knots (167 km/h; 104 mph) EAS
Stalling speed at max landing weight, flaps and landing gear down	73 knots (136 km/h; 85 mph) EAS
Max rate of climb at S/L	360 m (1,180 ft)/min
Service ceiling, one engine out, AUW of 9,072 kg (20,000lb)	3,500 m (11,500 ft)
Min ground turning radius about nosewheel	7.77 m (25 ft 6 in)
T-O distance (FAR Pt 25 and BCAR Gp A):	
ISA	1,042 m (3,420 ft)
ISA + 15°C	1,295 m (4,250 ft)
Landing distance, AUW of 9,072 kg (20,000 lb):	
BCAR	1,143 m (3,750 ft)
FAR	1,030 m (3,380 ft)
Runway LCN at max T-O weight	10.7
Range with max passenger payload, cruising at 3,050 m (10,000 ft), no reserves	473 nm (876 km; 544 miles)
Range with max fuel, cruising at 3,050 m (10,000 ft), no reserves:	
passenger version, 1,966 kg (4,335 lb) payload	915 nm (1,695 km; 1,053 miles)
cargo version, 2,306 kg (5,085 lb) payload	758 nm (1,403 km; 872 miles)

OPERATIONAL NOISE LEVELS (FAR Pt 36):

Take-off	88.9 EPNdB
Sideline	84.7 EPNdB
Approach	92.9 EPNdB

SHORTS 330-UTT

Shorts stated on 7 September 1982 that production had begun of this military utility tactical transport version of the Model 330. The Royal Thai Army took delivery of two (one in June 1984 and one in March 1985). The Royal Thai Border Police took two (in October 1984 and April 1985) and now operate also one of the Army UTTs.

The basic airframe and power plant remain unchanged, but max payload is increased to 3,630 kg (8,000 lb) and max operational necessity T-O weight to 11,158 kg (24,600 lb). Other changes include a strengthened cabin floor and reconfigured avionics panel. Cabin accommodation can be provided for up to 33 troops, 30 paratroops plus a jumpmaster (exit via inward opening rear door each side), or 15 stretchers plus four seated personnel.

PERFORMANCE:

Cruising speed at 3,050 m (10,000 ft), AUW of 9,979 kg (22,000 lb):	
high-speed cruise, max continuous power	201 knots (372 km/h; 231 mph)
long-range cruise	160 knots (296 km/h; 184 mph)
Max rate of climb at S/L at normal max T-O weight of 10,387 kg (22,900 lb):	
two engines	381 m (1,250 ft)/min
one engine	89 m (290 ft)/min
STOL T-O run at S/L, 15° flap	415 m (1,360 ft)
STOL T-O to 15 m (50 ft), 15° flap	644 m (2,110 ft)
STOL landing from 15 m (50 ft) at AUW of 9,525 kg (21,000 lb), flaps down, propeller reversal	488 m (1,600 ft)
STOL landing run, conditions as above	235 m (770 ft)
Range with 30 fully armed assault troops	600 nm (1,112 km; 691 miles)

SHORTS SHERPA
US Air Force designation: C-23A

The Sherpa is a freighter version of the Shorts 330-200. It retains many features of the all-passenger version, to allow utility passenger transport. The forward freight door and wide-body hold of the 330-200 are unchanged, but the Sherpa's design incorporates a full width rear cargo door, which permits through loading.

The hydraulically actuated rear ramp/door, which is operated from inside or outside the aircraft, can be lowered to a variety of positions to simplify loading from a wide range of ground equipment. The forward baggage compartment of the Shorts 330-200 is retained and this, being lockable, is suitable for high value cargo. Standard airline containers can be accommodated in the main cabin, up to the size of the LD3, making the Sherpa particularly suited for the operation of short-haul cargo feeder services. Typical loads can include two LD3 containers and nine passengers; four LD3 or seven CO8 containers; two half ton vehicles in the class of the Land-Rover, using load spreaders; and a wide range of bulky cargo. The cabin is suitable for the installation of specialist role equipment and, for example, lends itself readily to onboard sorting of letters and small packages. Roller conveyor systems, including pallet locks which pick up on the aircraft's standard seat rails, are available optionally (standard on the C-23A).

The prototype of the Sherpa was flown for the first time on 23 December 1982. In March 1984 the US Air Force ordered 18 Sherpas for use by the 10th Military Airlift Squadron of Military Airlift Command in the EDSA (European Distribution System Aircraft) role. The fleet is based at Zweibrücken in West Germany, for the transport of high priority spares between more than 20 peacetime US Air Force bases in Europe. The initial contract included ten years' logistic support and servicing. In addition, the US Air Force took options on a further 48 aircraft, which were extended in November 1986 for a further four years.

The first Sherpa, designated C-23A in the EDSA role, made its first flight on 6 August 1984; with the second aircraft, it was delivered in November 1984. The remaining 16 C-23As were delivered by 6 December 1985. Shorts' contractor logistics support (CLS) for these aircraft has consistently been rated as 'outstanding'.

In October 1988, the company was awarded a contract by the US Department of the Army to supply 10 C-23 Sherpa aircraft to the Army National Guard to replace elderly DHC-4 Caribous. Their main role will be to transport army aviation spares and components between ArNG bases and Aviation Classification Repair Activity Depots. The multi-role light military freighters can also be deployed in passenger transport, paratrooping and freight paradropping roles, and although similar to the USAF C-23s will embody the strengthened wings, more powerful PT6A-65AR turboprops and five-blade propellers of the Shorts 360 Advanced regional airliner. These aircraft will also have uprated landing gear, more advanced flight deck instrumentation and air-operable rear freight doors for supply dropping. The upper section of the ramp will retract inward and upward, while the bottom section will lower to provide a drop platform. Max payload is increased to 3,302 kg (7,280 lb). Deliveries to the ArNG were to begin in 1990.

A civilian-registered Sherpa was delivered to the Venezuelan government to support hydro-electric power development schemes. It was joined in 1988 by a Shorts 360-300.

The following details apply to the USAF C-23A:

TYPE: Twin-turboprop freight/utility aircraft.

AIRFRAME AND POWER PLANT: As described for Shorts 330-200 except for constant width rear fuselage with hydraulically actuated rear loading ramp/door.

ACCOMMODATION: Crew of two on flight deck, plus flight mechanic. Dual controls standard. Flight deck air-conditioned. Main cabin air-conditioning optional. Baggage compartment in nose (1.27 m³; 45 cu ft) with external access. Passenger door at rear of cabin on port side. Cargo door at front of cabin on port side. Hydraulically actuated full width rear loading ramp/door. In an all-cargo configuration the cabin can accommodate up to seven CO8 or four LD3 containers. Cabin floor is flat throughout its length and is designed to support 181 kg (400 lb) per foot run at 610.3 kg/m² (125 lb/sq ft). The locally reinforced centre cabin area is able to carry 272 kg (600 lb) per foot run at 732.4 kg/m² (150 lb/sq ft). A further 272 kg (600 lb) total load can be stowed on the ramp/door. Seat rails can be used as cargo lashing points. Freight loading is facilitated by the low level cabin floor. Alternative loads as Shorts 330-UTT.

AVIONICS AND EQUIPMENT: Avionics on the C-23As for the US Air Force include single UHF and HF radios, dual VHF-AM/FM, two flight directors, dual VOR/ILS, a Litton LTN-96 ring laser gyro inertial navigation system, Tacan, dual ADF, flight data recorder, cockpit voice recorder, IFF transponder, GPWS, radar altimeter, and a Collins RNS-300 colour weather radar with terrain mapping.

DIMENSIONS, EXTERNAL: As for 330-200 plus:
Rear loading door: Height	1.98 m (6 ft 6 in)
Width	1.98 m (6 ft 6 in)

DIMENSIONS, INTERNAL:
Cabin: Max length	9.09 m (29 ft 10 in)
Max width	1.98 m (6 ft 6 in)
Max height	1.98 m (6 ft 6 in)
Volume (all-cargo)	35.68 m³ (1,260 cu ft)
Baggage compartment (nose)	1.27 m³ (45 cu ft)

WEIGHTS AND LOADINGS (C-23A):
Max T-O weight	11,566 kg (25,500 lb)
Max ramp weight	11,612 kg (25,600 lb)
Max landing weight	11,340 kg (25,000 lb)
Max payload	3,220 kg (7,100 lb)
Max nose baggage load	227 kg (500 lb)

PERFORMANCE (C-23A at max T-O weight, ISA, except where indicated):
Max cruising speed at AUW of 9,525 kg (21,000 lb) at 3,050 m (10,000 ft)	190 knots (352 km/h; 218 mph)

Econ cruising speed at AUW of 9,525 kg (21,000 lb) at 3,050 m (10,000 ft) 157 knots (291 km/h; 181 mph)
Max rate of climb at S/L 360 m (1,180 ft)/min
Service ceiling, one engine out, AUW of 9,072 kg (20,000lb) 3,930 m (12,900 ft)
T-O run (at 11,566 kg; 25,500 lb) 561 m (1,840 ft)
T-O to 15 m (50 ft) 796 m (2,610 ft)
Landing from 15 m (50 ft) (at 11,566 kg; 25,500 lb) 579 m (1,900 ft)
Landing run 342 m (1,120 ft)
Range with max fuel, reserves for 45 min hold and 43 nm (80 km; 50 mile) diversion:
with 3,175 kg (7,000 lb) payload 195 nm (362 km; 225 miles)
with 2,268 kg (5,000 lb) payload 669 nm (1,239 km; 770 miles)

SHORTS 360-300

On 10 July 1980, Shorts released first details of the Model 360 stretched development of the Model 330, seating six more passengers in a lengthened fuselage and having strengthened outer wing panels and bracing struts, and a new tail unit, as well as more powerful and more fuel-efficient engines.

Designed specifically for short haul airline operation, over typical commuter average stage lengths of about 120 nm (222 km; 138 miles), the Shorts 360 retains the basic configuration of the Model 330, the major external differences being the lengthened fuselage (a 0.91 m; 3 ft plug is inserted forward of the wings) and the introduction of a sweptback single fin and rudder instead of the latter's twin assembly. Power plant is a higher rated version of the proven PT6A turboprop.

Pressurisation was considered unnecessary in view of the short stage lengths over which the aircraft would operate, and this enables the Shorts 360 to retain the same 'walkabout' headroom, square section wide-bodied interior, seating comfort, air-conditioning and other amenities as its predecessor. The new rear fuselage/tail configuration is designed to reduce drag, improve fuel efficiency, and provide even greater baggage capacity. Considerable emphasis is placed on the 360's ability to provide more than 0.20 m³ (7 cu ft) of baggage space for each of its 36 passengers.

The prototype (G-ROOM) made its first flight on 1 June 1981, some six months ahead of schedule, powered initially by PT6A-45 engines. The PT6A-65R power plant which had been selected for production aircraft was installed subsequently, and CAA certification was obtained on 3

September 1982. FAA certification, to FAR Pt 25 and Pt 36, followed in early November 1982. The first production 360 made its first flight on 19 August 1982, and entered commercial service with Suburban Airlines of Pennsylvania on 1 December 1982.

From November 1985, manufacture turned to the Shorts 360 Advanced, which was powered by two 1,062 kW (1,424 shp) PT6A-65AR turboprops. This has been superseded by the current variant, the **Shorts 360-300**.

Several enhancements are featured by the Series 300, including six-blade propellers with synchrophasing, new cambered wing lift struts, and engine nacelles with low-drag exhaust stubs. New lightweight seats offer improved passenger comfort and reduced maintenance. The improved power plant provides an increase in maximum cruising speed and substantially improved weight/altitude/temperature limits, giving better hot and high performance and an improved en-route climb performance, and permitting an increased maximum take-off weight.

Optional extras include a Category II autopilot, reclining seats, a wet sink facility in the toilet, a supplementary ground air-conditioning system, and protective liners for freight operations.

The first two Shorts 360-300 airliners, accepted by Philippine Airlines on 18 March 1987, represented part of an order for four being supplied under operating leases from the Shannon based GPA Jetprop company. In October 1987, Capital Airlines of the UK began operations with the first Shorts 360-300 to be certificated for the carriage of 39 passengers.

By January 1990 orders and options for all versions of the Shorts 360 totalled 170, of which 164 had been delivered, including 14 in 1988.

TYPE: Twin-turboprop commuter transport.

WINGS: Generally as for Shorts 330-200.

FUSELAGE: As Shorts 330-200, but lengthened by 0.91 m (3ft) forward of wings. Rear fuselage modified to cater for redesigned tail unit.

TAIL UNIT: Cantilever all-metal two-spar structure, with single sweptback fin and rudder and constant chord non-swept tailplane. Trim tabs in each elevator. Heavy-duty floor panels for freight handling in Series 300.

LANDING GEAR: Similar to Shorts 330-200, but of Dowty design with Dunlop tyres. Mainwheel tyres size 37 × 11.75-16, pressure 5.38 bars (78 lb/sq in). Maxaret anti-skid units standard. Nosewheel steerable ± 55°.

POWER PLANT: Two 1,062 kW (1,424 shp) Pratt & Whitney Canada PT6A-67R turboprops, each driving a Hartzell advanced technology six-blade constant-speed fully-feathering propeller with spinner. New engine nacelles

Shorts C-23A Sherpa in US Air Force service

Shorts 360-300 commuter transport (two P&WC PT6A-67R turboprop engines) *(Pilot Press)*

Shorts 360-300 commuter transport operated by Formosa Airlines

with low-drag exhaust stubs on Series 300. Fuel capacity 2,182 litres (576 US gallons; 480 Imp gallons).

ACCOMMODATION: Crew of two on flight deck, plus cabin attendant. Dual controls standard. Main cabin accommodation similar to Shorts 330-200, but seating 36 passengers in 12 rows of three (optionally, 39 passengers). Standard ground and in-flight air conditioning. Large overhead baggage lockers. Baggage compartments in nose and to rear of cabin, each with external access, giving equivalent of almost 0.17 m³ (6 cu ft) of baggage space per passenger (0.20 m³; 7.2 cu ft per passenger if locker space is included). Self-contained passenger stairs.

SYSTEMS: Generally as for Shorts 330-200 except for electrical system, which has Lear Siegler 28V 300A DC starter/generators and three 400VA single-phase static inverters for AC power. Full de-icing and anti-icing systems standard.

AVIONICS: From Collins Pro Line II range, including dual FDS-65 flight director systems, dual VHF-21A com, dual VIR-32 VHF nav, dual DME-42, dual TDR-90 transponders, dual RMI-36, ADF-60A, dual MCS-65 magnetic compasses, and WXR-220 colour weather radar, plus Sundstrand Mk II GPWS, Honeywell YG7500 radar altimeter, Fairchild A100A voice recorder and Plessey PV1584G data recorder. Options include Collins HF-230 HF com, APS-65 Cat II autopilot and second ADF.

DIMENSIONS, EXTERNAL: As for Shorts 330-200 except:

Wing span	22.80 m (74 ft 9½ in)
Length overall	21.58 m (70 ft 9⅝ in)
Height overall	7.27 m (23 ft 10¼ in)
Tailplane span	7.19 m (23 ft 7 in)
Wheelbase	7.06 m (23 ft 2 in)
Propeller diameter	2.74 m (9 ft 0 in)
Propeller ground clearance	1.78 m (5 ft 10 in)
Rear door sill height	0.98 m (3 ft 2¼ in)

DIMENSIONS, INTERNAL:

Cabin: Length	11.02 m (36 ft 2 in)
Max width	1.93 m (6 ft 4 in)
Max height	1.93 m (6 ft 4 in)
Passenger compartment volume	41.06 m³ (1,450 cu ft)
Baggage compartment volume:	
forward	1.27 m³ (45 cu ft)
rear	4.81 m³ (170 cu ft)
lockers	1.47 m³ (52 cu ft)

AREAS: As for Shorts 330-200 except:

Wings, gross	42.18 m² (454 sq ft)
Vertical tail surfaces (total)	8.49 m² (91.4 sq ft)
Horizontal tail surfaces (total)	9.85 m² (106.0 sq ft)

WEIGHTS:

Typical operating weight empty	7,870 kg (17,350 lb)
Max payload:	
36 passengers and baggage	3,184 kg (7,020 lb)
cargo	3,765 kg (8,300 lb)
Max fuel load	1,741 kg (3,840 lb)
Max T-O weight	12,292 kg (27,100 lb)
Max ramp weight	12,337 kg (27,200 lb)
Max landing weight	12,020 kg (26,500 lb)

PERFORMANCE (to FAR Pt 25: at max T-O weight except where indicated):

Cruising speed at 3,050 m (10,000 ft) and 11,340 kg (25,000 lb) aircraft weight	
	216 knots (400 km/h; 249 mph)
Max rate of climb at S/L: ISA	290 m (952 ft)/min
ISA +15°C	282 m (925 ft)/min
Single-engine ceiling	2,665 m (8,750 ft)
Min ground turning radius about nosewheel	
	8.21 m (26 ft 11 in)
Balanced T-O field length: ISA	1,305 m (4,280 ft)
ISA +15°C	1,402 m (4,600 ft)
Landing distance at max landing weight:	
ISA	1,220 m (4,000 ft)

Runway LCN	14.1

Range at 3,050 m (10,000 ft), cruising at 216 knots (400 km/h; 249 mph), 50 nm (93 km; 57 mile) diversion, 45 min hold, 54 kg (119 lb) fuel allowance, 36 passengers with baggage at 86 kg (190 lb) each
402 nm (745 km; 463 miles)
Range as above at 182 knots (337 km/h; 210 mph) with 31 passengers with baggage
636 nm (1,178 km; 732 miles)

SHORTS 360-300F

Capitalising on the 360's low noise levels (well within FAR Pt 36 and ICAO Annex 16), Shorts is promoting an all-freight adaptation of the 360-300 directed towards the overnight parcels market. The 360-300F was originally proposed with a windowless cargo hold and a large rear freight door. In present form, and as purchased (two aircraft delivered from March 1989) by the initial customer, Rheinland Air Service of Dusseldorf, West Germany, it is basically similar to the standard 360-300. Up to 4,536 kg (10,000 lb) of payload may be carried. Optional modifications include enlargement of the port forward cargo door to enable five LD3-size containers to be loaded aboard. This will be retrospectively embodied in the Rheinland AS aircraft, once certification has been achieved. In addition, an integrated handling system is available in the form of a roller conveyor with pallet locks; directional transfer mat; side guidance rails; and a forward cargo restraint barrier.

SHORTS S312 TUCANO
RAF designation: Tucano T. Mk 1

Under the terms of a co-operation agreement between Shorts and Embraer of Brazil, announced in May 1984, Shorts undertook to develop from the basic EMB-312 Tucano (see Embraer entry in Brazilian section) a new version of the turboprop trainer that would meet or exceed all requirements of the UK Ministry of Defence Air Staff Target 412 for a Jet Provost replacement.

The UK Government announced on 21 March 1985 that the Shorts Tucano had been selected for this role. The decision ended a competition that had lasted two years. The

decisive consideration, according to the UK Secretary of State for Defence, was the "cost factor", the Shorts offer being the least expensive "by a clear margin". Initially, 130 Tucanos are being built for the Royal Air Force.

To exceed Air Staff Target 412, the Shorts Tucano embodies significant modifications compared with the basic EMB-312. These include a changed power plant to improve speed, particularly at low altitude, and provide an increased rate of climb; a ventral airbrake to control speed during descent; structural strengthening for increased manoeuvre loads and fatigue life; a new cockpit layout to meet RAF requirements; and wide use of UK equipment. For export sales purposes, the design incorporates four wing strong-points to provide armament training and light attack capability. The Shorts Tucano has a safe design fatigue life of 12,000 hours.

The first flight of a Tucano with a Garrett engine (PP-ZTC), as chosen for the RAF version, took place in Brazil on 14 February 1986. After completing 14.35 hours of test flying there, it was airfreighted to the UK, reassembled in Belfast, and made its first flight with a British test flight serial (G-14-007, later G-BTUC) on 11 April 1986. The first Shorts-built production Tucano T. Mk 1 (ZF135) flew on 30 December 1986, although the formal rollout ceremony did not take place until 20 January 1987. It was delivered to the Aeroplane & Armament Experimental Establishment at Boscombe Down on 26 June 1987, followed on 1 October 1987 by ZF136, both being engaged on provisional type certification trials. Deliveries to the RAF began with ZF138 to the Central Flying School (CFS) at Scampton on 16 June 1988, and formal hand-over of the first aircraft took place on 1 September 1988. Flying by the Tucano Course Design Team (part of the CFS) began in early August 1988.

Following instructor conversion, student flying on the Tucano began at No. 7 FTS, Church Fenton, in December 1989, on the first of 25 aircraft assigned to the school. Following disbandment of the Design Team in November 1989, the future Tucano Squadron of CFS was building to an establishment of 15. Deliveries of 30 Tucanos to No. 3 FTS at RAF College, Cranwell, were scheduled to begin in October 1990, followed by 39 to No. 1 FTS at Linton-on-Ouse in 1991. Final recipients will be the

Shorts S312 Tucano basic trainer (Garrett TPE331-12B turboprop) *(Pilot Press)*

Refresher Flying Flight at Church Fenton and navigator school, No. 6 FTS at Finningley, where approximately nine are required.

The baseline Tucano course is 146 h 30 min (1 h less than the Jet Provost syllabus), for students who have received prior piston-engined training of 30-60 hours. They then progress to Hawks for advanced training and weapons instruction. Helicopter pilots receive only 63½ Tucano hours, and future multi-engine pilots terminate the Tucano phase at 140 hours. Estimates indicate that the Tucano will have direct operating costs only 49 per cent of those of the Jet Provost. Shorts is responsible for logistic supplies at RAF stations operating the Tucano. Maintenance contracts are assigned individually by base: Airwork at Church Fenton and Field Aircraft at Cranwell. Five Ferranti simulators are being delivered from 1990 onwards to Church Fenton (one), Cranwell (two) and Linton (two). Following changes introduced on the production line, Shorts was contracted in January 1990 to modify the first 50 Tucanos with strengthened flying controls, revised communications/navigation equipment and structural changes to extend fatigue life.

Two overseas contracts have been received for the Shorts Tucano. Kenya placed an order for 12 **T. Mk 51s** in 1988, and in February 1989 a contract was signed with the Kuwait Ministry of Defence for 16 **T. Mk 52s** and support equipment, including a flight simulator. The first Kenyan aircraft (temporarily ZH203) flew on 11 October 1989. Kenyan Tucanos will be armed and used for weapons training. By 31 December 1989, 38 Shorts Tucanos had flown, including one for export.

The main description of the Tucano can be found under the Embraer heading in the Brazilian section, although UK aircraft have only 25 per cent commonality. The Shorts Tucano T. Mk 1 for the RAF differs in the following respects:

WINGS: Incidence 1° 13′. Aluminium alloy two-spar torsion box structure of 7075-T73511 and 7075-T76 and 2024-T3 sheet. Leading-edge strengthened for bird strike protection.

FUSELAGE: Hydraulically actuated ventral airbrake.

LANDING GEAR: Nosewheel unit supplied by Fairey Hydraulics. Dunlop wheels and tyres, size 22 × 6.75-10 on mainwheels, 5.00-5 on nosewheel. Dunlop hydraulic single-disc brakes on mainwheels.

POWER PLANT: One 820 kW (1,100 shp) Garrett TPE331-12B turboprop, driving a Hartzell four-blade constant-speed fully-feathering reversible-pitch propeller with spinner. Additional 38 kW (51 ehp) derived from exhaust. Two integral fuel tanks in each wing, total capacity 694 litres (183.3 US gallons; 152.7 Imp gallons). Gravity refuelling point in each wing upper surface. Provision for two external tanks with total capacity of 660 litres (174 US gallons; 145 Imp gallons). Oil capacity 4.25 litres (1.13 US gallons; 0.94 Imp gallon).

ACCOMMODATION: Instructor and pupil in tandem, on Martin-Baker Mk 8LCP lightweight ejection seats under Lucas canopy. No pressurisation: practical service ceiling 7,620 m (25,000 ft).

SYSTEMS: Cockpit air-conditioning by engine bleed air plus recirculated cockpit air through a regenerative turbofan system. Alternative freon system available for hot climates. Single hydraulic system, pressure 207 bars

Shorts Tucano T. Mk 1 of the RAF's Central Flying School with ventral airbrake extended *(Paul Jackson)*

(3,000 lb/sq in), for landing gear extension and retraction, and airbrake. Accumulator to lower landing gear in emergency. DC electrical power provided by a 28V 200A starter/generator and two 24Ah alkaline batteries. Static inverter for 115V and 26V AC power at 400Hz. Normalair-Garrett oxygen system supplied from a single bottle, capacity 2,250 litres (80 cu ft). Emergency oxygen bottle, capacity 70 litres (2.5 cu ft), mounted on each ejection seat. Engine air intake de-iced by engine bleed air; propeller, pitot head, static vents, and stall warning system de-iced electrically. Optional windscreen anti-icing.

AVIONICS AND EQUIPMENT: Standard avionics include VHF/UHF/audio by Marconi, Plessey and Dowty; gyromagnetic compass, VOR/ILS/marker beacon receiver, GEC Sensors AD2780 Tacan, and Narco transponder.

ARMAMENT: Optional provision on export variant for up to 454 kg (1,000 lb) of weapons distributed on four underwing pylons fitted with ML Aviation ejector release units. Details as for Embraer Tucano. Equipment specified for Kenya includes FN Herstal rocket pods and Forges de Zeebrugge 12.7 mm gun pods; and an ML Aviation stores management system, including Avimo weapon sights, Base Ten weapon control electronics and other equipment from Dowty and Guardian Electronics. Guardian Electronics.

DIMENSIONS, EXTERNAL:

Wing span	11.28 m (37 ft 0 in)
Propeller diameter	2.39 m (7 ft 10 in)
Propeller ground clearance	0.32 m (12.6 in)

AREAS:

Wings, gross	19.33 m² (208.08 sq ft)
Fin, excl dorsal fin	2.08 m² (22.40 sq ft)
Rudder, incl tab	1.46 m² (15.70 sq ft)
Tailplane, incl fillets	4.57 m² (49.20 sq ft)

WEIGHTS AND LOADINGS (A, aerobatic configuration; B, full weapons configuration):

Basic weight empty: A	2,017 kg (4,447 lb)
Max internal fuel: A, B	555 kg (1,223 lb)
Max ramp weight: A	2,900 kg (6,393 lb)
B	3,520 kg (7,760 lb)

Max T-O weight: A	2,900 kg (6,393 lb)
B	3,500 kg (7,716 lb)
Max landing weight: A	2,700 kg (5,952 lb)
B	2,900 kg (6,393 lb)
Max zero-fuel weight: A	2,110 kg (4,652 lb)
Max wing loading: A	139.7 kg/m² (28.61 lb/sq ft)
Max power loading: A	3.29 kg/kW (5.41 lb/shp)

PERFORMANCE (at T-O weight of 2,700 kg; 5,952 lb, except where indicated):

Never-exceed speed	
	300 knots (556 km/h; 345 mph) EAS
Max level and cruising speed at 3,050-4,575 m (10,000-15,000 ft) at 2,600 kg (5,732 lb)	
	274 knots (507 km/h; 315 mph)
Normal cruising speed (RAF)	
	240 knots (448 km/h; 276 mph)
Econ cruising speed at 6,100 m (20,000 ft)	
	220 knots (407 km/h; 253 mph)
Stalling speed, power off:	
flaps and landing gear up	
	75 knots (139 km/h; 87 mph) EAS
flaps and landing gear down	
	69 knots (128 km/h; 80 mph) EAS
Max rate of climb at S/L	1,070 m (3,510 ft)/min
Service ceiling	10,365 m (34,000 ft)
T-O run	308 m (1,010 ft)
T-O to 15 m (50 ft)	533 m (1,750 ft)
Landing from 15 m (50 ft) at 2,600 kg (5,732 lb)	
	585 m (1,920 ft)
Landing run	314 m (1,030 ft)
Radius of action with 454 kg (1,000 lb) of weapons at T-O weight of 3,275 kg (7,220 lb) with 5 min over target	
	390 nm (722 km; 449 miles)
Range at 7,620 m (25,000 ft) with max fuel, 30 min reserves:	
internal fuel only	900 nm (1,665 km; 1,035 miles)
with external fuel	1,790 nm (3,317 km; 2,061 miles)
Endurance at econ cruising speed at 7,620 m (25,000 ft), 30 min reserves	5 h 12 min
g limits:	+7/−3.6 aerobatic
	+4.4/−2.2 full weapons

SLINGSBY
SLINGSBY AVIATION LIMITED

Ings Lane, Kirkbymoorside, North Yorkshire YO6 6EZ
Telephone: 44 (751) 32474
Telex: 57597 SLINAV G
Fax: 44 (751) 31173

MANAGING DIRECTOR:
James S. Tucker, BSc (Eng), CEng, MRAeS
CHIEF DESIGNER: B. Mellers
MARKETING DIRECTOR, AIRCRAFT: John C. Dignan
PRODUCT SUPPORT MANAGER: Roger C. Bull, BSc (Eng)

Slingsby, formerly a manufacturer of sailplanes, is concentrating on development and production of the T67 two-seat aerobatic trainer aircraft. The company, which is a subsidiary of the Aerospace and Defence division of ML Holdings PLC, specialises in the application of modern composite materials, and is involved in the design and manufacture of hovercraft, large wind turbines for electricity generation and various marine structures and components. Slingsby is responsible for manufacture of the gondola, propulsion ducts, flying control surfaces, nosecone and battens of the Airship Industries Skyship 600 airships, and is also the main subcontractor to the Westinghouse Airship Industries consortium for the design and manufacture of the nosecone, battens, tail fins and control surfaces of the Sentinel 5000 airship (which see) for the US Navy.

Other subcontract work includes the design and development of carbonfibre components for the Bell/Boeing V-22 Osprey tilt-rotor aircraft, and metal assemblies for the Boeing 747.

MoD work includes technical support and repair and maintenance facilities for the RAF Air Cadets fleet of gliders and motor gliders, including a full-scale dynamic fatigue test of the Grob Viking sailplane, and re-covering

and painting of Chipmunk aircraft for the RAF, Royal Navy and Army Air Corps.

Slingsby is a major participant in the Chichester-Miles Leopard four-seat business jet project, with responsibility for building the composite airframe of the second prototype.

In early 1990, the firm's covered works area was approx 9,290 m² (100,000 sq ft) and it had a workforce of 230.

SLINGSBY T67 FIREFLY

The original T67A was a licence built version of the Fournier RF6B light aircraft. Production by Fournier, in France, was limited to 45 RF6B-100s and a single RF6B-120, which flew for the first time on 14 August 1980 and received FAR Pt 23 certification on 7 November 1980. Slingsby built ten T67As (similar to the RF6B-120), of which the first (G-BIOW) flew for the first time on 15 May 1981. This model, which was described in the 1982-83 *Jane's,* has been superseded by new Firefly versions, built primarily of GFRP instead of wood, including the military T67M (described separately). To speed the T67M programme, a T67A (G-BJNG) was modified to Firefly 160 standard by installation of a 119 kW (160 hp) engine and constant-speed propeller for tests that included spinning trials at extreme CG limits.

Current versions for civil use are as follows:

T67B. Basic version, of GFRP construction. Powered by an 86.5 kW (116 hp) Textron Lycoming O-235-N2A flat-four engine driving a two-blade fixed-pitch propeller with spinner. Received CAA certification 18 September 1984.

T67C. As T67B, but with 119 kW (160 hp) Textron Lycoming AEIO-320-D1B, metal fixed-pitch propeller, 24V 70A engine driven alternator and 24V 12Ah battery..

Received CAA certification 15 December 1987. Three sub-variants are available, all of which are certificated under the T67C designation: **T67C1** with normal fuselage fuel tank and one-piece canopy; **T67C2** with fuselage fuel and two-piece canopy; and **T67C3**, having wing fuel tanks and two-piece canopy.

By January 1990 more than 80 civil and military T67s had been delivered to customers in 10 countries. The military versions are described separately.

The following details apply to the T67C:

TYPE: Two-seat aerobatic, training and sporting aircraft.

WINGS: Cantilever low-wing monoplane. Wing section NACA 23015 at root, NACA 23013 at tip. Dihedral 3° 30′. Incidence 3°. Constructed entirely of GFRP. Single-spar structure, double skin comprising a plain outer skin to which is bonded a corrugated inner skin. Conventional ribs are used in positions of load concentration. Mass balanced Frise-type ailerons of GFRP construction with no tabs, operated manually through pushrods. Trailing-edge fixed hinge flaps of GFRP construction.

FUSELAGE: Oval section GFRP fuselage of conventional frame and top-hat stringer construction with a stainless steel firewall between cockpit and engine installation.

TAIL UNIT: Conventional fixed incidence GFRP tailplane of cantilever construction with single spar, having same skin construction as the wings. Tailplane incorporates a built-in VOR antenna. Fully mass balanced elevator with manually operated trim tab in port elevator. Fixed fin incorporating built-in VHF antenna. Conventional rudder. Spin strakes forward of tailplane roots.

LANDING GEAR: Non-retractable tricycle type. Oleo-pneumatic shock absorber in each unit. Steerable nosewheel. Mainwheel tyres size 6.00-6, pressure 1.4 bars (20 lb/sq in). Nosewheel tyre size 5.00-5, pressure 2.5 bars

(37 lb/sq in). Hydraulic disc brakes. Parking brake. GFRP mainwheel fairings optional.

POWER PLANT: One flat-four engine as described in model listings. Fuselage fuel tank, immediately aft of firewall, in T67C1 and T67C2, capacity 114 litres (30 US gallons; 25 Imp gallons). Refuelling point on fuselage upper surface, forward of windscreen. T67C3: wing fuel tanks as T67M. Oil capacity 4 litres (1.06 US gallons; 0.88 Imp gallon). Oil system permits short periods of inverted flight.

ACCOMMODATION: Two seats side by side, originally (T67C1) under one-piece transparent canopy, which swings upward and rearward for access to cockpit. T67C2/C3 have fixed windscreen, and rearward hinged and upward opening rear section. Dual controls standard. Adjustable rudder pedals. Cockpit heated and ventilated. Baggage space aft of seats.

SYSTEMS: Hydraulic system for brakes only. Vacuum system for blind-flying instrumentation. Electrical power supplied by 24V engine driven alternator and 24V 15Ah battery. (12V system in T67B.)

AVIONICS AND EQUIPMENT: Standard equipment includes artificial horizon and directional gyro, with vacuum system and vacuum gauge, electric turn co-ordinator, rate of climb indicator, recording tachometer, stall warning system, clock, outside air temperature gauge, accelerometer; cabin fire extinguisher, crash axe, heated pitot; instrument, landing, navigation and strobe lights; tiedown rings and towbar. Optional avionics, available to customer requirements, include equipment by Becker, Bendix/King and Narco, up to full IFR standard. Optional equipment includes T67M-type blue tinted canopy, external power socket (not on T67B), and wingtip mounted smoke system (not T67B).

DIMENSIONS, EXTERNAL:
Wing span	10.59 m (34 ft 9 in)
Wing chord: at root	1.53 m (5 ft 0¼ in)
at tip	0.83 m (2 ft 8¾ in)
Wing aspect ratio	8.9
Length overall	7.32 m (24 ft 0¼ in)
Height overall	2.36 m (7 ft 9 in)
Tailplane span	3.40 m (11 ft 1¾ in)
Wheel track	2.44 m (8 ft 0 in)
Wheelbase	1.50 m (4 ft 11 in)
Propeller diameter	1.88 m (6 ft 2 in)

DIMENSIONS, INTERNAL:
Cockpit: Length	2.05 m (6 ft 8¾ in)
Max width	1.08 m (3 ft 6½ in)
Max height	1.08 m (3 ft 6½ in)

AREAS:
Wings, gross	12.63 m² (136.0 sq ft)
Ailerons (total)	1.24 m² (13.35 sq ft)
Trailing-edge flaps (total)	1.74 m² (18.73 sq ft)
Fin	0.80 m² (8.61 sq ft)
Rudder	0.82 m² (8.8 sq ft)
Tailplane	1.65 m² (17.76 sq ft)
Elevators (incl tab)	0.99 m² (10.66 sq ft)

WEIGHTS AND LOADINGS:
Weight empty (basic): T67B	610 kg (1,345 lb)
T67C2	649 kg (1,430 lb)
T67C3	658 kg (1,450 lb)
Max fuel: T67B, T67C1/C2	82 kg (181 lb)
T67C3	114 kg (252 lb)
Max baggage: T67B	18 kg (40 lb)
T67C	30 kg (66 lb)
Max T-O, landing and aerobatic weights:	
T67B	862 kg (1,900 lb)
T67C2	907 kg (2,000 lb)
T67C3	952 kg (2,100 lb)
Max wing loading: T67B	68.21 kg/m² (13.97 lb/sq ft)
T67C2	71.82 kg/m² (14.71 lb/sq ft)
T67C3	75.38 kg/m² (15.44 lb/sq ft)
Max power loading: T67B	9.97 kg/kW (16.38 lb/hp)
T67C2	7.62 kg/kW (12.50 lb/hp)
T67C3	8.00 kg/kW (13.13 lb/hp)

PERFORMANCE (at max T-O weight):
Never-exceed speed:	
T67B	165 knots (305 km/h; 190 mph)
T67C	180 knots (333 km/h; 207 mph)
Max level speed at S/L:	
T67B	115 knots (213 km/h; 132 mph)
T67C	133 knots (246 km/h; 153 mph)
Max cruising speed (75% power) at 2,440 m (8,000 ft):	
T67B	110 knots (204 km/h; 126 mph)
T67C	125 knots (231 km/h; 144 mph)
Stalling speed, power off, flaps up:	
T67B	55 knots (102 km/h; 64 mph)
T67C2	52 knots (97 km/h; 60 mph)
T67C3	53 knots (99 km/h; 61 mph)
Stalling speed, power off, flaps down:	
T67B	46 knots (85 km/h; 53 mph)
T67C	49 knots (91 km/h; 57 mph)
Max rate of climb at S/L: T67B	201 m (660 ft)/min
T67C2	287 m (940 ft)/min
Service ceiling: T67B	3,660 m (12,000 ft)
T-O run: T67B	223 m (733 ft)
T67C2	201 m (660 ft)
T-O to 15 m (50 ft): T67B	537 m (1,760 ft)
T67C2	442 m (1,450 ft)
Landing from 15 m (50 ft): T67B	521 m (1,710 ft)
T67C2	533 m (1,750 ft)
Landing run: T67B	213 m (700 ft)
T67C2	232 m (760 ft)

Range with max fuel (65% power at 2,440 m; 8,000 ft), allowances for T-O and climb, 45 min reserves at 45%
power: T67B	451 nm (835 km; 519 miles)
T67C2	360 nm (666 km; 414 miles)
T67C3	565 nm (1,046 km; 650 miles)
Endurance at 65% power: T67B	4 h 20 min
T67C2	3 h 30 min
T67C3	4 h 50 min
g limits	+6/−3

SLINGSBY T67M Mk II FIREFLY

This military basic trainer version of the T67 is based on the T67B of GFRP construction. The description of the T67B applies also to the T67M, except as detailed below. A first flight of this version (G-BKAM), known as the Firefly 160, was made on 5 December 1982, and CAA certification was achieved on 20 September 1983.

With the change to a two-piece canopy, the designation is amended to T67M Mk II. Recent deliveries of this version include five to Trent Air Services at Cranfield and two to a Japanese airline training academy.

TYPE: Two-seat military basic trainer.

WINGS, FUSELAGE, TAIL UNIT AND LANDING GEAR: Generally as for T67B.

POWER PLANT: One 119 kW (160 hp) Textron Lycoming AEIO-320-D1B flat-four engine, driving a Hoffmann HO-V72 two-blade constant-speed composite propeller with spinner. Fuel and oil systems suitable for inverted flight. Fuel tanks in leading-edge of wings, capacity 159 litres (42 US gallons; 35 Imp gallons). Refuelling point in upper wing surface. Oil capacity 7.7 litres (2.0 US gallons; 1.7 Imp gallons).

ACCOMMODATION AND SYSTEMS: As for T67B, except that current aircraft have new blue tinted canopy with fixed windscreen and upward hinged and rearward opening rear section. Inertia reel lockable shoulder harness standard, and air-conditioning optional.

AVIONICS AND EQUIPMENT: Avionics to customer requirements. Blind-flying instrumentation standard.

DIMENSIONS AND AREAS: As for T67B

WEIGHTS AND LOADINGS:
Weight empty, equipped	658 kg (1,450 lb)
Max fuel weight	114 kg (252 lb)
Max T-O, aerobatic and landing weight	952 kg (2,100 lb)
Max wing loading	75.38 kg/m² (15.44 lb/sq ft)
Max power loading	8.00 kg/kW (13.12 lb/hp)

PERFORMANCE (at max T-O weight):
Never-exceed speed	180 knots (333 km/h; 207 mph)
Max level speed at S/L	136 knots (252 km/h; 157 mph)
Max cruising speed, 75% power at 2,440 m (8,000 ft)	127 knots (235 km/h; 146 mph)

Stalling speed, power off, flaps down
	49 knots (91 km/h; 57 mph)
Max rate of climb at S/L	335 m (1,100 ft)/min
Service ceiling	4,575 m (15,000 ft)
T-O run	190 m (623 ft)
T-O to 15 m (50 ft)	402 m (1,319 ft)
Landing from 15 m (50 ft)	533 m (1,750 ft)
Landing run	232 m (760 ft)

Range with max fuel at 75% power, at 2,440 m (8,000 ft), allowances for T-O, climb and 45 min reserves at 45%
power	529 nm (980 km; 608 miles)

Range with max fuel at 65% power, at 2,440 m (8,000 ft), allowances as above 565 nm (1,047 km; 650 miles)
Endurance at 75% power	4 h 20 min
at 65% power	5 h 05 min
g limits at 884 kg (1,950 lb) AUW	+6/−3

SLINGSBY T67M200 FIREFLY

A development of the T67M, this version has a 149 kW (200 hp) Textron Lycoming AEIO-360-A1E engine, driving a Hoffmann HO-V123 three-blade variable-pitch composite propeller. Fuel and oil systems for inverted flight. The description and dimensions of the T67M apply also to the T67M200; weight and performance data are given below. This version flew for the first time on 16 May 1985 and was certificated by the CAA on 13 October 1985. A representative airframe has undergone a long term fatigue test to simulate 75,000 flying hours. First customer was the Turkish Aviation Institute at Ankara, to which a total of 16 aircraft have been delivered since 1985, making it the world's largest operator of T67s. Dutch operator King Air flies three T67Ms and one T67M Mk II as screening trainers for prospective pilots of the RNethAF. Other operators include the Royal Hong Kong Auxiliary Air Force (four) and the Norwegian Government's Flying Academy (six). By January 1990 a total of 31 T67M200s were in service with operators in five countries.

DIMENSIONS, EXTERNAL:
Propeller diameter	1.80 m (5 ft 11 in)

WEIGHTS AND LOADINGS:
Weight empty	698 kg (1,540 lb)
Max fuel	114 kg (252 lb)
Max baggage	30 kg (66 lb)
Max T-O weight: Utility	1,020 kg (2,250 lb)
Aerobatic	975 kg (2,150 lb)
Max landing weight	975 kg (2,150 lb)
Max wing loading	80.75 kg/m² (16.54 lb/sq ft)
Max power loading	6.85 kg/kW (11.25 lb/hp)

PERFORMANCE:
Never-exceed speed	180 knots (333 km/h; 207 mph)
Max level speed at S/L	140 knots (259 km/h; 161 mph)

Slingsby T67M Mk II Firefly delivered to a Swiss customer *(John Dignan)*

Slingsby T67M Mk II Firefly (Textron Lycoming AEIO-320-D1B engine) *(Pilot Press)*

Max cruising speed (75% power, at 2,440 m; 8,000 ft)
　　　　　　　　　　　130 knots (241 km/h; 150 mph)
Stalling speed, power off, flaps down
　　　　　　　　　　　　51 knots (95 km/h; 59 mph)
Max rate of climb at S/L　　　　350 m (1,150 ft)/min
T-O run　　　　　　　　　　221 m (725 ft)
T-O to 15 m (50 ft)　　　　　　409 m (1,340 ft)
Landing from 15 m (50 ft)　　　564 m (1,850 ft)
Landing run　　　　　　　　　265 m (870 ft)
Range with max fuel (75% power at 2,440 m; 8,000 ft),
　　allowances for T-O and climb, 45 min reserves at 45%
　　power　　　　　　　　　480 nm (889 km; 552 miles)
Range with max fuel (65% power at 2,440 m; 8,000 ft),
　　allowances as above　　　500 nm (926 km; 575 miles)
Endurance: at 75% power　　　　　　　3 h 45 min
　　at 65% power　　　　　　　　　4 h 10 min
g limits　　　　　　　　　　　　　　+6/−3

Slingsby T67M200 Fireflies of the Royal Hong Kong Auxiliary Air Force *(John Dignan)*

WALLIS
WALLIS AUTOGYROS LTD
Reymerston Hall, Norfolk NR9 4QY
Telephone: 44 (362) 850418
MANAGING DIRECTOR:
　Wg Cdr K. H. Wallis, CEng, FRAeS, FRSA, RAF (Retd)

The first Wallis single-seat ultralight autogyro introduced many patented features, including a rotor head with offset gimbal system to provide hands and feet off stability and to eliminate pitch-up and 'tuck-under' hazards; a high speed flexible rotor spin-up shaft with positive disengagement during flight; an automatic system of controlling rotor drive on take-off which allows power to be applied until the last moment; centrifugal stops to control rotor blade teetering; and a novel safe starting arrangement.

Many other Wallis autogyros have since been completed. Wallis Autogyros does not engage in production for public sale; it builds these aircraft only for operation within the company. However, three Wallis autogyros (two WA-116s and a WA-117) have been evaluated by RARDE, Christchurch, in the role of airfield battle damage reconnaissance.

Wallis WA-116/F/S which holds Class E3 and E3a speed records, showing fixed foreplane surfaces

WALLIS WA-116 and WA-116-T
The WA-116 represents the original Wallis design, of which the prototype (G-ARRT) flew for the first time on 2 August 1961, powered by a 54 kW (72 hp) modified McCulloch 4318 piston engine. Four more WA-116s were built by Beagle and five by Wg Cdr Wallis, as described in the 1973-74 *Jane's*. The last of these was later dismantled for construction of the two-seat G-AXAS, a WA-116-T.

WA-116/Mc. The prototype (G-ARRT) is re-engined with a 67 kW (90 hp) McCulloch. This aircraft, and the 'James Bond' WA-116/Mc (G-ARZB), continue to perform well. The latter has appeared in more than 500 displays, as far afield as Australia and the USA.

WA-116/F. Designation applied following the refitting of G-ASDY in 1971 with a 44 kW (60 hp) Franklin 2A-120-A engine. It is currently fitted with a Franklin 2A-120-B engine, driving a specially designed two-blade propeller, and has carried out specialised aerial photographic work, as detailed in earlier editions of *Jane's*.

A particularly successful WA-116/F is G-ATHM which currently holds nine world rotorcraft records. This aircraft underwent more extensive conversion than its predecessors, mainly to increase fuel capacity and pilot comfort for special long range flights. It has a 50 litre (13.2 US gallon; 11 Imp gallon) internal fuel tank, and began test flying, for range, in April 1974. Fitted also with a 36 litre (9.6 US gallon; 8 Imp gallon) jettisonable long range ventral tank, it set up on 13 July 1974 new Class E3 and E3a world records, for nonstop distance in a closed circuit, of 361.91 nm (670.26 km; 416.48 miles). Additionally, this flight set new 100 km (Class E3a only) and 500 km (Class E3 and E3a) closed circuit speed records of 70.51 knots (130.67 km/h; 81.19 mph) and 68.07 knots (126.14 km/h; 78.38 mph) respectively, the latter record subsequently passing to

G-BLIK (see below). A 91 litre (24 US gallon; 20 Imp gallon) ventral tank was next fitted, and on 28 September 1975, with this tank containing some 70 litres (18.5 US gallons; 15.5 Imp gallons), Wg Cdr Wallis made a nonstop flight from Lydd, Kent, to Wick, Caithness. This flight set Class E3 and E3a records for nonstop distance in a straight line of 472.092 nm (874.315 km; 543.274 miles). The ventral tank was not jettisoned after being emptied, and G-ATHM landed with sufficient fuel remaining for a further 65 nm (121 km; 75 miles). Its time of 6 h 25 min is a record for duration in both Class E3 and Class E3a.

On 14 October 1984 **WA-116/F/S** G-BLIK set new Class E3 and E3a speed records over 15 km of 102.365 knots (189.58 km/h; 117.80 mph). On 17 April 1985 it set new Class E3 and E3a world speed records over 100 km of 102.81 knots (190.41 km/h; 118.31 mph); and on 18 September 1986 new speed records over 3 km of 104.5 knots (193.6 km/h; 120.3 mph). The first ever autogyro record for a 1,000 km closed circuit was established by G-BLIK on 5 August 1988 with a speed of 70.574 knots (130.789 km/h; 81.268 mph) over 541.09 nm (1,002.75 km; 623.08 miles). This distance was also an absolute record for an autogyro and was achieved in 7 h 39 min 59 s. An endurance record of 7 h 42 min 49 s was established on the same flight. G-BLIK also claimed the 500 km closed circuit from G-ATHM with a speed of 72.33 knots (134.042 km/h; 83.29 mph). The suffix S (Special) denotes numerous cleaning up refinements and the addition of small fixed foreplanes. Thus, WA-116s hold all the major autogyro world records for speed, range and endurance.

WA-116-T/Mc. The McCulloch engined WA-116-T/Mc, G-AXAS, is a tandem two-seat autogyro which flew for the first time on 3 April 1969. Recent activities include work utilising the slow flight and short take-off and landing capability, and also electrostatically charged spraying tests, employing a spray system that can be lowered in flight.

WEIGHTS (WA-116/F):
　Weight empty　　　　　　　　　143 kg (316 lb)
　Max T-O weight　　　　　　　317.5 kg (700 lb)
　WA-116/F/S with long-range tank　331 kg (730 lb)
PERFORMANCE (WA-116/F):
　Max level speed　　　　　　　not fully explored
　Cruising speed without long-range tank
　　　　　　　　　　　　87 knots (161 km/h; 100 mph)
　Max rate of climb at S/L　305 m (1,000 ft)/min
　Max range with long-range tank (WA-116/F/S, estimated)　　　701 nm (1,300 km; 808 miles)

WALLIS WA-116/X
In 1985 Wg Cdr Wallis began the development of a new autogyro for a particular reconnaissance role. The requirement calls for a day and night all-weather capability, together with very low vibration levels.

As part of the development programme a series of flight tests is being conducted with current and new technology engines. Current engines tested include a special version of the 59.6 kW (80 hp) Limbach L 2000, a 37 kW (50 hp) Fuji 440 cc two-cylinder aircooled two-stroke, and the 47.7 kW (64 hp) Rotax 520 Bombardier geared two-cylinder liquid cooled two-stroke engine. Modified engines include the Rootes Imp and a two-cylinder engine made from components of the Rolls-Royce Continental O-240. New technology engines in the programme include a special version of the Norton Motors P62 twin-rotor Wankel type and a supercharged or turbocharged 1,360 cc automobile engine. The radiator for the Rotax and Norton engines is in the nose of the cockpit nacelle, providing some cockpit heating in inclement weather conditions.

Airframes being used for these flight tests are a basic WA-116 (G-AVDG), with appropriate modifications, and a new one (G-BMJX) provisionally designated WA-116/X, the suffix X indicating the unknown quantity pending selection of a suitable engine, for which a twin-rotor Norton rotary power plant is being considered.

The WA-116/X programme is expected to lead to the next generation of Wallis autogyros, emphasis being placed on easy adaptation to new technology engines as they become available. Future aircraft will be equipped for night flying and the carriage of a range of sensors, and will be easily adaptable for military, police and similar roles.

WALLIS WA-117/R-R

Details of the WA-117, which combines the WA-116 airframe with a fully certificated engine, the 74 kW (100 hp) Rolls-Royce Continental O-200-B, can be found in the 1986-87 *Jane's*.

The WA-117/R-R was engaged during 1987 in important operations, under Ministry of Defence contracts, to demonstrate the effectiveness of Wallis autogyros for all-weather day and night damage reconnaissance of military airfields. It is shown in an accompanying illustration equipped with a British Aerospace miniature infra-red linescan and real-time ground link, and a 70 mm camera.

WALLIS WA-120/R-R

The WA-120 (G-AYVO) was last described in the 1987-88 *Jane's*.

WALLIS WA-121

The WA-121 is the smallest and lightest Wallis autogyro to date. Three versions were projected: a high-speed **WA-121/Mc** with a Wallis-McCulloch engine of about 74 kW (100 hp); a cross-country **WA-121/F** with a 44.5 kW (60 hp) Franklin 2A-120-B engine; and a high-altitude **WA-121/M Meteorite 2** with a supercharged 89 kW (120 hp) Meteor Alfa 1 radial two-stroke engine and transistorised ignition. There are currently no plans to proceed with construction of the two last-mentioned variants.

The prototype WA-121/Mc (G-BAHH) has a high-mounted tailplane and an open cockpit, and made its first flight on 28 December 1972. It employs a number of improvements in control system design, resulting in greater stability at speed, better head resistance and greater pilot comfort. It set new Class E3 and E3a height records on 20 July 1982, when Wg Cdr Wallis flew it to a height of 5,643.7 m (18,516 ft) at Boscombe Down. Special features in the rotor head suspension, incorporated originally in the WA-117 prototype G-AVJV, are incorporated also in the WA-120 and WA-121. Now fitted with an improved oxygen system, and a wider track main landing gear to standardise it with other autogyros in the Wallis range, the WA-121 is intended to undertake experimental flying using rotor blades designed for high speeds and may make an attempt to better its height record.

WALLIS WA-122/R-R

A two-seat trainer development of the similar WA-116-T (G-BGGW) first flew on 16 July 1980 as the WA-122/R-R. In 1988, the rear seat was replaced by an F52 camera fitted with a 900 mm (35.4 in) lens and mounted in the shallow oblique position for experiments in long-range surveillance.

Wallis WA-117/R-R equipped for airfield damage assessment research *(RAE Farnborough)*

Wallis WA-201 twin-engined research autogyro

Further details appeared in the 1987-88 and previous editions of *Jane's*.

WALLIS WA-201

The WA-201 is a research vehicle for a twin-engined version of the Wallis type of light autogyro. The aircraft is powered by two 47.7 kW (64 hp) Rotax 532 Bombardier geared two-cylinder liquid-cooled two-stroke engines, mounted separately in tandem so that the front engine drives a pusher propeller and the rear engine a tractor propeller. The two propellers are counter rotating and have no offset thrust. The power available is sufficient for take-off and flight using only one engine. The two engines give an exceptional lift-to-empty-weight ratio and rate of climb. Tests were continuing in 1990.

WESTLAND

WESTLAND GROUP PLC
Yeovil, Somerset BA20 2YB
Telephone: 44 (935) 75222
Telex: 46277 WHLYEO G
LONDON OFFICE: 4 Carlton Gardens, Pall Mall, SW1
Telephone: 44 (71) 839 4061
CHAIRMAN: Sir Leslie Fletcher, DSC, FCA
DEPUTY CHAIRMAN: Alec Daly
CHIEF EXECUTIVE: Alan Jones, FEng, FIProdE, MA
HEAD OF PUBLIC RELATIONS: David Bath

Westland Aircraft Ltd (now Westland Group plc) was formed in July 1935, to take over the aircraft branch of Petters Ltd, known previously as the Westland Aircraft Works, which had been engaged in aircraft design and construction since 1915. It entered the helicopter industry in 1947 by acquiring a licence to build the US Sikorsky S-51, which it produced as the Westland Dragonfly and Widgeon. This technical association with Sikorsky Division of United Technologies has continued since the decision was taken to concentrate on the design, development and construction of helicopters.

In 1959, Westland acquired Saunders-Roe Ltd. In 1960 it acquired the Helicopter Division of Bristol Aircraft Ltd and Fairey Aviation Ltd, and has been subsequently the only major helicopter design and manufacturing organisation in the United Kingdom.

In April 1983 the Aerospace Division of British Hovercraft Corporation was combined with the Westland Helicopters Industrial Division to form the Aerospace Division of Westland Group plc. In October 1985 three additional divisions were created: Helicopter Division, Helicopter Customer Support Division and Technologies Division. Early in 1987 the Helicopter Division and the Customer Support Division were amalgamated to create a new Helicopter Division with responsibility for both manufacturing and product support. The various Divisions subsequently became consolidated into limited liability companies, as Westland Helicopters Ltd, Westland Aerospace Ltd and Westland Technologies Ltd.

A shareholders' meeting in February 1986 approved a financial reconstruction package under which United Technologies (USA) and Fiat (Italy) acquired a minority holding in Westland Group plc. Fiat withdrew in 1988, allowing GKN to secure a 22 per cent holding in Westland.

Programmes on which Westland Aerospace is engaged include the production of centre wings for the Shorts 330 and 360 transport aircraft, composite engine cowlings for the Boeing Canada DHC-8 Dash 8, Dornier 328, missile and satellite structures, fuel pods and transmission components for Boeing CH-47 Chinook helicopters, and gears and gearboxes for other aerospace companies. Its latest products include composite structures for McDonnell Douglas, Boeing and Airbus aircraft.

The collaboration between Westland and Agusta of Italy, already well established with the EH 101 programme (see International section), has been extended to include design, manufacture and marketing across the joint product range.

A joint Westland/Agusta management company, EHI Limited, has been set up in London to support the EH 101 civil and military helicopter. EHI Inc is a subsidiary of EHI in the USA. It also has a Canadian subsidiary in Ottawa, known as EHI Canada.

Westland Group activities in the USA and Central America are represented by Westland Inc, a wholly owned subsidiary.

WESTLAND HELICOPTERS LIMITED
Yeovil, Somerset BA20 2YB
Telephone: 44 (935) 75222
Telex: 46277 WHL YEO G
Fax: 44 (935) 704201
MANAGING DIRECTOR: J. Varde
ENGINEERING DIRECTOR: R. I. Case

HEAD OF HM GOVERNMENT BUSINESS: G. N. Cole
HEAD OF EXPORT BUSINESS: D. L. Gardner
PUBLIC RELATIONS MANAGER: P. Hersfield

Helicopters in current production at Yeovil are the Sea King and Lynx. In addition, Westland Helicopters and Agusta of Italy are collaborating through a joint company named EH Industries Ltd to develop and produce the EH 101 naval, commercial and utility helicopter (see International section).

Composite main rotor blades, based on carbonfibre and glassfibre materials, are in production at Yeovil as direct replacements for metal blades on S-61, SH-3 and Westland Sea King helicopters.

Advanced design composite main rotor blades have been

successfully test flown on the Lynx, Westland TT300 and EH 101.

Under the terms of an agreement signed in June 1989, Westland has obtained co-production rights for the McDonnell Douglas Helicopters AH-64 Apache. Production of up to 150 Apaches is envisaged in the UK if the helicopter is selected by the Army Air Corps for anti-tank roles, the preferred version being the improved Longbow Apache.

WESTLAND SEA KING

The Westland Sea King development programme stemmed from a licence agreement for the S-61 helicopter concluded originally with Sikorsky in 1959. This permitted Westland to utilise the basic airframe and rotor system of the Sikorsky SH-3 now described under Agusta in the Italian section. Considerable changes were made in the power plant and in specialised equipment, initially to meet a Royal Navy requirement for an advanced anti-submarine helicopter with prolonged endurance. The Sea King can also undertake secondary roles, such as search and rescue, tactical troop transport, casualty evacuation, cargo carrying and long-range self-ferry. A land based general purpose version, the Commando, is described separately.

Current versions of the Sea King are as follows:

Sea King AEW. Mk 2A. Version developed in mid-1982 to provide Royal Navy with airborne early warning capability. By 1987, 10 (plus a trials vehicle) had been converted, of which only eight were operational at any one time due to availability of Thorn EMI Searchwater radars. A further two radars were ordered in 1989. Described and illustrated in 1986-87 edition.

Sea King HAR. Mk 3. Uprated version for SAR duties with the Royal Air Force. Provision for flight crew of two pilots, air electronics/winch operator and loadmaster/winchman; up to six stretchers, or two stretchers and 11 seated survivors, or 19 persons. Nav system includes Decca TANS F computer, accepting inputs from Mk 19 Decca nav receiver and Type 71 Doppler. MEL radar. First HAR. Mk 3 flew on 6 September 1977; deliveries of 16 completed in 1979. Three more ordered in 1983 were delivered in 1985. Operated by No. 202 Squadron at Finningley (HQ) and detachments at Boulmer, Brawdy, Manston, Lossiemouth and Leconfield; plus No. 78 Squadron on Falkland Islands. Latter's aircraft fitted with radar warning receivers and chaff/flare dispensers. A follow-on RAF order for between six and eight was under discussion in 1990.

Sea King HC. Mk 4. Utility version of Commando Mk 2 (which see) for Royal Navy.

Sea King HAS. Mk 5. Updated ASW and SAR version for the Royal Navy. Thirty new-build aircraft ordered in three batches (17, 8 and 5), of which the first two (ZA126/127) were handed over officially on 2 October 1980. The final five were delivered between January and July 1986. Fleet Air Arm workshops had brought all surviving older Sea Kings up to recent standards by early 1987. Of 56 HAS. Mk 1s, 47 were converted to HAS. Mk 2A (including 35 subsequently to HAS. Mk 5 and 11 to AEW. Mk 2A) and one directly to HAS. Mk 5. All except one of the 21 new-build HAS. Mk 2s also became Mk 5s.

The nav/attack system of the Sea King HAS. Mk 5 utilises Tans G coupled to Decca 71 Doppler and MEL Sea Searcher radar. Also fitted are Racal MIR-2 ESM, passive sonobuoy dropping equipment, and associated GEC Avionics LAPADS acoustic processing and display equipment. The Mk 5's search radar has a larger dorsal radome.

Using this new equipment, the Sea King can pinpoint the position of an enemy submarine at far greater range than has been possible in the past, and attack it with torpedoes. In addition to monitoring signals from its own sonobuoys, the Sea King can handle information from buoys dropped by RAF Nimrod in a joint search. It can remain on station, up to 87 nm (160 km; 100 miles) from its parent ship, for long periods.

The Sea King HAS. Mk 5 carries a crew of four, with the dunking sonar operator also monitoring the LAPADS equipment at an additional crew station. To make room for the extra equipment, the cabin has been enlarged by moving the rear bulkhead 1.72 m (5 ft 7¾ in) further into the tail, increasing cabin length to 7.59 m (24 ft 11 in). Max T-O weight of the Sea King HAS. Mk 5 is 9,525 kg (21,000 lb).

In 1987-88, four Mk 5s were stripped of ASW avionics for SAR duties with No. 771 Squadron at Culdrose, becoming operational on 1 April 1988 as **Sea King HAR. Mk 5.**

Sea King HAS. Mk 6. Updated ASW version for the Royal Navy. Four new-build aircraft ordered October 1987 and fifth soon thereafter, although new-build helicopters were preceded by first conversions from Mk 5. Initial 25 Mk 5s being retrofitted to this standard by the RN workshop at Fleetlands with Westland-supplied kits. Further 44 update kits to be acquired by RN through competitive tender.

The principal change introduced by the Mk 6 is a modification of the sonar system under a contract awarded to the Maritime Aircraft Systems Division of GEC Avionics in 1987. Previously fitted with two separate stand-alone systems (Plessey 195 dipping sonar and GEC Avionics AQS-902C sonobuoy processing), the HAS. Mk 5 will be retrofitted to Mk 6 standard with a new and enhanced combined system known as AQS-902G-DS. This will replace the analog computing element of the Plessey 195 with a digital processor (changing its designation to Ferranti 2069), and present integrated information from both the free sonobuoys and the dipping sonar on a single CRT display. The contract provides for 31 new AQS-902G-DS systems, plus the modification of 112 AQS-902C systems to the upgraded standard. The initial Type 2069 order is for 44 units. Associated changes include modifications to increase sonar 'dunking' depth from 75 m (245 ft) to some 213 m (700 ft).

In addition, the Mk 6 will have Plessey PTR 446 improved IFF; upgraded ESM to Orange Reaper standard; and two GEC Signals AD3400 VHF/UHF secure speech radios in place of three older communications sets. CAE Electronics internal MAD was first installed in May 1988 for clearance trials which had been satisfactorily completed by 1989. Retrofit programme anticipated. Performance slightly improved over HAS. Mk 5 as the result of 227-363 kg (500-800 lb) weight saving, being equivalent of fuel for additional 30 min endurance.

The first Mk 6 (a conversion of Mk 5 XZ581) first flew at Yeovil on 15 December 1987. The initial new-build Mk 6, ZG816, flew on 7 December 1989. Entered service on 15 April 1988 (ZA136) with the Intensive Flight Trials Unit formed within No. 824 Squadron and detached from Culdrose to Prestwick. Later helicopters will be issued to existing Mk 5 operators, Nos. 810, 814, 819, 820, 826 and 706 Squadrons. In January 1990, the RN had 60 HAS. Mk 5, eight Mk 6 conversion, 10 AEW and five HAR. Mk 5 SAR Sea Kings in service, plus one trials Mk 2 and two Sikorsky-built SH-3s.

Sea King HAS. Mk 7. Provisional designation for projected Mk 6 upgrade with new main gearbox and composite tail rotors.

Advanced Sea King. Version with 1,092 kW (1,465 shp) Rolls-Royce Gnome H.1400-1T engines, uprated main gearbox with emergency lubrication and strengthened main lift frames. Other changes include composite main and tail rotor blades, and improved search radar. Maximum AUW increased to 9,752 kg (21,500 lb) to give an improved payload/range performance. Through life costs reduced.

Sea King Mk 42B. ASW version of the Advanced Sea King of which 12 were ordered for the Indian Navy in July 1983, followed by eight more and a further small batch of undisclosed size against a further requirement for up to 15. Features include GEC Avionics AQS-902 sonobuoy processor and tactical processing system; MEL Super Searcher radar; integrated Alcatel HS-12 dipping sonar; Chelton 700 sonics homing; Marconi Hermes ESM; and ability to carry British Aerospace Sea Eagle long-range anti-ship missiles. First aircraft (IN513) flown 17 May 1985. Following contractual and fiscal problems, first two (IN515 and IN516) handed over on 16 January 1989 to begin crew training at Yeovil. Seventeen delivered by end of 1989.

Recent developments concerning other variants of Sea King are:

Sea King Mk 41. Deliveries totalled 22 in 1973-75 for SAR. Three have been converted by MBB to anti-ship configuration as explained in the German section.

Sea King Mk 43B. One additional helicopter to be delivered to the Norwegian Air Force in June 1992. Eleven Mk 43s received 1972-78, of which nine survivors to be raised to Mk 43B standard with additional Bendix nose radar, Racal Doppler 91, R-NAV2 and Mk 32 Decca, plus 2000F FLIR. Re-deliveries to begin in August 1992.

Sea King Mk 48. Five helicopters, delivered to the Belgian Air Force in 1976, re-equipped with composite main rotor blades by March 1988. In 1989, Westland was contracted to update navigation systems with new Doppler and TANS.

Other versions, for which orders have been completed, were described in the 1983-84 *Jane's* and included the Sea King HAS. Mk 1 (56 Royal Navy), Sea King HAS. Mk 2 (21 Royal Navy), Sea King Mk 4X (two Royal Aerospace Establishment), Sea King Mk 42/42A/42C (12/3/6 India), Sea King Mk 45 (six Pakistan Navy), Sea King Mk 47 (six Egyptian Navy) and Sea King Mk 50 (12 Royal Australian Navy). One further Pakistani Mk 42C is included in RN Mk 5 production. Several of these operators have retrofitted their Sea Kings with Westland-produced composite blades.

A total of 324 Sea Kings and Commandos had been ordered by 1 January 1990, of which 311 had been delivered.

The following details apply to current production Advanced Sea Kings:

AIRFRAME: Generally similar to Agusta-Sikorsky ASH-3H (see Italian section), but with main and tail rotor blades of composite materials. Stabiliser on starboard side of tail pylon is unbraced. New five-blade tail rotor to give increased capability in side wind.

POWER PLANT: Two 1,238 kW (1,660 shp) (max contingency rating) Rolls-Royce Gnome H.1400-1T turboshafts, mounted side by side above cabin. Transmission rating 2,200 kW (2,950 shp). Fuel in six underfloor bag tanks, total capacity 3,714 litres (981 US gallons; 817 Imp gallons). Internal auxiliary tank, capacity 863 litres (228 US gallons; 190 Imp gallons) may be fitted for long range ferry purposes. Pressure refuelling point on starboard side, two gravity points on port side. Flat plate debris guard for engine air intakes. Optional Centrisep air cleaner unit.

Westland Sea King AEW. Mk 2A of 'A' Flight, 849 Squadron, RN *(Paul Jackson)*

Westland Sea King HAS. Mk 5 anti-submarine helicopter *(Pilot Press)*

Indian Sea King Mk 42B destined for INS *Vikrant*

ACCOMMODATION: Crew of four in ASW role; accommodation for up to 22 survivors – or 18 if radar fitted – in SAR role; and up to 28 troops in utility role. Alternative layouts for nine stretchers and two attendants; or 15 VIPs. Two-section airstair door at front on port side, cargo door at rear on starboard side. Entire accommodation heated and ventilated. Cockpit doors and windows, and two windows each side of cabin, can be jettisoned in an emergency.

SYSTEMS: Three main hydraulic systems. Primary and auxiliary systems operate main rotor control. System pressure 103.5 bars (1,500 lb/sq in); flow rate 22.7 litres/min at 87.9 bars (6 US gallons; 5 Imp gallons/min at 1,275 lb/sq in). Unpressurised reservoir. Utility system for main landing gear, sonar and rescue winches, blade folding and rotor brake. System pressure 207 bars (3,000 lb/sq in); flow rate 41 litres/min at 186.2 bars (10.8 US gallons; 9 Imp gallons/min at 2,700 lb/sq in). Unpressurised reservoir. Electrical system includes two 20kVA 200V three-phase 400Hz engine driven generators, a 26V single-phase AC supply fed from the aircraft's 40Ah nickel-cadmium battery through an inverter, and DC power provided as a secondary system from two 200A transformer-rectifier units.

OPERATIONAL EQUIPMENT (ASW models): As equipped for this role, the Sea King is a fully integrated all-weather hunter/killer weapon system, capable of operating independently of surface vessels, and the following equipment and weapons can be fitted to achieve this task: Ferranti 2069, Plessey Type 195, Bendix AN/AQS-13B or Alcatel HS-12 dipping sonar, GEC Avionics Doppler navigation system, MEL Super Searcher radar in dorsal radome, transponder beneath rear fuselage, Honeywell AN/APN-171 radar altimeter, Honeywell GM7B Gyro-syn compass system, Louis Newmark Mk 31 automatic flight control system, two No. 4 marine markers, four No. 2 Mk 2 smoke floats, Ultra Electronics mini-sonobuoys, up to four Mk 46, Whitehead A244S or Sting Ray homing torpedoes, or four Mk 11 depth charges or one Clevite simulator. Observer/navigator has tactical display on which sonar contacts are integrated with search radar and navigational information. Radio equipment comprises Collins ARC-182 UHF/VHF and homer, Ultra D 403M standby UHF, Collins 718U-5 HF radio, Racal B693 intercom, Telebrief system and IFF provisions. CAE Electronics AN/ASQ-504(V) internal MAD ordered for RN Sea Kings in 1987 and fitted from 1988 onwards. Whittaker Electronic Systems ALQ-167 Yellow Veil modular jamming equipment installed internally in Mk 5 from about 1986. For secondary role a mounting is provided on the rear frame of the starboard door for a general purpose machine-gun. The Mk 31 AFCS provides radio altitude displays for both pilots; artificial horizon displays; three-axis stabilisation in pilot controlled manoeuvres; attitude hold, heading hold and height hold in cruising flight; controlled transition manoeuvres to and from the hover; automatic height control and plan position control in the hover; and an auxiliary trim facility.

OPERATIONAL EQUIPMENT (non-ASW models): A wide range of radio and navigation equipment may be installed, including VHF/UHF communications, VHF/UHF homing, radio compass, Doppler navigation system, radio altimeter, VOR/ILS, radar and transponder, of Collins, Plessey, Honeywell and GEC Avionics manufacture. A Honeywell compass system and a Louis Newmark automatic flight control system are also installed. Sea Kings equipped for search and rescue have in addition a Breeze BL 10300 variable speed hydraulic rescue hoist of 272 kg (600 lb) capacity mounted above the starboard side cargo door. Second hoist optional. Automatic main rotor blade folding and spreading is standard; for shipboard operation the tail pylon can also be folded.

DIMENSIONS, EXTERNAL:
Main rotor diameter	18.90 m (62 ft 0 in)
Tail rotor diameter	3.16 m (10 ft 4 in)
Length overall (rotors turning)	22.15 m (72 ft 8 in)
Length of fuselage	17.02 m (55 ft 10 in)
Length overall:	
main rotor folded	17.42 m (57 ft 2 in)
rotors and tail folded	14.40 m (47 ft 3 in)
Height overall: rotors turning	5.13 m (16 ft 10 in)
rotors spread and stationary	4.85 m (15 ft 11 in)
Height to top of rotor head	4.72 m (15 ft 6 in)
Width overall (rotors folded):	
with flotation bags	4.98 m (16 ft 4 in)
without flotation bags	4.77 m (15 ft 8 in)
Width of fuselage	2.16 m (7 ft 1 in)
Wheel track (c/l of shock absorbers)	3.96 m (13 ft 0 in)
Wheelbase	7.14 m (23 ft 5 in)
Cabin door (port): Height	1.68 m (5 ft 6 in)
Width	0.91 m (3 ft 0 in)
Cargo door (stbd): Height	1.52 m (5 ft 0 in)
Width	1.73 m (5 ft 8 in)
Height to sill	1.14 m (3 ft 9 in)

DIMENSIONS, INTERNAL:
Cabin: Length	7.59 m (24 ft 11 in)
Max width	1.98 m (6 ft 6 in)
Max height	1.92 m (6 ft 3½ in)
Floor area (incl area occupied by radar, sonar etc)	13.94 m² (150 sq ft)
Volume	28.03 m³ (990 cu ft)

AREAS:
Main rotor disc	280.6 m² (3,020.3 sq ft)
Tail rotor disc	7.8 m² (83.9 sq ft)

WEIGHTS AND LOADINGS (A: anti-submarine, B: anti-surface vessel, C: airborne early warning, D: SAR, E: troop transport, F: external cargo, G: VIP):
Basic weight: with sponsons	5,393 kg (11,891 lb)
without sponsons	5,373 kg (11,845 lb)
Weight equipped (typical): A	7,428 kg (16,377 lb)
B	7,570 kg (16,689 lb)
C	7,776 kg (17,143 lb)
D	6,241 kg (13,760 lb)
E	5,712 kg (12,594 lb)
F	5,686 kg (12,536 lb)
G	7,220 kg (15,917 lb)
Max T-O weight	9,752 kg (21,500 lb)
Max underslung or internal load	3,628 kg (8,000 lb)
Max disc loading	34.75 kg/m² (7.12 lb/sq ft)
Max power loading	4.44 kg/kW (7.29 lb/shp)

PERFORMANCE (at max T-O weight, ISA):
Never-exceed speed (British practice) at S/L	122 knots (226 km/h; 140 mph)
Cruising speed at S/L	110 knots (204 km/h; 126 mph)
Max rate of climb at S/L	619 m (2,030 ft)/min
Max vertical rate of climb at S/L	246 m (808 ft)/min
Service ceiling, one engine out	1,220 m (4,000 ft)
Max contingency ceiling (1 hour rating)	1,067 m (3,500 ft)
Hovering ceiling: IGE	1,982 m (6,500 ft)
OGE	1,433 m (4,700 ft)

Radius of action:
A (2 h on station, including three torpedoes)	125 nm (231 km; 144 miles)
B (2 h on station, including two Sea Eagles)	110 nm (204 km; 126 miles)
C (2 h 24 min on station)	100 nm (185 km; 115 miles)
D (picking up 20 survivors)	220 nm (407 km; 253 miles)
E (28 troops)	range 300 nm (556 km; 345 miles)
F (1,814 kg; 4,000 lb external load)	225 nm (417 km; 259 miles)
G	580 nm (1,075 km; 668 miles)
Range with max standard fuel, at 1,830 m (6,000 ft)	800 nm (1,482 km; 921 miles)
Ferry range with max standard and auxiliary fuel, at 1,830 m (6,000 ft)	940 nm (1,742 km; 1,082 miles)

PERFORMANCE (at typical mid-mission weight):
Never-exceed speed (British practice) at S/L	146 knots (272 km/h; 169 mph)
Cruising speed at S/L	132 knots (245 km/h; 152 mph)

WESTLAND COMMANDO

First flown on 12 September 1973, the Commando is a tactical helicopter based on the Sea King.

The payload/range performance and endurance capabilities of the Sea King have been optimised in the design of the Commando, which is intended to operate with maximum efficiency in the primary roles of tactical troop transport, logistic support and cargo transport, and casualty evacuation. In addition, the Commando can operate effectively in the secondary roles of air-to-surface strike and SAR.

Export orders for the Commando have totalled 40 for Egypt (five Mk 1s, 17 Mk 2s, two Mk 2Bs and four Mk 2Es) and Qatar (three Mk 2As, one Mk 2C and eight Mk 3s). Additional details in the 1989-90 and earlier editions of *Jane's*. In 1990, work began on conversion of Qatari Mk 2s to Mk 3 standard with new nav/com equipment. Six Indian Sea King Mk 42Cs are essentially to Commando standard, as is the UK's Sea King HC. Mk 4.

Sea King HC. Mk 4. Utility version of Commando Mk 2 for Royal Navy. Has folding main rotor blades and folding tail pylon of Sea King, but retains non-retractable wheeled landing gear of Commando. Designed to carry up to 28 fully equipped troops, or 2,720 kg (6,000 lb) of cargo, and to operate in Arctic and tropical conditions. Max slung load 3,628 kg (8,000 lb). Equipped for parachuting and abseiling. Revised avionics, including Decca TANS with chart display and Decca 71 Doppler navigation system. One cabin mounted 7.62 mm machine-gun. In service with Nos. 707, 845 and 846 (Naval Air Commando) Squadrons and 772 (SAR) Squadron. First flight (by ZA290) 26 September 1979; first handed over to the Royal Navy in November 1979.

RN orders total 40, of which 37 had been delivered by April 1987 and three were due in mid-1990. A further three, lacking some operational equipment, ordered for MoD(PE), comprising two **Mk 4X**s delivered in 1982-83 to the Royal Aerospace Establishment (including Blue Kestrel radar trials) and one **Mk 4** (ZG829) to the Empire Test Pilots' School on 3 May 1989. In January 1990, 34 HC. Mk 4s were in service, sole losses being three in the 1982 Falklands War. The 28th HC.Mk 4 (ZF115) was the first production Sea King to fly from the start with composites main rotor blades, on 14 November 1985, although others had been retrofitted.

The following data apply to current production aircraft:
TYPE: Twin-turboshaft tactical military helicopter.
ROTOR SYSTEM: Five-blade main and tail rotors, of composite construction. Main rotor blades, of NACA 0012 section, attached to hub by multiple bolted joint. Rotor brake fitted. Automatic folding of main rotor blades available as an option.
ROTOR DRIVE: Twin input four-stage reduction main gearbox, with single bevel intermediate and tail gearboxes. Main rotor/engine rpm ratio 93.43; tail rotor/engine rpm ratio: 15.26.
FUSELAGE: Light alloy stressed skin structure, unpressurised. Sea King sponsons replaced by stub wings.

Westland Sea King Mk 4X testbed for Blue Kestrel radar at RAE Bedford *(Paul Jackson)*

TAIL UNIT: Similar to Advanced Sea King, with starboard side stabiliser at top of fixed tail rotor pylon. Folding tail pylon available as an option.

LANDING GEAR: Non-retractable tailwheel type, with twin-wheel main units. Oleo-pneumatic shock absorbers. Mainwheel tyres size 6.50-10, tailwheel tyre size 6.00-6.

POWER PLANT: As for current versions of Advanced Sea King.

ACCOMMODATION: Crew of two on flight deck. Seats along cabin sides, and single jump seat, for up to 28 troops. Overload capacity 45 troops. Two-piece airstair door at front on port side, cargo door at rear on starboard side. Entire accommodation heated and ventilated. Cockpit doors and windows, and two windows each side of main cabin, are jettisonable in an emergency.

SYSTEMS: Primary and secondary hydraulic systems for flight controls. No pneumatic system. Electrical system includes two 20 kVA alternators.

AVIONICS AND EQUIPMENT: Wide range of radio, radar and navigation equipment available to customer's requirements. Cargo sling and rescue hoist optional.

ARMAMENT: Wide range of guns, missiles, etc may be carried, to customer's requirements: typically, pintle-mounted machine-gun (7.62 mm or 20 mm) in cabin doorway and machine-gun pod (0.5 in or 7.62 mm) on each side of forward fuselage with reflector sight for pilot. If fitted, sponsons may mount one rocket pod each (FZ M159C 2.75 in; Matra F4 68 mm; Thomson-Brandt 68-22 68 mm; Medusa 81 mm; or SNIA HL-12 80 mm).

DIMENSIONS, EXTERNAL:

Main rotor diameter	18.90 m (62 ft 0 in)
Tail rotor diameter	3.16 m (10 ft 4 in)
Distance between rotor centres	11.10 m (36 ft 5 in)
Main rotor blade chord	0.46 m (1 ft 6¼ in)
Length overall (rotors turning)	22.15 m (72 ft 8 in)
Length of fuselage	17.02 m (55 ft 10 in)
Height overall (rotors turning)	5.13 m (16 ft 10 in)
Height to top of rotor head	4.72 m (15 ft 6 in)
Wheel track (c/l of shock absorbers)	3.96 m (13 ft 0 in)
Wheelbase	7.21 m (23 ft 8 in)
Passenger door (fwd, port):	
Height	1.68 m (5 ft 6 in)
Width	0.91 m (3 ft 0 in)
Cargo door (rear, stbd): Height	1.52 m (5 ft 0 in)
Width	1.73 m (5 ft 8 in)

DIMENSIONS, INTERNAL: As Advanced Sea King (SAR version)

AREAS: As for Advanced Sea King, plus:

Main rotor blades (each)	4.14 m² (44.54 sq ft)
Tail rotor blades (each)	0.23 m² (2.46 sq ft)
Tailplane	1.80 m² (19.40 sq ft)

WEIGHTS:

Operating weight empty (troop transport, 2 crew, typical)	5,620 kg (12,390 lb)
Max T-O weight	9,752 kg (21,500 lb)
Max underslung load	3,628 kg (8,000 lb)

PERFORMANCE (at max T-O weight): As given for Advanced Sea King, plus:

Range with max payload (28 troops), reserves for 30 min standoff	214 nm (396 km; 246 miles)

WESTLAND LYNX

The Lynx is one of three types of aircraft (Puma, Gazelle and Lynx) covered by the Anglo-French helicopter agreement first proposed in February 1967 and confirmed on 2 April 1968. Westland has design leadership in the Lynx, which fulfils general purpose and naval roles.

The first of 13 Lynx prototypes (XW835) flew for the first time on 21 March 1971 and was followed by XW837, the third prototype (second Lynx to fly), on 28 September 1971. Details of subsequent development aircraft can be found in the 1975-76 *Jane's*. Production versions are as follows:

Lynx AH. Mk 1. General purpose and utility version for British Army. Total of 113 built of which 107 remained in service at January 1990, some converted to AH. Mk 7 (which see). Described in 1986-87 and earlier editions of *Jane's*.

Lynx HAS. Mk 2. Version for Royal Navy, for advanced shipborne anti-submarine and other duties. Gem 2 engines. Ferranti Seaspray search and tracking radar in modified nose. Capable of operation on anti-submarine classification and strike, air to surface vessel search and strike, search and rescue, reconnaissance, troop transport, fire support, communication and fleet liaison, and vertical replenishment duties. Total of 60 delivered, plus 26 to French Navy, designated **HAS. Mk 2(FN)**. First production aircraft (XZ227) flown on 20 February 1976. First operational RN unit, No. 702 Squadron, formed on completion of Navy intensive flight trials in December 1977. Able to carry Sea Skua anti-ship missiles. In late 1985, the Royal Navy workshops at Yeovilton began converting HAS. Mk 2s to Mk 3 standard (see below). By 1989, all 53 active RN first-series Lynx had been modified to Mk 3 or later standards.

Lynx HAS. Mk 3. Royal Navy aircraft with uprated power plant, comprising two 835 kW (1,120 shp) Rolls-Royce Gem 41-1 turboshaft engines. Delivery of original series of 20, plus three Falklands War replacements, began in March 1982 and was completed in April 1985. One (ZD560) was built for the Empire Test Pilots' School and

Westland Lynx HAS. Mk 3 aerodynamic prototype of Mk 8 with Sea Owl thermal imager and chin radome

delivered in April 1988 in approximate Mk 7 configuration. Seven more were ordered in July 1985 and delivered from November 1987 to November 1988. Eleven Lynx, used by the Armilla Patrol in the Arabian Gulf, modified to **HAS. Mk 3GM** (Gulf Mod) with a more effective cooling system. Prior to introduction of the Mk 8 (which see), approximately 12 Lynx were modified by the RN Aircraft Yard at Fleetlands from April 1989 to **HAS. Mk 3S** standard. These helicopters have a RAMS 4000 central tactical system which will be used by crews to acquire experience of this aspect of the Mk 8. Lynx operations centred on Portland, where 815 and 829 Squadrons provide detachments of one or two helicopters to RN warships, and 702 Squadron is training unit.

Lynx Mk 4. Second batch of 14 aircraft ordered for French Navy in May 1980 with Gem 41-1 engines and uprated transmission to permit an increase in AUW to 4,763 kg (10,500 lb). Deliveries began on 28 April 1982 and were completed in September 1983. All supplied 'green' for equipment installation by Aerospatiale and subsidiaries.

Lynx AH. Mk 5. Similar to AH. Mk 1. Two trials aircraft ZD285 and ZD559 (see 1989-90 *Jane's*). Nine AH. Mk 5s ordered for Army Air Corps. Initial example (ZE375) flew on 23 February 1985 and was used for engine trials. Remainder transferred to AH. Mk 7 contract, although ZE376 flew initially as Mk 5.

RAE Farnborough testbed ZD285 was fitted in 1989 with an advanced fibre optic MIL-STD-1553B databus, hardware being provided by STC. At RAE Bedford, ZD559 received pressure sensors to support the proposed Lynx ACT programme, in which it is planned to equip a Lynx with active control technology. The intended recipient is the ETPS's ZD560 (see above), which would become the world's first true FBW helicopter.

Lynx AH. Mk 7. Uprated aircraft to meet GSR 3947 requirement for the British Army. As Mk 5 but with improved systems, reversed-direction (clockwise when seen from port side) tail rotor with improved composite blades,

and 4,876 kg (10,750 lb) AUW. The more powerful tail rotor reduces noise and improves the ability to hover for extended periods at high weights, important during anti-tank operations. Eight transferred from AH. Mk 5 contract, plus five more ordered in 1985. Last aircraft from each batch was cancelled. First AH. Mk 7 (ZE376) flew on 7 November 1985. Deliveries completed with 11th helicopter in July 1987.

Conversion of Mk 1 Lynx to Mk 7 standard is proceeding at the Royal Navy workshops at Wroughton. The first thus modified (XZ641) was returned to service on 30 March 1988 and one quarter of the Mk 1 fleet had been modified by the end of 1989. Box-type exhaust diffusers added to Mk 7s from early 1989.

Lynx HAS. Mk 8. Current development proposed for the RN, equivalent to **Super Lynx** (described separately), having passive identification system, increased max T-O weight to 5,125 kg (11,300 lb), improved (reversed-direction) tail rotor control, BERP composite main rotor blades and a Racal RAMS 4000 central tactical system (CTS). The CTS will ease the crew's workload by centrally processing all sensor data and presenting mission information on a multi-function electronic display. First flight of the CTS took place in 1987. Lynx HAS. Mk 8 is basically similar to export **Super Lynx** (described separately). Originally intended to receive 360° radar in chin-mounted radome – either MEL Super Searcher or Ferranti Seaspray Mk 3 – but requirement cancelled by MoD on cost grounds in early 1988. As alternative, current Seaspray Mk 1 to be repackaged in chin radome (continuing to scan only 180°) and original radar position employed as mounting for GEC Sensors Sea Owl thermal imager. Sea Owl is a ×5 or ×30 magnifying system on a gimballed mount: elevation +20° to –30°; azimuth +120° to –120°. In addition, MIR-2 ESM equipment is to be updated. Following a 1987 order for 15 systems, main batch of 106 RAMS 4000s purchased in September 1989, followed in October by Sea Owl.

Westland Lynx HAS. Mk 3 anti-submarine helicopter for the Royal Navy (*Pilot Press*)

Three Lynx Mk 3s have been converted to participate in the Mk 8 development programme, not including the radome aerodynamic testbed ZD249. Of these, XZ236 flew on 25 January 1989 as the tactical system testbed, followed on 30 March 1989 by ZD267, fitted with a dummy Sea Owl and a chin radome. ZD266, with Mk 8 avionics, was due to follow.

Introduction of Mk 8s to RN service will be a three-phase programme beginning with Phase 1 modification of Mk 3s with radios and other, simpler items. Phase 2 involves addition of the RAMS 4000 CTS. In 1991, full Mk 8 standard is to be achieved with fitment of Sea Owl and CAE internal MAD. Experience of CTS has been accumulating since delivery of Lynx HAS. Mk 3S helicopters (which see) to the Operational Flight Trials Unit at Portland in September 1989.

Lynx AH. Mk 9. UK Army Air Corps equivalent of export **Battlefield Lynx** (described separately) with tricycle wheel landing gear, max T-O weight of 5,125 kg (11,300 lb), advanced technology composites main rotor blades, and exhaust diffusers as standard, but no TOW missile capability. Prototype, converted from company development Lynx XZ170, first flown 29 November 1989. Sixteen ordered in 1987 for delivery from 1991, together with eight conversions from Mk 1, to equip newly-formed Nos. 672 and 673 Squadrons of 9 Regiment, based at Dishforth for support of rapid intervention 24th Airmobile Brigade. Some to be outfitted as advanced command posts; remainder for tactical transport.

Other versions, for which orders have been completed (described in the 1983-84 *Jane's*), comprise Lynx Mk 2 (FN) (14 French Navy), Mk 21 (nine Brazilian Navy), Mk 23 (two Argentine Navy), Mk 25 (six Netherlands Navy UH-14A), Mk 27 (ten Netherlands Navy SH-14B), Mk 28 (three Qatar Police), Mk 80 (eight Danish Navy), Mk 81 (eight Netherlands Navy SH-14C), Mk 86 (six Norwegian Air Force/Coast Guard), Mk 88 (19 West German Navy), Mk 89 (three Nigerian Navy) and Mk 90 (two, plus conversions, Danish Navy). All Danish Mk 80s and 90s will standardise on Mk 90 from 1991 onwards. Versions not built were: Mk 6 (Royal Marines), Mk 22 (Egyptian Army), Mk 24 (Iraqi Army), Mk 26 (Iraqi Army – armed), Mk 82 (Egyptian utility export), Mk 83 (Saudi Army), Mk 84 (Qatar Army), Mk 85 (United Arab Emirates Army) and Mk 87 (Argentine Navy – embargoed).

Further orders for the Super Lynx are detailed separately. The Royal Netherlands Navy plans to upgrade its Lynx to a common standard, locally designated **SH-14D**. This involves five utility transport UH-14As and eight SH-14Cs (delivered with MAD, which since removed) being fitted with Alcatel dipping sonar, as installed in nine SH-14Bs. All will additionally receive UHF radios, a radar warning receiver, new navigation instruments, a new radar altimeter and modified engines.

Lynx production by 1 January 1990 totalled 337, including two demonstrators but excluding 13 prototypes. Orders totalled 380. Production is shared in the ratio of 70 per cent by Westland to 30 per cent by Aerospatiale.

On 11 August 1986, the Lynx demonstrator G-LYNX set the current world's absolute speed record for helicopters by averaging 216.45 knots (400.87 km/h; 249.09 mph) over a 15/25 km course. The Lynx was modified for the attempt, with BERP III main rotor blades, Westland 30 type tail surfaces and other performance enhancements (see 1986-87 *Jane's*).

In a series of agility trials conducted by Lynx AH. Mk 7 XZ170 in 1989, the helicopter demonstrated at S/L, 55 knots (102 km/h; 63 mph) sideways to port and starboard; 70 knots (130 km/h; 81 mph) backwards; spot turns up to 80°/s, port and starboard; and 170 knots (315 km/h; 196 mph) in level flight. At 2,440 m (8,000 ft) the Lynx further achieved a maximum speed of 165 knots (306 km/h; 190

Westland Lynx AH. Mk 7 conversion from Mk 1 with reversed-direction tail rotor and box-type exhaust diffusers

mph) IAS; +2.4/−0.5 g at 125 knots (232 km/h; 144 mph) IAS; and 55° sustained bank turns at the last-mentioned speed.

The following description applies to both the military general purpose and naval versions with the Gem 2 power plant, except where indicated:

TYPE: Twin-engined multi purpose helicopter.

ROTOR SYSTEM: Single four-blade semi-rigid main rotor and four-blade tail rotor. Each blade is attached to the main rotor hub by titanium root attachment plates and a flexible arm. The rotor hub and inboard portions of the flexible arms are built as a complete unit, in the form of a titanium monobloc forging. Tail rotor blades have a light alloy spar, stainless steel leading-edge sheath, and rear section similar to that of main rotor blades. Main blades can be folded. (Composites construction on Mks 8/9.)

ROTOR DRIVE: Drives are taken from the front of the engines into the main gearbox, which is mounted above the cabin forward of the engines. In flight, the accessory gears, which are all at the front of the main gearbox, are driven by one of the two through shafts from the first stage reduction gears. Rotor head controls are actuated by three identical tandem servo jacks, trunnion mounted from the main rotor gearbox and powered by two independent hydraulic systems. Control system incorporates a simple stability augmentation system. Each engine embodies an independent control system which provides full authority rotor speed governing, pilot control being limited to selection of the desired rotor speed range. In the event of an engine failure, this system will restore power up to single engine maximum contingency rating. On naval versions, the main rotor can provide negative thrust to increase stability on deck after touchdown. Tail rotor drive is taken from the main ring gear. A hydraulically operated rotor brake is mounted on the main gearbox.

FUSELAGE AND TAIL UNIT: Conventional semi-monocoque pod and boom structure, mainly of light alloy. Glassfibre components used for access panels, doors and fairings. Single large window in each of the main cabin sliding doors. Provision for internally mounted defensive armament, and for universal flange mountings on each side of the exterior to carry weapons or other stores. Tailboom is a light alloy monocoque structure bearing the sweptback vertical fin/tail rotor pylon, which has a half tailplane near the tip on the starboard side. Tail pylon leading- and trailing-edges, and bullet fairing over tail rotor gearbox, are of glassfibre. Tail pylon of naval version can be folded and spread manually, to reduce overall length for stowage.

LANDING GEAR (general purpose military version): Non-retractable tubular skid type. Provision for a pair of adjustable ground handling wheels on each skid. Flotation gear optional.

LANDING GEAR (naval versions): Non-retractable oleo-pneumatic tricycle type. Single-wheel main units, carried on sponsons, are fixed at 27° toe-out for deck landing, and can be manually turned into line and locked fore and aft for movement of aircraft into and out of ship's hangar. Twin-wheel nose unit can be steered hydraulically through 90° by the pilot to facilitate independent take-off into wind. Sprag brakes (wheel locks) fitted to each wheel prevent rotation on landing or inadvertent deck roll. These locks are disengaged hydraulically and will re-engage automatically in the event of hydraulic failure. Max vertical descent 2.29 m (7½ ft)/s; max lateral drift 0.91 m (3 ft)/s for deck landing. Flotation gear, and hydraulically actuated harpoon deck lock securing system, optional.

POWER PLANT: Two Rolls-Royce Gem 2 turboshafts, each with max contingency rating of 671 kW (900 shp) in Lynx AH. 1, HAS. 2 and early export variants. Later versions have Gem 41-1 or 41-2 engines, each with max contingency rating of 835 kW (1,120 shp), or Gem 42-1 engines, each with max contingency rating of 846 kW (1,135 shp). Engines of British and French Lynx in service being converted to Mk 42 standard during regular overhauls from 1987 onwards. Engine oil tank capacity 6.8 litres (1.8 US gallons; 1.5 Imp gallons). Main rotor gearbox oil capacity 28 litres (7.4 US gallons; 6.2 Imp gallons). Usable fuel capacity 973 litres (257 US gallons; 214 Imp gallons) in five internal tanks. Optional 214 litres (56.4 US gallons; 47 Imp gallons) beneath bench seat in rear of cabin. For ferrying, two tanks, each of 436 litres (115.3 US gallons; 96 Imp gallons) in cabin, replacing bench tank. Max usable fuel 1,845 litres (488 US gallons; 406 Imp gallons). Naval Lynx equipped with bench tank as standard, and ferry tanks for long-range surveillance, thus gross capacities: 1,200 litres (317 US gallons; 264 Imp gallons) standard; 1,862 litres (492 US gallons; 409.5 Imp gallons) maximum. Pressure or gravity refuelling.

ACCOMMODATION: Pilot and co-pilot or observer on side by side seats. Dual controls optional. Individual forward hinged cockpit door and large rearward sliding cabin door on each side; all four doors jettisonable. Cockpit accessible from cabin area. Maximum high density layout (general purpose version) for one pilot and 10 armed troops or paratroops, on lightweight bench seats in soundproofed cabin. Alternative VIP layouts for four to seven passengers, with additional cabin soundproofing. Seats can be removed quickly to permit the carriage of up to 907 kg (2,000 lb) of freight internally. Tiedown rings are provided. In the casualty evacuation role, with a crew of two, the Lynx can accommodate three standard stretchers and a medical attendant. Both basic versions have secondary capability for search and rescue (up to nine survivors) and other roles.

SYSTEMS: Two independent hydraulic systems, pressure 141 bars (2,050 lb/sq in). A third hydraulic system is provided in the naval version when sonar equipment, MAD or a hydraulic winch system is installed. No pneumatic system. 28V DC electrical power supplied by two 6kW engine driven starter/generators and an alternator. External power sockets. 24V 23Ah (optionally 40Ah) nickel-cadmium battery fitted for essential services and emergency engine starting. 200V three-phase AC power available at 400Hz from two 15kVA transmission driven alternators. Optional cabin heating and ventilation system. Optional supplementary cockpit heating system. Electric anti-icing and demisting of windscreen, and electrically operated windscreen wipers, standard; windscreen washing system optional.

AVIONICS AND FLIGHT EQUIPMENT: All versions equipped as standard with navigation, cabin and cockpit lights; adjustable landing light under nose and anti-collision beacon. Avionics common to all roles (general purpose and naval versions) include GEC Avionics duplex three-axis automatic stabilisation equipment; BAe (Honeywell) GM9 Gyrosyn compass system; Decca

Westland Super Lynx (see page 334), advanced export version of Navy Lynx (*Pilot Press*)

Prototype Lynx AH. Mk 9 conversion, fitted with wheel landing gear but lacking TOW sight and missiles

tactical air navigation system (TANS); Decca 71 Doppler, E2C standby compass; and Racal intercom system. Optional role equipment for both versions includes GEC Avionics Mk 34 automatic flight control system (AFCS); Collins VOR/ILS; DME; Collins ARN-118 Tacan; I-band transponder (naval version only); Plessey PTR 446, Collins APX-72, Siemens STR 700/375 or Italtel APX-77 IFF; and vortex sand filter for engine air intakes. Additional units are fitted in naval version, when sonar is fitted, to provide automatic transition to hover and automatic Doppler hold in hover.

ARMAMENT AND OPERATIONAL EQUIPMENT: For armed escort, anti-tank or air-to-surface strike missions, general purpose version can be equipped with two 20 mm cannon mounted externally so as to permit the carriage also of anti-tank missiles or a pintle-mounted 7.62 mm machine-gun inside the cabin. External pylon can be fitted on each side of cabin for a variety of stores, including two Minigun or other self-contained gun pods; two rocket pods; or up to eight Aerospatiale/MBB Hot, Rockwell Hellfire, Hughes TOW, or similar air-to-surface missiles. An additional six or eight missiles can be carried in cabin, for rearming in forward areas, and a stabilised sight is fitted for target detection and missile direction. British Army Lynx aircraft equipped with TOW missiles have roof mounted Hughes sight manufactured under licence by British Aerospace. The TOW roof sight is being upgraded to have a night vision capability in the far infra-red waveband to increase operational versatility in low-light night conditions or poor daylight visibility, and the first test firing of TOW with an added GEC Sensors thermal imager took place in October 1988. The Lynx can transport anti-tank teams of three gunners with missiles and launchers. Sanders AN/ALQ-144 infra-red jammer installed beneath tailboom of some British Army Lynx from 1987 pending availability of exhaust diffusers. Requirement for radar warning receiver satisfied by 1989 selection of Ferranti AWARE-3 system. For search and rescue role, with three crew, both versions can have a waterproof floor and a 272 kg (600 lb) capacity clip-on hoist on starboard side of cabin. Cable length 30 m (98 ft). Optional equipment, according to role, can include lightweight sighting system with alternative target magnification, vertical and/or oblique cameras, flares for night operation, low light level TV, infra-red linescan, searchlight, and specialised communications equipment. Naval version can carry out a number of these roles, but has specialised equipment for its primary duties. For ASW role, this includes two Mk 44, Mk 46 or Sting Ray homing torpedoes, one each on an external pylon on each side of fuselage, and six marine markers; or two Mk 11 depth charges. Detection of submarines is by means of dipping sonars or magnetic anomaly detector. The dipping sonars are operated by a hydraulically powered winch and cable hover mode facilities within the AFCS. CAE Electronics AN/ASQ-504(V) internal MAD ordered for RN Lynx in 1987. Tracor M-130 chaff/flare dispensers, FN HMP .50 machine-gun and Whittaker Microwave Systems AN/ALQ-167(V) D-J band anti-anti-ship missile jamming pods installed on RN Lynx patrolling Arabian Gulf, 1987. Ferranti ARI5979 Seaspray Mk 1 lightweight search and tracking radar, for detecting small surface targets in low visibility/high sea conditions. Armament includes four BAe Sea Skua semi-active homing missiles for attacking light surface craft; alternatively on French Navy Lynx, four AS.12 or similar wire guided missiles can be employed in conjunction with AF 530 or APX-334 lightweight stabilised optical sighting system.

DIMENSIONS, EXTERNAL (A: general purpose version; N: naval version):

Main rotor diameter (A, N)	12.80 m (42 ft 0 in)
Tail rotor diameter (A, N)	2.21 m (7 ft 3 in)
Length overall:	
A, N, both rotors turning	15.163 m (49 ft 9 in)
N, main rotor blades and tail folded	
	10.618 m (34 ft 10 in)

Width overall, main rotor blades folded:	
A	3.75 m (12 ft 3¾ in)
N	2.94 m (9 ft 7¾ in)
Height overall, both rotors stopped:	
A	3.504 m (11 ft 6 in)
N	3.48 m (11 ft 5 in)
Height overall, main rotor blades and tail folded:	
N	3.20 m (10 ft 6 in)
Tailplane half-span	1.78 m (5 ft 10 in)
Skid track: A	2.032 m (6 ft 8 in)
Wheel track: N	2.778 m (9 ft 1.4 in)
Wheelbase: N	2.94 m (9 ft 7¾ in)

DIMENSIONS, INTERNAL:

Cabin, from back of pilots' seats:	
Min length	2.057 m (6 ft 9 in)
Max width	1.778 m (5 ft 10 in)
Max height	1.422 m (4 ft 8 in)
Floor area	3.72 m² (40.04 sq ft)
Volume	5.21 m³ (184 cu ft)
Cabin doorway: Width	1.37 m (4 ft 6 in)
Height	1.19 m (3 ft 11 in)

AREAS:

Main rotor disc	128.7 m² (1,385.4 sq ft)
Tail rotor disc	3.84 m² (41.28 sq ft)

WEIGHTS (A: general purpose version, N: naval version):

Manufacturer's empty weight: A	2,578 kg (5,683 lb)
N	2,740 kg (6,040 lb)
Manufacturer's basic weight: A	2,658 kg (5,860 lb)
N	3,030 kg (6,680 lb)
Operating weight empty, equipped:	
A, troop transport (pilot and 10 troops)	
	2,787 kg (6,144 lb)
A, anti-tank strike (incl weapon pylons, firing equipment and sight)	3,072 kg (6,772 lb)
A, search and rescue (crew of three)	
	2,963 kg (6,532 lb)
N, anti-submarine strike	3,343 kg (7,370 lb)
N, reconnaissance (crew of two)	3,277 kg (7,224 lb)
N, anti-submarine classification and strike	
	3,472 kg (7,654 lb)
N, air to surface vessel search and strike (crew of two and four Sea Skuas)	3,414 kg (7,526 lb)
N, search and rescue (crew of three)	
	3,416 kg (7,531 lb)
N, dunking sonar search and strike	
	3,650 kg (8,047 lb)
Max T-O weight: A	4,535 kg (10,000 lb)
N	4,763 kg (10,500 lb)

PERFORMANCE (at normal max T-O weight at S/L, ISA, except where indicated. A: general purpose version; N: naval version):

Max continuous cruising speed:	
A	140 knots (259 km/h; 161 mph)
N	125 knots (232 km/h; 144 mph)
A (ISA + 20°C)	130 knots (241 km/h; 150 mph)
N (ISA + 20°C)	114 knots (211 km/h; 131 mph)
Speed for max endurance:	
A, N (ISA and ISA + 20°C)	
	70 knots (130 km/h; 81 mph)
Max forward rate of climb: A	756 m (2,480 ft)/min
N	661 m (2,170 ft)/min
A (ISA + 20°C)	536 m (1,760 ft)/min
N (ISA + 20°C)	469 m (1,540 ft)/min
Max vertical rate of climb:	
A	472 m (1,550 ft)/min
N	351 m (1,150 ft)/min
A (ISA + 20°C)	390 m (1,280 ft)/min
N (ISA + 20°C)	244 m (800 ft)/min
Hovering ceiling OGE: A	3,230 m (10,600 ft)
N	2,575 m (8,450 ft)

Typical range, with reserves:

A, troop transport   292 nm (540 km; 336 miles)

Radius of action, out and back at max sustained speed, allowances for T-O and landing, 30 min loiter in search area, 3 min hover for each survivor, and 10% fuel reserves at end of mission:

N, search and rescue (crew of 3 and 2 survivors)
115 nm (212 km; 132 miles)

N, search and rescue (crew of 3 and 7 survivors)
96 nm (178 km; 111 miles)

Time on station at 50 nm (93 km; 58 miles) radius, out and back at max sustained speed, with 2 torpedoes, smoke floats and marine markers, allowances for T-O and landing and 10% fuel reserves at end of mission:

N, anti-submarine classification and strike, loiter speed on station	2 h 0 min
N, anti-submarine strike, loiter on station	2 h 29 min
N, dunking sonar search and strike, 50% loiter speed and 50% hover on station	1 h 5 min

Time on station at 50 nm (93 km; 58 miles) radius, out and back at max sustained speed, with crew of 2 and 4 Sea Skuas, allowances and reserves as above:

N, air to surface vessel strike, en-route radar search and loiter speed on station   1 h 36 min

Max range: A	340 nm (630 km; 392 miles)
N	320 nm (593 km; 368 miles)
Max endurance: A	2 h 57 min
N (ISA + 20°C)	2 h 50 min
Max ferry range with auxiliary cabin tanks:	
A	724 nm (1,342 km; 834 miles)
N	565 nm (1,046 km; 650 miles)

WESTLAND SUPER LYNX AND BATTLEFIELD LYNX

The Super Lynx and Battlefield Lynx are upgraded export versions of the helicopter approximately equivalent to the naval Mk 8 and army Mk 9 respectively. Principal changes comprise a 5,125 kg (11,300 lb) max T-O weight, all-weather day and night capability, extended payload/range performance and advanced technology composites main rotor blades, plus the Mk 7's dynamic improvements (reversed direction tail rotor, etc).

A mockup of the Battlefield Lynx was displayed at the 1988 Farnborough air show, converted from the company demonstrator G-LYNX, fitted with wheel landing gear, exhaust diffusers and provision for anti-helicopter missiles on each side of the forward fuselage. A wheeled prototype, the converted trials AH. Mk 7 (ex-Mk 1) XZ170, flew on 29 November 1989. In mid-1991, Westland is due to fly a Battlefield Lynx re-engined with a pair of LHTEC T800 turboshaft engines, each rated at 895 kW (1,200 shp). The joint demonstration programme includes engines, speed reduction gearboxes and support provided by LHTEC.

First sales of the Super Lynx were achieved in 1988 when South Korea purchased 12, to be equipped with Racal Avionics Doppler 71/TANS N navigation system, Seaspray Mk 3 360° radar and Sea Skua anti-ship missiles. The first, 90-0701 (temporarily ZH219), flew on 16 November 1989 as the initial Lynx to be fitted with Seaspray Mk 3. South Korean Lynx, designated Mk 99, will be delivered in

Westland Battlefield Lynx for export is equivalent to the British Army's Lynx Mk 9

1990-91 for service aboard 'Sumner' and 'Gearing' class destroyers. Also in 1989, Portugal ordered five Super Lynx, including two to be converted from RN Mk 3s. Delivery is due from December 1990 for 'Vasco da Gama' class (MEKO 200) frigates and equipment will include US items, including dipping sonar. Three further options are held by Portugal.

Data as for standard Lynx, except:

ROTOR SYSTEM: Advanced technology swept-tip (BERP) composites main blades offering improved speed and aerodynamic efficiency and reduced vibration. Reversed direction tail rotor for improved control.

LANDING GEAR: Battlefield Lynx equipped with non-retractable tricycle landing gear. Twin nosewheels; single mainwheels. Oleo-pneumatic struts capable of absorbing 1.83 m (6 ft)/s descent rate.

POWER PLANT: Two Rolls-Royce Gem 42-1 turboshafts, each rated at 835 kW (1,120 shp). Exhaust diffusers for infra-red suppression optional on Battlefield Lynx.

ARMAMENT AND OPERATIONAL EQUIPMENT: Super Lynx has Seaspray Mk 3 or Bendix RDR 1500 360° scan radars in chin fairing. (UK Mk 8 has Seaspray Mk 1 re-packaged, plus GEC Sensors Sea Owl thermal imaging equipment above nose.) Four Sea Skua or two Penguin anti-ship missiles; or four Stinger anti-helicopter missiles. Vinten Vicon 78 chaff dispenser; Vinten Vipa 1 reconnaissance pod; or Agiflite reconnaissance camera system. Other weapons as listed under standard Lynx. Battlefield Lynx may be equipped with Goodyear AN/ALE-39 chaff/flare dispensers and (subject to development) Dalmo-Victor AN/APR-39 radar warning receiver. Secure speech radio. Decca Doppler 71 and TANS 8447 navigation; Honeywell/Smiths AN/APN-198 radar altimeter; Collins 206A ADF; Cossor 2720 IFF; Collins VIR 31A VOR/ILS. Ferranti M126 sight for fixed armament, including two GIAT 20 mm cannon pods; two FN pods with two 7.62 mm machine-guns each; or two M.159C pods containing nineteen 2.75 in rockets each. Eight TOW anti-tank missiles on modified mounting, with BAe sight for gunner. Optionally HOT or Hellfire missiles. Vipa 1 and Agiflite cameras as Super Lynx.

DIMENSIONS, EXTERNAL (A: Battlefield Lynx; N: Super Lynx):
Tail rotor diameter 2.36 m (7 ft 9 in)
Length overall:
A, N, both rotors turning 15.24 m (50 ft 0 in)
N, main rotor blades and tail folded
10.85 m (35 ft 7¼ in)
A, rotors folded 13.24 m (43 ft 5¼ in)
Width overall, main rotor blades folded:
A 3.29 m (10 ft 9½ in)
N 2.94 m (9 ft 7¾ in)
Height overall, tail rotor turning:
A 3.73 m (12 ft 3 in)
N 3.79 m (12 ft 5¼ in)
Height overall, main rotor blades and tail folded:
N 3.25 m (10 ft 8 in)
Wheel track: A 2.80 m (9 ft 2¼ in)
Wheelbase: A, N 3.02 m (9 ft 11 in)
AREA:
Tail rotor disc 4.37 m² (47.04 sq ft)
WEIGHTS:
Basic weight empty: A 3,178 kg (7,006 lb)
N 3,291 kg (7,255 lb)

Prototype of the Westland/Sikorsky WS 70 (two General Electric T700 turboshaft engines)

Operating weight empty (including crew and appropriate armament):
A, anti-tank (eight TOW) 3,949 kg (8,707 lb)
A, reconnaissance 3,444 kg (7,592 lb)
A, transport (unladen) 3,496 kg (7,707 lb)
N, anti-submarine warfare 4,207 kg (9,276 lb)
N, ASV (four Sea Skua) 4,252 kg (9,373 lb)
N, ASV (two Penguin) 4,461 kg (9,834 lb)
N, surveillance and targeting 3,597 kg (7,929 lb)
N, search and rescue 3,658 kg (8,064 lb)
Max underslung load 1,361 kg (3,000 lb)
Max T-O weight 5,125 kg (11,300 lb)
PERFORMANCE:
Max continuous cruising speed:
A 138 knots (256 km/h; 159 mph)
Range:
A, tactical transport 370 nm (685 km; 426 miles)
Radius of action:
A, anti-tank, 2 h on station with four TOWs
25 nm (46 km; 29 miles)
N, anti-submarine, 2 h 20 min on station, dipping sonar and one torpedo 20 nm (37 km; 23 miles)
N, point attack with four Sea Skuas
148 nm (274 km; 170 miles)
N, surveillance, 4.1 h on station
75 nm (139 km; 86 miles)

WESTLAND WS 70L

Following agreement of full partnership with United Technologies, Westland received US State Department approval to produce a version of the Sikorsky Black Hawk helicopter designated WS 70. The Westland board set aside £3 million for a demonstrator (ZG468), which was assembled from a Sikorsky kit to US Army UH-60A battlefield transport standards. Powered by two General Electric T700 turboshaft engines, it flew for the first time on 1 April 1987 and is used for training and market support activities. In July 1988, Saudi Arabia signed a provisional agreement with the UK Government covering (among other equipment) the supply of 88 Westland helicopters, all of which are understood to be WS 70s. These will be to current Sikorsky UH-60L standard, and are designated WS 70L.

The details given for the UH-60L Black Hawk in the US section apply to the Westland WS 70L except as follows:
POWER PLANT: Two 1,239 kW (1,662 shp) General Electric T700-GE-701C turboshafts.
AVIONICS AND EQUIPMENT (recommended): Communications equipment includes UHF and V/UHF and VHF/FM homing. Navigation equipment includes AN/ASN-43 compass, Doppler, plus customer specified equipment.
WEIGHTS:
Weight empty 5,174 kg (11,406 lb)
Mission T-O weight 7,632 kg (16,825 lb)
Max alternative T-O weight 9,979 kg (22,000 lb)
PERFORMANCE:
Range with 1,814 kg (4,000 lb) payload
300 nm (556 km; 345 miles)
Ferry range 1,145 nm (2,122 km; 1,318 miles)

EH 101

Details of this programme, in which Westland is in partnership with Agusta of Italy, can be found in the International section.

UNITED STATES OF AMERICA

AAC
AIRCRAFT ACQUISITION CORPORATION
This company has acquired manufacturing and marketing rights to the Helio and Taylorcraft ranges of light aircraft, under whose entries in this section details may be found. Additional information is also contained in the New Technik entry and under Taylor Kits in the Sport Aircraft section.

AAI
AMERICAN AVIATION INDUSTRIES
16700 Roscoe Boulevard, Van Nuys, California 91406

Telephone: 1 (818) 786 1921

Telex: 662903 ACI USA

CHIEF EXECUTIVE OFFICER: Geoff Miller

VICE-PRESIDENT, MARKETING: Don Sterling

AAI FANSTAR
Aviation Consultants Inc formed American Aviation Industries to re-engine Lockheed JetStar business jets with new turbofans. The modified aircraft is known as the FanStar. Conversion involves the removal of the four 14.68 kN (3,300 lb st) Pratt & Whitney JT12 turbojets or the four 16.46 kN (3,700 lb st) Garrett TFE731-3 turbofans from Lockheed JetStar I and II aircraft respectively, and replacing them with two General Electric CF34-3A high bypass turbofans, each rated at 40.70 kN (9,150 lb st) with automatic power reserve (APR), 38.48 kN (8,650 lb) without APR, installed in new translating sleeve, short-cowl nacelles with cascade type thrust reversers. The proof of concept prototype, a JetStar Dash 8 (N380AA), was delivered in May 1985 to General Electric's Mojave Flight Test Center in California, and made its first flight, with lower rated CF34-1A engines, on 5 September 1986. No recent information has been received. A description and photograph of the FanStar may be found in the 1989-90 and earlier editions of *Jane's*.

ACA
ACA INDUSTRIES INC
28603 Trailriders Drive, Rancho Palos Verdes, California 90274

Telephone: 1 (213) 539 7121

PRESIDENT: Dr Julian Wolkovitch

In 1974 Dr Julian Wolkovitch flew a proof-of-concept glider featuring his patented joined wing configuration which comprises two sets of wings arranged to form diamond shapes in plan and front view. The configuration was adopted subsequently for the Summit Trident T-3 microlight aircraft (see Sport Aircraft section of 1987-88 *Jane's*).

The Defense Advanced Research Projects Agency (DARPA), NASA and the US Army and Navy have supported research into the joined wing concept for application to aircraft and missiles. Claimed benefits of the configuration, drawn from wind tunnel tests and structural analyses, include lighter weight, greater stiffness, less induced drag, lower wave drag, higher trimmed maximum lift coefficient and inbuilt direct lift and sideforce capabilities.

Studies by its Ames Research Center having shown that a joined wing weighs some 40 per cent less than aerodynamically equivalent conventional wing and tail surfaces, NASA awarded ACA a contract to design a manned research aircraft. ACA is studying applications for joined wings, which may include transport and general aviation aircraft, fighters, VTOL aircraft, agricultural aircraft and RPVs, and is providing consultancy services to Rockwell International and other manufacturers working on joined wing aircraft projects.

ACA JW-1, JW-2 and JW-3
In March 1986 ACA Industries began work on redesigning the Ames/NASA AD-1 oblique wing research aircraft (described in the 1981-82 *Jane's*) as a joined wing technology demonstrator. It proposes to use the fuselage, engines and landing gear of the AD-1 mated to a new joined wing which will have removable tip panels, enabling the aircraft to be progressively modified to configurations with the wing joint located at 60 per cent, 80 per cent and 100 per cent of span. Initially the aircraft will be configured with the joint at 60 per cent span, and designated **JW-1**. The tip panels will subsequently be removed in two phases to create the **JW-2** (joint at 80 per cent span) and **JW-3** (joint at 100 per cent span). NASA wind tunnel tests of one-sixth scale models of the JW-1, JW-2 and JW-3 were completed during 1987. Detail design work was completed in 1989 and has been approved by NASA. Further progress awaits release of NASA funds for prototype construction and flight testing.

TYPE: Single-seat research aircraft.

WINGS: Front and rear wings in joined wing configuration. Two-spar fail-safe structure of composite materials. Wing section specially designed by NASA. Thickness/chord ratio 11.3 per cent on front wing, 12.1 per cent on rear wing. Dihedral 5° on front wing. Anhedral 20° on rear wing. Sweepback 30° 28' on front wing. Sweepforward at quarter-chord 31° 50' on rear wing. In JW-1 configuration front wing has six trailing-edge control surfaces, rear wing four trailing-edge control surfaces, which can operate in a variety of combinations to provide pitch, roll and direct lift control.

FUSELAGE: Fail-safe structure of composite materials.

TAIL UNIT: Single vertical fin with rudder. Streamlined bullet fairing at junction with rear wing.

LANDING GEAR: Non-retractable tricycle type.

POWER PLANT: Two Ames Industrial Corporation TRS 18-046 turbojets, each rated at 0.978 kN (220 lb st), mounted in pods aft of front wing/fuselage junction.

ACCOMMODATION: Pilot only, in enclosed cockpit with canopy. Cockpit is not pressurised.

DIMENSIONS, EXTERNAL (A: JW-1, B: JW-2, C: JW-3):

Wing span, front: A		12.19 m (40 ft 0 in)
	B	9.84 m (32 ft 3½ in)
	C	7.31 m (24 ft 0 in)
rear, all		7.31 m (24 ft 0 in)
Wing chord: at root: all		1.19 m (3 ft 11 in)
at tip: A		0.48 m (1 ft 6¾ in)
	B	0.61 m (2 ft 0 in)
	C	0.76 m (2 ft 6 in)
Wing aspect ratio, front: A		11.18
	B	8.07
	C	5.21

AREAS:

Wings, gross: A		13.29 m² (143.1 sq ft)
	B	12.01 m² (129.3 sq ft)
	C	10.27 m² (110.6 sq ft)
Front wing: A		10.17 m² (109.5 sq ft)
	B	8.89 m² (95.7 sq ft)
	C	7.15 m² (77.0 sq ft)
Rear wing: all		3.12 m² (33.6 sq ft)

WEIGHT AND LOADINGS:

Max T-O weight		973 kg (2,145 lb)
Max wing loading: A		73.21 kg/m² (14.99 lb/sq ft)
	B	81.01 kg/m² (16.59 lb/sq ft)
	C	94.72 kg/m² (19.39 lb/sq ft)

PERFORMANCE (estimated):

Max level speed at 2,135 m (7,000 ft):		
A		276 knots (511 km/h; 318 mph)
B		283 knots (524 km/h; 326 mph)
C		291 knots (539 km/h; 335 mph)
Max rate of climb at S/L, ISA:		
A, B, C		518 m (1,700 ft)/min
Rate of climb at S/L, ISA, one engine out:		
A, B		152 m (500 ft)/min
C		91 m (300 ft)/min

Models of the ACA JW-1 (left) and JW-2 long- and medium-span versions of NASA's joined wing research aircraft

ADVANCED AIRCRAFT
ADVANCED AIRCRAFT CORPORATION
2016 Palomar Airport Road, Carlsbad, California 92008

Telephone: 1 (619) 438 1964

Telex: 249075 (ATSD UR)

PRESIDENT: Neil F. Martin

GENERAL MANAGER: Leland L. Dimon III

This company was formed on 1 July 1983. It has acquired the production facilities of the former Riley Aircraft Manufacturing Inc (see 1983-84 *Jane's*). The following conversions of Cessna aircraft were available in 1987, since when no further information has been received.

ADVANCED AIRCRAFT TURBINE P-210
The basic Cessna Model 210 Centurion, and the variations for the Pressurised Centurion, have been described fully under the Cessna entry in previous editions of *Jane's*. The Advanced Aircraft Turbine P-210 (previously known as the Spirit 750) is a turboprop conversion of the Pressurised Centurion, developed by Riley Aircraft Manufacturing. The Turbine P-210 is powered by a 559 kW (750 shp) PT6A-135 turboprop, flat rated at 335.5 kW (450 shp) and driving a Hartzell three-blade constant-speed fully-feathering and reversible-pitch Q-tip propeller with spinner. The conversion includes modified control surfaces, the addition of a ventral fin, installation of a glassfibre aerodynamic cowling with inertial separator and electric induction air lip de-icing, electric propeller de-icing, a SIADS Inc 28V 200A starter/generator, a 28V 50A standby generator, Gill 639T heavy duty battery, fuel computer, a new engine instrument panel, a 24V electrical system to meet FAA requirements, Flint wingtip fuel tanks with a combined capacity of 62.5 litres (16.5 US gallons; 13.7 Imp gallons), and 3M Stormscope radar.

DIMENSIONS, EXTERNAL: As for Cessna Centurion, except:

Length overall	9.17 m (30 ft 1 in)
Propeller diameter	1.98 m (6 ft 6 in)

WEIGHTS AND LOADINGS:

Weight empty	1,199 kg (2,621 lb)
Max ramp weight	1,822 kg (4,016 lb)
Max T-O weight	1,814 kg (4,000 lb)

Max landing weight	1,723 kg (3,800 lb)
Max wing loading	102.53 kg/m² (21.0 lb/sq ft)
Max power loading	5.41 kg/kW (8.88 lb/shp)

PERFORMANCE (at max T-O weight except where indicated):

Max cruising speed at 7,010 m (23,000 ft)	
	253 knots (470 km/h; 292 mph)
Econ cruising speed	213 knots (394 km/h; 245 mph)
Stalling speed:	
flaps up	67 knots (125 km/h; 78 mph) IAS
30% flap	63 knots (117 km/h; 73 mph) IAS
flaps down	58 knots (108 km/h; 67 mph) IAS
Max rate of climb at S/L	549 m (1,800 ft)/min
Service ceiling	above 7,010 m (23,000 ft)
T-O to 15 m (50 ft) at AUW of 1,542 kg (3,400 lb)	
	334 m (1,095 ft)
Landing from 15 m (50 ft) at AUW of 1,542 kg (3,400 lb)	
	394 m (1,291 ft)
Range with max fuel, ISA, max cruise power at 7,010 m (23,000 ft), allowances for start, taxi, take-off, climb and descent, 45 min reserves	
	1,008 nm (1,868 km; 1,160 miles)

ADVANCED AIRCRAFT REGENT 1500

Known formerly as the Riley Turbine Eagle 421, this modification unites the Cessna 421C Golden Eagle airframe with Pratt & Whitney Canada PT6A turboprops, mounted in new low-drag nacelles. The Riley prototype flew for the first time in late November 1979, at Palomar Airport, and the certification programme was completed during 1980.

A description of the Cessna 421C Golden Eagle appeared under the Cessna entry in the 1985-86 edition; it applies also to the Regent 1500 (421CP), except as follows:

POWER PLANT: Two Pratt & Whitney Canada PT6A-135 turboprops, each flat rated at 559 kW (750 shp), and driving Hartzell three-blade constant-speed autofeathering reversible-pitch propellers with Q-tips and spinners. Standard fuel as for Cessna 421C, but auxiliary tanks in rear of nacelles with combined capacity of 568 litres (150 US gallons; 125 Imp gallons). Optionally, rear of nacelles can be replaced by new all-glassfibre fuel tanks which increase standard fuel capacity by a total of 605 litres (160 US gallons; 133 Imp gallons). Advanced aerodynamic cowlings incorporate inertial separators. Electric de-icing of propellers and air intakes.

SYSTEMS: Generally as for Cessna 421C, except bleed air unit for pressurisation system; electrical system with 200A starter/generators and heavy duty battery; engine fire detection system; and pneumatic leading-edge de-icing boots for wings and tail unit.

WEIGHTS:

Weight empty	2,404 kg (5,300 lb)
Max T-O weight	3,447 kg (7,600 lb)
Max zero-fuel weight	2,993 kg (6,600 lb)
Max landing weight	3,266 kg (7,200 lb)

PERFORMANCE (at max T-O weight except where indicated):

Max cruising speed, at max cruise power, AUW of 3,220 kg (7,100 lb):	
at 8,230 m (27,000 ft)	315 knots (584 km/h; 363 mph)
at 6,705 m (22,000 ft)	278 knots (515 km/h; 320 mph)
at 4,875 m (16,000 ft)	251 knots (465 km/h; 289 mph)

Advanced Aircraft Turbine P-210 turboprop conversion of Cessna Pressurised Centurion, before addition of ventral fin

Advanced Aircraft Regent 1500, with Pratt & Whitney Canada PT6A-135 turboprops

Max rate of climb at S/L:		
at max T-O weight	945 m (3,100 ft)/min	
at 3,175 kg (7,000 lb) AUW	1,310 m (4,300 ft)/min	
Service ceiling	9,145 m (30,000 ft)	
Service ceiling, one engine out, at 3,175 kg (7,000 lb) AUW	7,620 m (25,000 ft)	
T-O run	462 m (1,517 ft)	
T-O to 15 m (50 ft)	694 m (2,277 ft)	
Landing from 15 m (50 ft) with propeller reversal	606 m (1,988 ft)	
Landing run with propeller reversal	324 m (1,064 ft)	
Range with max fuel, ISA, allowances for start, taxi, take-off, climb and descent, 45 min reserves:		

max cruise power:	
at 4,875 m (16,000 ft)	832 nm (1,542 km; 958 miles)
at 6,705 m (22,000 ft)	
	987 nm (1,829 km; 1,136 miles)
at 8,230 m (27,000 ft)	
	1,169 nm (2,166 km; 1,346 miles)
max range power:	
at 5,485 m (18,000 ft)	
	908 nm (1,682 km; 1,045 miles)
at 6,705 m (22,000 ft)	
	1,112 nm (2,060 km; 1,280 miles)
at 8,230 m (27,000 ft)	
	1,276 nm (2,364 km; 1,469 miles)

AERODIS
AERODIS AMERICA INC

D. W. Hooks Airport, 8319 Thora, Spring, Texas 77379
Telephone: 1 (713) 370 0394
Telex: 792835
Fax: 1 (713) 251 3633
PRESIDENT: Leonard E. Wolff

Aerodis America Inc was formed in October 1982 to design, manufacture and market light aircraft for civilian and military purposes. The company has commissioned the well-known light aircraft engineer David B. Thurston of Thurston Aeromarine Corporation to design three all-composite aircraft based on a common airframe. Aerodis has entered into an agreement with P. T. Cipta Restu Sarana Svaha of Indonesia for the manufacture of composite components for the aircraft, which will be assembled by Asian Aviation International of Bangkok, Thailand. Marketing in Asia, the Middle East and Pacific basin will be undertaken by Aerodis (HK) Company Limited of Hong Kong.

AERODIS AA200 ORION

Design work started on this four-seat low-wing T tail cabin aircraft in April 1988 and construction of a prototype began in July 1989, with first flight expected in May 1990. Despite its name and similar appearance, Aerodis says the AA200 is not related to the French Grinvalds G-802 Orion homebuilt, described in the Sport Aircraft section of the 1988-89 and earlier editions of *Jane's*. Although full FAA certification will not be sought initially, the Orion has been designed to meet or exceed FAR Pt 23 Amendment 34 requirements.

TYPE: Four-seat light cabin monoplane.
WINGS: Cantilever low-wing monoplane. NASA-developed laminar-flow wing section GA40U-A215 at root, GA37U-A212 at tip. Thickness/chord ratio 15 per cent at root, 12 per cent at tip. Dihedral 3°. Incidence 1.5° at root.

Artist's impression of the Aerodis AA200 Orion all-composite four-seat light aircraft

Fail-safe and damage-tolerant wing of two-spar construction of graphite/glassfibre/Nomex honeycomb composites with D-section leading-edge torque box. Wings have quick-detach fittings for ease of maintenance. Frise-type ailerons of Rohacell foam/glassfibre construction are electrically actuated, maximum deflection 30°. Slotted flaps of similar construction to ailerons.

FUSELAGE: Fail-safe and damage-tolerant monocoque structure of reinforced graphite/glassfibre/Nomex honeycomb/Rohacell foam composites, constructed in two halves and bonded at centreline with stringers and

seven bulkheads. Structural reinforcement of cabin area provides rollover protection for occupants.

TAIL UNIT: Cantilever T tail of moulded honeycomb core with glassfibre skins. Dorsal and ventral fins. Fixed tailplane. Electrically actuated trim tab in central position on one-piece elevator. Rudders in dorsal and ventral fins.

LANDING GEAR: Electro-hydraulically retractable tricycle type with steerable nosewheel. Mainwheels retract inward into wing, nosewheel forward. Oleo-strut shock absorbers in all units. Cleveland mainwheels, size 6.00 ×

6, pressure 3.45 bars (50 lb/sq in). Cleveland nosewheel, size 5.00 × 5, pressure 2.76 bars (40 lb/sq in). Cleveland disc brakes.

POWER PLANT: One 134 kW (180 hp) Textron Lycoming O-360-A4A flat-four engine, mounted to rear of cabin and driving a three-blade constant-speed composite MT pusher propeller via a graphite/epoxy drive shaft and flexidyne coupler. 149 kW (200 hp) Textron Lycoming IO-360-A1B6 engine optional. Fuel contained in integral wing leading-edge tanks, maximum capacity 227 litres (60 US gallons; 50 Imp gallons). Fuel filler cap in upper surface of each wing. Oil capacity 7.6 litres (2 US gallons; 1.67 Imp gallons).

ACCOMMODATION: Enclosed cabin with four individual seats. Baggage compartment aft of seats. Single door on port side of fuselage, horizontally divided, upper half opening upwards while lower portion contains integral entrance step. Emergency exit in forward cabin window on starboard side. Cabin is stressed to withstand 20*g* impact. Inertia-reel shoulder harnesses and seatbelts, cabin soundproofing, heating and ventilation, standard.

SYSTEMS: Electrical system supplied by 28V 60A alternator.

AVIONICS AND EQUIPMENT: IFR avionics to customer choice. Dual controls (sticks) optional.

DIMENSIONS, EXTERNAL:
Wing span	9.13 m (29 ft 11½ in)
Wing chord: at root	1.60 m (5 ft 3 in)
at tip	1.12 m (3 ft 8 in)
Wing aspect ratio	6.55
Length overall	7.75 m (25 ft 5 in)
Height overall	2.62 m (8 ft 7 in)
Tailplane span	3.30 m (10 ft 10 in)
Wheel track	3.23 m (10 ft 7 in)
Wheelbase	2.86 m (9 ft 4½ in)
Propeller diameter	1.88 m (6 ft 2 in)
Propeller ground clearance	0.53 m (1 ft 8¾ in)
Passenger door: Height	1.00 m (3 ft 3¼ in)
Width	1.00 m (3 ft 3¼ in)
Height to sill	0.65 m (2 ft 1½ in)

DIMENSIONS, INTERNAL:
Cabin: Length	2.48 m (8 ft 1½ in)
Max width	1.07 m (3 ft 6 in)
Height	1.14 m (3 ft 8¾ in)
Floor area	2.46 m² (26.43 sq ft)
Volume	2.62 m³ (92.5 cu ft)

AREAS:
Wings, gross	12.73 m² (137.0 sq ft)
Ailerons (total)	0.99 m² (10.67 sq ft)
Trailing-edge flaps (total)	1.68 m² (18.07 sq ft)
Vertical tail surfaces (total)	1.55 m² (16.7 sq ft)
Tailplane	3.14 m² (33.8 sq ft)
Elevator, incl tab	1.21 m² (13.0 sq ft)

WEIGHTS AND LOADINGS:
Weight empty	635 kg (1,400 lb)
Max fuel weight	163 kg (360 lb)
Max T-O weight	1,134 kg (2,500 lb)
Max wing loading	89.1 kg/m² (18.25 lb/sq ft)
Max power loading	8.46 kg/kW (13.89 lb/hp)

PERFORMANCE (estimated, at max T-O weight, ISA):
Never-exceed speed	190 knots (352 km/h; 218 mph)
Max level speed	180 knots (334 km/h; 207 mph)
Max cruising speed at 2,285 m (7,500 ft)	165 knots (306 km/h; 190 mph)
Stalling speed, 30° flap	54 knots (100 km/h; 62 mph)
Max rate of climb at S/L	311 m (1,020 ft)/min
Service ceiling	4,420 m (14,500 ft)
Range with max fuel	780 nm (1,445 km; 898 miles)

Artist's impression of Aerodis AA300 Rigel two-seat primary jet trainer

AERODIS AA300 RIGEL AND AA330 THETA

The AA300 Rigel is a tandem two-seat civilian or military primary jet trainer based on the AA200 Orion airframe, the general configuration of which can be seen in the accompanying artist's impression. A prototype was under construction in early 1990 with a first flight anticipated in September. Aerodis is proposing the AA300 Rigel for the USAF's Joint Primary Aircraft Training System (JPATS) requirement. The AA330 Theta is a single-seat tactical light jet on which design work started in September 1988. Both aircraft are aerobatic and stressed to +9*g*/−6*g*. The data for the AA200 Orion apply also to the AA300 Rigel and AA330 Theta except as follows:

WINGS: Single stores hardpoint under each wing.

FUSELAGE: Rear section detachable for engine change or maintenance. Single stores hardpoint beneath fuselage on centreline.

TAIL UNIT: As for Orion, but small strake instead of ventral fin.

LANDING GEAR: Mainwheel size 18.5 × 5.5. Tyre pressures: mainwheels 5.86 bars (85 lb/sq in); nosewheel 2.07 bars (30 lb/sq in). Maximum nosewheel steering angle ±30°.

POWER PLANT: One 8.45 kN (1,900 lb st) Garrett TFE109-3 or Williams FJ44 turbofan, derated to 5.34 kN (1,200 lb st). Maximum internal fuel capacity 757 litres (200 US gallons; 166.5 Imp gallons). Refuelling point in each wingtip.

ACCOMMODATION: Two in tandem in pressurised and air-conditioned cockpit in Rigel, one in Theta, on McDonnell Douglas Mini-Pac or Martin-Baker Mk 15 lightweight ejection seats. Sideways-opening bubble canopy, hinged on starboard side. Sliding canopy optional on Theta.

SYSTEMS: 28V 300A electrical system. Pressurisation system, maximum differential 0.45 bars (6.5 lb/sq in). Oxygen system standard.

DIMENSIONS, EXTERNAL:
Wing span	8.85 m (29 ft 0½ in)
Wing aspect ratio	6.39
Length overall	7.90 m (25 ft 11 in)
Height overall	2.64 m (8 ft 8 in)
Wheel track	2.95 m (9 ft 8 in)
Wheelbase	3.16 m (10 ft 4½ in)

DIMENSIONS, INTERNAL:
Cockpit (Rigel): Length	2.81 m (9 ft 2½ in)
Max width	0.78 m (2 ft 6½ in)
Height	1.12 m (3 ft 8 in)
Floor area	2.00 m² (21.5 sq ft)

AREAS:
Wings, gross	12.26 m² (132.0 sq ft)
Fin	1.05 m² (11.26 sq ft)
Rudder	0.365 m² (3.93 sq ft)

WEIGHT:
Max T-O weight	1,519 kg (3,350 lb)

PERFORMANCE (estimated, at max T-O weight, ISA):
Max level speed at 9,150 m (30,000 ft)	370 knots (686 km/h; 426 mph)
Max cruising speed at 9,150 m (30,000 ft)	335 knots (621 km/h; 386 mph)
Econ cruising speed at 9,150 m (30,000 ft)	220 knots (408 km/h; 253 mph)
Stalling speed, 30° flap	61 knots (113 km/h; 71 mph)
Max rate of climb at S/L	more than 915 m (3,000 ft)/min
Range with max internal fuel, 45 min reserves	1,050 nm (1,945 km; 1,209 miles)

AERO UNION
AERO UNION CORPORATION

PO Box 247, Municipal Airport, 100 Lockheed Avenue, Chico, California 95926
Telephone: 1 (916) 896 3000
Telex: 171359 AEROUNION CICO
Fax: 1 (916) 893 8585
PRESIDENT: Dale P. Newton
DIRECTOR, SALES AND MARKETING: John Oswald
DIRECTOR, INTERNATIONAL MARKETING:
Robert E. Fitzsimmons

This company was established in 1959 as an aerial firefighting operation, using converted war surplus aircraft for aerial retardant delivery. It manufactures tank systems for such aircraft as the Douglas DC-3, DC-4, DC-6 and DC-7, Fairchild C-119 and Grumman S-2. Aero Union also manufactures a variety of equipment, including aircraft fuel tanks, airstairs, environmental control systems, cargo pallet roller systems, retardant delivery and aerial spraying systems, and dorsal fin assemblies, and is the sole manufacturer of the Model 1080 Air Refuelling Store (ARS) originally developed by Beech Aircraft Corporation and acquired by Aero Union in 1985.

AERO UNION MODULAR AIRBORNE FIRE FIGHTING SYSTEM (MAFFS)

Designed for cargo aircraft such as the Lockheed C-130 which use the USAF 463L pallet system, the Aero Union MAFFS comprises five retardant tank modules with a total capacity of 11,356 litres (3,000 US gallons; 2,498 Imp

Lockheed C-130 of the United States Air Force equipped with Aero Union MAFFS

gallons), a control module, and a dispensing module with two retractable nozzles providing a retardant swath 13-61 m (43-200 ft) wide, and 180-610 m (590-2,000 ft) long, depending on aircraft altitude and speed. The MAFFS, which has an installed weight, empty, of 2,177 kg (4,800 lb), is powered by compressed air stored in reservoirs at each tank module. The control module is battery powered. An

installation time of less than one hour is claimed for the C-130 if the MAFFS is assembled on a loader outside the aircraft, with a typical turnaround time of 15 minutes for replenishing the system in operational use. The MAFFS can be operated at altitudes of 30-150 m (98-492 ft) and at speeds of 130-140 knots (241-259 km/h; 150-161 mph). Aero Union has delivered 16 MAFFS to the USAF.

AERO UNION C-130 AUXILIARY FUEL SYSTEM

Aero Union has developed an auxiliary fuel system for the Lockheed C-130/L-100 which can be used for in-flight refuelling, extra fuel capacity, or fuel transportation. The system consists of a 6.1 m (20 ft) platform on which two cylindrical tanks are mounted side by side by means of a pair of cradles and loaded using a standard 463L cargo handling system. The plumbing is in compliance with MIL-F-17874 and offers a flow rate of 1,136 litres (300 US gallons; 250 Imp gallons)/minute. The unit interfaces with the Lockheed air refuelling manifold, and a passage is provided for crew access fore and aft of the tank installation. Tank capacity (total) 13,627 litres (3,600 US gallons; 2,998 Imp gallons); length 5.26 m (17 ft 3 in); width 3.0 m (9 ft 10¼ in); height, excluding plumbing, 1.68 m (5 ft 6 in); weight empty approx 1,542 kg (3,400 lb).

AERO UNION HELIBORNE AERIAL FIRE FIGHTING SYSTEM (HAFFS)

The Heliborne Aerial Fire Fighting System is a second generation development of MAFFS, designed for installation in large helicopters such as the Boeing CH-47/Model 234 series. It has a capacity of 7,571 litres (2,000 US gallons; 1,665 Imp gallons). Extinguishing agent is dispersed through a remotely operated, variable pattern foam cannon capable of delivering up to 2,271 litres (600 US gallons; 500 Imp gallons)/min at a standoff distance of more than 61 m (200 ft). All or part of the payload may also be dropped directly on a fire in under 10 s. The HAFFS will saturate a half-acre area at a density of 40.3 litres/m² (0.99 US gallon; 0.82 Imp gallon/sq ft). Empty weight of the installation is 1,749 kg (3,857 lb). A smaller system, capacity 2,650-3,785 litres (700-1,000 US gallons; 583-833 Imp gallons), is being developed for Boeing CH-46/Kawasaki KV107 helicopters. Aero Union is also evaluating derivative designs for such helicopters as the Aerospatiale AS 332, EHI EH 101, Mil Mi-8 and Sikorsky UH-60.

AERO UNION (GRUMMAN) HU-16B ALBATROSS TANKER CONVERSION

Aero Union has developed a firefighting conversion of the standard HU-16B Albatross amphibian that enables the aircraft to carry 3,785 litres (1,000 US gallons; 833 Imp gallons) of water or retardant in two side by side tanks in the fuselage. The tanks can be filled from two retractable probes which extend into the water while the aircraft is planing on the step, or on land by a single filling point in the fuselage side. The retardant tanks can be emptied individually or simultaneously, and refilled from a body of water within 10 s at a speed of 70 knots (130 km/h; 81 mph).

WEIGHTS:
Weight empty	9,956 kg (21,950 lb)
Max T-O weight	15,036 kg (33,150 lb)

PERFORMANCE:
Max level speed	220 knots (408 km/h; 253 mph)
Cruising speed	162 knots (300 km/h; 186 mph)

AERO UNION SP-2H FIRESTAR TANKER CONVERSION

Aero Union has developed a civilianised air tanker version of the Lockheed P2V-7/SP-2 Neptune maritime patrol aircraft, known as the SP-2H Firestar, the prototype of which (N701AU) entered service in 1988. Conversion involved removal of the Neptune's podded Westinghouse J34 auxiliary turbojet engines and other military equipment, and installation of a fire retardant delivery system comprising a 7,570 litre (2,000 US gallon; 1,665 Imp gallon) capacity tank weighing 318 kg (700 lb) and two computer controlled, electro-hydraulically actuated dispersal doors which can deliver precisely metered flow rates from 189-2,650 litres (50-700 US gallons; 41.6-583 Imp gallons) per second. Computerised digital logic allows the pilot to select the retardant coverage level and quantity to produce the required drop pattern, resulting in drops that are continuous and uniform in density, with no overlaps or gaps. Incremental volumes of one eighth, one quarter, one half or all of tank capacity may be selected. The system maintains a constant rate of flow regardless of the amount of retardant remaining in the tank, and is claimed to provide drop patterns 50 per cent longer than typical multi-door drop systems using the same volume of retardant.

WEIGHTS:
Weight empty	16,692 kg (36,800 lb)
Max payload	8,164 kg (18,000 lb)
Max T-O and landing weight	30,617 kg (67,500 lb)

PERFORMANCE (at max T-O weight):
Never-exceed speed	270 knots (500 km/h; 311 mph)
Econ cruising speed	195 knots (361 km/h; 225 mph)
Max airdrop speed	145 knots (268 km/h; 167 mph)

Aero Union Firestar tanker conversion of the Lockheed SP-2H Neptune

Stalling speed, landing gear and flaps down
93 knots (172 km/h; 107 mph)
Max rate of climb at S/L	488 m (1,600 ft)/min
Rate of climb at S/L, one engine out	122 m (400 ft)/min
Certificated ceiling	5,485 m (18,000 ft)
Service ceiling, one engine out	5,365 m (17,600 ft)

Max ferry range, 30 min reserves
1,300 nm (2,409 km; 1,497 miles)

AERO UNION C-130 AIR TANKER CONVERSION

Aero Union's initial C-130 air tanker conversion was performed on a C-130A Hercules, but is adaptable to later models. It employs a retardant tank of 11,356 litres (3,000 US gallons; 2,498 Imp gallons) capacity, but all other elements of the dispersal system are similar to that of the SP-2H Firestar conversion described above. First flight of the aircraft was scheduled for early 1990, with service entry planned for the Spring.

AERO UNION P-3A ORION AIR TANKER CONVERSION

In early 1990 Aero Union was converting a Lockheed P-3A Orion maritime patrol aircraft for firefighting use. It was to be equipped temporarily with a ventrally mounted 11,356 litre (3,000 US gallon; 2,498 Imp gallon) retardant tank with eight drop doors, pending development of a new computer-controlled tank similar to those of the SP-2H and C-130 conversions, for installation in Spring 1991.

AERO UNION CESSNA 208/208B CARAVAN AIR TANKER CONVERSION

Aero Union has developed a lightweight firefighting kit for the Cessna Model 208/208B utility aircraft. Known as the **Caravan Fire Fighter**, it comprises a ventrally mounted retardant tank of aluminium construction, capacity 1,893 litres (500 US gallons; 416 Imp gallons) which attaches to standard Caravan cargo pod mountings. The tank weighs 163 kg (360 lb) and is equipped with two hydraulically actuated drop doors extending virtually its whole length. The computer-modulated doors maintain a standard preset drop rate, variable in eight increments from 3.8-30.3 litres (1-8 US gallons; 0.8-6.7 Imp gallons) per 9.3 m² (100 sq ft). An integral injection system provides sufficient foaming agent for 10 drops before refilling. An optional spray manifold kit permits conversion to an aerial insecticide sprayer.

AERO UNION C-130 AERIAL SPRAY SYSTEM

This self-contained modular system is mounted on a standard 463L pallet and is designed for installation in unmodified Lockheed C-130 aircraft. It comprises dual Aero Union bulk fuel transfer tanks of 6,813 litres (1,800 US gallons; 1,498 Imp gallons) each which have been modified with an external line to supply fluids to a spray module attached to the aircraft's cargo loading ramp. The spray module has a hydraulically actuated sprayboom which deploys below the fuselage in free airstream, and can be fully retracted into the aircraft and the cargo ramp closed when spraying has finished. Interchangeable spray nozzles permit application rate to be varied. Ultra-low-volume rotary atomisers may also be installed. Pressure and liquid flow rate to the booms are monitored and controlled from a portable electronic control panel operated by the aircraft loadmaster.

AIR TRACTOR
AIR TRACTOR INC

PO Box 485, Municipal Airport, Olney, Texas 76374
Telephone: 1 (817) 564 5616
Telex: 910 890 4792
Fax: 1 (817) 564 2348
PRESIDENT: Leland Snow

The Air Tractor series of agricultural aircraft embodies more than 30 years' experience by their designer, Mr Leland Snow, who designed, developed, certificated and put into production the earlier Snow S-2 series of agricultural aircraft. The latter, which later became the Rockwell S-2R Thrush, have been described in previous editions of *Jane's*.

Six versions of the Air Tractor series were available in 1990: the Models AT-401 and AT-501 with radial engines; and the AT-400, AT-402, AT-502 and AT-503 with various types of Pratt & Whitney Canada PT6A turboprop.

AIR TRACTOR MODEL AT-401/401A AIR TRACTOR

The AT-401 version of the Air Tractor was developed during 1986 and is based on the Pratt & Whitney R-1340 powered Model AT-301, but with an increased wing span and a larger capacity hopper. By January 1990 a total of 58 AT-401s had been delivered to customers in Australia, Brazil, Colombia, Spain and the United States.

In early 1990 Air Tractor was developing the AT-401A, which is powered by a Polish 441.5 kW (592 hp) Pezetel PZL-3S Series 2 radial engine driving a four-blade constant-speed US-132000/A-4 Hydromatic propeller, diameter 2.63 m (8 ft 7½ in). The PZL-3S engine installed in the AT-401A is a special version developed for Air Tractor and featuring cylinders with increased cooling fin area, Simplex piston rings and a carburettor with manual mixture control, and will be offered as an alternative to the AT-401's Pratt & Whitney power plant. FAA certification of the AT-401A was expected in early Summer 1990, to be followed by extensive service testing by Air Tractor dealers before production is launched.

TYPE: Single-seat agricultural aircraft.

WINGS: Cantilever low-wing monoplane. Wing section NACA 4415. Dihedral 3° 30′. Incidence 2°. No sweepback. Conventional two-spar structure of 2024-T3 light alloy, with alloy steel lower spar cap and bonded doubler on inside of wing leading-edge for impact damage resistance. Glassfibre wingroot fairings. Ailerons of light alloy construction, interconnected with trailing-edge flaps to droop 10° at maximum flap deflection of 30°. Aileron boost tabs. Electrically operated Fowler trailing-edge flaps of light alloy construction. Wing ribs and wing skins zinc chromated before assembly. Wingroot and skin overlaps sealed against chemical entry.

FUSELAGE: Welded structure of 4130N steel tube, oven stress relieved and oiled internally. Quickly detachable skins of 2024-T3 light alloy, with Camloc fasteners. Rear fuselage lightly pressurised to prevent chemical ingress.

TAIL UNIT: Light alloy structure, with cantilever fin and strut braced tailplane. Metal skinned rudder and elevators, sealed against chemical ingress. Boost tabs in each elevator and in rudder.

LANDING GEAR: Non-retractable tailwheel type. Cantilever heavy duty E-4340 spring steel main gear, thickness 28.6 mm (1.125 in); flat spring suspension for castoring and lockable tailwheel. Cleveland mainwheels with tyre size 8.50-10 (8-ply), pressure 2.83 bars (41 lb/sq in). Tailwheel tyre size 5.00-5. Cleveland four-piston brakes with heavy duty brake discs.

POWER PLANT: One remanufactured 447 kW (600 hp) Pratt & Whitney R-1340 aircooled radial engine with speed ring cowling, driving a Pacific Propeller 22D40/AG200-2 Hydromatic two-blade constant-speed metal propeller without spinner. Hydromatic 23D40 three-blade propeller, diameter 2.59 m (8 ft 6 in), optional. 441.5 kW (592 hp) Pezetel PZL-3S Series 2 in AT-401A, as detailed above. Fuel in two integral wing tanks with combined capacity of 477 litres (126 US gallons; 105 Imp gallons). Refuelling points on upper surface of wings at root. Oil capacity 30 litres (8 US gallons; 6.7 Imp gallons).

ACCOMMODATION: Single seat with nylon mesh cover in enclosed cabin which is sealed to prevent chemical ingress. Downward hinged window/door on each side. 'Line of sight' instrument layout, with swing-down lower instrument panel for ease of access for instrument maintenance. Baggage compartment in bottom of fuselage, aft of cabin, with door on port side. Cabin ventilation by 0.10 m (4 in) diameter airscoop.

SYSTEMS: Agricultural dispersal system comprises a 1,514 litre (400 US gallon; 333 Imp gallon) Derakane vinylester resin/glassfibre hopper mounted in forward fuselage with hopper window and instrument panel mounted hopper quantity gauge; 0.97 m (3 ft 2 in) wide Transland gatebox; Transland 5 cm (2 in) bottom loading valve; Agrinautics 6.4 cm (2½ in) spraypump with Transland on/off valve and two-blade wooden fan, and 41-nozzle stainless steel spray system with streamlined booms. 24V electrical system, supplied by 35A engine-driven alternator.

AVIONICS AND EQUIPMENT: Optional avionics include Bendix/ King KX 155 nav/com and Narco ELT-10 emergency locator transmitter. Standard equipment includes ground start receptacle and three-colour polyurethane paint finish. Optional equipment includes night flying package comprising strobe and navigation lights; night working lights; retractable 600W landing light in port wingtip, and ferry fuel system. Alternative agricultural equipment includes Transland 22358 extra high volume spreader, Transland 54401 NorCal Swathmaster, and 40 extra spray nozzles for high volume spraying.

DIMENSIONS, EXTERNAL:

Wing span	14.97 m (49 ft 1¼ in)
Wing chord, constant	1.83 m (6 ft 0 in)
Wing aspect ratio	8.2
Length overall	8.23 m (27 ft 0 in)
Height overall	2.59 m (8 ft 6 in)

AREAS:

Wings, gross	27.31 m² (294.0 sq ft)
Ailerons (total)	3.55 m² (38.2 sq ft)
Trailing-edge flaps (total)	3.75 m² (40.4 sq ft)
Fin	0.90 m² (9.7 sq ft)
Rudder	1.30 m² (14.0 sq ft)
Tailplane	2.42 m² (26.0 sq ft)
Elevators, incl tabs	2.36 m² (25.4 sq ft)

WEIGHTS AND LOADINGS:

Weight empty, spray equipped	1,875 kg (4,135 lb)
Max T-O weight	3,565 kg (7,860 lb)
Max landing weight	2,721 kg (6,000 lb)
Max wing loading	130.51 kg/m² (26.73 lb/sq ft)
Max power loading	7.97 kg/kW (13.1 lb/hp)

PERFORMANCE (at max T-O weight, ISA, except where indicated):

Max cruising speed at S/L, hopper empty	
	135 knots (251 km/h; 156 mph)
Cruising speed at 1,220 m (4,000 ft)	
	124 knots (230 km/h; 143 mph)
Typical working speed	
	104-122 knots (193-225 km/h; 120-140 mph)
Stalling speed at 2,721 kg (6,000 lb):	
flaps up	64 knots (118 km/h; 73 mph)
flaps down	53 knots (98 km/h; 61 mph)
Stalling speed as usually landed	
	47 knots (87 km/h; 54 mph)
Max rate of climb at S/L:	
at max landing weight	335 m (1,100 ft)/min
at max T-O weight	158 m (520 ft)/min
T-O run	402 m (1,318 ft)
Range, econ cruising speed at 2,440 m (8,000 ft), no reserves	547 nm (1,014 km; 630 miles)

AIR TRACTOR MODEL AT-400 and 402 TURBO AIR TRACTOR

These versions of the Air Tractor incorporate a 1,514 litre (400 US gallon; 333 Imp gallon) hopper and 0.97 m (3 ft 2 in) wide gatebox. The **AT-400** is powered by a 507 kW (680 shp) Pratt & Whitney Canada PT6A-15AG, -27 or -28 turboprop, the **AT-402** by the same engines, either new or customer-furnished, in each case driving a Hartzell three-blade constant-speed reversible-pitch propeller. All models have steel alloy wing lower spar caps for unlimited fatigue life, and a reinforced leading-edge to prevent bird strike damage; size 29-11 high-flotation tyres and wheels as standard; and a 250A starter/generator and two 24V 21Ah batteries. Standard fuel capacity is 477 litres (126 US gallons; 105 Imp gallons). Optional fuel capacities 818 litres (216 US gallons; 180 Imp gallons) and 886 litres (234 US gallons; 195 Imp gallons). Optional equipment includes Transland extra high volume dispersal system.

The Air Tractor AT-402 was first flown in August 1988 and received FAA certification in November of that year. This model combines the fuselage, tail surfaces and landing gear of the Model AT-400 with the long span wings of the Model AT-401. The first AT-402 was delivered in late 1988.

A total of 86 AT-400s and nine AT-402s had been delivered by 1 January 1990.

WEIGHTS AND LOADINGS:

Weight empty, spray equipped	1,696 kg (3,739 lb)
Certificated gross weight (FAR 23)	2,721 kg (6,000 lb)

Air Tractor Model AT-501 with Pratt & Whitney radial engine

Typical operating weight (CAM 8)	3,538 kg (7,800 lb)
Max wing loading	141.1 kg/m² (28.9 lb/sq ft)
Max power loading	6.98 kg/kW (11.47 lb/shp)

PERFORMANCE (at max T-O weight except where indicated):

Max level speed at S/L, clean	
	174 knots (322 km/h; 200 mph)
Max level speed at S/L with dispersal equipment	
	160 knots (298 km/h; 185 mph)
Cruising speed at 283.3 kW (380 shp) at 2,440 m (8,000 ft)	
	142 knots (264 km/h; 164 mph)
Typical working speed	
	113-126 knots (209-233 km/h; 130-145 mph)
Stalling speed at 2,721 kg (6,000 lb) AUW:	
flaps up	64 knots (118 km/h; 73 mph)
flaps down	53 knots (99 km/h; 61 mph)
Stalling speed as usually landed	
	46 knots (86 km/h; 53 mph)
Max rate of climb at S/L, dispersal equipment installed, AUW of 2,721 kg (6,000 lb)	495 m (1,625 ft)/min
Max rate of climb at S/L, dispersal equipment installed, AUW of 3,565 kg (7,860 lb)	305 m (1,000 ft)/min
T-O run at AUW of 3,565 kg (7,860 lb)	247 m (810 ft)
Landing run as usually landed	122 m (400 ft)

AIR TRACTOR MODEL AT-501

The original Model AT-500, which was described briefly in the 1985-86 *Jane's,* was a market research prototype for a new series of larger Air Tractors, and resulted in the production AT-501 variant which was certificated on 23 June 1987 with subsequent delivery of eight aircraft. The AT-501 is powered by a 447 kW (600 hp) Pratt & Whitney R-1340-S3H1G radial engine, driving a three-blade Hydromatic propeller, but may be converted to turboprop AT-502 configuration in the field, since the two models are identical aft of the engine firewall. Fuel capacity is 477 litres (126 US gallons; 105 Imp gallons); hopper capacity 1,900 litres (502 US gallons; 418 Imp gallons).

DIMENSIONS, EXTERNAL:

Wing span	15.24 m (50 ft 0 in)
Wing chord, constant	1.83 m (6 ft 0 in)
Length overall	9.05 m (29 ft 8½ in)
Height overall	2.99 m (9 ft 9½ in)
Wheel track	3.11 m (10 ft 2½ in)
Propeller diameter	3.30 m (10 ft 10 in)

AREA:

Wings, gross	27.87 m² (300.0 sq ft)

WEIGHTS:

Weight empty	2,086 kg (4,600 lb)
Design gross weight	3,629 kg (8,000 lb)
Normal operating weight	4,173 kg (9,200 lb)

PERFORMANCE:

Max level speed, with spray equipment	
	139 knots (257 km/h; 160 mph)
Cruising speed	121 knots (225 km/h; 140 mph)
Working speed	
	104-121 knots (193-225 km/h; 120-140 mph)
Stalling speed at normal landing weight	
	49 knots (91 km/h; 56 mph)

AIR TRACTOR MODEL AT-502

Increased usage of low-density nitrogen based fertilisers such as urea in various parts of the world prompted development of the Air Tractor AT-502, which has a larger chemical hopper than the AT-400, increased wing span, and safety glass centre windscreen with wiper. The AT-502 is designed for installation of a variety of Pratt & Whitney Canada PT6A turboprops. The AT-502 was first flown in April 1987, FAA type certification was granted on 23 June 1987. By 1 January 1990 a total of 68 AT-502s had been ordered, of which 29 had been delivered. Combined AT-401/AT-502 production was running at nine aircraft per month in early 1990. Differences from the AT-400 are as follows:

WINGS: As for AT-400 but with 1.52 m (5 ft 0 in) increase in span, alloy steel lower spar cap and bonded doubler on inside of wing leading-edge for increased resistance to impact damage, and glassfibre wingroot fairings.

FUSELAGE: Length increased by 0.56 m (1 ft 10 in), width increased by 0.25 m (10 in), and larger diameter tubular frame members used to cater for increased max T-O weight.

LANDING GEAR: As for AT-503.

POWER PLANT: One 507 kW (680 shp) Pratt & Whitney Canada PT6A-15AG, PT6A-27, PT6A-28, or 559 kW (750 shp) PT6A-34 or PT6A-34AG turboprop, driving a Hartzell HCB3TN-3D/T10282+4 three-blade metal propeller with spinner. Standard fuel capacity 477 litres (126 US gallons; 105 Imp gallons). Optional capacities 818 litres (216 US gallons; 180 Imp gallons) and 886 litres (234 US gallons; 195 Imp gallons).

ACCOMMODATION: As for AT-400, but with new quick-detachable instrument panel and removable fuselage skin panels for ease of maintenance.

SYSTEMS: Agricultural dispersal system comprises a 1,900 litre (502 US gallon; 418 Imp gallon) Derakane vinylester resin/glassfibre hopper mounted in forward fuselage with hopper window and instrument panel mounted hopper quantity gauge; 0.96 m (3 ft 2 in) wide Transland gatebox; Transland 5 cm (2 in) bottom loading valve; Agrinautics 6.4 cm (2½ in) spraypump with Transland on/off valve and two-blade wooden fan, and 40-nozzle stainless steel spray system with streamlined booms. Two 24V 42Ah batteries and 250A starter/generator. Optional dispersal equipment includes 7.6 cm (3 in) spray system with 119 spray nozzles, and automatic flagman.

AVIONICS AND EQUIPMENT: Optional avionics include Bendix/ King KX 155 nav/com and KR 87 ADF, KY 196 Com radio, KT 76A transponder and Narco ELT-10 emergency locator transmitter. Standard equipment includes safety glass centre windscreen panel, ground start receptacle and three-colour polyurethane paint finish. Optional equipment includes night flying package comprising strobe and navigation lights; night working lights; retractable 600W landing light in port wingtip, windscreen washer and wiper, fuel flowmeter, fuel totaliser and ferry fuel system. Alternative agricultural equipment includes Transland 22356 extra high volume spreader, Transland 54401 NorCal Swathmaster, 41 extra spray nozzles for high volume spraying, and eight-unit Micronair Mini Atomiser unit.

DIMENSIONS, EXTERNAL:

Wing span	15.24 m (50 ft 0 in)
Wing chord, constant	1.83 m (6 ft 0 in)
Wing aspect ratio	8.3
Length overall	9.91 m (32 ft 6 in)
Height overall	2.99 m (9 ft 9½ in)
Wheel track	3.11 m (10 ft 2½ in)
Wheelbase	6.64 m (21 ft 9½ in)
Propeller diameter	2.69 m (8 ft 10 in)

AREAS:

Wings, gross	27.87 m² (300.0 sq ft)
Ailerons (total)	3.53 m² (38.0 sq ft)
Trailing-edge flaps (total)	3.75 m² (40.4 sq ft)
Fin	0.90 m² (9.7 sq ft)
Rudder	1.30 m² (14.0 sq ft)
Tailplane	2.41 m² (26.0 sq ft)
Elevators (total, incl tab)	2.44 m² (26.3 sq ft)

Air Tractor Model AT-400 Turbo Air Tractor (P&WC PT6A-15AG turboprop)

WEIGHTS AND LOADINGS:

Weight empty, spray equipped	1,870 kg (4,123 lb)
Max T-O weight (CAM 8)	4,173 kg (9,200 lb)
Max landing weight	3,629 kg (8,000 lb)
Max wing loading	138.36 kg/m² (28.33 lb/sq ft)
Max power loading	7.61 kg/kW (12.5 lb/shp)

PERFORMANCE (at max T-O weight, except where indicated, with spray equipment installed):

Never-exceed speed and max speed at S/L, hopper empty	156 knots (290 km/h; 180 mph)
Cruising speed at 2,440 m (8,000 ft), 283.3 kW (380 shp)	136 knots (253 km/h; 157 mph)
Typical working speed	104-126 knots (193-233 km/h; 120-145 mph)
Stalling speed at 3,629 kg (8,000 lb):	
flaps up	72 knots (134 km/h; 83 mph)
flaps down	60 knots (111 km/h; 69 mph)
Stalling speed as usually landed	46 knots (86 km/h; 53 mph)
Max rate of climb at S/L, AUW of 3,629 kg (8,000 lb):	
with PT6A-15AG	311 m (1,020 ft)/min
with PT6A-34AG	360 m (1,180 ft)/min
Max rate of climb at S/L, AUW of 4,173 kg (9,200 lb):	
with PT6A-15AG	232 m (760 ft)/min
with PT6A-34AG	282 m (925 ft)/min
T-O run at AUW of 3,629 kg (8,000 lb):	
with PT6A-15AG	244 m (800 ft)
with PT6A-34AG	222 m (730 ft)
T-O run at AUW of 4,173 kg (9,200 lb):	
with PT6A-15AG	356 m (1,170 ft)
with PT6A-34AG	302 m (990 ft)
Range with max fuel	435 nm (805 km; 500 miles)

AIR TRACTOR MODEL AT-503

Design of the AT-503 began in September 1985 in response to a US State Department requirement for aerial application aircraft suitable for eradication of narcotics crops. The AT-503 is larger than previous Air Tractor models and is the company's first two-seat design. It is intended for special purpose operations such as fire-bombing, forest spraying in mountainous terrain and high-volume seeding or fertiliser applications, in addition to anti-drug enforcement operations. The prototype made its first flight on 25 April 1986, flown by its designer, Mr Leland Snow. An FAA Type Certificate for the AT-503 was granted on 2 October 1986. The prototype was exhibited at the 1989 Paris Air Show and was subsequently delivered to a customer in Spain.

TYPE: Two-seat agricultural aircraft.

WINGS: As for AT-400 except increased wing and flap spans and heavier gauge skins.

FUSELAGE: As for AT-400 except length increased by 0.56 m (1 ft 10 in), width by 0.25 m (10 in), and larger diameter tubular members employed for increased MTOW.

TAIL UNIT: As for AT-401. Elevator trim tabs actuated electrically.

LANDING GEAR: Non-retractable tailwheel type. Cantilever spring steel main units; flat spring suspension for castoring and lockable tailwheel. Cleveland mainwheels with Goodyear high flotation tyres, size 29-11, pressure 2.96 bars (43 lb/sq in). Tailwheel size 5.00-5. Cleveland three-piston disc brakes.

POWER PLANT: One Pratt & Whitney Canada PT6A-45R turboprop, flat rated at 820 kW (1,100 shp), driving a Hartzell five-blade feathering and reversible-pitch constant-speed metal propeller with spinner. Frakes Aviation Jet Thrust exhaust outlets. Fuel in two integral tanks and two self-sealing bladder tanks in wings, total usable capacity 984 litres (260 US gallons; 216.5 Imp gallons). Self-sealing tanks are of FTL No. 1 type, resistant to 0.50 in rounds.

ACCOMMODATION: Two seats in tandem in enclosed cabin, which is sealed to prevent chemical ingress and protected with overturn structure. Four downward hinged doors, two on each side, with 25.4 mm (1 in) square chromoly tube frames. Rear seat position windows are bulged to

Air Tractor Model AT-503 two-seat agricultural aircraft

Air Tractor Model AT-503A dual-control agricultural training aircraft

provide downward and forward view for observer/instructor. Windscreen is constructed of bulletproof laminated acrylic/polycarbonate. Windscreen washer/wiper system optional. Separate ram airscoops for ventilation of each cockpit.

SYSTEM: Integral chemical hopper, capacity 1,900 litres (502 US gallons; 418 Imp gallons).

DIMENSIONS, EXTERNAL:

Wing span	14.63 m (48 ft 0 in)
Wing chord, constant	1.83 m (6 ft 0 in)
Wing aspect ratio	8.0
Length overall	10.21 m (33 ft 6 in)
Height overall	2.99 m (9 ft 9½ in)
Wheel track	3.11 m (10 ft 2½ in)
Wheelbase	6.64 m (21 ft 9½ in)
Propeller diameter	2.82 m (9 ft 3 in)

AREAS:

Wings, gross	26.76 m² (288.0 sq ft)
Ailerons (total)	3.53 m² (38.0 sq ft)
Trailing-edge flaps (total)	3.40 m² (36.6 sq ft)
Fin	0.90 m² (9.70 sq ft)
Rudder	1.30 m² (14.0 sq ft)
Tailplane	2.41 m² (26.0 sq ft)
Elevators (total, incl tab)	2.44 m² (26.3 sq ft)

WEIGHTS AND LOADINGS:

Weight empty, equipped	2,109 kg (4,650 lb)
Max T-O weight (CAM 8)	4,754 kg (10,480 lb)
Max landing weight	3,629 kg (8,000 lb)
Max wing loading	177.65 kg/m² (36.39 lb/sq ft)
Max power loading	5.80 kg/kW (9.53 lb/shp)

PERFORMANCE (at max T-O weight except where indicated):

Max level speed at S/L	191 knots (340 km/h; 220 mph)
Max cruising speed at 2,440 m (8,000 ft)	182 knots (338 km/h; 210 mph)
Ferry speed	156 knots (290 km/h; 180 mph)
Stalling speed, power off, flaps down, at max landing weight	60 knots (111 km/h; 69 mph)
Max rate of climb at S/L, no hopper load	1,067 m (3,500 ft)/min
Service ceiling	10,975 m (36,000 ft)
T-O run	85 m (280 ft)
Range with max fuel	695 nm (1,287 km; 800 miles)
g limit	+3.8

AIR TRACTOR MODEL 503A

The Air Tractor Model 503A combines the two-seat fuselage of the AT-503 with the wings of the AT-502. Power plant options are 559 kW (750 shp) Pratt & Whitney Canada PT6A-34 or PT6A-34AG turboprops. The AT-503A is intended as a trainer, and has full dual controls, but can also be equipped with a 1,893 litre (500 US gallon; 416 Imp gallon) hopper and dispersal system for agricultural or firefighting use. Specifications, external dimensions, weights and performance are identical to those of the AT-502.

ALLISON

ALLISON GAS TURBINE DIVISION GMC

PO Box 420-SC U13A, Indianapolis, Indiana 46206-0420
Telephone: 1 (317) 230 3158
Telex: 276411
Fax: 1 (317) 230 5100
PUBLIC RELATIONS OFFICER: Anthony A. Perona

ALLISON PROP-JET BONANZA

Allison has sold the supplemental type certificate for this turboprop conversion of the Beechcraft Model A36 Bonanza to Tradewind Turbines of Amarillo, Texas, under whose entry in this section a full description and photograph appear.

ALLISON TURBINE MENTOR

In conjunction with Soloy Conversions Ltd and Mentors Unlimited, Allison has developed a turboprop conversion of the Beechcraft T-34 Mentor (Model 45) two-seat military trainer which involves replacement of the 152.9 kW (225 hp)

and 212.5 kW (285 hp) Continental piston engines originally installed with a 313 kW (420 shp) Allison 250B-17D turboprop, employing a similar engine mount to that developed for the Allison (now Tradewind Turbines) Prop-Jet Bonanza. Part of the space gained by the more forward location of the turboprop is used for an electrical bay and baggage compartment. Other modifications include strengthening of the wing to withstand a maximum load of 6g, and additional fuel tanks which increase standard capacity from 189 litres (50 US gallons; 41.6 Imp gallons) to 303 litres (80 US gallons; 66.6 Imp gallons). Wingtip tanks, each of 76 litres (20 US gallons; 16.6 Imp gallons) capacity, are optional. The Allison conversion can be carried out on T-34A and T-34B Mentors. An alternative version of the Allison 250 power plant with 372.8 kW (500 shp) rating will be available on production aircraft. The prototype Turbine Mentor (N4CN) made its public debut at the Paris Air Show in June 1987 and was demonstrated subsequently to a number of potential military operators. Orders from several countries were being negotiated in early 1990.

DIMENSIONS, EXTERNAL AND INTERNAL:

Wing span	10.00 m (32 ft 9⅞ in)
Wing chord: at root	2.13 m (7 ft 0 in)
at tip	1.07 m (3 ft 6 in)
Wing aspect ratio	6.1
Length overall	8.56 m (28 ft 1 in)
Height overall	2.92 m (9 ft 7 in)
Tailplane span	3.71 m (12 ft 2⅛ in)
Wheel track	2.92 m (9 ft 7 in)
Propeller diameter	2.29 m (7 ft 6 in)
Propeller ground clearance	0.31 m (1 ft 0¼ in)
Baggage door, rear:	
Height	0.48 m (1 ft 7⅛ in)
Max width	0.54 m (1 ft 9⅛ in)
Baggage door, forward:	
Height	0.35 m (1 ft 2 in)
Width	0.30 m (1 ft 0 in)
Baggage capacity, total	0.30 m³ (10.5 cu ft)

AREAS:

Wings, gross	16.50 m² (177.6 sq ft)
Ailerons (total)	1.07 m² (11.5 sq ft)

Flaps (total)	1.98 m² (21.3 sq ft)
Fin, incl dorsal fin	1.06 m² (11.46 sq ft)
Rudder, incl tab	0.62 m² (6.63 sq ft)
Tailplane	2.07 m² (22.25 sq ft)
Elevators (total, incl tabs)	1.39 m² (15.0 sq ft)

WEIGHTS:

Weight empty	916 kg (2,020 lb)
Max aerobatic T-O weight	1,338 kg (2,950 lb)
Max T-O weight	1,542 kg (3,400 lb)

PERFORMANCE:

Never-exceed speed	219 knots (406 km/h; 252 mph)
Max level speed at S/L	200 knots (370 km/h; 230 mph)
Max cruising speed at 3,050 m (10,000 ft)	205 knots (380 km/h; 236 mph)
Max rate of climb at S/L	640 m (2,100 ft)/min
Service ceiling	7,620 m (25,000 ft)
T-O run	137 m (450 ft)
T-O to 15 m (50 ft)	213 m (700 ft)
Landing from 15 m (50 ft)	229 m (750 ft)
Landing run	107 m (350 ft)
Range	1,080 nm (2,001 km; 1,244 miles)
g limits	+6/−3

Prototype Allison Turbine Mentor turboprop conversion of the Beech T-34 trainer

AMECO-HAWK
AMECO-HAWK INTERNATIONAL
PO Box 6292, Olympia, Washington 98502
Telephone: 1 (206) 842 1093
PRINCIPALS: Ronald C. Karzmar
Ronald W. Wright

In 1989 Ameco, a holding company specialising in aerospace engineering and manufacturing, joined Hawk International to continue development of the GafHawk 125, designed in 1977 by Ernest Hawk.

AMECO-HAWK GAFHAWK 125-200
Features considered of prime importance in design of the GafHawk (General Aviation Freighter) included STOL capability for operation into and from small unprepared strips, a turboprop power plant for economic operation, a square-section fuselage for maximum utilisation of internal capacity including the ability to carry vehicles or up to three LD3 containers, undertail loading of bulk cargo at truckbed height, and a single engine for economy, ease of certification and single-pilot operation.

A small scale flying testbed known as the MiniHawk, which consisted of an extensively rebuilt Piper Tri-Pacer light aircraft, made its first flight in 1978 and was described and illustrated in the 1980-81 *Jane's.*

The GafHawk 125 prototype (N101GH) was flown for the first time on 19 August 1982, powered by an 893 kW (1,198 shp) Pratt & Whitney Canada PT6A-45R turboprop, and by early 1990 had completed more than 75 test flights.

At that time modifications were being made to the design involving a fuselage stretch to enable containers to be carried and to revise the aircraft's centre of gravity to improve handling. The modified aircraft is known as the GafHawk 125-200, and will initially be certificated under FAR Pt 23 which currently restricts gross weight to 5,670 kg (12,500 lb), although it would be capable of operating at a max T-O weight of 6,577 kg (14,500 lb).

TYPE: Single-engined all-metal turboprop freighter.

WINGS: Strut braced high-wing monoplane, with dual steel alloy struts enclosed in an aluminium fairing to provide redundancy, plus short dual auxiliary struts on each side. Wing section NASA-GAW-1, modified by use of a leading-edge cuff. Thickness/chord ratio 17 per cent. No dihedral. Constant chord fail-safe structure of light alloy, comprising a leading-edge tubular spar, a box spar, a second tubular spar aft of the box, a total of 78 one-piece ribs, and light alloy skins. Electrically actuated full-span trailing-edge flaps of similar construction. Half-span spoiler/aileron ('rolleron') hinged to top surface within slot between wing and flap in outer half of each wing, operating differentially through a range of 60.5° up and 10.5° down. 'Rolleron' trimming by bungee.

FUSELAGE: Rectangular structure of welded square-section chrome-molybdenum steel tubing, covered with non-structural Alclad light alloy skins attached by clips, to facilitate replacement of damaged sections.

TAIL UNIT: Cantilever light alloy structure. Construction similar to wings, but with only fore and aft tubular spars in fin and tailplane. Horn balanced rudder and one-piece elevator. Dorsal fin. Rudder and elevator have servotabs and electrically actuated trim tabs.

LANDING GEAR: Non-retractable tricycle type, with single wheel on each unit. All units have shock absorption by rubber elastomer in compression. Goodyear tyres and

Prototype Ameco-Hawk GafHawk 125 single-engined turboprop freighter

wheels of the same size on all three units, tyre size 15.00-12. Dual mainwheels optional. Goodyear hydraulic disc brakes. Parking brake.

POWER PLANT: One Pratt & Whitney Canada PT6A-65AR turboprop, with a max continuous rating of 910 kW (1,220 shp), driving a Hartzell five-blade reversible-pitch constant-speed metal propeller with spinner. Fuel tank, made of light alloy and with a capacity of 1,363 litres (360 US gallons; 300 Imp gallons), mounted above forward fuselage, directly over the wing, and providing gravity feed to engine. Refuelling point on upper surface of tank. Two aluminium fuel tanks, with a combined capacity of 3,785 litres (1,000 US gallons; 833 Imp gallons), can be installed in the main cargo hold for long ferry flights. Oil capacity 11.5 litres (3.5 US gallons; 2.9 Imp gallons). Engine air intake incorporates an ice ramp and foreign particle separator. Electrically heated de-icing boots for propeller and engine air intake.

ACCOMMODATION: Pilot and co-pilot on flight deck. Dual controls and full blind-flying instrumentation for both pilots standard. Door to flight deck on each side of fuselage; communicating door between flight deck and cargo hold in forward bulkhead. Cabin door on each side, aft of wing. Electrically actuated upward/inward-opening main cargo door, in undersurface of upswept rear fuselage, can be opened in flight. Heavy duty corrugated light alloy floor in cargo hold, with cargo tiedowns along walls at each fuselage gusset frame, and tailgate for loading. Main cabin volume augmented by useable space under flight deck, accommodating pipes and timber up to 9.14 m (30 ft) in length with rear loading door closed. Accommodation heated and ventilated.

SYSTEMS: Electrical system powered by 28V 250A SIADS Inc starter/generator and 28V storage battery. Hydraulic system for brakes only. Vacuum system standard. De-icing system optional.

AVIONICS AND EQUIPMENT: Standard avionics include Bendix/King dual nav/com, dual ILS, HSI on pilot's side, ADF, DME, radar altimeter, transponder, switching panel and VOR/localiser-coupled autopilot. Standard equipment includes dual blind-flying instrumentation including turn co-ordinator and rate of climb indicator, dual ASIs, dual altimeters, one encoding, OAT gauge, compass, annunciator panel, eight-day clock, adjustable

crew seats with armrests, instrument post-lighting. landing, navigation, taxi and wingtip strobe lights, two rotating beacons, control locks, and heated pitot head.

DIMENSIONS, EXTERNAL:

Wing span	21.79 m (71 ft 6 in)
Wing chord (constant)	2.08 m (6 ft 10 in)
Wing aspect ratio	10.4
Length overall	15.98 m (52 ft 5 in)
Height overall	5.49 m (18 ft 0 in)
Tailplane span	7.01 m (23 ft 0 in)
Wheel track (c/l outer tyres)	3.38 m (11 ft 1 in)
Wheelbase	4.39 m (14 ft 5 in)
Propeller diameter	2.74 m (9 ft 0 in)
Rear ramp/door: Height	1.93 m (6 ft 4 in)
Width	1.96 m (6 ft 5 in)

DIMENSIONS, INTERNAL:

Cabin: Length at floor level, excl flight deck	6.40 m (21 ft 0 in)
Max width	1.96 m (6 ft 5 in)
Max height	2.36 m (7 ft 9 in)
Volume	26.9 m³ (950 cu ft)
Forward cargo hold under flight deck:	
Height	0.66 m (2 ft 2 in)
Width	1.22 m (4 ft 0 in)

AREA:

Wings, gross	45.8 m² (493.0 sq ft)

WEIGHTS AND LOADINGS:

Weight empty	3,085 kg (6,800 lb)
Max T-O weight	5,670 kg (12,500 lb)
Max wing loading	123.5 kg/m² (25.3 lb/sq ft)
Max power loading	6.23 kg/kW (10.24 lb/shp)

PERFORMANCE (prototype, at max design T-O weight):

Cruising speed (75% power) at 3,050 m (10,000 ft)	123 knots (229 km/h; 142 mph)
Econ cruising speed (55% power) at 3,050 m (10,000 ft)	113 knots (209 km/h; 130 mph)
Stalling speed, 30° flap, partial power	49 knots (91 km/h; 57 mph)
Max rate of climb at S/L	354 m (1,160 ft)/min
Service ceiling	5,485 m (18,000 ft)
T-O run	208 m (680 ft)
T-O to 15 m (50 ft)	506 m (1,660 ft)
Landing from 15 m (50 ft)	436 m (1,430 ft)
Landing run	201 m (660 ft)

AMERICAN GENERAL
AMERICAN GENERAL AIRCRAFT COMPANY
Greenville, Mississippi
CHAIRMAN: Leonard H. Seawell
PRESIDENT: James Cox
VICE-PRESIDENT, SALES: Robert Martin

In June 1989 this company purchased from Gulfstream Aerospace Corporation production and marketing rights for the Gulfstream American AA-1 Lynx, AA-5A Cheetah, AA-5B Tiger and GA-7 Cougar series of light aircraft, described in the 1980-81 and earlier editions of *Jane's.* American General intends to restore these aircraft to production, beginning with a trainer derivative of the

four-seat AA-5A Cheetah and an improved version of the AA-5B Tiger. Some 20 aircraft will be completed in the first year of production, rising to 200 aircraft in the second year and 400 in the third. Assembly will take place at Greenville Airport, using parts and components supplied by vendors and subcontractors and a large stock of finished components that had been held in storage by Gulfstream.

ARCTIC

ARCTIC AIRCRAFT COMPANY

PO Box 6-141, Anchorage International Airport, Alaska
99502
Telephone: 1 (907) 243 1580
PRESIDENT: William A. Diehl

The S1B2 Arctic Tern is an updated and much improved version of the Interstate S1A, first flown in 1940. Built to CAR.04a (aerobatic) standard, it was certificated for operation on optional Edo floats on 20 January 1981. No recent information has been received concerning numbers built.

ARCTIC AIRCRAFT INTERSTATE S1B2 ARCTIC TERN

TYPE: Two-seat sporting and general utility aircraft.
AIRFRAME: See 1987-88 *Jane's*.
POWER PLANT: One 112 kW (150 hp) Textron Lycoming O-320 flat-four engine, driving a McCauley two-blade fixed-pitch metal propeller. One fuel tank in each wing, total capacity 151 litres (40 US gallons; 33.3 Imp gallons). Underbelly auxiliary fuel tank optional.
ACCOMMODATION: Two seats in tandem; rear seat removable to provide additional space for cargo. Cabin door on starboard side, beneath wing. Cabin step. Baggage space in rear fuselage, with external door on starboard side, capacity 45 kg (100 lb). Tinted windows and cabin skylight optional. Safety belts and fittings standard. Dual controls standard. Cabin soundproofed, heated and ventilated. Windscreen de-icing by hot air.
SYSTEM: Electrical system includes 55A engine driven alternator, 12V DC storage battery and engine starter.
AVIONICS AND EQUIPMENT: A range of radios and equipment is available (see 1987-88 edition for details).
DIMENSIONS, EXTERNAL:

Wing span	11.18 m (36 ft 8 in)
Wing chord (constant)	1.57 m (5 ft 2 in)
Length overall: landplane	7.01 m (23 ft 0 in)
seaplane	7.32 m (24 ft 0 in)
Height overall	2.13 m (7 ft 0 in)
Tailplane span	3.35 m (11 ft 0 in)

DIMENSIONS, INTERNAL:

Cabin: Max width	0.66 m (2 ft 2 in)
Volume	1.38 m³ (48.7 cu ft)
Baggage compartment volume	0.84 m³ (29.63 cu ft)

AREA:

Wings, gross	17.30 m² (186.2 sq ft)

WEIGHTS AND LOADINGS (A: landplane; B: seaplane with Edo 2000 floats):

Weight empty: A	487 kg (1,073 lb)
B	521.5 kg (1,150 lb)
Max T-O weight: A	862 kg (1,900 lb)
B	965 kg (2,127 lb)

Arctic Aircraft Interstate S1B2 Arctic Tern (*Neil A. Macdougall*)

Max wing loading: A	49.8 kg/m² (10.2 lb/sq ft)
B	55.7 kg/m² (11.4 lb/sq ft)
Max power loading: A	7.7 kg/kW (12.67 lb/hp)
B	8.62 kg/kW (14.18 lb/hp)

PERFORMANCE:

Never-exceed speed: A	152 knots (282 km/h; 175 mph)

Max cruising speed at S/L, 75% power:

A	102 knots (188 km/h; 117 mph)
B	91 knots (169 km/h; 105 mph)

Cruising speed, 65% power at optimum altitude:

A	96 knots (178 km/h; 111 mph)

Stalling speed, flaps down:

A, B	30 knots (55 km/h; 34 mph)

Max rate of climb at S/L, at max T-O weight:

A	389 m (1,275 ft)/min
B	305 m (1,000 ft)/min
Service ceiling: A, B	5,790 m (19,000 ft)
T-O run at max T-O weight: A	99 m (325 ft)

T-O to 15 m (50 ft) at max T-O weight:

A	152 m (500 ft)
Landing from 15 m (50 ft): A	137 m (450 ft)

Range with max fuel, 45 min reserves:

A, 75% power	479 nm (888 km; 552 miles)
A, 65% power	566 nm (1,049 km; 652 miles)

Range with max fuel, no reserves:

B	499 nm (925 km; 575 miles)

ARCTIC AIRCRAFT INTERSTATE PRIVATEER

During 1988 it was reported that Arctic Aircraft was developing this four-seat version of the Arctic Tern.

Development was continuing in early 1990. The following details are provisional:
POWER PLANT: One 119 kW (160 hp) Textron Lycoming O-320-B2B flat-four engine, driving a McCauley two-blade fixed-pitch metal propeller, diameter 2.08 m (6 ft 10 in). Total fuel capacity 151 litres (40 US gallons; 33.3 Imp gallons).
LANDING GEAR: Cleveland mainwheel tyres size 8.50 × 6; 203 mm (8 in) diameter Maule tailwheel standard. Cleveland brakes on mainwheels.
ACCOMMODATION: Four seats. Cabin and rear baggage area provide onboard sleeping accommodation for two.
EQUIPMENT: Dual controls, toe-brakes, cabin heater and windscreen defroster standard.
WEIGHTS:

Weight empty	521 kg (1,148 lb)
Max T-O weight	1,021 kg (2,250 lb)

PERFORMANCE:
Cruising speed:

75% power at 1,065 m (3,500 ft)	107 knots (198 km/h; 123 mph)
65% power at 1,065 m (3,500 ft)	103 knots (191 km/h; 119 mph)
Stalling speed, flaps down	33 knots (61 km/h; 38 mph)
Max rate of climb at S/L	317 m (1,040 ft)/min
Service ceiling	5,790 m (19,000 ft)
T-O to and landing from 15 m (50 ft)	153 m (500 ft)

Range: at 75% power cruising speed at 915 m (3,000 ft), 45 min reserves 600 nm (1,112 km; 691 miles)
at 65% power, reserves as above 650 nm (1,204 km; 748 miles)

ASI (Now AAS)

AERODYNAMICS & STRUCTURES INC

450 Pat Kennedy Way SW, Olympia, Washington 98532
Telephone: 1 (206) 754 7000
CHIEF EXECUTIVE OFFICER AND GENERAL MANAGER: Darius Sharifzadeh
MARKETING MANAGER: Bill Hubbard
For latest details, see Addenda.

ASI JET CRUZER

Mr Darius Sharifzadeh, a former airline pilot, formed Aerodynamics & Structures Inc to develop a six-seat, all-composites canard turboprop aircraft known as the Jet Cruzer, the prototype of which made its debut at the National Business Aircraft Association convention in Dallas, Texas, in October 1988. Aerodynamic design work was undertaken during 1984-85 by Mr 'Sandy' Burns, while layout details were the responsibility of well-known US light aircraft designer Mr Ladislao Pazmany, and structural design was performed in the United Kingdom by Mr David Kent of Designability Ltd. Wind tunnel tests were performed at the University of San Diego.

The general configuration of the Jet Cruzer can be seen in the accompanying photograph. ASI intends to market the aircraft for both civilian and military roles, and may also adapt it for use as an RPV. The Jet Cruzer has an external load capability for sensor or weapons systems, and is said to possess minimal noise, infra-red and radar signatures, which can be further reduced by an optional shrouded propeller system. An instrument panel based on CRT displays will be standard in production aircraft. The prototype (N5369M) first flew on 11 January 1989, since when no further information has been received. The following description applies to the prototype:
TYPE: All-composites multi-role business/utility aircraft.
WINGS: Cantilever low-wing monoplane with 20° sweepback at quarter-chord. Wing section NACA 2412. Incidence 0°. Dihedral 4°. Tip fins at wingtips extend above and below wing, each incorporating a horn balanced rudder.
FUSELAGE: Unpressurised monocoque structure of composites construction.
FOREPLANE: Cantilever mid-wing monoplane, unswept, NASA LS 0417 (Mod) section. Incidence 4°. Dihedral 0°. Full span horn balanced elevator each side.

ASI Jet Cruzer six-seat business and utility aircraft (*Jay Miller/Aerofax*)

LANDING GEAR: Retractable tricycle type. Main units have spring steel legs.
POWER PLANT: One 313 kW (420 shp) Allison 250-C20S turboprop, driving a Hartzell three-blade reversible-pitch metal pusher propeller. A 335.5 kW (450 shp) Allison 250-B17F turboprop will be standard in production aircraft. Usable fuel capacity, 598 litres (158 US gallons; 131.5 Imp gallons).
ACCOMMODATION: Standard seating for six, including pilot. Three cabin windows on each side. Door on starboard side, height 1.09 m (3 ft 7 in), width 1.75 m (5 ft 9 in); door on port side, height 1.09 m (3 ft 7 in), width 0.97 m (3 ft 2 in).
DIMENSIONS, EXTERNAL:

Wing span	11.02 m (36 ft 2 in)
Wing aspect ratio	7.5
Foreplane span	4.83 m (15 ft 10 in)
Length overall	6.96 m (22 ft 10 in)
Fuselage length	3.76 m (12 ft 4 in)
Height overall	2.62 m (8 ft 7 in)
Propeller diameter	2.03 m (6 ft 8 in)
Propeller ground clearance	0.58 m (1 ft 11 in)

DIMENSIONS, INTERNAL:

Cabin: Length	3.61 m (11 ft 10 in)
Volume	4.15 m³ (146.5 cu ft)

AREAS:

Wings, gross	16.17 m² (174.0 sq ft)
Ailerons (total)	1.03 m² (11.1 sq ft)
Fins, (total)	2.00 m² (21.5 sq ft)
Rudders, (total)	0.85 m² (9.2 sq ft)
Foreplane, incl elevators	5.39 m² (58.0 sq ft)
Elevators, (total, incl tabs)	1.79 m² (19.3 sq ft)

WEIGHTS AND LOADINGS:
Weight empty   953 kg (2,100 lb)
Max T-O weight   1,769 kg (3,900 lb)
PERFORMANCE (estimated):
Never-exceed speed   247 knots (457 km/h; 284 mph)

Max cruising speed:
at 3,050 m (10,000 ft)   230 knots (426 km/h; 265 mph)
at S/L   220 knots (408 km/h; 253 mph)
Max rate of climb at S/L   704 m (2,310 ft)/min
T-O run   137 m (450 ft)

T-O to 15 m (50 ft)   213 m (700 ft)
Landing from 15 m (50 ft)   229 m (750 ft)
Landing run   107 m (350 ft)
Max range at 3,050 m (10,000 ft)
                            1,250 nm (2,317 km; 1,440 miles)

AVSTAR
AVSTAR INC
Seattle, Washington

AVSTAR SUPER MUSTANG T-100
At the 1988 Farnborough Air Show it was announced
that Avstar Inc, in collaboration with Shenyang Aircraft
Corporation of the People's Republic of China (which see),
Pacific Marketing Consultants Inc of San Francisco and

Plymouth Ltd of Hong Kong, planned to revive the Temco
TT-1 Super Pinto tandem two-seat light jet trainer, 14 of
which were built in 1956 for evaluation by the US Navy. The
Pinto was previously revived in the early 1970s by American
Jet Industries, and licensed to, but not manufactured by the
Philippine Aerospace Development Corporation as the
T-610 Cali. Under the terms of an agreement in principle
between the four parties the Super Mustang T-100 would be
built at Shenyang under licence from Plymouth, with final
assembly and avionics installation taking place in the USA,

and marketed by the two US companies. A prototype,
powered by a General Electric J85 turbojet, was being flight
tested in the USA in 1988, but no recent information has
been received. Production T-100s are expected to be
powered by either that engine or a Williams International
FJ44 turbofan. Provisional specifications include: max T-O
weight 2,313 kg (5,100 lb); max cruising speed 326 knots
(604 km/h; 375 mph); stalling speed 58 knots (108 km/h; 67
mph); max rate of climb at S/L 2,440 m (8,000 ft)/min.

AVTEK
AVTEK CORPORATION
4680 Calle Carga, Camarillo, California 93010
Telephone: 1 (805) 482 2700
Telex: 183218 AVTEK UD
Fax: 1 (805) 987 0068
PRESIDENT: Robert F. Adickes
SENIOR VICE-PRESIDENT, ENGINEERING: Niels Andersen
DIRECTOR OF MARKETING: Robert D. Honeycutt

Avtek Corporation was established in 1982 to design,
develop and certificate the Avtek Model 400A all-composite
twin-turboprop six/ten-seat business aircraft of canard
configuration. The aircraft was designed initially by the late
Al W. Mooney, founder of Mooney Aircraft Corporation,
and later refined by Niels Andersen, Ford Johnston and
Irvin Culver. NASA provided computer analysis of the
aerodynamic configuration, and wind tunnel testing. The
company benefits also from research by Dow Chemical
Company and Dr Leo Windecker, designer of the
Windecker Eagle which was the first all-composite aircraft
to gain FAA certification. Dow Chemical Company has
licensed its basic patents developed during the Eagle
programme to Avtek Corporation.

E. I. DuPont de Nemours, Dow Chemical Company, Air
Rotor GmbH of West Germany, Nomura Securities of
Japan, and Valmet Corporation of Finland are investors in
Avtek Corporation. In September 1988 the Michigan state
government announced that it was entering into a
partnership with Avtek and local development agencies to
establish an assembly facility at W.K. Kellogg Regional
Airport, Battle Creek, Michigan.

AVTEK MODEL 400A
Design of the Avtek 400A was initiated in March 1981,
and construction of the first prototype started on 1 January
1982. This proof of concept (POC) aircraft (N400AV) flew
for the first time on 17 September 1984.

Major changes made in the Spring of 1985 included a
fuselage stretch of 0.20 m (8 in) forward and 0.76 m (2 ft 6 in)
aft of the forward pressure bulkhead; an increase in cabin
width; a new wing incorporating additional fuel capacity in
large wingroot leading-edge extensions; a new foreplane of
greater span and reduced chord; ventral strakes known as
delta fins; relocated main landing gear legs; and specially
developed Pratt & Whitney PT6A-3 turboprops, mounted
closer to the wing.

On 20 March 1985 Valmet Corporation of Finland
purchased an option to build an Explorer derivative of the
Avtek 400A for special missions such as maritime
surveillance, liaison, coastal patrol, aerial survey, search
and reconnaissance, and ESM, tailored to individual
customer requirements. DuPont has an option to build the
first 100 production airframes, which would be constructed
primarily from its proprietary polyaramid materials. The
Avtek 400A is all-composite, comprising 72
per cent DuPont Kevlar and Nomex, 16 per cent
graphite/carbonfibre, and smaller quantities of R-glass,
S-glass, aluminium and nickel fibres. The structure
incorporates a wire mesh core to provide protection against
lightning strikes.

Avtek Corporation is reported to have received deposit
payments for more than 100 Avtek 400As, and plans to
achieve FAA certification in 1992.

A description of the proof of concept prototype can be
found in the 1985-86 *Jane's*. This aircraft was retrofitted
and flown with PT6A-135M engines (PT6A-35s with
counter-rotating gearboxes from the PT6A-66) and four-
blade propellers, but it is not otherwise planned to modify it
to production configuration. The following details apply to
the pre-production second prototype, which was expected
to fly in late 1990:
TYPE: Six/ten-seat business aircraft.
WINGS: Cantilever low-wing monoplane, with large wingroot
leading-edge extensions. Wing section Avtek 12. Anhedral 2° 30′ from roots. Sweepback 50° inboard of
nacelles, 15° 30′ outboard. All-composites fail-safe
structure. Mass balanced two-section ailerons of composite construction, inner sections functioning as pitch
trim stabilisers. All control surfaces operated through

bellcranks and rigid pushrods. Pitch trim tabs on
trailing-edge of wing inboard of ailerons, electrically
actuated. No trailing-edge flaps. Pneumatic de-icing
boots on leading-edges.
FOREPLANE: Cantilever structure of composite materials,
located on upper fuselage above forward end of cabin.
Dihedral 1°. Conventional elevators, mass balanced and
operated through bellcranks and pushrods. No trim tabs.
Electric or engine bleed air de-icing of leading-edges.
FUSELAGE: All-composites fail-safe monocoque structure.
Cabin and cabin baggage compartment pressurised.
TAIL UNIT: Conventional sweptback vertical fin and rudder,
of all-composites construction. Rudder mass balanced
and operated through bellcranks and pushrods. No trim
tab. Pneumatic de-icing of fin leading-edge. Two large
triangular ventral fins under tailcone, each at 45°
anhedral angle.
LANDING GEAR: Hydraulically retractable tricycle type,
main units retracting inward and nosewheel forward.
Emergency extension system. Oleo-pneumatic shock
absorber in each unit. Single wheel on each unit,
mainwheels size 6.00-6 with Goodyear tyres size 17.5-6.25
× 7.5, pressure 7.0 bars (102 lb/sq in). Steerable
nosewheel unit with wheel size 5.00-5 and Goodyear tyre
size 14.2-5.5 × 6.5, pressure 5.0 bars (73 lb/sq in).
Cleveland hydraulic disc brakes.
POWER PLANT: Two Pratt & Whitney Canada PT6A-3L/R
turboprops, derived from the PT6A-135 and flat rated at
507 kW (680 shp), one mounted within nacelle above each
wing. Hartzell four-blade constant-speed fully-feathering
reversible-pitch pusher propellers (metal blades on
prototype, Kevlar on production version). Propellers are
opposite rotating, with automatic synchrophasing, full
Beta control reversing and autofeathering. In-flight
start capability. Integral fuel tank in each wingroot
leading-edge. Total fuel capacity 1,003 litres (265 US
gallons; 221 Imp gallons), of which 18.9 litres (5 US
gallons; 4.2 Imp gallons) are unusable. Refuelling point
in upper surface of each wing. Dual anti-icing inlets for
each engine.
ACCOMMODATION: Pilot and five to nine passengers according to interior layout. Optional configurations include
eight-passenger Pullman or Salon; eight-passenger
Lounge; six-passenger Conference; Ambulance with
stretcher, medical equipment and seats for three ambulatory patients or medical attendants; and Cargo with seats
for pilot and one passenger. Two-section door on port
side of cabin, with step incorporated in lower half.
Emergency exit on starboard side opposite cabin door.
Baggage compartment at rear of cabin with internal
access. Unpressurised baggage compartment in nose
with external door on port side. Accommodation is
pressurised, air-conditioned, heated and ventilated.

SYSTEMS: AiResearch bleed air pressurisation system with
max differential of 0.52 bars (7.6 lb/sq in), and air cycle
air-conditioning system. Electrically driven hydraulic
pump provides pressure of 138 bars (2,000 lb/sq in) for
landing gear actuation. Electrical system includes dual
28V 300A engine driven generators, dual 29Ah storage
batteries and external power socket. Oxygen system of
1.39 m³ (49 cu ft) capacity, pressure 128 bars (1,850 lb/sq
in), provides constant flow for passengers and demand
flow for pilot. Anti-icing of windscreen by electrical
system, of propellers by engine efflux; alcohol anti-icing
of wing and fin leading-edges optional; electrically heated
pitot. Engine fire extinguishing system optional.
AVIONICS AND EQUIPMENT: Wide range of optional avionics
by Bendix/King, Collins and Honeywell, including EFIS
and EICAS, and colour radar by RCA. Full IFR
instrumentation optional.

DIMENSIONS, EXTERNAL:
Wing span   10.67 m (35 ft 0 in)
Foreplane span   6.92 m (22 ft 8½ in)
Length overall   11.99 m (39 ft 4 in)
Length of fuselage   10.41 m (34 ft 2 in)
Height overall   3.47 m (11 ft 4¾ in)
Propeller diameter   1.93 m (6 ft 4 in)
Passenger door (port): Height   1.17 m (3 ft 10 in)
  Width   0.76 m (2 ft 6 in)
  Height to sill   0.76 m (2 ft 6 in)
Baggage door (port, nose): Height   0.51 m (1 ft 8 in)
  Width   0.56 m (1 ft 10 in)
  Height to sill   0.79 m (2 ft 7 in)
Emergency exit (stbd): Height   0.51 m (1 ft 8 in)
  Width   0.67 m (2 ft 2½ in)
DIMENSIONS, INTERNAL:
Cabin: Length   3.14 m (10 ft 3½ in)
  Max width   1.40 m (4 ft 7¼ in)
  Max height   1.37 m (4 ft 6 in)
Baggage hold volume:
  nose   0.62 m³ (22.0 cu ft)
  cabin   1.24 m³ (44.0 cu ft)
AREAS:
Wings, gross   13.40 m² (144.2 sq ft)
Foreplane, gross   4.52 m² (48.7 sq ft)
Foreplane elevators (total)   0.92 m² (9.9 sq ft)
Ailerons (total)   0.60 m² (6.5 sq ft)
Fin   1.16 m² (12.5 sq ft)
Rudder   0.90 m² (9.7 sq ft)
WEIGHTS:
Weight empty, equipped   1,714 kg (3,779 lb)
Max ramp weight   2,976 kg (6,560 lb)
Max T-O and landing weight   2,948 kg (6,500 lb)
PERFORMANCE (estimated):
Max level speed at S/L   255 knots (473 km/h; 294 mph)

Avtek Model 400A six/ten-seat twin-turboprop business aircraft *(Pilot Press)*

Max cruising speed:

at 3,050 m (10,000 ft)	297 knots (550 km/h; 342 mph)	
at 6,700 m (22,000 ft)	364 knots (675 km/h; 419 mph)	
at 12,500 m (41,000 ft)	338 knots (626 km/h; 389 mph)	
Stalling speed	83 knots (154 km/h; 96 mph)	

Max rate of climb at S/L	1,411 m (4,630 ft)/min
Rate of climb at S/L, one engine out	
	578 m (1,897 ft)/min
Service ceiling	12,950 m (42,500 ft)
Service ceiling, one engine out	10,060 m (33,000 ft)

T-O to 15 m (50 ft)	463 m (1,520 ft)
Landing from 15 m (50 ft)	390 m (1,280 ft)
Range with max fuel:	
no reserves	2,276 nm (4,218 km; 2,621 miles)
NBAA IFR reserves	1,922 nm (3,562 km; 2,213 miles)

AYRES
AYRES CORPORATION
PO Box 3090, Albany, Georgia 31708-5201
Telephone: 1 (912) 883 1440
Telex: 547629 AYRESPORT ABN
Fax: 1 (912) 439 9790
SALES MANAGERS: Marvin H. Wilson (Domestic)
Bill Brodbeck (International)

AYRES THRUSH S2R-600
Ayres Corporation purchased the manufacturing and world marketing rights of the Rockwell Thrush Commander-600 and -800 from Rockwell International's General Aviation Division in late November 1977, and now offers the following versions of this large agricultural aircraft:

Thrush S2R-600. Basic version with Pratt & Whitney R-1340 Wasp aircooled radial engine. Previously known as S2R-R1340. Available with one or two seats.

Bull Thrush S2R-R1820. As Thrush S2R-600, but with a Wright R-1820 engine. Described separately.

Turbo-Thrush S2R. As Thrush S2R-600, but with a Pratt & Whitney Canada PT6A-11, -15, -34 or -65AG turboprop. Described separately.

The Thrush S2R-600 has a corrosion-proof polyurethane finish, and is certificated to both CAR 3 Normal category and CAM 8 Restricted category requirements.

The following details refer to the basic single-seat Thrush S2R-600, but apply also to the Bull Thrush, except as described in the separate entry for the latter aircraft.

TYPE: Single-seat (optionally two-seat) agricultural aircraft.

WINGS: Cantilever low-wing monoplane. Dihedral 3° 30'. Two-spar structure of light alloy throughout, except for main spar caps of 4130 chrome molybdenum steel. Leading-edge formed by heavy main spar and the nose skin. Light alloy plain ailerons. Electrically operated flaps. Wingroots sealed against chemical entry. Wing extensions, adding 2.79 m² (30 sq ft) of effective lifting surface, are standard on S2R-600, optional on Turbo-Thrush.

FUSELAGE: Welded chrome molybdenum steel tube structure covered with quickly removable light alloy panels. Underfuselage skin of stainless steel.

TAIL UNIT: All-metal aluminium alloy structure with cantilever fin and strut braced tailplane. Trim tab in each elevator. Deflector cable from cockpit to fin tip.

LANDING GEAR: Non-retractable tailwheel type. Main units have rubber in compression shock absorption and 29 × 11.00-10 wheels with 10-ply tyres. Hydraulically operated disc brakes. Parking brakes. Wire cutters on main gear. Steerable, locking tailwheel, size 12.5 × 4.5 in.

POWER PLANT: One 447 kW (600 hp) Pratt & Whitney R-1340 Wasp nine-cylinder aircooled radial engine, driving a Hamilton Standard type 12D40/EAC AG-100-2 two-blade constant-speed metal propeller, is standard. Fuel contained in wing tanks with combined capacity of 401 litres (106 US gallons; 88.3 Imp gallons).

ACCOMMODATION: Single adjustable mesh seat in 'safety pod' sealed cockpit enclosure is standard, with steel tube overturn structure. Dual tandem seating optional, with forward or rear facing second seat. Dual controls optional with forward facing rear seat, for pilot training. Adjustable rudder pedals. Downward hinged door on each side. Tempered safety glass windscreen. Cockpit wire cutter. Dual inertia reel safety harness with optional second seat. Baggage compartment standard on single-seat aircraft. Windscreen wiper and washer.

SYSTEM: Electrical system powered by a 24V 50A alternator. Lightweight 24V 35Ah battery.

AVIONICS: To customer's requirements.

EQUIPMENT: Transland glassfibre hopper forward of cockpit with capacity of 1.50 m³ (53 cu ft) can hold 1,514 litres (400 US gallons; 333 Imp gallons) of liquid or 1,487 kg (3,280 lb) of dry chemical. Hopper has a 0.33 m² (3.56 sq ft) lid, openable by two handles, and cockpit viewing window. Standard equipment includes Universal spray system with external 50 mm (2 in) stainless steel plumbing, 50 mm pump with wooden fan, Transland gate, 50 mm valve, quick-disconnect pump mount and strainer. Streamlined spraybooms with outlets for 68 nozzles. Micro-adjust valve control (spray) and calibrator (dry). A 63 mm (2.5 in) side loading system is installed on the port side. Stainless steel rudder cables. Navigation lights, instrument lights and two strobe lights. Optional equipment includes a rear cockpit to accommodate aft facing crew member, or forward facing seat for passenger, or flying instructor if optional dual controls installed; space can be used alternatively for cargo. Other optional items are a Transland high-volume spreader, agitator installation; ten-unit AU5000 Micronair installation in lieu of standard booms and nozzles; Transland gatebox with stiffener casting; quick-disconnect flange

Ayres Bull Thrush S2R-R1820 (1,200 hp Wright R-1820 engine)

Ayres Turbo-Thrush NEDS dedicated narcotics eradication aircraft

and kit; night working lights including landing light and wingtip turn lights; cockpit fire extinguisher; and water bomber configuration.

DIMENSIONS, EXTERNAL:

Wing span	14.48 m (47 ft 6 in)
Length overall (tail up)	8.95 m (29 ft 4½ in)
Height overall	2.79 m (9 ft 2 in)
Tailplane span	5.18 m (17 ft 0 in)
Wheel track	2.72 m (8 ft 11 in)
Propeller diameter	2.74 m (9 ft 0 in)

AREA:

Wings, gross	33.13 m² (356.6 sq ft)

WEIGHTS AND LOADINGS:

Weight empty, equipped	1,678 kg (3,700 lb)
Max T-O weight: CAR 3	2,721 kg (6,000 lb)
CAM 8	3,130 kg (6,900 lb)
Max wing loading	103.0 kg/m² (21.1 lb/sq ft)
Max power loading	6.99 kg/kW (11.5 lb/hp)

PERFORMANCE (with spray equipment installed and at CAR 3 max T-O weight, except where indicated):

Max level speed	122 knots (225 km/h; 140 mph)
Max cruising speed, 70% power	
	108 knots (200 km/h; 124 mph)
Working speed, 70% power	
	91-100 knots (169-185 km/h; 105-115 mph)
Stalling speed: flaps up	58 knots (108 km/h; 67 mph)
flaps down	55 knots (101 km/h; 63 mph)
Stalling speed at normal landing weight:	
flaps up	47 knots (87 km/h; 54 mph)
flaps down	45 knots (84 km/h; 52 mph)
Max rate of climb at S/L	317 m (1,040 ft)/min
Service ceiling	4,575 m (15,000 ft)
T-O run	215 m (705 ft)
Landing run	139 m (455 ft)

Ferry range with max fuel at 70% power
350 nm (648 km; 403 miles)

AYRES BULL THRUSH S2R-R1820/510
Claimed by Ayres to be the most powerful production agricultural aircraft in the world, the Bull Thrush is generally similar to the Thrush S2R-600 except for smaller wings and the installation of a Wright R-1820 engine and a chemical hopper of increased capacity. The description of the Thrush S2R-600 applies also to the Bull Thrush, except as follows:

POWER PLANT: One 895 kW (1,200 hp) Wright R-1820 Cyclone nine-cylinder aircooled radial engine, driving a Hamilton Standard three-blade constant-speed metal propeller. Fuel system as for Thrush, but total usable fuel capacity 863 litres (228 US gallons; 190 Imp gallons).

AVIONICS AND EQUIPMENT: Generally as for Thrush, except that the chemical hopper is of 1.93 m³ (68.2 cu ft) or 1,930 litres (510 US gallons; 425 Imp gallons) capacity.

DIMENSIONS, EXTERNAL: As for Thrush, except:

Wing span	13.54 m (44 ft 5 in)
Length overall	9.60 m (31 ft 6 in)
Height overall	2.92 m (9 ft 7 in)
Wheel track	2.74 m (9 ft 0 in)

AREA:

Wings, gross	30.34 m² (326.6 sq ft)

WEIGHTS:

Weight empty, equipped	2,263 kg (4,990 lb)
Typical operating weight (CAM 8)	4,536 kg (10,000 lb)

PERFORMANCE (with spray equipment, at CAM 8 max T-O weight, except where indicated):

Max level speed	138 knots (256 km/h; 159 mph)
Cruising speed, 50% power	
	135 knots (249 km/h; 155 mph)

Ayres Thrush S2R-600 (600 hp Pratt & Whitney R-1340 Wasp engine)

Terr-Mar Aviation Corporation Turbo Sea Thrush conversion of the Ayres Turbo-Thrush agricultural aircraft

Working speed, 30-50% power
87-130 knots (161-241 km/h; 100-150 mph)
Stalling speed: flaps up   61 knots (113 km/h; 70 mph)
    flaps down   58 knots (107 km/h; 66 mph)
Stalling speed at normal landing weight:
    flaps up   52 knots (95 km/h; 59 mph)
    flaps down   50 knots (92 km/h; 57 mph)
Max rate of climb at S/L   620 m (2,033 ft)/min
Service ceiling   8,535 m (28,000 ft)
T-O run   168 m (550 ft)
Landing run at normal landing weight   290 m (950 ft)
Ferry range at 40% power
582 nm (1,078 km; 670 miles)

AYRES TURBO-THRUSH S2R and TERR-MAR TURBO SEA THRUSH
Six versions of the turbine engined Turbo-Thrush S2R are currently available:
Turbo-Thrush S2R-T11: Version with a 373 kW (500 shp) Pratt & Whitney Canada PT6A-11AG turboprop and available only with the standard 1,514 litre (400 US gallon; 333 Imp gallon) chemical hopper.
Turbo-Thrush S2R-T15: Version with a 507 kW (680 shp) Pratt & Whitney Canada PT6A-15AG turboprop, available with a 1,514 litre (400 US gallon; 333 Imp gallon) or, optionally, 1,930 litre (510 US gallon; 425 Imp gallon) chemical hopper.
Turbo-Thrush S2R-T34: This version has a 559 kW (750 shp) Pratt & Whitney Canada PT6A-34AG turboprop and is available with standard and optional chemical hoppers as above.
Turbo-Thrush S2R-T65/400 NEDS: Ayres has developed a special version of the Turbo-Thrush, known as the Narcotics Eradication Delivery System (NEDS), for the US State Department, to which nine aircraft were delivered during 1983-85. This aircraft is powered by a 1,026 kW (1,376 shp) Pratt & Whitney Canada PT6A-65AG turboprop driving a five-blade propeller of 2.82 m (9 ft 3 in) diameter and features a two-seat armoured cockpit, armour protection around the engine compartment and a 75.7 litre (20 US gallon; 16.7 Imp gallon) self-sealing auxiliary fuel tank mounted in a bulletproof structure in addition to standard Turbo-Thrush wing fuel tanks. The aircraft are operated by the State Department's International Narcotics Matters Bureau and have been used on 'Operation Roundup' drug eradication missions in such countries as Burma, Colombia and Thailand against poppy crops, in Mexico against marijuana and poppies, and in Belize and Guatemala against marijuana. A chemical herbicide known as 'Roundup' is carried in a 1,514 litre (400 US gallon; 333 Imp gallon) tank and is sprayed on the plants to make them overfertilise, grow rapidly, then wilt and die. Delivery rate, at a working speed of 104-113 knots (193-209 km/h; 120-130 mph), is some 265 litres (70 US gallons; 60 Imp gallons) per acre, a typical marijuana field being about 0.3 ha (0.7 acre). In Belize, Turbo-Thrush NEDS have operated under escort

from an armed Pilatus Britten-Norman Defender which could provide fire support in an emergency, such as forced landing. The Turbo-Thrush NEDS is usually operated by two crew in case of injury from groundfire, and is equipped with King VLF Omega 660, ADF, VOR, HF and VHF avionics.
V-1-A Vigilante. Multi-mission version of Turbo-Thrush NEDS, described separately.
Terr-Mar Turbo Sea Thrush. Terr-Mar Aviation Corporation of Vancouver, Canada, holds FAA type approval for a water bombing version of the Turbo-Thrush mounted on twin Wipline 6000 amphibious floats. A Terr-Mar probe enables the 1,930 litre (510 US gallon; 425 Imp gallon) hopper to be filled while water-planing in 10-15 s. A gravity activated drop door beneath the hopper is closed by airflow.
With the exception of the Turbo-Thrush NEDS and Vigilante, in each case the turboprop drives a Hartzell three-blade constant-speed fully-feathering and reversible-pitch metal propeller with spinner. To compensate for the small size and light weight of the turboprop, it is mounted well forward of the firewall, in a slender cowling. Current installations have cowlings which comprise individual panels to improve access. Standard and optional equipment is generally as detailed for the basic Thrush. Total usable fuel capacity is 863 litres (228 US gallons; 190 Imp gallons).

Advantages claimed for this conversion include greatly improved take-off and climb performance; improved short landing capability; a 454 kg (1,000 lb) increase in payload due to reduced power plant weight; ability to operate on aviation turbine fuel, or diesel fuel; a TBO of 3,500 h; quieter operation; and the ability to feather the propeller during fuelling and loading operations without shutting down the engine, because of the free-turbine configuration.
DIMENSIONS, EXTERNAL, AND AREA: As for Bull Thrush
S2R-R1820 except:
Length overall   10.06 m (33 ft 0 in)
Height overall   2.79 m (9 ft 2 in)
WEIGHTS AND LOADINGS (A: standard hopper; B: optional 1,930 litre; 510 US gallon; 425 Imp gallon hopper):
Weight empty: A   1,633 kg (3,600 lb)
    B   1,769 kg (3,900 lb)
Max T-O weight (CAR 3): A, B   2,721 kg (6,000 lb)
Typical operating weight (CAM 8):
    A   3,719 kg (8,200 lb)
    B   3,856 kg (8,500 lb)
Max wing loading   127.1 kg/m² (26.0 lb/sq ft)
Max power loading   7.6 kg/kW (14.17 lb/shp)
PERFORMANCE (A and B with PT6A-34AG power plant, at max T-O weight except where indicated):
Max level speed with spray equipment
138 knots (256 km/h; 159 mph)
Cruising speed, 50% power
130 knots (241 km/h; 150 mph)
Working speed, 30-50% power
82-130 knots (153-241 km/h; 95-150 mph)
Stalling speed: flaps up   61 knots (113 km/h; 70 mph)
    flaps down   57 knots (106 km/h; 66 mph)
Stalling speed at normal landing weight:
    flaps up   51 knots (95 km/h; 59 mph)
    flaps down   50 knots (92 km/h; 57 mph)
Max rate of climb at S/L   530 m (1,740 ft)/min
Service ceiling   7,620 m (25,000 ft)
T-O run   183 m (600 ft)
Landing run   152 m (500 ft)
Landing run with propeller reversal   91 m (300 ft)
Ferry range at 40% power
664 nm (1,231 km; 765 miles)

AYRES V-1-A VIGILANTE
Ayres developed this multi-mission version of the Turbo-Thrush NEDS in co-operation with the US State Department and US Army Electro-Optical Survivability Programme, and first flew the prototype (N3100A) in May 1989. In addition to a two-seat armoured cockpit and self-sealing auxiliary fuel tank as fitted to the NEDS aircraft, the Vigilante features four standard NATO stores hardpoints under each wing and three tandem stores hardpoints under the fuselage. The three outboard hardpoints on each wing have a capacity of 159 kg (350 lb), while the inboard pylons have a capacity of 544 kg (1,200 lb). A wide variety of stores can be carried, including 0.50 in calibre, 7.62 mm and 20 mm gun pods; 2.75 in air-to-ground rockets, 500 lb bombs, Stinger missiles, land and sea mines, torpedoes, anti-tank missiles and ECM equipment. Surveillance systems which have been installed in the Vigilante include Honeywell, Westinghouse, Lockheed Gimbol/Texas Instruments and Lockheed Gimbol/Kollmorgen FLIR systems; multi-spectral LLTV and laser-gate LLTV cameras, Honeywell line scanner and BMS data link and receiver. The surveillance systems operator occupies the rear seat and can control all systems and communications radios. Onboard recorders can record data from two surveillance systems simultaneously and transmit it via data link in real time or as secure frozen imagery to a ground station at ranges up to 100 nm (185 km;

Ayres V-1-A Vigilante close air support and surveillance aircraft

115 miles). A high resolution video monitor combined with two VHS VCRs is installed in the rear position; the front cockpit has a small video display monitor.

During the Spring of 1989 Ayres conducted night surveillance demonstration flights with the Vigilante for the US Border patrol in Arizona and Texas, during which the aircraft's FLIR equipment successfully detected several groups of illegal immigrants. Ayres anticipates a market for the Vigilante as a low-cost surveillance and close support aircraft in such areas as North Africa and Central and South America, but will not seek FAA certification until a launch customer has been found.

The description of the Turbo-Thrush NEDS applies also to the Vigilante, except as follows:
WINGS: Wing section NACA 4412. Dihedral 1.5°. Incidence 2.5°.
LANDING GEAR: Tyre pressures: mainwheels 3.45 bars (50 lb/sq in); tailwheel 6.21 bars (90 lb/sq in).
POWER PLANT: Centrifugal air filtration system standard. External underwing fuel tanks, each capacity 1,514 litres (400 US gallons; 333 Imp gallons), optional.
SYSTEMS: 400A 28V DC electrical systems with AC inverter available. Parker Hannifin electric air-conditioning system and oxygen system standard. Wing and tail leading-edge, windscreen and propeller de-icing optional.
AVIONICS AND EQUIPMENT: Standard avionics include Bendix/King KY 196A nav/com, KNR 634 nav, dual KMA 24H audio panel, KDM 706A DME, dual KDI 573B DME indicators, KR 87 digital ADF, KT 76A transponder, KEA 130 encoding altimeter, KRA 10A radar altimeter, KI 250 altitude indicator, KA 35A marker beacon receiver, KCS 55A HSI, dual KI 229 RMI, KFS 564A, and KNS 660 VLF/Omega, HF, 3M Stormscope, Loran C, Rockwell Collins 182 UHF/VHF/FM multi-band transceiver with secure voice provisions, SATCOM, Have Quick and SINCGARS. Radar and IR warning receivers, IR paint, exhaust suppression system, hush kit and chaff/flare dispensers are optional. Armament and surveillance equipment as detailed above.

DIMENSIONS, EXTERNAL:
Wing chord, constant	2.29 m (7 ft 6 in)
Length overall	10.06 m (33 ft 0 in)
Height overall	2.90 m (9 ft 6 in)
Tailplane span	5.11 m (16 ft 9 in)
Wheel track	2.74 m (9 ft 0 in)
Wheelbase	5.31 m (17 ft 5 in)
Propeller diameter	2.69 m (8 ft 10 in)
Propeller ground clearance	0.91 m (3 ft 0 in)

AREA:
Wings, gross	31.22 m² (336 sq ft)

WEIGHTS AND LOADINGS:
Weight empty	2,223 kg (4,900 lb)
Max fuel weight: internal	952 kg (2,100 lb)
external	1,270 kg (2,800 lb)
Max T-O and landing weight	4,762 kg (10,500 lb)
Max wing loading	151.36 kg/m² (31.01 lb/sq ft)
Max power loading	4.64 kg/kW (7.5 lb/shp)

PERFORMANCE (at max T-O weight, ISA, except where indicated):
Never-exceed speed	191 knots (354 km/h; 220 mph) IAS
Max level speed	220 knots (408 km/h; 253 mph)
Max cruising speed	200 knots (371 km/h; 230 mph)
Econ cruising speed	150 knots (278 km/h; 173 mph)
Stalling speed, flaps down	50 knots (93 km/h; 58 mph)
Max rate of climb at S/L:	
at AUW of 2,721 kg (6,000 lb)	1,067 m (3,500 ft)/min
at max T-O weight	610 m (2,000 ft)/min
Service ceiling	7,620 m (25,000 ft)
T-O run: at AUW of 2,998 kg (6,500 lb)	121 m (395 ft)
at max T-O weight	381 m (1,250 ft)
Landing run, with reverse thrust:	
at AUW of 2,948 kg (6,500 lb)	153 m (500 ft)
at AUW of 3,855 kg (8,500 lb)	229 m (750 ft)
Range: with max internal fuel	900 nm (1,667 km; 1,036 miles)
with external fuel	1,750 nm (3,243 km; 2,015 miles)
Endurance, internal fuel, 60 knots (111 km/h; 69 mph) loiter speed	7 h

BALDWIN
BALDWIN AIRCRAFT INTERNATIONAL
CHIEF EXECUTIVE OFFICER: Gary Baldwin

BALDWIN ASP-XJ
In May 1988 Baldwin Aircraft International's ASP-XJ (Armed Surveillance and Patrol - Experimental Jet) two-seat all-composite jet surveillance and patrol aircraft was displayed at the Air/Space America 88 air show held at San Diego, California. Its first flight was scheduled to take place at Mojave, California, on 15 July 1988, but was delayed by late delivery of cockpit multi-function displays. No more recent news of the aircraft's status has been received. A brief description and photograph of the ASP-XJ can be found in the 1989-90 edition of *Jane's*.

BASLER
BASLER TURBO CONVERSIONS INC
7405 Hayvenhurst Place, Van Nuys, California 91406
Telephone: 1 (818) 782 8856
Fax: 1 (818) 782 9733
and at
255 West 35th Avenue, PO Box 2305, Oshkosh, Wisconsin 54903-2305
Telephone: 1 (414) 236 7820
Fax: 1 (414) 236 7833
PRESIDENT: Warren Basler
VICE-PRESIDENT: Bob Clark

BASLER TURBO-67 DC-3 CONVERSION
Basler Turbo Conversions has developed a turboprop conversion of the Douglas DC-3 transport which involves replacing the standard Pratt & Whitney Double Wasp radial piston engines with two 1,061 kW (1,424 shp) Pratt & Whitney Canada PT6A-67R turboprops, driving Hartzell five-blade feathering and reversing propellers, diameter 2.92 m (9 ft 7 in). The wings are reinforced to permit increased payload, and modified to improve flight characteristics. In addition, the fuselage is lengthened by means of a 1.02 m (3 ft 4 in) plug inserted forward of the wing centre-section to maintain the aircraft's centre of gravity envelope, and the DC-3's aft cargo door is enlarged to permit loading of standard LD3 cargo containers, five of which can be accommodated. A new electrical system is installed, conforming to FAR Pt 25, together with an upgraded hydraulic system to speed landing gear retraction, and a modified fuel system compatible with jet fuel. Long-range fuel tanks can be installed, to increase capacity to 5,837 litres (1,542 US gallons; 1,284 Imp gallons).

By early 1990 the second Turbo-67 conversion was nearing completion at Van Nuys, and six more were under way at a new facility at Oshkosh, Wisconsin, which has capacity to complete 30 installations each year, and to manufacture up to 100 conversion kits annually for installation by customers.

Two converted Turbo-67 DC-3s have been ordered by the USAF for delivery to El Salvador under the Foreign Military Assistance Programme.

Basler Turbo-67 DC-3 conversion (two P&WC PT6A-67R turboprops)

WEIGHTS:
Basic operating weight	7,180 kg (15,827 lb)
Max T-O weight	13,040 kg (28,750 lb)

PERFORMANCE (at max T-O weight):
Max cruising speed at 3,050 m (10,000 ft)	205 knots (380 km/h; 236 mph)
Normal cruising speed at 3,050 m (10,000 ft)	195 knots (361 km/h; 225 mph)
Stalling speed:	
wheels and flaps up	70 knots (130 km/h; 81 mph) IAS
wheels and flaps down	63 knots (117 km/h; 73 mph) IAS
Max rate of climb at S/L	387 m (1,270 ft)/min
Rate of climb at S/L, one engine out	75 m (245 ft)/min
Certificated ceiling	7,620 m (25,000 ft)
Service ceiling, one engine out	4,315 m (14,150 ft)
T-O run	606 m (1,988 ft)
T-O to 10 m (35 ft)	914 m (2,997 ft)
Landing from 15 m (50 ft)	949 m (3,111 ft)
Range: with standard fuel, 45 min reserves	981 nm (1,818 km; 1,129 miles)
with long-range tanks	2,088 nm (3,869 km; 2,404 miles)

BEECH
BEECH AIRCRAFT CORPORATION
(Subsidiary of Raytheon Company)
9709 East Central, Wichita, Kansas 67201-0085
Telephone: 1 (316) 681 7111
Telex: 71 203603 BEECH UR
Fax: 1 (316) 681 8867
BRANCH DIVISION: Salina, Kansas
CHAIRMAN EMERITUS, AND CHAIRMAN OF BEECH AIRCRAFT FOUNDATION: Mrs Olive Ann (Walter H.) Beech
CHAIRMAN: Thomas L. Phillips
PRESIDENT AND CHIEF EXECUTIVE OFFICER: Max E. Bleck
EXECUTIVE VICE-PRESIDENT:
Charles W. Dieker (Marketing)
VICE-PRESIDENTS:
C. Don Cary (Product Marketing)
William R. Coughenour (Aerospace)
Robert D. Dickerson (Engineering)
Thomas G. Keough (Airline Marketing)
George D. Rodgers (Sales and Marketing Services)
Donald E. Wells (TTTS Programme)
DIRECTOR, CORPORATE AFFAIRS: James M. Gregory
MANAGER, PUBLIC RELATIONS: Michael S. Potts

Beech Aircraft Corporation was founded jointly in 1932 by Mrs Olive Ann Beech and the late Walter H. Beech, pioneer designer and builder of light aeroplanes in the USA. On 8 February 1980 it became a wholly owned subsidiary of Raytheon. It continues to operate as a separate entity, and is currently engaged in the production of civil and military aircraft, missile targets, and aircraft and missile components.

Deliveries by Beech in 1989 were made up of 108 King Airs, 33 Barons, 178 Bonanzas, 5 Model 1300 Commuters, 42 Model 1900 Airliners and 10 Beechjets. By 1 January 1990 Beech had delivered 5,588 pressurised aircraft since introducing the King Air 90 in 1964. Total production of Beech aeroplanes reached 49,206 by the beginning of 1990.

A wholly owned subsidiary, Beech Aerospace Services Inc (BASI), of Jackson, Mississippi, is currently responsible for worldwide logistic support of Army/Air Force/Navy C-12s, and Beech MQM-107 targets, in more than 74 locations in 37 countries.

US Navy Beechcraft T-34C in experimental high-visibility white and yellow paint scheme *(Howard Levy)*

Beechcraft T-34C-1 turboprop powered training/light attack aircraft *(Pilot Press)*

Beech Aircraft has about 9,000 employees worldwide and occupies 327,111 m² (3,521,000 sq ft) of plant area at its two major facilities in Wichita and Salina, Kansas.

The Salina division supplies all wings, non-metallic interior components, nosecones and tailcones used in Wichita production, and is responsible for manufacture and final assembly of the T-34C trainer. Work performed in Wichita includes manufacture under subcontract of composites and aluminium alloy winglets, and composites landing gear doors, for the McDonnell Douglas C-17 military transport aircraft.

Wholly owned subsidiaries of the parent company include Beech Acceptance Corporation Inc, engaged in business aircraft retail finance and leasing; Beechcraft AG, in Zurich, Switzerland, which supports European sales, liaison and other activities of the parent company; Travel Air Insurance Company Ltd, a Bermuda-based company organised to provide aircraft liability insurance; Beech Holdings Inc, which provides marketing support to the parent company; Beech Aerospace Services Inc, which provides worldwide support of Beech military aircraft, missile targets and related products; and the following sales outlets which are wholly owned subsidiaries of Beech Holdings Inc: Beechcraft East Inc, Farmingdale, New York, and Bedford, Massachusetts; Hangar One Inc, Atlanta Hartsfield, DeKalb-Peachtree and Fulton County airports, Georgia; Birmingham, Alabama; and Opa Locka, Orlando and Tampa, Florida; United Beechcraft Inc, Wichita, Kansas; Beechcraft West, Ontario; Hayward, Van Nuys, and Fresno, California; Indiana Beechcraft Inc, Indianapolis, Indiana, where Beech's Commuter Spare Parts Supply operation is based; and Hartzog Aviation, Rockford, Illinois.

BEECHCRAFT T-34C
US Navy designation: T-34C

The original piston engined Beechcraft Model 45 was built as the T-34A Mentor for the USAF (450) and as the similar T-34B for the US Navy (423). Design of the upgraded T-34C, with a PT6A-25 turboprop and updated avionics, began in March 1973, and the first of two YT-34C prototypes flew on 21 September that year. Under successive US Navy contracts, Beech delivered 334

new-production T-34Cs between November 1977 and April 1984. Six T-34Cs were transferred to the US Army's Airborne Special Operations Test Board at Fort Bragg, North Carolina, where they serve as chase and photographic aircraft. In May 1987 the US Navy ordered a further 19 T-34Cs, deliveries of which were completed in April 1990. By mid-1989 the US Navy's T-34C fleet had logged more than one million flight hours and had established the lowest accident rate for aircraft in the service's current inventory. An export civil version, known as the **Turbine Mentor 34C**, is in service at the Algerian national pilot training school, which received six in 1979.

A **T-34C-1** armament systems trainer version is also available and, in addition to its basic role, is capable of carrying out forward air control (FAC) and tactical strike training missions. A total of 139 T-34C-1s were delivered, including aircraft for Argentina (Navy 15), Ecuador (Air

Force 20, Navy 3), Gabon (Presidential Guard 4), Indonesia (Air Force 25), Morocco (Air Force 12), Peru (Navy 7), Taiwan (Air Force 40) and Uruguay (Navy 3).

No further T-34C production is anticipated. Details of the T-34C and T-34C-1 appeared in the 1989-90 *Jane's*.

BEECHCRAFT BONANZA MODEL F33A/C

The **F33A** version of the Bonanza is a four/five-seat single-engined executive aircraft, similar in general configuration to the Bonanza Model V35B, but distinguished by a conventional tail unit with sweptback vertical surfaces. The prototype flew for the first time on 14 September 1959, and the production models were known as Debonairs until 1967. The 1985 model introduced as standard equipment a large cargo door, three-blade propeller, super soundproofing, and the avionics and equipment listed in the appropriate paragraph, representing full IFR standard.

The Mexican Air Force received 21 aerobatic **F33Cs** in 1986 and three other F33Cs, built to special order, were delivered to civilian customers in late 1986/early 1987. Earlier F33C recipients included the Imperial Iranian Air Force (16), Mexican Navy (5), Netherlands Government Flying School (16), and Spanish Air Force/Air Ministry (74). This model remains available to special order. The large cargo door, air-conditioning and fifth seat are not available for the Bonanza F33C.

A total of 2,979 Model 33s had been built by 1 January 1990.

TYPE: Four/five-seat light cabin monoplane.

WINGS: Cantilever low-wing monoplane. Wing section Beech modified NACA 23016.5 at root, modified NACA 23012 at tip. Dihedral 6°. Incidence 4° at root, 1° at tip. Sweepback 0° at quarter-chord. Each wing is a two-spar semi-monocoque box-beam of conventional aluminium alloy construction. Symmetrical section ailerons and single-slotted three-position flaps of aluminium alloy construction. Ground adjustable trim tab in each aileron.

FUSELAGE: Conventional aluminium alloy semi-monocoque structure. Hat section longerons and channel type keels extend forward from cabin section, making the support structure for the engine and nosewheel an integral part of the fuselage.

TAIL UNIT: Conventional cantilever all-metal stressed-skin structure, primarily of aluminium alloy but with beaded magnesium skin on elevators. Large trim tab in each elevator. Fixed tab in rudder.

LANDING GEAR: Electrically retractable tricycle type, with steerable nosewheel. Mainwheels retract inward into wings, nosewheel rearward. Beech oleo-pneumatic shock absorbers in all units. Cleveland mainwheels, size 6.00-6, and tyres, size 7.00-6, pressure 2.28-2.76 bars (33-40 lb/sq in). Cleveland nosewheel and tyre, size 5.00-5, pressure 2.76 bars (40 lb/sq in). Cleveland ring-disc hydraulic brakes. Parking brake. Magic Hand landing gear system optional.

POWER PLANT: One 212.5 kW (285 hp) Continental IO-520-BB flat-six engine, driving a McCauley three-blade constant-speed metal propeller with spinner. Propeller de-icing optional. Manually adjustable engine cowl flaps. Two standard fuel tanks in wing leading-edges, with total usable capacity of 280 litres (74 US gallons; 61.6 Imp gallons). Refuelling points above tanks. Oil capacity 11.5 litres (3 US gallons; 2.5 Imp gallons).

ACCOMMODATION: Enclosed cabin with four individual seats in pairs as standard, plus optional forward facing fifth seat (F33A only). Baggage compartment and hat shelf aft of seats. Passenger door and baggage compartment door on starboard side. Heater standard. Large cargo door, on starboard side of fuselage, standard on F33A. F33C has removable seat cushions, to accommodate parachutes, and a quick-release passenger door.

Beechcraft Model F33A Bonanzas used for pilot training by Lufthansa

SYSTEMS: Optional 12,000 BTU refrigeration type air-conditioning system (F33A only) comprises evaporator located beneath pilot's seat, condenser on lower fuselage and engine mounted compressor. Air outlets on centre console, with two-speed blower. Electrical system supplied by 28V 60A alternator, 24V 15.5Ah battery; a 100A alternator is available as an option, as is a standby generator. Hydraulic system for brakes only. Pneumatic system for instrument gyros and refrigeration type air-conditioning system optional. Oxygen system and electric propeller de-icing optional.

AVIONICS AND EQUIPMENT: Standard avionics include Bendix/King KX 155 760-channel com transceiver, 200-channel nav/glideslope receiver/converter with KI 209 VOR/ILS indicator, Bendix/King KY 155 760-channel com transceiver, 200-channel nav receiver/converter with KI 208 VOR/LOC indicator, KR 87 ADF with 227-00 indicator, KN 63 DME with KDI 572 indicator, DME hold and nav 1/nav 2 switching, KT 76A transponder, KMA 24-03 audio control/marker beacon receiver, microphone, headset, cabin speaker and static wicks. A wide range of optional avionics is available, including Bendix/King KFC 150 autopilot, and 3M/Ryan WX-1000 Stormscope. Standard equipment includes LCD digital chronometer, electric clock, exhaust gas temperature gauge, outside air temperature gauge, rate of climb indicator, sensitive altimeter, turn co-ordinator, 3 in horizon and directional gyros, four fore and aft adjustable and reclining seats, armrests, headrests, single diagonal strap shoulder harness with inertia reel for all occupants, pilot's storm window, sun visors, ultraviolet-proof windscreen and windows, large cargo door (F33A only), emergency locator transmitter, stall warning device, alternate static source, heated pitot, rotating beacon, three light strobe system, carpeted floor, super soundproofing, control wheel map lights, entrance door courtesy light, internally lit instruments, coat hooks, glove compartment, in-flight storage pockets, approach plate holder, utility shelf, cabin dome light, reading lights, instrument post lights, control wheel map light, electroluminescent sub-panel lighting, landing light, taxi light, full-flow oil filter, three-colour polyurethane exterior paint, external power socket and towbar. Optional equipment includes encoding altimeter, dual controls, co-pilot's wheel brakes, air-conditioning (F-33A only), fifth seat (F-33A only), fresh air vent blower and ground com switch. F33C has accelerometer, second boost pump with indicator light, non-baffled fuel cells, heavy-gauge rudder cables and reinforced fuselage, wings and tail surfaces as standard.

DIMENSIONS, EXTERNAL:

Wing span	10.21 m (33 ft 6 in)
Wing chord: at root	2.13 m (7 ft 0 in)
at tip	1.07 m (3 ft 6 in)
Wing aspect ratio	6.2
Length overall	8.13 m (26 ft 8 in)
Height overall	2.51 m (8 ft 3 in)
Tailplane span	3.71 m (12 ft 2 in)
Wheel track	2.92 m (9 ft 7 in)
Wheelbase	2.13 m (7 ft 0 in)
Propeller diameter	2.13 m (7 ft 0 in)
Passenger door: Height	0.91 m (3 ft 0 in)
Width	0.94 m (3 ft 1 in)
Cargo door (F33A): Height	0.57 m (1 ft 10½ in)
Width	0.96 m (3 ft 2 in)
Baggage compartment door:	
Height	0.57 m (1 ft 10½ in)
Width	0.47 m (1 ft 6½ in)

DIMENSIONS, INTERNAL:

Cabin, aft of firewall: Length	3.07 m (10 ft 1 in)
Max width	1.07 m (3 ft 6 in)
Max height	1.27 m (4 ft 2 in)
Volume	3.31 m³ (117 cu ft)
Baggage space	0.99 m³ (35 cu ft)

AREAS:

Wings, gross	16.80 m² (181 sq ft)
Ailerons (total)	1.06 m² (11.4 sq ft)
Trailing-edge flaps (total)	1.98 m² (21.3 sq ft)
Fin	0.93 m² (10.0 sq ft)
Rudder, incl tab	0.52 m² (5.6 sq ft)
Tailplane	1.75 m² (18.82 sq ft)
Elevators, incl tabs	1.67 m² (18.0 sq ft)

WEIGHTS AND LOADINGS:

Weight empty	1,015 kg (2,237 lb)
Max T-O and landing weight	1,542 kg (3,400 lb)
Max T-O weight, F33C in Aerobatic category	
	1,270 kg (2,800 lb)
Max ramp weight	1,548 kg (3,412 lb)
Max wing loading	91.8 kg/m² (18.8 lb/sq ft)
Max power loading	7.26 kg/kW (11.93 lb/hp)

PERFORMANCE (at max T-O weight, except cruising speeds at mid-cruise weight):

Max level speed at S/L	182 knots (338 km/h; 209 mph)
Cruising speed:	
75% power at 1,830 m (6,000 ft)	
	172 knots (319 km/h; 198 mph)
66% power at 3,050 m (10,000 ft)	
	168 knots (311 km/h; 193 mph)
55% power at 3,660 m (12,000 ft)	
	157 knots (291 km/h; 181 mph)

Beechcraft Model A36 Bonanza four/six-seat cabin monoplane

45% power at 2,440 m (8,000 ft)
    136 knots (253 km/h; 157 mph)

Stalling speed, power off:

flaps up	64 knots (118 km/h; 74 mph) IAS
30° flap	51 knots (94 km/h; 59 mph) IAS
Max rate of climb at S/L	353 m (1,157 ft)/min
Service ceiling	5,443 m (17,858 ft)
T-O run	305 m (1,000 ft)
T-O to 15 m (50 ft)	530 m (1,740 ft)
Landing from 15 m (50 ft)	396 m (1,300 ft)
Landing run	232 m (760 ft)

Range with max usable fuel, allowances for engine start, taxi, T-O, climb and 45 min reserves at 45% power:

75% power at 1,830 m (6,000 ft)
    715 nm (1,325 km; 823 miles)
66% power at 3,050 m (10,000 ft)
    777 nm (1,440 km; 894 miles)
55% power at 3,660 m (12,000 ft)
    838 nm (1,553 km; 964 miles)
45% power at 2,440 m (8,000 ft)
    889 nm (1,648 km; 1,023 miles)

BEECHCRAFT BONANZA MODEL A36

The current version of the A36, introduced on 3 October 1983, succeeded the earlier 212.5 kW (285 hp) Continental IO-520-BB powered model. It is a full six-seat utility aircraft developed from the Bonanza Model V35B, but has a conventional tail unit with sweptback vertical surfaces, similar to that of the Bonanza F33 series. In addition, the A36 has large double doors on the starboard side aft of the wingroot, to facilitate loading and unloading of bulky cargo when used in a utility role. The cabin volume is increased by 0.54 m³ (18.9 cu ft) compared with the F33, due to a fuselage extension of 0.25 m (10 in), and an increase of 0.28 m³ (10 cu ft) in the baggage compartment volume.

Like all Bonanzas, the Model A36 is licensed in the FAA Utility category at full gross weight, with no limitation of performance. The current model has as standard a Continental IO-550-B engine, redesigned instrument panels with 40 per cent more space for instruments and avionics, dual controls, throttle control power levers, altitude-compensating fuel pump, exhaust gas temperature gauge, automatically-dimming landing gear and annunciator lights for night operation, a three-blade propeller and a standby vacuum system. Landing gear and flap controls have been repositioned to conform to GAMA recommendations. Optional extras include instrument post lights, internally-lit instruments, courtesy lights for entrance door and rear step, co-pilot's vertically adjusting seat, refrigeration type air-conditioning system and all other items mentioned under the Model F33A Bonanza entry, except for the large cargo door.

A total of 2,954 Model 36 Bonanzas had been delivered by 1 January 1990. In April 1985 Saudia (Saudi Arabian Airlines) received four Model A36 Bonanzas for pilot training. The Finnair Training Centre at Pori, Finland, took delivery of three Model A36 Bonanzas during 1987.

TYPE: Four/six-seat utility light cabin monoplane.
WINGS: As for Model F33A.
FUSELAGE: As F33A but lengthened by 0.25 m (10 in).
TAIL UNIT: As for Model F33A.
LANDING GEAR: As for Model F33A; new landing gear warning system introduced in 1989.
POWER PLANT: One 224 kW (300 hp) Continental IO-550-B flat-six engine, driving a McCauley three-blade constant-speed propeller. The engine is equipped with an altitude-compensating fuel pump which automatically leans and enriches the fuel/air mixture during climb and descent respectively. Fuel capacity as for Model F33A.
ACCOMMODATION: Enclosed cabin seating four to six persons on individual seats. Pilot's seat is vertically adjustable. Dual controls standard. Two rear removable seats and two folding seats permit rapid conversion to utility configuration. Optional club seating with rear facing third and fourth seats, executive writing desk, refreshment cabinet, headrests for third and fourth seats, reading lights and fresh air outlets for fifth and sixth seats. Double doors of bonded aluminium honeycomb construction on starboard side facilitate loading of cargo. As an air ambulance, one stretcher can be accommodated with ample room for a medical attendant and/or other passengers. Extra windows provide improved view for passengers. Stowage for 181 kg (400 lb) of baggage.
SYSTEMS: Electrical system as for F33A. Hydraulic system for brakes only. Pneumatic system for instrument gyros, and refrigeration type air-conditioning system, optional.
AVIONICS AND EQUIPMENT: Standard avionics include Bendix/King KX 155 760-channel nav/com, with KI 208 VOR/LOC Omni converter/indicator, but a wide range of optional avionics is available. An optional ground communication switch permits use of one com radio without turning on the battery master switch. Optional equipment is as detailed for the F33A Bonanza, except as noted.

DIMENSIONS, EXTERNAL AND AREAS: As for F33A except:

Length overall	8.38 m (27 ft 6 in)
Height overall	2.62 m (8 ft 7 in)
Wheelbase	2.39 m (7 ft 10¼ in)
Rear passenger/cargo door: Height	1.02 m (3 ft 4 in)
Width	1.14 m (3 ft 9 in)

DIMENSIONS, INTERNAL:

Cabin, aft of firewall: Length, incl extended baggage compartment	3.84 m (12 ft 7 in)
Max width	1.07 m (3 ft 6 in)
Max height	1.27 m (4 ft 2 in)
Volume	3.85 m³ (135.9 cu ft)

WEIGHTS AND LOADINGS:

Weight empty, standard	1,028 kg (2,266 lb)
Max T-O weight	1,655 kg (3,650 lb)
Max ramp weight	1,661 kg (3,663 lb)
Max wing loading	98.6 kg/m² (20.2 lb/sq ft)
Max power loading	7.40 kg/kW (12.2 lb/hp)

PERFORMANCE (max speed at minimum weight; cruising speeds at mid-cruise weight):

Max level speed	184 knots (340 km/h; 212 mph)
Max cruising speed:	
2,500 rpm at 1,830 m (6,000 ft)	
	176 knots (326 km/h; 202 mph)
2,300 rpm at 2,440 m (8,000 ft)	
	167 knots (309 km/h; 192 mph)
2,100 rpm at 1,830 m (6,000 ft)	
	160 knots (296 km/h; 184 mph)
2,100 rpm at 3,050 m (10,000 ft)	
	153 knots (283 km/h; 176 mph)

Stalling speed, power off:

flaps up	68 knots (126 km/h; 78 mph) IAS
30° flap	59 knots (109 km/h; 68 mph) IAS
Max rate of climb at S/L	368 m (1,208 ft)/min
Service ceiling	3,640 m (18,500 ft)
T-O run: flaps up	360 m (1,182 ft)
12° flap	296 m (971 ft)
T-O to 15 m (50 ft): flaps up	640 m (2,100 ft)
12° flap	583 m (1,913 ft)

Beechcraft Baron Model 58 four/six-seat cabin monoplane

Landing from 15 m (50 ft)   442 m (1,450 ft)
Landing run   280 m (920 ft)
Range with max usable fuel, with allowances for engine
  start, taxi, T-O, climb and 45 min reserves at econ
  cruise power:
  2,500 rpm at 3,660 m (12,000 ft)
                               875 nm (1,621 km; 1,008 miles)
  2,300 rpm at 3,660 m (12,000 ft)
                               903 nm (1,672 km; 1,039 miles)
  2,100 rpm at 1,830 m (6,000 ft)
                               910 nm (1,686 km; 1,048 miles)

BEECHCRAFT TURBO BONANZA MODEL B36TC

Beech introduced a turbocharged version of the A36 Bonanza in 1979, following FAA certification on 7 December 1978, and 271 of the initial A36TC version were delivered. In 1982 Beech introduced the improved B36TC, with a wing of greater span and increased fuel capacity, and 500 of this model had been delivered by 1 January 1990. The B36TC is generally similar to the A36, except as follows:

WINGS: Wing section NACA 23010.5 at tip. Incidence 0° at tip.

POWER PLANT: One 223.7 kW (300 hp) Continental TSIO-520-UB turbocharged flat-six engine, driving a three-blade constant-speed metal propeller with spinner. Fixed engine cowl flaps. Two fuel tanks in each wing leading-edge, with total usable capacity of 386 litres (102 US gallons; 85 Imp gallons). Refuelling points above tanks. Oil capacity 11.5 litres (3 US gallons; 2.5 Imp gallons).

ACCOMMODATION AND SYSTEMS: Air-conditioning optional.

AVIONICS AND EQUIPMENT: As for Model A36, except that exhaust gas temperature gauge is not available. Turbine inlet temperature gauge is standard.

DIMENSIONS, EXTERNAL: As for Model A36, except:
  Wing span   11.53 m (37 ft 10 in)
  Wing chord at tip   0.91 m (3 ft 0 in)
  Wing aspect ratio   7.6
  Propeller diameter   1.98 m (6 ft 6 in)
DIMENSIONS, INTERNAL: As for Model A36
AREA:
  Wings, gross   17.47 m² (188.1 sq ft)
WEIGHTS AND LOADINGS:
  Weight empty, standard   1,093 kg (2,410 lb)
  Max T-O and landing weight   1,746 kg (3,850 lb)
  Max ramp weight   1,753 kg (3,866 lb)
  Max wing loading   100.1 kg/m² (20.5 lb/sq ft)
  Max power loading   7.81 kg/kW (12.8 lb/hp)
PERFORMANCE (at max T-O weight, except speeds are at mid-cruise weight):
  Max level speed at 6,700 m (22,000 ft)
                                  213 knots (394 km/h; 245 mph)
  Cruising speed at 7,620 m (25,000 ft):
    79% power   200 knots (370 km/h; 230 mph)
    75% power   195 knots (361 km/h; 224 mph)
    69% power   188 knots (348 km/h; 216 mph)
    56% power   173 knots (320 km/h; 199 mph)
  Stalling speed, power off:
    flaps up   65 knots (120 km/h; 75 mph) IAS

30° flap   57 knots (106 km/h; 66 mph) IAS
Max rate of climb at S/L   321 m (1,053 ft)/min
Service ceiling   over 7,620 m (25,000 ft)
T-O run, 15° flap   311 m (1,020 ft)
T-O to 15 m (50 ft), 15° flap   649 m (2,130 ft)
Landing run   298 m (976 ft)
Range with max fuel, allowances for engine start, taxi,
  T-O, cruise climb, descent, and 45 min reserves at 50%
  power:
  79% power at 7,620 m (25,000 ft)
                                  956 nm (1,770 km; 1,100 miles)
  75% power at 7,620 m (25,000 ft)
                                  984 nm (1,822 km; 1,132 miles)
  69% power at 7,620 m (25,000 ft)
                                  1,022 nm (1,892 km; 1,176 miles)
  56% power at 6,100 m (20,000 ft)
                                  1,092 nm (2,022 km; 1,256 miles)

BEECHCRAFT BARON MODEL 58

Beech introduced this new version of the Baron in late 1969. Developed from the Baron D55, it differed by having the forward cabin section extended by 0.254 m (10 in), allowing the windscreen, passenger door, instrument panel and front seats to be moved forward and so provide a more spacious cabin. This change was made without affecting the wing main spar location, but the wheelbase was extended by moving the nosewheel forward, to improve ground handling. New features included double passenger/cargo doors on the starboard side, extended propeller hubs, redesigned engine nacelles to improve cooling, and a fourth window on each side. The Model 58 was licensed by the FAA in the Normal category on 19 November 1969.

Beech had delivered 2,213 of this Baron series (including Baron 58Ps and 58TCs) by 1 January 1990. Deliveries include four for the Indonesian Civil Flying Academy, Java, three for the Centre Multi-National Formation Aviation Civile of M'Vengue, Gabon, and eight for the US Federal Aviation Administration's staff pilot proficiency training programme. Lufthansa has received 19 for pilot training.

TYPE: Four/six-seat cabin monoplane.

WINGS: Cantilever low-wing monoplane. Wing section NACA 23016-5 at root, NACA 23010-5 at tip. Dihedral 6°. Incidence 4° at root, 0° at tip. No sweepback. Each wing is a two-spar semi-monocoque box beam of conventional aluminium alloy construction, with beaded skins. Electrically operated single-slotted light alloy trailing-edge flaps, with beaded skins. Manually operated trim tab in port aileron. Pneumatic rubber de-icing boots optional.

FUSELAGE: Semi-monocoque aluminium alloy structure. Hat section longerons and channel type keels extend forward from the cabin section, making the support structure for the forward nose section and nosewheel gear an integral part of the fuselage.

TAIL UNIT: Cantilever all-metal structure. Elevators have smooth magnesium alloy skins. Manually operated trim tab in each elevator and in rudder. Pneumatic rubber de-icing boots optional.

LANDING GEAR: Electrically retractable tricycle type. Main units retract inward into wings, nosewheel aft. Beech

oleo-pneumatic shock absorbers in all units. Steerable nosewheel with shimmy damper. Cleveland wheels, with mainwheel tyres size 6.50-8, pressure 3.59-3.96 bars (52-56 lb/sq in). Nosewheel tyre size 5.00-5, pressure 3.79-4.14 bars (55-60 lb/sq in). Cleveland ring-disc hydraulic brakes. Heavy duty brakes optional. Parking brake. New warning system introduced in 1989.

POWER PLANT: Two 224 kW (300 hp) Continental IO-550-C flat-six engines, each driving a McCauley three-blade constant-speed fully feathering metal propeller with spinner. The standard fuel system has a usable capacity of 514 litres (136 US gallons; 113 Imp gallons), with optional usable capacity of 628 litres (166 US gallons; 138 Imp gallons). Optional 'wet wingtip' installation also available, increasing usable capacity to 734 litres (194 US gallons; 161.5 Imp gallons).

ACCOMMODATION: Standard model has four individual seats in pairs in enclosed cabin, with door on starboard side. Single diagonal strap shoulder harness with inertia reel standard on all seats. Vertically adjusting pilot's seat is standard. Vertically adjusting co-pilot's seat, folding fifth and sixth seats, or club seating comprising folding fifth and sixth seats and aft facing third and fourth seats, are optional. Executive writing desk available as option with club seating. Baggage compartment in nose, capacity 136 kg (300 lb). Double passenger/cargo doors on starboard side of cabin provide access to space for 181 kg (400 lb) of baggage or cargo behind the third and fourth seats. Pilot's storm window. Openable windows adjacent to the third and fourth seats are used for ground ventilation and as emergency exits. Cabin heated and ventilated. Windscreen defrosting standard.

SYSTEMS: Cabin heated by Janitrol 50,000 BTU heater, which serves also for windscreen defrosting. Oxygen system of 1.41 m³ (49.8 cu ft) or 1.87 m³ (66 cu ft) capacity optional. Electrical system includes two 28V 60A engine driven alternators with alternator failure lights and two 12V 25Ah batteries. Two 100A alternators optional. Hydraulic system for brakes only. Pneumatic pressure system for air driven instruments, and optional wing and tail unit de-icing system. Oxygen system optional. Cabin air-conditioning and windscreen electric anti-icing systems optional.

AVIONICS AND EQUIPMENT: Standard avionics include Bendix/King KX 155-09 760-channel com transceiver with audio amplifier, 200-channel nav receiver with KI 208 VOR/LOC converter/indicator, KR 87 ADF with KI 227-00 indicator, Bendix/King combined loop/sense antenna, microphone, headset, cabin speaker, nav and com antennae. Bendix weather radars optional. Optional avionics by Bendix/King and Collins. Standard equipment includes dual controls, blind-flying instruments, control wheel clock, outside air temperature gauge, sensitive altimeter, turn co-ordinator, pilot's storm window, sun visors, ultraviolet-proof windscreen and cabin windows, armrests, adjustable rudder pedals (retractable on starboard side), emergency locator transmitter, heated pitot head, instrument panel floodlights, map light, lighted trim tab position indicator, step and entrance door courtesy lights, reading lights, navigation and position lights, steerable taxi light, dual landing lights, cabin carpeting and soundproofing, headrests, heated fuel vents, cabin dome light, door ajar warning light, nose baggage compartment light, heated fuel and stall warning vanes, external polyurethane paint finish, EGT and CHT gauges, synchroscope, engine winterisation kit, towbar and external power socket. Options include a true airspeed indicator, engine and flight hour recorders, instantaneous vertical speed indicator, alternate static source, internally illuminated instruments, rotating beacon, strobe lights, electric windscreen anti-icing, wing ice detection light, static wicks, cabin club seating, executive writing desk, refreshment cabinet, cabin fire extinguisher, ventilation blower, super soundproofing, and approach plate holder.

DIMENSIONS, EXTERNAL:
  Wing span   11.53 m (37 ft 10 in)
  Wing chord: at root   2.13 m (7 ft 0 in)
    at tip   0.90 m (2 ft 11.6 in)
  Wing aspect ratio   7.2
  Length overall   9.09 m (29 ft 10 in)
  Height overall   2.97 m (9 ft 9 in)
  Tailplane span   4.85 m (15 ft 11 in)
  Wheel track   2.92 m (9 ft 7 in)
  Wheelbase   2.72 m (8 ft 11 in)
  Propeller diameter   1.98 m (6 ft 6 in)
  Rear passenger/cargo doors:
    Max height   1.02 m (3 ft 4 in)
    Width   1.14 m (3 ft 9 in)
  Baggage door (fwd): Height   0.56 m (1 ft 10 in)
    Width   0.64 m (2 ft 1 in)
DIMENSIONS, INTERNAL:
  Cabin, incl rear baggage area:
    Length   3.84 m (12 ft 7 in)
    Max width   1.07 m (3 ft 6 in)
    Max height   1.27 m (4 ft 2 in)
    Floor area   3.72 m² (40 sq ft)
    Volume   3.85 m³ (135.9 cu ft)
  Baggage compartment: fwd   0.49 m³ (17.2 cu ft)
AREAS:
  Wings, gross   18.51 m² (199.2 sq ft)

Ailerons (total)	1.06 m² (11.40 sq ft)
Trailing-edge flaps (total)	1.98 m² (21.30 sq ft)
Fin	1.46 m² (15.67 sq ft)
Rudder, incl tab	0.81 m² (8.75 sq ft)
Tailplane	4.95 m² (53.30 sq ft)
Elevators, incl tabs	1.84 m² (19.80 sq ft)

WEIGHTS AND LOADINGS:

Weight empty	1,579 kg (3,481 lb)
Max T-O weight	2,495 kg (5,500 lb)
Max landing weight	2,449 kg (5,400 lb)
Max ramp weight	2,506 kg (5,524 lb)
Max wing loading	143.4 kg/m² (27.6 lb/sq ft)
Max power loading	5.60 kg/kW (9.2 lb/hp)

PERFORMANCE (at max T-O weight, except cruising speeds at average cruise weight):

Max level speed at S/L 208 knots (386 km/h; 239 mph)
Max cruising speed, 2,500 rpm at 1,525 m (5,000 ft)
  203 knots (376 km/h; 234 mph)
Cruising speed, 2,500 rpm at 3,050 m (10,000 ft)
  198 knots (367 km/h; 228 mph)
Econ cruising speed, 2,100 rpm at 3,660 m (12,000 ft)
  163 knots (302 km/h; 188 mph)
Stalling speed, power off:
  flaps up 84 knots (156 km/h; 97 mph) IAS
  flaps down 75 knots (139 km/h; 86 mph) IAS
Max rate of climb at S/L 529 m (1,735 ft)/min
Rate of climb at S/L, one engine out 119 m (390 ft)/min
Service ceiling 6,306 m (20,688 ft)
Service ceiling, one engine out 2,220 m (7,284 ft)
T-O run 427 m (1,400 ft)
T-O to 15 m (50 ft) 701 m (2,300 ft)
Landing from 15 m (50 ft) 747 m (2,450 ft)
Landing run 434 m (1,425 ft)
Range with 734 litres (194 US gallons; 161.5 Imp gallons) usable fuel, with allowances for engine start, taxi, T-O, climb and 45 min reserves at econ cruise power:
  max cruising speed (power/altitude settings as above)
  1,150 nm (2,130 km; 1,324 miles)
  cruising speed (power/altitude settings as above)
  1,411 nm (2,615 km; 1,625 miles)
  econ cruising speed (power/altitude settings as above)
  1,575 nm (2,919 km; 1,814 miles)

BEECHCRAFT KING AIR MODEL C90A

The King Air C90A is a pressurised six/ten-seat twin-turboprop business aircraft which superseded the Models 90, A90, B90, C90 and C90-1 King Air. In April 1987 Beech announced structural changes which result in a 204 kg (450 lb) increase in max T-O weight, permitting two more passengers and additional baggage to be carried. Deliveries of the higher gross weight Model C90A began in the fourth quarter of 1987. Recent customers have included Japan Air Lines and the Japan Civil Aviation College, which uses the aircraft for commercial pilot training.

Beech delivered 38 Model C90As during 1989. A total of 1,226 commercial and 226 military King Air 90/A90/B90/C90/C90-1/C90As had been delivered by 1 January 1990.

TYPE: Six/ten-seat twin-turboprop business aircraft.

WINGS: Cantilever low-wing monoplane. Wing section NACA 23014.1 (modified) at root, NACA 23016.22 (modified) at outer end of centre-section, NACA 23012 at tip. Dihedral 7°. Incidence 4° 48′ at root, 0° at tip. No sweepback at quarter-chord. Two-spar aluminium alloy structure. All-metal ailerons of magnesium, with adjustable trim tab on port aileron. Single-slotted aluminium alloy flaps. Automatic pneumatic de-icing boots on leading-edges are standard.

FUSELAGE: Aluminium alloy semi-monocoque structure.

TAIL UNIT: Cantilever all-metal structure with sweptback vertical surfaces. Fixed incidence tailplane, with 7° dihedral. Trim tabs in rudder and each elevator. Automatic pneumatic de-icing boots on leading-edges of fin and tailplane are standard.

LANDING GEAR: Hydraulically retractable tricycle type. Nosewheel retracts rearward, mainwheels forward into engine nacelles. Mainwheels protrude slightly beneath nacelles when retracted, for safety in a wheels-up emergency landing. Fully castoring steerable nosewheel with shimmy damper. Beech oleo-pneumatic shock absorbers. Goodrich mainwheels with tyres size 8.50-10, pressure 3.79 bars (55 lb/sq in). Goodrich nosewheel with tyre size 6.50-10, pressure 3.59 bars (52 lb/sq in). Goodrich heat-sink and aircooled multi-disc hydraulic brakes. Parking brakes.

POWER PLANT: Two 410 kW (550 shp) Pratt & Whitney Canada PT6A-21 turboprops, each driving a Hartzell three-blade constant-speed fully-feathering propeller with spinner. Propeller electrothermal anti-icing, auto ignition system, environmental fuel drain collection system, magnetic chip detector, automatic propeller feathering, and propeller synchrophaser standard. Fuel in two tanks in engine nacelles, each with usable capacity of 231 litres (61 US gallons; 50.8 Imp gallons), and auxiliary bladder tanks in outer wings, each with capacity of 496 litres (131 US gallons; 109 Imp gallons). Total usable fuel capacity 1,454 litres (384 US gallons; 320 Imp gallons). Refuelling points in top of each engine nacelle and in wing leading-edge outboard of each nacelle. Oil capacity 13.2 litres (3.5 US gallons; 2.9 Imp gallons) per

Beechcraft King Air Model C90A business aircraft of Japan Airlines

engine. Engine anti-icing system standard. Engine fire detection and extinguishing system optional.

ACCOMMODATION: Two seats side by side in cockpit with dual controls standard. Normally, four reclining seats in main cabin, in pairs facing each other fore and aft. Standard furnishings include cabin forward partition, with fore and aft partition curtain and coat rack, hinged nose baggage compartment door, seat belts and inertia reel shoulder harness for all seats. Optional arrangements seat up to eight persons, with lateral tracking chairs, and refreshment cabinets. Baggage racks at rear of cabin on starboard side, with optional toilet on port side. Door on port side aft of wing, with built-in airstairs. Emergency exit on starboard side of cabin. Entire accommodation pressurised, heated and air-conditioned. Electrically heated windscreen, windscreen defroster and windscreen wipers standard.

SYSTEMS: Pressurisation by dual engine bleed air system with pressure differential of 0.34 bars (5.0 lb/sq in). Cabin heated by 45,000 BTU dual engine bleed air system and auxiliary electrical heating system. Hydraulic system for landing gear actuation. Electrical system includes two 28V 250A starter/generators, 24V 45Ah aircooled nickel-cadmium battery with failure detector. Complete de-icing and anti-icing equipment. Oxygen system, 0.62 m³ (22 cu ft), 1.39 m³ (49 cu ft) or 1.81 m³ (64 cu ft) capacity, optional. Vacuum system for flight instruments.

AVIONICS AND EQUIPMENT: Standard Collins Pro Line II avionics package includes APS-65 autopilot/flight director with ADI-84 FDI and EFD-74 EHSI; dual VHF-22A transceivers with CTL-22 controls; dual VIR-32 VOR/LOC/GLS/MKR receivers with CTL-32 controls; ADF-60A with CTL-62 control; DME-42 with IND-42 indicator; RMI-30; dual MCS-65 compass systems; WXR-270 colour weather radar; dual TDR-90 transponders; ALT-50A radio altimeter; dual DB systems Model 415 audio systems; pilot's United 5506-S encoding altimeter; dual Flite-Tronics PC-250 inverters; dual 2 in electric turn-and-bank indicators; co-pilot's 3 in horizon indicator; co-pilot's HSI; avionics master switch; edgelite radio panel; ELT; ground clearance switch to comm 1; control wheel push-to-talk switches; dual hand microphones; dual Telex headsets; and sectional instrument panel. Optional avionics include Bendix/King Silver Crown and Gold Crown packages; Foster LNS-616B RNAV/Loran C; and 3M WX-1000+ Stormscope. Standard equipment includes dual blind flying instrumentation with sensitive altimeters and dual instantaneous VSIs; standby magnetic compass; OAT gauge; LCD digital chronometer clock; vacuum gauge; de-icing pressure gauge; cabin rate of climb indicator; cabin altitude and differential pressure indicator; flight hour recorder; automatic solid state warning and annunciator panel; pilot and co-pilot's four-way adjustable seats with shoulder harness and lap belts; dual cockpit speakers; adjustable sun visors; map pocket; cigarette lighter; two ashtrays; fresh air outlets; coffee cup holders; oxygen outlets with overhead mounted diluter demand masks with microphones; pilot and co-pilot's approach plate/map cases; four fully-adjustable cabin seats in club arrangement with removable headrests; shoulder harnesses, lap belts, adjustable reading lights, retractable inboard armrests, fresh air outlets, ashtrays and cupholders; cabin floor carpeting; adjustable polarised sunshades; cabin coat cable with hangars; magazine rack; removable low profile toilet with shoulder harness, lap belt, baggage webbing and relief tube; aisle-facing storage seat with air, light, ashtray, water tank, ice chest drawer, removable bottle/decanter rack and padded partition; two cabinets, forward left and right sides of

cabin, with ice chest, heated liquid container and storage drawers; two cabin tables; cabin fire extinguisher; 'No smoking — Fasten seat belt' sign with audible chime; internal corrosion proofing; urethane exterior paint; towbar; propeller restraints; wing ice lights; dual landing lights; nosewheel taxi light; flush position lights; dual rotating beacons; dual map lights; indirect cabin lighting; two overhead cabin spotlights; entrance door light; aft compartment lights; primary and secondary instrument lighting systems; rheostat-controlled white cockpit lighting; entrance door step lights; wingtip recognition lights; wingtip and tail strobe lights; and vertical tail illumination lights. Optional equipment includes lateral tracking cabin seats; cabin door support cable; cabin partition sliding doors; central aisle carpet runner; electric flushing toilet; engine fire detection system; 1.81 m³ (64 cu ft) oxygen bottle; cockpit relief tube; co-pilot's control wheel digital chronometer; cabinet with three drawers and stereo tape deck storage; pilot-to-cabin paging with four stereo speakers; ADF audio to cabin paging; control wheel frequency transfer and memory advance switch; co-pilot's control wheel transponder ident switch; and passenger stereo headsets.

DIMENSIONS, EXTERNAL:

Wing span	15.32 m (50 ft 3 in)
Wing chord: at root	2.15 m (7 ft 0½ in)
at tip	1.07 m (3 ft 6 in)
Wing aspect ratio	8.6
Length overall	10.82 m (35 ft 6 in)
Height overall	4.34 m (14 ft 3 in)
Tailplane span	5.26 m (17 ft 3 in)
Wheel track	3.89 m (12 ft 9 in)
Wheelbase	3.73 m (12 ft 3 in)
Propeller diameter	2.36 m (7 ft 9 in)
Propeller ground clearance	0.305 m (1 ft 0 in)
Passenger door: Height	1.30 m (4 ft 3½ in)
Width	0.69 m (2 ft 3 in)
Height to sill	1.22 m (4 ft 0 in)

DIMENSIONS, INTERNAL:

Total pressurised length	5.43 m (17 ft 10 in)
Cabin: Length	3.86 m (12 ft 8 in)
Max width	1.37 m (4 ft 6 in)
Max height	1.45 m (4 ft 9 in)
Floor area	6.50 m² (70 sq ft)
Volume	8.88 m³ (313.6 cu ft)
Baggage compartment, rear	1.51 m³ (53.5 cu ft)

AREAS:

Wings, gross	27.31 m² (293.94 sq ft)
Ailerons (total)	1.29 m² (13.90 sq ft)
Trailing-edge flaps (total)	2.72 m² (29.30 sq ft)
Fin	2.20 m² (23.67 sq ft)
Rudder, incl tab	1.30 m² (14.00 sq ft)
Tailplane	4.39 m² (47.25 sq ft)
Elevators, incl tabs	1.66 m² (17.87 sq ft)

WEIGHTS AND LOADINGS:

Weight empty	2,985 kg (6,580 lb)
Max T-O weight	4,581 kg (10,100 lb)
Max ramp weight	4,608 kg (10,160 lb)
Max landing weight	4,354 kg (9,600 lb)
Max wing loading	167.7 kg/m² (34.4 lb/sq ft)
Max power loading	5.59 kg/kW (9.2 lb/shp)

PERFORMANCE (at max T-O weight except where indicated):
Max cruising speed at AUW of 3,855 kg (8,500 lb):
  at 3,660 m (12,000 ft) 242 knots (448 km/h; 278 mph)
  at 4,880 m (16,000 ft) 247 knots (457 km/h; 284 mph)
  at 6,400 m (21,000 ft) 243 knots (450 km/h; 280 mph)
Stalling speed, power off:
  wheels and flaps up
  88 knots (163 km/h; 101 mph) IAS

wheels and flaps down
                    78 knots (144 km/h; 90 mph) IAS
Max rate of climb at S/L   610 m (2,003 ft)/min
Rate of climb at S/L, one engine out 169 m (554 ft)/min
Service ceiling   8,809 m (28,900 ft)
Service ceiling, one engine out   4,346 m (14,260 ft)
Min ground turning radius   10.82 m (35 ft 6 in)
T-O run   574 m (1,885 ft)
T-O to 15 m (50 ft)   785 m (2,577 ft)
Accelerate/stop distance   1,232 m (4,042 ft)
Landing from 15 m (50 ft) at max landing weight, with
   propeller reversal   633 m (2,078 ft)
Landing run at max landing weight, with propeller
   reversal   316 m (1,036 ft)
Range with max fuel at max cruising speed, incl
   allowance for starting, taxi, take-off, climb, descent
   and 45 min reserves at max range power, ISA, at:
   6,400 m (21,000 ft)   1,075 nm (1,992 km; 1,238 miles)
   4,875 m (16,000 ft)   933 nm (1,729 km; 1,074 miles)
   3,660 m (12,000 ft)   866 nm (1,605 km; 997 miles)
Max range at econ cruising power, allowances as above,
   at:
   6,400 m (21,000 ft)   1,277 nm (2,366 km; 1,470 miles)
   4,875 m (16,000 ft)   1,155 nm (2,140 km; 1,330 miles)
   3,660 m (12,000 ft)   1,054 nm (1,953 km; 1,214 miles)

Beechcraft Super King Air B200 eight/fifteen-seat pressurised transport

BEECHCRAFT SUPER KING AIR B200
Swedish Air Force designation: Tp 101

Design of the Super King Air 200 began in October 1970.
The first prototype (c/n BB1) flew for the first time on 27
October 1972. FAA certification under FAR Part 23 was
awarded on 14 December 1973, the aircraft satisfying also
the icing requirements of FAR Part 25.

In February 1977 Beech delivered to the French Institut
Géographique National two specially modified Super King
Airs. These have twin Wild RC-10 Superaviogon camera
installations and Doppler navigation systems, and were the
first Super King Airs to be equipped with optional wingtip
fuel tanks, which increase the total usable fuel capacity from
2,059 litres (544 US gallons) to 2,460 litres (650 US gallons)
to provide a max endurance of 10.3 h. Designated **Model
200T**, they are fitted with high-flotation main landing gear,
and are operated under a special French airworthiness
certificate which allows max T-O and landing weights of
6,350 kg (14,000 lb) and 6,123 kg (13,500 lb) respectively.
They can be operated with or without the wingtip tanks, for
high-altitude photography and weather observation.

A specially equipped **Maritime Patrol** version of the
Super King Air, is described separately.

A Super King Air supplied to the Egyptian government in
1978 is used to conduct water, uranium and other natural
resources exploration in the Sinai and Egyptian deserts.
This aircraft is equipped with remote sensing equipment,
specialised avionics, and sophisticated cameras. In June
1978, Beech delivered to the government of Taiwan a Super
King Air equipped to check ground based navigation
systems; and Malaysia uses two Super King Airs for airways
calibration and flight inspection. A second special mission
aircraft was delivered to Taiwan's Ministry of the Interior in
May 1979. Two Super King Airs were delivered to the
Royal Hong Kong Auxiliary Air Force in 1986 and 1987.
Three Super King Air 200s were delivered during 1989 to
the Swedish Air Force, which operates them under the
designation **Tp 101**.

The **Super King Air B200**, introduced in March 1981,
is generally similar to the Super King Air 200, except for
the installation of Pratt & Whitney Canada PT6A-42
turboprops, which provide better cruise and altitude
performance than the PT6A-41s in the original Super King
Air 200. In addition, max zero-fuel weight is increased by
272 kg (600 lb) and cabin pressure differential is increased
from 0.41 bars (6.0 lb/sq in) to 0.44 bars (6.5 lb/sq in).
Design of the B200 began in March 1980, the prototype
being a modified Super King Air 200 (c/n BB343).
Manufacture of production aircraft began in May 1980,
and FAA certification was granted on 13 February 1981.
Seven versions are available:

Super King Air B200. Basic version.
Super King Air B200C. As Super King Air B200, but
with a 1.32 × 1.32 m (4 ft 4 in × 4 ft 4 in) cargo door.
Super King Air B200T. Generally similar to Maritime
Patrol 200T, with standard provision to carry removable
wingtip tanks to increase maximum fuel capacity by 401
litres (106 US gallons; 88.25 Imp gallons), to a total of 2,460
litres (650 US gallons; 541 Imp gallons). Span without
tip tanks 16.92 m (55 ft 6 in).
Super King Air B200CT. Version with both cargo
door and wingtip tank provisions as standard.
Super King Air 300 and **Super King Air 300LW**.
Described separately.
Super King Air 350. Described separately.

Beech delivered 32 Super King Air B200s in 1989 and by
1 January 1990 had delivered a total of 1,480 to commercial
and private operators and 282 military versions (described
separately) to the US armed forces and foreign customers.

The following description applies to the B200:
TYPE: Twin-turboprop passenger, cargo or executive light
transport.
WINGS: Cantilever low-wing monoplane, with constant
chord centre-section and tapered outer panels. Leading-

**Beechcraft Super King Air B200 twin-turboprop transport, with additional side view of Maritime
Patrol 200T (centre right); scrap views of wingtip tanks and centre-fuselage of photo survey aircraft
for IGN** *(Pilot Press)*

edges extended forward just outboard of engine nacelles.
Wing section NACA 23018 and 23016.5 at root, NACA
23012 at tip. Dihedral 6°. Incidence 3° 48′ at root, –1° 7′ at
tip. No sweepback at quarter-chord. Two-spar light
alloy structure. Conventional ailerons of light alloy
construction, with trim tab in port aileron. Single-slotted
trailing-edge flaps of light alloy construction. Pneumatic
de-icing boots standard.
FUSELAGE: Light alloy semi-monocoque structure of safe-life
design.
TAIL UNIT: Conventional cantilever T tail structure of light
alloy with swept vertical and horizontal surfaces. Dorsal
fin, and shallow ventral fin. Fixed incidence tailplane.
Trim tab in each elevator. Anti-servo tab in rudder.
Pneumatic de-icing boots standard, on leading-edge of
tailplane only.
LANDING GEAR: Hydraulically retractable tricycle type, with
twin wheels on each main unit. Single wheel on steerable
nose unit, with shimmy damper. Main units retract
forward, nosewheel rearward. Beech oleo-pneumatic
shock absorbers. Goodrich mainwheels and tyres size 18
× 5.5, pressure 7.25 bars (105 lb/sq in). Oversize and/or
10-ply mainwheel tyres optional. Goodrich nosewheel
size 6.50 × 10, with tyre size 22 × 6.75-10, pressure 3.93
bars (57 lb/sq in). Goodrich hydraulic multiple-disc
brakes. Parking brake.
POWER PLANT: Two 634 kW (850 shp) Pratt & Whitney
Canada PT6A-42 turboprops, each driving a Hartzell
three-blade constant-speed fully-feathering reversible-
pitch metal propeller with spinner. Bladder fuel cells in
each wing, with main system capacity of 1,461 litres (386
US gallons; 321.5 Imp gallons) and auxiliary system
capacity of 598 litres (158 US gallons; 131.5 Imp gallons).
Total usable fuel capacity 2,059 litres (544 US gallons;
453 Imp gallons). Two refuelling points in upper surface

of each wing. Wingtip tanks optional, providing an
additional 401 litres (106 US gallons; 88.25 Imp gallons)
and raising maximum usable capacity to 2,460 litres (650
US gallons; 541 Imp gallons). Oil capacity 29.5 litres (7.8
US gallons; 6.5 Imp gallons). Anti-icing of engine air
intakes by hot air from engine exhaust, electrothermal
anti-icing for propellers and automatic feathering and
synchrophaser standard.
ACCOMMODATION: Pilot only, or crew of two side by side, on
flight deck, with full dual controls and instruments as
standard. Six cabin seats standard, each equipped with
seat belts and inertia reel shoulder harness; alternative
layouts for a maximum of 13 passengers in cabin and 14th
beside pilot. Partition with sliding door between cabin
and flight deck, and partition at rear of cabin. Door at
rear of cabin on port side, with integral airstair. Large
cargo door optional. Inward opening emergency exit on
starboard side over wing. Lavatory and stowage for up to
249 kg (550 lb) baggage in rear fuselage. Maintenance
access door in rear fuselage; radio compartment access
doors in nose. Cabin is air-conditioned and pressurised,
with radiant heat panels to warm cabin before engine
starting.
SYSTEMS: Cabin pressurisation by engine bleed air, with a
maximum differential of 0.44 bars (6.5 lb/sq in). Cabin
air-conditioner of 34,000 BTU capacity. Auxiliary cabin
heating by radiant panels standard. Oxygen system for
flight deck, and 0.62 m³ (22 cu ft) oxygen system for
cabin, with automatic drop-down face masks; standard
system of 1.39 m³ (49 cu ft); 1.81 m³ (64 cu ft) or 2.15 m³
(76 cu ft) optional. Dual vacuum system for instruments.
Hydraulic system for landing gear retraction and
extension, pressurised to 171-191 bars (2,475-2,775 lb/sq
in). Separate hydraulic system for brakes. Pneumatic
system for wing and tailplane de-icing. Electrical system

has two 250A 28V starter/generators and a 24V 45Ah aircooled nickel-cadmium battery with failure detector. AC power provided by dual 250VA inverters. Engine fire detection system standard; engine fire extinguishing system optional.

AVIONICS AND EQUIPMENT: Standard Collins Pro Line II avionics and cockpit equipment generally as for King Air C90A except: dual DME-42, dual RMI-30; pilot's ALT-80A encoding altimeter; cockpit-to-cabin paging; dual maximum allowable airspeed indicators; flight director indicator; co-pilot's 24 hour clock; oxygen pressure indicator and blue-white cockpit lighting standard. Optional avionics include Collins Pro Line II with 5 in FCS; EFIS-85B(-14); Honeywell SPZ-4000 autopilot with 4 in or 5 in flight director systems or EDZ-605 three-tube EFIS; Bendix/King Gold Crown avionics packages; Bendix RDS-84VP colour weather radar; Fairchild 17M-700-274 flight data recorder; Fairchild A-100A cockpit voice recorder; Bendix/King KHF-950 or Collins HF-230 HF transceiver; Bendix/King CC-2024C or Collins DCP-270 radar checklist; Foster LNS-616B RNAV/Loran C; Bendix/King KNS-660 RNAV/VLF/Omega; 3M WX-1000+ Stormscope; and Wulfsberg Flitefone VI. Standard/optional equipment generally as for King Air C90A except fluorescent cabin lighting, one-place couch with storage drawers, flushing toilet (B200) or chemical toilet (B200C), cabin radiant heating, cockpit/cabin partition with sliding doors, and airstair door with hydraulic snubber and courtesy light, standard. FAR Pt 135 operational configuration includes cockpit fire extinguisher and 2.15 m³ (76 cu ft) oxygen bottle as standard. A range of optional cabin seating and cabinetry configuration is available, including quick-removable fold-up seats.

DIMENSIONS, EXTERNAL:
Wing span	16.61 m (54 ft 6 in)
Wing chord: at root	2.18 m (7 ft 1¾ in)
at tip	0.90 m (2 ft 11⅝ in)
Wing aspect ratio	9.8
Length overall	13.34 m (43 ft 9 in)
Height overall	4.57 m (15 ft 0 in)
Tailplane span	5.61 m (18 ft 5 in)
Wheel track	5.23 m (17 ft 2 in)
Wheelbase	4.56 m (14 ft 11½ in)
Propeller diameter	2.50 m (8 ft 2½ in)
Propeller ground clearance	0.37 m (1 ft 2½ in)
Distance between propeller centres	5.23 m (17 ft 2 in)
Passenger door: Height	1.31 m (4 ft 3½ in)
Width	0.68 m (2 ft 2¾ in)
Height to sill	1.17 m (3 ft 10 in)
Cargo door (optional): Height	1.32 m (4 ft 4 in)
Width	1.24 m (4 ft 1 in)
Nose avionics service doors (port and stbd):	
Max height	0.57 m (1 ft 10½ in)
Width	0.63 m (2 ft 1 in)
Height to sill	1.37 m (4 ft 6 in)
Emergency exit (stbd): Height	0.66 m (2 ft 2 in)
Width	0.50 m (1 ft 7¾ in)

DIMENSIONS, INTERNAL:
Cabin (from forward to rear pressure bulkhead):	
Length	6.71 m (22 ft 0 in)
Max width	1.37 m (4 ft 6 in)
Max height	1.45 m (4 ft 9 in)
Floor area	7.80 m² (84 sq ft)
Volume	11.10 m³ (392 cu ft)
Baggage hold, rear of cabin:	
Volume	1.51 m³ (53.5 cu ft)

AREAS:
Wings, gross	28.15 m² (303.0 sq ft)
Ailerons (total)	1.67 m² (18.0 sq ft)
Trailing-edge flaps (total)	4.17 m² (44.9 sq ft)
Fin	3.46 m² (37.2 sq ft)
Rudder, incl tab	1.40 m² (15.1 sq ft)
Tailplane	4.52 m² (48.7 sq ft)
Elevators, incl tabs	1.79 m² (19.3 sq ft)

WEIGHTS AND LOADINGS:
Weight empty	3,656 kg (8,060 lb)
Max fuel	1,653 kg (3,645 lb)
Max T-O and landing weight	5,670 kg (12,500 lb)
Max ramp weight	5,710 kg (12,590 lb)
Max zero-fuel weight	4,990 kg (11,000 lb)
Max wing loading	201.6 kg/m² (41.3 lb/sq ft)
Max power loading	4.47 kg/kW (7.35 lb/shp)

PERFORMANCE (at max T-O weight ISA, except where indicated):
Never-exceed speed	259 knots (480 km/h; 298 mph) IAS
Max operating Mach No.	0.52
Max level speed at 7,620 m (25,000 ft), average cruise weight	294 knots (545 km/h; 339 mph)
Max cruising speed at 7,620 m (25,000 ft), average cruise weight	289 knots (536 km/h; 333 mph)
Econ cruising speed at 7,620 m (25,000 ft), average cruise weight, normal cruise power	282 knots (523 km/h; 325 mph)
Stalling speed:	
flaps up	99 knots (183 km/h; 114 mph) IAS
flaps down	75 knots (139 km/h; 86 mph) IAS
Max rate of climb at S/L	747 m (2,450 ft)/min
Rate of climb at S/L, one engine out	226 m (740 ft)/min

Service ceiling	over 10,670 m (35,000 ft)
Service ceiling, one engine out	6,675 m (21,900 ft)
T-O run, 40% flap	566 m (1,856 ft)
T-O to 15 m (50 ft), 40% flap	786 m (2,579 ft)
Landing from 15 m (50 ft):	
without propeller reversal	867 m (2,845 ft)
with propeller reversal	632 m (2,074 ft)
Landing run	536 m (1,760 ft)

Range with max fuel, allowances for start, taxi, climb, descent, and 45 min reserves at max range power, ISA: max cruise power at:
5,485 m (18,000 ft)	1,190 nm (2,205 km; 1,370 miles)
8,230 m (27,000 ft)	1,550 nm (2,872 km; 1,785 miles)
9,450 m (31,000 ft)	1,750 nm (3,243 km; 2,015 miles)
10,670 m (35,000 ft)	1,965 nm (3,641 km; 2,263 miles)

econ cruise power at:
5,485 m (18,000 ft)	1,517 nm (2,811 km; 1,747 miles)
8,230 m (27,000 ft)	1,860 nm (3,447 km; 2,142 miles)
9,450 m (31,000 ft)	1,974 nm (3,658 km; 2,273 miles)

BEECHCRAFT MARITIME PATROL B200T

Beech announced on 9 April 1979 that it had begun to flight test a maritime patrol version of its Super King Air 200 twin-turboprop light transport, for FAA certification as the Maritime Patrol 200T.

In production form, the current B200T can be equipped for missions such as surface and subsurface monitoring of exclusive economic zones, detecting pollution, inspecting offshore installations, and conducting search and rescue flights. Special missions for which it could also be used include aerial photography, environmental and ecological research, airways and ground based navigation equipment checks, target towing, and ambulance duties.

Modifications to the standard Super King Air to adapt it to Maritime Patrol B200T configuration include fitting new outboard wing assemblies, with mountings for a 200.5 litre (53 US gallon; 44 Imp gallon) removable fuel tank at each wingtip; strengthened landing gear to cater for higher take-off and landing weights; two bubble observation windows in the rear of the cabin for visual search and photography; a hatch for dropping survival equipment; and a search radar with 360° scan in a radome beneath the fuselage. Advanced navigation equipment is available; standard avionics include VLF/Omega which provides ground stabilisation and is coupled with the autopilot. This permits a search pattern to be programmed before take-off or en route. An integrated systems approach is utilised, with controls and displays located on the cabin operator's console.

Deliveries include 17 Maritime Patrol 200Ts to Japan's Maritime Safety Agency, two for the Algerian Ministry of Defence, five to the Peruvian Navy, one to Puerto Rico and one to the Uruguayan Navy.

The description of the Super King Air B200 applies also to the B200T, except as follows:

TYPE: Maritime patrol or multi-mission aircraft.

WINGS: As for Super King Air B200, except for new outboard wing panels redesigned to permit mounting of removable wingtip tanks. Optional wingtip ESM antennae.

LANDING GEAR: Strengthened to cater for higher operating weights.

POWER PLANT: As for Super King Air B200, including removable wingtip tanks which increase maximum usable fuel capacity by 401 litres (106 US gallons; 88.25 Imp gallons), to a total of 2,460 litres (650 US gallons; 541 Imp gallons).

AVIONICS AND EQUIPMENT: Standard items as detailed in introductory description. Optional avionics include ESM integrated with INS, VHF-FM com, HF and VHF com, Northrop Seehawk FLIR, LLLTV, sonobuoys and processor, OTPI, multispectral scanner, tactical navigation computer, and two alternative search radar systems, both with 360° scan and weather avoidance capability and integrated with INS.

DIMENSIONS, EXTERNAL: As for Super King Air B200, except:
Wing span over tip tanks	17.25 m (56 ft 7 in)
Wing aspect ratio	10.5

DIMENSIONS, INTERNAL: As for Super King Air B200, except:
Cabin: Length (excl flight deck)	5.08 m (16 ft 8 in)

WEIGHTS (A: Normal category; B: Restricted category):
Weight empty: A, B	3,744 kg (8,255 lb)
Max T-O weight: A	5,670 kg (12,500 lb)
B	6,350 kg (14,000 lb)
Max landing weight: A	5,670 kg (12,500 lb)
B	6,123 kg (13,500 lb)

PERFORMANCE (at max T-O weight except where indicated):
Max cruising speed, AUW of 4,990 kg (11,000 lb) at 4,265 m (14,000 ft)	265 knots (491 km/h; 305 mph)
Typical patrol speed	140 knots (259 km/h; 161 mph)
Range with max fuel, patrolling at 227 knots (420 km/h; 261 mph) at 825 m (2,700 ft), 45 min reserves	1,790 nm (3,317 km; 2,061 miles)
Typical endurance at 140 knots (259 km/h; 161 mph), at 610 m (2,000 ft), 45 min reserves	6 h 36 min
Max time on station, with wingtip fuel tanks	9 h

BEECHCRAFT SUPER KING AIR 200/B200 (MILITARY VERSIONS)
US military designation: C-12

The first three production Super King Airs were acquired by the US Army in 1974 as RU-21Js, as noted in previous editions of Jane's. In August 1974, Beech received an initial contract to build and support 34 modified military versions of the Super King Air designated C-12A. Worldwide deployment of the C-12s began in July 1975. They are described as "standard off-the-shelf Super King Air types, modified slightly to meet military flight requirements and to orient the control systems for two-pilot operation which is standard military practice". Accommodation is provided for eight passengers, plus two pilots, with easy conversion to cargo and other missions. The large baggage area has provisions for storing survival gear.

Orders for the C-12 series totalled 317 by 1 January 1990, of which 308 had been delivered. The following versions have been announced:

C-12A. Initial Model A200 for US Army (60) and US Air Force (31, one of which was transferred to Greek Air Force), with two 559 kW (750 shp) Pratt & Whitney Canada PT6A-38 turboprops and Hartzell three-blade constant-speed fully-feathering reversible-pitch propellers. Wing span 16.61 m (54 ft 6 in); auxiliary tanks. Weights, loadings and performance given in 1980-81 Jane's. Army aircraft later refitted with PT6A-41 engines are redesignated C-12C; USAF C-12As refitted with PT6A-42s are redesignated C-12E. Total of 91 delivered. Entered service July 1975.

UC-12B. US Navy/Marine Corps version (Model A200C), with 634 kW (850 shp) PT6A-41 turboprops, cargo door and high-flotation landing gear. Total of 66 (49 Navy, 17 Marine Corps) delivered by May 1982.

C-12C. As C-12A, for US Army (14), but built from outset with PT6A-41 engines. Deliveries completed.

C-12D (Model A200CT). As C-12C, for US Army, but with cargo door, high flotation landing gear and provisions for tip tanks. Wing span (over tip tanks) 16.92 m (55 ft 6 in). Total of 51 delivered, including 27 for the US Army and six for the US Air Force. Five of the 51 were converted to RC-12Ds for Israel and 13 for the US Army.

RC-12D Improved Guardrail V (Model A200CT). Special mission US Army version, acquired to supplement

Retouched photograph of US Army RC-12D in Improved Guardrail V configuration

Beechcraft C-12F operational support aircraft of USAF Military Airlift Command *(Mike Jerram)*

earlier unpressurised RU-21H Guardrail V aircraft and used for battlefield duties in Europe. The RC-12D serves as the aerial platform for the AN/USD-9 Improved Guardrail remotely controlled communications intercept and direction finding system, with direct reporting to tactical commanders at corps level and below. It is configured with an aircraft survivability equipment (ASE) suite, a Carousel IV-E inertial platform and Tacan set, and mission equipment including a radio data link, AN/ARW-83(V)5 airborne relay facility, associated antennae above and below the wings, and ECM in wingtip pods which increase overall span to 17.63 m (57 ft 10 in). Other system components are an AN/TSQ-105(V)4 integrated processing facility, AN/ARM-63(V)4 AGE flightline van, and AN/TSC-87 tactical commander's terminal. Thirteen RC-12Ds are included in total given for C-12D, with deliveries from Summer 1983. Prime system contractor is ESL Inc, with Beech as mission equipment integrator. Max T-O weight 6,441 kg (14,200 lb).

C-12E. Designation of 29 upgraded C-12A for US Air Force, when refitted with PT6A-42 engines.

C-12F. Operational support aircraft (OSA), generally similar to Model B200C, with PT6A-42 engines and hydraulically retractable landing gear. Forty purchased for US Air Force following initial five-year lease contract. First C-12F delivered in May 1984. Alternative payloads include eight passengers, more than 1,043 kg (2,300 lb) of cargo, or two litter patients with attendants. Cargo door standard. Produced also for US Army (17 delivered) and Air National Guard, which has taken delivery of six.

UC-12F. US Navy equivalent of US Air Force C-12F with PT6A-42 engines and hydraulically retractable landing gear. Twelve delivered beginning 1986, of which two modified to RC-12F Range Surveillance Aircraft (RANSAC) configuration.

RC-12H Improved Guardrail V. Special mission US Army version, similar to RC-12D, but with increased max T-O weight of 6,804 kg (15,000 lb). Six delivered in 1988.

C-12J. Variant of Beechcraft 1900C (which see), not Super King Air.

RC-12K Guardrail Common Sensor. Electronics special missions aircraft. Nine ordered by US Army in October 1985. A further nine ordered in 1989, with five options, for delivery commencing February 1992. PT6A-67 turboprops, large cargo door and oversized landing gear standard. Max T-O weight 7,257 kg (16,000 lb).

UC-12M. US Navy equivalent of US Air Force C-12F. Twelve delivered beginning 1987, of which two modified to RC-12M RANSAC configuration under 1988 contract.

BEECHCRAFT SUPER KING AIR 300

The Super King Air 300 is an improved version of the Model B200 with two 783 kW (1,050 shp) Pratt & Whitney Canada PT6A-60A engines, increased maximum take-off and landing weights to FAA SFAR 41C standards, redesigned 'pitot cowl' engine air inlets of 451 cm² (70 sq in) area compared with 567 cm² (88 sq in) on the B200, aerodynamically faired exhausts, a 12.7 cm (5 in) forward extension of the inboard wing leading-edges, 13.2 cm (5.2 in) forward extension of the propeller line, hydraulically actuated landing gear and numerous interior and equipment changes.

Design began in August 1980. A modified Model 200 testbed began flight trials in October 1981; a production prototype made its first flight in September 1983 and was awarded FAA type certification on 24 January 1984. Customer deliveries of the Model 300 began in the Spring of 1984 and totalled 206 by 1 January 1990. In June 1989, two were ordered by Finnair for pilot training, under the designation **300AT** (for Airline Training).

The US Federal Aviation Administration has taken delivery of 19 Super King Air 300s for airways calibration duties. These aircraft are equipped with an onboard

automatic flight inspection system (AFIS), with accommodation for a flight inspection technician, observer, passenger/observer and a flight crew of two.

At the Farnborough Air Show in September 1988 Beech introduced a new **Super King Air 300LW** (Light Weight), designed specifically for the European market, where airways user fees are based on the max T-O weight of aircraft. This aircraft has a max T-O weight of 5,670 kg (12,500 lb) and a max ramp weight of 5,715 kg (12,600 lb), but is otherwise similar to the Model 300 described below. Beech had delivered 14 Model 300LWs by January 1990.

The Super King Air 300 was to be replaced on the production line by the Super King Air 350 in early 1990.

The following description applies to those features of the Model 300 which differ from the Super King Air 200 series:

WINGS: Inboard leading-edges extended forward and fitted with strakes.

LANDING GEAR: Hydraulically retractable tricycle type. Goodrich mainwheels and tyres size 19 × 6.75-8, pressure 6.20 bars (90 lb/sq in) at max T-O weight. Goodrich nosewheel and tyre size 22 × 6.75-10, pressure 3.79-4.13 bars (55-60 lb/sq in). Beech brake de-icing optional.

POWER PLANT: Two 783 kW (1,050 shp) Pratt & Whitney Canada PT6A-60A turboprops, each driving a Hartzell four-blade constant-speed fully-feathering reversible-pitch metal propeller with spinner. Bladder cells and integral tanks in each wing, with total capacity of 1,438 litres (380 US gallons; 316.5 Imp gallons); auxiliary tanks inboard of engine nacelles, capacity 601 litres (159 US gallons; 132.5 Imp gallons). Total fuel capacity 2,039 litres (539 US gallons; 449 Imp gallons). No provision for wingtip tanks. Oil capacity 30.2 litres (8 US gallons; 6.66 Imp gallons).

ACCOMMODATION: As for Model B200, except for additional emergency exit on port side of cabin, opposite starboard emergency exit and of the same dimensions. Pilot and co-pilot storm windows standard. Cabin features single-piece upper sidewall panels, indirect overhead lighting system with rheostat controls, stereo system with graphic equaliser and overhead speakers, larger executive tables incorporating magnetic game boards, seats with inflatable lumbar support adjustment, fore-and-aft, reclining and lateral tracking movement as standard. Crew seats have 2.5° or 5° tilt positions. Emergency exit lighting standard. Electric heating on ground standard. Optional radiant heat panels of B200 not available.

SYSTEMS: As for Model B200, except for automatic bleed air type heating and 22,000 BTU cooling system with high

capacity ventilation system; 2.18 m³ (77 cu ft) oxygen system standard; hydraulic landing gear retraction and extension system; two 300A 28V starter/generators with triple bus electrical distribution system.

AVIONICS AND EQUIPMENT: Generally as for Model B200.

DIMENSIONS, EXTERNAL: As for Model B200 except:

Length overall	13.36 m (43 ft 10 in)
Height overall	4.37 m (14 ft 4 in)
Propeller diameter	2.67 m (8 ft 9 in)
Propeller ground clearance	0.25 m (10 in)

DIMENSIONS, INTERNAL: As for Model B200 except:

Emergency exit doors (each side of cabin, above wing):

Height	0.66 m (2 ft 2 in)
Width	0.95 m (1 ft 7¾ in)

WEIGHTS AND LOADINGS:

Weight empty	3,851 kg (8,490 lb)
Max baggage weight	249 kg (550 lb)
Max T-O and landing weight	6,350 kg (14,000 lb)
Max ramp weight	6,396 kg (14,100 lb)
Max zero-fuel weight	5,216 kg (11,500 lb)
Max wing loading	225.6 kg/m² (46.2 lb/sq ft)
Max power loading	4.05 kg/kW (6.7 lb/shp)

PERFORMANCE (A: Model 300; B: Model 300LW at max T-O weight, ISA):

Never-exceed speed	259 knots (480 km/h; 298 mph) IAS
Max operating Mach No.	0.58
Max level speed	317 knots (587 km/h; 365 mph)
Max cruising speed	315 knots (583 km/h; 363 mph)
Econ cruising speed	307 knots (568 km/h; 353 mph)

Stalling speed:

flaps up	100 knots (185 km/h; 115 mph) IAS
flaps down	81 knots (150 km/h; 93 mph) IAS
Max rate of climb at S/L: A	867 m (2,844 ft)/min
B	999 m (3,277 ft)/min
Rate of climb at S/L, one engine out	264 m (867 ft)/min
Max certificated ceiling	10,670 m (35,000 ft)
Service ceiling, one engine out: A	6,970 m (22,875 ft)
B	7,882 m (25,855 ft)

T-O run, 40% flap, at T-O weight 5,670 kg (12,500 lb)
411 m (1,350 ft)

T-O to 15 m (50 ft), 40% flap, at T-O weight 5,670 kg (12,500 lb)
607 m (1,992 ft)

Accelerate/stop distance, 40% flap	1,122 m (3,682 ft)
Landing from 15 m (50 ft)	886 m (2,907 ft)

Landing run, without propeller reversal
514 m (1,686 ft)

Range with max fuel, allowances for start, taxi, T-O, climb, descent and 45 min reserves at max range power:

max cruise power at:

5,485 m (18,000 ft)
1,055 nm (1,955 km; 1,215 miles)

7,315 m (24,000 ft)
1,240 nm (2,298 km; 1,428 miles)

8,535 m (28,000 ft)
1,400 nm (2,594 km; 1,612 miles)

10,670 m (35,000 ft)
1,748 nm (3,235 km; 2,010 miles)

max range power at:

5,485 m (18,000 ft)
1,429 nm (2,647 km; 1,645 miles)

8,535 m (28,000 ft)
1,795 nm (3,326 km; 2,067 miles)

10,670 m (35,000 ft)
1,959 nm (3,630 km; 2,256 miles)

BEECHCRAFT SUPER KING AIR 350

At the 1989 National Business Aircraft Association convention in Atlanta, Georgia, Beech introduced the Super King Air 350, the first example of which (N120SK) had made its first flight in September 1988. This aircraft has replaced the Super King Air 300 in production and differs from it in having a 0.86 m (2 ft 10 in) fuselage stretch achieved with two plugs, one of 0.37 m (1 ft 2½ in) forward of the main spar and one of 0.49 m (1 ft 7½ in) aft; wing span

Beechcraft Super King Air 300, with side view and scrap view of wing of Model 350 (lower right)
(Pilot Press)

increased by 0.46 m (1 ft 6 in) with 0.61 m (2 ft 0 in) high NASA winglets of composites construction; and two additional cabin windows on each side. The longer fuselage permits standard cabin seating for eight passengers in double club arrangement. A further two passengers can be accommodated on optional jump seats in the extreme rear of the cabin and on the toilet, bringing total capacity to 11 in two-crew operations or 12 with a single pilot. Other improvements include increased area rudder anti-servo tab, aerodynamic cleanup of the ailerons and rudder, an automatic cable tensioner in the aileron control circuit, and a larger elevator bobweight. The first customer delivery of a Super King Air 350 was made on 6 March 1990 to Tecumseh Products Company of Michigan.

DIMENSIONS, EXTERNAL:

Wing span over winglets	17.65 m (57 ft 11 in)
Wing aspect ratio	10.79
Length overall	14.22 m (46 ft 8 in)
Height overall	4.37 m (14 ft 4 in)
Tailplane span	5.61 m (18 ft 5 in)
Passenger door: Height	1.31 m (4 ft 3½ in)
Width	0.68 m (2 ft 2¾ in)

DIMENSIONS, INTERNAL:

Cabin, excl cockpit: Length	5.94 m (19 ft 6 in)
Max width	1.37 m (4 ft 6 in)
Height	1.45 m (4 ft 9 in)

AREA:

Wings, gross	28.80 m² (310.0 sq ft)

WEIGHTS AND LOADINGS:

Weight empty	4,105 kg (9,051 lb)
Max T-O and landing weight	6,804 kg (15,000 lb)
Max ramp weight	6,849 kg (15,100 lb)
Max zero-fuel weight	5,670 kg (12,500 lb)
Max wing loading	236.3 kg/m² (48.4 lb/sq ft)
Max power loading	4.34 kg/kW (7.14 lb/shp)

PERFORMANCE:

Max level speed	314 knots (582 km/h; 362 mph)

Max cruising speed, AUW of 5,443 kg (12,000 lb) at:

7,315 m (24,000 ft)	313 knots (580 km/h; 360 mph)
10,670 m (35,000 ft)	295 knots (547 km/h; 340 mph)

Cruising speed, normal cruising power, AUW of 5,443 kg (12,000 lb) at:

7,315 m (24,000 ft)	303 knots (562 km/h; 349 mph)
10,670 m (35,000 ft)	286 knots (530 km/h; 329 mph)

Cruising speed, maximum range power, AUW of 5,443 kg (12,000 lb) at:

5,485 m (18,000 ft)	206 knots (382 km/h; 237 mph)
10,670 m (35,000 ft)	237 knots (439 km/h; 273 mph)

Stalling speed, at max landing weight, flaps and wheel down	81 knots (150 km/h; 94 mph)

Max rate of climb at S/L, AUW of 6,350 kg (14,000 lb)
  908 m (2,979 ft)/min
Rate of climb at S/L, one engine out, AUW of 6,350 kg (14,000 lb)
  278 m (912 ft)/min

Service ceiling	above 10,670 m (35,000 ft)

Service ceiling, one engine out, AUW of 6,350 kg (14,000 lb)
  7,360 m (24,150 ft)
T-O balanced field length, AUW of 6,350 kg (14,000 lb)
  1,122 m (3,680 ft)
Landing from 15 m (50 ft) at AUW of 6,350 kg (14,000 lb)
  765 m (2,508 ft)

Landing run	388 m (1,272 ft)

Range with 2,040 litres (539 US gallons; 449 Imp gallons) usable fuel, allowances for start, T-O, climb and descent plus 45 min reserves: max cruising power at:
  5,485 m (18,000 ft)
  1,043 nm (1,932 km; 1,201 miles)
  7,315 m (24,000 ft)
  1,230 nm (2,279 km; 1,416 miles)
  8,535 m (28,000 ft)
  1,387 nm (2,570 km; 1,597 miles)
  10,670 m (35,000 ft)
  1,722 nm (3,191 km; 1,983 miles)
normal cruising power, allowances as above:
  5,485 m (18,000 ft)
  1,061 nm (1,966 km; 1,221 miles)
  7,315 m (24,000 ft)
  1,286 nm (2,383 km; 1,480 miles)
  8,535 m (28,000 ft)
  1,456 nm (2,698 km; 1,676 miles)
  10,670 m (35,000 ft)
  1,778 nm (3,295 km; 2,047 miles)
max range power, allowances as above:
  5,485 m (18,000 ft)
  1,424 nm (2,639 km; 1,639 miles)
  8,535 m (28,000 ft)
  1,788 nm (3,313 km; 2,059 miles)
  10,670 m (35,000 ft)
  1,965 nm (3,641 km; 2,263 miles)
NBAA VFR range, 4 passengers, 30 min reserves
  2,038 nm (3,776 km; 2,346 miles)

BEECHCRAFT MODEL 1300 COMMUTER

In January 1988 Beech announced development of this regional airliner variant of the Super King Air B200, designed for operations on long routes with light passenger loads. The Model 1300 provides accommodation for 13 passengers with individual air, light and oxygen outlets at every seat, and is equipped with dual overwing emergency exits. The adoption of panel mounted avionics as standard

Beechcraft Super King Air 350 eight/eleven-passenger turboprop business aircraft

has enabled a baggage compartment to be provided in the aircraft's nose, volume 0.37 m³ (13 cu ft). Three-blade propellers with autofeathering, rudder boost for engine-out operations, hydraulically actuated landing gear, airframe anti- and de-icing systems, air-conditioning, cabin paging system, front-mounted post lit instruments interchangeable with those of the Beech 99 Airliner and Beech 1900, and radiant heat cabin warming, are standard. A belly cargo pod, volume 1.25 m³ (44 cu ft), engine fire extinguishing system, and landing gear and brake de-icing systems, are optional. Dual outward-canted ventral fins are installed for increased stability at low airspeeds and high angles of attack.

Launch customer for the Beechcraft 1300 Commuter is Mesa Airlines of Farmington, New Mexico, which has ordered ten, the first of which was delivered on 30 September 1988. Ten had been delivered by 1 January 1990.

The description of the Beech Super King Air B200 applies to the Model 1300 Commuter except as follows:

ACCOMMODATION: Crew of two and maximum of 13 passengers. Nose baggage compartment, capacity 159 kg (350 lb), and aft baggage compartment, capacity 231 kg (510 lb), standard (aft compartment not usable when two rear seats installed for maximum passenger capacity). Belly cargo pod, capacity 206 kg (455 lb), optional.

WEIGHT:

Empty weight, typical	3,573 kg (7,877 lb)

PERFORMANCE (at max T-O weight, ISA, except where indicated):

Max level speed at S/L	272 knots (504 km/h; 313 mph)
Max operating speed	260 knots (482 km/h; 299 mph) IAS

Max cruising speed, weight 4,990 kg (11,000 lb):

at 3,050 m (10,000 ft)	252 knots (467 km/h; 290 mph)
at 7,620 m (25,000 ft)	269 knots (499 km/h; 310 mph)

Stalling speed:

flaps up	96 knots (178 km/h; 111 mph)
flaps down	74 knots (137 km/h; 86 mph)
Max rate of climb at S/L	732 m (2,400 ft)/min
Rate of climb at S/L, one engine out	152 m (500 ft)/min
Max certificated ceiling	7,620 m (25,000 ft)

Service ceiling, one engine out:

at max T-O weight	5,067 m (16,625 ft)
at 4,990 kg (11,000 lb)	6,325 m (20,750 ft)
Landing from 15 m (50 ft)	784 m (2,572 ft)
Landing run	471 m (1,544 ft)

Range with max payload, ISA, zero wind, 1,800 rpm at 7,620 m (25,000 ft)
  381 nm (706 km; 438 miles)

Ferry range	1,235 nm (2,288 km; 1,422 miles)

BEECHCRAFT MODEL 1900C AIRLINER and 1900 EXEC-LINER

US Air Force designation: C-12J

Beech began design of the basic 1900 commuter airliner during 1979, and the first flight of the performance prototype (UA-1) was made on 3 September 1982, followed by the systems prototype (UA-2) on 30 November 1982. The third prototype (UA-3) was used for function and reliability testing, equipment certification, and demonstration; it is now in operational service. FAA certification under SFAR Pt 41C, obtained on 22 November 1983, included single pilot approval under FAR 135 Appendix A.

The Beech 1900C is offered in two variants: **Model 1900C Airliner** with cargo door, the first of which was delivered in February 1984; and **1900 Exec-Liner**, which is the corporate version. By May 1990 nearly 200 Model 1900C Airliners and 1900 Exec-Liners had been delivered. They were in service with 17 regional airlines in the United States and seven international operators. The first delivery of an Exec-Liner (N34GT) was made to General Telephone Company of Illinois in the Summer of 1985. Exec-Liners are operating in Africa, Australia, Europe and the USA.

In March 1986 the United States Air Force ordered six Model 1900Cs for delivery commencing September 1987. These aircraft, designated **C-12J**, serve as Air National Guard mission support aircraft, and replaced Convair C-131s.

Six Model 1900Cs (of eight ordered) have been delivered to the Egyptian Air Force. Four are configured for electronic surveillance missions, and two as maritime patrol

Beechcraft Model 1300 Commuter airliner of New Mexico based Mesa Airlines

Beechcraft Model 1900C twin-turboprop commuter airliner of Danish carrier Business Flight

Beechcraft Model 1900C Airliner with rear cargo door *(Pilot Press)*

aircraft. For this latter role the aircraft are equipped with Litton search radar, Motorola sideways looking airborne multi-mode radar (SLAMMR) and Singer S-3075 ESM systems. Deliveries of 12 Model 1900Cs for the Chinese Nationalist Air Force began in January 1988.

From aircraft c/n UC-1 onwards, all Beechcraft 1900 series aircraft (including those for the US Air Force and Egyptian Air Force) are equipped with a wet wing providing a maximum fuel capacity of 2,593 litres (685 US gallons; 570 Imp gallons).

In March 1989 Beech announced development of a new **Model 1900D**, described separately.

The description which follows applies to the commercial Models 1900C and 1900 Exec-Liner:

TYPE: Twin-turboprop commuter/cargo airliner and executive transport.

WINGS: Cantilever low-wing monoplane. Wing section NACA 23018 modified at root, NACA 23102 modified at tip. Dihedral 6°. Incidence 3° 29′ at root, –1° 4′ at tip. No sweepback at quarter-chord. Semi-monocoque fail-safe structure of aluminium alloy, riveted and bonded, with a continuous main spar. Single-slotted trailing-edge flaps, in two sections on each wing, of aluminium alloy construction; symmetrical ailerons of similar construction. Trim tab at inboard end of port aileron. Pneumatic de-icing boots on wing leading-edges.

FUSELAGE: Semi-monocoque fail-safe pressurised structure of aluminium alloy, mainly of bonded construction but including some riveting. Small horizontal vortex generator on each side of fuselage, immediately forward of wing leading-edge.

TAIL UNIT: Aluminium alloy structure comprising a cantilever T tail with sweptback vertical and horizontal surfaces. Small fin (tail-let) beneath each side of tailplane, near tip; and auxiliary fixed horizontal tail surface (stabilon) on each side of rear fuselage. Trim tabs in elevators and rudder. Pneumatic de-icing boots on leading-edges of tailplane and stabilons.

LANDING GEAR: Hydraulically retractable tricycle type. Main units retract forward and nose unit rearward. Beech oleo-pneumatic shock absorber in each unit. Twin Goodyear wheels on each main unit, size 6.50 × 10, with

Goodyear tyres size 22 × 6.75-10, pressure 6.07 bars (88 lb/sq in); Goodrich steerable nosewheel size 6.5 × 8, with Goodrich tyre size 19.5 × 6.75-8, pressure 6.07 bars (88 lb/sq in). Multiple-disc hydraulic brakes. Beech/Hydro-Aire anti-skid units and power steering optional.

POWER PLANT: Two Pratt & Whitney Canada PT6A-65B turboprops, each flat rated at 820 kW (1,100 shp) and driving a Hartzell four-blade constant-speed fully-feathering reversible-pitch composite propeller with spinner. 'Wet wing' fuel storage, with a total capacity of 2,593 litres (685 US gallons; 570 Imp gallons), of which 2,525 litres (667 US gallons; 555 Imp gallons) are usable. Refuelling point in each wing leading-edge, inboard of engine nacelle. Oil capacity (total) 27.2 litres (7.2 US gallons; 6 Imp gallons).

ACCOMMODATION: Crew of one (FAR Pt 91) or two (FAR Pt 135) on flight deck, with standard accommodation in cabin of commuter version for 19 passengers, in single seats on each side of centre aisle. Forward and rear carry-on baggage lockers, underseat baggage stowage, rear baggage compartment and nose baggage compartment. Forward and rear doors, incorporating airstairs, on port side. Upward hinged cargo door instead of rear passenger door on Model 1900C. Two emergency exits over wing on starboard side, plus one on port side (1900C only). Accommodation is air-conditioned, heated, ventilated and pressurised. Exec-Liner has 12/18-passenger cabin with forward and rear compartments, combination lavatory/passenger seat and two beverage bars at cabin compartment division. Club and double club seating optional. Customised interiors to customer choice.

SYSTEMS: Bleed air cabin heating and pressurisation, max differential 0.33 bars (4.8 lb/sq in). Air cycle and vapour cycle air-conditioning. Hydraulic system, pressure 207 bars (3,000 lb/sq in) for landing gear actuation. Electrical system includes two 300A engine starter/generators and one 22Ah nickel-cadmium battery. Constant flow oxygen system of 4.33 m³ (153 cu ft) capacity standard.

AVIONICS: Duplicated Bendix/King com/nav, glideslope receiver, transponder, audio, ADF, DME, marker beacon receiver and Bendix RDR-160 weather radar. Honeywell EFIS, and Collins autopilot and Pro Line II equipment, optional.

DIMENSIONS, EXTERNAL:

Wing span	16.60 m (54 ft 5¾ in)
Wing chord: at root	2.18 m (7 ft 1¾ in)
at tip	0.91 m (2 ft 11¾ in)
Wing aspect ratio	9.8
Length overall	17.63 m (57 ft 10 in)
Height overall	4.54 m (14 ft 10¾ in)
Tailplane span	5.63 m (18 ft 5¾ in)
Wheel track	5.23 m (17 ft 2 in)
Wheelbase	7.26 m (23 ft 10 in)
Propeller diameter	2.78 m (9 ft 1½ in)
Propeller ground clearance	0.36 m (1 ft 2 in)
Distance between propeller centres	5.23 m (17 ft 2 in)
Passenger doors (fwd and rear, port, each):	
Height	1.32 m (4 ft 4 in)
Width	0.68 m (2 ft 2¾ in)
Height to sill: fwd	1.28 m (4 ft 2½ in)
rear	1.15 m (3 ft 9¼ in)
Cargo door (rear, port): Height	1.32 m (4 ft 4 in)
Width	1.32 m (4 ft 4 in)
Height to sill	1.15 m (3 ft 9¼ in)
Baggage door (nose, port):	
Max height	0.56 m (1 ft 10 in)
Width	0.66 m (2 ft 2 in)
Height to sill	1.45 m (4 ft 9 in)
Emergency exits (two stbd; plus one port on 1900C only;	
all overwing): Height	0.70 m (2 ft 3½ in)
Width	0.51 m (1 ft 8 in)

DIMENSIONS, INTERNAL:

Cabin, incl flight deck and rear baggage compartment:	
Length	12.02 m (39 ft 5½ in)
Max width	1.37 m (4 ft 6 in)
Max height	1.45 m (4 ft 9 in)
Floor area	15.28 m² (164.5 sq ft)
Pressurised volume	20.00 m³ (706 cu ft)
Volume of passenger cabin	14.10 m³ (498 cu ft)
Baggage space:	
Cabin:	
1900C, fwd: standard	0.42 m³ (15.0 cu ft)
optional	1.19 m³ (41.9 cu ft)
rear (both)	4.36 m³ (154.0 cu ft)
Nose compartment	0.38 m³ (13.5 cu ft)

AREAS:

Wings, gross	28.15 m² (303.0 sq ft)
Ailerons (total)	1.67 m² (18.0 sq ft)
Trailing-edge flaps (total)	4.17 m² (44.9 sq ft)
Fin	3.42 m² (36.85 sq ft)
Rudder (incl tab)	1.106 m² (11.9 sq ft)
Tail-lets (total)	0.305 m² (3.28 sq ft)
Tailplane	4.52 m² (48.7 sq ft)
Elevator (incl tab)	1.79 m² (19.3 sq ft)
Stabilons (total, exposed)	1.44 m² (15.46 sq ft)

WEIGHTS AND LOADINGS:

Weight empty (typical)	4,327 kg (9,540 lb)
Max fuel (usable)	2,027 kg (4,469 lb)
Max baggage	866 kg (1,910 lb)
Max T-O weight	7,530 kg (16,600 lb)
Max ramp weight	7,580 kg (16,710 lb)
Max landing weight	7,302 kg (16,100 lb)
Max zero-fuel weight	6,350 kg (14,000 lb)
Max wing loading	267.5 kg/m² (54.8 lb/sq ft)
Max power loading	4.59 kg/kW (7.55 lb/shp)

PERFORMANCE (at max T-O weight except where indicated):

Max cruising speed at AUW of 6,350 kg (14,000 lb):

at 2,440 m (8,000 ft)	267 knots (495 km/h; 307 mph)
at 4,875 m (16,000 ft)	267 knots (495 km/h; 307 mph)
at 7,620 m (25,000 ft)	254 knots (471 km/h; 292 mph)

T-O speed, 20° flap
    105 knots (194 km/h; 121 mph) CAS

Approach speed at max landing weight
    113 knots (209 km/h; 130 mph) CAS

Stalling speed at max T-O weight:
  wheels and flaps up
    104 knots (193 km/h; 120 mph) IAS

Beechcraft Model 1900C electronic surveillance aircraft of the Egyptian Air Force *(Ivo Sturzenegger)*

wheels down and approach flaps
91 knots (169 km/h; 105 mph) IAS
Stalling speed at max landing weight, wheels and flaps
down   88 knots (163 km/h; 102 mph) IAS
Max rate of climb at S/L   719 m (2,360 ft)/min
Rate of climb at S/L, one engine out   149 m (490 ft)/min
Service ceiling
   exceeds certificated ceiling of 7,620 m (25,000 ft)
Service ceiling, one engine out   3,960 m (13,000 ft)
Turning circle based on nosewheel   8.17 m (26 ft 9½ in)
T-O run, approach flap   671 m (2,200 ft)
T-O to 15 m (50 ft), approach flap   994 m (3,260 ft)
Landing from 15 m (50 ft) at max landing weight
                                      780 m (2,560 ft)
Landing run at max landing weight   466 m (1,530 ft)
Accelerate/stop distance, 20° flap 1,158 m (3,800 ft)
Range with 10 passengers, at long range cruise power,
with allowances for starting, taxi, T-O, climb and
descent:
   with VFR reserves
                        1,569 nm (2,907 km; 1,806 miles)

BEECHCRAFT MODEL 1900D

At the 1989 meeting of the US Regional Airline
Association in Washington, DC, Beech announced development of a new version of the Model 1900 Airliner
designated Model 1900D. This aircraft features a new cabin
design with flat floor offering stand-up headroom and 28.5
per cent more volume than the Model 1900C. Other new
features include larger cabin windows and door, an increase
in cabin pressurisation differential to 0.34 bars (5.0 lb/sq in),
winglets for enhanced hot day/high elevation performance,
and twin ventral strakes to enhance directional stability and
improve turbulence penetration. The prototype Model
1900D (N5584B) made its first flight on 1 March 1990. FAA
certification for single-pilot operation is expected in early
1991, with a planned production rate of four per month
thereafter. Continued production of the Model 1900C after
introduction of the Model 1900D will depend on customer
demand.

The description of the Model 1900C Airliner applies to
the Model 1900D except as follows:

POWER PLANT: Two Pratt & Whitney Canada PT6A-67D
turboprops, each rated at 954.5 kW (1,280 shp).
Maximum usable fuel capacity 2,525 litres (667 US
gallons; 555 Imp gallons). Maximum oil capacity 29.5
litres (7.8 US gallons; 6.5 Imp gallons).

ACCOMMODATION: Airline-standard seats with underseat
baggage stowage and forward wardrobe standard. Rear
lavatory optional.

SYSTEMS: Pressurisation system, max differential 0.34 bars
(5.0 lb/sq in). Engine inlet screen anti-ice protection,
exhaust heated engine inlet lips, fuel vent heating, electric
propeller and windscreen de-icing and pneumatic wing
and tailplane leading-edge de-icing systems standard.
Brake de-icing optional.

AVIONICS AND EQUIPMENT: EFIS, cockpit voice recorder and
flight data recorder standard.

DIMENSIONS, EXTERNAL:
Wing span   17.65 m (57 ft 10¾ in)
Passenger door: Height   1.59 m (5 ft 2½ in)
   Width   0.62 m (2 ft 0¼ in)
Baggage door, forward: Height 1.50 m (4 ft 11 in)
   Width   1.32 m (4 ft 4 in)
Baggage door, rear: Height   1.32 m (4 ft 4 in)
   Width   1.32 m (4 ft 4 in)
DIMENSIONS, INTERNAL:
Passenger cabin: Max width   1.39 m (4 ft 6¾ in)
   Height   1.80 m (5 ft 11 in)
   Volume   18.12 m³ (640 cu ft)
Pressurised volume, total, incl flight deck and rear
   baggage compartment   25.99 m³ (918.0 cu ft)
Baggage space:
   Cabin: underseat   0.91 m³ (32.3 cu ft)

forward   0.48 m³ (17.0 cu ft)
rear   4.96 m³ (175.0 cu ft)
WEIGHTS AND LOADING:
Typical operating weight empty   4,612 kg (10,167 lb)
Max baggage   857 kg (1,890 lb)
Max payload   2,132 kg (4,700 lb)
Max T-O weight   7,688 kg (16,950 lb)
Max ramp weight   7,738 kg (17,060 lb)
Max zero-fuel weight   6,804 kg (15,000 lb)
Max landing weight   7,303 kg (16,100 lb)
Max power loading   4.03 kg/kW (6.62 lb/shp)
PERFORMANCE (at 7,031 kg; 15,500 lb T-O weight, ISA,
   except where indicated):
Max cruising speed:
   at 3,050 m (10,000 ft)   271 knots (502 km/h; 312 mph)
   at 6,100 m (20,000 ft)   291 knots (539 km/h; 335 mph)
   at 7,620 m (25,000 ft)   287 knots (532 km/h; 330 mph)
Stalling speed, 35° flap, at max landing weight
                            87 knots (162 km/h; 100 mph)
Range with 19 passengers, high-speed cruise power at
typical operating weight of 4,612 kg (10,167 lb), IFR
reserves for diversion to 100 nm (185 km; 115 mile)
alternate and 45 min hold:
   at 2,440 m (8,000 ft)   500 nm (926 km; 575 miles)
   at 3,660 m (12,000 ft)   540 nm (1,000 km; 621 miles)
   at 4,880 m (16,000 ft)   570 nm (1,056 km; 656 miles)
   at 7,620 m (25,000 ft)   690 nm (1,278 km; 794 miles)
Max range, VFR   1,380 nm (2,557 km; 1,589 miles)

BEECHCRAFT MODEL 2000 STARSHIP 1

The first flight took place on 29 August 1983 of an 85 per
cent scale proof of concept prototype of this Beechcraft
turboprop powered corporate aircraft. It was built by
Scaled Composites Inc (which see), and provided data for
the full size Starship 1.

Six pre-production Starship 1s were built, three for flight
testing and one each for static, damage tolerance and
pressure cycle testing. Bell Aerospace was contracted to
manufacture the CFRP foreplanes for these aircraft. The
first full scale prototype (N2000S) made its first flight
from Wichita on 15 February 1986, followed by a
commemorative first flight on 24 February. This aircraft
was powered initially by PT6A-65A-4 engines pending
delivery of the production standard PT6A-67A power
plants, and has now been retired from the test programme.
A second prototype (N3042S), fitted with the Collins
advanced integrated avionics system specified for production Starships, joined the flight test programme on 14
June 1986, and was followed on 5 January 1987 by the third
prototype (N3234S; c/n NC-3), which had a furnished cabin
and performed function and reliability testing.

In June 1987 NC-3/N3234S was flown to France, where it
made its first public appearance outside the USA at the
Paris Air Show. Basic certification was granted by the FAA
on 14 June 1988, and full certification for two-crew

Retouched photograph and three-view drawing *(Pilot Press)* **of Beech Model 1900D commuter airliner**

First production Beechcraft Starship 1 all-composite twin-turboprop business aircraft

Beechcraft Starship 1 eight/eleven-seat business aircraft *(Pilot Press)*

operation followed in December 1989, at which time the FAA was to undertake a crew determination study. Single-pilot certification, requiring an operating autopilot and flight management system, followed in May 1990.

The first production aircraft (N2000S, c/n NC-4), left Beech's composites facility assembly line on 30 December 1988 for installation of engines, systems and interior furnishings prior to its first flight on 25 April 1989 and subsequent use for customer demonstration flights. Beech expected to deliver 10 Starship 1s during 1990. The first overseas delivery, to a European operator, is expected in 1991. In January 1990 Beech held orders for more than 40 Starships, representing more than three years' production at planned rates, from customers in Canada, Europe, the United States and United Kingdom.

The description applies to the production Starship 1:

TYPE: Eight/eleven-seat business aircraft.

WINGS: Cantilever mid/low-wing monoplane. Specially developed wing section. Dihedral 1° 18′ 36″. Incidence 2° at root. Sweepback 24° 24′ at quarter-chord. Continuous tip to tip structure of Nomex honeycomb and graphite/epoxy monocoque, semi-monocoque and honeycomb sandwich, with titanium used in high stress areas such as landing gear mountings and wing/tipsail junctions. B.F. Goodrich Silver Estane pneumatic de-icing boots on leading-edges. Wingtip stabilisers (which the company terms tipsails) of composite construction, incorporating rudders, trim tabs and yaw dampers. Elevons and electrically actuated Fowler flaps of composite construction. Electric trim tab in each rudder.

FUSELAGE: Circular section fuselage of fail-safe construction, using similar materials to wings, produced by manual lay-up method. Fixed ventral fin serves as tail-bumper.

FOREPLANES: Low-set, electrically operated variable geometry foreplanes, of similar construction to wings, each with vortex generators and an elevator. Foreplane sweep

is electronically interconnected with the flaps to counter pitch moment changes, over sweep range 4° forward to 30° back. Trim tabs on elevators. B.F. Goodrich Silver Estane pneumatic de-icing boots on leading-edges.

LANDING GEAR: Retractable tricycle type, hydraulically operated with emergency backup. Main units retract inward, nose unit forward. Beech oleo-pneumatic shock absorbers. Twin Goodyear mainwheels with tyres size 19.5 × 6.75-10, pressure 5.38 bars (78 lb/sq in). Single Goodrich nosewheel with tyre size 19.5 × 6.75-8, pressure 5.38 bars (78 lb/sq in). Goodyear multi-disc anti-skid brakes with carbon heat sink.

POWER PLANT: Two Pratt & Whitney Canada PT6A-67A turboprops, each flat rated at 895 kW (1,200 shp) and driving a Hartzell five-blade fully-feathering and reversible-pitch metal pusher propeller with spinner. Fuel, total usable capacity 2,120 litres (560 US gallons, 466 Imp gallons), contained in integral wing tanks with flush refuelling point in upper surface of each wing.

ACCOMMODATION: Certificated for single pilot operation, but provision for two crew with dual controls on four-way adjustable reclining seats on flight deck, separated from cabin by bulkhead with door. Standard seating for eight passengers, six in double club arrangement with centre aisle in swivelling, reclining, lateral tracking, and fore and aft adjustable seats with retractable inboard armrests, and two on forward facing couch at rear of cabin, each with shoulder harness, lap belt, adjustable headliner-mounted reading light and fresh air outlet, individual magazine compartment with tambour door, cup holder, ashtray. Four folding work tables with vinyl tops at forward and rear club seating positions. Fail-safe dual pane cabin windows with electrically powered Polaroid dimming. Upright pyramid refreshment cabinet with heated liquid container, cup dispenser, ice chest, four decanters, waste container and overboard drain on forward port side; low pyramid bar with ice and general stowage between each

double club arrangement. Centre aisle stowage container. Low nap wool carpet, vinyl carpet protector, and No smoking and Fasten seat belt signs with audible chime, standard. Forward baggage compartment with flushing toilet, relief tube and cabin privacy door. Rear baggage compartment, accessible in flight via door in rear partition. Cabin is pressurised, electrically heated on ground, bleed air heated in flight, with vapour cycle cooling and high capacity ventilation systems. Single airstair door at forward end of cabin on port side with courtesy light. Emergency exit at rear end of cabin on starboard side, over wing.

SYSTEMS: Pressurisation system with max differential of 0.58 bars (8.4 lb/sq in) to provide a cabin altitude of 2,455 m (8,060 ft) at 12,495 m (41,000 ft). Freon vapour cycle cooling system. Engine bleed air provides pressurisation, heating and ventilation. 28V DC three-bus electrical system supplied by single aircooled 34Ah battery and 300A 28V starter/generator mounted on each engine and connected in parallel. Oxygen cylinder capacity 2.18 m³ (77 cu ft) rated at 124 bars (1,800 lb/sq in), mounted in nose, provides passenger oxygen supply automatically via drop-down masks until cabin altitude reaches 4,115 m (13,500 ft). Quick-donning masks for crew. B.F. Goodrich fully automatic self-initiating ice detection and de-icing system with Silver Estane pneumatic boots on wing and foreplane leading-edges, and anti-icing systems for windscreen, engine air inlets, fuel vents, pitot static probes and stall warning sensor.

AVIONICS AND EQUIPMENT: Collins integrated avionics package comprising 12 colour and two monochrome CRT displays in 'all glass' cockpit. Pilot and co-pilot have duplicated instrument panels, each with two 15.2 × 17.8 cm (6 × 7 in) EFIS displays for primary flight and navigation functions and two 10.2 × 10.2 cm (4 × 4 in) airspeed indicator and altitude/vertical speed indicator CRTs. Monochrome sensor display units (SDUs) provide heading and VOR, FMS and ADF bearings, and serves as secondary nav display. Dual control/display units (CDUs) control EFIS, weather radar, navigation radios and flight management functions. Engine indication caution and advisory system (EICAS) provides nearly 100 specific pieces of information in analog or digital form on a 15.2 × 17.8 cm (6 × 7 in) colour CRT display, with a priority message system to override extraneous information. Dual multi-function displays (MFDs) provide weather radar images from Collins TWR-850 Doppler turbulence weather radar system, maps, checklists and diagnostic and maintenance data, and serve as backup to EICAS. Two radio tuning units provide gas discharge tube alphanumerics for displaying navigation and transponder frequencies and codes, and can be used for display of engine parameters if EICAS fails. Dual flight management system (FMS) keyboards control all navigation frequencies, selected from onboard microdisc storage which is updated every 28 days. Standard avionics also include dual Collins com and nav receivers, dual transponders, ADF, DME, radio altimeter, dual compass system with strapdown attitude/heading reference system, and dual audio system with pilot/co-pilot interphone, aural warnings to flight deck, cabin speaker system, and emergency locator transmitter. Dual clocks, altitude awareness panels, a course heading panel, reversionary switching panels and standby electromagnetic airspeed indicator, gyro horizon and altimeter are provided. Information from sensors and data acquisition units located throughout the aircraft is available to all instruments through an ARINC 429 digital databus system. Teledyne stall warning system. Stick pusher limits max attainable angle of attack. Standard cockpit equipment includes dual audio speakers, dual hand-held microphones and crew headsets, avionics master switch, primary and secondary instrument lighting systems, dual map lights, indirect cockpit lighting and overhead crew reading lights, electrically heated windscreen and cockpit side windows, hot air windscreen defroster, dual adjustable sun visors, cigarette lighter, two ashtrays, fresh air outlets, coffee cup holders, oxygen outlets and console mounted diluter demand crew oxygen masks with microphones, pilot and co-pilot map cases, and lighted control wheel approach plate holder. Other equipment includes nosewheel bay microphone/earphone jack plug and ground clearance switch linked to com 1, external power receptacle, external oxygen filler ports and pressure gauge, dual heated pitot and static heads, heated stall warning system, wing ice-detection lights, dual landing lights, nosewheel-mounted taxi light, position lights, selectable high- and low-intensity anti-collision strobe lights, entrance door light, aisle courtesy light, indirect cabin lighting with passenger dimming feature, rear compartment lights, cabin fire extinguisher, towbar, pitot tube covers, static wicks, and control locks.

DIMENSIONS, EXTERNAL:

Wing span (reference)	16.60 m (54 ft 4¾ in)
Winglet height, each	2.45 m (8 ft 0½ in)
Foreplane span: sweptforward	7.79 m (25 ft 6½ in)
sweptback	6.63 m (21 ft 9¼ in)
Length overall	14.05 m (46 ft 1 in)
Fuselage: Length	13.67 m (44 ft 10 in)
Diameter (constant section)	1.78 m (5 ft 10 in)

Height overall	3.96 m (13 ft 0 in)
Wheel track	5.13 m (16 ft 10 in)
Wheelbase	6.86 m (22 ft 6 in)
Propeller diameter	2.64 m (8 ft 8 in)
Propeller ground clearance	0.89 m (2 ft 11 in)
Distance between propeller centres	3.07 m (10 ft 1 in)
Passenger door: Height	1.28 m (4 ft 2½ in)
Width	0.71 m (2 ft 4 in)
Emergency exit: Height	0.56 m (1 ft 10 in)
Width	0.66 m (2 ft 2 in)

DIMENSIONS, INTERNAL:

Cabin, excl flight deck: Length	5.08 m (16 ft 8 in)
Max width	1.68 m (5 ft 6 in)
Max height	1.61 m (5 ft 3½ in)
Floor area	5.94 m² (64 sq ft)
Volume (between pressure bulkheads)	13.45 m³ (475 cu ft)
Baggage holds: forward	0.40 m³ (14.0 cu ft)
rear	0.99 m³ (35 cu ft)

AREAS:

Wings, gross	26.09 m² (280.9 sq ft)
Elevons (total)	1.59 m² (17.1 sq ft)
Trailing-edge flaps (total)	4.78 m² (51.5 sq ft)
Ventral fin	1.25 m² (13.5 sq ft)
Foreplane (forward position)	5.67 m² (61.0 sq ft)
Elevators (total)	1.01 m² (10.9 sq ft)
Winglets (total)	4.92 m² (53.0 sq ft)
Rudders (total, incl tabs)	1.04 m² (11.2 sq ft)

WEIGHTS AND LOADINGS:

Weight empty, equipped	4,484 kg (9,887 lb)
Max baggage weight	351 kg (775 lb)
Max payload	1,152 kg (2,539 lb)
Max fuel weight	1,702 kg (3,752 lb)
Max T-O weight	6,531 kg (14,400 lb)
Max ramp weight	6,581 kg (14,510 lb)
Max zero-fuel weight	5,534 kg (12,200 lb)
Max landing weight	6,205 kg (13,680 lb)
Max wing loading	250.18 kg/m² (51.27 lb/sq ft)
Max power loading	3.65 kg/kW (6.00 lb/shp)

PERFORMANCE (at max T-O weight, ISA, except where indicated):

Never-exceed speed	Mach 0.76
Max cruising speed:	
at 7,620 m (25,000 ft)	335 knots (621 km/h; 386 mph)
at 10,670 m (35,000 ft)	304 knots (563 km/h; 350 mph)
Econ cruising speed at 10,670 m (35,000 ft)	295 knots (546 km/h; 340 mph)
Stalling speed: flaps up	99 knots (184 km/h; 114 mph)
flaps down	97 knots (180 km/h; 112 mph)
Max rate of climb at S/L	983 m (3,225 ft)/min
Rate of climb at S/L, one engine out	259 m (850 ft)/min
Max certificated altitude	12,495 m (41,000 ft)
Service ceiling	10,605 m (34,800 ft)
Service ceiling, one engine out	5,575 m (18,300 ft)
T-O to 15 m (50 ft)	1,182 m (3,875 ft)
Landing from 15 m (50 ft)	802 m (2,630 ft)
Range at 10,670 m (35,000 ft), max usable fuel, with reserves:	
at max cruise power	1,600 nm (2,965 km; 1,842 miles)
at econ cruise power	1,620 nm (3,002 km; 1,865 miles)
at max range power	1,690 nm (3,132 km; 1,946 miles)

BEECHCRAFT MODEL 400A BEECHJET
US Air Force designation: T-1A Jayhawk

In December 1985 Beech Aircraft Corporation acquired from Mitsubishi Heavy Industries and Mitsubishi Aircraft International the Diamond II business jet programme. The aircraft is now known as the Beechjet, for which Beech has worldwide marketing rights outside Japan. Mitsubishi Aircraft International (see 1986-87 *Jane's*) ceased all general aviation operations outside of Japan on 31 March 1986, but initially supplied assemblies and subassemblies for final assembly by Beech. In June 1989 Beech completed transfer of all Beechjet manufacturing to its facilities at Salina and Wichita.

Beech, through its dealer network, is providing support for existing Mitsubishi aircraft delivered prior to its acquisition of the Diamond II/Beechjet, including the MU-2 turboprop series and the Diamond I and IA business jets. Details of the development of the Mitsubishi Diamond series can be found under the MAI entry in the 1985-86 edition of *Jane's*.

The first Beech assembled aircraft was rolled out on 19 May 1986, and deliveries began in the following month. By 1 January 1990 a total of 56 Beechjets had been delivered.

At the 1989 National Business Aircraft Association convention in Dallas, Texas, Beech announced the Beechjet 400A, which features increases in payload and certificated ceiling, greater cabin volume achieved by relocating the rear fuselage fuel tank beneath the cabin floor, improved soundproofing, rear lavatory, and Collins Pro Line 4 EFIS avionics as standard. The first production Beechjet 400A flew on 22 September 1989. Customer deliveries were expected to begin in mid-1990. By early March 1990 Beech held orders for 73 Beechjet 400As, with commercial delivery positions committed until mid-1993.

Beechcraft Model 400A Beechjet twin-turbofan business aircraft

On 21 February 1990 the US Air Force announced that it had selected McDonnell Douglas, Beech and Quintron Corporation to provide its Tanker Transport Training System (TTTS), for which Beech will provide 211 **Beechjet 400T**s, a version of the Model 400A developed for the TTTS requirement and designated **T-1A Jayhawk** by USAF. Deliveries are scheduled to begin in October 1991. If the full contract options are exercised, a further 28 will be delivered in 1992, 36 in 1993, 48 in 1994, 39 in 1995, 43 in 1996 and 16 in 1997. Beech's Wichita Plant IV facility will be expanded by some 9,290 m² (100,000 sq ft) by mid-1991 to cater for Jayhawk production.

The Jayhawk will feature flight deck seating for a student on the left, instructor on the right and a third seat for another observing student behind the instructor's seat. Other modifications include strengthened landing gear, reinforced windscreen and tail surfaces for enhanced bird-strike protection, fewer cabin windows, an additional fuselage fuel tank, and single point pressure refuelling. Avionics, by Rockwell Collins, will include a five-tube EFIS, turbulence detection radar, digital autopilot, central diagnostic and maintenance system and a Tacan with air-to-air capability. IOC for USAF Jayhawks is scheduled for September 1992 when the aircraft will enter service at Reese AFB on the Air Training Command's Specialised Undergraduate Pilot Training (SUPT) programme. Jayhawks will be based at Williams AFB, Arizona, Columbus AFB, Mississippi, Vance AFB, Oklahoma, and Randolph, Reese and Laughlin AFBs, Texas (82nd, 14th, 71st, 12th, 64th and 47th FTWs, respectively), and will be used to train future crews for such aircraft as the KC-10, KC-135, C-5 and C-17.

TYPE: Twin-turbofan business aircraft.

WINGS: Cantilever low-wing monoplane. Mitsubishi MAC510 computer-designed wing sections: thickness/chord ratio 13.2 per cent at root, 11.3 per cent at tip. Dihedral 2° 30′. Incidence 3° at root, −3° 30′ at tip. Washout 6° 30′. Sweepback 20° at quarter-chord. Wings are of machine milled aluminium alloy, built in two panels. Each has two primary box beam spars, forming an integral fuel tank. Narrow chord Fowler type flaps over most of trailing-edges, actuated hydraulically and having double-slotted inboard and single-slotted outboard segments. Immediately forward of flaps are long span narrow chord spoilers, for roll control; these also serve as airbrakes, and can be used as lift dumpers to assist braking on touchdown. Outboard of each outer trailing-edge flap is a small, short span aileron for roll trim. Leading-edges anti-iced by hot air.

FUSELAGE: Pressurised, fail-safe fatigue resistant semi-monocoque structure, of oval cross-section with flattened cabin floor. Construction is mainly of aluminium alloy, using multiple load paths, bonded doublers and small skin panels in the principal load-bearing members. Built in three main portions: forward (including flight deck), centre and rear.

TAIL UNIT: Cantilever T tail, with sweepback on all surfaces; construction generally similar to that of wings. Curved dorsal fin, plus small underfin. A small horizontal strake is fitted on each side of rear fuselage, abreast of main fin, to assist airflow control. Trim tab in base of rudder. Variable incidence tailplane, with elevators.

LANDING GEAR: Retractable tricycle type, with single wheel and oleo-pneumatic shock absorber on each unit. Hydraulic actuation, controlled electrically. Emergency free-fall extension. Nosewheel, which is steerable by rudder pedals, retracts forward; mainwheels retract inward into fuselage. Goodyear wheels, with Goodrich tyres, on all units. Goodyear brakes.

POWER PLANT: Two Pratt & Whitney Canada JT15D-5 turbofans, each rated at 12.9 kN (2,900 lb st) for take-off. Rohr thrust reversers optional. Total usable fuel capacity 2,790 litres (737 US gallons; 614 Imp gallons). One refuelling point in top of each wing, and one in rear fuselage for fuselage tank, capacity 806 litres (213 US gallons; 177 Imp gallons). Oil capacity 7.7 litres (2 US gallons; 1.7 Imp gallons).

ACCOMMODATION: Crew of two on flight deck. Standard double club layout seats eight passengers in pressurised cabin, with eight tracking, reclining seats in facing pairs, each with integral headrest and armrest and shoulder harness. Fold-out writing table between each pair of seats. Private flushing lavatory at rear with sliding doors and optional lighted vanity unit and hot water supply. With seat belts, this compartment can serve as an additional passenger seat. Interior options include substitution of carry-on luggage compartment, volume 0.34 m³ (12.0 cu ft), for one of the forward club seats, and hot and cold service refreshment centre with integral stereo entertainment system. Independent temperature control for flight deck and cabin heating systems standard. In-flight telephone optional. Rear baggage compartment with external access, capacity 204 kg (450 lb).

SYSTEMS: Pressurisation system, with normal differential of 0.63 bars (9.1 lb/sq in). Backup pressurisation system, using engine bleed air, for use in emergency. Hydraulic system, pressure 103.5 bars (1,500 lb/sq in), for actuation

Beechcraft Model 400A (two P&WC JT15D-5 turbofans) *(Pilot Press)*

of flaps, landing gear and other services. Each variable volume output engine driven pump has a maximum flow rate of 14.76 litres (3.9 US gallons; 3.25 Imp gallons)/min, and one pump can actuate all hydraulic systems. Reservoirs, capacity 4.16 litres (1.1 US gallons; 0.9 Imp gallon), pressurised by filtered engine bleed air at 1.03 bars (15 lb/sq in). All systems are, wherever possible, of modular conception: for example, entire hydraulic installation can be removed as a single unit. Stick shaker as backup stall warning device.

AVIONICS: Standard avionics include pilot's integrated Collins Pro Line 4 EFIS featuring two-tube colour CRT primary flight display (PFD) and multi-function display (MFD) units mounted side by side, and control/display unit. PFD displays airspeed, altitude, vertical speed, flight director, attitude and horizontal situation information, while MFD displays navigation, radar, map, checklist and fault annunciation information. Smaller, single or dual CRTs mounted on central console function as independent navigation sensor displays or backup displays for main CRTs. Co-pilot's PFD, MFD optional. EFIS installation features EICAS engine instrumentation, strapdown attitude/heading referencing system, electronic map navigation display, airspeed trend information and V-speeds on Mach airspeed display, and solid state Doppler turbulence detection radar. Bendix/King three- or five-tube EFIS optional.

DIMENSIONS, EXTERNAL:

Wing span	13.25 m (43 ft 6 in)
Wing aspect ratio	7.5

Length overall	14.75 m (48 ft 5 in)
Fuselage: Length	13.15 m (43 ft 2 in)
Max width	1.68 m (5 ft 6 in)
Max depth	1.85 m (6 ft 1 in)
Height overall	4.19 m (13 ft 9 in)
Tailplane span	5.00 m (16 ft 5 in)
Wheel track	2.84 m (9 ft 4 in)
Wheelbase	5.86 m (19 ft 3 in)
Crew/passenger door: Height	1.27 m (4 ft 2 in)
Width	0.71 m (2 ft 4 in)

DIMENSIONS, INTERNAL:
Cabin:

Max length, incl flight deck	6.37 m (20 ft 11 in)
Length, excl flight deck	4.76 m (15 ft 7 in)
Max width	1.50 m (4 ft 11 in)
Max height	1.45 m (4 ft 9 in)
Volume: incl flight deck	11.69 m³ (413 cu ft)
excl flight deck	9.00 m³ (318 cu ft)
Baggage compartment volume	0.93 m³ (33 cu ft)

AREAS:

Wings, net	22.43 m² (241.4 sq ft)
Trailing-edge flaps (total)	5.22 m² (56.4 sq ft)
Spoilers (total)	0.57 m² (6.2 sq ft)
Fin, incl dorsal fin	5.91 m² (63.6 sq ft)
Rudder, incl yaw damper	1.12 m² (12.1 sq ft)
Tailplane	5.25 m² (56.5 sq ft)
Elevators, incl tab	1.56 m² (16.8 sq ft)

WEIGHTS AND LOADINGS:

Basic operating weight, incl crew, avionics and interior fittings	4,817 kg (10,620 lb)
Max fuel weight	2,240 kg (4,938 lb)
Max T-O weight	7,303 kg (16,100 lb)
Max ramp weight	7,393 kg (16,300 lb)
Max zero-fuel weight	5,896 kg (13,000 lb)
Max landing weight	6,450 kg (14,220 lb)
Max wing loading	325.6 kg/m² (66.69 lb/sq ft)
Max power loading	284.26 kg/kN (2.78 lb/lb st)

PERFORMANCE (at max T-O weight except where indicated):

Never-exceed speed	Mach 0.785
Max level speed at 8,230 m (27,000 ft)	
	467 knots (865 km/h; 538 mph)
Typical cruising speed at 12,500 m (41,000 ft)	
	450 knots (834 km/h; 518 mph)
Long-range cruising speed at 12,500 m (41,000 ft)	
	395 knots (732 km/h; 455 mph)
Stalling speed, flaps down, idling power	
	87 knots (161 km/h; 100 mph) IAS
Max operating altitude	13,715 m (45,000 ft)
FAA (FAR 25) T-O to 10.7 m (35 ft) at S/L, ISA	
	1,245 m (4,082 ft)
FAA landing distance from 15 m (50 ft) at S/L, ISA, max landing weight	862 m (2,830 ft)

Range with four passengers, max fuel, ISA, zero wind, with allowance for climb and descent, long-range cruise power:
NBAA VFR reserves
1,909 nm (3,537 km; 2,198 miles)

BELL
BELL HELICOPTER TEXTRON INC
(Subsidiary of Textron Inc)
PO Box 482, Fort Worth, Texas 76101
Telephone: 1 (817) 280 2011
Telex: 75 8229 and 75 8313
PRESIDENT: Leonard M. Horner
SENIOR VICE-PRESIDENTS:
  COMMERCIAL BUSINESS, AND GENERAL MANAGER, CUSTOMER SUPPORT AND SERVICE DIVISION: Gainor J. Lindsey
  RESEARCH & ENGINEERING: Robert R. Lynn
  GOVERNMENT BUSINESS: Charles R. Rudning
VICE-PRESIDENTS:
  COMMERCIAL MARKETING: James A. Hamilton
  INTERNATIONAL MARKETING: Philip S. Prince
  ENGINEERING, V-22 JOINT PROJECT OFFICE: Stanley Martin
  MILITARY BUSINESS DEVELOPMENT: Ray Swindell
DIRECTOR, PUBLIC AFFAIRS: Carl L. Harris

From 1970-81 Bell Helicopter Textron was an unincorporated division of Textron Inc. Since 3 January 1982 it has been a wholly owned subsidiary of Textron Inc.

In early 1990 a total of 7,436 people were employed in the USA by Bell, which, with its licensees, has manufactured more than 30,000 helicopters. Of these, more than 9,000 have been civilian.

In October 1983 Bell Helicopter Canada (see entry in Canadian section) was formed under a contract with the Canadian government to establish a manufacturing plant at Mirabel, near Montreal, Quebec. To make more space available at Fort Worth for the V-22 Osprey programme, Bell completed the transfer of its Model 206B JetRanger and Model 206L LongRanger production lines to Mirabel in January 1987. The lines for the Models 212 and 412 were transferred in mid-1988 and early 1989 respectively.

Available details of the range of military and commercial helicopters in current production or under development by Bell Helicopter Textron are published in this entry and under the Bell heading in the Canadian section. Several models are also built under licence by Agusta in Italy and Fuji in Japan (which see). Korea Bell Helicopter Company (KBHC, which see) will co-produce helicopters in the Republic of Korea with Bell Helicopter Textron.

Bell Helicopter de Venezuela CA, a joint venture with Maquinarias Mendoza CA and Aerotecnica SA, was established in early 1984, in Caracas, to provide marketing and support services in Venezuela. Bell Helicopter Asia (Pte) Ltd is a wholly owned Singapore-based company providing marketing and support for the Southeast Asia region.

BELL MODEL 205
US and Brazilian military designations: UH-1D/H/ V, EH-1H and HH-1H Iroquois
Canadian military designation: CH-118 Iroquois
Spanish military designations: HU.10B/HE.10B
Japanese military designation: HU-1H

Although basically similar to the earlier Model 204 (see 1971-72 *Jane's*), the Model 205 introduced a longer fuselage, increased cabin space to accommodate a much larger number of passengers, and other changes. Details of the full range of military variants have been recorded in previous editions of *Jane's*. The final production version is the **UH-1H**. Deliveries of this version to the US Army began in September 1967 and totalled 3,573. Production of the UH-1H continued subsequently to satisfy export orders, which totalled 1,317 by Spring 1985. It ended temporarily in December 1980, but was restarted in order to build 55 for

Turkey. Deliveries of these were completed in 1987. The Model 205 was also manufactured by Agusta in Italy, and (as the HU-1H) is still produced by Fuji in Japan, to which section reference should be made for technical and performance data. In addition, under a licensing agreement, 118 UH-1Hs were produced for the Nationalist Chinese Army, with much of the manufacturing and assembly carried out by AIDC.

The US Army plans to retain some 2,700 UH-1Hs in service beyond the year 2000. These have received upgraded avionics and composite main rotor blades, as have EH-1H ECM and UH-1V casualty evacuation helicopters. Further details of these modifications have appeared in the 1989-90 and earlier editions of *Jane's*.

BELL MODELS 206B JETRANGER III and 206L-3 LONGRANGER III

By January 1990, Bell and its licensees had manufactured well over 7,000 helicopters of the Model 206 series, more than 4,600 of them for commercial customers. Production of the JetRanger and LongRanger is now centred on Bell Helicopter Canada's plant at Mirabel, near Montreal. Details of these helicopters may be found in the Canadian section.

BELL MODEL 406 (AHIP)
US Army designation: OH-58D Kiowa Warrior

The US Army announced on 21 September 1981 that Bell's Model 406 proposal had been selected as winner of its Army Helicopter Improvement Program (AHIP)

competition to develop a near-term scout helicopter. Its configuration includes an MDAC/Northrop mast mounted sight and a Honeywell cockpit control and display subsystem. The US Army planned to modify at least 477 existing OH-58A Kiowa helicopters in 1985-91, under the designation **OH-58D**. Of these 243 had been funded by FY 1990, in seven lots (16, 44, 39, 36, 36, 36 and 36). The programme was then terminated. Deliveries by early February 1990 included 16 of an armed version known as the **OH-58D Kiowa Warrior**.

The first of five prototype OH-58Ds made its first flight on 6 October 1983. Deliveries began in December 1985, and to units in Europe on 11 June 1987, when 12 OH-58Ds were loaded on board a single C-5A Galaxy. By February 1990, Bell had delivered 163, including 54 serving in West Germany and six in South Korea. Production was continuing in 1990 at three per month.

Among improvements scheduled to be incorporated in the OH-58D are provision for Sanders AN/ALQ-144 infra-red jammer, Perkin Elmer AN/AVR-2 laser warning receiver, ITT SINCGARS secure radios, Tracor M130 flare/chaff dispensers, optical enhancements to the mast mounted sight to afford protection against battlefield lasers, and provision for M43 chemical/biological masks for crew. Under Stage 1 of a Multi Stage Improvement programme (MSIP) the OH-58D will also be equipped with a Global Positioning System receiver, improved Doppler, a digital data loader, flight data recorder and MIL-STD-1750 processors.

Bell began work on what was then known as the Armed OH-58D in September 1987 to meet an urgent requirement

Bell OH-58D (AHIP) with mast mounted sight

from the Special Forces. Under the 'Prime Chance' programme, the first of 15 conversions was delivered to the 160th Special Operations Aviation Regiment in the following December and soon afterwards deployed aboard a converted oil platform repair barge in the Arabian Gulf for operations against Iranian gunboats threatening international shipping. Modifications included weapons pylons attached to the ends of an aluminium tube running through the rear of the cabin; Stinger and Hellfire missiles; 0.50 in machine-guns and 2.75 in rocket pods; and a higher engine gas temperature to permit longer use of maximum power through a transmission re-rated at 380 kW (510 shp).

The US Army has decided to arm, through production and retrofit programmes, all 243 OH-58Ds currently authorised, assigning the name of Kiowa Warrior in early 1990. Compared with the 'Prime Chance' helicopters, future conversions will have a new engine diffuser providing 15 per cent additional power; transmission rated at 429 kW (575 shp); weapons stations added to the fuselage structure; structural improvements; and an integrated weapons control system. The two last-mentioned measures reduce weight by some 113 kg (250 lb) compared with 'Prime Chance'. Up to 81 of the 243 helicopters will be further modified for special duties with a 'squatting' landing gear; folding main blades; and tilting vertical stabiliser to allow them to fly within 10 minutes of being taken from the hold of a C-130 Hercules transport aircraft. These Multi-Purpose Light Helicopters (MPLH) will also receive a cargo hook for loads up to 907 kg (2,000 lb); and external attachments for six troop seats or four medevac litters. The last 18 of the FY 1989 OH-58D purchase, due to be delivered in January 1991, introduce Stinger missile modifications and are regarded as the first true Kiowa Warriors. FY 1990 helicopters will have engine diffuser and transmission upgrades, plus provision for air-to-surface weapons. Max weight growth to 2,495 kg (5,500 lb) is envisaged.

TYPE: Two-seat scout helicopter.

ROTOR SYSTEM: Four-blade soft-in-plane main rotor. Blade section BHTI M406183. Glassfibre composite blades, with hollow spar, and afterbody skins supported by Nomex honeycomb core. Main rotor head has glassfibre yoke and elastomeric bearings. Each blade attached to head by two side by side pins. Main rotor blades fold and have a bendable tab at 60 per cent radius. No rotor brake. Two-blade non-lubricated tail rotor on port side of tailboom; blades of glassfibre composite with nickel coated abrasion strip.

ROTOR DRIVE: Steel spiral bevel and planetary gear transmissions in aluminium and magnesium cast housings. Transmission rating 454 kW (609 shp) maximum, 339 kW (455 shp) continuous. Main gearbox beneath main rotor, tail rotor gearbox at tail rotor. Main rotor/engine rpm ratio 0.065668:1. Tail rotor/engine rpm ratio 0.39584:1.

FUSELAGE: Stressed aluminium semi-monocoque fail-safe structure incorporating skins, longerons, two upper longitudinal roof beams and a lower curved honeycomb sandwich underfuselage panel. Tapered stressed aluminium semi-monocoque tailboom, composed of bulkheads and skins.

TAIL UNIT: Fixed stabiliser of aluminium monocoque construction with inverted aerofoil section. Fixed vertical fin in sweptback upper and ventral sections.

LANDING GEAR: Light alloy tubular skids bolted to extruded cross-tubes.

POWER PLANT: One Allison 250-C30R turboshaft, with an intermediate power rating of 485 kW (650 shp) at S/L ISA. One self-sealing crash resistant fuel cell, capacity 399 litres (105.4 US gallons; 87.8 Imp gallons) located aft of the cabin area. Refuelling point on starboard side of fuselage. Oil capacity 5.7 litres (1.5 US gallons; 1.2 Imp gallons).

ACCOMMODATION: Pilot and co-pilot/observer seated side by side. Door on each side of fuselage. Accommodation is heated and ventilated.

SYSTEMS: Single hydraulic system, pressure 69 bars (1,000 lb/sq in) for main and tail rotor controls and SCAS system. Maximum flow rate 11.36 litres (3 US gallons; 2.5 Imp gallons)/min. Open-type reservoir. Primary electrical power provided by 10kVA 400Hz three-phase 120/208V AC alternator with 200A 28V DC transformer/rectifier unit for secondary DC power. Backup power provided by 500VA 400Hz single-phase 115V AC solid state inverter and 200A 28V DC starter/generator.

AVIONICS AND EQUIPMENT: Multi-function displays for vertical and horizontal situation indication, mast mounted sight day/night viewing and communications control, with selection via control column handgrip switches. Five com transceivers, data link and secure voice equipment. Doppler, strapdown INS. Equipped for day/night VFR. Mast mounted sight houses 12x magnification TV camera, auto-focusing IR thermal imaging sensor and laser rangefinder/designator, with automatic target tracking and in-flight automatic boresighting. Night vision goggles; AHRS; and airborne target handoff subsystem (ATHS). Germany-based OH-58Ds have real-time video downlink which can be relayed via Guardrail-capable aircraft. Phase 1 additions, introduced on production line in 1990, include doubled computer capacity to 88K, added weapons selection/

Bell Model 406 CS Combat Scout of the Royal Saudi Land Forces

aiming and multi-target acquisition/track displays, IR jammer, second RWR and laser warning, video recorder, data transfer system, SINCGARS and Have Quick II radios, ANVIS display and symbology system, NBC mask and EMV hardening.

ARMAMENT: Four Stinger air-to-air or Hellfire air-to-surface missiles, or two seven-round 2.75 in rocket pods, or two Global Helicopter Technology CFD-5000 pods for 7.62 mm and 0.50 in machine-guns, mounted on outriggers on cabin sides. IR jammer standard on armed version.

DIMENSIONS, EXTERNAL:
Main rotor diameter	10.67 m (35 ft 0 in)
Main rotor blade chord	0.24 m (9½ in)
Tail rotor diameter	1.65 m (5 ft 5 in)
Length: overall, rotors turning	12.85 m (42 ft 2 in)
fuselage, excl rotors	10.31 m (33 ft 10 in)
Width, rotors folded	1.97 m (6 ft 5½ in)
Height: to top of rotor head	2.59 m (8 ft 6 in)
overall	3.90 m (12 ft 9½ in)
Skid track	1.88 m (6 ft 2 in)
Cabin doors (port and stbd, each):	
Height	1.04 m (3 ft 5 in)
Width	0.91 m (3 ft 0 in)
Height to sill	0.66 m (2 ft 2 in)

AREAS:
Main rotor blades (each)	1.30 m² (13.95 sq ft)
Tail rotor blades (each)	0.13 m² (1.43 sq ft)
Main rotor disc	89.37 m² (962.0 sq ft)
Tail rotor disc	2.14 m² (23.04 sq ft)
Fin	0.85 m² (9.1 sq ft)

WEIGHTS AND LOADINGS:
Weight empty	1,281 kg (2,825 lb)
Max fuel weight	321 kg (707 lb)
Max T-O and landing weight	2,041 kg (4,500 lb)
Max zero-fuel weight	1,711 kg (3,773 lb)
Max disc loading	22.95 kg/m² (4.7 lb/sq ft)
Max power loading	6.27 kg/kW (10.3 lb/shp)

PERFORMANCE (at max T-O weight, clean):
Never-exceed speed	130 knots (241 km/h; 149 mph)
Max level speed at 1,220 m (4,000 ft)	128 knots (237 km/h; 147 mph)
Max cruising speed at 610 m (2,000 ft)	120 knots (222 km/h; 138 mph)
Econ cruising speed at 1,220 m (4,000 ft)	110 knots (204 km/h; 127 mph)
Max rate of climb: at S/L, ISA	469 m (1,540 ft)/min
at 1,220 m (4,000 ft), 35°C (95°F)	over 152 m (500 ft)/min
Vertical rate of climb: at S/L, ISA	232 m (760 ft)/min
at 1,220 m (4,000 ft), 35°C (95°F)	over 152 m (500 ft)/min
Service ceiling	over 3,660 m (12,000 ft)
Hovering ceiling: IGE, ISA	over 3,660 m (12,000 ft)
OGE, ISA	3,415 m (11,200 ft)
OGE, 35°C (95°F)	1,735 m (5,700 ft)
Range with max fuel, no reserves	300 nm (556 km; 345 miles)
Endurance	2 h 30 min

BELL MODEL 406 CS

The Model 406 CS (for Combat Scout) is a lighter and simplified variant of the AHIP OH-58D, equipped with a quick-change weapons system. First flown in June 1984, this multi-mission helicopter omits the MMS, specialised avionics and integrated multiplex cockpit of the AHIP 406, but incorporates many OH-58D features including AHIP dynamics and drive train, mated to a damage-resistant, 10,000 hour fail-safe four-blade rigid rotor of composites construction and a high-thrust composites tail rotor. Power plant is a 485 kW (650 shp) Allison 250-C30U turboshaft; transmission rating is 380 kW (510 shp) continuous. Armament can comprise two GIAT 20 mm M621 gun pods, each with 180 rds, four TOW 2 or Hellfire anti-tank missiles, or a mix of Stinger air-to-air missiles, 70 mm rockets and 7.62 mm or 0.50 in machine-guns.

In 1987 a Combat Scout successfully completed simulated air-to-air combat trials at NAS Patuxent River, Maryland, armed with a Lucas Aerospace gun turret and laser designator.

From June 1990, the 406 CS has been offered with increased fuel capacity of 455 litres (120 US gallons; 100 Imp gallons); transmission uprated to 410 kW (550 shp); and a max T-O weight of 2,268 kg (5,000 lb). Planned developments include TOW integration, a laser designator/rangefinder, uprated engine, 429 kW (575 shp) transmission rating and 2,495 kg (5,500 lb) max T-O weight.

Saudi Arabia has ordered 15 Combat Scouts under the designation MH-58D. These will incorporate a hybrid cockpit developed by SFENA, with conventional flight instruments and CRT displays for TOW and communications control. Sighting via Saab-Emerson HeliTOW system. Delivery began in mid-1990.

WEIGHTS:
Weight empty	1,028 kg (2,266 lb)
Max T-O weight	2,041 kg (4,500 lb)

PERFORMANCE (at max T-O weight):
Max level speed	124 knots (230 km/h; 143 mph)
Max cruising speed	120 knots (222 km/h; 138 mph)
Hovering ceiling: IGE	6,035 m (19,800 ft)
OGE	5,210 m (17,100 ft)
Range with max fuel	217 nm (402 km; 250 miles)
Endurance	2 h 30 min

BELL MODEL 209 HUEYCOBRA, SEACOBRA and SUPERCOBRA

US Army designations: AH-1G and AH-1Q
US Navy/Marine Corps designations: AH-1J, AH-1T and AH-1W

Bell initiated the Model 209 in March 1965 as a company funded development of the UH-1B/C Iroquois intended specifically for armed helicopter missions. The prototype made its first flight on 7 September 1965, and the US Army's intention to order the aircraft was announced on 11 March 1966, the initial model being the AH-1G HueyCobra. Total orders to date for all versions of the HueyCobra/SeaCobra exceed 1,800.

The following versions have been built:

AH-1G HueyCobra. Original version for US Army (1,075). Production totalled 1,127, including 38 diverted to USMC, six to Israel and eight to Spain. Some conversions to TH-1G dual-control trainer and single JAH-1G temporary armament testbed.

AH-1J SeaCobra. Initial twin-turboshaft version for US Marine Corps (67) and Imperial Iranian Army Aviation (202). Production completed in February 1975; last described in 1987-88 Jane's.

AH-1Q HueyCobra. Interim (92 converted AH-1G) anti-armour version for US Army; production completed. Details in 1982-83 and earlier Jane's.

AH-1S HueyCobra. Advanced and modernised TOW-capable version for US Army, some variants retrospectively designated AH-1P, AH-1E and AH-1F. In production.

AH-1T Improved SeaCobra. Improved version of twin-engined AH-1J for US Marine Corps, described in 1987-88 and earlier editions of Jane's. Total of 62 built; production completed, but March 1988 contract provides for survivors to be upgraded to AH-1W configuration.

AH-1W SuperCobra. Most recent production version, originating from April 1980 flight test by Bell of a USMC AH-1T powered by two General Electric T700-GE-700 turboshafts with a combined output in excess of 2,386 kW (3,200 shp). Improvements, proposed subsequently for retrofit to existing AH-1Ts, include installation of General Electric T700-GE-401 turboshafts with a combined output of 2,423 kW (3,250 shp); a new combining gearbox; and a number of detail improvements. The T700-GE-401 has intermediate and contingency ratings of 1,260 kW (1,690 shp) and 1,285 kW (1,723 shp) respectively. The fuel system is designed to survive 23 mm shell damage. A T700-GE-401 testbed helicopter (161022), then designated AH-1T+,

Bell AH-1W SuperCobra armed with TOW missiles

made its first flight on 16 November 1983 and in early 1984 Congressional approval was given for the procurement of 44 production AH-1W SuperCobras, 22 each in FYs 1985 and 1986. The first AH-1W was delivered on 27 March 1986 for a seven-month test programme with Naval Air Systems Command. A second AH-1W began a three-month electromagnetic interference test programme in the Spring of 1986. Deliveries of all 44 AH-1Ws and one TAH-1W trainer had been completed by August 1988 to HML/A-169, -267, -367 and -369 at Camp Pendleton, California. Two aircraft have been equipped with an interim FLIR capability. In August 1988 the US Marine Corps ordered a further 34 AH-1Ws for delivery between June 1990 and the end of June 1991. Six more were funded in FY 1990. The USMC also plans to update its fleet of 39 AH-1Ts to AH-1W standard for HML/A-167 and -269 at New River, North Carolina. First conversion delivered on 26 January 1989, and 17 completed by February 1990. The Turkish Army has plans to acquire five AH-1Ws.

An AH-1W variant fitted with a four blade rotor and designated AH-1(4B)W is described separately.

Missions assigned to the AH-1W include anti-armour, troop carrying helicopter escort, multiple weapon fire support, armed reconnaissance, and search and target acquisition. Night capability for the AH-1W M65 TOW sight, consisting of FLIR and a laser ranger/designator, is being jointly developed by US Marines and Israel based on Tamam equipment. It is known in Israel as CLNAS, but as Night Targeting System in the US. All US and exported NTS will be manufactured and supported by Kollsman. A Teledyne AN/APN-217 Doppler-based navigation system is under consideration for retrofit, whilst the USMC began testing an enhanced electronic warfare system in August 1989. The description below refers to the AH-1W SuperCobra:

TYPE: Twin-engined close support and attack helicopter.

ROTOR SYSTEM AND DRIVE: Two-blade main rotor system, similar to that of Bell Model 214, with strengthened main rotor head incorporating Lord Kinematics Lastoflex elastomeric and Teflon faced bearings. Main rotor blades, section Wortmann FX69-H-098, have aluminium spar with steel leading-edge and aluminium faced honeycomb material aft of spar. Single tab on each main rotor blade. Tail rotor also similar to that of Model 214, with increased diameter and blade chord, constructed from aluminium honeycomb with stainless steel skin and leading-edge. Main rotor brake standard. Main rotor/engine rpm ratio: 1 : 64.354. Tail rotor/engine rpm ratio 1 : 13.708.

WINGS: Small mid-mounted stub-wings, to carry armament, of conventional all-metal construction. Section NACA 0024-0030. Dihedral 0°. Incidence 14°. Sweepback at quarter-chord 14° 42′.

FUSELAGE: Conventional all-metal semi-monocoque fail-safe structure, with low silhouette and narrow profile.

TAIL UNIT: Sweptback vertical fin/tail rotor pylon. Elevator, of inverted aerofoil section and conventional construction, mid-mounted on tailboom forward of fin.

LANDING GEAR: Non-retractable tubular skid type. Ground handling wheels optional.

POWER PLANT: Two General Electric T700-GE-401 turbo-shafts, each rated at 1,260 kW (1,690 shp). Fuel contained in two interconnected self-sealing rubber fuel cells in fuselage, with protection from damage by 0.50 in ballistic ammunition, total capacity 1,153 litres (304.5 US gallons; 253.5 Imp gallons). Fire protection for wet area provided by passive powder filled panels and for ullage by on board inert gas generating system (OBIGGS). Gravity refuelling point in forward fuselage, pressure refuelling point in rear fuselage. Provision for carriage on underwing stores stations of two or four external fuel tanks each of 295 litres (78 US gallons; 65 Imp gallons) capacity; or two 378 litre (100 US gallon; 83 Imp gallon) tanks; or two 100 and two 78 US gallon tanks. Oil capacity 19 litres (5 US gallons; 4.2 Imp gallons).

ACCOMMODATION: Crew of two in tandem, with co-pilot/gunner in front seat and pilot at rear. Cockpit is heated,

ventilated and air-conditioned. Dual controls; lighting compatible with AN/AVS-6 night vision goggles, and armour protection standard. Forward crew door on port side and rear crew door on starboard side, both upward opening.

SYSTEMS: Three independent hydraulic systems, pressure 207 bars (3,000 lb/sq in), for flight controls and other services. Electrical system comprises three 28V 400A DC generators, two 24V 34.5Ah batteries and three inverters: main 115V AC, 1kVA, single-phase at 400Hz, standby 115V AC, 750VA, three-phase at 400Hz and a dedicated 115V AC 365VA single-phase for AIM-9 missile system. AiResearch environmental control unit.

AVIONICS: AN/ASN-75B compass set, AN/ARN-89B ADF, AN/APX-100(V) transponder, AN/ARN-118 Tacan, AN/APN-154(V) radar beacon set, AN/ARC-182(V), AN/APN-194 radar altimeter, AN/APR-39(V) pulse radar signal detecting set, AN/APR-44(V) CW radar warning system, KY-58 TSEC secure voice set and AN/ALQ-144(V) IR countermeasures set. Improved countermeasures suite in USMC AH-1Ws replaces APR-39 and APR-44 by AN/APR-39(XE2) radar warning and adds AN/AVR-2 laser warner and AN/AAR-47 plume detecting set.

ARMAMENT: Electrically operated General Electric under-nose GTK4A/A turret housing an M197 three-barrel 20 mm gun. A 750-rd ammunition container is located in the fuselage directly aft of the turret; firing rate is 690 rds/min; a 16-round burst limiter is incorporated in the firing switch. Gun can be tracked 110° to each side, 18° upward, and 50° downward, but barrel length of 1.52 m (5 ft) makes it imperative that the M197 is centralised before wing stores are fired. Underwing attachments for up to four LAU-61A (19 tube), LAU-68A, LAU-68A/A, LAU-68B/A or LAU-69A (seven-tube) 2.75 in Hydra 70 rocket launcher pods; two CBU-55B fuel-air explosive weapons; four SUU-44/A flare dispensers; two M118 grenade dispensers; Mk 45 parachute flares; or two GPU-2A or SUU-11A/A Minigun pods. Provision for carrying totals of up to eight TOW missiles, eight AGM-114 Hellfire missiles, two AIM-9L Sidewinder or AGM-122A Sidearm missiles, on outboard underwing stores stations. Canadian Marconi TOW/Hellfire control system enables AH-1W to fire both TOW and Hellfire missiles on same mission. Dual AN/ALE-39 chaff system with one MX-7721 dispenser mounted on each stub wing.

DIMENSIONS, EXTERNAL:
Main rotor diameter	14.63 m (48 ft 0 in)
Main rotor blade chord	0.84 m (2 ft 9 in)
Tail rotor diameter	2.97 m (9 ft 9 in)
Tail rotor blade chord	0.305 m (1 ft 0 in)
Distance between rotor centres	8.89 m (29 ft 2 in)
Wing span	3.23 m (10 ft 7 in)
Wing aspect ratio	3.74
Length overall, rotors turning	17.68 m (58 ft 0 in)
Length of fuselage	13.87 m (45 ft 6 in)
Width overall	3.28 m (10 ft 9 in)
Height to top of rotor head	4.11 m (13 ft 6 in)
Height overall	4.32 m (14 ft 2 in)
Elevator span	2.11 m (6 ft 11 in)
Width over skids	2.13 m (7 ft 0 in)

AREAS:
Main rotor blades (each)	6.13 m² (66.0 sq ft)
Tail rotor blades (each)	0.45 m² (4.835 sq ft)
Main rotor disc	168.11 m² (1,809.56 sq ft)
Tail rotor disc	6.94 m² (74.70 sq ft)
Vertical fin	2.01 m² (21.70 sq ft)
Horizontal tail surfaces	1.41 m² (15.20 sq ft)

WEIGHTS:
Weight empty	4,627 kg (10,200 lb)
Mission fuel load	946 kg (2,086 lb)
Max useful load (fuel and disposable ordnance)	
	2,065 kg (4,552 lb)
Max T-O and landing weight	6,690 kg (14,750 lb)

PERFORMANCE (at max T-O weight, ISA):
Never-exceed speed	190 knots (352 km/h; 219 mph)
Max level speed at S/L	152 knots (282 km/h; 175 mph)
Max cruising speed	150 knots (278 km/h; 173 mph)
Rate of climb at S/L, one engine out	244 m (800 ft)/min
Service ceiling	more than 4,270 m (14,000 ft)
Service ceiling, one engine out	
	more than 3,660 m (12,000 ft)
Hovering ceiling: IGE	4,495 m (14,750 ft)
OGE	915 m (3,000 ft)
Range at S/L with standard fuel, no reserves	
	343 nm (635 km; 395 miles)

BELL MODEL 209 HUEYCOBRA (MODERNISED VERSIONS)
US Army designations: AH-1E, AH-1F, AH-1P, AH-1S and TH-1S

The AH-1S was introduced as an advanced version of the single-engined HueyCobra for the US Army, with TOW missile capability, upgraded power plant, gearbox, transmission and many other improvements. The first of a succession of US Army contracts was placed in 1975, involving both the conversion of earlier AH-1G Cobras and a three-stage production programme of new-build aircraft with varying degrees of upgrading. The four versions were all designated AH-1S until March 1987, when new-build helicopters were retrospectively assigned the dormant suffixes (from the general H-1 Iroquois family) AH-1P, -1E and -1F.

AH-1S. Formerly AH-1S(MOD). Conversion of 179 helicopters (92 AH-1Qs up to 1979 and 87 AH-1Gs in

Bell AH-1T Improved SeaCobra, with added side view (bottom) of AH-1W SuperCobra *(Pilot Press)*

1986-88) with 1,342 kW (1,800 shp) Textron Lycoming T53-L-703 turboshaft engine, Kaman rotor blades (see AH-1P), and (ex-AH-1Gs only) TOW missile system, but retaining original canopies. Total includes 15 in **TH-1S** 'Night Stalker' configuration, to give US Army pilots experience in operation of the Martin Marietta FLIR-based night vision system and Honeywell integrated helmet and display sighting system (IHADSS) fitted to AH-64 Apache helicopters.

AH-1P. First batch of new-production TOW Cobras (formerly Production AH-1S), of which 100 delivered to US Army in 1977-78, beginning with 76-22567 and including two AH–IF prototypes. Flat-plate canopy, upturned exhaust, improved nap-of-the-earth (NOE) instrument panel layout, continental United States (CONUS) navigation equipment, radar altimeter, improved communication radios, uprated engine and transmission, push/pull anti-torque controls, and (from the 67th aircraft, 77-22729, onwards) Kaman developed composite rotor blades with tapered tips.

AH-1E (formerly Enhanced Cobra Armament System or 'Up-gun' AH-1S). Next 98 new-build aircraft, beginning at 77-22673, with improvements detailed for AH-1P plus universal 20/30 mm gun turret (invariably fitted with long-barrel, 20 mm cannon), improved wing stores management system for the 2.75 in rockets, automatic compensation for off-axis gun firing, and a 10kVA alternator to provide the necessary additional electric power. Delivered in 1978-79.

AH-1F. Fully upgraded TOW version (previously designated Modernised AH-1S). Production for US Army totalled 149 (beginning 78-23095) in 1979-86, of which 50 to the Army National Guard. In addition, 378 AH-1Gs converted to full AH-1F standard between November 1979 and June 1982, including 41 TAH-1F trainers. To the improvements already mentioned for the AH-1P and AH-1E are added a new fire control subsystem (comprising a laser rangefinder and tracker, ballistics computer, low-airspeed sensor probe on starboard side of cockpit, and pilot's head-up display), Doppler navigation system, IFF transponder, infra-red jammer above engine, hot metal and plume infra-red suppressor, closed circuit refuelling, new secure voice communications, and new composite rotor blades developed by Kaman.

Subsequent modification programmes have included C-Nite, ATAS (air-to-air Stinger), C-Flex (Cobra fleet life extension), engine air filter, redesigned swashplate, M-43 nuclear/biological/chemical mask, AN/AVR-2 laser warning, and improved SCAS (stability control augmentation system) roll modifications. **C-Nite**, which was applied to about 50 US Army AH-1Fs, was devised to detect, acquire and engage targets during reduced visibility and at night. **ATAS** will provide a mid-range defensive and offensive air-to-air capability. The **C-Flex** programme adds several service life extension modifications, of which the Night Fix lighting, AH-1G to S upgrade, and K-Flex driveshaft efforts have been completed. Remaining C-Flex efforts are rotor improvements, improved TOW test set, and radio upgrade. These and other improvements significantly enhance the safety of the aircraft and crew, as well as providing reliability and maintainability that will extend the life and increase the operational readiness of the Cobra fleet.

Given sufficient demand from operators, Bell and Textron Lycoming will launch a Cobra update package including a conversion kit to uprate T53-L-703 turboshaft engines to -70X standard, with a rating of 1,491 kW (2,000 shp); retrofit a 14.02 m (46 ft 0 in) diameter Bell 412 main rotor (but with a composite yoke, replacing the titanium main rotor hub); stretch the tailboom by 51 cm (20 in) to provide main rotor clearance; a needle-bearing tail rotor (as on Bell 412s and Israeli AH-1Fs); a three-axis digital stability augmentation system; and reliability and maintainability improvements. Thus modified, the AH-1F would be capable of carrying a further 454 kg (1,000 lb) of weapons and to manoeuvre at down to 0.5g. Anticipated hot-and-high performance gains include a 1,067 m (3,500 ft) OGE hover at 4,990 kg (11,000 lb) aircraft weight at ISA +20°C.

AH-1F production continues at the rate of three per month for export. Japan received two new AH-1Es for evaluation, converting these subsequently to AH-1F standard. Licence manufacture by Fuji (which see) of the AH-1F is in progress against a total of 70 funded up to, and including, FY 1990. Other Bell customers for the AH-1F comprise Israel (30), Jordan (24), Pakistan (20, plus 10 on order), South Korea (42 with C-Nite plus 28 on option) and Thailand (four). Overseas operators of Bell AH-1s have shown interest in retrofitting the C-Nite sighting system.

The major differences between the modernised versions and earlier single-engined HueyCobras may be summarised as follows:

TYPE: Anti-armour attack helicopter.

ROTOR SYSTEM AND DRIVE: Upgraded gearbox and transmission, the latter rated at 962 kW (1,290 shp) for take-off, 845 kW (1,134 shp) continuous. From 67th AH-1P onward, main rotor blades of composite construction are fitted, developed by Kaman Aerospace Corporation and equipped with tungsten carbide bearing sleeves. The outer 15 per cent of these blades, which are tolerant of damage by weapons of up to 23 mm calibre, is tapered in both chord and thickness.

Bell AH-1F HueyCobra of the US Army

Bell AH-1F HueyCobra (Textron Lycoming T53-L-703 turboshaft) *(Pilot Press)*

FUSELAGE: Tailboom strengthened to increase survivability against weapons of up to 23 mm calibre. Entire airframe has an infra-red-suppressant paint finish.

POWER PLANT: One 1,342 kW (1,800 shp) Textron Lycoming T53-L-703 turboshaft. Closed circuit refuelling on AH-1F. Fuel capacity 980 litres (259 US gallons; 216 Imp gallons). Upward-facing exhaust on AH-1E; IR-suppression nozzle on AH-1F.

ACCOMMODATION: Flat-plate canopy has seven planes of viewing surfaces, designed to minimise glint and reduce possibility of visual detection during nap-of-the-earth (NOE) flying; it also provides increased headroom for pilot. Improved instrument layout and lighting, compatible with use of night vision goggles. Improved, independently operating window/door ballistic jettison system to facilitate crew escape in emergency.

SYSTEMS: 10kVA 400Hz AC alternator with emergency bus added to electrical system. Hydraulic system pressure 103.5 bars (1,500 lb/sq in), maximum flow rate 22.7 litres (6 US gallons; 5 Imp gallons)/min. Open reservoir. Battery driven Abex standby pump, for use in event of main hydraulic system failure, can be used for collective pitch control and for boresighting turret and TOW missile system. Improved environmental control and fire detection systems.

AVIONICS AND EQUIPMENT: Standard lightweight avionics equipment (SLAE) in AH-1S includes AN/ARC-114 FM, AN/ARC-164 UHF/AM voice com, and E-Systems (Memcor Division) AN/ARC-115 VHF/AM voice com (compatible with KY-58 single-channel secure voice system). Other avionics include AN/ASN-128 Doppler nav system in AH-1F; HSI; VSI; radar altimeter; push/pull anti-torque controls for tail rotor; co-pilot's standby magnetic compass. C-Flex upgrade includes introduction of Magnavox AN/ARC-164(V) UHF/AM, Collins AN/ARC-186 VHF/AM-FM, ITT AN/ARC-201 (SINCGARS) VHF/FM, and LaBarge AN/ARN-89B D/F.

ARMAMENT AND OPERATIONAL EQUIPMENT: M65 system with eight Hughes TOW missiles, disposed as two two-round clusters on each of the outboard underwing stations. The inboard wing stations remain available for other stores. Beginning with the first AH-1E, the M28 (7.62/40 mm) turret in earlier HueyCobras was replaced by a new electrically powered General Electric universal turret, designed to accommodate either a 20 mm or a 30 mm

weapon and to improve standoff capability, although 30 mm weapon seldom carried. The 20 mm M197 three-barrel cannon (with 750 rds) is mounted in this turret. Rate of fire is 730 rds/min. Turret position is controlled by the pilot or co-pilot/gunner through helmet sights, or by the co-pilot using the M65 TOW missile system's telescopic sight unit. Field of fire is up to 110° to each side of aircraft, 20.5° upward and 50° downward. Also from the first AH-1E, the helicopter is equipped with a Baldwin Electronics M138 wing stores management subsystem, providing the means to select and fire, singly or in groups, any one of five types of external 2.75 in rocket store. These are mounted in launchers each containing from 7 to 19 tubes, and are additional to the TOW missile capability.

In addition to these installations the first AH-1F introduced a fire control subsystem which includes a Kaiser head-up display for the pilot, Teledyne Systems digital fire control computer for the turreted weapon and underwing rockets, omnidirectional airspeed system to improve cannon and rocket accuracy, Hughes laser rangefinder (accurate over 10,000 m; 32,800 ft), and a Rockwell AN/AAS-32 automatic airborne laser tracker. Other operational equipment includes a Hughes LAAT stabilised sight (see 1987-88 *Jane's*), a GEC Avionics M-143 air data subsystem, Bendix/King AN/APX-100 solid-state IFF transponder, Sanders AN/ALQ-144 infra-red jammer (above engine), suppressor for infra-red signature from engine hot metal and exhaust plume, and AN/APR-39 radar warning receiver.

DIMENSIONS, EXTERNAL:

Main rotor diameter	13.41 m (44 ft 0 in)
Main rotor blade chord (from 67th AH-1P onward)	0.76 m (2 ft 6 in)
Tail rotor diameter	2.59 m (8 ft 6 in)
Tail rotor blade chord	0.305 m (1 ft 0 in)
Wing span	3.28 m (10 ft 9 in)
Length overall, rotors turning	16.18 m (53 ft 1 in)
Width of fuselage	0.99 m (3 ft 3 in)
Height to top of rotor head	4.09 m (13 ft 5 in)
Width over TOW pods	3.56 m (11 ft 8 in)
Elevator span	2.11 m (6 ft 11 in)
Width over skids	2.13 m (7 ft 0 in)

AREAS:

Main rotor disc	141.26 m² (1,520.23 sq ft)
Tail rotor disc	5.27 m² (56.75 sq ft)

WEIGHTS (AH-1S):
Operating weight empty   2,993 kg (6,598 lb)
Mission weight   4,524 kg (9,975 lb)
Max T-O and landing weight   4,535 kg (10,000 lb)
PERFORMANCE (AH-1S at max T-O weight, ISA):
Never-exceed speed (TOW configuration)
                                      170 knots (315 km/h; 195 mph)
Max level speed (TOW configuration)
                                      123 knots (227 km/h; 141 mph)
Max rate of climb at S/L, normal rated power
                                      494 m (1,620 ft)/min
Service ceiling, normal rated power   3,720 m (12,200 ft)
Hovering ceiling IGE   3,720 m (12,200 ft)
Range at S/L with max fuel, 8% reserves
                                      274 nm (507 km; 315 miles)
g limits   +2.5/−0.5

Bell AH-1(4B)W SuperCobra fitted with Model 680 bearingless research rotor making its first flight on 24 January 1989

BELL AH-1(4B)W

The first AH-1T converted to AH-1W standard for the USMC has been further modified with a four-blade bearingless rotor based on the Bell 680 research project last fully described in the 1989-90 *Jane's*. Designated AH-1(Four-Blade)W, it first flew on 24 January 1989 and was expected to be demonstrated to the USMC in 1990.

The helicopter offers several improvements over the basic AH-1W SuperCobra, including a gross weight increased by 930 kg (2,050 lb), speed increased by 20 knots (37 km/h; 23 mph); expanded g envelope, digital flight control system, uprated transmission, night targeting sights and Doppler navigation.

Data generally as for AH-1W except:

ROTOR SYSTEM: Four-blade composite bearingless rotor with blade roots of controlled flexibility to allow pitch, flap and lead/lag movements. These roots are surrounded by rigid cuffs which transfer pitch-change commands from the hub to the aerodynamic portion of each blade. Two blades may be folded manually, so that the AH-1(4B)W requires no more storage space than an AH-1W.

ARMAMENT: Cranked, six-station stub-wings, including overwing position for two Sidearm ARMs at each tip. Total ordnance capacity 1,444 kg (3,184 lb), including 750 rds for nose cannon and two chaff/flare dispensers.

DIMENSION:
Main rotor blade chord   0.63 m (2 ft 1 in)
WEIGHT:
Max T-O and landing weight   7,620 kg (16,800 lb)
PERFORMANCE (at 6,120 kg; 13,494 lb mid-mission weight):
Never-exceed speed over 200 knots (371 km/h; 230 mph)
Max level speed   170 knots (315 km/h; 196 mph)
Max cruising speed   160 knots (297 km/h; 184 mph)
g limits   +3.39/0

BELL MODELS 212 and 412

The production lines for these two helicopters have been transferred to Bell's Canadian facility (in mid-1988 and January 1989 respectively), and their descriptions can therefore now be found in the Canadian section.

BELL MODEL 214ST SUPERTRANSPORT

The Model 214ST was developed originally for major production and service in Iran. It was expected to serve primarily as a military transport helicopter; but Bell has since developed the 214ST also as a commercial transport with multi-mission capability. Originally, the suffix ST indicated Stretched Twin: it now indicates SuperTransport.

The prototype 214ST flew for the first time in February 1977, and construction of three pre-production examples began in 1978. The decision to manufacture an initial series of 100 production 214STs was announced in November 1979. FAA and CAA certification for two-pilot IFR operation was obtained in 1982, and deliveries started soon afterwards. The Model 214ST has been certificated under transport category airworthiness requirements in Canada,

Bell Model 214ST SuperTransport helicopter for the People's Republic of China

Japan, the United Kingdom and United States. The CAA has approved it for flight into icing conditions with added icing kit.

Initial contracts included three for British Caledonian Helicopters for offshore support in the North Sea. To enhance the helicopter's value for such missions, on which it is now operated worldwide, the FAA approved a new configuration with seats for a crew of two and 18 (instead of the original 16) passengers in Spring 1982. Other orders include four for the People's Republic of China, and one for the North Slope Borough Search and Rescue team based at Barrow, Alaska, equipped for emergency medical service and SAR duties.

Military transport models have been sold to Brunei (one), Iraq (45), Peru (11), Thailand (nine) and Venezuela (four).

By early 1990 a total of 98 Bell 214STs had been delivered.

TYPE: Twin-turboshaft commercial transport helicopter.

ROTOR SYSTEM: Two-blade advanced technology main rotor. Each blade has a unidirectionally laid glassfibre spar, with a ±45°-wound torque casing of glassfibre cloth. The trailing-edge is also of unidirectional glassfibre, and the space between spar and trailing-edge is filled by a Nomex honeycomb core. The entire blade is then bonded together by glassfibre wrapping, with the leading-edge protected by a titanium abrasion strip and the tip by a replaceable stainless steel cap. Two-blade tail rotor; interchangeable blades, each with a stainless steel

leading-edge spar and covering, aluminium honeycomb core and glassfibre trailing-edge strip. Main rotor head incorporates elastomeric bearings. Second-generation Noda-Matic nodal suspension system. Nodal beam requires no lubrication. Main rotor brake standard.

ROTOR DRIVE: Main transmission has a maximum rating of 1,752 kW (2,350 shp), maximum continuous rating of 1,454 kW (1,950 shp), and single-engine rating of 1,286 kW (1,725 shp). Combining, intermediate and tail rotor gearboxes, each with one-hour run-dry capability.

FUSELAGE: Conventional all-metal semi-monocoque structure, incorporating rollover protection ring.

TAIL SURFACE: Electronically controlled elevator, which minimises trim changes with alterations of power and CG, and improves longitudinal stability.

LANDING GEAR: Choice of energy absorbing non-retractable tubular skid type or tricycle type wheeled landing gear.

POWER PLANT: Two 1,212 kW (1,625 shp) General Electric CT7-2A turboshafts, connected to a combining gearbox. In the event of an engine failure, the remaining engine is capable of developing 1,286 kW (1,725 shp) to provide continued flight capability. Standard fuel capacity 1,647 litres (435 US gallons; 362 Imp gallons), contained in seven interconnected rupture resistant cells, arranged to provide two independent fuel systems as required by FAR Pt 29. Single-point refuelling. Auxiliary fuel system optional, consisting of two tanks in rear of cabin, each of 329 litres (87 US gallons; 72 Imp gallons) capacity; 95 litre (25 US gallon; 21 Imp gallon) underseat auxiliary fuel tanks also available. Engine anti-icing and inlet screens standard.

ACCOMMODATION: Standard seating for pilot, co-pilot and up to 18 passengers. Dual controls standard. Crew seats adjustable. Passenger seats in three rows across cabin plus a two-place bench seat on each side of rotor mast. Standard configuration offers utility or deluxe interiors with contemporary or energy attenuating seats. Jettisonable crew door each side. Large cabin door on each side for passengers or easy loading of cargo. Glass windscreens, with standard anti-icing system. Two emergency exits on each side. Baggage space aft of cabin, capacity 1.84 m³ (65 cu ft). Passenger seating removable to provide 9.23 m³ (326 cu ft) of cargo capacity. Cabin heated and ventilated.

SYSTEMS: Dual engine driven hydraulic pumps for fully redundant hydraulic power for flight control system; pressure 207 bars (3,000 lb/sq in), maximum flow rate 25.4 litres (6.7 US gallons; 5.6 Imp gallons)/min for primary control system; 19 litres (5 US gallons; 4.2 Imp gallons)/min for utility system. Closed bootstrap pressurised reservoirs. Third system operates oil cooler blower for transmission and combiner gearbox. Redun-

Bell Model 214ST SuperTransport (two General Electric CT7-2A turboshafts) *(Pilot Press)*

dant electrical system with dual engine driven generators. Stability and control augmentation system (SCAS). Main rotor blade in-flight tracking system. Attitude/altitude retention system (AARS). Computer controlled fly by wire automatic elevator trim system.

AVIONICS AND EQUIPMENT: Standard avionics include dual com, dual nav, R/Nav, ADF, transponder, DME, air data computer, and standby attitude indicator to provide IFR capability. Avionics options include radar, nav coupling, and VLF nav system. Optional equipment includes anti-icing kit, emergency flotation gear, external cargo suspension system, internal rescue hoist, and two pneumatically ejected 10- or 12-person liferafts inside engine cowl fairing forward of rotor mast.

DIMENSIONS, EXTERNAL:

Main rotor diameter	15.85 m (52 ft 0 in)
Tail rotor diameter	2.95 m (9 ft 8 in)
Main rotor blade chord	0.84 m (2 ft 9 in)
Tail rotor blade chord	0.36 m (1 ft 2 in)
Length: overall, rotors turning	18.95 m (62 ft 2¼ in)
fuselage	15.02 m (49 ft 3½ in)
Height overall	4.84 m (15 ft 10½ in)
Skid track	2.64 m (8 ft 8 in)
Wheel track	2.83 m (9 ft 3½ in)

DIMENSIONS, INTERNAL:

Cabin: Length, instrument panel to centre rear bulkhead	3.42 m (11 ft 2¾ in)
Max length	4.13 m (13 ft 6¾ in)
Max width	2.41 m (7 ft 11 in)
Volume	8.95 m³ (316 cu ft)

AREAS:

Main rotor disc	197.30 m² (2,123.7 sq ft)
Tail rotor disc	6.82 m² (73.39 sq ft)

WEIGHT:

Max T-O weight:	
internal or external load	7,938 kg (17,500 lb)

PERFORMANCE (at max T-O weight except where indicated):

Normal cruising speed at S/L, at average cruise weight	140 knots (259 km/h; 161 mph)
Max cruising speed at 1,220 m (4,000 ft)	138 knots (256 km/h; 159 mph)
Max rate of climb at S/L, ISA	543 m (1,780 ft)/min
Service ceiling, one engine out, ISA	1,460 m (4,800 ft)
Hovering ceiling IGE	1,950 m (6,400 ft)
Range at 1,220 m (4,000 ft) with max standard fuel, no reserves	463 nm (858 km; 533 miles)
Range, ISA, VFR, standard fuel, no reserves	439 nm (813 km; 505 miles)
Ferry range with auxiliary fuel, pilot only, no payload, no reserves	over 550 nm (1,019 km; 633 miles)

BELL MODEL 222

The first of five prototypes of the Model 222, described as the first commercial light twin-engined helicopter to be built in the USA, flew for the first time on 13 August 1976. FAA certification for a Model 222 in pre-production configuration was received on 16 August 1979. The production 222 received approval for VFR operation on 20 December, and the first delivery, to Petroleum Helicopters Inc, was made on 16 January 1980. FAA certification for single-pilot IFR operations in Category I weather conditions was granted on 15 May 1980. A Model 222 delivered to Omniflight Helicopters on 18 January 1981 was the 25,000th Bell helicopter built. Another became a flying testbed for Bell's Model 680 rotor system (see 1989-90 *Jane's*).

Current production aircraft are available in the following configurations:

Basic 222B. Basic model, as described. On 29 July 1982 the 222B became the first transport category helicopter to be certificated by the FAA for single-pilot IFR flight without stability augmentation.

222B Executive. Fully equipped for both single and dual pilot IFR flight. Honeywell coupled automatic flight control system to provide stability augmentation and automatic hold for attitude, altitude, heading and airspeed, plus VOR/LOC course and glideslope hold during approach. Collins Pro Line avionics include dual VHF com, dual VOR nav with glideslope, ADF, marker beacon receiver, transponder, DME and area navigation. Luxury accommodation for five or six passengers, with automatic temperature control, fluorescent and reading lights, window curtains and ceiling speakers. Optional stereo system and refreshment cabinet.

222UT (Utility Twin). Utility version of the Model 222, incorporating the improvements and power plant detailed for the Model 222B. Retractable tricycle landing gear replaced by tubular skid gear with lock-on ground handling wheels. Fuselage mounted flotation system optional. Standard seating for a pilot and six or seven passengers. Optional layout for a pilot and eight passengers. VFR and single-pilot IFR certification received in Spring 1983; customer deliveries began in September 1983. Customers include Lloyd Helicopters of Australia, which has six intended primarily for offshore oil support, the New York City Police Department, and the Port Authority of New York and New Jersey. This model is used widely for air ambulance duties.

By January 1990 a total of 182 Model 222s had been delivered.

Bell Model 222B Executive helicopter

The following details refer to the basic Model 222B, except where indicated:

TYPE: Twin-turbine light commercial helicopter.

ROTOR SYSTEM: Two-blade main rotor. Blade section Wortmann 090. Thickness/chord ratio 8 per cent. Each blade has a stainless steel spar with bonded glassfibre safety straps to retard crack propagation and offer secondary load path; replaceable stainless steel leading-edge; and afterbody of Nomex honeycomb covered with glassfibre skin. Each blade is attached to the rotor head by two chordwise bolts. Small trim tab on each blade. Completely dry titanium main rotor hub has conical elastomeric bearings. Two-blade tail rotor of stainless steel construction, with preconing, underslung feathering axis and skewed flapping axis. Rotor blades do not fold. A rotor brake is standard.

ROTOR DRIVE: Rotors shaft driven through gearbox with two spiral bevel reductions and one planetary reduction. Transmission rating (two engines) 690 kW (925 shp). Single-engine rating 548 kW (735 shp). Main rotor/engine rpm ratio 1:27.4; tail rotor/engine rpm ratio 1:5.08.

SPONSONS: Short span cantilever sponson set low on each side of fuselage, serving as main landing gear housings, fuel tanks and work platforms. Section NACA 0035. Dihedral 3° 12′. Incidence 5°. Sweepback at quarter-chord 3° 30′. All-metal structure of light alloy sheet and honeycomb. No movable surfaces.

FUSELAGE: Semi-monocoque structure of light alloy, with limited use of light alloy honeycomb panels. Fail-safe structure in critical areas. One-piece nosecone tilts forward and down for access to avionics and equipment bay.

TAIL UNIT: Cantilever structure of light alloy. Fixed vertical fin in sweptback upper and lower sections. Tailplane, with slotted leading-edge and endplate fins, mounted midway along rear fuselage. Small skid below ventral fin for protection in tail-down landing.

LANDING GEAR: Hydraulically retractable tricycle type. All units retract forward, mainwheels into sponsons. Free-fall extension in emergency. Oleo-pneumatic shock absorbers, with scissored yoke. Self-centring nosewheel, swivelling through 360°. Single wheel and tyre on each unit. Mainwheel tyres size 6.00-6, pressure 5.18 bars (75 lb/sq in). Nosewheel tyre size 5.00-5, pressure 4.14 bars (60 lb/sq in). Hydraulic disc brakes. New type

water-activated emergency pop-out floats optional. Model 222UT has skid type landing gear and lock-on ground handling wheels, with fuselage mounted flotation system optional.

POWER PLANT: Two Textron Lycoming LTS 101-750C-1 turboshafts, each rated at 510 kW (684 shp) for take-off, mounted in a streamline housing above the cabin and aft of the rotor pylon. Bell focused pylon with nodalisation. Fuel contained in five crash resistant internal bladders, in fuselage and sponsons, with total capacity of 710 litres (187.5 US gallons; 156.1 Imp gallons) in Model 222B. Model 222UT has max fuel capacity of 931 litres (246 US gallons; 204.8 Imp gallons). Rear seat fuel tank, capacity 246 litres (65 US gallons; 54.1 Imp gallons), and parcel shelf fuel tank, capacity 181 litres (48 US gallons; 40 Imp gallons), optional on both models. Single-point refuelling on starboard side of fuselage. Oil capacity 6.5 litres (1.7 US gallons; 1.43 Imp gallons) per engine.

ACCOMMODATION: Pilot and seven passengers in standard 2-3-3 layout; alternatively pilot, co-pilot and six passengers. Two additional passengers can be accommodated in a high-density 2-2-3-3 arrangement. Energy attenuating seats, all with shoulder harness in Model 222B. Crew door at forward end of cabin on each side; cabin door on each side immediately forward of wing. Space for 1.05 m³ (37 cu ft) of baggage aft of cabin, with external door on starboard side. Ventilation standard; air-conditioning and heating optional.

SYSTEMS: Dual hydraulic systems, pressure 103.5 bars (1,500 lb/sq in). Maximum flow rate 15.1 litres (4 US gallons; 3.3 Imp gallons)/min. Open reservoir. Electrical system of Model 222B supplied by dual 150A DC generators, dual 250VA AC inverters, and 17Ah nickel-cadmium storage battery. Dual inverters deleted in Model 222UT, and 17Ah battery replaced by one of 34Ah capacity.

AVIONICS AND EQUIPMENT: Standard avionics in 222B comprise VHF transceiver and intercom system. Collins Pro Line and Bendix/King Gold Crown Series III avionics optional. Honeywell SPZ-7000 digital automatic flight control system approved for single-pilot IFR operation in 222UT. Other avionics, blind-flying instrumentation and equipment, including Honeywell Helipilot system, Bendix RDR-1400 weather radar and 1,270 kg (2,800 lb) capacity cargo hook kit, to customer's

Bell Model 222B twin-turbine light commercial helicopter (*Pilot Press*)

requirements. Bristol Aerospace/Aeronautical Accessories Inc wire strike protection system optional.

DIMENSIONS, EXTERNAL:

Main rotor diameter	12.80 m (42 ft 0 in)
Tail rotor diameter	2.10 m (6 ft 10½ in)
Main rotor blade chord	0.66 m (2 ft 2 in)
Tail rotor blade chord	0.254 m (10 in)
Sponson chord: at root	1.55 m (5 ft 1 in)
at tip	1.49 m (4 ft 10¾ in)
Length: overall, rotors turning	15.36 m (50 ft 4¾ in)
fuselage	12.85 m (42 ft 2 in)
Width overall	3.46 m (11 ft 4 in)
Height overall	3.51 m (11 ft 6 in)
Wheel track: 222B	2.77 m (9 ft 1 in)
Wheelbase: 222B	3.70 m (12 ft 1¾ in)
Passenger doors (each): Height	1.30 m (4 ft 3 in)
Width	0.99 m (3 ft 3 in)
Height to sill	0.46 m (1 ft 6 in)
Baggage door (stbd, rear): Height	0.62 m (2 ft 0½ in)
Width	0.89 m (2 ft 11 in)
Height to sill	1.14 m (3 ft 9 in)

DIMENSIONS, INTERNAL:

Cabin (passenger area): Length	2.01 m (6 ft 7 in)
Max width	1.41 m (4 ft 7½ in)
Max height	1.30 m (4 ft 3 in)
Volume, incl crew area	5.52 m³ (195 cu ft)
Baggage hold	1.05 m³ (37 cu ft)
Hatbox (aft of cabin seats)	0.14 m³ (5 cu ft)

AREAS:

Main rotor blades (each)	4.23 m² (45.50 sq ft)
Tail rotor blades (each)	0.23 m² (2.45 sq ft)
Main rotor disc	128.7 m² (1,385.4 sq ft)
Tail rotor disc	3.46 m² (37.2 sq ft)
Vertical tail surfaces (total)	1.44 m² (15.5 sq ft)
Horizontal tail surfaces (total)	1.37 m² (14.8 sq ft)

WEIGHTS AND LOADING (A: 222B; B: 222UT):

Weight empty: A	2,223 kg (4,900 lb)
B	2,210 kg (4,874 lb)
Max T-O and landing weight:	
internal payload	3,742 kg (8,250 lb)
Max disc loading:	
internal payload	29.1 kg/m² (5.95 lb/sq ft)

PERFORMANCE (at max T-O weight, ISA. A: 222B; B: 222UT):

Never-exceed speed:	
at S/L: A, B	150 knots (278 km/h; 172 mph)
at 1,220 m (4,000 ft):	
A, B	156 knots (289 km/h; 179 mph)
Econ cruising speed, S/L to 1,220 m (4,000 ft):	
A	140 knots (259 km/h; 161 mph)
B	133 knots (246 km/h; 153 mph)
Max rate of climb at S/L: A, B	512 m (1,680 ft)/min
Service ceiling: A, B	4,815 m (15,800 ft)
Service ceiling, one engine out:	
A, B	2,285 m (7,500 ft)
Hovering ceiling: IGE: A, B	2,165 m (7,100 ft)
OGE: A, B	1,950 m (6,400 ft)
Range with max fuel at 1,220 m (4,000 ft), 20 min reserves: A	287 nm (532 km; 330 miles)
B	373 nm (691 km; 429 miles)
Range with max fuel at S/L, 20 min reserves:	
A	255 nm (472 km; 294 miles)
B	330 nm (610 km; 380 miles)

BELL MODEL 230

At the National Business Aircraft Association Convention at Atlanta, Georgia in October 1989 Bell announced development of the Model 230 twin-turbine helicopter which is intended to replace the Model 222. The Model 230 will be available in retractable tricycle landing gear and fixed skid variants and in Executive and Utility configurations similar to those described for the Model 222. The first 50 production aircraft will be powered by two 522 kW (700 shp) Allison 250-C30G2 turboshafts, but Lycoming LTS 101 engines will be optional on later airframes. From c/n 15 onwards the Model 230 will incorporate Bell's liquid inertia vibration elimination system (LIVE), and adoption of the Model 680 four-blade rotor system is also being considered.

Launch customer for the Model 230 was Mitsui & Co Ltd of Tokyo, which has ordered 20 for delivery beginning in January 1992 following FAA certification anticipated in December 1991.

The following data are provisional:

TYPE: Twin-turbine light commercial helicopter.

ROTOR DRIVE: Main transmission T-O rating 690 kW (925 shp), max continuous 652.5 kW (875 shp), single engine 548 kW (735 shp).

POWER PLANT: Two Allison 250-C30G2 turboshafts, each rated at 522 kW (700 shp), 464 kW (622 shp) max continuous, intermediate engine-out rating of 581 kW (779 shp) for 2½ min. Standard fuel capacity 931 litres (246 US gallons; 205 Imp gallons) in Utility model, 712 litres (188 US gallons; 156.5 Imp gallons) in wheel landing gear model. Auxiliary fuel tanks, capacities 182 litres (48 US gallons; 40 Imp gallons) and 246 litres (65 US gallons; 54 Imp gallons), optional.

ACCOMMODATION: Pilot and five to nine passengers in various arrangements, either all forward-facing or with club seating.

Artist's impression of the Bell Model 230 twin-turbine utility and executive transport helicopter

DIMENSIONS, EXTERNAL: As for Model 222 except:

Length: overall, rotors turning	15.38 m (50 ft 5½ in)
fuselage	12.97 m (42 ft 6¾ in)
Height overall, on skids	3.66 m (12 ft 0¼ in)
Skid track	2.39 m (7 ft 10 in)

DIMENSIONS, INTERNAL:

Cabin (passenger area):	
Length	2.21 m (7 ft 3 in)
Max width	1.47 m (4 ft 10 in)
Max height	1.45 m (4 ft 9 in)
Volume, incl crew area	5.53 m³ (195.4 cu ft)
Baggage hold	1.05 m³ (37.2 cu ft)
Baggage access area aft of seats	0.17 m³ (6.0 cu ft)

WEIGHTS:

Weight empty (Utility)	2,224 kg (4,903 lb)
Max T-O weight	3,742 kg (8,250 lb)

PERFORMANCE (at max T-O weight, ISA, except where indicated. A: Utility, B: wheeled version):

Max cruising speed: A	136 knots (252 km/h; 157 mph)
B	140 knots (259 km/h; 161 mph)
Service ceiling, one engine out: A	2,285 m (7,500 ft)
B	2,315 m (7,600 ft)
Range, standard fuel: A	421 nm (780 km; 484 miles)
B	329 nm (609 km; 379 miles)

BELL MODEL 301 (XV-15)

Bell's two tilt-rotor technology demonstrators first flew in 1977 and 1979 and were continuing with trials programmes in 1990. Technical data and details of achievements have appeared in several previous volumes of *Jane's*, but were last summarised in the 1989-90 edition.

BELL/BOEING V-22 OSPREY

This joint programme is described under a separate Bell/Boeing main heading.

BELL MODEL 680 ROTOR

The 680 rotor system, which has been test flown on a Bell 222 and AH-1W (which see), was last described in the 1989-90 edition of *Jane's*. A derivative is proposed for the LH combat helicopter, described below.

BELL/MCDONNELL DOUGLAS LH

In 1982 the US Army invited manufacturers to submit design concepts for its Light Helicopter Experimental (LHX) programme, originally proposing procurement of 5,000 replacements for UH-1, AH-1, AH-58 and OH-6 helicopters. In 1987, this was drastically reduced to 2,096 LHXs, principally through elimination of the UH-1 follow-on. These will supplant 3,000 helicopters in current service. A request for proposals was issued on 21 June 1988, and on the following 31 October, competing designs by Bell/McDonnell Douglas and Boeing/Sikorsky were awarded 23-month demonstration/validation contracts. It is intended that one will be chosen in December 1990 for full-scale development. A related programme is the LHTec T800 turboshaft engine, specified for both competing designs.

Bell and its partner, McDonnell Douglas Helicopter Company, are concentrating on a single main rotor design incorporating an advanced bearingless four-blade main rotor system, composite materials adapted from the ACAP programme, MDHC's NOTAR anti-torque system, and twin T800 turboshafts. In accordance with US Army specifications it will be designed to fire Hellfire and Stinger missiles and other advanced weapons. Other members of the Bell/McDonnell Douglas Helicopter team include McDonnell Aircraft Company, AIL Eaton, General Electric, Honeywell, Hughes Aircraft Company, Litton Systems Canada, Northrop, and Texas Instruments.

A major supporting contract for the LHX was the now completed Advanced Rotorcraft Technology Integration

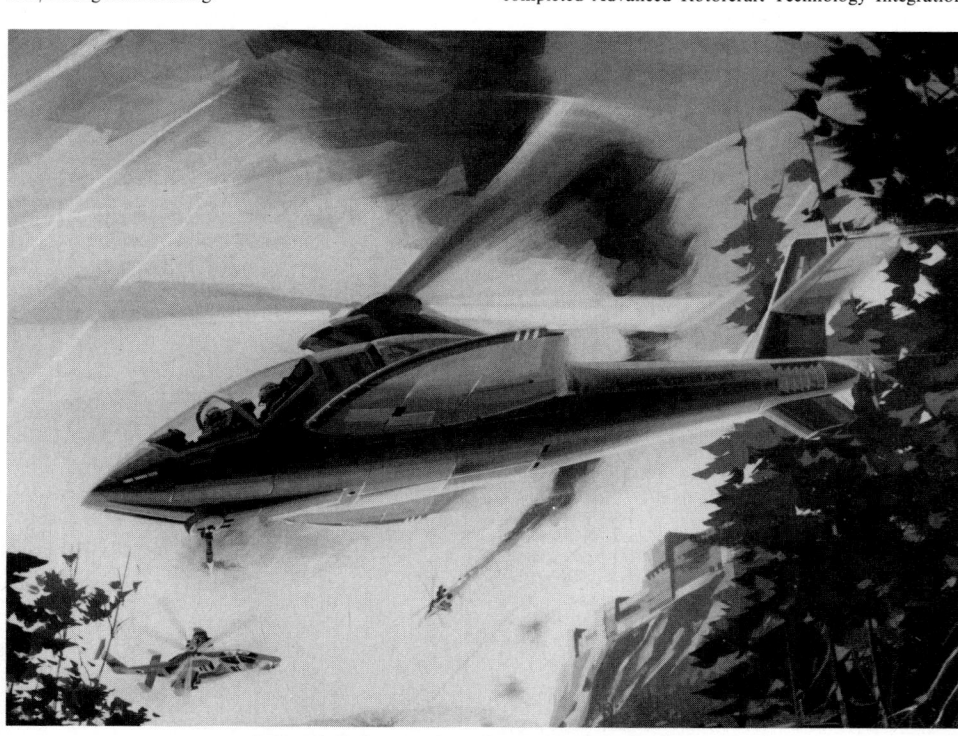

Bell artist's impression of possible LHX contender

(ARTI) effort for which Bell, in partnership with Sperry Flight Systems, Honeywell Inc and Texas Instruments, flight tested the digital fly by wire AFCS using the experimental YAH-1S four-blade Model 249 HueyCobra as the testbed aircraft.

During 1989, the LHX rotor system underwent 400 of a planned 1,400 hours of wind tunnel testing. Simultaneously, the OH-6 NOTAR trials helicopter, modified with a V-tail, was conducting tests of the complete system of rotor, tailboom and thruster and spent 12 weeks in the NASA wind tunnel at Ames Research Center.

Early in 1990 the experimental designation was deleted, and the programme became LH, although assignment of the type number AH-66 is anticipated. A prototype of the successful LH is intended to fly in August 1993. An initial order for 24 production helicopters will be placed in 1994, manufacture beginning in November of that year. First deliveries are due in March 1996, leading to IOC in November 1996. Yearly contracts will build to a peak 216 per annum, the selected team splitting to bid for each contract. Customer-specified details common to both LHs are given below.

TYPE: Attack/reconnaissance/air combat helicopter.
ROTORS: Super-light blades with bearingless systems.
FUSELAGE: Construction 90 per cent of composites (carbon-fibre, carbon-carbon and Kevlar).
POWER PLANT: Two 895 kW (1,200 shp) class LHTec T800 turboshaft engines. Fuel for 2 h 30 min flying.
ACCOMMODATION: Pilot and WSO in stepped cockpit.
AVIONICS AND EQUIPMENT: Night Vision Pilotage System and helmet mounted display; integrated cockpit, second-generation FLIR targeting, and digital map display. Dual anti-jam VHF-FM and UHF-AM Have Quick tactical communications, VHF-AM, anti-jam HF-SSB, Airborne Target Handover System, Navstar-GPS, IFF and radar altimeter. Laser warning and radar warning receivers, RF and IR jammers. Maximum avionics commonality required with US Navy A-12 and USAF F-22/F-23 ATF programmes.
ARMAMENT: Turret mounted gun with 500 rds; conformal weapons pods for eight Hellfire anti-tank and two Stinger anti-helicopter missiles (attack role); or four Hellfires and four Stingers (armed reconnaissance); or two Hellfires and eight Stingers (air combat).
DIMENSIONS (approx):
Main rotor diameter	12.50 m (41 ft 0 in)
Fuselage length	12.19 m (40 ft 0 in)

WEIGHTS:
Weight empty	3,402 kg (7,500 lb)
Max T-O weight (hot/high)	5,080 kg (11,200 lb)

PERFORMANCE:
Cruising speed	170 knots (315 km/h; 196 mph)
Ferry range with external tanks	
	1,260 nm (2,335 km; 1,451 miles)

BELL/BOEING

BELL HELICOPTER TEXTRON and BOEING HELICOPTERS

PROGRAMME MANAGER: Brig Gen Harry W. Blot, USMC

BELL/BOEING V-22 OSPREY

Bell Helicopter Textron and Boeing Helicopters are teamed in a joint programme to meet the US Defense Department's Joint Services Advanced Vertical Lift Aircraft (formerly JVX) requirement. This was initiated as an Army-led programme in FY 1982, but was transferred in January 1983 to the US Navy as executive service, the Army subsequently withdrawing from the programme. The selected aircraft, based on the technology of Bell's Model 301/XV-15 tilt-rotor research aircraft, was named V-22 Osprey in January 1985. Bell is responsible for the wings, nacelles, rotor and transmission systems, and engine integration; Boeing's contribution is the fuselage, tail unit, landing gear, fairings, and avionics integration.

A 24-month preliminary design contract was awarded by Naval Air Systems Command on 26 April 1983, and in January 1984 Bell began a simulated V-22 flight test programme using data from wind tunnel tests and analyses. Formal evaluation by military pilots, using NASA/Ames simulation, began in the following March. Boeing built a two-thirds scale rotor/wing model to prove hover performance predictions, and a fuselage mockup, and testing of critical structural components was co-ordinated by both partners.

A seven-year FSED phase started in FY 1986 with the award on 2 May of a first instalment contract covering the manufacture of six flying prototypes (Nos. 1, 3 and 6 by Bell, Nos. 2, 4 and 5 by Boeing), plus three non-flying airframes for static, ground and fatigue testing. The first flying prototype (BuAer number 163911) was rolled out at Bell's Flight Research Center at Arlington, Texas, on 23 May 1988, and made its first flight on 19 March 1989, followed by No. 2 (also at Arlington, despite being Boeing-built) on 9 September and No. 4 (in MV-22A configuration and camouflage) on 21 December 1989. The third V-22, first flown on 9 May 1990, was to undertake the Osprey's first sea trials later in the year; and the two remaining prototypes also were due to fly in 1990.

Osprey production deliveries were planned to begin in late 1991/early 1992 to the US Marine Corps, 1993 to the US Air Force, and 1995 to the US Navy. However, proposed funding for initial production was deleted from the FY 1990 and FY 1991 defence budgets.

The test programme was still funded in early 1990. It was originally to include more than 4,000 hours of flight testing. V-22 No. 1 will be used to expand the flight envelope and explore aeroelastic loads, and was also the first to make transitional flights. No. 2 will test the fly by wire system; No. 3 will be used to examine flight loads, vibrations and acoustics and conduct sea trials; No. 4 will be used for initial shipboard compatibility tests and propulsion studies; No. 5 will test avionics, flight controls and associated equipment, and will test USAF mission equipment; and No. 6 will test mission equipment for the US Navy and US Marine Corps. The first in-flight transition from helicopter to aeroplane mode was achieved by No. 1 on 14 September 1989, and on 19 October 1989 the V-22 exceeded 260 knots (482 km/h; 299 mph). The V-22 was originally planned in the following versions:

MV-22A. First and major production variant, for US Marine Corps, which has a requirement for 552 as amphibious troop assault and support transports to replace CH-46 Sea Knight and CH-53 Sea Stallion helicopters. Flight crew of three. Required to carry 24 combat-equipped Marines or equivalent cargo at a speed of 250 knots (463 km/h; 288 mph) over an operational radius of 200 nm (370 km; 230 miles), with the ability to hover midway through the mission at 915 m (3,000 ft) at an ambient air temperature of 33°C (91.4°F).

HV-22A. Combat search and rescue, special warfare and fleet logistics support variant for US Navy (requirement for 50), to replace HH-3 helicopters. Normal crew of five. In CSAR roles the Osprey would be required to operate at 250 knots (463 km/h; 288 mph) over a 460 nm (852 km; 530 mile) radius and hover mid-mission for 15 min at 915 m (3,000 ft) OGE, with accommodation for four survivors.

CV-22A. Long-range special operations variant for US Air Force, which has a requirement for 55 (originally 80) such aircraft, each able to carry 12 special forces troops or up to 1,306 kg (2,880 lb) of internal cargo over a 520 nm (964 km; 599 mile) mission radius at 250 knots (463 km/h; 288 mph), with capability to hover OGE at 1,220 m (4,000 ft) at 35°C (95°F).

The following variant is also under consideration:
SV-22A. The US Navy has expressed an interest in up to 300 V-22s for anti-submarine warfare duties, to replace the fixed-wing S-3 Viking. Features would include AN/APS-137 radar, dipping sonar, sonobuoy racks, external fuel tanks, FLIR, torpedoes and anti-shipping and self-defence missiles. Development go-ahead deferred to allow USN to study sensor requirements and to examine an alternative option of re-opening the S-3 production line.

The US Army, although not involved in the development phase, originally had plans to procure 231 aircraft in the Marine Corps configuration for multi-mission transport duties, but has since withdrawn its requirement, although maintaining a presence in the V-22 programme office.

Additional requirements specified by one or more of the services for the V-22 include an unrefuelled ferry range of 2,100 nm (3,892 km; 2,418 miles) for self-deployability; in-flight refuelling capability; ability to carry outsize external loads of up to 4,536 kg (10,000 lb); all-weather low-altitude capability; self-protection; and low maintenance. To meet the Navy/Marine Corps requirement for operation from US Navy amphibious assault ships, the wing and rotor system must fold in 90 seconds.

TYPE: Twin-turboshaft multi-mission tilt-rotor aircraft.
AIRFRAME (general): Approx 59 per cent of aircraft is constructed of advanced composites, of which principal ones are Hercules IM-6 graphite/epoxy for wings and Hercules AS4 for fuselage and tail unit. Metal in the V-22's structure accounts for only about 454 kg (1,000 lb) of aircraft empty weight. Safe emergency flotation is provided by fuselage sponsons, with engine nacelles serving as pontoons for additional stability on water.
ROTOR SYSTEM: Two Bell counter-rotating three-blade propeller/rotors, with graphite/glassfibre, tapered, statically and aerodynamically balanced blades of high-twist design, elastomeric spherical bearings, and glassfibre spinners. Three Bendix swashplate actuators in each rotor head, each actuator being triple redundant electrically and dual redundant hydraulically. Rotor braking standard. Litton Poly-Scientific folding and de-icing systems for rotor blades. Stage 1 of shipboard stowage sequence begins with aircraft in helicopter mode (nacelles vertical), rotors then being braked with one blade positioned inboard and parallel to wing leading-edge. Remaining blades are sequenced automatically to fold inward alongside first blade; nacelles are then tilted to horizontal position prior to unlocking and rotating the wing.
ROTOR DRIVE: Each rotor is driven by individual engine via engine coupling and one prop/rotor gearbox in each nacelle. Prop/rotor gearboxes are interconnected by gearboxes and driveshafts to permit single-engine operation. Main transmission rated at 3,408 kW (4,570 shp) for normal operation and 4,415 kW (5,920 shp) with one engine inoperative.
WINGS: Cantilever high-wing monoplane, with constant chord and slight forward sweep. Main wing built by Bell, with control surfaces and fixed trailing-edge by Lockheed-Georgia. Construction is mainly of composites, with one-piece moulded two-spar torsion box, moulded graphite/epoxy ribs, bonded stringers, and continuous one-piece upper and lower moulded skin panels. Trailing-edge of fixed portion is of graphite. Three-segment detachable leading-edge on each side, of aluminium alloy with Nomex honeycomb core. Two-segment single-slotted graphite flaperon, with titanium fittings, on each trailing-edge, operated by FBW signalling of Moog hydraulic actuators. No tabs. Pneumatic boot de-icing of leading-edges. Second stage of shipboard stowage sequence, after rotor blade folding and tilting of nacelles to horizontal position, involves unlocking wing and rotating it clockwise through 90° on a 2.31 m (7 ft 7 in) diameter stainless steel carousel, to lie fore and aft along top of fuselage with port nacelle at front. Wing locking/unlocking and rotation is performed hydraulically via Lucas Aerospace actuators. A Litton wire-twist capsule maintains integrity of electrical connections passing through carousel during rotation sequence.
FUSELAGE: Semi-monocoque structure of rectangular cross-section, built by Boeing Helicopters. So-called black aluminium structure with carbon frames, stringers and skins joined with metal rivets. Large overwing fairings,

V-22 prototype No. 1 (top) in aeroplane mode overtakes No. 2 in slow-speed flight housing wing rotation carousel and some equipment bays. Sponson on each side of lower centre-fuselage to house main landing gear, fuel and environmental control unit.

TAIL UNIT: Cantilever structure, manufactured by Grumman, comprising horizontal surfaces mounted on top of rear fuselage with twin sweptback endplate fins and rudders. Entire structure built of Hercules AS4 graphite/epoxy laminates except for hinges, fittings and fasteners. Three hydraulic actuators (by Moog) on elevator and one (by Dowty Aerospace) on each rudder, all signalled electrically by FBW system. No elevator or rudder tabs. Pneumatic boot de-icing of fin and tailplane leading-edges.

LANDING GEAR: Dowty hydraulically actuated retractable tricycle type, with twin wheels and oleo-pneumatic shock absorbers on each unit, Menasco Canada steerable nose unit. Dowty Toronto two-stage shock absorption in main gear is designed for landing impacts of up to 3.66 m (12 ft)/s normal, 4.48 m (14.7 ft)/s maximum, and has been drop tested to 7.32 m (24 ft)/s. All units retract rearward, main gear into sponsons on lower sides of centre-fuselage. Manual and nitrogen pressurised standby systems for emergency extension. Parker Bertea wheels and multi-disc hydraulic carbon brakes.

POWER PLANT: Two Allison T406-AD-400 (501-M80C) turboshafts, each with T-O and intermediate rating of 4,586 kW (6,150 shp) and max continuous rating of 4,392 kW (5,890 shp), installed in Bell built tilting nacelles at wingtips. Each nacelle has GFRP cowling panels and pylon support structures, and a Garrett infra-red emission suppressor at the rear. Air particle separator and Lucas inlet/spinner ice protection system for each engine. Lucas Aerospace full authority digital engine control (Fadec) for each engine, with analog electronic backup control. Pratt & Whitney originally named as second production source for engines, starting with production lot 5. Internal fuel (JP-5) in up to 13 crash resistant, self-sealing (nitrogen pressurised) cells: one 1,431 kg (3,155 lb) forward cell in each sponson, a 925 kg (2,040 lb) cell in rear of starboard sponson, four 227 kg (500 lb) auxiliary cells in each wing leading-edge, and a 306 kg (675 lb) engine feed cell outboard of the auxiliary tanks in each wing. (Not all versions have all tanks.) Pressure refuelling point in starboard wing leading-edge; gravity point in upper surface of each wing. Simmonds fuel management system. Provision for a further 7,235 kg (15,950 lb) of fuel to be carried in two additional tanks in main cabin for self-deployment mission. In-flight refuelling probe in lower starboard side of forward fuselage.

ACCOMMODATION: Normal crew complement of pilot (in starboard seat), co-pilot and crew chief in USMC variant. Flight crew accommodated on Simula Inc crashworthy armoured seats capable of withstanding strikes from 0.30 calibre armour piercing ammunition, 30g forward and 14.5g vertical decelerations. Seats are manufactured from a boron carbide/polyethylene laminate. Flight deck has overhead and knee-level side transparencies in addition to large windscreen and main side windows, plus an overhead rearview mirror. Main window frame is of titanium. Main cabin has composites floor panels, and can accommodate up to 24 combat-equipped troops, on inward facing foldaway seats, plus two gunners; up to 12 litters plus medical attendants; or an equivalent cargo load with energy absorbing tiedowns. Cargo handling provisions include a 907 kg (2,000 lb) capacity cargo winch and pulley system and removable roller rails. Main cabin door at front on starboard side, top portion of which opens upward and inward, lower portion (with built-in steps) downward and outward. Full width rear loading ramp/door in underside of rear fuselage, operated by Parker Bertea hydraulic actuators. Emergency exit windows on port side; escape hatch in fuselage roof aft of wing.

SYSTEMS: Environmental control system, utilising engine bleed air; control unit in rear of port main landing gear sponson. Three hydraulic systems (two independent main systems and one standby), all at operating pressure of 345 bars (5,000 lb/sq in), with Parker Bertea reservoirs. Electrical power supplied by two 40kVA constant frequency AC generators, two 50/80kVA variable frequency DC generators (one driven by APU), rectifiers, and a 15Ah battery. General Electric Aerospace triple redundant digital fly by wire flight control system, incorporating triple primary FCS (PFCS) and triple automatic FCS (AFCS) processors, and dual flight control computers (FCC) each linked to a MIL-STD-1553B databus; two PFCSs and one AFCS are fail-operational. FBW system signals hydraulic actuation of flaperons, elevator and rudders, controls aircraft transition between helicopter and aeroplane modes, and can be programmed for automatic management of airspeed, nacelle tilting and angle of attack. FCCs provide interfaces for swashplate, conversion actuator, flaperon, elevator, rudder and pylon primary actuators, flight deck central drive, force feel, and nosewheel steering. Dual 1750A processors for PFCS and single 1750A for AFCS incorporated in each FCC. Non-redundant standby analog computer provides control of aircraft, including Fadec and pylon actuation, in the

MV-22 development aircraft (prototype No. 4) at the hover

Bell/Boeing V-22 Osprey multi-mission tilt-rotor aircraft *(Pilot Press)*

event of FBW system failure. Sundstrand Turbomach 261 kW (350 shp) APU, in rear portion of wing centre-section, provides power for mid-wing gearbox which, in turn, drives two electrical generators and an air compressor. Anti-icing of windscreens and engine air intakes; de-icing of rotor blades and spinners. Clifton Precision combined oxygen (OBOGS) and nitrogen (OBIGGS) generating systems for cabin and fuel tank pressurisation respectively. Systron Donner pneumatic fire protection systems for engines, APU and wing dry bays.

AVIONICS AND EQUIPMENT: VHF/AM-FM, HF/SSB and (USAF only) UHF secure voice com; Tacan, VOR/ILS, AHRS, radar altimeter and digital map displays; IFF; Honeywell AN/AAR-47 missile warning system; radar/infra-red warning system; J.E.T. ADI-350W standby attitude indicator; Aydin Vector data acquisition and storage system. Major tactical sensors are a Hughes Aircraft AN/AAQ-16 FLIR detector in undernose fairing and (USAF and USN only) a Texas Instruments AN/APQ-174 terrain following multifunction radar in offset (to port) nose thimble, with two Allied Signal IP-1555 full colour multifunction displays. Two Control Data AN/AYK-14 mission computers, with Boeing/IBM software. Pilots' night vision system and Honeywell integrated helmet display system. Chaff/flare dispensers. Provision for rescue hoist over forward (starboard) cabin door.

DIMENSIONS, EXTERNAL:

Rotor diameter, each	11.58 m (38 ft 0 in)
Rotor blade chord: at root	0.87 m (2 ft 10¼ in)
at tip	0.56 m (1 ft 10 in)
Wing span, excl nacelles	14.02 m (46 ft 0 in)
Wing chord, constant	2.54 m (8 ft 4 in)
Distance between rotor centres	14.19 m (46 ft 6¾ in)
Width overall, rotors turning	25.78 m (84 ft 6.8 in)
Length: fuselage	17.47 m (57 ft 4 in)
overall, wings stowed/blades folded	19.09 m (62 ft 7.6 in)
Height: over tail fins	5.38 m (17 ft 7.8 in)
wings stowed/blades folded	5.51 m (18 ft 1 in)

overall, nacelles vertical (= rotor ground clearance)	6.35 m (20 ft 10 in)
Nacelle ground clearance, nacelles vertical	1.58 m (5 ft 2½ in)
Tail span, over fins	5.61 m (18 ft 5 in)
Wheel track (c/l of outer mainwheels)	4.62 m (15 ft 2 in)
Dorsal escape hatch: Length	1.02 m (3 ft 4 in)
Width	0.74 m (2 ft 5 in)

DIMENSIONS, INTERNAL:

Cabin: Length	7.37 m (24 ft 2 in)
Max width	1.80 m (5 ft 11 in)
Max height	1.83 m (6 ft 0 in)
Usable volume	24.3 m³ (858 cu ft)

AREAS:

Rotor discs, each	105.4 m² (1,134 sq ft)
Rotor blades (each)	12.15 m² (130.76 sq ft)
Wing, total incl flaperons and fuselage centre section	35.49 m² (382.0 sq ft)
Flaperons, total	4.12 m² (44.4 sq ft)
Tailplane	8.22 m² (88.5 sq ft)
Elevators, total	4.79 m² (51.54 sq ft)
Vertical tail surfaces, incl rudder (each)	12.45 m² (134.0 sq ft)
Rudders (each)	1.64 m² (17.6 sq ft)

WEIGHTS AND LOADING:

Weight empty, equipped	approx 14,463 kg (31,886 lb)
Max fuel weight: standard	6,215 kg (13,700 lb)
with self-ferry cabin tanks	13,450 kg (29,650 lb)
Max internal payload (cargo)	9,072 kg (20,000 lb)
Cargo hook capacity: single	4,536 kg (10,000 lb)
two hooks (combined weight)	6,804 kg (15,000 lb)
Rescue hoist capacity	272 kg (600 lb)
Normal mission T-O weight: VTO	21,545 kg (47,500 lb)
STO	24,947 kg (55,000 lb)
Max STO weight for self-ferry	27,442 kg (60,500 lb)
Max cabin floor loading (cargo)	1,464 kg/m² (300 lb/sq ft)

PERFORMANCE (estimated):

Max cruising speed:	
at S/L, helicopter mode	100 knots (185 km/h; 115 mph)

at S/L, aeroplane mode
275 knots (509 km/h; 316 mph)
at optimum altitude, aeroplane mode
300 knots (556 km/h; 345 mph)
Max forward speed with max slung load
200 knots (370 km/h; 230 mph)
Service ceiling 7,925 m (26,000 ft)

T-O run at normal mission STO weight
less than 152 m (500 ft)
Range:
VTO at 21,146 kg (46,619 lb) gross weight, incl 5,443 kg
(12,000 lb) payload
1,200 nm (2,224 km; 1,382 miles)

STO at 24,947 kg (55,000 lb) gross weight, incl 9,072 kg
(20,000 lb) payload
1,800 nm (3,336 km; 2,073 miles)
STO at 27,442 kg (60,500 lb) self-ferry gross weight, no
payload 2,100 nm (3,892 km; 2,418 miles)

BELLANCA
BELLANCA INC
PO Box 964, Alexandria, Minnesota 56308
Telephone: 1 (612) 762 1501

Viking Aviation acquired in 1982 the assets of the former Bellanca Aircraft Corporation (see 1981-82 and earlier editions of *Jane's*), which went into liquidation in 1981. Viking Aviation Inc was subsequently renamed Bellanca

Inc and resumed production of the Bellanca Viking in 1984, but no details of recent deliveries has been received. Details and an illustration of the Viking can be found in the 1986-87 *Jane's*.

BOEING
THE BOEING COMPANY
PO Box 3707, Seattle, Washington 98124
Telephone: 1 (206) 655 2121
Telex: 329430
Fax: 1 (206) 655 1171
ESTABLISHED: July 1916
CHAIRMAN AND CHIEF EXECUTIVE OFFICER:
Frank A. Shrontz
VICE-CHAIRMAN: Malcolm T. Stamper
EXECUTIVE VICE-PRESIDENT & CHIEF FINANCIAL OFFICER:
Harold W. Haynes

On 2 January 1990, Boeing Defense and Space Group (B. Dan Pinick, President) was formed to co-ordinate the activities of the Aerospace & Electronics, Helicopters, Military Airplanes and Advanced Systems divisions of The Boeing Company. Simultaneously, the former Military Airplanes division at Wichita was reduced in size by the transfer of some activities to Boeing Commercial Airplane Group. Wichita is now a subsidiary of re-organised Military Airplanes division based in Seattle and absorbing Advanced Systems.

Operating components of The Boeing Company include:
BOEING DEFENCE AND SPACE GROUP
Boeing Aerospace & Electronics
See next entry
Boeing Helicopters
See pages 384-388
Boeing Military Airplanes
See pages 388-391
BOEING COMMERCIAL AIRPLANE GROUP
See pages 372-384

BOEING AEROSPACE AND ELECTRONICS
PO Box 3999, Seattle, Washington 98124
PRESIDENT: B. Dan Pinick
EXECUTIVE VICE-PRESIDENT: Art Hitsman
Telephone: 1 (206) 773 2121
Telex: 32 9430

Boeing Aerospace and Electronics, formed on 1 May 1989 by consolidation of the former Boeing Aerospace and Boeing Electronics operating divisions, has its headquarters at the space centre at Kent, Washington, some 12 miles south of Seattle. It consists of four major divisions: Electronic Systems, Missile Systems, Space Systems and Huntsville. Subsidiary companies are: Boeing Agri-Industrial Company; Boeing Technical Operations; Boeing Technical and Management Services and Boeing Petroleum Services. Major programmes and activities concern airborne warning and control, the E-6 Tacamo and E-8 J-STARS aircraft, the Inertial Upper Stage, Minuteman ICBM, Peacekeeper ICBM ground support system, SRAM II air-launched cruise missile and Avenger air defence system. Responsible for much of Boeing's military and space effort, it has a labour force of approximately 20,000.

BOEING E-3 SENTRY
USAF designation: E-3
RAF designation: E-3D Sentry AEW. Mk 1
The E-3 Sentry AWACS (Airborne Warning And Control System) is effectively a mobile, flexible, survivable and jamming-resistant high capacity radar station, command, control and communications centre, installed within a Boeing 707 airframe. It offers the potential of long-range high or low level surveillance of all air vehicles, manned or unmanned, and provides detection, tracking and identification capability within its surveillance capacity during all weathers and above all kinds of terrain. The radar system of later production aircraft also incorporates a maritime surveillance mode. Each of these aircraft is able to support a variety of tactical and/or air defence missions with no change in configuration. Its data storage and processing capability can provide real-time assessment of enemy action, and of the status and position of friendly resources.

In US Air Force service, the E-3 has a dual use: as a command and control centre to support quick-reaction deployment and tactical operations by Tactical Air Command units; and as a survivable early warning airborne command and control centre for identification, surveillance and tracking of airborne enemy forces, and for the command and control of NORAD (North American Air Defense) forces over the continental USA. The E-3 provides comprehensive surveillance out to a range of more than 200 nm (370 km; 230 miles) from the aircraft for low-flying targets, and still further for targets at higher altitudes.

Design of the E-3A is based on the airframe of the Model 707-320B commercial jet transport, but with a strengthened fuselage and powered by Pratt & Whitney TF33 turbofans. Two aircraft, with the prototype designation EC-137D, were modified initially for comparative trials with two prototype downward looking radars, of which that produced by Westinghouse was eventually selected. The full scale development test programme, completed at the end of 1976, involved three aircraft completely equipped with mission avionics, and a fourth aircraft equipped for airworthiness testing. Thirty-five E-3s (including upgraded prototypes) were delivered subsequently to the USAF, the last of them in June 1984. A further 18 were built for NATO.

These USAF and NATO AWACS have been developed and produced to four differing standards, as follows:

Core E-3A. Initial form of the first 24 production Sentries delivered to USAF. Equipment as detailed in 1987-88 *Jane's*.

E-3B. Under the USAF Block 20 modification programme, the two EC-137Ds and 22 USAF core-configured E-3As (aircraft Nos. 4 to 9 and 11 to 26) are being updated to E-3B standard by the installation of ECM-resistant voice communications; one more HF (making three in all) and five more UHF radios (making 12); a new and faster IBM CC-2 computer with much expanded memory and greatly increased processing speed compared with the original CC-1; five additional SDCs (making 14); and an austere maritime surveillance capability which Westinghouse developed for incorporation in the basic radar system. The E-3B also has provisions for Have Quick anti-jamming improvements to UHF radios, self defence, and a radio teletypewriter. First E-3B was re-delivered to USAF, after modification, on 18 July 1984. Remaining 23 are being modified by USAF at Tinker AFB, using Boeing kits.

US/NATO Standard E-3A. Original standard for USAF aircraft Nos. 27 to 35, of which delivery began in December 1981, and of the updated aircraft No. 3. Radar modified to embody full maritime surveillance capability; CC-2 computer; additional HF radios; ECM-resistant voice communications; radio teletypewriter; provisions for self defence and ECM. The 18 NATO aircraft are to this standard and retain E-3A designation.

E-3C. Under USAF Block 25 modification programme, begun in 1984, 10 USAF Standard E-3As upgraded to E-3C configuration by adding five more SDCs, five more UHF radios, and provisions for Have Quick anti-jamming improvements.

The USAF Electronic Systems Division has proposed a $425 million MSIP for the E-3, phased over five years, to give the radar greater detectability, add passive sensors, and make other improvements. Eventually, all USAF, RAF and NATO E-3s will be equipped with the Joint Tactical Information Distribution System (JTIDS) for anti-jam communications.

As a first step, in May 1987, Boeing was awarded a $241.5 million USAF contract for E-3 improvements that include full-scale development and integration into US and NATO

E-3s of an ESM system to detect signals emitted by both hostile and friendly targets. Additional enhancements to be made to US E-3s, under what is known as the Block 30/35 programme, include a radar sensitivity improvement programme (RSIP), upgrading of JTIDS to TADIL-J (tactical digital information link-J) capability; CC-2 computer memory upgrade, using VLSI (very large scale integration) and bubble memory electronics technologies; and ability to employ the GPS (Global Positioning System). IOC for the Block 30/35 improvements is scheduled for 1993.

In this connection, Westinghouse was awarded in 1989 a development contract to upgrade the APY-1/2 radars of USAF E-3s with new processors, displays and a pulse compressed waveform, thereby doubling performance against small targets such as cruise missiles. If approved, the modification will be applied to all 35 E-3B/Cs from 1994 onwards. Also in 1989 Boeing was authorised to retrofit Have Quick A-NET, an improved communications system.

The first production core-configured E-3A Sentry was delivered on 24 March 1977 to Tactical Air Command's 552nd Airborne Warning and Control Wing, based at Tinker AFB, Oklahoma. E-3As achieved initial operational status in April 1978, and have since completed deployments to Iceland, West Germany, Saudi Arabia, Sudan, the Mediterranean area, South West Asia and the Pacific. The Saudi detachment, 'Elf One', flew 86,500 hours from October 1980 until disbanded on 17 April 1989. E-3 aircraft are also employed in support of the US drug enforcement programme.

E-3As began to assume a role in US continental air defence on 1 January 1979, when NORAD personnel started to augment E-3A flight crews from TAC on all operational NORAD missions from Tinker AFB. The operating component was redesignated 552nd AWAC Wing in April 1985; it consists of several subordinate units. At Tinker, these include the 963rd, 964th and 965th AWAC Squadrons, the 966th AWAC Training Squadron, the 552nd Aircraft Generation Squadron (systems support), the 552nd Component Repair Squadron, and the 8th Tactical Deployment Control Squadron (flying EC-135K aircraft). Overseas units include the 960th, 961st and 962nd AWAC

Boeing E-3A Sentry with lower side view and wing scrap view of Royal Air Force E-3D Sentry AEW. Mk 1 *(Pilot Press)*

The first Boeing E-3D Sentry AEW. Mk 1 for the British Royal Air Force

Squadrons, based respectively at NAS Keflavik, Iceland, Kadena AB, Okinawa, Japan, and Elmendorf AFB, Alaska. They provide command and control capability to CINCLANT (through the Commander, Iceland Defence Force) and CINCPAC.

Much of the avionics for NATO E-3As were produced in West Germany, with Dornier as systems integrator. NATO funded a third HF radio, to cover the maritime environment; a new data analysis and programming group; underwing hardpoints for self defence system stores; and a radio teletype to link the AWACS with the Organisation's maritime forces and commands. The first NATO production E-3A flew at Renton on 18 December 1980, was delivered to Dornier on 19 March 1981, and was handed over to NATO on 22 January 1982. The final aircraft was delivered on 25 April 1985.

NATO E-3As are assigned to Nos 1, 2 and 3 Squadrons and the Training Centre of the E-3A Component, NATO Airborne Early Warning Force, based at Geilenkirchen (West Germany). RAF aircraft (see below) will become the E-3D Component, NAEWF. Up to six E-3As are detached to forward operating locations at Konya (Turkey), Previza (Greece), Trapani/Birgi (Italy) and the forward operating location at Ørland (Norway). The NAEWF has the status of a NATO Command, and its E-3A Component is staffed by personnel from Belgium, Canada, Denmark, Greece, Italy, the Netherlands, Norway, Portugal, Turkey and the USA, plus Luxembourg as a non-aircrew participant.

The sale of five E-3 AWACS aircraft to the Royal Saudi Air Force was approved during October 1981, under a programme known as Peace Sentinel. Also included in the sale were six **KE-3A** tanker aircraft which, despite their designation, have only fuel-carrying and transport capability. During 1984 the Saudi government exercised an option to increase the number of KE-3As to eight. In the same year, agreement was reached to equip the RSAF aircraft with 97.9 kN (22,000 lb st) CFM56-2A-2 engines, fitted with Hispano-Suiza thrust reversers. The first Saudi E-3 was handed over on 30 June 1986, and delivery of all 13 E-3s and KE-3As was completed by 24 September 1987. These aircraft are not believed to be equipped with JTIDS, the latest-standard ECCM or Have Quick provisions.

On 18 December 1986 the British Government announced its intention to order six E-3 AWACS aircraft for the Royal Air Force, and exercised an option on a seventh in October 1987. RAF E-3s are designated **E-3D Sentry AEW. Mk 1**. The first, ZH101, was rolled out at Renton on 11 July 1989 before aerial delivery to Boeing Field, Seattle in September 1989 for avionics outfitting. RAF Sentries have CFM56 engines, a refuelling probe offset to starboard above the cockpit, wingtip ESM pods, trailing-edge HF radio antenna immediately inboard of these pods, and Have Quick communications. ZH101's first fully equipped flight occurred on 5 January 1990, and delivery to the UK was due in September 1990 after flight trials including joint UK-French airworthiness certification and in-flight refuelling tests. Second aircraft, ZH102, was intended to precede it to Waddington, UK, where a consortium led by British Aerospace (which see) is responsible for installation and checkout prior to the first handover in Spring 1991. The final E-3D, ZH107 is due to be rolled out in May 1991 as the last of the Boeing 707 family and will be delivered in January 1992. No. 8 Squadron, RAF, will be declared operational with E-3Ds on 1 July 1991.

In February 1987, France ordered three CFM56-powered aircraft, designated **E-3F** and fitted with refuelling probes, adding a fourth in August 1987, but allowing two options to lapse in August 1988. Deliveries, beginning in October 1990, alternate with RAF aircraft. Operating unit is Unite de Détection Aéroporté 02/290 at Avord. Both France and the UK have obtained 130 per cent industrial offsets from Boeing.

Constructional details of the E-3 have appeared in the 1987-88 and previous editions of *Jane's*. The following applies specifically to the USAF E-3A, except where indicated:

TYPE: Airborne early warning and command post aircraft.

AIRFRAME: RAF aircraft have additional wing stringers and stiffeners outboard of Nos. 1 and 4 engines as the result of being fitted with tip pods and trailing-edge HF antennae.

POWER PLANT: Four Pratt & Whitney TF33-PW-100/100A turbofans, each rated at 93.4 kN (21,000 lb st), mounted in pods beneath the wings. Fuel contained in integral wing tanks. Provision for in-flight refuelling, with receptacle for boom over flight deck. Four 97.9 kN (22,000 lb st) CFM56-2A-2 turbofans on French, Saudi and UK aircraft. In-flight refuelling probe on E-3D and E-3F.

ACCOMMODATION: Basic operational crew of 20 includes a flight crew complement of four plus 16 AWACS specialists, though this latter number can vary for tactical and defence missions. Aft of flight deck, from front to rear of fuselage, are communications, data processing and other equipment bays; multi-purpose consoles; communications, navigation and identification equipment; and crew rest area, galley and parachute storage rack.

SYSTEMS: A liquid cooling system provides protection for the radar transmitter. An air cycle pack system, a draw-through system, and two closed loop ram-cooled environmental control systems ensure a suitable environment for crew and avionics equipment. Electrical power generation has a 600kVA capability. Distribution centre for mission equipment power and remote avionics in lower forward cargo compartment. Lower forward cargo compartment houses radar transmitter and an APU. External sockets allow intake of power when aircraft is on ground. Two separate and independent hydraulic systems power essential flight and mission equipment, but either system can satisfy requirements of both equipment groups in an emergency.

AVIONICS AND EQUIPMENT: Elliptical cross-section rotodome of 9.14 m (30 ft) diameter and 1.83 m (6 ft) max depth, mounted 3.35 m (11 ft) above fuselage, comprises four essential elements: a turntable, strut mounted above rear fuselage, supporting rotary joint assembly to which are attached sliprings for electrical and waveguide continuity between rotodome and fuselage; structural centre section of aluminium skin and stiffener supporting the Westinghouse AN/APY-1 surveillance radar (AN/APY-2 from No. 25 onwards, and in all export E-3s) and IFF/TADIL C antennae, radomes, auxiliary equipment for radar operation and environmental control of the rotodome interior; liquid cooling of the radar antennae; and two radomes of multi-layer glassfibre sandwich material, one for surveillance radar and one for IFF/TADIL C array.

For surveillance operations rotodome is hydraulically driven at 6 rpm, but during non-operational flights it is rotated at only ¼ rpm, to keep bearings lubricated. Radar operates in S-band and can function as both a pulse and/or a pulse-Doppler radar for detection of aircraft targets. A similar pulse radar mode with additional pulse compression and sea clutter adaptive processing is used to detect maritime/ship traffic. Radar is operable in six modes: PDNES (pulse-Doppler non-elevation scan), when range is paramount to elevation data; PDES (pulse-Doppler elevation scan), providing elevation data with some loss of range; BTH (beyond the horizon), giving long-range detection with no elevation data; Maritime, for detection of surface vessels in various sea states; Interleaved, combining available modes for all-altitude longer-range aircraft detection, or for both aircraft and ship detection; and Passive, which tracks enemy ECM sources without transmission-induced vulnerability. Radar antennae, spanning about 7.32 m (24 ft), and 1.52 m (5 ft) deep, scan mechanically in azimuth, and electronically from ground level up into the stratosphere. Heart of the data processing capability of the first 24 aircraft in their original core E-3A form is an IBM 4 Pi CC-1 high-speed computer (see 1987-88 *Jane's* for details). From 25th aircraft, the new and improved IBM CC-2 computer was installed from the start, with a main storage capacity of 665,360 words. Data display and control are provided by Hazeltine high resolution colour situation display consoles (SDC) and auxiliary display units (ADU). The E-3B carries 14 SDCs and two ADUs. Navigation/guidance relies upon two Delco AN/ASN-119 Carousel IV inertial navigation platforms, a Northrop AN/ARN-120 Omega set which continuously updates the inertial platforms, and a Teledyne Ryan AN/APN-213 Doppler velocity sensor to provide airspeed and drift information. Communications equipment provides HF, VHF and UHF channels through which information can be transmitted or received in clear or secure mode, in voice or digital form. A Bendix weather radar is carried in the nose. Identification is based on an Eaton (AIL) AN/APX-103 interrogator set which is the first airborne IFF interrogator to offer complete AIMS Mk X SIF air traffic control and Mk XII military identification friend or foe (IFF) in a single integrated system. Simultaneous Mk X and Mk XII multi-target and multi-mode operations allow the operator to obtain instantaneously the range, azimuth and elevation, code identification, and IFF status, of all targets within radar range. NATO E-3As carry, and USAF aircraft have provisions for, a radio teletype. All aircraft from No 25 have an inboard underwing hardpoint on each side. There is no immediate requirement for either USAF or NATO AWACS to carry weapons; but on NATO E-3As these hardpoints can be used to mount additional podded items of ECM equipment. E-3Ds carry Loral 1017 'Yellow Gate' ESM pods at the wingtips.

DIMENSIONS, EXTERNAL:

Wing span	44.42 m (145 ft 9 in)
Length overall	46.61 m (152 ft 11 in)
Height overall	12.73 m (41 ft 9 in)

WEIGHT:

Max T-O weight	151,953 kg (335,000 lb)

PERFORMANCE:

Max level speed	460 knots (853 km/h; 530 mph)

Boeing E-6A Tacamo II prototype pictured during flight testing over Puget Sound, Washington

Service ceiling	over 8,850 m (29,000 ft)
Endurance on station, 870 nm (1,610 km; 1,000 miles)	
from base	6 h
Max unrefuelled endurance	more than 11 h

BOEING E-6A TACAMO II

On 29 April 1983, Boeing Aerospace received a contract from the US Navy to develop a survivable airborne communications system to provide an on-station/all-ocean link between the US National Command Authorities and the US Navy's Trident ballistic nuclear submarine (SSBN) fleet. Designated E-6A, the new aircraft will replace the EC-130Q version of the Lockheed Hercules used currently for this mission, known as Tacamo (TAke Charge And Move Out), and is fitted with the EC-130Q's existing AVLF avionics.

The airframe of the E-6A is almost identical with that of the E-3 Sentry, and is assembled on the same production line. The prototype (162782) made its first short flight from Renton to Boeing Field, Seattle, on 19 February 1987. After installation of the aircraft's avionics, full flight testing began on 1 June 1987. Two production E-6As were ordered in FY 1986 followed by three, three and seven in FYs 1987-89 to complete the requirement for 16. Two were delivered to VQ-3 trials squadron of the USN at Barber's Point, Hawaii, on 2 August 1989, and five were in service by October (initially for crew training only). VQ-3 will have eight aircraft for the Pacific area and VQ-4 at Patuxent River, Maryland, seven for the Atlantic area.

The following details apply to the E-6A prototype:

TYPE: Long endurance communications relay aircraft, to carry the US Navy's airborne very low frequency (AVLF) communications systems.

AIRFRAME: Retains more than 75 per cent commonality with that of the E-3A, main differences being deletion of the dorsal radome and its support structure, the addition of wingtip ESM/Satcom pods and HF antenna fairings, and increased corrosion protection. Also retained is the nuclear/EMP (electro-magnetic pulse) hardening of the E-3A airframe. Additions include incorporation of the large forward freight door of the commercial Boeing 707-320C. Landing gear is identical to that of the E-3A.

POWER PLANT: Four 106.76 kN (24,000 lb st) CFM International F108-CF-100 (CFM56-2A-2) turbofans in individual underwing pods, as on some export E-3s. Fuel contained in integral tanks in wings, with single-point refuelling. In-flight refuelling via boom receptacle above flight deck.

ACCOMMODATION: Basic militarised interior sidewalls, ceilings and lighting are similar to those of the E-3A. Interior divided into three main functional areas: forward of wings (flight deck and crew rest area), overwing (five-man mission crew), and aft of wings (equipment). Forward crew area, 50 per cent common with that of E-3A, accommodates a four-man crew on flight deck. Compartment immediately aft contains dining, toilet, and eight-bunk rest area for spare crew carried on extended or remote deployment missions. Crew enter by ladder and hatch in floor of this compartment. Overwing compartment with communications and other consoles, their operators, and an airborne communications officer (ACO). To the rear is compartment containing R/T

racks, transmitters, trailing wire antennae and their reels. Bale-out door at rear on starboard side.

SYSTEMS: Some 75 per cent of the E-6A's systems are the same as the E-3A. Among those retained are the liquid cooling system for the transmitters, 'draw-through' cooling system for other avionics, the 600kVA electrical power generation system, APU, liquid oxygen system, and MIL specification hydraulic oil.

AVIONICS AND OPERATIONAL EQUIPMENT: Three Collins AN/ARC-182 VHF/UHF com transceivers, all with secure voice capability; five Collins AN/ARC-190 HF com (one transceiver, one receive only); and Hughes Aircraft AIC-32 crew intercom with secure voice capability. External aerials for Satcom UHF reception in each wingtip pod; fairings beneath each pod house antenna for standard HF reception. Navigation by triplex Litton LTN-90 ring laser gyro-based inertial reference system integrated with a Litton LTN-211 VLF/Omega system and duplex Smiths Industries SFM 102 digital/analog flight management computer system (FMCS). Bendix AN/APS-133 colour weather radar, in nosecone, with capability for short-range terrain mapping, tanker beacon homing, and waypoint display. Honeywell APN-222 high/low-range (0-15,240 m; 0-50,000 ft) radio altimeter, and Collins low-range (0-762 m; 0-2,500 ft) radio altimeter, with ILS and GPWS. General Instruments AN/ALR-66(V)4 electronic support measures (ESM), in each wingtip pod, provide information on threat detection, identification, bearing and approximate range. In overwing compartment, overseen by ACO, is a new communications central console, which incorporates ERCS (emergency rocket communications system) receivers, cryptographic equipment, new teletypes, tape recorders, and other communications equipment, all hardened against electro-magnetic interference. In each operational area the E-6A links upward with airborne command posts and the Presidential E-4, to satellites, and to the ERCS; and downward to VLF ground stations and the SSBN fleet. The main VLF antenna is a 7,925 m (26,000 ft) long trailing wire aerial (LTWA), with a 41 kg (90 lb) drogue at the end, which is reeled out from the middle part of the rear cabin compartment through an opening in the cabin floor. The LTWA, with its drogue, weighs about 495 kg (1,090 lb) and creates some 907 kg (2,000 lb) of drag when fully deployed. Acting as a dipole is a much shorter (1,220 m; 4,000 ft) trailing wire (STWA), winched out from beneath the tailcone. At patrol altitude, with the LTWA deployed, the aircraft enters a tight orbit and the wire stalls, causing it to be almost vertical (70 per cent verticality is required for effective sub-sea communications). Signals transmitted through the trailing wire antennae use 200kW of power, and can be received by submerged SSBNs via a towed buoyant wire antenna. Mean time between failures of complete mission avionics is less than 20 h, but the E-6 is able to carry spares, and a spare crew, to permit extended missions of up to 72 h with in-flight refuelling, and/or deployment to remote bases, where it is capable of autonomous operation.

ARMAMENT: None.

DIMENSIONS, EXTERNAL:

Wing span	45.16 m (148 ft 2 in)
Length overall	46.61 m (152 ft 11 in)
Height overall	12.93 m (42 ft 5 in)

Wheel track	6.73 m (22 ft 1 in)
Wheelbase	17.98 m (59 ft 0 in)
Forward cargo door: Height	2.34 m (7 ft 8 in)
Width	3.40 m (11 ft 2 in)
Height to sill	3.20 m (10 ft 6 in)

AREA:

Wings, gross	283.4 m² (3,050.0 sq ft)

WEIGHTS:

Operating weight empty	78,378 kg (172,795 lb)
Max fuel	70,305 kg (155,000 lb)
Max T-O weight	155,128 kg (342,000 lb)

PERFORMANCE (S/L, ISA, estimated):

Dash speed	530 knots (981 km/h; 610 mph)
Cruising speed at 12,200 m (40,000 ft)	
	455 knots (842 km/h; 523 mph)
Patrol altitude	7,620-9,150 m (25,000-30,000 ft)
Service ceiling	12,800 m (42,000 ft)
Critical field length	2,042 m (6,700 ft)
Max effort T-O run	1,646 m (5,400 ft)
Max effort T-O run with fuel for 2,500 nm (4,630 km; 2,875 miles)	732 m (2,400 ft)
Landing run at max landing weight	793 m (2,600 ft)
Mission range, unrefuelled	
	6,350 nm (11,760 km; 7,307 miles)
Endurance: unrefuelled	15 h 24 min
on-station, 1,000 nm (1,850 km; 1,150 miles) from T-O	
	10 h 30 min
with one refuelling	28 h 54 min
with multiple refuelling	72 h

BOEING 767 AOA

In July 1984, Boeing Aerospace received a contract from the US Army Strategic Defense Command to evaluate the technical feasibility of using airborne optical sensors to provide early warning and tracking of hostile intercontinental ballistic missile warheads. The project is called Airborne Optical Adjunct (AOA). The aircraft modified under this 67-month programme is the original prototype of the Boeing 767 commercial transport (N767BA), now known as the 767 AOA. Identified by a large equipment housing, called the cupola, above its cabin, and two ventral fins, it flew for the first time in its new form on 21 August 1987 and was recertificated in October 1987.

Equipment for the AOA task is supplied by Boeing's two principal subcontractors. Hughes Aircraft Company delivered the infra-red sensor in July 1988, for evaluation in flight. The AOA's computers were delivered by the Space and Strategic Avionics Division of Honeywell in 1987.

Eventual testing of the complete AOA system, as an element of the SDI programme, will be conducted over the Pacific, with the aircraft flying at normal airline cruising heights. It will carry a crew of 10 to 15 personnel on four- to six-hour missions. The targets for its sensors will be inert ICBM warheads.

BOEING (LOCKHEED) P-3C UPDATE IV

After competitive bidding against Lockheed, Boeing Aerospace was selected by the US Navy to develop ASW mission avionics for the P-3C Orion Update IV programme. The contract, awarded on 10 July 1987, includes development and installation of a new technology distributed processing databus architecture based on 68020 microprocessors and a dual, high-speed 32-bit databus; programmable colour displays and controls; enhanced acoustic, non-acoustic, communications and navigation subsystems; and a considerable amount of automated operator aids to take advantage of more and better sensors. Major equipment suppliers include Texas Instruments for AN/APS-137 radar, General Instrument for AN/ALR-66(V)5 ESM, and AT&T for AN/UYS-2 Enhanced Modular Signal Processor (EMSP).

A trial installation is being made in a P-3C delivered to Boeing in August 1987, with redelivery to the Naval Air Test Center at Patuxent River NAS scheduled for early 1991. Present plans envisage retrofit of the Update IV avionics in 109 existing P-3C Update I and II Orions, and installation as standard equipment in the 125 new P-7A Long-Range Air ASW-Capability Aircraft (LRAACA) required by the US Navy to follow completion of Orion production.

Boeing's Airborne Optical Adjunct conversion of the prototype 767, an element of the SDI programme, now the responsibility of the Missile Systems Division of Boeing Aerospace & Electronics

Boeing/Grumman E-8A J-STARS prototype during European trials at Mildenhall, UK, February 1990
(Bob Archer)

BOEING/GRUMMAN E-8A J-STARS

On 27 September 1985, Grumman Corporation received a $657 million contract for full scale development of the USAF/US Army Joint Surveillance Target Attack Radar System (J-STARS). Boeing has modified two C-18A (former American Airlines Boeing 707-323C transports) airframes as E-8A testbeds for the airborne equipment. Grumman is responsible for subsystems installation, integration and flight testing of the equipment, which includes a Norden multi-mode side looking radar antenna in a canoe shape radome some 9.1 m (30 ft) long, under the front fuselage of each aircraft. The radar will operate in synthetic aperture radar (SAR) mode to detect and locate stationary objects such as parked tanks over ranges up to 81-95 nm (150-175 km; 93-109 miles) behind the front line, and will alternate between SAR and Doppler to locate slow moving targets. The J-STARS system will then direct attack on the targets, via the Joint Tactical Information Distribution System (JTIDS).

The first aircraft to be modified arrived at Boeing Military Airplanes' Wichita facility in January 1986 and was delivered to Grumman's Melbourne Systems Division on 31 July 1987. A second Boeing 707-323C arrived at Wichita for modification in June 1986, for delivery to Grumman in Autumn 1988. Each is able to carry a crew of 17 US Army and USAF specialists to man the radar processing and communications consoles in the cabin.

The first completed E-8A testbed aircraft (N770JS) flew

for the first time in full J-STARS configuration on 22 December 1988, and the second (N8411) on 31 August 1989. That same August the first aircraft achieved instantaneous transmission of data to a ground station. A demonstration programme, including trials in Europe by N770JS during February/March 1990, is due to end in 1991, when a decision will be made on purchase of up to 22 production versions, plus over 100 ground stations to receive data transmitted by the aircraft.

It was intended that J-STARS carrier aircraft would be based on the E-6A Tacamo II airframe, with F108 (CFM56) turbofan engines. However, the Boeing 707 family assembly line will have closed before the end of evaluation, so prompting the alternative solution of re-engining second-hand 707 airframes. IOC is expected in 1993, or later.

BOEING COMMERCIAL AIRPLANE GROUP

PO Box 3707, Seattle, Washington 98124
Telephone: 1 (206) 237 2121
Telex: 0650 329430 BOEING Co C
Fax: 1 (206) 237 1706
PRESIDENT: Dean D. Thornton
SENIOR VICE-PRESIDENT, GOVERNMENT AND INTERNATIONAL AFFAIRS: L. W. Clarkson
EXECUTIVE VICE-PRESIDENTS:
R. R. Albrecht
Philip M. Condit (General Manager, New Airplane Division)
SENIOR VICE-PRESIDENT: Ben A. Cosgrove
VICE-PRESIDENT, MARKETING: J. B. Hayhurst
VICE-PRESIDENT, SALES: J. C. Longridge
VICE-PRESIDENT, COMMUNICATIONS: Gerald A. Hendin

Boeing Commercial Airplane Group, with headquarters at the company's Renton, Washington, facility just south of Seattle, was reorganised in 1983 into three divisions. Renton Division is responsible for manufacture of 707, 737 and 757 series aircraft; the Everett Division handles the 747 and 767 programmes; and the Fabrication Division serves the other operating groups with its massive NC machine capability. A Materiel Division was created in 1984 to consolidate activities of purchasing, quality control and vendor supplies.

Including military derivatives, 7 Model 707s, 146 Model 737s, 45 Model 747s, 51 Model 757s and 37 Model 767s were delivered in 1989. Workforce stood at 63,000 in mid-1989. On 10 March 1990, Boeing delivered its 6,000th jet airliner, a 767-200 to Britannia Airways. Total Jetliner orders then stood at 7,700.

BOEING MODEL 707
USAF designations: VC-137, E-6A and E-8

The prototype for the Boeing Model 707, designated Model 367-80, made its first flight on 15 July 1954, and a developed version was ordered in large numbers as a flight refuelling tanker/transport for the US Air Force under the designation KC-135 (Boeing Model 717). Commercial developments of the prototype, with the basic designations of Boeing 707 and 720, were manufactured in many versions. Details can be found in the 1980-81 and earlier editions of *Jane's*. The last commercially configured example, a 707-320C for the Moroccan government, was delivered in March 1982.

Manufacture has continued solely to provide airframes for the military AWACS and other defence programmes,

details of which can be found in other Boeing sections of this entry. Orders for all commercial and military models totalled 999 by 31 March 1990, of which 986 had been delivered. Military 707s still to be delivered comprised 12 E-3s (one for USAF, four for France, seven for the UK) and one E-6A. The E-8A J-STARS (which see above) will no longer be new-build airframes, but re-engined civil 707s. Boeing Military Airplanes is offering tanker/transport conversions of ex-airline 707s, as described under its entry. Other 707 and 720 conversions are available from Israel Aircraft Industries (which see).

BOEING MODEL 737-200
USAF designation: T-43A

The original Model 737 was designed to utilise many components and assemblies already in production for the Boeing 727. Design began on 11 May 1964, and the first Model 737 flew on 9 April 1967. Deliveries began before the end of 1967, following FAA certification on 15 December. Details of the early production versions of the Model 737, and of subsequent design development, can be found in the 1974-75 *Jane's*.

The Boeing 737 was the third commercial transport to reach a sales total of one thousand, and in June 1987 became the world's best selling commercial airliner when orders for all models surpassed the previous record total of 1,831 sales set by the Boeing 727. They passed the 2,000 mark on 3 March 1988. By 31 March 1990 Boeing 737 orders totalled 2,773, of which 1,833 had been delivered. On 19 February 1990 Boeing rolled out the 1,832nd Boeing 737. It was subsequently delivered to the Australian leasing company Ansett Worldwide and leased to the UK carrier British Midland Airways. By 21 March 1990 the worldwide fleet of Boeing 737s had carried an estimated 2.6 billion passengers, recorded 37 million revenue hours and covered a combined distance of nearly 24.5 billion miles.

Production of the Model 737-200 ended in Summer 1988, after delivery of 1,114 aircraft, including 19 T-43As. It was built in the following commercial versions:

Advanced 737-200. Standard model, with max ramp weight of 52,615 kg (116,000 lb) and max T-O weight of 52,390 kg (115,500 lb). JT8D-15A engines (each 68.9 kN; 15,500 lb st) standard; JT8D-17A (71.2 kN; 16,000 lb st) optional; basic fuel capacity of 19,532 litres (5,160 US gallons; 4,296 Imp gallons). Accommodation for 120 passengers and baggage, with 81 cm (32 in) pitch seating, or

up to 130 passengers in 76 cm (30 in) pitch seating with no reduction in cabin facilities. Use of graphite composites in place of former aluminium honeycomb in later production aircraft reduced the weight of the rudder, elevators and ailerons. Coupled with further use of composites in a new advanced technology interior, this resulted in a total weight reduction of more than 454 kg (1,000 lb).

Advanced 737-200C/QC. Convertible passenger/cargo model with strengthened fuselage and floor, and a large two-position upper deck cargo door with effective opening of 2.15 m × 3.40 m (7 ft 0½ in × 11 ft 2 in). The quick change (QC) feature allows more rapid conversion by using palletised passenger seating and other special interior furnishings. Typical mixed interior configuration provides accommodation for three cargo pallets and 65 passengers with 81 cm (32 in) pitch seating. Total of 104 built and included in overall total of 1,114 Model 737-200s.

Corporate version. Same as standard Advanced 737-200, except interiors are adapted to special business and executive luxury requirements. Additional fuel capacity offered by installation of fuel cells in lower cargo compartments. With max fuel this model can carry a 1,134 kg (2,500 lb) payload up to 4,000 nm (7,412 km; 4,606 miles).

Advanced 737-200 High Gross Weight Structure. Higher gross weight models of the Advanced 737-200/200C, for longer-range use, in two versions. One has a maximum ramp weight of 56,700 kg (125,000 lb) and a maximum T-O weight of 56,472 kg (124,500 lb) with JT8D-15A or JT8D-17A engines, and a fuel capacity of either 21,009 litres (5,550 US gallons; 4,621 Imp gallons) or 22,598 litres (5,970 US gallons; 4,971 Imp gallons). The additional capacity for increased range capability is provided by a 1,476 litre (390 US gallon; 325 Imp gallon) or a 3,066 litre (810 US gallon; 674 Imp gallon) fuel tank installed in the aft lower cargo compartment. The second version, with a maximum ramp weight of 58,332 kg (128,600 lb), maximum T-O weight of 58,105 kg (128,100 lb), design landing weight of 48,534 kg (107,000 lb), and maximum zero-fuel weight of 43,091 kg (95,000 lb), has approximately 650 nm (1,204 km; 748 miles) greater range capability than the standard Advanced 737-200. Sectors of 2,300 nm (4,262 km; 2,648 miles) can be served with a 130-passenger payload and typical fuel reserves. Aircraft is identical to the Advanced 737-200 except for the auxiliary fuel tank, new wheels, tyres and brakes.

Most 737-200 versions meet FAR Pt 36 and ICAO Annex 16 in respect of noise characteristics.

In January 1987 the Boeing 737-200 with JT8D-9/9A/15/15A/17/17A engines received FAA approval for extended range operations, permitting flights over water or undeveloped land areas by these twin-engined commercial airliners without their being subject to restrictions requiring such aircraft to remain within one hour's flying time of a suitable airport at single-engine cruising speeds. Operators must, however, apply for regulatory permission to operate extended range services with the aircraft.

An FAA certificated kit is available which enables the Model 737 to operate from unpaved or gravel runways. The kit includes a vortex dissipator for each engine, consisting of a short hollow boom that protrudes from under each engine's forward edge. The boom is capped by a plug with downward facing orifices. Pressurised engine bleed air forced through these orifices destroys any ground level vortex and prevents small pieces of gravel being ingested by the engines. Other items include a gravel deflection 'ski' on the nosewheel, deflectors between the main landing gear wheels, protective shields over hydraulic tubing and speed brake cable on the main gear strut, glassfibre reinforcement of lower inboard flap surfaces, application of Teflon-base paint to fuselage and wing undersurfaces and provision of more robust DME, ATC and VHF antennae.

British Airways Advanced 737-200s, known as Super 737s, are equipped with advanced flight deck avionics, including a Honeywell SP-177 digital automatic flight control system. Lufthansa took delivery of 38 Advanced 737-200s with similar equipment. Category IIIA certification of these AFCS versions was granted on 2 December 1981.

Surveiller. Specially equipped maritime surveillance 737-200 for Indonesian Air Force (three built), fitted also with 14 first class and 88 tourist class seats so that they can be used for government transport purposes. Details in 1987-88 and earlier editions of *Jane's*.

The description which follows applies to the commercial versions of the 737-200:

TYPE: Twin-turbofan short-range transport.

WINGS: Cantilever low-wing monoplane. Special Boeing wing sections. Average thickness/chord ratio 12.89%. Dihedral 6°. Incidence 1° at root. Sweepback at quarter-chord 25°. Aluminium alloy dual-path fail-safe two-spar structure. Ailerons of graphite composite construction. Triple-slotted trailing-edge flaps of aluminium, with trailing-edges of aluminium honeycomb. Aluminium alloy Krueger flaps on leading-edge, inboard of nacelles. Three leading-edge slats of aluminium alloy with aluminium honeycomb trailing-edge on each wing from engine to wingtip. Two aluminium honeycomb flight spoilers on each outer wing serve both as airbrakes in the air and for lateral control, in association with ailerons. Two aluminium honeycomb ground spoilers on each wing, one outboard and one inboard of engine, are used only during landing. Ailerons are powered by two hydraulic systems with manual reversion. Trailing-edge flaps are hydraulically powered, with electrical backup. Leading-edge slats and Krueger flaps are symmetrically powered by one hydraulic system normally, and by a second hydraulic system for alternate extension. Flight spoilers are symmetrically powered by the two main individual hydraulic systems. Engine bleed air for anti-icing supplied to engine nose cowls and all wing leading-edge slats.

FUSELAGE: Aluminium alloy semi-monocoque fail-safe structure.

TAIL UNIT: Cantilever aluminium alloy multi-spar structure, with graphite composite control surfaces. Variable incidence tailplane. Elevator has dual hydraulic power, with manual reversion. Rudder is powered by a dual actuator from two main hydraulic systems, with a standby hydraulic actuator and system. Tailplane trim has dual electric drive motors, with manual backup. Elevator control tabs for manual reversion are locked out during hydraulic actuation.

LANDING GEAR: Hydraulically retractable tricycle type, with free-fall emergency extension. Nosewheels retract forward, main units inward. No main-gear doors: wheels form wheel well seal. Twin wheels on each main and nose unit. Boeing oleo-pneumatic shock absorbers. Mainwheels and tyres size 40 × 14-16 (low pressure 40 × 18-17 tyres, or C40 × 14-21/H40 × 14.5-19 tyres with heavy duty wheel brakes, are available optionally). Nosewheels and tyres size 24 × 7.7 (low pressure 24.5 × 8.5 tyres available optionally). Bendix or Goodrich multi-disc brakes. Hydro-Aire Mk III anti-skid units and automatic brakes standard.

POWER PLANT: Two Pratt & Whitney JT8D turbofans (details under individual model listings), in underwing pods. High performance target type thrust reversers, with full sound attenuation quiet nacelles. All models have standard fuel capacity of up to 19,532 litres (5,160 US gallons; 4,296 Imp gallons), with integral fuel cells in wing centre-section as well as two integral wing tanks. Long-range version has auxiliary fuel tank in rear lower cargo compartment, giving max fuel capacity of 22,598 litres (5,970 US gallons; 4,971 Imp gallons). Single-point pressure refuelling through leading-edge of starboard wing. Fuelling rate 1,135 litres (300 US gallons; 250 Imp gallons)/min. Auxiliary overwing fuelling points. Total oil capacity 41.5 litres (11 US gallons; 9.1 Imp gallons).

ACCOMMODATION: Crew of two side by side on flight deck. Details of passenger accommodation given under individual model descriptions. Passenger versions are equipped with forward airstair; a rear airstair is optional. Convertible passenger/cargo versions have the rear airstair as standard and forward airstair optional. One plug type door at each corner of cabin, with passenger doors on port side and service doors on starboard side. Overwing emergency exit on each side. Basic passenger cabin has one lavatory and one galley at each end. Large-volume hand baggage overhead bins. Provision for a wide variety of interior arrangements. Freight holds forward and aft of wing, under floor.

SYSTEMS: Air-conditioning and pressurisation system utilises engine bleed air. Max differential 0.52 bars (7.5 lb/sq in). Two functionally independent hydraulic systems with a third standby system, using fire resistant hydraulic fluid, for flying controls, flaps, slats, landing gear, nosewheel steering and brakes; pressure 207 bars (3,000 lb/sq in). No pneumatic system. Electrical supply provided by engine driven generators. Garrett APU for air supply and electrical power in flight and on the ground, as well as engine starting.

AVIONICS AND EQUIPMENT: Equipment to satisfy FAA Category II low weather minimum criteria is standard, as well as a SIADS Inc performance data computer system. Autopilot, specially designed for ILS localiser and glideslope control, with control wheel steering. Optional equipment will permit Category IIIA capability. Very low frequency (VLF-Omega) navigation systems, and a range of flight management systems with various levels of automation, including autothrottle and automatic flight control, are available as options.

DIMENSIONS, EXTERNAL:

Wing span	28.35 m (93 ft 0 in)
Wing chord: at root	4.71 m (15 ft 5.6 in)
at tip	1.60 m (5 ft 3 in)
Wing aspect ratio	8.8
Length overall	30.53 m (100 ft 2 in)
Length of fuselage	29.54 m (96 ft 11 in)
Height overall	11.28 m (37 ft 0 in)
Tailplane span	10.97 m (36 ft 0 in)
Wheel track	5.23 m (17 ft 2 in)
Wheelbase	11.38 m (37 ft 4 in)
Main passenger door (port, fwd):	
Height	1.83 m (6 ft 0 in)
Width	0.86 m (2 ft 10 in)
Height to sill	2.62 m (8 ft 7 in)
Passenger door (port, rear): Height	1.83 m (6 ft 0 in)
Width	0.76 m (2 ft 6 in)
Width with airstair	0.86 m (2 ft 10 in)
Height to sill	2.74 m (9 ft 0 in)
Emergency exits (overwing, port and stbd, each):	
Height	0.97 m (3 ft 2 in)
Width	0.51 m (1 ft 8 in)
Galley service door (stbd, fwd):	
Height	1.65 m (5 ft 5 in)
Width	0.76 m (2 ft 6 in)
Height to sill	2.62 m (8 ft 7 in)
Service door (stbd, rear): Height	1.65 m (5 ft 5 in)
Width	0.76 m (2 ft 6 in)
Height to sill	2.74 m (9 ft 0 in)
Freight hold door (stbd, fwd): Height	1.22 m (4 ft 0 in)
Width	1.30 m (4 ft 3 in)
Height to sill	1.30 m (4 ft 3 in)
Freight hold door (stbd, rear): Height	1.22 m (4 ft 0 in)
Width	1.22 m (4 ft 0 in)
Height to sill	1.55 m (5 ft 1 in)

DIMENSIONS, INTERNAL:

Cabin, incl galley and toilet: Length	20.88 m (68 ft 6 in)
Max width	3.53 m (11 ft 7 in)
Max height	2.13 m (7 ft 0 in)
Floor area	63.8 m² (687 sq ft)
Volume	131.28 m³ (4,636 cu ft)
Freight hold (fwd) volume	10.48 m³ (370 cu ft)
Freight hold (rear) volume	14.30 m³ (505 cu ft)

AREAS:

Wings, gross	102.00 m² (1,098.0 sq ft)
Ailerons (total)	2.49 m² (26.8 sq ft)
Trailing-edge flaps (total)	16.87 m² (181.6 sq ft)
Slats (total)	6.52 m² (70.2 sq ft)
Ground spoilers (total)	3.68 m² (39.6 sq ft)
Flight spoilers (total)	2.64 m² (28.4 sq ft)
Fin	20.81 m² (224.0 sq ft)
Rudder	5.22 m² (56.2 sq ft)
Tailplane	28.99 m² (312.0 sq ft)
Elevators, incl tabs (total)	6.55 m² (70.5 sq ft)

WEIGHTS AND LOADINGS (standard aircraft at brake release weight of 52,390 kg; 115,500 lb except where indicated):
Operating weight empty (JT8D-17A engines):

200	27,445 kg (60,507 lb)
200C all-passenger	28,828 kg (63,555 lb)
200C all-cargo	27,231 kg (60,034 lb)
200QC all-passenger	30,141 kg (66,450 lb)
200QC all-cargo	27,500 kg (60,629 lb)
Max payload: 200	15,645 kg (34,493 lb)
200C all-passenger	14,263 kg (31,445 lb)
200C all-cargo	15,860 kg (34,966 lb)
200QC all-passenger	12,950 kg (28,550 lb)
200QC all-cargo	15,590 kg (34,371 lb)

Max T-O weight (all-models):	
basic	52,390 kg (115,500 lb)
optional	53,070 kg (117,000 lb)
	or 56,472 kg (124,500 lb)
	or 58,105 kg (128,100 lb)
Max ramp weight (all models):	
basic	52,615 kg (116,000 lb)
optional	53,295 kg (117,500 lb)
	or 56,700 kg (125,000 lb)
	or 58,332 kg (128,600 lb)
Max zero-fuel weight (all models):	
basic	43,091 kg (95,000 lb)
optional for 200C	44,906 kg (99,000 lb)
Max landing weight (all models):	
basic	46,720 kg (103,000 lb)
optional	47,627 kg (105,000 lb)
	or 48,534 kg (107,000 lb)
Wing loading (all models):	
basic	575.5 kg/m² (117.9 lb/sq ft)
max optional	638.2 kg/m² (130.7 lb/sq ft)
Power loading (JT8D-17A engines, all models):	
basic	368 kg/kN (3.61 lb/lb st)
max optional	408 kg/kN (4.00 lb/lb st)

WEIGHTS AND LOADINGS (at brake release weight of 56,472 kg; 124,500 lb):

Operating weight empty	27,574 kg (60,790 lb)
Max payload	15,517 kg (34,210 lb)
Max T-O weight	56,472 kg (124,500 lb)
Max ramp weight	56,700 kg (125,000 lb)
Max zero-fuel weight	43,091 kg (95,000 lb)
Max landing weight	48,534 kg (107,000 lb)
Max wing loading	620.24 kg/m² (127.04 lb/sq ft)
Max power loading (JT8D-17A engines)	397 kg/kN (3.9 lb/lb st)

PERFORMANCE (ISA, with JT8D-17A engines):
Max operating speed, all models
Mach 0.84 (350 knots; 648 km/h; 402 mph EAS)
Max cruising speed, at an average cruise weight of 45,359 kg (100,000 lb) at 10,060 m (33,000 ft)
462 knots (856 km/h; 532 mph)
Econ cruising speed at 10,060 m (33,000 ft) Mach 0.73
Stalling speed, flaps down, at 46,720 kg (103,000 lb) landing weight 102 knots (189 km/h; 117 mph)
Runway LCN (at max ramp weight of 52,615 kg; 116,000 lb, optimum tyre pressure and 20 in flexible pavement):

40 × 14-16 tyres	53
C40 × 14-21 tyres	53
C40 × 18-17 tyres	38

FAR T-O distance to 10.7 m (35 ft), 737-200 at 49,435 kg (109,000 lb) AUW and 28.9°C (84°F):

JT8D-9A engines	2,027 m (6,650 ft)
JT8D-17A engines	1,615 m (5,300 ft)

FAR landing distance from 15 m (50 ft), 737-200 at landing weight of 46,720 kg (103,000 lb)
1,372 m (4,500 ft)
Min ground turning radius 17.58 m (57 ft 8 in)
Range, JT8D-17A engines, FAR domestic reserves, cruising at 10,060 m (33,000 ft), at 52,615 kg (116,000 lb) ramp weight with 115 passengers and 19,533 litres (5,160 US gallons; 4,296 Imp gallons) fuel
1,855 nm (3,437 km; 2,136 miles)
Range, conditions as above, except 58,332 kg (128,600 lb) ramp weight and 22,599 litres (5,970 US gallons; 4,971 Imp gallons) fuel 2,530 nm (4,688 km; 2,913 miles)
Range, conditions as above, with 130 passengers
2,255 nm (4,179 km; 2,596 miles)
OPERATIONAL NOISE LEVELS (JT8D-9 engines and nacelle acoustic treatment, FAR Pt 36):
T-O at 52,390 kg (115,500 lb) brake release weight
95.3 EPNdB
Sideline at 52,390 kg (115,500 lb) brake release weight
100.6 EPNdB
Approach at 46,720 kg (103,000 lb) max landing weight
101.1 EPNdB

BOEING MODEL 737-300

Work on the 737-300 was started in early 1980. Lengthening of the fuselage, to accommodate additional passengers and underfloor freight, and the installation of new-generation turbofan engines, offer much reduced fuel consumption per seat-mile and lower noise levels compared with the earlier model. It has the same approval for extended range overwater operations as the 737-200 (which see).

Following production go-ahead in March 1981, work began in mid-1982 and the prototype 737-300 made its first flight on 24 February 1984. A second aircraft joined the flight test programme on 2 March. Certification was granted on 14 November 1984, with the first delivery (to US Air) on 28 November. The first revenue service with a 737-300 was flown by Southwest Airlines on 7 December 1984.

The executive version of the 737-300 is equipped typically for about 20 passengers, with conference room, bedroom, bathroom and full dining facilities. Three had been sold by 31 March 1990, including one to the Royal Thai Air Force. By that date a total of 948 Model 737-300s had been ordered and 602 delivered.

The description of the 737-200 applies also to the 737-300, except as follows:

Boeing 737-300 short-range transport of Aéromaritime of France

WINGS: Generally similar to the 737-200 except: modified aerofoil section for leading-edge slats outboard of engine nacelles; revised trailing-edge flap sections and flap track fairings aft of engines; additional spoilers outboard; wing structure strengthened; and each wingtip extended by 0.28 m (11 in).

FUSELAGE: As for 737-200, but lengthened by a total of 2.64 m (8 ft 8 in), by insertion of a 1.12 m (3 ft 8 in) plug forward of the wing, and a 1.52 m (5 ft 0 in) plug aft of the wing carry-through structure. In addition to providing increased passenger capacity, this stretch gives a lower freight hold volume 5.47 m³ (193 cu ft) greater than that of the standard 737-200.

TAIL UNIT: As for 737-200, except dorsal fin area and tailplane span increased. Some fins manufactured by the Xian Aircraft Co in the People's Republic of China. Composite material rudders manufactured by Short Brothers in the UK.

LANDING GEAR: Generally as for 737-200, but nose unit repositioned downwards by 13 cm (5 in) and modified to ensure adequate ground clearance for larger engine nacelles. Twin nosewheels have tyres size 27 × 7.75. Main units have heavy duty wheels, H40 × 14.5-19 heavy duty tyres, and Bendix or Goodrich heavy duty wheel brakes as standard. Mainwheel tyre pressure 13.45-14.00 bars (195-203 lb/sq in). Nosewheel tyre pressure 11-45-11.85 bars (166-172 lb/sq in).

POWER PLANT: Two 88.97 kN (20,000 lb st) CFM International CFM56-3B-1 or B-2 turbofans, pylon mounted one on each wing. Nacelles are forward of wings, and higher than those of 737-200; each is fitted with an aerodynamic fence. Standard fuel capacity up to 20,104 litres (5,311 US gallons; 4,422 Imp gallons), with integral fuel cells in wing centre-section and integral wing tanks. Optional fuel capacities of 21,580 litres (5,701 US gallons; 4,747 Imp gallons) and 23,170 litres (6,121 US gallons; 5,097 Imp gallons). Single-point pressure refuelling through leading-edge of starboard wing.

ACCOMMODATION: Crew of two side by side on flight deck (unchanged from 737-200). Alternative cabin layouts seat from 128 to 149 passengers. Typical arrangements offer 8 first class seats four-abreast at 96.5 cm (38 in) pitch and 120 tourist class seats six-abreast at 81 cm (32 in) in mixed class; and 141 or 149 all-tourist at seat pitches of 81 cm (32 in) or 76 cm (30 in) respectively. One plug type door at each corner of cabin, with passenger doors on port side and service doors on starboard side. Airstair for forward cabin door optional. Overwing emergency exit on each side. One or two galleys and one lavatory forward, and one or two galleys and lavatories aft, depending on configuration. New lightweight interior, using advanced crushed core materials, providing total overhead baggage capacity of 6.80 m³ (240 cu ft), equivalent to 0.048 m³ (1.7 cu ft) per passenger. Underfloor freight holds, forward and aft of wing, with access doors on starboard side.

SYSTEMS: Generally as for 737-200. AiResearch bleed air control system for air-conditioning and thermal anti-icing systems; Garrett GTCP 85-129(C) APU.

AVIONICS AND EQUIPMENT: Equipped to FAA Category II low weather minimum criteria as standard. Flight management computer system (FMCS), with performance and navigation functions, includes FAA Category II SP-300 digital autopilot with optional Category IIIA capability, inertial reference system (IRS) with laser gyros in lieu of gimbal type, 12.7 cm (5 in) electro-mechanical flight displays, 10 cm (4 in) electrical air data displays, dual digital air data computers, and full-range digital autothrottle. Other items include dual nav/com, VHF nav, colour digital radar, and digital autobrake. Optional equipment includes VLF/Omega nav system and dual INS. An EFIS installation received FAA certification on 24 July 1986. Also FAA approved is Boeing's windshear detection and guidance system.

DIMENSIONS, EXTERNAL:

Wing span	28.88 m (94 ft 9 in)
Wing chord at root	4.71 m (15 ft 5.6 in)
Length overall	33.40 m (109 ft 7 in)
Height overall	11.13 m (36 ft 6 in)
Tailplane span	12.70 m (41 ft 8 in)
Wheel track	5.23 m (17 ft 2 in)
Wheelbase	12.45 m (40 ft 10 in)
Passenger, service and freight hold door sizes	as for 737-200

DIMENSIONS, INTERNAL:

Cabin, incl galley and toilet:	
Length	23.52 m (77 ft 2 in)
Max width	3.45 m (11 ft 4 in)
Max height	2.13 m (7 ft 0 in)
Freight hold (fwd) volume	12.03 m³ (425.0 cu ft)
Freight hold (rear) volume	18.21 m³ (643.0 cu ft)

AREAS: As for 737-200 except:

Wings, gross	105.4 m² (1,135.0 sq ft)
Slats (total)	7.23 m² (77.8 sq ft)
Ground spoilers (total)	5.00 m² (53.8 sq ft)
Fin	23.13 m² (249.0 sq ft)
Tailplane	31.31 m² (337.0 sq ft)

WEIGHTS:

Operating weight empty	31,479 kg (69,400 lb)
Max payload: standard	16,148 kg (35,600 lb)
optional	16,828 kg (37,100 lb)
Max T-O weight: standard	56,472 kg (124,500 lb)
optional	62,822 kg (138,500 lb)
Max ramp weight: standard	56,700 kg (125,000 lb)
optional	63,049 kg (139,000 lb)
Max zero-fuel weight: standard	47,625 kg (105,000 lb)
optional	48,307 kg (106,500 lb)
Max landing weight	51,710 kg (114,000 lb)

PERFORMANCE: (A: at brake release weight of 56,472 kg; 124,500 lb. B: at optional BRW of 62,822 kg; 138,500 lb):

T-O field length, S/L, at 29°C (84°F):	
A	2,027 m (6,650 ft)
B	2,749 m (9,020 ft)
Wet landing field length, 40° flap, at max landing weight:	
A, B	1,603 m (5,260 ft)
Still air range with 141 passengers, T-O at S/L:	
A	1,563 nm (2,897 km; 1,800 miles)
B	2,457 nm (4,554 km; 2,830 miles)

BOEING MODEL 737-400

Details of this new variant were announced in June 1986. The Model 737-400 offers all the new technology of the 737-300, but has a fuselage lengthened by 3.05 m (10 ft 0 in) by means of two plugs, one of 1.83 m (6 ft 0 in) forward of the wing and one of 1.22 m (4 ft 0 in) aft. The aircraft is powered by either two CFM International CFM56-3B-2 turbofans, each rated at 97.86 kN (22,000 lb st), or two CFM56-3C turbofans, each rated at 104.5 kN (23,500 lb st). The outer wings and landing gear are strengthened to permit a maximum landing weight of 54,885-56,245 kg (121,000-124,000 lb). A tail bumper is standard. In typical mixed-class configuration the 737-400 seats 146 passengers and up to 170 passengers in inclusive-tour charter configuration; lower cargo hold volume is 38.93 m³ (1,375 cu ft).

The first 737-400 (N73700) was rolled out on 26 January 1988 and made it first flight on 19 February, followed by the second aircraft on 25 March. A third 737-400 joined the test programme in June, and certification to carry up to 188 passengers was achieved on 2 September 1988. First delivery, to Piedmont Airlines, was made on 15 September.

Firm orders for the 737-400 totalled 224 by 31 March 1990, of which 84 had been delivered.

A 737-400 with high gross weight structure was rolled out on 23 December 1988. This model features a strengthened wing and landing gear, revised avionics software, increased fuel capacity and two 111.2 kN (25,000 lb st) CFM56-3C1 turbofans. Max ramp weight is 68,265 kg (150,500 lb).

The general specification of the 737-300 applies also to the 737-400 except as follows:

DIMENSION, EXTERNAL:

Length overall	36.45 m (119 ft 7 in)

Three-view drawing of Boeing Model 737-400, with additional side elevations of 737-500 (top) and 737-300 (centre) *(Pilot Press)*

Boeing 737-400 in the insignia of USAir

DIMENSION, INTERNAL:
Cabin, incl galley and toilet:	
Length	27.18 m (89 ft 2 in)

WEIGHTS:
Operating weight empty: standard	33,370 kg (73,570 lb)
optional	34,130 kg (75,250 lb)
Max payload: standard	17,885 kg (39,430 lb)
optional	18,935 kg (41,750 lb)
Max T-O weight: standard	62,822 kg (138,500 lb)
optional	68,039 kg (150,000 lb)
Max ramp weight: standard	63,049 kg (139,000 lb)
optional	68,265 kg (150,500 lb)
Max zero-fuel weight: standard	51,256 kg (113,000 lb)
optional	53,070 kg (117,000 lb)
Max landing weight: standard	54,885 kg (121,000 lb)
optional	56,245 kg (124,000 lb)

PERFORMANCE (A: at T-O weight of 62,822 kg; 138,500 lb. B: at optional T-O weight of 68,039 kg; 150,000 lb):
T-O field length, S/L, at 30°C: A	2,316 m (7,600 ft)
B, with optional CFM56-3C engines	
	2,499 m (8,200 ft)
Wet landing field length, 40° flap:	
A at 54,885 kg (121,000 lb) landing weight	
	1,722 m (5,650 ft)
B at 56,245 kg (124,000 lb) landing weight	
	1,850 m (6,070 ft)
Still air range with 146 passengers, T-O at S/L:	
A	2,160 nm (4,003 km; 2,487 miles)
B	2,500 nm (4,633 km; 2,879 miles)

BOEING MODEL 737-500

Known initially as the 737-1000 during early design studies, this variant was announced on 20 May 1987 and combines the advanced technology of the 737-300 and -400 with a fuselage shortened to give an overall length of 31.0 m (101 ft 9 in), providing accommodation for 108-132 passengers and lower hold volume of 23.3 m³ (823 cu ft). The aircraft is powered by two CFM International CFM56-3B-1 turbofans, each rated at 88.97 kN (20,000 lb st) or derated to 82.29 kN (18,500 lb st) according to customer preference, and is available with a choice of max T-O weights from 52,163 to 60,554 kg (115,000-133,500 lb). When equipped with auxiliary fuel tanks and the more powerful engines, a high gross weight 737-500 with mixed class accommodation for 108 passengers has a maximum range of 2,996 nm (5,552 km; 3,450 miles).

Major launch customers for the 737-500 were Braathens SAFE of Norway, which ordered 25 aircraft, and Southwest Airlines which ordered 20 and placed options on a further 20. Firm orders totalled 192 by 31 March 1990, from 19 customers. The first 737-500 was flown for the first time on 30 June 1989. FAA certification was achieved on 12 February 1990 after a flight test programme lasting 375 hours. The first customer delivery was made on 28 February 1990 to Southwest Airlines at Dallas, Texas. The 737-500 has replaced the 737-200 in the Boeing range.

BOEING MODEL 747

First details of this wide-body commercial transport were announced on 13 April 1966, simultaneously with the news that Pan American had ordered 25 Boeing 747s, including spares. Programme go-ahead followed on 25 July 1966.

The first 747 (designated RA001) flew for the first time on 9 February 1969. FAA certification of the basic 747 was granted on 30 December 1969. The first 747 was delivered to Pan American on 12 December 1969, and entered commercial service on the airline's New York/London route on 22 January 1970.

By 31 March 1990 a total of 982 Model 747s of all versions, commercial and military, had been ordered, of which 777 had been delivered. The order total passed the 1,000 mark on 24 May 1990. Earlier that month it was announced that only the Model 747-400 would continue to be offered for sale. At that time outstanding deliveries of other versions comprised four Model 747-200F Freighters and one Model 747-300M Combi.

Boeing delivered a total of 45 Model 747s during 1989. On 21 January 1990 the Boeing 747 celebrated 20 years in commercial service. By that time the worldwide fleet had flown 13.9 billion miles in a total of 27.5 million flight hours, and had carried nearly one billion passengers.

Versions of the Boeing 747 are as follows:

747-100. The original 747-100 was introduced into commercial service in January 1970, and 167 were sold. (Two of these have since been converted to -200B Combis and are included in the total given for that version.) The -100B (nine built) incorporates strengthened wing, fuselage and landing gear structure. Initial order, with 213.5 kN (48,000 lb st) JT9D-7F engines, was placed by Iran Air in 1978, and this aircraft was delivered on 5 July 1979. Subsequent versions, with max taxi weights of 323,411 kg

(713,000 lb), 334,751 kg (738,000 lb), and 341,555 kg (753,000 lb), allow for the installation of a variety of optional engines in addition to the basic CF6-45A2, including the CF6-50E2, and RB211-524D4.

747SP. Lighter weight, shorter bodied derivative of the 747-100B. Described separately.

747-100SR. This short-range version of the 747-100B embodies structural changes required for high take-off and landing cycles. It is available at max taxi weights up to 273,515 kg (603,000 lb) with the same engines as the 747-100B. The first 747-100SR flew on 4 September 1973 and was delivered on 26 September 1973. Total of 29 built.

747-200B. Passenger version, with same accommodation as 747-100B. First flown on 11 October 1970 and certificated on 23 December 1970; deliveries began on 15 January 1971. Available at taxi weights up to 379,200 kg (836,000 lb). Standard engines include 243.5 kN (54,750 lb st) JT9D-7R4G2, 233.5 kN (52,500 lb st) CF6-50E2 and 236.25 kN (53,110 lb st) RB211-524D4. Optional engines include 252.2 kN (56,700 lb st) CF6-80C2B1 and 236.25 kN (53,110 lb st) RB211-524D4-B. Total of 226 ordered and 224 delivered by 31 March 1990. Other two ordered by US Air Force for Presidential transport to replace VC-137 aircraft (further details in Boeing Military Airplanes entry, under VC-25A 'Air Force One' heading).

747-200C Convertible. Version of 747-200 which can be converted from all-passenger to all-cargo, or five combinations of both. The first 747-200C flew on 23 March 1973, was certificated on 17 April, and was delivered to World Airways on 27 April 1973. Max T-O weight of 377,840 kg (833,000 lb) with Pratt & Whitney JT9D-7R4G2, Rolls-Royce RB211-524D4, General Electric CF6-50E2 or CF6-80C2 engines. Thirteen ordered and delivered.

747-200F Freighter. Version of the 747-200 capable of delivering 90,720 kg (200,000 lb) of palletised cargo over a range of 4,480 nm (8,300 km; 5,159 miles). Described separately.

747-200M. Combi version of the basic 747-200B, incorporating a cargo door in the port side of the fuselage, aft of the wing. This permits main deck layouts for passengers only, or for passengers and up to 12 main deck pallets/containers, with passenger and cargo areas separated by removable bulkhead. The first modification to Combi configuration was carried out on a Sabena 747-100, and redelivery was made in February 1974. The first production

First production Boeing 737-500, delivered to Southwest Airlines on 28 February 1990

Combi was delivered to Air Canada in March 1975. Total of 77 ordered and delivered.

747-300. Version with extended upper deck to increase passenger accommodation. Described separately.

747-300M. Combi version of 747-300; described separately.

747-300SR. Short-range version of 747-300. Described separately.

747-400, 400F and 400M. Advanced, Freighter and Combi versions of 747-300; described separately.

E-4. Advanced Airborne Command Post version of 747, developed for US Air Force. Four built. Described under Boeing Aerospace heading in 1986-87 *Jane's*.

747 modification programmes. A major modification to enhance capability is available to operators of 747-100 and -200B aircraft. Performed at Boeing facilities, it includes installation of a side cargo door. The side cargo door modification enables an operator to convert 747-100 or -200B passenger aircraft into a version with main deck cargo capability. Variations include an all-cargo Special Freighter, a 6- or 12-pallet Combi, and an all-passenger or all-cargo Convertible. Like the Combi, the Convertible configuration can also be operated in a mixed passenger/cargo mode. The major elements of the side door modification include installation of a 3.05 m (10 ft 0 in) high by 3.40 m (11 ft 2 in) wide side cargo door, strengthened main deck floor, a fully powered or manual cargo handling system, and an option to increase certificated design weights of the aircraft. Boeing Military Airplanes (which see) has modified 19 Pan American 747s into the passenger/convertible configuration to support the US Air Force's CRAF (Civil Reserve Air Fleet) enhancement programme. The last converted aircraft was redelivered to Pan American in February 1990. These aircraft are known by the military designation **C-19A**.

The 747 can be fitted, or retrofitted, with a performance management system (PMS) developed by Boeing and Delco. The PMS computer memory is programmed with airline economic factors and the performance characteristics of the individual aircraft/engine combination, and receives continuous inputs of altitude, airspeed, air temperature, fuel flow, wind velocity and other data during flight. Using these data, coupled with existing autopilot, autothrottle and inertial navigation systems, the PMS calculates, displays and controls automatically the optimum or desired airspeed, engine power setting, attitude and flight path of the aircraft for minimum fuel burn and/or minimum operating cost. The first complete system was delivered for airline service in June 1982. Results of in-service airline evaluations show trip fuel burn reductions in excess of one per cent.

The following details apply specifically to the basic Model 747-100B/-200B passenger airliner:

TYPE: Four-turbofan heavy commercial transport.

WINGS: Cantilever low-wing monoplane. Special Boeing wing sections. Thickness/chord ratio 13.44% inboard, 7.8% at mid-span, 8% outboard. Dihedral 7°. Incidence 2°. Sweepback 37° 30′ at quarter-chord. Aluminium alloy dual-path fail-safe structure. Low-speed outboard ailerons; high-speed inboard ailerons. Triple-slotted trailing-edge flaps. Six aluminium honeycomb spoilers on each wing, comprising four flight spoilers outboard and two ground spoilers inboard. Ten variable camber leading-edge flaps outboard and three-section Krueger flaps inboard on each wing leading-edge. All controls fully powered.

FUSELAGE: Conventional semi-monocoque structure, consisting of aluminium alloy skin, longitudinal stiffeners and circumferential frames. Structure is of fail-safe design, utilising riveting, bolting and structural bonding.

TAIL UNIT: Cantilever aluminium alloy dual-path fail-safe structure. Variable incidence tailplane. No trim tabs. All controls fully powered.

LANDING GEAR: Hydraulically retractable tricycle type. Twin-wheel nose unit retracts forward. Main gear comprises four four-wheel bogies: two, mounted side by side under fuselage at wing trailing-edge, retract forward; two, mounted under wings, retract inward. Cleveland Pneumatic oleo-pneumatic shock absorbers. All 18 wheels and tubeless tyres of Model 747-100B are size 46 × 16 Type VII. Tyre pressure: mainwheels 14.49 bars (210 lb/sq in), nosewheels 13.11 bars (190 lb/sq in). Mainwheels and tyres size 49 × 17 on 747-200B model, pressure 14.15 bars (205 lb/sq in). The high gross weight aircraft has 49 × 19 tyres at a pressure of 13.46 bars (195 lb/sq in). Disc brakes on all mainwheels, with individually controlled anti-skid units.

POWER PLANT: Four Pratt & Whitney, General Electric or Rolls-Royce turbofans, as detailed in model listings, in pods pylon-mounted on wing leading-edges. Fuel in seven integral tanks. Capacity of centre wing tank varies according to version: 747-100B, 49,966 litres (13,200 US gallons; 10,991 Imp gallons); 747-200, 64,973 litres (17,164 US gallons; 14,292 Imp gallons). Remaining tanks common to all versions: two inboard main tanks, each 47,492 litres (12,546 US gallons; 10,447 Imp gallons); two outboard main tanks, each 16,966 litres (4,482 US gallons; 3,732 Imp gallons); two inboard reserve tanks, each 2,021 litres (534 US gallons; 445 Imp gallons). Outboard main tanks reduced by 1,234 litres (326 US gallons; 271 Imp gallons) when CF6-50E2 or CF6-80C2 engines are installed. 747-200 also available with two outboard reserve tanks, each 2,983 litres (788 US gallons; 656 Imp gallons). Fuselage tank, capacity 6,511 litres (1,720 US gallons; 1,432 Imp gallons) optional. Total capacity, including manifolds: 747-100B, 183,380 litres (48,445 US gallons; 40,339 Imp gallons); 747-200, 204,355 litres (53,985 US gallons; 44,952 Imp gallons). Refuelling point on each wing between inboard and outboard engines. Total usable oil capacity 19 litres (5 US gallons; 4.2 Imp gallons).

ACCOMMODATION: Normal operating crew of three, on flight deck above level of main deck. Observer station and provision for second observer station are provided. Crew rest area available as option at rear of upper deck. Basic accommodation for 452 passengers, made up of 32 first class and 420 economy class, which includes a 32-passenger upper deck (extended on 747-300, which see). Alternative layouts accommodate 447 economy class passengers in nine-abreast seating or 516 ten-abreast, with 32 passengers on upper deck. All versions have two aisles. Five passenger doors on each side, of which two forward of wing on each side are normally used. Freight holds under floor, forward and aft of wing, with doors on starboard side. One door on forward hold, two on rear hold. Aircraft is designed for fully mechanical loading of baggage and freight. An optional side cargo door is available for passenger, convertible and freighter versions of the Model 747. Installed aft of door 4 on the port side of the fuselage, it allows the carriage of main deck cargo on passenger versions. Addition of this door to the freighter allows loads up to 3.05 m (10 ft) in height to be accommodated aft of the flight deck, and also makes possible simultaneous nose and side cargo handling.

SYSTEMS: Air cycle air-conditioning system. Pressure differential 0.61 bars (8.9 lb/sq in). Four independent hydraulic systems, pressure 207 bars (3,000 lb/sq in), maximum capacity 265 litres (70 US gallons; 58 Imp gallons)/min at 196.5 bars (2,850 lb/sq in), each with one engine driven and one pneumatically driven pump. The latter pumps supplement or substitute for engine driven pumps. Reservoir in each system, pressurised by engine bleed air via a pressure regulation module. Reservoir relief valve pressure is nominal 4.48 bars (65 lb/sq in). A small AC powered electric pump is installed to charge the brake accumulator during towing of the aircraft. Electrical supply from four air-cooled 60kVA generators mounted one on each engine. Two 60kVA generators (supplemental cooling allows 90kVA each) mounted on APU for ground operation and to supply primary electrical power when engine mounted generators are not operating. Three-phase 400Hz constant frequency AC generators, 115/200V output. 28V DC power obtained from transformer-rectifier units. 24V 36Ah nickel-cadmium battery for selected ground functions and as in-flight backup. Gas turbine APU for pneumatic and electrical supplies.

AVIONICS AND EQUIPMENT: Standard avionics include three ARINC 566 VHF communications systems, two ARINC 533A HF communications systems, one ARINC 531 Selcal, three ARINC 547 VOR/ILS navigation systems, two ARINC 570 ADF, marker beacon receiver, two ARINC 568 DME, two ARINC 572 ATC, three ARINC 552 low-range radio altimeters, two ARINC 564 weather radar units, three ARINC 561 inertial navigation systems, two heading reference systems, ARINC 412 interphone, ARINC 560 passenger address system, multiple passenger service and entertainment system, ARINC 573 flight recorder, ARINC 557 cockpit voice recorder, integrated electronic flight control system with autothrottle and rollout guidance to provide automatic stabilisation, path control and pilot assist functions for Category II and III landing conditions, two ARINC 565 central air data systems, stall warning system, central instrument warning system, ground proximity warning system, attitude and navigation instrumentation, and standby attitude indication.

DIMENSIONS, EXTERNAL:

Wing span	59.64 m (195 ft 8 in)
Wing chord: at root	16.56 m (54 ft 4 in)
at tip	4.06 m (13 ft 4 in)
Wing aspect ratio	7.0
Length overall	70.66 m (231 ft 10 in)
Length of fuselage	68.63 m (225 ft 2 in)
Height overall	19.33 m (63 ft 5 in)
Tailplane span	22.17 m (72 ft 9 in)
Wheel track	11.00 m (36 ft 1 in)
Wheelbase	25.60 m (84 ft 0 in)
Passenger doors (ten, each): Height	1.93 m (6 ft 4 in)
Width	1.07 m (3 ft 6 in)
Height to sill	approx 4.88 m (16 ft 0 in)
Baggage door (front hold): Height	1.68 m (5 ft 6 in)
Width	2.64 m (8 ft 8 in)
Height to sill	approx 2.64 m (8 ft 8 in)
Baggage door (forward door, rear hold):	
Height	1.68 m (5 ft 6 in)
Width	2.64 m (8 ft 8 in)
Height to sill	approx 2.69 m (8 ft 10 in)
Bulk loading door (rear door on rear hold):	
Height	1.19 m (3 ft 11 in)
Width	1.12 m (3 ft 8 in)
Height to sill	approx 2.90 m (9 ft 6 in)
Optional cargo door (port): Height	3.05 m (10 ft 0 in)
Width	3.40 m (11 ft 2 in)

DIMENSIONS, INTERNAL:

Cabin, incl toilets and galleys:	
Length	57.00 m (187 ft 0 in)
Max width	6.13 m (20 ft 1½ in)
Max height	2.54 m (8 ft 4 in)
Floor area, passenger deck	327.9 m² (3,529 sq ft)
Volume, passenger deck	789 m³ (27,860 cu ft)
Baggage hold (fwd, containerised) volume	
	78.4 m³ (2,768 cu ft)
Baggage hold (rear, containerised) volume	
	68.6 m³ (2,422 cu ft)
Bulk volume	28.3 m³ (1,000 cu ft)

AREAS:

Wings, reference area	511 m² (5,500 sq ft)
Ailerons (total)	20.6 m² (222 sq ft)
Trailing-edge flaps (total)	78.7 m² (847 sq ft)
Leading-edge flaps (total)	48.1 m² (518 sq ft)
Spoilers (total)	30.8 m² (331 sq ft)
Fin	77.1 m² (830 sq ft)
Rudder	22.9 m² (247 sq ft)
Tailplane	136.6 m² (1,470 sq ft)
Elevators	32.5 m² (350 sq ft)

WEIGHTS (letters are used to denote engine installations as follows: A: JT9D-7R4G2, B: CF6-45A2, C: CF6-50E2, D: CF6-80C2, and E: RB211-524D4):

Operating weight empty (approx) for max available gross weights:

747-100SR (550 pass): B		162,431 kg (358,100 lb)
747-100B (366 pass): B		169,417 kg (373,500 lb)
E		171,866 kg (378,900 lb)
747-200B (366 pass): A		169,961 kg (374,700 lb)
C		171,548 kg (378,200 lb)
D		172,728 kg (380,800 lb)
E		173,998 kg (383,600 lb)
747-200M (257 pass and 7 pallets):		
A		171,821 kg (378,800 lb)
C		173,408 kg (382,300 lb)
D		174,587 kg (384,900 lb)
E		175,858 kg (387,700 lb)
747-200C (366 pass): A		175,313 kg (386,500 lb)
C		176,901 kg (390,000 lb)
D		178,080 kg (392,600 lb)
E		179,350 kg (395,400 lb)

Boeing 747-200B four-turbofan heavy transport aircraft (P&W JT9D engines) *(Pilot Press)*

Boeing 747-200F Freighter of Nippon Cargo Airlines

747-200C (28 pallets): A	163,973 kg (361,500 lb)
C	165,561 kg (365,000 lb)
D	166,740 kg (367,600 lb)
E	168,010 kg (370,400 lb)

Max fuel weight:

747-100B, 747-100SR:	
B, C	147,181 kg (324,480 lb)
E	148,324 kg (327,000 lb)
747-200B, 747-200M, 747-200C:	
A, E	165,289 kg (364,400 lb)
C, D	164,141 kg (361,870 lb)

Max structural payload:

747-100SR (550 pass): B	76,385 kg (168,400 lb)
747-100B (366 pass): B, C	69,399 kg (153,000 lb)
E	66,950 kg (147,600 lb)
747-200B (366 pass): A	68,855 kg (151,800 lb)
C	67,268 kg (148,300 lb)
D	66,088 kg (145,700 lb)
E	64,818 kg (142,900 lb)
747-200M (257 pass and 7 pallets):	
A	75,387 kg (166,200 lb)
C	73,799 kg (162,700 lb)
D	72,620 kg (160,100 lb)
E	71,350 kg (157,300 lb)
747-200C (366 pass): A	92,306 kg (203,500 lb)
C	90,718 kg (200,000 lb)
D	89,539 kg (197,400 lb)
E	88,269 kg (194,600 lb)
747-200C (28 pallets): A	103,646 kg (228,500 lb)
C	102,058 kg (225,000 lb)
D	100,879 kg (222,400 lb)
E	99,609 kg (219,600 lb)

Max T-O weight:

747-100SR: B	235,870 kg (520,000 lb)
	or 272,155 kg (600,000 lb)
747-100B: B, E	322,050 kg (710,000 lb)
	or 333,390 kg (735,000 lb)
	or 340,195 kg (750,000 lb)
747-200B, -200M, -200C:	
A, C, D, E	351,534 kg (775,000 lb)
	or 356,070 kg (785,000 lb)
	or 362,875 kg (800,000 lb)
	or 371,945 kg (820,000 lb)
	or 377,840 kg (833,000 lb)

Max ramp weight:

747-100B: B, C, E	341,555 kg (753,000 lb)
747-200B, -200M, -200C:	
A, C, D, E	379,200 kg (836,000 lb)

Max zero-fuel weight:

747-100SR: B	238,815 kg (526,500 lb)
747-100B: B, E	238,815 kg (526,500 lb)
747-200B: A, C, D, E	238,815 kg (526,500 lb)
747-200M: A, C, D, E	247,205 kg (545,000 lb)
747-200C: A, C, D, E	267,620 kg (590,000 lb)

Max landing weight:

747-100SR: B	229,065 kg (505,000 lb)
	or 238,135 kg (525,000 lb)
747-100B: B, E	255,825 kg (564,000 lb)
747-200B: A, C, D, E	255,825 kg (564,000 lb)
	or 265,350 kg (585,000 lb)
	or 285,765 kg (630,000 lb)
747-200M: A, C, D, E	285,765 kg (630,000 lb)
747-200C: A, C, D, E	285,765 kg (630,000 lb)

PERFORMANCE (747-100B at max T-O weight of 340,195 kg; 750,000 lb, and 747-200B at max T-O weight of 377,840 kg; 833,000 lb, except where indicated. Engines as designated under 'Weights'):

Max level speed at 9,150 m (30,000 ft):

747-100B at AUW of 272,160 kg (600,000 lb):	
B	525 knots (973 km/h; 604 mph)
747-200B at AUW of 317,515 kg (700,000 lb):	
A	527 knots (977 km/h; 607 mph)
C	523 knots (968 km/h; 602 mph)
D	530 knots (981 km/h; 610 mph)
E	522 knots (967 km/h; 601 mph)
Cruise ceiling, all versions	13,715 m (45,000 ft)
Min ground turning radius	22.86 m (75 ft 0 in)

Runway LCN (W: 334,750 kg; 738,000 lb, X: 341,555 kg; 753,000 lb, Y: 366,500 kg; 808,000 lb, Z: 379,200 kg; 836,000 lb max taxi weight on h = 0.51 m; 20 in flexible pavement):

W	81
X	83
Y	86
Z	88

Runway LCN (weights as above, on 11.02 m; 40 in rigid pavement):

W	87
X	89
Y	93
Z	95

FAR T-O distance to 10.7 m (35 ft) at S/L, ISA:

747-100B: B	3,050 m (10,000 ft)
747-200B: A	3,170 m (10,400 ft)
C	3,292 m (10,800 ft)
D	3,079 m (10,100 ft)
E	3,155 m (10,350 ft)

FAR landing field length:

747-100B, -200B at 255,825 kg (564,000 lb)
 1,881 m (6,170 ft)
747-200B at 265,350 kg (585,000 lb)
 1,942 m (6,370 ft)
747-200B at 285,765 kg (630,000 lb)
 2,112 m (6,930 ft)

Range, long-range cruise, typical international reserves of 5% trip fuel, 200 nm (371 km; 230 mile) alternate, 30 min hold at 457 m (1,500 ft):

747-100B with 366 passengers and baggage:	
B	5,500 nm (10,193 km; 6,333 miles)
747-200B with 366 passengers and baggage:	
A	6,550 nm (12,138 km; 7,542 miles)
C	6,350 nm (11,760 km; 7,307 miles)
D	6,900 nm (12,778 km; 7,940 miles)
E	6,600 nm (12,223 km; 7,595 miles)

Ferry range, long-range cruise, reserves as above:

747-100B: B	7,300 nm (13,520 km; 8,400 miles)
747-200B: A	7,450 nm (13,797 km; 8,573 miles)
C	7,200 nm (13,334 km; 8,285 miles)
D	7,900 nm (14,630 km; 9,091 miles)
E	7,500 nm (13,890 km; 8,631 miles)

OPERATIONAL NOISE LEVELS (as per FAR Pt 36, A: RB211-524C2 engines at brake release weight (BRW) of 340,195 kg; 750,000 lb and landing weight of 265,350 kg; 585,000 lb, B: JT9D-7R4G2 at BRW of 377,840 kg; 833,000 lb and landing weight of 285,765 kg; 630,000 lb):

T-O: A	104 EPNdB
B	106 EPNdB
Approach: A	107 EPNdB
B	107 EPNdB
Sideline: A	97 EPNdB
B	99 EPNdB

BOEING MODEL 747-200F FREIGHTER

The 747-200F Freighter is a version of the standard Model 747-200, capable of delivering 90,720 kg (200,000 lb) of containerised or palletised main deck cargo over a range of more than 4,500 nm (8,340 km; 5,180 miles). The first 747-200F flew for the first time on 30 November 1971. It was certificated on 7 March 1972 and delivered to Lufthansa two days later. A total of 72 had been ordered by 31 March 1990, of which 68 had been delivered.

To ensure maximum utilisation, the 747-200F has a special loading system that enables two men to handle and stow the maximum load of up to 112,400 kg (247,800 lb) in 30 min. This system was fully described in the 1977-78 *Jane's*.

The 747-200F can carry up to 29 containers measuring 3.05 × 2.44 × 2.44 m (10 ft long, 8 ft high and 8 ft wide), plus 30 lower-lobe containers, each of 4.90 m³ (173 cu ft) capacity, and 22.65 m³ (800 cu ft) of bulk cargo. The main deck can accommodate ANSI/ISO containers of up to 12.2 m (40 ft) in length, and many combinations of pallets and igloos. The lower hold can accommodate combinations of IATA-A1 or -A2, and ATA LD1 or LD3 half-width containers, full-width or main-deck baggage containers, and many combinations of pallets and igloos.

The nose loading door, which is hinged just below the flight deck to allow it to swing forward and upward, gives clear access to the main deck to facilitate the handling of long or large loads. A side cargo door is available as an option, allowing simultaneous nose and side loading. The side cargo door will accept palletised loads up to 3.05 m (10 ft 0 in) in height.

The description of the Model 747-200B applies also to the Model 747-200F except as follows:

TYPE: Four-turbofan heavy commercial freighter.

FUSELAGE: As for Model 747-200B, except for nose cargo loading door, which is hinged at the top and opens forward and upward. No windows in freight hold.

ACCOMMODATION: Normal operating crew of three on flight deck. Nose cargo loading door, hinged at top. Lower lobe cargo doors, on starboard side, one forward and one aft of wing. Bulk compartment cargo door, on starboard side, aft of lower lobe cargo door. Two doors for crew on port side of aircraft. Aircraft is designed for fully mechanical loading of freight.

DIMENSIONS, EXTERNAL: As for Model 747-200B except:

Crew doors (two, each): Height	1.93 m (6 ft 4 in)
Width	1.07 m (3 ft 6 in)
Height to sill	approx 4.88 m (16 ft 0 in)
Nose cargo loading door: Height	2.49 m (8 ft 2 in)
Width at top (min)	2.67 m (8 ft 9 in)
Max width	3.81 m (12 ft 6 in)
Height to sill	approx 4.90 m (16 ft 1 in)

DIMENSIONS, INTERNAL:

Main cargo deck: Height	2.54 m (8 ft 4 in)
Max width at floor level	5.92 m (19 ft 5 in)
Lower lobe: Width at floor level	3.18 m (10 ft 5 in)
Total cargo volume	687.0 m³ (24,260 cu ft)

AREAS: As for Model 747-200B

WEIGHTS (letters are used to denote engine installations as follows: A: JT9D-7R4G2, B: CF6-50E2, C: CF6-80C2, and D: RB211-524D4):

Operating weight empty (approx) for max available gross weights:

A	155,219 kg (342,200 lb)
B	156,807 kg (345,700 lb)
C	157,986 kg (348,300 lb)
D	159,256 kg (351,100 lb)
Max fuel weights	as for 747-200B

Max payload (29 pallets):

A	112,400 kg (247,800 lb)
B	110,812 kg (244,300 lb)
C	109,633 kg (241,700 lb)
D	108,363 kg (238,900 lb)

Boeing 747-300 of Egypt Air with extended upper deck

Max T-O weight: A, B, C, D   351,535 kg (775,000 lb)
        or 356,070 kg (785,000 lb)
        or 362,875 kg (800,000 lb)
        or 371,945 kg (820,000 lb)
        or 377,840 kg (833,000 lb)
Max ramp weight: A, B, C, D   379,200 kg (836,000 lb)
Max zero-fuel weight:
 A, B, C, D   267,620 kg (590,000 lb)
Max landing weight:
 A, B, C, D   285,765 kg (630,000 lb)
PERFORMANCE (at max T-O weight of 377,840 kg; 833,000 lb, except where indicated. Engines as designated under 'Weights'):
Max level speed at AUW of 317,515 kg (700,000 lb), at 9,150 m (30,000 ft):
 A   527 knots (977 km/h; 607 mph)
 B   523 knots (968 km/h; 602 mph)
 C   530 knots (981 km/h; 610 mph)
 D   522 knots (967 km/h; 601 mph)
Cruise ceiling   13,715 m (45,000 ft)
Min ground turning radius   22.86 m (75 ft 0 in)
FAR T-O distance to 10.7 m (35 ft) at S/L, ISA:
 A   3,170 m (10,400 ft)
 B   3,292 m (10,800 ft)
 C   3,079 m (10,100 ft)
 D   3,155 m (10,350 ft)
FAR landing field length:
 at AUW of 255,825 kg (564,000 lb)   1,881 m (6,170 ft)
 at AUW of 265,350 kg (585,000 lb)   1,942 m (6,370 ft)
 at AUW of 285,765 kg (630,000 lb)   2,112 m (6,930 ft)
Range, long-range step cruise, typical international reserves of 5% trip fuel, 200 nm (371 km; 230 mile) alternate, 30 min hold at 457 m (1,500 ft), with 90,720 kg (200,000 lb) payload:
 A   4,700 nm (8,704 km; 5,408 miles)
 B   4,550 nm (8,426 km; 5,236 miles)
 C   4,900 nm (9,075 km; 5,639 miles)
 D   4,650 nm (8,612 km; 5,351 miles)
Ferry range, long-range step cruise, reserves as above:
 A   7,900 nm (14,630 km; 9,091 miles)
 B   7,650 nm (14,168 km; 8,803 miles)
 C   8,300 nm (15,371 km; 9,551 miles)
 D   7,950 nm (14,723 km; 9,148 miles)

BOEING MODEL 747SP

A lower-weight longer-range version of the basic Model 747, the 747SP (special performance) was introduced for use on lower-density routes. Retaining a 90 per cent commonality of components with the standard Model 747, the major change is a reduction in overall length of 14.35 m (47 ft 1 in). It made its first flight on 4 July 1975, and FAA certification was received on 4 February 1976. First delivery was made on 5 March that year. To date, 45 have been ordered and delivered.

The description of the basic Model 747-100B/-200B applies also to the 747SP, except for the following details:
WINGS: As Model 747, except that trailing-edge flaps are of single-slotted variable pivot type, and wing structural materials are of reduced gauge. Large flap track fairings replaced by small link fairings. New wing/body fairings and leading-edge fillets.

FUSELAGE: As Model 747, except length reduced.
TAIL UNIT: Similar to 747, but tailplane span increased by 3.05 m (10 ft). Two-segment elevators. Height of fin increased by 1.52 m (5 ft 0 in). Double-hinged rudder.
LANDING GEAR: As Model 747, except structural weight reduced. Mainwheel tyres size 46 × 16, pressure 12.63 bars (183 lb/sq in). Nosewheel tyres size 49 × 17, pressure 13.8 bars (200 lb/sq in). Higher gross weight aircraft use 747-100 wheels and brakes. Modified 747-100 steel brakes by Bendix.
POWER PLANT: Four General Electric CF6-45A2 or CF6-50E2F turbofans, each of 206.8 kN (46,500 lb st); four Pratt & Whitney JT9D-7A turbofans, each of 205.7 kN (46,250 lb st); four Rolls-Royce RB211-524B2 turbofans, each of 222.8 kN (50,100 lb st), RB211-524C2 engines each of 229.5 kN (51,600 lb st), or RB211-524D4 engines each of 236.25 kN (53,110 lb st). Fuel system and oil capacity as for Model 747-100B, but with an additional 5,966 litres (1,576 US gallons; 1,312 Imp gallons) reserve fuel, providing a total capacity of 190,625 litres (50,359 US gallons; 41,932 Imp gallons).
ACCOMMODATION: Normal operating crew of three on flight deck above level of main deck. Observer station and provision for second observer station are provided. Crew rest area, as described for Model 747-400, is optional. Accommodation for 299 passengers on main deck, with 28 first class seats in forward area and ten-abreast seating throughout the major part of the main cabin. Seating for 32 passengers on upper deck, giving total capacity of 331 passengers. Max high-density accommodation for 440 passengers. Four doors on each side, two forward and two aft of the wing. Crew door on starboard side giving access to upper deck. Freight holds under floor, forward and aft of wing box, each with one door on starboard side.
SYSTEMS, AVIONICS AND EQUIPMENT: As for Model 747.
DIMENSIONS, EXTERNAL: As for 747-100B/200B except:
 Length overall   56.31 m (184 ft 9 in)
 Height overall   19.94 m (65 ft 5 in)
 Tailplane span   25.22 m (82 ft 9 in)
 Wheelbase   20.52 m (67 ft 4 in)
DIMENSIONS, INTERNAL:
 Cabin, incl toilets and galleys:
  Length   42.27 m (138 ft 8 in)
  Max width   6.13 m (20 ft 1½ in)
  Max height   2.54 m (8 ft 4 in)
 Floor area, passenger deck   253.2 m² (2,725 sq ft)
 Volume, passenger deck   613.34 m³ (21,660 cu ft)
 Baggage hold volume (fwd)   48.99 m³ (1,730 cu ft)
 Baggage hold volume (rear, containerised)
   48.99 m³ (1,730 cu ft)
 Bulk compartment volume (rear)   11.33 m³ (400 cu ft)
AREAS: As for 747-100B/200B except:
 Ailerons (total)   20.37 m² (219.3 sq ft)
 Trailing-edge flaps (total)   78.78 m² (848.0 sq ft)
 Fin   82.22 m² (885.0 sq ft)
 Tailplane   142.51 m² (1,534 sq ft)
WEIGHTS: (RB211-524D4 engines):
 Operating weight empty (approx, with 276 passengers):
   151,454 kg (333,900 lb)
 Max fuel weight   149,361 kg (329,285 lb)

Max payload   34,518 kg (76,100 lb)
      or 41,322 kg (91,100 lb)
Max T-O weight (dry engines)   285,765 kg (630,000 lb)
      or 299,370 kg (660,000 lb)
      or 303,905 kg (670,000 lb)
      or 312,980 kg (690,000 lb)
      or 315,700 kg (696,000 lb)
      or 317,515 kg (700,000 lb)
Max ramp weight   284,485 kg (636,000 lb)
      or 302,090 kg (666,000 lb)
      or 306,630 kg (676,000 lb)
      or 315,700 kg (696,000 lb)
      or 318,875 kg (703,000 lb)
Max zero-fuel weight   185,975 kg (410,000 lb)
      or 192,775 kg (425,000 lb)
Max landing weight   204,115 kg (450,000 lb)
      or 210,920 kg (465,000 lb)
PERFORMANCE (with RB211-524D4 engines), at T-O weight of 317,515 kg; 700,000 lb, except where indicated):
Never-exceed speed   Mach 0.92
Max level speed, AUW of 226,795 kg (500,000 lb) at 9,150 m (30,000 ft)   538 knots (996 km/h; 619 mph)
Service ceiling   13,745 m (45,100 ft)
Min ground turning radius over outer wingtip
   22.25 m (73 ft 0 in)
Runway LCN (Y: 302,090 kg; 666,000 lb, Z: 317,515 kg; 700,000 lb taxi weight on h = 0.51 m; 20 in flexible pavement): Y   70
 Z   75
Runway LCN (weights as above, on l = 1.02 m; 40 in rigid pavement): Y   76
 Z   80
FAR T-O distance to 10.7 m (35 ft) at S/L, ISA
   2,347 m (7,700 ft)
FAR landing field length:
 at AUW of 204,115 kg (450,000 lb)   1,594 m (5,230 ft)
 at AUW of 210,920 kg (465,000 lb)   1,646 m (5,400 ft)
Range, long-range step cruise, typical international reserves, with 276 passengers and baggage
   6,650 nm (12,324 km; 7,658 miles)
Ferry range, long-range step cruise, typical international reserves   8,000 nm (14,826 km; 9,212 miles)

BOEING MODEL 747-300

On 12 June 1980, Boeing announced an option for the Model 747 which incorporates structural changes to the aircraft's upper deck area to increase passenger carrying capacity and provide an optional crew rest area, as described for the Model 747-400. The upper forward fuselage is extended aft by 7.11 m (23 ft 4 in) to increase upper deck accommodation from 32 to a maximum of 69 passengers in all-economy class configuration. Seating is six abreast, with a single aisle, and panniers between the outer seats and cabin wall are provided for hand baggage. Alternative configurations include 26 first class sleeper seats on the extended upper deck. In addition, seven additional seats can be accommodated on the main deck as a result of deleting the standard circular stairway. It is replaced by a new straight stairway at the rear of the upper deck area. Two new doors 1.83 m (6 ft 0 in) high and 1.07 m (3 ft 6 in) wide replace the existing 1.22 × 0.61 m (4 ft 0 in × 2 ft 0 in)

Small winglets are a distinctive feature of the Boeing 747-400

upper deck exits. Other structural changes include the provision of a new emergency exit and additional windows. The extended upper deck option was made available initially on existing aircraft of the 747-100 and -200 series, which then became known as **747-300s**; maximum take-off weights are unchanged, but operating weight empty is increased by about 4,220 kg (9,310 lb). Most efficient high speed cruise is increased from Mach 0.84 to Mach 0.85 by the revised upper contours. Flight testing with JT9D-7R4G2 engines began on 5 October 1982, followed on 10 December by the first 747-300 with CF6-50E2 engines, and FAA certification of the -300 was announced by Boeing on 7 March 1983. Initial deliveries were to Swissair and UTA, with whom the aircraft entered service on 28 March and 1 April 1983 respectively. Orders for new 747-300s totalled 81, including four short-range **747-300SRs** (for Japan Air Lines) and 21 **747-300M** Combis, by 31 March 1990. At that date 80, including the four 300SRs and 20 of the -300Ms, had been delivered.

The detailed specification for the Boeing 747-100B/-200B applies also to the 747-300 except as follows:
WEIGHTS (A: JT9D-7R4G2, B: CF6-50E2, C: CF6-80C2, and D: RB211-524D4):
Operating weight empty (approx) for max available gross weights:

747-300 (400 pass): A	174,134 kg (383,900 lb)	
B	175,721 kg (387,400 lb)	
C	176,901 kg (390,000 lb)	
D	178,171 kg (392,800 lb)	
747-300M (289 pass and 7 pallets):		
A	175,585 kg (387,100 lb)	
B	177,173 kg (390,600 lb)	
C	178,352 kg (393,200 lb)	
D	179,622 kg (396,000 lb)	

Max fuel weights   as for 747-200B
Max payload:

747-300 (400 pass): A	68,538 kg (151,100 lb)
B	66,950 kg (147,600 lb)
C	65,771 kg (145,000 lb)
D	64,501 kg (142,200 lb)
747-300M (289 pass and 7 pallets):	
A	80,694 kg (177,900 lb)
B	79,106 kg (174,400 lb)
C	77,927 kg (171,800 lb)
D	76,657 kg (169,000 lb)

Max T-O weight:

747-300, -300M: A, B, C, D	351,535 kg (775,000 lb)
	or 356,070 kg (785,000 lb)
	or 362,875 kg (800,000 lb)
	or 371,945 kg (820,000 lb)
	or 377,840 kg (833,000 lb)

Max ramp weight:
747-300, -300M: A, B, C, D   379,200 kg (836,000 lb)
Max zero-fuel weight:

747-300: A, B, C, D	242,670 kg (535,000 lb)
747-300M: A, B, C, D	256,280 kg (565,000 lb)

Max landing weight:

747-300: A, B, C, D	260,360 kg (574,000 lb)
	or 265,350 kg (585,000 lb)
	or 285,765 kg (630,000 lb)
747-300M: A, B, C, D	285,765 kg (630,000 lb)

PERFORMANCE (at max T-O weight of 377,840 kg; 833,000 lb, except where indicated. Engines as designated under 'Weights'):
Max level speed at AUW of 317,515 kg (700,000 lb) at 9150 m (30,000 ft): A   530 knots (982 km/h; 610 mph)

B	529 knots (979 km/h; 608 mph)
C	538 knots (996 km/h; 619 mph)
D	526 knots (974 km/h; 605 mph)

FAR T-O distance to 10.7 m (35 ft) at S/L, ISA:

A	3,170 m (10,400 ft)
B	3,292 m (10,800 ft)
C	3,079 m (10,100 ft)
D	3,155 m (10,350 ft)

FAR landing field length:
at AUW of 255,825 kg (564,000 lb)   1,881 m (6,170 ft)

at AUW of 265,350 kg (585,000 lb)   1,942 m (6,370 ft)
at AUW of 285,765 kg (630,000 lb)   2,112 m (6,930 ft)
Range, long-range cruise, typical international reserves of 5% trip fuel, 200 nm (371 km; 230 mile) alternate, 30 min hold at 457 m (1,500ft), with 400 passengers and baggage: A   6,300 nm (11,675 km; 7,254 miles)

B	6,100 nm (11,297 km; 7,020 miles)
C	6,700 nm (12,408 km; 7,710 miles)
D	6,250 nm (11,575 km; 7,192 miles)

Ferry range, long-range cruise, reserves as above:

A	7,250 nm (13,436 km; 8,348 miles)
B	7,000 nm (12,964 km; 8,055 miles)
C	7,750 nm (14,353 km; 8,918 miles)
D	7,300 nm (13,520 km; 8,400 miles)

BOEING MODEL 747-400

Boeing announced in May 1985 development of the Model 747-400, an advanced long-range version of the 747-300. Improvements include 258.0 kN (58,000 lb st) class CF6-80C2, PW4056 or RB211-524G engines, a modern two-crew digital flight deck, more flexible interior configurations, increased range and better fuel economy. It is now the only version of the Model 747 marketed by Boeing.

The 747-400 shares the extended upper deck fuselage of the 747-300. A 1.83 m (6 ft 0 in) extension has been added to each wingtip, with a 1.83 m (6 ft 0 in) winglet, canted outboard at an angle of 22° and sweptback 60°, the combined tip extension and winglet installation offering a claimed increase in range of some three per cent. By employing advanced aluminium alloys developed for the Models 757 and 767 in the 747-400's wing structure, Boeing engineers have achieved a weight saving of 2,721 kg (6,000 lb). Substitution of carbon brakes for steel brakes, and new 0.56 m (1 ft 10 in) wide wheels with low-profile tyres, has provided a further weight saving of 816 kg (1,800 lb) in the aircraft's landing gear. New engine nacelles and support pylons have been designed, offering commonality with those of the Boeing 767. The 747-400's flight deck is configured for two-crew operation with digital avionics, sharing many common features with the 757/767 and resulting in a 60 per cent reduction in the number of instruments and gauges on the 747 flight deck. The final flight deck configuration may include a head-down display of fuel status on the engine indicating and crew alerting (EICAS) CRT displays rather than on overhead panels.

Improvements to the cabin area of the 747-400 include increased overhead storage facilities, alternative galley and toilet positions, a wireless cabin entertainment system in which audio and visual signals are picked up from floor mounted transmitters, and greater flexibility in interior design to permit airlines to react quickly to changes in market requirements which demand different mixes of first, business and economy class seating. An overhead crew rest area located above the main deck in the aft section of the passenger cabin is optional, with accommodation for four bunks and four seats; or eight bunks and two seats; or two bunks, two seats and five sleeper seats. A Combi cargo/passenger variant is designated **747-400M**.

An all-cargo version, launched during 1989, is designated **747-400F** and will carry a payload 19,960 kg (44,000 lb) greater than that of the 747-200F at ranges up to 5,210 nm (9,656 km; 6,000 miles). The 747-400F will be externally similar to the passenger variant except that it will not feature the extended upper deck. Launch customer for this variant was Air France, which has ordered five with CF6-80C2 engines for delivery commencing in August 1993, followed by Cathay Pacific, which has ordered two with RB211-524H engines.

A new feature of the 747-400 is provision for the carriage of 12,492 litres (3,300 US gallons; 2,748 Imp gallons) of fuel in the horizontal tail surfaces, in tanks located between the front and rear spars. No provision is made for transferring this fuel as a means of adjusting longitudinal trim or maintaining aft centre of gravity. As a result of the increased fuel capacity, greater fuel economy of new generation engines and structural weight savings, the 747-400 can offer a 1,000 nm (1,853 km; 1,151 mile) increase in range over the 747-300. Depending on the engines selected, the 747-400 is claimed to burn 9-12 per cent less fuel than a 747-300 and to offer fuel burned per passenger seat reductions of up to 24 per cent over a 747-200. A Pratt & Whitney Canada APU is installed in the tailcone.

Design go-ahead for the 747-400 was granted in July 1985. Construction of the first aircraft (N401PW) began in mid-1986 with rollout occuring on 26 January 1988, and first flight on 29 April 1988. Three further aircraft joined the test programme, leading to FAA certification of the PW4056 engined aircraft on 9 January 1989. Certification of the CF6-80C2 and RB211-524G variants was achieved in 1989. In October 1985 Northwest Orient Airlines became the launch customer for the 747-400 with an order for 10

Boeing 747-400 advanced long-range version of the 747-300 (General Electric CF6-80C2 engines)
(Pilot Press)

Boeing 757-200 (Rolls-Royce 535E4 turbofans) in the insignia of Royal Brunei Airlines

aircraft, powered by PW4000 series engines. The Northwest Orient aircraft are configured for 420 passengers. First delivery was made on 26 January 1989, and the aircraft began route proving flights five days later, initially entering service on Northwest Orient's domestic route between Minneapolis, Minnesota, and Phoenix, Arizona, pending completion of crew training for the introduction of New York-Tokyo. Total 747-400 firm orders, including 7 Freighters and 27 Combis, had reached 279 by 25 May 1990, of which 70 had been delivered.

On 17 August 1989 a Boeing 747-400 of Qantas Airlines set a new world record by flying non-stop from London to Sydney, a distance of 9,688 nm (17,950 km; 11,156 miles), in 20 h 8 min while on its delivery flight to the Australian airline.

DIMENSIONS, EXTERNAL: As for 747-100/200, except:

Wing span   64.31 m (211 ft 0 in)

WEIGHTS (letters are used to denote engine installations as follows: A: PW4256, B: CF6-80C2, and C: RB211-524D4D):

Operating weight empty (approx) for max available gross
weights: A   177,354 kg (391,000 lb)
  B   177,218 kg (390,700 lb)
  C   178,661 kg (393,880 lb)
Max fuel weights: A, C   175,392 kg (386,674 lb)
  B   174,553 kg (384,824 lb)
Max payload:
  A   65,317 kg (144,000 lb)
  B   65,453 kg (144,300 lb)
  C   64,011 kg (141,120 lb)
Max T-O weight   362,875 kg (800,000 lb)
            or 385,555 kg (850,000 lb)
            or 394,625 kg (870,000 lb)
Max ramp weight   364,235 kg (803,000 lb)
            or 386,915 kg (853,000 lb)
            or 395,986 kg (873,000 lb)
Max zero-fuel weight   242,670 kg (535,000 lb)
Max landing weight   260,360 kg (574,000 lb)
            or 285,765 kg (630,000 lb)
PERFORMANCE (estimated, at T-O weight of 394,625 kg; 870,000 lb except where indicated. Engines as designated under 'Weights'):
Max level speed at 9,150 m (30,000 ft):
  A   529 knots (979 km/h; 608 mph)
  B   532 knots (985 km/h; 612 mph)
  C   527 knots (976 km/h; 606 mph)
FAR T-O distance to 10.7 m (35 ft) at S/L, ISA:
  A   3,383 m (11,100 ft)
  B   3,353 m (11,000 ft)
  C   3,323 m (10,900 ft)
FAR landing field length at max landing weight of 285,765 kg (630,000 lb): A, B, C   2,134 m (7,000 ft)
Range, long-range cruising speed, 412 passengers and baggage, typical international reserves:
  A, B, C   7,300 nm (13,528 km; 8,406 miles)
Ferry range, typical international reserves:
  A, B, C   8,400 nm (15,569 km; 9,673 miles)

BOEING MODEL 757

In the early months of 1978, Boeing announced a proposal to develop a new family of advanced technology commercial aircraft, to which it gave the Model designations 757, 767 and 777. The short/medium-range 757 was intended to differ considerably from the other two, being based on the Boeing 727 fuselage. Improved performance would come from two new high bypass engines, and an advanced technology wing with less sweepback than that of the Model 727.

On 31 August 1978 Eastern Air Lines and British Airways announced their intention to purchase 21 and 19 Model 757s respectively, the former taking an option on an additional 24, and the latter on 18. Following the signature

in early 1979 of formal contracts by both of these airlines, Boeing announced on 23 March 1979 that the company had initiated full production of the Model 757. The first 757 (N757A) made its first flight on 19 February 1982. This, and the next four aircraft off the production line, were used in the certification programme, which resulted in type certification by the FAA on 21 December 1982 and the UK CAA on 14 January 1983. Deliveries to Eastern Air Lines and British Airways began on 22 December 1982 and 25 January 1983, with respective revenue services starting on 1 January and 9 February 1983. Aircraft for these two airlines are designated **Model 757-200** and were powered initially by 166.4 kN (37,400 lb st) Rolls-Royce 535C turbofans. This was the first time that Boeing had launched a new airliner with a non-American engine. The first PW2037 engined 757 made its first flight on 14 March 1984; it was certificated in October and deliveries to Delta began on 5 November 1984. The first 757 with uprated Rolls-Royce 535E4 engines was delivered to Eastern on 10 October 1984. With the 535C engines, the 757-200 provides 53 per cent more seat miles per unit of fuel than earlier medium-range aircraft. With 535E4 and PW2037 engines the advantage is 76 per cent. A corporate/executive transport version and an extended range variant are available. The first extended range model was delivered to Royal Brunei Airlines in May 1986.

Boeing announced in January 1986 a dedicated freighter version of the 757-200 designated Model **757-200PF** (Package Freighter). This aircraft features a large side cargo door in the forward fuselage, a single crew door and a windowless interior which will accept up to 15 standard 2.24 × 3.18 m (88 × 125 in) cargo pallets on the main deck. United Parcel Service has ordered 30 Model 757-200PFs powered by PW2040s; Ansett Worldwide has ordered two and Ethiopia one. The first 757-200PF was certificated on 3 September 1987 and delivered to UPS the same day. Sixteen had been delivered by 31 March 1990.

In February 1986 Boeing announced the **Model 757-200M** Combi, which, unlike the 757-200PF, retains all passenger windows and doors but has a mixed cargo/passenger configuration with an upward opening 3.40 × 2.18 m (134 × 86 in) cargo door on the port side of the forward fuselage. The 757-200M can carry up to three 2.24 m × 2.74 m (88 × 108 in) cargo containers and 150 passengers. Royal Nepal Airlines is launch customer for the Combi, with an order for a single aircraft which flew for the first time on 15 July 1988.

In December 1986 the Boeing 757 with Rolls-Royce 535E4 engines received FAA approval for extended range operations (EROPS) over water or undeveloped land areas. Boeing's windshear detection and guidance system also received FAA approval for commercial operation on 757s in the following month. EROPS approval with PW2037/2040 engines was received in April 1990.

On 8 April 1988 a Boeing 757-200 on delivery to Air Europe set a distance record for the type, flying the 4,988 nm (9,244 km; 5,744 miles) from Seattle to Palma de Mallorca in 10 h 21 min. By 31 March 1990 orders for 757-200/200M/200PFs totalled 632, of which 270 had been delivered.

The Model 757 retains the same fuselage cross-section as the 707/727/737 family. The original design provided for a T tail configuration, but as a result of wind tunnel testing it was decided to mount the tailplane on the fuselage.

TYPE: Twin-turbofan short/medium-range transport aircraft.

WINGS: Cantilever low-wing monoplane. Special Boeing wing sections. Dihedral 5°. Incidence 3° 12'. Sweepback at quarter-chord 25°. All aluminium alloy two-spar fail-safe wing box structure, manufactured by Boeing, with wing in-spar ribs by Hawker de Havilland of Australia. Centre-section continuous through fuselage. All-speed fully-powered ailerons outboard of double-

slotted inboard and outboard trailing-edge flaps. Inboard flaps manufactured by Shorts of Northern Ireland; outboard flaps by CASA of Spain. High-lift full span leading-edge slats, in five sections on each wing, manufactured by Boeing Renton; Boeing Helicopters fixed leading-edges. Five flight spoilers and one ground spoiler on wing upper surface forward of trailing-edge flaps, manufactured by Grumman. Lateral control provided by ailerons, plus flight spoilers operated differentially. Spoilers operated collectively as speed brakes. Extensive use of honeycomb, and graphite composites and laminates, in construction of ailerons, flaps and spoilers. Thermal anti-icing of wing leading-edges. Wing/fuselage fairings and flap track fairings, of graphite/Kevlar, manufactured by Heath Tecna; wingtips by Schweizer.

FUSELAGE: All-metal semi-monocoque fail-safe structure, cross-section based on two circular arcs of different radii, the larger above, and faired into a smooth contoured oval. Flight deck manufactured by Boeing Military Airplanes at Wichita; main cabin sections by Boeing Renton; extreme rear fuselage by LTV.

TAIL UNIT: Tailplane consists of full span torque boxes of conventional light alloy construction, and is attached at pivot points and to an actuator. The fin comprises a three-spar dual-cell light alloy torque box attached to the fuselage. Elevators and rudder have graphite/epoxy honeycomb skins, supported by honeycomb and laminated spar and rib assemblies. Fin and tailplane manufactured by LTV; rudder and elevators of graphite by Boeing.

LANDING GEAR: Retractable tricycle type, with main and nose units manufactured by Menasco. Each main unit comprises a four-wheel bogie, fitted with Dunlop wheels, carbon brakes and tyres. Twin-wheel nose unit, also with Dunlop tyres. All landing gear doors of graphite/Kevlar.

POWER PLANT: Two 166.4 kN (37,400 lb st) Rolls-Royce 535C, 170 kN (38,200 lb st) Pratt & Whitney PW2037, 178.4 kN (40,100 lb st) Rolls-Royce 535E4, or 185.5 kN (41,700 lb st) Pratt & Whitney PW2040 turbofans, mounted in underwing pods. Engine support struts supplied by Rohr Industries. Fuel capacity 42,597 litres (11,253 US gallons; 9,370 Imp gallons).

ACCOMMODATION: Crew of two on flight deck, with provision for an observer. Five to seven cabin attendants. Nine standard interior arrangements for 178 (16 first class/162 tourist), 186 (16 first class/170 tourist), 202 (12 first class/190 tourist), 208 (12 first class/196 tourist) mixed class passengers, or 214, 220, 223, 224 or 239 all-tourist passengers. First class seats are four-abreast, at 96.5 cm (38 in) pitch; tourist seat pitch is 81 or 86 cm (32 or 34 in), basically six-abreast, in mixed class arrangements. Large overhead bins of Kevlar provide approximately 0.054 m³ (1.9 cu ft) of stowage per passenger. Choice of two cabin door configurations, with either three passenger doors and two overwing emergency exits on each side (used with 186, 208, 220 and 224 seat interiors), or four doors on each side (used with 178, 202, 214, 223 and 239 seat interiors). All versions have a galley at the front on the starboard side and another at the rear (two on 178 and 186 passenger versions and three on the 239 version plus one amidships); a toilet at the front on the port side and three more at the rear (186, 202, 208, 220, 224 passengers) or two at the rear (239) or amidships (178, 214, 223 passengers). Coat closet at front of first class cabins and 214/220 passenger interiors. Baggage/cargo hold doors on starboard side.

SYSTEMS: AiResearch environmental control system; General Electric engine thrust management system; Honeywell-Vickers engine driven hydraulic pumps; four Abex electric hydraulic pumps. Hydraulic system maximum flow rate 140 litres (37 US gallons; 30.8 Imp gallons)/min at T-O power on engine driven pumps; 25.4-34.8 litres (6.7-9.2 US gallons; 5.6-7.7 Imp gallons)/min on electric motor pumps; 42.8 litres (11.3 US gallons; 9.4 Imp gallons)/min on ram air turbine. Independent reservoirs, pressurised by air from pneumatic system, maximum pressure 207 bars (3,000 lb/sq in) on primary pumps. Sundstrand electrical power generating system and ram air turbine; and Garrett GTCP331-200 APU.

AVIONICS: Collins FCS-700 autopilot flight director system (AFDS), EFIS-700 electronic flight instrument system, engine indication and crew alerting system (EICAS), RMI-743 radio distance magnetic indicator (RDMI) and optional radio magnetic indicator (RMI). Avionics also include a Honeywell inertial reference system (IRS). In this IRS, conventional mechanical gyroscopes are replaced by laser gyroscopes, and utilisation, in both the Models 757 and 767, represents their first commercial application. The IRS provides position, velocity and attitude information to flight deck displays, and the flight management computer system (FMCS) and digital air data computer (DADC) supplied by Honeywell. The FMCS provides automatic en-route and terminal navigation capability, and also computes and commands both lateral and vertical flight profiles for optimum fuel efficiency, maximised by electronic linkage of the FMCS with automatic flight control and thrust management systems. Boeing windshear detection and guidance system is optional. Aircraft for British Airways and Monarch Airlines have Bendix ARINC 700 series avionics, including colour weather radar and seven digital com, nav and identification systems.

DIMENSIONS, EXTERNAL:

Wing span	38.05 m (124 ft 10 in)
Wing chord: at root	8.20 m (26 ft 11 in)
at tip	1.73 m (5 ft 8 in)
Wing aspect ratio	7.8
Length overall	47.32 m (155 ft 3 in)
Length of fuselage	46.96 m (154 ft 10 in)
Height overall	13.56 m (44 ft 6 in)
Tailplane span	15.21 m (49 ft 11 in)
Wheel track	7.32 m (24 ft 0 in)
Wheelbase	18.29 m (60 ft 0 in)

Passenger doors (two, fwd, port):

Height	1.83 m (6 ft 0 in)
Width	0.84 m (2 ft 9 in)
Passenger door (rear, port): Height	1.83 m (6 ft 0 in)
Width	0.76 m (2 ft 6 in)
Service door (fwd, stbd): Height	1.65 m (5 ft 5 in)
Width	0.76 m (2 ft 6 in)

Service door (stbd, opposite second passenger door):

Height	1.83 m (6 ft 0 in)
Width	0.84 m (2 ft 9 in)
Service door (rear, stbd): Height	1.83 m (6 ft 0 in)
Width	0.76 m (2 ft 6 in)

Emergency exits (four, overwing):

Height	0.97 m (3 ft 2 in)
Width	0.51 m (1 ft 8 in)

Emergency exits, optional (two, aft of wings):

Height	1.32 m (4 ft 4 in)
Width	0.61 m (2 ft 0 in)

DIMENSIONS, INTERNAL:

Cabin (aft of flight deck to rear pressure bulkhead):

Length	36.09 m (118 ft 5 in)
Max width	3.53 m (11 ft 7 in)
Max height	2.13 m (7 ft 0 in)
Floor area	116.04 m² (1,249 sq ft)
Passenger area volume	230.50 m³ (8,140 cu ft)

Underfloor cargo volume (bulk loading):

fwd	19.82 m³ (700 cu ft)
rear	30.87 m³ (1,090 cu ft)

AREAS:

Wings, gross	185.25 m² (1,994 sq ft)
Ailerons (total)	4.46 m² (48.0 sq ft)
Trailing-edge flaps (total)	30.38 m² (327 sq ft)
Leading-edge slats (total)	18.39 m² (198 sq ft)
Flight spoilers (total)	10.96 m² (118 sq ft)
Ground spoilers (total)	12.82 m² (138 sq ft)
Fin	34.37 m² (370 sq ft)
Rudder	11.61 m² (125 sq ft)
Tailplane	50.35 m² (542 sq ft)
Elevators (total)	12.54 m² (135 sq ft)

WEIGHTS AND LOADINGS (with 186 passengers. A: 535E4 engines, B: PW2037s, C: PW2040s):

Operating weight empty: A	57,180 kg (126,060 lb)
B, C	57,039 kg (125,750 lb)
Max basic T-O weight: A, B, C	99,790 kg (220,000 lb)

Max T-O weight (medium-range):

A, B, C	104,325 kg (230,000 lb)

Max T-O weight (long-range):

A, B, C	113,395 kg (250,000 lb)
Max landing weight: A, B, C	89,810 kg (198,000 lb)
757-200PF	95,255 kg (210,000 lb)
Max zero-fuel weight: A, B, C	83,460 kg (184,000 lb)
757-200PF	90,720 kg (200,000 lb)

Max wing loading:

A, B, C at max basic T-O weight	538.5 kg/m² (110.3 lb/sq ft)
A, B, C at long-range max T-O weight	587.8 kg/m² (120.4 lb/sq ft)

First Boeing 757-200PF Package Freighter for United Parcel Service

Boeing 757-200 twin-turbofan short/medium-range transport aircraft (Pilot Press)

Max power loading:

at max basic T-O weight:

A	279.68 kg/kN (2.74 lb/lb st)
B	293.5 kg/kN (2.88 lb/lb st)
C	268.97 kg/kN (2.64 lb/lb st)

at long-range max T-O weight:

A	317.81 kg/kN (3.12 lb/lb st)
B	333.51 kg/kN (3.27 lb/lb st)
C	305.1 kg/kN (3.00 lb/lb st)

PERFORMANCE (nominal, with 186 passengers, US mixed class operations; at max basic T-O weight, except where indicated, and with engines as above):

Max operating speed: A, B, C	Mach 0.86
Cruising speed: A, B, C	Mach 0.80

Approach speed at S/L, flaps down, max landing weight:

A, B, C	132 knots (245 km/h; 152 mph) EAS
Initial cruising height: A	11,878 m (38,970 ft)
B, C	11,674 m (38,300 ft)

Min ground turning radius: over wingtip 29.87 m (98 ft)

nose gear 21.64 m (71 ft)

Runway LCN at ramp weight of 100,244 kg (221,000 lb), optimum tyre pressure and subgrade C flexible pavement: H40 × 14.5-19.0 tyres 36

T-O field length (S/L, 29°C):

at max basic T-O weight: A 1,646 m (5,400 ft)

B	1,791 m (5,875 ft)
C	1,637 m (5,370 ft)

at long-range max T-O weight: A 2,134 m (7,000 ft)

B	2,792 m (9,160 ft)
C	2,118 m (6,950 ft)

Landing field length at max landing weight:

A	1,411 m (4,630 ft)
B, C	1,460 m (4,790 ft)

Range with 186 passengers:

at max basic T-O weight:

A	2,820 nm (5,226 km; 3,247 miles)
B, C	2,980 nm (5,522 km; 3,431 miles)

at long-range max T-O weight:

A	3,820 nm (7,079 km; 4,399 miles)
B, C	4,000 nm (7,408 km; 4,603 miles)

757-200PF, max long-range T-O weight, 22,680 kg (50,000 lb) payload:

A	3,700 nm (6,857 km; 4,261 miles)
B, C	3,885 nm (7,200 km; 4,474 miles)

OPERATIONAL NOISE LEVELS (FAR Pt 36 Stage 3):

T-O, at max basic T-O weight, cutback power:

A	82.2 EPNdB
B	86.2 EPNdB
C (estimated)	84.7 EPNdB

Approach at max landing weight, 30° flap:

A	95.0 EPNdB
B, C	97.7 EPNdB

Sideline: A 93.3 EPNdB

B	94.0 EPNdB
C (estimated)	94.6 EPNdB

BOEING MODEL 767

On 14 July 1978, Boeing announced its intention to launch full scale development of the twin-turbofan Model 767, following receipt of an order for 30 from United Air Lines. Construction of the first Model 767 began on 6 July 1979, with a fuselage 1.17 m (3 ft 10 in) wider than that of the Model 757, permitting a two-aisle seating layout. A 220-passenger version known as the **767-200** was selected as the basic model. The first Model 767 (N767BA) made its first flight on 26 September 1981, powered by Pratt & Whitney JT9D turbofans. The fifth aircraft, the first powered by General Electric CF6-80A engines, flew for the first time on 19 February 1982.

FAA certification of the initial JT9D-7R4D version was received on 30 July 1982, and on 30 September 1982 for the CF6-80A version. Delivery of the first 767, to United Air Lines, was made on 19 August 1982, this airline operating its initial revenue service on 8 September. The first CF6-engined 767 was delivered to Delta on 25 October and entered service on 15 December 1982.

As well as the basic model, an optional medium-range version of the 767-200 with reduced fuel capacity, and an optional higher gross weight version, certificated in June 1983, are available. In addition, an extended-range **767-200ER** (first flown on 6 March 1984), with still higher gross weight and increased fuel capacity, is in production. The basic extended-range version, with gross weight increased to 156,490 kg (345,000 lb) and increased fuel capacity due to wing centre-section tanks, was first delivered, to Ethiopian Airlines on 23 May 1984. Versions with optional gross weights of 159,210 kg (351,000 lb), 172,365 kg (380,000 lb) and 175,540 kg (387,000 lb) and with additional fuel capacity are also available.

In February 1983 Boeing announced the addition to the line of a 269-seat **767-300**, with the same max T-O weight as the basic 767-200ER, strengthened main and nose landing gear, and additional metal thickness in certain areas of the fuselage and wing lower surface. The fuselage is extended by a 3.07 m (10 ft 1 in) plug forward of the wing, and a 3.35 m (11 ft) plug aft of the wing. Flight deck, cabin cross-section and systems are as for the other 767 models; power plant options are as for the 767-200ER. The first order for the 767-300 was received on 29 September 1983. The first 767-300 flew for the first time on 30 January 1986, powered by JT9D-7R4D engines, and was certificated on 22 September 1986, at which time the version with CF6-80A2s was also certificated. Deliveries (to JAL) began on 25 September 1986. In August 1987 British Airways ordered 11 767-300s to which a further six were added in October 1988, all with Rolls-Royce RB211-524H engines, for delivery commencing November 1989.

In January 1985 Boeing began development of an extended range, higher gross weight version of the 767-300, designated **767-300ER**. This version, with optional gross weights of 172,365 kg (380,000 lb), 175,540 kg (387,000 lb)

Boeing 767-200ER of Air Mauritius photographed during a record-setting delivery flight in April 1988

or 181,439 kg (400,000 lb), and further enlarged wing centre-section fuel tanks, is powered by advanced General Electric CF6-80C2, Pratt & Whitney PW4000 series or Rolls-Royce RB211-524H engines. Structural changes have been incorporated to accommodate the increased fuel capacity and higher gross weight. Launch customer for the 767-300ER was American Airlines, which ordered 15 for delivery commencing in February 1988. Certification of the 767-300ER was obtained in late 1987.

In January 1987 the 767-200 with JT9D-7R4 and CF6-80A or A2 engines received FAA approval for extended range operations (EROPS) over water or undeveloped land areas. By February, the FAA had also approved the installation on 767-200s and -300s of Boeing's windshear detection and guidance system. EROPS approval with PW4000 engines, for both series, was obtained in April 1990.

On 27 July 1988 a Boeing 767-200ER established a distance record for a twin-jet commercial airliner, flying from Grand Rapids, Michigan, to the island of Mahe in the Indian Ocean, a distance of 7,723 nm (14,310 km; 8,893 miles). The aircraft, which was on its delivery flight to Air Seychelles, completed the journey in 16 h 49 min.

By 31 March 1990 orders for the Model 767-200/200ER/ 300/300ER totalled 483, of which 293 had been delivered. Modification of the original prototype as an element of the SDI programme is described in the 767 AOA entry under Boeing Aerospace and Electronics.

Boeing awarded Model 767 manufacturing subcontracts to Grumman Aerospace Corporation (wing centre-section, an adjacent lower fuselage section, and fuselage bulkheads), to LTV (horizontal tail), and to Canadair (rear fuselage). In other major work-sharing programmes, Aeritalia of Italy and member companies of the Japanese aerospace industry participate as follows:

Aeritalia: Wing control surfaces, flaps and leading-edge slats; wingtips; elevators; fin and rudder; and nose radome.

Fuji: Wing fairings and main landing gear doors.

Kawasaki: Centre-fuselage body panels, exit hatches and wing in-spar ribs.

Mitsubishi: Rear-fuselage body panels, stringers, passenger and cargo doors, and dorsal fin.

The following details apply to the basic Model 767-200, except where indicated:

TYPE: Twin-turbofan medium-range commercial transport.
WINGS: Cantilever low-wing monoplane. Special Boeing wing sections. Thickness/chord ratio 15.1% at root, 10.3% at tip. Dihedral 6°. Incidence 4° 15′. Sweepback 31° 30′ at quarter-chord. Fail-safe structure of aluminium alloy. Plain inboard (all-speed) and outboard (low-speed) ailerons with extensive use of graphite hybrid composites. Single-slotted linkage-supported aluminium outboard trailing-edge flaps; double-slotted inboard flaps. Conventional inboard and outboard spoilers of graphite composite construction are provided for roll control, to act as airbrakes, and for lift dumping. Track mounted leading-edge slats of light alloy construction. Roll trim through spring feel system. All control surfaces are powered hydraulically. Anti-icing of outboard wing leading-edges.
FUSELAGE: Conventional semi-monocoque structure of aluminium alloy, consisting of skin, longitudinal stringers and circumferential frames. Structure is of fail-safe design, and is pressurised except for tailcone aft of passenger cabin, landing gear wheel wells and air cycle machine wells.
TAIL UNIT: Cantilever fail-safe structure of aluminium alloy and aluminium honeycomb. Variable incidence tailplane. Elevators of single hinge type with redundant parallel actuators. No trim tabs. All controls are powered hydraulically. Yaw trim through spring feel system. No anti-icing.
LANDING GEAR: Hydraulically retractable tricycle type. Menasco twin-wheel nose unit retracts forward. Cleveland Pneumatic main gear, comprising two four-wheel bogies which retract inward. Oleo-pneumatic shock absorbers. Bendix wheels and brakes. Mainwheel tyres size 45 × 17-20, pressure 12.6 bars (183 lb/sq in). Nosewheel tyres size 37 × 14-15, pressure 10.0 bars (145 lb/sq in). Steel disc brakes on all mainwheels. Electronically controlled anti-skid units.
POWER PLANT: Two high bypass turbofans in pods, pylon-mounted on the wing leading-edges. Alternative engines available for all models of the Boeing 767 are the General Electric CF6-80A and Pratt & Whitney JT9D-7R4D, both rated at 213.5 kN (48,000 lb st), and the CF6-80A2, JT9D-7R4E and JT9D-7R4E4, rated at 222.4 kN (50,000 lb st). Additionally, the 767-200,

767-200ER and 767-300 are available with the Pratt & Whitney PW4050 rated at 222.4 kN (50,000 lb st), PW4052 rated at 231.3 kN (52,000 lb st) and the General Electric CF6-80C2B2 rated at 233.5 kN (52,500 lb st). The General Electric CF6-80C2B4, rated at 257.5 kN (57,900 lb st), is available on the 767-200ER, 767-300 and 767-300ER. The Pratt & Whitney PW4056, rated at 252.4 kN (56,750 lb st), and the PW4060 and General Electric CF6-80C2B6 rated at 266.9 kN (60,000 lb st), are available only on extended range versions. The Rolls-Royce RB211-524G, rated at 269.6 kN (60,600 lb st), will be available on 767s entering service from early 1990. Fuel in one integral tank in each wing, and in a centre tank, with total capacity of 63,216 litres (16,700 US gallons; 13,905 Imp gallons) in 200/300; 767-200ER has additional 14,195 litres (3,750 US gallons; 3,122 Imp gallons) in a second centre-section tank, raising total capacity to 77,412 litres (20,450 US gallons; 17,028 Imp gallons). The 767-300ER has a further expanded wing centre-section tank (optional on the -200ER), bringing total capacity to 91,039 litres (24,050 US gallons; 20,026 Imp gallons). Refuelling point in port outer wing. Anti-icing of engine air inlets.
ACCOMMODATION: Normal operating crew of two on flight deck, with third position optional. Basic accommodation in -200 models for 216 passengers, made up of 18 first class passengers forward in six-abreast seating at 96.5 cm (38 in) pitch, and 198 tourist class in mainly seven-abreast seating at 87 cm (34 in) pitch. Type A inward opening plug doors are provided at both the front and rear of the cabin on each side of the fuselage, with a Type III emergency exit over the wing on each side. A total of five toilets is installed, two centrally in the main cabin, two aft in the main cabin, and one forward in the first class section. Galleys are situated at forward and aft ends of the cabin. Alternative single class layouts provide for 230 tourist passengers, seated seven-abreast at 86 cm (34 in) pitch; 242 passengers seated seven-abreast at 81 cm (32 in) pitch; 255 passengers mainly seven-abreast (two-three-two) at 76 cm (30 in) pitch, or eight-abreast (two-four-two) at 81 cm (32 in) pitch. Max seating capacity in -200 models (requiring additional overwing emergency exit) is 290 passengers, mainly eight-abreast, at 76 cm (30 in) pitch; capacity in -300 is 290 passengers seven-abreast. Underfloor cargo holds of -200 versions can accommodate, typically, up to 22 LD2 or 11 LD1 containers. The 767-300 underfloor cargo holds can accommodate 30 LD2 or 15 LD1 containers. Forward and rear cargo doors of equal size are standard on the 767-200 and 767-300, but a larger (1.75 by 3.40 m; 5 ft 9 in by 11 ft 2 in) forward cargo door is standard on the 767-200ER and 767-300ER and optional on 767-200 and 767-300, to permit loading of Type 2 pallets, three such pallets being accommodated in the -200/200ER and four in the -300/300ER. Bulk cargo door at rear on port side. Overhead stowage for carry-on baggage. Cabin is air-conditioned, cargo holds heated.
SYSTEMS: AiResearch dual air cycle air-conditioning system. Pressure differential 0.59 bars (8.6 lb/sq in). Electrical supply from two engine driven 90kVA three-phase 400Hz constant frequency AC generators, 115/200V output. 90 kVA generator mounted on APU for ground operation or for emergency use. Three hydraulic systems at 207 bars (3,000 lb/sq in), for flight control and utility functions, supplied from engine driven pumps and a Garrett bleed air powered hydraulic pump or APU. Maximum generating capacity of port and starboard systems is 163 litres (43 US gallons; 35.8 Imp gallons)/min; centre system 185.5 litres (49 US gallons; 40.8 Imp gallons)/min, at 196.5 bars (2,850 lb/sq in). Reservoirs pressurised by engine bleed air via a pressure regulation module. Reservoir relief valve pressure is nominally 4.48 bars (65 lb/sq in). An additional hydraulic motor driven

Boeing 767-300 wide-bodied medium-range commercial transport aircraft *(Pilot Press)*

Boeing 767-300 of the Dutch carrier Martinair

generator, to provide essential functions for extended range operations, is standard on the 767-200ER and 767-300ER and optional on the 767-200 and 767-300. Nitrogen chlorate oxygen generators in passenger cabin, plus gaseous oxygen for flight crew. Anti-icing for air data sensors and windscreen. APU in tailcone to provide ground and in-flight electrical power and pressurisation.

AVIONICS AND EQUIPMENT: Standard avionics include ARINC 700 Series equipment (Bendix VOR/marker beacon receiver, ILS receiver, radio altimeter, transponder, DME, ADF and RDR-4A colour weather radar in aircraft for All Nippon, Britannia and Transbrasil). Collins caution annunciator, dual digital flight management systems, and triple digital flight control computers, including FCS-700 flight control system, EFIS-700 electronic flight instrument system and RMI-743 radio distance magnetic indicator. Honeywell IRS, FMCS and DADC, as described in Boeing Model 757 entry. Options include Boeing's windshear detection and guidance system.

DIMENSIONS, EXTERNAL:
Wing span	47.57 m (156 ft 1 in)
Wing chord: at root	8.57 m (28 ft 1¼ in)
at tip	2.29 m (7 ft 6 in)
Wing aspect ratio	7.9
Length overall: 200/200ER	48.51 m (159 ft 2 in)
300/300ER	54.94 m (180 ft 3 in)
Length of fuselage: 200/200ER	47.24 m (155 ft 0 in)
300/300ER	53.67 m (176 ft 1 in)
Fuselage: Max width	5.03 m (16 ft 6 in)
Height overall	15.85 m (52 ft 0 in)
Tailplane span	18.62 m (61 ft 1 in)
Wheel track	9.30 m (30 ft 6 in)
Wheelbase: 200/200ER	19.69 m (64 ft 7 in)
300/300ER	22.76 m (74 ft 8 in)
Passenger doors (two, fwd and rear, port):	
Height	1.88 m (6 ft 2 in)
Width	1.07 m (3 ft 6 in)
Galley service door (two, fwd and rear, stbd):	
Height	1.83 m (6 ft 0 in)
Width	1.07 m (3 ft 6 in)
Emergency exits (two, each): Height	0.97 m (3 ft 2 in)
Width	0.51 m (1 ft 8 in)
Cargo doors (two, fwd and rear, stbd):	
Height	1.75 m (5 ft 9 in)
Width	1.78 m (5 ft 10 in)
Optional cargo door (fwd, port):	
Height	1.75 m (5 ft 9 in)
Width	3.40 m (11 ft 2 in)

DIMENSIONS, INTERNAL:
Cabin, excl flight deck:	
Length: 200/200ER	33.93 m (111 ft 4 in)
300/300ER	40.36 m (132 ft 5 in)
Max width	4.72 m (15 ft 6 in)
Max height	2.87 m (9 ft 5 in)
Floor area: 200/200ER	154.9 m² (1,667 sq ft)
300/300ER	184.0 m² (1,981 sq ft)
Volume: 200/200ER	428.2 m³ (15,121 cu ft)
300/300ER	483.9 m³ (17,088 cu ft)
Volume, flight deck	13.5 m³ (478 cu ft)
Baggage holds (containerised), volume:	
200/200ER	74.8 m³ (2,640 cu ft)
300/300ER	101.9 m³ (3,600 cu ft)
Bulk cargo hold volume:	
all models	12.2 m³ (430 cu ft)
Combined baggage hold/bulk cargo hold volume:	
200/200ER	87.0 m³ (3,070 cu ft)
300/300ER	114.1 m³ (4,030 cu ft)
Total cargo hold volume:	
200/200ER	111.3 m³ (3,930 cu ft)
300/300ER	147.0 m³ (5,190 cu ft)

AREAS:
Wings, gross	283.3 m² (3,050 sq ft)
Ailerons (total)	11.58 m² (124.6 sq ft)
Trailing-edge flaps (total)	36.88 m² (397.0 sq ft)
Leading-edge slats (total)	28.30 m² (304.6 sq ft)
Spoilers (total)	15.83 m² (170.4 sq ft)
Fin	30.19 m² (325.0 sq ft)
Rudder	15.95 m² (171.7 sq ft)
Tailplane	59.88 m² (644.5 sq ft)
Elevators (total)	17.81 m² (191.7 sq ft)

WEIGHTS (A: 767-200 basic/JT9D-7R4D engines, B: 767-200 basic/CF6-80A, C: medium-range version/JT9D-7R4D, D: medium-range version/CF6-80A, E: 767-200ER/PW4050, F: 767-200ER/CF6-80C2B2, G: 767-200ER/PW4056, H: 767-200ER/CF6-80C2B4, J: 767-300/PW4050, K: 767-300/CF6-80C2B2, L: 767-300 higher gross weight version/PW4050, M: 767-300 higher gross weight version/CF6-80C2B2, N: 767-300ER/PW4056, P: 767-300ER/CF6-80C2B4, Q: 767-300ER/PW4060):

Manufacturer's weight empty:
A, C	74,752 kg (164,800 lb)
B, D	74,344 kg (163,900 lb)
E	76,339 kg (168,300 lb)
F	76,249 kg (168,100 lb)
G	76,566 kg (168,800 lb)
H	76,476 kg (168,600 lb)
J, L	79,560 kg (175,400 lb)
K, M	79,379 kg (175,000 lb)
N	80,785 kg (178,100 lb)
P	80,603 kg (177,700 lb)
Q	81,374 kg (179,400 lb)

Operating weight empty:
A, C	80,921 kg (178,400 lb)
B, D	80,512 kg (177,500 lb)
E	83,552 kg (184,200 lb)
F	83,461 kg (184,000 lb)
G	83,778 kg (184,700 lb)
H	83,688 kg (184,500 lb)
J, L	87,135 kg (192,100 lb)
K, M	86,953 kg (191,700 lb)
N	89,312 kg (196,900 lb)
P	89,131 kg (196,500 lb)
Q	89,902 kg (198,200 lb)

Max payload (767-200, 216 passengers; 767-200ER, 174 passengers; 767-300, 261 passengers; 767-300ER, 210 passengers):
A, B, C, D	19,595 kg (43,200 lb)
E, F, G, H	16,574 kg (36,540 lb)
J, K, L, M	23,677 kg (52,200 lb)
N, P, Q	20,003 kg (44,100 lb)

Max fuel weight:
A, B, C, D, J, K, L, M	51,131 kg (112,725 lb)
E, F	62,613 kg (138,038 lb)
G, H, N, P, Q	73,635 kg (162,338 lb)

Max T-O weight:
A, B	136,078 kg (300,000 lb)
C, D	142,881 kg (315,000 lb)
E, F, J, K	156,489 kg (345,000 lb)
G, H, N, P	175,540 kg (387,000 lb)
L, M	159,211 kg (351,000 lb)
Q	181,437 kg (400,000 lb)

Max ramp weight:
A, B	136,985 kg (302,000 lb)
C, D	143,789 kg (317,000 lb)
E, F, J, K	157,396 kg (347,000 lb)
G, H, N, P	175,994 kg (388,000 lb)
L, M	159,664 kg (352,000 lb)
Q	181,890 kg (401,000 lb)

Max zero-fuel weight:
A, B	112,491 kg (248,000 lb)
C, D	113,398 kg (250,000 lb)
E, F	114,757 kg (253,000 lb)
G, H	117,934 kg (260,000 lb)
J, K, L, M, N, P	126,098 kg (278,000 lb)
Q	130,634 kg (288,000 lb)

Max landing weight:
A, B	122,470 kg (270,000 lb)
C, D	123,377 kg (272,000 lb)
E, F	126,098 kg (278,000 lb)
G, H	129,273 kg (285,000 lb)
J, K, L, M, N, P	136,078 kg (300,000 lb)
Q	145,149 kg (320,000 lb)

PERFORMANCE (at max T-O weight except where indicated):
Normal cruising speed, all versions Mach 0.80
Approach speed at max landing weight:
A, B, C, D	136 knots (252 km/h; 157 mph)
E	138 knots (256 km/h; 159 mph)
F, G, H	140 knots (259 km/h; 161 mph)
J, K, L, M, N, P	141 knots (261 km/h; 162 mph)
Q	145 knots (269 km/h; 167 mph)

Initial cruise altitude:
A	11,950 m (39,200 ft)
B	12,100 m (39,700 ft)
C	11,650 m (38,200 ft)
D	11,800 m (38,700 ft)
E	11,215 m (36,800 ft)
F	11,460 m (37,600 ft)
G	10,925 m (35,850 ft)
H	10,850 m (35,600 ft)
J, M	11,250 m (36,900 ft)
K	11,340 m (37,200 ft)
L	11,125 m (36,500 ft)
N, P	10,600 m (34,800 ft)
Q	10,400 m (34,100 ft)

Service ceiling, one engine out:
A, C	6,525 m (21,400 ft)
B, D	6,430 m (21,100 ft)
E	6,850 m (22,500 ft)
F	7,200 m (23,600 ft)
G	7,250 m (23,800 ft)
H	7,375 m (24,200 ft)
J, L	6,035 m (19,800 ft)
K, M	6,150 m (20,200 ft)
N, P	6,615 m (21,700 ft)
Q	6,550 m (21,500 ft)

T-O field length:
A, B	1,798 m (5,900 ft)
C	1,951 m (6,400 ft)
D	1,981 m (6,500 ft)
E	2,347 m (7,700 ft)
F	2,316 m (7,600 ft)
G, H	2,774 m (9,100 ft)
J	2,560 m (8,400 ft)
K	2,469 m (8,100 ft)
L, M	2,652 m (8,700 ft)
N	2,926 m (9,600 ft)
P	2,956 m (9,700 ft)
Q	2,774 m (9,100 ft)

Design range:
A	3,160 nm (5,856 km; 3,639 miles)
B	3,220 nm (5,967 km; 3,708 miles)
C	3,795 nm (7,033 km; 4,370 miles)
D	3,850 nm (7,135 km; 4,433 miles)
E	5,365 nm (9,942 km; 6,178 miles)
F	5,410 nm (10,026 km; 6,230 miles)
G	6,770 nm (12,546 km; 7,796 miles)
H	6,805 nm (12,611 km; 7,836 miles)
J	4,000 nm (7,413 km; 4,606 miles)
K	4,020 nm (7,450 km; 4,629 miles)
L	4,230 nm (7,839 km; 4,871 miles)
M	4,260 nm (7,895 km; 4,905 miles)
N	5,740 nm (10,637 km; 6,610 miles)
P	5,760 nm (10,674 km; 6,633 miles)
Q	6,060 nm (11,230 km; 6,978 miles)

OPERATIONAL NOISE LEVELS (FAR Pt 36, Stage 3):
T-O at max basic T-O weight: B	87.1 EPNdB
H	90.4 EPNdB
Approach at max landing weight: B	101.6 EPNdB
H	101.7 EPNdB
Sideline: B	95.4 EPNdB
H	96.6 EPNdB

BOEING MODEL 767-X

On 8 December 1989 Boeing announced brief details of a proposed Model **767-X** which, if launched, will be known as the Boeing 777. The aircraft is a twin-aisle twin-jet intended to fit into the Boeing range between the 767-300 and 747-400. It will feature a new wing design and a fuselage wider than that of the Boeing 767, with accommodation for a variety of seating layouts from six to ten abreast.

Japanese companies were arranging to take a risk-sharing participation of eight to ten per cent, the greatest ever conceded by Boeing in a commercial programme.

BOEING HELICOPTERS

Boeing Center, PO Box 16858, Philadelphia, Pennsylvania 19142
Telephone: 1 (215) 591 2121
Telex: 510 669 2217 BOEMORA MOR
PRESIDENT AND GENERAL MANAGER: Edward J. Renouard
VICE-PRESIDENT, RESEARCH AND ENGINEERING:
  John Diamond
DIRECTOR, COMMUNICATIONS: Robert Torgerson

Boeing Helicopters, established in 1960 as Boeing Vertol Company, has produced and delivered more than 2,500 tandem-rotor helicopters to the US military services, as well as to many foreign nations. Its primary production programme involves modernisation of early model CH-47 Chinooks to CH-47D configuration for the US Army. Production of H-46 Sea Knight SR&M improvement kits for the US Navy and Marine Corps was completed in January 1989.

Boeing Helicopters is teamed with Bell Helicopter Textron to develop and produce the V-22 Osprey, as described under the Bell/Boeing entry in this section. On 3 June 1985 Boeing Helicopters signed a memorandum of understanding with Sikorsky Aircraft to enter a joint design to meet the US Army's LHX (now LH) light helicopter requirement, with Boeing Military Airplanes responsible for the avionics integration. Under a US Army contract Boeing Helicopters has developed an all-composite main rotor blade for the Bell UH-1H helicopter. The first Boeing-manufactured blades were scheduled for delivery to the Army Engineering Flight Agency at Edwards AFB, California, in June 1989 for flight testing for interchangeability with similar blades manufactured by Bell.

Boeing Helicopters also produces the fixed portions of the wing leading-edges of the Model 737, 747, 757 and 767 commercial transports, and metal leading-edge slats for the 757.

In early 1987 an 11,055 m² (119,000 sq ft) development facility and a 17,466 m² (188,000 sq ft) office/computer centre were added to Boeing Helicopters' Philadelphia headquarters.

Employment within Boeing Helicopters stood at 6,300 at the beginning of 1990. The manufacturing plant at Ridley Township, PA, includes 325,150 m² (3,500,000 sq ft) of covered areas, whilst the flight test centre at Greater Wilmington, DE, accounts for a further 8,565 m² (92,200 sq ft).

BOEING HELICOPTERS MODEL 107
USN and USMC designations: CH-46/UH-46 Sea Knight

Development of the Helicopter Emergency Flotation System (HEFS) of rapid-inflating flotation bags for CH-46Es was completed during 1985. When deflated, the bags are stowed in fuselage side panels measuring approximately 1.78 m × 0.81 m (5 ft 10 in × 2 ft 8 in). All US Navy and US Marine Corps CH-46s are to be fitted with provisions for the equipment, beginning in 1990.

Under a US Navy contract received in September 1987, Boeing Helicopters is developing kits to increase the fuel capacity of 171 US Marine Corps H-46Es. Boeing is also under contract for Doppler 217 navigation systems.

Details of previous H-46 upgrades appeared in the 1989-90 and earlier editions.

In 1990, the USMC was considering further CH-46 improvements and re-launched production of a CH-46X version with modern avionics as an alternative to the Bell/Boeing V-22 Osprey.

BOEING HELICOPTERS MODELS 114 and 414
US Army designation: CH-47 Chinook
Canadian Armed Forces designation: CH-147
Royal Air Force designation: Chinook HC. Mk 2
Spanish Army designation: HT.17

Development of the CH-47 Chinook began in 1956, to meet a US Army requirement for an all-weather medium transport helicopter. The first of five YCH-47As made its initial hovering flight on 21 September 1961. Details of the initial production **CH-47A** (354 for US Army) and **CH-47B** (108 for US Army) can be found in the 1974-75 edition of *Jane's*. Transmissions of some existing US Army As and Bs were later uprated to CH-47C standard.

Current domestic and export versions are as follows:

CH-47C. Increased performance from a combination of strengthened transmissions, two 2,796 kW (3,750 shp) T55-L-11A engines and increased integral fuel capacity. First flight 14 October 1967; deliveries of 270 to US Army began in Spring 1968. Total of 182 US Army CH-47Cs have been retrofitted with glassfibre rotor blades.

A crashworthy fuel system and an integral spar inspection system (ISIS) were introduced from 1973,

RAF Chinook HC.Mk 1B retrofitted with fore and aft radar warning receiver antennae, chaff dispenser boxes each side of rear fuselage, and flare dispensers each side of rear rotor mast *(Paul Jackson)*

incorporation of the crashworthy fuel system on US Army CH-47Cs being accomplished by retrofit kits. Chinooks delivered to Australia also have this system, which provides a total fuel capacity of 3,944 litres (1,042 US gallons; 867.6 Imp gallons). Nine CH-47Cs, designated **CH-147**, were delivered to Canada from September 1974. Details of these can be found in the 1985-86 and earlier editions. There is a full description of the CH-47C in the 1980-81 edition. Nine of the Spanish Army's remaining Chinooks are CH-47Cs.

CH-47D. Under a 1976 US Army contract Boeing Helicopters modified three earlier model CH-47s (one A, one B and a C) as D standard prototypes, the first one being flown on 11 May 1979. In October 1980 the initial CH-47D 'production' modernisation contract was awarded by the US Army, and the first 'production' example made its initial flight as a CH-47D on 26 February 1982. It was handed over to the US Army on 20 May 1982. Initial operational capability for the CH-47D was achieved on 28 February 1984, with the aircraft first equipping the 101st Airborne Division. On 13 January 1989 Boeing Helicopters was awarded a second multi-year procurement contract for CH-47D modernisation covering 144 aircraft, bringing the total number of CH-47Ds (and MH-47Es) funded for remanufacture to this much modified and modernised standard to 472, extending the service life of the Army's Chinook fleet into the next century. By February 1990, a total of 287 CH-47Ds had been redelivered and conversions were continuing at the rate of four per month, with completion scheduled for October 1993. Equipment of active army units is to be completed by January 1991; the reserve and National Guard operators to be similarly modernised by 1994. Eight CH-47Ds were delivered to the Texas National Guard in 1988.

The CH-47D remanufacturing programme involves stripping the Chinooks down to their basic airframes before refitting them with improved components and systems to bring them up to the new standard. Any necessary body or other repairs and modifications are done at the same time.

Thirteen major improvements are involved in the conversion. Textron Lycoming T55-L-712 turboshafts replace the lower-rated T55-L-7C or -11 engines of earlier models. Rotor transmission rating is increased, with integral lubrication and cooling, and composite rotor blades are fitted. The flight deck is reconfigured to reduce pilot workload. Other changes include redundant and improved electrical systems, modular hydraulic systems, an advanced flight control system, improved avionics, aircraft survivability equipment, and night vision goggle compatibility. A Solar T62-T-2B APU runs the accessory gear drive, thereby operating all hydraulic and electrical systems, and a single-point pressure refuelling system and triple cargo hooks are installed. Some 10-15 per cent (by weight) of the CH-47D airframe is of composite construction. The basic airframe structure, landing gear and seats are the only major components not replaced or rebuilt. Some 300 subcontractors are engaged in the conversion programme.

At a max gross weight of 22,680 kg (50,000 lb) in US Army service, the CH-47D has more than double the useful load capability of the CH-47A (10,334 kg; 22,783 lb compared with 4,990 kg; 11,000 lb). Its versatility covers a variety of combat and support missions, including troop movement, artillery emplacement, and battlefield resupply.

Boeing Helicopters CH-47D military helicopter. Broken lines show rear loading ramp lowered *(Pilot Press)*

It is the prime mover for the Army's M198 towed 155 mm howitzer; this artillery piece, plus 32 rounds of ammunition and an 11-man gun crew, represents a combined internal/external load of approx 9,980 kg (22,000 lb). The CH-47D is the only Army helicopter capable of lifting the 11,225 kg (24,750 lb) D5 caterpillar bulldozer, using the centre underfuselage hook. It is able to airlift Army Milvans (supply containers) at speeds of up to 138 knots (256 km/h; 159 mph), and carry (using all three hooks) up to seven 1,893 litre (500 US gallon; 416 Imp gallon), 1,587 kg (3,500 lb) rubber fuel blivets in a single mission. According to the US Army, the CH-47D offers more than a 100 per cent increase in performance over the A model Chinook when operated in a standard European climate, and a 68 per cent increase in hot and high conditions.

Following successful in-flight refuelling trials conducted by the US Army Aviation Engineering Flight Activity unit based at Edwards AFB, California, using a US Air Force HC-130 tanker aircraft, five CH-47Ds have been equipped with an in-flight refuelling system comprising a single-piece graphite boom with aluminium fuel tube mounted on the lower starboard side of the helicopter. Qualification was achieved in July 1988. Refuelling has been accomplished at speeds of up to 120 knots (222 km/h; 138 mph), at night and in moderate turbulence, at a refuelling rate of 568 litres (150 US gallons; 125 Imp gallons)/min, permitting the CH-47D to be refuelled completely in six minutes. The first in-flight refuelling equipped CH-47D was delivered to the US Army in July 1988.

Pending availability of the MH-47E (see below), the 2nd Battalion of the 160th Special Operations Aviation Regiment at Fort Campbell, KY and its 3rd Battalion at Savannah, GA, were equipped with **CH-47D SOA** (Special Operations Aircraft) Chinooks fitted with refuelling probes, thermal imagers, Bendix RDR-1300 weather radar, improved communications and navigation equipment, and two pintle-mounted 7.62 mm machine guns. Navigator/commander's station was installed in some SOAs.

MH-47E. On 2 December 1987 Boeing Helicopters received an $81.8 million contract to develop a prototype MH-47E variant of the Chinook for the US Army's Special Operations Forces, based on a modified CH-47D. Eventual requirement is 51 MH-47Es, of which the first 17 were funded in FYs 1988-89, all deducted from the proposed 472 CH-47D conversions. The prototype, 88-0267 (originally built in 1968 as CH-47C 68-15838), was rolled out on 6 December 1989. Deliveries of the initial 17 will be made between January and September 1992 to the 160th Special Operations Aviation Regiment's 2nd Battalion at Fort Campbell, KY, the 3rd Battalion at Hunter AAR, Savannah, GA, and the 4th Battalion, Oklahoma National Guard.

Operating parameters specified for the MH-47E include a 5½-hour deep-penetration covert mission over a 300 nm (560 km; 345 mile) radius in adverse weather, day or night, over all terrain, with a 90 per cent probability of success. The helicopter is required to have an in-flight refuelling probe and the capability to self-deploy to Europe, seating for 44 troops, and powerful defensive weapons and ECM. Accordingly, the MH-47E has an IBM-Allied Bendix integrated avionics system with four-screen EFIS cockpit compatible with NVGs; two dual high-speed MIL-STD-1553 digital databuses; AN/ASN-145 AHRS; jam-resistant radios; Rockwell-Collins CP1516-ASQ automatic target handover system; inertial, AN/ASN-137 Doppler, Rockwell-Collins AN/ASN-149(V)2 GPS/Navstar and terrain-referenced navigation systems; Rockwell-Collins ADF-149; laser (Perkin-Elmer AN/AAR-47), radar (E-Systems AN/APR-39A) and missile (Honeywell AN/AAR-47) warning systems; ITT AN/ALQ-136(V)2 pulse jammer and Northrop AN/ALQ-162 CW jammer; Tracor M-130 chaff/flare dispensers; Texas Instruments AN/APQ-174 radar with terrain following (down to 30 m; 100 ft), terrain-avoidance, air-to-ground ranging and ground mapping modes; Hughes AN/AAQ-16 FLIR in a chin turret; a digital moving-map display; uprated T55-L-714 turboshaft engines with FADEC; increased fuel tankage; additional troop seating; OBOGS; a rotor brake; 272 kg (600 lb) rescue hoist with 61 m (200 ft) usable cable; two M2 0.50 in window-mounted (port forward; starboard aft) machine-guns; and provision for later fitment of Stinger AAMs, using the FLIR for sighting. There is high equipment commonality with the Sikorsky MH-60K (which see).

The MH-47E's nose section is from the Commercial Chinook, allowing later addition of weather radar, if required. The forward landing gear is moved 1.02 m (3 ft 4 in) farther to the nose to allow installation of all-composite external fuel pods which double the helicopter's basic capacity. Brooks & Perkins internal cargo handling system.

Chinook HC.Mk 2. The RAF's remaining 35 (of 41) Chinooks (designation CH47-352) have been upgraded to HC.Mk 1B standard, as described in the 1989-90 and earlier editions of *Jane's*. In October 1989, Boeing was authorised by the UK MoD to proceed with a mid-life update for the helicopters, raising them to HC.Mk 2 standard (equivalent to the CH-47D). Changes include a new automatic flight control system, updated modular hydraulics, strengthened transmission, improved T-62T-2B APU and airframe reinforcements. Conversion will begin in 1991 at Philadelphia and end in 1995. In a related programme, Chinook

MH-47E prototype prior to first flight, showing extended nose and refuelling probe

HC.Mk 1B, ZA718, began flight testing during October 1989 of a Chandler Evans/Hawker Siddeley dual-channel full-authority digital engine control system which will be installed during the Mk 2 conversion process.

HT.17 Chinook. Ten CH-47Cs (one of which was lost) and nine CH-47Ds were delivered to the Spanish Army. Under an agreement of December 1989, the CH-47Cs will be converted by Boeing in the USA to CH-47D standard, following initial preparation in Spain by AISA. The first will be returned to service in mid-1991, followed by four in each of the years 1992 and 1993.

Model 234. Commercial version, described separately.

Model 414. International military version of CH-47C, described in 1985-86 *Jane's*. Now superseded by CH-47D International Chinook (which see). Eight delivered to Spanish Army Aviation's 5th Helicopter Transport Battalion (Bheltra-V) at Colmenar Viejo, Madrid; last six of these have nose mounted Bendix RDR-1400 weather radar.

CH-47D International Chinook. Model 414-100, starting with aircraft for the Japanese programme which began in Spring 1984 when the Japan Defence Agency approved the purchase of two for the JGSDF and one for the JASDF. The first production International CH-47D (N7425H) made its first flight in January 1986 and, with the second, was shipped to Kawasaki Heavy Industries of Japan in April 1986 for avionics and interior installation prior to a co-production arrangement in which Kawasaki is manufacturing 21 CH-47Ds using some Boeing Helicopters' supplied components and some locally produced assemblies. Deliveries of the two Boeing Helicopters assembled Chinooks to the JGSDF and JASDF were made in November and December 1986 respectively. Further details of the Japanese (**CH-47J**) programme, expected to cover at least 54 helicopters, are given under the entry for Kawasaki. In January 1989 the Chinese People's Liberation Army (PLA) placed an order, later embargoed, for six CH-47D International Chinooks. The Royal Thai Army has ordered three, and deliveries were undertaken in 1989 of the first seven of 18 for South Korea.

Total US Army procurement of CH-47A/B/C models was 732. Other military customers for US built Chinooks include Argentina (5), Australia (12), Canada (9), Japan (2, + 1 CKD), Spain (19), Taiwan (3—see Boeing 234 MLR), Thailand (4 ex-US Army and 3 new-build), and the UK (41). Twelve have gone to civilians, two for trials, three to an undisclosed operator and 45 were kits for Italy (40) and Japan. Orders for Agusta/EM built CH-47Cs have been received from Egypt (15), Greece (10), Iran (68), Italy (32), Libya (20) and Morocco (9), with 11 more now in service with the Pennsylvania Army NG.

The following data apply generally to the CH-47D and International CH-47D, except where a specific version is indicated:

TYPE: Twin-engined medium transport helicopter.
ROTOR SYSTEM: Two three-blade rotors in tandem, rotating in opposite directions and driven through interconnecting shafts which enable both rotors to be driven by either engine. Rotor blades, of glassfibre, have Boeing Helicopters VR7 and VR8 aerofoil sections, cambered leading-edge, D shaped glassfibre spar, and a fairing assembly consisting of Nomex honeycomb core with crossply glassfibre laminates for skin. Blades can survive hits by 23 mm API and HEI munitions and still provide a 'fly home' capability. All blades can be folded manually by four men in 40 min. Rotor heads fully articulated with pitch, flapping and drag hinges. All bearings submerged

completely in oil. Provisions for optional rotor brake.
ROTOR DRIVE: Power transmitted from each engine through individual overrunning clutches, into the combiner transmission, thereby providing a single power output to the interconnecting shafts. Rotor/engine rpm ratio 1 : 67. Combined transmission rating 5,593 kW (7,500 shp) and single-engine transmission emergency rating of 3,430 kW (4,600 shp) in CH-47D, International CH-47D and MH-47E at 225 rpm.
FUSELAGE: Semi-monocoque mainly metal structure comprising flight deck, cabin, rear fuselage, and pylon sections. The cabin is of constant cross-section, with the lower half sealed during manufacture to form a watertight compartment that provides water landing capability. Rear of fuselage contains cargo ramp and door.
LANDING GEAR: Non-retractable quadricycle type, with twin wheels on each forward unit and single wheels on each rear unit. Oleo-pneumatic shock absorbers in all units. Rear units fully castoring and steerable; power steering installed on starboard rear unit. All wheels are size 24 × 7.7-VII, with tyres size 8.50-10-III, pressure 4.62 bars (67 lb/sq in). Two single-disc hydraulic brakes. Provision for fitting detachable wheel-skis.
POWER PLANT: Two Textron Lycoming T55-L-712 turboshafts, pod-mounted on sides of the rear pylon, and each with a standard power rating of 2,796 kW (3,750 shp) and emergency rating of 3,356 kW (4,500 shp). Textron Lycoming T55-L-712 SSB engine has standard power rating of 3,264 kW (4,378 shp) and emergency rating of 3,451 kW (4,628 shp). Self-sealing pressure refuelled crashworthy fuel tanks in external fairings on sides of fuselage. Total fuel capacity 3,899 litres (1,030 US gallons; 858 Imp gallons). Oil capacity 14 litres (3.7 US gallons; 3.1 Imp gallons). MH-47E uses two Textron Lycoming T55-L-714 turboshafts, each with a standard power rating of 3,065 kW (4,110 shp) continuous and emergency rating of 3,749 kW (5,028 shp). Total fuel capacity 7,828 litres (2,068 US gallons; 1,722 Imp gallons). CH-47D SOA and MH-47E have 8.53 m (24 ft 0 in) refuelling probe on starboard side of forward fuselage. Provision for additional fuel cells in cabin for long-range deployment.
ACCOMMODATION: Two pilots on flight deck, with dual controls. Jump seat for crew chief or combat commander. Jettisonable door on each side of flight deck. Depending on seating arrangement, 33 to 55 troops can be accommodated in main cabin, or 24 litters plus two attendants, or vehicles and freight. Rear loading ramp can be left completely or partially open, or can be removed to permit transport of extra-long cargo and in-flight parachute or free-drop delivery of cargo and equipment. Main cabin door, at front on starboard side, comprises upper hinged section which can be opened in flight, and lower section with integral steps. Lower section is jettisonable. Triple external cargo hook system, as on Model 234, with centre hook rated to carry max load of 11,793 kg (26,000 lb) and the forward and rear hooks 7,711 kg (17,000 lb) each or 10,433 kg (23,000 lb) in unison. Provisions are installed for a power-down ramp and water dam to permit ramp operation on water, for forward and rear cargo hooks, ferry fuel tanks, external rescue hoist, and windscreen washers.
SYSTEMS: Cabin heated by 200,000 BTU heater/blower. Hydraulic system provides pressure of 207 bars (3,000 lb/sq in) for flying controls. Max flow rate 53.0 litres (14

CH-47D CHINOOK WEIGHTS AND PERFORMANCE

	Condition 1	Condition 2	Condition 3	Condition 4
Take-off condition				
Altitude	1220 m (4,000 ft)	Sea level	1,220 m (4,000 ft)	Sea level
Temperature	35°C (95°F)	15°C (59°F)	35°C (95°F)	15°C (59°F)
Empty weight	10,500 kg (23,149 lb)	10,500 kg (23,149 lb)	10,423 kg (22,980 lb)	10,265 kg (22,630 lb)
T-O weight	19,178 kg (42,280 lb)	22,679 kg (50,000 lb)	19,657 kg (43,336 lb)	22,679 kg (50,000 lb)
Payload: external	7,081 kg (15,612 lb)	10,455 kg (23,049 lb)	—	—
internal	—	—	6,423 kg (14,160 lb)	—
Max level speed, S/L, ISA,				
max continuous power, no external load	161 knots (298 km/h; 185 mph)	161 knots (298 km/h; 185 mph)	154 knots (285 km/h; 177 mph)	—
Average cruising speed	120 knots (222 km/h; 138 mph)	132 knots (245 km/h; 152 mph)	134 knots (248 km/h; 154 mph)	138 knots (256 km/h; 159 mph)
Max rate of climb, S/L,				
ISA, intermediate rated power	669 m (2,195 ft)/min	464 m (1,522 ft)/min	640 m (2,100 ft)/min	464 m (1,522 ft)/min
Hovering ceiling OGE, ISA, max power	3,215 m (10,550 ft)	1,524 m (5,000 ft)	2,972 m (9,750 ft)	1,524 m (5,000 ft)
Mission radius	30 nm (55.5 km; 34.5 miles)	30 nm (55.5 km; 34.5 miles)	100 nm (185 km; 115 miles)	—
Ferry range	—	—	—	1,111 nm (2,059 km; 1,279 miles)

Condition 1
T-O weight is gross weight for 61 m (200 ft)/min vertical rate of climb to hover OGE at 1,220 m/35°C (4,000 ft/95°F). External payload is carried outbound only. Fuel reserve is 30 min cruise fuel. Max speed shown is at T-O weight less external payload.

Condition 2
T-O gross weight is max structural T-O weight for which vertical climb capability at S/L, ISA is 271 m (890 ft)/min. Otherwise same as Condition 1.

Condition 3
T-O weight is gross weight for hover OGE at 1,220 m/35°C (4,000 ft/95°F). Radius is with inbound payload 50 per cent of outbound internal payload. Fuel reserve is 30 min cruise fuel. Max speed shown is at T-O weight.

Condition 4
T-O weight is max structural T-O weight. Max ferry range (internal and external auxiliary fuel). Optimum cruise climb to 2,440 m (8,000 ft) and complete cruise at 2,440 m (8,000 ft). Fuel reserve is 10 per cent of initial fuel.

US gallons; 11.65 Imp gallons) per minute. Spherical hydraulic reservoir, volume 5,326 cm³ (325 cu in), pressurised to 1.72 bars (25 lb/sq in). Utility hydraulic system, pressure 231 bars (3,350 lb/sq in), max flow rate 51.5 litres (13.6 US gallons; 11.3 Imp gallons) per minute. Piston type reservoir, volume 7,014 cm³ (428 cu in), of which 5,326 cm³ (325 cu in) are usable, pressurised to 3.86 bars (56 lb/sq in). Electrical system includes two 40kVA air-cooled alternators driven by transmission drive system. Solar T62-T-2B APU runs accessory gear drive, thereby operating all hydraulic and electrical systems.

AVIONICS AND EQUIPMENT (International CH-47D: US Army CH-47D assumed to be generally similar. Avionics for RAF HC. Mk 1 listed in 1985-86 and earlier editions): Standard avionics include ARC-102 HF com radio, Collins ARC-186 UHF/AM-FM, Magnavox ARC-164 UHF/AM com; C-6533 intercom; Allied Signal/Bendix AN/APX-100 IFF; APN-209 radar altimeter; AN/ARN-89B ADF; AN/ARN-118 Tacan; AN/ARN-123 VOR/ glideslope/marker beacon receiver; and AN/ASN-43 gyromagnetic compass. Flight instruments are standard for IFR, and include an AQU-6A horizontal situation indicator. AFCS maintains helicopter stability, eliminating the need for constant small correction inputs by the pilot to maintain desired attitude. The AFCS is a redundant system using two identical control units and two sets of stabilisation actuators. Standard equipment includes a hydraulically powered winch for rescue and cargo handling, rearview mirror, plus integral work stands and step for maintenance. Provisions for static lines, and maintenance davits for removal of major components.

DIMENSIONS, EXTERNAL:
Rotor diameter (each)	18.29 m (60 ft 0 in)
Rotor blade chord (each)	0.81 m (2 ft 8 in)
Distance between rotor centres	11.86 m (38 ft 11 in)
Length overall, rotors turning	30.14 m (98 ft 10¾ in)
Length of fuselage	15.54 m (51 ft 0 in)
Width, rotors folded: CH-47D	3.78 m (12 ft 5 in)
MH-47E	4.78 m (15 ft 8 in)
Height to top of rear rotor head	5.68 m (18 ft 7.8 in)
Wheel track (c/l of shock absorbers):	
CH-47D	3.20 m (10 ft 6 in)
MH-47E	3.63 m (11 ft 11 in)
Wheelbase: CH-47D	6.86 m (22 ft 6 in)
MH-47E	7.87 m (25 ft 10 in)
Passenger door (fwd, stbd): Height	1.68 m (5 ft 6 in)
Width	0.91 m (3 ft 0 in)
Height to sill	1.09 m (3 ft 7 in)
Rear loading ramp entrance: Height	1.98 m (6 ft 6 in)
Width	2.31 m (7 ft 7 in)
Height to sill	0.79 m (2 ft 7 in)

DIMENSIONS, INTERNAL:
Cabin, excl flight deck:
Length CH-47D	9.19 m (30 ft 2 in)
MH-47E	9.30 m (30 ft 6 in)
Width (mean)	2.29 m (7 ft 6 in)
Width at floor	2.51 m (8 ft 3 in)
Height	1.98 m (6 ft 6 in)
Floor area	21.0 m² (226.0 sq ft)
Usable volume	41.7 m³ (1,474 cu ft)
Length of fuselage: Army CH-47D	15.54 m (51 ft 0 in)
International CH-47D and MH-47E	15.87 m (52 ft 1 in)

AREAS:
Rotor blades (each)	7.43 m² (80.0 sq ft)
Rotor discs (total)	525.3 m² (5,655 sq ft)

WEIGHTS (International CH-47D):
Operating weight empty	10,627 kg (23,429 lb)
Max underslung load: Army CH-47D	11,793 kg (26,000 lb)
International CH-47D	12,701 kg (28,000 lb)
Internal payload over 100 nm (185 km; 115 mile) radius at 1,220 m (4,000 ft), 35°C day, hovering OGE at T-O, 20 min reserves	7,040 kg (15,520 lb)
External payload over 100 nm (185 km; 115 mile) radius at 1,220 m (4,000 ft), 35°C day, hovering OGE at T-O, 20 min reserves	6,837 kg (15,073 lb)
Internal payload over 100 nm (185 km; 115 mile) radius at 1,525 m (5,000 ft), ISA, hovering OGE at T-O, 20 min reserves	10,200 kg (22,488 lb)
External payload over 100 nm (185 km; 115 mile) radius at 1,525 nm (5,000 ft), ISA, hovering OGE at T-O, 20 min reserves	10,057 kg (22,173 lb)
Design gross weight	14,968 kg (33,000 lb)
Alternative gross weight	20,865 kg (46,000 lb)
Max T-O weight	24,494 kg (54,000 lb)

PERFORMANCE (International CH-47D, at max continuous power, ISA, at gross weights of A: 22,680 kg; 50,000 lb, B: 20,865 kg; 46,000 lb, C: 14,968 kg; 33,000 lb):
Max level speed at S/L:
A	149 knots (276 km/h; 171 mph)
B	154 knots (285 km/h; 177 mph)
C	163 knots (302 km/h; 188 mph)
Service ceiling, max continuous power:	
A	2,775 m (9,100 ft)
B	3,690 m (12,100 ft)
C	6,735 m (22,100 ft)
Hovering ceiling OGE, T-O power:	
A	1,860 m (6,100 ft)
B	2,710 m (8,900 ft)
C	5,395 m (17,700 ft)

BOEING HELICOPTERS MODEL 234 COMMERCIAL CHINOOK

This development of the military CH-47 Chinook is produced as a commercial passenger transport, cargo carrier, and for specialised tasks such as servicing offshore oil and natural gas rigs, remote resources exploration and extraction, logging, and construction work. The airframe is based on that of the latest military Chinook, but includes features such as wide chord glassfibre rotor blades; redesigned fuselage side fairings; a lengthened nose to accommodate the weather radar antenna; and repositioning further forward of the front landing gear units.

Boeing Helicopters Model 234 LR long-range Commercial Chinook *(Pilot Press)*

Initial order was placed by British Airways Helicopters, which ordered three Model 234 LRs in 1978 (later increased to six), primarily for North Sea oil rig support operations. First flight was made on 19 August 1980. FAA and UK CAA certification was received on 19 and 26 June 1981 respectively. The first 234 LR went into service with BAH (now British International Helicopters) on 1 July 1981, and all six had been delivered by 1 June 1982. FAA and CAA certification of a 234 LR combi was received in the Summer of 1982.

Three basic versions of the Model 234 are offered:

Long-range model (234 LR). Identified by continuous fuselage-side fairings, approximately twice as large as those of the military Chinook and containing large fuel tanks. Equipped to airline standards as a passenger, passenger/freight combi, or all-cargo transport. Six built for BAH/BIH and three for Helicopter A/S of Norway in 1981-85. Five former BIH aircraft now operated by Columbia Helicopters of Portland, Oregon for logging and firefighting duties. Two second-hand Boeing 234s were delivered to Trump Air in 1989 and have operated on the airline's route between New York and Atlantic City, New Jersey.

Extended-range model (234 ER). Version of 234 LR with two internal auxiliary fuel tanks and fewer seats. Typical configuration has 17 seats for passengers and fuel for up to 875 nm (1,621 km; 1,008 miles). Can also be configured for 32 passengers and a single internal fuel tank where maximum range is not required. FAA certification granted in May 1983 for operation with internal and external loads at the max T-O weights listed. Leased to Arco Alaska (two in 1983) and ERA Helicopters (one in 1985); no other customers known.

Utility model (234 UT). Fuselage side fuel tanks replaced by two drum shaped internal tanks, mounted longitudinally side by side at front of cabin. Fuselage-side fairings removed, leaving only an individual blister around each landing gear mounting. Received supplemental type certification from FAA in October 1981 at a max gross weight of 23,133 kg (51,000 lb) for external cargo lift operations. The FAA approval included also the carriage of 24 passengers, external loads of up to 12,700 kg (28,000 lb) on the aircraft's single cargo hook, and external cargo lift missions at altitudes of up to 3,660 m (12,000 ft) under max gross weight conditions. No orders known.

Multi-purpose long-range model (234 MLR). Similar to 234 LR but with airline standard interior

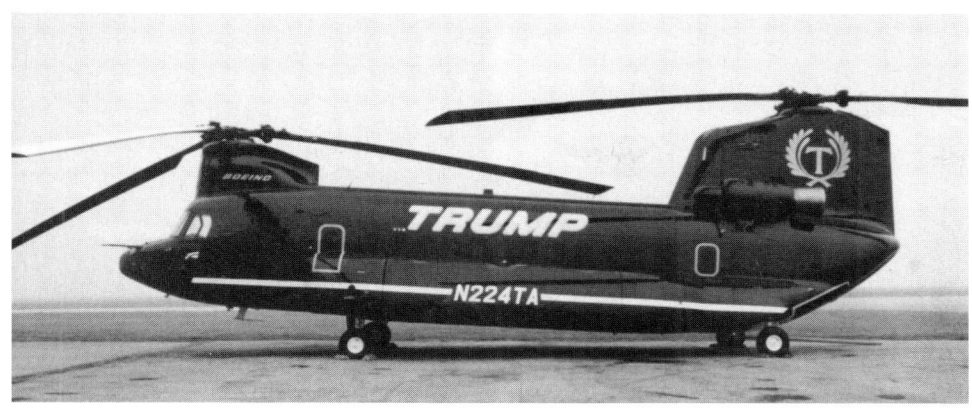

Boeing 234 Commercial Chinook of Trump Air, providing a shuttle service between New York and the casinos of Atlantic City, NJ

replaced by utility interior. Three delivered to a Far East government operator in 1985.

Conversion from one configuration of the Model 234 to another is estimated to take eight hours, and requires four persons to handle the fuel tanks of the utility model and the ramp baggage bins of the passenger carrying helicopter.

TYPE: Twin-turbine commercial transport helicopter.

ROTOR SYSTEM: Similar to that of International CH-47D. Wide chord glassfibre blades, with VR7 section over inboard 85 per cent of span, and VR8 section on outer 15 per cent of span; thickness/chord ratio 12% and 8% respectively. Overall blade twist 12°. An aluminium screen inserted in the skin provides lightning protection, discharging strikes via the titanium leading-edge. Outboard 25 per cent of leading-edge capped with replaceable nickel section. Blade balancing by tracking weights in tips. Two blades of each rotor can be folded manually. Heads fully articulated, with pitch, flapping and drag hinges. All bearings submerged completely in oil. Blades embody electric de-icing blankets, permitting addition of a de-icing kit if required. Rotor rpm 225.

ROTOR DRIVE: As described for CH-47D. Auxiliary transmission lubrication system enables flight to be completed after total loss of oil in primary system. Transmission rated at 5,033 kW (6,750 shp) at 225 rotor rpm, and 3,430 kW (4,600 shp) for single-engine operation.

FUSELAGE: All-metal semi-monocoque structure of basically square section. Loading ramp forms undersurface of upswept rear fuselage. External fuel pods of long-range model made of advanced composites, including glassfibre, graphite/epoxy and Nomex nylon honeycomb. These fairing pods provide flotation capability adequate to meet British airworthiness requirements applicable to a sea state seven (9.15 m; 30 ft waves. Wave length-to-height ratio 15) without added flotation gear.

LANDING GEAR: As described for CH-47D, but with tyre pressures of 8.55 bars (124 lb/sq in) on forward gear, 7.20 bars (104.4 lb/sq in) on rear gear.

POWER PLANT: Two Textron Lycoming AL 5512 turboshafts, pod-mounted on sides of rear rotor pylon. Each engine has max T-O rating of 3,039 kW (4,075 shp), max continuous rating of 2,975 kW (2,975 shp), and 30 min contingency rating of 3,247 kW (4,355 shp). Long-range model has two fuel tanks, one in each fuselage side fairing, with total capacity of 7,949 litres (2,100 US gallons; 1,749 Imp gallons). Utility model has two drum-shape internal tanks, with total capacity of 3,702 litres (978 US gallons; 814 Imp gallons). Extended-range model has both fuselage side and internal drum tanks. Single-point pressure refuelling.

ACCOMMODATION: Two pilots side by side on flight deck, with dual controls. Passenger cabin of long-range model seats up to 44 persons four-abreast, with centre aisle. Each seat has overhead bin and underseat stowage for carry-on baggage; larger items are stowed over the rear ramp in the main baggage compartment. Galley, with cabin attendant's seat, and toilet, are standard, between flight deck and cabin. Basic FAA/CAA approved combi versions offer 8-32 passenger seats, with cargo at rear of cabin, loaded via rear ramp; or 22-32 passenger seats, with cargo stowed on only one side of cabin's centre aisle. All passenger facilities can be removed, and heavy duty floor installed, for freight-only service. Passenger door at front of cabin on starboard side. Crew door on each side of flight deck. Cabin floor supported by dynamically tuned fittings to reduce vibration. Hydraulically powered cargo ramp can be stopped at any intermediate position to match the level of the loading vehicle being used. Single central cargo hook is standard on utility model for carrying external loads of up to 12,700 kg (28,000 lb). Optional dual tandem hooks for precision operations and for load stability in high-speed flight; or three tandem hooks for delivering multiple loads.

SYSTEMS: Heating and ventilation systems maintain comfortable flight deck/cabin temperature in ambient temperatures down to –32°C. Duplicated flying control, hydraulic and electrical systems, as described for CH-47D/Model 414. Solar T62T-2B APU, rated at

71 kW (95 shp), drives auxiliary gearbox on rear transmission to start engines and provide power for two flying control system hydraulic pumps and two alternators. All critical systems heated to inhibit ice build-up.

AVIONICS AND EQUIPMENT: Duplicated full blind-flying instrumentation, weather radar, and dual four-axis automatic flight control system with built-in test equipment, provide all-weather capability. Optional equipment includes passenger interior furnishings for the utility model, combi interior, downward-shining cargo load light, rescue hoist of 272 kg (600 lb) capacity, glassfibre wheel-skis, an ice detector probe, and ditching equipment that includes two liferafts, each with an overload capacity of 36 persons. Standard items include integral work platforms, and a maintenance panel that allows 26 separate checks to be made from a single ground-level position.

DIMENSIONS, EXTERNAL: As CH-47D except:

Length of fuselage	15.87 m (52 ft 1 in)
Width over fuselage side fairings	4.78 m (15 ft 8 in)
Wheel track:	
fwd landing gear	3.20 m (10 ft 6 in)
rear landing gear	3.40 m (11 ft 2 in)
Wheelbase	7.87 m (25 ft 9.9 in)

DIMENSIONS, INTERNAL:

Passenger cabin	as for CH-47D
Baggage compartment volume	4.42 m³ (156.0 cu ft)
Utility model, cargo hold volume	41.03 m³ (1,449 cu ft)

WEIGHTS:

Manufacturer's weight empty:	
LR	11,748 kg (25,900 lb)
ER	12,020 kg (26,500 lb)
MLR	11,113 kg (24,500 lb)
UT	9,797 kg (21,600 lb)
Operating weight empty: LR	12,292 kg (27,100 lb)
ER	12,406 kg (27,350 lb)
MLR	11,400 kg (25,134 lb)
UT	10,002 kg (22,050 lb)
Fuel load: LR, MLR	6,391 kg (14,091 lb)
ER	9,368 kg (20,653 lb)
UT	2,976 kg (6,562 lb)
Max payload: LR, MLR, internal	9,072 kg (20,000 lb)
ER, UT, internal	8,731 kg (19,250 lb)
ER, MLR, UT, external	12,700 kg (28,000 lb)

Max T-O weight:

ER, LR, MLR, internal load	22,000 kg (48,500 lb)
UT, internal load	19,051 kg (42,000 lb)
ER, LR, MLR, UT, external load	23,133 kg (51,000 lb)

PERFORMANCE:

Never-exceed speed:	
ER, LR, MLR	150 knots (278 km/h; 173 mph)
UT	140 knots (259 km/h; 161 mph)
Max cruising speed at 610 m (2,000 ft):	
ER, LR, MLR, internal load, at 20,411 kg (45,000 lb) AUW	145 knots (269 km/h; 167 mph)
UT, internal load, at 19,051 kg (42,000 lb) AUW	140 knots (259 km/h; 161 mph)
Cruising speed for optimum range, at 610 m (2,000 ft):	
ER, LR, MLR, UT, internal load, at all gross weights	135 knots (250 km/h; 155 mph)
Max rate of climb at S/L at max T-O weight:	
ER, LR, MLR, internal load	360 m (1,180 ft)/min
UT, internal load	457 m (1,500 ft)/min
Operational ceiling:	
ER, LR, MLR, UT	4,570 m (15,000 ft)
Hovering ceiling IGE:	
ER, LR, MLR, internal load	2,590 m (8,500 ft)
UT, internal load	4,085 m (13,400 ft)
Hovering ceiling OGE:	
ER, LR, MLR, internal load	820 m (2,700 ft)
UT, internal load	3,505 m (11,500 ft)
Range with 45 min IFR reserves:	
LR, 44 passengers	530 nm (982 km; 610 miles)
ER, 17 passengers	830 nm (1,538 km; 956 miles)
LR, MLR, with max fuel	620 nm (1,149 km; 714 miles)
ER with max fuel	1,035 nm (1,918 km; 1,192 miles)
UT with max internal load	229 nm (424 km; 264 miles)
UT with max external load	145 nm (269 km; 167 miles)
Max endurance: LR, MLR, internal load	5 h 18 min
ER, internal load	8 h 25 min
UT, external load	2 h 18 min

BOEING HELICOPTERS MODEL 360

Boeing Helicopters has designed and built as a private venture the prototype of a twin-turboshaft twin-rotor cargo helicopter known as the Model 360. Similar in size to the CH-46/UH-46 Sea Knight, it makes extensive use of composites materials in the fuselage, rotor hubs, upper controls and drive system components. An advanced flight control and flight management system is installed. The helicopter (N360BV) made its first flight on 10 June 1987 and had accumulated more than 160 hours' flying by the beginning of 1990. Achievements up to that time included an airspeed of 214 knots (397 km/h; 246 mph). The Model 360 will continue to serve as a technology demonstrator into the mid-1990s. Boeing Helicopters will employ the advanced technologies developed for the Model 360 in other programmes.

TYPE: Twin-turbine medium-size cargo/utility helicopter.

ROTOR SYSTEM: Two four-blade rotors in tandem counter-rotating linked through interconnecting shafts to enable both rotors to be driven by either engine. All-composites rotor blades of new VR12 and VR15 aerofoil section, which improve hovering efficiency and high speed performance. Rotor head is constructed almost entirely of glassfibre and graphite composites, with elastomeric bearings. Automatic blade-folding motors and linkages

Boeing Helicopters Model 360 advanced technology demonstrator

Artist's impression of the Boeing/Sikorsky LH in day attack configuration

are integrated with the lead-lag damping system. Many transmission and control system components made of carbonfibre or glassfibre, including rotor shafts and rotor swashplates.

FUSELAGE: Basic structure of graphite fuselage frames and longerons, covered by preformed panels of Kevlar diagonal-weave skins with Nomex honeycomb core; graphite reinforcement is provided at the panel edges and for all cut-outs. Panels attached to structure by combination of cold bonding and metallic fasteners. The floor is formed as a separate assembly incorporating the fuel tanks and cargo handling roller system, and is suspended on sprung counterweights to isolate it from vibration; the entire flight deck is mounted similarly. The rear of the fuselage, containing the one-piece cargo ramp and door, is of new drag-reducing design.

LANDING GEAR: Retractable tricycle type with twin wheels on each unit. Main landing gear retraction beams are of carbonfibre composites.

POWER PLANT: Two Textron Lycoming AL5512 turboshafts, mounted one in each side of the rear fuselage, each with a standard power rating of 3,132 kW (4,200 shp). Fuel in one 901 litre (238 US gallon; 198 Imp gallon) self-sealing tank at rear and two 1,109 litre (293 US gallon; 244 Imp gallon) tanks forward, giving total capacity of 3,119 litres (824 US gallons; 686 Imp gallons).

SYSTEMS: Hydraulic and electrical system components are modular in nature, and grouped to allow systems and structure to be integrated during construction.

AVIONICS AND EQUIPMENT: Full nav/com equipment. Doppler radar and optional remote map reader. Honeywell digital automatic flight control system forms part of Bendix integrated flight control and flight management system incorporating six CRT displays with multi-function keyboards, and computer controlled EADI and EHSI displays for pilot and co-pilot, linked to a heading and attitude reference system via a multiplex databus.

DIMENSIONS, EXTERNAL:
Length of fuselage	15.54 m (51 ft 0 in)
Height overall	5.91 m (19 ft 4¾ in)
Wheel track	3.96 m (13 ft 0 in)

DIMENSIONS, INTERNAL:
Cabin: Max width	3.99 m (13 ft 1 in)
Max height	3.43 m (11 ft 3 in)

WEIGHT (estimated):
Design T-O weight	13,834 kg (30,500 lb)

PERFORMANCE (estimated):
Dash speed	200 knots (370 km/h; 230 mph)
Normal cruising speed	180 knots (334 km/h; 207 mph)

BELL/BOEING V-22 OSPREY

Boeing Helicopters is teamed with Bell Helicopter Textron to develop the V-22 Osprey tilt-rotor aircraft to meet the US government's Joint Services Vertical Lift Aircraft requirement. A full description of the aircraft appears under the Bell/Boeing entry in this section.

BOEING HELICOPTERS/SIKORSKY LH

In June 1985 Boeing Helicopters and Sikorsky Aircraft (which see) announced the formation of a joint team to submit proposals for the US Army's Light Helicopter Experimental (LHX) programme. During October 1988, the Boeing/Sikorsky team revealed its design, the general configuration of which can be seen in the accompanying artist's impression. Features of the design include an all-composite airframe, five-blade main rotor, T tail with 'fan-in-fin' shrouded tail rotor, tandem two-seat cockpit, fly by light fibre optic flight control system, internal weapons bays, and a ventral turret mounted three-barrel 20 mm Gatling gun that can be slewed by movement of the pilot's helmet mounted sight. Other members of the Boeing/Sikorsky LH team include Boeing Aerospace and Electronics (flight control computer); Boeing Military Airplanes (mission equipment package and avionics systems integration); Collins Government Avionics Division (integrated avionics and multi-function displays and controls); General Electric Armament Systems Department (turreted gun and ammunition feed system); Hamilton Standard (flight control computer, wide field of view helmet mounted display system); Harris Corporation (3D digital map display, super high speed databus, sensor data distribution network); Kaiser Electronics (helmet mounted display system); Link Flight Simulation (operator training systems); Martin Marietta (electro-optical systems); and TRW Military Electronics Division with Westinghouse Defense and Electronics, supported by AT&T (VHSIC signal and data processors and aircraft survivability equipment).

In early 1990, Boeing/Sikorsky transferred the main LH development effort from Wichita to Philadelphia.

Details of the LH programme and a specification common to both contenders will be found under the Bell/McDonnell Douglas heading.

BOEING MILITARY AIRPLANES

PO Box 3707, Seattle, Washington 98124
PRESIDENT: C. G. King
MANUFACTURING CENTRE:
PO Box 7730, Wichita, Kansas 67277-7730
Telephone: 1 (316) 687 2020
Telex: 910 741 6900 BOEWICA WIC
VICE-PRESIDENT AND GENERAL MANGER: John Dempster
COMMUNICATIONS MANAGER: Peter Dakan

Formerly the base of Boeing Military Airplanes, Wichita was redesignated on 2 January 1990 as a branch of a new Military Airplanes division based at Seattle and also absorbing the former Boeing Advanced Systems. Civil airliner activities at Wichita are now subordinated to Boeing Commercial Airplanes (which see).

Boeing Military Airplanes is responsible for all work on the B-52 Stratofortress bomber and KC-135 jet tanker/transport series, and the offensive avionics system of the Rockwell B-1B strategic bomber. It is avionics integrator for the Bell/Boeing V-22 Osprey programme (see Bell/Boeing entry) and Boeing/Sikorsky's development work for the LH helicopter competition, and is currently teamed with General Dynamics and Lockheed Burbank in development work for the YF-22A advanced tactical fighter (ATF) prototypes (which see, under Lockheed heading).

The Wichita facility occupies an area of more than 445.2 ha (1,100 acres), including 929,030 m² (10,000,000 sq ft) of covered space. Military Airplanes also has facilities in Huntsville, Alabama, Edwards AFB, California, Lake Charles, Louisiana, and Seattle, Washington. At the beginning of 1989, the company had a total Kansas workforce of 23,900 persons.

In May 1985 the company was selected to design, develop and produce replacement wings for the US Navy's fleet of Grumman A-6 Intruder attack aircraft. The new wing is made primarily of graphite/epoxy composites. Control surfaces are of aluminium alloy. Titanium is used in high-stress areas, such as the wing fold fittings. Design improvements include split fuel tanks, so that supply can be maintained if one is damaged in combat; enhanced lightning and fire protection; and easier repair and maintenance. Contracts for 179 new wings were placed up to March 1988. For newly built A-6Es, the wings are

being installed by Grumman. The retrofit programme is undertaken at US Navy maintenance and repair depots. First deliveries of production replacement wings to Grumman were made in May 1988, and flight testing began on 3 April 1989 at the Naval Air Test Center, NAS Patuxent River, Maryland. By February 1990, 45 wing sets had been delivered, and one new-build and four modified A-6Es placed in service.

A NASA contract to modify a Boeing 747-100 as a second carrier aircraft for Space Shuttle Orbiter vehicles was received in early 1988. Boeing Military Airplanes is undertaking an upgrade programme for the McDonnell Douglas F-4 Phantom which includes installation of advanced digital avionics systems and conformal fuel tanks or weapons pylons, and has been contracted to design and manufacture new navigation and weapons delivery systems for installation in some 600 Air National Guard, Air Force Reserve and USAF F-4s.

First flight of a Grumman A-6E Intruder fitted with Boeing composites wings, 3 April 1989

BOEING B-52 STRATOFORTRESS

The early development history of the B-52 has been recorded in previous editions of *Jane's*, and a structural description can be found in the 1964-65 edition. The two versions in squadron service are the **B-52G** and **B-52H**, of which a combined total of 247 remain operational (152 Gs and 95 Hs), serving with the 2nd, 7th, 42nd, 97th, 379th, 410th and 416th Bomb Wings of the Eighth Air Force; and the 5th, 43rd, 92nd and 93rd Bomb Wings of the Fifteenth Air Force.

Full scale development of B-52 carrier aircraft equipment for AGM-86 air-launched cruise missiles began in early 1978, and 98 B-52Gs and 95 B-52Hs have each been modified to carry 12 AGM-86s externally (six on each inboard underwing pylon), in addition to an internal load of SRAMs or other weapons.

SAC's 416th Bomb Wing at Griffiss AFB, NY, became the first unit to attain operational capability with the

Boeing B-52H Stratofortress, armed with AGM-129A Advanced Cruise Missiles

Boeing KC-135R (62-3554) 'Cherokee Rose', holder of 16 world time-to-height records *(Paul Jackson)*

AGM-86 in December 1982. It was followed by the 379th Wing at Wurtsmith AFB, Michigan. Other stations equipped with ALCM-equipped B-52s include Eaker AFB, Arkansas (97th) and Fairchild AFB, Washington (92nd). All 98 B-52Gs, and about 72 B-52Hs, had been equipped for external cruise missile carriage by late 1989. Completion of this phase of the programme is scheduled for FY 1990.

The B-52Hs are being further modified to carry eight more ALCMs, SRAMs, advanced cruise missiles or free-fall nuclear weapons on an internal common strategic rotary launcher (CSRL). This programme was initiated in 1982, and the first CSRL began flight testing in September 1985. A total of 104 CSRLs is to be produced. The Boeing Military Airplanes branch is building 95 B-52H modification kits and providing depot and base activation support. The production programme is managed by Oklahoma City Air Logistics Center at Tinker AFB, and modification and installation is being performed at Kelly AFB, Texas. The first fully modified aircraft was delivered to Carswell AFB, Texas, in April 1988, permitting the first B-52Hs to be put on full alert with both internal and external ALCMs by September 1989. The system should be fully operational at all SAC B-52H bases by August 1993, including Fairchild AFB, Washington (92nd BW); K. I. Sawyer AFB, Michigan (410th BW); and Minot AFB, North Dakota (5th BW). The 416th BW at Griffiss AFB, NY, will convert to B-52Hs from G versions in FY 1991. B-52Hs will also be equipped with the General Dynamics AGM-129A Advanced Cruise Missile, which will augment the AGM-86Bs currently in service. Captive carry tests of eight AGM-129As mounted on the underwing pylons of a B-52H began in early 1989. IOC for the AGM-129A is expected in 1992, with the 410th BW.

Cruise missile carrying B-52Gs have a distinctive fairing (known as a strakelet) at the leading-edge of each wingroot to give them a recognisable appearance in accordance with provisions of the unratified SALT II agreement. B-52Hs do not need strakelets, as all carry cruise missiles and are already recognisably different from other versions of the Stratofortress.

The 54 B-52Gs not modified for use as cruise missile carriers have been adapted for a long-range conventional force projection role. Thirty of them have also each been equipped to carry eight Harpoon anti-shipping missiles externally in a maritime support role. Two squadrons of Harpoon-equipped B-52Gs are now operational. All 69 aircraft are being fitted with an integrated conventional stores management system (ICSMS) permitting them to carry a variety of conventional weapons as required, by

CSRL installed in weapons bay of a B-52H

rearranging data stored in the weapons systems computer by means of a pre-programmed removable software cassette. IOC for ICSMS-equipped B-52Gs was achieved in 1988. More B-52G/Hs may in future be assigned to the conventional mission.

The following details apply to the B-52G and B-52H:
POWER PLANT (B-52G): Eight 61.2 kN (13,750 lb st) J57-P-43WB turbojets. Fuel capacity 174,130 litres (46,000 US gallons; 38,303 Imp gallons) internally, plus two 2,650 litre (700 US gallon; 583 Imp gallon) underwing drop tanks.
POWER PLANT (B-52H): Eight 75.6 kN (17,000 lb st) Pratt & Whitney TF33-P-3 turbofans. Fuel capacity as for B-52G.
ACCOMMODATION (B-52G/H): Crew of six (pilot and co-pilot, side by side on flight deck, navigator, radar navigator, ECM operator and gunner).
AVIONICS AND OPERATIONAL EQUIPMENT: All currently operational B-52Gs and Hs have an AN/ASQ-151 Electro-optical Viewing System (EVS) to improve low level penetration capability. The EVS sensors are housed in two steerable, side by side chin turrets. The starboard turret houses a Hughes Aircraft AAQ-6 forward-looking infra-red (FLIR) scanner, while the port turret contains a Westinghouse AVQ-22 low light level TV camera. Phase VI avionics include Motorola ALQ-122 SNOE (Smart Noise Operation Equipment) and Northrop AN/ALQ-

155(V) advanced ECM; an AFSATCOM kit which permits worldwide communication via satellite; a Dalmo Victor ALR-46 digital radar warning receiver; Westinghouse ALQ-153 pulse-Doppler tail warning radar; and improved versions of the ITT Avionics ALQ-117 ECM system (ALQ-172(V) ECM system) for the B-52G and B-52H. Boeing OAS (offensive avionics system), introduced from 1980, is a digital solid state system, and includes Tercom (terrain comparison) guidance, a Teledyne Ryan Doppler radar, Honeywell AN/ASN-131 gimballed electrostatic airborne inertial navigation system (GEANS), IBM/Raytheon ASQ-38 analog bombing/navigation system with IBM digital processing, SIADS Inc attitude heading and reference system, Honeywell radar altimeter, Honeywell controls and displays, and Norden Systems modernised strategic radar. Under Phase II of the programme, completed by FY 1989, all 152 B-52Gs and 95 Hs have been equipped with OAS.
ARMAMENT (B-52G): Four 0.50 in machine-guns in tail turret, remotely operated by AGS-15 fire control system, remote radar control, or closed circuit TV. Twelve AGM-86 air-launched cruise missiles, eight Boeing AGM-69 SRAM short-range attack missiles (on rotary launcher in internal weapons bay, plus nuclear free-fall bombs) on 98 aircraft. Other 54 aircraft equipped to carry conventional bombs and/or (on 30 aircraft) Harpoon air-to-surface missiles, as described in earlier paragraphs.
ARMAMENT (B-52H): Single 20 mm Vulcan multi-barrel cannon in tail turret instead of four machine-guns. All aircraft being equipped to carry 12 AGM-86 cruise missiles externally and eight internally on CSRL.
DIMENSIONS, EXTERNAL:
Wing span	56.39 m (185 ft 0 in)
Wing area, gross	371.6 m² (4,000 sq ft)
Length overall	49.05 m (160 ft 10.9 in)
Height overall	12.40 m (40 ft 8 in)
Wheel track (c/l of shock struts)	2.51 m (8 ft 3 in)
Wheelbase	15.48 m (50 ft 3 in)

DIMENSION, INTERNAL:
Weapons bay volume	29.53 m³ (1,043 cu ft)

WEIGHT:
Max T-O weight	more than 221,350 kg (488,000 lb)

PERFORMANCE:
Max level speed at high altitude
Mach 0.90 (516 knots; 957 km/h; 595 mph)
Cruising speed at high altitude
Mach 0.77 (442 knots; 819 km/h; 509 mph)
Penetration speed at low altitude   Mach 0.53 to 0.55
(352-365 knots; 652-676 km/h; 405-420 mph)
Service ceiling   16,765 m (55,000 ft)
T-O run: G   3,050 m (10,000 ft)
H   2,900 m (9,500 ft)
Range with max fuel, without in-flight refuelling:
G   more than 6,513 nm (12,070 km; 7,500 miles)
H   more than 8,685 nm (16,093 km; 10,000 miles)

BOEING KC-135 STRATOTANKER

Between 1957 and 1965, Boeing delivered to the USAF 729 KC-135A tankers, 18 C-135A and 30 C-135B transports, 14 EC-135C and three EC-135J command posts, and four RC-135A and 10 RC-135C survey aircraft, the B and C versions with turbofan engines. Additionally, 12 C-135F tankers (of which 11 remain) were supplied to France. The USAF continues to operate about 741 aircraft, many of which have been modified: 446 KC-135A/Rs, two C-135As, one NC-135A, 11 NKC-135As (excluding one US Navy), five EC-135As, five C-135Bs, seven WC-135Bs, three C-135Cs, 13 EC-135Cs, four KC-135Ds, three C-135Es, one NKC-135E, five EC-135Es, 138 KC-135Es, four EC-135Gs, five EC-135Hs, four EC-135Js, two EC-135Ks, five EC-135Ls, four EC-135Ps, 54 KC-135Qs, two RC-135Ss, one TC-135S, two RC-135Us, eight RC-135Vs, six RC-135Ws, one RC-135X and one EC-135Y.

From 1975 Boeing at Wichita was engaged in a programme to extend the flying life of every KC-135 by 27,000 hours, by replacing sections of the lower wing skins. This programme, completed on 7 November 1988, will enable the aircraft to remain fully operational well past the year 2020, and justified a further programme to retrofit modern technology engines, to improve fuel economy and reduce noise. Selection of the 97.9 kN (22,000 lb st) CFM International CFM56-2B-1 turbofan (military designation F108-CF-100) for evaluation on a KC-135A testbed aircraft was announced in early 1980, and the USAF will have acquired 375 modification kits by FY 1992.

The re-engined aircraft, the first of which (61-0293) made its first flight on 4 August 1982, have the new USAF designation **KC-135R**. Electrical, hydraulic, performance and fuel management, and flight control systems are also undergoing modification, the main landing gear is being strengthened, and dual APUs are being installed for quick engine starting. The first nine KC-135R 'production' conversions for the USAF were funded in the FY 1982 budget, and 306 modification kits (each of 54,000 parts) and 237 installations had been funded by 19 January 1990. On that date Wichita delivered the 200th kit for fitment in a KC-135 to be redelivered a few months later. Production continues at the rate of four per month. Eleven similar **C-135FR** conversions have been completed for the French

Air Force; the first of these was returned to service officially on 26 August 1985, and the 11th aircraft was redelivered on 13 April 1988.

Compared with the standard turbojet KC-135A, Boeing estimated that the KC-135R would be able to offload 65 per cent more fuel over a 1,500 nm (2,775 km; 1,725 mile) radius at average T-O gross weight, and 150 per cent more at 2,500 nm (4,630 km; 2,875 mile) radius. Increased thrust enables it to take off to 762 m (2,500 ft) before a KC-135A could leave the ground. Its noise footprint is 98 per cent smaller in terms of a 90 EPNdB landing/take-off contour. Max take-off weight of the KC-135R is 146,285 kg (322,500 lb), compared with 136,800 kg (301,600 lb) for the KC-135A. Max fuel load is 92,210 kg (203,288 lb) compared with the KC-135A's 86,047 kg (189,702 lb). On 19 November 1988, KC-135R (62-3554) 'Cherokee Rose', of the 19th ARW at Robins AFB, established 16 time-to-height world records in four weights classes, breaking three records held since 1981 by the USSR.

Air Force Systems Division is reported to have received funding for trials of Flight Refuelling Ltd Mk 32B hose-reel refuelling pods on a KC-135R, with a view to supplementing the aircraft's standard boom refuelling system.

To satisfy the near-term critical requirements for replacing the turbojets of Air National Guard and Air Force Reserve KC-135As with turbofans, the US Air Force acquired many retired commercial Boeing 707-100B/720B/320B/320C airliners, together with spare JT3D-3B turbofans. Between 1981 and January 1988, 161 C-135s were re-engined, comprising 23 special missions aircraft and all 138 KC-135As of the ANG and AFRes, the latter redesignated **KC-135E** as described in the 1987-88 and earlier editions of *Jane's*. Following ANG/AFRes tanker fleet expansion plans, a September 1989 contract covered 14 more KC-135E conversions to be undertaken between May and September 1990 by Boeing Louisiana Inc, of Lake Charles. These 14 will be shared between the 145th ARS, Ohio ANG; 168th ARS, Alaska ANG; 197th ARS, Arizona ANG; 336th ARS at March AFB; 314th ARS at Mather AFB; and 72nd ARS at Grissom AFB. Simultaneously with this modification, five-rotor wheel brakes and a Mark II/III anti-skid system were installed.

BOEING EC-18D

This designation applies to two USAF C-18As which are being modified as cruise missile mission control platforms by Electrospace Systems Inc, under whose entry in this section the modification is described.

BOEING 707 TANKER/TRANSPORT
Royal Saudi Air Force designation: KE-3A

In 1982 BMA initiated a programme to demonstrate the use of the commercial Model 707-320 Intercontinental airframe modified as an aerial refuelling tanker. A former TWA 707-320C was converted as a demonstration aircraft, making its first flight in this form in early 1983. This aircraft was equipped with three hose and drogue refuelling points, one on the fuselage centreline and one at each wingtip, the latter being housed in pods similar to those used on earlier tanker modifications of the Model 707 for such operators as the Canadian Armed Forces and the Royal Moroccan Air Force. The centreline station is a new modification. When not required for the tanker role the aircraft can be converted easily into an all-passenger, all-cargo, or combination passenger/cargo transport, and with special interiors for VIP or aeromedical transport. Seats, cargo handling equipment, as well as most executive interior partitions and furnishings, are mounted on permanently installed tracks with quick disconnect fittings.

A variety of refuelling system options is available, including a probe or receptacle in the nose, Beech or Sargent-Fletcher wingtip pods deploying a hose and drogue, a Sargent-Fletcher rear fuselage centreline hose and drogue installation, or a Boeing centreline boom refuelling installation of the type developed for the USAF's KC-135 tanker/transports. These can be combined to customer requirements, enabling the Boeing 707 tanker/transport to be equipped in a configuration that is compatible with any type of Western fighter. Increased fuel capacity can be provided by the installation of an optional 19,040 litre (5,030 US gallon; 4,188 Imp gallon) tank in the rear lower cargo hold. With this, the 707-320's standard 90,299 litre (23,855 US gallon; 19,863 Imp gallon) wing fuel tanks, and triple refuelling points, the tanker can rendezvous with fighters 1,000 nm (1,853 km; 1,151 miles) from its base and transfer 55,878 kg (123,190 lb) of fuel.

In addition to installation of the refuelling pods or boom, basic modifications include a refuelling control panel at the flight engineer's station; improved hydraulic system and fuel pumps; strengthening of the outer wing; new wingtips, military avionics and a TV scanner; and either a boom operator's or pod observer's station. Military avionics include dual UHF with DF, Tacan, IFF, weather radar, rendezvous radar, and dual INS. The quick-change capability of the interior makes the 707 tanker/transport easily adaptable for a range of military roles including coastal patrol, electronic countermeasures, maritime missions, and tactical command and control (C²). By the installation of wing hardpoints or dispensing bays, it could also be used as a platform for the deployment of sonobuoys

Boeing Model 707 tanker/transport demonstrator with its three hose and drogue refuelling systems deployed

or other ASW sensors, mines and bombs, air-to-air or standoff missiles, and chaff or flares.

Eight KE-3As for Saudi Arabia and four 707-3J9Cs for Iran (Beech 1800 wingtip pods installed by Boeing) were the sole new-build tanker-transports. Customers for refurbished second-hand Boeing 707s comprise Australia (four 707-338Cs with FRL Mk 32 wing pods converted by IAI); Brazil (four KC-137s with Beech pods converted by Boeing); Canada (two CC-137s with provision for Beech 1800 wingtip pods converted by Boeing); Israel (six 707s converted by IAI with Sargent-Fletcher Co 34-000 pods); Italy (four 707-382Bs with SFC 34-000 pods and FR 480C fuselage HDU being converted by Officine Aeronavali); Morocco (one 707-138B, Beech pods converted by AMIN); and Spain (two T.17s with SFC 34-000 pods converted by Boeing). Chile has a requirement for IAI-converted 707 tankers.

A description of the Model 707-320C can be found in the 1980-81 and earlier editions of *Jane's*.

BOEING VC-25A 'AIR FORCE ONE'

Two Boeing 747-2G3Bs (Srs 200Bs) have been purchased by the USAF for Presidential transportation, replacing a pair of Boeing VC-137Cs. Designated VC-25A, the pair were built at Everett, Washington, and flown to Wichita for conversion to 'Air Force One' standard—the name reflecting the radio call-sign used by aircraft of the 89th Military Airlift Wing at Andrews AFB, MD, when flying the US President. Delivery to the USAF was delayed as the result of difficulties with re-wiring (the VC-25A containing 384 km; 239 miles of wire, or more than twice a standard 747) and additional fire-suppression measures. The first aircraft (with contrived serial 82-8000) flew in modified configuration at Wichita on 26 January 1990 and was due for delivery to the 89th MAW on 30 September 1990. Second aircraft, 92-9000, is to follow on 30 June 1991.

Powered by four 252.4 kN (56,750 lb st) General Electric F103-GE-102 (CF6-80C2B1) turbofans, the VC-25As have a fuel capacity of 202,940 litres (53,611 US gallons; 44,640 Imp gallons), providing a range in excess of 6,200 nm (11,490 km; 7,139 miles) before recourse to the in-flight refuelling provision. Self-sufficiency is enhanced by utilising self-contained airstairs in the lower lobe and the addition of a second Garrett GTCP331-200 APU in the tail.

The new aircraft have a Bendix Aerospace EFIS-10 electronic flight instrument system and complete onboard state-of-the-art communications equipment, including secure voice terminals and cryptographic equipment for writing and deciphering classified messages. E-Systems and Rockwell-Collins provided the mission communication system kits, which Boeing installed along with normal aircraft communications equipment. Litton supplied the aircraft's ring laser gyro inertial navigation systems. Each VC-25A accommodates 70 passengers and 23 crew, including ground crew required to travel with the aircraft.

Extensively modified to meet presidential requirements, the 371.6 m² (4,000 sq ft) of interior floor space of each 'Air Force One' includes an executive suite with presidential office, stateroom and lavatory; two galleys, each capable of providing food for 50 persons; an emergency treatment medical facility; and work and rest areas for the presidential staff, news media representatives and USAF crew.

WEIGHTS:
Long-range mission T-O weight   364,552 kg (803,700 lb)
Max zero-fuel weight   238,816 kg (526,500 lb)
Design mission zero-fuel weight   202,302 kg (446,000 lb)
Max landing weight   285,763 kg (630,000 lb)

BOEING 747 CRAF PROGRAMME
US Air Force designation: C-19A

Under the CRAF (Civil Reserve Air Fleet) programme, Boeing Military Airplanes modified 19 Boeing 747s of Pan American World Airways to supplement military transport forces by providing airlift of bulk and oversize cargo during emergencies. The main deck floor of each aircraft is strengthened, and a cargo handling system and side cargo door installed. Empty weight of the aircraft is increased by 5,900 kg (13,000 lb), for which the airline receives compensation during commercial operations.

The first modified 747 (N655PA) was returned to Pan American on 31 May 1985 and continues to operate in all-passenger configuration. The programme was completed in February 1990.

BOEING CARGO AIRCRAFT GROUND MOBILITY SYSTEM

Under contract from the US Air Force, Boeing Military Airplanes, in conjunction with Textron Marine Systems, is developing an air cushion Cargo Aircraft Ground Mobility System (CAGMS) which would enable USAF Lockheed C-130 transport aircraft to operate from bomb-damaged airfields or other rough surfaces. The CAGMS, the general configuration of which was illustrated in the 1989-90 *Jane's*, would be used for landing and would enable a C-130 to touch down on soft, unstable terrain and to clear obstacles up to 0.46 m (1 ft 6 in) high. After touchdown the aircraft's conventional landing gear would be lowered to enhance slow-speed stability and manoeuvrability when parking. The CAGMS is a strap-on unit which could be attached to a C-130 when required, and quickly removed for normal airfield operations.

BOEING 727 AAT

Boeing Military Airplanes has modified a Boeing 720B airliner (N771BE) to serve as an Advanced Avionics Testbed (AAT) for the development of new electronic warfare technologies under a multi-contractor advanced electronic countermeasures programme (AECM) led by Boeing. Team members include the US Air Force, ITT Avionics, Loral Electronic Systems, Ferranti, FLIR Inc, Norden Systems, Raytheon's Sedco Division, Tracor Aerospace, and Electro-Radiation Inc. Avionics subsystems, including ITT ALQ-172 jamming equipment, Loral

Retouched photograph showing final configuration of Boeing VC-25A (747-200B) 'Air Force One'

AN/ALR-56C ESM and Norden and Sedco monopulse jammers, and a Tracor towed decoy, have been integrated into the test airframe by Boeing's systems integration laboratory in Seattle. Boeing is also providing a core system with databus, flexible controls, displays and test instrumentation, making the aircraft easily adaptable for testing a variety of avionics systems and subsystems. Airframe modifications include provision for support systems, test equipment and new instrumentation in the cabin, installation of antennae in the nose, wings and tail, and Tracor towed ECM equipment in the tailcone. The Boeing 720B AECM testbed made its first flight from Seattle on 26 January 1989, when it operated against a ground based tracking radar, surface-to-air missile radars and an airborne interceptor aircraft. A millimetre wave (MMW) radar, FLIR, terrain-referenced navigation system, and two-crew operator station were expected to be installed in the aircraft during 1989 to enable it to be tested at low level to demonstrate the system's ability to navigate without constant radar emissions, and to detect and identify typical strategic targets.

During 1989, trials included advanced system management using expert system hardware, real-time route planning, missile warning systems, and advanced inte-gration and control concepts. The 1990 programme included a positioned towed SRT sensor platform; sensor fusion for SRT applications; missile countermeasures and further integration concepts. Boeing believes that AECM technology could be applied to special operations aircraft, tankers, transports, and to future upgrades of the Rockwell B-1B strategic bomber.

F-4 PHANTOM NWDS

Boeing Military Airplanes won a contract in 1986 to develop and install a modern digital avionics suite and weapons delivery system in more than 300 Tactical Air Command F-4Es and RF-4Cs. The NWDS (navigation and weapons delivery system) upgrade includes a databus link to a ring laser gyro inertial navigation unit, a new mission computer, avionics interface unit, data transfer system and new cockpit controls and displays. Using a technology employed in B-1B, F-16 and A-6 aircraft, the NWDS enables F-4E aircrews to deliver weapons with accuracy equal to newer front-line fighter-bombers. The system's ring laser gyro computes the aircraft's position and allows for precision navigation reconnaissance and accurate weapons delivery.

Work has been undertaken at the aircraft's home base, the first return to service being an F-4E of the 163rd TFS, Indiana ANG, at Fort Wayne on 8 September 1989. The programme was due for completion in September 1990.

BOEING 747 FREIGHTER CONVERSIONS

Boeing Military Airplanes has proposed a programme for converting commercial passenger Boeing 747-100/-200s into freighter aircraft. Modifications, which would be carried out at Wichita using parts and support supplied by Boeing Commercial Airplanes and Boeing Georgia Inc, would involve removing the passenger interior and ceiling to accommodate 3.05 m (10 ft) high containers, replacement of the floor and floor beams, strengthening of the main deck floor, and installation of a side cargo door and powered cargo handling system. The modification line, which could convert up to five aircraft per year, was scheduled to open in 1990 subject to a minimum launch order for four conversions. A second line could be added if required. Boeing Military Airplanes performed a similar freighter modification to Boeing 747-100s in the 1970s and has also modified 747 upper decks and converted the aircraft from passenger to passenger/cargo aircraft.

BRANSON
BRANSON AIRCRAFT CORPORATION

3790 Wheeling Street, Denver, Colorado 80239
Telephone: 1 (303) 371 9112
Telex: 45-4577 BRANSON DVR
Fax: 1 (303) 371 1813
PRESIDENT: Carl F. Branson
EXECUTIVE VICE-PRESIDENT: Roger P. Kirwan

Founded in 1966, Branson Aircraft Corporation provides engineering and custom manufacturing services for aircraft manufacturers and owners. The company has developed a series of auxiliary fuel tanks for business aircraft such as the Beechcraft Beechjet, Canadair Challenger, Cessna Citation, Learjet family and Mitsubishi Diamond, and has also designed conformal supplementary cargo bay fuel tanks commercial jet airliners. Other activities include the design, manufacture and installation of special equipment for medical transport, weather research and aerial photography.

CITATION EXTENDED RANGE FUEL SYSTEM

Branson holds an FAA FAR Pt 25 supplemental type certificate for its 454 litre (120 US gallon: 100 Imp gallon) auxiliary fuel tank installation in the Cessna Model 500 Citation, Citation I, II and S/II business jets. The tank installation and associated structural work weighs 36 kg (80 lb) empty and permits a 295 kg (650 lb) increase in the aircraft's maximum gross weight, enabling Citation I operators to carry an additional three passengers, plus 27 kg (60 lb) of baggage, and provides an extended maximum range of 1654 nm (3,065 km; 1,905 miles).

DIAMOND IA LONG-RANGE TANK

Branson has developed a 363 litre (96 US gallon; 80 Imp gallon) long-range fuel tank for the Mitsubishi Diamond IA and Beechcraft Model 400 Beechjet. In the latter aircraft the tank is standard equipment. The tank mounts in the aircraft's fuselage against the rear pressure bulkhead. Also available for the Diamond IA is a transfer system for filling the aircraft's fuselage fuel tank from the port wing tank, eliminating the need for manual filling of the fuselage tank; and a Branson tailcone baggage compartment, capacity 0.93 m³ (33 cu ft), maximum load 204 kg (450 lb). Branson has also received FAA approval for a gross weight increase kit for the Diamond IA which increases max T-O weight to 7,031 kg (15,500 lb).

LEARJET 55 LONG-RANGE TANKS

Branson's long-range auxiliary fuel tanks for the Learjet Model 55 business jet provide an additional 378.5 litres (100 US gallons; 83.5 Imp gallons) or 757 litres (200 US gallons; 167 Imp gallons) of fuel. The installation takes approximately four weeks for the 378.5 litre tank and five weeks for the 757 litre tank, which extends the aircraft's range by 400 nm (741 km; 461 miles)

CITATION EXTENDED WIDTH CARGO DOOR

Branson's cabin door modification for Cessna Citation I, II and S/II business jets provides an 0.91 m (3 ft 0 in) wide door permitting the loading of full size medical stretchers, palletised cargo, research equipment, large aerial cameras and other outsize items. The installation weighs 28.6 kg (63 lb), does not interfere with existing cabin seating or furnishings, meets FAA FAR Pt 25 requirements and takes six weeks to complete.

CITATION AIR AMBULANCE EQUIPMENT

Branson's medical equipment installation package for the Cessna Citation I, II and S/II includes installation of the extended width cabin door, single or dual stretchers, medical oxygen supply, compressed air, vacuum and electrical outlets. The first such installation was completed on a Citation II operated by Air Express of Oslo, Norway.

BRANSON F27/FH-227 LARGE CARGO DOOR

Branson has purchased from Fairchild Aircraft the FAA FAR Pt 25 supplemental type certificate for installation of a large cargo door on Fairchild FH-227 and Fokker F27 Friendship aircraft. The door, measuring 1.83 m (6 ft 0 in) high by 2.30 m (7 ft 6½ in) wide, is positioned just aft of the flight deck on the port fuselage side and is electrically actuated, opening to 110° and 170° positions. A crew entry door is incorporated. The conversion adds approximately 238 kg (525 lb) to aircraft empty weight. Cargo door conversions will be carried out in the United States, Europe and Asia.

BRANTLY
BRANTLY HELICOPTER INDUSTRIES USA CO LTD

Wilbarger County Airport, PO Box 113, Vernon, Texas 76384
Telephone: 1 (817) 552 5451
Fax: 1 (817) 552 2703
PRESIDENT: James T. Kimura

In March 1989 Japanese-American businessman James T. Kimura acquired from Hynes Aviation Industries type certificates and manufacturing and marketing rights to the Brantly B-2B and Model 305 light helicopters and formed Brantly Helicopter Industries on 8 May 1989. The new company has established a 2,787 m² (30,000 sq ft) facility at Wilbarger County Airport, Vernon, Texas, and expected to manufacture 10-12 B-2Bs and 5-8 Model 305s in 1990. The previously announced sale by Hynes of manufacturing and marketing rights to Naras Aviation Pvt Ltd of Madras, India (see 1989-90 *Jane's*) did not materialise, nor did Turkish interest in licence assembly or manufacture of the aircraft.

BRANTLY B-2B

TYPE: Two-seat light helicopter.
ROTOR SYSTEM: Three-blade main rotor. Articulated inboard flapping hinges offset 0.07 m (2.67 in) from hub, and coincident flap and lag hinges offset 1.31 m (4 ft 3¾ in) from rotor head. Symmetrical blade section with 29% thickness/chord ratio on inboard portion; NACA 0012 section outboard of hinge. Blades are semi-rigid at hub and fully articulated at inboard/outboard junction (40% blade span) to eliminate ground resonance. Inboard portion of each blade is built around a steel spar, outboard portion has an extruded aluminium leading-edge spar and polyurethane core; aluminium skin is bonded to core and riveted to spar. Blades are attached to

Brantly Helicopter Industries B-2B two-seat light helicopter *(Brian M. Service)*

head by flapping links; they do not fold, but can be quickly separated at inboard/outboard junction for easy storage. A rotor brake is standard equipment. Two-blade all-metal anti-torque tail rotor.
ROTOR DRIVE: Through automatic centrifugal clutch and planetary reduction gears. Bevel gear take-off from main transmission with flexible coupling via intermediate and upper gearboxes to tail rotor driveshaft. Main rotor/engine rpm ratio 1:6.0. Tail rotor/engine rpm ratio 1:1.

FUSELAGE: Stressed skin all-metal structure with conical tail section and small fixed horizontal stabilisers. Tail rotor on swept-up boom extension.
LANDING GEAR: Alternative skid, wheel or float gear. Skid type has small retractable wheels for ground handling, fixed tailskid and four shock absorbers with rubber in compression. Inflatable pontoons, which attach to standard skids, are available to permit operation from water. Alternative non-retractable tricycle landing gear has oleo-pneumatic shock absorbers in all units, with

single wheels on main units and twin castoring nosewheels. Goodyear tyres size 10 × 3½, pressure 2.07 bars (30 lb/sq in), on mainwheels; tyre pressure 1.93 bars (28 lb/sq in) on nosewheels. Goodyear mainwheel brakes.

POWER PLANT: One 134 kW (180 hp) Textron Lycoming IVO-360-A1A flat-four engine, mounted vertically, with dual fan cooling system. Rubber bag type fuel tank under engine, capacity 117 litres (31 US gallons; 25.8 Imp gallons). Refuelling point on port side of fuselage. Oil capacity 5.7 litres (1.5 US gallons; 1.25 Imp gallons).

ACCOMMODATION: Totally enclosed circular section cabin for two persons seated side by side. Forward hinged door on each side. Dual controls, cabin heater and demisting fan standard. Compartment for 22.7 kg (50 lb) baggage in forward end of tail section.

AVIONICS AND EQUIPMENT: Provision for all standard nav/com radios. Blind-flying instrumentation available as an option, but the Model B-2B is not certificated for instrument flight. Twin landing lights in nose.

DIMENSIONS, EXTERNAL:
Main rotor diameter	7.24 m (23 ft 9 in)
Main rotor blade chord: inboard	0.225 m (8.85 in)
outboard	0.203 m (8.0 in)
Tail rotor diameter	1.30 m (4 ft 3 in)
Length overall, rotors turning	8.53 m (28 ft 0 in)
Length of fuselage	6.62 m (21 ft 9 in)
Height overall	2.06 m (6 ft 9 in)
Skid track	1.73 m (5 ft 8½ in)
Passenger doors (each): Height	0.79 m (2 ft 7 in)
Width	0.86 m (2 ft 9¾ in)
Baggage compartment door:	
Mean height	0.25 m (9¾ in)
Length	0.55 m (1 ft 9¾ in)

DIMENSIONS, INTERNAL:
Cabin: Length	1.83 m (6 ft 0 in)
Max width	1.19 m (3 ft 11 in)
Max height	0.99 m (3 ft 3 in)
Floor area	2.60 m² (28.0 sq ft)
Volume	2.78 m³ (98.0 cu ft)
Baggage compartment	0.17 m³ (6.0 cu ft)

AREAS:
Main rotor blades (each)	0.69 m² (7.42 sq ft)
Main rotor disc	41.16 m² (443.0 sq ft)
Tail rotor disc	1.32 m² (14.19 sq ft)

WEIGHTS AND LOADINGS:
Weight empty: with skids	463 kg (1,020 lb)
with floats	481 kg (1,060 lb)
Max T-O weight	757 kg (1,670 lb)
Max disc loading	18.40 kg/m² (3.77 lb/sq ft)
Max power loading	5.65 kg/kW (9.27 lb/hp)

PERFORMANCE (at max T-O weight):
Max level speed at S/L	87 knots (161 km/h; 100 mph)
Max cruising speed (75% power)	
	78 knots (145 km/h; 90 mph)
Max rate of climb at S/L	580 m (1,900 ft)/min
Service ceiling	3,290 m (10,800 ft)
Hovering ceiling IGE	2,040 (6,700 ft)
Range with max fuel, with reserves	
	217 nm (400 km; 250 miles)

Brantly Helicopter Industries Model 305 five-seat light helicopter

BRANTLY MODEL 305

The Model 305 is a five-seat helicopter of similar configuration to the B-2B, but larger in every respect. The prototype flew for the first time in January 1964, and FAA type approval was received on 29 July 1965. The following description applies to the certificated passenger carrying version, about 44 of which were built in the mid-1960s. By mid-January 1990 an improved prototype, with redesigned rotor head and new blade section, had completed about 30h test flying.

TYPE: Five-seat light helicopter.

ROTOR SYSTEM AND DRIVE: As described for B-2B, except rotor/engine rpm ratio 1:6.6.

FUSELAGE AND TAIL UNIT: As described for B-2B.

LANDING GEAR: Choice of skid, wheel or float gear. Skid type has four oleo struts, two on each side, and small retractable ground handling wheels. The wheel gear has single mainwheels and twin nosewheels, all with oleo-pneumatic shock absorbers. Goodyear mainwheels and tyres size 6.00-6, pressure 2.07 bars (30 lb/sq in); Goodyear nosewheels and tyres size 5.00-5, pressure 1.93 bars (28 lb/sq in). Goodyear single-disc hydraulic brakes on mainwheels.

POWER PLANT: One 227.4 kW (305 hp) Textron Lycoming IVO-540-B1A flat-six engine, mounted vertically, with dual cooling fans. One rubber fuel cell under engine, capacity 163 litres (43 US gallons; 35.8 Imp gallons). Refuelling point in port side of fuselage. Oil capacity 9.5 litres (2.5 US gallons; 2.1 Imp gallons).

ACCOMMODATION: Two individual seats side by side, with dual controls. Rear bench seat for three persons. Door on each side. Rear compartment for 113 kg (250 lb) of baggage, with downward hinged door on starboard side.

AVIONICS AND EQUIPMENT: Bendix/King or Narco radio, to customer's specification. Blind-flying instrumentation is available, but helicopter is not certificated for instrument flight.

DIMENSIONS, EXTERNAL:
Main rotor diameter	8.74 m (28 ft 8 in)
Main rotor blade chord (constant)	0.254 m (10 in)
Tail rotor diameter	1.30 m (4 ft 3 in)
Length overall, rotors turning	10.03 m (32 ft 11 in)
Length of fuselage	7.44 m (24 ft 5 in)
Height overall	2.44 m (8 ft 1 in)
Wheel track	2.10 m (6 ft 10¾ in)
Wheelbase	2.15 m (7 ft 0½ in)
Passenger doors (each): Height	0.82 m (2 ft 8½ in)
Width	1.02 m (3 ft 3⅞ in)
Baggage compartment door:	
Mean height	0.30 m (1 ft 0¼ in)
Width	0.69 m (2 ft 3 in)

DIMENSIONS, INTERNAL:
Cabin: Length	2.30 m (7 ft 6½ in)
Max width	1.39 m (4 ft 6¾ in)
Max height	1.22 m (4 ft 0½ in)
Baggage compartment	0.47 m³ (16.7 cu ft)

AREAS:
Main rotor blades (each)	0.09 m² (11.79 sq ft)
Tail rotor blades (each)	0.05 m² (0.50 sq ft)
Main rotor disc	59.96 m² (645.4 sq ft)
Tail rotor disc	1.32 m² (14.19 sq ft)

WEIGHTS:
Weight empty	816 kg (1,800 lb)
Max T-O and landing weight	1,315 kg (2,900 lb)
Max zero-fuel weight	1,224 kg (2,900 lb)

PERFORMANCE (at max T-O weight):
Max level speed at S/L	104 knots (193 km/h; 120 mph)
Max cruising speed at S/L	
	96 knots (177 km/h; 110 mph)
Max rate of climb at S/L	297 m (975 ft)/min
Service ceiling	3,660 m (12,000 ft)
Hovering ceiling IGE	1,245 m (4,080 ft)
Range with max fuel and max payload, 15 min reserves	
	191 nm (354 km; 220 miles)

BROMON

BROMON AIRCRAFT CORPORATION
4085 Nevso Drive, Las Vegas, Nevada 89103

Telephone: 1 (702) 362 7121

Telex: 510 1002000 BROMON

Fax: 1 (702) 362 8931

CHAIRMAN OF THE BOARD: James T. Roe III

VICE-CHAIRMAN: James H. Brown

SENIOR VICE-PRESIDENT: Joseph A. Micó-Monaco

DIRECTOR OF ENGINEERING: Dale Ruhmel

MANAGER, MARKETING COMMUNICATIONS: Randy Horsley

BROMON BR2000

In June 1987 Bromon Aircraft Corporation announced that it was developing the BR2000 twin-turboprop aircraft, which it believes will meet commercial and military requirements for a sturdy STOL transport fulfilling such roles as commuter airliner, overnight package carrying, tactical troop transport, LAPES delivery, helicopter refuelling, gunship, medevac, border patrol, drug enforcement, coastal patrol, disaster relief, forestry patrol, surveillance and scientific mission work.

Key features of the concept, which was inspired by the four-engined Ahrens 404 transport (last described in the 1981-82 edition of *Jane's*), are simplicity, systems redundancy, accessibility and ease of maintenance combined with reliability, low acquisition and operating costs and quiet operation. The BR2000 has been designed to meet FAR Pt 25 certification requirements.

Design of the BR2000 began in 1985. Detail design continued in 1988, with construction of the first of three prototypes beginning in January 1989. The BR2000 was being built at Boringuen Airport, Aquadilla, Puerto Rico, but in October 1989 financial difficulties led to the suspension of all operations, since when no further news has been received.

A full description, artist's impression and three-view drawing of the BR2000 may be found in the 1989-90 edition of *Jane's*.

BUSH

BUSH CONVERSIONS INC
Box 431, Udall, Kansas 67146
Telephone: 1 (316) 782 3851
VICE-PRESIDENT: Barbara Williams

BOLEN 'TAILDRAGGER' CONVERSIONS

Bush Conversions Inc is offering the 'Taildragger' modification which the former Ralph Bolen Inc designed as a tailwheel landing gear conversion for Cessna 150/152, 172/Skyhawk, R172K and 175 aircraft. Flight testing has indicated an average 8.5-10.5 knots (16-19.5 km/h; 10-12 mph) increase in speed resulting from removal of the nosewheel unit; but this change in landing gear configuration is intended also to improve performance from short fields and rough surfaces, to permit a tighter turn radius on narrow strips, and to simplify operation on floats or skis when this is desirable.

Bolen 'Taildragger' conversion of a Cessna Model 150 *(Mike Jerram)*

The conversion is carried out by the addition of two bulkheads in the front fuselage and a new main landing gear attachment box, just forward of the existing box, to which new cantilever main legs are installed in the case of Cessna Models 172 and 175. Cessna 150 series F, G, H, J and K, and Cessna 152s, retain their existing main legs, but these are removed from their original mounting and attached to the new forward box. Earlier versions require new legs of the design fitted to Cessna 150s of the above series, so that the

now-standard wheel with 15 × 6.00-6 tyre and wheel brake can be installed. The remainder of the conversion covers the removal of the nose gear, and the installation of a new tailwheel unit that includes a Scott 3200 wheel. This unit is attached by stress plates and stringers, so that the tailwheel assembly becomes an integral part of the fuselage structure. No skin removal is required for the conversion.

The 'Taildragger' modification of the landing gear has been so designed that on completion there is no shift in the

CG position. The STC for most of the Cessna Model 150/152 series, and for the Model 172, R172K and 175, covers operation on Fluidyne snow skis. No weight penalty results from conversion of Model 150/152 aircraft; the longer and stronger main legs introduced on the Models 172/175, and accompanying structure, increase weight by 13.6 kg (30 lb).

CALIFORNIA HELICOPTER

CALIFORNIA HELICOPTER INTERNATIONAL
2935 Golf Course Drive, Ventura, California 93003-7604
Telephone: 1 (805) 644 5800
Telex: 6831165 CHI UW
Fax: 1 (805) 644 5132
PRESIDENT: Gary A. Podolny
VICE-PRESIDENT AND GENERAL MANAGER:
 W. E. 'Jake' Dangle

CALIFORNIA HELICOPTER (SIKORSKY) S-58T
On 22 December 1981, California Helicopter acquired from Sikorsky all rights to the S-58T helicopter, a twin-turbine (Pratt & Whitney Canada PT6T-6) conversion of the piston engined Sikorsky S-58. Details of the conversion can be found under the Sikorsky entry in the 1978-79 and earlier editions of *Jane's*; that company had delivered approximately 146 converted aircraft and/or conversion kits when negotiations with California Helicopter were finalised in 1981. The rights cover manufacture of turbine conversion kits and spare parts, and support of the worldwide fleet of S-58/S-58T aircraft.

California Helicopter also offers a dynamic component exchange programme for the S-58 and S-58T.

The S-58T is operated commercially on a variety of services ranging from passenger transport to heavy lift external cargo. The FAA and British Civil Aviation Authority have approved the aircraft for IFR operation.

New York Airways uses four S-58Ts with 14-passenger configuration on its shuttle operation from Manhattan to the New York metropolitan airports. Others are operated throughout the world.

The Indonesian Air Force has converted and delivered to

California Helicopter conversion of Sikorsky S-58 to twin-turbine S-58T configuration

its own units a total of 12 S-58Ts. The Royal Thai Air Force has acquired 18 S-58Ts. The Thai Ministry of Agriculture uses the S-58T as a VIP transport. California Helicopter delivered three S-58Ts to South Korea in 1988.

WEIGHTS AND LOADINGS:
Weight empty	3,437 kg (7,577 lb)
Max T-O and landing weight	5,896 kg (13,000 lb)
Max disc loading	25.8 kg/m² (5.29 lb/sq ft)
Max power loading	4.72 kg/kW (7.76 lb/shp)

PERFORMANCE (at max T-O weight. A: PT6T-3, B: PT6T-6):
Max level speed at S/L:
A, B	120 knots (222 km/h; 138 mph)

Cruising speed:
A, B	110 knots (204 km/h; 127 mph)
Hovering ceiling OGE: A	1,433 m (4,700 ft)
B	1,980 m (6,500 ft)
Single-engine absolute ceiling: A	640 m (2,100 ft)
B	1,280 m (4,200 ft)

Range with 1,071 litres (283 US gallons; 236 Imp gallons) usable fuel, including 20 min reserves at cruising speed:
A	260 nm (481 km; 299 miles)
B	242 nm (447 km; 278 miles)

CAVENAUGH

CAVENAUGH AVIATION INC
15600 Drummet Boulevard, Suite 730, Houston, Texas 77032
Telephone: 1 (713) 442 3500
Fax: 1 (713) 442 3559
PRESIDENT: Dudley N. Cavenaugh.
DIRECTOR OF MARKETING: William H. Reynolds

CAVENAUGH CARGOLINER
Cavenaugh Aviation commenced design work on this cargo conversion of the Mitsubishi MU-2 pressurised twin-turboprop business transport in mid-1984, and began construction of a prototype modification a year later, subsequently obtaining FAA certification. The Cargoliner is based on the long fuselage MU-2G, MU-2J, MU-2L, MU-2N and Marquise models of the aircraft, last described under the MAI heading in the US section of the 1985-86 *Jane's*.

The conversion involves substitution of a crew door, hinged at its forward edge and with integral step, for the flight deck window on the port or starboard side of the fuselage; installation of a bulkhead, stressed to 9g, between flight deck and cabin area and containing a door for access to the cargo area; the addition of a smooth plastic liner in the former cabin area, and cargo nets which divide the area into three compartments, each accessible from the front or rear of the aircraft. A one-piece upward opening cargo

Cavenaugh Cargoliner conversion of the Mitsubishi MU-2, with optional rear cargo door

door, 1.22 m (4 ft 0 in) high × 1.42 m (4 ft 8 in) wide, is optional and replaces the MU-2's standard door on the port side of the fuselage. The MU-2's pressurisation system is not affected by the conversion. By November 1988, when the last update was received, Cavenaugh Aviation had completed 20 Cargoliners, including the prototype.

DIMENSIONS, EXTERNAL:
Crew door: Height	0.61 m (2 ft 0 in)
Width: at top edge	0.41 m (1 ft 4 in)
at bottom edge	0.84 m (2 ft 9 in)

DIMENSIONS, INTERNAL:
Cargo hold: Length	4.90 m (16 ft 1 in)
Max height: at forward bulkhead	1.29 m (4 ft 3 in)
at rear bulkhead	1.17 m (3 ft 10 in)
Volume	7.64 m³ (270.0 cu ft)

CESSNA

CESSNA AIRCRAFT COMPANY (Subsidiary of General Dynamics Corporation)
PO Box 7704, Wichita, Kansas 67277
Telephone: 1 (316) 946 6000
Telex: 417 400
Fax: 1 (316) 946 7250
CHAIRMAN AND CHIEF EXECUTIVE OFFICER:
 Russell W. Meyer Jr
SENIOR VICE-PRESIDENT, AIRCRAFT MARKETING:
 Roy H. Norris
VICE-PRESIDENT, PROPELLER AIRCRAFT MARKETING:
 Melvin S. Nichols
DIRECTOR OF PUBLIC RELATIONS: H. Dean Humphrey

Cessna Aircraft Company was founded by the late Clyde V. Cessna, a pioneer in US aviation in 1911, and was incorporated on 7 September 1927. Its former Pawnee and Wallace aircraft divisions in Wichita were consolidated as

production facilities within the company's Aircraft Division in mid-1984. In 1985 General Dynamics Corporation acquired the company as a wholly owned subsidiary.

Subsidiary companies owned by Cessna are the McCauley Accessory Division of Dayton, Ohio, and Cessna Finance Corporation in Wichita. In February 1989 Cessna sold its 49 per cent interest in Reims Aviation of France to Compagnie Francaise Chaufour Investissement (CFCI) of Paris, which will continue to manufacture the Cessna F406 Caravan II, and holds an option to assemble Cessna's single-engine piston aircraft when Cessna resumes production of these models.

By 31 December 1989, the company had produced a total of 177,382 aircraft. During 1989, it delivered a total of 183 aircraft, including 89 Caravan Is, 12 Caravan IIs, 32 Citation IIs, one Citation S/II, 16 Citation IIIs and 33 Citation Vs. Total employment within the company stood at 4,150 on 1 January 1990.

The company's announced range of production aircraft for 1990 consisted of eight types: the Caravan I and II, and six models of the Citation business jet. Restoration of piston engined models to the production line is not anticipated before 1992.

CESSNA MODEL 152
A total of 7,500 standard Model 152s and Model 152 Aerobats had been built by 31 December 1986, including 640 built by Reims Aviation in France. Manufacture of the Aerobat has ended. Production of the standard Model 152 has been suspended. Descriptions of both can be found in the 1984-85 *Jane's*.

CESSNA SKYHAWK
The Skyhawk is certificated for operation as a floatplane, and can be fitted with skis. A version designated F 172 is produced in France by Reims Aviation.

A total of 35,773 commercial aircraft in the Model 172/Skyhawk series had been built by 31 December 1987, including 2,144 F 172s built in France. In addition, 864 were built during 1966-1983 as T-41A, T-41B, T-41C and T-41D Mescalero military basic trainers.

Production of the Skyhawk has been suspended. A description can be found in the 1985-86 *Jane's*.

CESSNA CUTLASS RG

The Cutlass RG combined the airframe of the Model 172 Skyhawk with the retractable landing gear developed for the Skylane RG.

A total of 1,159 Cutlass RGs had been sold by 31 December 1987. Production has been suspended. A description can be found in the 1985-86 *Jane's*.

CESSNA SKYLANE

A total of 19,812 Model 182/Skylanes of various models had been built by 31 December 1987, including 169 F 182s built by Reims Aviation. Production of the Model 182/Skylane has been suspended. A description appeared in the 1985-86 *Jane's*.

CESSNA SKYLANE RG and TURBO SKYLANE RG

Production of these retractable landing gear versions of the Skylane has been suspended.

By 31 December 1987 a total of 2,102 Skylane RGs had been built, including 73 assembled by Reims Aviation in France as Reims 182 Skylane RGs. A description can be found in the 1985-86 *Jane's*.

CESSNA MODEL 185 SKYWAGON

A total of 4,356 Model 185 Skywagons, including 497 military U-17A/B/Cs, had been built by 31 December 1987. Skywagon production has been suspended. A full description and illustration can be found in the 1985-86 *Jane's*.

CESSNA AG TRUCK and AG HUSKY

Production of both of these agricultural aircraft was suspended in 1985. Sales of the Ag Truck totalled 1,949, and 386 examples of the Ag Husky were delivered. Abbreviated descriptions of both models can be found in the 1985-86 *Jane's*, with a full description of the Ag Truck in the 1984-85 edition.

CESSNA STATIONAIR 6 and TURBO STATIONAIR 6

US Air Force designation: U-26A (Turbo Stationair)

Cessna first renamed the former U206 Skywagon and TU206 Turbo Skywagon as the Stationair and Turbo Stationair respectively. In 1978 a further name change to Stationair 6 and Turbo Stationair 6 highlighted the six-seat capacity of these cargo/utility aircraft. Production of the U206G and TU206G models has been suspended. Full descriptions of both can be found in the 1985-86 *Jane's*.

A total of 7,652 Model 206 Skywagons and Stationairs had been built by 31 December 1987, including 643 de luxe Super Skylanes of similar basic design.

CESSNA MODEL 208 CARAVAN I/U-27A

First flown on 9 December 1982, the engineering prototype of the Caravan I (N208LP) bore little resemblance to any previous Cessna design. The aircraft was claimed by the company to be the first all-new single-engined turboprop general aviation aircraft, and was intended to supplement or replace the thousands of de Havilland Canada Beavers and Otters, and Cessna 180s, 185s and 206s, operated throughout the world in a variety of utility roles.

The Caravan I's basic ability to fly fast with a heavy load, to get into and out of unprepared airstrips, and to offer economy and reliability with minimum maintenance, can be supplemented by the addition of weather radar, air-conditioning and oxygen systems. Other packages of optional equipment enable it to perform aerial firefighting, photographic, agricultural spraying, ambulance/hearse, border patrol, parachuting and supply dropping, surveillance, and a variety of government utility duties, on wheels and floats.

The first production Caravan I was rolled out in August 1984. FAA certification was obtained on 23 October, in landplane configuration, with full production beginning in 1985. FAA certification of an amphibian version was obtained in March 1986. The first production amphibian was delivered to the Royal Canadian Mounted Police for use in remote areas of the Province of Quebec. Three Caravan Is are in service with the Brazilian Air Force, with four more ordered, and one with the Liberian Army. Ten have been supplied to the Royal Thai Army.

In December 1983 Federal Express Corporation of Memphis, Tennessee, placed an initial order for 30 **Model 208A** Caravan Is, and subsequently ordered nine more of

Turboprop powered Cessna Model 208 Caravan I

Cessna Model 208B Caravan I operated by Union Flights of Sacramento, California, on behalf of Federal Express *(John Wegg)*

this model, which differs from the standard aircraft in having a Bendix/King avionics installation, no cabin windows or starboard side rear door, more freight tiedowns, an additional cargo net, an underfuselage cargo pannier constructed from composites materials, a 15.2 cm (6 in) vertical extension to the fin/rudder, realigned exhaust outlet to keep exhaust gases clear of the pannier, and a max T-O weight of 3,629 kg (8,000 lb).

On 3 March 1986 the prototype (N9767F) of a stretched version of the Caravan I made its first flight. This aircraft, known as the **Model 208B** and developed at the request of Federal Express Corporation, has a 1,587 kg (3,500 lb) payload and 12.7 m³ (450 cu ft) of cargo space, including belly cargo pod. Certification was achieved in October 1986. In November 1989 Federal Express ordered a further 50 Caravan Is, for delivery between September 1990 and January 1992, and took options on another 100. If exercised, the options would take Federal Express's total order to 349, with deliveries extending until October 1994. Two hundred and ten of the total of 249 Caravan Is on order for Federal Express are stretched versions, which have a 1.22 m (4 ft 0 in) increase in fuselage length achieved by plug inserts fore and aft of the wing centre-section. The first Model 208B was delivered to Federal Express Corporation on 31 October 1986, and a total of 172 Caravan Is of both models had been delivered by 31 December 1989. At that time the carrier's Caravan Is had logged more than 240,000 hours with a 99.8 per cent despatch reliability rate. Deliveries to Federal Express, which operates the aircraft in Canada, France, Hawaii, Ireland, Sweden, the United States and the US Virgin Islands, continued in 1990 at the rate of three per month.

The all-freight versions of the Model 208A and Model 208B developed for Federal Express are known as the **Cargomaster** and **Super Cargomaster** respectively.

The Caravan I is the first single-engined aircraft to achieve FAA certification for Category II ILS operations. Federal Express will equip 104 of its aircraft for Cat II operations. In 1989 Federal Express obtained approval to operate its Caravan Is as cargo carriers under IFR conditions in France and Ireland, which are the first European countries to approve single-engined Public Transport IFR operations.

In December 1988 Cessna announced that it had signed an agreement with Toyota Aviation, a subsidiary of the Japanese car manufacturer Toyota Motor Corporation, for the marketing, distribution and support of the Caravan I and Caravan II in the People's Republic of China.

In the Spring of 1985 Cessna released details of a military utility/special mission derivative of the Caravan I with the designation **U-27A**. This aircraft can be equipped with six underwing hardpoints and a fuselage centreline hardpoint for external stores carriage; surveillance/observation windows, including bubble windows for vertically downwards viewing; a centreline reconnaissance pod; the 2.8 m³ (84 cu ft) cargo pannier of the Model 208A; and a flight-openable electrically operated 'roll-up' cargo door with slipstream deflector. Cessna foresees a market for the U-27A in such roles as air cargo, logistic support, paratroop or supply dropping, medevac, electronic surveillance, forward air control, passenger/troop transport, C³I, maritime patrol, SAR, psychological warfare, radio relay/RPV control, military base support, range safety patrol, reconnaissance and fire suppression.

Cessna is marketing the U-27A as a Low Intensity Conflict Aircraft (LICA). In a reconnaissance role the aircraft is equipped with a removable General Dynamics underbelly pod which can carry a variety of film and electro-optical sensors, including Zeiss Avionics KS-153 80 mm Tri-Lens and 600 mm high resolution cameras, Texas Instruments RS730 IR linescanner, Honeywell four-channel encrypted data link, Fairchild RECCE interface unit, two RCA video recorders, Control Data video management system and SIADS Inc 9000C or JET VG204 roll gyros, permitting real/near-real time reporting via voice or data link to control centres or battlefield commanders. The pod could also house a SLAR unit for standoff reconnaissance. The pod, which is 4.39 m (14 ft 5 in) long, 0.72 m (2 ft 4½ in) deep and 0.63 m (2 ft 1 in) wide, and weighs 454-567 kg (1,000-1,250 lb) depending on the sensor configuration, is compatible with the Advanced Tactical Air Reconnaissance System (ATARS) and can be mounted on other aircraft, including the General Dynamics F-16. General Dynamics planned to install a retractable FLIR turret for 360° lower-hemisphere coverage in the U-27A during 1989, and has proposed a variant equipped with Stinger anti-aircraft missiles for self-defence in a combined reconnaissance/forward air control role. The U-27A is also being proposed to meet a gunship requirement for the USAF Special Operations Command, in which role it would be equipped with a door-mounted General Electric GECAL 50 12.7 mm three-barrel Gatling gun. During the Autumn of 1988 a U-27A in LICA configuration undertook a demonstration tour of Europe after making its debut at the Farnborough Air Show. The stretched Model 208B Caravan I is also available in U-27A configuration.

Two U-27As equipped with long-range VLF/Omega navigation systems are in service with the US State Department for use in its narcotics control, eradication and interdiction operations. More than 10 per cent of the Caravan Is sold are reported to be in military or paramilitary use, some with the CIA.

By 31 December 1989 Cessna had delivered a total of 372 Caravan Is.

The name Caravan II applies to the unrelated twin turboprop business and utility transport developed jointly by Cessna and CFCI of France, and described under the latter company's entry. The following description applies to Cessna's single-engined Model 208 Caravan I:

TYPE: Single-engined turboprop utility aircraft.

WINGS: Braced high-wing monoplane. Wing section NACA 23017.424 at root, NACA 23012 at tip. Dihedral 3° from roots. Incidence 2° 37' at root, –0° 36' at tip. Fail-safe two-spar structure. Single streamline section bracing strut each side. Electrically actuated wide span single-slotted flaps occupy more than 70 per cent of wing trailing-edge, and extend to 30° setting for low landing speeds. Ailerons operate in conjunction with slot-lip spoilers for positive roll control. Aileron trim standard.

FUSELAGE: Conventional semi-monocoque structure.

TAIL UNIT: Cantilever structure, with long dorsal fin. All control surfaces horn balanced. Large trim tab in starboard elevator. Rudder trim standard. Floatplane versions have an auxiliary fin mounted on the leading-edge of the tailplane on each side.

LANDING GEAR: Non-retractable tricycle type, with single wheel on each unit. Tubular spring cantilever main units; oil-damped spring nosewheel unit. Mainwheel tyres size 6.50-10; nosewheel 6.50-8. Oversize tyres, mainwheels 8.50-10, nosewheel 22 × 8.00-8 and extended nosewheel fork optional. Hydraulically actuated single-disc brake on each mainwheel. Certificated in floatplane and amphibian versions, with floats by Wipline.

POWER PLANT: One Pratt & Whitney Canada PT6A-114 turboprop, flat rated at 447 kW (600 shp) to 3,800 m (12,500 ft), and driving a Hartzell three-blade constant-speed reversible-pitch and feathering composites propeller type HC-B3MN3/M10083 with spinner. Integral fuel tanks in wings, total capacity 1,268 litres (335 US gallons; 279 Imp gallons), of which 1,257 litres (332 US gallons; 276.5 Imp gallons) are usable.

ACCOMMODATION: Pilot and up to nine passengers or 1,360 kg (3,000 lb) of cargo. Maximum seating capacity with FAR Pt 23 waiver is 14. Cabin has a flat floor with Brownline cargo track attachments for a combination of two- and three-abreast seating, with an aisle between the seats. Forward hinged door for pilot, with direct vision window, on each side of forward fuselage. Airstair door for passengers at rear of cabin on starboard side. Cabin is heated and ventilated. Optional air-conditioning. Two-section horizontally split cargo door at rear of cabin on port side, flush with floor at bottom and with square corners. Upper portion hinges upward, lower portion forward 180°. Electrically operated, flight openable tambour roll-up door with airflow deflecting spoiler optional. In a cargo role cabin will accommodate typically two D-size cargo containers or up to ten 208 litre (55 US gallon; 45.8 Imp gallon) drums.

SYSTEMS: Electrical system is powered by 28V 200A starter/generator and 24V 45Ah lead-acid battery (24V 40Ah nickel-cadmium battery optional). Standby electrical system, with 95A alternator, optional. Hydraulic system for brakes only. Oxygen system, capacity 3.31 m³ (116.95 cu ft), optional. Vacuum system standard. Cabin air-conditioning system optional on c/n 208-00030 onwards. De-icing system, comprising electric propeller de-icing boots, pneumatic wing, wing strut and tail surface boots, electric heated windscreen panel, heated pitot/static probe, ice detector light and standby electrical system, all optional.

AVIONICS AND EQUIPMENT: Standard avionics include Bendix/King Silver Crown package comprising a single nav/com, ADF, transponder and audio console. Optional avionics include Bendix RDS-82 colour weather radar in pod mounted on starboard wing leading-edge. Standard equipment includes vertical altimeter, electric clock, magnetic compass, attitude and directional gyros, true airspeed indicator, turn and bank indicator, vertical speed indicator, ammeter/voltmeter, fuel flow indicator, ITT indicator, oil pressure and temperature indicator, windscreen defrost, ground service plug receptacle, variable intensity instrument post lighting, map light, overhead courtesy lights (3) and overhead floodlights (pilot and co-pilot), approach plate holder, cargo tiedowns, internal corrosion proofing, vinyl floor covering, emergency locator beacon, partial plumbing for oxygen system, adjustable fore/aft/vertical/reclining pilot's seat with five-point restraint harness, tinted windows, control surface bonding straps, heated pitot and stall warning systems, retractable crew steps (port side), tiedowns and towbar. Optional equipment includes co-pilot's and passenger seats, stowable, folding utility seats, digital clock, fuel totaliser, turn co-ordinator, flight hour recorder, fire extinguisher, dual controls, co-pilot flight instruments, floatplane kit (on c/n 208-00030 onwards), hoisting rings (for floatplane), inboard fuel

Cessna U-27A LICA aircraft with underbelly reconnaissance pod, underwing hardpoints and roll-up cabin door

Three-view of Cessna U-27A Low Intensity Conflict Aircraft (LICA) with side views, top to bottom, of 208A Caravan I, U-27A, 208A amphibian and 208B Super Cargomaster for Federal Express (Pilot Press)

filling provisions (included in floatplane kit), ice detection light, courtesy lights on wing leading-edges, passenger reading lights, omniflash beacon, rudder gust lock, retractable crew step for starboard side, oversized tyres, electric trim system, oil quick drain valve and fan driven ventilation system.

DIMENSIONS, EXTERNAL (Model 208):

Wing span	15.88 m (52 ft 1 in)
Wing chord: at root	1.98 m (6 ft 6 in)
at tip	1.22 m (4 ft 0 in)
Wing aspect ratio	9.6
Length overall: landplane	11.46 m (37 ft 7 in)
Height overall: landplane	4.32 m (14 ft 2 in)
amphibian (on land)	5.33 m (17 ft 6 in)
Tailplane span	6.25 m (20 ft 6 in)
Wheel track: landplane	3.56 m (11 ft 8 in)
amphibian	3.25 m (10 ft 8 in)
Wheelbase: landplane	3.54 m (11 ft 7½ in)
amphibian	4.44 m (14 ft 7 in)
Propeller diameter	2.54 m (8 ft 4 in)
Airstair door: Height	1.27 m (4 ft 2 in)
Width	0.61 m (2 ft 0 in)
Cargo door: Height	1.27 m (4 ft 2 in)
Width	1.24 m (4 ft 1 in)

DIMENSIONS, INTERNAL (Model 208):

Cabin: Length, excl baggage area	4.57 m (15 ft 0 in)
Max width	1.57 m (5 ft 2 in)
Max height	1.30 m (4 ft 3 in)
Volume	9.67 m³ (341.4 cu ft)

AREAS:

Wings, gross	25.96 m² (279.4 sq ft)
Vertical tail surfaces (incl dorsal fin)	3.57 m² (38.41 sq ft)
Horizontal tail surfaces	6.51 m² (70.04 sq ft)

WEIGHTS AND LOADINGS (Civil Model 208. L: landplane, F: floatplane, A: amphibian):

Weight empty: L	1,724 kg (3,800 lb)
F	2,020 kg (4,454 lb)
A	2,177 kg (4,799 lb)
Max baggage (all)	147 kg (325 lb)
Max fuel (all)	1,009 kg (2,224 lb)
Max ramp weight: L	3,327 kg (7,335 lb)
F, A	3,463 kg (7,635 lb)

Max T-O and landing weight, and max zero-fuel weight:

L	3,311 kg (7,300 lb)
F, A	3,447 kg (7,600 lb)
Max wing loading: L	127.4 kg/m² (26.1 lb/sq ft)
F, A	132.8 kg/m² (27.2 lb/sq ft)
Max power loading: L	7.41 kg/kW (12.2 lb/shp)
F, A	7.71 kg/kW (12.7 lb/shp)

WEIGHTS (U-27A: L and A as above):

Weight empty, standard: L	1,752 kg (3,862 lb)
A	2,233 kg (4,922 lb)
Max ramp weight: L	3,645 kg (8,035 lb)
A	3,463 kg (7,635 lb)
Max T-O weight: L	3,629 kg (8,000 lb)
A	3,447 kg (7,600 lb)
Max landing weight: L	3,538 kg (7,800 lb)
A	3,311 kg (7,300 lb)

PERFORMANCE (Civil Model 208. L: landplane, F: floatplane, A: amphibian):

Max operating speed (all)	175 knots (325 km/h; 202 mph) IAS
Max cruising speed at 3,050 m (10,000 ft):	
L	184 knots (341 km/h; 212 mph)
F	159 knots (295 km/h; 183 mph)
A	153 knots (283 km/h; 176 mph)
Stalling speed, power off:	
L, flaps up	73 knots (135 km/h; 84 mph) CAS
L, flaps down	60 knots (111 km/h; 69 mph) CAS
F, A, landing configuration	58 knots (107 km/h; 67 mph) CAS
Max rate of climb at S/L: L	370 m (1,215 ft)/min
F	306 m (1,004 ft)/min
A	290 m (952 ft)/min
Service ceiling: L	8,410 m (27,600 ft)
F	7,285 m (23,900 ft)
A	7,010 m (23,000 ft)
Max operating altitude (all)	9,145 m (30,000 ft)
T-O run: L	296 m (970 ft)
T-O run, water: F	468 m (1,535 ft)
A	469 m (1,540 ft)
T-O to 15 m (50 ft): L	507 m (1,665 ft)
T-O to 15 m (50 ft), water: F	843 m (2,765 ft)
A	859 m (2,820 ft)
Landing from 15 m (50 ft): L	472 m (1,550 ft)
Landing run: L	197 m (645 ft)
Range with max fuel, at max cruise power, allowances for start, taxi and reserves stated:	
L at 3,050 m (10,000 ft), 45 min	970 nm (1,797 km; 1,117 miles)

L at 6,100 m (20,000 ft), 45 min
1,275 nm (2,362 km; 1,468 miles)
F at 3,050 m (10,000 ft), 30 min
898 nm (1,664 km; 1,034 miles)
A at 3,050 m (10,000 ft), 30 min
868 nm (1,608 km; 999 miles)
Range with max fuel at max range power, allowances as above:
L at 3,050 m (10,000 ft)
1,115 nm (2,066 km; 1,284 miles)
L at 6,100 m (20,000 ft)
1,370 nm (2,539 km; 1,578 miles)
g limits   +3.8/−1.52

PERFORMANCE (U-27A: L and A as above):
Max cruising speed at 3,050 m (10,000 ft):
| L | 184 knots (341 km/h; 212 mph) |
| A | 163 knots (302 km/h; 188 mph) |
Stalling speed in landing configuration:
| L | 61 knots (113 km/h; 71 mph) |
| A | 58 knots (107 km/h; 67 mph) |
Max rate of climb at S/L: L   320 m (1,050 ft)/min
A   274 m (900 ft)/min
Service ceiling: L   7,770 m (25,500 ft)
A   6,100 m (20,000 ft)
T-O run at S/L: L   368 m (1,205 ft)
T-O run at S/L, water: A   500 m (1,640 ft)
T-O to 15 m (50 ft) at S/L: L   674 m (2,210 ft)
T-O to 15 m (50 ft) at S/L, water: A   872 m (2,860 ft)
Landing from 15 m (50 ft) at S/L, without propeller reversal: L   505 m (1,655 ft)
A   560 m (1,835 ft)
Landing run at S/L, without propeller reversal:
| L | 227 m (745 ft) |
| A | 297 m (975 ft) |
Range at 3,050 m (10,000 ft) at max cruise power, allowances for T-O, climb, cruise, descent, and 45 min reserves: L   1,085 nm (2,011 km; 1,249 miles)
A   955 nm (1,770 km; 1,100 miles)

CESSNA CENTURION, TURBO CENTURION and PRESSURISED CENTURION

A total of 8,453 Model 210/Centurions, plus an additional 51 Pressurised Centurions, had been delivered by 31 December 1987. Production of all models of the Centurion has been suspended. Full descriptions can be found in the 1985-86 *Jane's*.

CESSNA MODEL T303 CRUSADER

Production of this six-seat, turbocharged twin-engined aircraft has been suspended. A total of 297 T303 Crusaders had been delivered by 31 December 1987. The aircraft was fully described and illustrated in the 1985-86 *Jane's*.

CESSNA MODEL 402C

Production of the Model 402C Utililiner and Model 402C Businessliner has been suspended. A total of 1,540 Model 402s had been delivered by 31 December 1987. Full descriptions and illustrations can be found in the 1985-86 *Jane's*.

REIMS-CESSNA MODEL F 406/CARAVAN II

Details of this joint programme for a twin-turboprop business/utility transport can be found under the Reims Aviation entry in the French section.

CESSNA MODEL 414A CHANCELLOR

Production of the pressurised Model 414A Chancellor has been suspended. By 31 December 1987 Cessna had delivered 1,067 Model 414/Chancellors. A full description of the Model 414A appeared in the 1985-86 *Jane's*.

CESSNA MODEL 421 GOLDEN EAGLE

The prototype of this six/eight-seat pressurised twin-engined business aircraft flew for the first time on 14 October 1965. FAA type approval was received on 1 May 1967 and deliveries began in the same month.

Two developed versions were produced subsequently as the 421B Golden Eagle and 421B Executive Commuter, remaining in production until replaced by the Model 421C Golden Eagle in 1976.

A total of 1,909 Model 421s had been delivered. Production was suspended in 1985. A full description and illustration can be found in the 1985-86 *Jane's*.

CESSNA MODEL 425 CONQUEST I

Known as the Corsair until late 1982, the Conquest I is a twin-turboprop business aircraft based on the airframe of the Model 421 Golden Eagle. FAA certification was gained by mid-1980. Initial deliveries of production aircraft were made in November 1980, and 132 Corsairs were delivered. A total of 232 Corsairs and Conquest Is had been delivered

Artist's impression of Cessna CitationJet six-seat light business jet

by 31 December 1987. Production of the Conquest I has been suspended. A full description and illustrations can be found in the 1986-87 *Jane's*.

CESSNA MODEL 441 CONQUEST II

Production of the twin-turboprop Conquest II has been suspended. A total of 360 had been delivered by 31 December 1987. A full description and illustrations of the Conquest II, together with brief details of the Pratt & Whitney Canada PT6A-engined **Model 435**, may be found in the 1986-87 *Jane's*.

CESSNA MODEL 525 CITATIONJET

At the 1989 National Business Aircraft Association convention in Atlanta, Georgia, Cessna announced development of the six-seat Model 525 CitationJet, which will succeed the original Citation 500 and its replacement, the Citation I, production of which ceased in 1985.

Compared to the Citation I, the CitationJet has a fuselage shortened by 0.27 m (10¾ in), and wing span reduced by 0.57 m (1 ft 10½ in). Cabin height is increased by 13 cm (5 in) achieved by lowering the centre aisle. A new supercritical laminar-flow wing section has been developed and a T-tail introduced. The main landing gear is of the trailing-link type. Power plant is two 8.45 kN (1,900 lb st) Rolls-Royce/Williams International FJ44 turbofans, which Cessna began flight testing in a Citation 500 airframe in April 1990. First flight of the prototype CitationJet is scheduled for Spring 1991, with a second aircraft joining the test programme in the Autumn. FAA certification for single-pilot operation is anticipated in October 1992, with customer deliveries starting in December of that year. Orders for 50 CitationJets were placed at the NBAA convention, and Cessna was receiving further orders at the rate of five per month in early 1990. The company anticipates a market for up to 1,000 CitationJets over 10 years.

The following data are provisional:
DIMENSIONS, EXTERNAL:
Wing span   13.78 m (45 ft 2½ in)

Wing aspect ratio	8.5
Length overall	12.98 m (42 ft 7¼ in)
Height overall	4.18 m (13 ft 8½ in)
Wheel track	3.84 m (12 ft 7¼ in)
Wheelbase	4.54 m (14 ft 10¾ in)
Tailplane span	4.99 m (16 ft 4¾ in)

Crew/passenger door:
| Height | 1.29 m (4 ft 2¾ in) |
| Width | 0.60 m (1 ft 11½ in) |

DIMENSIONS, INTERNAL:
Cabin:
Length between pressure bulkheads
4.85 m (15 ft 10¾ in)
| Max width | 1.49 m (4 ft 10¾ in) |
| Height | 1.46 m (4 ft 9½ in) |

AREAS:
Wings, gross	22.30 m² (240.0 sq ft)
Horizontal tail surfaces, incl tab	5.03 m² (54.1 sq ft)
Vertical tail surface, incl tab	4.74 m² (51.0 sq ft)

WEIGHTS:
Weight empty	2,599 kg (5,730 lb)
Max fuel weight	1,393 kg (3,070 lb)
Max T-O weight	4,536 kg (10,000 lb)
Max ramp weight	4,581 kg (10,100 lb)
Max zero-fuel weight	3,461 kg (7,630 lb)
Max landing weight	4,309 kg (9,500 lb)

PERFORMANCE (estimated):
Max operating speed:
S/L to 9,300 m (30,500 ft)
260 knots (482 km/h; 299 mph) IAS
Above 10,820 m (35,500 ft)   Mach 0.70
Max cruising speed at 10,670 m (35,000 ft)
380 knots (704 km/h; 438 mph)
Stalling speed, landing configuration
81 knots (150 km/h; 94 mph)
Rate of climb at S/L, one engine out
326 m (1,070 ft)/min
Service ceiling   12,500 m (41,000 ft)
T-O balanced field length (FAR Pt 25)   903 m (2,960 ft)
FAR Pt 25 landing field length at max landing weight
854 m (2,800 ft)
Range with one crew, four passengers, 45 min reserves
1,500 nm (2,780 km; 1,727 miles)

Cessna CitationJet (two Rolls-Royce/Williams International FJ44 turbofans, 8.45 kN; 1,900 lb st each)
(Pilot Press)

CESSNA MODEL 550 CITATION II

Announced on 14 September 1976, the Citation II introduced a fuselage lengthened by 1.14 m (3 ft 9 in) compared with the Citation I, an increased span high aspect ratio wing, increased fuel and baggage capacities, and Pratt & Whitney Canada JT15D-4 turbofan engines. The prototype (N550CC) flew for the first time on 31 January 1977, and certification to FAR Pt 25 Transport Category requirements was received in late March 1978 for two-pilot operation. The Model 551 Citation II/SP was subsequently introduced for single-pilot operation, with up to 10 passengers, at a max T-O weight of 5,670 kg (12,500 lb), conforming to FAR Pt 23 requirements.

Production of the Citation II was phased out during 1984 in favour of the improved Citation S/II (which see), at which time 503 Citation IIs had been delivered. At the National Business Aircraft Association convention at New Orleans in September 1985, Cessna announced that it would resume production of the Citation II. By 31 December 1989 a total of 597 Citation IIs had been delivered, 32 of them in 1989. The following description applies to the current production Model 550 (c/n 0550 and later) unless otherwise indicated:

TYPE: Eight/twelve-seat twin-turbofan executive transport.

WINGS: Cantilever low-wing monoplane without sweepback. Wing section at c/l NACA 23014 (modified), at wing station 247.95 NACA 23012. Incidence 2° 30′ at c/l, –0° 30′ at wing station 247.95. Dihedral 4°. All-metal fail-safe structure with two primary spars, an auxiliary spar, three fuselage attachment points, and conventional ribs and stringers. Manually operated ailerons, with manual trim on port aileron. Electrically operated single-slotted trailing-edge flaps. Hydraulically operated aerodynamic speed brakes. Wing leading-edge forward of each engine is electrically anti-iced. Pneumatic de-icing boots on outer leading-edges.

FUSELAGE: All-metal pressurised structure of circular section. Fail-safe design, providing multiple load paths.

TAIL UNIT: Cantilever all-metal structure. Horizontal surfaces with dihedral of 9°. Large dorsal fin and smaller ventral fin. Manually operated control surfaces. Electric elevator trim with manual override; manual rudder trim.

LANDING GEAR: Hydraulically retractable tricycle type with single wheel on each unit. Main units retract inward into the wing, nose gear forward into fuselage nose. Free-fall and pneumatic emergency extension systems. Goodyear mainwheels with tyres size 22.0 × 8-10, 10-ply rating, pressure 6.90 bars (100 lb/sq in). Steerable nosewheel (±20°) with Goodyear wheel and tyre size 18.0 × 4.4, 10-ply rating, pressure 8.27 bars (120 lb/sq in). Goodyear hydraulic brakes. Parking brake and pneumatic emergency brake system. Anti-skid system optional.

POWER PLANT: Two Pratt & Whitney Canada JT15D-4 turbofans, each rated at 11.12 kN (2,500 lb st) for take-off, pod-mounted on sides of rear fuselage. Integral fuel tanks in wings, with usable capacity of 2,808 litres (742 US gallons; 618 Imp gallons).

ACCOMMODATION: Crew of two on separate flight deck, on fully adjustable seats, with seat belts and inertia reel shoulder harness. Sun visors standard. Fully carpeted main cabin equipped with seats for six to ten passengers, with toilet in six/eight-seat versions. Main baggage area at rear of cabin. Second baggage area in nose. Total baggage capacity 522 kg (1,150 lb). Cabin is pressurised, heated and air-conditioned. Individual reading lights and air inlets for each passenger. Dropout constant-flow oxygen system for emergency use. Plug type door with integral airstair at front on port side and one emergency exit on starboard side. Doors on each side of nose baggage compartment. Tinted windows, each with curtains. Pilot's storm window, birdproof windscreen with de-fog system, anti-icing, standby alcohol anti-icing and bleed air rain removal system.

Cessna Citation S/II executive jet

SYSTEMS: Pressurisation system supplied with engine bleed air, max pressure differential 0.61 bars (8.8 lb/sq in), maintaining a sea level cabin altitude to 6,720 m (22,040 ft), or a 2,440 m (8,000 ft) cabin altitude to 12,495 m (41,000 ft). Hydraulic system, pressure 103.5 bars (1,500 lb/sq in), with two pumps to operate landing gear and speed brakes. Separate hydraulic system for wheel brakes. Electrical system supplied by two 28V 400A DC starter/generators, with two 350VA inverters and 24V 40Ah nickel-cadmium battery. Oxygen system of 0.62 m³ (22 cu ft) capacity includes two crew demand masks and five dropout constant flow masks for passengers. High capacity oxygen system optional. Engine fire detection and extinguishing systems.

DIMENSIONS, EXTERNAL:
Wing span	15.76 m (51 ft 8½ in)
Wing aspect ratio	8.3
Length overall	14.39 m (47 ft 2½ in)
Height overall	4.57 m (15 ft 0 in)
Wheel track	5.36 m (17 ft 7 in)
Wheelbase	5.55 m (18 ft 2½ in)
Min ground turning radius about nosewheel	8.38 m (27 ft 6 in)

DIMENSIONS, INTERNAL:
Cabin:	
Length, front to rear bulkhead	6.37 m (20 ft 10¾ in)
Max height	1.46 m (4 ft 9½ in)
Baggage capacity	1.84 m³ (65.0 cu ft)

AREAS:
Wings, gross	30.00 m² (322.9 sq ft)
Horizontal tail surfaces (total, incl tab)	6.56 m² (70.6 sq ft)
Vertical tail surfaces (total)	4.73 m² (50.9 sq ft)

WEIGHTS:
Weight empty, equipped	3,351 kg (7,388 lb)
Max fuel weight	2,272 kg (5,009 lb)
Max T-O weight	6,033 kg (13,300 lb)
Max ramp weight	6,123 kg (13,500 lb)
Max zero-fuel weight: standard	4,309 kg (9,500 lb)
optional	4,990 kg (11,000 lb)
Max landing weight	5,760 kg (12,700 lb)

PERFORMANCE (at max T-O weight, ISA, except where indicated):
Max operating speed:	
S/L to 4,265 m (14,000 ft)	262 knots (486 km/h; 302 mph) IAS
4,265 m (14,000 ft) to 8,530 m (28,000 ft)	277 knots (513 km/h; 319 mph) IAS
8,530 m (28,000 ft) and above	Mach 0.705
Cruising speed at average cruise weight of 4,990 kg (11,000 lb) at 7,620 m (25,000 ft)	385 knots (713 km/h; 443 mph)
Stalling speed, clean, at max T-O weight	94 knots (174 km/h; 108 mph) CAS
Stalling speed at max landing weight	82 knots (152 km/h; 95 mph) CAS
Max rate of climb at S/L	1,027 m (3,370 ft)/min
Rate of climb at S/L, one engine out	322 m (1,055 ft)/min
Max certificated altitude	13,105 m (43,000 ft)
Service ceiling, one engine out	7,680 m (25,200 ft)
T-O to 15 m (50 ft)	727 m (2,385 ft)
T-O balanced field length (FAR Pt 25)	912 m (2,990 ft)
FAR Pt 25 landing runway length at max landing weight	692 m (2,270 ft)
Range with max fuel, crew of two and six passengers, allowances for T-O, climb, cruise at 13,105 m (43,000 ft), descent, and 45 min reserves	1,662 nm (3,080 km; 1,914 miles)

OPERATIONAL NOISE LEVELS (FAR Pt 36):
T-O	80.1 EPNdB
Approach	90.5 EPNdB
Sideline	86.7 EPNdB

CESSNA MODEL S550 CITATION S/II
US Navy designation: T-47A

Cessna announced on 4 October 1983 first details of the Citation S/II, an eight/ten-seat version of the Citation II. The improvements were introduced on the production line from aircraft c/n 506, delivered in the late Summer of 1984. They include a new wing aerofoil section, utilising Citation III supercritical technology, to reduce high-speed drag while retaining the Citation II's slow-speed handling and short-field capability; a modified wing/fuselage fairing to improve localised airflow; an extended wing inboard leading-edge, increasing wing area/lift and providing greater fuel capacity; modified engine pylon contours to reduce drag; sealed aileron/speed brake gaps, and faired flap coves, to reduce drag and improve lift; hydraulically actuated Fowler flaps of graphite composite construction, in two panels on each wing, which extend further inboard to provide additional lift/drag; ailerons of graphite composite construction with geared trim tabs to improve roll access response; a TKS glycol anti-icing system for the wing leading-edges; and a new -4B version of the Citation II's Pratt & Whitney Canada JT15D turbofans, providing greater thrust at high altitudes. Tail unit anti-icing systems are no longer required.

Internal refinements include an increase in tailcone baggage volume to 0.79 m³ (28.0 cu ft); a headroom increase of 12.7 cm (5 in) in the totally private toilet area; soft-touch headliners that reduce sound levels; Citation III style seats with shoulder harness, lateral tracking for more head and elbow room, and built-in life jacket storage; and redesigned sidewall air ducts which improve cabin insulation and heating and also provide a better than ten per cent increase in aisle width. Options include a vanity unit for the toilet, refreshment centres of composite construction, a wide door for use in cargo, air ambulance and other special applications, and Honeywell EFIS. In April 1987 Cessna introduced high capacity brakes as standard. These units, available also for retrofit to earlier Model S550s, reduce landing distance at max landing weight by some 13 per cent.

The first production configuration Citation S/II made its first flight on 14 February 1984; FAA certification, with exemption for single-pilot operation, was granted in July 1984. In 1989, Cessna delivered 1 Citation S/II.

In late 1985 Cessna delivered its first Citation S/II ambulance aircraft to the Province of Manitoba, Canada.

Cessna Citation S/II (Pratt & Whitney Canada JT15D-4B turbofans) *(Pilot Press)*

Cessna T-47A, a US Navy training version of the Citation S/II

The aircraft can accommodate single or double stretchers, up to four medical attendants and large quantities of medical oxygen. Five specially-equipped Citation S/IIs have also been delivered to the Chinese government for use by the Airborne Remote Sensing Centre of the Chinese Academy of Sciences. They are operated by the Flight Test Research Institute in Xian.

Since 1985 the US Navy has operated 15 Citation S/IIs, known as the **Model 552** and designated **T-47A**, instead of the T-39Ds used previously to train personnel in use of air-to-air, air-to-surface, intercept and other radar equipment. These aircraft are part of a five-year programme, plus a three-year option, covering provision of the aircraft, simulators, maintenance and pilot services. The T-47As differ from standard Citation S/IIs in having JT15D-5 turbofans (each 12.89 kN; 2,900 lb st), a shorter wing span to increase rate of climb and make possible a speed of Mach 0.733 at 12,200 m (40,000 ft), and an Emerson nose mounted AN/APQ-159 radar. The crew normally comprises a civilian pilot, Navy instructor and three students. The first T-47A made its first flight on 15 February 1984 and received FAA certification on 21 November 1984.

General Dynamics, Cessna and the Link Division of CAE are teamed to offer a version of the Citation S/II, provisionally designated T-47B, for the USAF's Tanker Transport Training System (TTTS).

In January 1988 Cessna delivered its 1,500th Citation, a Model S/II for Executive Jet Aviation of Columbus, Ohio. At that time the worldwide Citation fleet, operating in 53 countries, had completed more than four million flight hours.

The following description applies to the current production Model S550 (c/n 0115 and later), except where indicated:

TYPE: Eight/ten-seat twin-turbofan executive transport.

WINGS: Cantilever low-wing monoplane without sweepback. Incidence 2° 30′ at c/l, –0° 30′ at wing station 247.95. Dihedral 4°. All-metal fail-safe structure with two primary spars, an auxiliary spar, three fuselage attachment points, and conventional ribs and stringers. Manually operated ailerons, of graphite composite construction, each with geared trim tab. Hydraulically operated trailing-edge Fowler flaps of graphite composite construction. Hydraulically operated aerodynamic speed brakes. Glycol anti-icing of leading-edges.

FUSELAGE: All-metal pressurised structure of circular section. Fail-safe design, providing multiple load paths.

TAIL UNIT: Cantilever all-metal structure. Horizontal surfaces have dihedral of 9°. Dorsal fin. Manually operated control surfaces. Electric elevator trim with manual override; manual rudder trim.

LANDING GEAR: Hydraulically retractable tricycle type with single wheel on each unit. Main units retract inward into the wing, nose gear forward into fuselage nose. Free-fall and pneumatic emergency extension systems. Goodyear mainwheels with tyres size 22.0 × 8-10, 12-ply rating, pressure 8.27 bars (120 lb/sq in). Steerable nosewheel with Goodyear wheel and tyre size 18.0 × 4.4, 10-ply rating, pressure 8.27 bars (120 lb/sq in). High capacity brakes manufactured by Aircraft Wheel and Brake Division of Parker Hannifin Corporation. Parking brake and pneumatic emergency brake system. Anti-skid system optional.

POWER PLANT: Two Pratt & Whitney Canada JT15D-4B turbofans, each rated at 11.12 kN (2,500 lb st) for take-off, pod-mounted on sides of rear fuselage. Integral fuel tanks in wings, with combined usable capacity of 3,263 litres (862 US gallons; 718 Imp gallons).

ACCOMMODATION: Crew of two on separate flight deck, on fully adjustable seats, with seat belts and inertia reel shoulder harness, and sun visors. Seating for six to eight passengers in main cabin. Standard interior configuration provides for six passenger seats, two forward and four aft facing, each with headrest, seat belt and diagonal inertia reel harness; flushing toilet aft; tracked refreshment centre; forward cabin divider with privacy curtain, aft cabin divider with sliding doors. Passenger service units containing an oxygen mask, air vent and reading light for each passenger. Three separate baggage areas, one in

nose section that is externally accessible, one in aft cabin area, and one in tailcone area, with a combined capacity of up to 658 kg (1,450 lb).

SYSTEMS: Pressurisation system supplied with engine bleed air, max pressure differential 0.61 bars (8.8 lb/sq in), maintaining a sea level cabin altitude to 6,962 m (22,842 ft), or a 2,440 m (8,000 ft) cabin altitude to 13,105 m (43,000 ft). Hydraulic system, pressure 103.5 bars (1,500 lb/sq in), with two pumps to operate landing gear and speed brakes. Separate hydraulic system for wheel brakes. Electrical system supplied by two 28V 300A engine driven DC starter/generators, with two 350VA inverters and 24V 40Ah nickel-cadmium battery. Oxygen system of 0.62 m³ (22 cu ft) capacity includes two crew demand masks and five dropout constant flow masks for passengers. High capacity oxygen system optional. Engine fire detection and extinguishing systems.

AVIONICS AND EQUIPMENT: Standard avionics package comprises Honeywell SPZ-500 integrated flight director/autopilot system, with single-cue command bars, Honeywell C-14D compass system, Honeywell RD-450 (starboard) HSI, dual Collins VHF-22A com transceivers, dual Collins VIR-32 nav receivers with VOR/LOC, glideslope and marker beacon receivers, dual Collins RMI-30, Collins DME-42 with 339F-12 indicator, TDR-90 transponder, Collins ADF-60, and Honeywell Primus 300SL colour weather radar. Optional advanced avionics and instrumentation are available according to customer choice, and include Bendix Series III integrated EFIS, nav/com and radar systems.

DIMENSIONS, EXTERNAL:

Wing span over lights: S/II	15.90 m (52 ft 2½ in)
T-47A	14.18 m (46 ft 6 in)
Wing chord (mean): S/II	2.06 m (6 ft 9 in)
Wing aspect ratio: S/II	7.8
Length overall: S/II	14.39 m (47 ft 2½ in)
T-47A	14.60 m (47 ft 10¾ in)
Height overall: S/II	4.57 m (15 ft 0 in)
T-47A	4.51 m (14 ft 9¾ in)
Wheel track	5.36 m (17 ft 7 in)
Wheelbase	5.55 m (18 ft 2½ in)
Tailplane span: S/II	5.79 m (19 ft 0 in)
Cabin door (S/II, optional): Height	1.14 m (3 ft 9 in)
Width	0.89 m (2 ft 11 in)

DIMENSIONS, INTERNAL (S/II):
Cabin:

Length, front to rear bulkhead	6.37 m (20 ft 10¾ in)
Max height	1.45 m (4 ft 9½ in)
Max width	1.49 m (4 ft 10¾ in)
Baggage capacity (total)	2.27 m³ (80.0 cu ft)

AREAS (S/II):

Wings, gross	31.83 m² (342.6 sq ft)
Horizontal tail surfaces (total)	6.48 m² (69.8 sq ft)
Vertical tail surfaces (total)	4.73 m² (50.9 sq ft)

WEIGHTS AND LOADINGS:

Weight empty, equipped: S/II	3,655 kg (8,059 lb)
T-47A	4,098 kg (9,035 lb)
Max baggage weight (S/II): internal	272 kg (600 lb)
external	385 kg (850 lb)
Max ramp weight: S/II	6,940 kg (15,300 lb)
Max fuel weight: S/II	2,640 kg (5,820 lb)
Max T-O weight: S/II	6,849 kg (15,100 lb)
T-47A	6,804 kg (15,000 lb)
Max landing weight: S/II	6,350 kg (14,400 lb)
Max zero-fuel weight: S/II	4,990 kg (11,200 lb)
Max wing loading: S/II	215.17 kg/m² (44.07 lb/sq ft)
Max power loading: S/II	1.42 kg/kN (3.02 lb/lb st)

PERFORMANCE (S/II at max T-O weight, except where indicated):

Max operating speed:	
S/L to 2,440 m (8,000 ft)	
	261 knots (483 km/h; 300 mph) IAS
2,440 m (8,000 ft) to 8,935 m (29,315 ft)	
	276 knots (511 km/h; 318 mph)
above 8,935 m (29,315 ft)	Mach 0.721
Cruising speed at mid-cruise weight of 5,443 kg (12,000 lb) at 10,670 m (35,000 ft)	
	403 knots (746 km/h; 463 mph)
Stalling speed, clean, at max T-O weight	
	94 knots (174 km/h; 108 mph) CAS
Stalling speed at max landing weight	
	82 knots (152 km/h; 94 mph) CAS
Max rate of climb at S/L	926 m (3,040 ft)/min
Rate of climb at S/L, one engine out	
	262 m (860 ft)/min
Max operating altitude	13,105 m (43,000 ft)
Service ceiling, one engine out	7,315 m (24,000 ft)
T-O balanced field length (FAR Pt 25)	
	987 m (3,240 ft)
FAR 25 landing runway length at max landing weight (high capacity brakes)	805 m (2,640 ft)
Range with four passengers, two crew and baggage, zero wind, IFR reserves	1,739 nm (3,223 km; 2,002 miles)
Range with max fuel	1,998 nm (3,701 km; 2,300 miles)

OPERATIONAL NOISE LEVELS (FAR Pt 36):

T-O	78.0 EPNdB
Approach	91.0 EPNdB
Sideline	90.4 EPNdB

CESSNA MODEL 560 CITATION V

Cessna announced development of the Model 560 Citation V at the 1987 National Business Aircraft Association convention in New Orleans, following the first flight of the engineering prototype (N560CC) during August. The Citation V is a development of the Citation S/II, powered by two 12.89 kN (2,900 lb st) Pratt & Whitney Canada JT15D-5A turbofans and with a fuselage lengthened by nearly 0.6 m (2 ft) to provide increased passenger space and a fully enclosed private toilet/vanity area in its eight-seat cabin. Apart from its longer fuselage, the principal external change is the addition of a seventh cabin window on each side. Two baggage compartments, outside the main passenger cabin area, with a total volume of 1.16 m³ (41 cu ft), can accommodate up to 385 kg (850 lb) of baggage.

The Citation V features a new anti-ice/de-ice system, comprising inboard wing cuff leading-edges heated by engine bleed air and 'silver' low profile de-icer boots on the leading-edges of the outer wing panels and tailplane. Standard equipment includes Category II avionics, comprising an integrated Honeywell autopilot and flight

Cessna Model 560 Citation V (two Pratt & Whitney Canada JT15D-5A turbofans) *(Pilot Press)*

guidance system, EFIS in the pilot's panel, a Global GNS-X navigation management system, advanced weather radar, dual transponders, encoding and radio altimeters; thrust reversers; engine synchronisers; a 1.8 m³ (64 cu ft) oxygen system; recognition lights; and an in-flight telephone.

The prototype Citation V was used for low speed aerodynamic certification and primary systems development. A second pre-production prototype, which joined the test programme in early 1988, was used for high speed aerodynamic and systems certification. The two aircraft flew a total of 1,029 hours in nearly 750 flights during the certification programme. FAA certification of the Citation V was received on 9 December 1988, with first delivery in April 1989. By 31 December 1989 Cessna had delivered 33 Citation Vs, and had a backlog of orders extending until October 1991.

The following data are provisional:

DIMENSIONS, EXTERNAL: As for Citation S/II except:
Length overall	14.90 m (48 ft 10¾ in)
Tailplane span	6.55 m (21 ft 6 in)
Wheelbase	6.06 m (19 ft 10¾ in)

DIMENSIONS, INTERNAL: As for Citation S/II except:
Length, front to rear bulkhead	6.89 m (22 ft 7¼ in)

AREAS: As for Citation S/II except:
Horizontal tail surfaces (total)	7.88 m² (84.8 sq ft)

WEIGHTS:
Weight empty, equipped	4,004 kg (8,828 lb)
Max fuel weight	2,640 kg (5,820 lb)
Max T-O weight	7,212 kg (15,900 lb)
Max ramp weight	7,303 kg (16,100 lb)
Max landing weight	6,895 kg (15,200 lb)
Max zero-fuel weight	5,080 kg (11,200 lb)

PERFORMANCE:
Max operating speed:
at 2,440 m (8,000 ft) to 8,810 m (28,900 ft)	292 knots (541 km/h; 336 mph) IAS
above 8,810 m (28,900 ft)	Mach 0.755
Cruising speed at 10,060 m (33,000 ft)	427 knots (791 km/h; 492 mph)
Stalling speed, clean, at max T-O weight	87 knots (161 km/h; 100 mph)
Max rate of climb at S/L	1,112 m (3,650 ft)/min
Rate of climb at S/L, one engine out	360 m (1,180 ft)/min
Max operating altitude	13,700 m (45,000 ft)
Service ceiling, one engine out	9,480 m (31,100 ft)
T-O balanced field length (FAR 25)	963 m (3,160 ft)
FAR 25 landing field length, S/L, ISA, at max landing weight	890 m (2,920 ft)

Range with six passengers, two crew, zero wind, at high-speed cruise speed with allowances for T-O, climb, cruise, descent and VFR reserves
1,920 nm (3,558 km; 2,211 miles)

CESSNA MODEL 650 CITATION III

The Citation III represented Cessna's entry into the high-speed medium-size business jet market. First flight of the first prototype (N650CC) was made on 30 May 1979. The second prototype flew for the first time on 2 May 1980, and FAA certification under FAR Pt 25 Transport Category requirements was gained on 30 April 1982. Flight test experience allowed the maximum operating speed to be increased to Mach 0.83. A maximum speed of Mach 0.90 was demonstrated successfully in a dive.

The first production Citation III was delivered to the Citation Marketing Division in December 1982. It was used as a demonstrator, together with the second and third production aircraft, prior to the start of deliveries to customers in Spring 1983. By 31 December 1989 Citation III deliveries totalled 174 aircraft, including 16 in 1989. The Citation III was certificated by the United Kingdom Civil Aviation Authority in April 1988. Within Europe, it is also certificated in Austria, Denmark, France, West Germany, Italy, Spain, Sweden and Switzerland.

At the 1988 National Business Aircraft Association convention in Dallas, Cessna introduced a new 'Masterpiece' interior for the Citation III. Features of the interior design include recessed switches and handles, single-surface cabin walls, writing tables that blend into the cabin walls, controls for overhead reading lights and electric window shades at armrest level, tailored double-stitched upholstery from custom fabrics, hand-woven carpeting, floorline lighting, a restyled refreshment centre, expanded vanity top and larger wash basin in the private lavatory area, and new reclining, swivelling and tracking passenger seats with adjustable arm- and headrests and optional reclining footrests.

TYPE: Twin-turbofan eight/eleven-seat long-range executive transport.

WINGS: Cantilever low-wing monoplane. NASA-developed supercritical section. Dihedral 3°. Sweepback at quarter-chord 25°. Conventional two-spar fail-safe structure of light alloy, utilising bonded and riveted construction and built in three sections. Electrically actuated trailing-edge flaps, in three sections on each wing, are of Kevlar and graphite composites construction. Four hydraulically actuated spoilers on the upper surface of each wing, immediately forward of the flaps. The two centre spoilers on each wing can be operated as airbrakes in flight. All eight spoilers can be used for emergency descent, and for

Cessna Model 560 Citation V eight-seat business jet

lift dumping after touchdown. Hydraulically powered ailerons, with manual reversion, are complemented by the outboard spoiler panel on each wing, which provides additional roll authority after approx 3° of aileron deflection. Stall strips and a stall fence are mounted at approx semi-span of each outer wing panel. Anti-icing of wing leading-edges by engine bleed air.

FUSELAGE: Conventional semi-monocoque light alloy structure of circular cross-section. Fail-safe in pressurised area.

TAIL UNIT: Cantilever T tail structure of light alloy, with swept horizontal and vertical surfaces. Variable incidence tailplane has 3° anhedral. Electric anti-icing of tailplane leading-edges. Fin leading-edge is not anti-iced. Rudder incorporates a boost system to minimise yaw in asymmetric thrust conditions.

LANDING GEAR: Hydraulically retractable tricycle type. Main units retract inward into the undersurface of the wing centre-section, nosewheel forward and upward into the nose. Main units of trailing link type, each with twin wheels; steerable nose unit has a single wheel, max steering angle ± 70-80°. Oleo-pneumatic shock absorber in each unit. Hydraulically powered nosewheel steering, with an accumulator to provide steering after a loss of normal hydraulic power. Emergency landing gear extension by manual release and free-fall to locked position; pneumatic blowdown system for backup. Mainwheel tyres size 22.0 × 5.75, 10-ply rating, pressure 10.20 bars (148 lb/sq in). Nosewheel tyre size 18.0 × 4.4, 10-ply rating, pressure 8.62 bars (125 lb/sq in). Fully modulated hydraulically powered anti-skid brake system. In the event of hydraulic system failure, an electrically driven standby pump provides pressure for the brakes. Emergency pneumatic brake system. Parking brake.

POWER PLANT: Two Garrett TFE731-3B-100S turbofans, each rated at 16.24 kN (3,650 lb st) for take-off, pod-mounted on sides of rear fuselage. Hydraulically operated Rohr target type thrust reversers standard. Two

independent fuel systems, with integral tanks in each wing; usable capacity 4,183 litres (1,105 US gallons; 920 Imp gallons). Additional fuel cell behind rear fuselage bulkhead. Single-point pressure refuelling on starboard side of fuselage, to rear of wing trailing-edge. Gravity refuelling point on upper surface of each wing. A boost pump in the port wing fills the fuselage tank when pressure refuelling is not available. Engine intake anti-icing system.

ACCOMMODATION: Crew of two on separate flight deck, and up to nine passengers. Standard interior has six individual seats, with toilet at rear of cabin. The fuselage nose incorporates a radome, high resolution radar, avionics bay and a storage compartment for crew baggage. Electrically heated baggage compartment in rear fuselage with external door on port side. Airstair door forward of wing on port side. Overwing emergency escape hatch on starboard side. Cabin is pressurised, heated and air-conditioned. Windscreen anti-icing by engine bleed air, with alcohol spray backup for port side of the windscreen. Windscreen defogging by warm air, and rain removal by engine bleed air and a mechanically actuated airflow deflector.

SYSTEMS: Environmental control system, with separate control of flight deck and cabin conditions. Direct engine bleed pressurisation system, with nominal pressure differential of 0.67 bars (9.7 lb/sq in) cabin environment to max certificated altitude and can maintain a sea level cabin environment to approx 7,620 m (25,000 ft). Electrical system includes two 28V 400A DC starter/generators, two 200/115V 5kW three-phase engine driven alternators, two 115V 400Hz solid state static inverters, two 24V 22Ah nickel-cadmium batteries and an external power socket in the tailcone. Hydraulic system of 207 bars (3,000 lb/sq in) powered by two engine driven pressure compensated pumps for operation of spoilers, brakes, landing gear, nosewheel steering and thrust reversers. Hydraulic reservoir with

Cessna Citation III (two Garrett TFE731 turbofans) *(Pilot Press)*

Cessna Citation III eight/eleven-seat executive transport

integral reserve and an electrically driven hydraulic pump to provide emergency power. Oxygen system of 1.39 m³ (49 cu ft) capacity with automatic dropout constant-flow oxygen mask for each passenger and a quick-donning pressure demand mask for each crew member. Engine fire detection and extinguishing system.

AVIONICS AND EQUIPMENT: Standard avionics include a Honeywell SPZ-650 integrated flight director/autopilot system with AD650A ADI, RD650A HSI and C-14D compass system; Honeywell GH-14 ADI and RD450 HSI with C-14D compass system for co-pilot; AA-300 radio altimeter; dual Collins VHF-22A 720-channel com transceivers, dual VIR-32 nav receivers which include VOR, localiser, glideslope and marker beacon receivers, dual RMI-30, DME-42 DME, and TDR-90 transponder; Honeywell Primus 300SL colour weather radar; Collins ADF-60 ADF; J.E.T. standby attitude gyro; Teledyne angle of attack system; air data computer; dual Avtech audio amplifiers; and Telex microphones, headsets and speakers. A wide range of optional avionics is available including Bendix Series III integrated EFIS, nav/com and radar system. Standard equipment includes dual altimeters, Mach/airspeed indicators, angle of attack indicator, digital clock, instantaneous rate of climb indicators, outside air temperature gauge, crew seats with vertical, fore, aft and recline adjustments, seat belts, shoulder harnesses and inertia reels, six individual passenger seats, three forward and three aft facing with vertical, fore and aft adjustment, lateral tracking and recline adjustments, seat belts and shoulder harnesses, sun visors, flight deck divider with curtain, map case, openable storm windows, electroluminescent and edge-lit instrument panels, stall warning system, cockpit and cabin fire extinguishers, indirect cabin lighting, cabin aisle lights, door courtesy lights, 'Fasten seat belt—No smoking' signs, refreshment centre, cup holders, ashtrays, executive table, aft cabin divider with curtain, emergency exit signs, internal corrosion proofing, emergency battery pack, emergency portable cabin oxygen, navigation and recognition lights, dual landing and taxi lights, dual anti-collision strobe lights, red flashing beacon, dual wing ice lights, lightning protection, static discharge wicks and tiedown provisions.

DIMENSIONS, EXTERNAL:
Wing span	16.31 m (53 ft 6 in)
Wing mean aerodynamic chord	2.08 m (6 ft 9¾ in)
Wing aspect ratio	8.9
Length overall	16.90 m (55 ft 5½ in)
Height overall	5.12 m (16 ft 9½ in)
Tailplane span	5.60 m (18 ft 4½ in)
Wheel track	2.84 m (9 ft 4 in)
Wheelbase	6.50 m (21 ft 4 in)
Turning circle based on nosewheel	6.63 m (21 ft 9 in)
Cabin door: Width	0.61 m (2 ft 0 in)
Height	1.37 m (4 ft 6 in)

DIMENSIONS, INTERNAL:
Cabin:
Length, front to rear bulkhead	7.01 m (23 ft 0 in)
Length, aft of cockpit divider	5.66 m (18 ft 7 in)
Max width	1.73 m (5 ft 8 in)
Max height	1.78 m (5 ft 10 in)
Baggage capacity (aft)	1.88 m³ (66.4 cu ft)
Crew baggage compartment (nose)	0.17 m³ (6.0 cu ft)

AREAS:
Wings, gross	29.00 m² (312.0 sq ft)
Horizontal tail surfaces (total)	6.26 m² (67.4 sq ft)
Vertical tail surfaces (total)	6.04 m² (65.0 sq ft)

WEIGHTS:
Weight empty, standard	5,357 kg (11,811 lb)
Max fuel weight	3,349 kg (7,384 lb)
Max payload	1,583 kg (3,489 lb)
Max T-O weight	9,979 kg (22,000 lb)
Max ramp weight	10,070 kg (22,200 lb)
Max landing weight	9,072 kg (20,000 lb)
Max zero-fuel weight	6,940 kg (15,300 lb)

PERFORMANCE (at max T-O weight, ISA, except where indicated):
Max operating speed:
S/L to 2,440 m (8,000 ft)
305 knots (565 km/h; 351 mph) IAS
at 11,132 m (36,524 ft)
278 knots (515 km/h; 320 mph) IAS
above 11,132 m (36,524 ft) Mach 0.851
Max cruising speed at 10,670 m (35,000 ft) and 7,257 kg (16,000 lb) cruise weight
472 knots (874 km/h; 543 mph)
Stalling speed, clean, at max T-O weight
125 knots (232 km/h; 144 mph) CAS
Stalling speed, flaps and wheels down, at max landing weight 97 knots (515 km/h; 112 mph) CAS
Max rate of climb at S/L 1,127 m (3,700 ft)/min
Rate of climb at S/L, one engine out 245 m (805 ft)/min
Time to 13,100 m (43,000 ft) 33 min
Certificated ceiling 15,545 m (51,000 ft)
Ceiling, one engine out 7,165 m (23,500 ft)
FAR 25 T-O field length at S/L 1,579 m (5,180 ft)
FAR 25 landing field length at max landing weight
884 m (2,900 ft)
Range, zero wind, with allowances for T-O, climb, descent and 45 min reserves:
2 crew, 4 passengers
2,346 nm (4,348 km; 2,701 miles)
g limits +3.2/−1

OPERATIONAL NOISE LEVELS (FAR Pt 36):
T-O	74.0 EPNdB
Approach	85.0 EPNdB
Sideline	81.0 EPNdB

CESSNA MODEL 670 CITATION IV

At the 1989 National Business Aviation Association convention in Atlanta, Georgia, Cessna announced this development of the Citation III which offers increased range and enhanced short-field performance. It features a fuselage 0.98 m (3 ft 2½ in) longer than that of the Citation III, with cabin length increased by 0.43 m (1 ft 4¾ in) and wing span increased by 1.68 m (5 ft 6 in). Power plant is two 17.79 kN (4,000 lb st) Garrett TFE731-4 turbofans, with all fuel contained in wing tanks. The extended fuselage and space made available by elimination of the Citation III's rear fuselage fuel tank provides more flight deck space and increased legroom in the standard eight-passenger cabin, which has stand-up headroom extending to the enlarged aft toilet. Baggage compartment volume has been increased by 20 per cent, with external loading door. Other improvements include simplified fuel system wiring and plumbing, and introduction of an electrically heated windscreen. Standard avionics includes a digital autopilot and five-tube EFIS displays.

First flight of the Citation IV prototype is scheduled for Spring 1991, with a second aircraft expected to join the test programme six months later. FAA certification is anticipated by the end of 1992, with customer deliveries starting in Spring 1993. Cessna announced in May 1990 that it was terminating development of the Citation IV. See Addenda.

DIMENSIONS, EXTERNAL:
Wing span	17.98 m (59 ft 0 in)

Cessna Citation IV (two 17.79 kN; 4,000 lb st Garrett TFE731-4 turbofans) *(Pilot Press)*

Wing aspect ratio	8.75
Length overall	17.89 m (58 ft 8½ in)
Height overall	5.27 m (17 ft 3½ in)
Tailplane span	6.46 m (21 ft 2½ in)

DIMENSIONS, INTERNAL:
Cabin:
Length between pressure bulkheads

	7.68 m (25 ft 2½ in)
Max width	1.73 m (5 ft 8 in)
Height	1.78 m (5 ft 10 in)

AREA:

Wings, gross	36.12 m² (388.8 sq ft)

WEIGHTS:

Weight empty	5,751 kg (12,680 lb)
Max fuel weight	3,946 kg (8,700 lb)
Max T-O weight	10,886 kg (24,000 lb)
Max ramp weight	10,977 kg (24,200 lb)
Max zero-fuel weight	7,439 kg (16,400 lb)
Max landing weight	9,071 kg (20,000 lb)

PERFORMANCE (estimated):
Max cruising speed at 9,450 m (31,000 ft)
473 knots (877 km/h; 545 mph)
Stalling speed, landing configuration
92 knots (171 km/h; 106 mph) CAS
Rate of climb at S/L, one engine out 271 m (890 ft)/min
Time to 13,100 m (43,000 ft) 39 min
Service ceiling 15,545 m (51,000 ft)
T-O balanced field length (FAR Pt 25) 1,494 m (4,900 ft)

Artist's impression of Cessna Model 670 Citation IV business jet

FAR Pt 25 landing field length at max landing weight
823 m (2,700 ft)

Range with 45 min reserves
2,710 nm (5,022 km; 3,120 miles)

CHADWICK
CHADWICK HELICOPTERS INC
PO Box 6179, Aloha, Oregon 97007-6179

A description and photograph of the Chadwick C-122S single-seat ultralight helicopter may be found in the 1988-89 *Jane's*. No further information has been received on the project.

CHRISTEN
CHRISTEN INDUSTRIES INC
(Aircraft Manufacturing Division)
PO Box 547, Afton, Wyoming 83110
Telephone: 1 (307) 886 3151
Fax: 1 (307) 886 9674
PRESIDENT AND GENERAL MANAGER: E. H. Andersen Jr

In November 1983 Christen Industries, whose Eagle biplanes are described in the Sport Aircraft section, acquired the former Pitts Aerobatics company, together with manufacturing and marketing rights to the Pitts Special series of aerobatic biplanes designed by Mr Curtis Pitts. The former Pitts Aerobatics facility at Afton, Wyoming, was retained as the corporate headquarters of Christen Industries, where manufacture, assembly and testing of the aircraft take place. In early 1990 Christen Industries had a workforce of 70 people.

Christen A-1 Husky two-seat light cabin monoplane *(Mike Jerram)*

CHRISTEN A-1 HUSKY
Work began in November 1985 on the design of a new utility aircraft designated A-1 Husky, which Christen Industries believes is suitable for a range of duties such as bush flying, border patrol, fish and wildlife protection, and pipeline inspection. Although it is externally similar in appearance to the Piper Super Cub, the Husky is entirely new, created with computer-aided design (CAD) techniques. The prototype (N6070H) began flight testing in 1986, and received FAA certification in 1987. The Husky is certificated for operation on Edo 2000 floats, and skis. The US Border Patrol service operates 15 Huskys, which have replaced its fleet of Piper Super Cubs. Christen delivered 49 Huskys in 1989, and had delivered a total of 130 by January 1990.

TYPE: Two-seat light cabin monoplane.
WINGS: Braced high-wing monoplane, with steel tube V bracing struts each side. Wing section modified Clark Y USA 35B. Aluminium spars and ribs, aluminium sheet leading-edge, with Dacron covering overall. Drooped Plane Booster wingtips. Slotted flaps and symmetrical section ailerons of light alloy construction with metal skin, each with spade type aerodynamic counterbalance. No tabs.
FUSELAGE: Welded full-depth truss structure of 4130 chrome molybdenum steel tubing, metal skinned to rear of cabin area, the remainder Dacron covered.
TAIL UNIT: Wire and strut braced structure of welded steel tubes and channels, covered with Dacron. Internal bungee trim system exerts trim forces on elevator control rods.
LANDING GEAR: Non-retractable tailwheel type. Two faired side Vs and half-axles hinged to bottom of fuselage, with internal (under front seat) bungee cord shock absorption. Cleveland mainwheels, tyres size 8.00-6. Oversize 'tundra' tyres optional. Cleveland mainwheel brakes. Steerable leaf-spring tailwheel. Skis and floats optional.
POWER PLANT: One 134 kW (180 hp) Textron Lycoming O-360-C1G flat-four engine, driving a Hartzell two-blade constant-speed metal propeller with spinner. Fuel contained in two metal tanks, one in each wing, total capacity 208 litres (55 US gallons; 45.75 Imp gallons), of which 189 litres (50 US gallons; 41.6 Imp gallons) are

usable. Fuel filler point in upper surface of each wing, near root.
ACCOMMODATION: Enclosed cabin seating two in tandem, with dual controls. Downward-hinged door on starboard side, with upward-hinged window above. Skylight window in roof.
SYSTEM: Electrical system includes lights and 60A alternator.
DIMENSIONS, EXTERNAL:

Wing span	10.73 m (35 ft 2½ in)
Length overall	6.88 m (22 ft 7 in)
Height overall	2.01 m (6 ft 7 in)
Propeller diameter	1.93 m (6 ft 4 in)

AREAS:

Wings, gross	16.72 m² (180.0 sq ft)
Ailerons (total)	1.43 m² (15.4 sq ft)
Trailing-edge flaps (total)	2.09 m² (22.5 sq ft)
Fin	0.43 m² (4.66 sq ft)
Rudder	0.62 m² (6.76 sq ft)
Tailplane	1.48 m² (15.9 sq ft)
Elevators, incl tabs	1.31 m² (14.1 sq ft)

WEIGHTS AND LOADINGS:

Weight empty	540 kg (1,190 lb)
Max T-O weight	816 kg (1,800 lb)
Max baggage weight	22.7 kg (50 lb)
Max wing loading	48.8 kg/m² (10.0 lb/sq ft)
Max power loading	7.45 kg/kW (10.0 lb/hp)

PERFORMANCE:

Never-exceed speed	132 knots (245 km/h; 152 mph)

Cruising speed:

75% power at 1,220 m (4,000 ft)	
	122 knots (226 km/h; 140 mph)
55% power	115 knots (212 km/h; 132 mph)

Stalling speed: flaps up	48 knots (80 km/h; 49 mph)
flaps down	37 knots (68 km/h; 42 mph)
Max rate of climb at S/L	457 m (1,500 ft)/min
Service ceiling	6,100 m (20,000 ft)
T-O run	46 m (150 ft)
T-O to 15 m (50 ft)	229 m (750 ft)
Landing from 15 m (50 ft)	427 m (1,400 ft)
Landing run, full flap	107 m (350 ft)

Range with max fuel, 75% power, 45 min reserves
550 nm (1,019 km; 633 miles)

PITTS SPECIAL S-1 SERIES
The original single-seat Pitts Special was designed in 1943-44. Construction of a prototype began in 1944 and it flew in September of that year.

The current production version of the S-1 is the **S-1T**, described below. Details of the earlier S-1S factory built aircraft may be found in the 1987-88 and earlier editions of *Jane's*. Christen Industries no longer markets kits or plans for Pitts designs.

PITTS S-1T SPECIAL
Production of this advanced version of the S-1 series began in early 1981, and it is available as a factory built aircraft to special order only. Generally similar to other versions of the S-1, it has symmetrical ailerons and wing sections, and the wings have been moved forward 11.5 cm (4½ in) to compensate for the installation of a more powerful engine. FAA type certification was gained in the Autumn of 1982. Christen delivered 3 S-1Ts during 1989, and had delivered a total of 54 by January 1990.

TYPE: Single-seat sporting biplane.
WINGS: Braced biplane type, with single faired interplane strut each side and N type cabane struts. Dual streamline flying and landing wires. Wing section M6. Thickness/chord ratio 12%. Dihedral 0° on upper wing, 3° on lower wings. Incidence 1° 30' on upper wing, 0° on lower wings. Sweepback at quarter-chord 6° 40' on upper wing only. Wooden structure, with fabric covering. Frise ailerons on both upper and lower wings, of similar construction to wings. No flaps or tabs.
FUSELAGE: Welded steel tube structure with wooden stringers, with aluminium top decking and side panels, remainder fabric covered.
TAIL UNIT: Wire braced steel tube structure, fabric covered. Fixed incidence tailplane. Trim tab in each elevator.
LANDING GEAR: Non-retractable tailwheel type. Rubber cord shock absorption. Cleveland mainwheels with 6-ply tyres, size 5.00-5, pressure 2.07 bars (30 lb/sq in). Cleveland hydraulic disc brakes. Steerable tailwheel. Glassfibre fairing on mainwheels.

Christen Pitts two-seat Model S-2B operated in the UK by Firebird Aerobatics

FUSELAGE: Welded 4130 steel tube structure with wooden stringers, covered with Dacron except for aluminium top decking and side panels.

TAIL UNIT: Wire braced 4130 steel tube structure. Fixed surfaces metal covered, control surfaces fabric covered. Trim tab in each elevator.

LANDING GEAR: Non-retractable tailwheel type. Rubber cord shock absorption. Steerable tailwheel. Streamlined fairings on mainwheels.

POWER PLANT: One 194 kW (260 hp) Textron Lycoming AEIO-540-D4A5 flat-six engine, driving a McCauley Type 1A/200 two-blade constant-speed metal propeller with spinner. Fuel tank in fuselage, immediately aft of firewall, capacity 110 litres (29 US gallons; 24 Imp gallons). Refuelling point on fuselage upper surface forward of windscreen. Oil capacity 11.35 litres (3 US gallons; 2.5 Imp gallons). Inverted fuel and oil systems standard.

ACCOMMODATION: Two seats in tandem cockpits, with dual controls. Sideways opening one-piece canopy covers both cockpits. Space for 9.1 kg (20 lb) baggage aft of rear seat when flown in non-aerobatic category.

SYSTEM: Electrical system powered by 12V 40A alternator and non-spill 12V battery.

DIMENSIONS, EXTERNAL:
Wing span: upper	6.10 m (20 ft 0 in)
lower	5.79 m (19 ft 0 in)
Wing chord (constant, both)	1.02 m (3 ft 4 in)
Length overall	5.71 m (18 ft 9 in)
Height overall	2.02 m (6 ft 7½ in)

AREA:
Wings, gross	11.6 m² (125.0 sq ft)

WEIGHTS AND LOADINGS:
Weight empty	521 kg (1,150 lb)
Max T-O weight	737 kg (1,625 lb)
Max wing loading	63.55 kg/m² (13.0 lb/sq ft)
Max power loading	3.80 kg/kW (6.25 lb/hp)

PERFORMANCE (at max T-O weight):
Never-exceed speed	182 knots (338 km/h; 210 mph)
Max cruising speed	152 knots (282 km/h; 175 mph)
Stalling speed	52 knots (97 km/h; 60 mph)
Max rate of climb at S/L	823 m (2,700 ft)/min
Service ceiling	6,400 m (21,000 ft)
Range with max fuel, 55% power, 30 min reserves	277 nm (513 km; 319 miles)

POWER PLANT: One 149 kW (200 hp) Textron Lycoming AEIO-360-A1E flat-four engine, driving a Hartzell two- or three-blade constant-speed propeller with spinner. Fuel tank aft of firewall, capacity 75 litres (20 US gallons; 16.6 Imp gallons). Refuelling point on upper surface of fuselage, forward of windscreen. Oil capacity 7.5 litres (2 US gallons; 1.7 Imp gallons). Inverted fuel and oil systems standard.

ACCOMMODATION: Single seat. Sliding cockpit canopy standard.

DIMENSIONS, EXTERNAL:
Wing span, upper	5.28 m (17 ft 4 in)
Wing chord (constant, both)	0.91 m (3 ft 0 in)
Wing aspect ratio	5.8
Length overall	4.72 m (15 ft 6 in)
Height overall	1.91 m (6 ft 3 in)
Tailplane span	1.98 m (6 ft 6 in)
Propeller diameter	1.93 m (6 ft 4 in)

AREA:
Wings, gross	9.15 m² (98.5 sq ft)

WEIGHTS AND LOADINGS:
Weight empty	376 kg (830 lb)
Max T-O weight	521 kg (1,150 lb)
Max wing loading	57.05 kg/m² (11.68 lb/sq ft)
Max power loading	3.50 kg/kW (5.75 lb/hp)

PERFORMANCE (at max T-O weight):
Never-exceed speed	176 knots (326 km/h; 203 mph)
Max level speed at S/L	161 knots (298 km/h; 185 mph)
Max cruising speed at S/L	152 knots (282 km/h; 175 mph)
Stalling speed	56 knots (103 km/h; 64 mph)
Max rate of climb at S/L	853 m (2,800 ft)/min
Range with max fuel, 55% power, 30 min reserves	268 nm (497 km; 309 miles)
g limits	+9/−4.5

PITTS MODEL S-2B

This two-seater differs from the earlier S-2A (described in the 1987-88 and earlier editions of *Jane's*) in having a 194 kW (260 hp) Textron Lycoming AEIO-540-D4A5 flat-six engine, and is intended to be capable of unlimited aerobatics carrying two persons. The heavier power plant necessitated moving the wings and landing gear forward about 15 cm (6 in), and made possible more room in the front cockpit.

The prototype S-2B was completed during September 1982. Its capability was demonstrated shortly afterwards when Clint McHenry, carrying a passenger, took first place in the Advanced Category at the US Nationals held at Sherman, Texas.

The S-2B was awarded FAA type certification in the Spring of 1983, in the Aerobatic category, under FAR Pt 23. Christen delivered 23 S-2Bs in 1989.

TYPE: Two-seat aerobatic biplane.

WINGS: Braced biplane type, with single faired interplane strut each side and N type cabane struts. Wing section NACA 6400 series on upper wing, 00 series on lower wings. Two-spar spruce structure with fabric covering. Ailerons on both upper and lower wings, with aero-dynamic spade balances on lower ailerons. No flaps or tabs.

PITTS MODEL S-2S

Production of this single-seat version of the S-2A began in late 1978. It has a forward fuselage shortened by 0.36 m (14 in) to accommodate a 194 kW (260 hp) Textron Lycoming AEIO-540-D4A5 flat-six engine, driving a McCauley Type 1A/200 two-blade fixed-pitch metal propeller with spinner. It also differs from the S-2A by having a maximum fuel capacity of 132.5 litres (35 US gallons; 29.1 Imp gallons) and an oil capacity of 11.4 litres (3 US gallons; 2.5 Imp gallons). The first flight of the prototype was made on 9 December 1977; full type certification was gained in June 1981. The Model S-2S is available to special order only. A total of 30 had been delivered by January 1990.

DIMENSIONS, EXTERNAL: As for Model S-2B except:
Length overall	5.28 m (17 ft 4 in)

WEIGHTS AND LOADINGS:
Weight empty	499 kg (1,100 lb)
Max T-O weight	680 kg (1,500 lb)
Max wing loading	58.6 kg/m² (12.0 lb/sq ft)
Max power loading	3.51 kg/kW (5.77 lb/hp)

PERFORMANCE (at max T-O weight):
Never-exceed speed	176 knots (326 km/h; 203 mph)
Max level speed at S/L	162 knots (301 km/h; 187 mph)
Max cruising speed at S/L	152 knots (282 km/h; 175 mph)
Stalling speed	51 knots (94 km/h; 58 mph)
Max rate of climb at S/L	853 m (2,800 ft)/min
g limits	+9/−4.5

CLASSIC

CLASSIC AIRCRAFT CORPORATION
Capital City Airport, Lansing, Michigan 48906
Telephone: 1 (517) 321 7500
Fax: 1 (517) 321 5845
PRESIDENT: Richard S. Kettles
ENGINEERING MANAGER: Donald P. Zurfluh
SALES MANAGER: Donald C. Kettles

CLASSIC WACO CLASSIC F-5

In March 1984 Classic Aircraft Corporation began construction of a prototype Waco Classic F-5 biplane, based on the original Waco YMF-5 and built under the same FAA type certificate. The prototype (N1935B) made its first flight on 20 November 1985 and FAA certification was received on 11 March 1986. Although externally similar to the earlier Waco YMF-5, the Waco Classic F-5 incorporates modern constructional techniques, tolerances and materials.

By February 1989 a total of 20 Waco Classic F-5s had been delivered, since when no further information has been received.

TYPE: Three-seat sporting biplane.

WINGS: Braced biplane, with N type interplane struts. Streamline section stainless steel landing and flying wires. Wing section Clark Y. 2° dihedral on upper and lower wings. 0° incidence on upper and lower wings. No sweepback. All-wood structure, with Dacron covering. Ailerons on upper and lower wings of all-aluminium construction with chordwise external stiffening. No flaps or tabs.

FUSELAGE: Welded 4130 steel tube with internal oiling for corrosion protection. Wooden bulkheads with overall Dacron covering.

TAIL UNIT: Braced welded steel tube structure with Dacron covering. Tailplane incidence manually adjustable from cockpit via screwjack actuator. Ground adjustable trim tab on rudder.

LANDING GEAR: Non-retractable tailwheel type. Shock absorption by oil and spring shock struts. Steerable tailwheel. Cleveland 30-67F hydraulic brakes on mainwheels only. Cleveland 40-101A mainwheels, tyre size 7.50-10; Cleveland 40-199A tailwheel, tyre size 3.50-4. Mainwheel fairings standard, tailwheel fairing optional. Float and amphibious landing gear optional.

POWER PLANT: One 205 kW (275 hp) Jacobs R-755-B2 air-cooled radial engine (remanufactured), driving a two-blade fixed-pitch wooden propeller. Constant-speed propeller with spinner optional. Engine enclosed with streamline aluminium 'bump' cowling. Fuel contained in two aluminium tanks in upper wing centre-section, total capacity 182 litres (48 US gallons; 40 Imp gallons). Refuelling point for each tank in upper wing surface. Auxiliary tanks, capacity 45 litres (12 US gallons; 10 Imp gallons) each, optional in either or both inboard upper wing panels. Standard oil capacity 15 litres (4 US gallons; 3.33 Imp gallons); with auxiliary fuel tanks 19 litres (5 US gallons; 4.2 Imp gallons).

ACCOMMODATION: Three seats in tandem open cockpits, two side by side in front position, single seat at rear. Dual controls, seat belts with shoulder harness, and pilot's adjustable seat, standard. Front baggage compartment, capacity 11.3 kg (25 lb); rear baggage compartment, volume 0.2 m³ (7.5 cu ft), capacity 34 kg (75 lb).

SYSTEMS: 24V electrical system with battery, alternator and starter for electrical supply to navigation, strobe and rear cockpit lights. Hydraulic system for brakes only.

AVIONICS AND EQUIPMENT: Emergency locator transmitter standard. VFR or IFR avionics packages to customer's choice including Bendix/King and Narco nav/com, ADF, DME, transponder and encoding altimeter; Apollo, Arnav, Foster, II Morrow and Northstar Loran-C systems; 3M Stormscope WX-8 and 1000 series; Bendix/King KCS 55A slaved compass system with KN 72 VOR/LOC converter; NAT voice-activated intercom; Bendix/King KX 99 and TR 720 hand-held transceivers, and Astrotech LC-2 digital clock. Toe brakes standard in rear cockpit. Compass, airspeed indicator, turn and bank indicator, rate of climb indicator, sensitive altimeter, recording tachometer, cylinder head temperature gauge and oil pressure and oil temperature gauges standard in rear cockpit. Front cockpit instruments optional. Front and rear windscreens (front removable), front and rear cockpit covers, instrument post lighting, heated pitot, tie-down rings and three colour paint scheme with choice of two designs, also standard. Optional equipment includes exhaust gas temperature gauge, carburettor temperature gauge, g meter, vacuum- or electrically-driven gyro system, Hobbs meter, outside air temperature gauge, manifold gauge, oil cooler for wooden propeller, ground service plug, landing and taxi lights, front and rear cockpit heaters, flight-approved metal front cockpit cover, map case, glider tow hook, deluxe interior with carpet, leather sidewalls and interior trim, and special exterior paint designs.

DIMENSIONS, EXTERNAL:

Wing span: upper	9.14 m (30 ft 0 in)
lower	8.18 m (26 ft 10 in)
Length overall	7.10 m (23 ft 3⅝ in)
Height overall	2.57 m (8 ft 5⅜ in)
Wheelbase	1.95 m (6 ft 5 in)
Propeller diameter	2.44 m (8 ft 0 in)

Classic Waco Classic F-5 re-creation of the Waco YMF-5 three-seat biplane *(Geoffrey P. Jones)*

AREA:

Wings, gross	21.69 m² (233.5 sq ft)

WEIGHTS AND LOADINGS:

Basic weight empty	880 kg (1,940 lb)
Max T-O and landing weight	1,256 kg (2,770 lb)
Max wing loading	52.26 kg/m² (10.71 lb/sq ft)
Max power loading	6.21 kg/kW (10.20 lb/hp)

PERFORMANCE (at max T-O weight):

Never-exceed speed	186 knots (344 km/h; 214 mph)
Max level speed at S/L	117 knots (217 km/h; 135 mph)

Max cruising speed at S/L	104 knots (193 km/h; 120 mph)
Econ cruising speed at 2,440 m (8,000 ft)	95 knots (177 km/h; 110 mph)
Stalling speed, power off	51 knots (94 km/h; 58 mph)
Max rate of climb at S/L	235 m (770 ft)/min
T-O run	152 m (500 ft)
Range, standard fuel, 30 min reserves	286 nm (531 km; 330 miles)

COLEMILL

COLEMILL ENTERPRISES INC

PO Box 60627, Cornelia Fort Air Park, Nashville, Tennessee 37206
Telephone: 1 (615) 226 4256
Telex: 555 197
Fax: 1 (615) 226 4702
PRESIDENT: Ernest Colbert
Colemill specialises in performance improvement conversions of light single- and twin-engined aircraft.

COLEMILL PANTHER NAVAJO

Colemill's conversion of the Navajo or Navajo C/R involves a power plant change, redesigned nacelles, additional continuous running fuel pumps, a digital fuel totaliser, heavy duty brakes, and wingtip mounted landing lights. Conversion normally takes 10-14 days. Colemill has also developed 'Zip-Tip' winglets for Panther Navajo and Chieftain conversions which improve stability in the lower-speed flight zone, down to stalling speed, and provide cruising speed increases of 4-9 knots (8-16 km/h; 5-10 mph) at altitudes between 3,960 and 7,620 m (13,000 and 25,000 ft), at engine power settings between 45% and 65% of maximum power. The resulting aircraft are therefore able to match the cruising speed of the standard Panther Navajo (without winglets) at power settings which offer greater fuel economy.

Following the award of a Supplemental Type Certificate in Summer 1982, operators of Panther conversions of Navajo and Chieftain aircraft can specify winglets from new or as retrofit modifications, replacing the normal extended wingtips of the conversion. They increase wing span to 13.16 m (43 ft 2 in) and wing area by 0.56 m² (6 sq ft).

The basic description of the Navajo, which can be found under the Piper entry in the 1982-83 *Jane's*, applies also to the Panther Navajo, except as follows:
WINGS: New wingtips with marked undercamber, which increase wing span and area; or alternative choice of winglets, as described in opening paragraphs.
LANDING GEAR: Cleveland four-spot heavy duty disc brakes.
POWER PLANT: Two 261 kW (350 hp) Textron Lycoming TIO-540-J2BD turbocharged engines, each driving a Hartzell four-blade constant-speed fully-feathering metal propeller with Q-tips. Pressurised magnetos, Woodward propeller governors, synchrophasers and unfeathering accumulators standard. Fuel system as for basic Navajo, except for the addition of continuous running electrically operated fuel pumps.
EQUIPMENT: Generally as for standard Navajo, but existing fuel flow gauges are replaced by a Shadin Digiflow fuel management computer giving digital readout of fuel remaining/fuel consumed. Supplemental wingtip landing lights can be operated independently of the standard nosewheel mounted landing light, prior to lowering of landing gear.

DIMENSION, EXTERNAL:

Wing span	13.00 m (42 ft 8 in)

LOADING:

Max power loading	5.65 kg/kW (9.3 lb/hp)

PERFORMANCE (at max T-O weight):

Max level speed	269 knots (498 km/h; 309 mph)

Colemill Panther Navajo with winglets

Max cruising speed, 75% power at optimum altitude	248 knots (459 km/h; 285 mph)

Cruising speed, 65% power:

at 7,315 m (24,000 ft)	235 knots (435 km/h; 270 mph)
at 3,660 m (12,000 ft)	206 knots (381 km/h; 237 mph)
Max rate of climb at S/L	610 m (2,000 ft)/min
Rate of climb at S/L, one engine out	122 m (400 ft)/min
Short-field T-O run	229 m (750 ft)
T-O to 15 m (50 ft)	458 m (1,500 ft)
Landing from 15 m (50 ft)	427 m (1,400 ft)

COLEMILL PANTHER II

Colemill's Panther II conversion is based on the Piper Chieftain and includes the installation of new 261 kW (350 hp) Textron Lycoming TIO-540-J2BD and LTIO-540-J2BD turbocharged engines, each driving a Hartzell four-blade constant-speed fully-feathering metal propeller with Q-tips. A digital fuel management computer, Woodward propeller governors and synchrophaser, and Cleveland four-spot heavy duty brakes, are also standard. 'Zip-Tip' winglets are optional.

COLEMILL EXECUTIVE 600

The Executive 600 is a Cessna 310, of Model F to Q series, fitted by Colemill with two 224 kW (300 hp) Continental IO-520-E flat-six engines, each driving a McCauley three-blade propeller. Dimensions are unchanged; empty weight is increased by about 14 kg (30 lb); other data are as follows:

WEIGHT:

Max T-O weight:	2,358 kg (5,200 lb)

PERFORMANCE (at max T-O weight):

Max cruising speed (75% power):	205 knots (379 km/h; 236 mph)

Colemill Panther II conversion with winglets

Cruising speed (65% power)
        195 knots (361 km/h; 224 mph)
Stalling speed, wheels and flaps down
        64 knots (119 km/h; 74 mph)
Max rate of climb at S/L   762 m (2,500 ft)/min
Service ceiling   5,940 m (19,500 ft)
T-O to 15 m (50 ft)   518 m (1,700 ft)
Landing from 15 m (50 ft)   unchanged
Range with max fuel, 45 min reserves
        1,050 nm (1,944 km; 1,208 miles)

COLEMILL PRESIDENT 600

The President 600 is a Beechcraft B55 Baron re-engined by Colemill with two 224 kW (300 hp) Continental IO-520-E flat-six engines, each driving a three-blade propeller. Some 250 President 600 conversions have been delivered. Dimensions are unchanged; empty weight is increased by about 14 kg (30 lb); other data are as follows:
WEIGHT:
  Max T-O weight   2,313 kg (5,100 lb)
PERFORMANCE (at max T-O weight):
  Max cruising speed (75% power)
        203 knots (376 km/h; 233 mph)
  Cruising speed (65% power)
        193 knots (357 km/h; 222 mph)
  Stalling speed, wheels and flaps down
        66 knots (123 km/h; 76 mph)
  Max rate of climb at S/L   823 m (2,700 ft)/min
  Service ceiling   5,940 m (19,500 ft)
  T-O to 15 m (50 ft)   497 m (1,631 ft)
  Landing from 15 m (50 ft)   unchanged
  Range with max fuel, 45 min reserves
        1,050 nm (1,944 km; 1,208 miles)

COLEMILL FOXSTAR BARON

The Foxstar is a Beechcraft Baron Model 55 or 58 re-engined with two 224 kW (300 hp) Teledyne Continental IO-550C engines with heavy duty crankcases, each driving a Hartzell Sabre Blade four-blade Q-tip propeller. Other modifications include the installation of Woodward propeller governors and synchrophase system, Shadin Digiflow fuel computer, 'Zip-Tip' winglets, and 60A alternators. The Foxstar conversion is FAA STC approved for all Model C55, D55, E55 and Model 58 Barons, and offers improvements in rate of climb, cruising speed, engine-out performance, and cabin noise and vibration levels.
WEIGHT:
  Max T-O weight   2,449 kg (5,400 lb)
PERFORMANCE (at max T-O weight):
  Max cruising speed, 75% power
        205 knots (380 km/h; 236 mph)
  Cruising speed, 65% power
        200 knots (371 km/h; 230 mph)
  Stalling speed, landing gear and flaps down
        74 knots (137 km/h; 85 mph)
  Max rate of climb at S/L   561 m (1,840 ft)/min
  Service ceiling   6,400 m (21,000 ft)
  T-O to 15 m (50 ft)   610 m (2,000 ft)
  Landing from 15 m (50 ft)   734 m (2,410 ft)
  Range with max fuel, 45 min reserves
        1,131 nm (2,096 km; 1,302 miles)

Colemill Foxstar Baron

Colemill Starfire Bonanza

COLEMILL STARFIRE BONANZA

The Starfire is a Beechcraft Bonanza re-engined with a 224 kW (300 hp) Teledyne Continental IO-550B engine, driving a Hartzell Sabre Blade four-blade Q-tip propeller. Other modifications include the installation of a Woodward propeller governor, Shadin Digiflow fuel computer/ totaliser, 'Zip-Tip' winglets, and a 60A alternator. The Starfire conversion has received FAA STC approval for all Beechcraft Model C33A, E33A, F33A, S35, V35A, V35B and A36 Bonanzas. The conversion offers improvements in rate of climb, cruising speed and cabin noise and vibration levels.

PERFORMANCE:
  Cruising speed   176 knots (326 km/h; 203 mph)
  Max rate of climb at S/L   369 m (1,210 ft)/min
  T-O run   296 m (971 ft)
  T-O to 15 m (50 ft)   583 m (1,912 ft)

COMMANDER
COMMANDER AIRCRAFT COMPANY
Wiley Post Airport, 7200 NW 63rd Street, Bethany, Oklahoma 73008
Telephone: 1 (405) 495 8080
Fax: 1 (405) 495 8383
PRESIDENT: Randall Greene
VICE-PRESIDENTS:
  David R. Ellis (Engineering)
  Lynn D. Jones (Manufacturing)
  Roy D. Pickens (Operations)

In the Summer of 1988 Commander Aircraft Company acquired from Gulfstream Aerospace Corporation the manufacturing, marketing and product support rights for the Rockwell Commander 112 and 114 series of single-engined light aircraft, last described in the 1978-79 edition of *Jane's*. The company is providing spares and product support services for existing aircraft from its product support centre and manufacturing in Oklahoma, from which deliveries of new Commander 114Bs were expected to begin in June 1990. Improvements to the Commander 114A airframe include a new cowling design, improved cooling and induction systems, a specially developed McCauley three-blade metal propeller, NACA scoop on the dorsal fin, new interior trim and seats, better soundproofing, inflatable door seals, and strengthened tail surface and landing gear attachment fittings. In early 1990

Commander Aircraft Company held orders for some 160 Commander 114Bs, which will be leased rather than sold to US customers.

A production rate of four aircraft per month is planned for 1991. Future developments of the Commander 114B which are under consideration include a version powered by a Teledyne Continental Voyager-series liquid-cooled power plant, a turbocharged version, and a pressurised model.
POWER PLANT: One 194 kW (260 hp) Textron Lycoming IO-540-T4B5 piston engine, driving a McCauley three-blade constant-speed metal propeller type B3B 32C 419/82NHA-5. Fuel contained in two integral wing tanks, max capacity 265 litres (70 US gallons; 58.3 Imp gallons), of which 257 litres (68 US gallons; 56.6 Imp gallons) are usable. Max oil capacity 7.6 litres (2 US gallons; 1.67 Imp gallons).
DIMENSIONS, EXTERNAL:
  Wing span   9.98 m (32 ft 9 in)
  Length overall   7.59 m (24 ft 11 in)
  Height overall   2.57 m (8 ft 5 in)
  Tailplane span   4.10 m (13 ft 5½ in)
  Wheel track   3.34 m (10 ft 11½ in)
  Wheelbase   2.11 m (6 ft 11 in)
  Propeller diameter   1.96 m (6 ft 5 in)
  Propeller ground clearance   0.19 m (7½ in)
DIMENSIONS, INTERNAL:
  Cabin: Length   1.91 m (6 ft 3 in)
    Max width   1.19 m (3 ft 11 in)
    Max height   1.24 m (4 ft 1 in)
  Volume   2.83 m³ (100.0 cu ft)
  Baggage compartment volume   0.62 m³ (22.0 cu ft)
AREA:
  Wings, gross   14.12 m² (152.0 sq ft)
WEIGHTS AND LOADINGS:
  Weight empty   927 kg (2044 lb)
  Max T-O weight   1474 kg (3250 lb)
  Max ramp weight   1479 kg (3260 lb)
  Max wing loading   104.5 kg/m² (21.4 lb/sq ft)
  Max power loading   7.62 kg/kW (12.54 lb/hp)
PERFORMANCE (estimated at max T-O weight, ISA, except where indicated):
  Max level speed   174 knots (322 km/h; 200 mph)
  Cruising speed:
    75% power   164 knots (304 km/h; 189 mph)
    65% power   152 knots (282 km/h; 175 mph)
  Stalling speed:
    flaps and wheels up   61 knots (113 km/h; 71 mph)
    flaps and wheels down   56 knots (104 km/h; 65 mph)
  Max rate of climb at S/L   335 m (1,100 ft)/min
  Service ceiling   5,335 m (17,500 ft)
  T-O run   317 m (1,040 ft)
  T-O to 15 m (50 ft)   610 m (2,000 ft)
  Landing from 15 m (50 ft)   366 m (1,200 ft)
  Landing run   220 m (720 ft)
  Range: at 75% power   672 nm (1,245 km; 773 miles)
    at 65% power   705 nm (1,306 km; 811 miles)

COMTRAN

COMTRAN LTD

8507 Broadway, San Antonio, Texas 78217
Telephone: 1 (512) 821 6301
Telex: 767438 COMTRAN UD
Fax: 1 (512) 822 7766
PROGRAMME DIRECTOR: John T. Jennings

COMTRAN SUPER Q

Comtran Ltd has developed a modification and upgrading programme for Boeing 707 jet airliners known as the Comtran Super Q. The extensive refurbishment includes installation of Comtran Q-707 engine nacelle hush kits which enable the aircraft to meet FAR 36 Stage 2 and ICAO Annex 16, Chapter 2 noise requirements. The hush kit uses Rohr Industries' DynaRohr surface liner material within a modified engine nacelle on which the engine inlet and fan exit ducts are lengthened, and results in a claimed reduction in the 100 EPNdB footprint area from 5.6 nm (10.4 km; 6.4 miles) for a standard Boeing 707 to 2.8 nm (5.2 km; 3.2 miles) for the Super Q. Hush kit installation does not interfere with existing engine systems such as anti-icing and thrust reversers.

The Super Q also features a new passenger cabin with wide-body styling incorporating new technology lightweight passenger seats, overhead storage bins, a new cabin entertainment system with video monitors and individual seat mounted controls, new cabin soundproofing, new cabin headliner with 'wash' lighting, headliner and aisle illuminated emergency escape lighting systems, overhauled galleys and lavatories fore and aft, new liferafts, lifejackets and emergency exit chutes, and new floor and side panel liners in the baggage compartments. The cabin provides accommodation for up to 186 passengers in four-class configuration. Optional interior arrangements provide for standard first and tourist class, high-density single class, combined passenger/cargo and all-cargo

Cutaway drawing of Comtran Super Q conversion of the Boeing 707 in Combi configuration

configurations. Use of fireblocking materials in all seats, and non-toxic polycarbonate composite materials for overhead panels and seat trim, plus supplementary emergency floor lighting, enables the Super Q to meet ICAO, FAA and European S-2000 fire, safety and toxicity standards.

The Super Q's flight deck features upgraded Collins avionics including FD109Y flight directors, long-range navigation systems, colour weather radar, a new cockpit audio system, and new wiring and switching as required.

For a typical mission carrying a full complement of passengers and crew, and 65,975 kg (145,450 lb) of fuel including 9,072 kg (20,000 lb) reserves, at a max brake release weight of 150,955 kg (332,800 lb), cruising at Mach 0.8 at 10,670 m (35,000 ft), the Super Q has an estimated range of 4,365 nm (8,089 km; 5,026 miles).

DEE HOWARD

THE DEE HOWARD COMPANY

9610 John Saunders Road, International Airport, PO Box 17300, San Antonio, Texas 78217
Telephone: 1 (512) 828 1341
Telex: 767380
CHAIRMAN OF THE BOARD: Dee Howard
PRESIDENT AND CHIEF EXECUTIVE: Philip Greco
VICE-PRESIDENT, ENGINEERING: David White
VICE-PRESIDENT, MARKETING AND SALES: Roger Munt
DIRECTOR OF MARKETING COMMUNICATIONS: Brian Loflin

A 60 per cent holding in The Dee Howard Company was acquired by Aeritalia (see Italian section) in the Spring of 1989.

DEE HOWARD XR LEARJET

The Dee Howard Company has developed an overall performance improvement system suitable for retrofit on all Model 24 and 25 Learjets having General Electric CJ610-6 or -8A turbojets. The improvements incorporated in the XR Learjet include a new centre-section glove which reduces drag, improves spanwise lift, and accommodates an additional 245 kg (540 lb) of fuel; a new engine pylon/nacelle configuration that eliminates adverse flow pressure characteristics and channel flow Mach problems, and also improves engine bay cooling; two small span flow limiters, boundary layer energisers and stall turbulators at the junction of the inboard and outboard leading-edge on each wing, to produce stall buffet and improve overall stall performance; a new leading-edge profile to optimise cruise drag and low-speed stall characteristics; improved ailerons, trailing-edge flaps, outer wing panels, and new tip tank fin cuffs to improve cruise performance; a new engine exhaust nozzle that improves specific fuel consumption; and installation of a Teledyne angle of attack system, or retention of the Conrac angle of attack system if the modified aircraft has the Century III wing.

Conversion of a suitable Model 24 or 25 to XR Learjet configuration provides an extra 400 nm (741 km; 460 miles)

Artist's impression of Dee Howard BAC 1-11 re-engined with Rolls-Royce Tay 650 turbofans

of range at a constant cruising speed of Mach 0.78, plus an increase of 680 kg (1,500 lb) in maximum take-off weight, and increased payload.

DEE HOWARD BAC 1-11

In February 1986 The Dee Howard Company signed agreements with Rolls-Royce and British Aerospace leading to certification of the 67.17 kN (15,100 lb st) Rolls-Royce Tay 650 turbofan in BAC One-Eleven Series 400, 475 and 500 aircraft. All prototype modification and flight test work is undertaken at the company's San Antonio facility. The first converted aircraft was rolled out in March 1990, with the first flight then anticipated in April. Replacement of the One-Eleven's Spey 511 engines with the Tay power plant is expected to provide corporate

configured 400 series aircraft with an NBAA IFR range of 3,100 nm (5,745 km; 3,570 miles) and to offer a reduction in balanced field length requirements of as much as 30 per cent under hot and high conditions. The modification includes new engine nacelles and Dee Howard-developed thrust reversers, and will enable the aircraft to meet FAR Pt 36 Stage 3 and ICAO Annex Chapter 3 noise requirements. At the time of its agreement with the engine and airframe manufacturers, the company held several orders for the conversion, which is available to corporate and airline operators of the BAC One-Eleven. Dee Howard foresees a potential market for up to 75-100 conversions. After completion of the first three aircraft, the conversion is expected to take between two to three months, depending on work required by customers.

DMAV

DUAL MODE AIR VEHICLE INC

2205 West Division, Unit C-5, Arlington, Texas 76012
Telephone: 1 (817) 265 8843
Fax: 1 (817) 274 1379
CHIEF OF AERODYNAMICS: J. David Kocurek, PhD

This company, in conjunction with the Ishida Corporation of Japan, has completed initial design studies and wind tunnel tests of a tilt-wing V/STOL aircraft known as the **TW-68**, intended for military and civilian roles. The aircraft will be of conventional aluminium alloy construction and may be powered by two Pratt & Whitney

Canada PT6A-67R turboprops. DMAV was building a mockup in early 1990; further details can be found in the Japanese section.

DYNAC

DYNAC INTERNATIONAL CORPORATION

New York
PRINCIPAL: Guenter Schnoor

During 1989 this company announced that it had acquired the type certificate, tooling, manufacturing and marketing rights for the former Aero Commander Lark Commander four-seat high-wing light aircraft, production of which ceased in 1971. DYNAC plans to develop two

redesigned versions of the Lark Commander as the **DYNAC C180** and **C235XP** with, respectively, 134 kW (180 hp) and 175 kW (235 hp) Textron Lycoming engines, the latter with a constant-speed propeller. No further details are known.

ELECTROSPACE SYSTEMS

ELECTROSPACE SYSTEMS INC
(Subsidiary of The Chrysler Corporation)

PO Box 831359, 1301 East Collins Boulevard, Richardson,
Texas 75083-1359
Telephone: 1 (214) 783 2000
Telex: 163590 ESI UT
Fax: 1 (214) 470 2466
PRESIDENT: James R. Lightner
VICE-PRESIDENT, MARKETING: Donald E. Heitzman

Electrospace Systems undertakes specialist conversions
for the US Department of Defense, one of its recent
contracts concerning modification of a McDonnell Douglas
DC-8 to EC-24A standard, as last described in the 1989-90
Jane's. The current programme, also an airliner conversion,
is the EC-18D.

ELECTROSPACE SYSTEMS (BOEING) EC-18D

Under a $42.6 million fixed-price USAF Aeronautical
Systems Division contract awarded in October 1988,
Electrospace Systems is modifying two Boeing 707 aircraft
for use as Cruise Missile Mission Control Aircraft
(CMMCA) under the designation EC-18D. Conversion of
the aircraft was due to begin in July 1989 and will include
structural modifications to the Boeing 707s' forward
fuselages and installation and integration of avionics
including Hughes Aircraft AN/APG-63 surveillance radar,
telemetry receiver and weather radar. Flight testing of the
first EC-18D was expected to begin during 1990, with
completion of the modification programme scheduled for
October 1991. When operational with the ASD's 4950th
Test Wing in FY 1991, the EC-18Ds will provide
stand-alone support for Strategic Air Command and US
Navy cruise missile test missions, including the capability to
fly the missile if necessary in addition to airborne radar
tracking and surveillance functions.

ENSTROM

THE ENSTROM HELICOPTER CORPORATION

PO Box 277, 2209 North 22nd Street, Twin County Airport,
Menominee, Michigan 49858
Telephone: 1 (906) 863 9971
Telex: 261912 ENST UR
Fax: 1 (906) 863 6821
PRESIDENT: Robert M. Tuttle
VICE-PRESIDENT, SALES AND SERVICE: Richard E. Loynachan

The history of Enstrom, since the company was founded
in 1959, has been outlined in previous editions of *Jane's*.
Ownership passed to Bravo Investments BV of the
Netherlands in January 1980. In September 1984 Enstrom
was acquired by a group of American investors then headed
by Mr Dean Kamen and Mr Robert Tuttle.

A total of more than 865 Enstrom helicopters had been
built by 1 January 1990.

ENSTROM MODELS F28 and 280

Details of the basic Model F-28A and the Model 280
Shark can be found in the 1978-79 *Jane's*. They were
replaced by turbocharged versions of both models, under
the designations F28C and 280C respectively. These
received FAA certification on 8 December 1975 and were
last described in the 1984-85 *Jane's*. Production of these
models ceased in November 1981. They were succeeded by
the Models F28F, 280F Shark (described in 1985-86 *Jane's*
and now out of production), and the Model 280FX.
Currently available versions are as follows:

F28F Falcon. Basic version, which received FAA
certification in January 1981. Recent developments, applicable to all Enstrom models, include a redesigned main
rotor gearbox with heavy wall main rotor shaft and a
lightweight exhaust muffler system which offers reductions
in noise levels of 40 per cent in the hover and 30 per cent
when flying at an altitude of 152 m (500 ft). The new main
rotor gearbox is fitted as standard on current production
helicopters and may be retrofitted to earlier 'F' series
Enstroms. The muffler assembly is available as an option on
new helicopters, and may also be retrofitted to Models
F28F, 280F and 280FX. Recent improvements introduced
on all models include a lightweight high efficiency starter
motor and optional pneumatic door opener.

An Enstrom wet or dry dispersal agricultural kit is
available for fitment to the F28F. It comprises two
side-mounted hoppers with large quick-fill openings, and
spraybooms with a normal span of 9.04 m (29 ft 8 in), but
extendable to 11.07 m (36 ft 4 in). A manually operated
clutch provides positive control of the centrifugal pump,
which has a liquid capacity of 227 litres (60 US gallons; 50
Imp gallons)/min. Dry discharge rate is variable from 0 to
272 kg (600 lb)/min. Weight of the entire quickly removable
dispersal system is 48 kg (105 lb). Hopper capacity is 303
litres (80 US gallons; 67 Imp gallons) of liquid or 0.5 m³
(17.4 cu ft) of dry chemicals.

F28F-P Sentinel. Dedicated police patrol version of
the F28F, developed for the Pasadena Police Department in
California, which took delivery of its first F28F-P in
October 1986. The F28F-P may be fitted with a Locator B,
Spectrolab SX-5 or Carter searchlight, and specialised
police radio packages. Specifications and performance are
identical to those of the standard F28F Falcon.

Model 280FX. Modified version of the Model 280F
Shark, which began flight testing in December 1983 and
received FAA certification under CAR Pt 6 on 14 January
1985. The Model 280FX features completely faired landing
gear, a redesigned air inlet system, redesigned horizontal
and vertical tail surfaces incorporating endplate fins on the
horizontal stabiliser, covered tail rotor shaft, and a tail
rotor guard. New seats including lumbar support and
energy-absorbing foam have been installed. Range can be
increased to 339 nm (627 km; 390 miles) by installing an
internal auxiliary tank. Fifteen Model 280FXs are operated
by the Chilean Army.

TYPE: Three-seat light helicopter.
ROTOR SYSTEM: Fully articulated metal three-blade main
rotor. Blades are of bonded light alloy construction, each
attached to hub by retention pin and drag link. Blade
section NACA 0013.5. Two-blade teetering tail rotor,
with blades of bonded light alloy construction. Tail rotor
on port side. Blades do not fold.
ROTOR DRIVE: Poly V-belt drive system. Right angle drive
reduction gearbox. Main rotor/engine rpm ratio 1 : 8.678;
tail rotor/engine rpm ratio 1 : 1.213.

Enstrom F28F Falcon three-seat light helicopter

FUSELAGE: Glassfibre and light alloy cab structure, with
welded steel tube centre-section. Semi-monocoque aluminium tailcone structure.
TAIL UNIT: Horizontal stabiliser forward of tail rotor, with
endplate fins.
LANDING GEAR: Skids carried on Enstrom oleo-pneumatic
shock absorbers. Air Cruiser inflatable floats available
optionally.
POWER PLANT: One 168 kW (225 hp) Textron Lycoming
HIO-360-F1AD flat-four engine with Rotomaster
3BT5EE10J2 turbocharger. Two fuel tanks, each of 79.5
litres (21 US gallons; 17.5 Imp gallons). Total standard
fuel capacity 159 litres (42 US gallons; 35 Imp gallons), of
which 151 litres (40 US gallons; 33.3 Imp gallons) are
usable. Auxiliary tank, capacity 49 litres (13 US gallons;
10.8 Imp gallons), can be installed in the baggage
compartment. Oil capacity 9.5 litres (2.5 US gallons; 2.1
Imp gallons).
ACCOMMODATION: Pilot and two passengers, side by side on
bench seat; centre place removable. Fully transparent
removable door on each side of cabin. Baggage space aft
of engine compartment, capacity 49 kg (108 lb), with
external access door. Cabin heated and ventilated.
SYSTEM: Electrical power provided by 12V 70A engine
driven alternator; 24V 70A system optional on F28F,
standard on 280FX.
AVIONICS AND EQUIPMENT: Standard equipment includes
airspeed indicator, sensitive altimeter, graphic engine
monitor, compass, outside air temperature gauge,
turn-and-bank indicator, rotor/engine tachometer, low
rotor rpm warning light, manifold pressure/fuel flow
gauge, fuel pressure warning lights, gearbox and oil
temperature gauges, cylinder head temperature gauge,
fuel quantity gauge, overboost, low fuel pressure and
clutch disengagement warning lights. Also standard are
ground handling wheels with handle, kick-in service
steps, floor carpeting, lap belts for all seats, shoulder
harnesses for two seats, instrument lighting with dimmer
control, position light on each horizontal stabiliser tip,
anti-collision strobe light, landing lights, adjustable nose
light, soundproofing, main and tail rotor covers and
blade tiedowns. Additionally, the Model 280FX has as
standard an annunciator warning panel, and custom
seating. Optional equipment includes dual controls,
cabin heater, fire extinguisher, first aid kit, custom
interior and custom paint scheme, floor switch, external
power receptacle, third shoulder harness, auxiliary fuel
tank, sliding vent windows, eight-day clock, baggage
compartment, floats, cargo hook, hardpoints for agricultural equipment or night sign, and wet or wet/dry
agricultural dispersal systems. Optional instrumentation
includes R. C. Allen attitude gyro and turn co-ordinator,
directional gyro, instantaneous vertical speed indicator,
and a variety of avionics fits from AR Nav, Bendix/King
II Morrow and Northstar. Bose noise-attenuating
headsets are optional on all models.
DIMENSIONS, EXTERNAL:

Main rotor diameter	9.75 m (32 ft 0 in)
Tail rotor diameter	1.42 m (4 ft 8 in)
Distance between rotor centres	5.56 m (18 ft 3 in)
Main rotor blade chord	0.24 m (9½ in)
Tail rotor blade chord	0.11 m (4½ in)

Enstrom Model 280FX three-seat light helicopter

Length overall, rotors stationary	8.92 m (29 ft 3 in)
Height to top of rotor head	2.79 m (9 ft 2 in)
Skid track	2.21 m (7 ft 3 in)
Cabin doors (each): Height	1.04 m (3 ft 5 in)
Width	0.84 m (2 ft 9 in)
Height to sill	0.64 m (2 ft 1 in)
Baggage door: Height	0.55 m (1 ft 9½ in)
Width	0.39 m (1 ft 3½ in)
Height to sill	0.86 m (2 ft 10 in)

DIMENSIONS, INTERNAL (A: F28F, B: 280FX):

Cabin: Max width: A	1.55 m (5 ft 1 in)
B	1.50 m (4 ft 11 in)
Baggage compartment volume	0.18 m³ (6.3 cu ft)

AREAS:

Main rotor disc	74.69 m² (804.0 sq ft)
Tail rotor disc	1.66 m² (17.88 sq ft)

WEIGHTS AND LOADINGS (A: F28F Normal category, B: 280FX):

Weight empty, equipped: A	712 kg (1,570 lb)
B	719 kg (1,585 lb)
Max T-O weight: A, B	1,179 kg (2,600 lb)
Max disc loading: A, B	15.77 kg/m² (3.23 lb/sq ft)
Max power loading: A, B	7.02 kg/kW (11.55 lb/hp)

PERFORMANCE (both versions at AUW of 1,066 kg; 2,350 lb, except where indicated):

Never exceed speed:	
A	97 knots (180 km/h; 112 mph)
B	102 knots (189 km/h; 117 mph)
Max level speed, S/L to 915 m (3,000 ft):	
A	97 knots (180 km/h; 112 mph) IAS
B	102 knots (189 km/h; 117 mph) IAS
Max cruising speed: A	97 knots (180 km/h; 112 mph)
B	102 knots (188 km/h; 117 mph)
Econ cruising speed: A	89 knots (165 km/h; 102 mph)
B	93 knots (172 km/h; 107 mph)
Max rate of climb at S/L	442 m (1,450 ft)/min
Certificated operating ceiling	3,660 m (12,000 ft)
Hovering ceiling:	
IGE at AUW of 1,179 kg (2,600 lb)	2,345 m (7,700 ft)
OGE at AUW of 1,066 kg (2,350 lb)	2,650 m (8,700 ft)
Max range, standard fuel, no reserves:	
A	228 nm (423 km; 263 miles)
B	260 nm (483 km; 300 miles)
Max endurance	3 h 30 min

ENSTROM MODEL 480
Military designation: TH-28

Enstrom launched this four-seat turbine-powered light helicopter at the Helicopter Association International Heli Expo '90 at Dallas, Texas, in February 1990. A proof of concept turboshaft conversion of a Model 280FX was first

Artist's impression of Enstrom Model 480 four-seat turbine-powered light helicopter

flown in December 1988, powered by an Allison 250 engine. The definitive four-seat wide-cabin prototype (N8631E) made its first flight on 7 October 1989 and by early 1990 had completed structural proof tests and initial exploration of the flight test envelope, including demonstrated cruising speeds up to 109 knots (203 km/h; 126 mph).

The Model 480 retains the three-blade rotor and dynamic system components of the piston-engined Model 280FX, but is powered by a 313 kW (420 shp) Allison 250-C20W turboshaft, derated to 212.5 kW (285 shp) with a maximum continuous power rating of 186.4 kW (250 shp). Fuel is contained in three interconnected crashworthy tanks, total capacity 363 litres (96 US gallons; 80 Imp gallons).

Enstrom is proposing a three-seat trainer version, designated **TH-28**, for the US Army's new training helicopter (NTH) requirement. In trainer configuration the aircraft has seating for instructor and pupil side-by-side with dual controls, and a third seat in the rear centre of the cabin for a second, observing, pupil. In commercial Model 480 four-seat configuration the front seats are slightly staggered and two rear seats are offset to the right, with provision for quick conversion to three-seat trainer, three-seat executive transport with a single front seat, or single-seat cargo transport. Enstrom expected to obtain FAA certification of the Model 480 in late 1990, with deliveries beginning shortly thereafter.

DIMENSIONS, EXTERNAL: As for 280FX except:

Distance between rotor centres	5.64 m (18 ft 6 in)
Height to top of rotor head	2.90 m (9 ft 6 in)
Skid track	2.46 m (8 ft 1 in)

DIMENSION, INTERNAL:

Cabin: Max width	1.73 m (5 ft 8 in)

WEIGHTS:

Weight empty	671 kg (1,480 lb)
Max T-O weight	1,202 kg (2,650 lb)

PERFORMANCE (provisional, at max T-O weight, ISA, except where indicated):

Never-exceed speed	123 knots (228 km/h; 142 mph)
Max cruising speed	109 knots (203 km/h; 126 mph)
Econ cruising speed	100 knots (185 km/h; 115 mph)
Max rate of climb at S/L:	
at AUW of 1,066 kg (2,350 lb)	494 m (1,620 ft)/min
at AUW of 1,202 kg (2,650 lb)	372 m (1,220 ft)/min
Service ceiling	4,570 m (15,000 ft)
Hovering ceiling: IGE:	
at AUW of 1,066 kg (2,350 lb)	4,635 m (15,200 ft)
at AUW of 1,202 kg (2,650 lb)	3,170 m (10,400 ft)
OGE:	
at AUW of 1,066 kg (2,350 lb)	3,870 m (12,700 ft)
at AUW of 1,202 kg (2,650 lb)	1,280 m (4,200 ft)
Max range	364 nm (676 km; 420 miles)
Endurance	4 h 12 min

EXCALIBUR
EXCALIBUR AVIATION COMPANY
8337 Mission Road, San Antonio, Texas 78214
Telephone: 1 (512) 927 6201
PRESIDENT: Michael M. Davis

Excalibur Aviation continues to produce its improved versions of the Beechcraft Queen Air. These modified aircraft, named Queenaire 800 and Queenaire 8800, continue to be completed at the rate of one per month, notably for operators in South America. In addition to this continuing programme, Excalibur Aviation is currently modifying military U-8F (Beech Queen Air 65) aircraft for the US National Guard Bureau, Washington, DC. The conversions provide improved reliability, speed and range, together with reduced operating costs.

By early 1990 Excalibur Aviation had completed a total of 166 Queenaire conversions, including 51 for the US Army. Some 45 Beech Model 50 Twin-Bonanzas have also been modified by the company.

An Excalibur Queenaire 800 conversion of a Beech U-8F for the Missouri Army National Guard

EXCALIBUR QUEENAIRE 800 and 8800
The Excalibur modification of Queen Air 65s and 80s includes installation of two 298 kW (400 hp) Textron Lycoming IO-720-A1B eight-cylinder engines, each driving a Hartzell three-blade constant-speed and fully-feathering metal propeller with spinner; new engine mountings; new exhaust system; new low drag engine nacelles; new (or zero-time overhauled and certificated) accessories; and Excalibur fully enclosed wheel well doors. Modifications of the Beechcraft Queen Air 65, A65 and 80 of all serial numbers are designated Queenaire 800; similar modifications to the Queen Air A80 and B80 of all serial numbers have the designation Queenaire 8800.

WEIGHTS (A: Queenaire 800, B: Queenaire 8800):

Weight empty, equipped (average):	
A	2,449 kg (5,400 lb)
B	2,631 kg (5,800 lb)
Max T-O weight: A	3,628 kg (8,000 lb)
B	3,991 kg (8,800 lb)
Max landing weight: A	3,447 kg (7,600 lb)
B	3,792 kg (8,360 lb)

PERFORMANCE (at max T-O weight):

Cruising speed, 75% power:	
A, B at 2,530 m (8,300 ft)	201 knots (372 km/h; 231 mph)
Cruising speed, 65% power:	
A, B at 3,050 m (10,000 ft)	195 knots (362 km/h; 225 mph)
Cruising speed, 45% power:	
A, B at 3,050 m (10,000 ft)	172 knots (319 km/h; 198 mph)
Stalling speed, gear and flaps up:	
A	80 knots (148 km/h; 92 mph)
B	86 knots (160 km/h; 99 mph)
Stalling speed, gear and flaps down:	
A	68 knots (126 km/h; 78 mph)
B	70 knots (129 km/h; 80 mph)
Max rate of climb at S/L: A	468 m (1,535 ft)/min
B	454 m (1,490 ft)/min
Rate of climb at S/L, one engine out:	
A	110 m (360 ft)/min
B	76 m (250 ft)/min
Service ceiling: A	6,005 m (19,700 ft)
B	5,700 m (18,700 ft)
Service ceiling, one engine out:	
A	3,595 m (11,800 ft)
B	3,110 m (10,200 ft)
T-O to 15 m (50 ft): A	520 m (1,706 ft)
B	625 m (2,050 ft)
Landing from 15 m (50 ft): A	663 m (2,176 ft)
B	747 m (2,450 ft)
Range with max fuel at 3,050 m (10,000 ft), with 113.5 litres (30 US gallons; 20.8 Imp gallons) reserves:	
A	1,322 nm (2,451 km; 1,523 miles)
B	1,547 nm (2,867 km; 1,782 miles)

FAIRCHILD AIRCRAFT
FAIRCHILD AIRCRAFT CORPORATION

PO Box 790490, San Antonio, Texas 78279-0490
Telephone: 1 (512) 824 9421
Telex: 767-315
Fax: 1 (512) 820 8690
PRESIDENT: Ron McKelvey

In December 1987 Fairchild Industries completed the sale of Metro Aviation, which owned 97 per cent of the stock of Fairchild Aircraft Corporation, to GMF Investments Inc. In February 1990 Fairchild Aircraft sought protection under Chapter 11 of US bankruptcy laws, and closed all but essential operations pending revised financing arrangements. At that time the company had a backlog of orders for 25 aircraft and had 11 in the process of final assembly, two of which were subsequently delivered to Air Sardinia in February 1990.

FAIRCHILD MODEL SA227-AC METRO III and EXPEDITER I
Swedish Air Force designation: Tp88
US military designation: C-26A/B

The **Metro III** is a 19/20-passenger all-weather pressurised, air-conditioned airliner, certificated under the FAA's Special Federal Air Regulations 41 and 41B, which provide for compliance with ICAO Annex 8 specifications for operation at a gross weight in excess of 5,670 kg (12,500 lb). The standard Metro III is certificated for operation at a max T-O weight of 6,577 kg (14,500 lb), providing a useful load of 2,354 kg (5,190 lb). The optional high gross weight version of the Metro III has a max T-O weight of 7,257 kg (16,000 lb). British CAA certification was achieved in August 1988, following modifications that include a new dual-redundant stall avoidance system, dual continuous alcohol/water injection system, externally operable escape hatches, and a modified aileron aerofoil section. Britavia of the UK assisted Fairchild in carrying out the modifications.

The changes from the Metro II include a 3.05 m (10 ft 0 in) increase in wing span; more powerful engines, each driving a slow-turning four-blade propeller; new main landing gear doors, to improve take-off and landing performance and provide better access for maintenance; new streamline nacelle cowlings, with quick-action latches and hinged at the rear to improve engine access; improved handling characteristics; and new fire prevention and containment features, with all inflammable fluid pipework isolated physically from all electric current-carrying components and wiring. The Metro III is certificated for flight into known icing conditions, and has lightning strike protection which the company claims is equal to that in the latest generation of commercial jet transports.

One Metro III was delivered to the Swedish Air Force for use as a VIP transport, and is known in Swedish service as the **Tp88**. In March 1988 Fairchild received an order for six Metro IIIs, later increased to 13. By 1 May 1990, ten of these had been delivered to the US Air National Guard under the designation **C-26A**. Subsequent orders included one **C-26B** and a further nine aircraft in FY 1990. The aircraft, which serve in the ANGOSTA (Air National Guard Operational Support Transport Aircraft) role, were delivered from March 1989. They have a quick-change interior, enabling passenger seats to be replaced by a medevac or all-cargo carrying configuration.

The all-cargo version, known as the **Expediter I**, has cabin air-conditioning ducts repositioned to increase cargo space, reinforced cabin floor, cargo nets and guards, and a reduced empty weight which permits a max cargo payload of more than 2,268 kg (5,000 lb). First operator of the Expediter was SAT-AIR, on behalf of United Parcel Service. In April 1985 the first of ten Expediter Is was

Fairchild Metro III commuter airliner (two Garrett TPE331 turboprops) *(Pilot Press)*

delivered to the US small package carrier DHL Worldwide Courier Express. This version has structurally reinforced landing gear and main spar to permit an increase in max T-O weight to 7,257 kg (16,000 lb).

Fairchild delivered 12 Metro IIIs during 1989.

TYPE: Twin-turboprop 19/20-passenger commuter airliner.

WINGS: Cantilever low-wing monoplane. Wing section NACA 65_2A215 at root, NACA 64_2A415 at tip. Dihedral 5°. Incidence 1° at root, −2° 30′ at tip. Sweepback at quarter-chord 0° 54′. All-metal two-spar fail-safe structure of aluminium alloy, constructed in one piece. The main spar beams have laminated caps and these, in the centre-section, have titanium laminations. Hydraulically operated double-slotted trailing-edge flaps. Manually controlled trim tab in each aileron. Goodrich pneumatic de-icing boots on wing leading-edges, with automatic bleed air cycling system.

FUSELAGE: All-metal cylindrical semi-monocoque fail-safe structure of 2024 aluminium alloy, flush riveted throughout. All but the nose section is pressurised. Glassfibre honeycomb nosecap can accommodate a 0.46 m (18 in) weather radar antenna.

TAIL UNIT: Cantilever all-metal structure with sweptback surfaces and dorsal fin. Small ventral fin. Electrically adjustable variable incidence tailplane. Manually controlled rudder trim. Goodrich pneumatic de-icing boots on tailplane leading-edges, with automatic bleed air cycling system.

LANDING GEAR: Retractable tricycle type with twin wheels on each unit. Hydraulic retraction, with dual actuators on each unit. All wheels retract forward, main gear into engine nacelles, nosewheels into fuselage. Ozone Aircraft Systems oleo-pneumatic shock absorber struts. Nosewheel steerable, maximum steering angle 63° either side of centre. Free-fall emergency extension system, with backup of hand operated hydraulic pump. Goodrich mainwheels with low-pressure tubeless tyres, size 19.5 × 6.75-8, type VII. Jay-Em nosewheels and Goodyear low-pressure tubeless tyres, size 18 × 4.40, type VII. Tyre pressures: nosewheel at standard T-O weight 3.79 bars

(55 lb/sq in), at optional increased T-O weight 4.76 bars (69 lb/sq in); mainwheels at standard T-O weight 5.60 bars (87 lb/sq in), at optional T-O weight 7.10 bars (103 lb/sq in). Goodrich self-adjusting hydraulically operated disc brakes and anti-skid system.

POWER PLANT: Two 745.5 kW (1,000 shp) dry/820 kW (1,100 shp) wet Garrett TPE331-11U-612G turboprops with continuous alcohol/water injection system, each driving a McCauley four-blade constant-speed fully-feathering reversible-pitch metal propeller with spinner. Automatic propeller synchrophasing, and full Beta control reversing, standard. In-flight windmill start capability. Integral fuel tank in each wing, each with a usable capacity of 1,226 litres (324 US gallons; 270 Imp gallons). Total usable fuel capacity 2,452 litres (648 US gallons; 540 Imp gallons). Refuelling point on each outer wing panel. Automatic fuel heating. Oil capacity 15.1 litres (4 US gallons; 3.3 Imp gallons). Alcohol/water tank in nose, capacity 60.5 litres (16 US gallons; 13.3 Imp gallons), with two pumps to pump fluid to engines. Engine inlet de-icing by bleed air. Electric oil cooler inlet anti-icing. Electric propeller de-icing. Flush mounted fuel vents. Single-point rapid defuelling provisions. Negative torque sensing, single red line/autostart, automatic engine temperature limiting, and engine fire extinguishing systems.

ACCOMMODATION: Crew of two on flight deck, each with four-way adjustable seat with folding armrests and shoulder harness, separated from passenger/cargo area by partial bulkhead on port side and armrest height curtain on starboard side. Dual controls standard. Bulkhead between cabin and flight deck optional. Standard accommodation for 19-20 passengers seated two abreast, on each side of centre aisle. 'No smoking' and 'Fasten seat belt' signs. High-back, tracking, quickly-removable passenger seats standard. Interior convertible to all-cargo or mixed passenger/cargo configuration with movable bulkhead between passenger and cargo sections. Snap-in carpeting. Self-stowing aisle filler. Tiedown fittings for cargo at 0.76 m (30 in) spacing. Integral-step passenger door on port side of fuselage, immediately aft of flight deck. Large cargo loading door

Fairchild Expediter I twin-turboprop cargo aircraft of DHL Worldwide Courier Express

on port side of fuselage at rear of cabin, hinged at top. Three window emergency exits, one on the port, two on the starboard side. Forward baggage/avionics compartment in nose, capacity 363 kg (800 lb). Pressurised rear cargo compartment, capacity 385 kg (850 lb). Cabin air-conditioned and pressurised. Electric windscreen de-icing. Two-speed windscreen wipers.

SYSTEMS: AiResearch automatic cabin pressure control system: max differential 0.48 bars (7.0 lb/sq in), providing a sea level cabin altitude to 5,120 m (16,800 ft). Engine bleed air heating, dual air cycle cooling system, with automatic temperature control. Air blower system for on-ground ventilation. Independent hydraulic system for brakes. Dual engine driven hydraulic pumps, using fire resistant MIL-H-83282 hydraulic fluid, provide 138 bars (2,000 lb/sq in) to operate flaps, landing gear actuators and nosewheel steering. Hydraulic system flow rates 30.3 litres (8 US gallons; 6.7 Imp gallons)/min at idle power, both engines; 46.7 litres (12.34 US gallons; 10.27 Imp gallons)/min at T-O and climb power. Air/oil reservoir, pressure 2.27 bars (33 lb/sq in). Electrical system supplied by two 300A 28V DC starter/generators. Fail-safe system with overload and overvoltage protection. Redundant circuits for essential systems. Two 350VA solid state inverters supply 115V and 26V AC. Two SAFT 24V 23Ah nickel-cadmium batteries for main services. Engine fire detection system and fire extinguishing system standard. Wing overheat detection system. Oxygen system of 1.39 m³ (49 cu ft) capacity with flush outlets at each seat; system with capacity of 5.04 m³ (178 cu ft) optional. Stall avoidance system comprising angle indicator, visual and aural warning.

AVIONICS AND EQUIPMENT: Two flight deck and four cabin speakers standard; provisions for installation of remotely mounted or panel mounted avionics, customer furnished weather radar and autopilot. Standard equipment includes pilot and co-pilot foot warmers; edge lit consoles, pedestal and switch panels; integrally lit instruments; annunciator panel with 48 indicators; internally operated control locks, individual reading lights and air vents for each passenger; heated pitot; heated static sources; baggage compartment, cargo compartment, entrance, map and instrument panel, ice inspection, retractable landing, navigation, rotating beacon and taxi lights; automatic engine start cycle; external power socket; and static wicks.

DIMENSIONS, EXTERNAL:

Wing span	17.37 m (57 ft 0 in)
Wing mean aerodynamic chord	1.84 m (6 ft 0⅓ in)
Wing aspect ratio	10.5
Length overall	18.09 m (59 ft 4¼ in)
Height overall	5.08 m (16 ft 8 in)
Tailplane span	4.86 m (15 ft 11½ in)
Wheel track	4.57 m (15 ft 0 in)
Wheelbase	5.83 m (19 ft 1½ in)
Propeller diameter	2.69 m (8 ft 10 in)
Passenger door (fwd): Height	1.35 m (4 ft 5 in)
Width	0.64 m (2 ft 1 in)
Cargo door (rear): Height	1.30 m (4 ft 3¼ in)
Width	1.35 m (4 ft 5 in)
Height to sill	1.30 m (4 ft 3¼ in)
Forward baggage doors (two, each):	
Height	0.64 m (2 ft 1 in)
Width	0.46 m (1 ft 6 in)
Emergency exits (three, each):	
Height	0.71 m (2 ft 4 in)
Width	0.51 m (1 ft 8 in)

DIMENSIONS, INTERNAL:

Cabin, excl flight deck and rear cargo compartment:	
Length	7.75 m (25 ft 5 in)
Max width	1.57 m (5 ft 2 in)
Max height (aisle)	1.45 m (4 ft 9 in)
Floor area	13.01 m² (140.0 sq ft)
Volume	13.88 m³ (490.0 cu ft)
Rear cargo compartment (pressurised):	
Length	2.34 m (7 ft 8 in)
Max width	1.57 m (5 ft 2 in)
Max height	1.32 m (4 ft 4 in)
Volume	4.06 m³ (143.5 cu ft)
Nose cargo compartment (unpressurised):	
Length	1.75 m (5 ft 9 in)
Volume	0.85 m³ (30.0 cu ft)

Fairchild Merlin IV C twin-turboprop corporate transport

AREAS:

Wings, gross	28.71 m² (309.0 sq ft)
Ailerons (total)	1.31 m² (14.12 sq ft)
Trailing-edge flaps (total)	3.78 m² (40.66 sq ft)
Fin, incl dorsal fin	3.40 m² (36.62 sq ft)
Rudder, incl tab	1.80 m² (19.38 sq ft)
Tailplane	5.08 m² (54.70 sq ft)
Elevators	1.98 m² (21.27 sq ft)

WEIGHTS AND LOADINGS:

*Operating weight empty:	
Commuter	4,268 kg (9,410 lb)
Expediter	4,137 kg (9,120 lb)
Max fuel weight	1,969 kg (4,342 lb)
Max T-O weight: standard	6,577 kg (14,500 lb)
optional	7,257 kg (16,000 lb)
Max ramp weight: standard	6,622 kg (14,600 lb)
optional	7,303 kg (16,100 lb)
Max zero-fuel weight	6,305 kg (13,900 lb)
Max landing weight: standard	6,350 kg (14,000 lb)
optional	7,031 kg (15,500 lb)
Max wing loading	252.8 kg/m² (51.78 lb/sq ft)
Max power loading	4.42 kg/kW (7.27 lb/shp)

*increased by 38 kg (84 lb) for aircraft with optional T-O weight of 7,257 kg (16,000 lb)

PERFORMANCE (at max T-O weight of 6,577 kg; 14,500 lb, ISA, except where indicated):

Design diving speed	
	311 knots (576 km/h; 358 mph) CAS
Max operating speed	
	248 knots (459 km/h; 285 mph) CAS
Max operating Mach No.	0.52
Max cruising speed at mid-cruise weight of 5,670 kg (12,500 lb):	
at 4,575 m (15,000 ft)	
	279 knots (517 km/h; 321 mph)
at 6,100 m (20,000 ft)	
	274 knots (508 km/h; 316 mph)
at 7,620 m (25,000 ft)	
	263 knots (487 km/h; 303 mph)
Long-range cruising speed at 7,620 m (25,000 ft)	
	252 knots (467 km/h; 290 mph)
Min single-engine control speed (VMC)	
	91 knots (169 km/h; 105 mph) IAS
Stalling speed:	
flaps and wheels up	
	98 knots (182 km/h; 113 mph) IAS
flaps and wheels down	
	85 knots (158 km/h; 98 mph) IAS
Max rate of climb at S/L	722 m (2,370 ft)/min
Rate of climb at S/L, one engine out	225 m (740 ft)/min
Service ceiling	8,140 m (26,700 ft)
Service ceiling, one engine out	4,420 m (14,500 ft)
Min turning radius: about nosewheel	6.55 m (21 ft 6 in)
about wingtip	11.73 m (38 ft 6 in)
T-O to 15 m (50 ft), dry power	1,020 m (3,340 ft)
Landing from 15 m (50 ft)	747 m (2,450 ft)

Range with max fuel, 252 knots (467 km/h; 290 mph) at 8,230 m (27,000 ft), allowances for start, T-O, climb and descent, plus 45 min reserves:

at max T-O weight of 6,577 kg (14,500 lb)
    384 nm (711 km; 442 miles)
at max T-O weight of 7,257 kg (16,000 lb)
    1,063 nm (1,970 km; 1,224 miles)

FAIRCHILD SPECIAL MISSION AIRCRAFT

Fairchild offers a variety of aircraft, designed specifically for special mission applications, some 35 examples of which have been delivered. Variations based on the Metro III include models for maritime patrol, anti-submarine warfare, flight navigation systems inspection, photo reconnaissance, electronic intelligence, airborne early warning and airborne critical care missions. The maritime patrol variant has a 360° scan Litton AN/APS-504(V), (V)5, or AIL AN/APS-128D radar in an underbelly blister fairing, an Omega nav system linked to hand held cameras, and two bulged observation windows, staggered one on each side of the rear fuselage. The ASW version carries sonobuoys and a sonobuoy signal processor, an OTP indicator, and MAD tailboom. Optional equipment for both versions includes a searchlight, IR linescanner, low light level TV, FLIR, side-looking TV, Doppler radar, droppable liferafts and survival kits, and two 288 litre (76 US gallon; 63 Imp gallon) underwing auxiliary fuel tanks. At a max T-O weight of 7,257 kg (16,000 lb), and with underwing tanks, the surveillance versions can complete a 10 hour mission over a radius of 1,050 nm (1,946 km; 1,209 miles) from base, at a height of 7,620 m (25,000 ft) and with 45 min fuel reserves.

In 1982 the Swedish Defence Materiel Administration (FMV) contracted Fairchild Aircraft Corporation to begin studies for an airborne early warning variant of the Metro III incorporating an active array radar housed in a dorsal antenna. Initial wind tunnel testing was conducted in LTV's Dallas facility during 1983, and in early 1986 the FMV ordered a Metro III to test the Ericsson PS-890 static, electronically scanned E/F band radar, which scans one side at a time in a 120° arc. The aircraft was first flown in October 1986 with a mockup antenna, and completed 116 hours of aerodynamic and handling tests with Fairchild before it was delivered to Sweden in early October 1987 for installation and integration of mission electronics and data link by Ericsson Radio and other subcontractors. The aircraft was exhibited at the 1988 Farnborough Air Show and was expected to make its first flight with an operating radar in early 1990.

The radar is carried in a 9.14 m (30 ft) long housing of composite construction which is mounted on pylons on top of the fuselage. A ram air cooling intake is incorporated in the forward end of the housing, and an exhaust outlet at the rear. The antenna is inclined at an incidence of −2°, permitting the Metro III to be flown at the high angle of attack/low airspeeds dictated by the FMV's requirement for long endurance while maintaining the antenna in a horizontal position. Sweptback vertical auxiliary fins or 'tail-lets' have been added to the upper and lower surfaces of the tailplane, and a larger ventral fin installed to enhance directional stability. 60kVA of electrical power for the radar is provided by a Turbomach T-62T APU, installed in an E-Systems pod carried on a centreline stores station beneath the wing centre-section. Other modifications include the installation of a periscope sight in the flight deck roof, and a larger emergency exit on the port side of the cabin. No decision has been announced on the choice of data link that will connect the radar with Sweden's STRIL 60/90 air defence system. Provisional performance data include loiter speeds of 135-146 knots (250-270 km/h; 155-168 mph) with flaps at 50 per cent, 164-175 knots (305-325 km/h; 189-202 mph) with flaps at 25 per cent, and an endurance of 4-6 h in a patrol area 100 nm (185 km; 115 miles) away from base. Sweden has a requirement for 10-15 such surveillance aircraft.

FAIRCHILD MERLIN IV C (SA227-AT)

The Merlin IV C is a corporate version of the Metro III commuter airliner, differing primarily in its internal configuration. It has reclining passenger seats, couches, and a more luxurious standard of interior furniture, decor and lighting. The refreshment and entertainment centre includes

Fairchild Metro III Special Missions Aircraft with dorsal antenna housing for Ericsson PS-890 radar
(Mike Jerram)

a large buffet cabinet with beverage and food storage and preparation facilities, television and stereo equipment. At the rear of the cabin, separated by a bulkhead and hinged door, are a toilet and baggage compartment.

The Merlin IV C is certificated under SFAR Pt 41B and ICAO Annex 8 specifications, and has a max T-O and landing weight of 6,577 kg (14,500 lb) or, optionally, 7,257 kg (16,000 lb). Its large cabin volume, and the availability of movable bulkheads and interchangeable cabin furnishings, makes it easily convertible to meet a company's airlift requirements in virtually any arrangement of passengers and/or cargo. By January 1990 a total of 24 Merlin IV Cs had been delivered.

The description and specification of the Metro III apply also to the Merlin IV C, except as follows:
TYPE: Eleven/fourteen-passenger corporate transport.
AVIONICS AND EQUIPMENT: In late 1986 the Merlin IV C was certificated for a Bendix/King KFC 400 flight control system with KNS 660 flight management system integrated with the Bendix EFIS-10 five-tube electronic flight instrument system comprising two ADIs, two HSIs and a multi-function display.
WEIGHTS AND LOADINGS: As Metro III, except:
Weight empty, equipped   4,472 kg (9,860 lb)
PERFORMANCE (at max T-O weight, ISA, except where indicated):
Max cruising speed, at mid-cruise weight of 5,670 kg (12,500 lb):
at 3,050-4,575 m (10,000-15,000 ft)
                              283 knots (524 km/h; 326 mph)
at 6,100 m (20,000 ft)   281 knots (521 km/h; 323 mph)
at 7,620 m (25,000 ft)   273 knots (506 km/h; 314 mph)
Max rate of climb at S/L   803 m (2,635 ft)/min
Rate of climb at S/L, one engine out   198 m (650 ft)/min

Range with max standard fuel, max cruise power at 7,925 m (26,000 ft), 45 min reserves:
  eight occupants   1,578 nm (2,924 km; 1,817 miles)
  thirteen occupants   1,036 nm (1,920 km; 1,193 miles)
Ferry range, conditions and allowances as above, but with two flight crew only
                         2,071 nm (3,838 km; 2,384 miles)

FAIRCHILD METRO V (SA228-AE)
Development of this proposed T tail, twin-turboprop commuter airliner was discontinued in 1989.

FAIRCHILD METRO 25 (SA227-DC)
In October 1989 Fairchild Aircraft announced development of the Metro 25, a 25-seat modification of the 19-20 seat Metro III commuter airliner. Additional passenger accommodation has been provided by installing six seats in the Metro III's rear baggage area. Three additional windows have been added to the rear cabin on the left side, and two on the right, with an additional emergency exit at mid-cabin on each side. The Metro III's large cargo door is eliminated. A ventral cargo pod of sheet metal construction with glassfibre fairings compensates for loss of internal baggage stowage, and has a volume of 3.54 m³ (125 cu ft), with two doors on the port side: forward, height 1.22 m (4 ft 0 in), width 0.44 m (1 ft 5½ in); rear, height 1.52 m (5 ft 0 in), width 0.44 m (1 ft 5½ in). Other changes planned for production aircraft include uprated 820 kW (1,100 shp) Garrett TPE331-12 turboprops giving more reserve power for hot-and-high take-offs; and modification of wing spars, addition of dual cable control systems, eyebrow windows in the cockpit roof, additional emergency lighting, and cockpit voice and flight data recorders to meet FAR 25 certification requirements. Max T-O weight is 7,710 kg (17,000 lb).

A prototype (N2671V) based on a modified Metro III airframe, made its first flight on 25 September 1989 and was being used to assess preliminary handling performance and flight characteristics prior to a production decision. FAA certification and first customer deliveries are anticipated in early 1992. Customers for the Metro 25 include Air Sardinia, which has options on two aircraft.

In late 1989 Fairchild was also studying a possible turbofan version of the Metro 25, powered by Garrett TFE731 power plants, with a cruising speed of 400 knots (741 km/h; 460 mph). The engines would be mounted within the existing nacelle structure, with much of the aircraft being manufactured on existing tooling.

Fairchild 25-passenger Metro 25 (two 820 kW; 1,100 shp Garrett TPE331-12 turboprops) *(Pilot Press)*

FANSTAR
FANSTAR PARTNERS
Bryn Mawr, Pennsylvania

This company is developing the **Fanstar 200T** four-seat piston engined ducted fan aircraft, based on the Rhein-Flugzeugbau Fantrainer military trainer, which is described in the German section of this edition. The Fanstar 200T, general configuration of which is shown in the accompanying artist's impression, features wings, movable tail surfaces and cabin of composites materials, with all-metal rear fuselage and fixed tail surfaces. The power plant is a 261 kW (350 hp) Teledyne Continental TSIO(L)-550 turbocharged liquid-cooled engine mounted at the rear of the cabin and driving a five-blade ducted fan. Electronic fuel control and ignition systems, and 'single lever' power control, are standard. Fuel is contained in integral wing tanks and optional underwing slipper tanks. Standard equipment will include Narco IFR avionics and an S-Tec autopilot.

Fanstar Partners was expecting to conclude an agreement with Rhein-Flugzeugbau in Spring 1990 to enable it to proceed with design, construction, certification and flight testing of two prototype Fanstar 200Ts, and was seeking funding for production. The following data are provisional:
DIMENSIONS, EXTERNAL:
Wing span   10.52 m (34 ft 6 in)
Length overall   8.53 m (28 ft 0 in)
Height overall   2.98 m (9 ft 9½ in)
WEIGHTS:
Weight empty   1,050 kg (2,315 lb)
Max fuel weight: standard tanks   329 kg (725 lb)
  with slipper tanks   465 kg (1,025 lb)
Max T-O weight   1,701 kg (3,750 lb)
PERFORMANCE (estimated):
Max cruising speed   230 knots (426 km/h; 265 mph)

Artist's impression of the Fanstar 200T four-seat ducted fan light aircraft

Cruising speed, 80% power
                     212 knots (393 km/h; 244 mph)
Stalling speed   56 knots (104 km/h; 65 mph)
Max rate of climb at S/L   427 m (1,400 ft)/min
T-O run   299 m (980 ft)

Landing run   275 m (900 ft)
Range, 80% power:
  with standard fuel   1,173 nm (2,173 km; 1,350 miles)
  with auxiliary tanks 1,651 nm (3,059 km; 1,901 miles)

GARRETT
GARRETT GENERAL AVIATION SERVICES DIVISION
(Division of Allied Signal Aerospace Company)
Los Angeles International Airport, 6201 West Imperial Highway, Los Angeles, California 90045
Telephone: 1 (213) 568 3700
Telex: 181827 A/B AIRE AVI LSA
Fax: 1 (213) 568 3790
VICE-PRESIDENT, MARKETING & SALES: Richard A. Graser

GARRETT 731 FALCON 20 RETROFIT PROGRAMME
In May 1987 Garrett General Aviation Services announced plans to offer an engine retrofit to operators of Dassault Aviation Mystère-Falcon 20 business jets. The modification, developed in conjunction with the French manufacturer, involves replacing the Falcon 20's General Electric CF700 power plant with Garrett TFE731-5AR turbofans. Dassault Aviation (which see, in the French section of this edition) developed a new engine pylon with improved aerodynamics for the conversion, which uses engine nacelles identical to those of the Falcon 900.

The first development aircraft, a Falcon 20F (F-WTFE), made its first flight with TFE731 engines from Bordeaux-Mérignac on 7 October 1988, and was followed by a Falcon 20C (F-WTFF) on 26 January 1989, leading to certification in France and the United States in March 1989.

The TFE731 retrofit increases the range of Falcon 20s by up to 50 per cent, and enables them to meet FAR Pt 36 Stage 3 noise standards. The range of a C model is increased to

2,040 nm (3,780 km; 2,349 miles); of a D or E model to 2,230 nm (4,132 km; 2,567 miles); and of an F model to 2,260 nm (4,188 km; 2,602 miles). In each case a payload of eight passengers is assumed, operating at a speed of Mach 0.72 with NBAA IFR fuel reserves.

The 731 Falcon 20 retrofit can be undertaken by Garrett General Aviation Services facilities at Los Angeles, California, or Springfield, Illinois; Falcon Jet Service Center in Little Rock, Arkansas; Europe Falcon Service, Le Bourget Airport, Paris; and TransAirCo, Geneva, Switzerland. Modified aircraft are identified by a -5 suffix to their designations (eg Falcon 20F-5). By the end of January 1990 a total of 22 Falcon 20s of all models had undergone retrofits, including the first to be completed in Europe, a Falcon 20C-5 for Hennessy-Moet et Cie delivered on 6 July 1989 after modification by Europe Falcon Service. Dee Howard TR-5020 thrust reversers have been certificated for the Garrett 731 Falcon and are available as an option.

Garrett 731 Falcon 20C-5 (TFE731-5AR turbofans)

GATES LEARJET — *See Learjet Corporation*

GENERAL DYNAMICS
GENERAL DYNAMICS CORPORATION
Pierre Laclede Center, St Louis, Missouri 63105
Telephone: 1 (314) 889 8200
Telex: 6841036
Fax: 1 (314) 889 8839
CHAIRMAN AND CHIEF EXECUTIVE OFFICER: Stanley C. Pace
PRESIDENT AND CHIEF OPERATING OFFICER:
  Herbert F. Rogers
Convair Division:
PO Box 85357, San Diego, California 92138
Telephone: 1 (619) 573 8000
CORPORATE VICE-PRESIDENT AND GENERAL MANAGER:
  John E. McSweeny
VICE-CHAIRMAN: William A. Anders
VICE-PRESIDENT, RESEARCH AND ENGINEERING:
  J. William Vega
Fort Worth Division:
PO Box 748, Fort Worth, Texas 76101
Telephone: 1 (817) 777 2000
CORPORATE VICE-PRESIDENT AND GENERAL MANAGER:
  Charles A. Anderson
VICE-PRESIDENT, F-16 PROGRAMME DIRECTOR: D. M. Hancock
VICE-PRESIDENT, F-16 ENGINEERING: J. D. Engelland
VICE-PRESIDENT, RESEARCH AND ENGINEERING:
  E. M. Petrushka
VICE-PRESIDENT, PROGRAMME DEVELOPMENT:
  A. D. Mayfield
General Dynamics conducts its US aerospace activities at Convair Division, with operations at San Diego, California; Fort Worth Division, with operations at Fort Worth, Texas; Pomona Division, with headquarters at Pomona, California; Electronics Division, with headquarters in San Diego; Valley Systems Division, with headquarters at Rancho Cucamonga, California; Space Systems Division, with headquarters in San Diego; and, since acquisition in March 1985, at Cessna Aircraft Company, Wichita (which see). Convair Division is responsible for the design, development and production of offensive missile systems and aircraft structures. Fort Worth Division is engaged in the design, development and production of military aircraft and electronics. Pomona Division is engaged in the development and production of tactical missile and gun systems. Electronics Division is involved in new technology to support the development and production of advanced electronic systems. Valley Systems Division produces Stinger and RAM missiles, and is developing terminally guided submunitions.

Fort Worth is currently responsible for production of the F-16 Fighting Falcon multi-role fighter; spares, support and modification/update for the F-111 fighter-bomber; development, in association with Lockheed and Boeing Military Airplanes, of the YF-22A Advanced Tactical Fighter (see under US Air Force Systems Command); and various ground based radar systems. Convair Division retains detailed tooling for high usage spares for the Convair-Liner 240/340/440 series of piston-engined transports, and continues to manufacture components for these types.

GENERAL DYNAMICS F-111
Details of F-111 upgrade and modification programmes can be found under the Rockwell and US Air Force headings in this section and under BAe in the UK section.

GENERAL DYNAMICS/MCDONNELL DOUGLAS A-12
Details of the A-12 Avenger II programme are given under a separate General Dynamics/McDonnell Douglas heading.

GENERAL DYNAMICS F-16 and A-16 FIGHTING FALCON
The F-16 had its origin in the US Air Force's Lightweight Fighter (LWF) prototype programme, in 1972. The history of this programme and a description of the YF-16 prototypes can be found in the 1978-79 and 1977-78 editions of *Jane's* respectively.

The first of two YF-16 prototypes (72-01567) made its official first flight on 2 February 1974 and was followed by the second YF-16 (72-01568) on 9 May 1974. On 13 January 1975 the Secretary of the US Air Force announced that the F-16 had been selected for full scale engineering development. The original YF-16 requirement for an air superiority day fighter was expanded, to give equal emphasis to the air-to-surface role, including provision of radar and all-weather navigation capabilities. The manufacture of eight pre-production aircraft, comprising six single-seat **F-16As** and two two-seat **F-16Bs**, began in July 1975. The first full scale development F-16A made its first flight on 8 December 1976, and the first F-16B on 8 August 1977.

Initially, the US Air Force planned to procure a total of 650 F-16s. This was increased first to 1,388 aircraft, including 204 two-seaters, to replace McDonnell Douglas F-4s in the active force and to modernise the Air Force Reserve and Air National Guard, and subsequently to a planned total of 2,799, of which 2,474 had been contracted and 1,583 delivered by 1 January 1990. Excluding two prototypes and eight pre-series aircraft (two of them tandem-seat), the USAF ordered 665 F-16As and 121 F-16Bs up to FY 1983. Orders for later versions placed in FY 1983-87 covered 623 F-16Cs and 105 F-16Ds, whilst a further 960 F-16C/Ds are covered by FY 1988-FY 1993 multi-year contracts. In addition, 16 other air forces have ordered a total of 1,300 F-16s (for details see 1986-87 *Jane's*). Production at Fort Worth for the USAF continues at the rate of 180 a year for FY 1990-93 multi-year contracts. By January 1990 deliveries to all customers from Fort Worth totalled 2,006, with a further 510 delivered from European assembly lines in Belgium, the Netherlands and Turkey.

Current operational, experimental and planned or proposed versions of the F-16 are as follows:

A-16. Proposed close air support (CAS)/battlefield air interdiction (BAI) version for US Air Force, based on modified aircraft from current procurement. Under the Bush Administration's FY 1990/91 budget proposals, 146 F-16s will be modified to meet USAF requirements, supplementing 225 updated Fairchild Republic A-10As. Potential exists for use of new and/or additional retrofit F-16s and a dedicated CAS/BAI role with only minor upgrades to communications and target cueing capability. Ballistic hardening and night capability options are being considered. In the Spring of 1989 the first Air National Guard unit, the 138th TFS at Syracuse, NY, converted from A-10As to F-16As in the dedicated CAS/BAI role. The aircraft were modified to carry the GPU-5/A 30 mm gun pod on the centreline station. Incorporation of an automatic target hand-off system (ATHS) is planned.

F-16A. First production version, for air-to-air and air-to-surface roles. Production for USAF completed in March 1985, but still available to other customers. Pratt & Whitney F100-PW-200 turbofan, rated at approx 106.0 kN (23,830 lb st) with afterburning. Westinghouse AN/APG-66 pulse-Doppler range and angle track radar. First aircraft (78-0001) flew for the first time on 7 August 1978. Entered service with USAF's 388th Tactical Fighter Wing at Hill AFB, Utah, on 6 January 1979, and achieved combat-ready status in October 1980, in which year the name **Fighting Falcon** was adopted. Standard equipment in TAC, USAFE, PACAF, ANG and AFRES, and with the Thunderbirds air demonstration squadron. Operated also by the air forces of Belgium, Denmark, Egypt, Indonesia, Israel, the Netherlands, Norway, Pakistan, Singapore, Thailand and Venezuela. Portugal will acquire 17 F-16As and three F-16Bs from new production. Extension of fin root fairing houses Loral Rapport ECM in Israeli F-16As and F-16Bs, a braking parachute in aircraft for Norway, Indonesia, Netherlands (retrofit) and Venezuela, and will be retrofitted with ESD Carapace ECM on Belgian F-16s. The F-16s of the Pakistan Air Force carry Thomson-CSF Atlis laser target designation pods. Further details of service history may be found in the 1986-87 and earlier editions of *Jane's*.

USAF and NATO operators are co-operating in an operational capabilities upgrade (OCU) programme to

General Dynamics F-16C (GE F110 engine) with extra side view of two-seat F-16D (P&W F100)
(Pilot Press)

enable F-16A/Bs to utilise next-generation air-to-air and air-to-surface weapons systems. Changes will be made to existing radar systems and software, and the aircraft's fire control and stores management computers will be improved. A data transfer unit and combined altitude radar altimeter will be installed. Reliability/maintainability improvements in the early 1990s include a ring laser gyro INS and an upgrade of the F100-PW-200 engine to the F100-PW-220E configuration.

The next major upgrade being planned for the F-16A/B is the Mid-Life Update (MLU). Changes include an advanced cockpit similar to the F-16C/D including a wide angle HUD, cockpit compatibility with night vision goggles, a modular mission computer to replace three existing computers, digital terrain system, fire control radar upgrade to the APG-66(V2A) configuration, GPS/Navstar, automatic target hand-off system, and provisions for a microwave landing system. Inlet hardpoints and associated wiring for FLIR pods will be added to pre-Block 15 aircraft. Options include advanced IFF interrogator/transponder and a helmet-mounted display. Current plans are to begin development in 1991 and modify at least 500 aircraft for the USAF and four western European countries beginning in 1996 in a co-development/co-production effort.

F-16(ADF). In October 1986 the USAF awarded General Dynamics a contract to modify a total of 270 Block 15 F-16As and Bs as air defence fighters (ADF) to replace F-4s and F-106s in eleven Air National Guard continental air defence squadrons. F-16(ADF) modifications include upgrading of the aircraft's Westinghouse AN/APG-66 radar to enhance small-target detection; provision of an AMRAAM data link; improved ECCM; Bendix/King AN/ARC-200 HF/SSB radio; Teledyne/E-Systems advanced IFF; provisions for GPS/Navstar; low altitude warning; voice message unit; and a night identification light. The aircraft are also modified to carry two AIM-7 Sparrow missiles. The first successful guided launch of an AIM-7 from an F-16 was made at the Pacific Missile Test Center at Point Mugu, California, in February 1989 as part of the ADF programme. Alternatively the F-16(ADF) can carry up to six AIM-120 AMRAAM or AIM-9 Sidewinder missiles, or combinations of all three air-to-air weapons, and retains the M61 20 mm gun. Under the provisions of the contract General Dynamics is producing ADF modification kits for installation by the US Air Force's Ogden Air Logistics Center, Utah, in conjunction with the F-16A/B OCU programme.

In 1990, developmental flight testing was due to be completed at Edwards AFB, and follow-on operational test and evaluation begun at the 57th Fighter Weapons Wing at Nellis AFB, Nevada. The first ADF-modified F-16 was delivered to the 114th Tactical Fighter Training Squadron at Kingsley Field, Oregon, on 1 March 1989. IOC was achieved in 1989 with the 194th Fighter Interceptor Wing, California ANG, at Fresno, and by the end of that year a total of four interceptor squadrons (119, 159, 186 and 194) were flying the ADF version. During 1990, six more interceptor squadrons were to convert from F-4Ds to standard F-16A/Bs.

F-16B. Two-seat variant of F-16A with two cockpits in tandem, each fully systems-operational. Service use as for F-16A. Length unchanged.

F-16C/D. Single-seat (F-16C) and two-seat (F-16D) versions embodying results of USAF Multinational Staged Improvement Programme (MSIP) implemented in February 1980. MSIP expands the aircraft's growth capability to incorporate systems for ground attack and beyond-visual-range intercept missions by day and night, and in all weather conditions. Stage I of the programme, introduced on Block 15 F-16A and F-16B aircraft delivered from November 1981, included wiring and structural provisions for emerging systems. Stage II, applicable to Block 25 production deliveries of F-16C and F-16D aircraft from July 1984, incorporates core avionics, cockpit and other airframe changes. Stage III involves selected installation of advanced systems as these become available.

The only external feature distinguishing the F-16C from the F-16A is a slightly expanded forward tail fin root fairing to house ASPJ (airborne self-protection jamming) when it becomes available. Internal changes include a Westinghouse AN/APG-68 multi-mode radar offering increased range, sharper resolution, expanded modes and advanced ECCM by comparison with the AN/APG-66; an advanced cockpit with improved pilot/vehicle interface, including up-front controls, two multi-function displays, radar altimeter, GEC Avionics wide-angle HUD and Fairchild mission data transfer equipment; avionics growth capability through increases in both the speed and memory of core computers; increased capacity electrical power and cooling systems; structural changes for increased max T-O weight and gross weight manoeuvring limits; and MIL-STD-1760 weapons interface to provide compatibility with advanced smart weapons such as AMRAAM and AGM-65D Maverick imaging infra-red missiles.

At Block 30/32 (July 1986 deliveries) a common engine bay was incorporated which facilitated installation of either the Pratt & Whitney F100-PW-220 (Block 32) or the General Electric F110-GE-100 (Block 30) engine developed under the USAF's Alternate Fighter Engines programme. Other changes included computer memory expansion and seal-bonded fuselage fuel tanks. First USAF wing to receive

First General Dynamics F-16C Block 40 'Night Falcon' equipped with LANTIRN pods

First guided launch of an AIM-7 Sparrow missile from an F-16(ADF) in February 1989

F-16C/Ds with F110 engines was the 86th TFW at Ramstein AB, West Germany, from October 1986. Additions in 1987 included a voice message unit, Shrike anti-radiation missiles, crash survivable flight data recorder, and a modular common inlet duct which provides more air and full available thrust from the F110 engine at lower airspeeds. One Block 30 F-16D was diverted to Calspan Corporation as the NF-16D (which see). Early in 1988, a software upgrade provided full level IV multi-target compatibility with AMRAAM. In May 1989, AIM-7F and -7M Sparrow missiles were fired from an F-16C, completing a successful industry-sponsored programme that will lead to radar missile capability for several F-16 users, starting in mid-1991. Missiles are guided using pulse-Doppler illumination while tracking the targets in a high PRF mode of the APG-68 radar.

Block 40/42 (December 1988 deliveries) upgrades include AN/APG-68(V) radar, capable of more than 100 hours operation before maintenance, full compatibility with Martin Marietta LANTIRN (low altitude navigation and targeting infra-red for night) pods, four-channel digital flight control system, expanded capacity core computers, diffractive optics HUD, enhanced-envelope gunsight, GPS/Navstar, improved leading-edge flap drive system, improved cockpit ergonomics, heavyweight landing gear for increased max T-O weight, structural strengthening, and provisions for advanced EW equipment. LANTIRN (used operationally in Europe from late 1989) allows automatic target acquisition and standoff target identification by day and night, automatic target handoff for multiple launch of Maverick missiles, autonomous laser guided bomb delivery and precision air-to-ground laser ranging. In 1990, the Combat Edge pressure breathing system was to be installed to provide increased g tolerance for pilots during combat manoeuvres.

Block 50/52 (October 1991 deliveries) upgrades include increased performance engines (IPE) (the F110-GE-129 and F100-PW-229) advanced programmable signal processor employing VHSIC technology in the APG-68(V5) fire control radar, Have Quick IIA VHF radio, ALR-56M advanced radar warning receiver and provisions for the automatic target hand-off system (ATHS) and Have Sync VHF anti-jam radio. Changes planned for 1993 include full integration of HARM/Shrike anti-radiation missiles, an upgraded programmable display generator with digital terrain system (DTS) provisions and scope for digital map capability, installation of ATHS, a ring laser gyro INS and the ALE-47 advanced chaff dispenser.

Upgrades being considered for 1995 include a digital terrain system with colour map, colour multi-function displays, modular core computer suite, head-steered FLIR with helmet-mounted display, airborne self protection jammer (ASPJ) or alternative, and on-board oxygen generation system (OBOGS).

The first F-16C for the US Air Force (83-118) was delivered on 19 July 1984; the first F-16D was delivered in September 1984; first operational unit to equip with these models was the 33rd TFS at Shaw AFB, South Carolina. F-16Cs and F-16Ds have been ordered also by Bahrain (12 F-16C/Ds with F110-GE-100 engines); Egypt (34 F-16Cs and 6 F-16Ds, the first of which, with an F100-PW-220 engine, was handed over at Fort Worth on 15 August 1986, plus 41 of the Block 40 version with F110-GE-100 engines to be delivered from 1991); Greece (40, with F110-GE-100 engines, deliveries completed 1989); Israel (60 F-16Cs and 15 F-16Ds with F110-GE-100s, deliveries of which were completed in 1988, plus a further 60, deliveries to begin in 1991); South Korea (30 F-16Cs and 10 F-16Ds with F100-PW-220 engines, the first delivered in March 1986); and Turkey (136 F-16Cs and 24 F-16Ds with F110-GE-100 engines; of which 152 being built locally by TAI). Greek and Turkish F-16s have braking parachute. Turkish aircraft to share 60 LANTIRN pods.

F-16Cs and F-16Ds of USAF's 52nd TFW at Spangdahlem AB, West Germany, have interim HARM/Shrike capability and are operated alongside F-4G Phantoms on 'Wild Weasel' defence suppression missions. The definitive version will have special operational equipment housed in a large rectangular-section dorsal spine, extending from the canopy to beyond the jet nozzle.

In 1989, F-16C/Ds became operational with the USAF in the aggressor role at Nellis AFB, Nevada, and RAF Bentwaters, UK, most of these fully combat-capable aircraft wearing MiG-type camouflage. Further units at Kadena (Japan) and Tyndall AFB, Florida, were cancelled due to budget cuts, which also forced disbandment of the 527th AS at Bentwaters, 26th AS at Clark AFB, Philippines, and 64th AS at Nellis.

NF-16D. Under a $31.5 million contract awarded in December 1988, an F-16D Block 30 was modified as variable stability in-flight simulator test aircraft (VISTA), replacing earlier NT-33A variable stability testbed. VISTA features include vertical surface direct-force generators above and below wings, variable stability flight control system and fully programmable cockpit controls and displays. The NF-16D will be used for research into flying qualities, displays and flight control, and for test pilot training. First flight was expected in 1990.

F-16N. Selected in January 1985 as US Navy supersonic adversary aircraft (SAA). Contract for 26 aircraft, of which deliveries began in Spring 1987 and were completed in 1988. The airframe is derived from that of Block 30 F-16Cs with minor structural modifications involving the substitution of titanium for aluminium in lower wing fittings and cold working the lower wing skin holes to meet the increased frequency of g loading in adversary roles. The F-16N configuration includes the General Electric F110-GE-100 engine, substitution of the APG-66 radar for the APG-68,

USAF 'Aggressor' F-16C in Soviet-type camouflage

The first Indonesian F-16A, TS-1605, handed over in December 1989

and deletion of the M61 gun. The F-16N normally carries only wingtip launchers for practice AIM-9 missiles and ACMI AIS pods, but is capable of carrying the full complement of F-16 fuel tanks and other external stores. Four aircraft are two-seat versions, similar to the F-16D and designated **TF-16N**. F-16Ns and TF-16Ns serve with the ('Top Gun') Fighter Weapons School (eight) and VF-126 (six) at NAS Miramar, CA; VF-45 (six) at NAS Key West, FL, and VF-43 (six detached from VF-45) at NAS Oceana, VA.

F-16 Agile Falcon and FS-X. Agile Falcon is proposed successor to F-16C/D with composites wings of same planform but with area increased, and lighter in weight, with refined aerodynamics, updated avionics and an improved performance engine (IPE). Pre-FSD studies were completed in 1989 under joint government/industry by the US and four European nations. Several air forces operating the F-16 have expressed an interest in future buys, but development funding had not been allocated.

On 19 October 1987 the Japan Defence Agency announced that it had selected a derivative version of the F-16 for its FS-X fighter requirement. Further details will be found under Mitsubishi in the Japanese section.

F-16 Recce. A reconnaissance capability is being designed for the F-16, using pod mounted sensors and requiring only minor changes to any existing F-16 model. Compatibility has been flight demonstrated with four existing European built sensor pods, including that used on the Tornado. F-16s have been operational as tactical reconnaissance aircraft with the Royal Netherlands Air Force, as F-16A(R)s, since 1983.

An extensive flight test programme conducted in 1986 verified the suitability of a new General Dynamics designed underbelly reconnaissance pod built especially for the F-16, and the feasibility and effectiveness of near-real-time reconnaissance capability. The semi-conformal pod, installed on an F-16B (75-0752), housed advanced electro-optical and infra-red sensors for day/night operation, at all speeds and altitudes, and with stand-off capability. The three multi-position sensors served the function of seven cameras in current fixed-mount arrangements. The system provided real-time cockpit viewing and sensor positioning, imagery review/manipulation/frame selection, and digital data link of selected frames to distant ground stations. Ground station operators were able to analyse, annotate and disseminate this imagery and their reports electronically only minutes after the images were taken, compared with the hours required to process film-based systems. The USAF wishes to replace its RF-4C fleet with some 200 F-16s carrying ATARS reconnaissance pods by the mid-1990s, and would designate these RF-16s.

AFTI/F-16. Modified F-16A testbed aircraft for Air Force Systems Command's Advanced Fighter Technology Integration (AFTI) programme; first flown on 10 July 1982. Digital flight control system and twin fuselage-mounted ventral foreplanes, permitting decoupled or six degrees of freedom flight modes and also providing integrated manoeuvring capability for making flat (unbanked) turns without sideslip and manoeuvre enhancement/gust alleviation. Detailed account of programme in 1986-87 *Jane's*, and of the automated manoeuvre and attack system (AMAS) programme (completed April 1987) in 1987-88 edition. A new test programme, begun in 1988, is aimed at

improving communications between aircraft and ground troops during close air support missions. Aircraft modifications include a Rockwell Collins CP-1516 automatic target hand-off system (ATHS) data link with forward air controllers, refinement of terrain management and display system and its Sandia software, and improvements to FLIR/laser tracker and pilot's helmet sight. The close air support test flights will also continue work begun in the AMAS programme to provide a ground collision avoidance system. Future plans call for upgrades of AFTI/F-16's core avionics to a Block 40 baseline and to add a night FLIR system.

F-16XL. NASA has leased the two prototype F-16XL aircraft from General Dynamics for a three to four year test programme which will evaluate concepts for sustained high-speed flight. The F-16XLs had been held in flyable storage at General Dynamics' Fort Worth plant since 1985, and the single-seat No. 1 aircraft began flying again on 9 March 1989. NASA is modifying the aircraft at its Dryden facility (Edwards AFB) with an experimental wing glove perforated with thousands of tiny laser cut holes connected to an air pump to produce an uninterrupted airflow over the cranked-arrow wing in supersonic flight, decreasing drag, turbulence and fuel consumption. The No. 2 aircraft (two-seat with GE F110 engine) was expected to be deployed to Edwards AFB in 1990. A full description and photograph of the F-16XL can be found in the 1985-86 and earlier editions of *Jane's*.

Extensive flight demonstrations of enhanced systems for night and close air support (CAS) began in 1985. Systems include Terprom digital terrain system, automatic target hand-off system, night cockpit lighting, night vision goggles, navigation FLIR pods, head-steered FLIR, and head-mounted displays. These systems have enabled a single-seat pilot to fly a high speed/low altitude survivable profile; receive target instructions without voice transmission; successfully locate, recognise, and attack a vehicular target on the first pass; and operate at night/under-the-weather using daylight tactics.

A Falcon Century programme has been instituted to monitor and evaluate developments and to maintain a master plan for F-16 developments into the next century.

The following description applies to the Block 40 F-16C and F-16D:

TYPE: Single-seat day/night multi-role fighter (F-16C) and two-seat fighter/trainer (F-16D).

WINGS: Cantilever mid-wing monoplane, of blended wing/body design and cropped delta planform. The blended wing/body concept is achieved by flaring the wing/body intersection, thus not only providing lift from the body at high angles of attack but also giving less wetted area and increased internal fuel volume. In addition, thickening of the wingroot gives a more rigid structure, with a weight saving of some 113 kg (250 lb). Basic wing is of NACA 64A-204 section, with 40° sweepback on leading-edges. Structure is mainly of aluminium alloy, with 11 spars, 5 ribs and single upper and lower skins, and is attached to fuselage by machined aluminium fittings. Leading-edge manoeuvring flaps are programmed automatically as a function of Mach number and angle of attack. The increased wing camber maintains effective lift coefficients at high angles of attack. These flaps are one-piece bonded aluminium honeycomb sandwich structures and are driven by rotary actuators. The trailing-edges carry large flaperons (flaps/ailerons), which are interchangeable left with right and are actuated by integrated servo-actuators. The maximum rate of flaperon movement is 52°/s.

FUSELAGE: Semi-monocoque all-metal structure of frames and longerons, built in three main modules: forward (to just aft of cockpit), centre and aft. Nose radome built by Brunswick Corporation. Highly swept vortex control strakes along the fuselage forebody increase lift and improve directional stability at high angles of attack.

TAIL UNIT: Cantilever structure with sweptback surfaces. Fin is multi-spar multi-rib aluminium structure with graphite epoxy skins, aluminium tip and dorsal fin. Optional extension of rear root fairing to house brake-chute or portion of an internal ECM. Interchangeable all-moving tailplane halves, constructed of graphite epoxy composite laminate skins mechanically attached to a corrugated aluminium substructure. Each tailplane half has an aluminium pivot shaft, and a removable full depth bonded honeycomb leading-edge. Ventral fins have bonded aluminium honeycomb core with aluminium skins. Split speed-brakes inboard of rear portion of each horizontal tail surface, each deflecting 60° from the closed position.

LANDING GEAR: Menasco hydraulically retractable type, nose unit retracting rearward and main units forward into fuselage. Nosewheel is located aft of intake to reduce the risk of foreign objects being thrown into the engine during ground operation, and rotates 90° during retraction to lie horizontally under engine air intake duct. Oleo-pneumatic struts in all units. Aircraft braking systems, mainwheels and brakes; Goodyear or Goodrich mainwheel tyres, size 27.75 × 8.75-14.5, pressure 14.48-15.17 bars (210-220 lb/sq in) at T-O weights less than 13,608 kg (30,000 lb). Steerable nosewheel with Goodyear, Goodrich, or Dunlop tyre, size 18 × 5.7-8, pressure 20.68-21.37 bars (300-310 lb/sq in) at T-O weights less than 13,608 kg (30,000 lb). All but two main unit components interchangeable. Brake by wire system on main gear, with Aircraft Braking Systems anti-skid units. Runway arresting hook under rear fuselage. Landing/taxi lights on nose landing gear door.

POWER PLANT: One General Electric F110-GE-100, rated at 122.8 kN (27,600 lb st) with afterburning, or one Pratt & Whitney F100-PW-220 turbofan, rated at 104.3 kN (23,450 lb st) with afterburning, as alternative standard engines, mounted in rear fuselage. Over 70 per cent of FY 1984-91 production for USAF fitted with F110. Fixed geometry intake, with boundary layer splitter plate, beneath fuselage. Standard fuel contained in wing and five seal-bonded fuselage cells which function as two tanks; see under 'Weights' for quantities. In-flight refuelling receptacle in top of centre-fuselage, aft of cockpit. Auxiliary fuel can be carried in drop tanks on underwing and underfuselage hardpoints.

ACCOMMODATION: Pilot only in F-16C, in air-conditioned cockpit. McDonnell Douglas ACES II zero/zero ejection seat. Bubble canopy made of polycarbonate advanced plastics material. Inside of USAF F-16C/D canopy (and most Netherlands F-16A/Bs) coated with gold film to dissipate radar energy. In conjunction with radar-absorbing materials in air intake, this reduces frontal radar signature by 40 per cent. Windscreen and forward canopy are an integral unit without a forward bow frame, and are separated from the aft canopy by a simple support structure which serves also as the breakpoint where the forward section pivots upward and aft to give access to the cockpit. A redundant safety lock feature prevents canopy loss. Windscreen/canopy design provides 360° all-round view, 195° fore and aft, 40° down over the side, and 15° down over the nose. To enable the pilot to sustain high g forces, and for pilot comfort, the seat is inclined 30° aft and the heel line is raised. In normal operation the canopy is pivoted upward and aft by electrical power; the pilot is also able to unlatch the canopy manually and open it with a backup handcrank. Emergency jettison is provided by explosive unlatching devices and two rockets. A limited displacement, force sensing control stick is provided on the right hand console, with a suitable armrest, to provide precise control inputs during combat manoeuvres. The F-16D has two cockpits in tandem, equipped with all controls, displays, instruments, avionics and life support systems required to perform both training and combat missions. The layout of the F-16D second station is similar to the F-16C, and is fully systems-operational. A single-enclosure polycarbonate transparency, made in two pieces and spliced aft of the forward seat with a metal bow frame and lateral support member, provides outstanding view from both cockpits.

SYSTEMS: Regenerative 12kW environmental control system, with digital electronic control, uses engine bleed air for pressurisation and cooling of crew station and avionics compartments. Two separate and independent hydraulic systems supply power for operation of the primary flight control surfaces and the utility functions. System pressure (each) 207 bars (3,000 lb/sq in), rated at 161 litres (42.5 US gallons; 35.4 Imp gallons)/min. Bootstrap type reservoirs, rated at 5.79 bars (84 lb/sq in). Electrical system powered by engine driven Westinghouse 60kVA main generator and 10kVA standby generator (including ground annunciator panel for total electrical system fault reporting), with Sundstrand constant speed drive and powered by a Sundstrand accessory drive gearbox. Four dedicated, sealed cell batteries provide transient electrical power protection for the fly-by-wire flight control system. Application of the control configured vehicle (CCV) principle of relaxed static stability produces a significant reduction in trim drag, especially at high load factors and supersonic speeds. The aircraft centre of gravity is allowed to move aft, reducing both the tail drag and the change in drag on the wing due to changes in lift required to balance the download on the tail. Relaxed static stability imposes a requirement for a highly reliable, full-time-operating, stability augmentation system, including reliable electronic, electrical and hydraulic provisions. The signal paths in this quad-redundant system are used to control the aircraft, replacing the usual mechanical linkages. Pilot commands are processed by a four-channel Bendix digital flight control computer which generates the electrical signals for the servo

actuators. An onboard Sundstrand/Solar jet fuel starter is provided for engine self-start capability. Simmonds fuel measuring system. Garrett emergency power unit automatically drives a 5kVA emergency generator and emergency pump to provide uninterrupted electrical and hydraulic power for control in the event of the engine or primary power systems becoming inoperative.

AVIONICS AND EQUIPMENT: Westinghouse AN/APG-68(V) pulse-Doppler range and angle track radar, with planar array in nose. Provides air-to-air modes for range-while-search, uplook search, velocity search, air combat, track-while-scan (ten targets), raid cluster resolution, single target track and (later) high PRF track to provide target illumination for AIM-7 missiles; and air-to-surface modes for ground mapping, Doppler beam sharpening, ground moving target, sea target, fixed target track, target freeze after pop-up, beacon, and air-to-ground ranging. Forward avionics bay, immediately forward of cockpit, contains radar, air data equipment, inertial navigation system, flight control computer, and combined altitude radar altimeter (CARA). Rear avionics bay contains ILS, Tacan and IFF, with space for future equipment. A Dalmo Victor AN/ALR-69 radar warning system (to be replaced by Loral AN/ALR-56M advanced RWR) is installed. Communications equipment includes Magnavox AN/ARC-164 UHF 'Have Quick' transceiver; provisions for a Magnavox KY-58 secure voice system; Collins AN/ARC-186 VHF AM/FM transceiver; government furnished AN/AIC-18/25 intercom; and SCI advanced interference blanker. Honeywell central air data computer. Litton LN-39 standard inertial navigation system; Collins AN/ARN-108 ILS; Collins AN/ARN-118 Tacan; Teledyne Electronics AN/APX-101 IFF transponder with a government furnished IFF control; government furnished National Security Agency KIT-1A/TSEC cryptographic equipment; GEC Astronics stick force sensors; GEC Avionics wide-angle holographic electronic head-up display with raster video capability and integrated keyboard; Collins GPS/Navstar; General Dynamics enhanced stores management computer; Teledyne Systems general avionics computer; Honeywell multi-function display set; data entry/cockpit interface and dedicated fault display by Litton-Canada and General Dynamics, Fort Worth; Fairchild data transfer set; and Astronautics cockpit/TV set. Cockpit and core avionics integrated on two MIL-STD-1553B multiplex buses. Optional equipment includes VIR-130 VOR/ILS and ARC-190 HF radio. Essential structure and wiring provisions are built into the airframe to allow for easy incorporation of future avionics systems under development for the F-16 by the US Air Force. Israeli Air Force F-16s have been extensively modified with Israeli designed and manufactured equipment, as well as optional US equipment, to tailor them to the IAF defence role.

ARMAMENT: General Electric M61A1 20 mm multi-barrel cannon in the port side wing/body fairing, equipped with a General Electric ammunition handling system and an enhanced envelope gunsight (part of the head-up display system) and 515 rounds of ammunition. There is a mounting for an air-to-air missile at each wingtip, one underfuselage centreline hardpoint, and six underwing hardpoints for additional stores. For manoeuvring flight at 5.5g the underfuselage station is stressed for a load of up to 1,000 kg (2,200 lb), the two inboard underwing stations for 2,041 kg (4,500 lb) each, the two centre underwing stations for 1,587 kg (3,500 lb) each, the two outboard underwing stations for 318 kg (700 lb) each, and the two wingtip stations for 193 kg (425 lb) each. For manoeuvring flight at 9g the underfuselage station is stressed for a load of up to 544 kg (1,200 lb), the two inboard underwing stations for 1,134 kg (2,500 lb) each, the two centre underwing stations for 907 kg (2,000 lb) each, the two outboard underwing stations for 204 kg (450 lb) each, and the two wingtip stations for 193 kg (425 lb) each. There are mounting provisions on each side of the inlet shoulder for the specific carriage of sensor pods (electro-optical, FLIR, etc); each of these stations is stressed for 408 kg (900 lb) at 5.5g, and 250 kg (550 lb) at 9g. Typical stores loads can include two wingtip mounted AIM-9L/M/P Sidewinders, with up to four more on the outer underwing stations; centreline GPU-5/A 30 mm

cannon; Sargent-Fletcher 1,400 litre (370 US gallon; 308 Imp gallon) or 2,271 litre (600 US gallon; 500 Imp gallon) drop tanks on the inboard underwing stations; a 1,136 litre (300 US gallon; 250 Imp gallon) drop tank on the underfuselage station; a Martin Marietta Pave Penny laser spot tracker pod along the starboard side of the nacelle; and single or cluster bombs, air-to-surface missiles, or flare pods, on the four inner underwing stations. Stores can be launched from Aircraft Hydro-Forming MAU-12C/A bomb ejector racks, Hughes LAU-88 launchers, or Orgen triple or multiple ejector racks. Westinghouse AN/ALQ-119 and AN/ALQ-131 ECM (jammer) pods can be carried on the centreline and two underwing stations. Provision for future internal installation of Westinghouse/ITT AN/ALQ-165 airborne self-protection jammer (ASPJ) instead of ECM pods. ALE-40 internal chaff/flare dispensers. Current capabilities include air-to-air combat with gun and Sidewinder missiles; and air-to-ground attack with gun, rockets, conventional bombs, special weapons, laser guided and electro-optical weapons. Specific structure, wiring provisions, and system architecture, are built in to ensure acceptance of future sensor and weapon systems, including electro-optical and FLIR pods, and advanced beyond-visual-range missiles. Weapons launched successfully from F-16s, in addition to Sidewinders and AMRAAM, include radar guided Sparrow and Sky Flash air-to-air missiles, French Magic 2 infra-red homing air-to-air missiles, AGM-65A/B/D/G Maverick air-to-surface missiles, HARM and Shrike anti-radiation missiles, and Penguin Mk 3 anti-ship missile. F-16s of the Norwegian Air Force carry Penguin anti-shipping missiles. F-16s can be equipped with a variety of reconnaissance pods (eg, Orpheus on RNethAF aircraft) and the Thomson-CSF Atlis laser designator pod, as carried by those of Pakistan Air Force.

DIMENSIONS, EXTERNAL (F-16C, D):

Wing span over missile launchers	9.45 m (31 ft 0 in)
Wing span over missiles	10.00 m (32 ft 9¾ in)
Wing aspect ratio	3.0
Length overall	15.03 m (49 ft 4 in)
Height overall	5.09 m (16 ft 8½ in)
Tailplane span	5.58 m (18 ft 3¾ in)
Wheel track	2.36 m (7 ft 9 in)
Wheelbase	4.00 m (13 ft 1½ in)

AREAS (F-16C, D):

Wings, gross	27.87 m² (300.0 sq ft)
Flaperons (total)	2.91 m² (31.32 sq ft)
Leading-edge flaps (total)	3.41 m² (36.72 sq ft)
Vertical tail surfaces (total)	5.09 m² (54.75 sq ft)
Rudder	1.08 m² (11.65 sq ft)
Horizontal tail surfaces (total)	5.92 m² (63.70 sq ft)

WEIGHTS AND LOADINGS:

Weight empty:	
F-16C: F100-PW-220	8,273 kg (18,238 lb)
F110-GE-100	8,627 kg (19,020 lb)
Max internal fuel: F-16C	3,104 kg (6,846 lb)
F-16D	2,567 kg (5,659 lb)
Max external fuel (both)	3,066 kg (6,760 lb)
Max external load (both)	5,443 kg (12,000 lb)
Typical combat weight:	
F-16C (F110)	10,780 kg (23,765 lb)
Max T-O weight:	
air-to-air, no external tanks:	
F-16C (F110)	12,331 kg (27,185 lb)
with external load:	
F-16C	19,187 kg (42,300 lb)
Wing loading:	
at 12,927 kg (28,500 lb) AUW	464 kg/m² (95.0 lb/sq ft)
at 19,187 kg (42,300 lb) AUW	688 kg/m² (141.0 lb/sq ft)
Thrust/weight ratio (clean)	1.1 to 1

PERFORMANCE:

Max level speed at 12,200 m (40,000 ft)	above Mach 2.0
Service ceiling	more than 15,240 m (50,000 ft)
Radius of action	more than 500 nm (925 km; 575 miles)
Ferry range, with drop tanks	more than 2,100 nm (3,890 km; 2,415 miles)
Max symmetrical design g limit with full internal fuel	+9

GENERAL DYNAMICS/ MCDONNELL DOUGLAS

PRINCIPAL PROGRAMME OFFICE: General Dynamics Corporation, Fort Worth Division, PO Box 748, Fort Worth, Texas 76101
Telephone: 1 (817) 777 2000

GENERAL DYNAMICS/MCDONNELL DOUGLAS ATA
US Navy designation: A-12A Avenger II

On 23 December 1987 the US Navy announced that it had selected General Dynamics and McDonnell Douglas to

develop its A-12A low-observable carrier-based Advanced Tactical Aircraft (ATA). A fixed-price incentive contract valued at $4.379 billion was allocated for the development programme, and in November 1988 General Dynamics and McDonnell Douglas were awarded a $7.9 million contract for an 11-month concept definition study of a US Air Force version of the aircraft as a possible replacement for F-111 attack aircraft. Both air-to-air and air-to-surface radar modes and weapons are included. Few details have yet been released for the aircraft, which will be subsonic, powered by two General Electric F412 (F404 derivative) turbofans, operated by a two-man crew, and feature integrated avionics and electronic warfare systems. Prototype rollout was scheduled for the Autumn of 1990.

Announced subcontractors on the A-12A include AiResearch and Ball Aerospace and Loral Randtron Systems (door mechanical drive group), Bendix (main landing gear, wheels and carbon brakes), Garrett (air data computer), Garrett Auxiliary Power Division (airframe-mounted accessory drive gearbox system), General Electric Aircraft Electronics Division (missile warning system), Harris (multi-function antenna system), Honeywell (digital flight control system), Honeywell/Litton (integrated inertial sensor assembly), Litton (inertial navigation and electronic surveillance measures systems), Martin Marietta (navigational FLIR), Parker Bertea Aerospace (in-flight refuelling probe), Pilkington PLC's Swedlow Inc subsidiary (cockpit transparencies), SCI Technology Inc (amplifier control intercommunications set), Sundstrand Turbomach Division (auxiliary power unit), Teledyne Ryan Electronics (radar altimeter), and Westinghouse (multi-function radar and combined function FLIR). The US Navy has a requirement for at least 450 ATAs by 2005, initial

procurement plans of January 1989 covering 106 aircraft up to FY 1994 at a cost of $10.2 billion. In later production lots, GD and McDonnell Douglas may compete annually. The A-12A will replace Grumman A-6E Intruders from the late 1990s onwards and is being studied by the USAF.

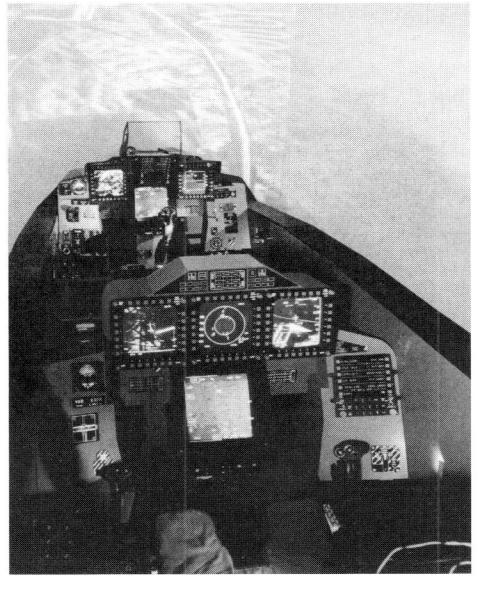

A cockpit mockup was the sole illustrative material released on the A-12 up to early 1990

GLOBAL
GLOBAL HELICOPTER TECHNOLOGY INC
8900 Trinity Boulevard, Fort Worth, Texas 76053.
Telephone: 1 (817) 284 1212
Fax: 1 (817) 284 8846
PRESIDENT: Clem Bailey
VICE-PRESIDENT, MARKETING: Mike Robbins

Global Helicopter Technology has developed a number of modifications for Bell Model 206 series helicopters, which are described under the Bell Helicopter Textron entry in the Canadian section of this edition.

It has developed an armed version of the Bell Model 206L-3 LongRanger helicopter, known as **NightRanger**.

The conversion, which can be carried out on new or re-manufactured LongRanger airframes, involves installation of a FLIR Systems FLIR 2000 forward-looking infra-red system, Crouzet T100 sight, outrigger stores carriers developed for the Bell Model 406 CS Combat Scout, armoured seats for pilot and co-pilot, cabin-mounted machine-gun pintles with swivelling gunners' seats and sliding cabin doors, and night vision goggles-compatible cockpit lighting. The Emerson HeliTOW missile system and a two- or three-axis autopilot are also available. Armament includes two 7.62 mm machine-guns with 2,000 rds, or two seven-tube or two 19-tube 2.75 in rocket pods. The NightRanger has an empty weight, equipped, of 1,134 kg (2,500 lb) and a useful load of 816 kg (1,800 lb).

Global Helicopters Technology is developing a modification of the Bell UH-1H utility helicopter which involves installation of 1,342 kW (1,800 shp) Textron Lycoming T53-L-703 turboshafts, Bell Model 212 drivetrain, upgraded transmission and a Frahm vibration absorber. The modified helicopter is known as the **UH-1HP** (High Performance). Max T-O weight is 5,080 kg (11,200 lb) and useful load 2,540 kg (5,600 lb).

In conjunction with Soloy Conversions Ltd (which see), Global Helicopter Technology is developing a twin-engined conversion of the Bell 206L series in which a Soloy Dual Pac incorporating twin Allison 250 series power sections would replace the single Allison 250 power plant of the standard helicopter.

GRUMMAN
GRUMMAN CORPORATION
1111 Stewart Avenue, Bethpage, New York 11714-3580
Telephone: 1 (516) 575 0574
Telex: 961430
CHAIRMAN, PRESIDENT AND CHIEF EXECUTIVE OFFICER: John O'Brien
VICE-CHAIRMAN, TECHNOLOGY: Renso L. Caporali
VICE-PRESIDENT, MARKETING: David L. Walsh
VICE-PRESIDENT, PUBLIC AFFAIRS: Weyman B. Jones

Grumman Aircraft Engineering Corporation was incorporated on 6 December 1929. Important changes in its corporate structure were announced in 1969, resulting in the

formation of Grumman Corporation as a small holding company, with Grumman Aerospace Corporation, Grumman Allied Industries Inc and Grumman Data Systems Corporation. In February 1985 Grumman Corporation announced the creation of ten operating divisions, each matched to a specific market: Aerostructures; Aircraft Systems; Allied (Vehicles and Marine); Data Systems; Electronics Systems; International; Melbourne Systems; Space Systems; St Augustine; and Technical Services. Melbourne Systems Division is prime contractor and responsible for avionics installation in the E-8A Joint STARS (modified Boeing 707) aircraft, of which further details are given under the entry for Boeing Aerospace &

Electronics. A Corporate Services Division provides legal, purchasing, contracts and other common services to all the operating divisions. A Space Station Program Support division was formed during 1987. Aerostructures and St Augustine divisions became units of the Aircraft Systems division in 1988. In Spring 1988 it was announced that Electronics Systems, Melbourne Systems and Space Systems divisions were to be consolidated into a unified Systems Group.

Employment within the corporation totalled 30,100 in 1989.

GRUMMAN AIRCRAFT SYSTEMS DIVISION
PRESIDENT: Peter B. Oram

Current aircraft products of this division include versions of the A-6 Intruder, EA-6B Prowler, E-2C Hawkeye and F-14 Tomcat for the US Navy. It has also designed and built two examples of a small forward swept wing (FSW) technology demonstrator designated X-29A, under contract from the US Defense Advanced Research Projects Agency. A contract to manufacture 270 shipsets of engine nacelles and thrust reversers for the Tay turbofans of Gulfstream IV and Fokker 100 transport aircraft was received in February 1984. An initial contract covering design and manufacture of complete tail sections of the Bell/Boeing V-22 Osprey advanced vertical lift aircraft (see Bell/Boeing entry) was received in August 1984. In April 1987 Grumman announced that it had been awarded an initial $28 million contract for the manufacture of two sets of composite structure ailerons, elevators and rudders for the McDonnell Douglas C-17A tactical airlifter.

Since October 1987, Grumman Aircraft Systems has been responsible for engineering and logistic support of A-10 Thunderbolt II close air support aircraft in the US Air Force inventory. On 5 August 1987 the US Air Force awarded Grumman contracts totalling $245 million for the development, installation and flight testing of 55 avionics upgrade kits for Chinese Shenyang J-8 II fighter aircraft. Further details of this programme are given under the SAC heading in the Chinese section. Under the CAC heading in the same section can be found details of the proposed Super-7 update of the Chinese F-7M fighter, which Grumman has been studying jointly with Chengdu Aircraft Corporation.

GRUMMAN HAWKEYE
US Navy designations: E-2B, E-2C and TE-2C
The E-2 Hawkeye was developed as a carrier borne early warning aircraft, but is suitable also for land based

operations. The first of three prototypes flew on 21 October 1960; these were followed by 59 E-2As, all operational examples of which had been updated to E-2B standard by the end of 1971 apart from two TE-2A trainers and two converted to E-2C prototypes. Details of these versions have appeared in earlier editions of *Jane's.*

The first of the two E-2C prototypes flew on 20 January 1971. Manufacture began in mid-1971 and the first flight of a production aircraft was made on 23 September 1972. Orders for this version now cover 164 aircraft; over 130 of these had been delivered by the beginning of 1990, and it is planned for production to continue at the rate of six per year until the early 1990s. Four E-2Cs were supplied to Israel in 1981; Japan accepted four each in 1982 and 1984, and bought three in FY 1989 and two in FY 1990. Egypt has accepted five aircraft, the last three of which were delivered in October 1987 and ordered a sixth in 1989. The government of Singapore took delivery of four aircraft in 1987. The US Coast Guard and US Customs Service each have two aircraft for use in anti-narcotics smuggling operations. These four aircraft were taken from the US Navy inventory, and replaced by increasing FY 1988 procurement from six aircraft to ten.

The E-2C entered service, with airborne early warning squadron VAW-123 at NAS Norfolk, VA, in November 1973, and went to sea on board USS *Saratoga* in late 1974. Eighteen other squadrons, including two naval reserve, have received E-2C aircraft, and two **TE-2C** training aircraft are also in service. They are VAW-110 and 112 to 117 at Miramar, CA, with VAW-88 of the Reserves; and VAW-120 to 127 and 132, plus Reserves VAW-78 at Norfolk, VA. VAW-110 and 120 are training units.

The Hawkeye can maintain patrol on naval task force defence perimeters in all weathers, at an operating height of about 9,150 m (30,000 ft), and can detect and assess any threat from approaching enemy aircraft over ranges approaching 260 nm (480 km; 300 miles). An AN/APS-139 radar system superseded the earlier AN/APS-125 and

AN/APS-138 in new production E-2Cs in 1989. A retrofit programme is in progress for all previously delivered aircraft. The system includes a new total radiation aperture control antenna (TRAC-A) to reduce sidelobes and offset increased jamming threats. The radar is capable of detecting airborne targets anywhere in a three million cubic mile surveillance envelope while simultaneously monitoring maritime traffic. Long-range detection, automatic target track initiation and high-speed processing combine to enable each E-2C to track, automatically and simultaneously, more than 2,000 targets and to control more than 40 airborne intercepts. A Randtron Systems AN/APA-171 antenna system is housed in a 7.32 m (24 ft) diameter saucer-shaped rotodome, mounted above the rear fuselage of the aircraft, which revolves in flight at 6 rpm. The Yagi type radar arrays within the rotodome are interfaced to the onboard avionic systems, providing radar sum and difference signals plus IFF. AN/APS-139 and -427 versions of the T56 power plant constitute the 'Group 1' update, the first operational aircraft being 163538, delivered to VAW-112 on 8 August 1989.

The AN/APS-139 search radar can detect targets as small as a cruise missile at ranges in excess of 145 nm (268 km; 167 miles). It also monitors movement of enemy ships and land vehicles. The AN/ALR-73 passive detection system (PDS) alerts operators to the presence of electronic emitters at distances up to twice the detection range of the radar system, thus expanding significantly the surveillance capability of the E-2C's avionics systems were described more fully in the 1979-80 *Jane's.*

In 1986, the US Navy began evaluation of an E-2C with new Grumman/General Electric AN/APS-145 radar system, able to track more targets, at greater ranges, decrease the effects of jamming, and offer sharper overland detection. The AN/APS-145 is expected to go into production aircraft towards the end of 1991. Work continues on further improvements to the E-2C's radar

Grumman E-2C Hawkeye early warning and control aircraft of the US Navy *(Paul Jackson)*

Grumman E-2C Hawkeye twin-turboprop airborne early warning and control aircraft *(Pilot Press)*

detection and processing capabilities, a new IFF system, and on a wing strengthening programme.

E-2Cs are used to monitor air traffic in the Florida skies surrounding Cape Canaveral during Space Shuttle launches and to direct US Coast Guard and US Customs fixed-wing and helicopter crews in many successful interceptions of drug smuggling aircraft. They are also used to direct Israeli fighters engaged in combat missions in the Middle East.

The following details apply to the E-2C Hawkeye:

TYPE: Airborne early warning aircraft.

WINGS: Cantilever high-wing monoplane of all-metal construction. Incidence 4° at root, 1° at tip. Centre-section is a structural box consisting of three beams, ribs and machined skins. Hinged leading-edge is non-structural and provides access to flying and engine controls. The outer panels fold rearward about skewed-axis hinge fittings mounted on the rear beams, to stow parallel with the rear fuselage on each side. Folding is done through a double acting hydraulic cylinder. Trailing-edges of outer panels and part of centre-section consist of long span ailerons and hydraulically actuated Fowler flaps. When flaps are lowered, ailerons are drooped automatically. All control surfaces are power operated and incorporate devices to produce artificial feel forces. Automatic flight control system (AFCS) can be assigned sole control of the system hydraulic actuators, or AFCS signals can be superimposed on the pilot's mechanical inputs for stability augmentation. Pneumatically inflated rubber de-icing boots on leading-edges.

FUSELAGE: Conventional all-metal semi-monocoque structure.

TAIL UNIT: Cantilever structure, with four fins and three double-hinged rudders. Tailplane dihedral 11°. Portions of tail unit made of glassfibre to reduce radar reflection. Power control and artificial feel systems as for ailerons. Pneumatically inflated rubber de-icing boots on all leading-edges.

LANDING GEAR: Hydraulically retractable tricycle type. Pneumatic emergency extension. Steerable nosewheel unit retracts rearward. Mainwheels retract forward, and rotate to lie flat in bottom of nacelles. Twin wheels on nose unit only. Oleo-pneumatic shock absorbers. Mainwheel tyres size 36 × 11 Type VII 24-ply, pressure 17.9 bars (260 lb/sq in) on ship, 14.5 bars (210 lb/sq in) ashore. Hydraulic brakes. Hydraulically operated retractable tailskid. A-frame arrester hook under tail.

POWER PLANT: Two 3,661 kW (4,910 ehp) Allison T56-A-425 turboprops, driving Hamilton Standard type 54460-1 four-blade fully-feathering reversible-pitch constant-speed propellers. These have foam filled blades which have a steel spar and glassfibre shell. Spinners and blades incorporate electric anti-icing. Production E-2Cs delivered from 1989 onwards have T56-A-427 engines

which provide a two per cent power increase and lower fuel consumption.

ACCOMMODATION: Normal crew of five on flight deck and in ATDS compartment in main cabin, consisting of pilot, co-pilot, combat information centre officer, air control officer and radar operator. Downward hinged door, with built-in steps, on port side of centre-fuselage.

AVIONICS: Randtron AN/APA-171 rotodome (radar and IFF antennae), General Electric AN/APS-139 advanced radar processing system (ARPS) with overland/overwater detection capability (with AN/APS-145 scheduled for introduction in 1991 and eventual retrofit in all E-2Cs), RT-988/A IFF interrogator with Hazeltine OL-76/AP IFF detector processor, Litton AN/ALR-73 passive detection system, Hazeltine AN/APA-172 control indicator group, Litton OL-77/ASQ computer programmer (L-304), ARC-158 UHF data link, ARQ-34 HF data link, ASM-440 in-flight performance monitor, Collins ARC-51A UHF com, AIC-14A intercom, Litton AN/ASN-92 (LN-15C) CAINS carrier aircraft inertial navigation system, GEC Avionics standard central air data computer, AN/APN-153 (V) Doppler, AN/ASN-50 heading and attitude reference system, AN/ARN-52 (V) Tacan, Collins ARA-50 UHF ADF, ASW-25B ACLS and Honeywell AN/APN-171 (V) radar altimeter.

DIMENSIONS, EXTERNAL:

Wing span	24.56 m (80 ft 7 in)
Wing chord: at root	3.96 m (13 ft 0 in)
at tip	1.32 m (4 ft 4 in)
Wing aspect ratio	9.3
Width, wings folded	8.94 m (29 ft 4 in)
Length overall	17.54 m (57 ft 6¾ in)
Height overall	5.58 m (18 ft 3¾ in)
Diameter of rotodome	7.32 m (24 ft 0 in)
Tailplane span	7.99 m (26 ft 2½ in)
Wheel track	5.93 m (19 ft 5¾ in)
Wheelbase	7.06 m (23 ft 2 in)
Propeller diameter	4.11 m (13 ft 6 in)

AREAS:

Wings, gross	65.03 m² (700.0 sq ft)
Ailerons (total)	5.76 m² (62.0 sq ft)
Trailing-edge flaps (total)	11.03 m² (118.75 sq ft)
Fin, incl rudder and tab:	
outboard (total)	10.25 m² (110.36 sq ft)
inboard (total)	4.76 m² (51.26 sq ft)
Tailplane	11.62 m² (125.07 sq ft)
Elevators (total)	3.72 m² (40.06 sq ft)

WEIGHTS:

Weight empty	17,265 kg (38,063 lb)
Max fuel (internal, usable)	5624 kg (12,400 lb)
Max T-O weight	23,556 kg (51,933 lb)

PERFORMANCE (at max T-O weight):

Max level speed	323 knots (598 km/h; 372 mph)
Max cruising speed	311 knots (576 km/h; 358 mph)

Cruising speed (ferry)	268 knots (496 km/h; 308 mph)
Approach speed	103 knots (191 km/h; 119 mph)
Stalling speed (landing configuration)	
	74 knots (138 km/h; 86 mph)
Service ceiling	9,390 m (30,800 ft)
Min T-O run	610 m (2,000 ft)
T-O to 15 m (50 ft)	793 m (2,600 ft)
Min landing run	439 m (1,440 ft)
Ferry range	1,394 nm (2,583 km; 1,605 miles)
Time on station, 175 nm (320 km; 200 miles) from base	
	3-4 h
Endurance with max fuel	6 h 6 min

GRUMMAN C-2A GREYHOUND

Production of the C-2A Greyhound is now complete. The aircraft was last described in the 1989-90 edition.

GRUMMAN A-6E INTRUDER
US Navy designations: A-6E, EA-6A and KA-6D

The basic A-6A (originally A2F-1) Intruder was conceived as a carrier-borne low-level attack bomber equipped specifically to deliver nuclear or conventional weapons on targets completely obscured by weather or darkness. Of more than 660 A-6s built, in successive versions, approximately 350 currently equip operational US Navy and Marine Corps squadrons, and three readiness training squadrons.

The A-6A, A-6B and A-6C early models, last described in the 1978-79 *Jane's*, are no longer operational, most available examples having been converted to A-6E/TRAM or EA-6A configuration or into KA-6D tankers (78 converted from A-6A and seven from A-6E, details in 1980-81 *Jane's*). The latest **KA-6D** configuration deletes all weapon systems capability and includes provision for the carriage of five 1,514 litre (400 US gallon; 333 Imp gallon) drop tanks.

The following versions of the A-6 are still in production:

EA-6B Prowler. Advanced electronics development of the EA-6A, described separately.

A-6E Intruder. First produced as an advanced conversion of the A-6A (240 converted) with multi-mode radar and an IBM computer similar to that first tested in the EA-6B. First flight of an A-6E was made on 10 November 1970. First squadron deployment was made in September 1972, and the A-6E was approved officially for service use in December 1972. Procurement of new airframes totalled 195 up to and including FY 1987, of which approx 176 had been delivered by the end of 1987. A further contract for 10 new production A-6Es was awarded to Grumman in June 1988, the aircraft to be built between December 1990 and September 1991. Current Intruders are to **A-6E/TRAM** (target recognition and attack multisensor) standard, first flown in October 1974. Delivery of fully provisioned TRAM aircraft began on 14 December 1978, and the first carrier deployment was completed successfully in May 1980. All older A-6Es were converted to TRAM standard by 1988. A-6E/TRAM training is carried out using Grumman TC-4C (modified Gulfstream I) aircraft, eight of which are in US Navy/US Marine Corps service.

Navy squadrons equipped with the A-6E are VA-52, 95, 115, 128 (training), 145, 165, 195 and 196 at Whidbey Island, WA (with two rotated to Atsugi, Japan); VA-34, 35, 36, 42 (training), 55, 65, 75, 85 and 176 at Oceana, VA; and Reserves' VA-305 at Point Mugu, CA, plus VA-205 at Atlanta, GA, to convert in 1990. Marines squadrons are VMA(AW)-224, 242, 332 and 533 at Cherry Point, CA (including one rotated to Atsugi, Japan).

Fifty A-6Es were equipped to carry McDonnell Douglas Harpoon anti-shipping missiles (four per aircraft). Harpoon-capable A-6Es began to be deployed during 1981, and all subsequent new production and converted aircraft are equipped to carry this missile.

The last metal-winged A-6E was delivered in September 1988, but the final 21 production aircraft are being fitted with composite wings, as described above. These 21, produced from late 1989 onwards, also have features of the Systems Weapons Integration Program (SWIP), including provision to carry stand-off weapons (such as AGM-88 HARM, AGM-84 Harpoon and AGM-65 Maverick), installation of uprated Pratt & Whitney J52-P-408/409 turbojets, digital cockpit displays and controls, an advanced multi-mode attack radar, GEC Avionics wide angle HUD and night attack navigation system (NANS), provision for AMRAAM missiles, additional chaff/flare and air-to-air weapons stations, and various airframe improvements. Some 342 existing A-6Es will receive the SWIP modifications, including the entire Marine Corps inventory of over 50, which is being transferred to the US Navy.

Boeing Military Airplanes has a contract to develop and manufacture new graphite/epoxy wings for the A-6, to overcome fatigue problems believed to result from operation at heavier weights and higher load factors than were envisaged when the original A-6 was designed. Flight trials, started on 3 April 1989, were intended to lead to production of the new wings for all existing and future A-6s, and to provide an 8,800-hour service life. The initial contracts covered manufacture of 179 wings, with options for a total of 327. Up to 102 existing A-6s were to be re-winged by Boeing (which see for illustration), but the programme faced the possibility of cutback due to budgetary restrictions.

A-6F Intruder II and A-6G. See separate entry.
The following description applies to the A-6E:

TYPE: Two-seat carrier-based bomber for all-weather close air support, interdiction and deep strike missions.

WINGS: Cantilever mid-wing monoplane, with 25° sweepback at quarter-chord. All-metal structure. Hydraulically operated almost full span leading-edge slats and trailing-edge single-slotted, tracked, Fowler type flaps, with inset spoilers (flaperons) of same span as flaps forward of trailing-edge flaps for roll control. Trailing-edge of each wingtip, outboard of flap, splits to form speed-brakes which project above and below wing when extended. Two short fences above each wing. Outer panels fold upward and inward.

FUSELAGE: Conventional all-metal semi-monocoque structure. Bottom is recessed between engines to carry semi-exposed store.

TAIL UNIT: Cantilever all-metal structure. All-moving tailplane, without separate elevators. Electronic antenna in rear part of fin, immediately above rudder.

LANDING GEAR: Hydraulically retractable tricycle type. Twin-wheel nose unit retracts rearward. Single-wheel main units retract forward and inward into air intake fairings. A-frame arrester hook under rear fuselage.

POWER PLANT: Two 41.4 kN (9,300 lb st) Pratt & Whitney J52-P-8B turbojets. Max internal fuel capacity 8,873 litres (2,344 US gallons; 1,952 Imp gallons). Provision for up to five external fuel tanks under wing and centreline stations, each of 1,135 litres (300 US gallons; 250 Imp gallons) or 1,514 litres (400 US gallons; 333 Imp gallons) capacity. Removable flight refuelling probe projects upward immediately forward of windscreen.

ACCOMMODATION: Crew of two on Martin-Baker GRU7 ejection seats, which can be reclined to reduce fatigue during low-level operations. Bombardier/navigator slightly behind and below pilot to starboard. Hydraulically operated rearward sliding canopy.

SYSTEMS: AiResearch environmental control system for cockpit and avionics bay. Dual hydraulic systems for operation of flight controls, leading-edge and trailing-edge flaps, wingtip speed-brakes, landing gear brakes and cockpit canopy, each rated at 119.4 litres (31.5 US gallons; 26.2 Imp gallons) per min, with air/oil separated reservoir, pressurised at 2.76 bars (40 lb/sq in). One electrically driven hydraulic pump provides restricted flight capability by supplying the tailplane and rudder actuators only, each rated at 11.4 litres (3 US gallons; 2.5 Imp gallons) per min, with internally pres-

Grumman KA-6D in-flight refuelling tanker aircraft *(Katsumi Hinata)*

surised reservoir, pressurised at 1.08 bars (15.7 lb/sq in). Electrical system powered by two Garrett constant speed drive units that combine engine starting and electric power generation, each delivering 30 kVA. A Garrett ram air turbine, mounted so that it can be projected into the airstream above the port wing root, provides in-flight emergency electric power for essential equipment.

AVIONICS AND EQUIPMENT: Single Norden AN/APQ-148 simultaneous multi-mode nav/attack radar, replaces two earlier radar systems in A-6A. IBM and Fairchild nav/attack computer system and interfacing data converter. Conrac Corporation armament control unit. RCA video tape recorder for post-strike assessment of attacks. Litton AN/ALR-67 radar warning receiver. Norden radar provides simultaneous ground mapping; identification, tracking, and rangefinding of fixed or moving targets; and terrain clearance or terrain following manoeuvres. During 1981-83, it was updated by an improved AMTI (airborne moving target indication) to enhance its ability to detect moving targets. Cockpit displays for pilot and bombardier/navigator; terrain data presented on vertical display indicator ahead of pilot. IBM AN/ASQ-133 solid state digital computer is coupled to A-6E's radar, inertial and Doppler navigational equipment, communications and AFCS. As mission data is measured in flight by onboard aerodynamic and electronic sensors, computer compares data with pro-

grammed information, computes differences, and provides corrective data to alter parameters of mission. Fairchild signal data converter accepts analog input data from up to 60 sensors, converting data to a digital output that is fed into nav/attack system computer. Conrac armament control unit (ACU) provides all inputs and outputs necessary to select and release weapons. Master arming switch has a 'practice' position that allows ACU to be cycled up to point of firing command. Kaiser AN/AVA-1 multi-mode display serves as a primary flight aid for navigation, approach, landing and weapons delivery. Basic vertical display indicator (VDI) is a 0.20 m (8 in) CRT which shows a synthetic landscape, sky and electronically generated command flight path that move to simulate the motion of these features as they would be seen by pilot through windscreen. Symbols are superimposed to augment basic attitude data, and for attack a second set of superimposed information provides a target symbol, steering symbol, and release and pull-up markers. A solid state radar data scan converter can provide on the same display an apparent real-world perspective of terrain, ten shades of grey defining terrain elevation at ten different segmented contour intervals up to 8.7 nm (16 km; 10 miles) ahead of aircraft. This makes it possible for pilot to fly in either terrain following or terrain avoidance mode at low altitude. Flight path and attack symbols can be superimposed over terrain elevation data on VDI, enabling pilot to attack while avoiding or following terrain in target area. Kaiser micromesh filter prevents 'washout' of data displayed on VDI in sunlight. Naval pilots use VDI as a primary flight instrument, for precise steering in navigation, weapons cues, progress, and status information during attack. For carrier landing, unit is used as a flight director and, linked to the APQ-148 radar, presents steering information, allowing pilot to select descent angle for final approach. Aircraft fitted with TRAM package have, in addition, an undernose precision-stabilised turret, with a sensor package containing both infra-red and laser equipment; INS updated with Litton AN/ASN-92 CAINS; new communications-navigation-identification (CNI) equipment including AN/ARC-159 UHF, AN/ARN-84 Tacan and AN/APX-72 IFF transponder; and automatic carrier landing capability. Sensor package is integrated with multi-mode radar, providing capability to detect, identify and attack a wide range of targets (as well as view the terrain) under adverse weather conditions, and with improved accuracy, using conventional or laser guided weapons. Bombardier/navigator operates TRAM system by first acquiring target on his radar screen. He then switches to FLIR (forward looking infra-red) system, using an optical zoom to enlarge target's image. After identifying and selecting his targets, bombardier uses a laser designator to mark target with a laser spot, on which his own laser guided weapons, or those from another aircraft, will home. Using TRAM's laser spot detector, A-6E can also acquire a target being illuminated from another aircraft, or designated by a forward air controller on the ground. GEC Sensors Ltd FLIR system, for night attack navigation, under development in 1988.

ARMAMENT: Five weapon attachment points, each with a 1,633 kg (3,600 lb) capacity (max external stores load 8,165 kg; 18,000 lb). Typical weapon loads are twenty-eight 500 lb bombs in clusters of six, or three 2,000 lb general purpose bombs plus two 1,135 litre (300 US gallon; 250 Imp gallon) drop tanks. AIM-9 Sidewinder missiles can be carried for air-to-air use. Harpoon missile capability added to weapons complement of A-6E/TRAM. The HARM missile has been test flown on the A-6E. Flight and firing tests have been carried out with the AGM-123A Skipper II, also on an A-6E.

DIMENSIONS, EXTERNAL:

Wing span	16.15 m (53 ft 0 in)
Wing mean aerodynamic chord	3.32 m (10 ft 10¾ in)
Width, wings folded	7.72 m (25 ft 4 in)

Grumman A-6E/TRAM Intruder of VA-55 'War Horses' Squadron landing on USS *Coral Sea*
(Brian M. Service)

Grumman A-6E/TRAM, with additional side views of EA-6A (centre) and EA-6B (bottom) *(Pilot Press)*

Grumman EA-6B Prowler ICAP-2 tactical jamming aircraft

Length overall	16.69 m (54 ft 9 in)
Height overall	4.93 m (16 ft 2 in)
Tailplane span	6.21 m (20 ft 4½ in)
Wheel track	3.32 m (10 ft 10½ in)
Wheelbase	5.24 m (17 ft 2¼ in)
AREAS:	
Wings, gross	49.1 m² (528.9 sq ft)
Flaperons (total)	3.81 m² (41.0 sq ft)
Trailing-edge flaps (total)	9.66 m² (104.0 sq ft)
Leading-edge slats (total)	4.63 m² (49.8 sq ft)
Fin	5.85 m² (62.93 sq ft)
Rudder	1.52 m² (16.32 sq ft)
Tailplane	10.87 m² (117.0 sq ft)
WEIGHTS AND LOADING:	
Weight empty	12,132 kg (26,746 lb)
Fuel load: internal	7,230 kg (15,939 lb)
external (five tanks)	4,558 kg (10,050 lb)
Max external load	8,165 kg (18,000 lb)
Max T-O weight: catapult	26,582 kg (58,600 lb)
field	27,397 kg (60,400 lb)
Max zero-stores weight	20,166 kg (44,460 lb)
Max landing weight: carrier	16,329 kg (36,000 lb)
field	20,411 kg (45,000 lb)
Max wing loading	557. kg/m² (114.2 lb/sq ft)
PERFORMANCE (no stores, except where stated):	
Never-exceed speed	700 knots (1,297 km/h; 806 mph)
Max level speed at S/L	
	560 knots (1,037 km/h; 644 mph)
Cruising speed at optimum altitude	
	412 knots (763 km/h; 474 mph)
Approach speed	110 knots (204 km/h; 127 mph)
Stalling speed:	
flaps up	142 knots (264 km/h; 164 mph)
flaps down	98 knots (182 km/h; 113 mph)
Max rate of climb at S/L	2,323 m (7,620 ft)/min
Rate of climb at S/L, one engine out	
	646 m (2,120 ft)/min
Service ceiling	12,925 m (42,400 ft)
Service ceiling, one engine out	6,400 m (21,000 ft)
Min T-O run	1,185 m (3,890 ft)
T-O to 15 m (50 ft)	1,390 m (4,560 ft)
Landing from 15 m (50 ft)	774 m (2,540 ft)
Min landing run	521 m (1,710 ft)
Range with max military load	
	878 nm (1,627 km; 1,011 miles)
Ferry range with max external fuel:	
tanks retained	2,380 nm (4,410 km; 2,740 miles)
tanks jettisoned when empty	
	2,818 nm (5,222 km; 3,245 miles)

GRUMMAN A-6F INTRUDER II and A-6G

Design work on the **A-6F** (details in 1988-89 *Jane's*) began in July 1984, and construction of a prototype was started during 1985. The programme called for five development prototypes taken from the A-6E contract, the first of which (162183) first flew on 25 August 1987, the second on 23 November 1987 and the third, an A-6 digital systems development aircraft intended to flight test the new systems of the A-6F, on 26 August 1988.

Funding for the A-6F programme was withdrawn by Congress in FY 1989 US defence budget cuts, and a number of alternatives was considered, including the upgrading of a total of 167 (later revised to 113) A-6Es to **A-6G** configuration. The A-6G would have included all of the planned digital avionics upgrades of the A-6F, but would have been powered by J52-P-408/409 turbojets, obviating the need for major airframe redesign. On 13 January the US Navy terminated the A-6E improvement and digital systems development (DSD) programme, which would have led to the A-6G, in favour of an A-6E upgrade programme (see A-6E entry for details).

GRUMMAN EA-6B PROWLER

The EA-6B is an advanced electronics development of the EA-6A for which Grumman received a prototype design and development contract in the Autumn of 1966. Except for a 1.37 m (4 ft 6 in) longer nose section and large fin pod, the external configuration of this version is similar to that of the basic A-6.

The longer nose section provides accommodation for a total crew of four, the two additional crewmen being necessary to operate the more advanced ECM equipment. This comprises high-powered electronic jammers and modern computer-directed receivers, which provided the US Navy with its first aircraft designed and built specifically for tactical electronic warfare. The prototype EA-6B flew for the first time on 25 May 1968.

Deliveries of the first 12 production aircraft began in January 1971, and a total of 149 EA-6Bs had been ordered up to and including FY 1988, of which 127 had been delivered. Grumman delivered 12 EA-6Bs in 1988, and expected to produce 12 in 1989, 12 in 1990, and seven in 1991. No EA-6Bs were included in the President's initial FY 1990 budget proposals, which does not affect deliveries until 1992.

ICAP (increased capability) versions of the EA-6B, with substantially increased jamming efficiency, are now standard. The first 21 production EA-6Bs were modified by Grumman to ICAP-1 configuration, and new-built aircraft up to 1983 were also to this standard. Modifications included an expanded onboard tactical jamming system with eight frequency bands, reduced response time, and a new multi-format display. In addition, an automatic carrier landing system (ACLS) to permit carrier recovery in zero-zero weather, a new defensive electronic counter-measures system (DECM) and new communications-navigation-identification (CNI) equipment are installed.

The prototype of a more advanced ICAP-2 version, with further improved jamming capability, made its first flight on 24 June 1980, and aircraft delivered since early 1984 have been to this higher standard. Each of the five pods carried under the EA-6B's wings and fuselage originally generated signals within a single frequency band. An ICAP-2 exciter in each pod generates signals in any one of seven frequency bands, and each pod can jam in two different bands simultaneously. ICAP-2 attained IOC in 1984 on new aircraft; some early EA-6Bs are being updated to ICAP-2 standard.

To follow this, an ADVCAP (advanced capability) programme was initiated in 1983, when Litton Industries' Amecom Division, with Texas Instruments and ITT as subcontractors, received a contract to develop a new receiver/processor group for the EA-6B's tactical jamming system. The ADVCAP EA-6B will carry HARM anti-radar missiles or drop tanks on two inboard underwing stations, with an additional outboard station under each wing for ECM pods. A prototype (156482) rebuilt to ADVCAP standard flew on 29 October 1989. Retrofit of up to 100 ICAP-2 Prowlers starts in 1991 with funding for three, to be delivered in FY 1994.

A prime feature of ADVCAP is the Lockheed-Sanders AN/ALQ-149 communications jammer, which requires the addition of a ventral group of antennae. In early 1989 Sanders Associates Inc delivered the last of seven engineering development models of its AN/ALQ-149 tactical communications countermeasures systems for flight trials on an EA-6B. The AN/ALQ-149 is contained in eight assemblies installed in the aircraft's equipment bay and comprises all antennae, receivers, signal recognisers, computers and controls necessary to detect, identify, evaluate and jam hostile communications signals and long-range early warning radar systems. Under its contract with Naval Air Systems Command, Sanders holds options for the supply of a further 95 production AN/ALQ-149 sets.

Other ADVCAP changes include improvement of the ALQ-99 jamming system by addition of a 7-18 GHz transmitter to complement the present 0.5-7 GHz capability; provision for a Westinghouse AN/ALQ-165 self-defence jammer; two additional (making three) AN/ALE-39 chaff/flare dispensers; provision for JTIDS; GPS/Navstar; a disc-based recorder/onboard programme loader; improved cooling system; substitution of 53.4 kN (12,000 lb st) J52-P-409 turbojets to accommodate an increased T-O

weight approaching 29,500 kg (65,036 lb); a 0.5 m (19¾ in) increase in fin height; re-contoured slats and flaps; drooped wing leading edges; and forward fuselage strakes.

Fourteen US Navy squadrons (VAQ-129 for training, 130, 131, 132, 133, 134, 135, 136, 137, 138, 139, 140, 141 and 142, all at Whidbey Island, WA, including one rotated to Atsugi, Japan) were equipped with the Prowler by 1989. The first detachment of US Marine Corps Prowler squadron VMAQ-2 began training on the EA-6B in September 1977 and the detachment deployed in late 1978. Two additional detachments have since completed training, and at least one is deployed at all times from the main base at Cherry Point, NC. Deployment with reserve units began in June 1989 with conversion of VAQ-309 at Whidbey, from EA-6As. VAQ-209 follows in 1991.

As part of the US Navy's vehicle improvement programme (VIP) for the EA-6B, Grumman modified one aircraft in 1988 as a VIP testbed for airframe changes aimed at improving stall and manoeuvring limitations. Narrow triangular glove strakes were added immediately forward of the wingroot; the tail fin was extended 0.46 m (1 ft 6 in) above the fin pod; wingtip speed brakes were modified to operate also as ailerons, deflecting with the flaperons for roll control; droop of the inboard and outboard leading-edge slats was increased; and the rear undersurface of the wings, including the trailing-edge flaps, was reconstructed. The VIP testbed aircraft was also refitted with more powerful (53.4 kN; 12,000 lb st) J52-P-409 turbojets.

The description of the standard A-6E Intruder applies also to the EA-6B, except as follows:

TYPE: Four-seat carrier- or land-based advanced ECM aircraft.

WINGS: As for A-6E, but reinforced to cater for increased gross weight, fatigue life and 5.5g load factor.

FUSELAGE: As for A-6E, but reinforcement of underfuselage structure in areas of arrester hook and landing gear attachments, and lengthened by 1.37 m (4 ft 6 in).

TAIL UNIT: As for A-6E, except for provision of a large fin-tip pod to house ECM equipment.

LANDING GEAR: As for A-6E, except for reinforcement of attachments, A-frame arrester hook, and upgrading of structure to cater for increased gross weight.

POWER PLANT: Two Pratt & Whitney J52-P-408 turbojets, each rated at 49.8 kN (11,200 lb st).

ACCOMMODATION: Crew of four under two separate upward opening canopies. Martin-Baker GRUEA 7 ejection seats for flight crew. The two additional crewmen are ECM Officers to operate the ALQ-99 equipment from the rear cockpit. Either ECMO can independently detect, assign, adjust and monitor the jammers. The ECMO in the starboard front seat is responsible for communications, navigation, defensive ECM and chaff dispensing.

SYSTEMS: Generally as for A-6E.

AVIONICS: AN/ALQ-99F tactical jamming system, in five integrally powered pods, with a total of 10 jamming transmitters. Each pod covers one of seven frequency bands. Sensitive surveillance receivers in the fin-tip pod for long-range detection of radars; emitter information is fed to a central digital computer (AYK-14 in ICAP-2 aircraft) that processes the signals for display and recording. Detection, identification, direction-finding and jammer-set-on sequence can be performed automatically or with manual assistance from crew. PRB Associates AN/TSQ-142 tactical mission support system. Teledyne Systems AN/ASN-123 navigation system with digital display group.

ARMAMENT: Originally unarmed, but currently being developed to carry Texas Instruments AGM-88A HARM anti-radar missiles underwing (due to enter flight test in 1989). Four underwing hardpoints on ICAP-2 aircraft, six on ADVCAP EA-6B.

DIMENSIONS, EXTERNAL: As for A-6E, except:

Width, wings folded	7.87 m (25 ft 10 in)
Length overall	18.24 m (59 ft 10 in)
Height overall	4.95 m (16 ft 3 in)
Wheelbase	5.23 m (17 ft 2 in)
WEIGHTS AND LOADING:	
Weight empty	14,588 kg (32,162 lb)
Internal fuel load	6,995 kg (15,422 lb)
Max external fuel load	4,547 kg (10,025 lb)
T-O weight from carrier in standoff jamming configuration (5 ECM pods)	24,703 kg (54,461 lb)
T-O weight from field in ferry range configuration (max internal and external fuel)	27,492 kg (60,610 lb)
Max T-O weight, catapult or field	
	29,483 kg (65,000 lb)
Max zero-fuel weight	17,708 kg (39,039 lb)
Max landing weight, carrier or field	
	20,638 kg (45,500 lb)
Max wing loading	600.5 kg/m² (123 lb/sq ft)
PERFORMANCE (A: no stores, B: 5 ECM pods):	
Never-exceed speed	710 knots (1,315 km/h; 817 mph)
Max level speed at S/L:	
A	566 knots (1,048 km/h; 651 mph)
B	530 knots (982 km/h; 610 mph)
Cruising speed at optimum altitude:	
A, B	418 knots (774 km/h; 481 mph)
Stalling speed, flaps up, max power:	
A	124 knots (230 km/h; 143 mph)

Grumman F-14A Tomcat of US Navy Squadron VF-33 from USS *America (Paul Jackson)*

Grumman F-14A(Plus) Tomcat carrier based multi-role fighter *(Pilot Press)*

Stalling speed, flaps down, max power:

A	84 knots (156 km/h; 97 mph)
Max rate of climb at S/L: A	3,932 m (12,900 ft)/min
B	3,057 m (10,030 ft)/min

Rate of climb at S/L, one engine out:

A	1,189 m (3,900 ft)/min
Service ceiling: A	12,550 m (41,200 ft)
B	11,580 m (38,000 ft)
Service ceiling, one engine out: A	8,930 m (29,300 ft)
T-O run: B	814 m (2,670 ft)
T-O to 15 m (50 ft): A	869 m (2,850 ft)
B	1,065 m (3,495 ft)
Landing from 15 m (50 ft): A	823 m (2,700 ft)
Landing run: A	579 m (1,900 ft)
B	655 m (2,150 ft)

Range with max external load, 5% reserves plus 20 min at S/L: B   955 nm (1,769 km; 1,099 miles)

Ferry range with max external fuel:

tanks retained	1,756 nm (3,254 km; 2,022 miles)
tanks jettisoned when empty	2,085 nm (3,861 km; 2,399 miles)

GRUMMAN TOMCAT
US Navy designation: F-14

The Tomcat was declared winner of the US Navy's VFX carrier-based fighter competition on 15 January 1969, and the first of 12 development aircraft made its initial flight on 21 December 1970. Originally, the planned programme was intended to provide 497 Navy Tomcats, including the 12 development aircraft, but this total is now to be increased considerably, extending production into the 1990s. By the end of 1987 the US Navy was scheduled to have 28 Tomcat squadrons, including four reserve and two training squadrons, operating from 12 aircraft carriers and the Naval Air Stations at Miramar, California, Oceana, Virginia, and Dallas, Texas.

Production versions are as follows:

F-14A. Initial version, deployed from October 1972, initially with USN squadrons VF-1 and VF-2. Total of 557, including the 12 R & D aircraft, delivered to US Navy by April 1987, when production of this version ended. Early aircraft powered by TF30-P-412A turbofans, but those delivered from FY 1983 (final 102 aircraft) have improved TF30-P-414As of the same rating. Thirty-two are being upgraded to F-14A(Plus) standard, with F110 engines. In addition, 79 F-14As were delivered to Iran in 1976-78; those

retained the Phoenix weapon system but had slightly different ECM equipment from US Navy Tomcats.

F-14A Squadrons are VF-1, 2, 21, 24, 51, 111, 114, 124 (training), 154, 211, 213, 301 (Reserve) and 302 (Reserve) at Miramar, CA; VF-11, 14, 31, 32, 33, 41, 74, 84, 101 (training), 103, 142 and 143 at Oceana, VA; and VF-201 and 202 of the Reserve at Dallas, TX.

F-14A(Plus). Interim updated version, produced pending introduction of F-14D derivative. Development began in July 1984, when Grumman was awarded a $984 million fixed price contract for an F-14A update programme which provided for development of the F-14A(Plus) 'Super Tomcat' with F110-GE-400 engines but otherwise mostly unchanged, and for the F-14D with F110-GE-400s, digital avionics and a new radar. Grumman is prime contractor for the engine and avionics upgrades, with General Electric and Hughes Aircraft as subcontractors. The F110-GE-400 is rated at 62.3 kN (14,000 lb st) dry and 102.75 kN (23,100 lb st) with max afterburning, and offers 82 per cent parts commonality with the F110-GE-100 engine for the USAF's F-15s and F-16s. A 1.27 m (4 ft 2 in) plug is inserted in the afterburner section to match the engine to F-14A inlet position and airframe contours, and only secondary structure requires modification to accept the new engine. Operational improvements conferred by the new engine include unrestricted throttle movement throughout the aircraft's flight envelope and fewer compressor stalls.

Grumman's full scale development programme involved five aircraft, including the F-14B prototype (157986) which first flew with definitive F110-GE-400 engines on 29 September 1986 as part of the F-14A(Plus) programme. Three, the first of which was flown on 24 November 1987, were used for avionics and radar development, in conjunction with a TA-3B Skywarrior aircraft. One was to be completed to full F-14D standard and to join that programme after serving on the F-14A(Plus) development programme. The development schedule included some 36 months of flight testing. Production of the F-14A(Plus) followed completion of the F-14A programme, with the first of 38 aircraft (18, 15 and five, funded in FYs 1986-88) flown for the first time on 14 November 1987 and delivered to VF-101 at NAS Oceana, Virginia, on 11 April 1988. Sixteen more F-14A(Plus) Tomcats were delivered in 1988, with 17 scheduled for delivery in 1989. IOC with two US Navy fleet squadrons was achieved in early 1989, and completion of F-14A(Plus) deliveries by May 1990. In

addition, 32 F-14As will be upgraded to F-14A(Plus) standard, with F110 engines. The Plus variant has been issued to F-14A squadrons VF-24, 74, 101, 103 and 211.

F-14D. The F-14D upgrade modifies some 60 per cent of the F-14A's analog avionics, providing new weapons management, navigation, displays and control functions, with digital bus integration of the Litton AN/ALR-67 threat warning and recognition system, Westinghouse/ITT AN/ALQ-165 airborne self protection jammer (ASPJ), joint tactical information distribution system (JTIDS), General Electric Aerospace Electronic Systems infra-red search and track sensor (IRST) and television camera set (TCS), with emphasis on hardware and software commonality with F/A-18 and latest A-6 programmes. The new Hughes radar, designated AN/APG-71, is based on the AN/AWG-9 radar, with improved ECCM capability and incorporating monopulse angle tracking, digital scan control, target identification and raid assessment. The AN/APG-71 features non-co-operative target identification and is able to counter sophisticated ECM by means of a low-sidelobe antenna and sidelobe blanking guard channel, frequency agility, and a new high-speed digital signal processor based on elements of the USAF's multi-stage improvement programme (MSIP) of the F-15's AN/APG-70 radar. Provision is also made for integration of the AMRAAM missile. The F-14D is equipped with Martin-Baker Navy aircrew common ejection seats (NACES).

Funding of new production F-14Ds totalled 37 (seven, 12 and 18 in FYs 1988-90) towards a planned 127 before the programme was cancelled as an economy measure in 1989. Plans to remanufacture approximately 400 F-14A and F-14A(Plus) aircraft to F-14D standard are unaffected by the cancellation of new production. Six conversions were funded in FY 1990 and 12 are planned for FY 1991.

The F110-GE-400 powered F-14A(Plus) and F-14D show significant performance benefits resulting from the engine's 43 per cent increase in afterburning and 37 per cent increase in military (non-afterburning) thrust over the Pratt & Whitney TF30-P-414A engine. Specific excess energy is increased by 20 per cent, afterburning specific fuel consumption is reduced by 30 per cent, and deck launch intercept radius and combat air patrol time on station are expected to be increased by 62 and 34 per cent respectively, as a result of lower fuel burns and the F110 engined Tomcat's ability to be launched without use of afterburner. Time to 10,670 m (35,000 ft) is expected to be reduced by 61 per cent, and acceleration time by 43 per cent.

Grumman is studying an advanced F-14, designated **Tomcat-21**, that could satisfy US Navy requirements for a strike fighter in the next century. The company-funded effort is aimed at defining an economical alternative to the Navy version of the USAF's Advanced Tactical Fighter (ATF). It suggests that the Tomcat-21 would have 90 per cent of the advertised capability of the ATF for 60 per cent of the cost.

The following description applies to the current operational F-14A:

TYPE: Two-seat carrier based multi-role fighter.

WINGS: Variable geometry mid-wing monoplane, with 20° of leading-edge sweep in the fully forward position and 68° when fully swept. Oversweep position of 75° for carrier stowage. Wing position is programmed automatically for optimum performance throughout the flight regime, but manual override is provided. A short movable wing outer panel, needing only a comparatively light pivot structure, results from the wide fuselage and fixed centre-section 'glove', with pivot points 2.72 m (8 ft 11 in) from the centreline of the airframe. The inboard wing sections, adjacent to the fuselage, arc upward slightly to minimise cross-sectional area and wave drag, and consist basically of a one-piece electron beam-welded assembly, 6.70 m (22 ft) in span, made from Ti-6A1-4V titanium alloy. Small canard surfaces, known as glove vanes, swing out from the leading-edge of the fixed portion of the wing, to a maximum of 15° in relation to the leading-edge, as Mach number is increased. Spoilers on upper surfaces of wing. Stabilisation in pitch, provided by the canard surfaces, leaves the differential tailplane free to perform its primary control function. Trailing-edge flaps extend over almost entire span. Leading-edge slats.

FUSELAGE: All-metal semi-monocoque structure, with machined frames, main longerons of titanium, and light alloy stressed skin. The centre-fuselage section is a simple, fuel-carrying box structure; forward fuselage section comprises cockpit and upward hinged nose giving access to radar. The aft section has a tapered aerofoil shape to minimise drag, with a fuel dump pipe projecting from the rear. Speed brakes located on the upper and lower surfaces, between the bases of the vertical tail fins. Rear fuselage and vertical tail surfaces manufactured by Fairchild Republic.

TAIL UNIT: Twin vertical fins, mounted at the rear of each engine nacelle. Fins and rudders of light alloy honeycomb sandwich. Outward canted ventral fin under each nacelle. The all-flying multi-spar horizontal surfaces have skins of boron epoxy composite material and honeycomb trailing-edges.

LANDING GEAR: Retractable tricycle type. Twin-wheel nose unit and single-wheel main units retract forward, main units inward into bottom of engine air intake trunks.

Original beryllium brakes were replaced with Goodyear lightweight carbon brakes from Spring 1981. Arrester hook under rear fuselage, housed in small ventral fairing. Nose-tow catapult attachment on nose unit.

ENGINE INTAKES: Straight two-dimensional external compression inlets. A double-hinged ramp extends down from the top of each intake, and these are programmed to provide the correct airflow to the engines automatically under all flight conditions. Each intake is canted slightly away from the fuselage, from which it is separated by some 0.25 m (10 in) to allow sufficient clearance for the turbulent fuselage boundary layer to pass between fuselage and intake without causing turbulence within the intake. Engine inlet ducts and aft nacelle structures are manufactured by Rohr Corporation. The inlet duct, constructed largely of aluminium alloy honeycomb, is about 4.27 m (14 ft) long; the aft nacelle structure, of bonded aluminium alloy honeycomb and conventional aluminium alloy sheet, is about 4.88 m (16 ft) in length.

POWER PLANT: Early aircraft have two Pratt & Whitney TF30-P-412A turbofans of 93 kN (20,900 lb st) each with afterburning, mounted in ducts which open to provide 180° access for ease of maintenance. F-14As delivered from 1984-87 have TF30-P-414As of the same rating. Garrett ATS200-50 air turbine starter. Integral fuel tanks in outer wings, each with capacity of 1,117 litres (295 US gallons; 246 Imp gallons); between engines in rear fuselage, with capacity of 2,453 litres (648 US gallons; 539 Imp gallons); and forward of wing carry-through structure, capacity 2,616 litres (691 US gallons; 575 Imp gallons); plus two feeder tanks with combined capacity of 1,726 litres (456 US gallons; 380 Imp gallons). Total internal fuel capacity 9,029 litres (2,385 US gallons; 1,986 Imp gallons). An external auxiliary fuel tank can be carried beneath each intake trunk, each containing 1,011 litres (267 US gallons; 222 Imp gallons). Retractable flight refuelling probe on starboard side of fuselage near front cockpit.

ACCOMMODATION: Pilot and naval flight officer seated in tandem on Martin-Baker GRU7A rocket assisted zero/zero ejection seats, under a one-piece bubble canopy, hinged at the rear and offering all-round view.

AVIONICS: Hughes AN/AWG-9 weapons control system, with ability to detect airborne targets at ranges of more than 65-170 nm (120-315 km; 75-195 miles) according to their size, and ability to track 24 enemy targets and attack six of them simultaneously at varied altitudes and distances. Fairchild AN/AWG-15F fire control set; CP-1066/A central air data computer; CP-1050/A computer signal data converter; AN/ASW-27B digital data link; AN/APX-76(V)1FF interrogator; AN/APX-72 IFF transponder; AN/ASA-79 multiple display indicator group; Kaiser Aerospace AN/AVG-12 vertical and head-up display system. AN/ARC-51 and AN/ARC-159 UHF com; AN/ARR-69 UHF auxiliary receiver; KY-28 cryptographic system; LS-460/B intercom; AN/ASN-92(V) INS; A/A24G39 AHRS; AN/APN-154 beacon augmentor; AN/APN-194(V) radar altimeter; ARA-63A receiver-decoder; AN/ARN-84 micro Tacan; AN/ARA-50 UHF ADF; AN/APR-27/50 radar receiver; AN/APR-25/45 radar warning set. TV optical unit in undernose pod.

ARMAMENT AND OPERATIONAL EQUIPMENT: One General Electric M61A-1 Vulcan 20 mm gun mounted in the port side of forward fuselage, with 675 rounds of ammunition. Four Sparrow air-to-air missiles mounted partially submerged in the underfuselage, or four Phoenix missiles carried on special pallets which attach to the bottom of the fuselage. Two wing pylons, one under each fixed wing section, can carry four Sidewinder missiles or two additional Sparrow or Phoenix missiles with two Sidewinders. Various combinations of missiles and bombs. ECM equipment includes Goodyear AN/ALE-29 and AN/ALE-39 chaff and flare dispensers, with integral jammers. Since 1979, Northrop Corporation has been manufacturing television camera sets (TCSs) for installation on F-14As. The TCS is a closed-circuit TV system, offering both wide-angle (acquisition) and telescopic (identification) fields of view. Mounted beneath the nose of the F-14A, the TCS automatically searches for, acquires and locks on to distant targets, displaying them on monitors for the pilot and flight officer. By allowing early identification of targets, the system permits crews to make combat decisions earlier than was possible previously. Small undernose pod for Sanders AN/ALQ-100/126 deception jamming system, relocated under camera package of aircraft with Northrop TCS. During 1980-81, a total of 49 F-14As were allocated to carry TARPS (tactical air reconnaissance pod system), containing a KS-87B frame camera, KA-99 low altitude panoramic camera, and AN/AAD-5 infra-red reconnaissance equipment, on underbelly attachment.

DIMENSIONS, EXTERNAL:

Wing span: unswept	19.54 m (64 ft 1½ in)
swept	11.65 m (38 ft 2½ in)
overswept	10.15 m (33 ft 3½ in)
Wing aspect ratio	7.28
Length overall	19.10 m (62 ft 8 in)
Height overall	4.88 m (16 ft 0 in)
Tailplane span	9.97 m (32 ft 8½ in)
Distance between fin tips	3.25 m (10 ft 8 in)

First Grumman X-29A FSW (forward swept wing) technology demonstrator

Grumman X-29A FSW demonstrator (General Electric F404-GE-400 turbofan) *(Pilot Press)*

Wheel track	5.00 m (16 ft 5 in)
Wheelbase	7.02 m (23 ft 0½ in)
AREAS:	
Wings, gross	52.49 m² (565.0 sq ft)
Leading-edge slats (total)	4.29 m² (46.2 sq ft)
Trailing-edge flaps (total)	9.87 m² (106.3 sq ft)
Spoilers (total)	1.97 m² (21.2 sq ft)
Fins (total)	7.90 m² (85.0 sq ft)
Rudders (total)	3.06 m² (33.0 sq ft)
Horizontal tail surfaces (total)	13.01 m² (140.0 sq ft)
WEIGHTS (P-414A engines):	
Weight empty	18,191 kg (40,104 lb)
Fuel (usable): internal	7,348 kg (16,200 lb)
external	1,724 kg (3,800 lb)
Max external weapon load	6,577 kg (14,500 lb)
T-O weight: clean	26,632 kg (58,715 lb)
with 4 Sparrow	27,086 kg (59,714 lb)
with 6 Phoenix	32,098 kg (70,764 lb)
max	33,724 kg (74,349 lb)
Design landing weight	23,510 kg (51,830 lb)
PERFORMANCE:	
Max level speed:	
at height	
Mach 2.34 (1,342 knots; 2,485 km/h; 1,544 mph)	
at low level	
Mach 1.2 (792 knots; 1,468 km/h; 912 mph)	
Max cruising speed	
400-550 knots (741-1,019 km/h; 460-633 mph)	
*Carrier approach speed 134 knots (248 km/h; 154 mph)	
*Stalling speed 115 knots (213 km/h; 132 mph)	
Max rate of climb at S/L over 9,140 m (30,000 ft)/min	
Service ceiling above 15,240 m (50,000 ft)	
Min T-O distance 427 m (1,400 ft)	
Min landing distance 884 m (2,900 ft)	
Max range with external fuel	
approx 1,735 nm (3,220 km; 2,000 miles)	

*carrier landing design gross weight

GRUMMAN OV-1/RV-1 MOHAWK

Various updates and improvements are being made to US Army OV-1Ds to enable them to continue operating effectively into the late 1990s. Funding for current updates, initiated in FY 1986, covers wing and fuselage strengthening of 18 aircraft to increase fatigue life from 7,000 to 12,000 hours, conducting of fatigue testing and monitoring, and the fitting of one aircraft with new com/nav equipment and cockpit display systems. The com/nav prototype was delivered to the Army for evaluation during 1988, when Grumman anticipated orders to modify at least 58 more OV-1Ds to this standard. Airframe strengthening of 20 more OV/RV-1s was approved in the FY 1987 budget, making 38 aircraft scheduled for this treatment. The 36

'Quick Look' AR-1C/Ds are due for replacement by Beechcraft RC-12Ks, beginning in 1991.

The US Army has flight tested in recent years an OV-1D fitted with more powerful engines, and Grumman has tested improved stall warning and electrical power/anti-icing systems for the Mohawk.

Equipment installed in the OV-1D and RV-1D conversions was detailed in the 1989-90 and previous issues of *Jane's*.

GRUMMAN MODEL 712 FORWARD SWEPT WING DEMONSTRATOR
US Air Force designation: X-29A

Grumman's FSW design offers the promise of a new generation of tactical aircraft that will be smaller, lighter in weight, less costly, but more efficient than contemporary fighters. The aerodynamic advantages of forward wing sweep include improved manoeuvrability, with virtually spin-proof characteristics, better low-speed handling, and reduced stalling speeds. In addition, such aircraft have the advantage of lower drag across the entire operational envelope, particularly at speeds approaching Mach 1, which will permit the use of a less powerful engine.

Early history of the X-29A programme was detailed in the 1989-90 and previous editions, together with a technical description. The first aircraft was grounded after its 242nd flight on 6 December 1988, but on 23 May 1989 the second X-29A began a series of high angle of attack trials. These extended to 40° at first, and later to a maximum of about 80°, exploring the aircraft's three-axis manoeuvrability and agility at high AOA at altitudes between 10,670-12,200 m (35,000-40,000 ft).

GRUMMAN S-2T TURBO TRACKER

Grumman received a $260 million US Navy foreign military sales contract for a turboprop modification of its S-2 Tracker anti-submarine warfare aircraft, which involves replacing the S-2's 1,141 kW (1,530 hp) Curtiss-Wright R-1820-82 piston engines with 1,227 kW (1,645 shp) Garrett TPE331-1-5AW turboprops driving four-blade Dowty advanced technology propellers. The Turbo Tracker has a 270 knot (500 km/h; 311 mph) maximum speed at 1,525 m (5,000 ft), a 500 kg (1,102 lb) increase in payload, and improvements in cruising speed, T-O and landing distances, single-engine rate of climb and engine TBO.

Prototype installation, in two S-2G aircraft, was carried out by Tracor Aviation. Included in the modification programme is a new avionics and ASW package which comprises a GEC Avionics MAPADS 902F acoustic processor, AN/ASQ-504(V) magnetic anomaly detector, AN/APS-509 radar, AN/ARR-84 acoustic receivers and an

AN/ASN-150 tactical navigation system coupled with the 72R inertial navigation system and Collins avionics. Thirty-two S-2Ts, including a pre-production aircraft, are to be supplied to Taiwan under a US Navy FMS contract. Grumman has converted two, and will supply conversion kits for local modification of the remainder. Other potential customers include Argentina, Brazil, Peru, Thailand, Turkey, Uruguay and Venezuela.

Retouched photograph showing engine configuration of Grumman S-2T Turbo Tracker with Garrett TPE331-1-5AW turboprops

GULFSTREAM AEROSPACE
GULFSTREAM AEROSPACE CORPORATION
PO Box 2206, Savannah International Airport, Savannah, Georgia 31402-2206
Telephone: 1 (912) 964 3000
Telex: 546470 GULF AERO
Fax: 1 (912) 964 3775
CHAIRMAN AND CHIEF EXECUTIVE OFFICER:
  Allen E. Paulson
PRESIDENT AND CHIEF OPERATING OFFICER:
  Albert H. Glenn
SENIOR VICE-PRESIDENT, ENGINEERING:
  Charles N. Coppi
SENIOR VICE-PRESIDENT, MARKETING:
  Robert H. Cooper
VICE-PRESIDENT, INTERNATIONAL SALES:
  Joseph E. Anckner
VICE-PRESIDENT, DOMESTIC MARKETING AND ADMINISTRATION:
  Herbert B. Franck
CORPORATE COMMUNICATIONS DIRECTOR:
  Alvin F. Balaban

On 13 February 1990 Mr Allen Paulson, Chairman and Chief Executive Officer of Gulfstream Aerospace Corporation, and Forstmann Little and Company announced that they had agreed to purchase the company from the Chrysler Corporation, which had acquired it from Mr Paulson in August 1985. The acquisition was formally concluded on 19 March 1990.

In March 1986 Gulfstream acquired a 9,290 m² (100,000 sq ft) aircraft completion facility at Long Beach International Airport, California, which had been operated formerly by AiResearch Aviation. This facility has since been expanded to 20,438 m² (220,000 sq ft) and is capable of handling outfitting and completion of up to 17 Gulfstream IVs at a time.

GULFSTREAM AEROSPACE GULFSTREAM IV
Design of this advanced version of the Gulfstream III was initiated in March 1983, and construction of four production prototypes (one for static testing) began in 1985. Rollout of the first aircraft (N404GA) occurred on 11 September 1985, with a first flight following on 19 September. The second prototype flew on 11 June 1986, followed by the third in August 1986. FAA certification was granted on 22 April 1987, following 1,412 hours of flight testing. By March 1990 Gulfstream Aerospace had delivered 130 Gulfstream IVs, including 40 in 1989, and expected to deliver 32 in 1990. At that time the order backlog stood at 15.

On 12 June 1987 the third production Gulfstream IV (N440GA), with company Chairman Mr Allen Paulson in command, flew from le Bourget Airport, Paris, on an attempt to set a westbound around-the-world record. Routing via fuel stops at Edmonton, Alberta; Midway Island; Kota Kinabalu, Malaysia; and Dubai, UAE, the aircraft returned to Paris on 14 June after covering a total distance of 19,887.9 nm (36,832.44 km; 22,886.6 miles) in 45 h 25 min 10 s at an average speed of 437.86 knots (810.93 km/h; 503.89 mph). Gulfstream achieved a total of 22 world records with this flight.

On 26/27 February 1988 a Gulfstream IV (N400GA) captained by Mr Paulson flew from Houston, Texas, on an attempt to set an eastbound around-the-world record. The aircraft, named *Pursuit of Perfection*, routed via fuel stops at Shannon, Ireland; Dubai, UAE; Taipei, Taiwan; and Maui, Hawaii, returning to Houston after covering a total distance of 20,028.68 nm (37,093.1 km; 23,048.6 miles) in 36 h 8 min 34 s, at an average speed of 554.15 knots (1,026.29 km/h; 637.71 mph). Gulfstream was awarded eleven records for the flight, which broke an around-the-world record set 30 days previously by a United Airlines Boeing 747SP. The Gulfstream IV was equipped with an additional fuel tank in its cabin, capacity 3,629 kg (8,000 lb),

Gulfstream Aerospace Gulfstream IV twin-turbofan executive transport *(Pilot Press)*

for the flight, for which its T-O weight was 34,782 kg (76,681 lb). This tank installation is available as an option for civil and SRA-4 versions of the Gulfstream IV.

Generally similar to the Gulfstream III, the Gulfstream IV differs primarily in having a structurally redesigned wing, incorporating 30 per cent fewer parts and offering a weight saving of 395 kg (870 lb) with provision for 453 kg (1,000 lb) more internal fuel capacity; a tailplane of increased span; a fuselage lengthened by 1.37 m (4 ft 6 in); a sixth window on each side of the cabin; rudder, ailerons and spoilers made of carbonfibre; Rolls-Royce RB183-03 Tay Mk 611-8 turbofans; and a flight deck incorporating advanced CRT displays and digital avionics.

TYPE: Twin-turbofan long-range executive transport.

WINGS: Cantilever low-wing monoplane of light alloy construction, with carbonfibre ailerons and spoilers; manufactured by Textron Aerostructures. Advanced sonic rooftop wing section. Thickness/chord ratio of 10% at wing station 50 and 8.6% at wing station 414. Dihedral 3°. Incidence 3° 30′ at root, −2° at tip. Sweepback at quarter-chord 27° 40′. NASA (Whitcomb) aluminium honeycomb winglets. Plain ailerons of aluminium alloy, hydraulically powered with manual reversion. Single-slotted Fowler trailing-edge flaps. Three spoilers on upper surface of each wing at 12 per cent chord, immediately forward of trailing-edge flaps, operated differentially to complement ailerons for roll control and collectively to serve as airbrakes. Trim tab in port aileron. Four vortilons and a single 'tripper' strip under leading-edge of each wing to enhance low speed stall characteristics. Anti-icing of leading-edges by engine bleed air.

FUSELAGE: Conventional semi-monocoque fail-safe pressurised structure of light alloy, with carbonfibre in cabin floor and flight deck areas.

TAIL UNIT: Cantilever T tail of light alloy, except for rudder and some tailplane components of carbonfibre. Swept horizontal and vertical surfaces. Trim tab in rudder and each elevator. Hydraulically powered controls with manual reversion.

LANDING GEAR: Retractable tricycle type with twin wheels on each unit. Main units retract inward, steerable nose unit forward. Mainwheel tyres size 34 × 9.25-16, pressure 12.07 bars (175 lb/sq in). Nosewheel tyres size 21 × 7.25-10, pressure 7.9 bars (115 lb/sq in). Loral aircooled carbon brakes, with Loral fully modulating anti-skid units. Loral digital electronic brake-by-wire system. Dowty electronic steer-by-wire system.

POWER PLANT: Two Rolls-Royce Tay Mk 611-8 turbofans, each flat rated at 61.6 kN (13,850 lb st) to ISA +15°C. Target type thrust reversers. Fuel in two integral wing tanks, with total capacity of 16,542 litres (4,370 US gallons; 3,639 Imp gallons). Single pressure fuelling point in leading-edge of starboard wing.

ACCOMMODATION: Crew of two or three. Standard seating for 14 to 19 passengers in pressurised and air-conditioned cabin. Galley, toilet and large baggage compartment, capacity 907 kg (2,000 lb), at rear of cabin. Integral airstair door at front of cabin on port side. Baggage compartment door on port side. Electrically heated wraparound windscreen. Six cabin windows, including one overwing emergency exit, on each side.

SYSTEMS: Cabin pressurisation system max differential 0.65 bars (9.45 lb/sq in). Air-conditioning system. Two independent hydraulic systems, each 207 bars (3,000 lb/sq in). Maximum flow rate 83.3 litres (22 US gallons; 18.3 Imp gallons)/min. Two bootstrap type hydraulic reservoirs, pressurised to 4.14 bars (60 lb/sq in). Garrett GTCP36-100 APU in tail compartment, flight rated to 9,150 m (30,000 ft). Electrical system includes two 36kVA alternators with two solid state 30kVA converters to provide 23kVA 115/200V 400Hz AC power and 250A of regulated 28V DC power; two 24V 40Ah nickel-cadmium storage batteries and external power socket.

AVIONICS AND EQUIPMENT: Standard items include a Honeywell SPZ-8000 digital automatic flight control system, Honeywell FMZ-800 Phase II flight management system and six 20.3 cm × 20.3 cm (8 in × 8 in) colour CRT displays, two each for primary flight instruments, navigation and engine instrument and crew alerting systems (EICAS); dual fail-operational flight guidance systems including auto throttles; dual air data systems; dual flight management systems with vertical and lateral navigation and performance management, and digital colour radar. System integration is accomplished through a Honeywell avionics standard communications bus (ASCB). Other factory-installed avionics include dual VHF/HF com; dual VOR/LOC/GS and markers; dual DME; dual ADF; dual radio altimeters; dual transponders; dual cockpit audio; dual flight guidance and performance computers; dual laser INS; attitude/heading reference system; and cockpit voice recorder. The system is designed to provide growth potential for interface with MLS, GPS and VLF Omega in future developments. Optional avionics include Racal Satfone satellite communications equipment.

Gulfstream Aerospace Gulfstream IV twin-turbofan executive transport

DIMENSIONS, EXTERNAL:

Wing span over winglets	23.72 m (77 ft 10 in)
Wing chord:	
at root (fuselage centreline)	5.94 m (19 ft 5⅞ in)
at tip	1.85 m (6 ft 0¾ in)
Wing aspect ratio	5.92
Length overall	26.92 m (88 ft 4 in)
Fuselage: Length	24.03 m (78 ft 10 in)
Max diameter	2.39 m (7 ft 10 in)
Height overall	7.57 m (24 ft 10 in)
Tailplane span	9.75 m (32 ft 0 in)
Wheel track	4.17 m (13 ft 8 in)
Wheelbase	11.61 m (38 ft 1¼ in)
Passenger door (fwd, port): Height	1.57 m (5 ft 2 in)
Width	0.91 m (3 ft 0 in)
Baggage door (rear): Height	0.72 m (2 ft 4½ in)
Width	0.91 m (2 ft 11¾ in)

DIMENSIONS, INTERNAL:

Cabin:

Length, incl galley, toilet and baggage compartment	
	13.74 m (45 ft 1 in)
Max width	2.24 m (7 ft 4 in)
Max height	1.85 m (6 ft 1 in)
Floor area	22.9 m² (247 sq ft)
Volume	47.62 m³ (1682 cu ft)
Cabin volume	42.84 m³ (1,513 cu ft)
Passenger area volume	30.50 m³ (1,077 cu ft)
Flight deck volume	3.51 m³ (124.0 cu ft)
Rear baggage compartment volume 4.78 m³ (169.0 cu ft)	

AREAS:

Wings, gross	88.29 m² (950.39 sq ft)
Ailerons (total, incl tab)	2.68 m² (28.86 sq ft)
Trailing-edge flaps (total)	11.97 m² (128.84 sq ft)
Spoilers (total)	7.46 m² (80.27 sq ft)
Winglets (total)	2.38 m² (25.66 sq ft)
Fin	10.92 m² (117.53 sq ft)
Rudder, incl tab	4.16 m² (44.75 sq ft)
Horizontal tail surfaces (total)	18.77 m² (202.0 sq ft)
Elevators (total, incl tabs)	5.22 m² (56.22 sq ft)

WEIGHTS AND LOADINGS:

Manufacturer's weight empty	16,102 kg (35,500 lb)
Typical operating weight empty	19,278 kg (42,500 lb)
Max payload	1,814 kg (4,000 lb)
Max usable fuel	13,381 kg (29,500 lb)
Max T-O weight	33,203 kg (73,200 lb)
Max ramp weight	33,384 kg (73,600 lb)
Max zero-fuel weight	21,092 kg (46,500 lb)
Max landing weight	26,535 kg (58,500 lb)
Max wing loading	375.9 kg/m² (77.02 lb/sq ft)
Max power loading	269.6 kg/kN (2.64 lb/lb st)

PERFORMANCE (at max T-O weight, ISA, except where indicated):

Max operating speed	
	340 knots (629 km/h; 391 mph) CAS
	or Mach 0.88
Max cruising speed at 9,450 m (31,000 ft)	
	509 knots (943 km/h; 586 mph)
Normal cruising speed at 13,715 m (45,000 ft)	
	Mach 0.80 (459 knots; 850 km/h; 528 mph)
Stalling speed at max landing weight:	
wheels and flaps up	122 knots (227 km/h; 141 mph)
wheels and flaps down	
	108 knots (200 km/h; 124 mph)
Approach speed at max landing weight	
	140 knots (259 km/h; 161 mph)
Max rate of climb at S/L	1,220 m (4,000 ft)/min
Rate of climb at S/L, one engine out	
	337 m (1,105 ft)/min
Max operating altitude	13,715 m (45,000 ft)
Runway LCN	35

FAA balanced T-O field length at S/L	
	1,609 m (5,280 ft)
Landing from 15 m (50 ft)	1,032 m (3,386 ft)
Range with max payload, normal cruising speed and NBAA IFR reserves	
	3,694 nm (6,845 km; 4,254 miles)
Range with max fuel, eight passengers, at Mach 0.80 and with NBAA IFR reserves	
	4,220 nm (7,820 km; 4,859 miles)

OPERATIONAL NOISE LEVELS (FAR Pt 36):

T-O	76.8 EPNdB
Approach	91.0 EPNdB
Sideline	87.3 EPNdB

GULFSTREAM AEROSPACE SRA-4

Gulfstream Aerospace has extended the special missions concept of the Gulfstream IV under the designation **SRA-4**. The aircraft is available with integrated systems and equipment for surveillance/reconnaissance, electronic warfare support, maritime patrol, anti-submarine warfare, medical evacuation, priority cargo and administrative transport roles, with cabin interiors configured to permit rapid changes of role. An upward opening cargo door 1.6 m (5 ft 3 in) high and 2.1 m (6 ft 11 in) wide can be installed in the starboard forward fuselage area, aft of the flight deck, to facilitate loading and unloading of bulky cargo, mission equipment or stretchers.

In typical maritime patrol configuration the SRA-4 is equipped with a nose mounted high definition surface search radar, forward looking infra-red detection system, electronic support measures, flare/marker launch tubes, radar/IRDS, nav/com and ESM consoles, positions for up to eight observers/console operators, stowage and deployment facilities for survival equipment, and a crew rest area. With a mission payload of 1,950-4,173 kg (4,300-9,200 lb), including 272 kg (600 lb) of expendable stores, the SRA-4 could operate over a 600 nm (1,112 km; 690 mile) radius of action, cruising to the patrol area at 12,500 m (41,000 ft) at 454 knots (841 km/h; 523 mph) and remain on station for four to six hours, manoeuvring at 61 m (200 ft) for up to 33 per cent of that time, and searching at 3,050 m (10,000 ft) for the remainder, returning to base at 13,715 m (45,000 ft).

A development aircraft for the electronic warfare support version of the SRA-4 was exhibited at the 1988 Farnborough Air Show. This aircraft (N413GA) featured a ventral fin to offset the effect of a belly-mounted pod for jamming antennae beneath the forward fuselage section, and a small pod for a DF/Omni antenna on top of the tail fin. The cabin of the production version will contain operators' consoles and equipment, including a microwave generator and amplifier rack, modulation generator rack,

radio racks, and chaff supply and cutters to simulate realistically the EW conditions created by an adversary's aircraft and missiles. As well as this primary training mission, the aircraft could be used for testing and evaluation of weapons systems, and for the development of effective electronic warfare tactics.

In electronic surveillance/reconnaissance roles the SRA-4 can be equipped with a variety of sensors, including side-looking synthetic aperture radar in a belly-mounted pod beneath the forward fuselage section, long-range oblique photographic camera (LOROP), ESM, VHF/UHF/HF communications for C³ functions, chaff dispensers, infra-red countermeasures housed in the tailcone, SAR equipment and accommodation for mission specialists for each sensor. A typical electronic surveillance mission profile with a total mission payload of 1,950 kg (4,300 lb) would permit 10.5 hours on station at loiter altitudes between 10,670 and 15,550 m (35,000-51,000 ft).

For anti-submarine warfare applications the SRA-4 can be equipped with a nose-mounted high definition maritime surveillance radar offering persicope/snorkel detection capability, FLIR, sonobuoy launchers and acoustic processor, a tailcone-mounted magnetic anomaly detector (MAD) boom, ESM, torpedo stowage in a weapons bay beneath the forward fuselage, and provision for carriage and launch of one anti-shipping missile on each underwing stores hardpoint. With a mission payload of 2,503 kg (5,518 lb), including six crew, an ASW SRA-4 could operate over a 1,000 nm (1,853 km; 1,151 mile) radius of action with 4.3 hours on station in hi-lo loitering and manoeuvring. In an anti-shipping role, with one anti-shipping missile under each wing, the SRA-4 could fly 1,350 nm (2,502 km; 1,554 miles) at high altitude, descend to 61 m (200 ft) for a 350 knot (649 km/h; 403 mph)/100 nm (185 km; 115 mile) attack run and launch a standoff weapon at 50 nm (93 km; 57 miles) range from target before climbing to 13,715 m (45,000 ft) for return to base.

In a medical evacuation role the SRA-4's cabin can accommodate up to 15 litter patients plus medical attendants; while for priority cargo transport, in addition to the cargo door, the aircraft can be equipped with a floor-mounted cargo roller system for rapid loading.

SUKHOI-GULFSTREAM AEROSPACE SSBJ

Following discussions held at the Paris Air Show in June 1989, Gulfstream Aerospace and the Sukhoi Design Bureau of the Soviet Union signed a memorandum of understanding dealing with "the feasibility of a joint venture in the development, manufacturing and marketing of a business type supersonic aircraft", details of which may be found in the International section of this edition.

Development prototype of the Gulfstream SRA-4 electronic warfare support aircraft *(J.M.G. Gradidge)*

GULFSTREAM AEROSPACE TECHNOLOGIES
(Oklahoma Operations)

Wiley Post Airport, Box 22500, Oklahoma City, Oklahoma 73123
Telephone: 1 (405) 789 5000
Telex: 747193
PRESIDENT: Robert N. Buckley

Gulfstream Aerospace's 55,740 m² (600,000 sq ft) Oklahoma facility, used formerly for the production of the Gulfstream Commander Jetprop series of turboprop business aircraft, now provides subcontracted manufacturing and engineering services for government agencies, aerospace equipment manufacturers and defence contractors. The Commander 112 and 114 single-engined range was sold by Gulfstream Aerospace in June 1988 to Commander Aircraft Company (which see), and manufacturing and marketing rights to the twin-engined Commanders were sold in December 1989 to Precision Airmotive Corporation of Everett, Washington. Further details of this sale may be found under Twin Commander Corporation in this section.

Under a major agreement announced on 2 May 1988, Gulfstream Aerospace Technologies has been authorised by McDonnell Douglas to manufacture spare parts for all out-of-production Douglas transport aircraft from the DC-3 up to and including the DC-10.

On 8 September 1989 the company announced a contract with British Aerospace (Commercial Aircraft) Ltd to design, tool and manufacture 200 wing sets for the BAe Jetstream 41 regional airliner, for delivery between 1990-2000.

HELI-AIR
HELI-AIR

119 Ida Road, Broussard, Louisiana 70518
Telephone: 1 (318) 837 9502
Telex: 5101010395
Fax: 1 (318) 837 2113
PRESIDENT: Gary J. Villiard
DIRECTOR OF OPERATIONS: David A. Brown

Heli-Air, a member of the Jaffe Group, has developed an engine conversion for Bell Model 222A, 222B and 222UT helicopters which involves replacing the standard 510 kW (684 shp) Textron Lycoming LTS 101-750C-1 turboshafts with two 522 kW (700 shp) Allison 250-C30G engines, which it is claimed offer reduced maintenance requirements and costs. Performance is unchanged except for an improvement in engine-out rate of climb and a 36 kg (80 lb) increase in useful load. The first Allison-engined Bell 222 conversion (N5008Q) began test flights on 10 November 1988, and the first production conversion flew on 12 January 1990. At that time the prototype had completed 400 hours of flight testing, with an FAA Supplemental Type Certificate expected by April 1990. In early 1990 Heli-Air held orders for 16 Bell 222 conversions.

HELIO
HELIO AIRCRAFT CORPORATION

PO Drawer 3350, 165 Scott Avenue, Suite 102, Morgantown, West Virginia 26505
Telephone: 1 (304) 291 2376
Fax: 1 (304) 292 1902
PRESIDENT: Darus H. Zehrbach

Helio Aircraft Corporation was founded in November 1989 by Aircraft Acquisition Corporation, which has acquired design, manufacturing and marketing rights to the Helio range of piston-engined and turboprop STOL light utility aircraft. The company has restored to production the piston-engined Courier Models 600, 800 and 900 and the turboprop H-550A Stallion, and in Spring 1990 was developing a new Courier 700 powered by a liquid-cooled 224 kW (300 hp) Teledyne Continental Voyager piston engine and a Super Courier powered by a 313 kW (420 shp) Allison 250-B17C turboprop, with certification for both models anticipated in the Autumn of that year.

Details of the early development, and full technical descriptions of the Courier and Stallion, may be found, respectively, in the 1978-79 and 1976-77 editions of *Jane's*. The following descriptions apply to current models.

HELIO COURIER 600, 700, 800 and 900

TYPE: Six-seat STOL utility aircraft.
WINGS: Cantilever high-wing monoplane. Wing section NACA 23012. Dihedral 1°. Constant chord wings with no sweepback. All-metal fail-safe structure. Fowler-type slotted all-metal trailing-edge flaps. Automatic full-span leading-edge slats.
FUSELAGE: All-metal structure. Cabin safety cage section of welded 4130 steel tube with light alloy covering. Rear section is of semi-monocoque construction with light alloy bulkheads, stringers and skin.
TAIL UNIT: Cantilever light alloy structure with all-moving tailplane. Two trim tabs on tailplane, one on rudder.
LANDING GEAR: Non-retractable tailwheel or tricycle type with spring steel main legs and oleo-pneumatic shock absorber on nosewheel leg. Goodyear crosswind landing gear, and Edo and PK floats and amphibious floats optional.
POWER PLANT: One 186.4 kW (250 hp) Textron Lycoming O-540 (Model 600), or liquid-cooled 224 kW (300 hp) Teledyne Continental Voyager (Model 700), or 261 kW (350 hp) turbocharged Textron Lycoming TIO-540 (Model 800), or 298 kW (400 hp) Textron Lycoming IO-720-A1B (Model 900), each driving a Hartzell three-blade constant-speed metal propeller. Fuel in two wing tanks, total capacity 227 litres (60 US gallons; 50 Imp gallons). Auxiliary wing tanks optional, bringing total capacity to 454 litres (120 US gallons; 100 Imp gallons). Refuelling points in upper surface of each wing.
ACCOMMODATION: Standard seating for pilot and five passengers in three rows of two. Door at forward end of cabin on port side and at mid-cabin on starboard side. Four doors optional.
SYSTEMS: Electrical system power supplied by 50A 12V alternator.
AVIONICS AND EQUIPMENT: Standard avionics comprise VHF com transceiver, transponder and encoder. Full IFR avionics, II Morrow Loran C, global positioning system and inertial navigation system optional.

DIMENSIONS, EXTERNAL:
Wing span	11.58 m (38 ft 0 in)
Wing chord, constant	1.83 m (6 ft 0 in)
Wing aspect ratio	6.6
Length overall	9.91 m (32 ft 6 in)
Height overall	4.32 m (14 ft 2 in)
Tailplane span	4.57 m (15 ft 0 in)
Wheel track	2.69 m (8 ft 10 in)
Wheelbase: tailwheel	7.26 m (23 ft 10 in)
nosewheel	3.10 m (10 ft 2 in)

Helio Courier 800 STOL utility aircraft on PK floats

Propeller diameter	2.44-257 m (8 ft 0 in-8 ft 5 in)
Propeller ground clearance	0.23 m (9 in)

AREAS:
Wings, gross	21.46 m² (231.0 sq ft)
Tailplane	3.48 m² (37.5 sq ft)

WEIGHTS (A: 600/700, B: 800/900):
Max T-O weight: A	1,542 kg (3,400 lb)
B	1,723 kg (3,800 lb)
Max zero-fuel weight: A	943 kg (2,080 lb)
B	1,146 kg (2,527 lb)

PERFORMANCE (at max T-O weight, ISA, except where indicated. A: 600, B: 700, C: 800, D: 900):
Max level speed: A	139 knots (259 km/h; 160 mph)
B, C	145 knots (269 km/h; 167 mph)
D	147 knots (272 km/h; 169 mph)
Max cruising speed at 1,525 m (5,000 ft):	
A, C	132 knots (245 km/h; 152 mph)
B	143 knots (266 km/h; 165 mph)
D	133 knots (246 km/h; 153 mph)
Econ cruising speed at 1,525 m (5,000 ft):	
A	115 knots (214 km/h; 133 mph)
B	130 knots (241 km/h; 150 mph)
C	122 knots (225 km/h; 140 mph)
D	123 knots (229 km/h; 142 mph)
Stalling speed, flaps down, power on:	
A	26 knots (49 km/h; 30 mph)
B	27 knots (50 km/h; 31 mph)
Max rate of climb at S/L: A	364 m (1,195 ft)/min
B	381 m (1,250 ft)/min
C	360 m (1,180 ft)/min
D	341 m (1,120 ft)/min
Service ceiling: A	4,630 m (15,200 ft)
B	6,250 m (20,500 ft)
C	8,840 m (29,000 ft)
D	6,400 m (21,000 ft)
T-O run: A	92 m (300 ft)
B	75 m (245 ft)
C	89 m (290 ft)
D	87 m (285 ft)
T-O to 15 m (50 ft): A	229 m (750 ft)
B	186 m (610 ft)
C	211 m (690 ft)
D	189 m (618 ft)
Landing from 15 m (50 ft): A, B	151 m (493 ft)
C, D	223 m (730 ft)
Landing run: A, B	74 m (240 ft)
C, D	70 m (228 ft)
Range with max fuel: A	1,118 nm (2,072 km; 1,288 miles)
B	1,198 nm (2,220 km; 1,380 miles)
C	924 nm (1,712 km; 1,064 miles)
D	851 nm (1,577 km; 980 miles)

HELIO SUPER COURIER

The following details are provisional:
POWER PLANT: One 313 kW (420 shp) Allison 250-B17C turboprop.

WEIGHTS:
Weight empty	812 kg (1,790 lb)
Max fuel weight	381 kg (840 lb)
Max T-O weight	1,723 kg (3,800 lb)

PERFORMANCE (estimated):
Max cruising speed at 5,180 m (17,000 ft), 70% power	152 knots (282 km/h; 175 mph)
Stalling speed	25 knots (45 km/h; 28 mph)
Max rate of climb at S/L	823 m (2,700 ft)/min
Service ceiling	7,620 m (25,000 ft)
T-O and landing run	46 m (150 ft)
Endurance	5 h 30 min

HELIO H-550A STALLION
US military designation: AU-24A

The description of the Helio Courier applies also to the Stallion except as follows:
TYPE: Eight/twelve-seat turboprop STOL utility aircraft.
WINGS: Spoilers on upper surfaces of wings inboard of ailerons. Electric aileron trim. Military version has two hardpoints for external stores under each wing, capacities 612 kg (1,350 lb) each outboard and 680 kg (1,500 lb) inboard.
FUSELAGE: Military version has centreline stores hardpoint, capacity 227 kg (500 lb).
TAIL UNIT: Swept fin and rudder with dorsal fin. Elevator trim is electric, rudder trim manual.
POWER PLANT: One 507 kW (680 shp) Pratt & Whitney Canada PT6A-27 turboprop, driving a three-blade constant-speed feathering and reversing Hartzell propeller. Fuel in four wing tanks, total capacity 454 litres (120 US gallons; 100 Imp gallons).
ACCOMMODATION: Standard seating for pilot and seven passengers in four rows of two. Three-abreast seating optional. Crew door on each side of cockpit, double cargo/passenger door on port side of cabin. Ventral airdrop hatch/emergency exit.
SYSTEMS: 150A 24V alternator.
AVIONICS: Bendix/King or Narco com transceiver, transponder, encoder and intercom standard. Full range of avionics by Bendix/King and Narco available to customer choice.
ARMAMENT: Military version has provision for the carriage of a range of weapons and stores including 20 mm and 7.62 mm miniguns, 500 lb Mk 82 bombs, FFARs, napalm and reconnaissance cameras.

DIMENSIONS, EXTERNAL:				
Wing span	12.50 m (41 ft 0 in)	Height	1.47 m (4 ft 10 in)	Stalling speed: A	37 knots (69 km/h; 43 mph)
Wing aspect ratio	6.83	Floor area	5.30 m² (57.0 sq ft)	B	41 knots (76 km/h; 48 mph)
Length overall	12.07 m (39 ft 7 in)	Volume	6.46 m³ (228.0 cu ft)	Max rate of climb at S/L: A	670 m (2,200 ft)/min
Height overall	2.82 m (9 ft 3 in)	AREA:		B	411 m (1,350 ft)/min
Tailplane span	5.49 m (18 ft 0 in)	Wings, gross	22.85 m² (246.0 sq ft)	Service ceiling: A	8,840 m (29,000 ft)
Wheel track	2.95 m (9 ft 8 in)	WEIGHTS (A: civil, B: military):		B	5,790 m (19,000 ft)
Propeller diameter	2.82 m (9 ft 3 in)	Weight empty	1,297 kg (2,860 lb)	T-O run: A	98 m (320 ft)
Passenger/cargo door: Height	1.22 m (4 ft 0 in)	Max fuel weight	326.5 kg (720 lb)	B	171 m (560 ft)
Width	1.63 m (5 ft 4 in)	Max T-O and landing weight: A	2,313 kg (5,100 lb)	T-O to 15 m (50 ft): A	202 m (660 ft)
Height to sill	0.76 m (2 ft 6 in)	B	2,857 kg (6,300 lb)	Landing from 15 m (50 ft): A	229 m (750 ft)
Ventral hatch: Length	1.09 m (3 ft 7 in)	PERFORMANCE (at max T-O weight, ISA, except where		Landing run: A	77 m (250 ft)
Width	0.58 m (1 ft 11 in)	indicated. (A: civil, B: military):		B	98 m (320 ft)
DIMENSIONS, EXTERNAL:		Max cruising speed at 3,050 m (10,000 ft):		Max range: A	640 nm (1,186 km; 737 miles)
Cabin: Length incl cockpit	4.19 m (13 ft 9 in)	A	188 knots (348 km/h; 216 mph)	B	450 nm (834 km; 518 miles)
Max width	1.35 m (4 ft 5 in)	B	156 knots (289 km/h; 180 mph)		
		Econ cruising speed: A	139 knots (258 km/h; 160 mph)		

HILLER — see Rogerson

HUGHES — see McDonnell Douglas Helicopter Company

HYNES — see Brantly

IAC

INTERNATIONAL AEROMARINE CORPORATION

1011 South Sanford Avenue, Sanford, Florida 32771
Telephone: 1 (305) 323 4360
PRESIDENT: Joseph W. Gurnow
VICE-PRESIDENT, ENGINEERING: David B. Thurston

International Aeromarine Corporation, which is partly owned by Thurston Aeromarine Corporation, was formed to develop and gain certification of the TA16 Seafire, the latest in a series of light amphibians designed by Mr David B. Thurston.

IAC TA16 SEAFIRE

Following design and development of the TA16 Trojan amphibian, of which 50 are under construction by Canadian and US homebuilders, Mr Thurston decided to market a production version. This has been named Seafire to distinguish it from the homebuilt version. The Seafire prototype (N16SA), completed in March 1982, was structurally designed and statically tested to the requirements of FAR Pt 23, Amendment 24. It flew for the first time on 10 December 1982. By mid-1987 the company held orders for ten Seafires, since when no further information has been received.

A description, specifications and photograph of the Seafire may be found in the 1989-90 and earlier editions of *Jane's*.

JAFFE — see Swearingen

JETCRAFT

JETCRAFT USA INC

3801 Highway 146, Las Vegas, Nevada 89124
Telephone: 1 (702) 361 0043
PRESIDENT AND CHAIRMAN: John E. Morgan
CHIEF ENGINEER: Floyd Snow

JetCraft USA has announced plans to develop a family of business jets, using airframe parts based on those of the de Havilland Vampire T. Mk 11 jet trainer, but of new manufacture. A British company, Strato Jet UK Ltd, is supplying all components for the aircraft, which will be assembled in a 9,290 m² (100,000 sq ft) factory in Las Vegas.

JETCRAFT EXECUTIVE MARK I

Initial model in the JetCraft range is a six/seven-passenger business jet called Executive Mark I. Certification is anticipated in July 1991 under FAR Pt 23. It has a new metal fuselage, with a conventional enclosed cabin pressurised to 0.59 bars (8.6 lb/sq in) forward of the wing main spar, and new fins and rudders mated to the Vampire's wings and tailbooms. The power plant is a Pratt & Whitney Canada JT15D-5 turbofan rated at 12.89 kN (2,900 lb st). Standard fuel capacity is 1,745 litres (461 US gallons; 384 Imp gallons), of which 1,703 litres (450 US gallons; 375 Imp gallons) are usable. Total fuel capacity with external fuel tanks is 2,653 litres (701 US gallons; 584 Imp gallons).

DIMENSIONS, EXTERNAL:	
Wing span	11.58 m (38 ft 0 in)
Length overall	12.50 m (41 ft 0 in)
Height overall	2.59 m (8 ft 6 in)
AREAS:	
Wings, gross	19.32 m² (208.0 sq ft)
Horizontal tail surfaces (total)	5.20 m² (56.0 sq ft)

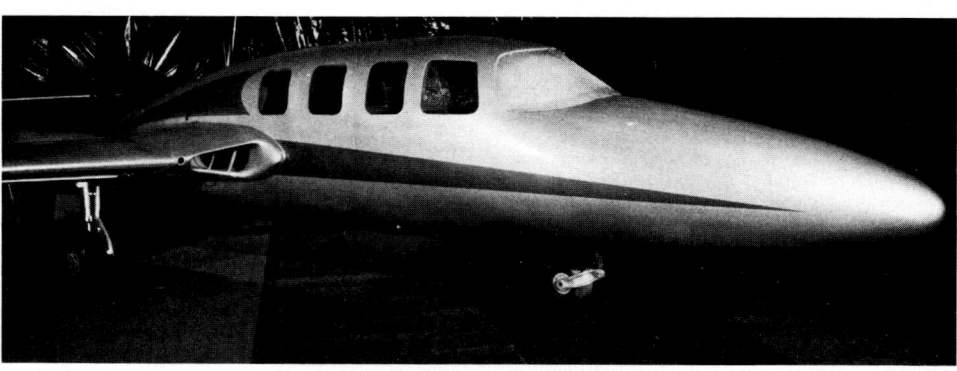

Prototype JetCraft Executive Mark I

WEIGHTS (estimated):	
Weight empty	2,372 kg (5,252 lb)
Max T-O and landing weight	
	4,672 kg (10,300 lb)
PERFORMANCE (estimated):	
Max operating speed	
	486 knots (901 km/h; 560 mph) IAS
	or Mach 0.82
Max cruising speed at 6,100 m (20,000 ft):	
	412 knots (764 km/h; 474 mph)
Stalling speed:	
landing gear and flaps up	
	80 knots (148 km/h; 92 mph)
landing gear and flaps down	
	75 knots (138 km/h; 86 mph)

Max rate of climb at S/L	1,067 m (3,500 ft)/min
T-O to 15 m (50 ft)	762 m (2,500 ft)
Max operating altitude	12,500 m (41,000 ft)
Range	2,084 nm (3,862 km; 2,400 miles)

JETCRAFT MARK II JET CRUISER

This six-passenger executive aircraft is generally similar to the Executive Mark I, but is projected with a Pratt & Whitney Canada PT6A-65AR turboprop in the same location as the Mark I's turbofan, driving a five-blade pusher propeller. Jetcraft plans to re-engine the prototype Mark I with a turboprop upon completion of certification of the turbofan version. Estimated range of the Mark II is 2,605 nm (4,828 km; 3,000 miles), with a max cruising speed of 347 knots (644 km/h; 400 mph).

KAMAN

KAMAN AEROSPACE CORPORATION
(a subsidiary of Kaman Corporation)

Old Windsor Road, PO Box No. 2, Bloomfield, Connecticut 06002
Telephone: 1 (203) 242 4461
Telex: 710 425 3411

PRESIDENT AND CHIEF EXECUTIVE OFFICER:
Walter R. Kozlow
VICE-PRESIDENT, ENGINEERING:
Dr Roger A. Massey
DIRECTOR, PUBLIC RELATIONS:
Kenneth J. Nasshan

The original Kaman Aircraft Corporation was founded in 1945 by Mr Charles H. Kaman, who is now President and Chairman of the Board of Kaman Corporation. Its initial programme was to develop and test a novel servo-flap control system for helicopter rotors, and the current production H-2 Seasprite naval helicopter continues to utilise this system.

Current research and development programmes under the sponsorship of the US Army, Air Force, Navy and NASA include the advanced design of helicopter rotor systems, blades and rotor control concepts, component fatigue life determination, and structural dynamic analysis and testing.

Kaman Aerospace is a major subcontractor in many aircraft and space programmes. This work includes design, tooling and fabrication of components in metal, metal honeycomb, bonded and composite construction, using techniques such as filament winding and braiding. Military and commercial aircraft programmes in which Kaman participates include the Grumman A-6 and F-14, Lockheed C-5B, Bell/Boeing V-22, Boeing 737, 747, 757 and 767, Sikorsky UH-60 and SH-60, and NASA Space Shuttle Orbiter. Kaman also supplies acoustic engine ducts for Pratt & Whitney JT8D engines, and thrust reversers for CF6 engines to General Electric Company.

Kaman designed, and since 1977 has been producing, all-composite rotor blades for Bell AH-1 HueyCobras in service with the US Army and other countries. Improved performance, life and operational features have been demonstrated. Kaman is participating in the AH-1 air-to-air Stinger programme, providing flight-test airworthiness qualification. Kaman is also a supplier of helicopters reconfigured as remotely piloted target drones for US Army weapons testing and training.

Through its diversified technologies operations, of which Kaman Aerospace is a part, Kaman Corporation provides scientific services and systems development primarily for the US armed services and government agencies; advanced technology products for military and commercial applications; helicopters, helicopter modifications and spare parts for the US Navy; and aerospace subcontracting for defence and commercial prime contractors.

KAMAN SEASPRITE
US Navy designations: HH-2 and SH-2

The prototype Seasprite flew for the first time on 2 July 1959, and many versions (described in previous editions of *Jane's*) were produced subsequently for the US Navy. Production of the SH-2F version was restarted in 1981.

From 1967, all single-engined UH-2A/B Seasprites were converted progressively to UH-2C twin-engined configuration, with 932 kW (1,250 shp) General Electric T58-GE-8B turboshafts in place of the former T58. They later underwent further modification, under the US Navy's Mk I LAMPS (Light Airborne Multi-Purpose System) programme, to provide helicopters for ASW (anti-submarine warfare), ASST (anti-ship surveillance and targeting), SAR (search and rescue), and utility operations operating from small ships. All of the US Navy's SH-2s were subsequently upgraded to SH-2F standard, with increased strength landing gear, T58-GE-8F engines and improved rotor system.

Operational deployment of HSL LAMPS Mk I squadrons began on 7 December 1971. By December 1989 more than 685,000 flight hours had been accumulated by LAMPS Mk I detachments deployed on successive long cruises on the following ship classes: FFG-7, DD-963, DDG-993, CG-47, FFG-1, FF-1052, FF-1040, CG-26, CGN-35, CGN-38 and BB-61. US Coast Guard WMEC and WHEC cutters are also being made capable of operating with the SH-2. In addition to the eight active Navy LAMPS Mk I HSL squadrons, formation of three Naval Air Reserve HSL squadrons began in 1984, and 24 SH-2Fs have been transferred to Reserve units as new production aircraft were delivered, these going to HSL-74, 84 and 94 at South Weymouth, MA, North Island, CA and Willow Grove, PA. Front-line squadrons are HSL-30, 32 and 34 at Norfolk, VA, and HSL-36 at Mayport, FL, for Atlantic-based vessels; and HSL-31, 33 and 35 at North Island, CA, and HSL-37 at Barber's Point, HI, for the Pacific. Active and Reserve LAMPS Mk I SH-2s are scheduled to remain operational at least to the year 2010.

The following versions were in service in January 1990:

HH-2D. One aircraft, without LAMPS modifications, assigned to oceanography work.

SH-2F. LAMPS Mk I version, of which 88 were delivered initially between May 1973 and 1982, plus 16 earlier SH-2Ds uprated to SH-2F configuration; first unit became operational with squadron HSL-33, deployed to the Pacific, on 11 September 1973. Seventy-five of original 88 remained in US Navy service in February 1989. Further 54 new production SH-2Fs ordered in FYs 1982-86 (18, 18, 6, 6, and 6), all of which had been delivered by December 1989. Further six, ordered in FY 1987, will instead be completed to T700 powered SH-2G configuration (see next heading). For description and illustrations of SH-2F, see 1987-88 *Jane's*. US Navy plans to retrofit SH-2F fleet to SH-2G standard, and June 1987 contract included funds to initiate the programme. Total of 14 conversion kits currently funded.

Fifteen SH-2Fs operating in the Arabian Gulf in 1987-88, during the Iran-Iraq war, were fitted with additional survival aids including Sanders AN/ALQ-144 IR jammers to the starboard side of the tail rotor driveshaft; Tracor AN/ALE-39 chaff/flare dispensers (two per side); General Instruments AN/ALR-66(V)1 radar warning system and AN/DLQ-3 missile warning equipment. Eight SH-2Fs thus equipped also added a Hughes AN/AAQ-16 FLIR beneath the nose.

SH-2G. Super Seasprite. To keep pace with the increasing threat, the US Navy initiated an SH-2F upgrade programme with FY 1987 production, under this designation. The primary airframe changes include the installation of new fuel-efficient T700-GE-401 engines to replace the T58-GE-8F engines, and incorporation of newly developed composite main rotor blades with a service life of 10,000 hours. Fuel consumption is improved by over 20 per cent. The avionics improvements include a MIL-STD-1553B digital databus, onboard acoustic processor, multi-function raster display, AN/ASN-150 tactical navigation display, and 99-channel sonobuoys. US Navy tests have proved the SH-2 suitable for dipping sonar operations, air-to-surface missile firing, forward looking infra-red sensors and equipment with various guns, rockets and countermeasures. Export models of the SH-2 are offered with this equipment.

The USN plans to acquire approx 103 SH-2Gs by new manufacture and (mostly) conversion, of which 61 retrofits are destined for the active fleet and are expected to add AN/AAQ-16 FLIR, AN/ALQ-144 jammers, Loral AN/AAR-47 missile warning equipment and Collins AN/ARC-182 secure radio. These are unofficially known as the SH-2G+ to differentiate them from the 36 lesser-equipped SH-2Gs destined for the Reserves. A further improvement, the as-yet unfunded Update II, is

Kaman SH-2G (ex YSH-2G) in production configuration during its first flight on 28 December 1989

Kaman SH-2G Super Seasprite LAMPS Mk I helicopter *(Pilot Press)*

intended to add dipping sonar to SH-2Gs. Classified equipment codenamed Magic Lantern and Demon is understood to concern use of lasers to detect mines and submarines below the surface.

An SH-2F, 161653, first flew as a T700 testbed in April 1985, designated YSH-2G. It was subsequently brought up to SH-2G operational equipment standard and flew again on 28 December 1989. Delivery will take place in 1991, followed by the six new-build helicopters ordered in FY 1987. Pakistan, Portugal and Thailand expressed interest in the Seasprite during 1988-89, but no orders have yet ensued.

The following description refers to the SH-2G Super Seasprite:

TYPE: Naval anti-submarine warfare and anti-ship surveillance and targeting helicopter, with secondary missions of search and rescue, observation and utility.

ROTOR SYSTEM: Four-blade main rotor utilising titanium hub and composite rotor blades, with composite servo-flap controls. Four-blade tail rotor. All eight blades folded manually. Main rotor rpm 298.

FUSELAGE AND TAIL UNIT: All-metal semi-monocoque structure, with flotation hull housing main fuel tanks. Nose split on centreline, to fold rearward on each side to reduce stowage space required. Fixed horizontal stabiliser on tail rotor pylon.

LANDING GEAR: Tailwheel type, with forward retracting twin mainwheels and non-retractable tailwheel. Liquid spring shock absorbers in main-gear legs; oleo-pneumatic shock absorber in tailwheel unit, which is fully castoring for taxying but locked fore and aft for T-O and landing. Mainwheels have 8-ply tubeless tyres size 17.5 × 6.25-11, pressure 17.25 bars (250 lb/sq in); tailwheel 10-ply tube-type tyre size 5.00-5, pressure 11.04 bars (160 lb/sq in).

POWER PLANT: Two 1,285 kW (1,723 shp) General Electric T700-GE-401 turboshafts, one on each side of rotor pylon structure. Basic fuel capacity of 1,802 litres (476 US gallons; 396 Imp gallons), including up to two external auxiliary tanks with a combined capacity of 757 litres (200 US gallons; 166.5 Imp gallons). Ship-to-air helicopter in-flight refuelling (HIFR).

ACCOMMODATION: Crew of three, consisting of pilot, co-pilot/tactical co-ordinator, and sensor operator. One passenger with LAMPS equipment installed; four

passengers or two litters with sonobuoy launcher removed. Provision for transportation of internal or external cargo. Space for additional troop seats.

AVIONICS, ARMAMENT AND OPERATIONAL EQUIPMENT: LAMPS Mk I mission equipment includes Canadian Marconi LN-66HP surveillance radar; General Instruments AN/ALR-66A(V)1 radar warning/ESM; Teledyne Systems AN/ASN-150 tactical management system; dual Collins AN/ARC-159(V)1 UHF radios; Texas Instruments AN/ASQ-81(V)2 magnetic anomaly detector; Computing Devices AN/UYS-503 acoustic processor; Rospatch AN/ARR-84 sonobuoy receiver; Tele-Dynamics AN/AKT-22(V)6 sonobuoy data link; 15 DIFAR and DICASS sonobuoys; AN/ALE-39 chaff dispensers; AN/ASQ-188 torpedo presetter; one or two Mk 46 or Mk 50 torpedoes; eight Mk 25 marine smoke markers; cargo hook for external loads, capacity 1,814 kg (4,000 lb); and folding rescue hoist, capacity 272 kg (600 lb). Provision for pintle-mounted 7.62 mm machine-gun in both cabin doorways. The US Navy plans to retrofit additional self-defence equipment in all fleet SH-2Gs, consisting of Hughes AN/AAQ-16 FLIR, Sanders AN/ALQ-144 IR jammers, Loral AN/AAR-47 missile warning and Collins AN/ARC-182 VHF/UHF secure radio.

DIMENSIONS, EXTERNAL:

Main rotor diameter	13.51 m (44 ft 4 in)
Main rotor blade chord	0.59 m (1 ft 11 in)
Tail rotor diameter	2.46 m (8 ft 1 in)
Tail rotor blade chord	0.236 m (9.3 in)
Length of fuselage, excl tail rotor	12.19 m (40 ft 0 in)
Length overall (rotors turning)	16.08 m (52 ft 9 in)
Length overall, nose and blades folded	11.68 m (38 ft 4 in)
Height overall (rotors turning)	4.58 m (15 ft 0½ in)
Height (blades folded)	4.14 m (13 ft 7 in)
Width overall, incl MAD	3.74 m (12 ft 3 in)
Stabiliser span	2.97 m (9 ft 9 in)
Wheel track (outer wheels)	3.30 m (10 ft 10 in)
Wheelbase	5.13 m (16 ft 10 in)
Tail rotor ground clearance	2.12 m (6 ft 11½ in)

AREAS:

Main rotor blades (each)	3.96 m² (42.63 sq ft)
Tail rotor blades (each)	0.295 m² (3.175 sq ft)
Main rotor disc	143.41 m² (1,543.66 sq ft)
Tail rotor disc	4.77 m² (51.32 sq ft)

WEIGHTS:
Weight empty	3,447 kg (7,600 lb)
Max T-O weight	6,124 kg (13,500 lb)

PERFORMANCE (ISA):
Max level speed at S/L	138 knots (256 km/h; 159 mph)
Normal cruising speed	120 knots (222 km/h; 138 mph)

Max rate of climb at S/L	762 m (2,500 ft)/min
Rate of climb at S/L, one engine out	530 m (1,740 ft)/min
Service ceiling	7,285 m (23,900 ft)
Service ceiling, one engine out	4,816 m (15,800 ft)

Hovering ceiling: IGE	6,340 m (20,800 ft)
OGE	5,486 m (18,000 ft)
Max range, 2 external tanks	478 nm (885 km; 500 miles)
Max endurance, 2 external tanks	5 h 0 min

KING'S
THE KING'S ENGINEERING FELLOWSHIP
Municipal Airport, Orange City, Iowa 51041
Telephone: 1 (712) 737 4444
PRESIDENT: Carl A. Mortenson

The Angel, developed for and by The King's Engineering Fellowship through donations, was designed by Mr Carl Mortenson, whose earlier light twin named Evangel was described in the 1974-75 and earlier editions of *Jane's*. Eight Evangels were built, of which seven were still serving with missionaries in Alaska, Colombia, Micronesia and Peru in 1988.

KING'S MODEL 44 ANGEL
The King's Angel is a twin-engined light transport intended for missionary aviation duties. Design goals included low manufacturing costs, STOL capability, suitability for rough and soft field operation, sturdiness, easy maintenance and repair in the field, and the ability to accommodate bulky cargo. The design phase involved more than 16,000 manhours of work on over 1,000 drawings, and the prototype (N44KE) was built on production tooling. It flew for the first time in January 1984, and had logged over 550 flying hours by January 1988. During the test programme, the engines were raised above the wing on pylons for a period, and outboard 'trimmerons' were added for improved single-engine control (roll control being normally by means of spoilers). Later, the engines were replaced immediately on top of the wings, in longer nacelles, to increase cruising speed by an estimated 13 knots (24 km/h; 15 mph).

Changes incorporated as a result of flight testing include increased span on the horizontal tail surfaces to improve pitch trim with power changes. Final performance testing has been completed, and structural testing was beginning in early 1990. Production is expected to begin no earlier than 1992.

TYPE: Twin-engined light utility transport.
WINGS: Cantilever low-mid wing monoplane. Wing section modified NACA 23018-23010 with modified leading-edge; thickness/chord ratio of 18% at root, 10% at tip. All-metal riveted structure, with built-up aluminium alloy capstrip spars and 19 die formed ribs each side. Near full span hydraulically actuated Fowler flaps, with 37° max deflection. Multiple small-plate spoilers, forward of flaps, for roll control, supplemented by outboard 'trimmeron' between flap and wingtip on each trailing-edge.
FUSELAGE: Conventional aluminium alloy riveted semi-monocoque structure.
TAIL UNIT: Cantilever aluminium alloy riveted structure, with sweptback vertical surfaces and long dorsal fin.

Prototype King's Angel light twin for missionary aviation duties (*Howard Levy*)

LANDING GEAR: Retractable tricycle type. Electro-hydraulic retraction, mainwheels inward into wingroots, nosewheel rearward. Emergency extension by handpump or gravity. Tyre size: mainwheels 8.50-10, nosewheel 8.50-6. Cleveland brakes.
POWER PLANT: Two 224 kW (300 hp) Textron Lycoming IO-540-M flat-six engines, mounted on top of the inboard wings and each driving a Hartzell three-blade constant-speed feathering pusher propeller. Total usable fuel capacity 855 litres (226 US gallons; 188 Imp gallons). Oil capacity 22.7 litres (6 US gallons; 5 Imp gallons).
ACCOMMODATION: Enclosed cabin seating up to eight persons, including pilot. Five seats can be removed for carrying cargo, including four 208 litre (55 US gallon; 46 Imp gallon) drums. Rearmost bench seat is fixed. Four large windows and one smaller circular window on each side of cabin. Horizontally divided 'clamshell' door on port side at front of cabin; emergency exit on starboard side. Heating and window air vents standard. Compartment for 90 kg (200 lb) of baggage at rear of fuselage, with door on port side.
SYSTEMS: Hydraulic system, with electric pump, for landing gear and flap actuation. Electrical system includes 12V battery in fuselage nose.
AVIONICS AND EQUIPMENT: Blind-flying instrumentation standard. Bendix/King avionics, including twin com/nav transceivers, glideslope, and dual ADF. Weather radar, Loran-C and HF com optional.

DIMENSIONS, EXTERNAL:
Wing span	12.19 m (40 ft 0 in)
Wing chord at root	2.29 m (7 ft 6 in)
Length overall	10.13 m (33 ft 3 in)
Height overall	3.51 m (11 ft 6 in)
Wheel track	3.96 m (13 ft 0 in)
Wheelbase	4.57 m (15 ft 0 in)

WEIGHTS:
Weight empty	1,701 kg (3,750 lb)
Max T-O weight	2,631 kg (5,800 lb)

PERFORMANCE:
Cruising speed, 65% power at 3,050 m (10,000 ft)	174 knots (322 km/h; 200 mph)
Landing speed	57 knots (105 km/h; 65 mph)
Service ceiling	5,790 m (19,000 ft)
Service ceiling, one engine out	2,135 m (7,000 ft)
T-O run	183 m (600 ft)
T-O to 15 m (50 ft)	366 m (1,200 ft)
Landing from 15 m (50 ft)	335 m (1,100 ft)
Landing run	183 m (600 ft)
Range with max fuel, with reserves	1,390 nm (2,575 km; 1,600 miles)
Endurance: with 8 occupants	4 h
with max fuel and 4 occupants	8 h

LAKE
LAKE AIRCRAFT INC
606 Dyer Boulevard, Kissimmee Airport, Kissimmee, Florida 32741
Telephone: 1 (407) 847 9000
Telex: 52-3258 LAKE AIR KISS
Fax: 1 (407) 847 4516
PRESIDENT: Armand E. Rivard
EXECUTIVE VICE-PRESIDENT: Gordon Collins
VICE-PRESIDENT, INTERNATIONAL: Haig Hagopian

LAKE LA4-200 AMPHIBIAN
The original C-1 Skimmer prototype flew for the first time in May 1948. From it were developed the improved C-2 Skimmer IV and the Lake LA-4, LA-4A, LA-4P, LA-4S and LA-4T, as described in previous editions of *Jane's*. By early 1990 more than 1,300 Lake amphibians had been delivered. The current LA4-200 received FAA certification in 1970, and is manufactured in two versions, as follows:
LA4-200 EP. Standard version, as described in detail, which introduced a 13 cm (5 in) longer propeller shaft to increase efficiency and reduce cabin noise; a Textron Lycoming IO-360-A1B6 engine, dynamically balanced for smoother operation; an aerodynamically improved engine nacelle, which reduces drag and noise; wing trailing-edge fillets at intersection of wingroot and fuselage, to improve low-speed stability and protect the propeller from water spray erosion; hull hydro boosters for improved on-water operation; reinforced floats and hull station 97 bulkhead; improved canopy; new instrument panel glareshield; new fresh air vents; additional corrosion proofing; and a new polyurethane paint finish.
LA4-200 EPR. Identical to above, but with reversible-pitch constant-speed propeller, which allows the aircraft to taxi in reverse during such on-water operations as docking or mooring.

Two Lake LA4-200 amphibians emerging from the water

TYPE: Single-engined four-seat amphibian.
WINGS: Cantilever shoulder-wing monoplane with tapered wing panels attached directly to sides of hull. Wing section NACA 4415 at root, NACA 4409 at tip. Dihedral 5° 30'. Incidence 3° 15'. Structure consists of duralumin leading- and trailing-edge torsion boxes separated by a single duralumin main spar. All-metal ailerons and hydraulically operated slotted flaps over 80 per cent of span. Ground adjustable trim tabs on ailerons. Wing balancer floats are light alloy monocoque structures.
HULL: Single-step all-metal structure, with double-sealed boat hull. Alodined and zinc chromated inside and out against corrosion, with polyurethane paint exterior finish.
TAIL UNIT: Cantilever all-metal structure. Outboard elevator section separate from inboard section and actuated hydraulically for trimming. Retractable water rudder in base of aerodynamic rudder.

LANDING GEAR: Hydraulically retractable tricycle type. Consolidated oleo-pneumatic shock absorbers in main gear, which retracts inward into wings. Nosewheel, with long-stroke oleo, retracts forward. Gerdes mainwheels with Goodyear tyres, size 6.00-6, pressure 2.41 bars (35 lb/sq in). Gerdes nosewheel with Goodyear tyre size 5.00-5, pressure 1.38 bars (20 lb/sq in). Gerdes disc brakes. Parking brake. Nosewheel is free to swivel 30° each side.
POWER PLANT: One 149 kW (200 hp) Textron Lycoming IO-360-A1B6 flat-four engine, mounted on pylon above hull and driving a Hartzell two-blade constant-speed metal pusher propeller. Rajay turbocharger, reversible-pitch and Q-tip propeller, optional. Standard usable fuel capacity 204 litres (54 US gallons; 45 Imp gallons); optional usable fuel capacity of 340 litres (90 US gallons; 75 Imp gallons). Oil capacity 7.5 litres (2 US gallons; 1.7 Imp gallons).

ACCOMMODATION: Enclosed cabin seating pilot and three passengers. Front and rear seats removable. Front seats have inertia reel shoulder harness as standard. Dual controls standard; dual brakes for co-pilot optional. Entry through two forward-hinged windscreen sections. Upward hinged gull wing cargo door standard. Baggage compartment, capacity 90.5 kg (200 lb), aft of cabin. Dual windscreen defroster system.

SYSTEMS: Vacuum system for flight instruments. Hydraulic system, pressure 86.2 bars (1,250 lb/sq in), for flaps, horizontal trim and landing gear actuation; handpump provided for emergency operation. Engine driven 12V 60A alternator and 12V 30Ah battery. Janitrol 30,000 BTU heater optional.

AVIONICS AND EQUIPMENT: Basic avionics installation includes com and nav antennae, cabin speaker, microphone and circuit breakers. An extensive range of avionics by Bendix/King, Collins and Narco, and autopilots by Brittain and Edo-Aire Mitchell, are available to customers' requirements. Standard equipment includes full blind-flying instrumentation, electric clock, manifold pressure gauge, outside air temperature gauge, recording tachometer, fuel pressure and quantity indicators, oil pressure and temperature indicators, cylinder head temperature gauge, ammeter, stall warning device, control locks, carpeted floor, four fresh air vents, tinted glass for all windows, dual windscreen defrosters, inertia reel shoulder harness on front seats, shoulder restraint on rear seats, map pocket on front seats, baggage tiedown straps, landing and taxi lights, navigation lights, strobe light, heated pitot, fuselage nose bumper, paddle, cleat, line, full flow oil filter, quick fuel drains, and inboard and outboard tiedown rings. Optional equipment includes hour meter, true airspeed indicator, shoulder harness for rear seats, alternate static source, manual/automatic bilge pump, cabin fire extinguisher, and external metallic paint finish.

DIMENSIONS, EXTERNAL:
Wing span	11.58 m (38 ft 0 in)
Wing chord, mean	1.35 m (4 ft 5.1 in)
Wing aspect ratio	8.7
Length overall	7.59 m (24 ft 11 in)
Height overall	2.84 m (9 ft 4 in)
Tailplane span	3.05 m (10 ft 0 in)
Wheel track	3.40 m (11 ft 2 in)
Wheelbase	2.69 m (8 ft 10 in)
Propeller diameter	1.88 m (6 ft 2 in)

DIMENSIONS, INTERNAL:
Cabin: Length	1.57 m (5 ft 2 in)
Max width	1.05 m (3 ft 5½ in)
Max height	1.32 m (3 ft 11½ in)
Floor area	approx 1.53 m² (16.5 sq ft)
Volume	approx 1.70 m³ (60.0 cu ft)
Baggage hold	0.24 m³ (8.5 cu ft)

AREAS:
Wings, gross	15.79 m² (170.0 sq ft)
Ailerons (total)	1.16 m² (12.5 sq ft)
Trailing-edge flaps (total)	2.28 m² (24.5 sq ft)
Fin	1.25 m² (13.5 sq ft)
Rudder	0.79 m² (8.5 sq ft)
Tailplane	1.45 m² (15.6 sq ft)
Elevators	0.78 m² (8.4 sq ft)

WEIGHTS AND LOADINGS:
Weight empty, equipped	753 kg (1,660 lb)
Max T-O and landing weight	1,220 kg (2,690 lb)
Max wing loading	74.2 kg/m² (15.2 lb/sq ft)
Max power loading	8.19 kg/kW (13.45 lb/hp)

PERFORMANCE (at max T-O weight. A: EP/EPR, B: EP/EPR with turbocharger):
Max level speed at S/L:
A	134 knots (248 km/h; 154 mph) IAS

Max cruising speed: 75% power at 2,440 m (8,000 ft):
A	130 knots (241 km/h; 150 mph)

75% power at 6,100 m (20,000 ft):
B	143 knots (265 km/h; 164 mph)

Lake Turbo 270 Renegade six-seat amphibian

Stalling speed:
A, B, flaps and landing gear up
	53 knots (98 km/h; 61 mph)

A, B, flaps and landing gear down
	39 knots (73 km/h; 45 mph)

Max rate of climb at S/L: A	299 m (980 ft)/min

Rate of climb at 2,440 m (8,000 ft):
B	244 m (800 ft)/min
Service ceiling: A	3,810 m (12,500 ft)
Max operating altitude: B	6,100 m (20,000 ft)
T-O run: on land: A	183 m (600 ft)
on water: A	335 m (1,100 ft)
Landing run on land: A	145 m (475 ft)
Alighting run on water: A	183 m (600 ft)

Range with max fuel, at normal cruising speed, with reserves: A   564 nm (1,046 km; 650 miles)
Max range with max fuel, with reserves:
A	716 nm (1,327 km; 825 miles)

Endurance (75% power):
A at 2,440 m (8,000 ft)	5 h 36 min
B at 6,100 m (20,000 ft)	5 h 12 min

LAKE LA-250 RENEGADE and TURBO 270 RENEGADE

The **Renegade** is basically a development of the LA4-200 with lengthened fuselage, providing six-seat accommodation, and has a more powerful engine, together with tail surfaces of greater area. It was designed for STOL capability and is able to make high-speed step turns on water. FAA certification was received in August 1983. It is available also in turbocharged form as the **Turbo 270 Renegade**. In the late Summer of 1988 the prototype Lake Turbo Renegade set a world altitude record for light single-engined amphibians, climbing to 7,465 m (24,500 ft) over Sanford, Maine. Lake delivered a total of 23 Renegades during 1989.

The **Special Edition Seafury** is a version of the Renegade and has as standard the salt water operating package, listing rings, stainless steel brake discs, custom interior and survival package. It was available in Summer 1990.

The description of the LA4-200 applies also to the LA-250, except as follows:

TYPE: Single-engined six-seat amphibian.

HULL: Generally as for LA4-200, but lengthened by 1.05 m (3 ft 5 in). Deeper V hull bottom and added hull strakes for improved water handling.

TAIL UNIT: Cantilever all-metal structure, with swept fin and rudder and dorsal fillet. High-set tailplane. Outboard portion of elevator on port side is actuated hydraulically and independently as large trim tab. Fin is notched at tailplane position to permit elevator movement. Small retractable water rudder in base of rudder.

LANDING GEAR: As for LA4-200, except wheelbase increased

by 0.43 m (1 ft 5 in), and oleo extension increased to provide greater ground clearance.

POWER PLANT: One 186 kW (250 hp) Textron Lycoming IO-540-C4B5 flat-six engine in Renegade, driving a Hartzell three-blade constant-speed Q-tip metal pusher propeller. Turbocharged TIO-540-AA1AD engine in Turbo Renegade. Standard usable fuel capacity 204 litres (54 US gallons; 45 Imp gallons); optional usable capacity of 340 litres (90 US gallons; 75 Imp gallons).

ACCOMMODATION: As for LA4-200, but lengthened cabin provides seating for a pilot and five passengers, with increased baggage capacity. Gull wing cargo door standard.

DIMENSIONS, EXTERNAL:
Wing span	11.68 m (38 ft 4 in)
Length overall	8.64 m (28 ft 4 in)
Height overall	3.05 m (10 ft 0 in)
Wheelbase	3.13 m (10 ft 3 in)
Propeller diameter	1.93 m (6 ft 4 in)

DIMENSION, INTERNAL:
Cabin: Length	2.03 m (6 ft 8 in)

WEIGHTS AND LOADINGS:
Weight empty, equipped: Renegade	839 kg (1,850 lb)
Turbo Renegade	875 kg (1,930 lb)
Max usable fuel	240 kg (528 lb)
Max ramp, T-O and landing weight	1,383 kg (3,050 lb)
Max wing loading	87.6 kg/m² (17.94 lb/sq ft)
Max power loading	7.42 kg/kW (12.2 lb/hp)

PERFORMANCE (at max T-O weight, S/L, ISA):
Never-exceed speed:
Renegade	148 knots (274 km/h; 170 mph)

Max level speed at 1,980 m (6,500 ft): Renegade
	139 knots (258 km/h; 160 mph)

Max cruising speed: Renegade, 75% power at 1,980 m (6,500 ft)   132 knots (245 km/h; 152 mph)
Turbo Renegade, 78% power at 6,100 m (20,000 ft)   148 knots (274 km/h; 170 mph)
Stalling speed, power off:
landing gear and flaps up
	54 knots (100 km/h; 62 mph) IAS

landing gear and flaps down
	48 knots (89 km/h; 56 mph) IAS

Max rate of climb at S/L	274 m (900 ft)/min
Service ceiling: Renegade	4,480 m (14,700 ft)
Turbo Renegade	6,100 m (20,000 ft)
T-O run: on land	268 m (880 ft)
on water	381 m (1,250 ft)

Range with max fuel, 30 min reserves:
Renegade	900 nm (1,668 km; 1,036 miles)

Endurance at 78% power: Turbo Renegade   5 h 18 min

LAKE SEAWOLF

The Seawolf, introduced in early 1985, is a military/maritime surveillance variant of the LA-250 Renegade, with an Alkan 6091 rack under each wing to carry a variety of external stores including bombs of up to 200 lb size, rocket launchers, cartridge launchers and machine-gun pods. The weapons boresight position is constant and repeatable even after store removal and re-installation. In addition, the Seawolf can carry and release wing mounted rescue pods designed for use at sea or over land, with contents suitable for desert, Arctic and sea survival. Sea search and rescue pods are equipped with a liferaft, rations, homing and signalling devices; while desert pods have tent, rations, water, and other necessary equipment for survival and rescue.

A variety of radar systems is available, with the antenna mounted at the forward face of the engine pod, between the cooling inlets. The systems offer colour weather detection, a range of 240 nm (445 km; 276 miles), and three search modes: Search 1, employing sea clutter rejection circuitry to assist in detecting small boats down to a minimum range of 275 m (900 ft); Search 2, designed for precision surface mapping where high target resolution is important; and Search 3, which offers normal surface mapping for such tasks as the detection and tracking of oil slicks.

Interface units are available to provide a moving map display, waypoint designation, checklists, beacon navigation and multiple indicators. Provision has also been

Lake Renegade six-seat amphibian (*Pilot Press*)

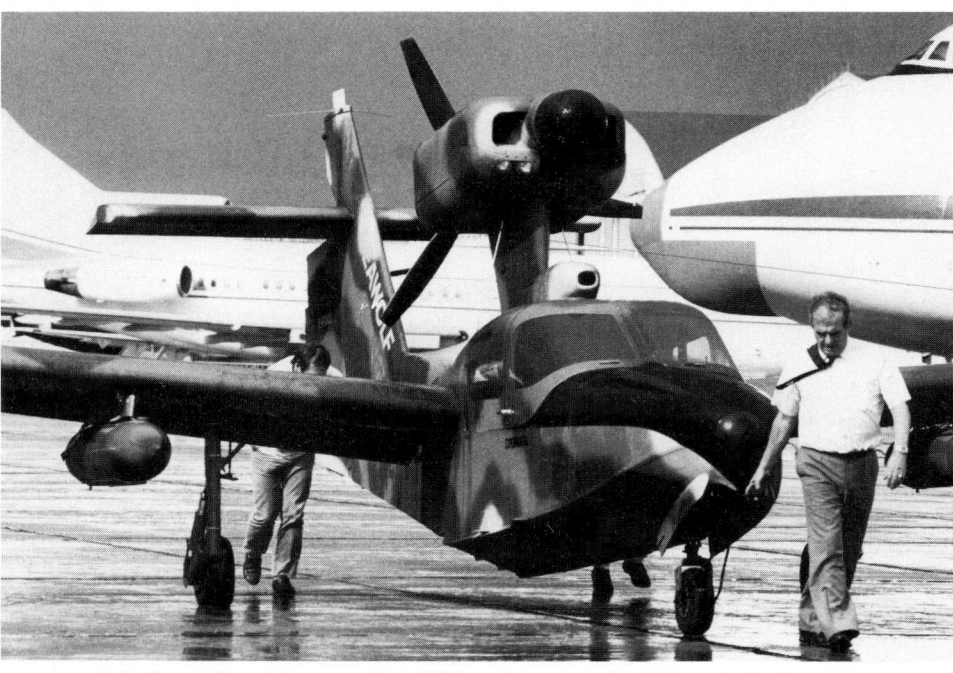

Lake Seawolf maritime patrol amphibian with underwing SAR pods *(Air Portraits)*

made for the installation of Loran or Omega navigation equipment.

Lake Aircraft claims that the Seawolf can fulfil a variety of paramilitary roles, including patrol and reconnaissance, search and rescue, special missions, liaison and logistics support, anti-smuggling duties, fish and wildlife protection, pollution control, law enforcement, and medevac duties. In medevac configuration the cabin can accommodate two litter patients and an attendant, as well as emergency medical equipment, once the passenger seats have been removed.

The prototype Seawolf (N1401G), which made its public debut at the 1985 Paris Air Show, retained the standard 12V electrical system of the civil Renegade; production versions have a 28V system.

Typical mission profiles for the Seawolf are:

Maritime patrol, with standard fuel and two gun pods; pilot only; take-off weight 1,485 kg (3,274 lb), 70 min fuel reserves; radius of action 100 nm (185 km; 115 miles); outbound leg flown at 120 knots (222 km/h; 138 mph) at

1,830 m (6,000 ft), with 6 h 30 min on station at 450 m (1,500 ft), returning to base at 120 knots at 2,440 m (8,000 ft).

Single strike mission, with standard fuel, and bombs or rockets; pilot only; take-off weight 1,517 kg (3,344 lb), 70 min fuel reserves; flying outbound to target 400 nm (740 km; 460 miles) from base at 120 knots at 6,000 ft, with ten min over target, returning to base at 125 knots (231 km/h; 144 mph) at 3,050 m (10,000 ft).

Multiple strike mission, with standard fuel and rockets; two crew; take-off weight 1,565 kg (3,450 lb), 1 h 50 min fuel reserves; flying to initial target 200 nm (370 km; 230 miles) distant at 6,000 ft, ten min over target, continuing to second target 150 nm (278 km; 172 miles) beyond, ten min over target, returning to base at 10,000 ft.

Search and rescue mission, with external fuel and two SAR packs; pilot only; take-off weight 1,568 kg (3,457 lb), 1 h 50 min fuel reserves; to search locality 250 nm (463 km; 287 miles) from base at 6,000 ft, time on station 8 hours, returning to base at 120 knots at 10,000 ft.

Photo reconnaissance mission, with standard fuel

and two reconnaissance pods; two crew; take-off weight 1,430 kg (3,152 lb), 1 h 30 min fuel reserves; flying at 120 knots to three locations at 50 nm (93 km; 57 mile) intervals from base, one hour loiter over each at 1,500 ft, returning 150 nm to base at 120 knots at 6,000 ft.

Ferry flight, with external fuel; two crew; take-off weight 1,563 kg (3,445 lb), 1 h 50 min fuel reserves; range 1,500 nm (2,775 km; 1,726 miles) at 120 knots; endurance 12 h 30 min.

The description of the Renegade applies also to the Seawolf, except as follows:
TYPE: Single-engined multi-role amphibian.
HULL: Interior LPS preservative spray optional.
POWER PLANT: Standard fuel capacity 333 litres (88 US gallons; 73.3 Imp gallons); optional capacity, with external tanks, 568 litres (150 US gallons; 125 Imp gallons).
ACCOMMODATION: Enclosed cabin capable of seating up to six persons. All seats except pilot's removable, with a variety of optional internal configurations according to mission. Entry through two forward-hinged windscreen sections. Upward hinged gull wing cargo door standard.
ARMAMENT: Standard Alkan 6091 stores mounts on underwing hardpoints, one inboard and one outboard of each wing balancer float, can accommodate a variety of stores, including external fuel tanks, parachute flares, SAR pods, ECM pods, gun pods, reconnaissance pods, rocket launchers, photo-reconnaissance pods, cartridge throwers, flare dispensers, hazardous material containers, practice and general purpose bombs. Inboard stores points can each carry up to 100 kg (220 lb), outboard points can each carry up to 35 kg (77 lb).
DIMENSIONS AND AREAS: As for Renegade
WEIGHTS:

Weight empty	998 kg (2,200 lb)
*Max ramp and T-O weight	1,565 kg (3,450 lb)
Max landing weight, on land	1,383 kg (3,050 lb)

*181 kg (400 lb) must be underwing stores
PERFORMANCE:
As for Renegade, except:
Cruising speed, 55% power

	110 knots (204 km/h; 127 mph)
Landing distance, land and water	230 m (755 ft)
Range with standard fuel at 120 knots (222 km/h; 138 mph), with 38 litres (10 US gallons; 8.3 Imp gallons) fuel reserves	876 nm (1,622 km; 1,008 miles)
Range with external tanks at 120 knots (222 km/h; 138 mph), with 38 litres (10 US gallons; 8.3 Imp gallons) fuel reserves	1,500 nm (2,780 km; 1,727 miles)
Endurance: with standard fuel	8 h 30 min
with external tanks	14 h 30 min

LEARJET
LEARJET CORPORATION
Mid-Continent Airport, PO Box 7707, Wichita, Kansas 67277
Telephone: 1 (316) 946 2000
Telex: 417441
CHAIRMAN AND CHIEF EXECUTIVE OFFICER: Brian Barents
SENIOR VICE-PRESIDENT, MARKETING AND SALES:
Robert C. Williams
VICE-PRESIDENT, OPERATIONS: Richard E. Hamlin
VICE-PRESIDENT CORPORATE AFFAIRS:
William G. Robinson
VICE-PRESIDENT RESALE MARKETING: Michael I. Berger
VICE-PRESIDENT ENGINEERING: William W. Greer

Founded in 1960 by the late William P. Lear Sr, this company was known originally as the Swiss American Aviation Corporation, which was formed to manufacture a high-speed twin-jet executive aircraft known as the Learjet 23 (formerly SAAC-23). In 1962 all company activities were relocated at Wichita, Kansas, and shortly afterwards the company became known as Lear Jet Corporation. In 1967 Mr Lear's interests (approx 60 per cent) were acquired by The Gates Rubber Company of Denver, Colorado, and in January 1970 the company name was changed to Gates Learjet Corporation. In early September 1987, Integrated Acquisition Inc acquired a 64.8 per cent interest in Gates Learjet, and renamed the company Learjet Corporation. In January 1988 the company announced that it would close its plant at Tucson, Arizona, and concentrate all Learjet manufacturing operations in Wichita, where employment exceeded 2,475 by the end of 1989, and total employment stood at 2,885. A customer service and aircraft modification centre is retained at Tuscon.

In March 1989 Learjet purchased manufacturing and marketing rights and tooling for Aeronca thrust reversers, which it manufactures and services for its own aircraft and for retrofit to those of other manufacturers.

In April 1990, Canada's Bombardier agreed to buy Learjet from its owner, Integrated Acquisition, for $75 million and to assume its debts.

Improved Century III models of the Learjet 24, 25 and 35/36, incorporating a cambered wing and other changes to reduce stall and approach speeds and balanced field length,

were introduced in late 1975. Further details of these improvements can be found in the 1981-82 *Jane's*.

Since 1 July 1979, all newly delivered Learjets have also embodied Softflite handling package to improve stall characteristics. Available for retrofit on earlier aircraft, this comprises a full chord shallow fence on each wing, small devices on the inboard leading-edge, and two rows of boundary layer energisers forward of each aileron, to energise the airflow and delay the onset of compressibility. Vortex generators are removed; the stick shaker/pusher is retained but unlikely to be required. A Softflite I performance kit was developed subsequently, and is FAA certificated for all early model Learjet 20 series aircraft with the so-called straight-wing or standard wing configuration, including the original Model 23. The modification incorporates a unique treatment of the wing leading-edge in place of conventional stall strips, and includes the full chord wing fences and boundary layer energisers that form part of the original Softflite package. Designed to improve low-speed performance and handling qualities, the Softflite I modification greatly enhances the aerodynamic stall characteristics of those early 20 series aircraft not equipped with Century III and original Softflite systems improvements.

Advanced models, with wings of increased span fitted with supercritical winglets, were announced in 1977. Designated Learjet 28/29 and Learjet 55, these subsequently joined the earlier models in production; manufacture of the Learjet 28/29 ended in 1982. Models 35, 36 and 55 continue in production, and were joined in 1988 by a new Model 31, combining the Learjet 35/36 fuselage and power plant with a wing similar to that of the earlier 28/29.

Learjet Corporation delivered a total of 25 Learjets during 1989.

LEARJET 35A and 36A
US Air Force designation: C-21A
A prototype turbofan powered Learjet (known originally as the Model 26) made its first flight with Garrett TFE731-2 engines on 4 January 1973. The production 35 and 36, announced in May 1973, are almost identical, differing in fuel capacity and accommodation. FAA certification was awarded in July 1974, and customer deliveries began later

that year. French and UK certification were gained during 1979.

Century III improvements, the Softflite handling package (see introductory notes) and engine synchronisers are standard for both models; a higher max T-O weight of 8,300 kg (18,300 lb), originally an option, is now standard on the current 35A/36A. Other improvements introduced in the Autumn of 1983 include the T/R-4000 thrust reverser system developed in co-operation with The Dee Howard Company (which see). The T/R-4000 has a hydraulic accumulator permitting operation even if the aircraft hydraulic system fails, single-engine deployment capability, quick removal hot section, a locking arrangement preventing deployment at high thrust settings, reverse thrust availability within two seconds after touchdown, throttle retard system, and lower engine (N_1) speed at equivalent reverser thrust. The T/R-4000 is optional on new Learjet 35A/36As, and is available for retrofit to all Century III 30-series Learjets.

A new special class interior for the Model 35A was introduced in Autumn 1985, offering increased leg and headroom. Four passengers can be accommodated in club seating on Erda seats which recline and have an electrically actuated inboard, fore and aft tracking facility. A centre console between the rear pair of seats contains stereo headsets and an in-flight telephone. Solid doors fore and aft of the lavatory area, electronic control of the adjustable washbasin cabinet, and 0.61 m (2 ft 0 in) wide fold-out conference/dining tables, are also featured in the new cabin configuration.

During 1984-85 the USAF received, originally on lease, 80 Model 35As, designated **C-21A**, for the Operational Support Aircraft (OSA) programme, to replace CT-39 Sabreliners in the Military Airlift Command inventory on high-priority and time-sensitive cargo delivery, passenger airlift and other operational support missions, including medical evacuation. In September 1986 USAF exercised its option to purchase the 80 C-21As for $180 million. They are based throughout the USA and in Japan and the Federal Republic of Germany. In the Summer of 1987 the Air National Guard acquired four C-21As to replace T-39s based at Andrews AFB, Maryland.

Learjet delivered 12 Model 35As and 36As in 1989, bringing total deliveries of those models to more than 710.
TYPE: Twin-turbofan light executive transport.

WINGS: Cantilever low-wing monoplane. Wing section NACA 64A 109 with modified leading-edge. Dihedral 2° 30'. Incidence 1°. Sweepback 13° at quarter-chord. All-metal eight-spar structure with milled alloy skins. Manually operated, aerodynamically balanced all-metal ailerons. The Softflite handling package consists of two rows of boundary layer energisers forward of each aileron, full-chord fences, and stall strips on the wing leading-edges. Hydraulically acutated all-metal single-slotted flaps. Hydraulically actuated all-metal spoilers ahead of flaps. Electrically operated trim tab in port aileron. Balance tab in each aileron. Anti-icing by engine bleed air ducted into leading-edges.

FUSELAGE: All-metal flush riveted semi-monocoque fail-safe structure.

TAIL UNIT: Cantilever all-metal sweptback structure, with electrically actuated variable incidence T tailplane and small ventral fin. Conventional manually operated control surfaces. Electrically operated trim tab in rudder. Electrically heated de-icing of tailplane leading-edges.

LANDING GEAR: Retractable tricycle type, with twin wheels on each main unit and single steerable nosewheel, maximum steering angle 45° either side of centreline. Hydraulic actuation, with backup pneumatic extension. Oleo-pneumatic shock absorbers. Goodyear multiple-disc hydraulic brakes. Pneumatic emergency braking system. Parking brakes. Fully modulated anti-skid system.

POWER PLANT: Two Garrett TFE731-2-2B turbofans, each rated at 15.6 kN (3,500 lb st), pod-mounted on sides of rear fuselage. Fuel in integral wing and wingtip tanks and a fuselage tank, with a combined usable capacity (Learjet 35A) of 3,500 litres (925 US gallons; 770 Imp gallons). Learjet 36A has a larger fuselage tank, giving a combined usable total of 4,179 litres (1,104 US gallons; 919 Imp gallons). Refuelling point on upper surface of each wingtip tank. Fuel jettison system. Engine nacelle leading-edges anti-iced by engine bleed air.

ACCOMMODATION: Crew of two on flight deck, with dual controls. Up to eight passengers in Learjet 35A; one on inward facing seat with toilet on starboard side at front, then two pairs of swivel seats which face fore and aft for take-off and landing, with centre aisle, and three on forward facing couch at rear of cabin. Two forward storage cabinets, one on each side; refreshment cabinet with hot and cold cup storage, coffee warmer, water dispenser, ice chest and serving surfaces; and two folding tables, standard. Alternative 'mid-cabin' arrangement, available optionally, places a refreshment area in the middle of the cabin, accessible from fore and aft club seating areas, each for four passengers. Learjet 36A can accommodate up to six passengers, one pair of swivel seats being removed. Toilet and stowage space under front inward facing seat which can be screened from remainder of cabin. Refreshment cabinet opposite this seat, aft of passenger door. Baggage compartment with capacity of 226 kg (500 lb) aft of cabin. Two-piece clamshell door at forward end of cabin on port side, with integral steps built into lower half. Emergency exit on starboard side of cabin. Birdproof windscreens.

SYSTEMS: Environmental control system comprises cabin pressurisation, ventilation, heating and cooling. Heating and pressurisation by engine bleed air, with a max pressure differential of 0.65 bars (9.4 lb/sq in), maintaining a cabin altitude of 1,980 m (6,500 ft) to an actual altitude of 13,715 m (45,000 ft). Freon R12 vapour cycle cooling system supplemented by a ram-air heat exchanger. Flight control system includes dual yaw dampers, dual stick pushers, dual stick shakers and Mach trim. Anti-icing system includes distribution of engine bleed air for wing, tailplane and engine nacelle leading-edges and windscreen; electrical heating of pitot heads, stall warning vanes and static ports; and alcohol spray on windscreen and nose radome. Hydraulic system supplied by two engine driven pumps, each pump capable of maintaining alone the full system pressure of 103.5 bars (1,500 lb/sq in), for operation of landing gear, brakes, flaps and spoilers. Hydraulic system maximum flow rate 15 litres (4 US gallons; 3.33 Imp gallons) per min. Cylindrical reservoir pressurised to 1.38 bars (20 lb/sq in). Electrically driven hydraulic pump for emergency operation of all hydraulic services. Pneumatic system of 124 to 207 bars (1,800 to 3,000 lb/sq in) pressure for emergency extension of landing gear and operation of brakes. Electrical system powered by two 30V 400A brushless generators, two 1kVA solid state inverters to provide AC power, and two 24V 37Ah lead-acid batteries. Oxygen system for emergency use, with crew demand masks and drop-out masks for each passenger.

AVIONICS: Standard Collins avionics include dual FIS-84/EHSI-74 flight directors, integrated with J.E.T. FC-530 FCS and dual yaw dampers; dual VHF-22A com transceivers with CTL-22 controls; dual VIR-32 nav receivers with CTL-32 controls; ADF-60 with CTL-62 control; dual DME-42 with IND-42C indicators; dual TDR-90 transponders with CTL-92 controls; ALT-55B radio altimeter with DRI-55 indicator; dual Allen 3137 RMIs; UNS-1 long-range nav system; Honeywell Primus 450 colour weather radar; dual J.E.T. VG-206D vertical gyros; dual J.E.T. DN-104B directional gyros; pilot's IDC electric encoding altimeter with altitude preselect

One of 80 Learjet C-21As sold to US Air Force for operational support missions *(Jay Miller/Aerofax)*

and IDC air data unit; co-pilot's IDC barometric altimeter; dual Teledyne SL2-9157-3 IVSIs; dual marker beacon lamps; dual D.B. audio systems; J.E.T. PS-835D emergency battery and AI-804 attitude gyro; dual Davtron 877 clocks; annunciator package; N_1 reminder; avionics master switch; chip detector; flap preselect; Wulfsberg Flitefone VI; Bendix/King KHF 950 HF; Frederickson Jetcal 5 Selcal; Rosemount air data system and SAS/TAT/TAS indicator.

EQUIPMENT: Standard equipment includes thrust reversers, dual angle of attack indicators, engine synchronisation meter, cabin differential pressure gauge, cabin rate of climb indicator, interstage and turbine temperature gauges, turbine and fan speed gauges, wing temperature indicator, alternate static source, depressurisation warning, engine fire warning lights, Mach warning system, dual stall warning system, fire axe, cabin fire extinguisher, cabin stereo cassette player, EEGO audio distribution system, flotation jackets for crew and passengers, sound-proofing; baggage compartment, courtesy, instrument panel, flood, map, cockpit dome, and reading lights; dual anti-collision, landing, navigation, recognition, strobe, taxi and maintenance lights, wing ice detection light; dual engine fire extinguishing systems with 'systems armed' and fire warning lights, maintenance interphone jack plugs, engine synchronisation system, control lock, external power socket, and lightning protection system.

DIMENSIONS, EXTERNAL:

Wing span over tip tanks	12.04 m (39 ft 6 in)
Wing chord: at root	2.74 m (9 ft 0 in)
at tip	1.55 m (5 ft 1 in)
Wing aspect ratio	5.7
Length overall	14.83 m (48 ft 8 in)
Height overall	3.73 m (12 ft 3 in)
Tailplane span	4.47 m (14 ft 8 in)
Wheel track	2.51 m (8 ft 3 in)
Wheelbase	6.15 m (20 ft 2 in)
Passenger door:	
Standard: Height	1.57 m (5 ft 2 in)
Width	0.61 m (2 ft 0 in)
Optional: Height	1.57 m (5 ft 2 in)
Width	0.91 m (3 ft 0 in)
Emergency exit: Height	0.71 m (2 ft 4 in)
Width	0.48 m (1 ft 7 in)

DIMENSIONS, INTERNAL (A: Learjet 35A, B: Learjet 36A):

Cabin: Length, incl flight deck: A	6.63 m (21 ft 9 in)
B	5.77 m (18 ft 11 in)
excl flight deck: A	5.21 m (17 ft 1 in)
B	4.06 m (13 ft 4 in)
Max width	1.50 m (4 ft 11 in)
Max height	1.32 m (4 ft 4 in)
Volume, incl flight deck: A	9.12 m³ (322.0 cu ft)
B	7.25 m³ (256.0 cu ft)
Baggage compartment: A	1.13 m³ (40.0 cu ft)
B	0.76 m³ (27.0 cu ft)

AREA:

Wings, gross	23.53 m² (253.3 sq ft)

WEIGHTS AND LOADINGS (Learjet 35A and 36A):

Weight empty, equipped	4,462 kg (9,838 lb)
Max payload	1,361 kg (3,000 lb)
Max T-O weight	8,300 kg (18,300 lb)
Max ramp weight	8,391 kg (18,500 lb)
Max landing weight	6,940 kg (15,300 lb)
Max wing loading	347.1 kg/m² (71.1 lb/sq ft)
Max power loading	261.7 kg/kN (2.57 lb/lb st)

PERFORMANCE (Learjet 35A and 36A, at max T-O weight, except where indicated):

Max operating speed	Mach 0.81
Max level speed at 7,620 m (25,000 ft)	
	471 knots (872 km/h; 542 mph)
Max cruising speed, mid-cruise weight, at 12,500 m	
(41,000 ft)	460 knots (852 km/h; 529 mph)
Econ cruising speed, mid-cruise weight, at 13,700 m	
(45,000 ft)	418 knots (774 km/h; 481 mph)
Stalling speed, wheels and flaps down, engines idling	
	96 knots (178 km/h; 111 mph) IAS
Max rate of climb at S/L	1,323 m (4,340 ft)/min
Rate of climb at S/L, one engine out	
	390 m (1,280 ft)/min
Service ceiling	13,715 m (45,000 ft)
Service ceiling, one engine out	7,620 m (25,000 ft)
Min ground turning radius, about nosewheel	
	6.43 m (21 ft 1 in)
T-O balanced field length, FAR Pt 25:	
at 7,711 kg (17,000 lb)	1,287 m (4,224 ft)
at 8,300 kg (18,300 lb)	1,515 m (4,972 ft)
Landing distance, FAR Pt 25, at max landing weight	
	937 m (3,075 ft)
Range with 4 passengers, max fuel and 45 min reserves:	
Learjet 35A	1,206 nm (2,236 km; 1,389 miles)
Learjet 36A	1,437 nm (2,664 km; 1,655 miles)

OPERATIONAL NOISE LEVELS (FAR Pt 36):

T-O	83.9 EPNdB
Approach	91.4 EPNdB
Sideline	86.7 EPNdB

LEARJET 35A/36A SPECIAL MISSIONS VERSIONS

In addition to the commercial Model 35A/36A, Learjet offers specialised aircraft for a wide range of civilian and paramilitary applications such as aerial survey, aeronautical research, airways calibration, anti-submarine warfare, atmospheric research, border patrol, ECM/ESM, geophysical survey, maritime patrol, pilot training, radar surveillance, reconnaissance, search and rescue, and weather modification. Special mission Learjets are operating in 20 countries, including Argentina, Australia, Bolivia, Brazil, Chile, the People's Republic of China, Finland, West Germany, Japan, Mexico, Peru, Saudi Arabia, Sweden, Switzerland, Thailand, the United Kingdom, USA and Yugoslavia. Most special missions modifications are applicable to the Models 35A and 36A, according to customer requirements.

Special missions Learjet U-36A of Japan's Maritime Self-Defence Force

The Learjet 31 eight-passenger twin-turbofan business aircraft

Versions announced to date are:

EC-35A. Electronic warfare version for EW training simulation or use as a standoff ECM/ESM platform.

PC-35A. Maritime patrol version. Equipment available includes 360° sea surveillance digital radar housed in underbelly radome; high resolution television; forward looking infra-red (FLIR); infra-red linescanner (IRLS); electronic support measures (ESM); magnetic anomaly detector; integrated tactical displays; VLF Omega and other long-range navigation systems; a hardpoint under each wing with an Alkan 165B ejector for the carriage and ejection of external stores weighing up to 453 kg (1,000 lb); drop hatch for rescue gear; multi-track digital recorders; direction finding (homing) systems; ASW sonobuoy drop and detection equipment, and data annotated hand-held cameras.

RC-35A. Reconnaissance version. Standard installations include long-range oblique photographic (LOROP) cameras, side looking synthetic aperture radar, and pod-mounted surveillance camera systems carried as external stores. Three RC-35As, each equipped with geological survey equipment, including Goodyear SLAR in an underbelly pack, were delivered to the People's Republic of China in 1985, to supplement two similarly equipped **RC-36As** delivered in 1984.

UC-35A. Utility version with configurations to suit such applications as aerial survey, airways calibration, cargo/passenger transport, medevac, target towing and weather modification. Certified tow target systems include the Hayes Universal Tow Target System (HUTTS) with or without MTR-101, Flight Refuelling LLHK, MRTT and EMT TGL targets, and Marquardt MTR-101 aerial target launch and recovery tow reel. Four Learjet 35As and Model 36As have been delivered to West Germany for military target towing, and three Learjet 35As are operated by the Finnish Air Force, equipped for aerial mapping, air ambulance, air pollution control, oblique photography, rescue and sea patrol mission, in addition to their primary role of target towing for the Air Force's BAe Hawk combat trainers. Other Learjet 35As and 36As are in use in Asia, Australia and the United States for target towing and electronic warfare missions.

U-36A. Extensively modified version of Learjet 36A for Japan's Maritime Self-Defence Force (JMSDF). Four delivered for target towing, anti-ship sea skimming missile simulation and ECM duties. To meet the Japan Defence Agency's mission profile for the aircraft, Learjet, in association with Shin Meiwa, introduced longer and increased diameter wingtip tanks to accommodate the HWQ-1T missile seeker simulator, ALQ-6 jammer and camera equipment; an underbelly fairing for long-range ocean surveillance radar; an ALE-43 chaff dispenser; an ARS-1-L high speed tow sleeve with scoring; a new two-piece windscreen with electric demisting system for increased speed during low level missions; expanded underwing stores capability; and increases in max T-O and landing weights to accommodate mission equipment. Further deliveries of U-36As to the JMSDF are anticipated during the 1990s.

PERFORMANCE (PC-35A):
Operating speed:
at 11,275-12,500 m (37,000-41,000 ft)
415 knots (769 km/h; 478 mph)
at 4,575-7,620 m (15,000-25,000 ft)
319 knots (590 km/h; 367 mph)
S/L to 610 m (2,000 ft)
250 knots (463 km/h; 288 mph)
Rate of climb at S/L   1,380 m (4,525 ft)/min
Range:
at high altitude   2,249 nm (4,168 km; 2,590 miles)
at medium altitude 1,617 nm (2,996 km; 1,862 miles)
at low altitude   1,060 nm (1,964 km; 1,220 miles)

LEARJET 31

Learjet introduced the Learjet Model 31 at the National Business Aircraft Association Covention at New Orleans in late September 1987. This aircraft combines the fuselage, eight-passenger cabin and 15.6 kN (3,500 lb st) Garrett TFE731-2-2B turbofans of the Learjet 35A and 36A with the wing of the 55. A new feature introduced on the Learjet 31 is a pair of outward-canted ventral strakes which Learjet calls Delta-Fins. Installed on each side of the lower rear fuselage, the aluminium and composite fins have a 65° leading-edge sweepback and exert a nose-down pitching moment as the aircraft approaches the stall, virtually eliminating Dutch Mach roll and improving handling at high Mach numbers. As a result, the Learjet 31 is not required to have a stick puller/pusher system, although a stick shaker is installed as a precaution, and the aircraft exhibits such improved yaw and Dutch roll characteristics that only a single yaw damper is required and is not a vital operational item for flight dispatch. The Learjet 31 is offered in standard and Model 31ER extended range variants.

The prototype Learjet 31, modified from a Learjet 35A airframe, first flew on 11 May 1987 and was used for aerodynamic testing. The first production aircraft (N311DF) served as systems testbed. FAA certification was obtained on 12 August 1988. A total of seven Learjet 31s was manufactured during 1989.

POWER PLANT: As for Learjet 35A/36A. Fuel capacities 2,320 litres (613 US gallons; 510 Imp gallons) standard, 2,597 litres (686 US gallons; 571 Imp gallons) on Model 31ER.

AVIONICS: Standard Collins avionics package comprises dual VHF-22A com with CTL-22 controls, dual VIR-32 nav receivers with CTL-32 controls, pilot's ADI-84A/HSI-70 and co-pilot's AIM-510-24HG/HSI-70 flight instruments integrated with J.E.T. FC-531 autopilot, ADF-60 with CTL-62 control, DME-42 with IND-42A indicator, TDR-90 with CTL-92 control, dual Allen 3137 RMIs, dual marker beacon receivers, dual DB audio systems, Bendix/King RDS-81 four-colour weather radar, dual J.E.T. DN-104B directional gyros, J.E.T. VG-206D vertical gyro, I.D.C. electric encoding altimeter with altitude alert and I.D.C. air data unit, co-pilot's I.D.C. barometric altimeter, dual Teledyne IVSIs, dual marker beacon systems, dual DB audio systems, dual Davtron 877 digital clocks, dual I.D.C. Mach/IAS indicators, J.E.T. PS-835D/AI-804 emergency battery and attitude gyro, avionics master switch, and single J.E.T. YD-531 yaw damper.

EQUIPMENT: Gravity flow fuel system, fuel filler screens, throttle-mounted landing gear warning mute and go-around switches, nacelle heat annunciator, engine synchroniser and synchroscope, dual Gill-Teledyne G-6381E high capacity lead-acid batteries, recognition light, wing ice light, emergency press override switches, transponder ident switch in pilot's control wheel, engine synchroniser and synchroscope, flap preselect, crew lifejackets, cockpit dome lights, cockpit speakers, crew oxygen masks and fire extinguisher are standard. Cabin furnishings include a three-seat divan, four individual tracking and reclining seats, side facing seat with toilet, two folding tables, refreshment cabinet with ice chest, baggage compartment, coffee warmer, water dispenser, cup and miscellaneous storage, coat rod, forward privacy curtain, overhead panels with reading lights, indirect lighting, air vents and oxygen masks, and passenger lifejackets.

Data as for Learjet 35A except:

DIMENSIONS, EXTERNAL:
Wing span	13.33 m (43 ft 9 in)
Length overall	14.83 m (48 ft 8 in)
Height overall	3.73 m (12 ft 3 in)

DIMENSIONS, INTERNAL (A: Learjet 31, B: Learjet 31ER):
Cabin:
Length, incl flight deck: A	6.63 m (21 ft 9 in)
B	6.27 m (20 ft 7 in)
Length, excl flight deck: A	5.21 m (17 ft 1 in)
B	4.85 m (15 ft 11 in)
Max width: A, B	1.50 m (4 ft 11 in)
Height: A, B	1.32 m (4 ft 4 in)
Volume, incl flight deck: A	9.12 m³ (322.0 cu ft)
B	8.83 m³ (312.0 cu ft)
Baggage compartment: A	1.13 m³ (40.0 cu ft)
B	0.85 m³ (30.0 cu ft)

AREA:
Wings, gross	24.57 m² (264.5 sq ft)

WEIGHTS AND LOADINGS (A: 31, B: 31ER):
Weight empty: A	4,497 kg (9,914 lb)
B	4,514 kg (9,953 lb)
Basic operating weight: A	4,678 kg (10,314 lb)
B	4,696 kg (10,353 lb)
Max payload: A	1,037 kg (2,286 lb)
B	1,019 kg (2,247 lb)
Payload with max fuel: A	595 kg (1,312 lb)
B	791 kg (1,744 lb)
Max fuel weight: A	1,870 kg (4,124 lb)
B	2,110 kg (4,653 lb)
Max T-O weight: A	7,030 kg (15,500 lb)
B	7,484 kg (16,500 lb)
Max ramp weight: A	7,144 kg (15,750 lb)
B	7,597 kg (16,750 lb)
Max zero-fuel weight	5,715 kg (12,600 lb)
Max landing weight	6,940 kg (15,300 lb)
Max wing loading: A	286.1 kg/m² (58.60 lb/sq ft)
B	304.6 kg/m² (62.38 lb/sq ft)
Max power loading: A	225.32 kg/kN (2.21 lb/lb st)
B	239.87 kg/kN (2.36 lb/lb st)

PERFORMANCE (at max standard T-O weight, S/L, ISA, except where indicated; A: 31, B: 31ER):
Never-exceed speed	300 knots (555 km/h; 345 mph) IAS
Max operating speed	Mach 0.78
Cruising speed at 13,715 m (45,000 ft)	447 knots (828 km/h; 515 mph)
Stalling speed at typical landing weight	93 knots (173 km/h; 107 mph)
Max rate of climb at S/L: A	1,670 m (5,480 ft)/min
B	1,555 m (5,100 ft)/min
Rate of climb at S/L, one engine out:	
A	576 m (1,890 ft)/min
B	466 m (1,530 ft)/min
Max certificated ceiling	15,545 m (51,000 ft)
Service ceiling, one engine out: A	9,510 m (31,200 ft)
B	8,840 m (29,000 ft)

Three-view drawing of Learjet 31 *(Pilot Press)*

T-O balanced field length, FAR Pt 25:

A	886 m (2,906 ft)
B	987 m (3,236 ft)
Turning radius, about nosewheel	11.91 m (39 ft 1 in)
FAR 91 landing distance: A	844 m (2,767 ft)
B	917 m (3,010 ft)

Range at econ cruising speed with four passengers, 45 min reserves:

A	1,660 nm (3,076 km; 1,911 miles)
B	1,897 nm (3,515 km; 2,184 miles)

OPERATIONAL NOISE LEVELS (FAR Pt 36):

T-O	79.6 EPNdB
Approach	92.6 EPNdB
Sideline	87.2 EPNdB

LEARJET 55C

The first of two Learjet 55 prototypes (N551GL) flew for the first time on 19 April 1979; the second (N552GL) flew on 15 November 1979, and the first production example on 11 August 1980. Certification under FAR Pt 25 was received on 18 March 1981. The initial customer delivery was made on 30 April 1981. Learjet delivered six Model 55s in 1989.

FAA certification was received in July 1983 of a Phase 1 performance improvement package for Model 55s, which included replacement of the original leading-edge stall strips with new strips each containing five small inverted triangular wedges approx 1.5 mm ($\frac{1}{16}$ in) thick, plus installation of seven individually mounted triangles at a location on the leading-edge forward of the ailerons; installation of automatic performance ground spoilers; and the addition of automatic performance reserve (APR) to the TFE731-3A-2B turbofans, automatically provides an additional 0.80 kN (180 lb) of thrust from one engine if thrust from the other engine drops by five per cent or more. Phase 1 improvements are incorporated in all Learjet 55s manufactured since 1 July 1983, and are available as a retrofit package for earlier production aircraft. A Garrett energy management system (GEMS) is available optionally as an extension of APR.

A further performance improvement package, Phase 1A, was introduced on the production line in the Spring of 1984. This features high-energy brakes with 13 per cent greater capacity and up to 50 per cent increased life claimed, new wheels, longer axles, and modified landing gear doors, fairings and actuators. The doors and fairings are manufactured from graphite/epoxy and Kevlar/epoxy, respectively. Phase 1A, certificated in February 1984, is available as a retrofit to earlier Model 55s, with Phase 1 as a prerequisite. The package offers substantial increases in the Learjet 55's high-altitude, hot-day performance. Other improvements introduced from c/n 55-107 included an optional 9,752 kg (21,500 lb) max T-O weight and 8,165 kg (18,000 lb) max landing weight.

In September 1986 Learjet announced the Learjet Model 55B which featured an all-digital flight deck, increased max T-O weight as standard, aerodynamic refinements to the wing, and interior changes, which provide better take-off performance, increased range and greater mission flexibility than those of earlier Learjet 55s. Details of the Model 55B can be found in the 1987-88 Jane's. The current model, announced at the 1987 NBAA Convention in New Orleans, is the **Learjet Model 55C**, which is similar to the Model 55B but incorporates ventral Delta-Fins, each 2.88 m (9 ft 3 in) long, which improve balanced field length performance and confer aerodynamic and handling benefits, particularly at low airspeed and high angles of attack. They also obviate the need for a stick pusher system and permit installation of a single yaw damper. New low-drag engine pylons have also been introduced on the 55C. FAA certification of the 55C was obtained in December 1988.

Three versions were available in 1990:

Learjet 55C. Basic version, as described in detail.

Learjet 55C/ER. Extended range version, with an additional fuel tank of 163 kg (359 lb) capacity in the tailcone baggage compartment. This tank is available for retrofit on standard 55s already delivered.

Learjet 55C/LR. Long-range version; as 55C/ER, plus an additional fuel tank of 386 litres (102 US gallons; 85 Imp gallons) capacity between the standard fuselage tank and rear cabin baggage compartment. Typical seating for seven passengers and two crew. Retrofit of existing 55s to this standard to be available.

TYPE: Twin-turbofan light executive transport.

WINGS: Cantilever low-wing monoplane. Sweepback 13° at quarter-chord. All-metal multi-spar structure with cavity milled wing skins. Wing upper surface skin tapers in thickness from wing root to wingtip to save weight. The design incorporates an advanced cambered leading-edge, the Softflite handling package (see introductory notes to company entry), boundary layer energisers and supercritical winglets. Manually operated ailerons. Electrically operated trim tab in port aileron. Hydraulically operated all-metal single-slotted trailing-edge flaps. Hydraulically operated all-metal spoilers mounted on wing upper surface just forward of flaps. Anti-icing by engine bleed air ducted into leading-edges.

FUSELAGE: All-metal flush riveted semi-monocoque fail-safe structure.

TAIL UNIT: Cantilever all-metal sweptback structure, with electrically actuated variable incidence T tailplane. Twin

Three-view drawing *(Pilot Press)* **and photograph of the Learjet 55C executive transport**

ventral Delta-Fins on lower rear fuselage, canted outward. Electrically heated de-icing of tailplane leading-edge.

LANDING GEAR: Hydraulically retractable tricycle type, with twin wheels on each main unit and single steerable nosewheel (± 55°). Mainwheel tyres size 17.5 × 5.75-8, 12 ply, pressure 12.4 bars (180 lb/sq in); nosewheel tyre size 18.0 × 4.4, 10 ply, pressure 7.24 bars (105 lb/sq in). High pressure pneumatic system for emergency extension. Oleo-pneumatic shock absorbers. Chined nosewheel tyre. Mainwheel doors are of composites construction. High energy hydraulic braking system, with pneumatic backup. Fully modulated anti-skid units.

POWER PLANT: Two Garrett TFE731-3A-2B turbofans, each rated at 16.46 kN (3700 lb st), plus 0.80 kN (180 lb st) automatic power reserve, pod-mounted on sides of fuselage aft of wing. Thrust reversers standard. Fuel in integral wing tanks and a fuselage bladder tank, with a combined usable capacity of 3,782 litres (999 US gallons; 832 Imp gallons) in standard Model 55C; 3,982 litres (1,052 US gallons; 876 Imp gallons) in Model 55C/ER; 4,353 litres (1,150 US gallons; 957 Imp gallons) in Model 55C/LR. Single-point refuelling. Engine nacelle leading-edges and fan hubs anti-iced by engine bleed air.

ACCOMMODATION: Crew of two on flight deck, with dual controls. IPECO fully adjustable crew seats. Seating for four to eight passengers in a choice of six interior layouts. Two folding tables. Carpeted floor. Galley refreshment cabinet. Toilet. Baggage space at rear of cabin, and in fuselage nose and tailcone of basic Model 55C. Tailcone baggage space reduced on long-range versions, but 55C/LR has baggage area at front of cabin. Two-piece clamshell door at forward end of cabin on port side, with integral steps built into the lower section. Emergency exit/baggage door on starboard side of cabin.

SYSTEMS: Environmental control system comprises cabin pressurisation, ventilation, heating and cooling. Heating and pressurisation are provided by engine bleed air, with a maximum pressure differential of 0.65 bars (9.4 lb/sq in), maintaining a cabin altitude of 2,440 m (8,000 ft) to 15,545 m (51,000 ft). Freon vapour-cycle cooling system, supplemented by a ram air system. Anti-icing system includes distribution of engine bleed air to wing leading-edges, engine nacelle leading-edges and fan hubs, and pilot and co-pilot windscreens; electric anti-icing of tailplane leading-edge, pitot heads, stall warning vanes and static ports; and alcohol anti-icing of windscreens. Hydraulic system supplied by two engine driven variable-volume constant-pressure pumps, one on each engine, each capable of maintaining alone the full system pressure of 103.5 bars (1,500 lb/sq in) for operation of landing gear, brakes, flaps and spoilers. Hydraulic system

maximum flow rate 15 litres (4 US gallons; 3.33 Imp gallons) per min. Cylindrical reservoir pressurised to 1.38 bars (20 lb/sq in). Electrically driven hydraulic pump for emergency operation of all hydraulic services. Pneumatic system of 124 to 207 bars (1,800 to 3,000 lb/sq in) pressure for emergency extension of landing gear and operation of brakes. Electrical system powered by two 28V 400A engine driven brushless generators, either of which is capable of maintaining adequate DC power to operate all electrical services; two 1kVA solid state inverters to provide AC power; and two 24V 37Ah lead-acid batteries. Oxygen system of 1.08 m³ (38 cu ft) capacity, with crew demand masks; dropout mask for each passenger, which is presented automatically if cabin altitude exceeds 4,265 m (14,000 ft). Sundstrand Turbomach APU optional (not on 55C/ER or 55C/LR).

AVIONICS: From aircraft c/n 134 onwards standard avionics include a Collins five-tube EFIS-85L-12 electronic flight instrumentation system with dual AHS-85 AHRS; Collins APS-85 digital autopilot with glareshield controller and dual flight data computers; dual ADC-82 air data systems; dual VHF-22A nav/coms with CTL-22 controls; dual VIR-32 nav receivers with CTL-32 controls; dual DME-42 with IND-42C indicators; ADF-60 with CTL-62 control; dual RMI-30; dual TDR-90 transponders with CTL-92 controls; ALT-55B radio altimeter, Collins WXR-350 Sensor weather radar, Universal UNS-1A long-range nav system; Bendix/King KHF 950 HF; Frederickson Jetcal-5 secal; Collins flight profile advisory system; and Wulfsberg Flitefone VI. Other standard flight deck equipment includes dual Collins encoding altimeters; MSI-80 Mach/airspeed indicators; VSI-80 instantaneous vertical speed indicators; Collins altitude pre-selector/alerter; TAS/SAT/TAT temperature indicator; IDC two-inch standby Mach/IAS indicator and altimeter; J.E.T. PS-835D and AI-804 emergency battery and attitude gyro; dual marker beacon systems; dual Avtech audio systems; dual Davtron 877 clocks; yaw damper; dual stall warning indicators; engine synchroniser and synchroscope; annunciator panels; avionics master switch; N_1 reminder, chip detector and flap preselect.

EQUIPMENT: Standard equipment includes sun visors; map lights; life jackets; fire extinguisher; writing tables; dome lights; oxygen masks; manual storage compartments, and dividing panel between flight deck and cabin. Cabin equipment includes two folding tables; four individual seats with tracking, swivel, recline and sideways motions; three-seat forward facing divan with storage and tracking and recline motions, single side facing seat, galley refreshment cabinet with decanters, bottle cooler, ice chest, oven, tray carrier, hot and cold liquid containers and storage area; forward coat closet; stereo and tape storage; magazine rack; convenience panel with reading lights, air vents, cabin speakers and oxygen masks; lighting control panel; opaque and tinted window shades; indirect lighting; aisle lighting; entrance step light; flushing toilet with vanity mirror and light; baggage compartment light; passenger life jackets; auxiliary cabin heater; fire extinguisher and axe; nose and tail baggage compartment lights; wing ice light and maintenance interphone jack plug sockets.

DIMENSIONS, EXTERNAL:

Wing span	13.34 m (43 ft 9 in)
Wing chord: at root	2.74 m (9 ft 0 in)
at tip	1.07 m (3 ft 6 in)
Wing aspect ratio	6.7
Length overall	16.79 m (55 ft 1 in)
Length of fuselage	15.93 m (52 ft 3 in)
Height overall	4.47 m (14 ft 8 in)
Tailplane span	4.47 m (14 ft 8 in)
Wheel track	2.51 m (8 ft 3 in)
Wheelbase	7.01 m (23 ft 0 in)
Cabin door: Height	1.70 m (5 ft 7 in)
Width	0.61 m (2 ft 0 in)

DIMENSIONS, INTERNAL:

Cabin: Length between pressure bulkheads:	
55C, 55C/ER	6.71 m (22 ft 0 in)
55C/LR	6.30 m (20 ft 8 in)
Length, cockpit/cabin divider to rear pressure bulkhead: 55C, 55C/ER	5.08 m (16 ft 8 in)
55C/LR	4.67 m (15 ft 4 in)
Max width	1.80 m (5 ft 11 in)
Max height	1.74 m (5 ft 8½ in)
Volume, incl flight deck:	
55C, 55C/ER	13.37 m³ (472 cu ft)
55C/LR	12.88 m³ (455 cu ft)
Baggage capacity: 55C rear cabin	0.93 m³ (33.0 cu ft)
nose	0.17 m³ (6.0 cu ft)
tail	0.52 m³ (18.5 cu ft)
55C/ER, total	1.36 m³ (48.0 cu ft)
55C/LR, total	1.81 m³ (64.0 cu ft)

AREAS:

Wings, gross	24.57 m² (264.5 sq ft)
Ailerons (total)	1.09 m² (11.70 sq ft)
Trailing-edge flaps (total)	3.42 m² (36.85 sq ft)
Winglets (total)	1.11 m² (12.00 sq ft)
Spoilers (total)	0.65 m² (7.05 sq ft)
Fin	4.67 m² (50.29 sq ft)
Rudder	0.99 m² (10.65 sq ft)
Tailplane	5.02 m² (54.00 sq ft)
Elevators (total)	1.31 m² (14.13 sq ft)

WEIGHTS AND LOADINGS:

Weight empty: 55C	5,832 kg (12,858 lb)
55C/ER	5,861 kg (12,922 lb)
55C/LR	5,920 kg (13,052 lb)
Typical operating weight empty:	
55C	6,013 kg (13,258 lb)
55C/ER	6,042 kg (13,322 lb)
55C/LR	6,101 kg (13,452 lb)
Payload with max fuel: 55C	590 kg (1,302 lb)
55C/ER	625 kg (1,379 lb)
55C/LR	268 kg (591 lb)
Max payload: 55C	790 kg (1,742 lb)
55C/ER	761 kg (1,678 lb)
55C/LR	702 kg (1,548 lb)
Max fuel weight: 55C	3,035 kg (6,690 lb)
55C/ER	3,197 kg (7,049 lb)
55C/LR	3,496 kg (7,707 lb)
Max T-O weight: 55C	9,525 kg (21,000 lb)
55C/ER & LR	9,752 kg (21,500 lb)
Max ramp weight: 55C	9,639 kg (21,250 lb)
55C/ER & LR	9,865 kg (21,750 lb)
Max zero-fuel weight:	
all versions	6,804 kg (15,000 lb)
Max landing weight:	
all versions	8,165 kg (18,000 lb)
Max wing loading:	
55C	387.6 kg/m² (79.4 lb/sq ft)
55C/ER & LR	396.9 kg/m² (81.3 lb/sq ft)
Max power loading:	
55C	289.3 kg/kN (2.84 lb/lb st)
55C/ER & LR	296.2 kg/kN (2.90 lb/lb st)

PERFORMANCE (at max T-O weight except where indicated):

Never-exceed speed:	
below 2,440 m (8,000 ft)	300 knots (555 km/h; 345 mph) IAS
2,440 m (8,000 ft) to 11,275 m (37,000 ft)	350 knots (648 km/h; 403 mph) IAS
11,275 m (37,000 ft) to 13,715 m (45,000 ft)	Mach 0.81 to Mach 0.79
above 13,715 m (45,000 ft)	Mach 0.79
Max level speed at 9,150 m (30,000 ft)	477 knots (884 km/h; 549 mph)
Max cruising speed at 12,500 m (41,000 ft)	455 knots (843 km/h; 524 mph)
Econ cruising speed at 14,325 m (47,000 ft)	419 knots (776 km/h; 482 mph)
Stalling speed	106 knots (197 km/h; 122 mph)
Max rate of climb at S/L: 55C	1,273 m (4,176 ft)/min
55C/ER & LR	1,237 m (4,059 ft)/min
Max rate of climb at S/L, one engine out:	
55C	378 m (1,240 ft)/min
55C/ER & LR	305 m (1,000 ft)/min
Max certificated ceiling	15,545 m (51,000 ft)
Min ground turning radius, about nosewheel	11.58 m (38 ft 0 in)
T-O balanced field length, FAR Pt 25:	
55C	1,536 m (5,039 ft)
55C/ER & LR	1,615 m (5,299 ft)
Landing distance, FAR Pt 91 at max landing weight	991 m (3,250 ft)
Range with crew of two, four passengers, allowances for taxi, T-O, climb, cruise at long-range power at 13,100 m (43,000 ft), descent and 45 min reserves:	
55C	2,189 nm (4,056 km; 2,520 miles)
55C/ER	2,305 nm (4,271 km; 2,654 miles)
55C/LR	2,397 nm (4,442 km; 2,760 miles)

OPERATIONAL NOISE LEVELS (FAR Pt 36):

T-O	86.3 EPNdB
Approach	90.7 EPNdB
Sideline	91.0 EPNdB

LOCKHEED
LOCKHEED CORPORATION

4500 Park Granada Boulevard, Calabasas, California 91399-0610
Telephone: (818) 712 2000

CHAIRMAN, PRESIDENT AND CHIEF EXECUTIVE OFFICER:
Daniel M. Tellep

VICE-CHAIRMEN:
Robert A. Fuhrman
Vincent N. Marafino

The early history of this company was outlined briefly in previous editions of *Jane's*. In September 1977 the former Lockheed Aircraft Corporation was renamed Lockheed Corporation, to reflect the company's diversified activities. These include the design and production of aircraft, electronics, satellites, space systems, missiles, ocean systems, information systems, and systems for strategic defence and for command, control, communications and intelligence.

Lockheed Corporation's total facilities cover more than 2,322,575 m² (25,000,000 sq ft). It has 86,800 employees in 25 US states and on worldwide company assignments. On 3

September 1987, it announced that its aircraft design, development, manufacturing and modification programmes, undertaken previously by Lockheed-California Company, Lockheed-Georgia Company and Lockheed Aircraft Service Company, were being integrated under three divisions of a new Lockheed Aeronautical Systems Group (LASG), with headquarters in Burbank, California. Lockheed Aircraft Service Company (LAS) reverted to its former status as a separate operating company within the Aeronautical Systems Group in February 1989.

LOCKHEED AERONAUTICAL SYSTEMS GROUP (LASG)

2555 North Hollywood Way (PO Box 551), Burbank, California 91520
Telephone: 1 (818) 847 6121
DIVISIONAL HEADQUARTERS: Burbank, California; Marietta, Georgia
PRESIDENT: Kenneth W. Cannestra
EXECUTIVE VICE-PRESIDENTS:
H. Bard Allison (General Manager, Georgia Operations)

E. Lloyd Graham (General Manager, Programmes)
Ben R. Rich (President, Advanced Development Company)
EXECUTIVE VICE-PRESIDENT AND GENERAL MANAGER, TECHNOLOGY AND ENGINEERING: Bart Krawetz
VICE-PRESIDENT, AND GENERAL MANAGER TEAM PROGRAMME OFFICE, F-22 ATF PROGRAMMES: Sherman N. Mullin
VICE-PRESIDENT, CIEM AND MODERNISATION AND INFORMATION SERVICES: William R. Sorenson
Lockheed Aeronautical Systems Group employs about

22,000 people at facilities in California, Georgia, Mississippi, Pennsylvania, South Carolina, Texas and West Virginia. Under plans announced in 1989 and 1990, major manufacturing activities are to be relocated from Burbank to Georgia and, to a lesser extent, Palmdale. In particular the much publicised Advanced Development Projects (Skunk Works), with a 4,000–5,000 workforce, becomes a separate company, and will be transferred largely to Palmdale. See also 'Advanced Reconnaissance Aircraft' in the USAF entry.

LASG BURBANK DIVISION

2555 North Hollywood Way (PO Box 551), Burbank, California 91520
Telephone: 1 (818) 847 6121
Telex: 67208

This division of LASG is responsible for production of the P-3 Orion land based anti-submarine warfare aircraft, special aircraft modification programmes, and formerly for components for the TR-1 high-altitude reconnaissance aircraft and Lockheed-Georgia's C-5B. It is engaged currently in several important research and development programmes, of which few details are yet available. One of them, covered in part by a $4.7 million USAF contract received in Spring 1986, is a four-year four-phase programme involving integrated vehicle and propulsion system concepts applicable to future supersonic cruise aircraft. Another, current in 1989, is for a supersonic advanced STOVL fighter with a hybrid fan vectored thrust engine and gross weight of about 19,050 kg (42,000 lb), being developed under a conceptual design contract from NASA.

The P-7A LRAACA programme is remaining at Burbank during the FSD phase, but will move to Georgia as it approaches the prototype and production phases. The ATF programme also will be transferred to Georgia if the competition ends in favour of the YF-22A.

LOCKHEED F-117A STEALTH FIGHTER

The F-117A was derived from a DARPA-funded contract from the USAF's Flight Dynamics Laboratory to develop a single-seat fighter/reconnaissance aircraft

featuring low radar, infra-red and optical signatures. Under the programme designated Have Blue, Lockheed Advanced Development Projects, the so-called Skunk Works at Burbank, built between five and seven proof of concept/demonstrator aircraft, known as **XST** (Experimental Stealth Technology), the prototype of which first flew from the secluded airfield at Groom Lake, Nevada, early in 1978, piloted by William C. Park.

The XST was reportedly a very small aircraft, powered by two 11.12-12.46 kN (2,500-2,800 lb st) General Electric CJ610 turbojets. Two XSTs crashed during trials, one (apparently the first prototype) on 4 May 1978. Concurrent development and production of the F-117A operational derivative, under the code name Senior Trend, was ordered in 1978 and the first flight followed only 31 months later, in June 1981. An initial US Air Force requirement for 100 F-117As was reduced to 59, of which the last was to be delivered in Autumn 1990.

The designations F-19 (for which no other application is known), RF-19, AR-19 and AR-2 were erroneously applied. Although US fighter designations re-started at F-1 in 1962, it is believed that Soviet-built aircraft acquired from friendly nations and brought to the US for secret evaluation have occupied the numbers F-112 to F-116. The designation, and a photograph of the F-117A, were released by the Department of Defense on 10 November 1988.

Clearly, the F-117A bears no relationship to the artist's conjectural impressions of a smooth-contoured airframe, or to the B-2 Stealth Bomber which employs such a shape. Resembling a multi-faceted pyramid with the apex immediately behind the cockpit, the F-117A appears to

have been designed to dissipate radar signals—particularly those from AEW aircraft looking down upon it—by deflecting them in numerous directions away from the searching radar. The aircraft's two engines are non-afterburning derivatives of the General Electric F404 turbofan. Although the F-117A programme was launched in November 1977, development of the -F1D2 version of F404 did not begin until 1980.

According to test pilot Park, the F-117A's design was dictated more by stealth requirements than aerodynamics. The XST demonstrated a tendency to sink rapidly onto the runway when in ground effect, and the F-117A's USAF nickname of 'Wobblin' Goblin' was derived from a controllability problem which is understood to have been improved since it entered service. Three F-117As have crashed. The aircraft is said to be capable of supersonic speeds, but to be restricted to subsonic operations reportedly following a tail surface detachment during high speed flight. The US Air Force defines maximum speed as 'high subsonic'.

The original F-117A unit was the 4450th Tactical Group formed at Tonopah Test Range Airfield, 140 miles north-west of Las Vegas, Nevada, in 1980, and was equipped with 18 A-7D Corsair IIs while awaiting delivery of the F-117A, the first of which arrived in 1982. Some civilian MU-2s were also used for communications. Initial operational capability was achieved on 26 October 1983. The unit first reported directly to Tactical Air Command, but passed under command of the Tactical Fighter Weapons Center at Nellis AFB in 1985.

Some of the Group's A-7Ds visited the UK, apparently to

test the F-117A sensors in the European environment, which resulted in reports that the F-117As themselves had flown from English bases. The F-117A with wings removed can be loaded into a C-5 for covert deployment.

At first, all flying was at night, but the broadening of operations forced the first public announcement of the existence of the F-117A in November 1988. A high profile was adopted from April 1990 when the F-117A made the first of several static appearances at public air displays.

The A-7Ds continued as introductory trainer and training chase aircraft for the F-117A until October 1989, when the 4450th was renamed 37th Tactical Fighter Wing and passed under control of 12th Air Force. Strength is now 46 F-117As in two squadrons (415th and 416th TFS). The A-7Ds were replaced by eight T/AT-38 Talons of the 417th TFTS. The Wing is expected to move to Holloman AFB, New Mexico, in 1992.

The F-117A's primary role appears to be one of defence suppression with AGM-88 HARM ARMs, AGM-65 Maverick ASMs and laser-guided bombs carried in an internal bay to maintain a minimal radar signature. Consistent with stealth principles, it appears to have no radar, although satellite-based navigation and possibly a terrain-referenced navigation system might be required for such pathfinding operations. Official statements refer only to "sophisticated navigation and attack systems integrated with a state-of-the-art digital avionics suite that increases mission effectiveness and reduces pilot workload". An operational debut was unexpectedly achieved on 21 December 1989 when two F-117As (of six flown directly from their base with aerial refuelling) each dropped a single 907 kg (2,000 lb) laser-guided bomb on a barracks at Rio Hato, during US Operation Just Cause to overthrow the Panamanian military government.

The following data has been obtained from several sources, but little has been verified by the manufacturer or operator and should thus be regarded as provisional.

TYPE: Twin-turbofan interdictor, optimised for radar energy dispersion and low IR emission.

WINGS: Cantilever low-wing monoplane. Sweepback of 67° 30′ is excessive for aircraft's design speed, and thus apparently dictated by stealth considerations and vortex lift generation from untwisted, sharp-edged aerofoil. Two-spar wings have equal-size ailerons and flaps along almost the entire trailing-edge. Highly original aerofoil section comprising three flat surfaces above and two beneath. Forward underside surface on same plane as forward underside of fuselage. Wings detachable to facilitate air transportation.

FUSELAGE: Conventional semi-monocoque all-metal construction, principally aluminium. Fuselage and wings further coated with several types of radar-absorbent materials. Pyramidal appearance with faceted exterior comprising flat surfaces attached to skeletal subframe and jointed without contour blending. Four small air data sensor probes around nose indicate quadruplex fly by wire control system. Internal weapons bay 4.70m (15 ft 5 in) long and 1.75m (5 ft 9 in) wide. Airfield arrester hook at rear.

TAIL UNIT: Two all-moving ruddervators in sharply-swept (approx 65°) V configuration, opposed at approx 85°.

LANDING GEAR: Tricycle type with single wheels all retracting forwards. All doors have serrated edges to suppress radar reflections. Braking parachute.

POWER PLANT: Two 48.0 kN (10,800 lb st) class General Electric F404-GE-F1D2 non-augmented turbofans. Rectangular overwing air intakes with 15 mm (⅝ in) square heated grid for anti-icing and low observability. Auxiliary air intake doors in horizontal surface immediately to the rear. Part of cold air ingested bypasses engine and is mixed with exhaust gases for cooling. Narrow-slot 'platypus' exhausts in rear fuselage, 1.65 m (5 ft 5 in) long and 0.10 m (4 in) high, with extended lower lip, surrounded by heat tiles of type used on Space Shuttle. In-flight refuelling receptacle in decking aft of cockpit. Braking parachute at base of tail fins.

ACCOMMODATION: Pilot only. Five individually-framed flat-plate windows, including single-piece windscreen. Transparencies gold-coated for radar dissipation. Canopy hinged to open upward and backward.

SYSTEMS: GEC Astronics quadruple-redundant fly by wire control system.

AVIONICS AND EQUIPMENT: Forward-looking infra-red (FLIR) sensor in recessed emplacement, covered by fine mesh screen, below windscreen. Retractable lower-sector FLIR and laser designator beneath forward fuselage to right of nosewheel bay. High-precision INS and GPS/Navstar integrated in digital nav/attack system with automated mission planning system augmented by pilot's night vision goggles. Retractable radio antennae beneath fuselage, ahead of port main landing gear.

ARMAMENT: "Full range of USAF tactical fighter ordnance" including one 907 kg (2,000 lb) BLU-109 low-level laser-guided bomb; or AGM-65 Maverick ASM. Internal carriage only.

DIMENSIONS, EXTERNAL:
Wing span	13.20 m (43 ft 4 in)
Length overall	20.08 m (65 ft 11 in)
Height overall	3.78 m (12 ft 5 in)

WEIGHT:
Max T-O weight	23,814 kg (52,500 lb)

Official pictures of Lockheed F-117A stealth fighter of the 37th Tactical Fighter Wing

Lockheed F-117A stealth fighter *(Jane's/Mike Keep)*

PERFORMANCE (* = not confirmed by USAF):
Max speed	Mach 1 + *
Normal max operating speed	Mach 0.9
T-O and landing speed	
	150 knots (227 km/h; 172 mph)*
g limit	+6

LOCKHEED YF-22A (ATF)

For available details of the US Air Force's Advanced Tactical Fighter (ATF) programme, see the US Air Force Systems Command entry in this section. Lockheed is contracted to build two YF-22A prototypes, in partnership with General Dynamics (Fort Worth Division) and Boeing Military Airplanes. Under the work division of the demonstration-validation phase of the programme, Lockheed is to maintain control and system integration responsibilities while the three companies will share the workload equally. Lockheed will oversee weapon system integration; develop and construct all forward fuselage structures and components, including crew station; spearhead avionics architecture and functional design, as well as displays, controls, air data system and apertures; and perform the testing and evaluation of the two prototype aircraft, with help from the other two companies. Boeing will develop and construct the wings, aft sections of the fuselage, and install the engines, nozzles and auxiliary power unit; and provide radar, infra-red search and track system (IRST), the avionics ground prototype and flying laboratory, to be installed aboard its company-owned 757 aircraft. General Dynamics is responsible for all mid-fuselage structures, tail assembly, nose and main landing gear, and key systems including electrical, hydraulic, fuel, flight controls, environment control system and armament; and will provide the tailored INEWS, tailored ICNIA, stores management systems, and inertial navigation systems.

Subcontractors so far announced include Curtiss-Wright (leading-edge flap drive), GEC Astronics (digital flight control computers), GEC Avionics (head-up display), Menasco (landing gear), National Water Lift and Parker Hannifin (flight control actuators), Sterer (nosewheel steering), Sundstrand Turbomach (APU), Texas Instruments (mission and display processing computer), and General Electric (liquid crystal displays).

First flight of the YF-22A was expected in mid-1990 at Palmdale. Unusually, the two YF-22As will have civilian registrations (N22YF and N22YX). If selected as ATF winner F-22 development and production will be transferred to Georgia.

LOCKHEED ER-2, U-2R and TR-1

After a three-phase production history spanning 34 years, the final aircraft of the U-2/TR-1 family (TR-1A 80-1099) was delivered to the USAF on 3 October 1989. Production totalled 55 U-2As in 1955-60, 12 U-2Rs in 1967-68 and a final batch in 1980-89 comprising seven U-2Rs, one U-2RT trainer, 25 TR-1As, two TR-1B trainers and two NASA ER-2s. Three TR-1s were later converted to U-2Rs.

In July 1989, a TR-1 began flight trials at Edwards AFB with the normal Pratt & Whitney J75-P-13B turbojet replaced by a lighter, 12 per cent more powerful, but still non-afterburning, General Electric F101-GE-F29 (believed to be a prototype F118). If successful, the trials are expected to lead to a re-engining of the TR-1/U-2R fleet (including six survivors of 1967-68 production) in order to offset increasing weight of sensors.

The final flying example of the smaller U-2A (a NASA-operated U-2C conversion, 66682/N709NA) was retired on 26 April 1989. Shortly before, on 17-18 April, it was permitted to demonstrate its capabilities publicly for the first time. Sixteen time-to-height records in classes C.1f and C.1g were broken by large margins, maximum altitude reached being 22,463 m (73,700 ft) in 16 min 0 s.

Further details of the TR-1 appeared in the 1989-90 *Jane's*. An illustration is overleaf.

Official artist's impression of Lockheed YF-22A Advanced Tactical Fighter

Lockheed U-2R fitted with a C-Span III communications pod for real-time transfer of reconnaissance data via satellite *(Bob Archer)*

LOCKHEED MODEL 185/285 ORION
US Navy designation: P-3
CAF designations: CP-140 Aurora/CP-140A Arcturus

In 1958 Lockheed won a US Navy competition for an off-the-shelf ASW aircraft with a developed version of its Electra four-turboprop commercial transport. An aerodynamic prototype flew for the first time on 19 August 1958. A second aircraft, designated YP-3A (formerly YP3V-1), with full avionics, flew on 25 November 1959.

Details of the P-3A initial production version and WP-3A can be found in the 1978-79 *Jane's*. The P-3B (144 built) and EP-3B were last described in the 1983-84 edition.

Unless South Korea places its proposed order for up to 16 Orions during 1990, the P-3 production line will close in September 1991 at the 642nd airframe. This total comprises one YP-3; 157 USN P-3As (of which 38 modified to UP-3A, seven to EP-3A, six to RP-3A, five to VP-3A, 12 to TP-3A, two to EP-3B and 10 to EP-3E standard); 124 USN P-3Bs (one to NP-3B); 267 USN P-3Cs (12 intended for EP-3E-II conversion); one USN RP-3D; two USN WP-3Ds; and 90 exports. The latter went to Australia (10 P-3B and 20 P-3C-II); Canada (18 CP-140 Aurora and three CP-140A Arcturus); Iran (six P-3F); Japan (three P-3C-II before local production); Netherlands (13 P-3C-II); New Zealand (five P-3K); Norway (five P-3B and four P-3C-III); and Pakistan (three P-3C-III). Transfers between operators comprise,

Australian P-3B: five to Portugal, one to New Zealand and two to US Customs as AEW&C; USN P-3A: four to US Customs as UP-3A; USN P-3B: two to Norway, seven to Spain and one to Australia; and Norwegian P-3B: five to Spain. Thailand plans to acquire three USN P-3Bs.

Production and conversion programmes since 1969 have included the following:

P-3C. Advanced version with the A-NEW system of sensors and control equipment, built around a Univac digital computer that integrates all ASW information and permits retrieval, display and transmission of tactical data in order to eliminate routine log keeping functions. First flight was made on 18 September 1968 and the P-3C entered service in 1969. The 267th and last USN P-3C (163295) was delivered in April 1990 to VP-91 at Moffett Field NAS, CA, which (with VP-62 at Jacksonville NAS, FL) is one of two Reserve squadrons issued with the P-3C. A further 11 reserve squadrons currently fly P-3A/Bs, augmenting 25 full-time patrol squadrons almost completely equipped with P-3Cs. Six more Orions remained to be delivered from Burbank in 1990-91, comprising three P-3Cs for Pakistan and three CP-140As for Canada.

Initial deliveries of 118 P-3Cs were followed from January 1975 onwards by 31 to **P-3C Update I** standard, with new avionics and electronics software developed to enhance their effectiveness. Equipment includes a magnetic drum that gives a sevenfold increase in computer memory

capacity, a new versatile computer language, Omega navigation system, improved DIFAR acoustic processing sensitivity, an AN/ASA-66 tactical display for two of the sensor stations, and an improved magnetic tape transport. **Update II**, initiated in 1976 and involving 44 aircraft, added an infra-red detection system (IRDS) and a sonobuoy reference system (SRS). The Harpoon missile and control system were incorporated into production aircraft from August 1977. The interim Update II.5 of 1981 covered a further 24 P-3Cs for the USN, having improved navigation and communications systems.

Update III, of which production deliveries began in May 1984, involves mainly ASW avionics, including a new IBM Proteus acoustic processor to analyse signals picked up from the sea, a new sonobuoy receiver which replaces DIFAR (directional acoustic frequency analysis and recording), an improved APU, and environmental controls to cater for increased heat from the avionics and to improve crew comfort further. Update III concerned the last 50 USN P-3Cs.

The P-3C remains in full scale production by Kawasaki of Japan (which see). Contracts placed up to, and including FY 1990, covered 69 P-3C.IIs (the first three included in US production totals), 27 P-3C.IIIs and two EP-3Cs, although the Update II aircraft will be retrospectively updated.

In addition to new production Update III aircraft, Lockheed has developed a retrofit kit, which was installed on a P-3C of VP-31 in early 1987. Installation of 18 more kits was scheduled to begin in June 1987, with the possibility of retrofitting a total of 113 Update II P-3Cs eventually.

Update IV, now being developed by Boeing for introduction in the early 1990s, will have improved processing capabilities, Texas Instruments AN/APS-137(V) radar, and a new family of acoustic sensors designed to counter the quieting trend of the Soviet submarine force. Aerodynamic trials by Lockheed of a P-3C equipped with an Eaton AIL Division AN/ALR-77 tactical electronic support measures (ESM) system were expected to be followed by technical and operational evaluation at the Naval Air Test Center, Patuxent River, Maryland. The AN/ALR-77 system comprises four wingtip quadrants providing 360° coverage with 36 interferometer antennae, each sub-band being covered by a triplet of antennae. Overall FSED contractor for Update IV is Boeing Aerospace and Electronics; up to 80 Update II P-3Cs are expected to receive Update IV modification.

EP-3C. Elint version of P-3C being developed by Kawasaki for JMSDF. First example funded in 1987, for delivery in March 1991. Eight more expected to be funded for operation by mid-1990s.

EP-3E Aries. Ten P-3As and two EP-3Bs were converted to EP-3E configuration. Identified by large canoe shape radars on upper and lower surfaces of fuselage and ventral radome forward of wing. EP-3E avionics suites are believed to comprise GTE-Sylvania AN/ALR-60 communications, interception and analysis sytem; Raytheon AN/ALQ-76 noise jamming pod; Loral AN/ALQ-78 automatic ESM system; Magnavox AN/ALQ-108 IFF jammer; Sanders AN/ALR-132 infra-red jammer; ARGO Systems AN/ALR-52 instantaneous frequency measuring equipment; Texas Instruments AN/APS-115 frequency agile search radar; Hughes AN/AAR-37 infra-red detector; Loral AN/ASA-66 tactical display; Cardion AN/ASA-69 scan converter; and Honeywell AN/ASQ-114 computer.

EP-3E Aries II. The USN is converting 12 low houred P-3Cs to replace the above EP-3Es currently serving with special reconnaissance squadrons VQ-1 at Agana NAS, Guam, and VQ-2 at Rota, Spain. Equipment is being transferred directly from the original EP-3Es. First conversion (156507) re-delivered to NATC Patuxent River in November 1988. Last aircraft due February 1991.

P-3F. Six aircraft, similar to mid-1970s US Navy P-3Cs, for Iranian Air Force.

CP-140 Aurora. Version for Canadian Armed Forces (18 built). Described in detail in 1981-82 *Jane's*.

CP-140A Arcturus. Three aircraft to be completed by September 1991, ending P-3 production. These differ significantly from the CP-140 Aurora in that no anti-submarine equipment is fitted. The Arcturus will assume fishery and environmental patrol duties from withdrawn CP-121 Trackers and release Auroras from these secondary duties. Principal equipment includes Texas Instruments AN/APS-134 radar, Honeywell AN/APN-194 RAWS, Bendix AN/ASW-502 AFCS, Canadian Marconi AN/APN-510 Doppler radar, Litton LN33 INS and a Leigh AN/ASH-502 flight recorder.

P-3 AEW&C. Airborne early warning and control variant. Prototype (N91LC), converted from ex-Royal Australian Air Force P-3B, made first flight on 14 June 1984, fitted with a 7.32 m (24 ft) diameter Randtron APA-171 rotodome above rear fuselage but without radar. For military AEW&C operations the aircraft would be equipped with General Electric AN/APS-139 radar (as on Grumman E-2C Hawkeye); a C³ system to receive, process and transmit tactical information through HF, UHF, VHF and Satcom channels; AR-187 satellite communications system; and Collins EFIS-86B five-tube colour CRT electronic flight instrument system. Testing of an installed APS-138 began in 1988.

In May 1987 the US Customs Service became launch customer for the P-3 AEW&C, with an order for one

The prototype Update III P-3C Orion photographed during test and evaluation by the US Navy

aircraft and options on three more. The first aircraft for US Customs is based on the company demonstrator airframe equipped with General Electric AN/APS-125 radar, with which it was flown for the first time on 8 April 1988. Other equipment includes a Control Data Corporation AN/AYK-14 computer with Honeywell 1601M array processor, dual Sanders Miligraphics touch-sensitive colour display screens providing digital target data, Hazeltine TPX-54 IFF, dual ARC-182 VHF/UHF com, dual ARC-207 HF, and dual Wulfsberg VHF/UHF FM radios. The aircraft, named *Blue Eagle*, was delivered to NAS Corpus Christi, Texas, on 17 June 1988, and is used for anti-drug smuggling operations in the Caribbean and Gulf of Mexico. A second P-3 AEW&C, named *Blue Eagle II* and equipped with an improved AN/APS-138 radar, was delivered to the US Customs Service in June 1989, and a third is on order. All three are ex-Australian P-3Bs. The General Electric AN/APS-145 radar will be available for the aircraft from late 1989.

P-3N. Two P-3Bs retained by Norway after delivery of P-3Cs are being divested of some anti-submarine equipment and will be used for EEZ surveillance, SAR and training.

P-3P. Designation of Portuguese P-3Bs obtained from Australia. One converted by Lockheed and five will be upgraded locally by OGMA (which see), with MIL-STD-1553 digital databus and systems similar to Update II, for Esquadra 601 at Ovar.

P-3W. Designation of Australian P-3C. These aircraft have AQS-901 processing system for Barra sonobuoys in place of Proteus and AQA-7 equipment of standard P-3C.

The following data refer to the P-3C, but are generally applicable to other versions, except for the details noted:

TYPE: Four-turboprop ASW aircraft.

WINGS: Cantilever low-wing monoplane. Wing section NACA 0014 (modified) at root, NACA 0012 (modified) at tip. Dihedral 6°. Incidence 3° at root, 0° 30′ at tip. Fail-safe box beam structure of extruded integrally stiffened aluminium alloy. Lockheed-Fowler trailing-edge flaps. Hydraulically boosted aluminium ailerons. Anti-icing by engine bleed air ducted into leading-edges.

FUSELAGE: Conventional aluminium alloy semi-monocoque fail-safe structure.

TAIL UNIT: Cantilever aluminium alloy structure with dihedral tailplane and dorsal fin. Fixed incidence tailplane. Hydraulically boosted rudder and elevators. Leading-edges of fin and tailplane have electric anti-icing system.

LANDING GEAR: Hydraulically retractable tricycle type, with twin wheels on each unit. All units retract forward, mainwheels into inner engine nacelles. Oleo-pneumatic shock absorbers. Mainwheels have size 40-14 type VII 26-ply tubeless tyres, pressures 7.58-12.41 bars (110-180 lb/sq in) at 36,287 kg (80,000 lb) T-O weight; 12.41 bars (180 lb/sq in) at 57,606 kg (127,000 lb) T-O weight; 13.10 bars (190 lb/sq in) at 61,235 kg (135,000 lb) max normal T-O weight. Nosewheels have size 28-7.7 type VII tubeless tyres, pressure 10.34 bars (150 lb/sq in). Hydraulic brakes. No anti-skid units.

POWER PLANT: Four 3,661 kW (4,910 ehp) Allison T56-A-14 turboprops, each driving a Hamilton Standard 54H60-77 four-blade constant-speed propeller. Fuel in one tank in

fuselage and four wing integral tanks, with total usable capacity of 34,826 litres (9,200 US gallons; 7,660 Imp gallons). Four overwing gravity fuelling points and central pressure refuelling point. Oil capacity (min usable) 111 litres (29.4 US gallons; 24.5 Imp gallons) in four tanks. Electrically de-iced propeller spinners.

ACCOMMODATION: Normal ten-man crew. Flight deck has wide-vision windows, and circular windows for observers are provided fore and aft in the main cabin, each bulged to give 180° view. Main cabin is fitted out as a five-man tactical compartment containing advanced electronic, magnetic and sonic detection equipment, an all-electric galley and large crew rest area.

SYSTEMS: Air-conditioning and pressurisation system supplied by two engine driven compressors. Pressure differential 0.37 bars (5.4 lb/sq in). Hydraulic system, pressure 207 bars (3,000 lb/sq in), for flaps, control surface boosters, landing gear actuation, brakes and bomb bay doors. Three hydraulic pumps, each rated at 30.3 litres (8.0 US gallons; 6.7 Imp gallons)/min at 0-151.7 bars (0-2,200 lb/sq in), 22.7 litres (6.0 US gallons; 5.0 Imp gallons)/min at 205.1 bars (2,975 lb/sq in). Class one non-separated air/oil reservoir, Type B pressurised. Electrical system utilises three 60kVA generators for 120/208V 400Hz AC supply. 24V DC supply. Integral APU with 60kVA generator for ground air-conditioning, electrical supply and engine starting.

Lockheed P-3C Orion four-turboprop anti-submarine aircraft, with added side elevation (centre) of AEW & C version *(Pilot Press)*

AVIONICS AND EQUIPMENT: The ASQ-114 general purpose digital computer is the heart of the P-3C system. Together with the AYA-8 data processing equipment and computer controlled display systems, it permits rapid analysis and utilisation of electronic, magnetic and sonic data. Nav/com system comprises two LTN-72 inertial navigation systems; AN/APN-227 Doppler; ARN-81 Loran A and C; AN/ARN-118 Tacan; two VIR-31A VOR/LOC/GS/MB receivers; ARN-83 LF-ADF; ARA-50 UHF direction finder; AJN-15 flight director indicator for tactical directions; HSI for long-range flight directions; glideslope indicator; on-top position indicator; two ARC-161 HF transceivers; two ARC-143 UHF transceivers; ARC-101 VHF receiver/transmitter; AGC-6 teletype and high-speed printer; HF and UHF secure communication units; ACQ-5 data link communication set and AIC-22 interphone set; APX-72 IFF transponder and APX-76 SIF interrogator. Electronic computer controlled display equipment includes ASA-70 tactical display; ASA-66 pilot's display; ASA-70 radar display and two auxiliary readout (computer stored data) displays. ASW equipment includes two ARR-72 sonar receivers which replaced in Update III by AN/ARR-78; two AN/AQA-7(V)8 DIFAR (directional acoustic frequency analysis and recording) sonobuoy indicator sets which replaced in Update III by AN/UYS-1 Proteus; hyperbolic fix unit; acoustic source signal generator; time

Lockheed P-3W upgraded Orion of the Royal Australian Air Force *(Paul Jackson)*

US Customs Service P-3 AEW & C *Blue Eagle* **airborne early warning and control version of the Orion**

code generator and AQH-4(V) sonar tape recorder; ASQ-81 magnetic anomaly detector; ASA-64 submarine anomaly detector; ASA-65 magnetic compensator; ALQ-78 electronic countermeasures set; APS-115 radar set (360° coverage); ASA-69 radar scan converter; undernose AAS-36 IRDS, KA-74 forward computer assisted camera; KB-18A automatic strike assessment camera with horizon-to-horizon coverage; RO-308 bathythermograph recorder. Additional equipment includes APN-194 radar altimeter; two APQ-107 radar altimeter warning systems; A/A24G-9 true airspeed computer and ASW-31 automatic flight control system. P-3Cs delivered from 1975 have the avionics/electronics package updated by addition of an extra 393K memory drum and fourth logic unit, Omega navigation, new magnetic tape transport, and an ASA-66 tactical display for the sonar operators. To accommodate the new systems a new operational software computer programme was written in CMS-2 language. GEC Avionics AQS-901 acoustic signal processing and display system in RAAF P-3Ws. AN/ALR-66 passive radar detection system (ESM), to be housed in wingtip pods, is under development for Update IV P-3C by General Instruments, and will also provide targeting data for the aircraft's Harpoon missiles. Also installed in Nowegian P-3C and as retrofit in P-3P and CP-140. Wing span increased by some 0.81 m (2 ft 8 in) to accommodate ESM antennae and receivers. Update IV FSED contract awarded to Boeing Aerospace and Electronics in Spring 1987, for completion in 1992. Subcontractors include Magnavox (acoustic system), Resdel (sonobuoy receiver), General Instrument (ESM), Honeywell (AN/AQH-4[V]2 data recorders) and M/A Com (satellite communications).

ARMAMENT: Bomb bay, 2.03 m wide, 0.88 m deep and 3.91 m long (80 in × 34.5 in × 154 in), forward of wing, and 10 underwing pylons. Maximum stores capabilities in weapons bay/underwing are Mk 46 torpedo 8/0; Mk 50 torpedo 6/0; Mk 54 depth bomb 8/10; B57 nuclear depth-charge 3/0; Mk 82 560 lb bomb 8/10; Mk 83 980 lb bomb 3/8; Mk 36 destructor 8/10; Mk 40 destructor 3/8; LAU-68A pod (seven 2.75 in rockets), or LAU-69A (nineteen 2.75 in rockets), or LAU-10A/C (four 5 in rockets), or SUU-44A (eight flares) 0/4; Mk 52 mine 3/8; Mk 55 or Mk 56 mine 1/6; Mk 60 torpedo 0/6; AGM-86 Harpoon anti-ship missile 0/8. Two AIM-9L Sidewinder AAMs underwing for self-defence. Searchlight replaces one wing pylon, starboard. Search stores, such as sonobuoys and sound signals, are launched from inside cabin area in the P-3A/B. In the P-3C sonobuoys are loaded and launched externally and internally. Max total weapon load includes six 2,000 lb mines under wings and a 3,290 kg (7,252 lb) internal load made up of two Mk 101 depth bombs, four Mk 44 torpedoes, pyrotechnic pistol and 12 signals, 87 sonobuoys, 100 Mk 50 underwater sound signals (P-3A/B), 18 Mk 3A marine markers (P-3A/B), 42 Mk 7 marine markers, two B.T. buoys, and

two Mk 5 parachute flares. Harpoon missiles are standard fit on a proportion of US Navy P-3Cs. Sonobuoys are ejected from P-3C aircraft with explosive cartridge actuating devices (CAD), eliminating the need for a pneumatic system. Australian P-3Ws use SSQ-801 Barra sonobuoys and will receive Elta (Israel) ESM systems.

DIMENSIONS, EXTERNAL:
Wing span	30.37 m (99 ft 8 in)
Wing chord: at root	5.77 m (18 ft 11 in)
at tip	2.31 m (7 ft 7 in)
Wing aspect ratio	7.5
Length overall	35.61 m (116 ft 10 in)
Height overall	10.27 m (33 ft 8½ in)
Fuselage diameter	3.45 m (11 ft 4 in)
Tailplane span	13.06 m (42 ft 10 in)
Wheel track (c/l shock absorbers)	9.50 m (31 ft 2 in)
Wheelbase	9.07 m (29 ft 9 in)
Propeller diameter	4.11 m (13 ft 6 in)
Cabin door: Height	1.83 m (6 ft 0 in)
Width	0.69 m (2 ft 3 in)

DIMENSIONS, INTERNAL:
Cabin, excl flight deck and electrical load centre:

Length	21.06 m (69 ft 1 in)
Max width	3.30 m (10 ft 10 in)
Max height	2.29 m (7 ft 6 in)
Floor area	61.13 m² (658.0 sq ft)
Volume	120.6 m³ (4,260 cu ft)

AREAS:
Wings, gross	120.77 m² (1,300.0 sq ft)
Ailerons (total)	8.36 m² (90.0 sq ft)
Trailing-edge flaps (total)	19.32 m² (208.0 sq ft)
Fin, incl dorsal fin	10.78 m² (116.0 sq ft)
Rudder, incl tab	5.57 m² (60.0 sq ft)
Tailplane	22.39 m² (241.0 sq ft)
Elevators, incl tabs	7.53 m² (81.0 sq ft)

WEIGHTS (P-3B/C):
Weight empty	27,890 kg (61,491 lb)
Max fuel weight	28,350 kg (62,500 lb)
Max expendable load	9,071 kg (20,000 lb)
Max normal T-O weight	61,235 kg (135,000 lb)
Max permissible weight	64,410 kg (142,000 lb)
Design zero-fuel weight	35,017 kg (77,200 lb)
Max landing weight	47,119 kg (103,880 lb)

PERFORMANCE (P-3B/C, at max T-O weight, except where indicated otherwise):
Max level speed at 4,575 m (15,000 ft) at AUW of 47,625 kg (105,000 lb)   411 knots (761 km/h; 473 mph)
Econ cruising speed at 7,620 m (25,000 ft) at AUW of 49,895 kg (110,000 lb)
        328 knots (608 km/h; 378 mph)
Patrol speed at 457 m (1,500 ft) at AUW of 49,895 kg (110,000 lb)   206 knots (381 km/h; 237 mph)
Stalling speed: flaps up   133 knots (248 km/h; 154 mph)
        flaps down   112 knots (208 km/h; 129 mph)
Max rate of climb at 457 m (1,500 ft)
        594 m (1,950 ft)/min
Time to 7,620 m (25,000 ft)   30 min
Service ceiling   8,625 m (28,300 ft)
Service ceiling, one engine out   5,790 m (19,000 ft)
T-O run   1,290 m (4,240 ft)
T-O to 15 m (50 ft)   1,673 m (5,490 ft)
Landing from 15 m (50 ft) at design landing weight
        845 m (2,770 ft)
Mission radius (3 h on station at 457 m; 1,500 ft)
        1,346 nm (2,494 km; 1,550 miles)
Max mission radius (no time on station) at 61,235 kg (135,000 lb)   2,070 nm (3,835 km; 2,383 miles)
Ferry range   4,830 nm (8,950 km; 5,562 miles)
Max endurance at 4,575 m (15,000 ft)
        two engines   17 h 12 min
        four engines   12 h 20 min

LOCKHEED LRAACA
US Navy designation: P-7A

In October 1988 the US Naval Air Systems Command selected Lockheed's proposal for its long-range air anti-submarine warfare capable aircraft (LRAACA), previously known as the P-3G, for which it has a requirement for 125 aircraft. A $52 million contract for full scale development was awarded in January 1989 to cover the design, development, manufacture and flight testing of two prototypes, designated P-7A. Rollout of the first aircraft is scheduled for September 1991, with first flight in December. This aircraft will be used initially for airframe testing, followed by avionics integration testing. The second prototype is to be delivered to the US Navy in March 1993 for technical and operational evaluation, leading to first production deliveries in 1994. Production is scheduled to reach 18 aircraft per year by 1996 and to continue at that

Lockheed P-7A long-range ASW capable aircraft *(Pilot Press)*

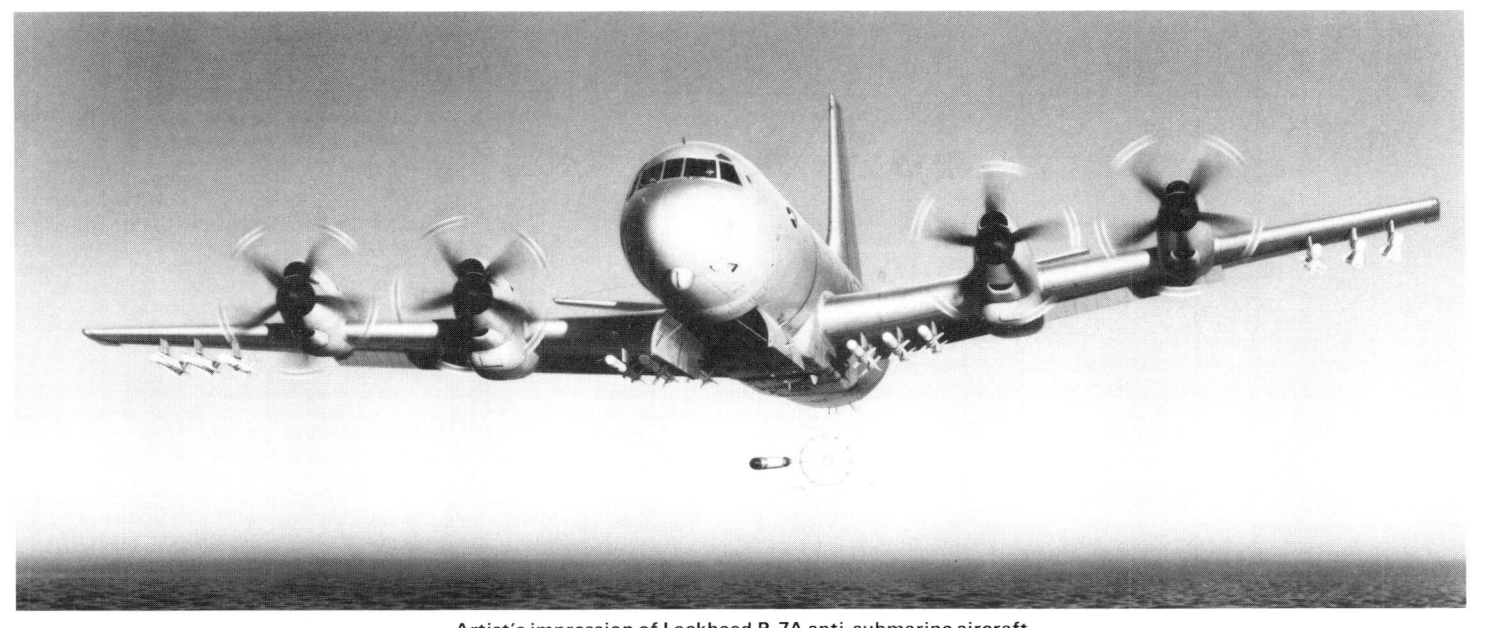

Artist's impression of Lockheed P-7A anti-submarine aircraft

rate until 2001, when the final 19 aircraft will be delivered, at an estimated unit cost of \$32-40 million.

The P-7A will replace early generation P-3 Orions in US Navy service, and has also been selected by the West German Navy to replace its Dassault Atlantic 1 anti-submarine aircraft from 1997. A total of 12 P-7As is required by the Marineflieger. In March 1989 the West German Government signed a memorandum of understanding covering industrial participation by Dornier in the project. Outer-wing panels subcontracted to Daewoo Heavy Industries of South Korea.

The P-7A is of similar overall configuration to the Orion. A 20 per cent commonality was envisaged, but a reassessment in late 1989 reduced this to virtually zero and was expected to introduce delays of between one and two years in the programme as a result of consequent redesign. Compared with the P-3C, the P-7A has double the payload, a two-man flight crew, a 67 per cent reduction in cockpit gauges and 50 per cent reduction in crew workload through fitment of a six-tube EFIS flight deck, a 40 per cent reduction in interior noise, and a 94 per cent reduction in fuel tank fire vulnerability. General Electric T407 turboprop engines offer 25 per cent better fuel consumption, and Hamilton Standard five-blade propellers give 12 per cent increased take-off thrust in addition to being 10 times more reliable than the previous units. Typically, for four hours on station the P-7 has double the P-3's range.

TYPE: Four-turboprop ASW aircraft.

WINGS: Similar to P-3. Elevators split for redundancy.

FUSELAGE: Aluminium alloy semi-monocoque fail-safe structure. Cabin elongated in comparison with P-3, but MAD boom omitted.

TAIL UNIT: Similar to P-3, but larger tailplane.

LANDING GEAR: Dowty Aerospace hydraulically retractable tricycle type, with twin wheels on each unit. All units retract forwards.

POWER PLANT: Four 3,729 kW (5,000 shp) class General Electric T407 turboprops driving Hamilton Standard 15WF five-blade modular composite propellers. Full-authority digital electronic controls. IR signature reducing exhausts. Internal fuel capacity 37,703 litres (9,953 US gallons; 8,294 Imp gallons). Garrett GTCP 131-7 APU providing air-conditioning plus 150kVA.

ACCOMMODATION: Two-man flight deck crew with provision for third seat. Six colour-screen EFIS. Pilot's hinged overhead mounted HUD. Tactical co-ordinator and four equipment operators in fuselage centre section, forward of which are computer banks and two rest bunks. Behind wing is sonobuoy launch compartment, also containing two visual observers and space for optional two equipment consoles. Toilet and restroom/galley at rear. Improved (40 per cent) soundproofing throughout.

SYSTEMS: Fly by wire digital flight control system. Three independent hydraulic systems with electric and engine-driven pumps, plus backup mechanical pump on No. 2 engine. Air-conditioning for crew and avionics by Barber-Colman Aerospace & Power Control Div. Dowty advanced electrical distribution system. Four 90kVA generators (with provision for further three). Walter Kidde Aerospace Halon 1301 dry bay fire suppression; nitrogen inerting system in fuel tanks.

AVIONICS AND EQUIPMENT: Update IV avionics suite developed by Boeing (which see). Advanced threat warning and countermeasures systems. Flight Dynamics HUD. Texas Instruments internal digital, self-compensating MAD. GEC Astronics Corp integrated flight control system. Rosemount Inc air data system and Canadian Marconi microwave landing system. SIADS

Inc flight management system. Litton LTN-92 ring laser gyro INS.

ARMAMENT: Up to 38 A size sonobuoys internally, launched via three chutes, plus two pre-loaded centre-section packs for 48 (forward pack) and 64 (aft). Further 150 may be carried in wing pods. Weapons bay for eight torpedoes or bombs; or four AGM-84 Harpoon ER anti-ship missiles. Twelve underwing stations (groups of three inboard and outboard of power plant pairs). Extreme outer positions (Nos. 9 and 20) accommodate only AGM-65 Maverick ASM, bomb or flare; Harpoon or other weapons on remaining 10. Control Data Co stores management system. Chaff/flare dispenser for self-protection.

DIMENSIONS EXTERNAL:

Wing span	32.49 m (106 ft 7¼ in)
Length overall	34.35 m (112 ft 8½ in)
Height overall	10.03 m (32 ft 8½ in)
Tailplane span	15.73 m (51 ft 7¼ in)
Weapons bay length	5.08 m (16 ft 8 in)
Wheel track (c/l shock absorbers)	
	11.64 m (38 ft 2⅜ in)
Wheelbase	11.64 m (38 ft 2⅜ in)

WEIGHTS:

Weight empty	33,520 kg (73,900 lb)
Max fuel weight	30,096 kg (66,350 lb)
Payload	17,411 kg (38,385 lb)
Manoeuvre weight (3.5 g)	
	62,142 kg (137,000 lb)
Max normal T-O weight (3.0 g)	
	74,843 kg (165,000 lb)
Max permissible weight	77,723 kg (171,350 lb)
Zero-fuel weight	47,627 kg (105,000 lb)

PERFORMANCE:

Cruise ceiling	10,668 m (35,000 ft)
Radius of action for 4 h on station	
	1,863 nm (3,453 km; 2,145 miles)
Time on station at 1,600 nm (2,965 km; 1,842 miles) from base	5 h 50 min

LOCKHEED VIKING
US Navy designation: S-3

Production of 187 **S-3As** (see 1978-79 *Jane's*) for the US Navy ended in mid-1978. All tooling was then placed in storage at Burbank pending a US Navy decision on further orders, and in early 1980 demonstrator versions of the **US-3A** (COD) and **KS-3A** (tanker) were evaluated by the Navy. In 1982 three of the earlier production S-3As were modified to US-3A configuration. The sole KS-3A was also converted to US-3A configuration in late 1983.

As an alternative to the KS-3A dedicated tanker configuration, tests of an S-3A with a Sargent-Fletcher 31-301 buddy refuelling pack under its port wing were conducted in 1984. This technique, which transfers fuel from the tanker's standard internal tanks, and an external tank under the starboard wing, without affecting its multi-mission capability, has been adopted for operational use.

Lockheed announced on 18 August 1981 the receipt of a full scale engineering development contract, from the US Naval Air Systems Command, for an improved avionics system for S-3A Vikings currently in service with the US Navy. With initial funding of \$14.5 million, it followed a contract awarded by the Navy in 1980, under which Lockheed developed the specifications for an S-3A weapons system improvement programme (WSIP).

Aircraft modified under the WSIP are redesignated **S-3B**. Improvements include increased acoustic processing

capacity, expanded electronic support measure capability, better radar processing, a new sonobuoy telemetry receiver system, and provisions for the Harpoon missile. It is anticipated that a total of 160 S-3As will be retrofitted under the programme. Two FSED (full scale engineering development) S-3As were modified initially, the first of which (159742) began flight testing on 13 September 1984; the flight test schedule was completed in August 1985, with redelivery to the US Navy in October. Following a three-month technical evaluation by the Naval Air Test Center at Patuxent River NAS, Maryland, the two S-3Bs undertook a six-month operational evaluation.

Two prototype kits to convert S-3As to S-3B production standard were delivered in 1987, and on 28 April 1986 the US Navy contracted Lockheed to supply a first production series of 22 modification kits, together with spares, support equipment and integrated logistics support, at the rate of two per month followed by a further contract for 24 kits awarded in December 1988 for completion of deliveries in August 1992. By January 1990, 42 Vikings had been retrofitted for Atlantic Fleet squadrons. Modification of S-3As to S-3B standard is undertaken at Cecil Field NAS, Florida, where the first modified S-3B was delivered to squadron VS-27 on 17 December 1987. Lockheed has submitted proposals for conversion of Pacific Fleet Vikings to S-3B standard.

In March 1988 Lockheed Aeronautical Systems Group was awarded a \$66 million US Navy contract for prototype development of an electronic reconnaissance variant of the S-3A, designated **ES-3A**. The ES-3A will supplant, but not fully replace the EA-3B Skywarrior as part of the USN's Battle Group Passive Horizon Extension System for long-range signals monitoring of potentially hostile forces. Lockheed took delivery of an S-3A (159401) from NAS Cecil Field, Florida, on 1 March 1988, in order to remove its ASW equipment and install government-furnished electronics. This aircraft was due to fly in the Summer of 1990 and complete trials in May 1991. Meanwhile, an aerodynamic prototype (former second development YS-3A, 157993) fitted with 60 aerials and domes, conducted a flight test programme between September 1989 and January 1990.

Conversion of the ES-3A involves employing the weapons bay for equipment (more of which is in the rear of the fuselage) and replacing the dual controls of the starboard front seat with tactical displays for the electronic warfare co-ordinating officer. As previously, two further crew members occupy an internal station, but with entirely modified displays. GPS/Navstar and Omega navigation is added, and three AN/AYK-14 processors replace the single AN/AYK-10. A MIL-STD-1553 databus, avionics cooling system, Link 11 data link, AN/APX-76 IFF interrogator, AN/APS-137 radar and OR-236 FLIR are among other equipment items. Operational equipment is a simplified version of that in the EP-3E Orion, including AN/ALR-76 ESM and possibly AN/ALR-52 frequency measuring radar and AN/ALR-60 communications analysis equipment.

The original ES-3A contract provided an option for the production of kits and modification of a further 15 aircraft. It was followed, in early 1989, by a \$56.2 million contract for the supply of nine modification kits, delivery to be completed in August 1991. Sanders Associates of Nashua, New Hampshire, is providing cockpit display screens; Lockheed Missiles and Space Company's Austin, Texas, division will provide wiring and electronics racks; and electronics installation will be undertaken by LASG at its Greenville, South Carolina, Aeromod Center after airframe modifications at Burbank. The ES-3A is expected to equip two new US Navy squadrons, VQ-5 and VQ-6, based

Lockheed ES-3A aerodynamic prototype, showing some of 60 additional antennae

LOCKHEED L-1011 (MODEL 385) TRISTAR

Details of the early history of the L-1011 TriStar, of which 250 were built, can be found in the 1983-84 and previous editions of *Jane's*.

Lockheed has delivered modification kits to Delta Air Lines for uprating six of its TriStars to **L-1011-250** extended range configuration. The kits increase total fuel capacity of each aircraft from 71,668 kg (158,000 lb) to 96,905 kg (213,640 lb), to provide a 2,000 nm increase in range to 5,085 nm (9,415 km; 5,850 miles) with 280 passengers and baggage. Key structural sections of the wings, fuselage and landing gear are strengthened to cater for an 18 per cent increase in max T-O weight to 231,330 kg (510,000 lb). The original engines are replaced by higher thrust Rolls-Royce RB211-524B4 turbofans under separately negotiated arrangements.

The Dash 250 modification is available for approximately 150 other TriStars (from c/n 1,052 onwards) produced after design changes were implemented to improve the CG envelope. The L-1011-500 version already incorporates the Dash 250 elements.

Under a similar contract from First Chicago Leasing Corporation, Lockheed is supplying kits to uprate four early production TriStars to a new **L-1011-150** extended range configuration. This modification, which is applicable also to about 50 L-1011-1 models, increases range from 2,800 nm (5,185 km; 3,220 miles) to 3,600 nm (6,665 km; 4,140 miles) and max T-O weight from 195,045 kg (430,000 lb) to 213,190 kg (470,000 lb).

Details of the L-1011 tanker/freighter conversion for the Royal Air Force can be found under the Marshall of Cambridge entry in the UK section of this edition. The **L-1011F** all-cargo conversion is described briefly under the Pemco Aeroplex entry in this section.

respectively at NAS Agana and NAS Rota in support of the Pacific and Atlantic/Mediterranean fleets.

AVIONICS, ARMAMENT AND OPERATIONAL EQUIPMENT (S-3B): AYS-1 Proteus acoustic signal processor; modified Sanders AN/OL-320/AYS data processing memory group integrated with IBM AN/UYS-1; updated Honeywell AYK-10A(V) air data computer, interfaced with Harpoon air-to-surface missile and other new systems; improved electronic support measures (ESM); Hazeltine AN/ARR-78 sonobuoy receiver system; Precision Echo AN/AQH-7 analog tape recorder, Cubic AN/ARS-4 sonobuoy reference system; Texas Instruments AN/APS-137(V)1 radar, incorporating inverse synthetic aperture radar (ISAR) techniques; modified Goodyear AN/ALE-39 chaff/flare dispensing system; IBM AN/ALR-76 ESM; and provision for future advanced navigation and communications systems including Global Positioning System and Joint Tactical Information Distribution System. S-3A/B weapon options include four Mk 46/50 torpedoes, two B57 nuclear depth-charges, four Mk 82 560 lb bombs or four Mk 36 destructors all stowed internally; plus underwing armament of six Mk 82/86s, two Mk 52/55/56 mines, two Mk 60 torpedoes, two AGM-84 Harpoon anti-ship missiles, or six LAU-10C/-68A/-69A rocket pods/SUU-44A flare pods.

LOCKHEED AERONAUTICAL SYSTEMS COMPANY (LASC)

86 South Cobb Drive, Marietta, Georgia 30063
Telephone: 1 (404) 494 4411
Telex: 542642 LOCKHEED MARA
PRESIDENT: Kenneth W. Cannestra
EXECUTIVE VICE-PRESIDENT AND GENERAL MANAGER:
H. Bard Allison
PUBLIC INFORMATION: Joseph E. Dabney

The main building occupied by Lockheed at Marietta is one of the world's largest aircraft production plants under a single roof. Aircraft in current production on its assembly lines are the C-130 Hercules turboprop transport and its commercial counterpart, the L-100. A major modification programme on USAF C-5A Galaxy transports was completed in 1987, and production of new C-5Bs was completed in March 1989. Future work will include prototype construction and production of the Lockheed P-7A, and subcontract work on the McDonnell Douglas C-17.

Lockheed had approximately 10,000 employees in Marietta in the Spring of 1990.

LOCKHEED MODEL 382 HERCULES

US Air Force designations: C-130, AC-130, DC-130, EC-130, HC-130, JC-130, LC-130, MC-130, NC-130, RC-130 and WC-130
US Navy designations: C-130, DC-130, EC-130 and LC-130
US Marine Corps designation: KC-130
US Coast Guard designation: HC-130
Canadian Armed Forces designation: CC-130
RAF designations: Hercules C. Mk 1K, C. Mk 1P, W. Mk 2 and C. Mk 3P
Spanish designations: T.10, TK.10 and TL.10
Export designations: C-130H, C-130H-30, KC-130H, C-130H-MP and VC-130H

The C-130 was designed to a specification issued by the US Air Force Tactical Air Command in 1951. Lockheed was awarded its first production contract for the C-130A in September 1952, and two prototypes, 231 C-130As, 230 C-130Bs and 491 C-130Es were manufactured. Details of these basic versions and of many variants for special duties can be found in previous editions of *Jane's*. Later military versions of the C-130 are as follows:

C-130H. Similar to earlier Hercules models except for updated avionics, improved wing, new corrosion protection technology, and more powerful engines: T56-A-15 turboprops rated at 3,661 kW (4,910 shp) for take-off, but limited to 3,362 kW (4,508 shp). Deliveries began in March 1965 to the Royal New Zealand Air Force. In service with 50 countries. At 31 December 1988 total orders for the C-130H and derivatives stood at 366 aircraft for the USAF, US Navy and US Coast Guard and 478 for international customers.

C-130H-MP. Maritime patrol, search and rescue version, based on C-130H. Max T-O weight 70,310 kg (155,000 lb). Max payload 18,630 kg (41,074 lb). Four 3,362 kW (4,508 ehp) T56-A-15 engines. Standard and optional equipment includes sea search radar, scanner seats with observation windows, computerised INS/Omega navigation system, crew rest and lavatory/galley slide-in module, flare launcher, loudspeaker system, rescue kit airdrop platform, side looking airborne radar, passive microwave imager, low light TV, infra-red scanner, camera

with data annotation, and ramp equipment pallet which includes a station for an observer. Search time at an altitude of 1,525 m (5,000 ft) is 2 h 30 min at a radius of 1,800 nm (3,333 km; 2,070 miles); 16 h 50 min at radius of 200 nm (370 km; 230 miles). One each delivered to the Indonesian Air Force and US Coast Guard, and three to the Royal Malaysian Air Force.

C-130H-30. Stretched version, with structural changes similar to those of RAF Hercules C.Mk 3 (see C-130K paragraph). Seven delivered to the Algerian Air Force, one to the Cameroun Air Force, one to the Dubai Air Wing, seven to the French Air Force, seven to the Indonesian Air Force, three to the Nigerian Air Force, one to Saudi Arabia, one to the Spanish Air Force, three to the Royal Thai Air Force, and four to South Korea. Two of the Nigerian aircraft are convertible into 90-passenger transports, by inserting 15-seat pallets into the cargo hold. Conversion takes less than one hour.

AC-130H 'Spectre'. Gunship version with side-firing 105 mm howitzer, 40 mm cannon and two 20 mm Vulcan cannon. Equipped with sensors and target acquisition systems including forward looking infra-red and low light level TV, and in-flight refuelling capability. In service with the 16th Special Operations Squadron at Hurlburt Field, FL. Improvement programme announced in Spring 1987 and known as SOFI (Special Operations/Forces Improvements) will include new fire control computers, navigation equipment and sensors, scheduled for completion in FY 1992.

EC-130H 'Compass Call'. Operated by 41st Electronic Combat Squadron at Davis-Monthan AFB, Arizona and the 43rd Electronic Combat Squadron at Sembach, West Germany. Works with ground mobile C³CM systems to jam enemy command control and communications systems.

HC-130H. Extended range version for Aerospace Rescue and Recovery Service of the US Air Force for aerial recovery of personnel or equipment and other duties; total of 43 delivered, of which the first was delivered in October

Lockheed C-130 Hercules of Military Airlift Command, USAF *(Paul Jackson)*

1964. Update programme announced in Spring 1987 includes self contained navigation system (SCNS), night vision goggles lighting and new communications and navigation equipment for 31 HC-130Hs, 21 of which will also be equipped for in-flight refuelling. The US Coast Guard subsequently ordered 29. Details in 1979-80 *Jane's*. Four modified as **JC-130H** with added equipment for aerial recovery of re-entering space capsules. Two modified to **DC-130H** for drone control duties.

KC-130H. Probe-drogue tanker version, very similar to the KC-130R. Exported to Argentina (2), Brazil (2), Israel (2), Morocco (2), Saudi Arabia (8), Spain (5) and Singapore (1).

LC-130H. Similar to LC-130R (which see). Four acquired by US Air Force Air Reserve Forces, and six by US Navy.

MC-130H. Combat Talon II version of C-130H, modified by USAF for special tactical missions including day/night infiltration and exfiltration, resupply of Special Operations ground forces, psychological warfare missions, aerial reconnaissance, and airdropping and surface-to-air retrieval of personnel. Crew of five. A larger nose radome houses Emerson Electric AN/APQ-170 precision ground mapping/weather/terrain following/terrain avoidance radar. Other equipment includes an inertial navigation system, automatic computed air release point, high-speed low-level aerial delivery and container release systems, ground acquisition receiver/interrogator, Texas Instruments AN/AAQ-15 infra-red detection system, eight multi-function displays, secure voice UHF/VHF/FM radios, retractable FLIR pod, angle of attack probe and ALQ-8 ECM pod under each wing, plus in-flight refuelling capability. Defensive equipment includes a Litton AN/ALR-69 radar warning receiver, ITT AN/ALQ-172 detector/jammer, Watkins-Johnson WJ-1840 signal detector, Cincinnati Electronics AN/AAR-44 launch warning receiver, Northrop QRC-8402 IR jammer, and chaff/flare dispensers. IBM Federal Systems Division is prime contractor for systems integration, with E-Systems as

Lockheed C-130H of the Republic of Singapore Air Force *(Paul Jackson)*

subcontractor for avionics installation and modification. Eighteen funded during FY 1983-88, with expected USAF MC-130H inventory of 24 aircraft by 1999. The first MC-130H began flight tests with E-Systems at Greenville, Texas, in the Spring of 1988. A formal 19-month flight test programme began at Edwards AFB, California, on 20 September 1988. MC-130Hs will supplement earlier MC-130Es with 8th SOS at Hurlburt Field from June 1990 and 16th SOS at the same base from 1992.

C-130J. Advanced Hercules proposed by Lockheed to USAF in 1989 as C-130E replacement from 1994. Entirely re-designed flight-deck with four liquid crystal display screens and two fold-down HUDs. Flight crew reduced from four to two. Series IV version of T56 power plant, driving new propellers. External fuel tanks deleted, with no loss of range, as result of increased fuel efficiency. Carbon brakes, with improved anti-skid system.

C-130K. This is basically a C-130H, modified to meet requirements of the Royal Air Force. Much of the avionics and instrumentation is of UK manufacture. Sixty-six delivered as **Hercules C. Mk 1**, beginning September 1966. One modified by Marshall of Cambridge (Engineering) Ltd in the UK (which see for further details) for use by the RAF Meteorological Research Flight, under the designation **Hercules W. Mk 2.** Thirty of the others have been lengthened by 4.57 m (15 ft 0 in)—2.54 m; 8 ft 4 in plug forward of wing, 2.03 m; 6 ft 8 in aft of wing—equivalent to commercial L-100-30 standard. This increases payload capacity to seven cargo pallets instead of five, or four Land-Rovers and four trailers (instead of 3 + 2), or 128 troops instead of 92, or 92 fully equipped paratroops instead of 64, or 97 stretcher patients instead of 74. The first aircraft was modified at Marietta in 1979; the remaining 29 were lengthened by Marshall of Cambridge (see UK section). After modification, these aircraft were redesignated **Hercules C. Mk 3.**

HC-130N. Search and rescue version of the C-130H for recovery of aircrew and retrieval of space capsules after re-entry, using advanced direction finding equipment. Fifteen delivered to US Air Force.

HC-130P. Version of the C-130H, modified to have capability of refuelling helicopters in flight and for mid-air retrieval of parachute-borne payloads. Twenty built for USAF Aerospace Rescue and Recovery Service. Details in 1979-80 *Jane's.*

EC-130Q. Similar to earlier EC-130G, but with improved equipment and crew accommodation, for US Navy command communications (Tacamo) duties. Described (before advent of Boeing E-6A) as "the only airborne, survivable, communications link with submarine forces, providing HF and VLF SIMOP (simultaneous operations) capability in a collocated environment". Eighteen built.

KC-130R. Probe-drogue tanker version of C-130H: 14 for US Marine Corps. Changes from earlier KC-130F (1975-76 *Jane's*) include engines of 3,362 kW (4,508 shp), increased T-O and landing weights, pylon mounted fuel tanks to provide additional 10,296 litres (2,720 US gallons; 2,265 Imp gallons) of fuel, and removable 13,627 litre (3,600 US gallon; 2,997 Imp gallon) fuel tank in cargo

compartment. All fuel can be used by tanker for extended range. Single-point fuelling of installed and removable tanks via normal filler in wheel well. Operating weight empty 36,279 kg (79,981 lb). Max T-O weight 79,378 kg (175,000 lb). Able to offload up to 20,865 kg (46,000 lb) of fuel, equivalent to 26,790 litres (7,077 US gallons; 5,893 Imp gallons), at mission radius of 1,000 nm (1,850 km; 1,150 miles). Maximum offload capability is 31,750 kg (70,000 lb), equivalent to 40,765 litres (10,769 US gallons; 8,967 Imp gallons).

LC-130R. Basically a C-130H with wheel-ski gear for US Navy Squadron VXE-6. Six converted, for service in the Antarctic. Details in 1979-80 *Jane's.*

KC-130T. Tanker for US Marine Corps (Reserve). Similar to KC-130R but with updated avionics, including 'state of the art' INS, Omega and Tacan, a new autopilot and flight director, and solid state search radar. KC-130Ts delivered in late 1984 featured Bendix AN/APS-133 colour radar, flush mounted antennae and orthopaedically designed crew seats. Able to refuel helicopters as well as

EC-130H 'Compass Call' jamming version of Lockheed Hercules *(Ivo Sturzenegger)*

Lockheed C-130H-30 stretched Hercules (RAF C. Mk 3), with upper side view of AC-130U Spectre and centre side view of EC-130E *(Pilot Press)*

Lockheed KC-130T tanker of US Marine Corps Squadron VMGR-452 based at Stewart International Airport, Newburgh, New York

fighters. Delivery of 16 to Marine Aerial Refueler Transport Squadron 234 (VMGR-234) of Marine Air Control Group 48 at NAS Glenview, Illinois, began in November 1983. Four advanced KC-130Ts delivered to Marine Corps Reserve squadron VMGR-452.

AC-130U 'Spectre'. New gunship version of C-130H. For details, refer to Rockwell International entry.

Commercial versions of the Hercules are described separately.

The C-130 is able to deliver single loads of up to 11,340 kg (25,000 lb) by the ground proximity extraction method. This involves making a flypast 1.2-1.5 m (4-5 ft) above the ground with the rear loading ramp open. The aircraft trails a hook which is attached by cable to the palletised cargo. The hook engages a steel cable on the ground and the cargo is extracted from the aircraft and brought to a stop on the ground in about 30 m (100 ft) by an energy absorption system manufactured by All American Engineering of Wilmington, Delaware. An alternative extraction technique known as LAPES (low altitude parachute extraction system) involves deploying a 6.70 m (22 ft) ribbon parachute to drag the pallet from the cabin. Loads of up to 22,680 kg (50,000 lb) have been delivered by this method.

By December 1989, over 1,900 Hercules had been delivered to 60 nations.

The following details refer specifically to the international C-130H, except where indicated otherwise:

TYPE: Medium/long-range combat transport.

WINGS: Cantilever high-wing monoplane. Wing section NACA 64A318 at root, NACA 64A412 at tip. Dihedral 2° 30′. Incidence 3° at root, 0° at tip. Sweepback at quarter-chord 0°. All-metal two-spar stressed skin structure, with integrally stiffened tapered machined skin panels up to 14.63 m (48 ft 0 in) long. Conventional aluminium alloy ailerons have tandem-piston hydraulic boost, operated by either of two independent hydraulic systems. Lockheed-Fowler aluminium alloy trailing-edge flaps. Trim tab in each aileron. Leading-edges anti-iced by engine bleed air.

FUSELAGE: Semi-monocoque structure of aluminium and magnesium alloys.

TAIL UNIT: Cantilever all-metal stressed skin structure. Fixed incidence tailplane, with Kevlar afterbody strake on undersurface at each side, close to fuselage. Trim tab in each elevator and rudder. Elevator tabs use AC electrical power as primary source and DC as emergency source. Control surfaces have tandem-piston hydraulic boost. Hot air anti-icing of tailplane leading-edge, by engine bleed air.

LANDING GEAR: Hydraulically retractable tricycle type. Each main unit has two wheels in tandem, retracting into fairings built on to the sides of the fuselage. Nose unit has twin wheels and is steerable through 60° each side of centre. Oleo shock absorbers. Mainwheel tyres size 56 × 20-20, pressure 6.62 bars (96 lb/sq in). Nosewheel tyres size 39 × 13-16, pressure 4.14 bars (60 lb/sq in). Goodyear aircooled multiple disc hydraulic brakes with anti-skid units. Retractable combination wheel-skis available.

POWER PLANT: Four 3,362 kW (4,508 shp) Allison T56-A-15 turboprops, each driving a Hamilton Standard type 54H60 four-blade constant-speed fully-feathering reversible-pitch propeller. Fuel in six integral tanks in wings, with total capacity of 26,344 litres (6,960 US gallons; 5,795 Imp gallons) and two optional underwing pylon tanks, each with capacity of 5,146 litres (1,360 US gallons; 1,132 Imp gallons). Total fuel capacity 36,636 litres (9,680 US gallons; 8,060 Imp gallons). Single pressure refuelling point in starboard wheel well. Overwing gravity fuelling. Oil capacity 182 litres (48 US gallons; 40 Imp gallons).

ACCOMMODATION: Crew of four on flight deck, comprising pilot, co-pilot, navigator and systems manager (fully performance qualified flight engineer on USAF aircraft). Provision for fifth man to supervise loading. Sleeping quarters for relief crew, and galley. Flight deck and main cabin pressurised and air-conditioned. Standard complements for C-130H are as follows: troops (max) 92, paratroops (max) 64, litters 74 and 2 attendants. Corresponding figures for C-130H-30 are 128 troops, 92 paratroops, and 97 litters. As a cargo carrier, loads can include heavy equipment such as a 12,080 kg (26,640 lb) type F.6 refuelling trailer or a 155 mm howitzer and its high-speed tractor, or up to five 463L pallets of freight (seven in C-130H-30). Hydraulically operated main loading door and ramp at rear of cabin. Paratroop door on each side aft of landing gear fairing. Two emergency exit doors standard; two additional doors optional on C-130H-30.

SYSTEMS: Air-conditioning and pressurisation system max pressure differential 0.52 bars (7.5 lb/sq in). Three independent hydraulic systems, utility and booster systems operating at a pressure of 207 bars (3,000 lb/sq in), rated at 65.1 litres (17.2 US gallons; 14.3 Imp gallons)/min for utility and booster systems, 30.3 litres (8.0 US gallons; 6.7 Imp gallons)/min for auxiliary system. Reservoirs are unpressurised. Auxiliary system has handpump for emergencies. Electrical system supplied by four 40kVA AC alternators, plus one 40kVA auxiliary alternator driven by APU in port main landing gear fairing. Four transformer-rectifiers for DC power. Current production aircraft incorporate systems and component design changes for increased reliability. There are differences between the installed components for US government and export versions. Babcock Power Ltd High Volume Mine Layer (HVML) system available as an option, using modular roll-on pallets.

AVIONICS: Dual 628T-2A HF com, dual 618M-3A VHF com, AN/ARC-164 UHF com, AN/AIC-13 PA system, AN/AIC-18 intercom, dual 621A-6A ATC transponders, DF-301E UHF nav, dual 51RV-4B VHF nav, CMA 771 Omega nav, LTN-72 INS, dual DF-206 ADF, 51Z-4 marker beacon receiver, dual 860E-5 DME, AL-101 radio altimeter, RDR-1F weather radar, dual C-12 compass systems, Mk II GPWS, AP-105V autopilot, and dual FD-109 flight directors.

DIMENSIONS, EXTERNAL:

Wing span	40.41 m (132 ft 7 in)
Wing chord: at root	4.88 m (16 ft 0 in)
mean	4.16 m (13 ft 8½ in)
Wing aspect ratio	10.1
Length overall:	
all except HC-130H and C-130H-30	29.79 m (97 ft 9 in)
C-130H-30	34.37 m (112 ft 9 in)
Height overall	11.66 m (38 ft 3 in)
Tailplane span	16.05 m (52 ft 8 in)
Wheel track	4.35 m (14 ft 3 in)
Wheelbase	9.77 m (32 ft 0¾ in)
Propeller diameter	4.11 m (13 ft 6 in)
Main cargo door (rear of cabin):	
Height	2.77 m (9 ft 1 in)
Width	3.05 m (10 ft 0 in)
Height to sill	1.03 m (3 ft 5 in)
Paratroop doors (each): Height	1.83 m (6 ft 0 in)
Width	0.91 m (3 ft 0 in)
Height to sill	1.03 m (3 ft 5 in)
Emergency exits (each): Height	1.22 m (4 ft 0 in)
Width	0.71 m (2 ft 4 in)

DIMENSIONS, INTERNAL:

Cabin, excl flight deck:	
Length without ramp:	
C-130H	12.22 m (40 ft 1¼ in)
C-130H-30	16.79 m (55 ft 1¼ in)
Length with ramp: C-130H	15.73 m (51 ft 8½ in)
C-130H-30	20.33 m (66 ft 8½ in)

Max width	3.12 m (10 ft 3 in)
Max height	2.81 m (9 ft 2¾ in)
Floor area, excl ramp: C-130H	39.5 m² (425.0 sq ft)
Volume, incl ramp: C-130H	127.4 m³ (4,500.0 cu ft)
C-130H-30	165.5 m³ (5,845.0 cu ft)

AREAS:

Wings, gross	162.12 m² (1,745.0 sq ft)
Ailerons (total)	10.22 m² (110.0 sq ft)
Trailing-edge flaps (total)	31.77 m² (342.0 sq ft)
Fin	20.90 m² (225.0 sq ft)
Rudder, incl tab	6.97 m² (75.0 sq ft)
Tailplane	35.40 m² (381.0 sq ft)
Elevators, incl tabs	14.40 m² (155.0 sq ft)

WEIGHTS AND LOADINGS:

Operating weight empty:	
C-130H	34,686 kg (76,469 lb)
C-130H-30	36,397 kg (80,242 lb)
Max fuel weight: internal	20,520 kg (45,240 lb)
external	8,020 kg (17,680 lb)
Max payload: C-130H	19,356 kg (42,673 lb)
C-130H-30	17,645 kg (38,900 lb)
Max normal T-O weight	70,310 kg (155,000 lb)
Max overload T-O weight	79,380 kg (175,000 lb)
Max normal landing weight	70,310 kg (155,000 lb)
Max overload landing weight	79,380 kg (175,000 lb)
Max zero-fuel weight, 2.5g	54,040 kg (119,142 lb)
Max wing loading	434.5 kg/m² (89 lb/sq ft)
Max power loading	5.23 kg/kW (8.6 lb/ehp)

PERFORMANCE (C-130H at max T-O weight, unless indicated otherwise):

Max cruising speed	325 knots (602 km/h; 374 mph)
Econ cruising speed	300 knots (556 km/h; 345 mph)
Stalling speed	100 knots (185 km/h; 115 mph)
Max rate of climb at S/L	579 m (1,900 ft)/min
Service ceiling at 58,970 kg (130,000 lb) AUW	10,060 m (33,000 ft)
Service ceiling, one engine out, at 58,970 kg (130,000 lb) AUW	8,075 m (26,500 ft)
Min ground turning radius:	
C-130H:	
about nosewheel	11.28 m (37 ft 0 in)
about wingtip	25.91 m (85 ft 0 in)
C-130H-30:	
about nosewheel	14.33 m (47 ft 0 in)
about wingtip	27.43 m (90 ft 0 in)
Runway LCN at 70,310 kg (155,000 lb) AUW:	
asphalt	37
concrete	42
T-O run	1,091 m (3,580 ft)
T-O to 15 m (50 ft)	1,573 m (5,160 ft)
Landing from 15 m (50 ft):	
at 45,360 kg (100,000 lb) AUW	731 m (2,400 ft)
at 58,967 kg (130,000 lb) AUW	838 m (2,750 ft)
Landing run at 58,967 kg (130,000 lb) AUW	518 m (1,700 ft)
Range with max payload, with 5% reserves and allowance for 30 min at S/L	2,046 nm (3,791 km; 2,356 miles)
Range with max fuel, incl external tanks, 7,081 kg (15,611 lb) payload, reserves of 5% initial fuel plus 30 min at S/L	4,250 nm (7,876 km; 4,894 miles)

LOCKHEED L-100 SERIES COMMERCIAL HERCULES

Details of initial versions of the commercial Hercules have appeared in previous editions of *Jane's*; current models are as follows:

L-100-20 (Model 382E). Certificated on 4 October 1968, this stretched version of the Hercules has a 2.54 m (100 in) fuselage extension. A 1.52 m (60 in) fuselage plug is inserted aft of the forward crew door and a 1.02 m (40 in) plug aft of the rear personnel doors. Allison 501-D22A engines. Military operators/owners include the Gabon Air Force (1), Peruvian Air Force (5) and Philippine Air Force (3). Commercial operators were Jamahirya Air Transport (2), Safair (1), Southern Air Transport (2), Tepper Aviation Inc (1), and Transafrik (2). Lockheed operates one L-100-20 as the HTTB testbed, described separately.

L-100-30 (Model 382G). Generally similar to the L-100-20, but with the fuselage extended a further 2.03 m (6 ft 8 in). Early models did not have aft personnel doors which are now standard. Saturn Airways was the first operator of this model, in December 1970. Military operators in 1989 included the air forces of Dubai (1), Ecuador (1), Gabon (2), Indonesia (1), Kuwait (4) and Pakistan (1). The largest commercial operator is Southern Air Transport with 15. Other operators/owners include AFI International (2), Air Algerie (3), Air Gabon (1), Bolivian Air Transport (1), China Air Cargo (2), Ethiopian Airlines (2), Jamahirya Air Transport (1), Jet Fret (1), LADE (1), MarkAir (3), Merpati Nusantara Airlines (2), Northwest Territorial Airways (1), Pelita Air Service (4), Petroleos Mexicanos (PEMEX) (1), Safair (7), Saudi Arabia (6), TAAG-Angola Airlines (1), The Pegasus Aviation Company (1), Transafrik (1), Uganda Air Cargo (1), Worldwide Trading Ltd (1), and Zimex (1).

In 1989 efforts to obtain an FAA supplemental type certificate with ditching provision to enable the civil L-100-30 to carry up to 100 passengers continued. All C-130 and L-100 aircraft delivered since April 1984 have two 0.61 × 1.22 m (24 × 48 in) emergency exits, one on each side of the aircraft, as standard equipment. Together with the current rear personnel doors, these provide the necessary exits for up to 79 passengers. An optional additional exit on each side of the fuselage will provide exits for 100 passengers. Various passenger, galley and toilet configurations are available, with a supplemental oxygen system for passengers.

Lockheed developed an airborne hospital version of the L-100-30, designated **L-100-30HS**. Five of this variant have been delivered to Saudi Arabia after modification by LAS (which see), with operating theatres and intensive care, advanced anaesthesia and X-ray facilities. Electrical generators and air conditioners contained in underwing pods enable the aircraft to function as remote emergency hospitals for up to 72 hours without external support. Described under LAS division entry.

A total of 111 commercial Hercules (all versions) had been delivered by December 1988. Details given for the C-130H apply also to the L-100-20 and L-100-30, except as follows:

TYPE: Medium/long-range transport.

LANDING GEAR: As for C-130H, except mainwheel tyre pressure 3.24-7.38 bars (47-107 lb/sq in) and nosewheel tyre pressure 4.14 bars (60 lb/sq in).

POWER PLANT: Four 3,362 kW (4,508 shp) Allison 501-D22A turboprops.

DIMENSIONS, EXTERNAL:

Length overall: L-100-20	32.33 m (106 ft 1 in)
L-100-30	34.37 m (112 ft 9 in)
Wheelbase: L-100-20	11.30 m (37 ft 1 in)
L-100-30	12.32 m (40 ft 5 in)
Crew door (integral steps): Height	1.14 m (3 ft 9 in)
Width	0.76 m (2 ft 6 in)
Height to sill	1.04 m (3 ft 5 in)

DIMENSIONS, INTERNAL:

Cabin, excl flight deck:	
Length: L-100-20	15.04 m (49 ft 4 in)
L-100-30: excl ramp	17.07 m (56 ft 0 in)
incl ramp	19.93 m (65 ft 4¾ in)
Max height	2.74 m (9 ft 0 in)
Floor area, excl ramp: L-100-20	46.36 m² (499.0 sq ft)
L-100-30	52.30 m² (563.0 sq ft)
Floor area, ramp	9.57 m² (103.0 sq ft)
Volume, incl ramp: L-100-20	150.28 m³ (5,307 cu ft)
L-100-30	171.5 m³ (6,057 cu ft)

WEIGHTS AND LOADINGS:

Operating weight empty:	
L-100-20	34,781 kg (76,680 lb)
L-100-30	35,260 kg (77,736 lb)
Max payload: L-100-20	23,637 kg (52,110 lb)
L-100-30	23,158 kg (51,054 lb)
Max ramp weight	70,670 kg (155,800 lb)
Max T-O weight	70,308 kg (155,000 lb)
Max landing weight	61,235 kg (135,000 lb)
Max zero-fuel weight	58,420 kg (128,790 lb)
Max fuel weight	29,380 kg (64,772 lb)

Lockheed L-100-30 'Super Hercules' of China Air Cargo

Max wing loading	433.5 kg/m² (88.8 lb/sq ft)
Max power loading	5.23 kg/kW (8.6 lb/ehp)

PERFORMANCE (at max T-O weight except where indicated):

Max cruising speed at 6,100 m (20,000 ft) at 54,430 kg (120,000 lb) AUW	308 knots (571 km/h; 355 mph)
Landing speed	124 knots (230 km/h; 143 mph)
Max rate of climb at S/L	518 m (1,700 ft)/min
Min ground turning radius: L-100-20	26.8 m (88 ft)
L-100-30	27.5 m (90 ft)
Runway LCN: asphalt	37
concrete	42
FAR T-O field length	1,905 m (6,250 ft)
FAR landing field length, at max landing weight	1,478 m (4,850 ft)
Range:	
with max payload, 45 min reserves	1,334 nm (2,472 km; 1,536 miles)
with zero payload	4,830 nm (8,951 km; 5,562 miles)

OPERATIONAL NOISE LEVELS (FAR Pt 36, Stage 2):

T-O sideline	96.7 EPNdB
T-O flyover: at T-O power	97.8 EPNdB
at cutback power	94.8 EPNdB
Approach fly over	98.1 EPNdB

LOCKHEED HTTB

The high technology testbed (HTTB) conversion of a commercial model L-100-20 Hercules, developed to provide a platform for evaluating new technologies in an airborne environment, first flew on 19 June 1984, registered N130X. It is being used to conduct STOL flight research, in the development of avionics subsystems, and to develop high lift systems, advanced flight controls, cockpit displays, navigation, guidance and enroute survivability systems for future tactical airlift aircraft. Externally apparent features

Lockheed's all-black high technology testbed (HTTB) Hercules, a converted L-100-20

include the addition of a long dorsal fin, similar extensions known as 'horsals' (horizontal dorsals) forward of each tailplane root, and an instrumentation sensor boom of composite materials forward of each wingtip.

Early trials programmes of the HTTB were described in the 1989-90 and previous editions of *Jane's*.

In the first quarter of 1989 LASC installed 3,915 kW (5,250 shp) Allison T-56 Series IV turboprops, driving 4.19 m (13 ft 9 in) Hamilton Standard propellers, in the HTTB to improve take-off performance, hot day performance, terrain following capability, and fuel economy. The engines include digital controls which continually monitor maximum power available with the given ambient conditions and provide a linear horsepower response to power lever angle. The controls also automatically limit torque and turbine temperature therefore reducing pilot workload. After a two-month lay-up, N130X returned to flying in November 1989 at the start of a series of trials to demonstrate 460 m (1,509 ft) take-offs and 365 m (1,198 ft) landings at a weight of 59,000 kg (130,073 lb).

In each phase of the HTTB modification programme LASC Georgia is inviting pilots and flight engineers from industry and service organisations to fly the aircraft, providing feedback which will be used in establishing future advanced tactical transport requirements. In addition to industry research programmes, the HTTB is being offered to university faculties and graduate students who will have opportunities to place experiments aboard the aircraft and to take part in the flight testing of their equipment.

LOCKHEED ARTB

Due for completion in 1990, the ARTB (advanced radar testbed) is a modified Lockheed NC-141A StarLifter four-turbofan transport aircraft for use by USAF's 4950th Test Wing at Wright-Patterson AFB, Ohio, to evaluate the response of modern airborne radars to jamming and other ECCM. The aircraft was modified by Lockheed Georgia, with Hughes and Westinghouse as subcontractors, and can accommodate a number of different radar antennae in interchangeable nose radomes. The programme, which is expected to improve the anti-jamming capabilities of current airborne radars in the B-1B, F-15, F-16 and ATF, is scheduled to run until the late 1990s.

LOCKHEED GALAXY

Major activities concerning the C-5 Galaxy are now at an end. Re-winging of 77 C-5As (remaining from 81 built) was completed in 1987, and conversion of two C-5As to take over-sized Space Shuttle cargo ended in 1989. The last of 50 new-built C-5Bs was handed over on 17 April 1989. Further details can be found in the 1989-90 and earlier editions of *Jane's*.

LOCKHEED GEORGIA/NASA PROPFAN

Details of this modified Gulfstream II last appeared in the 1989-90 edition.

LOCKHEED AIRCRAFT SERVICE COMPANY (LAS)

PO Box 33, Ontario International Airport, Ontario, California 91761-0033
Telephone: 1 (714) 395 2411
PRESIDENT: Harold T. Bowling
EXECUTIVE VICE-PRESIDENT: John S. McLellan
VICE-PRESIDENT, ENGINEERING: George L. Morgan
DIRECTOR, NEW BUSINESS DEVELOPMENT:
John J. Bamberger
DIRECTOR, PUBLIC RELATIONS: John R. Dailey

Lockheed Aircraft Service Company is claimed to be the world's largest aircraft maintenance and modification unit, with over 3,000 employees. LAS has designed and installed major modifications and airborne mechanical and

electronic systems, including cargo conversions and special interiors, for such aircraft as the Boeing KC-135 and 707; Douglas DC-8; and Lockheed C-130, C-141, L-188 Electra, L-1011 and P-3. LAS manufactures flight data recorders and portable airfield lighting systems, and operates an OMNILOG worldwide logistics support service which maintains information on over 20 million aircraft components on its databases. Lockheed Aeromod Center in Greenville, South Carolina, provides aircraft maintenance and modification services to military and commercial customers. Airod SDN BHD, a joint venture company formed in 1984 by Lockheed Aircraft Service International and Aerospace Industries Malaysia, performs aircraft maintenance, modification, repair and overhaul work at Subang International Airport, Kuala Lumpur.

LOCKHEED C-130 CONVERSIONS

Lockheed Aircraft Service Company specialises in engineering design and modification of aircraft for electronic warfare, command, control and communications, and other high technology systems, including Sigint. During 1981 it completed the modification of a C-130H to airborne emergency hospital configuration for the Royal Saudi Air Force (illustration in 1982-83 *Jane's*). Patients enter via a ramp at the rear of the aircraft, into a reception area; this is followed by three compartments comprising an examination room, operating theatre and intensive care unit. Non-standard underwing pods house APUs which draw fuel from the aircraft's wing tanks when the main engines are shut down. Each APU is able to provide essential ground power for up to 72 hours, including for the operation of medical equipment, environmental systems such as air-conditioning and heating, lighting, and communications. The aircraft is equipped with HF and UHF communications systems.

By the Spring of 1986, Saudi Arabia had a total of ten modified C-130 type aircraft employed in its nationwide rapid-response aeromedical service. The three latest aircraft are L-100-30HS stretched 'hospital ships'. The fleet includes aircraft which carry onboard four-wheel drive ambulances, a 52-patient air evacuation aircraft with onboard surgical capability, and an aircraft which can provide opthalmology, ear, nose and throat and dental examination and treatment. Three Saudi Arabian C-130 medical aircraft took part in the evacuation and emergency treatment of casualties from the hijacking and subsequent crash of a Boeing 737 near Arar on 25 December 1986.

In late 1985 LAS was awarded a US Air Force contract to update the Special Operations Forces' AC-130H gunships with new navigation and fire control systems. The company is also engaged in developing other Special Mission C-130s for the US Air Force, and in gunship modifications of C-130s for export customers. The first prototype of the 'Combat Talon I' MC-130E SOFI (special operations forces improvement) Hercules was delivered to the US Air Force in January 1988.

LOCKHEED P-3 CONVERSIONS

A P-3A Orion was modified by Lockheed Aircraft Service Company in 1984 for use by the US Customs Service, to interdict ships and aircraft smuggling illegal drugs into the USA. The original Texas Instruments nose radar was replaced by a Hughes AN/APG-63 radar and infra-red detection system, for all-weather day/night operations. Three more P-3As were subsequently modified for the US Customs Service by Lockheed Aeromod Center Inc at Greenville, South Carolina, using kits produced at Ontario. In addition to the AN/APG-63 radar, all of these aircraft have new inertial navigation systems and multi-frequency communications radios compatible with US Customs and Coast Guard ground stations, as well as civilian law enforcement agencies. LAS was also responsible for modifying the prototype P-3 AEW & C to carry its rotodome above the rear fuselage.

In 1985, LAS was awarded contracts by the US Navy for design and conversion of two VP special mission P-3s. A conversion in lieu of production (CILOP) contract was issued in 1986 for the EP-3E-II electronic surveillance Orion, described under the LASG Burbank heading.

LTV

LTV AIRCRAFT PRODUCTS GROUP
(A unit of The LTV Corporation)
9314 West Jefferson, PO Box 655907, Dallas, Texas 75265-5907
Telephone: 1 (214) 266 2011
PRESIDENT: Gordon L. Williams
SENIOR VICE-PRESIDENT:
  Robert J. Patton (Special Assignments)
DIRECTOR, PUBLIC RELATIONS AND ADVERTISING:
  Lynn J. Farris
VICE-PRESIDENT, COMMERCIAL PROGRAMMES:
  Frank S. Kipp
VICE-PRESIDENT, B-2 PROGRAMME:
  Henry L. Spence
VICE-PRESIDENT, A-7 AND SUPPORT PROGRAMMES:
  Steve H. Yarborough
VICE-PRESIDENT, C-17 PROGRAMME:
  Thomas W. Jackson

The former Chance Vought Aircraft Inc, founded in 1917 and a leading producer of aircraft for the US Navy throughout its history, became the Chance Vought Corporation on 31 December 1960. On 31 August 1961, it merged with Ling-Temco Electronics Inc, to form Ling-Temco-Vought Inc (now The LTV Corporation). On 29 September 1986, LTV reorganised its aerospace/defence operations into two groups: LTV Aircraft Products Group, which consists of the Commercial, B-2, A-7 and C-17 programmes based in Dallas, Texas; and LTV Missiles and Electronics Group, which consists of AM General Division, South Bend, Indiana, Sierra Research Division of Buffalo, New York, and Missiles Division of Grand Prairie, Texas.

Current aerospace products include Boeing 747 tail assemblies, complete tailplane assemblies for the Boeing Model 767, complete tail units for the Boeing 757, and engine nacelles for Canadair business jets. Two YA-7F prototypes have been produced. In 1986, the company was selected by McDonnell Douglas Corporation to manufacture engine nacelles and tail unit sections for the C-17A transport. As a major subcontractor to the Northrop Corporation, the company produces the intermediate sections of the B-2 bomber which constitute approximately one-third of the total airframe structure by weight. The company has a teaming agreement with Aerospatiale Helicopter Corporation and LHTEC to produce the Panther 800, a T800 engined version of the AS 365 Dauphin helicopter, for US government military applications.

In the Spring of 1988, LTV's Sierra Research Division was awarded a contract to undertake systems installation in six British Aerospace 125-800 business jets for the US Air Force's flight inspection (C-FIN) role, under the USAF designation C-29A. The first aircraft flew in August 1989 and was delivered in the following December. A contract to study a possible upgrade for NASA's 27 Northrop T-38s was awarded in 1989. This concentrates on flight safety improvements, avionics maintenance improvements and compatibility with the US air traffic control system. A HUD may also be added to improve realism in the Space Shuttle pilot training role. In a further venture, Sierra Research is installing a large, electronically steerable, dual-polarised phased-array antenna in the dorsal fin of a Lockheed EP-3A Orion as an airborne telemetry system for the Pacific Missile Test Range.

LTV A-7 CORSAIR UPDATE PROGRAMMES

An initial contract to develop and build three A-7As was awarded by the US Navy on 19 March 1964; first flight was made on 27 September 1965. Several versions of the A-7 were developed subsequently as Corsair IIs, for the US Navy, the US Air Force, the Hellenic Air Force and the Portuguese Air Force. Details of the A-7A, A-7B, A-7C, A-7D and A-7E can be found in the 1983-84, 1979-80 and earlier editions of *Jane's*. TA-7C, A-7H, TA-7H, A-7K, EA-7L and A-7P versions were last described in the 1989-90 edition.

Orders for all versions totalled 1,545 new-build aircraft when production ended in 1983.

Prototype YA-7F supersonic conversion of A-7D aircraft during its first flight

LTV YA-7F prototype for A-7 Plus (P&W F100-PW-220 or GE F100-GE-100 turbofan) *(Pilot Press)*

Current activity is centred on a series of update programmes for the Corsair II. A total of 83 Air National Guard A-7Ds and A-7Ks has been equipped with low-altitude night attack (LANA) capability under contracts awarded by the Air Force's Oklahoma City Air Logistics Center. The first LANA equipped aircraft, an A-7K (81-0076) of the 162nd TFTS, Arizona ANG, made its first flight from Dallas on 2 October 1986. Deliveries, to the 150th TFG of the New Mexico ANG at Kirtland AFB, began in the Summer of 1987. LTV retrofitted 75 A-7Ds and eight two-seat A-7Ks with forward looking infra-red (FLIR), a Singer tactical mission computer, and linking the Texas Instruments AN/APQ-126 radar with the aircraft's automatic flight control via an automatic terrain following (ATF) coupler, together with a new GEC Avionics wide angle HUD derived from that fitted to the F-16C/D, to provide around-the-clock, under-the-weather capability. LTV also manufactured 40 FLIR pods incorporating a Texas Instruments AN/AAR-49 IR seeker.

LTV, with Rockwell-Collins as major subcontractor, is replacing the A-7's existing AN/ASN-90 inertial measurement system with the replacement inertial measurement system (RIMS). LTV is responsible for integrating a Honeywell or Litton ring laser gyro, Rockwell-Collins bus system interface unit and cockpit display. A Singer tactical mission computer will be installed in A-7s which have not received LANA modifications. Future plans include AIM-9L Sidewinder air-to-air missile capability, and a one-piece birdproof windscreen which has already been tested on an A-7D.

On 7 May 1987, LTV received a contract from USAF Aeronautical Systems Division to upgrade two LANA equipped A-7D Corsair IIs to supersonic **A-7 Plus** (formerly Strikefighter) configuration, for prototype evaluation in 1989-90 as a potential improvement to the Air Force's air-to-ground support task, including close air support/battlefield air interdiction (CAS/BAI). These prototypes, modified under the designation **YA-7F**, feature a common engine bay enabling Pratt & Whitney F100-PW-220 or General Electric F110-GE-100 afterburning turbofans to be installed, but are being test flown with the Pratt & Whitney engine. Rated at 105.7 kN (23,770 lb st), this gives the YA-7F almost 50 per cent more power. Other modifications include a lengthened fuselage—75 cm (2 ft 5½ in) forward of the wing and 46 cm (1 ft 6⅛ in) aft; an entirely new rear fuselage angled upwards at 4° 20′; fe-designed tail surfaces including a 25 cm (10 in) fin tip extension and 5° 15′ tailplane anhedral; re-skinned wings; airframe mounted accessory drive unit for self-contained ground operation; a new technology trailing-edge flap system and lift dump/spoiler system to permit shorter landing run on unimproved or battle damaged runways; extended vertical tail surfaces; wingroot strakes; anhedral tailplane; improved avionics including a GEC Avionics head-up display and air data computer; improved environmental control system; and a molecular sieve oxygen generating system (MSOGS).

If the YA-7F is selected for production, up to 337 existing ANG Corsair IIs could be modified to the A-7 Plus standard, at a planned rate of six to seven per month. The first flight of a YA-7F took place on 29 November 1989 from LTV's Dallas area facility. After four test sorties, YA-7F 71-344 was flown to Edwards AFB, CA, on 20 December to begin a 10-month flight test programme. After completing four test flights from the Dallas area, the second YA-7F was flown to Edwards AFB in Spring 1990 to join the test programme. Trials are expected to demonstrate a maximum speed of Mach 1.2; improved short-field performance; and sustained 6g turns at Mach 0.9 (compared with 4g at Mach 0.7 for the A-7D).

Other developments under evaluation, but not incorporated in the YA-7F prototypes, include hands-on throttle and stick (HOTAS); a data link for improved close air support; advanced tactical hand-off system (ATHS); improved radar warning system; ground proximity warning system; and improved landing gear warning system. LTV stated that the A-7 Plus will offer 16 per cent greater speed (Mach 1.12 with afterburner), 45 per cent decrease in T-O roll and 30 per cent decrease in landing roll over existing A-7s and will provide greater agility and survivability while operating with minimal support in forward battle areas.

ARMAMENT (YA-7F): One internally mounted M 61 20 mm Gatling gun, with 1,000 rounds of ammunition. Six underwing and two fuselage weapon stations, capable of carrying all USAF, USN, and assorted NATO munitions (max external load more than 7,711 kg; 17,000 lb). Weapon carriers include MAU-12, MER-10N, and TER-9A bomb racks; LAU-3 and LAU-68l wing mounted rocket launchers; AERO-38 fuselage mounted missile launchers; and pods containing 20 or 30 mm guns, ECM, chaff, or auxiliary fuel. Provision also to carry Sargent-Fletcher 31-301 buddy air-to-air refuelling pods.

WEIGHTS (YA-7F):
Operating weight empty:
F100	10,463 kg (23,068 lb)
F110	10,825 kg (23,866 lb)
Max internal fuel	8,074 kg (17,800 lb)
Max stores weight	7,883 kg (17,380 lb)
Max T-O weight	20,865 kg (46,000 lb)

TYPICAL MISSION PERFORMANCE (YA-7F with F100-PW-220 at T-O weight of 17,078 kg; 37,651 lb, with six Mk 82 bombs and 1,000 rds of 20 mm ammunition):
Max level speed at S/L	642 knots (1,190 km/h; 737 mph)
Time to 9,150 m (30,000 ft)	1 min 36 s
T-O run	640 m (2,100 ft)

MACAVIA
MACAVIA INTERNATIONAL
2232 Airport Boulevard, Santa Rosa, California 95401
Telephone: 1 (707) 546 9435
Telex: 5106002077
Fax: 1 (707) 546 2037

MACAVIA TURBINE 207
Macavia International has developed a turboprop conversion of the seven-seat Cessna 207 utility aircraft which involves replacement of the standard 224 kW (300 hp) Teledyne Continental IO-520-F piston engine with a 313 kW (420 shp) Allison 250C-20S turboprop. A custom-designed ergonomic pilot workstation features new seats and soundproofing and standard avionics comprising dual VORs, HSI and RMI. Optional avionics include weather radar, 3M Stormscope, Loran C and HF transceivers. In cargo configuration the Turbine 207's cabin provides 2.83 m³ (100 cu ft) of cargo space.

POWER PLANT: One 313 kW (420 shp) Allison 250C-20S turboprop, driving a Hartzell three-blade constant-speed propeller. Fuel capacity 333 litres (88 US gallons; 73.3 Imp gallons).

DIMENSIONS, EXTERNAL: As Cessna 207 except:
Length overall	10.36 m (34 ft 0 in)
Propeller ground clearance	0.30 m (1 ft 0 in)

MacAvia International Turbine 207 turboprop conversion of the Cessna 207 utility aircraft *(Mike Jerram)*

WEIGHTS:
Weight empty	1,088 kg (2,400 lb)
Max T-O weight	1,814 kg (4,000 lb)
Max landing weight	1,723 kg (3,800 lb)

PERFORMANCE:
Max cruising speed:	
at S/L	148 knots (274 km/h; 170 mph)
at 1,525 m (5,000 ft)	157 knots (291 km/h; 181 mph)
at 3,050 m (10,000 ft)	161 knots (298 km/h; 185 mph)
T-O run	225 m (736 ft)
Range with max fuel	910 nm (1,686 km; 1,047 miles)

MACHEN
MACHEN INC
South 3608 Davison Boulevard, Spokane, Washington 99204
Telephone: 1 (509) 838 5326
Fax: 1 (509) 838 0831
EXECUTIVE VICE-PRESIDENT, MARKETING: James S. Christy

Machen's current products in 1990 were the Superstar 650, 680 and 700. By January 1990 Machen had modified more than 500 Aerostar aircraft.

MACHEN SUPERSTAR 650
Under the name Superstar 650, Machen Inc has developed a conversion of the Piper (Ted Smith) Aerostar 600, 601, 601P and 602P which provides new turbochargers, controllers, fuel pumps, fuel injection servos, and improved pressurisation components, as well as uprating each of the Textron Lycoming TIO-540-S1A5 engines to 242 kW (325 hp). Performance improvements include a better twin- and single-engine rate of climb, a higher single-engine service ceiling, and reduced take-off distance and noise levels.

Machen also markets and installs an FAA approved aerodynamic modification kit (SB 73-1) for the standard Aerostar 600 series and Superstar 650, which restores the unrestricted use of flaps and the original centre of gravity limits, following limitations imposed on the 600 series by the FAA in 1983. The kit comprises aileron and rudder hinge gap seals, a strake on the forward fuselage, leading-edge stall strips, and vortex generators on the lower wing surface and on the fin.

Machen announced in early 1987 that it had developed a compact turbo-intercooling system for turbocharged models of the Aerostar series. The system offers improvements in hot day take-off, cruise climb and single-engine climb performance.

The Aerostar 600 was described fully under the Piper entry in the 1982-83 *Jane's*, the 601 and 601P in the 1981-82 *Jane's*, and the 602P in the 1984-85 *Jane's*. The descriptions of these aircraft apply also to the Superstar 650, except as noted in this entry.

PERFORMANCE: As for appropriate Aerostar model except:
Cruising speed, average cruise weight at 7,620 m (25,000 ft): 75% power	240 knots (445 km/h; 276 mph)
65% power	226 knots (419 km/h; 260 mph)
Min single-engine control speed (VMC)	79 knots (146 km/h; 91 mph)
Max rate of climb at S/L	596 m (1,955 ft)/min
Rate of climb at S/L, one engine out	123 m (402 ft)/min
Service ceiling, one engine out	4,575 m (15,000 ft)
T-O to 15 m (50 ft)	604 m (1,980 ft)

Machen Superstar 650 conversion of the Piper Aerostar 601P

MACHEN SUPERSTAR 680
Machen Inc began producing in 1980 a further conversion of the Piper (Ted Smith) Aerostar 601P, known as the Superstar 680, to provide improved performance. The major element of this modification is the addition of induction air intercoolers to the Superstar 650 model. Four-blade Hartzell propellers are optional.

The description of the Aerostar 601P under the Piper entry in the 1981-82 *Jane's* applies also to the Machen Superstar 680 modification, except as noted. Changed full-conversion weight and performance figures include:

WEIGHTS:
Weight empty, equipped	1,863 kg (4,106 lb)
Max ramp weight	2,812 kg (6,200 lb)
Max T-O weight	2,812 kg (6,200 lb)
Max landing weight	2,721 kg (6,000 lb)

PERFORMANCE (at max T-O weight except where indicated):
Max cruising speed at 7,620 m (25,000 ft)	265 knots (491 km/h; 305 mph)
Cruising speed, average cruise weight at 7,620 m (25,000 ft):	
75% power	250 knots (463 km/h; 288 mph)
65% power	242 knots (448 km/h; 279 mph)
55% power	232 knots (430 km/h; 267 mph)
Min single-engine control speed (VMC)	79 knots (146 km/h; 91 mph)
Max rate of climb at S/L	596 m (1,955 ft)/min
Rate of climb at S/L, one engine out	122 m (402 ft)/min
Service ceiling	7,620 m (25,000 ft)
Service ceiling, one engine out	7,010 m (23,000 ft)
T-O to 15 m (50 ft)	603 m (1,980 ft)

Range, standard fuel, 45 min reserves	1,137 nm (2,107 km; 1,309 miles)
Range, auxiliary fuel	1,441 nm (2,670 km; 1,659 miles)

MACHEN SUPERSTAR 700
Machen Inc began producing in 1988 a further conversion of the Piper (Ted Smith) Aerostar 601P and 602P, known as the Superstar 700. The conversion involves installation of specially designed Rotomaster automatic turbochargers and Machen-developed nacelle mounted intercoolers which raise power output of the engines to 261 kW (350 hp) each, and low noise signature Hartzell three blade propellers. The modification permits an increase in max T-O weight to 2,864 kg (6,315 lb), providing a 120 kg (265 lb) increase in useful load. Additional improvements include reduced cabin and external noise levels, increased cabin air volume, and a more efficient pressurisation system.

The description of the Aerostar 601P and 602P under the Piper entry in the 1981-82 *Jane's* applies also to the Machen Superstar 700 modification, except as noted. Changed full conversion weight and performance figures include:

WEIGHTS:
Weight empty, equipped	1,862 kg (4,106 lb)
Max ramp and max T-O weight	2,864 kg (6,315 lb)
Max landing weight	2,721 kg (6,000 lb)

PERFORMANCE (at max T-O weight except where indicated):
Max cruising speed at 7,620 m (25,000 ft)	270 knots (500 km/h; 311 mph)
Cruising speed, at average cruise weight at 7,620 m (25,000 ft):	

75% power	255 knots (473 km/h; 294 mph)	Max rate of climb at S/L	
65% power	245 knots (454 km/h; 282 mph)	more than 610 m (2,000 ft)/min	
55% power	235 knots (435 km/h; 271 mph)	Rate of climb at S/L, one engine out	
Min single-engine control speed (VMC)			122 m (400 ft)/min
	79 knots (146 km/h; 91 mph)	Service ceiling	7,620 m (25,000 ft)

Service ceiling, one engine out	4,570 m (15,000 ft)
T-O to 15 m (50 ft)	535 m (1,755 ft)
Range, standard fuel, 45 min reserves	
	1,200 nm (2,224 km; 1,382 miles)
Range, auxiliary fuel	1,560 nm (2,891 km; 1,796 miles)

MAGNUM
MAGNUM T/R
Salinas, California

This company has announced plans to develop a tilt-rotor aircraft known as the **MTR-201**, which will use the wing, rotors, powertrain and flight controls of the Bell Model 301 (XV-15) experimental tilt-rotor aircraft mated to the fuselage of a Mitsubishi MU-2 twin turboprop business aircraft. Power plant will be two 1,305 kW (1,750 shp) Pratt & Whitney Canada turboshafts. Predicted performance includes a max cruise speed of 300 knots (556 km/h; 345 mph) and a range of 1,000 nm (1,853 km; 1,151 miles). First deliveries are anticipated in 1994.

MARSH
MARSH AVIATION COMPANY
5060 East Falcon Drive, Mesa, Arizona 85205
Telephone: 1 (602) 832 3770
Telex: 165 028
Fax: 1 (602) 985 2840
PRESIDENT: Floyd D. Stilwell
EXECUTIVE VICE-PRESIDENT: Bill Walker Jr

MARSH S2R-T TURBO THRUSH

Marsh Aviation converted the piston engined Rockwell Thrush Commander to turbine power by installing a Garrett TPE331-1-101 turboprop. Derated to 447 kW (600 shp) for this conversion, the engine drives a Hartzell constant-speed fully-feathering and reversible-pitch propeller, and the full 580 kW (778 shp) output of the TPE331 is available in an emergency. Single cycle air-conditioning and cockpit heating are provided by engine bleed air, which also operates the agricultural spraypump. The empty weight of the Turbo Thrush is 227 kg (500 lb) less than that of the standard Thrush Commander, providing increased payload capability and improved speed and performance. For agricultural operators working in remote areas, the TPE331 installation has the advantage that ordinary automotive diesel fuel can be used if jet fuel is not available.

Standard fuel capacity of the Turbo Thrush is 401 litres (106 US gallons; 88.3 Imp gallons). Standard hopper capacity is 1.50 m³ (53 cu ft) or 1,514 litres (400 US gallons; 333 Imp gallons). A larger hopper is available optionally, capacity 1.89 m³ (66.8 cu ft) or 1,892.5 litres (500 US gallons; 416 Imp gallons).

Following more than 600 h of flight by two prototypes, an FAA Supplemental Type Certificate was issued and the first production conversion was handed over in September 1976. Turbo Thrush deliveries totalled 75 by February 1985, the majority for operators in Africa, Europe, Mexico, the Middle East and the USA. A further four were delivered to US operators during 1989.

Details of the Rockwell Thrush Commander can be found in the 1977-78 *Jane's*, and weight and performance data for the Turbo Thrush in the 1987-88 edition.

MARSH G-164 C-T TURBO CAT

Marsh Aviation developed this turbine engine conversion for the Grumman/Gulfstream Aerospace/Schweizer G-164 Super Ag-Cat C by replacing the original piston engine with a 580 kW (778 shp) Garrett TPE331-1-101 turboprop, derated to 447 kW (600 shp).

Certification was gained in 1980, and six Turbo Cats (one A, four Bs and a C) had been completed by 1981. No more have been built since, although the aircraft remains available. Details of the Schweizer Super Ag-Cat C can be found in the 1981-82 *Jane's*, and of the Turbo Cat in the 1984-85 edition.

MARSH/GRUMMAN TURBO S-2 CONVERSION

Marsh Aviation has developed a turbine engine conversion for the Grumman S-2 Tracker anti-submarine aircraft. Modifications include extensive aerodynamic changes to the fuselage and engine nacelles, to reduce drag, and replacement of the S-2's original Wright R-1820 piston engines with 932 kW (1,250 shp) Garrett TPE331-14 or 1,227 kW (1,645 shp) TPE331-15 turboprops, housed in new cowlings of composite construction and each driving a Hartzell five-blade reversible-pitch propeller of 2.92 m (9 ft 7 in) diameter. Maximum usable fuel capacity 1,960 litres (518 US gallons; 431 Imp gallons). Other modifications include modern flight, engine and navigation instrumentation; a multiple bus electrical system; two batteries; Systron-Donner fire detection system; halon fire extinguisher system, and optional bleed air environmental control system. The aim was to increase cruising speed by 60 knots (111 km/h; 69 mph) by comparison with the standard S-2, with a 50 per cent reduction in fuel consumption at high speed. Other performance improvements were expected to include a 25 per cent reduction in take-off and landing runs, and an increase of about 230 m (750 ft)/min in single-engine rate of climb at max T-O weight.

The first Marsh Turbo S-2 conversion (N426DF) made its first flight on 21 November 1986, and during subsequent early testing, it demonstrated true airspeeds in excess of 287

Prototype Marsh Turbo S-2 conversion of the S-2 Tracker

Marsh Turbo Thrush conversion of the Rockwell International Thrush Commander

knots (531 km/h; 330 mph) and initial climb rates of up to 1,225 m (4,020 ft)/min. This aircraft has computerised engine controls to reduce pilot workload and enhance reliability.

Following certification, the Turbo S-2 was evaluated in the firefighting role by the California Forestry Department, and was exhibited at the 1989 Paris Air Show.

A military version of the Turbo S-2 is available with integrated mission equipment for maritime patrol and anti-submarine warfare roles, including search radar, FLIR, MAD, sonobuoy launchers, pictorial navigation avionics with automatic search and attack modes, six underwing stores positions and a torpedo bay.

In early 1990 Marsh Aviation was converting nine Turbo S-2s, and held orders for seven in military ASW configuration for unidentified foreign customers.

The TPE331-14 powered conversion is equipped with a 3,028 litre (800 US gallon; 666 Imp gallon) chemical retardant tank, while the TPE331-15 version has a 3,785 litre (1,000 US gallon; 833 Imp gallon) tank. Marsh Aviation foresees a market for between 60 and 80 conversions worldwide. The following specifications refer to the TPE331-14 powered Turbo S-2:

WEIGHTS:
Weight empty	6,278 kg (13,840 lb)
Max fuel weight	1,624 kg (3,580 lb)
Max T-O weight	11,340 kg (25,000 lb)
Max landing weight	11,113 kg (24,500 lb)

PERFORMANCE:
Cruising speed:	
at 3,050 m (10,000 ft)	230 knots (426 km/h; 265 mph)
at 7,925 m (26,000 ft)	270 knots (500 km/h; 311 mph)
Retardant drop speed	130 knots (241 km/h; 150 mph)
Max rate of climb at S/L	518 m (1,700 ft)/min
Max range at cruising speed of 210 knots (389 km/h; 242 mph) at 7,620 m (25,000 ft), no reserves	
	1,468 nm (2,720 km; 1,690 miles)

MAULE

MAULE AIR INC

Lake Maule, Route 5, Box 319, Moultrie, Georgia 31768
Telephone: 1 (912) 985 2045
Telex: 804613 MAULE MOUL
Fax: 1 (912) 890 2402
PRESIDENT: Belford D. Maule
SALES MANAGER: Don Ritchie

This company succeeded Maule Aircraft Corporation, which was formed to manufacture the M-4 four-seat light aircraft, production of which ended in 1975. The former company transferred to Moultrie, Georgia, in September 1968, and Maule Air Inc was formed in 1984 to continue production of the uprated M-5 Lunar Rocket and M-7 Super Rocket. The Lunar Rocket has since been discontinued, but the following versions of the Super Rocket and Star Rocket, and the turboprop Starcraft, are currently available:

MAULE STAR ROCKET and SUPER ROCKET

Models of the Star Rocket and Super Rocket available in 1990 were as follows:

M-6-235 Super Rocket. Generally similar to the earlier M-5-235C (1983-84 *Jane's*), but differs by having a revised wing of increased span, with changes to the ailerons and trailing-edge flaps. FAA certification awarded on 25 June 1981. Available as M-6-235 with a 175 kW (235 hp) Textron Lycoming O-540-J1A5D or IO-540-W1A5D engine, and with wheel landing gear or amphibious floats.

MX-7 Star Rocket. Certificated on 9 November 1984, the Star Rocket combines the shorter span wing of the former M-5 series with the glassfibre wingtips, increased fuel capacity, ailerons and five-position flaps of the M-7, and the fuselage of the M-6. It is available as the **MX-7-180** with 134 kW (180 hp) Textron Lycoming O-360-C1F, as the **MXT-7-180 Tri-Gear** with optional tricycle landing gear, or as the **MX-7-235** with 175 kW (235 hp) Textron Lycoming O-540-J1A5D or IO-540-W1A5D engine.

M-7-235 Super Rocket. This 1984 development of the earlier four-seat M-6-235 is a five-seater with a one-place rear bench. Wing span and weights are increased. Power plant is a 175 kW (235 hp) Textron Lycoming O-540-J1A5D or fuel injected IO-540-W1A5D flat-six engine. It is available as a landplane, on Edo 797-2500 amphibious floats or Edo 2440B or Aqua 2400 standard floats, or on FluiDyne FliLite 3000 Mk IIIA hydraulic wheel/skis.

Production of all versions totals more than 1,500, of which 35 were sold in 1989.

TYPE: Four-seat or five-seat STOL light aircraft.
WINGS: Braced high-wing monoplane. Streamline section V bracing strut each side. USA 35B (modified) wing section. Dihedral 1°. Incidence 0° 30′. All-metal two-spar structure with metal covering and glassfibre tips. All-metal ailerons and flaps. Ailerons linked with rudder tab, so that aircraft can be controlled in flight by using only the control wheel in the cockpit. Flaps have maximum deflection of 48°, with negative setting of –7° for enhanced cruise performance. Cambered wingtips standard.
FUSELAGE: Welded 4130 steel tube structure. Covered with Ceconite, except for metal doors, aluminium skin around cabin, and glassfibre cowling.
TAIL UNIT: Braced steel tube structure with Ceconite covering. Trim tab in port elevator. Servo tab in rudder linked to aileron movement. Starboard rudder trim via spring to starboard rudder pedal. Underfin on floatplane and amphibious versions.
LANDING GEAR: Non-retractable tailwheel type. Maule oleo-pneumatic shock absorbers in main units. Maule steerable tailwheel. Cleveland mainwheels with Goodyear or McCreary tyres size 17 × 6.00-6, pressure 1.79 bars (26 lb/sq in). Tailwheel tyre size 8 × 3.50-4, pressure 1.03-1.38 bars (15-20 lb/sq in). Cleveland hydraulic disc brakes. Parking brake. Oversize tyres, size 20 × 8.50-6 (pressure 1.24 bars; 18 lb/sq in), and fairings aft of mainwheels optional. Tricycle gear optional on MX-7. Provisions for fitting optional Edo Model 248B2440 floats or Edo Model 797-2500 amphibious floats, Aqua Model 2400 floats, or Federal Model C2200H or C3000 or Fli-Lite 3000 Mk IIIA skis.
POWER PLANT: One flat-four or flat-six engine, driving a Hartzell two-blade constant-speed propeller, as detailed in model listings. (Three-blade McCauley propeller optional.) Two fuel tanks in wings with total usable capacity of 151 litres (40 US gallons; 33 Imp gallons). Auxiliary fuel tanks in outer wings, to provide total capacity of 265 litres (70 US gallons; 58 Imp gallons), standard. Refuelling points on wing upper surface. Oil capacity 7.5 litres (2 US gallons; 1.7 Imp gallons) on all models except Super Rocket with O-540-J1A5D engine which has 9.5 litres (2.5 US gallons; 2.1 Imp gallons).
ACCOMMODATION: Pilot and three passengers in Star Rocket, four in Super Rockets, on two front bucket seats and rear bench seat, or optional quickly removed rear seat. One door on port side of fuselage, hinged at front edge and opening forward. Three doors on starboard side of fuselage, the forward and centre doors hinged at the front

Maule M-7-235 Super Rocket five-seat STOL aircraft

edge, the rear baggage door hinged at the rear edge. The centre and rear doors can be opened together to provide an opening 1.30 m (4 ft 3 in) wide to facilitate loading of bulky cargo. Plexiglas observation doors optional. Accommodation heated and ventilated. Tinted windscreen and windscreen defroster standard.
SYSTEMS: Hydraulic system for brakes only. Electrical system powered by 60A engine driven alternator. 28V electrical system optional.
AVIONICS AND EQUIPMENT: Standard avionics comprise Bendix/King KX 155 nav/com with glideslope and KI 208 indicator. Optional avionics include Bendix/King KX 155 digital nav/com; KN 62A DME; KR 21 marker beacon receiver; KR 87 ADF; KT 76A transponder; KN 75 glideslope receiver; KNS 80 integrated nav system; Narco ADF-841; AR-850 remote altitude encoder; AT-150 transponder; DME-890; IDME-891; Terra TX-720 com transceiver; AT-3000 altitude digitiser; TMA-230 audio panel; TRT-2350 transponder; David Clark Isocom or Sigtronics SPA-400 intercoms; Apollo II, ArNav 21 or North Star M1 Loran C, and Century 21 or IIB autopilots. Standard equipment includes airspeed indicator; altimeter; electric turn co-ordinator; full gyro panel; vertical speed indicator; tachometer; OAT, fuel pressure, oil pressure, oil temperature, manifold pressure, cylinder head temperature and electric fuel quantity gauges; compass; clock; ammeter; dual controls; cabin soundproofing; cloth velour upholstery; tinted windscreen with defroster; auxiliary cabin heater; ashtray; cigarette lighter; cabin steps; cargo tie-down straps; microphone and bracket; heated pitot; corrosion proofing; emergency locator transmitter; float reinforcements (235 models only); port wing landing light; instrument, dome, navigation and wingtip strobe lights; and tie-down rings. Optional equipment includes encoding altimeter; acoustic stall warner; engine hour meter; Alcor exhaust gas temperature gauge; cabin cool air kit; carburettor air temperature gauge; clear windscreen; observation window; swing out window; Plexiglas door; skylight window; door pockets; dual caliper brakes; fire extinguisher; Schweizer tow-release kit; jump seat in baggage area; shoulder harnesses with lap belts; starboard wing landing light; control wheel push-to-talk switch; radio cooling kit; radio master switch; Telex headset; McCauley three-blade propeller (235 models only); wheel fairings, and ventral fin (floatplanes).
DIMENSIONS, EXTERNAL:

Wing span: M-6	10.03 m (32 ft 11 in)
M-7	10.26 m (33 ft 8 in)
MX-7	9.40 m (30 ft 10 in)
Wing chord, constant: all	1.60 m (5 ft 3 in)
Wing aspect ratio: M-6	6.5
M-7	6.4
MX-7	6.0
Length overall: MX-7-180, MX-7-235/O-540	7.16 m (23 ft 6 in)
all others	7.19 m (23 ft 7¼ in)
Height overall: all (landplane)	1.93 m (6 ft 4 in)
all (amphibian)	3.20 m (10 ft 6 in)
Tailplane span: all	3.28 m (10 ft 9 in)
Wheel track: all	1.83 m (6 ft 0 in)
Wheelbase: all	4.82 m (15 ft 10 in)
Propeller diameter:	
M-6, MX-7-235, M-7: two-blade	2.06 m (6 ft 9 in)
MX/MXT-7-180	1.93 m (6 ft 4 in)
Cabin doors: all (fwd, each):	
Height	0.84 m (2 ft 9 in)
Width	0.76 m (2 ft 6 in)
Height to sill	0.94 m (3 ft 1 in)

Cabin door: all (centre, stbd):	
Height	0.75 m (2 ft 5½ in)
Width	0.69 m (2 ft 3 in)
Height to sill	0.76 m (2 ft 6 in)
Baggage door: all (rear, stbd):	
Height	0.58 m (1 ft 11 in)
Width	0.56 m (1 ft 10 in)
Height to sill	0.61 m (2 ft 0 in)
DIMENSION, INTERNAL:	
Cabin width: all	0.98 m (3 ft 2½ in)
AREAS:	
Wings, gross: M-6	15.38 m² (165.6 sq ft)
M-7	16.44 m² (177.0 sq ft)
MX-7	14.67 m² (157.9 sq ft)
Ailerons (total): MX-7, M-7	1.17 m² (12.56 sq ft)
M-6	1.20 m² (12.92 sq ft)
Trailing-edge flaps (total): MX-7	2.12 m² (22.78 sq ft)
M-6	2.32 m² (25.0 sq ft)
M-7	2.44 m² (26.25 sq ft)
Fin: all	1.22 m² (13.14 sq ft)
Rudder, incl tab: all	0.54 m² (5.83 sq ft)
Tailplane: all	1.32 m² (14.2 sq ft)
Elevators, incl tab: all	1.58 m² (17.0 sq ft)

WEIGHTS AND LOADINGS (L: landplane, F: floatplane, A: amphibian):

Weight empty:	
M-6 (L), M-7 (L)	681 kg (1500 lb)
M-6 (F), M-7 (F), MX-7-235 (F)	794 kg (1,750 lb)
M-6 (A), M-7 (A), MX-7-235 (A)	907 kg (2,000 lb)
MX-7-180 (L)	613 kg (1,350 lb)
MX-7-235 (L)	669 kg (1,475 lb)
Max baggage (all)	45 kg (100 lb)
Max cargo (all)	317 kg (700 lb)
Max T-O and landing weight:	
all models (L)	1,134 kg (2,500 lb)
all models (F, A)	1,247 kg (2,750 lb)
Max wing loading:	
M-6 (L)	73.69 kg/m² (15.10 lb/sq ft)
M-6 (F, A)	81.06 kg/m² (16.61 lb/sq ft)
M-7 (L)	68.91 kg/m² (14.12 lb/sq ft)
M-7 (F, A)	75.83 kg/m² (15.54 lb/sq ft)
MX-7 (L)	77.25 kg/m² (15.83 lb/sq ft)
MX-7 (F, A)	85.01 kg/m² (17.42 lb/sq ft)
Max power loading:	
M-6 (L), M-7 (L), MX-7-235 (L)	6.48 kg/kW (10.64 lb/hp)
M-6 (F, A), M-7 (F, A), MX-7-235 (F, A)	7.12 kg/kW (11.70 lb/hp)
MX-7-180 (L)	8.45 kg/kW (13.89 lb/hp)

PERFORMANCE (at max T-O weight, ISA: L, F and A as for 'Weights'):

Max level speed at S/L:	
M-6/O-540 (L), M-7/O-540 (L), MX-7-235/O-540 (L)	144 knots (267 km/h; 166 mph)
M-6/IO-540 (L), M-7/IO-540 (L), MX-7-235/IO-540 (L)	147 knots (273 km/h; 170 mph)
M-6 (F, A)	126 knots (233 km/h; 145 mph)
M-7 (F, A), MX-7-235 (F, A)	130 knots (241 km/h; 150 mph)
MX-7-180 (L)	134 knots (248 km/h; 154 mph)
Max cruising speed (75% power) at optimum altitude:	
M-6 (L), M-7 (L), MX-7-235 (L)	139 knots (257 km/h; 160 mph)
M-6 (F, A)	121 knots (224 km/h; 139 mph)
M-7 (F, A), MX-7-235 (F, A)	125 knots (232 km/h; 144 mph)
MX-7-180 (L)	126 knots (233 km/h; 145 mph)
MXT-7-180	122 knots (225 km/h; 140 mph)

Stalling speed, flaps down, power off:

M-6 (L), M-7 (L)	31 knots (57 km/h; 35 mph)
M-6 (F, A)	49 knots (91 km/h; 56 mph)
M-7 (F, A), MX-7-235 (F, A)	47 knots (87 km/h; 54 mph)
MX-7 (L), MXT-7-180	35 knots (65 km/h; 40 mph)

Max rate of climb at S/L:

M-6 (L), MX-7-235, M-7 (L)	610 m (2,000 ft)/min
M-6 (F, A), MX-7-235 (F, A)	381 m (1,250 ft)/min
M-7 (F, A)	411 m (1,350 ft)/min
MX-7-180 (L), MXT-7-180	366 m (1,200 ft)/min

Service ceiling:

M-6 (L), M-7 (L), MX-7-235 (L)	6,100 m (20,000 ft)
M-6 (F, A), M-7 (F, A), MX-7-235 (F, A)	5,180 m (17,000 ft)
MX-7-180 (L)	4,575 m (15,000 ft)

T-O run on land:

M-6 (L), M-7 (L), MX-7-235/IO-540 (L)	38 m (125 ft)
MX-7-235 (A), M-6 (A), M-7 (A)	69 m (225 ft)
MX-7-180 (L), MXT-7-180	61 m (200 ft)
MX-7-235/O-540 (L)	46 m (150 ft)

T-O run on water:

M-6 (F, A), M-7 (F, A)	305 m (1,000 ft)
MX-7-235 (F, A)	335 m (1,100 ft)

T-O to 15 m (50 ft) on land:

M-6 (L), M-7 (L), MX-7 (L), MXT-7-180	183 m (600 ft)
M-6 (A), M-7 (A), MX-7-235 (A)	152 m (500 ft)

T-O to 15 m (50 ft) on water:

M-6 (F, A), M-7 (F, A)	381 m (1,250 ft)
MX-7-235 (F, A)	412 m (1,350 ft)

Landing from 15 m (50 ft) on land:

M-6 (L), M-7 (L), MX-7 (L)	152 m (500 ft)
M-6 (A), M-7 (A), MX-7-235 (A)	305 m (1,000 ft)

Landing from 15 m (50 ft) on water:

M-6 (F, A), M-7 (F, A), MX-7-235 (F, A)	305 m (1,000 ft)

Landing run on land and water:

M-6 (A), M-7 (A), MX-7-235 (A)	244 m (800 ft)

Range with standard fuel:

M-6-235/O-540 (L), M-7-235/O-540 (L), MX-7-235/O-540 (L)	425 nm (788 km; 490 miles)
M-6-235/IO-540 (L), M-7-235/IO-540 (L), MX-7-235 (L)	460 nm (853 km; 530 miles)
MX-7-180 (L)	560 nm (1,038 km; 645 miles)
M-6-235/O-540 (F, A)	264 nm (490 km; 305 miles)
M-6-235/IO-540 (F, A)	299 nm (555 km; 345 miles)
M-7-235/O-540 (F, A)	286 nm (531 km; 330 miles)
M-7-235/IO-540 (F, A)	321 nm (595 km; 370 miles)

Range with auxiliary fuel:

M-6-235/O-540 (L), M-7-235/O-540 (L), MX-7-235/O-540 (L)	746 nm (1,384 km; 860 miles)
M-6-235/IO-540 (L), M-7-235/IO-540 (L), MX-7-235 (L)	807 nm (1,496 km; 930 miles)

Turboprop powered Maule M-7-420 Starcraft with Edo 797-2500 amphibious landing gear

MX-7-180 (L)	977 nm (1,810 km; 1,125 miles)
M-6-235/O-540 (F, A)	586 nm (1,086 km; 675 miles)
M-6-235-IO-540 (F, A)	647 nm (1,199 km; 745 miles)
M-7-235/O-540 (F, A)	608 nm (1,126 km; 700 miles)
M-7-235/IO-540 (F, A)	668 nm (1,239 km; 770 miles)

MAULE M-7 and MX-7 STARCRAFT

Maule is building turboprop versions of both the **MX-7-420** and **M-7-420**, powered in each case by an Allison 250-B17C engine. Named Starcraft, the turboprop models have airframes generally identical to those of the piston engined MX-7 and longer span M-7, with the same option of wheel, ski, float or Edo 797-2500 amphibious landing gear. Certification of both models was achieved in 1989.

POWER PLANT: One 313 kW (420 shp) Allison 250-B17C turboprop, driving a Hartzell HC-B3TF-7A three-blade metal propeller with autofeathering, reverse pitch and Beta control. Intake anti-icing. Fuel capacity (usable) is 265 litres (70 US gallons; 58 Imp gallons) standard, increasable to 378 litres (100 US gallons; 83 Imp gallons) with optional outer-wing tanks.

SYSTEMS: 28V DC electrical system standard, with 150A starter/generator, solid state regulators and 24V 19Ah battery.

AVIONICS AND EQUIPMENT: Standard and optional avionics and equipment generally as for piston-engined models except; airspeed warning system; chip detector light; engine inlet heater; torque indicator; fuel filter light;

propeller rpm indicator; 100A starter generator, turbine temperature indicator; turbine percentage rpm indicator, and volt/amp meter, standard.

DIMENSIONS, EXTERNAL: As for piston engined M-7/MX-7 except:

Length overall (landplane)	7.32 m (24 ft 0 in)
Propeller diameter: (L)	2.03 m (6 ft 8 in)
(A)	2.29 m (7 ft 6 in)

WEIGHTS AND LOADINGS:

Weight empty:

M-7-420: landplane	626 kg (1,380 lb)
amphibian	907 kg (2,000 lb)
MX-7-420: landplane	626 kg (1,380 lb)

Max T-O weight:

M-7-420 (amphibian)	1,247 kg (2,750 lb)
M-7-420, MX-7-420 (landplane)	1,134 kg (2,500 lb)

Max wing loading:

M-7-420	75.83 kg/m² (15.54 lb/sq ft)
MX-7-420	77.25 kg/m² (15.83 lb/sq ft)

Max power loading:

M-7-420 (amphibian)	3.99 kg/kW (6.55 lb/shp)
MX-7-420	3.62 kg/kW (5.95 lb/shp)

PERFORMANCE (at max T-O weight. A: MX-7-420 landplane, B: M-7-420 amphibian):

Max level speed at S/L:

A	174 knots (322 km/h; 200 mph)
B	161 knots (298 km/h; 185 mph)

Cruising speed, 75% power at optimum altitude:

A	169 knots (314 km/h; 195 mph)
B	156 knots (290 km/h; 180 mph)

Cruising speed, 50% power at optimum altitude:

A	156 knots (290 km/h; 180 mph)
B	143 knots (266 km/h; 165 mph)

Stalling speed, flaps down, power off:

A	44 knots (81 km/h; 50 mph)
B	47 knots (87 km/h; 54 mph)

Max rate of climb at S/L: A 1,430 m (4,700 ft)/min

B	762 m (2,500 ft)/min

Service ceiling: A, B	6,100 m (20,000 ft)
T-O run: A	61 m (200 ft)
B (land)	77 m (250 ft)
B (water)	229 m (750 ft)
Landing run: A, B (land)	92 m (300 ft)
B (water)	107 m (350 ft)

Range, 75% power, no reserves:

A	456 nm (846 km; 526 miles)
B	422 nm (782 km; 486 miles)

Range, 50% power, no reserves:

A	644 nm (1,194 km; 742 miles)
B	590 nm (1,094 km; 680 miles)

Maule MXT-7-180 with tricycle landing gear

MBB

MBB HELICOPTER CORPORATION
(Subsidiary of Messerschmitt-Bölkow-Blohm GmbH)
900 Airport Road, PO Box 2349,
West Chester, Pennsylvania 19380
Telephone: 1 (215) 431 4150
Telex: 173102 MBB HELIC WCHR
Fax: 1 (215) 436 9618
PRESIDENT AND CHIEF EXECUTIVE OFFICER: David O. Smith

SENIOR VICE-PRESIDENT, MARKETING: Andreas Aastad
DIRECTOR OF COMMUNICATIONS: Lynda Kate

Messerschmitt-Bölkow-Blohm of West Germany (which see) established this subsidiary company in the USA, in early 1979, to take over marketing and product support of the company's family of twin-turbine helicopters in North and Central America.

The MBB complex is located on a 17 hectare (42 acre) site adjacent to the Brandywine Airport, West Chester, Pennsylvania, comprising a 3,716 m² (40,000 sq ft)

completion centre, a 3,252 m² (35,000 sq ft) maintenance and training centre, and a 2,787 m² (30,000 sq ft) administration building.

MBB Helicopter Corporation is responsible for marketing, sales and technical support of the entire range of MBB helicopters, which includes the BO 105 CBS, BO 105 LS and BK 117, described in the German, Canadian and International sections respectively, in the United States, Mexico, Central America, the Caribbean, Colombia and Peru.

MCDONNELL DOUGLAS

MCDONNELL DOUGLAS CORPORATION
Box 516, St Louis, Missouri 63166
Telephone: 1 (314) 232 0232
Telex: 44-857
Corporate Office
CHAIRMAN AND CHIEF EXECUTIVE OFFICER:
John F. McDonnell
PRESIDENT: Gerald A. Johnston
DIRECTOR, PUBLIC RELATIONS: John L. Cooke

McDonnell Douglas Corporation was formed on 28 April 1967, by the merger of the former Douglas Aircraft Company Inc and the McDonnell company. It encompasses both of the original companies and their subsidiaries, and the former Hughes Helicopters Inc, which became a subsidiary in 1984.

At the end of March 1990 McDonnell Douglas employed 131,097 people worldwide. Total office, engineering, laboratory and manufacturing floor area was then 3.8 million m² (41 million sq ft).

Major operating components of McDonnell Douglas Corporation Aerospace Group are as follows:
McDonnell Aircraft Company
Follows this entry
Douglas Aircraft Company
Follows McDonnell Aircraft Co entry
McDonnell Douglas Helicopter Company
Follows Douglas Aircraft Co entry
McDonnell Douglas Astronautics Company

MCDONNELL AIRCRAFT COMPANY
(A Division of McDonnell Douglas Corporation)

Box 516, St Louis, Missouri 63166
Telephone: 1 (314) 232 0232
PRESIDENT: William S. Ross
EXECUTIVE VICE-PRESIDENT:
Irving L. Burrows (Programme Management)
VICE-PRESIDENT, INTERNATIONAL MARKETING:
James P. Caldwell
VICE-PRESIDENT, ENGINEERING: James M. Sinnett
VICE-PRESIDENT, ENGINEERING TECHNOLOGY:
Leonard F. Impellizzeri
VICE-PRESIDENT, GENERAL MANAGER NEW AIRCRAFT
PRODUCTS: Michael M. Sears
VICE-PRESIDENT, AIRCRAFT ENGINEERING:
Donald D. Snyder
DIRECTOR OF COMMUNICATIONS: Timothy J. Beecher

Development and production at St Louis continues to be concentrated on versions of the F-15 Eagle strike/attack aircraft, AV-8B Harrier II and F/A-18 Hornet strike fighter.

MCDONNELL DOUGLAS F-4 PHANTOM II

Improvement and upgrade programmes are being undertaken on Phantoms of several air arms. Recent and current projects affecting the USAF are detailed under the McDonnell Douglas heading in the 1989-90 edition and under Boeing Military Airplanes in the present volume. Data on foreign programmes will be found under MBB (Germany), IAI (Israel), Mitsubishi (Japan) and BAe (UK).

MCDONNELL DOUGLAS/BAe AV-8B HARRIER II

Details of the AV-8B Harrier II can be found in the International section.

MCDONNELL DOUGLAS F-15C/D EAGLE

An F-15C delivered on 3 November 1989 was the last of 894 air superiority Eagles (F-15A, B, C and D) for the USAF. This version is now temporarily out of production, but will be briefly reinstated in 1991-92 to meet residual orders from Israel (five) and Saudi Arabia (12). Production is currently concentrating on the F-15E, which is described separately, whilst promotion has begun of a new version, designated F-15F.

By the end of 1989, MDC had completed 70 F-15Es and 1,025 of other versions, including prototypes. The latter included 366 F-15As, 58 F-15Bs, 409 F-15Cs and 61 F-15Ds for the USAF; 19 F-15As (plus four ex-USAF), two F-15Bs, 24 F-15Cs and 15 F-15Ds for the Saudi AF; Israeli F-15A, B, C and Ds; and two F-15DJs for the Japan ASDF. Including the FY 1990 budget, Japanese orders from Mitsubishi (which see) and US production totalled 183. B and D versions are two-seat operational trainers.

The F-15C/D were introduced in 1979 and are able to carry two McDonnell low-drag conformal fuel tanks (CFT) developed specially for the F-15. Made in handed pairs, these attach to the sides of the engine air intake trunks, are designed to the same load factors as the basic aircraft, and can be removed in 15 minutes. CFTs can be configured to accommodate avionics such as reconnaissance sensors, radar detection and jamming equipment, a laser designator, low light level TV system, and reconnaissance cameras, in addition to fuel. All external stores stations remain available with the CFTs in use, and a special weapon attachment system can extend the operating radius with large external loads by up to 40 per cent. Known as tangential carriage, it involves the installation of rows of stub pylons on the lower corner and bottom of each CFT. Up to twelve 1,000 lb class or four 2,000 lb class weapons can be carried on these pylons. AIM-7F Sparrow missiles can also be attached directly to the CFTs.

The first F-15C (78-468) flew on 26 February 1979, and the first F-15D on 19 June of that year. In aircraft built since 1980 the radar can operate in a high-resolution raid assessment mode able to identify clustered targets individually. F-15Cs and F-15Ds delivered prior to availability of the programmable signal processor and expanded computer which provide this capability are retrofitted to bring them up to standard. Early F-15s had Pratt & Whitney F100-PW-100 turbofans, but the F100-PW-220 has been standard since 1985.

An initial multi-staged improvement programme (MSIP), first funded in 1983, covers the introduction of a Hughes AN/APG-70 radar with memory increase to 1,000K and trebled processing speed; upgrading the aircraft's central computer to store four times as much data and process it three times as quickly; and replacing the original armament control system panel by a single multi-purpose Honeywell colour video screen. Linked to a computer, the armament control system is programmable, allowing for the addition of advanced versions of the AIM-7, AIM-9 and AIM-120 AMRAAM. Other MSIP improvements include a tactical electronic system consisting of a Northrop enhanced AN/ALQ-135 internal countermeasures system, Loral AN/ALR-56C radar warning receiver, Tracor AN/ALE-45

McDonnell Douglas F-15C Eagles of the USAF's 57th FIS escorting a Tu-95 'Bear-D'

McDonnell Douglas F-15C Eagle single-seat air superiority fighter, with additional side view (top) of two-seat F-15B *(Pilot Press)*

chaff/flare dispenser, and Magnavox electronic warfare warning system. Flight testing of the new system began in December 1984. The first production F-15C built under MSIP was unveiled at McDonnell Douglas' St Louis plant on 20 June 1985. All other F-15C/Ds have been retrofitted.

McDonnell Douglas has proposed a version of the F-15 Eagle for the USAF's Follow-on Wild Weasel defence suppression aircraft requirement to replace F-4G Wild Weasels in the USAF inventory. As a private venture, the company developed a conformal reconnaissance pod designed to be carried on the centreline stores station of two-seat F-15s. The pod, which was flight tested in the Summer of 1987, could transmit imagery to ground stations via a data link, providing near real-time reconnaissance.

In 1990, MDC was seeking customers abroad for the **F-15F.** Although a single-seat aircraft optimised for air-to-air combat, this proposed version would have the AN/APG-70 radar, modern cockpit and wide-angle HUD of the F-15E. However, it would lack some radar air-to-ground modes and provision for conformal fuel tanks. As a fall-back for the ATF programme, the USAF has studied a minimally modified F-15X and a more extensively re-configured F-15XX (larger wing, F119 or F120 engines and new combat avionics).

The following description applies to the standard F-15C:
TYPE: Single-seat twin-turbofan air superiority fighter, with secondary attack role.
WINGS: Cantilever shoulder-wing monoplane. Wing uses NACA 64A aerofoil section with varying thickness/chord ratios, ranging from 6.6% at the root to 3% at the tip. Leading-edges modified with conical camber. Anhedral 1°. Incidence 0°. Sweepback at quarter-chord 38° 42'. Fail-safe structure, comprising a torque box with integrally stiffened machined skins and conventionally machined ribs, of light alloy and titanium. Leading- and trailing-edges are of conventional light alloy rib/skin construction, and wingtips of aluminium honeycomb. Plain ailerons and plain trailing-edge flaps of aluminium honeycomb. No spoilers or trim tabs. Powered controls, hydraulically operated by National Water Lift actuators. No anti-icing system.
FUSELAGE: All-metal semi-monocoque structure. Speedbrake on upper centre-fuselage, constructed of graphite/epoxy, aluminium honeycomb and titanium.
TAIL UNIT: Cantilever structure with twin fins and rudders. All-moving horizontal tail surfaces outboard of fins, with extended chord on outer leading-edges. Ronson

Hydraulic Units rudder servo actuators; National Water Lift actuators for horizontal surfaces. Moog boost and pitch compensator for control stick.
LANDING GEAR: Hydraulically retractable tricycle type, with single wheel on each unit. All units retract forward. Cleveland nose and main units, each incorporating an oleo-pneumatic shock absorber. Nosewheel and tyre by Goodyear, size 22 × 6.6-10, pressure 17.93 bars (260 lb/sq in). Mainwheels by Bendix, with Goodyear tyres size 34.5 × 9.75-18, pressure 23.44 bars (340 lb/sq in). Bendix carbon heat-sink brakes. Hydro-Aire wheel braking skid control system.
POWER PLANT: Two Pratt & Whitney F100-PW-220 turbofans, each rated at 104.3 kN (23,450 lb st) with afterburning for take-off. Internal fuel in eight Goodyear fuselage tanks, total capacity 7,836 litres (2,070 US gallons; 1,724 Imp gallons). Simmonds fuel gauge system. Optional conformal fuel tanks attached to side of engine air intakes, beneath wing, each containing 2,839 litres (750 US gallons; 624 Imp gallons). Provision for up to three additional 2,309 litre (610 US gallon; 508 Imp gallon) external fuel tanks. Max total internal and external fuel capacity 20,441 litres (5,400 US gallons; 4,496 Imp gallons).
ENGINE INTAKES: Straight two-dimensional external compression inlets, on each side of the fuselage. Air inlet controllers by Hamilton Standard. Air inlet actuators by National Water Lift.
ACCOMMODATION: Pilot only, on McDonnell Douglas ACES II ejection seat. Stretched acrylic canopy and windscreen. Windscreen anti-icing valve by Dynasciences Corporation.
SYSTEMS: AiResearch air-conditioning system. Three independent hydraulic systems (each 207 bars; 3,000 lb/sq in) powered by Abex engine driven pumps; modular hydraulic packages by Hydraulic Research and Manufacturing Company. SIADS Inc generating system for electrical power, with Sundstrand 40/50kVA generator constant speed drive units and Electro Development Corpn transformer-rectifiers. The oxygen system includes a Simmonds liquid oxygen indicator. Garrett APU for engine starting, and for the provision of electrical or hydraulic power on the ground independently of the main engines.
AVIONICS AND EQUIPMENT: General Electric automatic analog flight control system standard. Hughes Aircraft AN/APG-63 X-band pulse-Doppler radar (being up-

graded to AN/APG-70 under MSIP), equipped since 1980 with a Hughes Aircraft programmable signal processor, provides long-range detection and tracking of small high-speed targets operating at all altitudes down to treetop level, and feeds accurate tracking information to the IBM CP-1075 96K (24K on early F-15C/Ds) central computer to ensure effective launch of the aircraft's missiles or the firing of its internal gun. For close-in dogfights, the radar acquires the target automatically and the steering/weapon system information is displayed on a McDonnell Douglas Electronics AN/AVQ-20 head-up display. A Teledyne Electronics AN/APX-101 IFF transponder informs ground stations and other suitably equipped aircraft that the F-15 is friendly. It also supplies data on the F-15's range, azimuth, altitude and identification to air traffic controllers. A Hazeltine AN/APX-76 IFF interrogator informs the pilot if an aircraft seen visually or on radar is friendly. A Litton reply evaluator for the IFF system operates with the AN/APX-76. A Honeywell vertical situation display set, using a cathode ray tube to present radar, electro-optical identification and attitude director indicator formats to the pilot, permits inputs received from the aircraft's sensors and the central computer to be visible to the pilot under any light conditions. Honeywell also developed the AN/ASK-6 air data computer and AN/ASN-108 AHRS for the F-15, the latter also serving as a backup to the Litton AN/ASN-109 INS which provides the basic navigation data and is the aircraft's primary attitude reference. In addition to giving the aircraft's position at all times, the INS provides pitch, roll, heading, acceleration and speed information. Other specialised equipment for flight control, navigation and communications includes a Collins AN/ARN-118 Tacan; Collins HSI to present aircraft navigation information on a symbolic pictorial display; Collins ADF and AN/ARN-112 ILS receivers; Magnavox AN/ARC-164 UHF transceiver and UHF auxiliary transceiver. The communications sets have cryptographic capability. Dorne and Margolin glideslope localiser antenna, and Teledyne Avionics angle of attack sensors. Northrop (Defense Systems Division) Enhanced AN/ALQ-135(V) internal countermeasures set provides automatic jamming of enemy radar signals; Loral AN/ALR-56C radar warning receiver; Magnavox AN/ALQ-128 electronic warfare warning set; and Tracor AN/ALE-45 chaff dispenser. Bendix tachometer, fuel and oil indicators; Plessey feel trim actuators.

ARMAMENT: Provision for carriage and launch of a variety of air-to-air weapons over short and medium ranges, including four AIM-9L/M Sidewinders, four AIM-7F/M Sparrows or eight AMRAAM, and a 20 mm M61A1 six-barrel gun with 940 rounds of ammunition. General Electric lead-computing gyro. A Dynamic Controls Corporation armament control system keeps the pilot informed of weapons status and provides for their management. Three air-to-surface weapon stations (five if configured with conformal fuel tanks) allow for the carriage of up to 10,705 kg (23,600 lb) of bombs, rockets or additional ECM equipment. AN/AWG-20 armament control system.

DIMENSIONS, EXTERNAL:

Wing span	13.05 m (42 ft 9¾ in)
Length overall	19.43 m (63 ft 9 in)
Height overall	5.63 m (18 ft 5½ in)
Tailplane span	8.61 m (28 ft 3 in)
Wheel track	2.75 m (9 ft 0¼ in)
Wheelbase	5.42 m (17 ft 9½ in)

AREAS:

Wings, gross	56.5 m² (608.0 sq ft)
Ailerons (total)	2.46 m² (26.48 sq ft)
Flaps (total)	3.33 m² (35.84 sq ft)
Fins (total)	9.78 m² (105.28 sq ft)
Rudders (total)	1.85 m² (19.94 sq ft)
Tailplanes (total)	10.34 m² (111.36 sq ft)

WEIGHTS:

Weight empty, equipped (no fuel, ammunition, pylons or external stores)	12,973 kg (28,600 lb)
Max fuel load: internal	6,103 kg (13,455 lb)
CFTs (2, total)	4,422.5 kg (9,750 lb)
auxiliary tanks (3, total)	5,395.5 kg (11,895 lb)
max internal and external	15,921 kg (35,100 lb)
T-O weight (interceptor, full internal fuel and 4 Sparrows)	20,244 kg (44,630 lb)
T-O weight (incl three 2,309 litre; 610 US gallon; 508 Imp gallon drop tanks)	26,521 kg (58,470 lb)
Max T-O weight with CFTs	30,845 kg (68,000 lb)

PERFORMANCE:

Max level speed	more than Mach 2.5 (800 knots; 1,482 km/h; 921 mph CAS)
Approach speed	125 knots (232 km/h; 144 mph) CAS
T-O run (interceptor)	274 m (900 ft)
Landing run (interceptor), without braking parachute	1,067 m (3,500 ft)
Service ceiling	18,300 m (60,000 ft)
Ferry range: with external tanks, without CFTs	more than 2,500 nm (4,631 km; 2,878 miles)
with CFTs	3,100 nm (5,745 km; 3,570 miles)
Max endurance: with in-flight refuelling	15 h 0 min
unrefuelled, with CFTs	5 h 15 min
Design g limits	+9/–3

Conformal reconnaissance pod under development as a private venture for two-seat F-15s

MCDONNELL DOUGLAS F-15E EAGLE

The F-15E is a two-seat dual role version of the Eagle capable of performing long-range, deep interdiction, high ordnance payload air-to-ground missions by day or night, and in adverse weather, while retaining its proven air-to-air capabilities. An industry funded prototype, known initially as the Strike Eagle, was modified from a two-seat F-15B (71-291). The rear cockpit was upgraded with four multi-purpose CRT displays for radar, weapon selection, and monitoring of enemy tracking systems. Production F-15Es also have front cockpit modifications that include redesigned up front controls, a wide field of view HUD, and three colour CRTs providing multi-purpose displays for improved navigation, weapons delivery and systems operation, including moving map displays, weapons options, precision radar mapping, and terrain following.

For tactical target missions at night and in all-weather conditions, the F-15E has advanced radar and infra-red systems. A new high resolution synthetic aperture Hughes AN/APG-70 radar, wide-field forward looking infra-red (FLIR) and Martin Marietta AN/AAQ-14 LANTIRN navigation and targeting pods will ensure target detection/identification and improve the accuracy of weapons delivery. Successful integration of these systems was demonstrated during 1982 in flight tests at Edwards AFB, California, and Eglin AFB, Florida, resulting in accurate 'blind' weapons delivery. Integrated internal counter-measures equipment is fitted.

Some 60 per cent of the F-15's structure was redesigned to create the F-15E, the airframe of which is expected to have a fatigue life of 16,000 flying hours. To accommodate the new avionics, internal fuel capacity has been reduced slightly, to 7,643 litres (2,019 US gallons; 1,681 Imp gallons), by reducing the capacity of one fuselage tank, but for increased payload/range capability the F-15E can utilise standard F-15 conformal fuel tanks with a full complement of bombs carried on integral, tangential weapon racks. The conformal tanks add 5,678 litres (1,500 US gallons; 1,249 Imp gallons) of fuel for increased range, and can be used in conjunction with up to three 2,309 litre (610 US gallon; 508 Imp gallon) external fuel tanks. In addition to carrying a variety of guided and unguided bombs and other air-to-ground weapons, the F-15E retains its air superiority performance and weapons (AIM-7 Sparrow, AIM-9 Sidewinder and AIM-120 AMRAAM missiles).

A digital, triple redundant GEC Astronics flight control system is installed in the F-15E, permitting coupled automatic terrain following, and a Honeywell ring laser gyro INS provides quick reaction alignment and improved navigational accuracy. A new engine bay developed by

McDonnell Douglas enables the F-15E to be powered by either General Electric F110 or Pratt & Whitney F100 engines. The engine bay structure consists of large titanium sections manufactured with superplastic forming and diffusion bonding processes, and will permit future installation of growth versions of these engines, providing a total of up to 266.9 kN (60,000 lb st) in the aircraft's two-engine installation. An F-15 powered by the Pratt & Whitney improved F100-PW-220 was delivered to the 33rd TFW at Eglin AFB, Florida, in August 1986 for in-service evaluation. Subsequently, an F-15 was tested with an F100-PW-200 in one engine bay and an improved performance F100-PW-229 in the other. The F-15E incorporates digital electronic engine control, engine trimming and monitoring systems. Other improvements include foam filled fuel tanks for greater survivability, higher rated generators, and an improved environmental control system.

Product improvements for the F-15E were flight tested on four Eagles, including an F-15C, an F-15D and the prototype Strike Eagle, between November 1982 and April 1983. During these tests, an F-15 took off for the first time at a gross weight of 34,019 kg (75,000 lb), ie 3,175 kg (7,000 lb) more than the standard max T-O weight of the F-15C with conformal fuel tanks. On this occasion, the aircraft was equipped with two CFTs, three other external tanks, and eight 500 lb Mk 82 bombs. In the overall programme 16 different stores load configurations were tested, including the carriage of 2,000 lb Mk 84 bombs and BDU-38 and CBU-58 weapons, delivered by both visual and radar means.

Go-ahead for the dual role Eagle programme was announced by the USAF on 24 February 1984, and the first production F-15E (86-183) made its initial flight on 11 December 1986. The first F-15E delivery took place on 29 December 1988 to the 336th TFS, 4th TFW at Seymour Johnson AFB, North Carolina, which was declared operational in October 1989. By the end of 1989, re-equipment had also taken place of the 461st and 550th Tactical Fighter Training Squadrons of the 405th TTW at Luke AFB, AZ, and deliveries were under way to the 57th Fighter Weapons Wing at Nellis AFB, NV. European basing of F-15Es armed with SRAM-T nuclear missiles was under consideration early in 1990, with Bentwaters, UK, as the preferred location. Systems Command have a small number of F-15Es for trials with the 3246th Test Wing at Eglin AFB, FL, and 6512th TS/6510th TW at Edwards AFB, CA. Trials aircraft include 70180 with two F110-GE-129 turbofans as alternatives to F100s.

Funding of F-15Es has comprised 8, 42, 42, 36 and 36 in FY 1986-90. Although planned production was 392, it is now intended to end procurement with a FY 1991 order for 36, bringing the total to 200. The last of these will be completed in June 1993.

The following description refers to the F-15E where it differs from the F-15C:

TYPE: Two-seat dual role attack/air superiority fighter.

FUSELAGE: Upper rear fuselage, rear fuselage keel structure, main landing gear doors and some rear fuselage fairings incorporate superplastic-formed/diffusion bonded (SPF/DB) titanium structure, providing additional engine bay volume to permit compatibility with alternative engines. Sixty per cent of F-15D's structure strengthened to allow 9 g manoeuvres at increased design weight.

LANDING GEAR: Bendix wheels and Michelin AIR X radial tyres on all units. Nosewheel tyre size 22 × 7.75-9, mainwheel tyres size 36 × 11-18; tyre pressure 21.03 bars (305 lb/sq in) on all units. Bendix five-rotor carbon disc brakes.

POWER PLANT: As F-15C/D, but option of General Electric F110-GE-129s.

ACCOMMODATION: Two crew, pilot and weapon systems officer, in tandem on McDonnell Douglas ACES II ejection seats. Single-piece, upward-hinged canopy with increased bird resistance.

McDonnell Douglas F-15E Eagle equipped for high ordnance payload air-to-ground mission (*Pilot Press*)

ARMAMENT: 20 mm M61A1 six-barrel gun in starboard wing-root, with 512 rds. General Electric lead computing gyro. Provision on underwing (one per wing) and centreline pylons for air-to-air and air-to-ground weapons and external fuel tanks. Wing pylons use standard rail and ejection launchers for AIM-9 Sidewinder and AIM-120 AMRAAM air-to-air missiles; AIM-7 Sparrow and AIM-120 AMRAAM can be carried on launchers on centreline station or on tangential stores carriers on conformal fuel tanks (maximum total load four each AIM-7 or AIM-9, up to eight AIM-120). Single or triple rail launchers for AGM-65 Maverick air-to-ground missiles can be fitted to wing stations only. Tangential carriage on CFTs provides for up to six bomb racks on each tank, with provision for triple ejector racks on wing and centreline stations. The F-15E can carry a wide variety and quantity of guided and unguided air-to-ground weapons, including Mk 20 Rockeye (26), Mk 82 (26), Mk 84 (seven), BSU-49 (26), BSU-50 (seven), GBU-10 (seven), GBU-12 (15), GBU-15 (two), GBU-24 (five), CBU-52 (25), CBU-58 (25), CBU-71 (25), CBU-87 (25), CBU-89 (25), CBU-90 (25), CBU-92 (25) or CBU-93 (25) bombs; LAU-3A rockets (nine); SUU-20 training weapons (five); A/A-37 U-33 tow target (one); and B-57 and B61 series nuclear weapons (five). An AN/AXQ-14 data link pod is used in conjunction with the GBU-15; LANTIRN pod illumination is used to designate targets for the GBU-12 and -24 laser guided bombs. AN/AWG-27 armament control system.

WEIGHTS:

Basic operating weight empty	14,379 kg (31,700 lb)
Max weapon load	11,113 kg (24,500 lb)
Max fuel weight: internal	5,952 kg (13,123 lb)
external (two CFTs and three 610 US gallon drop tanks)	9,818 kg (21,645 lb)
Max T-O weight	36,741 kg (81,000 lb)
Max zero-fuel weight	28,440 kg (62,700 lb)
Max landing weight:	
unrestricted	20,094 kg (44,300 lb)
at reduced sink rates	36,741 kg (81,000 lb)

PERFORMANCE:

Max level speed at height	Mach 2.5
Max combat radius	685 nm (1,270 km; 790 miles)
Max range	2,400 nm (4,445 km; 2,765 miles)

MCDONNELL DOUGLAS F-15S/MTD

In October 1984 McDonnell Douglas was awarded a $117.8 million cost-sharing contract to develop and flight test for the US Air Force Wright Aeronautical Laboratories an advanced technology version of the F-15 with short take-off and landing (STOL) and new manoeuvring capabilities, designated F-15S/MTD (STOL/Manoeuvring Technology Demonstrator). The programme investigates four specific technologies: two-dimensional (2-D) thrust vectoring/reversing jet nozzles; integrated flight/propulsion control; rough/soft field STOL landing gear; and advanced pilot/vehicle interfaces.

McDonnell Douglas has modified the first prototype F-15B (71-0290) for the programme. Controllable foreplanes, adapted from the tailplanes of the F/A-18A Hornet, were installed above the F-15B's engine air intake trunks, forward of the wings. Mounted at a dihedral angle of 20°, the foreplanes operate symmetrically or asymmetrically to provide pitch and roll moments, and are used as stability maintaining surfaces rather than for primary flight control. They permit the F-15B's maximum allowable load factor to be increased from 7.33g to 9g without additional structural strengthening. Rectangular, two-dimensional vectoring nozzles manufactured from carbonfibre are installed at the rear of the aircraft's F100 engines, replacing the F-15B's standard afterburner ducts. The nozzles vector engine thrust by up to 20° upward or downward from the longitudinal axis to enhance take-off performance and flight manoeuvring. Thrust reverser vanes in the nozzles are flight-deployable for rapid deceleration in addition to their short landing roll function.

A digital fly by wire system integrates with the flight control system all functions of foreplanes, flaperons, horizontal tail surfaces and vectoring nozzles to provide high precision control of the aircraft's flight path for landing approach. Structurally reinforced landing gear permits 3.66 m (12 ft)/s landing impact loads. The F-15S/MTD employs F-15E avionics and cockpit displays. All flight control surfaces on the F-15S/MTD are actuated hydraulically, and McDonnell Douglas is using the requirements of this aircraft to design a new 552 bar (8,000 lb/sq in) hydraulic power system for future fighters.

The F-15S/MTD incorporates new aluminium-lithium alloy skins, 5 per cent stronger and 9 per cent lighter than the conventional aluminium parts they replace.

Performance parameters specified for the F-15S/MTD include take-off and landing runs of 457 m (1,500 ft) on a 15 m (50 ft) wide, hard, wet, rough surface runway, at night and in adverse weather, with fuel, gun, ammunition and a 2,721 kg (6,000 lb) external payload. McDonnell Douglas is aiming for take-off and landing runs of 305 m (1,000 ft) and 381 m (1,250 ft) respectively. A 6 to 7 per cent increase in manoeuvring performance over the standard F-15 is anticipated, with a 4,536 kg (10,000 lb) increase in payload when operating from a 457 m (1,500 ft) runway, a 27 per

McDonnell Douglas F-15E Eagle dual role fighters from Luke Air Force Base

McDonnell Douglas F-15S/MTD (STOL/Manoeuvring Technology Demonstrator) with two-dimensional vectoring nozzles

cent reduction in take-off run, 13 per cent improvement in cruise range, 24 per cent better roll rate and up to 100 per cent improvement in pitch rate.

The F-15S/MTD made its first flight on 7 September 1988 and its first transonic flight during the following month. The two-dimensional vectoring nozzles were installed in early 1989 and first flown on 10 May, at the start of a 100-flight, 13 month flight test programme at Edwards AFB, California. Reverse thrust was first applied in flight on 23 March 1990. Major subcontractors in the programme are Pratt & Whitney, Cleveland Pneumatic Corporation, General Electric's Flight Control Division, and the National Water Lift Division of Pneumo Corporation.

MCDONNELL DOUGLAS F/A-18 HORNET
US military designations: F/A-18A/B/C/D
Australian AF designations: AF-18A and ATF-18A
Canadian AF designations: CF-18A/B
Spanish Air Force designations: C.15 and CE.15

In the Spring of 1974 the US Department of Defense accepted a proposal from the US Navy to study a low-cost lightweight multi-mission fighter, then identified as the VFAX. In August of that year Congress terminated the VFAX concept, directing instead that the Navy should investigate versions of the General Dynamics YF-16 and Northrop YF-17 lightweight fighter prototypes then under evaluation for the USAF. McDonnell Douglas, deciding that the YF-17 could be redesigned to meet the Navy's requirements, teamed with Northrop to propose a derivative, for which it would serve as prime contractor. Identified as the Navy Air Combat Fighter (NACF), this was named Hornet when selected for development. Two seat versions were proposed originally, the F-18A for fighter duties and the A-18 for attack missions. Except for a small amount of operational equipment and missile armament, the two proved so similar that a single configuration, the

F/A-18, was able eventually to undertake both missions. Under a 1985 agreement, McDonnell Douglas became prime contractor for all existing and future versions of the aircraft, with Northrop as principal subcontractor.

The first Hornet (160775) made its first flight on 18 November 1978; the second flew on 12 March 1979, and all 11 development aircraft were flying by March 1980, including two F/A-18B two-seat combat-capable trainers.

F/A-18A. Initial single-seat production version, ordered as escort fighter/interdictor replacing F-4, armed with fuselage mounted Sparrows; and as attack aircraft replacing A-7, with FLIR and a laser tracker replacing the Sparrow missiles. Total of 410 (including two-seat F/A-18Bs) built for USN/USMC under FY 1979-1985 contracts. Deliveries began in May 1980 and were completed in 1987. Production for export customers (see later paragraphs) is continued until 1990. The first development squadron (VFA-125) was formed at NAS Lemoore, California, in November 1980, and the Hornet officially entered operational service on 7 January 1983, with Marine Fighter/Attack Squadron 314 at MCAS El Toro, California. On 1 February 1985 the first Atlantic Fleet F/A-18A operational squadrons began forming at Cecil Field NAS, Florida, after training at NAS Lemoore, California. Also in February, two F/A-18A squadrons, VFA-113 'Stingers' and VFA-25 'Fist of the Fleet', embarked in the aircraft carrier USS *Constellation* for the aircraft's first extended deployment at sea.

US Navy squadrons equipped with the F/A-18A/B are VFAs 15, 87, 106, 131, 132, 136, 137 and the Blue Angels display team, all at Cecil Field, FL; VFA-25, 113, 125, 136, 137 and 303 at Lemoore, CA; and VFA-151, 192 and 195 at Atsugi (Japan). Marine Corps squadrons are VMFA-122, 251, 312, 333 and 451 at Beaufort, SC; VMFA-314, 323, 531 and VMFAT-101 at El Toro, CA; and VMPF-115 at Atsugi (Japan). (25, 101 and 106 squadrons are training units also with F/A-18C/Ds; and 303 is manned by Reservists.) They first saw combat action in April 1986, when aircraft

McDonnell Douglas F/A-18A Hornet armed with Mk 83 bombs, Sidewinders and Sparrows

F/A-18D prototype of the McDonnell Douglas night attack Hornet

from VFA-131, VFA-132, VMFA-314 and VMFA-323, operating from USS *Coral Sea*, attacked targets in Libya.

F/A-18B. Tandem two-seat version of F/A-18A for training, with combat capability, formerly known as TF/A-18A. Fuel capacity reduced by under 6 per cent.

F/A-18C and F/A-18D. Single- and two-seat aircraft purchased from FY 1986 onwards: total of 390 funded between FYs 1986-90 (84, 84, 84, 72 and 66), of which one quarter are two-seaters. Similar to F/A-18A/B, but with provision for carriage of up to six AMRAAM weapons, two fuselage mounted and two on each outboard wing stores station; up to four imaging infra-red Maverick missiles, one on each wing station; provisions for AN/ALQ-165 airborne self-protection jammer (ASPJ), permitting interchangeability with AN/ALQ-126B; provisions for reconnaissance equipment; upgraded stores management set with 128K memory, Intel 8086 processor, upgraded armament multiplex bus to meet MIL-STD 1553B and MIL-STD 1760 weapons interface capability; flight incident recorder and monitoring set (FIRAMS) which incorporates an integrated fuel/engine indicator, data storage set for recording maintenance and flight incidents data, a signal data processor interfacing with the fuel system to provide overall system control, enhanced built-in-test capability and automatic adjustment of aircraft centre of gravity as fuel is consumed in flight; a maintenance status panel enabling avionics faults to be isolated at circuit card level; and new XN-6 mission computer with higher processing speed and double the memory of the F/A-18A/B's XN-5.

The first production F/A-18C flew on 3 September 1987 and was delivered to NATC Patuxent River on 21 September. All F/A-18Cs and Ds delivered from November 1989 (32 Cs and 15 Ds by 11 May 1990) have all-weather night attack capability, including provision for pilot's night vision goggles, a Hughes Aircraft AN/AAR-50 FLIR thermal imaging navigation set (TINS) which presents

TV-like images on the Kaiser AN/AVQ-28 raster head-up display, multi-function colour displays and a Honeywell colour digital moving map system. The F/A-18D also incorporates a fully mission capable rear cockpit featuring independent display selection. An F/A-18D equipped as the night attack prototype made its first flight on 6 May 1988. In the night attack role the control column and throttles are removed from the F/A-18D's rear cockpit and replaced by two stationary hand controllers with which a naval flight officer can operate the aircraft's weapon systems and three colour CRT display screens. After initial flight testing by the manufacturer, the night attack prototype underwent a test and evaluation programme at the Naval Weapons Center, NAS China Lake, California.

Deliveries of night attack Hornets began to the Naval Air Test Center at Patuxent River, MD, with F-18C 163985 and F-18D 163986 on 1 and 14 November 1989 respectively. All subsequent production is to this standard. The Marine Corps requires six squadrons of night attack F/A-18Ds, to replace Grumman A-6Es, McDonnell Douglas OA-4s and RF-4Bs in attack, FAC and reconnaissance roles. This requires 96 aircraft, only 48 of which are currently authorised. Deliveries began to VMFA(AW)-121 at El Toro, CA, early in 1990, and will continue to VMFA(AW)-242, 225 (reconnaissance), 224, 332 and 533 in FYs 1991-95, respectively. Composition of Navy squadrons will remain unaltered, with two-seat Hornets used for training.

Following flight trials by the US Navy and McDonnell Douglas, a fence measuring 0.203×0.81 m (8 in $\times$ 2 ft 8 in) is being retrofitted to the LEX strakes of USN aircraft. The fence broadens LEX vortices and reduces loads on the aircraft's tail unit, increasing fatigue life and improving directional control at angles of attack in excess of 45°.

F/A-18D(CR). The US Navy began evaluation of a simple reconnaissance conversion of the standard F/A-18A

(first prototype, 160775) in the Autumn of 1982. This involved removal of the gun from the aircraft's nose, and its replacement by a twin-sensor package with two windows in a slightly bulged underfairing. Flight testing of the first F/A-18 fitted with reconnaissance equipment (161214) began on 15 August 1984. A reconnaissance version of the F/A-18D is now being developed for the US Marine Corps as the F/A-18D(CR), incorporating the Advanced Tactical Airborne Reconnaissance System (ATARS) that is being developed separately. An all-weather reconnaissance pod for carriage on the centreline stores station houses a Loral UPD-4 SLAR high resolution synthetic aperture side-looking radar to supplement the F/A-18's nose mounted optical and infra-red sensors. Imagery is transmitted in real time via a datalink but could be displayed in the rear cockpit of the F/A-18D(CR), with growth potential within the pod for installation of an electro-optical camera. The pod, datalink and digital processing equipment have been successfully tested on a US Marine Corps RF-4B. It will be possible to convert the F/A-18D(CR) overnight to the fighter/attack configuration within the operational squadron.

Squadrons equipped with F/A-18C/Ds are VFA-81, 82, 83 and 86 at Cecil Field, FL; VFA-146 at Lemoore, CA; and Marines units VMFAT-212, 232 and 235 at Kanehoe Bay, HI.

Three export customers have purchased the F/A-18A/B and assigned their own designations, as under:

CF-18A. Version for Canadian Armed Forces, which purchased 138, including 40 **CF-18B** two-seaters. Selection announced on 10 April 1980. First example made its initial flight on 29 July 1982. Deliveries began with trainers 188901 and 188902 on 25 October 1982 and were completed in September 1988. First CAF unit was No. 410 OCU, based at CFB Cold Lake, Alberta, followed by Nos. 416 and 441 Squadrons at Cold Lake; 425 and 433 at Bagotville, Quebec, and Nos. 439, 409 and 421 Squadrons of No. 4 Fighter-Wing/No. 1 Air Division at Söllingen, West Germany. Usual complements are six As and 20 Bs with the OCU; 10 As and three Bs with each of the four other home-based squadrons; and 43 As and six Bs shared by the German squadrons. By comparison with US Navy version, CF-18 has different ILS, added spotlight on port side of fuselage for night identification of other aircraft in flight, and provision for carrying LAU-5003 rocket pods containing 19 CRV-7 70 mm (2.75 in) rockets. Other weapons carried are AIM-7M and AIM-9L AAMs, Mk 82 (227 kg/500 lb) bombs and Hunting BL755 CBUs. A comprehensive cold weather land survival pack is provided for the pilot.

AF-18A and ATF-18A. Versions for the Royal Australian Air Force. The intention to procure 75 Hornets was announced on 20 October 1981. Two two-seat ATF-18As, manufactured by McDonnell Douglas, were delivered to the RAAF on 17 May 1985. The first ATF-18A assembled by Aerospace Technologies of Australia (ASTA), which see) made its first flight on 26 February 1985 and was handed over to the RAAF's No. 2 operational conversion unit on 4 May. The first Australian manufactured aircraft (ATF-18A A21-104) made its first flight on 3 June 1985. The RAAF's Hornets (57 single-seat AF-18As and 18 two-seat ATF-18As) have replaced Dassault Mirage III-Os. Initial recipient was No. 2 OCU at Williamtown, followed by No. 3 Squadron (from August 1986) and 77 Squadron (from July 1987), both at the same base. No. 75 Squadron re-equipped from May 1988, but transferred to Tindal in October 1988, on becoming operational. The last Hornet was delivered in May 1990. Weapons include AIM-9L Sidewinder AAMs, AGM-88 HARM ARMs, AGM-84 Harpoon anti-ship missiles and 907 kg (2,000 lb) LGBs. All 74 surviving aircraft are being upgraded from 1990 onwards with F-18C/D-type avionics and provision for fitment of a Ford Aerospace AN/AAS-38 IR tracking and laser designating pod.

EF-18A and B. On 30 May 1983, Spain partly satisfied its Futuro Avión de Combate y Ataque or Future Fighter-Attack Aircraft requirement by ordering 60 single-seat Hornets with the local designation **C.15** and 12 two-seat versions, known as the **CE.15**. Financial problems had caused a reduction from the planned 84, and further problems saw the 1986-88 delivery schedule of 36, 24 and 12, stretched to a 1986-90 timetable with receipts of 11, 26, 15, 12 and eight. Maintenance is provided locally by CASA, which also has responsibility for Canadian Hornets in Europe and those of the USN deployed to the 6th Fleet in the Mediterranean.

Initial aircraft, CE.15-01, was unveiled at St Louis on 25 November 1985 and first flew on 4 December. Deliveries began on 10 July 1986 after crew training in the USA. All 12 trainers had been delivered by early 1987. Armament includes AIM-7F and AIM-9L AAMs, AGM-84 Harpoon anti-ship missiles, AGM-88 HARM ARMs and free-fall bombs. The initial 36 aircraft have Sanders AN/ALQ-126B deception jammers ordered in 1987; the final 36 received Northrop AN/ALQ-162(V) systems.

Ala de Caza 15 (15th Fighter Wing) formed at Zaragoza on 16 December 1985 and became operational in December 1987 with 30 A and six B versions shared between component Escuadrones 151 and 152. Early in 1989, Ala de Caza 12 at Torrejon (121 and 122 Squadrons) began receiving a similar complement to replace its F-4C(S) Phantoms, which were withdrawn in April. The last Hornet was due for delivery in July 1990.

McDonnell Douglas F/A-18C Hornet (two General Electric F404-GE-400 turbofans) *(Pilot Press)*

A further three export customers propose to operate the F/A-18C/D:

The Hornet was announced winner of Switzerland's Neue Jagdflugzeug competition in October 1988. It is intended to place a contract for 26 F-18Cs and eight F-18Ds (plus 81 General Electric F404-GE-402 engines rated at 78.3 kN; 17,600 lb st) in late 1990, to permit 1994 entry into service.

A contract was signed in September 1988 with Kuwait for 32 F-18Cs and eight F-18Ds, together with AGM-65G Maverick, AGM-84 Harpoon, AIM-7F Sparrow and AIM-9L Sidewinder AAMs. Delivery of the aircraft is to be completed by September 1993. Included in the agreement are 89 F404-GE-202 engines.

In December 1989, South Korea announced an order for 120 F-18C/Ds, of which only the first 12 will be flown in the USA. The next 36 will be assembled locally from CKD kits, beginning in 1992, and the final 72 co-produced by Samsung Aerospace, aided by Daewoo Industries and Korean Air. Power plant will be the F404-GE-202, and of 252 required, 27 assembled engines and 81 in CKD form will be supplied from the USA.

A total of 914 Hornets had been delivered by the 11 May 1990, including more than 150 F/A-18Cs and 38 F/A-18Ds for the US forces, the Canadian contract and the majority of those for Australia and Spain. Firm orders totalled 11 development and 800 production aircraft for the USA and 445 for export. Northrop builds the centre and rear fuselage sections, which are delivered totally assembled to McDonnell Douglas at St Louis, where final assembly and testing are centred. As part of the EF-18 industrial co-operation programme, CASA of Madrid manufactures horizontal tail surfaces, flaps, leading-edge extensions, speed brakes, rudders and rear side panels for all F/A-18s.

The following information applies to the single-seat US Navy F/A-18C, but is generally applicable to all versions:

TYPE: Single-seat multi-mission fighter.

WINGS: Cantilever mid-wing monoplane. Anhedral 3°. Sweepback 20° at quarter-chord. Multi-spar structure primarily of light alloy, with graphite/epoxy inter-spar skin panels and trailing-edge flaps. Boundary layer control achieved by wing roots slots. Full span leading-edge manoeuvring flaps have a maximum extension angle of 30°. Single-slotted trailing-edge flaps, actuated by Bertea hydraulic cylinders, deploy to a maximum of 45°. Ailerons, with Hydraulic Research actuators, can be drooped to 45°, providing the advantages of full span flaps for low approach speeds. Leading- and trailing-edge flaps are computer programmed to deflect for optimum lift and drag in both manoeuvring and cruise conditions, and ailerons and flaps are also deflected differentially for roll. Light alloy wingroot leading-edge extensions (LEX) permit flight at angles of attack exceeding 60°. Small dorsal fin above each LEX. Wings fold upward through 100°, by means of AiResearch mechanical drive, at the inboard end of each aileron.

FUSELAGE: Semi-monocoque basic structure, primarily of light alloy, with graphite/epoxy used for access doors/panels. Titanium firewall between engines. Air-brake in upper surface of fuselage between tail fins. Pressurised cockpit section of fail-safe construction.

TAIL UNIT: Cantilever structure with swept vertical and horizontal surfaces, made primarily of graphite/epoxy over light alloy honeycomb core. Twin 20° outward-canted fins and rudders, mounted forward of all-moving horizontal surfaces (stabilators), which have 2° anhedral and are actuated collectively and differentially by National Water Lift servo-cylinder hydraulic units for pitch and roll control.

LANDING GEAR: Retractable tricycle type, with twin-wheel nose and single-wheel main units. Nose unit retracts forward, mainwheels rearward, turning 90° to stow horizontally inside the lower surface of the engine air ducts. Bendix wheels and brakes. Nosewheel tyres size 22 × 6.6-10, 20 ply, pressure 24.13 bars (350 lb/sq in) for carrier operations, 10.34 bars (150 lb/sq in) for land operations. Mainwheel tyres size 30 × 11.5-14.5, 24 ply, pressure 24.13 bars (350 lb/sq in) for carrier operations, 13.79 bars (200 lb/sq in) for land operations. Ozone nosewheel steering unit. Nose unit towbar for catapult launch. Arrester hook, for carrier landings, under rear fuselage.

POWER PLANT: Two General Electric F404-GE-400 low bypass turbofans, each producing approx 71.2 kN (16,000 lb st) with afterburning. Self-sealing fuel tanks

and fuel lines; foam in wing tanks and fuselage voids. Internal fuel capacity approx 6.435 litres (1,700 US gallons; 1,415 Imp gallons). Provision for up to three 1,250 litre (330 US gallon; 275 imp gallon) external tanks. Flight refuelling probe retracts into upper starboard side of nose. Simmonds fuel gauging system. Fixed ramp air intakes.

ACCOMMODATION: Pilot only, on Martin-Baker SJU-5/6 ejection seat, in pressurised, heated and air-conditioned cockpit. Upward opening canopy, with separate windscreen.

SYSTEMS: Two completely separate hydraulic systems, each at 207 bars (3,000 lb/sq in). Max flow rate 212 litres (56 US gallons; 46.6 Imp gallons)/min. Bootstrap type reservoir, pressure 5.86 bars (85 lb/sq in). Quadruplex digital fly by wire flight control system, with direct electrical backup to all surfaces, and direct mechanical backup to stabilators. AiResearch air-conditioning system. General Electric electrical power system. Garrett GTC36-200 APU for engine starting and ground pneumatic, electric and hydraulic power. Oxygen system. Fire detection and extinguishing systems.

AVIONICS AND EQUIPMENT: Include an automatic carrier landing system (ACLS) for all-weather carrier operations; a Hughes Aircraft AN/APG-65 multi-mode digital air-to-air and air-to-ground tracking radar, with air-to-air modes which include velocity search (VS), range while search (RWS), track while scan (TWS), which can track ten targets and display eight to the pilot, and raid assessment mode (RAM). Ford AN/AAS-38 attack FLIR; Honeywell digital moving map display; Smiths Industries multi-purpose colour cockpit display; Collins AN/ARN-118 Tacan; AN/ARC-182 UHF/VHF com and DF-301E UHF/DF; Magnavox AN/ALR-50 and Litton AN/ALR-67 radar warning receivers; Ferranti Type 117 laser designator; Goodyear AN/ALE-39 chaff dispenser; Sanders AN/ALQ-126B ECM; Harris AN/ASW-25 radio data link; Eaton AN/ARA-63 receiver/decoder; Ferranti FID 2035 horizontal situation display; Bendix HSI; J.E.T. ID-1791/A flight director indicator; ITT/Westinghouse AN/ALQ-165 airborne self-protection jammer (ASPJ); General Electric quadruple-redundant fly by wire flight control system; two Control Data AN/AYK-14 digital computers; Litton AN/ASN-130A inertial navigation system; two Kaiser multi-function CRTs, central Ferranti/Bendix CRT and Kaiser AN/AVQ-28 head-up display; Conrac communications system control; Normalair-Garrett digital data recorder for Bendix maintenance recording system; flight incident recording and monitoring system (FIRAMS); Smiths standby altimeter; and Kearflex standby airspeed indicator, standby vertical speed indicator, and cockpit pressure altimeter.

ARMAMENT: Nine external weapon stations, comprising two wingtip stations for AIM-9 Sidewinder air-to-air missiles; two outboard wing stations for an assortment of air-to-air or air-to-ground weapons, including AIM-7 Sparrows, AIM-9 Sidewinders, AIM-120 AMRAAMs, AGM-84 Harpoons and AGM-65 Maverick missiles; two inboard wing stations for external fuel tanks, air-to-ground weapons or Brunswick TALD tactical air-launched decoy missiles; two nacelle fuselage stations for Sparrows or Martin Marietta AN/ASQ-173 laser spot tracker/strike camera (LST/SCAM) and Ford AN/AAS-38 FLIR pods; and a centreline fuselage station for external fuel or weapons. Air-to-ground weapons include GBU-10 and -12 laser guided bombs, Mk 82 and Mk 84 general purpose bombs, and CBU-59 cluster bombs. An M61 20 mm six-barrel gun, with 570 rounds, is mounted in the nose and has a McDonnell Douglas director gunsight, with a conventional sight as backup.

DIMENSIONS, EXTERNAL:

Wing span	11.43 m (37 ft 6 in)
Wing span over missiles	12.31 m (40 ft 4¾ in)
Wing chord: at root	4.04 m (13 ft 3 in)
at tip	1.68 m (5 ft 6 in)
Wing aspect ratio	3.5
Width, wings folded	8.38 m (27 ft 6 in)
Length overall	17.07 m (56 ft 0 in)
Height overall	4.66 m (15 ft 3½ in)
Tailplane span	6.58 m (21 ft 7¼ in)
Distance between fin tips	3.60 m (11 ft 9½ in)
Wheel track	3.11 m (10 ft 2½ in)
Wheelbase	5.42 m (17 ft 9½ in)

AREAS:

Wings, gross	37.16 m² (400.0 sq ft)
Ailerons (total)	2.27 m² (24.4 sq ft)
Leading-edge flaps (total)	4.50 m² (48.4 sq ft)
Trailing-edge flaps (total)	5.75 m² (61.9 sq ft)
Fins (total)	9.68 m² (104.2 sq ft)
Rudders (total)	1.45 m² (15.6 sq ft)
Tailplanes (total)	8.18 m² (88.1 sq ft)

WEIGHTS:

Weight empty	10,455 kg (23,050 lb)
Max fuel weight: internal	4,926 kg (10,860 lb)
external	3,053 kg (6,732 lb)
Max external stores load	7,710 kg (17,000 lb)
T-O weight: Fighter mission	16,651 kg (36,710 lb)
Attack mission	22,328 kg (49,224 lb)

PERFORMANCE:

Max level speed	more than Mach 1.8
Max speed, intermediate power	more than Mach 1.0
Approach speed	134 knots (248 km/h; 154 mph)
Acceleration from 460 knots (850 km/h; 530 mph) to 920 knots (1,705 km/h; 1,060 mph) at 10,670 m (35,000 ft)	under 2 min
Combat ceiling	approx 15,240 m (50,000 ft)
T-O run	less than 427 m (1,400 ft)

Combat radius:
Fighter mission
more than 400 nm (740 km; 460 miles)
Attack mission   575 nm (1,065 km; 662 miles)
Ferry range, unrefuelled
more than 2,000 nm (3,706 km; 2,303 miles)

MCDONNELL DOUGLAS HORNET 2000

As part of a study commissioned by the US Department of Defense in 1987, McDonnell Douglas is examining five potential configurations for an upgraded F/A-18 Hornet known as the Hornet 2000, for the development of which international partners are being sought. Configuration 1 features an enhanced performance engine; integrated communications, navigation and identification avionics (ICNIA) performing all communications, navigation and IFF functions; an optional active array antenna for the AN/APG-65 radar; and weapons system improvements, including replacement of existing cockpit displays, front control panel and HUD control panel by flat plate displays. In Configuration 2 the Hornet 2000 would also feature missile detection, laser warning and C³ receiver systems; a 50 per cent increase in wing stiffness to raise weapons carriage speeds; engines such as the projected General Electric Growth 2 F404, each delivering 88.97 kN (20,000 lb st); and a dorsal fuel tank increasing internal fuel capacity by 1,225 kg (2,700 lb). Configuration 3 would feature a new wing with 25 per cent greater area than that of the F/A-18; a dorsal tank containing an additional 1,678 kg (3,700 lb) of fuel; and enlarged horizontal tail surfaces. In Configuration 3A the larger wing and tail surfaces would be complemented by vertical surfaces of increased area, but an additional 1,225 kg (2,700 lb) of fuel would be carried in a 0.70 m (2 ft 3½ in) fuselage 'plug' tank rather than the dorsal tank. Configuration 4 features an entirely new wing of cranked-arrow planform, with forward canard surfaces; a 1,450 kg (3,197 lb) capacity fuselage fuel tank plug; and the power plant, avionics and defensive systems improvements previously described.

MCDONNELL DOUGLAS/BAe T45TS

US Navy aircraft designation: T-45A Goshawk

Details of the T-45 can be found under the McDonnell Douglas/BAe entry in the International section.

NORTHROP/MCDONNELL DOUGLAS YF-23A (ATF)

McDonnell Douglas and Northrop signed a teaming agreement covering their individual proposals for the US Air Force's Advanced Tactical Fighter. Northrop's design was one of two selected by the USAF on 31 October 1986. Northrop is prime contractor for all phases of the YF-23A programme and McDonnell Douglas is principal subcontractor. First flight of the YF-23A was expected in mid-1990. For further details of the ATF programme, see the USAF, Lockheed and Northrop entries.

GENERAL DYNAMICS/MCDONNELL DOUGLAS A-12A

See separate entry under General Dynamics/McDonnell Douglas heading in this section.

DOUGLAS AIRCRAFT COMPANY
(A Division of McDonnell Douglas Corporation)

HEADQUARTERS: 3855 Lakewood Boulevard, Long Beach, California 90846
Telephone: 1 (213) 593 5511
PRESIDENT: Robert H. Hood Jr
DEPUTY PRESIDENT: John P. Capellupo
VICE-PRESIDENTS:
Robert L. Clepper (General Manager, C-17)
Louis F. Harrington (General Manager, MD-11/DC-10 programmes)
Russell L. Ray (General Manager, Commercial Marketing)

John D. Wolf (General Manager, MD-80/DC-9 programmes)
MANAGER, COMMERCIAL COMMUNICATIONS:
Elayne P. Bendel

Douglas Aircraft Company operates plants at Long Beach and Torrance, California; Macon, Georgia; Columbus, Ohio; and Salt Lake City, Utah. The DC (Douglas Commercial) series of designations which had identified the company's civil designs since the DC-1 of 1933 was superseded in 1983 by a system using the McDonnell Douglas initials MD. First to bear an MD designation was the Super 80 series of DC-9 derivatives, now known as the MD-80 series. Existing DC-8, DC-9 and DC-10 designations remain unchanged.

On 19 September 1988 McDonnell Douglas delivered its 1,500th twin-jet airliner, an MD-80 to American Airlines. The company delivered 118 MD-80s during 1989. Firm orders were received for 423 MD-80s and 126 MD-11s.

MCDONNELL DOUGLAS MD-80 SERIES

Known previously as the Super 80, the MD-80 series was developed from the DC-9 specifically to meet the needs of operators on short/medium-range routes who require an aircraft of increased capacity. Compared with the DC-9 Series 50, the wings are increased in span by the insertion of root plugs and by a 0.61 m (2 ft 0 in) extension on each tip, and the fuselage is extended by plugs forward and aft of the

First McDonnell Douglas MD-87 for Swiss carrier CTA *(Anton Wettstein)*

wing. The cabin has 'wide look' decor, with large enclosed overhead baggage compartments, acoustic ceiling and soft fluorescent lighting. Standard fuel capacity is increased as a result of the larger wing. Systems improvements include a new digital electronics integrated flight guidance and control system; a 'dial a flap' system to permit more accurate selection of flap angle for optimum take-off and landing performance; flow-through cooling of the aircraft's avionics compartment; a larger capacity APU; a new recirculating system for ventilation air; and an advanced digital fuel quantity gauging system.

A performance management system (PMS) similar to that certificated for the DC-10 (which see) became standard on all MD-80s delivered from April 1983, and a flight management system providing vertical and horizontal guidance is available optionally. Other improvements include aerodynamic refinements; increased use of composites, such as a Kevlar wing/fuselage fillet that became standard during 1983; and cockpit and avionics changes, including advanced attitude and heading reference systems. A Honeywell EFIS system is offered as an optional replacement for electro-mechanical primary flight instrument displays, together with flat plate LED displays and flight management systems. Honeywell has also developed a windshear detection and guidance system for the MD-80 series, which received FAA certification on 15 June 1989. The windshear detection and guidance system is standard equipment on all new MD-80 series aircraft, and will be available for retrofit to aircraft already in service.

The first aircraft in the Super 80/MD-80 series made its initial flight on 18 October 1979; second and third prototypes (N1002G and N1002W) flew on 6 December 1979 and 29 February 1980 respectively. FAA certification was granted on 26 August 1980, and on 12 September the first production aircraft was delivered to Swissair, which had placed an order for 15 in October 1977.

Available models are as follows:

MD-81. Basic version, powered by two Pratt & Whitney JT8D-209 turbofans. Emergency thrust reserve becomes available automatically in an engine-out situation. Entered service, with Swissair, on 5 October 1980.

MD-82. Announced on 16 April 1979, with Pratt & Whitney JT8D-217 turbofans. Regarded as being particularly suitable for operation from hot and high airports. The higher thrust available makes possible an increased payload and range when operating from standard airports. First flown on 8 January 1981, and certificated on 30 July 1981 at a max T-O weight of 66,680 kg (147,000 lb), it entered commercial service in August 1981. Otherwise

generally similar to MD-81, with same fuel capacity and max landing weight. A second version, with JT8D-217A engines and higher max T-O weight, was certificated in mid-1982, and became available from Autumn 1982. On 12 April 1985 agreement was reached with the government of the People's Republic of China for the sale of 26 MD-82s, of which 25 were to be partially assembled in the United States and shipped to China for final completion by the Shanghai Aircraft Manufacturing Factory (SAMF), which in April 1990 received approval to assemble a further 20 aircraft. The sole US assembled aircraft arrived in China on 30 September 1985. First subassemblies were delivered to SAMF in January 1986; the first SAMF assembled MD-82 flew for the first time on 2 July 1987 and entered service with CAAC on 4 August, followed by delivery of the second aircraft on 18 December 1987. The FAA certificate was extended to Chinese built MD-82s on 9 November 1987. Fourteen had been completed by SAMF by April 1990.

MD-83. This longer-range version of the MD-80, powered by Pratt & Whitney JT8D-219 engines, was announced on 31 January 1983. These engines offer a 2 per cent improvement in fuel consumption by comparison with -217A turbofans; greater fuel capacity is provided by the introduction of two extra fuel tanks in the cargo compartment.

The MD-83 flew for the first time on 17 December 1984. FAA certification was received in 1985, with service entry with launch customers Alaska Airlines and Finnair taking place in early 1986. On 14 November 1985 Finnair's first MD-83 made the longest nonstop flight ever recorded by an MD-80 variant, flying from Montreal to Helsinki, a distance of 3,404 nm (6,308 km; 3,920 miles) in 7 h 26 min. On 9 September 1987 an MD-83 of the Swedish charter carrier Transwede flew the MD-80 series' first transatlantic revenue service, flying from Stockholm to Fort Lauderdale, Florida, a distance of 4,533 nm (8,401 km; 5,220 miles), routing via stops at Oslo, Norway, and Gander, Newfoundland.

MD-87. Announced on 3 January 1985, the MD-87 is a short-fuselage variant of the MD-80, with accommodation for 130 single class passengers or 109 passengers in mixed class configuration. Standard power plant is two Pratt & Whitney JT8D-217C engines, offering a 2 per cent improvement in fuel consumption over -217A engines. The JT8D-219 or other engines in the JT8D-200 series may be fitted in the MD-87. Standard fuel capacity can be increased by optional forward and rear auxiliary tanks, each of 2,139 litres (565 US gallons; 470.5 Imp gallons) capacity, in the cargo compartment. The MD-87 incorporates McDonnell

Douglas' MD-80 series cruise performance improvement package, which includes a fillet fairing between fuselage and engine pylons, a fairing on the APU, improved sealing on the horizontal tail surfaces, low drag flap hinge fairings, and an extended low drag tailcone. The MD-87 was also the first of the MD-80 series to have as standard an electronic flight instrument system, AHRS and head-up display.

Assembly of the first MD-87 began in April 1986, followed by the first flight on 4 December. Certification was received on 21 October 1987, permitting deliveries to begin to launch customers Finnair and Austrian Airlines.

MD-88. Announced on 23 January 1986, the MD-88 is powered by Pratt & Whitney JT8D-219 engines and features EFIS cockpit displays, a flight management system, an onboard windshear detection system and increased use of composites materials in the airframe. A new interior design provides accommodation for 142 passengers (14 first class and 128 coach class) in five-abreast seating, with wider aisle and redesigned overhead storage bins. First flight was made on 15 August 1987, and FAA certification was granted on 9 December. The first of 53 MD-88s ordered by launch customer Delta Air Lines, which has 57 more on option, entered service on 5 January 1988.

MD-80 Executive Jets. McDonnell Douglas offers corporate and executive variants of the MD-83 and MD-87. In typical corporate configuration seating 20 passengers, the MD-83 offers a maximum range of 4,100 nm (7,598 km; 4,721 miles), while the MD-87 has a maximum range of 4,500 nm (8,339 km; 5,182 miles), each being equipped with auxiliary fuel tanks.

By 1 April 1990 orders and options for the MD-80 series totalled 1,594, of which 711 had been delivered.

The following description applies specifically to the MD-81, and generally also to the other models, except where indicated:

TYPE: Twin-turbofan short/medium-range airliner.

WINGS: Cantilever low-wing monoplane. Mean thickness/chord ratio 11.0%. Dihedral 3°. Incidence 1° 15'. Sweepback at quarter-chord 24° 30'. All-metal construction, with two spars and spanwise stringers riveted to skin. Glassfibre trailing-edges on wings, ailerons and flaps. Manually controlled aileron on each wing. Wing mounted speed brakes. Full span leading-edge slats. Hydraulically actuated double-slotted trailing-edge flaps over 67 per cent of semi-span. Single boundary layer fence (vortillon) under each wing. Three spoilers per wing; two outboard segments act as flight and ground spoilers, inboard segment is ground spoiler only. Detachable wingtips. Thermal anti-icing of leading-edges.

FUSELAGE: All-metal semi-monocoque fail-safe structure of heat treated light alloy. Majority of cabin floor constructed of balsa or Nomex core composite. Engine pylons built by Calcor, fuselage panels by Aeritalia.

TAIL UNIT: Cantilever all-metal structure with electrically actuated variable incidence T tailplane. Manually controlled elevators with control tabs. Hydraulically controlled rudder with manual override. Glassfibre trailing-edges on control surfaces.

LANDING GEAR: Retractable tricycle type of Cleveland Pneumatic manufacture, with steerable nosewheels (±27° on MD-81/82/87/88; ±25° on MD-83). Hydraulic retraction, nose unit forward, main units inward. Twin Goodyear wheels and tyres on each unit. Mainwheel tyres size 44.5 × 16.5-20, pressure 11.38 bars (165 lb/sq in). Nosewheel tyres size 26 × 6.6-14, pressure 10.34 bars (150 lb/sq in). Goodyear disc brakes. Hydro-Aire Mk IIIA anti-skid units. Douglas ram air brake cooling.

POWER PLANT: Two Pratt & Whitney JT8D-209 turbofans in MD-81, pod mounted one each side of rear fuselage, and each rated at 82.3 kN (18,500 lb st), with emergency thrust reserve of 3.34 kN (750 lb st). MD-82 uses JT8D-217s, each rated at 89 kN (20,000 lb st), with emergency thrust reserve of 3.78 kN (850 lb st), or -217As of similar rating. MD-83 has JT8D-219 engines of 93.4 kN (21,000 lb st). MD-87 has JT8D-217C engines of 89 kN (20,000 lb st), with an emergency thrust reserve of

McDonnell Douglas MD-87, a short-fuselage variant of the MD-80 series of twin-turbofan transports
(Pilot Press)

First McDonnell Douglas MD-88 taking off on its first flight, in the markings of Delta Air Lines

3.78 kN (850 lb st). MD-88 has 93.4 kN (21,000 lb st) JT8D-219 turbofans. Standard fuel capacity in MD-81/82/87/88 is 21,876 litres (5,779 US gallons; 4,812 Imp gallons); increased in MD-83 (and, optionally, MD-87) to 26,260 litres (6,939 US gallons; 5,778 Imp gallons) by two 2,195 litre (580 US gallon; 483 Imp gallon) auxiliary tanks in cargo compartment. Pressure refuelling point in starboard wing leading-edge. Overwing gravity refuelling points.

ACCOMMODATION: Crew of two and observer on flight deck, plus cabin attendants. Seating arrangements are optional to meet specific airline requirements. Maximum optional seating capacity is for 172 passengers (139 in MD-87). Fully pressurised and air-conditioned. One toilet forward on port side, two at rear of cabin. Provisions for galley at both forward and rear ends of cabin. Passenger door at front of cabin on port side, with built-in electrically operated airstairs, and rear hydraulically operated ventral stairway, are standard. Servicing and emergency exit doors at starboard forward end and port rear end of cabin. Three cargo doors for underfloor holds on starboard side. Overwing emergency exits, two each side.

SYSTEMS: AiResearch dual air cycle air-conditioning and pressurisation system utilising engine bleed air, max differential 0.54 bars (7.77 lb/sq in). Two separate 207 bar (3,000 lb/sq in) hydraulic systems for operation of spoilers, flaps, slats, rudder, landing gear, nosewheel steering, brakes, rotated thrust reversers and ventral stairway. Maximum flow rate 30.3 litres (8 US gallons; 6.7 Imp gallons)/min. Airless bootstrap type reservoirs, output pressure 2.07 bars (30 lb/sq in). Pneumatic system, for air-conditioning/pressurisation, engine starting and ice protection, utilises 8th or 13th stage engine bleed air and/or APU. Electrical system includes three 40kVA 120/208V three-phase 400Hz alternators, two engine driven, one driven by APU. Oxygen system of diluter demand type for crew on flight deck; continuous flow chemical canister type with automatic mask presentation for cabin passengers. Anti-icing of wing and engine inlets, and de-icing of tailplane, by engine bleed air. Electric de-icing of windscreen. APU provides pneumatic and electrical power on ground, and electrical power in flight.

AVIONICS AND EQUIPMENT: All-digital avionics, including dual Honeywell integrated flight systems; Honeywell Cat IIIA autoland; autopilot and stability augmentation system; performance management system; speed command with digital full-time autothrottles; thrust rating indicator system; dual Honeywell air data systems; automatic reserve thrust; ADF system; and colour weather radar display. Sundstrand head-up display optional.

DIMENSIONS, EXTERNAL (all versions, except as indicated):

Wing span	32.87 m (107 ft 10 in)
Wing chord: at root	7.05 m (23 ft 1½ in)
at tip	1.10 m (3 ft 7½ in)
Wing aspect ratio	9.62
Length overall: except MD-87	45.06 m (147 ft 10 in)
MD-87	39.75 m (130 ft 5 in)
Length of fuselage:	
except MD-87	41.30 m (135 ft 6 in)
MD-87	36.30 m (119 ft 1 in)
Height overall: except MD-87	9.04 m (29 ft 8 in)
MD-87	9.30 m (30 ft 6 in)
Tailplane span	12.24 m (40 ft 2 in)
Wheel track	5.08 m (16 ft 8 in)
Wheelbase: except MD-87	22.07 m (72 ft 5 in)
MD-87	19.18 m (62 ft 11 in)
Passenger door (port, fwd):	
Height	1.83 m (6 ft 0 in)
Width	0.86 m (2 ft 10 in)
Height to sill	2.24 m (7 ft 4 in)

Servicing door (stbd, fwd): Height	1.22 m (4 ft 0 in)
Width	0.69 m (2 ft 3 in)
Height to sill	2.24 m (7 ft 4 in)
Servicing door (port, rear): Height	1.52 m (5 ft 0 in)
Width	0.69 m (2 ft 3 in)
Height to sill	2.67 m (8 ft 9 in)
Freight and baggage hold doors:	
Height	1.27 m (4 ft 2 in)
Width	1.35 m (4 ft 5 in)
Height to sill: fwd	1.17 m (3 ft 10 in)
centre	1.30 m (4 ft 3 in)
rear	1.52 m (5 ft 0 in)
Rear cargo door (MD-87): Height	1.27 m (4 ft 2 in)
Width	0.91 m (3 ft 0 in)
Emergency exits (overwing, port and stbd):	
Height	0.91 m (3 ft 0 in)
Width	0.51 m (1 ft 8 in)

DIMENSIONS, INTERNAL:

Cabin, excl flight deck, incl toilets:	
Length	30.78 m (101 ft 0 in)
Max width	3.07 m (10 ft 1 in)
Max height	2.06 m (6 ft 9 in)
Floor area	89.65 m² (965.0 sq ft)
Volume	191.9 m³ (6,778 cu ft)
Freight holds (underfloor, MD-81/82):	
fwd	13.14 m³ (464.0 cu ft)
centre	9.80 m³ (346.0 cu ft)
rear	12.54 m³ (443.0 cu ft)
Freight holds (underfloor, MD-83):	
total	29.1 m³ (1,028 cu ft)

AREAS:

Wings, gross	118 m² (1,270 sq ft)
Ailerons (total)	3.53 m² (38.0 sq ft)
Fin, excl dorsal fin	9.51 m² (102.4 sq ft)
Rudder	6.07 m² (65.3 sq ft)
Tailplane	29.17 m² (314.0 sq ft)

WEIGHTS AND LOADINGS (A: MD-81, B: MD-82, C: MD-83, D: MD-87, E: MD-88):

Operating weight empty: A	35,571 kg (78,421 lb)
B	35,629 kg (78,549 lb)
C	36,543 kg (80,563 lb)
D standard fuel	33,183 kg (73,157 lb)
D optional fuel	33,851 kg (74,629 lb)
Fuel load:	
A, B, D standard	17,748 kg (39,128 lb)
C, D optional	21,273 kg (46,900 lb)
Max payload (weight limited): A	17,952 kg (39,579 lb)
B	19,709 kg (43,451 lb)
C	18,795 kg (41,437 lb)
D standard	17,619 kg (38,843 lb)
D optional	16,951 kg (37,371 lb)
Max T-O weight: A (-217 engines), D standard	
	63,503 kg (140,000 lb)
A (-217A engines), B, D optional, E standard	
	67,812 kg (149,500 lb)
C, E optional	72,575 kg (160,000 lb)
Max zero-fuel weight: A	53,524 kg (118,000 lb)
B, C	55,338 kg (122,000 lb)
D	50,802 kg (112,000 lb)
Max landing weight:	
A, D standard	58,060 kg (128,000 lb)
B, D optional	58,967 kg (130,000 lb)
C	63,276 kg (139,500 lb)
Max wing loading:	
A, D standard	534.6 kg/m² (109.5 lb/sq ft)
B, D optional, E standard	574.7 kg/m² (117.7 lb/sq ft)
C, E optional	615.0 kg/m² (126.0 lb/sq ft)
Max power loading: A	385.8 kg/kN (3.78 lb/lb st)
B, D optional	381.0 kg/kN (3.74 lb/lb st)
C, E optional	388.5 kg/kN (3.81 lb/lb st)

D standard	356.8 kg/kN (3.50 lb/lb st)
E standard	363.3 kg/kN (3.56 lb/lb st)

PERFORMANCE (at max T-O weight except where indicated):

Max level speed (all)	500 knots (925 km/h; 575 mph)
Max cruising speed (all)	Mach 0.80
Normal cruising speed (all)	Mach 0.76
Min ground turning radius:	
about nosewheels:	
MD-81, 82, 83, 88	22.43 m (73 ft 7¼ in)
MD-87	19.54 m (64 ft 1¼ in)
about wingtip:	
MD-81, 82, 83, 88	21.21 m (69 ft 7¼ in)
MD-87	20.64 m (67 ft 8½ in)
FAA T-O field length: A	2,210 m (7,250 ft)
B	2,271 m (7,450 ft)
C	2,553 m (8,375 ft)
D	1,859 m (6,100 ft)
FAA landing field length, at max landing weight:	
A	1,478 m (4,850 ft)
B	1,500 m (4,920 ft)
C	2,585 m (5,200 ft)
D	1,430 m (4,690 ft)
Range with max fuel:	
D standard	2,980 nm (5,522 km; 3,431 miles)
D optional	3,650 nm (6,764 km; 4,203 miles)
Range (A, B, C with 155 passengers, domestic reserves; D with 130 passengers, domestic reserves):	
A	1,563 nm (2,896 km; 1,800 miles)
B	2,049 nm (3,798 km; 2,360 miles)
C	2,501 nm (4,635 km; 2,880 miles)
D standard	2,372 nm (4,395 km; 2,731 miles)
D optional	2,829 nm (5,243 km; 3,260 miles)

OPERATIONAL NOISE LEVELS (FAR Pt 36):

T-O: A, B, C	90.4 EPNdB
D estimated	88.7 EPNdB
Sideline: A, B, C	94.6 EPNdB
D estimated	92.8 EPNdB
Approach: A, B, C	93.3 EPNdB
D estimated	93.3 EPNdB

MCDONNELL DOUGLAS MD-90

On 14 November 1989 McDonnell Douglas launched the MD-90 series of twin-engine jet airliners, to be powered by two International Aero Engines V2500 turbofans. The MD-90 will employ the same fuselage cross-section, advanced high-lift wing and EFIS flight deck displays employed on the MD-80 series. The introduction of interchangeable, standardised modular fuselage components will enable the aircraft to be assembled on a common production line with MD-80s. Launch customer is Delta Air Lines, which has ordered 50, with options on a further 110. Other announced customers include Alaska Airlines (20 orders, 20 options), International Lease Finance Corporation (15 orders, 15 options), and Japan Air System (10 orders).

Three version of the MD-90 have been announced, as detailed below. McDonnell Douglas is modifying the MD-80 UHB propfan demonstrator (described in the 1989-90 edition of *Jane's*) to serve as the prototype for the MD90-30, with certification and first deliveries scheduled for the fourth quarter of 1994. MD90-10 certification is anticipated in the first quarter of 1995.

MD90-10. Basic version, with fuselage of same length as MD-87, accommodating 114 passengers (12 first class, 102 economy). Power plant is two 97.86 kN (22,000 lb st) IAE V2500-D2 turbofans.

MD90-30. Features MD-80 fuselage, lengthened forward of wing by 1.45 m (4 ft 9 in), and MD-87 tail surfaces. Accommodation for 153 passengers (12 first class, 141

Artist's impression of the McDonnell Douglas MD-90

McDonnell Douglas MD90-30, powered by two IAE V2500-D1 turbofans *(Pilot Press)*

economy). Power plant is two 111.21 kN (25,000 lb st) IAE V2500-D1 turbofans.

MD90-40. Accommodation for 180 passengers in mixed-class configuration. Power plant is two 124.55 kN (28,000 lb st) IAE V2500-D5 turbofans. Max fuel capacity for all models is 22,107 litres (5,840 US gallons; 4,863 Imp gallons). A European configuration with different fuel and payload capacities is being offered as the **MD90-40EC.**

The following data are provisional:

DIMENSIONS, EXTERNAL (A: MD90-10, B: MD90-30, C: MD90-40):

Wing span: A, B, C	32.85 m (107 ft 9½ in)
Length overall: A	39.75 m (130 ft 5 in)
B	48.04 m (157 ft 7¼ in)
C	52.30 m (171 ft 7¼ in)
Height overall: A	9.30 m (30 ft 6 in)
B, C	9.40 m (30 ft 10¾ in)
Wheel track: A, B, C	5.09 m (16 ft 8½ in)
Wheelbase: A	19.17 m (62 ft 10¾ in)
B	23.53 m (77 ft 2½ in)
C	26.91 m (88 ft 3½ in)

DIMENSIONS, INTERNAL:

Baggage volume (total): A	26.56 m³ (938.0 cu ft)
B	38.03 m³ (1,343 cu ft)
C	45.56 m³ (1,609 cu ft)

AREA:

Wings, gross: A, B, C	112.32 m² (1,209 sq ft)

WEIGHTS:

Operating weight empty: A	36,968 kg (81,500 lb)
B	39,415 kg (86,900 lb)
C	43,135 kg (95,100 lb)
Max T-O weight: A	63,050 kg (139,000 lb)
B	70,760 kg (156,000 lb)
C	74,160 kg (163,500 lb)
Max ramp weight: A	63,500 kg (140,000 lb)
B	71,215 kg (157,000 lb)
C	74,615 kg (164,500 lb)
Max zero-fuel weight: A	51,710 kg (114,000 lb)
B	58,965 kg (130,000 lb)
C	67,585 kg (149,000 lb)
Max landing weight: A	55,335 kg (122,000 lb)
B	64,410 kg (142,000 lb)
C	71,210 kg (157,000 lb)

PERFORMANCE (estimated, at max T-O weight, ISA, except where indicated):

Cruising speed at 10,670 m (35,000 ft): A, B, C	Mach 0.76
FAA T-O field length: A	1,802 m (5,910 ft)
B	2,098 m (6,880 ft)
C	2,104 m (6,900 ft)
FAA landing field length, at max landing weight:	
A	1,392 m (4,565 ft)
B	1,552 m (5,090 ft)
C	1,691 m (5,545 ft)

Range, with domestic reserves:

A	2,413 nm (4,472 km; 2,779 miles)
B	2,396 nm (4,441 km; 2,760 miles)
C	1,741 nm (3,226 km; 2,005 miles)

MCDONNELL DOUGLAS DC-10

The DC-10 was developed as an all-purpose commercial transport able to operate economically over ranges from 260 nm to 5,730 nm (480 to 10,620 km; 300 to 6,600 miles), according to series, and able to carry 270 mixed class passengers or a maximum of 380 passengers in an all-economy configuration.

There have been five basic civil production versions, as follows:

Series 10. Initial version at 185,970 kg (410,000 lb) max T-O weight for use on domestic services, powered by three General Electric CF6-6D or -6D1 turbofans, each rated at 178 kN (40,000 lb st) or 182.4 kN (41,000 lb st). First flight 29 August 1970. Type certificated by FAA on 29 July 1971. First scheduled passenger flight 5 August 1971, by American Airlines. Subsequent version at 206,385 kg (455,000 lb) max T-O weight, and with added centre-wing fuel. Details in 1987-88 and earlier *Jane's.*

Series 15. Basically as Series 10, but with max T-O weight of 206,385 kg (455,000 lb), and 207 kN (46,500 lb st) General Electric CF6-50C2F engines. First flight 8 January 1981. Certificated on 12 June 1981. Seven built. Details in 1987-88 and earlier *Jane's.*

Series 30. Extended range version for intercontinental operations, powered by three General Electric CF6-50A or -50C turbofans, each rated at 218 kN (49,000 lb st) or 227 kN (51,000 lb st) respectively. Initial deliveries at 251,745 kg (555,000 lb) max T-O weight. Later versions have CF6-50C1 or C2 engines rated at 233.5 kN (52,500 lb st), or C2B engines rated at 236 kN (53,000 lb st) and max T-O weight of up to 263,085 kg (580,000 lb). Increased fuel capacity. Wing span increased by 3.05 m (10 ft 0 in). Landing gear supplemented by additional dual-wheel bogie unit, mounted on the fuselage centreline between the four-wheel bogie main units. First flight 21 June 1972. FAA certification granted 21 November 1972, simultaneously with first deliveries of production aircraft to KLM and Swissair. Convertible and cargo versions, designated **Series 30CF** and **30F,** are described separately.

Series 30ER. Developed version of Series 30, with range extended still further by installing auxiliary fuel tank in rear of cargo compartment. More powerful (240.2 kN; 54,000 lb st) CF6-50C2B engines. First order (for two) placed by Swissair in July 1980, plus kits to convert two of its existing DC-10s to Srs 30ER configuration. Other customers include Thai Airways International and Toa Domestic Airlines of Japan.

Series 40. Extended range version for intercontinental operations, powered by three Pratt & Whitney turbofan engines. Twenty-two early models, built for Northwest

Orient Airlines, had JT9D-20 turbofans, each rated at 220 kN (49,400 lb st) with water injection. First flight 28 February 1972; FAA certification received 20 October 1972. Later versions, built for Japan Air Lines, equipped with JT9D-59A turbofans, each rated at 236 kN (53,000 lb st). First flight of a Series 40 with this latter power plant was on 25 July 1975.

In early 1983, FAA certification was received for a Delco Electronics performance management system (PMS) for installation on the DC-10, which is able to provide fuel savings of 1 to 3 per cent. The PMS is coupled through the autopilot and autothrottle systems to control automatically the aircraft's pitch and thrust to obtain maximum fuel efficiency during climb, cruise and descent. First PMS-equipped DC-10 to enter service, in March 1983, was a JAL Series 40.

McDonnell Douglas received firm orders for 386 commercial DC-10s, the last of which was delivered in Spring 1989.

The following description applies to the Series 30, 30ER and 40:

TYPE: Three-turbofan commercial transport.

WINGS: Cantilever low-wing monoplane of all-metal fail-safe construction. Several different Douglas wing sections. Thickness/chord ratio varies from slightly more than 12.2% at root to less than 8.4% at tip. Dihedral 5° 14.4′ inboard, 3° 1.8′ outboard. Incidence positive at wingroot, negative at tip. Sweepback at quarter-chord 35°. All-metal inboard and outboard ailerons, the former used conventionally, the latter only when the leading-edge slats are extended. Double-slotted all-metal trailing-edge flaps mounted on external hinges, with an inboard and outboard flap panel on each wing. Five all-metal spoiler panels on each wing, at the rear edge of the fixed wing structure, forward of the flaps. All spoilers operate in unison as lateral control, speed brake and ground spoilers. Full span three-position all-metal leading-edge slats. Ailerons are powered by Bertea hydraulic actuators, spoilers by Parker-Hannifin hydraulic actuators. Each aileron is powered by either of two hydraulic systems; each spoiler is powered by a single system. All leading-edge slat segments outboard of the engines are anti-iced with engine bleed air.

FUSELAGE: Aluminium alloy semi-monocoque fail-safe structure of circular cross-section. Except for auxiliary areas, the entire fuselage is pressurised.

TAIL UNIT: Cantilever all-metal structure standard. Variable incidence tailplane, actuated by Vickers hydraulic motors. Longitudinal and directional controls are fully powered and comprise inboard and outboard elevators, each segment powered by a Bertea tandem actuator; upper and lower rudder each powered by a Bertea actuator. Rudder standby power supplied by two Abex transfer motor pumps. Twelve DC-10s in current service have upper rudder segments made of graphite epoxy.

LANDING GEAR: Hydraulically retractable tricycle type, with gravity free-fall for emergency extension. Twin-wheel steerable nose unit (±68°) retracts forward; Menasco main units inward into fuselage. Main gear comprises two four-wheel bogies, with an additional dual-wheel main unit mounted on the fuselage centreline between the bogie units and retracting forward. Oleo-pneumatic shock absorbers in all units. Goodyear nosewheels and tyres size 40 × 15.5-16, pressure 12.41 bars (180 lb/sq in). Main units and centreline unit have Goodyear wheels and tyres size 52 × 20.5-23. The former have a pressure of 11.38 bars (165 lb/sq in), the latter 9.65 bars (140 lb/sq in). Goodyear disc brakes and anti-skid system, with individual wheel control.

POWER PLANT: Three turbofans (details under Series descriptions), two of which are mounted on underwing pylons, the third above the rear fuselage at the base of the fin. All engines are fitted with thrust reversers for ground operation. Engine air inlets have load carrying acoustically treated panels for noise attenuation, and each engine fan case and fan exhaust is similarly treated. Four integral wing fuel tanks and an auxiliary tank in the wing centre-section with a connected structural compartment fitted with a bladder cell, giving total capacity of approximately 138,165 litres (36,500 US gallons; 30,392 Imp gallons). Four standard pressure refuelling adapters, two in each wing outboard of the engine pylons. Lower cargo hold can be used to carry an optional long-range tank of either 5,807 litres (1,534 US gallons; 1,277 Imp gallons) or 12,556 litres (3,317 US gallons; 2,762 Imp gallons). Oil capacity (usable): Series 30, 34.1 litres (9 US gallons; 7.5 Imp gallons); Series 40, 56.8 litres (15 US gallons; 12.5 Imp gallons).

ACCOMMODATION: Crew of three (pilot, first officer, flight engineer), with seating for two observers, plus cabin attendants. Standard seating for 255 or 270 in mixed class versions, with a maximum of 380 passengers in an economy class arrangement. Two aisles run the length of the cabin, which is separated into sections by cloakroom dividers. In the first class section, with three pairs of reclining seats abreast, the aisles are 0.78 m (2 ft 7 in) wide. In the coach class section, four pairs of seats, with a table between the centre pairs, also have two aisles, these being 0.51 m (1 ft 8 in) wide. One pair of seats is exchanged for a three-seat unit in the nine-abreast high-density layout. Up to nine lavatories located

McDonnell Douglas DC-10 Series 30 in the insignia of Swissair, under charter to Air Afrique

throughout the passenger cabin. Cloakrooms of standard and elevating type distributed throughout the cabin. Overhead stowage modules, fully enclosed and providing stowage for passengers' personal effects, are located on the sidewalls and extend the full length of the cabin. Optional centreline overhead baggage racks available. Eight passenger doors, four on each side, open by sliding inward and upward into the above-ceiling area. Containerised or bulk cargo compartments located immediately forward and aft of the wing, with outward opening doors on the starboard side, max capacity 14 LD3 containers. A bulk cargo compartment is located in the lower rear section of the fuselage, with its door on the port side. Entire accommodation is fully air-conditioned, with five separate control zones for the below-floor galley configuration. Optional main cabin galley to replace the lower galley, and in this configuration there are four separate control zones for the air-conditioning. The lower deck galley is provided with five to eight high-temperature ovens, and with refrigerators, storage space for linen, china and other accessories. Serving carts are taken to cabin level by two electric elevators, to a buffet service centre, from where stewardesses serve passengers. To permit quick turnround at terminals, without interference to passenger movement in the main cabin, the kitchen is provisioned through the cargo doors at ground level.

SYSTEMS: Three parallel continuously operating and completely separate hydraulic systems supply the fully powered flight controls and wheel brakes. Normally, one of the systems supplies power for landing gear actuation. Two reversible motor pumps, each sized to deliver power from one of the other two systems for standby operation of landing gear, can also power any other hydraulically operated unit. Each hydraulic system is powered by two identical engine driven pumps, capable of delivering a total of 265 litres (70 US gallons; 58.3 Imp gallons)/min at 207 bars (3,000 lb/sq in) at take-off. All three hydraulic systems are applied to each primary control axis in a manner which ensures maximum control effectiveness in the event of single or dual hydraulic system failures. A Garrett TSCP-700-4 APU provides ground electrical and pneumatic power, including main engine starting and auxiliary electrical power in flight.

AVIONICS AND EQUIPMENT: A dual fail-operative landing system is installed to meet Category IIIA weather minima. Triple inertial navigation system meeting ARINC 561 requirements on Srs 30 and 40, with optional dual area navigation system capability.

DIMENSIONS, EXTERNAL:
Wing span	50.40 m (165 ft 4½ in)
Wing chord: at root	10.71 m (35 ft 1¾ in)
at tip	2.73 m (8 ft 11½ in)
Wing aspect ratio	7.5
Length overall	55.50 m (182 ft 1 in)
Fuselage: Length	51.97 m (170 ft 6 in)
Max width	6.02 m (19 ft 9 in)
Height overall	17.70 m (58 ft 1 in)
Tailplane span	21.69 m (71 ft 2 in)
Wheel track	10.67 m (35 ft 0 in)
Wheelbase: Series 30	22.05 m (72 ft 4 in)
Series 40	22.07 m (72 ft 5 in)

DIMENSIONS, INTERNAL:
Cabin: Length, from rear bulkhead of flight deck to rear cabin bulkhead   approx 41.45 m (136 ft 0 in)
Max width	5.72 m (18 ft 9 in)
Height (basic)	2.41 m (7 ft 11 in)

Series 30, 40 in lower-galley configuration:
Forward baggage and/or freight hold (forward of wing):
containerised volume	27.2 m³ (960.0 cu ft)
bulk volume	37.9 m³ (1,339 cu ft)

Centre baggage and/or freight hold (aft of wing):
containerised volume	36.2 m³ (1,280 cu ft)
bulk volume	43.9 m³ (1,552 cu ft)
Rear hold: bulk volume	22.8 m³ (805.0 cu ft)

Series 30, 40 in upper-galley configuration:
Forward baggage and/or freight hold (forward of wing):
containerised volume	72.5 m³ (2,560 cu ft)
bulk volume	86.2 m³ (3,045 cu ft)

Centre baggage and/or freight hold (aft of wing):
containerised volume	45.3 m³ (1,600 cu ft)
bulk volume	54.8 m³ (1,935 cu ft)
Rear hold: bulk volume	14.4 m³ (510.0 cu ft)

AREAS:
Wings, gross	367.7 m² (3,958 sq ft)
Ailerons: inboard (total)	7.68 m² (82.7 sq ft)
outboard (total)	9.76 m² (105.1 sq ft)
Trailing-edge flaps (total)	62.1 m² (668.2 sq ft)
Leading-edge slats (total)	43.84 m² (471.9 sq ft)
Spoilers (total)	12.73 m² (137.0 sq ft)
Fin	45.92 m² (494.29 sq ft)
Rudders (total)	10.29 m² (110.71 sq ft)
Tailplane	96.6 m² (1,040.2 sq ft)
Elevators (total)	27.7 m² (298.1 sq ft)

WEIGHTS AND LOADINGS:
Basic weight empty: Series 30	121,198 kg (267,197 lb)
Series 40	122,951 kg (271,062 lb)
Max payload: Series 30	48,330 kg (106,550 lb)
Series 40	46,243 kg (101,950 lb)

Max fuel weight:
standard	111,387 kg (245,566 lb)
small auxiliary tank installed	116,049 kg (255,844 lb)
large auxiliary tank installed	121,467 kg (267,790 lb)

Max T-O weight:
Series 30	259,450-263,085 kg (572,000-580,000 lb)
Series 40 (-20 engines)	251,745 kg (555,000 lb)
Series 40 (-59A engines)	259,450 kg (572,000 lb)

Max ramp weight:
Series 30	260,815 kg (575,000 lb)
Series 40 (-20 engines)	253,105 kg (558,000 lb)
Series 40 (-59A engines)	260,815 kg (575,000 lb)

Max zero-fuel weight:
Series 30, 40	166,922 kg (368,000 lb)

Max landing weight:
Series 30, 40	182,798 kg (403,000 lb)

Max wing loading:
Series 30	705.6 kg/m² (144.5 lb/sq ft)
Series 40 (-20 engines)	684.6 kg/m² (140.2 lb/sq ft)
Series 40 (-59A engines)	705.6 kg/m² (144.5 lb/sq ft)

PERFORMANCE (at max T-O weight except where indicated):
Never-exceed speed	Mach 0.95

Max level speed at 7,620 m (25,000 ft)
     Mach 0.88 (530 knots; 982 km/h; 610 mph)

Max cruising speed at 9,145 m (30,000 ft):
Series 30	490 knots (908 km/h; 564 mph)
Series 40 (-20 engines)	
	489 knots (906 km/h; 563 mph)
Series 40 (-59A engines)	
	498 knots (922 km/h; 573 mph)
Normal cruising speed, all versions	Mach 0.82

T-O speed (V₂):

Series 30 (-50C engines)
     189 knots (351 km/h; 218 mph)

Series 40 (-20 engines)
     187 knots (346 km/h; 215 mph)

Series 40 (-59A engines)
     178 knots (330 km/h; 205 mph)

Landing speed (with full load of passengers and baggage):
Series 30, 40	138 knots (256 km/h; 159 mph)

Max rate of climb at S/L:
Series 30	884 m (2,900 ft)/min
Series 40 (-20 engines)	829 m (2,720 ft)/min
Series 40 (-59A engines)	762 m (2,500 ft)/min

Service ceiling:
Series 30 at 249,475 kg (550,000 lb) AUW
     10,180 m (33,400 ft)
Series 40 (-20 engines) at 242,670 kg (535,000 lb) AUW   9,660 m (31,700 ft)
Series 40 (-59A engines)   9,965 m (32,700 ft)

En-route climb altitude, one engine out:
Series 30 at 251,744 kg (555,000 lb) AUW
     4,360 m (14,300 ft)
Series 40 (-20 engines) at 247,205 kg (545,000 lb) AUW   3,565 m (11,700 ft)
Series 40 (-59A engines) at 254,010 kg (560,000 lb) AUW   5,135 m (16,850 ft)

Min ground turning radius:
about nosewheels:
Series 10, 10F	24.02 m (78 ft 9½ in)
Series 30, 30CF, 40, 40CF	24.32 m (79 ft 9½ in)

about wingtip:
Series 10, 10F	33.65 m (110 ft 4¾ in)
Series 30, 30CF, 40, 40CF	35.39 m (116 ft 1¼ in)

FAA T-O field length:
Series 30 (-50C2 engines)	3,170 m (10,400 ft)
Series 40 (-59A engines)	3,135 m (10,280 ft)

FAA landing field length:
Series 30, 40	1,630 m (5,350 ft)

Range with max fuel, no payload:
Series 30	6,504 nm (12,055 km; 7,490 miles)
Series 40	6,305 nm (11,685 km; 7,260 miles)

Range with max payload at max zero-fuel weight:
Series 30	4,000 nm (7,413 km; 4,606 miles)

Series 40 (-20 engines)
     3,500 nm (6,485 km; 4,030 miles)
Series 40 (-59A engines)
     4,050 nm (7,505 km; 4,663 miles)

MCDONNELL DOUGLAS DC-10 SERIES 30CF and 30F

The **Series 30CF** is a convertible freighter version of the McDonnell Douglas DC-10 transport. Generally similar to the basic DC-10 Series 30 and 40, it was designed for easy conversion to either passenger or cargo configuration. Its payload can consist of 380 passengers and baggage or 64,860 kg (143,000 lb) of cargo over full intercontinental range; or up to 70,626 kg (155,700 lb) of cargo on domestic transcontinental routes.

The first Series 30CF was powered by three General Electric CF6-50A turbofans. It flew for the first time on 28 February 1973 and initial deliveries were made that year to Trans International Airlines and Overseas National Airways. In 1977, Overseas National Airways took delivery of two of the later DC-10 Srs 30CFs, powered by General Electric CF6-50C1 engines rated at 233.5 kN (52,500 lb st). More than 30 Series 30CFs were ordered, and this version also formed the basis for the USAF's **KC-10 Extender** tanker/transport described in a later entry.

In the passenger configuration, interior layout of the Series 30CF is generally similar to that of the DC-10, but the CF was designed to permit overnight conversion to an all-cargo configuration. This entails removal of seats, overhead baggage racks, forward food service centre, cloakrooms and carpeting from the main cabin, and installation of freight loading tracks and rollers, a cargo tiedown system and restraint nets. Coffee service fixtures and lavatories in the rear cabin may also be removed but are retained normally for regular cargo flights.

For cargo loading, two-channel network of roller conveyors, adjustable guide rails and pallet restraint fittings is installed in the seat tracks in the cabin floor by use of simple stud and locking pin devices. A 2.59 m high × 3.56 m wide (8 ft 6 in × 11 ft 8 in) cargo door in the side of the fuselage swings upward and allows easy loading of bulky freight.

A total of 30 standard 2.24 × 2.74 m (7 ft 4 in × 9 ft) cargo pallets, or 22 larger pallets measuring 2.24 × 3.18 m (7 ft 4 in × 10 ft 5 in) or 2.44 × 3.05 m (8 × 10 ft), can be accommodated in the main cabin. The Series 30CF with upstairs galleys also has 132.2 m³ (4,670 cu ft) of cargo space in the two lower cargo compartments for bulk freight, or for 26 half-size containers, or for five full-size pallets and 16 half-size containers.

The 60th production McDonnell Douglas KC-10A Extender, first to be equipped as a three-point tanker

The **Series 30F** is an all-freighter version of the DC-10. Generally similar to the Series 30CF, it does not incorporate those features which permit conversion to passenger configuration. Its payload capability is 80,282 kg (176,992 lb) of cargo over intercontinental range. The Series 30F is powered by CF6-50C2 engines. Nine DC-10 Series 30Fs were ordered by Federal Express. The first was delivered on 24 January 1986, and the last in October 1988.

The main deck cargo compartment can accommodate 23 standard 2.24 × 3.18 m (7 ft 4 in × 10 ft 5 in) cargo pallets, or 51 1.57 × 2.24 m (5 ft 2 in × 7 ft 4 in) demi containers, or 30 pallets measuring 2.24 × 2.74 m (7 ft 4 in × 9 ft). Below-deck forward and centre cargo compartments can accommodate a further 117.8 m³ (4,160 cu ft) of bulk freight using 13 full-width containers, or 116.3 m³ (4,108 cu ft) using 26 half-width containers. The rear below-deck compartment provides a further 14.4 m³ (510 cu ft) of cargo volume.

Weight and performance figures are generally similar to those for the DC-10 Series 30, except as follows:

WEIGHTS:

Weight empty: CF	108,385 kg (238,948 lb)	
F	106,505 kg (234,800 lb)	
Max T-O weight: CF	267,620 kg (590,000 lb)	
F	263,085 kg (580,000 lb)	
Max landing weight: CF	190,962 kg (421,000 lb)	
F	197,765 kg (436,000 lb)	

PERFORMANCE:

Landing speed at max landing weight:		
CF	149 knots (275 km/h; 171 mph)	
F	152 knots (282 km/h; 175 mph)	
FAA T-O field length at max T-O weight:		
CF	3,170 m (10,400 ft)	
F	3,292 m (10,800 ft)	
FAA landing field length at max landing weight:		
CF	1,868 m (6,130 ft)	
F	1,926 m (6,320 ft)	
Max range with max cargo:		
CF	3,581 nm (6,637 km; 4,124 miles)	
F	3,281 nm (6,080 km; 3,778 miles)	

MCDONNELL DOUGLAS EXTENDER
US Air Force designation: KC-10A

The US Air Force announced on 19 December 1977 that, following evaluation of the Boeing 747 and McDonnell Douglas DC-10 to meet its requirement for an advanced tanker/cargo aircraft (ATCA), the DC-10 was selected to fulfil this role. Subsequently, the aircraft was designated KC-10A and named Extender.

On 20 November 1978, the Air Force authorised McDonnell Douglas to begin production of two KC-10As. Four more were ordered in November 1979, six in February 1981 and four in January 1982. Then, in December 1982, the Air Force entered into a multi-year contract with McDonnell Douglas for the purchase of 44 more KC-10s during the fiscal years 1983 to 1987, bringing the total to 60. The last aircraft was delivered to the USAF in September 1988, but was subsequently used to flight test a hose-and-drogue capability (see later paragraph).

The first KC-10A (serial number 79-0433) made its first flight on 12 July 1980. The first to enter service (serial number 79-0434) was delivered on 17 March 1981 to Barksdale AFB, Louisiana, and the Extender is now in service with the US Air Force's 6th and 9th Air Refueling Squadron at March AFB, California, 2nd and 32nd ARS at Barksdale AFB, and the 344th ARS and 911th ARS at Seymour Johnson AFB, North Carolina. The Air Force Reserve's 77th ARS (Associate) at Seymour Johnson, the 78th ARS (Associate) at Barksdale and the 79th ARS (Associate) at March share the aircraft with the active duty squadrons at their respective bases. Since service entry USAF KC-10As have maintained a launch reliability of better than 99 per cent. The final KC-10A (87-0124) was delivered to the USAF on 4 April 1990, after manufacturer's trials with underwing pods.

The modifications necessary to convert the DC-10-30CF to KC-10A configuration included the installation of fuel cells in the lower fuselage compartment; provision of a boom operator station, an aerial refuelling boom, a refuelling receptacle, fuselage-mounted probe and drogue refuelling system, an improved cargo handling system, and some military avionics systems. Various seating layouts are available in the forward area to permit the transport of a fighter squadron's essential support personnel. Seven bladder fuel cells are installed in the lower fuselage compartments, three forward and four aft of the wing, mounted within framework that restrains and supports the cells. These are interconnected with the aircraft's basic fuel system, comprising 108,062 kg (238,236 lb). All can be used for extended range, or fuel from the lower deck cells and the aircraft's basic fuel system can be used for in-flight refuelling. The KC-10A is able to deliver 90,718 kg (200,000 lb) of fuel to a receiver 1,910 nm (3,540 km; 2,200 miles) from its home base, and return to base. In February 1985 a KC-10A made a nonstop, unrefuelled flight from Riyadh, Saudi Arabia, to March AFB, covering the 7,800 nm (14,455 km; 8,982 miles) in 17.8 hours and consuming 139,253 kg (307,000 lb) of fuel.

In June 1987 McDonnell Douglas was awarded a US Air Force contract to modify the 60th production KC-10A to three-point tanker configuration by fitting two Flight Refuelling Ltd Mk 32B underwing hose/drogue refuelling pods. Modification work included additional wiring controls in the flight engineer's and refuelling operator's stations, and structural work in the aircraft's wings. Other aircraft in the inventory will be modified to accept the pods, of which 39 more will be purchased. The pods will increase the KC-10A's fuel offload capability and offer system redundancy in over-water deployments of US Navy and US Marine Corps aircraft which use the probe and drogue method of in-flight refuelling. Each pod can offload fuel at a max rate of 1,590 litres (420 US gallons; 350 Imp gallons)/min.

The aerial refuelling operator's station, with access from the upper main deck, is sited in the lower rear fuselage and can accommodate the boom operator, an instructor and an observer, although only the boom operator is needed for a refuelling mission. The station has a rear window and a periscope observation system to give a wide field of view, and is pressurised and air-conditioned. The advanced aerial refuelling boom provides greater capability than the type installed in the KC-135; in particular, it has a greater transfer flow rate, being rated at 5,678 litres (1,500 US gallons; 1,249 Imp gallons)/min. The boom operator 'flies' it by means of a digital fly by wire control system supplied by Honeywell. A Sargent-Fletcher FR600 hose/reel unit for probe and drogue refuelling is also installed in the rear fuselage, so that the KC-10A can service US Navy, US Marine Corps and NATO aircraft, as well as older types of fighters still serving with Reserve and ANG units. This unit can offload fuel at a max rate of 2,271 litres (600 US gallons; 499.6 Imp gallons)/min.

The provision of a refuelling receptacle, above the flight deck of the KC-10A, allows greater flexibility on long-range cargo or refuelling operations, extending the range beyond the nominal 6,000 nm (11,112 km; 6,905 miles) with a 45,400 kg (100,000 lb) payload. The improved cargo handling system, by comparison with the basic DC-10-30CF, includes an increased floor area covered by omni-directional rollers, power rollers, and a portable winch to move cargo fore and aft.

Changes to the avionics are concerned chiefly with the deletion of equipment intended specifically for commercial operations, and the addition of UHF and secure com systems, Tacan, IFF, beacon transponder and a radar beacon mode. In addition to its tanker/transport role, the KC-10A can also act as a pathfinder for the aircraft it is refuelling, by providing supplementary navigation and communications services during long-range deployments.

The description of the DC-10 Series 30CF applies to the KC-10A, except as follows:

TYPE: Military flight refuelling/cargo aircraft.

WINGS, FUSELAGE, TAIL UNIT: As for DC-10-30, except for omission of most upper deck cabin windows and Srs 30CF lower deck cargo doors.

LANDING GEAR: As for DC-10-30, except nosewheel tyre pressure increased to 13.10 bars (190 lb/sq in); pressure in tyres on main units and centreline unit increased to 13.79 bars (200 lb/sq in) and 10.69 bars (155 lb/sq in) respectively.

POWER PLANT: Three 233.53 kN (52,500 lb st) General Electric CF6-50C2 turbofans. Basic aircraft fuel system comprises three integral main wing fuel tanks, and an integral auxiliary tank in the wing centre-section with a connected structural compartment fitted with a bladder cell, giving a total capacity of approximately 132,331 litres (34,958 US gallons; 29,108 Imp gallons). Details of transfer fuel loads given in introductory copy and under Avionics and Equipment. Oil capacity 34.1 litres (9 US gallons; 7.5 Imp gallons).

ACCOMMODATION: Three crew on flight deck. Various seating arrangements for a limited number of essential support personnel at forward end of main cabin. Aerial refuelling station, with accommodation and large observation windows for boom operator, instructor and a student observer at aft end of lower fuselage compartment. Five passenger doors on main deck. A 2.59 × 3.56 m (8 ft 6 in × 11 ft 8 in) cargo door on the port side of the fuselage permits loading of standard USAF 463L pallets, bulk cargo or wheeled vehicles. Maximum capacity for 25 pallets with access from both sides of the compartment, or 27 pallets with a single aisle on the starboard side.

SYSTEMS: As for DC-10-30.

AVIONICS AND EQUIPMENT: Include some additional military avionics, comprising navigation, communication, Tacan, IFF transponder, and modified commercial weather radar. Seven Goodyear Aerospace rubberised fabric fuel cells mounted in the lower fuselage compartments, with combined capacity of 53,446 kg (117,829 lb) of fuel, equivalent to approx 68,610 litres (18,125 US gallons; 15,092 Imp gallons), which are interconnected into the aircraft's basic fuel system. Flight refuelling boom mounted under rear fuselage, plus hose/reel unit for probe and drogue refuelling (24.4 m; 80 ft long hose and 66 cm; 26 in diameter drogue). Director lights to guide receiver. Flight refuelling receptacle mounted on fuselage upper surface above flight deck.

DIMENSIONS, EXTERNAL: As for DC-10-30 except:

Length overall	55.35 m (181 ft 7 in)
Height overall	17.70 m (58 ft 1 in)
Wheel track	10.57 m (34 ft 8 in)

AREAS: As for DC-10-30
WEIGHTS AND LOADING:

Operating weight empty:	
tanker	109,328 kg (241,027 lb)
cargo	110,945 kg (244,591 lb)
Fuel at T-O: tanker	158,291 kg (348,973 lb)
Design fuel capacity	161,508 kg (356,065 lb)
Max cargo payload	76,843 kg (169,409 lb)
Design max T-O weight	267,620 kg (590,000 lb)
Max wing loading	727.8 kg/m² (149.06 lb/sq ft)

PERFORMANCE:

Critical field length	3,124 m (10,250 ft)
Max range with max cargo	
	3,797 nm (7,032 km; 4,370 miles)
Max ferry range, unrefuelled	
	9,993 nm (18,507 km; 11,500 miles)

MCDONNELL DOUGLAS MD-11

First details of the MD-11, an advanced medium/long-range successor to the DC-10, were revealed at the 1985 Paris Air Show; development began in July 1985, with prototype construction commencing in March 1987. Derived from the DC-10, the aircraft features a longer fuselage than the DC-10 Series 30; aerodynamic improvements including upper and lower outward inclined winglets; an advanced horizontal tail design with cambered aerofoil, reduced sweepback and integral 'trim tank' with a fuel capacity of 7,571 litres (2,000 US gallons; 1,665 Imp gallons); extended tailcone; an advanced two-crew all-digital flight deck; and restyled passenger interior. Power plants are either three General Electric CF6-80C2D1F, three Pratt & Whitney PW4460, or three Rolls-Royce Trent 650 turbofans, providing a 27 per cent improvement in range over the DC-10 Series 30, with increased passenger capacity and a 31 per cent forecast reduction in seat/mile costs.

The use of composite materials is a key feature of the MD-11 design. More than 20 airframe components, including virtually all control surfaces on the wings and horizontal tail, engine inlets and cowls, and wing/fuselage fillets, are manufactured from composite materials such as carbonfibre, glassfibre and Kevlar. Aluminium-lithium fuselage floor beams will be introduced from the 14th production aircraft.

Three variants of the MD-11 are offered initially. The standard **MD-11** provides two-class accommodation for 323 passengers, with a maximum range of 7,008 nm (12,987 km; 8,070 miles). The **MD-11 Combi** is a mixed passenger/cargo aircraft capable of carrying 4-10 cargo pallets and 168-240 two-class passengers, depending on configuration, at maximum ranges between 5,210 nm (9,656 km; 6,000 miles) and 6,947 nm (12,875 km; 8,000 miles). The **MD-11F** is an all-freight variant.

Production of the MD-11 is expected to reach the rate of four per month by 1992.

On 3 December 1986 the (then) British Caledonian Airways became launch customer for the MD-11 with an order for nine aircraft. McDonnell Douglas officially launched the MD-11 programme on 30 December 1986. By 21 May 1990 a total of 145 firm orders, plus 201 options and reserves had been received from customers including: Aero Lloyd (10), Air Europe (6 orders, 12 options), Air Outre Mer (8), Air Zaïre (2), Alitalia (6 MD-11 Combis ordered, with 4 options), American Airlines (15 orders, 35 options), China Airlines (4), China Eastern Airlines (4 MD-11, 1 MD-11F), Delta Air Lines (42), Dragonair, Evergreen Airways (13), Federal Express Corporation (8 orders, 8 options for MD-11F), Finnair (4 orders, 2 options), Garuda Indonesia (9 orders, 1 option), Guinness Peat Aviation (12), International Lease Finance (5 orders, 2 options), Japan Air Lines (10 orders, 5 options), Korean Air (5 orders, 3 options), LTU (4 orders, 6 options), Minerve (4), Nigeria Airways (2), SAS (12), Singapore Airlines (5 orders, 15 options), Swissair (12 orders, 6 options), Thai Airways International (4 orders, 4 options), Varig (4 orders, 6 options), VIASA (2 orders, 1 option), Zambia Airways, (1), and ZAS Airline of Egypt (1 order, 1 option).

Assembly of the first MD-11, powered by CF6 engines, began on 9 March 1988. The aircraft made its first flight on 10 January 1990, and had completed 115 hours of flight testing at Yuma, Arizona, and Edwards AFB, California, by 15 March 1990. During that time it had achieved a maximum speed of Mach 0.945 and a maximum altitude of 11,900 m (39,000 ft). The second test aircraft, an MD-11F, was flown from Long Beach to Yuma on 1 March. It was joined on 26 April by the first PW4460 powered aircraft. Five MD-11s will share the test and certification programme, leading to FAA certification in late 1990.

McDonnell Douglas MD-11 medium/long-range transport *(Pilot Press)*

The first McDonnell Douglas MD-11 prototype, powered by three General Electric CF6-80C2 turbofans

Suppliers for the MD-11 programme include Aeritalia (fin, rudder, fuselage panels and winglets), AP Precision Hydraulics (centreline and nose landing gear), Bendix Brake and Strut (mainwheels and carbon brakes), CASA (horizontal tail surfaces), Convair Division of General Dynamics (fuselage sections), Embraer (outboard flap sections), Fischer GmbH (composite flap hinge fairings), Pneumo Abex Corporation (main landing gear), Rohr Industries (engine pylons), Honeywell (advanced flight deck) and Westland Aerospace (flap vane and inlet duct extension rings).

The following data apply to the standard MD-11, except where indicated:

TYPE: Three-turbofan commercial transport.

WINGS: Cantilever low-wing monoplane of all-metal fail-safe construction, comprising two-spar structural box and chordwise ribs and bulkheads, and skins with spanwise stiffeners. Aerofoil section is a Douglas design. Dihedral 6°. Incidence 5° 51′ at wing/fuselage intersection. Sweepback at quarter-chord 35°. Winglet extending above and below each wingtip. Upper winglet is of metal construction with ribs, spars and stiffened aluminium alloy skin, with carbonfibre trailing-edge; lower winglet is of carbonfibre construction. Inboard ailerons have metal structure with composites skin; outboard ailerons entirely of composites materials. Double-slotted trailing-edge flaps mounted on external hinges, with composite-skinned metal (inboard) and all-composites (outer flap) panel on each wing. Five all-metal spoiler panels on each wing, at rear edge of fixed wing structure, forward of flaps. Spoilers are of aluminium alloy honeycomb construction with aluminium alloy skinning. Full-span two-position all-metal leading-edge slats, eight segments per wing. Ailerons are powered by National Water Lift hydraulic actuators. All leading-edge outer slat segments are anti-iced with engine bleed air.

FUSELAGE: Aluminium alloy semi-monocoque fail-safe structure of circular cross-section. Passenger and cargo areas are pressurised.

TAIL UNIT: Electro-hydraulically actuated variable incidence tailplane has metal spars and ribs, aluminium alloy skinning, and carbonfibre trailing-edge. Slotted elevators of carbonfibre construction. Elevators powered by Parker Hannifin and Teijin Seiki actuators. Leading-edge of tailplane is anti-iced with bleed air from No. 2 engine.

LANDING GEAR: Hydraulically retractable tricycle type, with additional twin-wheel main unit mounted on the fuselage centreline. Nosewheel and centreline units retract forward, main units inward into fuselage. Twin-wheel steerable nose unit (±70°). Main gear comprises two four-wheel bogies. Oleo-pneumatic shock absorbers in all units. Loral nosewheels and Goodyear tyres size 40 × 15.5-16, pressure 13.44 bars (195 lb/sq in). Main and centreline units have Bendix wheels and Goodyear tyres size 54 × 21-24, pressure 13.79 bars (200 lb/sq in). Bendix carbon brakes with air convection cooling; Loral anti-skid system.

POWER PLANT: Three Pratt & Whitney PW4460 turbofans, each rated at 266.9 kN (60,000 lb st), or three General Electric CF6-80C2D1F turbofans, each rated at 273.57 kN (61,500 lb st), or three Rolls-Royce Trent 650 turbofans, each rated at 289-311 kN (65,000-70,000 lb st), two of which are mounted on underwing pylons, the third above the rear fuselage at the base of the fin. Rear engine inlet duct and fan cowl doors, and nose cowl outer barrels on wing-mounted engines, are of composites construction. Inner surfaces of engine nacelles are acoustically treated. Refuelling point in leading-edge of each wing.

ACCOMMODATION: Crew of two. Standard mixed class seating for 323 (MD-11) or 214 (Combi). Crew door and three passenger doors each side, all eight of which open sliding inward and upward. Two freight holds below cabin, forward and aft of wing, and one bulk cargo compartment in rear fuselage. Forward freight hold is heated and ventilated; rear freight hold heated only. MD-11 Combi has a cargo door in centre compartment on port side of fuselage for loading of pallets, a main deck cargo door on port rear side of cabin, and two additional emergency exit doors, one on each side of passenger cabin immediately forward of the main deck cargo door.

SYSTEMS: Air-conditioning system comprises three AiResearch air bearing air cycle units with two automatic digital pressure controllers and electro-manual backup. Cabin max pressure differential 0.59 bars (8.6 lb/sq in). Three independent hydraulic systems for operation of flight controls and braking, with motor/pump interconnects to allow one system to power another. Electrical system comprises three 400Hz, 100/120kVA integrated drive generators, one per engine; one 90kVA generator in APU; 50Ah battery; four transformer-rectifiers to convert AC power to DC; and 25kVA drop-out air driven emergency generator. Pneumatic system, max controlled pressure 0.27-0.41 bars (4-6 lb/sq in) at 230°C, supplies air-conditioning, anti-icing for wing (outer slats) and tailplane leading-edges, galley vent jet pump, and cargo compartment floor heating. Plumbed gaseous oxygen system for crew, using EROS equipment; chemical oxygen generators with automatically deploying masks for passengers. Portable oxygen cylinders for attendants and first aid. Engine bleed air anti-icing for wing and tailplane leading-edges and engine cowlings. De-icing for windscreens, angle-of-attack sensors, TAT probe and static port plate. Garrett TSCP700-4E APU.

AVIONICS: Avionics integrator, Honeywell, responsible for flight guidance/flight deck system consisting of 44 line-replaceable units. These include aircraft system controllers (ASC) that perform flight engineering control and monitoring functions, providing automated hydraulic, electrical, environmental and fuel systems; a central fault display system (CFDS); an electronic instrument system (EIS) using six 20 × 20 cm (8 × 8 in) colour CRTs; a flight management system (FMS); an automatic flight system (AFS) featuring Cat IIIB autoland, windshear detection and guidance computer with escape capability and full-time longitudinal stability augmentation; a laser inertial reference system (IRS); and a digital air data computer (DADC).

DIMENSIONS, EXTERNAL:

Wing span	51.66 m (169 ft 6 in)
Wing chord: at root	10.71 m (35 ft 1¾ in)
at tip	2.73 m (8 ft 11½ in)
Wing aspect ratio	7.5
Length overall	61.21 m (200 ft 10 in)
Fuselage: Length	58.65 m (192 ft 5 in)
Max diameter	6.02 m (19 ft 9 in)
Height overall	17.60 m (57 ft 9 in)
Tailplane span	18.03 m (59 ft 2 in)
Wheel track	10.57 m (34 ft 8 in)
Wheelbase	24.61 m (80 ft 9 in)
Crew doors (two, each): Height	1.93 m (6 ft 4 in)
Width	0.81 m (2 ft 8 in)
Passenger doors (six, each): Height	1.93 m (6 ft 4 in)
Width	1.07 m (3 ft 6 in)
* Forward cargo door: Height	1.68 m (5 ft 6 in)
Width	2.64 m (8 ft 8 in)
Centre cargo door (standard): Height	1.68 m (5 ft 6 in)
Width	1.78 m (5 ft 10 in)
Bulk cargo door: Height	0.91 m (3 ft 0 in)
Width	0.76 m (2 ft 6 in)
Combi main deck cargo door (port, rear):	
Height	2.59 m (8 ft 6 in)
Width	4.06 m (13 ft 4 in)
Combi emergency exits (two, each):	
Height	1.52 m (5 ft 0 in)
Width	0.71 m (2 ft 4 in)

* Centre cargo door of Combi also this size

DIMENSIONS, INTERNAL:
Cabin:

Length, flight deck door to rear bulkhead	
	46.51 m (152 ft 7¼ in)
Max width	5.71 m (18 ft 9 in)
Max height	2.41 m (7 ft 11 in)
Floor area, incl galleys and toilets	
	244.7 m² (2,634.0 sq ft)
Volume, incl galleys and toilets	
	599.3 m³ (21,165 cu ft)
Baggage holds, volume:	
forward	80.5 m³ (2,844 cu ft)
centre	62.6 m³ (2,212 cu ft)
rear	14.4 m³ (510 cu ft)

AREAS:

Wings, gross	338.9 m² (3,648 sq ft)
Winglets (total)	7.42 m² (80.0 sq ft)
Vertical tail surfaces (total)	56.2 m² (605.0 sq ft)
Horizontal tail surfaces (total)	85.5 m² (920.0 sq ft)

WEIGHTS (MD-11):

Operating weight empty	125,874 kg (277,500 lb)
Max payload	55,656 kg (122,700 lb)
Max fuel weight	117,480 kg (259,000 lb)
Max T-O weight	273,289 kg (602,500 lb)
Max zero-fuel weight	181,437 kg (400,000 lb)
Max landing weight	195,044 kg (430,000 lb)

PERFORMANCE (estimated: A: MD-11, B: MD-11F, C: MD-11 Combi):

Never-exceed speed: all	Mach 0.95
Max level speed at 8,230 m (27,000 ft): all	
	Mach 0.87 (519 knots; 962 km/h; 597 mph)
Max cruising speed at 9,150 m (30,000 ft):	
A, C	503 knots (932 km/h; 579 mph)
Econ cruising speed at 10,670 m (35,000 ft): all	
	473 knots (876 km/h; 544 mph)
Stalling speed, power on:	
10° flap:	
A, B, C	148 knots (274 km/h; 171 mph)
25° flap:	
A, B, C	142 knots (263 km/h; 164 mph)
Max rate of climb at S/L: A, B, C	844 m (2,770 ft)/min
Rate of climb at S/L, one engine out:	
A, B, C	414 m (1,360 ft)/min
Service ceiling: A, B, C	9,935 m (32,600 ft)
Service ceiling, one engine out:	
A, B, C	6,310 m (20,700 ft)
Min ground turning radius:	
about nosewheel	26.67 m (87 ft 6 in)
about wingtip	35.90 m (117 ft 9½ in)
T-O run: A, B, C	2,207 m (7,240 ft)
T-O to 10.7 m (35 ft): A, B, C	2,926 m (9,600 ft)

Landing from 15 m (50 ft) at max landing weight:

A	1,966 m (6,450 ft)
B	2,130 m (6,990 ft)
C	2,079 m (6,820 ft)
Runway LCN, rigid pavement, taxi weight of 276,010 kg	
(608,500 lb)	105
Runway ACN, conditions as above	65

Range with max payload, at max zero-fuel weight, with fuel to proceed to a 150 nm (278 km; 173 mile) alternate and make one missed approach, with FAR international reserves:

A	5,002 nm (9,270 km; 5,760 miles)
B	3,542 nm (6,564 km; 4,079 miles)
C	4,024 nm (7,457 km; 4,634 miles)

MCDONNELL DOUGLAS MD-12X

McDonnell Douglas is studying development of a stretched version of the MD-11, designated MD-12X. This aircraft would feature a fuselage 10.36 m (34 ft) longer than that of the MD-11, enabling it to carry an additional 83 passengers in three-class configuration. Max T-O weight would be 303,900 kg (670,000 lb) and range in excess of 6,000 nm (11,119 km; 6,909 miles). The MD-11's wing would be retained, with extended chord aft of the rear spar, and re-designed flaps. The centre landing gear would be strengthened. Also under study is a lower 'panorama' deck, which would increase the MD-12X's passenger capacity to 440. If launched during 1990, first flight of the MD-12X could take place in 1994, with certification following in mid-1995.

McDONNELL DOUGLAS C-17A

The US Air Force announced on 29 August 1981 that McDonnell Douglas had been selected as prime contractor to develop the new C-17A long-range cargo aircraft, following evaluation of three designs entered for its C-X competition.

The C-17A will be a long-range, heavy lift air-refuellable cargo transport, intended primarily to provide inter-theatre and theatre airlift of outsize loads, including tanks and infantry fighting vehicles, directly into airfields in potential conflict areas. Design requirements therefore include outstanding STOL performance.

In January 1982 the Air Force stated that it did not plan full scale development and production of the C-17A at that time. However, on 26 July 1982 McDonnell Douglas received a contract for a 'modestly paced' research and development programme, to include such C-17A technologies as would also benefit other airlift programmes, and preserving the option to proceed to full scale engineering development of the C-17A if eventually deemed appropriate. A full scale development contract, covering the construction of one flying prototype and two structural test aircraft was awarded on 31 December 1985.

Construction of the first C-17A (87-0025) began in 1987, and assembly started in August 1988, with the first flight scheduled for June 1991 and the FSD phase continuing until 1993. The first of two production C-17As ordered on 20 January 1988 is also due to fly in 1991. Before programme reductions were proposed early in 1990, the first four production aircraft and the prototype were to be used in the test programme. The USAF planned to acquire 210 aircraft by the year 2001, at a unit cost of $125 million. Planned production rate was to be 10-12 C-17s annually in FY 1990 and 1991, increasing to 24 by FY 1993. The 17th MAS at Charleston AFB, South Carolina, has been designated as the first C-17A unit, and is due to receive the fifth C-17A as its initial aircraft in 1991 and achieve IOC in September 1993. Reserve and Air National Guard squadrons were

provisionally assigned 48 new C-17As but defence cuts may now reduce production from 210 to 120.

Major subassemblies are produced at Macon, Georgia, where a new 18,580 m² (200,000 sq ft) facility was completed in July 1988. Subcontractors in the C-17A programme include Beech Aircraft Corporation (composite winglets); Delco Electronics Corporation (mission computer and electronic display system); Grumman Aerostructures (composite ailerons, rudder and elevators); GEC Avionics (advanced head-up displays); Lockheed (wing spars, stringers, ribs, bulkheads, leading-edge slats and main wing assembly) up to sixth aircraft only; LTV (vertical and horizontal stabilisers, engine nacelles and thrust reversers); Murdock Engineering Company (engine pylons); Reynolds Metals Company (wing skins); Plessey (fuel pumps); Pyrotector Division of Graviner Inc (smoke detection systems); and Honeywell (electronic flight control system and air data computers). McDonnell Douglas Helicopter Co will manufacture the tailcone, wing/fuselage fillets, wing trailing-edge panels, main landing gear fairings and flap hinge fairings, all of composites materials.

The C-17A, making use of technology developed for the company's earlier YC-15 advanced medium STOL transport prototypes (see 1979-80 *Jane's*), will be able to airlift outsize combat equipment which at present can be carried only by the Lockheed C-5 Galaxy, and offer a short field performance currently provided only by the C-130 Hercules. It will be able to operate from runways only 915 m (3,000 ft) long and 18.3 m (60 ft) wide; on the ground, it will be able to execute a three-point 180° turn in only 25 m (82 ft); and a fully loaded aircraft, using thrust reversal, will be able to reverse up a 1 in 50 gradient.

TYPE: Long-range heavy lift cargo transport.

AIRFRAME: General survivability features include ample provisions for crew and troop shielding; redundant load paths, to minimise the effects of battle damage; and facility for critical line-replaceable units (LRUs) to be replaced in flight.

WINGS: Cantilever high-wing monoplane, of supercritical section with 25° sweepback. NASA type 2.90 m (9.5 ft) tall winglet of composites construction at each tip, also of supercritical section. Full span leading-edge slats. Externally blown flap system, developed from that used on McDonnell Douglas YC-15, to reduce final approach and landing speeds by directing engine efflux over single-hinged, single-slotted Fowler trailing-edge flaps to provide extra lift. Flaps extend over approx two-thirds of each trailing-edge. Four-segment spoilers/lift dumpers forward of flaps on each wing. Ailerons are of composites construction.

FUSELAGE: Conventional semi-monocoque fail-safe structure, upswept at rear. Rear-loading ramp/door in underside of rear fuselage. Twin strakes under extreme rear of fuselage.

TAIL UNIT: Cantilever T tail. Sweptback fin, with small dorsal fillet; inset rudder, in upper and lower segments. Sweptback tailplane, with two inboard and two outboard elevators.

LANDING GEAR: Hydraulically retractable tricycle type, with free-fall emergency extension. Twin-wheel Menasco nose unit and two three-wheel main units, designed for sink rate of 4.57 m (15 ft)/s and suitable for operation from paved runways or unpaved strips. Mainwheel units, each consisting of two legs in tandem with three wheels on each leg, retract into fairings on lower fuselage sides; Menasco nose unit is forward retracting. Bendix wheels and carbon brakes.

POWER PLANT: Early aircraft will have 185.5 kN (41,700 lb st) Pratt & Whitney F117-PW-100 turbofans, pylon-mounted in individual underwing pods and each fitted

McDonnell Douglas C-17A long-range heavy lift cargo transport
(Pilot Press)

with a directed-flow thrust reverser deployable both in flight and on the ground. Power plant contract open to competition for later C-17As. Provision for in-flight refuelling.

ACCOMMODATION: Normal flight crew of pilot and co-pilot, side by side on flight deck, plus a loadmaster. Provision for additional crew members if required for special missions. Access to flight deck via downward opening airstair door on port side of lower forward fuselage. Bunks for crew immediately aft of flight deck area: crew comfort station at forward end of cargo hold. Main cargo hold able to accommodate Army wheeled vehicles, including five-ton expandable vans in two side by side rows, or three Jeeps, or up to three AH-64A Apache attack helicopters, with straight-in loading via hydraulically actuated rear loading ramp which forms underside of rear fuselage when retracted. Alternatively, aircraft can be equipped as a troop transport, with rows of stowable tip-up seats along each side wall and a row of seats which can be erected along the centreline, or with litters for medical evacuation mission. Airdrop capability includes single platforms of up to 27,215 kg (60,000 lb), multiple platforms of up to 49,895 kg (110,000 lb), or up to 102 paratroops. Equipped for low altitude parachute extraction system (LAPES) drops. The C-17A will be the only aircraft able to airdrop outsize firepower the size of the US Army's new infantry fighting vehicle; it will also be able to carry the M1 main battle tank in combination with other vehicles. The cargo handling system includes rails for airdrops and rails/rollers for normal cargo handling. Each row of rails/rollers can be converted quickly by a single loadmaster from one configuration to the other. Cargo tiedown rings, each with an 11,340 kg (25,000 lb) load restraint capability, are installed throughout the cargo area floor. Three quick-erecting litter stanchions, each supporting four litters, permanently carried. Main access to cargo hold is via rear loading ramp, which is itself capable of transporting 18,145 kg (40,000 lb) of cargo. Undersurface of rear fuselage aft of ramp is formed by door which moves upward inside fuselage to facilitate loading and unloading. Paratroop door at rear on each side, and two overwater emergency exits overhead, aft of the paratroop doors, and two overhead forward of the wing box.

SYSTEMS: Include AiResearch computer controlled cabin pressure control system; fully redundant flight control and hydraulic systems; independent fuel feed systems; electrical system; Garrett GTCP331 APU (in starboard landing gear pod), operable in flight, provides power for environmental control system, engine starting, and on-ground electronics requirements; onboard inert gas generating system (OBIGGS) for the explosion protection system, pressurised by engine bleed air at 4.1 bars (60 lb/sq in) to produce NEA 4 gas and governed by a Gull

Inc system controller; and fire suppression system. All phases of cargo operation and configuration change capable of being handled by one loadmaster.

AVIONICS AND EQUIPMENT: General Electric electronic flight control system; and Honeywell dual air data computers, with advanced digital avionics and four full-colour multi-function displays (MFDs), two GEC Avionics full flight regime head-up displays, plus integrated mission and communications keyboards (MCKs) and displays (MCDs). Primary flight data presented on HUD and a selectable mode for the MFD. Horizontal navigation situation computer-generated flight plan and weather radar overlay selectable on MFD. Station keeping (SKE), engine and flight control configuration data available on MFDs. All frequency tuning for nav/com accomplished from glareshield control panel. MCDs have frequency and channel pre-storage facility and provide for flight plan entry manually or by preprogrammed cassette, permitting insertion of in-flight planning changes without disturbing ongoing navigation. All MCD information for flight and navigation monitoring is presented on the HUD and MFDs. Teledyne Controls warning and caution system. Master warning caution annunciator provides automatic monitoring of all main systems and provides visual alerts on glareshields, aural and voice alerts on intercom. Cargo hold equipment includes integral rails and roller conveyors, in floor (incl ramp); sidewall rails; tiedown rings of 11,340 kg (25,000 lb) rating, spaced at 61 cm (24 in) intervals; cargo winch and retrieval winch; and Oxford type tow/release for cargo platforms. Other equipment suppliers include Bendix (AN/APS-133[V] weather/mapping radar), Delco Electronics (mission computer with MDC software; and electronic control system), Hamilton Standard (aircraft and propulsion data management computer), Honeywell (automatic test equipment, and support equipment data acquisition and control system), LTV (Sierra Research Division) (station keeping equipment), and Telephonic Corporation (radio management system). Development of defensive electronic systems was authorised in 1988.

DIMENSIONS, EXTERNAL:
Wing span	50.29 m (165 ft 0 in)
Length overall	53.04 m (174 ft 0 in)
Height overall	16.79 m (55 ft 1 in)

DIMENSIONS, INTERNAL:
Cargo compartment:
Length, incl 6.05 m (19 ft 10 in) rear loading ramp	26.82 m (88 ft 0 in)
Max width	5.49 m (18 ft 0 in)
Height under wing	3.76 m (12 ft 4 in)
Max height	4.11 m (13 ft 6 in)
Volume	592 m³ (20,900 cu ft)

AREAS:
Wings, gross	353 m² (3,800 sq ft)
Ailerons (total)	11.83 m² (127.34 sq ft)

WEIGHTS (target):
Operating weight empty	122,016 kg (269,000 lb)
Typical payload:	
inter-theatre logistics mission (2.5g load factor)	58,605 kg (129,200 lb)
heavy logistics mission (2.25g load factor)	71,895 kg (158,500 lb)
Max payload	78,108 kg (172,200 lb)
Max T-O weight	263,083 kg (580,000 lb)

PERFORMANCE (estimated):
Normal cruising speed at high altitude Mach 0.77
Max cruising speed at low altitude
350 knots (648 km/h; 403 mph) CAS
Airdrop speed:
at S/L 115-250 knots (213-463 km/h; 132-288 mph) CAS
at 7,620 m (25,000 ft)
130-250 knots (241-463 km/h; 150-288 mph) CAS
Approach speed with max payload
115 knots (213 km/h; 132 mph) CAS
Min ground turning radius:
three-point turn	25 m (82 ft)
180° turn	34.74 m (114 ft)
wingtip/tailplane clearance	72.24 m (237 ft)
Runway LCN (paved surface) better than 40
T-O field length with 75,750 kg (167,000 lb) payload
2,320 m (7,600 ft)
Landing field length with 75,750 kg (167,000 lb) payload, using thrust reversal 915 m (3,000 ft)
Radius, T-O with 39,055 kg (86,100 lb) payload in 975 m (3,200 ft), land in 760 m (2,500 ft), T-O with similar payload in 885 m (2,900 ft) and land in 730 m (2,400 ft), all at load factor of 3g, no in-flight refuelling
500 nm (925 km; 575 miles)
Radius, T-O with 63,865 kg (140,800 lb) payload in 2,320 m (7,600 ft) at load factor of 2.25g, land in 915 m (3,000 ft), T-O with zero payload (load factor of 3g) in 730 m (2,400 ft) and land in 610 m (2,000 ft), no in-flight refuelling 1,900 nm (3,520 km; 2,190 miles)
Range with payloads indicated, with no in-flight refuelling:
75,750 kg (167,000 lb), T-O in 2,320 m (7,600 ft), land in 915 m (3,000 ft), load factor of 2.25g
2,400 nm (4,445 km; 2,765 miles)
71,895 kg (158,500 lb), T-O in 2,320 m (7,600 ft), land in 885 m (2,900 ft), load factor of 2.25g
2,700 nm (5,000 km; 3,110 miles)
58,605 kg (129,200 lb), T-O in 1,830 m (6,000 ft), land in 795 m (2,600 ft), load factor of 2.5g
2,800 nm (5,190 km; 3,225 miles)
self-ferry (zero payload), T-O in 1,100 m (3,600 ft), land in 610 m (2,000 ft), load factor of 2.5g
4,700 nm (8,710 km; 5,412 miles)

MCDONNELL DOUGLAS HELICOPTER COMPANY
(A Subsidiary of McDonnell Douglas Corporation)
5000 East McDowell Road, Mesa, Arizona 85205-9797
Telephone: 1 (602) 891 3000
Telex: 3719337 MD HC C MESA
Fax: 1 (602) 891 5599
OTHER WORKS: Culver City, California 90230
Telephone: 1 (213) 305 5000
Telex: 182436 HU HELI C CULV
PRESIDENT: Thomas M. Gunn
EXECUTIVE VICE-PRESIDENTS:
Al Haggerty (LH Division)
Norman B. Hirsh (General Products Division)
VICE-PRESIDENTS:
Dean C. Borgman (Advanced Project Development and Technology Division)
Leonard J. Devey (Business Support Division)
Stuart D. Dodge (AH-64 Division)
Paul K. Henney (Quality Management Systems Division)
J. James Schwalm (Production Support Division)
DIRECTOR, PUBLIC AFFAIRS: Dale M. Willis
On 6 January 1984, Hughes Helicopters Inc became a subsidiary of the McDonnell Douglas Corporation; on 27 August 1985 the company name was changed to McDonnell Douglas Helicopter Company. More than 4,000 of nearly 7,000 helicopters produced are in operation by civil and military operators in nearly 100 countries worldwide, and a series of advanced models is being developed. Research activities include work on composites rotor blades, hubs and tailbooms, metal insulation and IR suppression systems, the US Army's LH programme, and Chain Gun ordnance systems for air and ground applications.
Mesa, Arizona, the site of the company's main production and flight test facility, comprises a 52,955 m² (570,000 sq ft) Apache assembly, flight test and delivery centre, to which was added a further 123,980 m² (1,334,500 sq ft) complex of office, engineering and other buildings that were completed in 1986. In mid-1986 Mesa became the new official headquarters of the company, with a workforce

due to total 7,000 by 1990. The MD 500/530 line was transferred to Mesa from California in the Winter of 1986-87. The combined production rate of MD 500/530s and Apaches is about 16 per month.
In 1986 MDHC sold its Model 300 helicopter line to Schweizer Aircraft Corporation (which see) of Elmira, New York, which had been producing the helicopter under a licensing agreement since 1983. Licensees building McDonnell Douglas helicopters in 1989 were RACA in Argentina (500D and 500E civil variants); Kawasaki in Japan (500D civil and military variants); Korean Air in the Republic of Korea (500D and 500E civil and military, excluding TOW variants, and fuselages for all MD 500s sold worldwide); and Agusta in Italy (500D, 500E and 530F civil variants).

MCDONNELL DOUGLAS MD 500/520/530 (CIVIL VERSIONS)
The MD 500, which entered full scale production in November 1968, originated as a civil development of the OH-6A Cayuse military helicopter last described in the 1977-78 *Jane's*. From it have since been developed several military export versions; these are listed separately. Including the OH-6A, more than 4,000 helicopters of the MD 500/530 series had been built by early 1990.
Civil versions of the MD 500 are as follows:
MD 500. Initial basic production version, with Allison 250-C18A turboshaft.
MD 500C. Similar to MD 500, but with Allison 250-C20 engine and improved hot and high performance. Licence manufacture was also undertaken by RACA (Argentina) and Kawasaki (Japan). US production ended in 1978.
MD 500D. Announced in February 1975, the MD 500D is similar in size and general appearance to the MD 500C. It differs in having a derated Allison 250-C20B engine; a five-blade main rotor; and a T tail, which gives greater flight stability in both high and low speed regimes, as well as better handling characteristics in abnormal manoeuvres. First flight of the prototype took place in August 1974, and

the first flight of a production aircraft was made on 9 October 1975. Now replaced on US production line by MD 500E. Licence manufacture continues by RACA (Argentina), Agusta (Italy), Kawasaki (Japan) and Korean Air (South Korea). US production ended in 1983.
MD 500E. Longer and more streamlined nose, providing increased legroom for front seat occupants. Replaced MD 500D in 1982 as basic US production version. Available with Allison 250-C20B or (from late 1988) 250-C20R engine. Rear seat passengers have 12 per cent more headroom, additional legroom and, as a result of lowering the bulkhead between front and rear seats, a 50 per cent improvement in forward view. First flown (N5294A) on 28 January 1982, it incorporates improvements that include a new auxiliary fuel tank, better soundproofing around the transmission and cooling fan, longer main rotor blade abrasion strips, new endplate fins, new T grouping of flight instruments, and an improved heating system. A four-blade tail rotor, a fore-and-aft litter kit, and an air-conditioning system are optional. Deliveries began in December 1982, following FAA certification in the preceding month. By early 1990 more than 275 had been delivered. Dedicated law enforcement variants of the MD 500E are equipped with a 30 million candlepower SX-16 Nightsun searchlight, siren, emergency services communications systems and a rescue net. A four-blade Quiet Knight tail rotor has also been developed to reduce the helicopter's noise level from the ground. Recent customers for law enforcement variants include the Hungarian Police Aviation Force, which ordered six MD 500Es for delivery in 1990.
MD 520N and MD 530N. NOTAR developments of MD 500 and MD 530. Described separately.
MD 530F Lifter. Derived from the MD 500D, this version is intended for operation at high altitudes or high temperatures. It has the fuselage configuration of the 500E and a derated Allison 250-C30 turboshaft engine which fits into the same engine compartment as the 250-C20B. FAA approval to increase the T-O rating from 280 kW (375 shp) to 317 kW (425 shp) was granted on 11 July 1985. To provide additional lift capability, the main rotor has a 0.3 m (1 ft) increase in diameter, and diameter of the tail rotor is

McDonnell Douglas MD 500E of Washington, DC, Metropolitan Police

increased by 5 cm (2 in). A cargo hook kit is available, capable of lifting an external load of up to 907 kg (2,000 lb). First flight was made on 22 October 1982. FAA certification was granted on 29 July 1983 and the first customer aircraft was delivered to Rogers Helicopters Inc on 20 January 1984. Deliveries include 26 for Iraq, for use in training, transportation and agricultural roles.

McDonnell Douglas Helicopter Company received orders for 111 civil and military versions of the MD 500/530 series in 1989, and plans to increase the production rate of these models to 120 per year by 1992. Current production rate is 72 per year.

The following details apply to the current MD 500E and 530F, except where indicated:

TYPE: Turbine powered civil light helicopter.

ROTOR SYSTEM: Five-blade fully articulated main rotor, with blades attached to laminated strap retention system by means of quick-disconnect pins for folding. Each blade consists of an extruded aluminium spar hot-bonded to one-piece wraparound aluminium skin. Trim tab outboard on each blade. Main rotor blades can be folded. Two-blade tail rotor, each blade comprising a swaged steel tube spar and metal skin covering. Four-blade quiet tail rotor, and main rotor brake, optional.

ROTOR DRIVE: Three sets of bevel gears, three driveshafts and one overrunning clutch. Main rotor/engine rpm ratio 1 : 12.594. Tail rotor/engine rpm ratio 1 : 1.956.

FUSELAGE: Aluminium semi-monocoque structure of pod and boom type. Clamshell doors at rear of pod give access to engine and accessories.

TAIL UNIT: T tail with horizontal stabiliser at tip of narrow chord sweptback fin; small auxiliary fin at tip of tailplane on each side; narrow chord sweptback ventral fin with integral tailskid to protect tail rotor in tail-down attitude near ground.

LANDING GEAR: Tubular skids carried on McDonnell Douglas oleo-pneumatic shock absorbers. Utility floats, snow skis and emergency inflatable floats optional.

POWER PLANT: MD 500E is powered by a 313 kW (420 shp) Allison 250-C20B turboshaft, which is derated to 280 kW (375 shp) for T-O and has a max continuous rating of 261 kW (350 shp). Allison 250-C20R, rated at 280 kW (375 shp) for T-O and 261 kW (350 shp) max continuous, optional. MD 530F has a 485 kW (650 shp) Allison 250-C30 turboshaft, derated to 317 kW (425 shp) for take-off and 261 kW (350 shp) max continuous. Two interconnected bladder fuel tanks with combined usable capacity of 240 litres (63.4 US gallons; 52.8 Imp gallons). Self-sealing fuel tank optional. Refuelling point on starboard side of fuselage. Auxiliary fuel system, with 79.5 litre (21 US gallon; 17.5 Imp gallon) internal tank, available optionally. Oil capacity 5.7 litres (1.5 US gallons; 1.2 Imp gallons).

ACCOMMODATION: Forward bench seat for pilot and two passengers, with two or four passengers, or two litter patients and one medical attendant, in rear portion of cabin. Low-back front seats and individual rear seats, with fabric or leather upholstery, optional. Baggage space, capacity 0.31 m³ (11 cu ft), under and behind rear seat in five-seat form. Clear space for 1.19 m³ (42 cu ft) of cargo or baggage with only three front seats in place. Two doors on each side. Interior soundproofing optional.

SYSTEMS: Aero Engineering Corporation air-conditioning system or Fargo pod mounted air-conditioner optional.

AVIONICS AND EQUIPMENT (MD 500E): Optional avionics include dual Bendix/King KY 195 com, KX 175 nav/com, KR 85 ADF, and KT 76 transponder; dual Collins VHF-251 com, VHF-251/351 nav/com, IND-350 nav indicator, ADF-650 ADF, and TDR-950 transponder; intercom system, headsets, microphones; and public address system. Standard equipment includes outside air temperature gauge, 8-day clock, engine hour meter, five sets inertia reel shoulder harness, cargo tiedown fittings, fire extinguisher, first aid kit, passenger steps, ground handling wheels, external power socket, landing light, skid-tip position light, anti-collision strobe lights, navi-

gation lights, cockpit utility light, aft cabin light, and instrument lights. Optional equipment includes shatterproof glass, heating/demisting system, radios and intercom, attitude and directional gyros, rate of climb indicator, nylon mesh seats, dual controls, cargo hook, cargo racks, underfuselage cargo pod, heated pitot tube, extended landing gear, blade storage rack, litter kit, emergency inflatable floats and inflated utility floats. FAA supplemental certification has been received for installing a 30 million candlepower Spectrolab SX-16 Nightsun searchlight.

DIMENSIONS, EXTERNAL:

Main rotor diameter: 500E	8.05 m (26 ft 5 in)	
530F	8.33 m (27 ft 4 in)	
Main rotor blade chord	0.171 m (6¾ in)	
Tail rotor diameter: 500E	1.37 m (4 ft 6 in)	
530F	1.40 m (4 ft 7 in)	
Distance between rotor centres:		
500E	4.67 m (15 ft 4 in)	
530F	4.88 m (16 ft 0 in)	
Length overall, rotors turning:		
500E	9.40 m (30 ft 10 in)	
530F	9.78 m (32 ft 1 in)	
Length of fuselage	7.49 m (24 ft 7 in)	
Height to top of rotor head (standard skids)		
500E	2.67 m (8 ft 9 in)	
530F	2.67 m (8 ft 9 in)	
Tailplane span	1.65 m (5 ft 5 in)	
Skid track (standard)	1.91 m (6 ft 3 in)	
Cabin doors (each): Height	1.13 m (3 ft 8½ in)	
Max width	0.76 m (2 ft 6 in)	
Height to sill: 500E	0.79 m (2 ft 7 in)	
530F	0.76 m (2 ft 6 in)	
Cargo compartment doors (each):		
Height	1.12 m (3 ft 8¼ in)	
Width	0.88 m (2 ft 10½ in)	
Height to sill: 500E	0.71 m (2 ft 4 in)	
530F	0.66 m (2 ft 2 in)	

DIMENSIONS, INTERNAL:

Cabin: Length	2.44 m (8 ft 0 in)	
Max width	1.31 m (4 ft 3½ in)	
Max height	1.52 m (5 ft 0 in)	

AREAS:

Main rotor blades (each): 500E	0.62 m² (6.67 sq ft)	
530F	0.65 m² (6.96 sq ft)	
Tail rotor blades (each): 500E	0.063 m² (0.675 sq ft)	
530F	0.066 m² (0.711 sq ft)	
Main rotor disc: 500E	50.89 m² (547.81 sq ft)	
530F	54.58 m² (587.50 sq ft)	

Tail rotor disc: 500E	1.53 m² (16.47 sq ft)	
530F	1.65 m² (17.72 sq ft)	
Fin	0.56 m² (6.05 sq ft)	
Horizontal stabiliser	0.76 m² (8.18 sq ft)	

WEIGHTS AND LOADINGS:

Weight empty: 500E	654 kg (1,441 lb)	
530F	709 kg (1,564 lb)	
Max normal T-O weight: 500E	1,361 kg (3,000 lb)	
530F	1,406 kg (3,100 lb)	
Max overload T-O weight:		
500E, 530F	1,610 kg (3,550 lb)	
Max gross weight, external load:		
530F	1,701 kg (3,750 lb)	
Max normal disc loading:		
500E	26.76 kg/m² (5.48 lb/sq ft)	
530F	25.78 kg/m² (5.28 lb/sq ft)	
Max normal power loading:		
500E	4.35 kg/kW (7.14 lb/shp)	
530F	2.90 kg/kW (4.77 lb/shp)	

PERFORMANCE (A: 500E, B: 530F, at max normal T-O weight):

Never-exceed speed at S/L:		
A, B	152 knots (282 km/h; 175 mph)	
Max cruising speed at S/L:		
A	134 knots (248 km/h; 154 mph)	
B	133 knots (246 km/h; 153 mph)	
Max cruising speed at 1,525 m (5,000 ft):		
A	132 knots (245 km/h; 152 mph)	
B	134 knots (248 km/h; 154 mph)	
Econ cruising speed at S/L:		
A	129 knots (239 km/h; 149 mph)	
B	131 knots (243 km/h; 151 mph)	
Econ cruising speed at 1,525 m (5,000 ft):		
A, B	123 knots (228 km/h; 142 mph)	
Max rate of climb at S/L: A	536 m (1,760 ft)/min	
B	645 m (2,115 ft)/min	
Vertical rate of climb at S/L: A	248 m (813 ft)/min	
B	446 m (1,462 ft)/min	
Service ceiling: A, B,	4,875 m (16,000 ft)	
Hovering ceiling, IGE, ISA: A	2,590 m (8,500 ft)	
B	4,360 m (14,300 ft)	
ISA +20°C: A	1,830 m (6,000 ft)	
B	3,660 m (12,000 ft)	
Hovering ceiling, OGE, ISA: A	1,830 m (6,000 ft)	
B	3,660 m (12,000 ft)	
ISA +20°C: A	975 m (3,200 ft)	
B	2,970 m (9,750 ft)	
Range, 2 min warm-up, standard fuel, no reserves:		
A at S/L	233 nm (431 km; 268 miles)	
B at S/L	202 nm (374 km; 232 miles)	
A at 1,525 m (5,000 ft)	258 nm (478 km; 297 miles)	
B at 1,525 m (5,000 ft)	228 nm (422 km; 262 miles)	

MCDONNELL DOUGLAS MODEL 500/530 DEFENDER

US Army designations: AH-6, MH-6

Details of the 500MD Scout Defender, 500MD/TOW Defender, 500MD/ASW Defender, and 500MD Defender II variants of the MD 500 may be found in the 1987-88 and earlier editions of *Jane's*.

Military versions of the MD 500/530 available in 1990 were as follows:

500MG Defender. As 530MG, but with 313 kW (420 shp) Allison 250-C20B turboshaft and MD 500E rotor system. In July 1985 a **Paramilitary MG Defender** version was introduced which is intended as a low cost helicopter suitable for use by police, border patrol, rescue, narcotics control and internal security authorities. It is offered in both 500E and 530F configurations.

530MG Defender. Based on airframe and power plant of the commercial MD 530F Lifter. Development began in late 1982, and demonstrator (N530MG) flew for first time

McDonnell Douglas 530MG Defender, with TOW missiles and mast mounted sight *(Pilot Press)*

on 4 May 1984. Integrated crew station provides a compact multi-function display which enhances cockpit field of view and enables hands-on control of the helicopter at all times, with all weapons delivery, communications management, and flight control conducted via the collective and cyclic sticks. A 79.5 litre (21 US gallon; 17.5 Imp gallon) internal auxiliary fuel tank is optional.

The 530MG Defender is designed primarily for point attack and anti-armour missions, but is equally suitable for scout, day and night surveillance, utility, cargo lift, and light attack duties. A programme is under way to develop an over-the-horizon capability for naval applications.

Equipment includes Racal Avionics RAMS 3000 integrated control and display system for all-weather and NOE flight, designed to operate with a MIL-STD-1553B interface and comprising a processor interface unit (PIU), a control display unit (CDU), and a data transfer device (DTD) linked by a dual 1553B databus. A multi-function display incorporates a high resolution monochrome CRT with alpha-numeric and symbolic data overlay capability. The CDU incorporates a monochrome CRT with line keys and keyboard and can be used to conduct all normal flight planning, navigational, frequency selection, and subsystem management functions by use of dedicated keys on the CDU keyboard. Data are transferred to the DTD from a ground loader unit via an RS-232C serial data link which is placed in a cockpit receptacle for update transfer to the data base of the PIU. Other equipment includes Astronautics Corpn autopilot; Decca Doppler navigation system integrated with Racal Doppler velocity sensor; Ferranti FIN 1110 AHRS; twin Collins VHF/UHF AM/FM radios; Bendix/King HF radio, ADF/VOR, radar altimeter and transponder; Telephonics intercom; and SFENA attitude indicator. Optional avionics include Hughes Aircraft TOW mast mounted sight system, FLIR, radar warning receiver, IFF, GPWS and laser rangefinder.

Standard 14 in NATO racks are provided for external stores. Weapons qualified or tested include TOW 2 anti-armour missiles, FN pods containing two 7.62 mm or one 0.50 in machine-gun, and 2.75 in rockets in 7-tube or 12-tube launchers. Additional weapons are planned to include four General Dynamics Stinger air-to-air missiles and a 7.62 mm McDonnell Douglas Chain Gun automatic machine-gun. Chaff and infra-red decoy flares can be carried, with automatic chaff ejection on threat detection facility. Both cyclic sticks have triggers for gun or rocket firing; the co-pilot/gunner's visual image display has two handgrips for TOW/FLIR operation.

Nightfox. Introduced in January 1986 as low cost helicopter for night surveillance and military operations. Equipment includes a FLIR Systems Inc Series 2000 thermal imager and night vision goggles, with weapons as for 530MG. Available in both 500MG and 530MG configurations. Four MD 500MG Nightfoxes reportedly delivered to Colombian Air Force.

AH-6 and MH-6. Versions in limited service with US Army 160th Special Operations Aviation Group (Night Stalkers), based at Fort Campbell, Kentucky. Identified variants are **MH-6B, AH-6C** and **EH-6B** conversions from OH-6A, of which most withdrawn from operational service; **AH-6F** and **MH-6E**, based on MD 500MG, and **AH-6G** and **MH-6F** based on MD 530MG. All believed to be equipped with 7.62 mm Miniguns, machine-guns and rocket pods with provision for Stinger air-to-air missiles; MH-6E and MH-6F equipped with cockpit multi-function displays and FLIR, used in conjunction with night vision goggles. A total of 12 AH-6s and 17 MH-6s is believed to be in service. Aircraft of this type, flying from the frigate USS *Jarrett*, took part in the action against the Iranian minelayer *Iran Ajr* in the Persian Gulf in September 1987.

DIMENSIONS, EXTERNAL (A: 500MD/TOW, B: 530MG):
As for 500E/530F except:
Length of fuselage: A   7.62 m (25 ft 0 in)
     B   7.29 m (23 ft 11 in)

McDonnell Douglas 530MG Defender, with TOW missile launchers and nose mounted Hughes M65 sight

Height to top of rotor head: A	2.64 m (8 ft 8 in)	Hovering ceiling IGE: ISA: A	2,590 m (8,500 ft)	
B	2.62 m (8 ft 7 in)	B	4,360 m (14,300 ft)	
B with MMS	3.41 m (11 ft 2½ in)	ISA + 20°C: A	1,830 m (6,000 ft)	
Height over tail (endplate fins):		B	3,660 m (12,000 ft)	
A	2.71 m (8 ft 10½ in)	A, 35°C	1,341 m (4,400 ft)	
B	2.59 m (8 ft 6 in)	B, 35°C	2,680 m (8,800 ft)	
Width over skids: A	1.93 m (6 ft 4 in)	Hovering ceiling OGE: ISA: A	1,830 m (6,000 ft)	
B	1.96 m (6 ft 5 in)	B	3,660 m (12,000 ft)	
Width over TOW pods: A, B	3.23 m (10 ft 7¼ in)	ISA + 20°C: A	975 m (3,200 ft)	
Tailskid ground clearance: A	0.64 m (2 ft 1¼ in)	B	2,970 m (9,750 ft)	
B	0.61 m (2 ft 0 in)	A, 35°C	732 m (2,400 ft)	
WEIGHTS:		B, 35°C	2,120 m (6,950 ft)	
Weight empty, equipped: A	849 kg (1,871 lb)	Range, 2 min warm-up, standard fuel, no reserves:		
B	898 kg (1,979 lb)	A at S/L	203 nm (376 km; 233 miles)	
Max T-O weight: A, normal	1,361 kg (3,000 lb)	B at S/L	176 nm (326 km; 202 miles)	
A, max overload	1,610 kg (3,550 lb)	A at 1,525 m (5,000 ft)	227 nm (420 km; 261 miles)	
B, normal	1,406 kg (3,100 lb)	B at 1,525 m (5,000 ft)	200 nm (370 km; 230 miles)	
B, max overload	1,701 kg (3,750 lb)	Endurance with standard fuel, 2 min warm-up, no		
PERFORMANCE (at max normal T-O weight, except where		reserves: A at S/L	2 h 23 min	
indicated):		B at S/L	1 h 56 min	
Never-exceed speed at S/L:		A at 1,525 m (5,000 ft)	2 h 35 min	
A, B	130 knots (241 km/h; 150 mph)	B at 1,525 m (5,000 ft)	2 h 7 min	
Max cruising speed at S/L:				
A, B	121 knots (224 km/h; 139 mph)			

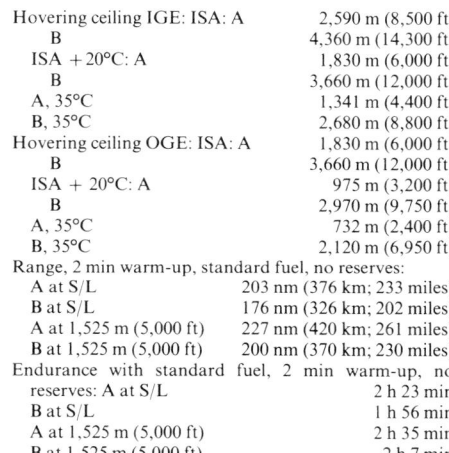

Max cruising speed at 1,525 m (5,000 ft):
A   120 knots (222 km/h; 138 mph)
B   123 knots (228 km/h; 142 mph)
Max rate of climb at S/L, ISA: A   520 m (1,707 ft)/min
B   626 m (2,055 ft)/min
Vertical rate of climb at S/L: A   248 m (813 ft)/min
B   445 m (1,660 ft)/min
Service ceiling: A   4,636 m (15,210 ft)
B   over 4,875 m (16,000 ft)

MCDONNELL DOUGLAS MD 520N and MD 530N NOTAR HELICOPTERS

Under a $2.2 million 24-month contract from the US Army Applied Technology Laboratory and the Defense Advanced Research Projects Agency, an Army OH-6A helicopter (65-12917) was modified to serve as the prototype of the no-tail-rotor (NOTAR) helicopter, and was flown for the first time in this form on 17 December 1981. Details of the programme can be found in the 1982-83 *Jane's*. During 1985 the NOTAR prototype was extensively modified, with a new forward fuselage similar in profile to that of the MD 500E, a 313 kW (420 shp) Allison 250-C20B turboshaft, a new fan with composite blades of smaller diameter and greater chord than the original metal bladed fan, and a second air circulation slot on the tailboom. Flight testing of the helicopter resumed on 12 March 1986 and was completed in June when more than 400 flight hours had been recorded. A photograph of the NOTAR testbed in final configuration may be found in the 1988-89 edition of *Jane's*. At the Helicopter Association International convention held at Anaheim, California, in February 1988, McDonnell Douglas Helicopter Company announced development of prototype NOTAR versions of the MD 500/530, designated MD 520N and MD 530N, for which detailed design work began in May 1988.

The MD 520N/530N, which were officially launched at the 1989 HAI convention in New Orleans, are powered by Allison 250-C20R-2 or 250-C30 turboshafts respectively, as detailed in the MD 500/530 model listings, and feature an increased diameter rotor, new tailboom of graphite composites construction, advanced NOTAR circulation fan, and new tail surfaces. Both the MD 520N and 530N feature a small horizontal tailplane with twin fins moving in synchronisation with the side-thrust vanes in the tail. The fins provide directional control during autorotation so that a power-off run-on landing can be made at less than 20 knots (37 km/h; 23 mph).

McDonnell Douglas AH-6F of the US Army's Task Force 160, fitted with Stinger missiles
(Ivo Sturzenegger)

McDonnell Douglas MD 530N with NOTAR tailboom

McDonnell Douglas MD 530N five-seat NOTAR helicopter *(Jane's/Mike Keep)*

The first prototype, an MD 530N (N530NT), made its first flight on 29 December 1989, the 520N following a few weeks later. FAA certification for both models was expected in September 1990. By early February 1990 McDonnell Douglas had received orders for 115 MD 520N/530N variants, including seven MD 520Ns to be delivered to the Police Department of Phoenix, Arizona. Deliveries of NOTAR models are scheduled to begin in early 1991. Military variants, similar to those described for the MD 500/530 series, are also being developed.

The following details, which should be regarded as provisional, refer to the MD 520N:

DIMENSIONS, EXTERNAL:

Main rotor diameter	8.62 m (28 ft 3½ in)
Length: overall, rotor turning	9.75 m (32 ft 0 in)
fuselage	7.62 m (25 ft 0 in)
Height to top of rotor head:	
standard skids	2.65 m (8 ft 8½ in)
extended skids	2.91 m (9 ft 6¾ in)
Height to top of fins	3.11 m (10 ft 2½ in)
Tailplane span	2.07 m (6 ft 9½ in)
Skid track	1.98 m (6 ft 6 in)

WEIGHTS:

Weight empty: standard	696 kg (1,534 lb)
industrial	650 kg (1,434 lb)
Max fuel weight	183 kg (403 lb)
Max hook capacity	907 kg (2,000 lb)
Max T-O weight: normal	1,519 kg (3,350 lb)
external load	1,746 kg (3,850 lb)

PERFORMANCE (estimated, at normal max T-O weight, ISA, except where indicated):

Never-exceed speed	152 knots (281 km/h; 175 mph)
Max cruising speed:	
at S/L	136 knots (251 km/h; 156 mph)
at 1,525 m (5,000 ft)	135 knots (249 km/h; 155 mph)
Max rate of climb at S/L: ISA	555 m (1,820 ft)/min
ISA + 20°C	479 m (1,570 ft)/min
Service ceiling	4,815 m (15,800 ft)
Hovering ceiling, IGE, ISA	3,078 m (10,100 ft)
OGE, ISA	2,230 m (7,310 ft)
ISA + 20°C	757 m (2,482 ft)
Maximum range, standard fuel:	
S/L	226 nm (418 km; 260 miles)
at 1,525 m (5,000 ft)	247 nm (458 km; 285 miles)
Endurance at S/L	2 h 27 min

MCDONNELL DOUGLAS MD 900 MDX

At the 1989 Helicopter Association International convention at New Orleans, Louisiana, McDonnell Douglas launched development of a new twin-engined commercial helicopter designated MDX, initial details of which had been announced at the previous year's HAI convention. In February 1989 Hawker de Havilland Limited of Australia became a partner in the MDX programme. It will be responsible for final design and airframe production for the helicopter, shipping airframes to Mesa (Arizona) for final assembly, power plant and systems installation and flight testing. Transmissions will be provided by Kawasaki Heavy Industries of Japan. Other international partners are expected to join the programme.

The MDX will seat eight in a passenger transport role, with three-abreast seating which can be removed for cargo carrying. Access to the main cabin area is via a large sliding door on each side. The MDX will employ the NOTAR anti-torque system, an all-composites five-blade flexbeam main rotor, advanced all-digital liquid crystal systems monitoring, and mechanical instruments for attitude, airspeed and altitude. Customers will have the choice of the Pratt & Whitney Canada PW206A turboshaft or, after the 100th helicopter, the Turbomeca TM319-2 turboshaft, each rated at 450 kW (603 shp). An initial production rate of 108 aircraft per year is planned. McDonnell Douglas anticipates a market for 800-1,000 MDXs in the first decade of production, and held orders for 271 by the end of 1989. First flight is scheduled for July 1992, with certification anticipated in October 1993 and first deliveries in December of that year.

The following data are provisional:

DIMENSIONS, EXTERNAL:

Main rotor diameter	10.32 m (33 ft 10¼ in)
NOTAR fan diameter	0.56 m (1 ft 10 in)
Main rotor blade chord	0.25 m (10 in)
Length overall, rotor turning	11.96 m (39 ft 3 in)
Fuselage length	10.49 m (34 ft 4¾ in)
Height to top of rotor head	3.43 m (11 ft 3 in)
Tailplane span	2.66 m (8 ft 8½ in)
Skid track	2.29 m (7 ft 6 in)
Passenger doors: Height	1.24 m (4 ft 1 in)
Width	1.27 m (4 ft 2 in)
Baggage door: Height	0.86 m (2 ft 10 in)
Width: top	0.61 m (2 ft 0 in)
bottom	0.80 m (2 ft 7½ in)

DIMENSIONS, INTERNAL:

Cabin: Length, excl cockpit	1.91 m (6 ft 3 in)
Max width	1.63 m (5 ft 4 in)
Max height	1.27 m (4 ft 2 in)
Floor area	3.09 m² (33.3 sq ft)
Volume	3.94 m³ (139.0 cu ft)
Baggage compartment volume	1.47 m³ (52.0 cu ft)

AREAS:

Main rotor blades (each)	1.00 m² (10.78 sq ft)
Main rotor disc	83.61 m² (900.0 sq ft)
Rudders (total)	2.52 m² (27.10 sq ft)
Tailplane	0.91 m² (9.77 sq ft)

WEIGHTS:

Weight empty	1,170 kg (2,580 lb)
Max payload, internal fuel	1,134 kg (2,500 lb)
Max fuel weight	485 kg (1,070 lb)
Max T-O weight	2,449 kg (5,400 lb)
Max zero-fuel weight	1,986 kg (4,380 lb)

PERFORMANCE (estimated, at max T-O weight):

Never-exceed speed	175 knots (324 km/h; 201 mph)
Max level and max cruising speed	150 knots (278 km/h; 173 mph)
Econ cruising speed	130 knots (241 km/h; 150 mph)
Max rate of climb at S/L	966 m (3,170 ft)/min
Vertical rate of climb at S/L	651 m (2,137 ft)/min
Service ceiling	6,100 m (20,000 ft)
Service ceiling, one engine out	3,350 m (11,000 ft)
Hovering ceiling: IGE	4,265 m (14,000 ft)
OGE	3,840 m (12,600 ft)
Range with max fuel	350 nm (648 km; 403 miles)

MCDONNELL DOUGLAS APACHE
US Army designation: AH-64A

The Hughes (now McDonnell Douglas Helicopter Company) Model 77 was designed to meet the US Army's requirement for an advanced attack helicopter (AAH) capable of undertaking a full day/night/adverse weather anti-armour mission, and of fighting, surviving and 'living

McDonnell Douglas MD 900 MDX eight/ten-seat commercial helicopter *(Jane's/Mike Keep)*

Model of the McDonnell Douglas MD 900 MDX twin-turboshaft NOTAR helicopter

with' troops in a front-line environment. Two YAH-64 flight test prototypes made their initial flights on 30 September and 22 November 1975 respectively. Details of the prototype and full scale engineering development programmes can be found in the 1984-85 and earlier editions of *Jane's*. Selection of the AH-64 for the US Army was announced in December 1976, and it was given the name Apache in late 1981.

Targets for US Apache procurement have varied. Current planning calls for the 807th and last, from FY 1990 funding, to be delivered in September 1993. Following the six prototype and pre-series helicopters, FY 1982-90 funding covered 11, 48, 112, 138, 116, 101, 77, 72 and 132 helicopters, completing procurement at 807 plus five flying prototypes. Deliveries began on 26 January 1984, and 539 had been produced by January 1990. Teledyne Ryan is responsible for building the AH-64 fuselage, wings, engine nacelles, avionics bays, canopy and tail unit.

Self-deployment capability was demonstrated on 4 April 1985, when the 14th production Apache, with four 871 litre (230 US gallon; 191 Imp gallon) external fuel tanks, made a 1,020 nm (1,891 km; 1,175 mile) nonstop flight from Mesa to Santa Barbara, landing with 30 minutes' fuel remaining. Such ferry range permits deployment from the USA to Europe via a northern Atlantic route, with stops at Goose Bay, Frobisher Bay, Søndrestrøm, Reykjavik and Prestwick. If the required deployment is farther than ferry range, the Apache can be carried in C-141B StarLifter and C-5 Galaxy transports (two and six Apaches respectively). Loading trials have also been conducted with a mockup of the McDonnell Douglas C-17A, which could accommodate up to three Apaches.

Initial operational capability was achieved in July 1986 by the 6th Cavalry Regiment's 3rd Squadron. By December 1989, 15 of the 30 projected Apache battalions were in operation, whilst establishment was planned in 1990 of a further seven. Combat debut was achieved in December 1989 when 11 Apaches participated in the US policing action in Panama. In addition to regular Army units, Apaches have been issued to the National Guard, beginning in 1987 with 1 Battalion/130 Aviation Regiment at Raleigh Durham, NC, and continuing with 1/151 AvRgt at MacEntire, SC, and 1/111 AvRgt at Craig Field, FL. A Utah ArNG Battalion was due to convert in 1990.

The 2/6 Cavalry Regiment at Illesheim, West Germany, became the first overseas Apache operator in September 1987. By 1990, AH-64As had replaced Bell AH-1 Cobras with the 5/6 Cav at Wiesbaden, 4/229 AvRgts at Illesheim, 2/227 and 3/227 AvRgts at Hanau and 2/1 and 3/1 AvRgts also at Hanau. Established battalion strength is 18 Apaches and 13 Bell OH-58 Kiowas. Over 200 Apaches will be based in Europe.

In October 1987 McDonnell Douglas Helicopter Company began a $10 million, 11 month programme to integrate General Dynamics Stinger air-to-air missiles with the Apache. The helicopter can carry up to four Stingers, mounted in pairs on the tips of each stub wing. Successful test firing of two AIM-9 Sidewinder air-to-air missiles was carried out in late November 1987 at the US Army's White Sands, New Mexico, range as part of a programme to explore the Apache's air-to-air combat capability. The firings were made in the hover, and in forward flight at a speed of 80 knots (148 km/h; 92 mph). The Apache also conducted laser ranging and tracking tests, using Bell UH-1 helicopters and LTV A-7 attack aircraft as aerial targets. The first phase of the programme culminated in February 1989 with live firings of Sidewinders. Army and company funds are also being used to develop other air-to-air missile installations for the helicopter, and to enhance the M230 Chain Gun for the air-to-air role. Stinger and Matra Mistral missiles have been integrated with the AH-64A's weapons system. Five test firings of Stingers, including one which destroyed a target drone, were made in early 1989 at the US Army's proving grounds at Yuma, Arizona. Two of the firings used telemetry to monitor the missile's launch and target acquisition, and one firing was done at night. Following a 15-month evaluation of test results which began in May 1989, and integration of a new missile control system manufactured by Base 10 Defense of Trenton, New Jersey, two further Stingers are scheduled to be fired from an AH-64A in 1990. On 25 April 1988 a Sidearm missile fired from an Apache at the US Naval Weapons Center hit an armoured vehicle containing an RF emitter. Captive carry tests of Mistrals had been completed by early 1989, with test firings of the missile planned for later in the year. Captive trials of the Shorts Starstreak missile are scheduled for 1990, with live firings to follow in 1991.

McDonnell Douglas Helicopter Company has received contracts from the US Army Aviation Applied Directorate to develop an advanced composite main rotor hub and fibre-reinforced thermoplastic secondary structures for the AH-64A, and to develop artificial intelligence applications for fault isolation and diagnosis of the helicopter's systems. A production AH-64A has been allocated for a five-year vibration analysis study funded by NASA's Langley Research Center.

In April 1987 MDHC announced preliminary details of a proposed **Advanced Apache**, based on studies for an advanced development for the US Army which had been under way for 18 months. This helicopter would include advanced avionics and fly by wire flight controls, a new Honeywell ring laser INS, a data transfer system permitting cassette loading of mission data, ATHS, 1,491 kW (2,000 shp) T700 engines with digital control, improved cockpit fields of view, provision for air-to-air Stinger missiles slaved to the gunner's helmet for off-axis aiming, rearward looking TV with a fin mounted video camera, and a gun with longer barrel, active recoil damping and digital turret control. The Advanced Apache would have 75 per cent commonality with the AH-64A.

Advanced Apache did not go ahead and neither did a multi-stage improvement programme (MSIP) which would have included upgrading of the Apache's weapon, sensor and fire control systems, digital databus and crew displays, although MSIP funds were provided in the FY 1988 budget, allowing initial work to begin in mid-1988.

The AH-64 update programme is now centred on the **Longbow** millimetre-wave radar being developed by Westinghouse and the Hellfire missile equipped by Martin Marietta with an RF seeker that goes with it, plus the aircraft modifications required to accommodate it. Two Apaches fitted with proof of concept Longbow radars completed Early User Test and Experimentation (EUT&E) in April 1990 with seven RF Hellfire shots, six of which hit moving and stationary tank targets. The decision to proceed with the four-year full-scale development (FSD) was to be taken in June 1990.

Longbow can track flying targets in clutter and stationary or moving ground targets through rain, fog and smoke conditions in which normal FLIR and TV will not work. The system allows the Hellfire to lock-on before launch over shorter ranges or to accept target co-ordinates from which it can lock-on after launch at longer ranges. Longbow scans through 360° against aerial targets and over 270° in 90° sectors against ground targets. The mast-mounted rotating antenna weighs 136 kg (300 lb).

Reduced budgets have forced the US Army to retrofit only 227 AH-64s, out of the 330 available, with the Longbow system. All AH-64s are to be retrofitted with

McDonnell Douglas AH-64A Apache twin-turboshaft attack helicopter, demonstrating its agility

McDonnell Douglas AH-64A Apache tandem two-seat advanced attack helicopter *(Pilot Press)*

more powerful General Electric T700-GE-701C engines each rated at 1,385 kW (1,857 shp). For the Longbow installation a new Smiths electrical power distribution system, handling doubled load of 70kVA, MIL-STD-1553B multiplex databus allied to dual 1750A processors, and a new Parker Hannifin vapour-cycle cooling system to allow for the Longbow electronics units, are all being incorporated. The cost per aircraft is estimated at a maximum \$4 million compared with the present complete flyaway cost of \$9 million. The US Army is considering a so-called manprint cockpit layout with large multi-function displays for Longbow. Further available as later retrofits are air-to-air Stinger, digital autostabiliser, improved navigation with Global Positioning System, digital communications, faster target hand-off system, and enhanced fault detection system with data transfer and recording.

In January 1990, the Pentagon announced proposals to supply Apaches powered by T700-GE-701 turboshafts to Israel (19) and Egypt (24) under FMS provisions. Both nations will also receive Hellfire missiles, and their aircrews were due to begin training in the USA late in 1990.

Data follows for the AH-64A Apache. Differences of the Longbow Apache are summarised above.

TYPE: Twin-engined attack helicopter.

ROTOR SYSTEM: Four-blade fully articulated main rotor and four-blade tail rotor; all blades manufactured by Tool Research and Engineering Corpn (Composite Structures Division). Main rotor blades are of high-camber aerofoil section and broad chord, with sweptback tips, and can be folded or removed for air transportation. Each blade has five stainless steel spars lined with structural glassfibre tubes, a laminated stainless steel skin and a composite rear section, bonded together. Blades are attached to hub by a laminated strap retention system, and are fitted with elastomeric lead/lag dampers and offset flapping hinges. Tail rotor comprises two pairs of blades, mounted on port side of pylon/fin support structure at optimum quiet setting of approx 55°/125° to each other. AEG-Telefunken blade de-icing system. Main rotor driveshaft rotates within a fixed, hollow outer shaft, permitting removal of main transmission without dismantling main rotor system. This results in improved drive system reliability, as flight loads are transmitted to airframe via static mast instead of through main transmission. Entire system is capable of flight in negative g conditions.

ROTOR DRIVE: Litton (Precision Gear Division) main transmission and engine nose gearbox; transmission to tail rotor via Aircraft Gear Corpn grease-lubricated intermediate and tail rotor gearboxes, with Bendix driveshafts and couplings. Garrett cooling fan for tail rotor gearbox. Main transmission designed to operate for one hour after loss of oil; gearboxes can tolerate ballistic damage and continue to operate for up to one hour without failure. Selected dynamic components constructed of 7049 aluminium and electro-slag remelt (ESR) steel; critical parts of transmission (eg, bearings) have ESR collars for protection against hits by 12.7 mm ammunition. Rotor/engine rpm ratios approx 1 : 72.4 for main rotor, approx 1 : 14.9 for tail rotor.

WINGS: Cantilever mid-mounted wings of low aspect ratio, located aft of the cockpit. Wings are removable, and attach to sides of fuselage for transport and storage. Two hardpoints beneath each wing for the carriage of mixed ordnance or ferry tanks.

FUSELAGE: Conventional semi-monocoque aluminium structure. Designed to survive hits by 12.7 mm and 23 mm ammunition.

TAIL UNIT: Bolted pylon structure, with tail rotor mounted on port side. Low-mounted all-moving tailplane, with Simmonds actuators and Hamilton Standard control electronics.

LANDING GEAR: Menasco trailing arm type, with single mainwheels and fully castoring, self-centring and lockable tailwheel. Mainwheel tyres size 8.50-10, tailwheel tyre size 5.00-4. Hydraulic brakes on main units. Main gear is non-retractable, but legs fold rearward to reduce overall height for storage and transportation. Energy absorbing main and tail gears are designed for normal descent rates of up to 3.05 m (10 ft)/s and heavy landings at up to 12.8 m (42 ft)/s. Take-offs and landings can be made at structural design gross weight on terrain slopes of up to 12° (head-on) and 10° (side-on).

POWER PLANT: Two 1,265 kW (1,696 shp) General Electric T700-GE-701 turboshafts, derated for normal operations to provide reserve power for combat emergencies, and with automatic one engine inoperative rating of 1,285 kW (1,723 shp). Engines mounted one on each side of fuselage, above wings, with key components armour-protected. Upper cowlings let down to serve as maintenance platforms. Two crash resistant fuel cells in fuselage, combined capacity 1,422 litres (376 US gallons; 313 Imp gallons).

ACCOMMODATION: Crew of two in tandem: co-pilot/gunner in front, pilot behind on 48 cm (19 in) elevated seat. Crew seats, by Simula Inc, are of lightweight Kevlar. Teledyne Ryan canopy, with PPG transparencies and transparent acrylic blast barrier between cockpits, is designed to provide optimum field of view. Crew stations are protected by Ceradyne Inc lightweight boron armour shields in cockpit floor and sides, and between cockpits,

Close-up of the Apache's nose mounted TADS/PNVS installation *(Brian M. Service)*

offering protection against 23 mm high explosive and armour piercing rounds. Sierracin electric heating of windscreen. Seats and structure designed to give crew a 95 per cent chance of surviving ground impacts of up to 12.8 m (42 ft)/s.

SYSTEMS: AiResearch totally integrated pneumatic system includes a shaft driven compressor, air turbine starters, pneumatic valves, temperature control unit and environmental control unit. Parker Bertea dual hydraulic systems, operating at 207 bars (3,000 lb/sq in), with actuators ballistically tolerant to 12.7 mm direct hits. Redundant flight control system for both rotors. In the event of a flying control system failure, the system activates Honeywell secondary fly by wire control. Bendix electrical power system, with two 35kVA fully redundant engine driven AC generators, two 300A transformer-rectifiers, and URDC standby DC battery. Garrett GTP 36-55(H) 93 kW (125 shp) APU for engine starting and maintenance checking.

AVIONICS AND EQUIPMENT: Main avionics bays are adjacent to co-pilot/gunner's position, in large fairings on sides of fuselage. Communications equipment includes AN/ARC-164 UHF, AN/ARC-186 UHF/VHF, Tempest C-10414 intercom, KY-28/58/TSEC crypto secure voice, and C-8157 secure voice control. Singer-Kearfott AN/ASN-128 lightweight Doppler navigation system, with Litton LR-80 (AN/ASN-143) strapdown attitude and heading reference system (AHRS). Doppler system, with AHRS, permits nap-of-the-earth navigation and provides for storing target locations. Avionics fit includes an AN/ARN-89B ADF and an AN/APX-100 IFF transponder with KIT-1A secure encoding. Honeywell digital automatic stabilisation equipment (DASE). Aircraft survivability equipment (ASE) consists of an Aerospace Avionics AN/APR-39 passive radar warning receiver, an AN/AVR-2 laser warning receiver, a Sanders AN/ALQ-144 infra-red jammer, chaff dispensers, and an AN/ALQ-136 radar jammer. Other avionics include Astronautics Corpn HSI, an AN/APU-209 radar altimeter video display unit, and remote magnetic indicator, and Pacer Systems omnidirectional air data system. A Honeywell all-raster symbology generator processes TV data from IR and other sensors, superimposes symbology, and distributes the combination to CRT and helmet mounted displays in the aircraft. 'Black Hole' IR suppression system protects aircraft from heat-seeking missiles: this eliminates an engine bay cooling fan, by operating from engine exhaust gas through ejector nozzles to lower the gas plume and metal temperatures. BITE fault detection/location system.

ARMAMENT AND OPERATIONAL EQUIPMENT: Armament consists of a McDonnell Douglas M230 Chain Gun 30 mm automatic cannon, located between the mainwheel legs in an underfuselage mounting with SIADS Inc electronic controls. Normal rate of fire is 625 rds/min of Honeywell TP (target practice), HE or HEDP (high explosive dual purpose) ammunition, which is interoperable with NATO Aden/DEFA 30 mm ammunition. Max ammunition load is 1,200 rds. Gun mounting is designed to collapse into fuselage between pilots in the event of a crash landing. Four underwing hardpoints, with Aircraft Hydro-Forming pylons and ejector units, on which can be carried up to sixteen Rockwell Hellfire anti-tank missiles; or up to seventy-six 2.75 in FFAR (folding fin aerial rockets) in their launchers; or a combination of Hellfires and FFAR. Hellfire remote electronics by Rockwell; Bendix aerial rocket control system; multiplex (MUX) system units by Honeywell. Co-pilot/gunner (CPG) has primary responsibility for firing gun and missiles, but pilot can override his controls to fire gun or launch missiles. Martin Marietta Orlando Aerospace target acquisition and designation sight and AN/AAQ-11 pilot's night vision sensor (TADS/PNVS) comprises two independently functioning systems mounted on the nose. The TADS consists of a rotating turret (±120° in azimuth, +30/−60° in elevation) that houses the sensor subsystems, an optical relay tube in the CPG's cockpit, three electronic units in the avionics bay, and cockpit-mounted controls and displays. It is used principally for target search, detection and laser designation, with the

CPG as primary operator (though it can also provide backup night vision to the pilot in the event of a PNVS failure). Once acquired by the TADS, targets can be tracked manually or automatically for autonomous attack with gun, rockets or Hellfire missiles. The TADS daylight sensor consists of a TV camera with narrow (0.9°) and wide angle (4.0°) fields of view; direct view optics (4° narrow and 18° wide angle); a laser spot tracker; and an International Laser Systems laser rangefinder/designator. The night sensor, in the starboard half of the turret, incorporates a FLIR sight with narrow, medium and wide angle (3.1, 10.1 and 50.0°) fields of view. The PNVS consists of a FLIR sensor (30° × 40° field of view) in a rotating turret (±90° in azimuth, +20/−45° in elevation) mounted above the TADS; an electronics unit in the avionics bay; and the pilot's display and controls. It provides the pilot with thermal imaging that permits nap-of-the-earth flight to, from and within the battle area at night or in adverse daytime weather, at altitudes low enough to avoid detection by the enemy. PNVS imagery is displayed on a single monocle in front of one of the pilot's eyes; flight information such as airspeed, altitude and heading is superimposed on this imagery to simplify the piloting task. The monocle is a part of the Honeywell Avionics integrated helmet and display sighting system (IHADSS) worn by both crew members.

DIMENSIONS, EXTERNAL:

Main rotor diameter	14.63 m (48 ft 0 in)
Main rotor blade chord	0.53 m (1 ft 9 in)
Tail rotor diameter	2.79 m (9 ft 2 in)
Length overall: tail rotor turning	14.68 m (48 ft 2 in)
both rotors turning	17.76 m (58 ft 3⅛ in)
Wing span	5.23 m (17 ft 2 in)
Height: over tail fin	3.52 m (11 ft 6½ in)
over tail rotor	4.30 m (14 ft 1¼ in)
to top of rotor head	3.84 m (12 ft 7 in)
overall (top of air data sensor)	4.66 m (15 ft 3½ in)
Distance between c/l of pylons:	
inboard pair	3.20 m (10 ft 6 in)
outboard pair	4.72 m (15 ft 6 in)
Tailplane span	3.40 m (11 ft 2 in)
Wheel track	2.03 m (6 ft 8 in)
Wheelbase	10.59 m (34 ft 9 in)

AREAS:

Main rotor disc	168.11 m² (1,809.5 sq ft)
Tail rotor disc	6.13 m² (66.0 sq ft)

WEIGHTS:

Weight empty	4,881 kg (10,760 lb)
Max internal fuel weight	1,157 kg (2,550 lb)
Max external stores weight	771 kg (1,700 lb)
Structural design gross weight	6,650 kg (14,660 lb)
Primary mission gross weight	6,552 kg (14,445 lb)
Alternate mission gross weight	8,006 kg (17,650 lb)
Max T-O weight	9,525 kg (21,000 lb)

GENERAL PERFORMANCE (at 6,552 kg; 14,445 lb AUW, ISA except where indicated):

Never-exceed speed	197 knots (365 km/h; 227 mph)
Max level and max cruising speed	
	160 knots (296 km/h; 184 mph)
Max vertical rate of climb at S/L	762 m (2,500 ft)/min
Service ceiling	6,400 m (21,000 ft)
Service ceiling, one engine out	3,290 m (10,800 ft)
Hovering ceiling: IGE	4,570 m (15,000 ft)
OGE	3,505 m (11,500 ft)
Max range, internal fuel	260 nm (482 km; 300 miles)
Ferry range, max internal and external fuel, still air	
	918 nm (1,701 km; 1,057 miles)
Endurance at 1,220 m (4,000 ft) at 35°C	1 h 50 min
Max endurance, internal fuel	3 h 9 min
g limits at low altitude and airspeeds up to 164 knots	
(304 km/h; 189 mph)	+3.5/−0.5

WEIGHTS FOR TYPICAL MISSION PERFORMANCE (A: anti-armour at 1,220 m/4,000 ft and 35°C, 4 Hellfire and 320 rds of 30 mm ammunition; B: as A, but with 1200 rds; C: as A, but with 6 Hellfire and 540 rds; D: anti-armour at 610 m/2,000 ft and 21°C, 8 Hellfire and 1,200 rds; E: air cover at 1,220 m/4,000 ft and 35°C, 4 Hellfire and 1,200 rds; F: as E but at 610 m/2,000 ft and 21°C, 4 Hellfire, 19 rockets, 1,200 rds; G: escort at 1,220 m/4,000 ft and 35°C, 19 rockets and 1,200 rds; H: escort at 610 m/2,000 ft and 21°C, 38 rockets and 1,200 rds):

Mission fuel: A	727 kg (1,602 lb)
G	741 kg (1,633 lb)
E	745 kg (1,643 lb)
C	902 kg (1,989 lb)
B	1,029 kg (2,269 lb)
D	1,063 kg (2,344 lb)
H	1,077 kg (2,374 lb)
F	1,086 kg (2,394 lb)
Mission gross weight: A	6,552 kg (14,445 lb)
E	6,874 kg (15,154 lb)
G	6,932 kg (15,282 lb)
B, C	7,158 kg (15,780 lb)
D	7,728 kg (17,038 lb)
F	7,813 kg (17,225 lb)
H	7,867 kg (17,343 lb)

TYPICAL MISSION PERFORMANCE (A-H as above):

Cruising speed at intermediate rated power:	
C	147 knots (272 km/h; 169 mph)
D	148 knots (274 km/h; 170 mph)

F	150 knots (278 km/h; 173 mph)	F, G	262 m (860 ft)/min	
B	151 knots (280 km/h; 174 mph)	E	293 m (960 ft)/min	
E, H	153 knots (283 km/h; 176 mph)	D	301 m (990 ft)/min	
A	154 knots (285 km/h; 177 mph)	A	448 m (1,470 ft)/min	
G	155 knots (287 km/h; 178 mph)	Mission endurance: A, E, G	1 h 50 min	
Max vertical rate of climb at intermediate rated power:		C	1 h 17 min	
B, C	137 m (450 ft)/min	D, F, H	2 h 30 min	
H	238 m (780 ft)/min	B	2 h 40 min	

MCDONNELL DOUGLAS/BELL LH

Details of revised requirements for the US Army's LH programme, for which McDonnell Douglas Helicopter Company and Bell Helicopter Textron are teamed, may be found under the Bell entry in this section.

MELEX

MELEX USA INC

1221 Front Street, Raleigh, North Carolina 27609
Telephone: 1 (919) 828 7645
Telex: 825868 MELEX UF
Fax: 1 (919) 834 7290
VICE-PRESIDENT: George Lundy

This company, a subsidiary of Pezetel (PZL) of Poland (which see), is responsible for sales and operational support of PZL Mielec M-18 and M-18A Dromader agricultural aircraft operating in the western hemisphere.

TURBINES INC/MELEX T45 TURBINE DROMADER

Turbines Inc of Terre Haute, Indiana, in co-operation with Melex USA Inc, has developed a turboprop conversion of the M-18, based on the 895 kW (1,200 shp) Pratt & Whitney Canada PT6A-45AG engine (derated to 735 kW; 986 shp) driving a five-blade propeller and known as the T45 Turbine Dromader. The prototype (N2856G) flew for the first time on 17 August 1985, and a supplemental type certificate was obtained on 25 April 1986.

The conversion, which reduces the Dromader's empty weight by about 363 kg (800 lb), provides an increase in normal operating speed of some 20 knots (37 km/h; 23 mph) and a 10 per cent decrease in take-off distance at max T-O weight. Standard fuel capacity has been increased to 719 litres (190 US gallons; 158 Imp gallons). Improvements have also been made to the hydraulic and electrical systems. A second occupant can be carried in a rearward facing seat, and a dual control trainer version is also available.

Prototype T45 Turbine Dromader conversion with Pratt & Whitney Canada PT6A-45AG engine

MELEX DROMADER WATER BOMBER

Melex USA is also developing a firefighting version of the Dromader which would be able to replenish its tanks by collecting water via scoops while taxying. In early 1990 the company was investigating the use of hydro-skis for stabilising the aircraft on water as a possible alternative to conventional float landing gear.

MID-CONTINENT

MID-CONTINENT AIRCRAFT CORPORATION

Drawer L, Highway 84 East, Hayti, Missouri 63851
Telephone: 1 (314) 359 0500
Telex: 447183
Fax: 1 (314) 359 0538
CHAIRMAN: Richard Reade
PRESIDENT: Ken Mauk

MID-CONTINENT KING CAT

Mid-Continent Aircraft Corporation, an operator and distributor of Schweizer (Grumman) Ag-Cats and Ayres Thrushes, has obtained an FAA supplemental type certificate for an aircraft known as the King Cat. This is an Ag-Cat re-engined with an 895 kW (1,200 hp) Wright R-1820-202A radial engine, driving a three-blade metal propeller. The engineering work for the STC was carried out by Serv-Aero Engineering Inc. The King Cat has since been certificated in Canada.

Based on the airframe of the Super Ag-Cat C, which has a hopper accommodating 1,893 litres (500 US gallons; 416 Imp gallons) of spray or 1,814 kg (4,000 lb) of dry chemicals, the King Cat offers improved high-altitude/high-temperature performance. It is available as a conversion of a Super Ag-Cat C, or a kit is obtainable for installation by the customer or his maintenance organisation. Options which are available include upper wing installation height increase of 20.3 cm (8 in), Serv-O ailerons, increased fuel capacity of 431.5 litres (114 US gallons; 95 Imp gallons), Collins cockpit air-conditioning and a 1,893 litre (500 US gallon; 416 Imp gallon) water bombing system for fire control.

WEIGHTS AND LOADINGS:
Weight empty: basic   2,184 kg (4,816 lb)

Mid-Continent King Cat, a Wright engined conversion of a Super Ag-Cat C

spray equipped	2,257 kg (4,976 lb)	Typical working speed
dust equipped	2,225 kg (4,906 lb)	87-113 knots (161-209 km/h; 100-130 mph)
Max T-O weight: FAR 23	2,857 kg (6,300 lb)	Stalling speed, power off, at AUW of 2,857 kg
CAM 8	3,855 kg (8,500 lb)	(6,300 lb) 60 knots (111 km/h; 69 mph) CAS
Max wing loading:		T-O run with 907 kg (2,000 lb) hopper load
FAR 23	78.5 kg/m² (16.07 lb/sq ft)	293 m (960 ft)
CAM 8	105.9 kg/m² (21.68 lb/sq ft)	T-O to 15 m (50 ft) with 907 kg (2,000 lb) hopper load
Max power loading:		427 m (1,400 ft)
FAR 23	3.19 kg/kW (5.25 lb/hp)	Landing from 15 m (50 ft) at weight of 2,257 kg
CAM 8	4.31 kg/kW (7.08 lb/hp)	(4,976 lb) 363 m (1,190 ft)
PERFORMANCE:		Landing run at weight of 2,257 kg (4,976 lb)
Ferry speed	117 knots (217 km/h; 135 mph)	179 m (588 ft)

MOLLER

MOLLER INTERNATIONAL

1222 Research Park Drive, Davis, California 95616
Telephone: 1 (916) 756 5086
Fax: 1 (916) 756 5179
PRESIDENT: Paul S. Moller
MARKETING DIRECTOR: Jack G. Allison

Since 1960 Moller International has undertaken research and development projects in aerodynamics, noise suppression and vehicle design, leading to the construction and testing of a number of experimental VTOL aircraft which are said to combine the best features of helicopters, fixed-wing aircraft and cars. Prototypes known originally as the Discojet and later designated Model **XM-4** and Model **200X** were of flying saucer configuration with two-piece glassfibre airframes. Accommodation was provided for two occupants in a centrally mounted cockpit, around which were mounted eight 37.3 kW (50 hp) Wankel rotary ducted fans which provided lift for hovering flight and thrust for forward flight.

A developed production version known as the **Moller 400 Volantor** will seat four occupants, and is illustrated in an accompanying photograph. Work on the prototype slowed down in 1988 due to increased interest in unmanned versions, but a limited number of Moller 400s are expected to be available as experimental civilian aircraft in the early 1990s, with FAA certification in the Powered-Lift Aircraft category to follow. The Moller 400 will be powered by eight twin-rotor rotary engines driving ducted fans. Three redundant systems provide stability in pitch, roll and yaw axes. A ballistic parachute recovery system is installed.

Projected variants include the tandem two-seat **Moller 150** with power plants totalling 477.2 kW (640 hp), giving a cruising speed of 287 knots (532 km/h; 330 mph).

MOLLER 400 VOLANTOR

All data is provisional:
POWER PLANT: Eight 111.8 kW (150 hp) air-cooled rotary engines driving ducted fans. Maximum fuel capacity 227 litres (60 US gallons; 50 Imp gallons).
DIMENSIONS, EXTERNAL:

Length overall	5.33 m (17 ft 6 in)
Width overall	2.87 m (9 ft 5 in)
Height overall	1.68 m (5 ft 6 in)

WEIGHTS:
Max payload	447 kg (985 lb)
Max T-O weight	1,123 kg (2,475 lb)

PERFORMANCE:
Max level speed	350 knots (649 km/h; 403 mph)
Cruising speed at 38% power	
	280 knots (518 km/h; 322 mph)
Rate of climb at 75% power	1,920 m (6,300 ft)/min
Hovering ceiling	2,896 m (9,500 ft)
Service ceiling	9,449 m (31,000 ft)
Max range	738 nm (1,368 km; 850 miles)

Scale model of the Moller 400 Volantor ducted fan VTOL craft

MOONEY
MOONEY AIRCRAFT CORPORATION
PO Box 72, Louis Schreiner Field, Kerrville, Texas 78029-0072
Telephone: 1 (512) 896 6000
Telex: Easylink 62913770 OESL UD
Fax: 1 (512) 257 4635
SALES AND MARKETING:
8901 Wetmore Road, San Antonio International Airport, San Antonio, Texas 78216
Telephone: 1 (512) 824 2727
Fax: 1 (512) 824 4221
CHAIRMAN AND PRESIDENT: Alexandre Couvelaire
GENERAL MANAGER, ENGINEERING AND MANUFACTURING:
Robert A. Kromer
GENERAL MANAGER, SALES AND MARKETING:
William B. Starkey

The original Mooney Aircraft Inc was formed in June 1948, in Wichita, Kansas, from where the single-seat Model M-18 Mooney Mite was produced until 1952. Its subsequent history and name changes were detailed in the 1987-88 and earlier *Jane's*.

In 1985 M Alexandre Couvelaire, President of the Paris based Euralair/Avialair jet charter and fixed base operator, and M Michel Seydoux, President of MSC, jointly acquired Mooney Aircraft.

In June 1987 Mooney and Aerospatiale of France announced joint development of the TBM 700 pressurised turboprop light aircraft, details of which can be found under TBM in the International section of this edition. Mooney delivered a total of 143 aircraft during 1989.

MOONEY 201SE (M20J)
The original Mooney 201 first flew in June 1976 and received FAA certification in September 1976. The current model is known as the Mooney 201SE, and incorporates the 28V electrical system and rounded cabin windows introduced on the Model 205, which it supersedes in the Mooney range. By early 1990 Mooney had delivered a total of 1,740 Model 201s, including 69 in 1989.

TYPE: Four-seat cabin monoplane.

WINGS: Cantilever low-wing monoplane. Wing section NACA 63₂-215 at root, NACA 64₁-412 at tip. Dihedral 5° 30′. Incidence 2° 30′ at root, 1° at tip. Sweepforward 2° 29′. Light alloy structure with flush riveted stretch formed wraparound skins. Full span main spar; rear spar terminates at mid-span of flaps. Sealed-gap differentially operated light alloy ailerons. Electrically operated single-slotted light alloy flaps over 70 per cent of trailing-edge. No tabs.

FUSELAGE: Composite all-metal structure. Cabin section is of welded 4130 chrome molybdenum steel tube with light alloy covering. Rear section is of semi-monocoque construction, with light alloy bulkheads and skin and extruded light alloy stringers.

TAIL UNIT: Cantilever light alloy structure, with variable incidence tailplane. All surfaces covered with wraparound metal skin.

LANDING GEAR: Electrically retractable levered suspension tricycle type with airspeed safety switch bypass. Nosewheel retracts rearward, main units inward into wings. Rubber disc shock absorbers in main units. Cleveland mainwheels, size 6.00-6, and steerable nosewheel, size 5.00-5. Tyre pressure, mainwheels 2.07 bars (30 lb/sq in), nosewheel 3.38 bars (49 lb/sq in). Cleveland hydraulic single-disc brakes on mainwheels. Parking brake.

POWER PLANT: One 149 kW (200 hp) Textron Lycoming IO-360-A3B6D flat-four engine, driving a McCauley B2D34C214/90DHB-16 two-blade constant-speed metal propeller. Two integral fuel tanks in wings, with combined usable capacity of 242 litres (64 US gallons; 53.3 Imp gallons). Refuelling points in wing upper surface. Oil capacity 7.5 litres (2 US gallons; 1.7 Imp gallons).

ACCOMMODATION: Cabin accommodates four persons in pairs on individual vertically adjusting seats with reclining back, armrests, and lumbar support. Dual controls standard. Overhead ventilation system. Cabin heating and cooling system, with adjustable outlets and illuminated control. One-piece wraparound windscreen. Tinted Plexiglas windows. Rear seats removable for freight stowage. Rear seats fold forward for carrying cargo. Single door on starboard side. Compartment for 54 kg (120 lb) baggage behind cabin, with access from cabin or through door on starboard side. Windscreen defrosting system standard.

SYSTEMS: Hydraulic system for brakes only. Electrical system includes 70A alternator, 28V 70Ah battery, voltage regulator and warning lights, together with protective circuit breakers.

AVIONICS AND EQUIPMENT: A complete range of digital IFR avionics, including autopilot and weather avoidance systems, is available as an option. Standard equipment includes 'Greystone' instrument panel, airspeed indicator, sensitive altimeter with blind encoder, vertical speed indicator, turn co-ordinator, magnetic compass, directional gyro, pictorial artificial horizon, emergency locator transmitter, ammeter, oil pressure gauge, oil temperature gauge, fuel pressure gauge, manifold pressure gauge, tachometer, FT101 digital fuel totaliser, fuel sight gauges in wings, two electric fuel quantity gauges, electric outside air temperature gauge, CHT and EGT gauges, alternate static source, instrument panel annunciator lights, internally lighted instruments, rheostat controlled glareshield post lights, navigation lights, landing/taxi light, cabin lighting, three high intensity strobe lights, grey tinted windscreen and cabin windows, seat belts and shoulder harnesses for all seats, assist straps and baggage straps, hatrack, multiple cabin fresh air vents, cargo tiedowns, wing jackpoints and external tiedowns, towbar, fuel tank quick drains and fuel sampler cup, auxiliary power plug, heated pitot tube, epoxy polymide anti-corrosion treatment, and overall external polyurethane paint finish. Optional equipment includes export altimeter with millibar subscale, co-pilot's toe brakes, and deluxe control wheels.

Mooney 201SE four-seat light aircraft (Textron Lycoming IO-360-A3B6D engine)

DIMENSIONS, EXTERNAL:
Wing span	11.00 m (36 ft 1 in)
Wing chord, mean	1.50 m (4 ft 11¼ in)
Wing aspect ratio	7.45
Length overall	7.52 m (24 ft 8 in)
Height overall	2.54 m (8 ft 4 in)
Tailplane span	3.58 m (11 ft 9 in)
Wheel track	2.79 m (9 ft 2 in)
Wheelbase	1.82 m (5 ft 11½ in)
Propeller diameter	1.88 m (6 ft 2 in)
Propeller ground clearance	0.24 m (9½ in)

DIMENSIONS, INTERNAL:
Cabin: Length	2.90 m (9 ft 6 in)
Max width	1.10 m (3 ft 7½ in)
Max height	1.13 m (3 ft 8½ in)
Baggage door: Width	0.53 m (1 ft 9 in)
Height	0.43 m (1 ft 5 in)
Baggage compartment volume	0.38 m³ (13.5 cu ft)

AREAS:
Wings, gross	16.24 m² (174.8 sq ft)
Ailerons (total)	1.06 m² (11.4 sq ft)
Trailing-edge flaps (total)	1.66 m² (17.9 sq ft)
Fin	0.73 m² (7.92 sq ft)
Rudder	0.58 m² (6.23 sq ft)
Tailplane	1.99 m² (21.45 sq ft)
Elevators (total)	1.11 m² (12.05 sq ft)

WEIGHTS AND LOADINGS:
Weight empty	809 kg (1,784 lb)
Max T-O and landing weight	1,243 kg (2,740 lb)
Max wing loading	76.5 kg/m² (15.67 lb/sq ft)
Max power loading	8.34 kg/kW (13.7 lb/hp)

PERFORMANCE (at max T-O weight):
Never-exceed speed	196 knots (364 km/h; 226 mph)
Max level speed at S/L	175 knots (325 km/h; 202 mph)
Max cruising speed, 75% power at 2,470 m (8,100 ft)	
	168 knots (311 km/h; 193 mph)
Econ cruising speed, 55% power at 2,470 m (8,100 ft)	
	152 knots (282 km/h; 175 mph)
Stalling speed:	
flaps up	63 knots (117 km/h; 73 mph) IAS
wheels and flaps down	
	53 knots (98 km/h; 61 mph) CAS
Max rate of climb at S/L	314 m (1,030 ft)/min

Service ceiling	5,670 m (18,600 ft)
T-O to 15 m (50 ft)	463 m (1,517 ft)
Landing from 15 m (50 ft)	491 m (1,610 ft)
Landing run	235 m (770 ft)
Range: 55% power, no reserves	
	1,059 nm (1,962 km; 1,219 miles)
75% power, no reserves	
	951 nm (1,762 km; 1,095 miles)

MOONEY 201AT ADVANCED TRAINER (M20J)

In 1989 Mooney introduced the Model 201AT Advanced Trainer version of the Model 201SE. Principal differences in standard equipment are: 14V DC electrical system; 70A 12V alternator; three-position manually operated cowl flaps; dual brakes; hard-wearing interior trim with fore- and aft-, up- and down- and reclining front seats without armrests but with lumbar support and inertia reel shoulder harness and lapbelts; larger oil access door; instructor and pupil approach plate holders; white instrument panel with black control wheels; standby vacuum system; three strobe lights; auxiliary power plug and cables; high visibility striped external paint scheme; and ram-air system eliminated. Standard Bendix/King IFR training avionics package comprises KMA 24 audio panel; dual KX 155 nav/com; KN 64 DME; KR 87 ADF; KT 76A transponder; Terra blind encoder; 100T microphone; and David Clark four-position intercom. Embry Riddle Aeronautical University of Florida has taken delivery of eight Advanced Trainers, and Florida Institute of Technology has received three.

MOONEY 252TSE (M20K)

Mooney introduced the Model 252TSE (Turbo Special Edition) in late 1985 as a replacement for the Turbo Mooney 231, described in the 1985-86 *Jane's*. A total of 889 Model 231s was manufactured. Externally similar to the Model 231, the Mooney 252TSE differs in having a 156.5 kW (210 hp) Continental TSIO-360-MB-1 engine with Garrett TE04 turbocharger with automatic wastegate operation, an intercooler, electric cowl flap, NACA duct for induction air, a 28V electrical system and new landing gear doors which fully enclose the main legs and wheels when retracted. Principal external difference is the rounded cabin window design. By early 1990 Mooney had delivered a total of 230 Model 252TSEs, including 19 in 1989.

TYPE: Four-seat cabin monoplane.

WINGS: As for 201SE except vacuum operated, electrically controlled speedbrake optional, in upper surface of each wing at quarter span/two-thirds chord.

FUSELAGE AND TAIL UNIT: As for 201SE.

LANDING GEAR: Electrically retractable tricycle type. Steerable nosewheel retracts rearward, main units inward into wings. All wheels faired by doors when retracted. Shock absorption of nosewheel and mainwheel units by Lord rubber discs. Cleveland wheels, with mainwheel tyres size 6.00-6 (6-ply), pressure 2.90 bars (42 lb/sq in). Nosewheel tyre size 5.00-5 (6-ply), pressure 3.38 bars (49 lb/sq in). Cleveland hydraulic brakes. Parking brake.

POWER PLANT: One 156.5 kW (210 hp) Continental TSIO-360-MB-1 flat-six turbocharged and intercooled engine, driving a McCauley 2A34C216/90DHB-16E constant-speed metal propeller. Goodrich propeller de-icing optional. Two integral fuel tanks in inner wings, with combined capacity of 297.5 litres (78.6 US gallons; 65.4 Imp gallons), of which 286 litres (75.6 US gallons; 63 Imp gallons) are usable. Refuelling points in upper surface of the inboard section of each wing. Oil capacity 7.5 litres (2 US gallons; 1.7 Imp gallons).

ACCOMMODATION: Cabin accommodates four persons in pairs on individual seats. Front seats fully adjustable, with lumbar support. Rear seats fold flat for carriage of bulky items of cargo. Dual controls standard. Forward hinged door on starboard side. Baggage space aft of rear seat, accessible from cabin and via baggage door on starboard side. Accommodation heated and ventilated.

SYSTEMS: Hydraulic system for brakes only. 28V DC electrical system powered by a 70A engine driven alternator. Dual 70A alternators optional. 24V 22Ah battery. Electric standby vacuum system standard. Oxygen system, capacity 3.26 m³ (115.0 cu ft).

AVIONICS AND EQUIPMENT: Avionics options as for Mooney 201SE. Standard and optional equipment generally as for Mooney 201SE except that vacuum indicator, standby vacuum system with annunciator, push/pull vernier primary engine controls, turbine inlet temperature gauge, pressurised magnetos, air/oil separator, oil quick-drain, alternator loadmeter/voltmeter, fuel flow totaliser with memory, flight hour recorder, panel-mounted OAT gauge, electric clock, rheostat-controlled panel wash lighting, wingtip recognition lights, epoxy polymide and zinc chromate anti-corrosion treatment and sun visor with power chart standard, and dual alternators, oxygen system, hot-prop de-icing system, speed brakes, and leather interior optional.

DIMENSIONS, EXTERNAL AND INTERNAL:
As Mooney 201SE, except:

Length overall	7.75 m (25 ft 5 in)
Cabin door (stbd, over wing):	
Height	1.13 m (3 ft 8½ in)
Width	0.74 m (2 ft 5 in)
Baggage door (stbd, aft): Height	0.52 m (1 ft 8½ in)

Mooney Model 201AT Advanced Trainer in high visibility colour scheme

Mooney 252TSE (turbocharged Continental TSIO-360-MB-1 engine)

Width	0.43 m (1 ft 5 in)
Height to sill	1.17 m (3 ft 10 in)
AREAS:	
Fin	0.72 m² (7.80 sq ft)
Rudder	0.58 m² (6.25 sq ft)
Tailplane	1.99 m² (21.42 sq ft)
Elevators (total)	1.21 m² (13.0 sq ft)
WEIGHTS AND LOADINGS:	
Weight empty	871 kg (1,920 lb)
Max baggage	54 kg (120 lb)
Max ramp, T-O and landing weight	1,315 kg (2,900 lb)
Max wing loading	80.97 kg/m² (16.6 lb/sq ft)
Max power loading	8.4 kg/kW (13.8 lb/hp)
PERFORMANCE (at max T-O weight):	
Max level speed	219 knots (406 km/h; 252 mph)
Max cruising speed, 78.6% power at 8,535 m (28,000 ft)	
	202 knots (374 km/h; 233 mph)
Econ cruising speed, 55% power at 7,010 m (23,000 ft)	
	178 knots (330 km/h; 205 mph)
Stalling speed:	
landing gear and flaps up	
	61 knots (113 km/h; 71 mph)
landing gear and flaps down	
	59 knots (110 km/h; 68 mph)
Max rate of climb at S/L	329 m (1,080 ft)/min
Certificated ceiling	8,535 m (28,000 ft)
T-O to 15 m (50 ft)	655 m (2,150 ft)
Endurance at max cruising speed	5 h 48 min

MOONEY PFM (M20L)

Design started in April 1986 of the Mooney M20L, the engineering prototype of which (N20PM) made its first flight in May 1987. Known as the Mooney PFM, the aircraft is powered by a Porsche PFM 3200-N03 power plant. The airframe is generally similar to that of the Mooney 252TSE, but with an increase in fuselage length aft of the cabin area. The first production standard Mooney PFM (N10MP) made its first flight in October 1987 and was officially rolled out at the company's Kerville headquarters on 12 November. FAA certification was received in May 1988, when first customer deliveries began. By early 1990 Mooney had delivered a total of 41 PFMs.

The description for the Mooney 201SE and 252TSE applies also to the PFM except as follows:

FUSELAGE: Generally as for Mooney 201SE, 205 and 252TSE, but with cabin tubular structure extended aft of rear seats by 0.305 m (1 ft 0 in) and nosewheel mounting point moved forward by 0.20 m (8 in).

LANDING GEAR: As for previously described models, except that the inner pair of main landing gear doors is deleted and mainwheels are unfaired when retracted.

POWER PLANT: One 162 kW (217 hp) Porsche PFM 3200-N03 flat-six aircooled engine attached to three-point overhead tubular mount structure and driving a two-blade constant-speed composite construction Hartzell BHC-J2YF-1BF/B7421 propeller via 0.442:1 reduction gearing. Engine has Bosch K-Jetronic fuel injection with automatic mixture control, dual solid-state Magneti Marelli electronic ignition systems, and single lever power control. Two integral fuel tanks in inboard wing leading-edges, with combined capacity of 252 litres (66.5 US gallons; 55.4 Imp gallons), of which 229 litres (60.5 US gallons; 50.4 Imp gallons) are usable. Oil capacity 12.8 litres (3.375 US gallons; 2.8 Imp gallons).

ACCOMMODATION: Porsche AG-styled interior standard.

SYSTEMS: Dual 28V DC electrical systems including 70A alternators, dual 24V 22Ah batteries and dual bus systems. Scott oxygen system and propeller de-icing system optional.

AVIONICS AND EQUIPMENT: Optional digital nav/com avionics packages from Bendix/King and Narco including R/Nav systems. Other avionics options include Bendix/King KI 227 slaved ADF heading indicator, KI 229 RMI, KN 62A-03 DME, KN 63-06 DME with KDI 572 indicator, KR 87-03 ADF, KRA 10A-00 radar altimeter, KT 79-00 digital transponder, KMA 24H-71 intercom, KT 96-00 radio telephone, KFC 150 flight director with HSI and electric artificial horizon, autopilot nav 1/2 selector, Bendix/King KLN 88 Loran C, Vortac R/Nav, II Morrow Apollo 612 Loran C, Northstar M1 Loran C, Argus 5000 moving map display, and 3M Stormscope

First production Mooney PFM (Porsche PFM 3200 engine)

WX-8 or WX-1000/1000+. Standard equipment includes true airspeed indicator, sensitive altimeter, magnetic compass, vertical speed indicator, turn co-ordinator, electric directional gyro, blind encoder, electric pictorial artificial horizon, dual deluxe control wheels, dual alternator output loadmeter/voltmeter, digital engine monitoring gauges, oil pressure gauge, fuel pressure gauge, oil temperature gauge, tachometer, fuel flow indicator, OAT and CHT gauges, electric clock/flight hour recorder, alternate static source, internally lit instruments, glareshield panel dimmer control, auxiliary power receptacle point, vertically adjustable seats, adjustable sun visors, and custom designed exterior paint finish. Optional equipment includes second altimeter, co-pilot's brakes, Halon fire extinguisher, instantaneous vertical speed indicator, propeller de-icing, polished spinner, rotating beacon, rudder pedal extensions, windscreen defroster/blower, and leather interior.

DIMENSIONS, EXTERNAL:
Length overall	15.44 m (26 ft 11 in)
Wheel track	2.76 m (9 ft 0¾ in)
Wheelbase	2.02 m (6 ft 7½ in)
Propeller ground clearance	0.28 m (11 in)
Passenger door: Height	0.89 m (2 ft 11 in)
Width	0.74 m (2 ft 5 in)
Baggage door: Height	0.52 m (1 ft 8½ in)
Width	0.43 m (1 ft 5 in)
Height to sill	1.19 m (3 ft 10 in)

DIMENSIONS, INTERNAL:
Cabin: Length	3.20 m (10 ft 6 in)
Floor area	3.53 m² (38.0 sq ft)
Volume	3.88 m³ (137 cu ft)
Baggage compartment volume	0.64 m³ (22.6 cu ft)

AREA:
Wings, gross	16.23 m² (174.7 sq ft)

WEIGHTS AND LOADINGS:
Weight empty	959 kg (2,114 lb)
Max T-O and landing weight	1,315 kg (2,900 lb)
Max wing loading	81.0 kg/m² (16.6 lb/sq ft)
Max power loading	8.13 kg/kW (13.36 lb/hp)

PERFORMANCE (at max T-O weight):
Never-exceed speed	195 knots (361 km/h; 224 mph)
Max level speed at S/L	171 knots (317 km/h; 197 mph)
Max cruising speed at S/L	168 knots (311 km/h; 193 mph)
Cruising speed at 2,745 m (9,000 ft):	
75% power	160 knots (296 km/h; 184 mph)
65% power	152 knots (282 km/h; 175 mph)
55% power	145 knots (269 km/h; 170 mph)
Stalling speed, power off:	
clean	64 knots (119 km/h; 74 mph)
wheels and flaps down	57 knots (106 km/h; 66 mph)
Max rate of climb at S/L	314 m (1,030 ft)/min
Service ceiling	5,883 m (19,300 ft)
T-O run	396 m (1,300 ft)
T-O to 15 m (50 ft)	792 m (2,600 ft)
Landing from 15 m (50 ft)	579 m (1,900 ft)
Landing run	244 m (800 ft)
Range, with allowances for T-O, climb and descent, and 45 min reserves:	

Mooney 257TLS four-seat turbocharged light aircraft

with max fuel	921 nm (1,706 km; 1,060 miles)	
with max payload	500 nm (927 km; 576 miles)	
Endurance	6 h 42 min	

MOONEY 257 TLS (M20M)

On 2 February 1989 Mooney announced the Model M20M, which is known as the Mooney TLS (Turbocharged Lycoming Sabre), a prototype of which (N20XM) was then being flight tested. It combines the stretched-fuselage airframe of the Mooney PFM with a turbocharged and intercooled Textron Lycoming TIO-540-AF1A engine, driving a McCauley three-blade propeller. Certification was achieved in 1989 and by early 1990 a total of 40 had been delivered.

The description of the Mooney 252TSE applies also to the 257TLS except as follows:

POWER PLANT: One 201.3 kW (270 hp) turbocharged and intercooled Textron Lycoming TIO-540-AF1A engine, driving a McCauley three-blade metal propeller. Two integral fuel tanks in inboard wing leading-edges, with a combined capacity of 363 litres (96 US gallons; 80 Imp gallons), of which 341 litres (90 US gallons; 75 Imp gallons) are usable. Two-piece nose cowling is of composite glassfibre/graphite construction.

ACCOMMODATION: All seats have centre and side armrests (removable in rear seats) and European-style headrests. Rear seats moved aft by 10 cm (4 in) to increase legroom. Pilot and co-pilot seats have inertia reel shoulder harnesses.

SYSTEM: Oxygen system, capacity 3.26 m³ (115 cu ft), with masks and overhead outlets, standard.

AVIONICS AND EQUIPMENT: Full range of Bendix/King avionics packages available as options, including EFIS, EHI-40 coupled to KLN 88 Loran C with moving map display, flight director, altitude and vertical speed preselect, R/Nav, and weather avoidance systems. Standard equipment includes attitude indicator, IFR directional gyro, fuel flow indicator, annunciator panel with press-to-test, electric/manual elevator trim and electric rudder trim with console- or panel-mounted LED indicators, avionics master switch, forward centre console, console-mounted chart holder, pilot's and co-pilot's map lights, high speed electric starter, dual batteries, console-mounted weight-and-balance computer, chrome-plated collapsible towbar, cigarette lighter and ashtrays, cabin, baggage door and ignition locks, and speedbrakes.

DIMENSIONS, EXTERNAL: as for Model 252TSE except:
Length overall	8.15 m (26 ft 9 in)
Height overall	2.51 m (8 ft 3 in)
Propeller diameter	1.91 m (6 ft 3 in)

DIMENSIONS, INTERNAL: as for Mooney PFM
WEIGHTS AND LOADINGS:
Weight empty	913 kg (2,012 lb)
Max T-O weight	1,451 kg (3,200 lb)
Max wing loading	89.35 kg/m² (18.3 lb/sq ft)
Max power loading	7.21 kg/kW (11.85 lb/hp)

PERFORMANCE (at max T-O weight, ISA, except where indicated):
Max cruising speed:	
at 3,960 m (13,000 ft)	200 knots (371 km/h; 230 mph)
at 7,620 m (25,000 ft)	223 knots (413 km/h; 257 mph)
Stalling speed:	
flaps and wheels up	65 knots (121 km/h; 75 mph)
flaps and wheels down	60 knots (111 km/h; 69 mph)
Max rate of climb at S/L	375 m (1,230 ft)/min
Certificated ceiling	7,620 m (25,000 ft)
Range with max fuel	1,070 nm (1,983 km; 1,232 miles)

MORRISEY

MORRISEY AIRCRAFT COMPANY
PO Box 27889, Las Vegas, Nevada 89126

No recent information has been received on Mr Bill Morrisey's plan to manufacture the Morrisey Model 2000 version of his earlier Nifty light aircraft. A brief description and photograph may be found in the 1989-90 edition.

MU-2

MU-2 MODIFICATIONS INC
Box 7331, Dallas, Texas 75209
Telephone: 1 (214) 358 3528
Fax: 1 (214) 350 9261
PRESIDENT: Steve Gage
MARKETING: Barron Thomas Aviation Inc, Love Field, Dallas, Texas 75209

MU-2 EXPRESS CONVERSIONS

MU-2 Modifications Inc has developed and certificated cargo and medevac conversions of the long-fuselage variants of the Mitsubishi MU-2 twin-turboprop business aircraft. Work commenced on the first conversion in April 1985, and FAA certification by supplemental type certificate was obtained in September and October of that year for the company's crew and cargo door modifications respectively.

The **MU-2 Express** conversion involves installation of a crew door in place of the cockpit window on the port side of the flight deck, hinged at its forward edge; a rear cargo door measuring 1.22 m (4 ft 0 in) high by 1.35 m (4 ft 5 in) wide in place of the aircraft's standard cabin door on the fuselage port side; and cargo nets in the cabin area. The rear cargo door can be a one-piece unit hinged at the top, or a twin door, vertically divided, hinged at front and rear, with a window in the forward door portion. It is available for use in either pressurised or unpressurised form. The MU-2 Express provides a total of 7.64 m³ (270.0 cu ft) of cargo space.

MU-2 Modifications Inc MU-2 Express twin-turboprop cargo aircraft

The **MU-2 Medi-Vac Express** is a dedicated emergency medical services aircraft which incorporates the crew door and a pressurised rear cargo door and provides accommodation for three stretcher patients, three medical attendants and associated life-support equipment. Other variants offered include a commuter aircraft with accommodation for ten passengers, a Combi passenger/cargo aircraft, and an Executive/Cargo quick-change aircraft. An optional weight reduction programme carried out concurrently with the other modifications increases the aircraft's useful load to 1,678 kg (3,700 lb).

NASA
NATIONAL AERONAUTICS AND SPACE ADMINISTRATION (Office of Aeronautics and Space Technology)
600 Independence Avenue SW, Washington, DC 20546
Telephone: 1 (202) 453 1000
Telex: 89530 NASA WSH
Fax: 1 (202) 426 4256
ACTING ASSOCIATE ADMINISTRATOR:
  Dr William F. Ballhaus Jr
DIRECTOR OF AERONAUTICS: Cecil C. Rosen
DIRECTOR OF NASP OFFICE: Dr. J. Robert Barthelmy

NASA has several research programmes involving the use of specially developed, specially equipped or modified aircraft. Details of some of these follow:

NATIONAL AERO-SPACE PLANE
In his State of the Union address on 4 February 1986, President Reagan announced plans for an "aerospace plane" that "could shrink travel times between Washington, DC, and Tokyo . . . to less than two hours".

NASA and the US Department of Defense then initiated plans for a joint National Aero-Space Plane (NASP) research programme which could lead to a new generation of economic, reusable aerospace vehicles for the 21st century. The programme brings together hypersonic research programmes undertaken separately by DoD and NASA over a number of years, and follows an initial research phase of concept studies for a Trans-Atmospheric Vehicle (TAV) conducted by aerospace manufacturers during 1984-85 under the Defense Advanced Research Projects Agency.

The National Aero-Space Plane concept is based on an air-breathing hydrogen-fuelled aircraft, which would probably embody hybrid power plants combining rockets for take-off with supersonic combustion ramjets (scramjets), and be capable of horizontal take-off and landing. The objective is to provide technology to make single-stage entry into space. Other vehicles which use some NASP technologies could cruise in the upper atmosphere at sustained hypersonic velocities of Mach 5 to Mach 15 (5,250 to 15,750 km/h; 3,000 to 10,000 mph) at altitudes around 32,000 m (105,000 ft).

Research is being conducted in the areas of hypersonic propulsion, advanced materials and structures, fluid dynamics, supersonic combustion ramjet theory, development of lightweight, high strength, high temperature structural materials. Results of this work and the availability of supercomputers for engine and airframe design integration, suggests that a research version of such aircraft could fly before the year 2000.

Aero-Space Planes, in various configurations, are expected to have both military and commercial applications. They could serve as low-cost satellite and orbital payload launch vehicles, long-range air defence interceptors, and space platforms for systems of the kind proposed for the Strategic Defense Initiative (SDI) programme.

The US Air Force has been assigned overall responsibility for the NASP research programme, with NASA responsible for overall technology maturation and commercial applications. The current technology development phase of the NASP programme involves five major contractors for propulsion and airframe development. General Dynamics, McDonnell Douglas and Rockwell International received the airframe contracts. The propulsion contracts were awarded to Rocketdyne and Pratt & Whitney. In July 1988 The Marquardt Company of Van Nuys, California, received an $18 million contract to assist Pratt & Whitney in the development of scramjet engines, and in January 1989 Rocketdyne successfully tested a one-seventh scale model of its scramjet power plant.

The contractors formed a consortium in January 1990 to develop advanced materials. Each contractor has responsibility for a specific class of materials, leadership being entrusted to Rockwell. General Dynamics is taking the lead in studying carbon structures, while McDonnell Douglas studies silicone carbide fibre reinforced titanium and Rockwell pursues titanium aluminide honeycomb.

In the subsequent phase of the programme, a consortium made up of the five principal contractors involved will design and build two flight research vehicles, designated **X-30**, which will be of similar size to a McDonnell Douglas MD-80 series airliner and will be used to develop, prove and demonstrate Aero-Space Plane technologies throughout the flight envelope for hypersonic cruise and acceleration to low Earth orbit. A programme go-ahead decision is expected in 1993, with selection of power plant and airframe configuration in the middle of that year, leading to a first flight by the late 1990s.

NASA HIDEC F-15
The Highly Integrated Digital Electronic Control (HIDEC) programme is being used to evaluate performance gains provided by the integration of propulsion and flight control systems, and is being conducted jointly by NASA, the US Air Force and industry.

A McDonnell Douglas F-15 Eagle (NASA 287) has been modified with a digital flight control system, advanced digitally controlled Pratt & Whitney PW1128 engines, and integrating hardware connecting the two systems. Initial testing began on 25 June 1986 and demonstrated significant

Rockwell International artist's impression of the X-30 National Aero-Space Plane in Earth orbit

NASA-modified Convair F-106B with wing leading-edge vortex flaps

General Dynamics/NASA/Boeing Canada E-7A STOVL fighter design being tested in NASA-Ames wind tunnel

improvement in aircraft performance and fuel economy. Additional testing was continuing in 1990 with a self-repairing flight control system under a $6.3 million, three-year Air Force-funded contract. NASA 287 is equipped with unique software that detects faults and determines which flight components caused them. The system then alters flight controls to aid pilots in regaining full control of the aircraft. It is also able to diagnose electronic and hydraulic failures, thus enabling ground crews to make repairs faster and so reducing maintenance costs. At NASA-Dryden, tests have shown that the system can reconfigure controls after failure of the right horizontal stabilator and that the system allows pilots to control adequately the aircraft at the specified flight condition.

Development of a self-repairing system with additional capabilities, including flight control reconfigurations using a thrust vectoring engine nozzle, was expected to be funded after this phase of development ended in September 1990.

NASA LEADING-EDGE VORTEX FLAP RESEARCH
Following a 3,000-hour programme of wind tunnel and scale model tests which began in 1985, NASA Langley has modified a Convair F-106B delta-wing jet fighter (N816NA) with variable deflection wing leading-edge vortex flaps that are expected to yield increases in lift/drag ratio, enhancing the manoeuvrability of sweptwing aircraft at transonic speeds. The port wing of the aircraft features an array of 165 flow direction cones that measure vortex behaviour around the flap. The modified F-106B made its first flight on 2 August 1988, during which handling, low cruising speed, structural dynamics and landing characteristics were evaluated with the vortex flaps positioned at 40°. Flap settings between 20° and 50° were tested later in the programme, which was expected to include about 50 flights.

NASA high AoA F/A-18A Hornet immediately prior to installation of a thrust-vectoring system

NASA ATOPS

NASA's Advanced Transport Operating System (ATOPS) programme is exploring technology to enhance the safety of commercial air travel, using its Boeing 737-100 Transport Systems Research Vehicle (see 1986-87 *Jane's*). The aircraft, known as TSRV, features a conventional Boeing 737 flight deck and a fully operational research flight deck installed in the passenger cabin. The 'all-glass' research cockpit presents information to the crew on eight 203 mm × 203 mm (8 in × 8 in) square colour CRT screens driven by onboard computers and specially developed computer software which provide clearer displays than electromechanical and first-generation electronic instrument systems in current aircraft. Centre panel displays are used to monitor and manage engine and systems performance and will be used for research into improving situational awareness, air traffic control communications, flight management and traffic awareness. The TSRV has been used to evaluate a NASA Langley-developed take-off performance monitor system which displays graphically on a single CRT screen all information critical to successful take-off, including the aircraft's position on the runway and key performance indicators. Onboard computers predict at what point and speed take-off will occur, and an aural warning is sounded if the performance is inadequate to achieve safe take-off.

In a joint programme with McDonnell Douglas Corporation, NASA is testing a helmet-mounted display concept for possible use in windowless aircraft or in other applications where crews have no outside view. During 1990 the TSRV was scheduled to undertake experiments with airborne use of onboard sensors for windshear detection and the study of aircraft/air traffic control technology integration aimed at improving traffic flow near airports.

NASA HIGH-ALPHA RESEARCH F/A-18A

NASA's Ames-Dryden Research Center is conducting a high angle of attack (AoA) technology programme to research flight control concepts which employ various combinations of aerodynamics and thrust vector control at subsonic and high alpha flight conditions. Flow visualisation is measured using various methods. Testing resumed on 16 March 1989 after a five-month lay-up for flap modifications and addition of a spin recovery system. NASA has contracted McDonnell Douglas Corporation to modify its F/A-18A Hornet (160780/NASA 840) high-alpha research aircraft with a thrust vector control system for pitch and yaw axes. Flight testing was due to begin in 1990.

NASA STOVL TECHNOLOGY DEVELOPMENT PROGRAMMES

NASA's Ames Research Center undertook wind tunnel testing during 1988-89 of a STOVL fighter featuring ejector augmentor lift system for vertical lift. Designated E-7A, the design is based on a General Dynamics concept using a Boeing Canada de Havilland division ejector and a NASA-Ames designed wing. The non-flying E-7A test model is powered by a 46.70 kN (10,500 lb st) Rolls-Royce Spey Mk 801 turbofan initially, though plans are to refit it with a General Electric F110 to simulate full airflow. It has a length of 15.06 m (49 ft 5 in) and a span of 9.88 m (32 ft 4¾ in).

NEW TECHNIK
NEW TECHNIK INCORPORATED

Flight Vehicle Division
PO Drawer 3350, 165 Scott Avenue, Suite 102, Morgantown, West Virginia 26505
Telephone: 1 (304) 291 2376
Fax: 1 (304) 292 1902
PRESIDENT: Darus H. Zehrbach

In February 1990 Aircraft Acquisition Corporation, which had acquired the Taylorcraft Aircraft Corporation (see entry in this section), formed New Technik Inc to develop and market a line of two- and four-seat light aircraft based on the Taylorcraft Models L-2, 15 and 20, and to provide product support to owners of the original aircraft. These designs have been re-engineered in conjunction with the Department of Mechanical and Aerospace Engineering at West Virginia University and the Concurrent Engineering Research Center in Morgantown, West Virginia. Work is also proceeding on design of a new two-seat twin-engined light trainer. Models planned in early 1990 are described below.

NEW TECHNIK MODEL L-2M TECH 2

TYPE: Two-seat trainer/sporting aircraft.
WINGS: Braced high-wing monoplane with V bracing struts each side. Wing section NACA 23013. Dihedral 1°. Composite structure with aluminium I beam spars, stamped metal ribs and fabric covering. Frise ailerons of similar construction. Sheet aluminium spoiler in upper surface of each wing.
FUSELAGE: Welded structure of 4130 steel tube with fabric covering.
TAIL UNIT: Wire braced welded steel tube structure with fabric covering.
LANDING GEAR: Non-retractable tailwheel type. Bungee cord suspension. Mainwheel tyres size 6.00 × 6. Cleveland disc brakes. Wheel fairings optional. Floats optional.
POWER PLANT: One 88 kW (118 hp) Textron Lycoming O-235-L2C flat-four engine, driving a Sensenich two-blade fixed-pitch metal propeller. One fuel tank in each wing, combined capacity 151 litres (40 US gallons; 33.3 Imp gallons). Oil capacity 5.7 litres (1.5 US gallons; 1.2 Imp gallons).
ACCOMMODATION: Two seats in tandem. Rear seat rotates 180° to face aft. Single entrance door on starboard side.
SYSTEM: Electrical system powered by 12V 35A engine driven alternator, with 12V 35Ah battery.
AVIONICS AND EQUIPMENT: Standard avionics comprise single com transceiver, transponder and encoder. IFR avionics optional.
DIMENSIONS, EXTERNAL:

Wing span	10.80 m (35 ft 5¼ in)
Wing chord (constant)	1.60 m (5 ft 3 in)
Wing aspect ratio	5.1
Length overall	6.83 m (22 ft 5 in)
Height overall	1.98 m (6 ft 6 in)
Wheel track	1.93 m (6 ft 4 in)
Wheelbase	4.94 m (16 ft 2½ in)
Propeller diameter	1.83 m (6 ft 0 in)
Propeller ground clearance	0.23 m (9 in)

DIMENSION, INTERNAL:

Cabin: Max width	0.91 m (3 ft 0 in)

AREAS:

Wings, gross	17.07 m² (183.7 sq ft)
Spoilers (total)	0.19 m² (2.0 sq ft)

WEIGHT AND LOADINGS:

Max T-O weight	794 kg (1,750 lb)
Max wing loading	46.38 kg/m² (9.5 lb/sq ft)
Max power loading	9.02 kg/kW (14.8 lb/hp)

PERFORMANCE (estimated, at max T-O weight, ISA:

Never-exceed speed	134 knots (249 km/h; 155 mph)
Max level speed:	
at S/L	107 knots (198 km/h; 123 mph)
at 1,525 m (5,000 ft)	102 knots (188 km/h; 117 mph)
Econ cruising speed at 1,525 m (5,000 ft)	
	95 knots (175 km/h; 109 mph)
Stalling speed, power on	42 knots (78 km/h; 48 mph)
Max rate of climb at S/L	247 m (810 ft)/min
Service ceiling	5,485 m (18,000 ft)
T-O run	159 m (521 ft)
T-O to 15 m (50 ft)	214 m (700 ft)
Landing from 15 m (50 ft)	254 m (832 ft)
Landing run	170 m (556 ft)
Range with max fuel, 30 min reserves	
	590 nm (1,094 km; 680 miles)

NEW TECHNIK MODEL 20 TECH 4

TYPE: Four-seat light aircraft.
WINGS: As for Tech 2 except skinned with glassfibre, and slotted Fowler-type trailing-edge flaps of glassfibre construction standard.
FUSELAGE: As for Tech 2, except skinned with glassfibre.
TAIL UNIT: As for Tech 2, except skinned with glassfibre.
LANDING GEAR: Non-retractable tailwheel type. Tricycle landing gear optional. Bungee cord suspension on main gear for tailwheel type, spring steel main gear for tricycle configuration. Mainwheel tyres size 6.00 – 6; nosewheel tyre size 5.00 – 5. Cleveland disc brakes. Glassfibre wheel fairings standard.
POWER PLANT: One 171.5 kW (230 hp) Teledyne Continental O-470U engine, driving a Hartzell or McCauley two-blade constant-speed metal propeller. One fuel tank in each wing, combined capacity 250 litres (66 US gallons; 55 Imp gallons). Auxiliary fuselage tank, capacity 83 litres (22 US gallons; 18.3 Imp gallons), optional. Oil capacity 7.6 litres (2 US gallons; 1.7 Imp gallons).
ACCOMMODATION: Two adjustable seats in front, with two-seat bench in rear. Single child's seat aft of bench optional. Baggage compartment behind rear seat. Four doors, one front and rear on each side of cabin. Small baggage door.
SYSTEM: Electrical system powered by 12V 55A engine driven alternator, with 12V 35Ah battery.
AVIONICS AND EQUIPMENT: Standard avionics comprise single com transceiver, transponder and encoder. Full range of Bendix/King and Narco IFR avionics optional. II Morrow Loran C optional.
DIMENSIONS, EXTERNAL:

Wing span	10.57 m (34 ft 8 in)
Wing chord (constant)	1.57 m (5 ft 2 in)
Wing aspect ratio	6.7

Length overall	7.42 m (24 ft 4 in)
Height overall	2.18 m (7 ft 2 in)
Propeller diameter	2.08 m (6 ft 10 in)
Propeller ground clearance	0.23 m (9 in)

AREA:

Wings, gross	16.58 m² (178.5 sq ft)

WEIGHTS AND LOADINGS:

Max payload	510 kg (1,125 lb)
Max T-O weight	1,247 kg (2,750 lb)
Max wing loading	75.19 kg/m² (15.4 lb/sq ft)
Max power loading	7.27 kg/kW (11.96 lb/hp)

PERFORMANCE (estimated, at max T-O weight, ISA, except where indicated):

Never-exceed speed	149 knots (277 km/h; 172 mph)
Max level speed at 1,525 m (5,000 ft)	
	139 knots (257 km/h; 160 mph)
Max cruising speed at 1,525 m (5,000 ft)	
	130 knots (241 km/h; 150 mph)
Econ cruising speed at 1,525 m (5,000 ft)	
	119 knots (220 km/h; 137 mph)
Stalling speed, power on	49 knots (90 km/h; 56 mph)
Max rate of climb at S/L	305 m (1,000 ft)/min
Service ceiling	4,575 m (15,000 ft)
T-O run	222 m (728 ft)
T-O to 15 m (50 ft)	278 m (912 ft)
Landing from 15 m (50 ft)	263 m (862 ft)
Landing run	196 m (643 ft)
Range, with max fuel, 30 min reserves	
	868 nm (1,609 km; 1,000 miles)

NEW TECHNIK TWIN TECH

New Technik began design work on a two-seat light twin-engined trainer in January 1990 and expected to fly a prototype the following August.
TYPE: Two-seat twin-engined light trainer.
WINGS: As for Tech 2 except trailing-edge flaps standard and ailerons droop 11° 30' to increase effective flap area.
FUSELAGE: As for Tech 2.
TAIL UNIT: As for Tech 2, except manually adjustable trim tab in rudder.
LANDING GEAR: Non-retractable tricycle type. Bungee cord suspension on main gear, oleo-pneumatic on nosewheel. Goodyear tyres, mainwheel tyres size 6.00 – 6; nosewheel tyre size 5.25 – 5. Cleveland disc brakes. Glassfibre wheel
POWER PLANT: Two 88 kW (118 hp) Textron Lycoming O-235-L2L flat-four engines, each driving a Sensenich two-blade fixed-pitch metal propeller. Two 119 kW (160 hp) Textron Lycoming O-320 or 134 kW (180 hp) O-360 engines optional, each driving a McCauley two-blade constant-speed metal propeller. One fuel tank in each wing, combined capacity 318 litres (84 US gallons; 70 Imp gallons). Oil capacity (O-235) 11.3 litres (3 US gallons; 2.5 Imp gallons), (O-320/O-360) 15 litres (4 US gallons; 3.3 Imp gallons).
ACCOMMODATION: Two individual bucket seats, side by side for pilot and pupil/passenger.
SYSTEM: Electrical system powered by two 12V 35A engine driven alternators, with two 12V 25Ah batteries.
AVIONICS AND EQUIPMENT: Standard avionics comprise single com transceiver, transponder and encoder. Full range of

Bendix/King and Narco IFR avionics optional. II Morrow Loran C optional.

DIMENSIONS, EXTERNAL:

Wing span	10.97 m (36 ft 0 in)
Wing chord (constant)	1.60 m (5 ft 3 in)
Wing aspect ratio	7.1
Length overall	7.51 m (24 ft 7½ in)
Height overall	3.07 m (10 ft 1 in)
Tailplane span	3.05 m (10 ft 0 in)
Wheel track	1.98 m (6 ft 6 in)
Wheelbase	1.88 m (6 ft 2 in)
Propeller diameter: O-235	1.83 m (6 ft 0 in)
O-320/O-360	1.88 m (6 ft 2 in)
Propeller ground clearance	0.46 m (1 ft 6 in)

DIMENSIONS, INTERNAL:

Cabin: Length	2.74 m (9 ft 0 in)
Max width	1.02 m (3 ft 4¼ in)
Height	1.17 m (3 ft 10¼ in)
Floor area	2.42 m² (26.0 sq ft)

Volume	9.10 m³ (321.4 cu ft)
Baggage compartment volume	1.36 m³ (48.1 cu ft)

AREAS:

Wings, gross	17.19 m² (185.0 sq ft)
Ailerons (total)	1.86 m² (20.0 sq ft)
Trailing-edge flaps (total)	2.23 m² (24.0 sq ft)
Fin	1.23 m² (13.2 sq ft)
Tailplane	1.33 m² (14.3 sq ft)

WEIGHTS AND LOADINGS (O-320 engines):

Weight empty	640 kg (1,410 lb)
Max payload	373 kg (823 lb)
Max T-O weight	1,020 kg (2,250 lb)
Max ramp weight	1,027 kg (2,265 lb)
Max wing loading	59.57 kg/m² (12.2 lb/sq ft)
Max power loading	4.29 kg/kW (7.0 lb/hp)

PERFORMANCE (estimated, with O-320 engines and constant-speed propellers, at max T-O weight, ISA, except where indicated):

Never-exceed speed	174.5 knots (323 km/h; 201 mph)

Max level speed at 1,525 m (5,000 ft)
174 knots (322 km/h; 200 mph)
Max cruising speed at 1,525 m (5,000 ft)
161 knots (298 km/h; 185 mph)
Econ cruising speed at 1,525 m (5,000 ft)
155 knots (286 km/h; 178 mph)

Stalling speed, power on	37 knots (68 km/h; 42 mph)
Max rate of climb at S/L	640 m (2,100 ft)/min
Rate of climb at S/L, one engine out	274 m (900 ft)/min
Service ceiling	7,010 m (23,000 ft)
Service ceiling, one engine out	3,355 m (11,000 ft)
T-O run	61 m (200 ft)
T-O to 15 m (50 ft)	98 m (320 ft)
Landing from 15 m (50 ft)	160 m (525 ft)
Landing run	77 m (250 ft)

Range with max fuel, 75% power, IFR reserves
771 nm (1,429 km; 888 miles)

NORTHROP

NORTHROP CORPORATION

1840 Century Park East, Los Angeles, California 90067-2199
Telephone: 1 (213) 553 6262
Telex: 192893 NORTHROP 1
Fax: 1 (213) 201 3023, 553 2076, or 552 3104
PRESIDENT AND CHIEF EXECUTIVE OFFICER: Kent Kresa
SENIOR VICE-PRESIDENT, PUBLIC AFFAIRS:
Les Daly
VICE-PRESIDENT, PUBLIC INFORMATION: A. W. Cantafio

This company was formed in 1939 by John K. Northrop and others to undertake the design and manufacture of military aircraft. Although continuing its activities in the design, development and production of aircraft, missiles and target drone systems, Northrop broadened its scope of operation to include electronics, space technology, communications, support services and commercial products. To reflect this changing character of its business, the company changed its name from Northrop Aircraft Inc to Northrop Corporation in 1959. Since 1986, its operations have been handled by the Aircraft and B-2 (formerly Advanced Systems) Divisions, an Electronics Systems Group, and a subsidiary known as Northrop Worldwide Aircraft Services Inc.

The Aircraft Division is responsible for the design and manufacture of fighter aircraft, the manufacture of commercial aircraft major assemblies, and the work of Northrop Aircraft Division's Newbury Park site in missiles and unmanned aerial targets. Northtop is prime contractor for the air-launched Tacit Rainbow loitering anti-radar missile. B-2 Division manages a number of aerospace programmes and is prime contractor to the USAF for research and development of the B-2 advanced technology bomber. Northrop Worldwide Aircraft Services Inc, of Lawton, Oklahoma, provides technical and support services. The Electronics Systems Division in Hawthorne, CA, and its facility in Anaheim, CA, produce navigation and guidance equipment for strategic and tactical applications, passive sensor and tracking systems. Defense Systems Division is designer and manufacturer of electronic countermeasures systems, including the internal countermeasures set (ICS) for the US Air Force's F-15 Eagle. Precision Products Division in Norwood, MA, is a major producer of rate and rate-integrating gyroscopes and strapdown guidance systems.

Northrop had 41,000 employees in the Spring of 1990.

AIRCRAFT DIVISION

One Northrop Avenue, Hawthorne, California 90250
Telephone: 1 (213) 332 1000
Telex: 181861 NORTHR A HWTH
VICE-PRESIDENT AND AIRCRAFT DIVISION GENERAL MANAGER:
Stephen R. Smith
VICE-PRESIDENT, ADVANCED DESIGN: Delbert H. Jacobs
VICE-PRESIDENT, ENGINEERING: Dene Hauser
VICE-PRESIDENT, INFORMATION RESOURCES: Robert W. Slusser
Newbury Park Site
1515 Rancho Conejo Boulevard, Newbury Park, California 91320
Telephone: 1 (805) 373 2000
Telex: 683 9403 NOCVNP

Current production at Northrop's Aircraft Division, which has about 14,000 employees, is centred on the F/A-18 Hornet multi-mission fighter (see McDonnell Douglas entry), and major Boeing 747 subcontract work, which includes manufacture of the main fuselage section, the extra-large side loading cargo door, passenger doors and upper deck.

Northrop is principal subcontractor for the Hornet, with design and production responsibility for the centre and rear fuselage and the twin vertical tails, including internal systems such as fuel, the environmental control system and auxiliary power system. The 900th shipset of these components was delivered in September 1989.

Northrop is one of the two selected prime contractors in the USAF's advanced tactical fighter (ATF) programme, with McDonnell Douglas Corporation as principal subcontractor; and is engaged in research projects involving advanced simulators and composite materials.

The Newbury Park Site (formerly Northrop Ventura) became a unit of the Aircraft Division in 1987.

NORTHROP TIGER II
USAF designations: F-5E and F-5F

Although series production of the Northrop F-5 series ended in early 1987 with the delivery of two F-5Es to the Air Force of Bahrain, Northrop subsequently assembled five F-5Es and three F-5Fs from spares for the Singapore Air Force, the last of which was delivered in July 1989 as the 3,805th production aircraft in the F-5/T-38 family. Northrop was responsible for building 617 F-5As, 89 RF-5As, 183 F-5Bs, 792 F-5Es, 12 RF-5Es, 149 F-5Fs and 1,187 T-38As. Additional production or assembly abroad involved 164 F-5As and 76 F-5B/Ds by Canadair; 18 F-5As, 18 RF-5As and 34 F-5Bs by CASA in Spain; 48 F-5Es and 20 F-5Fs by KAL in South Korea; 84 F-5Es and six F-5Fs by F+W in Switzerland and 242 F-5Es and 66 F-5Fs by AIDC in Taiwan. Totals do not include three prototypes each of the T-38, F-5 and F-20 Tigershark or the two F-5E fuselages used for the Grumman X-29 programme.

Details of the F-5E, F-5F and RF-5E TigerEye may be found in the 1986-87 and earlier editions of *Jane's*.

NORTHROP YF-23A (ATF)

For available details of the US Air Force's Advanced Tactical Fighter (ATF) programme, see the US Air Force Systems Command entry in this section. Northrop is contracted to build two YF-23A prototypes, in partnership with McDonnell Douglas as principal subcontractor. These are assigned civilian registrations N231YF and N232YF, the first of which was due to fly in mid-1990. Other YF-23A subcontractors include a Hamilton Standard/General Electric team (flight control computer) and ATT/TRW (central digital processor).

B-2 DIVISION

8900 East Washington Boulevard, Pico Rivera, California 90660-3737
Telephone: 1 (213) 942 3000
PRESIDENT AND GENERAL MANAGER: Oliver C. Boileau

NORTHROP B-2A

The B-2A advanced technology bomber (ATB) has been developed from 1978 onwards to meet a USAF requirement, first outlined publicly in late 1981, for a highly survivable strategic penetration bomber to complement and eventually replace the Rockwell B-1B. Known popularly as the 'Stealth Bomber' due to its adoption of low-observables (LO) technology, it has been developed by Northrop as prime contractor, with assistance from Boeing Advanced Systems, General Electric and LTV, under an October 1981 contract (which included one prototype) from the USAF's Aeronautical Systems Division. A competing Lockheed-Rockwell ATB design was rejected in 1981. The design underwent considerable modification in 1983, to strengthen the structure for low-altitude, as well as high-altitude, missions. The wing leading- and trailing-edge configurations were also altered. The USAF awarded Northrop a $2 billion contract on 19 November 1987 to initiate B-2A production.

During seven years of B-2A development. Northrop conducted 20,000 h of wind tunnel trials; 16,000 h of engineering simulation; and 6,000 h of control system tests on a full-scale hydraulic and flight control bench. Avionics intended for the B-2A were reportedly being flown at Edwards in an unidentified testbed aircraft in the Spring of 1988.

Northrop B-2A prototype viewed from a KC-10A tanker, showing air intake and other details

Extensive use has been made of computer aided design and manufacturing techniques (CAD/CAM) in development of the B-2A. The external geometry, and the shape and location of every component, is maintained on a three-dimensional database that is used to control machine tools and industrial robots, to design tooling, and to generate data for tooling alignment. The database is shared between Northrop and its principal subcontractors, and released to other subcontractors as necessary. By late 1989, Northrop had announced 131 subcontractors; Boeing had a further 69, General Electric 52, and LTV 32.

Northrop is responsible for building the B-2A's forward centre section, including the cockpit, and performing integration and final assembly. Boeing Military Airplanes produces the aft centre section and outboard sections, fuel system, weapons delivery system and landing gear. LTV is responsible for intermediate fuselage sections, aluminium and titanium structural components and composite parts. The combined staff total is 26,000, including 10,000 at Boeing and 4,000 at LTV.

The USAF had a requirement for 133 B-2As, including the prototype, but only 75 may now be bought as the result of FY 1991 budget cuts. Six of these are assigned to initial trials, of which all but the second will later be refurbished for operational service. All except 12 of the SAC B-2As will have dual nuclear/conventional capabilities, as defined by MIL-STD-1760. Following the initial six aircraft and two airframes for structural tests, three B-2As were funded in FY 1989 and two in FY 1990. Cost of each aircraft over a 132 unit production run is $274 million in 1989 dollars, excluding R&D; and is expected to be $530 million in 1999 prices, including R&D.

The prototype B-2A (82-1066) was rolled out of the assembly building at USAF Plant 42 at Palmdale, California, on 22 November 1988. It made a 2 h 20 min first flight on 17 July 1989, landing at the nearby Air Force Flight Test Center at Edwards AFB. The Block 1 section of the flight test programme consists of 75 hours in 15 flights to test aerodynamic performance and airworthiness. Block 2 will include testing of the aircraft's low-observable characteristics. An initial in-flight refuelling was accomplished from a KC-10A during the seventh flight on 8 November 1989.

Achievements claimed by Northrop for the B-2 programme include successful completion of all planned objectives in the early test programme; development of the first three-dimensional computing capability combining design and manufacturing stages; manufacture of a prototype on production tooling and achievement of unprecedented tolerances of ± 6.3 mm ($\frac{1}{4}$ in) across the B-2A's wing span; and development of nearly 900 new materials and processes, allied to productivity gains in some manufacturing processes of 60:1.

The B-2A's initial operating base, from 1992-93, will be Whiteman AFB, Missouri, where 34 B-2A hangars and additional support facilities for the 509th BW are under construction. One other base will be designated later. Oklahoma Air Logistics Center has been selected as the primary depot facility for the B-2A, with other participating depots situated at Hill AFB, UT; Sacramento, CA; San Antonio, TX; and Warner-Robbins AFB, GA.

TYPE: Four-engined, low-observable strategic bomber.
WINGS: Flying wing design. Straight leading-edges, swept at 33°. Centre and tip sections have unconventionally-shaped leading-edges with sharp radii and concave lower surfaces. 'Double-W' trailing-edge incorporating eight movable surfaces (six elevons; two drag rudders) outboard of the engines, combining aileron, elevator and flap functions, and also obviating conventional fin and rudder. Two inboard pairs of surfaces (on same hinge line) act in unison as elevons for slow-speed flight control; outboard elevon pair employed in normal flight; outermost control surfaces, split horizontally, function as fast-moving drag rudders and speed-brakes, remaining partly deployed at most times. Latter set at $+45/-45°$ on landing approach. For normal flight control, lower halves of drag rudders deploy to 90°, followed by upper halves to extent required to execute manoeuvre. Control surfaces occupy approximately 15 per cent of wing area. No high-lift devices. Construction heavily reliant on graphite/epoxy (carbonfibre) and other advanced composite materials, with extensive use of honeycomb radar-absorbent structure (RAS) and radar-absorbent material (RAM) skinning. Leading-edges and wingtips have dielectric covering of aerofoil section to mask radar-dissipating 'sawtooth' construction. Dielectric panels each side of nosewheel well believed to be for Hughes radar antenna.
FUSELAGE: Blended centrebody comprising flight deck immediately behind wing leading-edge and weapons bay.
TAIL UNIT: No vertical stabilising surfaces. Moving 'beaver-tail' between exhausts functions in conjunction with elevons as gust-alleviation system.
LANDING GEAR: Tricycle type, adapted from Boeing 757/767. Inward-retracting four-wheel main bogies have large trapezoidal door of thick cross-section. Rearward-retracting two-wheel nose unit has small door with sawtooth edges and large rear door, also used for crew access. Two landing lights on nosewheel leg. Landing gear limiting speed 224 knots (415 km/h; 258 mph).
POWER PLANT: Four 84.5 kN (19,000 lb st) General Electric F118-GE-110 non-afterburning turbofans mounted in pairs within wing structure, each side of weapons bay, fed by S-shaped air ducts. Irregular-shaped air intakes feed each pair, with three-pointed splitter plates ahead of the inlets which draw in air, removing boundary layer and providing secondary airflow for cooling and infra-red emissions control. Upper lip of intake has single point. Two auxiliary air inlet doors mounted on top of intake trunks remain open on ground and in slow-speed flight. Two V-shaped overwing exhausts set well forward of trailing-edge. Heat-resistant material on wing surface behind engine outlet. Provision for mixing chloro-fluoro-sulfonic acid with exhaust gases to eliminate visible contrails. In-flight refuelling receptacle in centrebody spine. Garrett APU outboard of port engine bay, covered by triangular door flush with wing surface.
ACCOMMODATION: Two crew, with upward firing ejection seats: pilot to port, mission commander/instructor pilot to starboard. Provision for third member. Both forward positions have conventional control columns. Flight, engine, sensor and systems information presented on eight-tube IFIS display. Either crew member capable of flying complete mission, although data entry panels biased towards weapon systems officer on starboard seat. Four flight deck windows.
SYSTEMS: Quadruple-redundant digital fly by wire flight control system and sophisticated stability augmentation system, possibly incorporating fly by light technology.

Prototype Northrop B-2A banking with drag rudders in normal (slightly open) position and trailing static sensor cable extending from structure above the rear fuselage

Provisional three-view drawing of Northrop B-2A *(Pilot Press)*

Air data sensor system includes four small circular panels above windscreen, plus 12 more between leading-edge and flight deck and two pairs of four in wing undersides. Hydraulic system for flying controls operates at 276 bars (4,000 lb/sq in).

AVIONICS AND EQUIPMENT: Hughes AN/APQ-118 low-probability-of-intercept (LPI) covert strike radar. Rockwell Collins TCN-250 Tacan, VIR-130A ILS and ICS-150X intercom. To ease crew workload, three-position selector switch in cockpit activates/de-activates appropriate equipment for 'take-off' (transfer mission data tape, checklist and appropriate flight controls mode), 'go to war' (flight controls in 'stealthy' mode, weapons ready and radio emitters switched off) and 'land' (re-activate systems and perform checklist).

ARMAMENT: Boeing Advanced Applications Rotary Launcher in each of two side-by-side weapons bays in lower centrebody. Total capacity of 16 SRAM II or AGM-129 ACMs. Alternative weapons include B61 tactical/strategic and B83 strategic free-fall nuclear bombs, Mk 36 1,000 lb sea mines, Mk 82 500 lb bombs (maximum 80) and M117 750 lb fire bombs.

DIMENSIONS, EXTERNAL:
Wing span	52.43 m (172 ft 0 in)
Length overall	21.03 m (69 ft 0 in)
Height overall	5.18 m (17 ft 0 in)
Wheel track	12.20 m (40 ft 0 in)

AREA:
Lower surface	over 464.5 m² (5,000 sq ft)

WEIGHTS:
Weight empty	45,360 kg-49,900 kg (100,000-110,000 lb)
Max weapon load	22,680 kg (50,000 lb)
Max internal fuel capacity	81,650-90,720 kg (180,000-200,000 lb)
Max T-O weight	168,433 kg (371,330 lb)

PERFORMANCE:
Approach speed	140 knots (259 km/h; 161 mph)
Service ceiling	15,240 m (50,000 ft)

Range with eight SRAMs and eight B83 bombs, totalling 16,919 kg (37,300 lb), at max T-O weight:
hi-hi-hi	6,300 nm (11,675 km; 7,255 miles)
hi-lo-hi (1,000 nm; 1,853 km; 1,152 miles at low level)	
	4,400 nm (8,154 km; 5,067 miles)

Range with eight SRAMs and eight B61 bombs, totalling 10,886 kg (24,000 lb), at 162,386 kg (358,000 lb) T-O weight:
hi-hi-hi	6,600 nm (12,231 km; 7,600 miles)
hi-lo-hi (1,000 nm; 1,853 km; 1,152 miles at low level)	
	4,500 nm (8,339 km; 5,182 miles)

Range with one aerial refuelling
over 10,000 nm (18,532 km; 11,515 miles)

OMAC
OMAC INC
PO Box 3530, 1 Rockwell Avenue, Albany, Georgia 31708

Telephone: 1 (912) 436 2425

Fax: 1 (912) 436 2488

CHIEF EXECUTIVE OFFICER: Charles V. Mihaylo

VICE-PRESIDENT, ENGINEERING: Everett Cook

NATIONAL SALES MANAGER: David J. Rooney

PUBLIC RELATIONS MANAGER: Geoff Parker

OMAC was founded in Reno, Nevada, to develop and market a low cost high performance and economical six/eight-seat turboprop powered business aircraft of canard configuration, known as the Laser 300 (originally OMAC I). In January 1985 the company moved its operations to Albany Municipal Airport, Georgia.

OMAC LASER 300
The OMAC 1 prototype flew for the first time on 11 December 1981, but was slightly damaged in a ground accident in the Spring of 1982. In June of that year modifications were made to the original configuration, as detailed in earlier editions of *Jane's*. This aircraft had completed 249 flights by the Summer of 1987, when it was retired from the test programme and displayed in the Museum of Flight at Boeing Field, Seattle, Washington.

A second prototype (N81PH) flew for the first time on 19 February 1983, becoming an experimental testbed for further modification and design changes, including replacement of the original Textron Lycoming LTP 101-700A-1A turboprop with a similarly rated Garrett TPE331-9 in 1984, and the addition of larger wingtip fins. The production prototype Laser 300 (N301L), powered by a 559 kW (750 shp) Pratt & Whitney Canada PT6A-135A turboprop, was rolled out in early June 1988 and made its first flight on 29 July.

In December 1988 OMAC reduced staff levels at its Albany headquarters to a minimum while seeking additional financing for certification and production of the Laser 300, which was then expected to achieve FAA certification in May 1990. Flight testing of the production prototype was suspended in March 1989 when the company filed for protection under Chapter 11 of US bankruptcy laws. In September of that year the company was reported to be seeking a buyer for its production and engineering facilities, and was negotiating with South Korean companies for the manufacture of components for the Laser 300. No more recent information has been received. Details and a photograph of the prototype can be found in the 1989-90 and earlier editions of *Jane's*.

ORLANDO
ORLANDO HELICOPTER AIRWAYS INC
2774 Carrier Avenue, Building 141, Sanford, Florida 32771

Telephone: 1 (305) 323 1756

Telex: 52 9450

Fax: 1 (407) 330 2647

PRESIDENT: Fred P. Clark

VICE-PRESIDENT OF SALES: Troy E. Simmons

Orlando Helicopter Airways Inc was founded at Sanford, Florida, in 1964, since when the company has been engaged in the remanufacture, sale and operation of Sikorsky helicopters. The company has large stocks of parts and components for Sikorsky S-52, S-55/H-19 and S-58/H-34 helicopters and owns the FAA type certificates for all models of the H-19 series and the H-34. Rotorparts Inc, an affiliate company, claims the world's largest stocks of Sikorsky S-55 parts, and supplies components for S-55, S-58, S-61 and S-62 helicopters to many overseas governments. Total sales of Sikorsky helicopters remanufactured by Orlando Helicopter Airways exceed 100. Future plans include conversions of later models such as the S-61, S-62 and S-64 series as they are declared surplus by military forces; turbine engine conversions of piston engined helicopters; and experimentation with alternative fuels such as gasoline/alcohol and propane gas in helicopters for agricultural operation.

On 27 October 1985 an agreement was signed with the Guangzhou Machinery Tool Company for the production of Orlando OHA-S-55 Bearcat helicopters in the People's Republic of China. A new company, Guangzhou Orlando Helicopters (which see), is initially assembling US manufactured parts, leading to production of components in China. The 20-year joint venture includes the establishment and operation of helicopter passenger services in China, and will also offer rotor blade overhaul and repair facilities for Far East operators. Future plans include the assembly of larger helicopter types in China. Orlando Helicopter Airways and Bates Associates of Hong Kong have also formed Orlando Helicopter Far East Ltd to handle export marketing of helicopters manufactured in China.

Orlando Helicopter Airways 'Hind Look-alike' conversion of the Sikorsky H-19/S-55

ORLANDO/SIKORSKY S-55/H-19
Several remanufactured models of Sikorsky S-55/H-19 series helicopters are offered by Orlando Helicopter Airways:

Vistaplane. Passenger/air ambulance version seating eight passengers in standard version or 11 passengers in high density configuration. For ambulance work up to six litters and two attendants can be accommodated. Cabin floor viewing window optional.

Heli-Camper. VIP model with sleeping facilities for four passengers in fully carpeted and soundproofed cabin, hot and cold water, refrigerator, two-burner stove, shower and wash basin, toilet and air-conditioning. Other standard features include colour television and AM/FM stereo radio and tape deck, roll-up awning, tinted windows, bar and storage cabinets, dual flight controls, full night lighting and dual landing lights, interphone communication system,

Orlando Helicopter Airways OHA-S-55 Bearcat agricultural helicopter

Orlando Helicopter Airways S-58T Orlando Airliner

Orlando Helicopter Airways OHA-S-58T Viking twin-turbine conversion of the Sikorsky S-58
(Jane's/Mike Keep)

construction, a new tailboom, stub wings, weapon pylons, 'operational' blisters, and a new five-blade Rotaire main rotor. The new nose was designed by 3D Industries of Madison Heights, Michigan, which is supplying moulds and canopies for the aircraft. The drone flight control package is provided by Honeywell. Noise simulators will be installed to imitate the sound of the Mil Mi-24's Isotov turboshaft engines. By January 1989 three modified 'Hind Look-alikes' were being test flown, initially with standard H-19/S-55 three-blade main rotors. Thirteen of the converted helicopters will be configured for alternative manned or RPV operation.

ORLANDO/SIKORSKY S-58/H-34

Five remanufactured models of Sikorsky S-58/H-34 series helicopters are offered. The **Agricultural** and **Heavy Lift** versions have a 1,137 kW (1,525 hp) Wright Cyclone R-1820-84 piston engine and are similarly equipped to equivalent versions of the Orlando S-55/H-19.

Heli-Camper. Similarly equipped to S-55 Heli-Camper, but with additional standard features: 8.73 m² (94 sq ft) living area with sculptured carpeting, entertainment centre, separate bar, sleeping accommodation for six passengers, full-size four-burner stove and 0.11 m³ (3.9 cu ft) refrigerator, 3,500W generator, super soundproofing, tinted glass and wraparound windscreen. 1,137 kW (1,525 hp) Wright Cyclone R-1820-84 radial piston engine. Fuel capacity 992 litres (262 US gallons; 218 Imp gallons); max T-O weight 5,670 kg (12,500 lb); cruising speed 96 knots (177 km/h; 110 mph); range 304 nm (563 km; 350 miles).

Orlando Airliner. High density version of the Sikorsky S-58T twin-turbine helicopter (see California Helicopters entry in this section). Standard equipment includes dual flight controls; toe brakes; hydraulic rotor brake; two independent servo control systems; cabin, cockpit, instrument, position, night and landing lights; rotating beacon; 24V battery, 1,071 litre (283 US gallon; 235.6 Imp gallon) fuel system; 2,268 kg (5,000 lb) capacity cargo sling; new paintwork; an extended passenger cabin; 18 additional cabin windows (for a total of 22); 18 airline-standard seats (15 forward facing and three rearward facing, standard or lightweight); Flightex soundproofing; tinted cabin windows; and ram air scoop for cabin cooling. Options available for the Orlando Airliner include a 272 kg (600 lb) capacity rescue hoist; pop-out emergency floats; 568 litre (150 US gallon; 125 Imp gallon) capacity external auxiliary fuel tank; stereo system; toilet; air-conditioning; one-piece windscreen; and customer choice of avionics. The Orlando Airliner has a useful load of over 2,268 kg (5,000 lb), maximum speed at S/L of 120 knots (222 km/h; 138 mph), hovering ceiling OGE of 2,440 m (8,000 ft), and range (with auxiliary fuel and 20 min reserves) of 373 nm (692 km; 430 miles).

Flying Armoured Personnel Carrier. Military version of S-58T with extended passenger cabin and 18 opening cabin windows. The entire lower fuselage below the line of the cabin windows is protected with Kevlar soft armour plating. Fuel system similarly armoured, and incorporates self-sealing tanks. Pilot and co-pilot side windows are made from Lexan bullet resistant material, with 6.35 mm (¼ in) boiler plate panels for added crew protection, and soft Kevlar armour around and under seats and in engine compartment. Two additional doors, each 0.56 m × 1.17 m (22 in × 46 in) on port side of fuselage, supplementing main cabin sliding door on starboard side. Provision for mounting heavy weapons at door and window stations, and for carrying external stores.

A new version of the Orlando S-58 is under development, designated **OHA-S-58T Viking**. It will be powered by twin Pratt & Whitney Canada PT6 turbine engines mounted on the transmission deck and will have a redesigned streamlined nose.

Bendix/King 360-channel VHF transceiver and VOR, Bendix/King transponder, and emergency locator transmitter. Options include an electro-mechanical cargo sling, hydraulic hoist, amphibious floats, rotating spot light, and Bendix/King KT-96 radio telephone. The Heli-Camper has a stripped and remanufactured airframe, new instruments, new or overhauled dynamic components including main and tail rotor blades, and an overhauled 596 kW (800 hp) Wright Cyclone R-1300-3D piston engine. Fuel capacity 715 litres (189 US gallons; 157.5 Imp gallons); max T-O weight 3,266 kg (7,200 lb); cruising speed 78 knots (145 km/h; 90 mph); range 304 nm (563 km; 350 miles).

OHA-S-55 Nite-Writer. Aerial advertising model incorporating a 12.2 × 2.4 m (40 × 8 ft) Sky Sign Inc computerised electronic billboard, mounted at 40° to the side of the helicopter's fuselage. Continuously running messages, graphics and logos can be displayed on the sign, with a claimed night legibility range of up to 1.7 nm (3.2 km; 2 miles).

OHA-S-55 Bearcat. Designed for Orlando-developed combination spray and dry dispensing systems for quick conversion from liquid chemicals to dry fertilisers or seeds. Glassfibre chemical tank, capacity 946 litres (250 US gallons; 208 Imp gallons) standard. System also allows dry material to be carried internally rather than in underslung bucket. Also adaptable for firefighting. Orlando Helicopter

Airways has obtained FAA approval for S-55 helicopters using Pratt & Whitney R-1340 engines under FAR Parts 91 (Standard), 137 (Agricultural) and 133 (External Load) to use automobile fuel, and all Orlando-modified S-55s with R-1340 engines include this approval. The OHA-S-55 is equipped with a 'super quiet' engine muffler system. Kysor cockpit air-conditioning system optional.

Heavy Lift. External load model for logging, construction and firefighting operations, with 1,361 kg (3,000 lb) useful load.

As noted in the Chinese section of this edition, an **OHA-S-55T Challenger** version, with a 522 kW (700 shp) Textron Lycoming LTS 101-700A-3 turboshaft engine, is, together with the standard OHA-S-55, the subject of a co-production agreement with the People's Republic of China, where it will be known as the **Panda**. An **OHA-S-55T Phoenix** variant which was under construction in 1989 will feature Pratt & Whitney Canada PT6 single- or twin-turbine engines mounted on the transmission deck, and a new streamlined nose section.

Hind Look-alike. Under US Army Missile Command contract, Orlando is modifying 15 H-19/S-55s into simulated representations of the Soviet Mil Mi-24 'Hind-E' combat helicopter for use by troops in battlefield training and recognition, and as pilotless targets. Modification involves fitting a larger, reshaped nose of composites

---

PEMCO

PEMCO AEROPLEX
(Subsidiary of Precision Standard Inc)
PO Box 2287, Birmingham, Alabama 35201-2287
Telephone: 1 (205) 592 0011
Telex: (810) 733 3687
Fax: 1 (205) 595 6631

Precision Standard Inc of Denver, Colorado, acquired the former Hayes International Corporation in September 1988 and continues to market its cargo conversions for a number of jet airliners. In addition to those described below, the company has completed passenger to cargo conversions on Convair 240, 340, 580, 640, Douglas DC-6, DC-8, Gulfstream I and Boeing 727-100/200 aircraft.

PEMCO AEROPLEX BAe 146-200 CARGO CONVERSION

Pemco Aeroplex was appointed by British Aerospace to undertake the prototype conversion of a BAe 146 Series 200

(see UK section) to all-cargo configuration. Pemco Aeroplex designed, manufactured and installed a port-side upward opening door (3.30 m; 10 ft 10 in wide by 1.98 m; 6 ft 6 in deep) in the rear fuselage, forward of the rear passenger door; undertook the necessary structural strengthening; and installed interior furnishings and cargo handling equipment.

After such conversion, a BAe 146 is operable in either all-cargo or passenger/cargo combi configuration. It is marketed by BAe, but Pemco Aeroplex was responsible for obtaining the FAA supplemental type certificate and is undertaking production conversions. The company has also converted BAe 146 Series 200 and Series 300 aircraft to QC quick-change configuration.

PEMCO AEROPLEX LOCKHEED L-1011F TRISTAR

Under contract to Aircraft Sales Company, Pemco Aeroplex converted an ex-Eastern Air Lines Lockheed

L-1011-1 passenger airliner to all-cargo configuration, as the L-1011F. In addition to installing a 2.84 m × 4.32 m (9 ft 4 in × 14 ft 2 in) cargo door in the port side of the cabin, forward of the wing, the conversion required a 9g bulkhead aft of the flight deck, replacement of the cabin windows by blanking plates, and installation of tracks and roller conveyors on the upper and lower decks. Max payload is 54,430 kg (120,000 lb). FAA type approval was received after the L-1011F's first flight, on 7 May 1987. Further conversions can be made to order.

PEMCO AEROPLEX BOEING 747-100 CARGO CONVERSION

Pemco Aeroplex has completed modification of a former Trans World Airlines Boeing 747-100 passenger airliner to all-freighter configuration. The conversion involved installation of a 3.12 m × 3.48 m (10 ft 3 in × 11 ft 5 in) cargo door on the port side of the fuselage aft of the wing, replacement of cargo compartment floor beams, installation of a 9g bulkhead aft of the flight deck, modifications to the upper deck, replacement of cabin windows by blanking plugs, a new interior cabin liner, and provision of an electric cargo handling system. The 747's upper deck has capacity for 29 cargo containers, while the lower deck can accommodate a further 13, for a total payload of 91,625 kg (202,000 lb). The modification was granted an FAA supplemental type certificate in April 1988. Two Boeing 747-100s were modified at Pemco's Birmingham facility in 1989, and several more conversions are anticipated.

PEMCO AEROPLEX MCDONNELL DOUGLAS DC-9 CARGO CONVERSION

Pemco Aeroplex has completed the first conversion of a McDonnell Douglas DC-9 from passenger to all-cargo configuration. In addition to installation of a 2.06 m × 3.45 m (6 ft 9 in × 11 ft 4 in) cargo door on the port side of the fuselage aft of the wing, the conversion required a 9g net barrier, cockpit emergency exit, smoke detection system, overhead storage rack/bin modifications to accept cargo containers, interior panel alterations, and modifications to the aircraft's oxygen and air-conditioning systems. The DC-9 modification permits up to 15,876 kg (35,000 lb) of

cargo to be carried in the aircraft's main cabin without operational limitations.

PEMCO AEROPLEX BOEING 737 FREIGHTER AND QUICK-CHANGE CONVERSIONS

Pemco Aeroplex is developing conversions of the Boeing 737-300 to freighter or quick-change configuration. The first such conversion was expected to be completed during 1990.

PIASECKI

PIASECKI AIRCRAFT CORPORATION

2nd Street West, Essington, Pennsylvania 19029
Telephone: 1 (215) 521 5700
Fax: 1 (215) 521 5935
PRESIDENT: Frank N. Piasecki
VICE-PRESIDENT, ENGINEERING: Donald N. Myers
INDUSTRIAL ENGINEER: Kenneth R. Meenen

The Piasecki Aircraft Corporation was formed in 1955 by Mr Frank Piasecki, who was formerly Chairman of the Board and President of the Piasecki Helicopter Corporation (now Boeing Helicopters). The company has a wholly owned subsidiary, Piasecki Aircraft of Canada Ltd, in Ottawa, Ontario. Work on the hybrid VTOL Heli-Stat has ceased.

PIASECKI 16H-4 PATHFINDER III

On 29 March 1988 Piasecki Aircraft Corporation announced plans for the development of a high-speed compound helicopter known as the Model 16H-4 Pathfinder III, the general configuration of which can be seen in the accompanying artist's impression. The Pathfinder is intended to compete with fixed-wing corporate and commuter aircraft, carrying six passengers at cruising speeds in excess of 180 knots (335.5 km/h; 207 mph). It will be powered by two 1,339 kW (1,796 shp) General Electric T700 turboshafts, and will employ an advanced version of Piasecki's ring tail vertical thrust ducted propeller (VTDP) design which is being developed under contract from the US Army for prototype installation, and testing in NASA-Langley's wind tunnel. The VTDP concept was successfully demonstrated on the prototype Piasecki 16H-1A compound helicopter which achieved a maximum speed of 195 knots (362 km/h; 225 mph).

Piasecki is seeking domestic and overseas manufacturing and marketing partners for the Pathfinder project. The following data are provisional:

Artist's impression of Piasecki 16H-4 Pathfinder III compound helicopter

DIMENSIONS, EXTERNAL:	
Rotor diameter	13.48 m (44 ft 2¾ in)
Wing span	7.80 m (25 ft 7¼ in)
Wing chord: at root	1.77 m (5 ft 9½ in)
at tip	0.61 m (2 ft 0 in)
Wing aspect ratio	5.6
Length overall, rotor turning	16.46 m (54 ft 0 in)
Fuselage length	15.73 m (51 ft 7¼ in)
Height overall	5.04 m (16 ft 6½ in)
Wheel track	2.32 m (7 ft 7¼ in)
Wheelbase	6.35 m (20 ft 9⅞ in)
Ducted propeller diameter	2.29 m (7 ft 6 in)
Passenger door: Height	1.40 m (4 ft 7 in)
Width	0.70 m (2 ft 3½ in)
Height to sill	0.58 m (1 ft 11 in)
DIMENSIONS, INTERNAL:	
Cabin: Length	5.44 m (17 ft 10 in)
Max width	1.98 m (6 ft 6 in)
Max height	1.27 m (4 ft 2 in)
AREA:	
Wings, gross	10.87 m² (117.0 sq ft)
WEIGHTS:	
Basic operating weight	5,512 kg (12,153 lb)
Max payload	1,064 kg (2,347 lb)
Max fuel weight	1,043 kg (2,300 lb)
Max ramp, T-O, and landing weight	5,806 kg (12,800 lb)
Max zero-fuel weight	4,762 kg (10,500 lb)
PERFORMANCE (at max T-O weight):	
Never-exceed speed	230 knots (426 km/h; 265 mph)
Max level speed at S/L	196 knots (363 km/h; 226 mph)
Max cruising speed at S/L	181 knots (335 km/h; 208 mph)
Econ cruising speed at S/L	140 knots (259 km/h; 161 mph)
Max rate of climb at S/L	594 m (1,950 ft)/min
Rate of climb at S/L, one engine out	46 m (150 ft)/min
Service ceiling	3,050 m (10,000 ft)
Range with max fuel, 15% SFC allowance, 10% reserves	290 nm (537 km; 334 miles)

PIPER

PIPER AIRCRAFT CORPORATION

2926 Piper Drive, PO Box 1328, Vero Beach, Florida 32960
Telephone: 1 (305) 567 4361
Telex: 441426
Fax: 1 (305) 562 0299
CHAIRMAN: M. Stuart Millar
PRESIDENT AND CHIEF EXECUTIVE OFFICER:
  C. Raymond Johnson
SENIOR VICE-PRESIDENT, ADVANCED ENGINEERING:
  LeRoy LoPresti
VICE-PRESIDENT, PRODUCT ENGINEERING AND DOMESTIC
  MARKETING: Douglas H. Smith
VICE-PRESIDENT, MANUFACTURING: William D. Polk
DIRECTOR OF MARKETING: Joseph Ponte
DIRECTOR, INTERNATIONAL SALES: Andrew Cairns

Effective 1 March 1984, Piper Aircraft became a subsidiary of Lear Siegler Inc. The manufacturing and R&D facilities at Lock Haven, Pennsylvania, and sheet metal plant at Piper, Pennsylvania, were closed during the second half of 1984. The last of 76,992 aircraft to be manufactured at Lock Haven, a Piper Mojave, left the plant in August 1984, and phasing out of the Lakeland, Florida, facility was completed by October 1985. All Piper manufacturing activities are now concentrated at Vero Beach, where a new 12,077 m² (130,000 sq ft) plant was completed in October 1986, to accommodate production of the Cheyenne IIIA and 400 turboprop aircraft which had formerly been built at Lakeland.

On 12 May 1987 Piper was acquired by Mr M. Stuart Millar, a California businessman. In December 1987 a subsidiary company, LoPresti Piper Advanced Engineering Group, was established under the direction of Mr LeRoy LoPresti to explore and develop aerodynamic improvements to selected Piper aircraft models, including some out-of-production types.

In November 1989 Piper announced the formation of a subsidiary, Piper North Corporation (which see), at its former headquarters in Pennsylvania.

Piper has agreements with Chincul SA (which see) for the manufacture of a broad range of Piper products in

Argentina; with Embraer (which see) for the development, production and marketing of Piper aircraft in Brazil; and with PZL Mielec (which see) of Poland, which produces a modified version of the Piper Seneca II light twin-engined aircraft, known as the M-20 Mewa, in that country.

Piper delivered a total of 621 aircraft during 1989.

PIPER PA-18-150 SUPER CUB

The original Piper PA-18 with a 67 kW (90 hp) Continental C90-12F engine received FAA Type Approval on 18 November 1949. The PA-18-150, PA-18A-150 agricultural aircraft and PA-18S and PA-18AS seaplanes were all approved on 1 October 1954.

Piper restored the PA-18-150 Super Cub to production during 1988. The current model differs from earlier variants in having stamped aluminium wing ribs, Ceconite 7600 fabric covering which is pop-riveted to the wing structure, 7600 Flexi-gloss paint, electric fuel gauges, stainless steel control cables, and heavy-duty wing strut fork ends. In addition to the factory-built aircraft, the Super Cub is also available in kit form for home assembly, with all fuselage components ready welded, wing components pre-formed and fabric envelope pre-sewn. The builder can supply a used engine and propeller, or obtain new items from Piper.

By January 1990 Piper held orders for 88 Super Cubs, including 37 in kit form, and delivered a total of 48 in 1989.
TYPE: Two-seat light cabin monoplane.
WINGS: Braced high-wing monoplane, with steel tube V bracing struts each side. Wing section USA 35B. Thickness/chord ratio 12%. Dihedral 1°. No incidence at mean aerodynamic chord. Total washout of 3° 18′. Aluminium spars and stamped aluminium ribs, aluminium sheet leading-edge and aileron false spar, wingtip bow of ash, with Ceconite 7600 covering, pop-riveted to structure. Plain ailerons and trailing-edge flaps of light alloy construction and skinning.
FUSELAGE: Rectangular welded steel tube structure covered with Ceconite 7600.

TAIL UNIT: Wire braced structure of welded steel tubes and channels, covered with Ceconite 7600. Tailplane incidence variable for trimming. Balanced rudder and elevators.
LANDING GEAR: Non-retractable tailwheel type. Two side Vs and half axles hinged to bottom of fuselage. Rubber cord shock absorption. Mainwheel tyres size 6.00-6 (four-ply). Scott 20 cm (8 in) steerable leaf spring tailwheel. Dual brakes and parking brake standard. Floats optional.
POWER PLANT: One 112 kW (150 hp) Textron Lycoming O-320 flat-four engine, driving a Sensenich two-blade fixed-pitch metal propeller with spinner. Steel tube engine mount is hinged at firewall, allowing it to be swung to port for access to rear of engine. One 68 litre (18 US gallon; 15 Imp gallon) metal fuel tank in each wing. Total fuel capacity 136 litres (36 US gallons; 30 Imp gallons), of which 135.5 litres (35.8 US gallons; 29.8 Imp gallons) are usable. Refuelling points on top of wing.
ACCOMMODATION: Enclosed cabin seating two in tandem with dual controls. Adjustable front seat. Shoulder harness and seat belts standard for front and rear seats. Heater and adjustable fresh air control. Downward hinged door on starboard side, and upward hinged window above, can be opened in flight. Sliding window on port side. Baggage compartment aft of rear seat, capacity 22 kg (50 lb).
SYSTEM: Electrical system comprising 14V 55A alternator, 12V engine starter and 35Ah battery, standard.
AVIONICS AND EQUIPMENT: Optional Bendix/King KTS-1-18 avionics package comprising KX 155 nav/com, KI 208 VOR/LOC indicator and KT 76A transponder, or Narco NTC-1-18 package comprising MK-12D nav/com, ID-824 VOR/LOC indicator and AT-150 transponder, each with microphone, speaker, headset and jack plugs. Other optional avionics include Bendix/King KY 97A com transceiver, KT 76 transponder, Narco AR-850 encoder (compatible with Bendix/King equipment), II Morrow 612B and Northstar M1 Loran C systems, Sigtronics SPA-400 intercom system with control stick transmit switch, and Aero Pro 90 pilot's and passenger's headsets with boom microphones. Standard equipment includes

Piper PA-18-150 Super Cub two-seat light aircraft, restored to production in 1988

airspeed indicator, sensitive altimeter, fluid compass, combination oil pressure/temperature gauge, recording tachometer, carburettor heat control, stall warning system, emergency locator transmitter, vinyl headliner, tiedown rings, epoxy primer on all steel components, polyurethane finish on exposed steel, 7600 Flexi-gloss external paint finish in yellow with black trim, and 30 cm (12 in) registration letters. Optional equipment includes vacuum system with 3 in directional gyro, artificial horizon and vacuum driven or electric turn and bank indicator; vertical speed indicator; electric clock; OAT gauge; float attachment brackets; wingtip strobe lights; oversize 8.00-6 four-ply tyres; 52° pitch propeller; and night lighting package comprising three navigation lights, red tail strobe light, instrument panel lights, dome light, auxiliary cockpit light, and landing/taxy light.

DIMENSIONS, EXTERNAL:

Wing span	10.76 m (35 ft 3½ in)
Length overall	6.86 m (22 ft 6 in)
Height overall	2.05 m (6 ft 8½ in)
Propeller diameter	1.88 m (6 ft 2 in)

AREA:

Wings, gross	16.58 m² (178.5 sq ft)

WEIGHTS AND LOADINGS:

Weight empty	482 kg (1,062 lb)
Max T-O weight	794 kg (1,750 lb)
Max wing loading	47.9 kg/m² (9.8 lb/sq ft)
Max power loading	7.09 kg/kW (11.7 lb/hp)

PERFORMANCE (at max T-O weight, ISA, except where indicated):

Max level speed at S/L	113 knots (210 km/h; 130 mph)
Cruising speed, 75% power at 1,525 m (5,000 ft)	
	100 knots (185 km/h; 115 mph)
Stalling speed, flaps down	37 knots (69 km/h; 43 mph)
Max rate of climb at S/L	292 m (960 ft)/min
Service ceiling	5,790 m (19,000 ft)
Absolute ceiling	6,490 m (21,300 ft)
T-O run	61 m (200 ft)
T-O to 15 m (50 ft)	153 m (500 ft)
Landing from 15 m (50 ft)	270 m (885 ft)
Landing run	107 m (350 ft)
Range with max fuel, 75% power	
	400 nm (741 km; 460 miles)

PIPER PA-28-161 WARRIOR II

Design of the Warrior began in June 1972, an important feature being replacement of the earlier constant chord wings of the Cherokee series by a longer span wing with tapered outer panels. As a result of its introduction the Warrior, which at that time had essentially the same 112 kW (150 hp) engine as the discontinued Cherokee Cruiser, was certificated at a max T-O weight 79 kg (175 lb) greater. First flight of a prototype was made on 17 October 1972, and FAA certification of the original Model PA-28-151 was granted on 9 August 1973.

The current PA-28-161 Warrior II version, first flown on 27 August 1976, has a 119 kW (160 hp) engine which operates on 100 octane low-lead fuel.

A total of 3,042 Warrior IIs had been sold by 1 January 1990. Recent customers include the Singapore Air Force, which took delivery of 12 in 1989, and the British Aerospace-Ansett Flying College of Australia which has ordered 30 for delivery during 1990.

TYPE: Four-seat cabin monoplane.

WINGS: Cantilever low-wing monoplane. Wing section NACA 65₂-415 on inboard panels; outboard leading-edges incorporate modification No. 5 of NACA TN 2228. Dihedral 7°. Incidence 2° at root, −1° at tip. Sweepback at quarter-chord 5°. Light alloy single-spar structure with glassfibre wingtips. Plain ailerons of light alloy construction. Four-position manually actuated trailing-edge flaps of light alloy with ribbed skins.

FUSELAGE: Light alloy semi-monocoque structure with glassfibre nose cowl and tailcone.

TAIL UNIT: Cantilever structure of light alloy, except for glassfibre tips on fin and tailplane. Fin and rudder have ribbed light alloy skins. One-piece all-moving tailplane, with combined anti-servo and trim tab. Rudder trimmable, but no trim tab in rudder.

LANDING GEAR: Non-retractable tricycle type. Steerable nosewheel. Piper oleo-pneumatic shock absorbers; single wheel on each unit. Cleveland wheels with 4-ply tyres size 6.00-6 on main units, pressure 1.65 bars (24 lb/sq in). Cleveland nosewheel and 4-ply tyre size 5.00-5, pressure 1.65 bars (24 lb/sq in). Cleveland disc brakes. Parking brake. Glassfibre wheel fairings standard.

POWER PLANT: One 119 kW (160 hp) Textron Lycoming O-320-D3G flat-four engine, driving a Sensenich two-blade fixed-pitch metal propeller type 74DM6-0-60 with spinner. Fuel in two wing tanks, with total capacity of 189 litres (50 US gallons; 41.6 Imp gallons), of which 181.5 litres (48 US gallons; 40 Imp gallons) are usable. Refuelling point on upper surface of each wing. Oil capacity 7.5 litres (2 US gallons; 1.7 Imp gallons).

ACCOMMODATION: Four persons in pairs in enclosed cabin. Individual adjustable front seats with seat belts and shoulder harnesses; bench type rear seat with seat belts and shoulder harnesses. Dual controls and brakes standard. Large door on starboard side. Baggage compartment at rear of cabin, with volume of 0.68 m³ (24 cu ft) and capacity of 91 kg (200 lb). External baggage door on starboard side. Heating, ventilation and windscreen defrosting standard.

SYSTEMS: Hydraulic system for brakes only. Electrical system powered by 14V 60A engine driven alternator. 12V 35Ah battery standard. Dual vacuum system for blind-flying instrumentation standard, complete with vacuum gauge, regulator, filter, and annunciator light. Piper Aire air-conditioning system optional.

AVIONICS AND EQUIPMENT: Single Bendix/King nav/com, transponder and Narco AR-850 altitude reporter digitiser standard. Choice of three optional factory installed Bendix/King avionics groups including various combinations of nav/com, ADF, DME, RNAV, transponder, glideslope and marker beacon receivers, and Bendix/King autopilots, and electric pitch trim, with substitute equipment options in each group. Additional avionics options for all groups include II Morrow 612 and Northstar M1 Loran C, Argus 5000 moving map display, 3M Stormscope WX-1000 and 1000+, Bendix/King KMA 24-H-70 audio control panel with intercom, KAS 297B altitude/vertical speed preselect system, KRA 10A radio altimeter, KI 229 RMI, KI 204-02 or KI 203-00 nav indicator, ground clearance energy saving switch, United UI-5035-P23 encoding altimeter, transponder ident and press-to-talk buttons on pilot's control wheel, pilot's and co-pilot's boom microphones with control wheel buttons, and static discharge wicks. Standard equipment includes advanced instrument panel with 3 in gyro horizon and directional gyro, pictorial rate of turn indicator, rate of climb indicator and OAT gauge; electric clock; engine driven vacuum pump with indicator, regulator, filter, annunciator light and auxiliary electric vacuum pump with selector switch; EGT gauge; heated pitot head; Piper true airspeed indicator; magnetic compass; sensitive altimeter; ammeter; annunciator panel with press-to-test; recording tachometer; fuel quantity gauges; fuel pressure gauge; oil temperature and pressure gauges; vacuum gauge; wool carpet and vinyl sidewalls and headliner; fabric and vinyl pilot's and co-pilot's fore and aft adjustable and tilting seats with inertia reel shoulder harnesses, seatbelts, armrests and ashtrays; rear bench seat with inertia reel shoulder harnesses, seatbelts and side panel ashtrays; pilot's storm window; map pockets; pilot's and co-pilot's scuff pads and sun visors; door closing strap; soundproofing; ignition lock; carpeted luggage compartment with security straps; compass card with holder; tiedown rings; jack pads; cabin and rear baggage door locks; emergency locator beacon; zinc chromate corrosion protection; stainless steel control cables; exterior styling with single- or two-tone base colour in Piper acrylic enamel with a choice of two trim colours in three designs; instrument panel white backlighting and overhead blue lighting, cabin dome light, two navigation lights, landing/taxi light, shielded white wingtip and red tail strobe lights and avionics dimming; true airspeed indicator; alternate static source; 35Ah battery; entrance step; wheel fairings; engine primer system; and towbar. Optional **Deluxe** avionics and equipment package includes dual Bendix/King KX 165 nav/com; glideslope receiver; KR 87 digital ADF; KAP 100 autopilot with electric pitch trim; deluxe interior with headrests, window curtains and Sofsuede sidewalls; super soundproofing; ventilation fan; vertically adjustable pilot's and co-pilot's seats; cigarette lighter; crew cup holders; engine hour recorder; external power receptacle; wingtip recognition lights; and fin strobe light. Optional equipment in addition to the Deluxe package includes carburettor ice detector, digital clock in pilot's control wheel, approach plate holder (not with digital clock), lockable fuel caps, Piper-Aire air-conditioning system, hand fire extinguisher, leather trimmed or all-leather seats, entry/exit assist strap, DuPont IMRON polyurethane enamel exterior finish, third trim colour, and shadowed registration numbers.

DIMENSIONS, EXTERNAL:

Wing span	10.67 m (35 ft 0 in)
Wing chord: at root	1.60 m (5 ft 3 in)
at tip	1.07 m (3 ft 6¼ in)
Wing aspect ratio	7.2
Length overall	7.25 m (23 ft 9½ in)
Height overall	2.22 m (7 ft 3½ in)
Tailplane span	3.96 m (12 ft 11¾ in)
Wheel track	3.05 m (10 ft 0 in)
Wheelbase	2.03 m (6 ft 8 in)
Propeller diameter	1.88 m (6 ft 2 in)
Propeller ground clearance	0.21 m (8¼ in)
Cabin door: Height	0.89 m (2 ft 11 in)
Width	0.91 m (3 ft 0 in)
Baggage door: Height	0.51 m (1 ft 8 in)
Max width	0.56 m (1 ft 10 in)
Height to sill	0.71 m (2 ft 4 in)

Piper Warrior II four-seat light aircraft

DIMENSIONS, INTERNAL:
Cabin: Length (instrument panel to rear bulkhead)
        2.49 m (8 ft 2 in)
  Max width   1.05 m (3 ft 5¼ in)
  Max height   1.14 m (3 ft 8¾ in)
  Floor area   2.28 m² (24.5 sq ft)
  Volume (incl baggage area) 3.00 m³ (106.0 cu ft)
AREAS:
Wings, gross   15.8 m² (170.0 sq ft)
Ailerons (total)   1.23 m² (13.2 sq ft)
Trailing-edge flaps (total) 1.36 m² (14.6 sq ft)
Fin   0.69 m² (7.4 sq ft)
Rudder   0.38 m² (4.1 sq ft)
Tailplane, incl tab   2.46 m² (26.5 sq ft)
WEIGHTS AND LOADINGS:
Weight empty, equipped   653 kg (1,439 lb)
Max T-O and landing weight 1,106 kg (2,440 lb)
Max ramp weight   1,110 kg (2,447 lb)
Max wing loading 70.06 kg/m² (14.35 lb/sq ft)
Max power loading 9.33 kg/kW (15.25 lb/hp)
PERFORMANCE (at max T-O weight):
Never-exceed speed 153 knots (282 km/h; 176 mph)
Max level speed at S/L 127 knots (235 km/h; 146 mph)
Best power cruising speed:
  75% power at 2,745 m (9,000 ft)
     126 knots (233 km/h; 145 mph)
  65% power at 3,810 m (12,500 ft)
     118 knots (219 km/h; 136 mph)
  55% power at 3,810 m (12,500 ft)
     107 knots (198 km/h; 123 mph)
Best econ cruising speed:
  75% power at 2,745 m (9,000 ft)
     122 knots (225 km/h; 140 mph)
  65% power at 3,810 m (12,500 ft)
     116 knots (215 km/h; 134 mph)
  55% power at 3,810 m (12,500 ft)
     105 knots (195 km/h; 121 mph)
Stalling speed:
  flaps up 56 knots (104 km/h; 65 mph) CAS
  flaps down 50 knots (93 km/h; 58 mph) CAS
Max rate of climb at S/L 196 m (644 ft)/min
Service ceiling   3,355 m (11,000 ft)
T-O run   320 m (1,050 ft)
T-O to 15 m (50 ft)   503 m (1,650 ft)
Landing from 15 m (50 ft) 354 m (1,160 ft)
Landing run   191 m (625 ft)
Range with max fuel with allowances for taxi, T-O, climb
  and descent, and 45 min reserves at max range power:
  at best power settings:
    75% power at 2,745 m (9,000 ft)
      525 nm (972 km; 604 miles)
    65% power at 3,810 m (12,500 ft)
      553 nm (1,025 km; 637 miles)
    55% power at 3,810 m (12,500 ft)
      565 nm (1,047 km; 651 miles)
  at best econ power settings:
    75% power at 2,745 m (9,000 ft)
      590 nm (1,092 km; 679 miles)
    65% power at 3,810 m (12,500 ft)
      633 nm (1,173 km; 729 miles)
    55% power at 3,810 m (12,500 ft)
      640 nm (1,186 km; 737 miles)

PIPER PA-28-161 CADET

The Cadet, announced under this new name in April 1988, is a two/four-seat variant of the Warrior II with instrumentation optimised for VFR or IFR training. Other changes include deletion of the rear baggage compartment and third cabin window on each side. Piper delivered 275 Cadets during 1989. Recent customers include the Embry Riddle Aeronautical University (15 ordered), Florida Institute of Technology (15), Flight Safety International (50 delivered, with a further 50 options), Ohio University (2 ordered), and the University of North Dakota (29 ordered).

The description for the Warrior II applies also to the Cadet, except as follows:

TYPE: Two/four-seat cabin training aircraft.
LANDING GEAR: As for Warrior II, except wheel fairings not available.
ACCOMMODATION: Utility interior with individual fore and aft adjustable and tilting seats with inertia reel shoulder harnesses and seatbelts for instructor and pupil. Bench type rear seat optional. No external baggage door. Limited baggage storage in cabin and behind optional rear seat, capacity 23 kg (50 lb).
AVIONICS AND EQUIPMENT: **Basic Training Group (VFR)** package comprises Bendix/King KX 155-38 nav/com, KI 208 VOR/LOC indicator, KT 76A transponder, Telex 100T microphone and speaker, headset and two sets of microphone/earphone jack plugs; 3 in pictorial gyro horizon and directional gyro; pictorial turn rate indicator; rate of climb indicator; OAT gauge; engine driven vacuum pump with indicator, regulator, filter and annunciator light; basic lighting package comprising instrument panel white backlighting and overhead blue lighting, cabin dome light, two navigation lights, landing/taxy light, and avionics dimming; entrance step; fin strobe light; and emergency locator beacon.
Advanced Training Group (IFR) package includes instruments and equipment as above, plus electric

Piper Cadet two/four-seat VFR or IFR training aircraft

backup vacuum pump, alternate instrument static source and heated pitot head, and IFR avionics comprising dual Bendix/King KX 155-30/31 nav/coms with glideslope receiver, KI 209 VOR/LOC/glideslope indicator, KI 208 VOR/LOC indicator, KMA 24-03 audio selector panel/amplifier, marker beacon receiver, KR 86 ADF with KA 42B loop/sense antenna, KT 76A transponder, avionics master switch, speaker, and microphone headset. Other optional avionics include electric trim, Narco AR-850 altitude reporter, control wheel mounted transponder ident button, Bendix/King KAP 100 autopilot, KN 64 DME, KMA 24-H-70 audio control panel with intercom system, Telex Pro Comm PC-4 voice-activated intercom system, pilot's and co-pilot's control wheel microphone buttons, and static discharge wicks. Optional equipment includes engine hour recorder, engine primer system, carburettor ice detector, EGT gauge, true airspeed indicator, control wheel approach plate holder, external power receptacle and cable, wingtip and fuselage belly strobe lights, wingtip recognition lights, towbar, vertically adjustable pilot's and co-pilot's seats, bench-type rear passenger seat, tinted windscreen and side windows, overhead cabin vent system, floor-mounted rear air vents, ventilation fan, improved cabin sound-proofing, Piper-Aire air-conditioning, and fire extinguisher.

WEIGHTS AND LOADINGS:
Weight empty: VFR   631 kg (1,390 lb)
  IFR   642 kg (1,416 lb)
Max T-O weight: Normal 1,055 kg (2,325 lb)
  Utility   916 kg (2,020 lb)
Max ramp weight: Normal 1,058 kg (2,332 lb)
  Utility   919 kg (2,027 lb)
Max wing loading 66.9 kg/m² (13.7 lb/sq ft)
Max power loading 8.89 kg/kW (14.6 lb/hp)
PERFORMANCE (at mid-cruise weight):
Max level speed 121 knots (224 km/h; 139 mph)
Best power cruising speed:
  75% power at 2,745 m (9,000 ft)
    119 knots (220 km/h; 137 mph)
  65% power at 3,660 m (12,000 ft)
    110 knots (204 km/h; 127 mph)
  55% power at 3,660 m (12,000 ft)
    101 knots (187 km/h; 116 mph)
Best econ cruising speed:
  75% power at 2,745 m (9,000 ft)
    115 knots (213 km/h; 132 mph)
  65% power at 3,660 m (12,000 ft)
    110 knots (204 km/h; 127 mph)
  55% power at 3,660 m (12,000 ft)
    97 knots (180 km/h; 111 mph)
Stalling speed:
  flaps up 50 knots (93 km/h; 58 mph)
  flaps down 44 knots (82 km/h; 51 mph)
Max rate of climb at S/L 204 m (670 ft)/min
T-O run   290 m (950 ft)
T-O to 15 m (50 ft)   457 m (1,500 ft)
Landing from 15 m (50 ft) 320 m (1,050 ft)
Landing run   180 m (590 ft)
Range (estimated) with max fuel, allowances for start,
  T-O, climb and descent, plus 45 min reserves:
  at best power settings:
    75% power at 2,745 m (9,000 ft)
      490 nm (908 km; 564 miles)
    65% power at 3,660 m (12,000 ft)
      515 nm (954 km; 593 miles)
    55% power at 3,660 m (12,000 ft)
      530 nm (982 km; 610 miles)
  at best econ power settings:
    75% power at 2,745 m (9,000 ft)
      550 nm (1,019 km; 633 miles)
  65% power at 3,660 m (12,000 ft)
      590 nm (1,093 km; 679 miles)
  55% power at 3,660 m (12,000 ft)
      600 nm (1,112 km; 691 miles)

PIPER PA-28-181 ARCHER II

On 9 October 1972 Piper introduced the Cherokee Challenger as successor to the Cherokee 180. In 1974 this was superseded by the Cherokee Archer, with the same basic airframe and power plant, but with many additional equipment and avionics options. In 1976 this aircraft was redesignated PA-28-181 Cherokee Archer II, and in 1978 introduced the tapered wings of the Warrior II.

A total of 9,894 Cherokee 180s and PA-28-181 Archer IIs had been sold by 1 January 1990, including 53 delivered in 1989.

TYPE: Four-seat cabin monoplane.
WINGS: Cantilever low-wing monoplane. Wing section NACA 65₂-415 on inboard panels; outboard leading-edges have modification No. 5 of NACA TN 2228. Dihedral 7°. Incidence 2° at root, –1° at tip. Sweepback at quarter-chord 5°. Light alloy single-spar structure with glassfibre wingtips. Plain ailerons of light alloy construction. Light alloy trailing-edge flaps with ribbed skins.
FUSELAGE: Aluminium alloy semi-monocoque structure. Glassfibre engine cowling.
TAIL UNIT: Cantilever structure of aluminium alloy, except for glassfibre tips on fin and tailplane. Fin and rudder have corrugated metal skin. One-piece all-moving horizontal surface with combined anti-servo and trim tab. Trim tab in rudder.
LANDING GEAR: Non-retractable tricycle type. Steerable nosewheel. Piper oleo-pneumatic shock absorbers. Cleveland wheels and Schenuit tyres, size 6.00-6, 4-ply rating, on all three wheels. Mainwheel tyre pressure 1.65 bars (24 lb/sq in), nosewheel 1.24 bars (18 lb/sq in). Cleveland high capacity disc brakes. Parking brake. Wheel speed fairings standard.
POWER PLANT: One 134 kW (180 hp) Textron Lycoming O-360-A4M flat-four engine, driving a Sensenich two-blade fixed-pitch metal propeller with spinner. Fuel in two tanks in wing leading-edges, with total capacity of 189 litres (50 US gallons; 41.6 Imp gallons), of which 181.5 litres (48 US gallons; 40 Imp gallons) are usable. Oil capacity 7.5 litres (2 US gallons; 1.7 Imp gallons).
ACCOMMODATION: Four persons in pairs in enclosed cabin. Individual adjustable front seats, with dual controls; individual rear seats. Large door on starboard side. Baggage compartment at rear of cabin, with volume of 0.74 m³ (26 cu ft) and capacity of 90 kg (200 lb); door on starboard side. Rear seats removable to provide 1.25 m³ (44 cu ft) cargo space. Accommodation heated and ventilated. Windscreen defrosting.
SYSTEMS: Optional Piper Aire air-conditioning system. Electrical system includes 14V 60A alternator and 12V 35Ah battery. Hydraulic system for brakes only. Vacuum system standard.
AVIONICS AND EQUIPMENT: As for Warrior.
DIMENSIONS, EXTERNAL AND INTERNAL:
As for Warrior II except:
Tailplane span   3.92 m (12 ft 10½ in)
Wheelbase   2.00 m (6 ft 7 in)
Propeller diameter 1.93 m (6 ft 4 in)
Cabin: Width   1.06 m (3 ft 5¾ in)
  Height   1.14 m (3 ft 9 in)
Baggage compartment volume, incl hatshelf
    0.74 m³ (26.0 cu ft)
AREAS: As for Warrior II

Piper Archer II, which has the tapered wings introduced on the Warrior

WEIGHTS AND LOADINGS:
Weight empty, equipped (standard)	683.5 kg (1,507 lb)
Max T-O and landing weight	1,156 kg (2,550 lb)
Max ramp weight	1,160 kg (2,558 lb)
Max wing loading	73.2 kg/m² (15.0 lb/sq ft)
Max power loading	8.63 kg/kW (14.17 lb/hp)

PERFORMANCE (at max T-O weight):
Never-exceed speed
148 knots (275 km/h; 171 mph) CAS
Max level speed at S/L 129 knots (239 km/h; 148 mph)
Best power cruising speed:
75% power at 2,440 m (8,000 ft)
129 knots (239 km/h; 148 mph)
65% power at 3,660 m (12,000 ft)
125 knots (231 km/h; 144 mph)
55% power at 3,810 m (12,500 ft)
111 knots (206 km/h; 128 mph)
Best econ cruising speed:
75% power at 2,440 m (8,000 ft)
126 knots (233 km/h; 145 mph)
65% power at 3,660 m (12,000 ft)
121 knots (224 km/h; 140 mph)
55% power at 3,810 m (12,500 ft)
106 knots (196 km/h; 122 mph)
Stalling speed:
flaps up 59 knots (109 km/h; 68 mph) CAS
flaps down 53 knots (98 km/h; 61 mph) CAS
Max rate of climb at S/L 224 m (735 ft)/min
Service ceiling 4,160 m (13,650 ft)
Absolute ceiling 4,800 m (15,750 ft)
T-O run 265 m (870 ft)
T-O to 15 m (50 ft) 506 m (1,660 ft)
Landing from 15 m (50 ft) 424 m (1,390 ft)
Landing run 282 m (925 ft)
Range with max fuel, allowances for taxi, T-O, climb and
descent, and 45 min reserves at max range power:
at best power settings:
75% power at 2,440 m (8,000 ft)
520 nm (963 km; 599 miles)
65% power at 3,660 m (12,000 ft)
565 nm (1,047 km; 650 miles)
55% power at 3,810 m (12,500 ft)
580 nm (1,075 km; 668 miles)
at best econ power settings:
75% power at 2,440 m (8,000 ft)
600 nm (1,112 km; 691 miles)
65% power at 3,660 m (12,000 ft)
645 nm (1,196 km; 743 miles)
55% power at 3,810 m (12,500 ft)
670 nm (1,242 km; 772 miles)

PIPER PA-28R-201 ARROW and PA-28RT-201T TURBO ARROW

The Piper Arrow was derived from the Cherokee Arrow
II, which was generally similar to the Cherokee Archer II
but had a retractable landing gear, more powerful engine,
and the untapered wings of the 1975 PA-28-180 Archer. In
1977, Piper updated this model by fitting long span tapered
wings identical with those of the Archer II, but with
increased fuel capacity, giving improved performance. The
1978 version of this aircraft was named Arrow III, the
prototype of which flew for the first time on 16 September
1975, followed by the first production aircraft on 7 January
1977. Piper designation is PA-28R-201. The Turbo Arrow
III differed by having a turbocharged engine and the first
production example of this version flew on 1 December
1976.

In 1979 Piper introduced new models with all-moving T
tailplanes, but has since restored to production the earlier
low-tail Arrow and Turbo Arrow. A description and
photograph of the Turbo Arrow IV may be found in the
1988-89 and earlier editions of *Jane's*. Piper delivered 33
Arrows and 10 Turbo Arrows in 1989, including 12 Arrows
to the University of North Dakota and four to Korean Air.
The description of the Archer II applies also to the Arrow
and Turbo Arrow, except for the following details:
LANDING GEAR: Tricycle type, retracted hydraulically with
an electrically operated pump supplying the hydraulic
pressure. Main units retract inward into wings, nose unit
rearward. All units fitted with oleo-pneumatic shock
absorbers. Mainwheels and tyres size 6.00-6, 6-ply rating,
pressure 2.07 bars (30 lb/sq in). Nosewheel and tyre size
5.00-5, 4-ply rating, pressure 1.86 bars (27 lb/sq in). High
capacity dual hydraulic disc brakes and parking brake.
POWER PLANT: Arrow: One 149 kW (200 hp) Textron
Lycoming IO-360-C1C6 flat-four engine, driving a
McCauley two-blade constant-speed metal propeller
with spinner. Turbo Arrow: One 149 kW (200 hp)
Teledyne Continental TSIO-360-FB, driving a Hartzell
two-blade constant-speed metal propeller with spinner.
Fuel tanks in wing leading-edges with total capacity of
291 litres (77 US gallons; 64 Imp gallons), of which 273
litres (72 US gallons; 60 Imp gallons) are usable. Oil
capacity 7.5 litres (2 US gallons; 1.7 Imp gallons).
SYSTEMS: Generally as for Archer II and Warrior II except
for electro-hydraulic system for landing gear actuation.
An oxygen system of 1.37 m³ (48.3 cu ft) capacity is
available optionally.
AVIONICS AND EQUIPMENT: Standard and optional avionics
and standard equipment as for Archer II. Optional
equipment as for Archer II, plus cold weather start kit,
and integral or portable oxygen systems (Turbo models
only).
DIMENSIONS, EXTERNAL:
Wing span	10.80 m (35 ft 5 in)
Wing chord: at root	1.60 m (5 ft 3 in)
at tip	1.07 m (3 ft 6 in)
Length overall	7.52 m (24 ft 8 in)
Height overall	2.39 m (7 ft 10¼ in)
Tailplane span	3.92 m (12 ft 10½ in)
Wheel track	3.19 m (10 ft 5½ in)
Wheelbase	2.39 m (7 ft 10¼ in)
Propeller diameter	1.93 m (6 ft 4 in)
Cabin door (stbd): Width	0.91 m (3 ft 0 in)
Height	0.89 m (2 ft 11 in)
Baggage door (stbd): Width	0.56 m (1 ft 10 in)
Height	0.51 m (1 ft 8 in)

DIMENSIONS, INTERNAL:
Cabin:
Length, panel to rear bulkhead	2.42 m (7 ft 11¼ in)
Max width	1.06 m (3 ft 5¾ in)
Max height	1.14 m (3 ft 8¾ in)
Volume (incl baggage area)	3.00 m³ (106.0 cu ft)
Baggage compartment volume, incl hatshelf	
	0.74 m³ (26.0 cu ft)

AREA:
Wings, gross	15.79 m² (170.0 sq ft)

WEIGHTS AND LOADINGS (A: Arrow, B: Turbo Arrow):
Weight empty: A	731 kg (1,612 lb)
B	756 kg (1,667 lb)
Max T-O weight: A	1,247 kg (2,750 lb)
B	1,315 kg (2,900 lb)
Max ramp weight: A	1,252 kg (2,760 lb)
B	1,320 kg (2,912 lb)
Max wing loading: A	79.0 kg/m² (16.2 lb/sq ft)
B	83.3 kg/m² (17.0 lb/sq ft)
Max power loading: A	8.37 kg/kW (13.7 lb/hp)
B	8.83 kg/kW (14.5 lb/hp)

PERFORMANCE (at max T-O weight):
Max level speed:
A at S/L	152 knots (281 km/h; 175 mph)
B	178 knots (330 km/h; 205 mph)

Best power cruising speed at optimum altitude:
A, 75% power	143 knots (265 km/h; 165 mph)
A, 65% power	138 knots (255 km/h; 159 mph)
A, 55% power	131 knots (242 km/h; 151 mph)
B, 75% power	172 knots (318 km/h; 198 mph)
B, 65% power	167 knots (310 km/h; 192 mph)
B, 55% power	157 knots (291 km/h; 181 mph)

Best econ cruising speed at optimum altitude:
A, 75% power	135 knots (250 km/h; 155 mph)
A, 65% power	129 knots (239 km/h; 148 mph)
A, 55% power	122 knots (226 km/h; 140 mph)
B, 75% power	168 knots (311 km/h; 193 mph)
B, 65% power	164 knots (304 km/h; 189 mph)
B, 55% power	154 knots (285 km/h; 177 mph)

Stalling speed:
A, flaps up	60 knots (111 km/h; 69 mph)
B, flaps up	63 knots (117 km/h; 73 mph)
A, flaps down	55 knots (102 km/h; 64 mph)
B, flaps down	56 knots (104 km/h; 65 mph)
Max rate of climb at S/L: A	253 m (831 ft)/min
B	286 m (940 ft)/min
Service ceiling: A	4,935 m (16,200 ft)
B	6,100 m (20,000 ft)
T-O run: A	313 m (1,025 ft)
B	339 m (1,110 ft)
T-O to 15 m (50 ft): A	488 m (1,600 ft)
B	494 m (1,620 ft)
Landing from 15 m (50 ft): A	465 m (1,525 ft)
B	476 m (1,560 ft)
Landing run: A	188 m (615 ft)
B	197 m (645 ft)

Range with max fuel, allowances for start, T-O, climb
and descent, plus 45 min reserves:
at best power settings:
A, 75% power	725 nm (1,343 km; 835 miles)
A, 65% power	770 nm (1,427 km; 886 miles)
A, 55% power	795 nm (1,473 km; 915 miles)
B, 75% power	675 nm (1,250 km; 777 miles)
B, 65% power	705 nm (1,306 km; 811 miles)
B, 55% power	740 nm (1,371 km; 852 miles)

at best econ power settings:
A, 75% power	810 nm (1,501 km; 932 miles)

Piper Arrow used for training Korean Air pilots

A, 65% power	845 nm (1,566 km; 973 miles)
A, 55% power	875 nm (1,621 km; 1,007 miles)
B, 75% power	785 nm (1,455 km; 904 miles)
B, 65% power	830 nm (1,538 km; 955 miles)
B, 55% power	860 nm (1,593 km; 990 miles)

PIPER PA-28-236 DAKOTA

Piper introduced in 1978 an addition to the Warrior, Archer, Arrow line known as the PA-28-236 Dakota, which differs primarily by having a 175 kW (235 hp) Textron Lycoming engine to provide increased performance, and increased capacity fuel tanks to cater for this power plant.

The Dakota introduced the same standard items as listed for the Arrow, plus high performance wheel fairings. A **Deluxe** package as detailed for the Warrior II is also available, and adds 38 kg (83.8 lb) to aircraft basic weight. A range of Bendix/King and Narco avionics packages is also available optionally.

Licence assembly of the Dakota was undertaken by the Chilean aircraft industry (ENAER, which see); a total of 27 was completed. Ten Dakotas were delivered to Argentina's Instituto Nacional de Aviación Civil (INAC) in 1987 for airline pilot training. The aircraft carry Argentine Air Force markings. Piper delivered 12 Dakotas during 1989, bringing total sales to 742.

The description of the Archer II applies also to the Dakota, except as follows:

POWER PLANT: One 175 kW (235 hp) Textron Lycoming O-540-J3A5D flat-six engine, driving a Hartzell two-blade constant-speed metal propeller with spinner. Two integral fuel tanks in each wing, with a total capacity of 291.5 litres (77 US gallons; 64 Imp gallons), of which 272.5 litres (72 US gallons; 60 Imp gallons) are usable. Refuelling points on upper surface of each wing. Oil capacity 11.5 litres (3 US gallons; 2.5 Imp gallons).

AVIONICS AND EQUIPMENT: Avionics groups, optional avionics, standard equipment, and equipment options generally as for Arrow, except oxygen systems not available and heavy duty brakes and tyres and polished propeller spinner optional.

DIMENSIONS, EXTERNAL AND INTERNAL: As for Archer II except:

Length overall	7.54 m (24 ft 8¾ in)
Height overall	2.18 m (7 ft 2 in)
Wheelbase	1.98 m (6 ft 6 in)
Cabin: Height	1.14 m (3 ft 8¾ in)

WEIGHTS AND LOADINGS:

Weight empty	730 kg (1,610 lb)
Max T-O weight	1,361 kg (3,000 lb)
Max ramp weight	1,366 kg (3,011 lb)
Max wing loading	85.93 kg/m² (17.6 lb/sq ft)
Max power loading	7.78 kg/kW (12.8 lb/hp)

PERFORMANCE (at max T-O weight):

Max level speed at S/L	148 knots (274 km/h; 170 mph)

Best power cruising speed at optimum altitude:

75% power	144 knots (267 km/h; 166 mph)
65% power	139 knots (257 km/h; 160 mph)
55% power	130 knots (241 km/h; 150 mph)

Best econ cruising speed at optimum altitude:

75% power	139 knots (258 km/h; 160 mph)
65% power	134 knots (248 km/h; 154 mph)
55% power	126 knots (234 km/h; 145 mph)

Stalling speed:

flaps up	65 knots (120 km/h; 75 mph) CAS
flaps down	58 knots (108 km/h; 67 mph) CAS
Max rate of climb at S/L	338 m (1,110 ft)/min
Service ceiling	5,335 m (17,500 ft)
Absolute ceiling	5,945 m (19,500 ft)
T-O run	270 m (886 ft)
T-O to 15 m (50 ft)	371 m (1,216 ft)

Landing from 15 m (50 ft):

standard brakes	526 m (1,725 ft)
heavy duty brakes	466 m (1,530 ft)

Landing run: standard brakes | 252 m (825 ft)

heavy duty brakes	195 m (640 ft)

Range with max fuel, allowances for taxi, T-O, climb, cruise, descent, and 45 min reserves at max range power:

at best power settings at optimum altitude:

75% power	650 nm (1,205 km; 748 miles)
65% power	710 nm (1,315 km; 817 miles)
55% power	750 nm (1,390 km; 863 miles)

at best econ power settings at optimum altitude:

75% power	720 nm (1,334 km; 829 miles)
65% power	770 nm (1,427 km; 886 miles)
55% power	810 nm (1,501 km; 933 miles)

PIPER PA-32-301 SARATOGA

On 17 December 1979, Piper announced that it had begun production of a new family of six-seat single-engined aircraft known as Saratogas, to replace the PA-32 SIX 300 and T tail Lance series (all described in 1979-80 *Jane's*). All Saratogas have a common airframe, with a conventional low-mounted tailplane and a semi-tapered wing of longer span than the wing of the aircraft they supersede.

Two versions of the Saratoga were available in 1990:

PA-32-301 Saratoga. Basic version, as described in detail.

Piper Dakota, a four-seat aircraft with non-retractable landing gear

PA-32R-301 Saratoga SP. Retractable landing gear version of the Saratoga, described separately.

At 1 January 1990, sales of Saratoga models totalled 396, including 16 delivered in 1989.

TYPE: Six-seat cabin monoplane.

WINGS: Cantilever low-wing monoplane. Light alloy single-spar structure with glassfibre wingtips. Plain ailerons of light alloy construction. Electrically operated trailing-edge flaps of light alloy construction with ribbed skins.

FUSELAGE: Conventional semi-monocoque structure of light alloy. Glassfibre engine cowling.

TAIL UNIT: Cantilever structure of light alloy, except for glassfibre tips on fin and tailplane. Fin and rudder have ribbed metal skins. One-piece all-moving horizontal surface with combined anti-servo and trim tab. Trimmable rudder.

LANDING GEAR: Non-retractable tricycle type. Steerable nosewheel. Piper oleo-pneumatic shock absorbers. Single wheel on each unit. Mainwheel tyres size 6.00-6, 8-ply rating, pressure 3.79 bars (55 lb/sq in). Nosewheel tyre size 5.00-5, 6-ply rating, pressure 2.41 bars (35 lb/sq in). Nosewheel tyre size 6.00-6 optional. High capacity disc brakes. Parking brake. Wheel fairings optional. Heavy duty brakes and tyres optional.

POWER PLANT: One 224 kW (300 hp) Textron Lycoming IO-540-K1G5 flat-six engine, driving a Hartzell two-blade constant-speed metal propeller with spinner. Three-blade propeller optional. Polished spinner optional (three-blade propeller only). Two fuel tanks in each wing with combined capacity of 405 litres (107 US gallons; 89 Imp gallons), of which 386 litres (102 US gallons; 85 Imp gallons) are usable. Refuelling points on wing upper surface. Oil capacity 11.5 litres (3 US gallons; 2.5 Imp gallons).

ACCOMMODATION: Enclosed cabin, seating six people in pairs. Dual controls and toe brakes standard. Two forward hinged doors, one on starboard side forward, overwing, and one on port side at rear end of cabin. Space for 45 kg (100 lb) baggage at rear of cabin, with external baggage/utility door on port side. Additional baggage space, capacity 45 kg (100 lb), between engine fireproof bulkhead and instrument panel, with external door on starboard side. Pilot's storm window. Sun visors. Accommodation heated and ventilated. Windscreen defroster standard.

SYSTEMS: Piper Aire air-conditioning, vacuum and oxygen systems optional, including a built-in oxygen system of 1.81 m³ (64.0 cu ft) capacity. Hydraulic system for brakes only. Electrical system includes a 14V 60A engine driven alternator, and 28V 35Ah battery. Vacuum system standard.

AVIONICS AND EQUIPMENT: Single Bendix/King KX 155 nav/com, KAP 100 autopilot, Narco AR-850 altitude reporter/digitiser, and transponder standard. Three optional factory installed Bendix/King avionics groups including various single and dual combinations of nav/com, ADF, DME, RNAV, transponder, glideslope and marker beacon receivers, and electric pitch trim, with substitute equipment options in each group. Additional avionics options for all groups Bendix/King KAP 150 autopilot, KFC 150 flight control system, Bendix/King KLN 88, II Morrow 612 and Northstar M1 Loran C systems, Argus 5000 moving map display, 3M Stormscope WX-1000 and 1000+, Bendix/King KMA 24H-70 audio control panel with intercom, KHF 950 HF, KRA 10A radio altimeter, KI 229 RMI, KI 204-02 or KI 203-00 nav indicator, ground clearance energy saving switch, Wulfsberg Flitefone VI, press-to-talk buttons on pilot's control wheel, pilot's and co-pilot's boom microphones with control wheel buttons, and static discharge wicks. Standard equipment includes Piper true airspeed indicator; magnetic compass; sensitive altimeter; ammeter; annunciator panel with press-to-test; recording tachometer; fuel quantity gauges; fuel pressure gauge; manifold/fuel flow gauge, oil temperature and pressure gauges; engine driven vacuum system with indicator and annunciator light; electric standby vacuum pump; instrument panel white backlighting and overhead blue lighting, baggage door ajar warning light, four cabin reading lights, two map lights, navigation lights,

Piper PA-32-301 Saratoga six-seat cabin monoplane

landing/taxy light, wingtip strobe lights and avionics dimming; advanced instrument panel with 3 in gyro horizon, turn rate indicator, rate of climb indicator, OAT gauge and electric clock; heated pitot head; EGT gauge; 35Ah heavy duty battery; emergency locator beacon; entrance step; wheel fairings; wool carpet and Sofsuede sidewalls and headliner; fabric and vinyl pilot's and co-pilot's fore and aft adjustable reclining seats with inertia reel shoulder harnesses, seatbelts, armrests and ashtrays; four rear seats with inertia reel shoulder harnesses, seatbelts and side panel ashtrays; pilot's storm window; map pockets; pilot's and co-pilot's scuff pads and sun visors; conference interior with club seating, headrests for all seats; window curtains; assist strap; tinted windscreen and side windows; vertically adjustable crew seats; ventilation fan; alternate static source; external power receptacle; crew cup holders; and courtesy lighting package; door closing straps; soundproofing; ignition lock; carpeted luggage compartment with security straps; compass card with holder; stowable towbar, tiedown rings; jack pads; cabin and rear baggage door locks; zinc chromate corrosion protection; stainless steel control cables; and exterior styling in choice of three styles with single- or two-tone base colour in Piper acrylic enamel. Optional **Deluxe** avionics and equipment package comprises dual Bendix/King KX 165 nav/com; KAP 150 autopilot with electric pitch trim, VOR/LOC/GS coupling; KCS 55A HSI/slaved compass system; Lounge interior with refreshment console and fold-down armrest between fifth and sixth seats; improved cabin soundproofing; cigarette lighter; three-blade propeller; polished spinner; engine hour recorder; wingtip recognition lights; heavy duty brakes and tyres on main gear, and heavy duty tyre on nosewheel. Optional equipment in addition to the Deluxe package includes engine hour recorder, digital clock in pilot's control wheel, approach plate holder (not with digital clock), lockable fuel caps, strobe light on fin, Piper-Aire air-conditioning system, DeLuxe Lounge interior, executive writing table (with club seating only), fire extinguisher, DuPont IMRON polyurethane enamel exterior finish, third trim colour, and shadowed registration numbers.

DIMENSIONS, EXTERNAL:
Wing span	11.02 m (36 ft 2 in)
Length overall	8.44 m (27 ft 8½ in)
Height overall	2.49 m (8 ft 2 in)
Tailplane span	3.94 m (12 ft 11 in)
Wheel track	3.23 m (10 ft 7 in)
Wheelbase	2.36 m (7 ft 9 in)
Cabin door (fwd, stbd): Height	0.89 m (2 ft 11 in)
Width	0.91 m (3 ft 0 in)
Cabin door (rear, port): Height	0.72 m (2 ft 4½ in)
Width	0.71 m (2 ft 4 in)
Baggage door (fwd): Height	0.41 m (1 ft 4 in)
Width	0.56 m (1 ft 10 in)
Baggage/utility door (rear): Height	0.52 m (1 ft 8½ in)
Width	0.66 m (2 ft 2 in)

DIMENSIONS, INTERNAL:
Cabin: Length (instrument panel to rear bulkhead)	3.15 m (10 ft 4¼ in)
Max width	1.22 m (4 ft 0¼ in)
Max height	1.07 m (3 ft 6 in)
Volume (incl rear baggage area)	5.53 m³ (195.3 cu ft)
Baggage compartment volume:	
forward	0.23 m³ (8.0 cu ft)
rear	0.49 m³ (17.3 cu ft)

AREA:
Wings, gross	16.56 m² (178.3 sq ft)

WEIGHTS AND LOADINGS:
Weight empty, equipped	953 kg (2,101 lb)
Max T-O weight	1,633 kg (3,600 lb)
Max ramp weight	1,640 kg (3,615 lb)
Max wing loading	98.6 kg/m² (20.2 lb/sq ft)
Max power loading	7.30 kg/kW (12.0 lb/hp)

PERFORMANCE (at max T-O weight):
Max level speed at optimum altitude	152 knots (282 km/h; 175 mph)
Best power cruising speed at optimum altitude:	
at 75% power	150 knots (278 km/h; 173 mph)
at 65% power	146 knots (270 km/h; 168 mph)
at 55% power	136 knots (252 km/h; 156 mph)
Best econ cruising speed at optimum altitude:	
at 75% power	148 knots (274 km/h; 170 mph)
at 65% power	144 knots (267 km/h; 166 mph)
at 55% power	133 knots (246 km/h; 153 mph)
Stalling speed:	
flaps up	66 knots (122 km/h; 76 mph) CAS
flaps down	60 knots (111 km/h; 69 mph) CAS
Max rate of climb at S/L	302 m (990 ft)/min
Service ceiling	4,875 m (16,000 ft)
T-O run: 2-blade propeller	361 m (1,183 ft)
3-blade propeller	309 m (1,013 ft)
T-O to 15 m (50 ft): 2-blade propeller	536 m (1,759 ft)
3-blade propeller	479 m (1,573 ft)
Landing from 15 m (50 ft):	
standard brakes	491 m (1,612 ft)
heavy duty brakes	466 m (1,530 ft)
Landing run: standard brakes	223 m (732 ft)
heavy duty brakes	198 m (650 ft)

Range with max fuel, allowances for taxi, T-O, climb, descent, and 45 min reserves at max range power: best power settings at optimum altitude:

Piper Seneca III (two Teledyne Continental TSIO-360-KB turbocharged counter-rotating engines)

75% power	745 nm (1,381 km; 858 miles)
65% power	805 nm (1,492 km; 927 miles)
55% power	849 nm (1,573 km; 978 miles)

best econ power settings at optimum altitude:
75% power	823 nm (1,525 km; 948 miles)
65% power	911 nm (1,688 km; 1,049 miles)
55% power	960 nm (1,778 km; 1,105 miles)

PIPER PA-32R-301 SARATOGA SP

This is a retractable landing gear model of the Saratoga. At 1 January 1990 sales of the Saratoga SP totalled 418.

The description of the Saratoga applies also to the retractable landing gear versions, except as follows:

LANDING GEAR: Hydraulically retractable tricycle type with single wheel on each unit. Main units retract inward, nosewheel aft. Emergency free-fall extension system. Piper oleo-pneumatic shock absorbers. Steerable nosewheel. Mainwheels and tyres size 6.00-6, 8-ply rating, pressure 2.62 bars (38 lb/sq in). Nosewheel and tyre size 5.00-5, 6-ply rating, pressure 2.41 bars (35 lb/sq in). High capacity hydraulic disc brakes. Parking brake. Heavy duty tyres and brakes optional.

SYSTEMS: As for Saratoga, but electrically driven hydraulic pump for landing gear actuation.

DIMENSIONS, EXTERNAL: As for Saratoga, except:
Length overall	8.45 m (27 ft 8½ in)
Height overall	2.59 m (8 ft 6 in)
Wheel track	3.39 m (11 ft 1½ in)
Wheelbase	2.43 m (7 ft 11½ in)

WEIGHTS AND LOADINGS:
As for Saratoga, except:
Weight empty	972 kg (2,143 lb)

PERFORMANCE (at max T-O weight):
Max level speed at optimum altitude	164 knots (304 km/h; 189 mph)
Best power cruising speed at optimum altitude:	
at 75% power	159 knots (295 km/h; 183 mph)
at 65% power	153 knots (283 km/h; 176 mph)
at 55% power	144 knots (267 km/h; 166 mph)
Best econ cruising speed at optimum altitude:	
at 75% power	157 knots (291 km/h; 181 mph)
at 65% power	151 knots (280 km/h; 174 mph)
at 55% power	141 knots (261 km/h; 162 mph)
Stalling speed:	
flaps up	65 knots (121 km/h; 75 mph) CAS
flaps down	59 knots (110 km/h; 68 mph) CAS
Max rate of climb at S/L	308 m (1,010 ft)/min
Service ceiling	5,090 m (16,700 ft)
Absolute ceiling	5,595 m (18,350 ft)
T-O run, and T-O to 15 m (50 ft)	as for Saratoga
Landing from 15 m (50 ft) and landing run	as for Saratoga

Range with max fuel, allowances for taxi, T-O, climb, descent, and 45 min reserves at max range power: best power settings at optimum altitude:
75% power	784 nm (1,453 km; 903 miles)
65% power	828 nm (1,533 km; 953 miles)
55% power	869 nm (1,611 km; 1,001 miles)

best econ power settings at optimum altitude:
75% power	865 nm (1,603 km; 996 miles)
65% power	937 nm (1,736 km; 1,079 miles)
55% power	983 nm (1,822 km; 1,132 miles)

PIPER PA-34-220T SENECA III

On 23 September 1971, Piper announced a twin-engined light aircraft which had the company designation PA-34 and the name Seneca. Built at Piper's Vero Beach factory in Florida, the aircraft was redesignated Seneca II from 1975. On 15 February 1981 Piper introduced the improved PA-34-220T Seneca III, with more powerful engines.

The Seneca III has counter-rotating (C/R) engine and propeller installations. The retractable landing gear is operated by an electro-hydraulic system and includes an emergency extension system which allows the wheels to free

fall into the down and locked position. A dual-vane stall warning system provides warning by horn well in advance of the stall in either clean or gear/flaps-down configuration.

It was announced on 3 January 1977 that Piper had signed an agreement with Pezetel, the Polish foreign trade organisation, enabling PZL Mielec (which see) to assemble, manufacture and distribute the Seneca in Eastern Europe. These aircraft (several hundred are involved in the agreement) are powered by 164 kW (220 hp) PZL-F engines and are named **M-20 Mewa** (Gull). In June 1987 Pezetel awarded Western world marketing rights for the M-20 to the British company Aircraft International.

At 1 January 1990 a total of 4,464 Senecas had been delivered, including 46 in 1989. Recent orders include four for Korean Air, nine for the BAe-Ansett Flying College and four for Flight Safety International.

TYPE: Six-seat twin-engined light aircraft.

WINGS: Cantilever low-wing monoplane. Dihedral 7°. Single-spar wings, Frise ailerons, and wide span electrically operated slotted flaps, of light alloy construction. Glassfibre wingtips. Pneumatic de-icing boots for leading-edges optional.

FUSELAGE: Light alloy semi-monocoque structure.

TAIL UNIT: Cantilever structure of light alloy. One-piece all-moving horizontal surface with combined anti-balance and trim tab. Anti-servo tab in rudder. Pneumatic de-icing boots for fin and tailplane leading-edges optional.

LANDING GEAR: Hydraulically retractable tricycle type. Main units retract inward, nose unit forward. Oleo-pneumatic shock absorbers. Steerable nosewheel. Emergency free-fall extension system. Mainwheels and tyres size 6.00-6, 8-ply rating, pressure 3.79 bars (55 lb/sq in); nosewheel and tyre size 6.00-6, 6-ply rating, pressure 2.76 bars (40 lb/sq in). Nosewheel safety mirror. High capacity disc brakes. Parking brake. Heavy duty tyres and brakes optional.

POWER PLANT: One 164 kW (220 hp) Teledyne Continental TSIO-360-KB and one 164 kW (220 hp) LTSIO-360-KB flat-six turbocharged counter-rotating engine, each driving a Hartzell two-blade constant-speed fully-feathering metal propeller with spinner. Three-blade propellers, propeller de-icing, automatic unfeathering and propeller synchrophasers optional. Fuel in four tanks in wings, with a total capacity of 485 litres (128 US gallons; 106.6 Imp gallons), of which 466 litres (123 US gallons; 102.4 Imp gallons) are usable. Oil capacity 7.5 litres (2 US gallons; 1.7 Imp gallons). Glassfibre engine cowlings.

ACCOMMODATION: Enclosed cabin, seating six people in pairs on individual seats with 0.25 m (10 in) centre aisle. Dual controls standard. Pilot's storm window. Two forward hinged doors, one on starboard side at front, the other on port side at rear. Large utility door adjacent to rear cabin door provides an extra-wide opening for loading bulky items. Passenger seats easily removable to provide different seating/baggage/cargo combinations. Space for 45 kg (100 lb) baggage at rear of cabin, and for 45 kg (100 lb) in nose compartment with external door on port side. Cabin heated and ventilated. Windscreen defrosters standard. Electrically de-iced windscreen for pilot, and ice inspection light, optional.

SYSTEMS: Electro-hydraulic system for landing gear actuation. Electrical system powered by two 28V 60A alternators. 24V 35Ah battery. Oxygen system with six outlets, or built-in oxygen system of 1.81 m³ (64 cu ft), optional. Dual engine driven pneumatic pumps for flight instruments standard. Piper Aire air-conditioning system of 14,500 BTU capacity optional. Janitrol 45,000 BTU combustion heater standard.

AVIONICS AND EQUIPMENT: Standard Bendix/King avionics package comprises dual KX 155 nav/com; KAP 150 autopilot; transponder; and Narco AR-850 altitude reporter/digitiser. Choice of three optional factory installed Bendix/King avionics groups including various single and dual combinations of nav/com, ADF, DME, RNAV, transponder, glideslope and marker beacon receivers, and electric pitch trim, with substitute equipment options in each group. Additional avionics options for all groups include Bendix/King EFIS EHI-40, King KAP 150 autopilot, KFC 150 flight control system, Bendix/King KLN 88, Foster LNS 616B, II Morrow 612 and Northstar M1 Loran C systems, Argus 5000 moving map display, 3M Stormscope WX-1000 and 1000+, Bendix/King RDS-81 or Narco KWX-56 colour weather radar with nose radome; Bendix/King KMA 24H-70 audio control panel with intercom, KHF 950 HF, KRA 10A radio altimeter, KI 229 RMI, KI 204-02 or KI 203-00 nav indicator, ground clearance energy saving switch, Wulfsberg Flitefone VI, press-to-talk buttons on pilot's control wheel, pilot's and co-pilot's boom microphones with control wheel buttons, and static discharge wicks. Standard equipment includes advanced instrument panel with gyro horizon, directional gyro, turn rate indicator, rate of climb indicator, OAT gauge and electric clock; Piper true airspeed indicator; illuminated magnetic compass; sensitive altimeter; dual reading ammeter; annunciator panel with press-to-test; dual electric tachometers; dual fuel quantity gauges; dual fuel flow gauges; dual manifold pressure gauges; dual oil temperature and pressure gauges; dual CHT gauges; dual EGT gauges; pilot's and co-pilot's toe brakes; basic lighting package comprising instrument panel white backlighting and overhead blue lighting, four cabin reading lights, two map lights, navigation lights, landing/taxi lights, and avionics dimming; wingtip strobe lights; heated pitot head; dual engine driven pneumatic pumps with indicator and annunciator light; emergency locator beacon; wool carpet, Sofsuede sidewalls and white vinyl headliner; fabric and vinyl pilot's and co-pilot's fore and aft adjustable reclining seats with inertia reel shoulder harnesses, seatbelts, armrests and ashtrays; fabric and vinyl passenger seats with quick release feature, inertia reel shoulder harnesses on forward facing seats, seatbelts and side panel ashtrays; four rear seats with inertia reel shoulder harnesses, seatbelts and side panel ashtrays; pilot's storm window; map pockets; cigarette lighter; glove compartment with rollaway door; pilot's and co-pilot's scuff pads and sun visors; door closing straps; soundproofing; Janitrol 45,000 BTU combustion heater with six floor air/heat outlets, regulating levers and cabin air exhaust vents; six cabin fresh air vents; windscreen defrosters; luggage compartments with security straps; compass card with holder; power setting table and T-O/landing checklists on sun visor; tiedown rings; jack pads; cabin and forward baggage door locks; zinc chromate corrosion protection; stainless steel control cables; exterior styling in choice of three styles with single- or two-tone base colour in Piper acrylic enamel; conference interior with club seating, headrests for all seats, window curtains, tinted windscreen and side windows; vertically adjustable crew seats; ventilation fan; external power receptacle; crew cup holders; courtesy lighting package; nose baggage door ajar warning light; and stowable towbar. Optional **Deluxe** avionics and equipment package comprises dual Bendix/King KX 165 nav/com; KAP 150 autopilot with electric pitch trim, VOR/LOC/GS coupling; KCS 55A HSI/slaved compass system; Lounge interior with refreshment console and fold-down armrest between fifth and sixth seats; improved cabin soundproofing; three-blade propellers with synchrophasers; polished spinners; wingtip recognition lights; heavy duty brakes and tyres on main gear, and heavy duty tyre on nosewheel. Optional equipment in addition to the Deluxe package includes cold weather start kit, heater hour recorder, digital clock in pilot's control wheel, approach plate holder (not with digital clock), co-pilot's instrument panel (deletes glove compartment and not available with some avionics groups or weather radar), De-icing Group comprising wing and tail leading-edge pneumatic boots, electric propeller de-icing, pilot's windscreen de-icing plate, ice inspection light and luminous OAT gauge, lockable fuel caps, wingtip recognition lights, Piper-Aire air-conditioning system, executive writing table (with club seating only), six-outlet portable oxygen system (club seating only) mounted between third and fourth seats, built in oxygen system, capacity 1.81 m³ (64 cu ft) with remote filler, ventilation fan, fire extinguisher, DuPont IMRON polyurethane enamel exterior finish, third trim colour, and shadowed registration numbers.

DIMENSIONS, EXTERNAL:

Wing span	11.85 m (38 ft 10¾ in)
Wing chord, constant	1.60 m (5 ft 3 in)
Length overall	8.72 m (28 ft 7½ in)
Height overall	3.02 m (9 ft 10¾ in)
Tailplane span	4.14 m (13 ft 6¼ in)
Wheel track	3.38 m (11 ft 1 in)
Wheelbase	2.13 m (7 ft 0 in)
Propeller diameter	1.93 m (6 ft 4 in)
Distance between propeller centres	3.80 m (12 ft 5½ in)
Cabin door (stbd, fwd): Height	0.89 m (2 ft 11 in)
Width	0.91 m (3 ft 0 in)
Cabin door (port, rear): Height	0.72 m (2 ft 4½ in)
Width	0.71 m (2 ft 4 in)
Baggage door (stbd, rear): Height	0.52 m (1 ft 8½ in)
Width	0.66 m (2 ft 2 in)
Baggage door (port, fwd): Height	0.53 m (1 ft 9 in)
Width	0.61 m (2 ft 0 in)

DIMENSIONS, INTERNAL:

Cabin (incl flight deck): Length	3.15 m (10 ft 4¼ in)
Max width	1.24 m (4 ft 0¾ in)
Max height	1.07 m (3 ft 6 in)
Volume	5.53 m³ (195.3 cu ft)
Forward baggage compartment	0.43 m³ (15.3 cu ft)
Rear baggage compartment	0.49 m³ (17.3 cu ft)

AREAS:

Wings, gross	19.39 m² (208.7 sq ft)
Ailerons, incl tab (total)	1.17 m² (12.60 sq ft)
Trailing-edge flaps (total)	1.94 m² (20.84 sq ft)
Fin	1.14 m² (12.32 sq ft)
Rudder, incl tab	0.71 m² (7.62 sq ft)
Horizontal tail surfaces (total)	3.60 m² (38.74 sq ft)

WEIGHTS AND LOADINGS:

Weight empty, standard	1,362 kg (3,004 lb)
Max usable fuel weight	385 kg (738 lb)
Max T-O weight	2,154 kg (4,750 lb)
Max ramp weight	2,165 kg (4,773 lb)
Max zero-fuel weight	2,027 kg (4,470 lb)
Max landing weight	2,047 kg (4,513 lb)
Max wing loading	111.1 kg/m² (22.76 lb/sq ft)
Max power loading	6.57 kg/kW (10.8 lb/hp)

PERFORMANCE (at max T-O weight except where indicated):

Max level speed at optimum altitude, mid cruise weight	196 knots (363 km/h; 226 mph)
Cruising speed at optimum altitude, mid-cruise weight:	
75% power	193 knots (357 km/h; 222 mph)
65% power	191 knots (354 km/h; 220 mph)
45% power	168 knots (311 km/h; 193 mph)
Cruising speed at 3,050 m (10,000 ft), mid-cruise weight:	
75% power	179 knots (332 km/h; 206 mph)
65% power	175 knots (324 km/h; 202 mph)
45% power	143 knots (265 km/h; 165 mph)
Minimum single-engine control speed (V_{MC})	65 knots (120 km/h; 75 mph)
Stalling speed: flaps and landing gear up	66 knots (122 km/h; 76 mph) CAS
flaps and landing gear down	62 knots (115 km/h; 72 mph) CAS
Max rate of climb at S/L	427 m (1,400 ft)/min
Rate of climb at S/L, one engine out	73 m (240 ft)/min
Max certificated ceiling	7,620 m (25,000 ft)
Service ceiling, one engine out	3,750 m (12,300 ft)
T-O run	280 m (920 ft)
T-O to 15 m (50 ft)	369 m (1,210 ft)
Landing from 15 m (50 ft):	
standard brakes	658 m (2,160 ft)
heavy duty brakes	603 m (1,978 ft)
Landing run: standard brakes	427 m (1,400 ft)
heavy duty brakes	371 m (1,218 ft)
Accelerate/stop distance:	
standard brakes	732 m (2,400 ft)
heavy duty brakes	636 m (2,088 ft)
Range with standard fuel, allowances for taxi, T-O, climb, descent, and 45 min reserves at max range power:	
at optimum altitude:	
75% power	463 nm (858 km; 533 miles)
65% power	550 nm (1,018 km; 633 miles)
45% power	670 nm (1,240 km; 771 miles)
at 3,050 m (10,000 ft):	
75% power	450 nm (833 km; 517 miles)
65% power	535 nm (990 km; 615 miles)
45% power	632 nm (1,170 km; 727 miles)
Range with max optional fuel, allowances as above:	
at optimum altitude:	
75% power	665 nm (1,232 km; 765 miles)
65% power	785 nm (1,454 km; 904 miles)
45% power	990 nm (1,834 km; 1,140 miles)
at 3,050 m (10,000 ft):	
75% power	640 nm (1,186 km; 737 miles)
65% power	758 nm (1,405 km; 873 miles)
45% power	903 nm (1,673 km; 1,040 miles)

PIPER PA-42-720 CHEYENNE IIIA

Announced on 26 September 1977, the **Cheyenne III** differed from the I and II by having increased wing span, a lengthened fuselage, a T tail and more powerful PT6A-41 engines. The production prototype flew for the first time on 18 May 1979; FAA certification was gained in early 1980, and 89 had been delivered before the Cheyenne III was superseded by the **Cheyenne IIIA**.

Piper received FAA certification for the Cheyenne IIIA in March 1983. It differs principally in having PT6A-61 turboprop engines, and offers performance improvements which include increased max cruising speed and higher certificated ceiling. Other features include improvements to the interior layout, air-conditioning and electrical systems. A total of 47 Cheyenne IIIAs had been delivered at 1 January 1990.

A Cheyenne IIIA, equipped with special sensors, was delivered to the US Drug Enforcement Administration on 15 February 1984 for use on a variety of surveillance and identification missions by day and night, and in March 1985 an order for a further eight Cheyenne IIIA Customs High Endurance Tracker (CHET) aircraft was announced by Piper. These aircraft, equipped with AN/APG-66 radar and a Texas Instruments ventral FLIR turret, were delivered at one month intervals commencing in late September 1985.

Lufthansa German Airlines has taken delivery of five Cheyenne IIIAs, and has ordered a further two aircraft for delivery in 1990. The aircraft, which are equipped with Collins five-tube EFIS on flight decks configured to resemble those of Lufthansa's Airbus A310 jet transports, are used for pilot training by Lufthansa, the West German Air Force, the Spanish airline Iberia and the Swiss airline Swissair. Three Cheyenne IIIAs are used by the Italian carrier Alitalia for advanced pilot training; the Turkish Air League operates two; All Nippon Airways of Japan has ordered four, the first of which was delivered in March 1990; CAAC of China has ordered four for advanced airline pilot training at its flying college in Guanghan City; and Austrian Airlines has ordered two, for delivery in November 1990 and January 1991.

The Cheyenne IIIA is available with Standard and Executive interior options, and a Co-pilot Flight Group which adds 8.7 kg (19.2 lb) to the aircraft's basic empty weight, comprising airspeed and rate of climb indicator, altimeter, electric turn rate indicator, attitude and directional gyros, clock, heated pitot, static system with alternate source, co-pilot's toe brakes, and windscreen wiper.

A full IFR avionics package, including autopilot/flight director and weather radar, plus full icing protection, is standard equipment on the current Cheyenne IIIA, to which the following description applies:

TYPE: Six/eleven-seat corporate and commuter airline transport.

WINGS: Cantilever low-wing monoplane. Wing section NACA 63₂A415 (modified) at root, NACA 63₁A212 at tip. Dihedral 5°. Incidence 1° 30′. No sweepback. Three-spar safe-life structure of light alloy. Ailerons and trailing-edge flaps as for Cheyenne IA. Goodrich pneumatic de-icing boots for wing leading-edges are standard.

FUSELAGE: Conventional semi-monocoque safe-life structure of light alloy.

TAIL UNIT: Cantilever T tail of light alloy construction, with sweptback vertical surfaces. Fixed incidence tailplane. Elevators and rudder of light alloy. Servo tab in rudder; anti-servo tab in elevator. Goodrich de-icing equipment standard for leading-edges of tailplane and fin.

LANDING GEAR: Hydraulically retractable tricycle type with single wheel on each unit. Main units retract inward, nosewheel aft. Pneumatic blow-down system for emergency landing gear extension, with manually operated hydraulic system as backup. Piper oleo-pneumatic shock absorbers. Cleveland mainwheels with tyres size 6.50-10 12-ply Type III, pressure 6.90 bars (100 lb/sq in). Cleveland steerable nosewheel with tyre size 17.5 × 6.25, 10-ply rating Type III, pressure 4.83 bars (70 lb/sq in). Goodrich hydraulically operated disc brakes. Parking brake.

POWER PLANT: Two Pratt & Whitney Canada PT6A-61 turboprops, each flat rated at 537 kW (720 shp) and driving a Hartzell three-blade constant-speed feathering and reversible-pitch metal propeller with Q-tips. Automatic propeller feathering system and synchrophaser optional. Each wing has four interconnected fuel cells and a tip tank, with a combined total capacity of 2,158 litres (570 US gallons; 474.5 Imp gallons), of which 2,120 litres (560 US gallons; 466 Imp gallons) are usable. NACA type anti-icing and non-siphoning fuel vents incorporating flame arresters. Refuelling points on upper surface of each tip tank and engine nacelle. Oil capacity 24.6 litres (6.5 US gallons; 5.4 Imp gallons). Electric intake anti-icing and propeller de-icing.

ACCOMMODATION: Pilot and co-pilot on four-way adjustable seats with armrests, headrests, shoulder safety belts with inertia reels, and stowage for oxygen mask beneath seats. To be certificated for single pilot operation. Dual controls standard. Cabin seats up to nine passengers, but standard interior includes six reclining and adjustable passenger seats with armrests, headrests, and magazine storage on seat back. Four optional executive interiors available, plus a wide range of options for cabin furnishing. Door with built-in airstair on port side, with seven locking pins and inflatable pressurisation seal. Emergency exit window on starboard side. Baggage compartments in nose and rear of cabin, each with capacity of 136 kg (300 lb), and in each engine nacelle, with a capacity of 45 kg (100 lb), giving a maximum total baggage capacity of 363 kg (800 lb). Accommodation is pressurised, heated and air-conditioned. Pilot's windscreen heated; provisions for heating co-pilot windscreen. Pilot and co-pilot windscreen wipers standard.

SYSTEMS: AiResearch pressurisation system with max differential of 0.43 bars (6.3 lb/sq in), maintaining a cabin altitude of 3,050 m (10,000 ft) to a height of 10,060 m (33,000 ft). Environmental control system, combining the functions of heater, air-conditioner and dehumidifier. Hydraulic system supplied by dual engine driven pumps. Pneumatic system and vacuum system supplied by engine bleed air. Electrical system includes two 28V 250A engine driven generators and 24V 43Ah storage battery. Oxygen system of 0.62 m³ (22 cu ft) capacity with ten outlets. Pneumatic wing and tailplane de-icing boots, electric anti-icing of engine air intakes, heated pitots, electric propeller de-icing, and windscreen heating.

AVIONICS AND EQUIPMENT: Generally as for Cheyenne IA (1986-87 Jane's), including Bendix/King and Collins EFIS. Extensive standard installed equipment includes

Piper Cheyenne IIIA used for advanced civil pilot training by China's CAAC

'No smoking-Fasten seat belt' sign; carpeted floor; tinted cabin windows; pull-down window shades; curtain between flight deck and cabin; oxygen system with individual masks in storage compartments; indirect fluorescent lighting, individual reading lights, and courtesy lights. Optional equipment includes cabin chimes; stereo system; cabin instrument cluster giving digital readouts of altitude, outside air temperature, time, and true airspeed; cabin fire extinguisher; emergency locator transmitter; and engine fire extinguishing systems.

DIMENSIONS, EXTERNAL:

Wing span over tip tanks	14.53 m (47 ft 8 in)
Wing chord: at root	3.12 m (10 ft 3 in)
at tip	0.97 m (3 ft 2 in)
Wing aspect ratio	7.8
Length overall	13.23 m (43 ft 4¾ in)
Height overall	4.50 m (14 ft 9 in)
Tailplane span	6.65 m (21 ft 10 in)
Wheel track	5.72 m (18 ft 9 in)
Wheelbase	3.23 m (10 ft 7¼ in)
Propeller diameter	2.41 m (7 ft 11 in)
Distance between propeller centres	5.38 m (17 ft 8 in)
Passenger door: Height	1.12 m (3 ft 8 in)
Width	0.73 m (2 ft 5 in)
Baggage doors:	
Nose: Height	0.30 m (1 ft 0 in)
Width	0.61 m (2 ft 0 in)
Rear: Height	0.51 m (1 ft 8 in)
Width	0.66 m (2 ft 2 in)
Utility door (aft): Height	0.76 m (2 ft 6 in)
Width	0.43 m (1 ft 5 in)
Nacelle locker doors: Height	0.86 m (2 ft 10 in)
Width	0.61 m (2 ft 0 in)

DIMENSIONS, INTERNAL:

Cabin (incl flight deck and rear baggage area):	
Length	6.99 m (22 ft 11 in)
Max width	1.30 m (4 ft 3 in)
Max height	1.32 m (4 ft 4 in)
Volume	approx 9.91 m³ (350.0 cu ft)
Nose baggage compartment	0.46 m³ (16.25 cu ft)
Rear baggage compartment	0.88 m³ (31.0 cu ft)
Nacelle baggage locker (two, each)	0.16 m³ (5.6 cu ft)

AREAS:

Wings, gross	27.22 m² (293.0 sq ft)
Ailerons (total)	1.25 m² (13.5 sq ft)
Trailing-edge flaps (total)	3.98 m² (42.8 sq ft)
Fin	2.17 m² (23.36 sq ft)
Rudder, incl tab	1.88 m² (20.2 sq ft)
Tailplane	3.48 m² (37.5 sq ft)
Elevators, incl tab	2.26 m² (24.3 sq ft)

WEIGHTS AND LOADINGS:

Basic weight empty	3,101 kg (6,837 lb)
Max T-O weight	5,080 kg (11,200 lb)
Max ramp weight	5,119 kg (11,285 lb)
Max zero-fuel weight	4,241 kg (9,350 lb)
Max landing weight	4,685 kg (10,330 lb)
Max wing loading	186.6 kg/m² (38.22 lb/sq ft)
Max power loading	4.73 kg/kW (7.78 lb/shp)

PERFORMANCE (at max T-O weight except where indicated):

Max level speed at average cruise weight of 4,127 kg
(9,100 lb)   305 knots (565 km/h; 351 mph)
Cruising speed at max cruise power, at average cruise weight of 4,127 kg (9,100 lb):

at 6,700 m (22,000 ft)	305 knots (565 km/h; 351 mph)
at 7,620 m (25,000 ft)	302 knots (560 km/h; 348 mph)
at 9,460 m (31,000 ft)	293 knots (543 km/h; 337 mph)
at 10,670 m (35,000 ft)	282 knots (523 km/h; 325 mph)

Minimum single-engine control speed (V_{MC})
                                   91 knots (169 km/h; 105 mph)

Stalling speed, engines idling, at 5,080 kg (11,200 lb):
flaps and gear up   100 knots (186 km/h; 115 mph) IAS
flaps and gear down
                            87 knots (162 km/h; 100 mph) IAS

Rotation speed	95 knots (176 km/h; 110 mph) IAS
Approach speed	109 knots (202 km/h; 126 mph) IAS
Max rate of climb at S/L	725 m (2,380 ft)/min

Rate of climb at S/L, one engine out
                                   191 m (625 ft)/min

Service ceiling	10,925 m (35,840 ft)
Service ceiling, one engine out	6,460 m (21,200 ft)
T-O run	447 m (1,465 ft)
T-O to 15 m (50 ft)	695 m (2,280 ft)
Landing from 15 m (50 ft)	928 m (3,043 ft)

Landing from 15 m (50 ft) with propeller reversal
                                   788 m (2,586 ft)

Landing run	583 m (1,914 ft)
Landing run with propeller reversal	444 m (1,457 ft)
Accelerate/stop distance	1,025 m (3,363 ft)

Range with max fuel, allowances for taxi, T-O, climb, descent, 45 min reserves at max range power ISA:
max cruising power at:
6,700 m (22,000 ft)
                  1,372 nm (2,542 km; 1,580 miles)
7,620 m (25,000 ft)
                  1,510 nm (2,798 km; 1,739 miles)
9,460 m (31,000 ft)
                  1,840 nm (3,409 km; 2,118 miles)
10,670 m (35,000 ft)
                  2,055 nm (3,808 km; 2,366 miles)
max range power at:
6,700 m (22,000 ft)
                  1,803 nm (3,341 km; 2,076 miles)
7,620 m (25,000 ft)
                  1,945 nm (3,604 km; 2,240 miles)
9,460 m (31,000 ft)
                  2,170 nm (4,021 km; 2,499 miles)
10,670 m (35,000 ft)
                  2,270 nm (4,207 km; 2,614 miles)

PIPER PA-42-1000 CHEYENNE 400

Announced in September 1982, this eight-seat business aircraft (known initially as the Cheyenne IV and later as the Cheyenne 400 LS) combines the basic airframe structure, components and systems of the Cheyenne IIIA with a new power plant, updated electrical system and other changes to ensure optimum performance and economy of operation. The prototype Cheyenne 400 (N400PT) flew for the first time on 23 February 1983, followed by a second prototype on 23 June. FAA certification was obtained on 13 July 1984, and deliveries began with an aircraft handed over to the Garrett Turbine Engine Company on 26 July. By 1 January 1990 a total of 42 Cheyenne 400s had been delivered. Korean Air took delivery of a Cheyenne 400 in January 1990 and was to receive a second aircraft late in the year for use at KA's Cheju advanced pilot training facility.

In January 1990 Piper also delivered the 1,000th Cheyenne series aircraft, a Model 400 to a customer in Connecticut.

The 400 in the designation marks the claim by Piper that this is the only corporate turboprop aircraft capable of achieving 400 mph.

TYPE: Twin-turboprop eight-seat light business transport.

WINGS: Cantilever low-wing monoplane, basically similar to those of Cheyenne IIIA, adapted for new power plant and flush riveted throughout. Area inboard of each wheel well strengthened and modified to accept new main landing gear. Outer panels modified to incorporate integral fuel tanks and to carry wingtip tanks to supplement fuel capacity and provide endplate aerodynamic benefits.

FUSELAGE: Basically as for Cheyenne IIIA, but strengthened to cater for increased pressurisation and to embody new multi-ply stretched acrylic cabin windows. Flush riveted throughout.

TAIL UNIT: As for Cheyenne IIIA, with minor modifications to cater for higher speeds. Flush riveted throughout.

LANDING GEAR: Hydraulically retractable tricycle type, with single wheel on each unit. Main units retract inward into wings, nosewheel rearward. Redesigned by comparison with Cheyenne IIIA, for improved ground attitude and increased landing weight. Mainwheels and tyres size 6.50-10, 12-ply rating, pressure 7.58 bars (110 lb/sq in). Steerable nosewheel, size 6.00-6, with 17.5 × 6.25-6 tyre, 10-ply rating, pressure 5.52 bars (80 lb/sq in). Hydraulically actuated dual disc brakes, with multiple brake pads, on each mainwheel.

POWER PLANT: Two 1,226.5 kW (1,645 shp) Garrett TPE331-14A/14B counter-rotating turboprops, each flat rated at 746 kW (1,000 shp) and driving a Hartzell four-blade constant-speed reversible-pitch metal propeller. Blade design and construction incorporates protection from both erosion and lightning strike. The installation of each engine includes new mountings, a new nacelle enclosing the exhaust system, new inlet incorporating bleed air anti-icing, and an exhaust system which discharges the efflux over the wing. Propeller synchrophaser standard. Fuel system as for Cheyenne IIIA, except usable fuel capacity is 2,158 litres (570 US gallons; 474.5 Imp gallons). The engines have automatic negative torque control, automatic start sequencing, and use a micro-computer system to record in-flight performance data for engine trend monitoring.

ACCOMMODATION: Crew of two side by side on separate flight deck. Standard cabin has two rearward facing seats at front. Flat floor and table between these seats and two pairs of forward facing seats, with dropped aisle between each pair. Toilet, with solid divider and door, and walk-in baggage area (capacity 136 kg (300 lb)) at rear of cabin.

Piper Cheyenne 400 twin-turboprop eight-seat business transport (*Pilot Press*)

Piper Cheyenne 400, powered by Garrett TPE331-14A/14B turboprops

Alternative cabin layouts available. Airstair door at rear of cabin on port side. Cargo door immediately aft of this, to provide unobstructed wide opening. Double glazed windows. Emergency exit over wing on starboard side. Nose baggage compartment, capacity 136 kg (300 lb), with two doors on port side.

SYSTEMS: Environmental control system utilises engine bleed air from both engines for heating, cooling and pressurisation. Max pressure differential 0.51 bars (7.5 lb/sq in), maintaining a cabin altitude of 3,040 m (9,980 ft) at a height of 12,500 m (41,000 ft). Independent emergency bleed air pressurisation system. Completely new electrical system includes two engine driven generators and two batteries. Automatic dropout oxygen masks.

AVIONICS AND EQUIPMENT: A full Collins IFR avionics package, including autopilot/flight director and weather radar, plus full icing protection, is standard equipment. Complete optional system by Collins includes pilot's electronic ADI and electric HSI; multi-function display for radar and nav as well as system functions; co-pilot's mechanical ADI and electronic HSI; digital air data system, FCS 65 flight control system with latest technology digital autopilot; and a complete line of com, nav, radar and long range nav systems. Similar system by Bendix is in form of a five-tube EFIS display comprising pilot and co-pilot electronic ADI and electronic HSI; multi-function radar display; electronic engine instrument and crew alerting options; digital air data system; digital autopilot flight control system; and complete line of com, short and long range nav and radar systems.

DIMENSIONS, EXTERNAL: As for Cheyenne IIIA, except:

Height overall	5.18 m (17 ft 0 in)
Propeller diameter	2.69 m (8 ft 10 in)
Passenger door: Height	1.12 m (3 ft 8 in)
Width	0.74 m (2 ft 5 in)
Nose baggage doors:	
Fwd: height	0.30 m (1 ft 0 in)
width	0.60 m (2 ft 0 in)
Rear: height	0.66 m (2 ft 2 in)
width	0.51 m (1 ft 8 in)
Utility door (aft): Height	0.76 m (2 ft 6 in)
Width	0.43 m (1 ft 5 in)

DIMENSIONS, INTERNAL: As for Cheyenne IIIA, except:

Cabin: Max height	1.42 m (4 ft 8 in)
Baggage compartment volume:	
nose	0.48 m³ (17.0 cu ft)
rear	0.88 m³ (31.0 cu ft)

AREAS: As for Cheyenne IIIA, except:

Fin	2.68 m² (28.81 sq ft)
Rudder, incl tab	1.60 m² (17.25 sq ft)
Elevators, incl tabs	2.26 m² (24.30 sq ft)

WEIGHTS:

Weight empty, standard	3,431 kg (7,565 lb)
Max usable fuel	1,732 kg (3,819 lb)
Max T-O weight	5,466 kg (12,050 lb)
Max ramp weight	5,504 kg (12,135 lb)
Max landing weight	5,035 kg (11,100 lb)
Max zero-fuel weight	4,536 kg (10,000 lb)

PERFORMANCE (at max T-O weight except where indicated):

Max operating speed
Mach 0.62 (246 knots; 455 km/h; 283 mph EAS)
Cruising speed at max cruise power at AUW of 4,536 kg (10,000 lb):
at 7,620 m (25,000 ft) 358 knots (663 km/h; 412 mph)
at 12,500 m (41,000 ft) 335 knots (621 km/h; 386 mph)
Minimum single-engine control speed (VMC)
99 knots (183 km/h; 114 mph)

Stalling speed, engines idling:
flaps and landing gear up
93 knots (172 km/h; 107 mph) IAS
flaps and landing gear down
84 knots (156 km/h; 97 mph) IAS
Max rate of climb at S/L 988 m (3,242 ft)/min
Rate of climb at S/L, one engine out 304 m (997 ft)/min
Service ceiling 12,100 m (39,700 ft)
Service ceiling, one engine out
above 7,955 m (26,100 ft)
T-O run 435 m (1,425 ft)
T-O to 15 m (50 ft) 709 m (2,325 ft)
Landing from 15 m (50 ft) at max landing weight:
without reverse thrust 706 m (2,317 ft)
with reverse thrust 621 m (2,038 ft)
Landing run:
without reverse thrust 333 m (1,090 ft)
with reverse thrust 250 m (820 ft)
Accelerate/stop distance 969 m (3,180 ft)
Range at max cruise power at 10,670 m (35,000 ft), with allowances for start, taxi, T-O, climb, descent and 45 min reserves at max range power:
with 8 passengers 1,243 nm (2,304 km; 1,432 miles)
with 2 passengers 1,821 nm (3,375 km; 2,097 miles)
Max range, at max range power at 12,500 m (41,000 ft), allowances as above:
with 8 passengers 1,431 nm (2,652 km; 1,648 miles)
with 2 passengers 2,176 nm (4,033 km; 2,506 miles)

PIPER PA-44-180 SEMINOLE

The prototype Piper PA-44 Seminole lightweight twin-engined four-seat cabin monoplane first flew in May 1976, and the production version was announced on 21 February 1978. Two versions were produced: the basic Seminole, powered by two counter-rotating 134 kW (180 hp) Textron Lycoming O/LO-360-E1A6D engines, and the PA-44-180T Turbo Seminole with TO/LTO-360-E1A6D engines. Production of both variants was terminated in 1982 after a total of 361 Seminoles and 87 Turbo Seminoles had been built. The normally-aspirated Seminole was restored to production during 1988, and total deliveries stood at 390 at the end of 1990, including eight delivered in that year to the University of North Dakota, which will receive a further five in 1990.

TYPE: Twin-engined lightweight four-seat cabin monoplane.

WINGS: Cantilever low-wing monoplane. Conventional structure of light alloy. Plain ailerons and manually-operated four-position trailing-edge flaps of light alloy construction.

FUSELAGE: Conventional semi-monocoque structure, primarily of light alloy.

TAIL UNIT: Cantilever T tail of light alloy construction. All-moving tailplane with full-span tab. Rudder anti-servo tab.

LANDING GEAR: Hydraulically retractable tricycle type. Free-fall emergency extension system. Piper oleo-pneumatic shock absorbers. Mainwheels and tyres size 6.00-6, 8-ply, with tubes. Steerable nosewheel with tyre size 5.00-5, 6-ply, with tube. Dual toe-operated high capacity disc brakes. Heavy duty brakes and tyres optional.

POWER PLANT: Two 134 kW (180 hp) Textron Lycoming flat-four counter-rotating engines (one O-360-A1H6 and one LO-360-A1H6), each driving a Hartzell two-blade constant-speed fully-feathering metal propeller with spinner. One bladder-type fuel tank in each engine nacelle, with total capacity of 416 litres (110 US gallons; 91.5 Imp gallons), of which 409 litres (108 US gallons; 90 Imp gallons) are usable. Refuelling point on upper surface of each nacelle. Oil capacity 11.5 litres (3 US gallons; 2.5 Imp gallons).

ACCOMMODATION: Cabin seats four in two pairs of individual seats. Dual controls standard. Emergency exit on port side. Pilot's storm window. Baggage compartment at rear of cabin, capacity 91 kg (200 lb). Accommodation heated and ventilated. Windscreen defrosters.

SYSTEMS: Electro-hydraulic system for landing gear actuation and brakes. Electrical system includes two engine-driven 14V 70A alternators and 12V 35Ah battery. Janitrol combustion heater of 45,000 BTU capacity. Dual vacuum systems standard.

AVIONICS AND EQUIPMENT: Standard Bendix/King avionics fit comprising KY 197 com transceiver, KX 155 nav/com, KNS 80 integrated nav/RNAV/DME/ILS, KI 206 VOR/LOC/GS indicator, KI 208 VOR/LOC indicator, KR 87 ADF with KA 44B loop/sense antenna, KT 76A transponder, KR 21 marker beacon receiver and lights, AR-850 encoder, KFC 150 autopilot/flight director,

Piper PA-44-180 Seminole four-seat light twin-engined transport

KCS 55A slaved compass, KI 525 HSI, KI 256 attitude indicator, KMA 24H audio selector amplifier with integral intercom, avionics master switch, cabin speaker, pilot's and co-pilot's control wheel microphone buttons and headsets with boom microphones, and microphone/headphone jack plugs for pilot, co-pilot and observer. Standard equipment includes advanced black finish metal instrument panel with post lights; dual vacuum system with indicator; Piper true airspeed indicator; illuminated magnetic compass; sensitive altimeter; dual ammeters; annunciator panel with press-to-test; dual tachometers; engine hour meter; dual fuel quantity gauges; dual fuel pressure gauges; dual manifold pressure gauges; dual oil temperature and pressure gauges; dual CHT gauges; dual EGT gauges; heated pitot head; alternate instrument static source; instrument panel lights and overhead blue lighting; cabin dome light; navigation lights; two landing/taxy lights; wingtip strobe lights; avionics dimming; Janitrol 45,000 BTU heater with four floor air/heat outlets; heater hour recorder; four overhead cabin fresh air vents with vent fan; wool carpet and vinyl sidewalls and headliner in choice of four colours; fabric and vinyl pilot's and co-pilot's seats fore and aft and vertically adjustable reclining seats with inertia reel shoulder harnesses, seatbelts, armrests, ashtrays, magazine pockets and map pockets; quick-release fabric and vinyl rear passenger seats with inertia reel shoulder harnesses, seatbelts and side panel ashtrays; pilot's storm window; pilot's and co-pilot's scuff pads and sunvisors with power setting and T-O/landing checklists; compass card with holder; tinted windscreen and side windows; emergency exit window; assist strap; door closing strap; soundproofing; luggage compartment with security straps and hat shelf area; external power receptacle; static discharge wicks; tiedown rings; jack pads; nose gear safety mirror; stowable towbar; entrance step; cabin and baggage door locks; emergency locator beacon; full corrosion protection; stainless steel control cables; and exterior styling with single- or two-tone base colour (choice of seven) in Piper acrylic enamel with two trim colours (choice of 16) in two designs. **Training Equipment Group** comprises two propeller unfeathering accumulators, heavy duty brakes and tyres, flight time meter, wingtip recognition lights, Quietised cabin soundproofing, two control wheel approach plate holders, work table for third crew member, and hand-held fire extinguisher.

DIMENSIONS, EXTERNAL:

Wing span	11.7 m (38 ft 7¼ in)
Length overall	8.41 m (27 ft 7¼ in)
Height overall	2.59 m (8 ft 6 in)
Wheel track	3.20 m (10 ft 6 in)
Wheelbase	2.56 m (8 ft 4¾ in)
Propeller diameter	1.88 m (6 ft 2 in)
Cabin door (stbd): Height	0.89 m (2 ft 11 in)
Width	0.91 m (3 ft 0 in)
Baggage door: Height	0.51 m (1 ft 8 in)
Width	0.56 m (1 ft 10 in)

DIMENSIONS, INTERNAL:

Cabin, instrument panel to rear bulkhead:

Length	2.46 m (8 ft 1 in)
Max width	1.05 m (3 ft 5½ in)
Max height	1.25 m (4 ft 1 in)
Volume	3.00 m³ (106.0 cu ft)
Baggage compartment volume	0.74 m³ (26.0 cu ft)

AREA:

Wings, gross	17.08 m² (183.8 sq ft)

WEIGHTS AND LOADINGS:

Weight empty	1,068 kg (2,354 lb)
Max T-O, landing and zero fuel weight	1,723 kg (3,800 lb)
Max ramp weight	1,731 kg (3,815 lb)
Max wing loading	100.9 kg/m² (20.67 lb/sq ft)
Max power loading	6.43 kg/kW (10.55 lb/hp)

PERFORMANCE (at mid-cruise weight):

Max level speed	168 knots (311 km/h; 193 mph)

Best power cruising speed at optimum altitude:

75% power	167 knots (309 km/h; 192 mph)
65% power	164 knots (304 km/h; 189 mph)
55% power	156 knots (289 km/h; 180 mph)

Econ cruising speed at optimum altitude:

75% power	162 knots (300 km/h; 187 mph)
65% power	159 knots (295 km/h; 183 mph)
55% power	151 knots (280 km/h; 174 mph)

Stalling speed:

flaps and wheels up

57 knots (106 km/h; 66 mph) IAS

flaps and wheels down

55 knots (102 km/h; 64 mph) IAS

Max rate of climb at S/L	408 m (1,340 ft)/min
Rate of climb at S/L, one engine out	66 m (217 ft)/min
Service ceiling	5,210 m (17,100 ft)
Service ceiling, one engine out	1,250 m (4,100 ft)
T-O run	268 m (880 ft)
T-O to 15 m (50 ft)	427 m (1,400 ft)

Landing from 15 m (50 ft):

standard brakes	427 m (1,400 ft)
heavy-duty brakes	363 m (1,190 ft)

Landing run: standard brakes 180 m (590 ft)
heavy-duty brakes 117 m (383 ft)

Piper PA-46-350P Malibu Mirage cabin class, pressurised, piston powered single-engined aircraft

Range at optimum altitude with max fuel, allowances for start, T-O, climb and descent, plus 45 min reserves:

at best power settings:

75% power	690 nm (1,278 km; 794 miles)
65% power	725 nm (1,343 km; 834 miles)
55% power	765 nm (1,417 km; 881 miles)

at best econ power settings:

75% power	750 nm (1,445 km; 898 miles)
65% power	850 nm (1,575 km; 979 miles)
55% power	915 nm (1,695 km; 1053 miles)

PIPER PA-46-350P MALIBU MIRAGE

Piper announced on 20 November 1982 a new six-seat cabin monoplane, the PA-46-310P Malibu, which the company claimed to be the world's first cabin class, pressurised, piston powered single-engined aircraft. FAA certification was received in September 1983. Production deliveries began in November 1983, and totalled 402 aircraft. In October 1988 Piper introduced a new model designated PA-46-350P Malibu Mirage, which has replaced the earlier model and differs from it in having a 261 kW (350 hp) Textron Lycoming TIO-540-AE2A engine with dual turbochargers, intercoolers and vacuum pumps, pressurised magnetos and a revised cooling system in place of the Malibu's 231 kW (310 hp) Teledyne Continental TSIO-520-BE power plant. Other changes include the addition of dual 70A 28V alternators and a split bus electrical system, redesigned flight deck with new power quadrant and two-piece glareshield, regrouped switches and system controls, an 18 kg (40 lb) increase in useful load, and a range of additional options including a computerised fuel management system, electrically heated windscreen permitting flight into known icing conditions, and a supplemental cabin/cockpit heater. Piper delivered 89 Malibu Mirages in 1989 and at 1 January 1990 held orders for 73 more aircraft, all of which were expected to be delivered by the end of the year. Total orders reached 200 in May 1990.

TYPE: Six-seat all-metal cabin monoplane.

WINGS: Cantilever low-wing monoplane of high aspect ratio. Dihedral 4°. Conventional ailerons and hydraulically actuated trailing-edge flaps. Pneumatic de-icing boots on leading-edges optional.

FUSELAGE: Semi-monocoque structure, primarily of light alloy, with fail-safe construction in the pressurised area.

TAIL UNIT: Conventional tail unit, with swept vertical surfaces and an extended dorsal fin blended into the upper surface of the rear fuselage. Horn balanced control surfaces. Trim tab in elevator. Pneumatic de-icing boots on leading-edges optional.

LANDING GEAR: Hydraulically retractable tricycle type with single wheel on each unit; main units retract inward into wing roots, nosewheel rearward, rotating 90° to lie flat under baggage compartment. Oleo-pneumatic shock absorber in each unit. Mainwheel tyres, size 6.00-6, 8-ply; nosewheel tyre, size 5.00-5, 6-ply. Hydraulic brakes on mainwheels. Parking brake.

POWER PLANT: One 261 kW (350 hp) Textron Lycoming TIO-540-AE2A turbocharged and intercooled flat-six engine, driving a Hartzell two-blade constant-speed propeller with spinner. Fuel system capacity 462 litres (122 US gallons; 101.6 Imp gallons), of which 454 litres (120 US gallons; 100 Imp gallons) are usable. Oil capacity 11.5 litres (3 US gallons; 2.5 Imp gallons).

ACCOMMODATION: Pilot and five passengers in pressurised, heated and ventilated cabin. Centre and rear contoured reclining seats in facing pairs. Foldaway writing table. Airstair door immediately to rear of wing trailing-edge on port side. Overwing emergency exit on starboard side. Unpressurised baggage compartment in nose, and pressurised space at rear of cabin, each with capacity of 45 kg (100 lb). Heated windscreen optional.

SYSTEMS: Pressurisation system with max differential of 0.38 bars (5.5 lb/sq in), to provide a cabin altitude of 2,400 m

(7,900 ft) to a height of 7,620 m (25,000 ft). Hydraulic system pressure 107 bars (1,550 lb/sq in). Dual engine driven vacuum pumps standard. Standard electrical system has two 70A alternators; 24V 10Ah batteries. Full icing protection is optional, with pneumatic de-icing boots on wing and tail surfaces, electrically heated propeller, pilot's electrically heated anti-ice windscreen plate, wing ice inspection light, heated pitot head, heated lift detector, and dual alternators and vacuum pumps.

AVIONICS AND EQUIPMENT: Standard Bendix/King avionics package comprises KX 165-25 nav/com with VOR/LOC converter and glideslope receiver, KX 165-24 nav/com, KI 525A electric HSI with VOR/LOC/GS indicator for nav 1, KI 202-00 VOR/LOC indicator for nav 2, KG 258 horizon reference indicator, KCS 55A slaved compass system, KR 87 digital ADF with KI 227-00 indicator and K44B antenna, KT 76A transponder, KMA 24-02 audio selector panel with marker beacon receiver and lights, KN 62A DME, KAP 150 AFCS with electric pitch trim, VOR/LOC/GS coupling and KCS 55A HSI/compass system, United 5035P-P40 encoding altimeter, Piper avionics master switch, Telex 100T noise-cancelling microphone, Telex 600 OHM headset, and Truax static discharge wicks (16). Alternative Bendix/King package substitutes dual KY 196A-30 com, dual KN 53-00 nav 1, KN 53-01 nav 2, and nav 2 KI 203-00 VOR/LOC indicator, otherwise as above. Approved options to standard and alternative packages include KT 79 transponder, KNS 80 and KNS 81 integrated nav systems, second glideslope, nav 1/2 autopilot coupling switch, KI 227-01 slaved ADF indicator for use with KR 87, KN 63, DME, KMA 24H-70 audio control panel with intercom system, and KEA 346 encoding altimeter. Other avionics options include Bendix/King KFC 150 AFCS/Flight Director, KAS 297B altitude/vertical speed preselect/alerter, yaw damper, KA 185 autopilot mode annunciator, EHI-40 EFIS, KDI 572 second DME indicator, KN 63 DME, KRA 10 radio altimeter, KI 229 and KNI 582 RMIs, Bendix/King KLN 88, Foster LNS 616B Vortac, II Morrow 612 and Northstar M1 Loran C systems, 3M Stormscope WX-1000/1000+, Bendix/King RDS-81 colour weather radar with Piper radome, Bendix/King KHF 950 HF, Wulfsberg Flitefone VI, Flite-Tronics PC-50 static inverter, ground clearance energy saver switch, pilot's boom microphone and control wheel button, pilot's and co-pilot's control wheel microphone and transponder ident buttons, and co-pilot's control wheel electric trim button. Standard equipment includes true airspeed indicator; magnetic compass; Piper pictorial turn rate indicator; eight-day clock; 3 in artificial horizon and pictorial navigation indicator; gyro air filter; vacuum gauge; luminous OAT gauge; heated pitot head; ammeter/voltmeter; annunciator panel with push-to-test; electric tachometer; two-in-one fuel quantity gauges; manifold pressure/fuel flow gauge; oil temperature/pressure gauge; cylinder head temperature gauge with individual cylinder monitoring; TIT gauge; Hobbs meter; cabin altitude and differential pressure indicator; cabin pressure rate of climb indicator; cabin altitude warning light; alternate static source; pilot's and co-pilot's toe brakes; stall warning computer and horn; landing light; two taxi lights; two navigation lights; two strobe lights; instrument panel, switch and circuit breaker panel lighting; solid state dimming; two cabin dome lights; seven overhead cabin lights; nose baggage compartment light; cabin entrance light; interior baggage compartment light; Piper Aire freon vapour cycle air-conditioning system; supplemental electric heater; windscreen defrosters; six cabin air controls with electric fan; six floor mounted cabin heating/ventilating vents; choice of four interior colours; fabric, leather and vinyl side panels; wool carpeting; sheepskin covered fore and aft and vertically adjustable and reclining pilot's and co-pilot's seats with inertia reel shoulder harnesses, seatbelts, map holders

holders and ashtrays; pilot's storm window; emergency exit; pilot's and co-pilot's scuff pads and sun visors; compass card with holder; power setting table and T-O/landing checklists on sun visor; four fabric and leather reclining passenger seats in club arrangement with inertia reel shoulder harnesses, seatbelts and ashtrays; executive writing table; super soundproofing and inner passenger windows; window shades for passenger windows; passenger briefing cards; luggage compartment security straps; rear cabin compartment luggage retaining net; cabin entrance door with integral steps and pneumatic extender on upper door; DuPont IMRON polyurethane enamel exterior paint finish with single- or two-tone base colour with choice of two schemes in two trim colours; epoxy primer and zinc chromate corrosion protection; stainless steel control cables; retractable tiedown rings; stowable towbar; two jack pads; external power receptacle; and emergency locator transmitter. Optional **Executive** group comprises forward refreshment centre, cassette player cabin entertainment system, lockable fuel caps, hand-held fire extinguisher, and vinyl floor runner. Other options available in addition to those listed for Executive group include panel mounted digital clock, Lewis digital TIT gauge, co-pilot's flight instruments, backup mechanical altimeter for co-pilot, six-cylinder CHT gauge, Shadin Mini Flow fuel management system, AIM 2 in standby attitude gyro, De-icing Group comprising wing and tail pneumatic de-icing boots, electric propeller de-icing, pilot's electrically heated windscreen and ice inspection light; polished propeller spinner, lightweight canister emergency oxygen system, all-leather crew and passenger seats, relief tube, CD player, third exterior trim colour, Infinity Designer Edition exterior styling, and shadowed registration numbers.

DIMENSIONS, EXTERNAL:
Wing span	13.11 m (43 ft 0 in)
Length overall	8.72 m (28 ft 7¼ in)
Height overall	3.51 m (11 ft 6 in)
Tailplane span	4.42 m (14 ft 6 in)
Wheel track	3.75 m (12 ft 3½ in)
Wheelbase	2.44 m (8 ft 0 in)
Propeller diameter	2.03 m (6 ft 8 in)
Passenger door (port, rear):	
Height	1.17 m (3 ft 10 in)
Width	0.61 m (2 ft 0 in)
Baggage door (port, nose):	
Height	0.58 m (1 ft 11 in)
Width	0.48 m (1 ft 7 in)

Piper PA-46-350P Malibu Mirage, powered by Textron Lycoming TIO-540-AE2A *(Pilot Press)*

DIMENSIONS, INTERNAL:
Cabin: Length, instrument panel to rear pressure bulkhead	3.76 m (12 ft 4 in)
Max width	1.26 m (4 ft 1½ in)
Max height	1.19 m (3 ft 11 in)
Baggage compartment volume:	
nose	0.37 m³ (13.0 cu ft)
rear cabin	0.57 m³ (20.0 cu ft)

AREA:
Wings, gross	16.26 m² (175.0 sq ft)

WEIGHTS AND LOADINGS:
Weight empty, standard (estimated)	1,265 kg (2,790 lb)
Max T-O weight	1,950 kg (4,300 lb)
Max ramp weight	1,958 kg (4,318 lb)
Max zero-fuel weight	1,860 kg (4,100 lb)
Max landing weight	1,860 kg (4,100 lb)
Max wing loading	119.9 kg/m² (24.6 lb/sq ft)
Max power loading	7.47 kg/kW (12.3 lb/hp)

PERFORMANCE:
Max level speed at mid-cruise weight
232 knots (430 km/h; 267 mph)
Cruising speed at optimum altitude, mid-cruise weight:
High speed cruise power
225 knots (417 km/h; 259 mph)

Normal cruise power	215 knots (398 km/h; 247 mph)
Econ cruise power	199 knots (369 km/h; 229 mph)
Long range cruise power	
	168 knots (311 km/h; 193 mph)
Stalling speed:	
flaps and wheels up	71 knots (132 km/h; 82 mph)
flaps and wheels down	60 knots (111 km/h; 69 mph)
Max rate of climb at S/L	371 m (1,218 ft)/min
Max certificated ceiling	7,620 m (25,000 ft)
T-O run	467 m (1,530 ft)
T-O to 15 m (50 ft)	724 m (2,375 ft)
Landing from 15 m (50 ft)	599 m (1,964 ft)
Landing run	311 m (1,018 ft)

Range with max fuel, allowances for start, T-O, climb and descent, plus 45 min reserves, at optimum altitude:
High speed cruise power
990 nm (1,834 km; 1,140 miles)
Normal cruise power 1,056 nm (1,957 km; 1,216 miles)
Econ cruise power 1,184 nm (2,194 km; 1,363 miles)
Long range cruise power
1,450 nm (2,687 km; 1,669 miles)

PIPER NORTH
PIPER NORTH CORPORATION
Lock Haven, Pennsylvania
PRESIDENT AND CHIEF EXECUTIVE OFFICER: John R. Piper
VICE-PRESIDENT: William H. Piper
VICE-PRESIDENT, OPERATIONS, AND GENERAL MANAGER: Charles H. Bartholomew

On 17 November 1989 Piper announced formation of this company, a wholly owned subsidiary of Piper's parent company Romeo Charlie Inc., to be established at Piper's former headquarters at William T. Piper Memorial Airport in Lock Haven, Pennsylvania. It is proposed that Piper North will re-establish production of the Piper PA-31-350 Navajo Chieftain twin piston-engined business aircraft, last

described in the 1984-85 edition of *Jane's*, and may also manufacture the LoPresti-Piper SwiftFury, described below. Piper North expects to employ 700 personnel by the end of its fifth year of operations.

LOPRESTI PIPER
LOPRESTI PIPER AIRCRAFT ENGINEERING COMPANY
3215 26th Avenue, Hangar 19, Vero Beach, Florida 32960
PRESIDENT: LeRoy P. LoPresti
Under the direction of Mr LeRoy LoPresti, this subsidiary company is developing a number of improved versions of current and out-of-production Piper models and other aircraft.

LOPRESTI PIPER LP-1 SWIFTFURY
This derivative of the Globe/Temco GC-1B Swift light aircraft (last described in the 1951-52 *Jane's*) features many airframe and engineering refinements, and replacement of the original 93 kW (125 hp) Continental piston engine with a 149 kW (200 hp) Textron Lycoming IO-360. Aerodynamic improvements include replacement of the Swift's corrugated sheet metal wing skins with smooth skins, elimination of wing slots, installation of wingroot fairings, use of flush rivets and butt joints on panels throughout the airframe, fully-enclosed main landing gear, retractable tailwheel, and a more streamlined bubble canopy, resulting in a claimed 37 per cent reduction in drag. Other changes include use of independent pushrods instead of cables to operate control surfaces, addition of speedbrakes, control sticks instead of control wheels, a dual braking system, a curved instrument panel to eliminate viewing parallax, and incorporation of hands on throttle and stick (HOTAS) technology, with throttle-mounted switches for operation of speedbrakes, trailing-edge flaps, cowl flaps, landing, recognition and exterior lights, and control stick switches for electric pitch trim, autopilot override, transponder ident, push-to-talk and checklist display scrolling. The prototype SwiftFury (N207LP), modified from a 1946 model Globe Swift, made its first flight on 23 March 1989, and was displayed at the Experimental Aircraft Association's Sun'n'Fun Fly-ins in April 1989 and April 1990. By the latter date LoPresti Piper had received orders for 414 SwiftFuries. Certification is expected in late 1990 or early 1991.

LoPresti Piper LP-1 SwiftFury, derived from the Globe/Temco Swift

TYPE: Two-seat fully aerobatic light aircraft.
WINGS: Cantilever low-wing monoplane, with dihedral from roots. Wing section NACA 23015 at root, NACA 23009 at tip. Dihedral 6°. Incidence 2°. Conventional light alloy structure. Electrically operated single-slotted trailing-edge flaps of light alloy construction, maximum deflection 40°. Light alloy ailerons, maximum deflections +12°/-25°. Electrically operated speedbrake in upper surface of each wing. Fences and stall strips added in 1990.
FUSELAGE: Aluminium alloy semi-monocoque structure.

TAIL UNIT: Cantilever structure of aluminium alloy. Dihedral on tailplane. Trim tab in elevator. Ground adjustable trim tab in rudder. Small auxiliary fixed horizontal tail surface on each side of rear fuselage, forward of tailplane leading-edge.
LANDING GEAR: Retractable tailwheel type. Main units fully enclosed when retracted; tailwheel remains partially exposed. Dual redundant braking system.
POWER PLANT: One 149 kW (200 hp) Textron Lycoming IO-360 flat-four engine, driving a two-blade metal

constant-speed propeller. Max fuel capacity 189 litres (50 US gallons; 41.5 Imp gallons).

ACCOMMODATION: Cockpit accommodates two persons side by side. Dual controls standard.

DIMENSIONS, EXTERNAL:
Wing span	8.93 m (29 ft 3½ in)
Wing aspect ratio	6.375

AREA:
Wings, gross	12.54 m² (135.0 sq ft)

WEIGHTS AND LOADINGS:
Weight empty	635 kg (1,400 lb)
Max T-O weight	998 kg (2,200 lb)
Max wing loading	79.6 kg/m² (16.30 lb/sq ft)
Max power loading	6.70 kg/kW (11.0 lb/hp)

PERFORMANCE (provisional):
Max level speed	188 knots (348 km/h; 217 mph)
Max cruising speed	174 knots (322 km/h; 200 mph)
g limit	+ 10 ultimate

LOPRESTI PIPER SWIFTFIRE

LoPresti Piper Aircraft has developed this turbine engined version of the Globe Swift in which the standard 93 kW (125 hp) Continental piston engine has been replaced by a 313 kW (420 shp) Allison 250-B17C turboprop, driving a three-blade constant-speed feathering metal propeller. The prototype (N345LP) made its first flight on 19 July 1988 and subsequently made its public debut at the 1988 Experimental Aircraft Association Convention at Oshkosh, Wisconsin. Airframe modifications incorporated in the SwiftFire include moving the wing forward by 102 mm (4 in), changing the incidence of the tailplane, increasing tailplane dihedral, and aerodynamic and internal refinements as detailed for the SwiftFury. Provisional performance figures include a cruising speed of 300 knots (556 km/h; 345 mph) and max rate of climb of 1,220 m (4,000 ft)/min.

RAISBECK

RAISBECK ENGINEERING INC

7675 Perimeter Road South, Boeing Field International, Seattle, Washington 98108
Telephone: 1 (206) 763 2000
Fax: 1 (206) 767 7726
CHIEF EXECUTIVE OFFICER: James D. Raisbeck
VICE-PRESIDENT, SERVICE AND SALES: Robert P. Steinbach

Raisbeck Engineering Inc continues the work of its founder and Chief Executive Officer, James D. Raisbeck, of developing, certificating and marketing to the general aviation community advanced technology systems aimed at increasing aircraft performance, productivity and safety. Current products include a series of modifications for the Beech King Air and Super King Air turboprop business aircraft, which are available singly or in combination, and a 'Quiet Turbofan' modification for the DHC-6 Twin Otter, and King Air/Super King Air as described below.

Raisbeck wing lockers and dual aft-body strake modifications on a Beechcraft Super King Air 200

HARTZELL/RAISBECK QUIET TURBOFAN PROPELLER SYSTEM FOR BEECHCRAFT KING AIRS

In February 1985 Raisbeck certificated a four-blade propeller conversion for the Super King Air 200, known as the Raisbeck Quiet Turbofan. This is claimed to offer reduced vibration, reductions of between 7 and 10dBA in flight deck and cabin noise, shorter take-off and landing runs and improved rates of climb. The conversion utilises advanced technology lightweight 2.39 m (7 ft 10 in) diameter 'turbofan' propellers developed by Hartzell, and includes new timers, slip rings and a Goodrich hot propeller de-icing system. First flight of the propeller took place on a Mark VI-equipped Beechcraft Super King Air B200 on 25 June 1984. The Raisbeck Quiet Turbofan propeller system is also certificated for all models in the Beech King Air 90 series.

HARTZELL/RAISBECK QUIET TURBOFAN PROPELLER SYSTEM FOR DHC-6 TWIN OTTER

At the request of Scenic Airlines of Las Vegas, Nevada, Raisbeck developed the Quiet Turbofan system for de Havilland Canada DHC-6 Twin Otter Series 300 aircraft. The modification is similar to that described for the Beechcraft King Air series and reduces cabin and flight deck noise levels by 10-13 dBA, while also offering substantial decreases in external noise, increased engine inlet ram air and lower engine operating temperatures. FAA certification was achieved in May 1986, since when Scenic Airlines has equipped its entire Twin Otter fleet with Quiet Turbofans for operation on sightseeing flights over the Grand Canyon. A number of European Twin Otter operators have also had their aircraft modified to meet ICAO Annex 16 noise requirements.

RAISBECK SHORT-FIELD ENHANCEMENT SYSTEM

In June 1987 Raisbeck announced FAA certification and first production deliveries of its Short-Field Enhancement System for Super King Air 200/B200/300 aircraft. The modification comprises new composite constructed inboard wing leading-edges, intercooler ducting, wing-to-fuselage fairings, and flush mounted Goodrich de-icing boots.

When combined with the Hartzell/Raisbeck Quiet Turbofan propeller system, the modification provides a claimed 18 knot (33 km/h; 21 mph) reduction in flaps-up V_2 take-off speed; 35 per cent reduction in FAA T-O distance; 50 per cent reduction in FAA accelerate/go T-O distance; increased engine-out climb rate; reduced FAA-approved reference and approach speeds; and a 56 per cent reduction in stopping distance using maximum reverse thrust.

Raisbeck Short-Field Enhancement System modification for Beech Model 200 series Super King Airs

Other claimed benefits include increased outer wing fatigue life, smoother rotation at T-O, more efficient air-conditioning through the intercooler system, increased cruising speeds, reduced stalling speeds at all flap settings, and improved low speed handling and stall characteristics.

PERFORMANCE (at AUW of 5,670 kg; 12,500 lb, S/L, ISA. A: Super King Air 200/B200, B: Super King Air 300):

T-O speed (V_2): A		103 knots (191 km/h; 119 mph)
	B	114 knots (211 km/h; 131 mph)
Approach speed: A		97 knots (180 km/h; 112 mph)
	B	100 knots (185 km/h; 115 mph)
T-O to 15 m (50 ft): A		686 m (2,250 ft)
	B	707 m (2,320 ft)
Accelerate/go distance: A		1,061 m (3,480 ft)
	B	1,097 m (3,600 ft)
Accelerate/stop distance: A		988 m (3,240 ft)
	B	1,305 m (4,280 ft)

RAISBECK DUAL AFT-BODY STRAKE SYSTEM

Raisbeck Engineering Inc has developed for all Beechcraft King Air and Super King Air models dual ventral strakes which replace the standard single strake, enhancing stability, providing small increases in cruising speed and range through drag reduction, and eliminating rear cabin area vibration. On King Air F90 and Super King Air 200 series aircraft, installation of the dual strakes also removes the mandatory flight manual requirement for the aircraft's yaw damper to be operative before despatch.

RAISBECK WING LOCKERS

Raisbeck Engineering Inc has certificated, to FAA FAR Pt 135 requirements, engine nacelle wing lockers for all Beechcraft King Air and Super King Air models. The aerodynamic lockers, capacity 272 kg (600 lb), are installed at the rear of each nacelle, extending over and beyond the wing trailing-edge. They provide an additional 0.45 m³ (16.0 cu ft) of cargo space, and are claimed to enhance climb and cruising performance, reduce stalling speed, and reduce pitch axis trim changes when the aircraft is in landing configuration.

RAISBECK FULLY-ENCLOSED LANDING GEAR DOORS

Raisbeck fully-enclosed landing gear doors have been certificated for Beechcraft Super King Air 200 series aircraft which are equipped with the optional high flotation landing gear. The doors are of composites construction and provide increases in high altitude cruising speed of 8-12 knots (15-22 km/h; 9-14 mph), and increased two-engine and engine-out climb rates, whilst keeping the wheel wells clean and extending wheel, tyre and brake life.

RAISBECK STAINLESS EXHAUST STACK FAIRINGS

Raisbeck Engineering Inc has developed small fairings to fit over the fronts of the exhaust stacks on all Pratt & Whitney PT6A-powered Beechcraft King Air and Super King Air models. The fairings are held in place by camlocks and prevent power losses caused by hot air entering the forward cowling and inlet, and reduce drag by streamlining propeller wash. Two 'delta-wing' vortex generators on the fairings divert high-energy gases between exhaust and cowling, keeping nacelle and wing free of accumulated exhaust soot.

RAISBECK RAM AIR RECOVERY SYSTEM

Raisbeck Engineering Inc has developed a Ram Air Recovery System (RARS) for Beechcraft Super King Air 200 aircraft, which involves a more complete sealing of the engine nacelle air inlet section, a new fixed turning vane, the addition of a 'Coanda effect' curved surface on the rear portion of the movable inertial separator vane, and a new highly porous ice shedder screen. RARS, which was developed in association with Pratt & Whitney Canada, which manufactures the Super King Air 200's engines, has received FAA certification. The system provides increases in cruising speed, rates of climb, power plant flat rating, and engine power output with ice vanes deployed, and reduces block fuel consumption and engine ITT at equal torque.

RAM

RAM AIRCRAFT CORPORATION

Waco Regional Airport, PO Box 5219, Waco, Texas 76708-0219
Telephone: 1 (817) 752 8381
Telex: 910 894 5248
Fax: 1 (817) 752 3307

PRESIDENT: Jack M. Riley Jr (Engineering)
INTERNATIONAL SALES:
  Dick Belanger
  Bob Neal
SALES MANAGER: David Seesing
PRESS RELATIONS: Chuck Morrow

RAM Aircraft Corporation specialises in the modification of selected single- and twin-engined general aviation aircraft to provide increased performance and efficiency. This is achieved by the installation of engines of greater horsepower, driving propellers of advanced design. All of the resulting modifications have been FAA approved by the award of a supplemental type certificate (STC). Export STC modification kits are available, and these can include either new engines or RAM-remanufactured 100 per cent balanced versions of the Teledyne Continental TSIO-520 engine in N, NB, VB, WB, LB, E, EB, B, BB, C, F, H, M, P, AF, R and GE models and GTSIO-520-H, L and N. RAM remanufactured engines employ factory-new cylinders. RAM's Cessna 310, 320, 340 and 414A conversions are now identified as Series I (310 hp) and Series III (325 hp) when Teledyne Continental camshafts are fitted, and Series II and Series IV respectively with RAM economy camshafts developed by Crane Cams Inc of Daytona Beach, Florida, which afford easier starting, increased manifold pressure, and smoother idling, with claimed reductions in cruising power fuel consumption of 3-5 per cent. The company offers also an aircraft refurbishing service at its Waco works, including repainting and airframe maintenance.

Any performance figures not listed in this entry may be considered to be the same as specified by the aircraft's manufacturer.

RAM/CESSNA 172

RAM modifications of the Cessna 172, models D-N, involves the installation of a 119 kW (160 hp) Textron Lycoming O-320-D2G flat-four engine or a RAM-remanufactured Textron Lycoming O-320-E2D with power output increased from 112 kW (150 hp) to 119 kW (160 hp).

RAM/PIPER PA-28-140/PA-28-151

RAM modification of these two Piper models involves the installation of a 119 kW (160 hp) Textron Lycoming O-320-D3G flat-four engine.

RAM/CESSNA T206/210

RAM modification of these two Cessna models covers replacement of the 212 kW (285 hp) Teledyne Continental TSIO-520-C/H flat-six engine in early production aircraft by a 231 kW (310 hp) TSIO-520-M/R. This RAM-remanufactured engine provides performance generally the same as that of later model Cessna production aircraft powered by a 231 kW (310 hp) engine and offers a 200 h increase in TBO over the standard engine. A Hartzell Q-tip propeller or wide chord McCauley propeller can be included in the modification.

RAM/CESSNA T310

In this modification the 212 kW (285 hp) Teledyne Continental TSIO-520-B flat-six engines can be replaced by 224 kW (300 hp) TSIO-520-E, or 242 kW (325 hp) TSIO-520-NBR RAM-remanufactured engines. With 242 kW (325 hp) engines the modified aircraft is known as RAM 310 Series IV. The modification increases max T-O weight of Cessna T310P, Q and R models to 2,572 kg (5,670 lb), for a 122 kg (270 lb) increase in useful load on the T310P and 77 kg (170 lb) on the T310Q and R. Either separately or in conjunction with this modification, RAM can install aerial mapping/photo reconnaissance dual camera ports, the STC approved installation being suitable for cameras as large as the Wild RC10 and Zeiss RMKA 15/23.
PERFORMANCE (A: 224 kW; 300 hp, B: 242 kW; 325 hp engines, at max T-O weight of 2,572 kg; 5,670 lb):
Cruising speed, 75% power at 5,485 m (18,000 ft):

A		217 knots (402 km/h; 250 mph)
B		243 knots (450 km/h; 280 mph)
Max rate of climb at S/L: A		640 m (2,100 ft)/min
B		915 m (3,000 ft)/min

Rate of climb at S/L, one engine out:

A		152 m (500 ft)/min
B		183 m (600 ft)/min

RAM/CESSNA 340/340A

RAM's modification of the Cessna 340/340A replaces 212 kW (285 hp) Teledyne Continental TSIO-520-K engines by RAM-remanufactured 231 kW (310 hp) TSIO-520-Ns or 242 kW (325 hp) TSIO-520-NBRs. In 231 kW (310 hp) form the modified aircraft is known as the RAM 340 Series II, and in 242 kW (325 hp) form as the 340 Series IV. Hartzell Q-tip propellers are part of the Series IV modification package. With the 231 kW (310 hp) engines, useful load and max T-O weight of the Cessna 340 and 340A are increased by 75 kg (165 lb) and 68 kg (150 lb) respectively and, with the 242 kW (325 hp) engines, by 136 kg (300 lb).
PERFORMANCE (A: 231 kW; 310 hp engines with McCauley propellers, B: 242 kW; 325 hp engines, at max T-O weight of 2,853 kg; 6,290 lb):
Cruising speed, 75% power at 6,100 m (20,000 ft):

A		220 knots (408 km/h; 253 mph)
B		225 knots (417 km/h; 259 mph)
Max rate of climb at S/L: A		655 m (2,150 ft)/min
B		686 m (2,250 ft)/min

Rate of climb at S/L, one engine out:

A		105 m (345 ft)/min
B		114 m (375 ft)/min
Time to 5,485 m (18,000 ft): A		18 min
B		16 min
Acceleration to 87 knots (161 km/h; 100 mph): A		18 s
B		16 s

RAM/CESSNA 401/402A/402B/402C

In this modification RAM installs remanufactured 224 kW (300 hp) Teledyne Continental TSIO-520-E or 242 kW (325 hp) TSIO-520-VB engines in Cessna 401 and 402A-C aircraft. Standard equipment includes replacement of engine accessories with new or overhauled equipment, Slick 6220 pressurised magnetos, a red silicone rubber baffle seal kit, Alcor 46158 exhaust gas temperature gauge and combustion analyser. Options include an electronic fuel flow management system, Woodward propeller synchrophaser, RAM super soundproofing, Cleveland heavy duty brakes, polished and balanced propellers and three-colour polyurethane external paint finish.

RAM/CESSNA 414

In this modification RAM replaces the 231 kW (310 hp) Teledyne Continental TSIO-520-J engines installed in Cessna 414s built between 1970 and 1976 by 231 kW (310 hp) TSIO-520-Ns or 242 kW (325 hp) TSIO-520-NBRs, when they are known respectively as the RAM 414 Series II and IV. The installation includes the same standard and optional items as for the Cessna 340A and 402C. The Hartzell Q-tip propellers are available only for modifications with the 242 kW (325 hp) engines, with which they are standard.
PERFORMANCE (A: 231 kW; 310 hp, B: 242 kW; 325 hp engines, at max T-O weight of 2,953 kg; 6,510 lb):
Cruising speed, 75% power at 6,100 m (20,000 ft):

A		210 knots (389 km/h; 241 mph)
B		215 knots (398 km/h; 247 mph)
Max rate of climb at S/L: A		503 m (1,650 ft)/min
B		610 m (2,000 ft)/min

Rate of climb at S/L, one engine out:

A		76 m (250 ft)/min
B		104 m (340 ft)/min
Time to 5,485 m (18,000 ft): A		20 min
B		18 min
Acceleration to 87 knots (161 km/h; 100 mph): A		22 s
B		19 s

RAM/CESSNA 414AW

RAM's modification of the Cessna 414A replaces the standard 231 kW (310 hp) Teledyne Continental TSIO-520-N engines by remanufactured TSIO-520-N/NBs of the same power (Series II) or (in the 414AW Series IV) by 242 kW (325 hp) TSIO-520-NBRs, with Hartzell Q-tip propellers. FAA approval of this aircraft, which is fitted with 0.89 m (2 ft 11 in) high winglets at each wingtip, was received on 1 March 1983, and subsequently by the civil aviation authorities in Australia. The RAM/Cessna 414AW operates at a gross weight increase of 153 kg (337 lb), providing a 136 kg (300 lb) net increase in useful load.
PERFORMANCE (at max T-O weight: A with 231 kW; 310 hp engines, B with 242 kW; 325 hp engines):
Cruising speed, at 6,100 m (20,000 ft):
75% power:

A		210 knots (389 km/h; 242 mph)
B		215 knots (398 km/h; 247 mph)

55% power:

A		188 knots (348 km/h; 216 mph)
B		195 knots (361 km/h; 224 mph)

Max rate of climb at S/L:

A		494 m (1,620 ft)/min
B		533 m (1,750 ft)/min

Rate of climb at S/L, one engine out:

A		91 m (300 ft)/min
B		98 m (320 ft)/min
Time to 5,485 m (18,000 ft):		
A		22 min

RAM/Cessna 414AW Series V conversion with Teledyne Continental Voyager liquid-cooled engines

B		18 min
Acceleration to 87 knots (161 km/h; 100 mph):		
A		23 s
B		22 s

RAM/CESSNA 414AW SERIES V

This modification replaces the standard 231 kW (310 hp) Teledyne Continental TSIO-520-N/NB engines with new 261 kW (350 hp) Teledyne Continental TSIOL-550-A Voyager liquid-cooled engines driving McCauley three-blade propellers of new design. Apart from the engine change, the modification involves installation of a coolant radiator in the extended rear portion of each wing nacelle baggage locker, each with flush-mounted non-icing NACA air intake scoop; new engine nacelle nose caps of graphite/glassfibre composite with integral flush-mounted recognition/landing lights; and winglets. Cockpit instruments are provided for monitoring coolant temperature and pressure. The coolant used is a 60/40 mixture of Prestone anti-freeze and water, operating at a pressure of 2.07-2.76 bars (30-40 lb/sq in) and with a maximum pressure of 4.14 bars (60 lb/sq in). Coolant temperature is thermostatically controlled.

The RAM/Cessna 414AW-V includes the same standard and optional items as for the Model 414AW Series IV, with a 136 kg (300 lb) increase in max T-O weight and a 91 kg (200 lb) increase in useful load. The RAM/Cessna 414AW-V received FAA certification on 10 August 1989, and the first customer aircraft was delivered in the following November. Conversions were continuing at the rate of one per month in early 1990. RAM is planning a similar Voyager liquid-cooled engine conversion for the Cessna 340A, with first delivery anticipated in November 1990.
PERFORMANCE:
Cruising speed at 75%:
power at 7,010 m (23,000 ft):

	232 knots (430 km/h; 267 mph)
at 9,145 m (30,000 ft)	
	244 knots (452 km/h; 281 mph)
Max rate of climb, one engine out, at S/L	
	137 m (450 ft)/min
Time to 9,145 m (30,000 ft)	33 min

RAM/CESSNA 421C and 421CW

RAM's modification of the Cessna 421B and 421C Golden Eagle series includes RAM or TCM factory remanufactured GTSIO-520-L/N engines, propellers and accessories. The RAM engine conversion provides a 50 kg (110 lb) increase in useful load for the Cessna 421C. RAM replaces the standard engine cooling baffles, exhaust risers, slip joints and magnetos with a 'RAM Reliability Package' which includes new red silicone rubber/glassfibre cooling baffle seal material, remanufactured exhaust system and slip joints, and Bendix S6RN-1250 pressurised magnetos. Also included are a Hoskins computerised fuel management system and Alcor direct reading exhaust gas temperature system. In November 1984 RAM received FAA approval for the installation of 0.89 m (2 ft 11 in) winglets to Cessna 421C aircraft up to factory serial number 0799. The first converted aircraft, known as the RAM/Cessna 421CW, was delivered in October 1984, and 31 conversions had been completed by February 1990. Australian certification of the RAM/Cessna 421CW was obtained in 1987.

The winglet installation for the Cessna 421C involves removal of the standard 0.46 m (1 ft 6 in) wingtip and replacement with a wing extension and winglet assembly, each of which measures 0.93 m (3 ft 0½ in) to the base of the winglet. This adds a total of 0.94 m (3 ft 1 in) to the standard Cessna 421C's wing span. The RAM winglet is constructed from bidirectional carbon graphite cloth impregnated with epoxy resins, with an outer layer which includes interwoven aluminium cloth for electrical conductivity and lighting protection. Existing landing lights, position lights and wingtip strobe lights are installed in the new wingtip/winglet assembly. The RAM/Cessna 421CW Supplemental Type Certificate includes certification for flight into known icing conditions. With winglets installed the RAM/Cessna 421CW has a 23 kg (50 lb) increase in useful load over the standard Cessna 421C. RAM claims a 25 per cent increase in max rate of climb for the winglet equipped aircraft.

A description of the Cessna 421C can be found in the 1985-86 *Jane's*. The following details refer to the 421CW:

DIMENSIONS, EXTERNAL: As for Cessna 421C except:

Basic wing span	13.47 m (44 ft 2½ in)
Span, winglet tip to winglet tip	13.83 m (45 ft 4½ in)
Wing aspect ratio (basic)	8.64
Effective wing aspect ratio, including winglets	9.74
Winglet cant angle	10°
Winglet toe-out angle	2°

AREA
Wings, gross (basic)	21.0 m² (226.0 sq ft)

WEIGHTS AND LOADINGS:
Max T-O weight	3,429 kg (7,560 lb)
Max zero-fuel weight	2,963 kg (6,533 lb)
Max wing loading	163.3 kg/m² (33.45 lb/sq ft)
Max power loading	6.12 kg/kW (10.06 lb/hp)

PERFORMANCE:
Cruising speed at 75% power at 6,100 m (20,000 ft)
228 knots (422 km/h; 262 mph)
Cruising speed at 65% power at 6,100 m (20,000 ft)
223 knots (413 km/h; 257 mph)
Max rate of climb, one engine out at 1,525 m (5,000 ft), ISA 91 m (300 ft)/min
Time to 7,315 m (24,000 ft) 24 min

RAM conversion of a Cessna 421C with winglets, known as RAM/Cessna 421CW

RAM/BEECH BARON 58

This modification installs 231 kW (310 hp) Teledyne Continental TSIO-520-L/LB or 242 kW (325 hp) TSIO-520-WB engines in Beech Baron Models 58P and 58TC. Standard items include Alcor exhaust gas temperature gauge and combustion analyser, Airborne dry vacuum pumps, electronic fuel management system and red silicone rubber baffle seals. Optional equipment includes teflon fuel and oil hoses, polished and balanced propellers, and optional three-colour polyurethane external paint finish.

PERFORMANCE (Baron 58P. A: 231 kW; 310 hp, B: 242 kW; 325 hp):
Cruising speed, 75% power at 6,100 m (20,000 ft):
A 223 knots (413 km/h; 257 mph)
B 229 knots (424 km/h; 264 mph)
Max rate of climb at S/L: A 463 m (1,520 ft)/min
B 469 m (1,540 ft)/min
Rate of climb at S/L, one engine out:
A 67 m (220 ft)/min
B 97 m (320 ft)/min

RILEY

RILEY INTERNATIONAL CORPORATION

2206 Palomar Airport Road, Suite B-2, Carlsbad, California 92008
Telephone: 1 (619) 438 9089
Telex: 140414
Fax: 1 (619) 438 0578
PRESIDENT: Jack M. Riley

This company was formed by Mr Jack Riley to continue marketing his well-known conversions of commercially produced light aircraft. Those available in 1990 are described below.

RILEY ROCKET P-210

In 1983 Riley announced development of the Rocket conversion of the Cessna Model 210 Pressurised Centurion. This conversion involves the installation of a factory remanufactured 231 kW (310 hp) turbocharged Teledyne Continental TSIO-520-AF engine with Riley intercooler system. Riley claims that the induction air intercooler with flush NACA duct in the cowling reduces induction air temperatures by up to 45 per cent, greatly improving engine efficiency. Other standard equipment includes a dynamically-balanced, electrically de-iced three-blade McCauley propeller, heavy duty battery, dual vacuum pumps, alternative electrical system, Riley engine baffle system, new Cleveland wheels and brakes, new tyres, luxury interior (with leather seats, new fabrics, soundproofing and electro-pneumatic door and window seals), metal instrument panel with Bendix/King Silver Crown avionics and drag-reducing antennae, Northstar M1 Loran C, 3M WX-10A Stormscope, S-Tech flight director system, aerodynamic smoothing of the exterior, and Riley Rocket polyurethane paint finish. Flint wingtip fuel tanks, which increase the P-210's fuel capacity to 462 litres (122 US gallons; 102 Imp gallons), air-conditioning, airframe de-icing, and a STOL system, are optional.

The Riley Rocket P-210 received an FAA supplemental type certificate in late 1984. By early 1989 a total of 34 Rocket P-210s had been delivered. The Riley induction air intercooler has also received FAA approval for the Cessna Turbo Stationair 6, Turbo Stationair 7, Turbo Centurion, Pressurised Super Skymaster, and Piper Turbo Saratoga.

PERFORMANCE:
Cruising speed:
at 5,335 m (17,500 ft) 204 knots (378 km/h; 235 mph)
at 7,000 m (23,000 ft) 217 knots (402 km/h; 250 mph)
Max rate of climb at S/L 305 m (1,000 ft)/min
Time to 7,000 m (23,000 ft) 23 min
Service ceiling 7,000 m (23,000 ft)
Range, with IFR reserves
1,129 nm (2,092 km; 1,300 miles)

RILEY SUPER 310

The Super 310 (formal designation R310 Super) represents a similar conversion to that of the Super 340, the existing power plants in the Cessna 310/320 being replaced by 231 kW (310 hp) Teledyne Continental TSIO-520-Ns with intercoolers. The conversion is FAA approved for the Cessna 310I to 310R, 320B to 320F and T310P to T310R. Installation of the complete kit requires 12 working days.

A description of the Cessna Model 310 appears under the Cessna entry in the 1981-82 *Jane's*. It applies also to the Riley Super 310, except as follows:

POWER PLANT: As described for Riley Super 340, except installed engines are TSIO-520-Ns instead of TSIO-520-Js.

WEIGHTS AND LOADING: As for the appropriate Cessna 310/320 model except as follows:
Weight empty increased by 10 kg (22 lb)
Max payload reduced by 10 kg (22 lb)
Max power loading 5.11 kg/kW (8.4 lb/hp)

PERFORMANCE (at max T-O weight):
Max cruising speed, 75% power:
at 7,315 m (24,000 ft) 261 knots (483 km/h; 300 mph)
at 5,485 m (18,000 ft) 243 knots (451 km/h; 280 mph)
at 4,265 m (14,000 ft) 234 knots (435 km/h; 270 mph)
Max rate of climb at S/L 792 m (2,600 ft)/min
Rate of climb at S/L, one engine out
158 m (520 ft)/min
Service ceiling 10,670 m (35,000 ft)
Service ceiling, one engine out 7,620 m (25,000 ft)
T-O to 15 m (50 ft) 503 m (1,650 ft)
Landing from 15 m (50 ft) 546 m (1,790 ft)
Range with max fuel, max cruising speed at 7,315 m (24,000 ft), 30 min reserves
1,042 nm (1,931 km; 1,200 miles)
Range with max fuel, econ cruising speed at optimum altitude, 30 min reserves
1,737 nm (3,218 km; 2,000 miles)

RILEY SUPER 340

The Riley Super 340 (formal designation R340 Super) differs from the standard Cessna 340 primarily through replacement of the latter's TSIO-520-K engines by TSIO-

Riley Rocket P-210 conversion of the Cessna Pressurised Centurion

520-Ns. The most important change associated with this new engine installation is the addition of an intercooler which allows a higher power output and also improves specific fuel consumption, critical altitude, engine life and reliability.

The prototype Super 340 received FAA certification in June 1974. The standard Cessna 340A for 1976 was updated in a manner similar to that of the Riley Super 340. Consequently, only Cessna 340 aircraft constructed from 1972 until the last of the 1975 models were completed are suitable for this conversion, which is completed by Riley engineers in five working days.

A description of the Cessna Model 340A appears under the Cessna entry in the 1984-85 *Jane's*. It applies also to the Riley Super 340, except as follows:

POWER PLANT: Two 231 kW (310 hp) Teledyne Continental TSIO-520-J flat-six turbocharged and intercooled engines, each driving a McCauley three-blade propeller. Engine installation upgraded from Cessna 340 to Cessna 414 configuration. Fuel system as for Cessna 340. Optional aft nacelle fuel tanks, each of 75.7 litres (20 US gallons; 16.6 Imp gallons), provide max optional fuel capacity of 920 litres (243 US gallons; 202 Imp gallons) when used in conjunction with the Cessna optional 768 litre (203 US gallon; 169 Imp gallon) system.

WEIGHTS AND LOADINGS:
Weight empty 1,754 kg (3,868 lb)
Max payload 904 kg (1,993 lb)
Max T-O weight 2,710 kg (5,975 lb)
Max wing loading 158.6 kg/m² (32.47 lb/sq ft)
Max power loading 5.87 kg/kW (9.64 lb/hp)

PERFORMANCE (at max T-O weight):
Max level speed at 7,315 m (24,000 ft)
252 knots (467 km/h; 290 mph)
Max cruising speed, 75% power:
at 7,315 m (24,000 ft)
234 knots (435 km/h; 270 mph)

at 5,485 m (18,000 ft)
226 knots (418 km/h; 260 mph)
at 4,265 m (14,000 ft)
217 knots (402 km/h; 250 mph)
Econ cruising speed at 7,315 m (24,000 ft)
208 knots (386 km/h; 240 mph)
Max rate of climb at S/L   549 m (1,800 ft)/min
Cruise rate of climb at max cruising power
305 m (1,000 ft)/min
Rate of climb at S/L, one engine out
107 m (350 ft)/min
Service ceiling   9,755 m (32,000 ft)
Service ceiling, one engine out   4,875 m (16,000 ft)
T-O run   457 m (1,500 ft)
T-O to 15 m (50 ft)   594 m (1,950 ft)
Landing from 15 m (50 ft)   561 m (1,840 ft)
Landing run   233 m (765 ft)
Range with max fuel, max cruising speed at 7,315 m (24,000 ft), 30 min reserves
1,042 nm (1,931 km; 1,200 miles)
Range with max fuel, econ cruising speed at 7,315 m (24,000 ft), 30 min reserves
1,737 nm (3,218 km; 2,000 miles)

Riley Turbine Eagle 421 turboprop conversion of the Cessna 421 Golden Eagle business aircraft

RILEY TURBINE EAGLE 421

This Riley conversion of the pressurised Cessna 421 Golden Eagle involves installation of Pratt & Whitney Canada PT6A-135 turboprops, each rated at 634 kW (850 shp) but flat rated in this application to 559 kW (750 shp). Both the Cessna Model 421B and Model 421C are suitable for this conversion, which also includes Hartzell Q-tip three-blade autofeathering, reversing and electrically de-iced propellers with Hartzell spinners; auxiliary fuel tanks in the rear of the engine nacelles with combined capacity 568

litres (150 US gallons; 125 Imp gallons); new Cablecraft engine controls; fire detection system; fuel heaters; aerodynamic engine cowlings with inertial separator and B.F. Goodrich electric induction air inlet lip de-icing; wing, tailplane and fin leading-edge pneumatic de-icer boots; revised electrical system; SIADS Inc 200A starter/generator system; Gill 639T heavy duty battery; bleed air cabin pressurisation unit; jet air pump; new engine instruments; anti-siphon fuel caps with screens; eight-seat cabin interior and customised cockpit; and hydraulically actuated two-piece cabin door.

PERFORMANCE:
Cruising speed at 8,230 m (27,000 ft)
300-310 knots (556-574 km/h; 345-357 mph)
Max rate of climb at S/L   1,220 m (4,000 ft)/min
Rate of climb at S/L, one engine out
305 m (1,000 ft)/min
Service ceiling   above 9,145 m (30,000 ft)
Service ceiling, one engine out   7,620 m (25,000 ft)
Max range with IFR reserves
1,400 nm (2,594 km; 1,612 miles)

ROBINSON
ROBINSON HELICOPTER COMPANY INC
24747 Crenshaw Boulevard, Torrance, California 90505
Telephone: 1 (213) 539 0508
Telex: 18-2554
Fax: 1 (213) 539 5198
PRESIDENT: Franklin D. Robinson
VICE-PRESIDENT, MARKETING: Barbara K. Robinson

Robinson Helicopter Company was formed to design and manufacture the R22 as a lightweight helicopter competitive in price with current two/four-seat fixed-wing light aircraft. Design began in June 1973, the first prototype flew for the first time on 28 August 1975, and the second was completed in early 1977. FAA certification was granted on 16 March 1979, and deliveries of production R22s began in October 1979. United Kingdom CAA certification was gained in June 1981.

Three standard R22s operated by Ranger Helicopters set five Class E1a records in Canada on 11-12 May 1982. A speed of 95 knots (176 km/h; 109 mph) was achieved over both 3 km and 25 km courses. Average speed over a 100 km course was 92.233 knots (170.817 km/h; 106.140 mph). Distance records were set by flights of 142.340 nm (263.615 km; 163.802 miles) over a straight course, and 140.655 nm (260.494 km; 161.863 miles) in a closed circuit. On 11 March 1989 Mr Wayne Mulgrew established a new world altitude record of 5,938 m (19,480 ft) over Northern California.

FAA certification of the improved R22 Alpha was received in October 1983, permitting a 31.75 kg (70 lb) increase in gross weight, to allow development of the R22 for police work and for IFR training. The further improved R22 Beta model was announced on 5 August 1985.

Float equipped Robinson R22 Mariner

ROBINSON MODEL R22 BETA, MARINER and POLICE
Current standard version of the Robinson helicopter, from c/n 501 onwards, is the **R22 Beta**. It has been available also with floats and ground handling wheels, as the **R22 Mariner**, since 1985. Mariners are operating as tuna-spotters in Mexico (2) and Venezuela (8). A law enforcement variant, the **R22 Police**, is also available, with specialist equipment as detailed below.

A load carrying hook kit, complete with electric release switches for both pilots and mechanical emergency release, is available from Classic Helicopter Corporation, 6505 Perimeter Road, Boeing Field, Seattle, Washington 98108. Applicable to any R22 with a factory installed hardpoint, the kit is certificated for a max load of 181 kg (400 lb) and imposes a never-exceed speed of 75 knots (139 km/h; 86 mph) when in use. The installation weighs 2.3 kg (5 lb) and can be installed in approx six hours. It is expected to be used primarily for sling training.

The 1,000th production R22 was delivered on 30 March 1989. Robinson delivered 310 during 1989, including 53 to the United Kingdom, and expected to deliver a similar number during 1989. In January 1988 five R22 IFR trainers were delivered to Bristow Helicopters at Redhill Aerodrome, England, for use by the company's commercial helicopter pilot school. Two others are operated by the Indira Gandhi Memorial Flying Academy in India. Production was continuing at the rate of 10 per week in early 1990.

TYPE: Two-seat lightweight helicopter.
ROTOR SYSTEM: Two-blade semi-articulated main rotor, with a tri-hinged underslung rotor head to reduce blade flexing, rotor vibration and control force feedback and an elastic teeter hinge stop to prevent blade/boom contact when starting or stopping the rotor in high winds. Main rotor blade section NACA 63-015 (modified). Rigid in plane, and free to flap, these blades are of bonded all-metal construction, with a stainless steel spar and leading-edge, light alloy skin and light alloy honeycomb core. One fixed trim tab on main rotor blades. The two-blade tail rotor, mounted on the port side, is of light alloy bonded construction. Rotor brake standard.
ROTOR DRIVE: V belt drive with sprag type overrunning clutch. The main and tail gearboxes each utilise spiral bevel gears. Maintenance-free flexible couplings of proprietary manufacture are used in both the main and tail rotor drive systems. Main rotor/engine rpm ratio 1:5. Tail rotor/engine rpm ratio 1.28:1.
FUSELAGE: Welded steel tube and light alloy primary structure for cabin, rotor pylon and engine mounting, with full monocoque tailcone. Cabin skins of light alloy and glassfibre.
TAIL UNIT: Cruciform light alloy structure with fixed horizontal stabiliser and vertical fin. Small spring skid (small float on Mariner version) beneath lower half of fin to give protection in a tail-down landing.
LANDING GEAR: Welded steel tube and light alloy skid landing gear, with energy absorbing crosstubes. Twin float/skid gear on Mariner.

POWER PLANT: One 119 kW (160 hp) Textron Lycoming O-320-B2C flat-four engine (derated to 97.5 kW; 131 hp for T-O), mounted in the lower rear section of the main fuselage, and partially exposed to improve cooling and simplify maintenance. Light alloy main fuel tank in upper rear section of the fuselage on port side, usable capacity 72.5 litres (19.2 US gallons; 16 Imp gallons). Optional auxiliary fuel tank, capacity 39.75 litres (10.5 US gallons; 8.7 Imp gallons). Oil capacity 5.7 litres (1.5 US gallons; 1.25 Imp gallons).
ACCOMMODATION: Two seats side by side in enclosed cabin, with inertia reel shoulder harness. Cyclic control stick mounted between seats, with dual grips on yoke so that aircraft can be flown from either seat. Conventional dual collective and throttle controls mounted at the port side of each seat. Cyclic control pivots to either side to simplify entry and exit and to permit resting control hand on knee while flying, for more relaxed piloting position. Curved two-panel windscreen. Removable door, with window, on each side. Police version has observation doors with bubble windows, which are also available as options on other models. Baggage space beneath each seat. Cabin heated and ventilated.
SYSTEM: Electrical system, powered by 12V DC alternator, includes navigation, panel and map lights, dual landing lights, anti-collision light and battery. Second battery optional.
AVIONICS AND EQUIPMENT: A Bendix/King KY 197 com transceiver is standard; optional avionics include a KN 53 nav receiver, Apollo II, Bendix/King or Northstar

Robinson R22 Beta two-seat light helicopter

Main rotor blade chord	0.18 m (7.2 in)
Distance between rotor centres	4.39 m (14 ft 5 in)
Length overall (rotors turning)	8.76 m (28 ft 9 in)
Length of fuselage	6.30 m (20 ft 8 in)
Fuselage: Max width	1.12 m (3 ft 8 in)
Height overall	2.67 m (8 ft 9 in)
Skid track	1.93 m (6 ft 4 in)

DIMENSION, INTERNAL:

Cabin: Max width	1.12 m (3 ft 8 in)

AREAS:

Main rotor blades (each)	0.70 m² (7.55 sq ft)
Tail rotor blades (each)	0.037 m² (0.40 sq ft)
Main rotor disc	46.21 m² (497.4 sq ft)
Tail rotor disc	0.89 m² (9.63 sq ft)
Fin	0.21 m² (2.28 sq ft)
Stabiliser	0.14 m² (1.53 sq ft)

WEIGHTS AND LOADINGS:

Weight empty (without auxiliary fuel tank)	379 kg (835 lb)
Fuel weight: standard	52 kg (115 lb)
auxiliary	28.6 kg (63 lb)
Max T-O and landing weight	621 kg (1,370 lb)
Max zero-fuel weight	569 kg (1,255 lb)
Max disc loading	13.43 kg/m² (2.75 lb/sq ft)
Max power loading	5.22 kg/kW (8.56 lb/hp)

PERFORMANCE (at max T-O weight):

Never-exceed speed without sling load	102 knots (190 km/h; 118 mph)
Max level speed	97 knots (180 km/h; 112 mph)
Cruising speed, 75% power at 2,440 m (8,000 ft)	96 knots (177 km/h; 110 mph)
Econ cruising speed	82 knots (153 km/h; 95 mph)
Max rate of climb at S/L	366 m (1,200 ft)/min
Rate of climb at 1,525 m (5,000 ft)	323 m (1,060 ft)/min
Service ceiling	4,265 m (14,000 ft)
Hovering ceiling IGE	2,125 m (6,970 ft)
Range with auxiliary fuel and max payload, no reserves	319 nm (592 km; 368 miles)
Endurance at 65% power, auxiliary fuel, no reserves	3 h 20 min

Loran-C, KT 76A transponder and KR 87 ADF. Standard equipment includes rate of climb indicator, sensitive altimeter, quartz clock, hour meter, low rotor rpm warning horn, temperature and chip warning lights for main gearbox and chip warning light for tail gearbox, high-capacity oil cooler, rotor brake, windscreen cover, rotor blade tiedowns, soundproofing, and ground handling wheels. Optional equipment includes Hamilton vertical compass, AIM 305-1AL artificial horizon, AIM-205-1AL directional gyro, remote altitude encoder, cabin heater/demister, engine primer, rotor rpm governor, removable port side controls, leather seats, ventral hardpoint and fire extinguisher.

Police version standard equipment as above plus: dual com control panel, Wulfsberg Flitefone 40 VHF or UHF radio, removable port side controls, 70A alternator

and fire extinguisher. Police version optional equipment: searchlight with dual lamps, PA speaker and siren, second Wulfsberg Flitefone 40 VHF or UHF radio and Bendix/King KT 76A transponder.

IFR trainer standard avionics and equipment: AIM 305-1AL DVF artificial horizon, Bendix/King KEA 129 encoding altimeter, Astronautics DC turn co-ordinator, Bendix/King KCS 55A HSI, KR 87 ADF, KX 165 nav/com digital display radio, KT 76A transponder and KR 22 marker beacon receiver, and Astro Tech LC-2 digital clock. Standard equipment is the same as for basic Beta. IFR trainer optional avionics: Bendix/King KN 63 DME.

DIMENSIONS, EXTERNAL:

Main rotor diameter	7.67 m (25 ft 2 in)
Tail rotor diameter	1.07 m (3 ft 6 in)

ROBINSON R44

In the Summer of 1986 Robinson Helicopter Company announced that it was developing a four-seat version of its R22 helicopter, to be designated R44. The R44 will be powered by a 194 kW (260 hp) Textron Lycoming O-540 piston engine driving a two-blade main rotor.

A prototype was under construction in early 1990, with first flight expected later in the year. Production could start by 1993/94. The following data are provisional:

DIMENSIONS, EXTERNAL:

Main rotor diameter	10.06 m (33 ft 0 in)
Tail rotor diameter	1.47 m (4 ft 10 in)
Height overall	3.28 m (10 ft 9 in)
Skid track	2.18 m (7 ft 2 in)

WEIGHT:

Max T-O weight	1,066 kg (2,350 lb)

ROCKWELL INTERNATIONAL

ROCKWELL INTERNATIONAL CORPORATION

600 Grant Street, Pittsburgh, Pennsylvania 15219
Telephone: 1 (412) 565 2000
Telex: 866213
CHAIRMAN AND CHIEF EXECUTIVE OFFICER:
   Donald R. Beall
EXECUTIVE VICE-PRESIDENT, STRATEGIC DEFENCE AND TECHNOLOGY:
   George W. Jeffs
SENIOR VICE-PRESIDENT, RESEARCH AND ENGINEERING:
   Robert L. Cattoi

VICE-PRESIDENT, AND PRESIDENT AEROSPACE OPERATIONS:
   Sam F. Iacobellis
DIRECTOR OF MEDIA RELATIONS: William D. Mellon

North American Aviation Inc, incorporated in Delaware in 1928 and a manufacturer of aircraft of various kinds from 1934, and Rockwell-Standard Corporation of Pittsburgh, Pennsylvania, a manufacturer of automotive components and builder of the Aero Commander line of civilian aircraft, merged on 22 September 1967 to form North American Rockwell Corporation.

This adopted its present name in 1973, to reflect its expanding international business. The corporation applies advanced technology to a wide range of products in its four

major businesses: **Aerospace**, which is engaged in the research, development and manufacture of military aircraft, manned and unmanned space systems and rocket engines, advanced space-based surveillance systems and high energy laser and other directed energy programmes; **Automotive**; **Electronics**, engaged in research, development, manufacture and marketing of a broad range of defence and commercial electronics systems and products for precision guidance and control, tactical weapons command, control, communications and intelligence, precision navigation, avionics, telecommunications and semiconductor applications; and **General Industries**.

NORTH AMERICAN AIRCRAFT

100 North Sepulveda Boulevard, El Segundo, California 90245
Telephone: 1 (213) 647 1000
PRESIDENT: John J. Pierro
Palmdale Facility:
2825 East Avenue P, Palmdale, California 93550
Telephone: 1 (805) 273 6000
VICE-PRESIDENT AND GENERAL MANAGER: C. W. Bright
Tulsa Facility:
2000 North Memorial Drive, Tulsa, Oklahoma 74158
Telephone: 1 (918) 835 3111
VICE-PRESIDENT AND GENERAL MANAGER:
   William P. Swiech

In addition to the programmes of which details follow, Rockwell's North American Aircraft unit is one of the three airframe contractors selected for current work on the US National Aero-Space Plane (see NASA entry in this section). It is also teamed with British Aerospace in offering a modified BAe 125 aircraft as a candidate for the US Air Force's Tanker Transport Training System (TTTS)

programme. Rockwell would also serve as prime contractor, with Panavia as a major subcontractor, if the Panavia Tornado (see International section) was chosen for the US Air Force's Follow-on Wild Weasel programme.

ROCKWELL INTERNATIONAL BRONCO
US military designation: OV-10

In July 1988 Rockwell International was awarded a Department of the Navy contract for the modification of 42 US Marine Corps OV-10A Bronco aircraft to OV-10D configuration. The work is being undertaken at Rockwell's Palmdale plant and involves installation of 775.5 kW (1,040 shp) Garrett T76-G-420/421 turboprops, new avionics, FLIR, and a reconfigured cockpit. The contract also provides for supply of service life extension package (SLEP) kits which will enable the US Navy to convert a further 14 OV-10Ds to OV-10D(SLEP) standard. Delivery of the first 15 OV-10Ds converted by Rockwell will be completed in early 1991. Details and an illustration of the OV-10 can be found in the 1986-87 and earlier editions of *Jane's*.

GENERAL DYNAMICS F-111

Rockwell's Palmdale division, in conjunction with the USAF's Sacramento Air Logistics Center, began the 'Pacer Strike' update programme for 79 F-111Ds and 84 F-111Fs in September 1989, allowing them to remain in service until 2010. The programme will bring the F-111 fleet to an essentially common avionics standard (the F-111A, EF-111A and F-111E having been upgraded earlier by Grumman). To a ring-laser gyro INS and GPS/Navstar will be added an integrated cockpit display and complete re-wiring of the avionics bay. Two prototype conversions are being undertaken at Palmdale, the first of which will fly in April 1991, prior to three months of contractor's testing and a further year of USAF trials.

Delivery of 'production' kits for conversion will begin in August 1993. F-111Ds of the 27th TFW at Cannon AFB, NM, will be converted by the Sacramento ALC, but F-111Fs of the 48th TFW at RAF Lakenheath, UK, are to receive their new avionics at BAe's Bristol plant. (BAe is also to install avionics modernisation programme equipment in 20th TFW F-111Es from RAF Upper Heyford, following testing of a prototype digital flight control systems conversion of FB-111A 68-0254 at McClellan and Edwards AFBs in 1989.) Early in 1990, Rockwell was bidding for the proposed update contract for 22 Australian F-111s.

Details of other F-111 programmes will be found under the USAF heading.

ROCKWELL INTERNATIONAL B-1B LANCER

Production of B-1B bombers for the USAF was completed on rollout of the 100th aircraft on 20 January 1988. The B-1B was last described fully in the 1989-90 edition.

Early in 1990, AIL Systems was expecting to receive a USAF contract to bring the first 19 B-1Bs up to a common avionics standard. The firm has also made a bid to modify the AN/ALQ-161 defensive avionics suite of the B-1B in order to improve its capabilities, although the USAF is considering replacement of the system by a more effective unit. The US Air Force gave the B-1B the name Lancer in May 1990. Of the original batch, 97 remain in service or in reserve.

ROCKWELL (LOCKHEED) AC-130U 'SPECTRE'

It was announced on 6 July 1987 that the USAF had awarded a $155,233,489 contract to Rockwell's North American Aircraft Operations to cover research and development of this new gunship version of the Lockheed Hercules. The prototype conversion was funded in the FY 1986 budget, followed by six in FY 1989 and five in FY 1990. The first AC-130U (87-0128) was completed in unarmed form by Lockheed at Marietta in 1988 and delivered to Rockwell at Palmdale for fitting-out. First flight was due in June 1990, followed by 10 months of trials at Edwards AFB, CA. Remaining AC-130s, all produced from new airframes, are to be delivered to the 16th Special Operations Squadrons at Hurlbert Field, FL, in 1991-92.

Armament is installed in the port side of the fuselage and comprises (front to rear) a General Electric GAU-12/U 25 mm six-barrel Gatling-type gun with 3,000 rds, a Bofors 40 mm gun and a 105 mm gun based on the US Army's howitzer. Weapons can be slaved to Hughes AN/APG-80 (modified AN/APG-70) digital fire control radar, Texas Instruments AN/AAQ-117 FLIR or Ball Aerospace LLL TV, permitting night and/or adverse weather operations against ground targets. There is a prone observer's position in the rear ramp, a starboard-side observer's window to the rear of the cockpit, and a battle-management centre in the cabin with seven positions at monitoring consoles and four IBM AP-102 computers. Crew totals 13, including flight deck personnel and gun loaders. Defensive aids are believed to be similar to those installed in the MC-130H. Modified fuel tank pylons contain IR countermeasures equipment. Total of 300 chaff bundles and 90 MJU7 or 180 M206 flares in three launchers beneath the fuselage. ITT Avionics AN/ALQ-172 jammer installed at base of fin. Other equipment includes a HUD, combined INS and GPS/Navstar, triple MIL-STD-1553B databuses and Spectra/ceramic armour protection.

Attacks will be undertaken using the banked circular (pylon) turn technique, but absolute precision is no longer required. Provided that the aircraft is kept within certain parameters, the guns are trained automatically, allowing the Hercules to cover a less predictable flight path. Apart from its primary role of precision fire suppression, the flight-refuellable AC-130U will be capable of performing other special operations roles, including escort, surveillance, search, rescue and armed reconnaissance/interdiction.

Full details of the basic C-130H can be found in the LASC Georgia entry in this section.

AEROSPACE BUSINESSES
2230 East Imperial Highway, El Segundo, California 90245
Telephone: 1 (213) 647 5000
VICE-PRESIDENT AND CHIEF OPERATING OFFICER:
Sam F. Iacobellis
Satellite & Space Electronics Division
2600 Westminster Boulevard, Seal Beach, California 90740-7644
Telephone: 1 (213) 797 3311
PRESIDENT: Richard E. Derr
Rocketdyne Division
6633 Canoga Avenue, Canoga Park, California 91303
Telephone: 1 (818) 710 6300
PRESIDENT: Robert D. Paster
Space Transportation Systems Division
12214 Lakewood Boulevard, Downey, California 90241
Telephone: 1 (213) 922 2111
PRESIDENT: Robert G. Minor

The Space Transportation Systems Division is responsible for Rockwell International Corporation's engineering design and development, fabrication and assembly, test and evaluation and integration of both manned and unmanned space systems.

Under contract to NASA, the Rockwell group designed, built and tested the four Shuttle spacecraft (Orbiters) and is constructing a fifth.

Rockwell's space group, with its major facilities in Downey and Palmdale, California, has contractual support units based in NASA Centers at the Johnson Space Center, Texas, the Kennedy Space Center, Florida, the Marshall Space Flight Center, Alabama, and the John C. Stennis Space Center, Mississippi.

Space Operations Company
600 Gemini Avenue, Houston, Texas 77058
Telephone: 1 (713) 282 2000
PRESIDENT: Glen S. Lunney

Rockwell's Space (formerly Shuttle) Operations Company performs mission support operations for Johnson Space Center under a contract which consolidated work previously performed by 17 different contractors. Its tasks include project management, maintenance and operations of Mission Control Center at Houston, Shuttle Mission Simulator, Shuttle Avionics Integration Laboratory, Software Production Facility, Central Computing Facility and the Mockup and Integration Laboratory; and sustaining engineering, flight preparation requirements and analyses, flight preparation production, and direct mission operations, testing and support for Space Shuttle operations at the Johnson Space Center. The Rockwell team includes Bendix Field Engineering Corporation, UNISYS, Omniplan Corporation, RMS Technologies Incorporated, and System Management American Corporation.

SPACE TRANSPORTATION SYSTEM
The NASA Space Shuttle was the world's first reusable space transportation system, and will be the keystone of America's space programme for the remainder of this century.

The Shuttle system includes the Rockwell International Shuttle spacecraft (see next entry), an external propellant tank and two solid propellant rocket boosters. Other prime contractors are Martin Marietta for the external tank, and Thiokol for the boosters. In operation, the Shuttle is launched vertically, with all engines firing. At an altitude of about 43 km (27 miles), the booster stages separate and descend into the sea by parachute, for recovery. The Shuttle spacecraft continues under its own power, and jettisons its large external propellant tank just before attaining orbit.

In space, the Shuttle spacecraft manoeuvres by means of the two orbital manoeuvring engines. The reaction control engines are used for minor course corrections and adjustments of attitude. Its main tasks are to place satellites into orbit, retrieve satellites from orbit, and repair and service satellites in orbit. It can also be used to put propulsive stages and satellites into precise low Earth orbit, for subsequent transfer to synchronous orbit or to an 'escape' mission into space. It can be used for short duration scientific and applications missions, as an orbiting research laboratory or reconnaissance vehicle, for space rescue, as a tanker for space refuelling, and for support of orbiting space stations.

On some flights a pressurised Spacelab, developed by ten European countries under the leadership of the European Space Agency, is carried in the payload bay. Spacelab is the means by which man-associated experiments can be performed in the payload bay. It includes a pressurised enclosure housing support equipment (to make it habitable) as well as the experimental equipment. When sensors require direct exposure to the space environment, a pallet is used in association with the pressurised enclosure. On other types of mission, a pallet may be used alone, with control of the instruments being exercised from the Shuttle spacecraft cabin or even from the ground. The Spacelabs are designed around a basic seven-day mission.

On conclusion of its mission, the Shuttle spacecraft flies back into the atmosphere towards its land base, protected by a form of heat shielding which is designed to survive 100 missions, unlike ablative heatshields. Once through the re-entry phase, the Shuttle spacecraft is able to glide up to 950 nm (1,760 km; 1,100 miles) to its base, steered by aerodynamic controls.

Essential details of missions flown in 1981-85 can be found in previous editions of *Jane's*. Before resumption of the programme in September 1988, the boosters were redesigned.

Details of the boosters and the external tank used with the spacecraft in its original form are as follows:

BOOSTERS (STS-8 and subsequent missions): Two Thiokol solid propellant rocket boosters (each 14,679 kN; 3,300,000 lb st for lift-off) are attached one on each side of the external propellant tank. The inert weight of each solid rocket booster is 87,090 kg (192,000 lb). The booster cases are designed for 20 re-uses.
EXTERNAL PROPELLANT TANK: Contains the main propellants for the Orbiter. It is of aluminium alloy semi-monocoque construction, with a 25 mm (1 in) thick foam external insulation. In the forward end of the tank is a 554 m³ (19,563 cu ft) tank holding 617,774 kg (1,361,936 lb) of liquid oxygen; in the rear end is a 1,514 m³ (53,518 cu ft) tank holding 103,257 kg (227,641 lb) of liquid hydrogen. Total propellant weight 721,031 kg (1,589,577 lb). Between propellant tanks is an unpressurised intertank which houses instrumentation and electrical components. Current missions use a lightweight tank weighing 750,980 kg (1,655,600 lb) when filled.
Basic dimensions and weights of the complete Space Transportation System are as follows:
DIMENSIONS, EXTERNAL:

Length overall	56.14 m (184 ft 2¼ in)
Length of external tank	46.88 m (153 ft 9⅝ in)
Length of boosters	45.46 m (149 ft 2 in)
Height overall	23.35 m (76 ft 7¼ in)

WEIGHTS:
Shuttle system complete (STS-26)
    2,050,365 kg (4,520,276 lb)
Shuttle spacecraft (STS-26, *Discovery* dry weight)
    77,754 kg (171,419 lb)

External tank (full)	750,980 kg (1,655,600 lb)
Boosters (2), each	586,051 kg (1,292,000 lb)

THRUST:

Total, at lift-off	34,613 kN (7,781,400 lb st)

Shuttle main engines (3), each at S/L at 104%
    1,751 kN (393,800 lb st)

Boosters (2), each	14,679 kN (3,300,000 lb st)

PERFORMANCE:
Payload, for 177 km (110 mile) orbit
  due east (*Discovery* or *Atlantis*)
    24,948 kg (55,000 lb)

due east, 57° inclination	21,319 kg (47,000 lb)
98° polar orbit	13,426 kg (29,600 lb)

ROCKWELL INTERNATIONAL SHUTTLE SPACECRAFT
The Shuttle spacecraft, primary component of NASA's Space Transportation System, lifts off from Earth like a rocket, operates in orbit as a spacecraft, and returns to land in a manner similar to that of a conventional aeroplane.

Shuttle spacecraft *Columbia* (OV-102) made the first successful, 36-orbit, test flight in April 1981, manned by astronauts John Young (commander) and Capt Robert Crippen (pilot), and has since completed eight more successful orbital missions. After STS-5, the orbiter was modified at Kennedy Space Center to enable it to carry Spacelab and to accommodate a six-man crew to fly the spacecraft and conduct experiments. After STS-9, *Columbia* returned to Rockwell's Palmdale facility for major modifications, including the installation of operational systems, and returned to service in early 1986.

Challenger (OV-099), the second Earth orbital flight spacecraft, made its first flight on 4 April 1983. It became the first operational spacecraft, with all onboard systems qualified to operate for a minimum of 100 missions without major overhaul. *Challenger* was destroyed in a post-launch explosion during mission 51L on 28 January 1986. *Discovery* (OV-103) made its first flight on 30 August 1984. *Atlantis* (OV-104) was launched for the first time on 3 October 1985, on military mission 51J. *Discovery* and *Atlantis* are approximately 3,116 kg (6,870 lb) lighter than *Colombia* due to various weight-saving measures. In August 1986 President Reagan ordered a new Shuttle spacecraft to replace *Challenger*. This, *Endeavour* (OV-105), is scheduled for rollout in April 1991 and first flight in February 1992. The programme resumed on 29 September 1988 with STS-26, on which *Discovery* placed a Tracking Data Relay Satellite (TDRS-C) in orbit by means of an Inertial Upper Stage (IUS).

Before this resumption of the programme, the orbiter's main engines were improved and more than 200 modifications were made to the spacecraft. They included improvements to the wheel brakes, main propulsion system disconnect valves between the orbiter and external tank, and APU tank shut-off valves. The thermal protection system was improved in the elevon cove region, and on the nose landing gear door, lower wing surface trailing-edge and elevon leading-edge. A pyrotechnically jettisoned side hatch, crew parachutes and survival gear, and a curved telescoping pole to aid the crew in clearing the wing, were added to give a bale-out capability in the event of an emergency where runway landing is not possible; and an egress slide was added to facilitate post-landing evacuation of the vehicle in an emergency.

The following description refers to the spacecraft in its original form:
TYPE: Reusable space transportation vehicle.
WINGS: Cantilever low-wing monoplane, of ogival planform. Wing section NACA 0010 (modified). Sweepback 81° on inner leading-edges, 45° on outer leading-edges. Dihedral 3° 30' on trailing-edges. The main wing assembly, for which Grumman is responsible, is primarily a conventional aluminium alloy structure made up of a corrugated spar web, truss ribs, and riveted skin/stringer

and honeycomb skins. Wing has a very blunt leading-edge and is more than 1.52 m (5 ft) deep at the thickest point. Two-segment hydraulically actuated elevons on each trailing-edge, for pitch and roll control, are of aluminium honeycomb construction with a titanium rubbing strip on each of their leading-edges. Hinged panels on the wing upper surface, of titanium and Inconel sandwich, are used to seal the wing/elevon gap; these are the only areas of the wing not covered by the thermal protection system.

FUSELAGE: Conventional semi-monocoque aluminium alloy structure, built in three main portions. Forward fuselage contains the crew module, three forward electronics bays, forward reaction control system and nosewheel unit. The mid fuselage portion is an 18.28 m (60 ft) long section of primary load carrying structure, built by General Dynamics (Convair), and includes the wing carry-through structure. Upper half of the mid fuselage consists of structural payload bay doors, hinged along the side and meeting at the top centreline. These doors are of graphite epoxy bonded honeycomb sandwich construction, with a Nomex core. The forward 9.14 m (30 ft) of each door incorporates Vought radiator panels that are deployed in orbit. Fixed radiator panels are attached to the remaining inner surface on the front of each aft door. The rear of the aft doors can be fitted with fixed radiator panels if required by a specific mission. The rear fuselage interfaces with the removable orbital manoeuvring system (OMS)/reaction control system (RCS) pods, the wing rear spar, the vertical tail assembly, the body flap, the external tank rear supports, the main propulsion system, the launch umbilical panel, the three rear electronics bays, and other discrete system equipment. A bulkhead heatshield at the rear of the vehicle protects the main engine systems. A large body flap at the rear of the fuselage protects the main engine nozzles during re-entry, and is actuated hydraulically to serve also as a trimming surface.

TAIL UNIT: Vertical surfaces only, built by Fairchild Republic, of wedge section with 45° sweepback on fin leading-edge. Fin is a conventional aluminium alloy structure. The rudder/speed brake assembly has an aluminium honeycomb skin and is divided into upper and lower sections. Each of these is also split longitudinally and actuated individually to serve as both rudder and speed brake, operated by a Sundstrand hydraulic rotary actuator. The Inconel honeycomb seal over these is the only part of the vertical tail not covered by the thermal protection system. Mission requirements call for a locked rudder/speed brake during boost, orbit and re-entry. The speed brake control is provided from approx Mach 10 to Mach 5; from Mach 5 to landing the rudder and speed brake controls are combined as required. Primary system control is automatic, with manual override.

THERMAL PROTECTION SYSTEM: The thermal protection system (TPS) consists of materials applied externally to maintain the airframe outer skins within an acceptable temperature limit of 176°C (350°F) during re-entry. The TPS materials are designed to perform a minimum of 100 missions, in which temperatures will range from −156°C (−250°F) in space to re-entry temperatures of nearly 1,648°C (3,000°F). Reinforced carbon-carbon is used on the wing leading-edges, the nose cap (including chin panel area immediately aft on the lower surface), and the immediate area around the forward orbiter/external tank structural attachment. RCC protects areas where temperatures exceed 1,260°C (2,300°F) during entry. Coated Nomex felt reusable surface insulation (FRSI) is used where temperatures are less than 371°C (700°F), on the upper portion of the payload bay doors, mid and rear fuselage sides, upper wing, and part of the orbital manoeuvring system (OMS) pods. Low-temperature reusable surface insulation (LRSI) white tiles (about 700) are used where temperatures are below 649°C (1,200°F) and above 371°C (700°F) nominal. These tiles are used in selected areas on the forward, mid and aft sections of the fuselage, and the vertical tail, upper wing, and OMS/RCS pods. Advanced flexible reusable surface insulation (AFRSI) quilted fabric blankets are used in the majority of the areas below 649°C (1,200°F) and above 371°C (700°F) on the forward, mid and aft of fuselage, vertical tail, upper wing and OMS/RCS pods. High-temperature reusable surface insulation (HRSI) tiles are used where temperatures are below 1,260°C (2,300°F) and above 648°C (1,200°F). The areas are the forward fuselage, lower mid fuselage, lower wing, selected areas of the vertical tail, a portion of the OMS pods, and around the forward fuselage windows. The HRSI has two different densities: one weighs 4 kg/m³ (9 lb/cu ft) and is used in all areas except around the nose and main landing gear doors, nose cap interface, wing leading-edge, reinforced carbon-carbon/HRSI interface, external tank umbilical doors, vent doors, and fin leading-edge. These areas use HRSI tiles with a density of 9.9 kg/m³ (22 lb/cu ft) and have a black surface coating for entry emittance. When the higher density HRSI tiles have been expended, fibrous refractory insulation (FRCI) tiles will be used instead. The FRCI-12 tiles have a density of 5.4 kg/m³ (12 lb/cu ft), and improved strength, durability and resistance to cracking.

LANDING GEAR: Retractable tricycle type, with twin wheels and Menasco oleo-pneumatic shock absorbers on each unit. Hydraulic release, with a pyrotechnic backup for

STS launching system at the Kennedy Space Center

deployment in flight. Landing gear cannot be retracted in flight, after release. Nose unit is retracted forward into fuselage and main units forward into wings before launch. Nose unit is steerable; main units are fitted with Goodrich brakes and Hydro-Aire anti-skid units. All units have Goodrich wheels and tyres. Landing gear is designed to facilitate safe landing at speeds of up to 225 knots (415 km/h; 258 mph). The main gear tyres are rated at 20,410 kg (45,000 lb) and the brakes at 240 × 10⁶ ft-lb.

MAIN PROPULSION: Three Rocketdyne SSME (Space Shuttle Main Engines) high-pressure liquid oxygen/liquid hydrogen engines, each rated at 1,668 kN (375,000 lb st) at sea level and 2,091 kN (470,000 lb thrust) in vacuum at 100 per cent; 1,752 kN (393,800 lb) at sea level and 2,174 kN (488,800 lb) vacuum at 104 per cent; 1,856.2 kN (417,300 lb) at sea level and 2,283.0 kN (513,250 lb) vacuum at 109 per cent. The engines can be throttled over a range of 65 to 109 per cent of their rated power level. Each engine is designed for 7h 30 min of operation, with 55 starts.

ORBIT MANOEUVRING ENGINES: Two Aerojet Liquid Rocket Company (ALRC) bipropellant liquid rocket engines, running on monomethylhydrazine (MMH) and nitrogen tetroxide (N_2O_4), are used for the Orbiter's orbit manoeuvring subsystem (OMS). These engines are housed in pods, one on each side of the Orbiter's rear fuselage. The OMS engines, for which a usable total of 10,830 kg (23,876 lb) of propellant is carried, are used to position the spacecraft in orbit; each develops 26.7 kN (6,000 lb thrust) in space.

REACTION CONTROL ENGINES: The reaction control subsystem (RCS) utilises 38 Marquardt R-40A bipropellant liquid rocket engines (each 3.88 kN; 872 lb vacuum thrust) and six Marquardt R-1E-3 bipropellant liquid rocket vernier thrusters (each 0.11 kN; 24 lb vacuum thrust). Fourteen of the R-40A engines are on the nose and 24 on the aft end, 12 in each OMS/RCS pod; there are two of the R-1E verniers on the nose and two in each aft pod. Propellants are the same as for the OMS engines; 1,096 kg (2,418 lb) is carried in the RCS tanks, and there is provision for crossfeed between the aft OMS and aft RCS tanks.

CREW COMPARTMENT: Self-contained crew module has a fuselage side hatch for access, a hatch into the airlock

from the mid section, and a hatch from the airlock into the payload bay. It is divided into three levels, the upper (flight deck) level having side by side seating for two flight crewmen with dual controls. Behind them are seats for two mission specialists. On the middle deck provisions are made for three more seats, bunks and a galley, dependent upon particular flight requirements, hygiene section, airlock, three electronics bays, and payload bay access. For rescue missions, seats for three more persons can be fitted in place of the bunks. The lower deck contains environmental control equipment and crew equipment storage.

PAYLOAD BAY: In centre of fuselage, 18.29 m (60 ft) long and 4.57 m (15 ft) in diameter. Retractable manipulator arm on left hand side if required for a particular flight (with provision for a second one on the right), for deploying and retrieving payloads. Complete closed circuit TV system by RCA Astro-Electronics includes a colour camera in the crew compartment and several black and white and or colour cameras in the cargo bay and on the manipulator arm. These facilitate payload handling and provide TV coverage for engineers and the general public on Earth.

SYSTEMS: Environmental control and life support system, made up of four subsystems: atmosphere revitalisation subsystem (ARS), to control atmospheric environment for occupants and thermal environment for electronics; food, water and waste subsystem (FWW), to provide hygiene, and other life support functions; active thermal control subsystem (ATCS), to maintain subsystems and components within specified temperature limits and to provide, via payload door radiator panels, active heat rejection to protect payloads; and an airlock support subsystem. Three redundant hydraulic systems, each of 207 bars (3,000 lb/sq in), supply actuators for the elevons, body flap, rudder/speed brake, and power to actuate main engine thrust vector controls, landing gear, brakes and steering. Electrical power subsystem (EPS) consists, functionally, of a fuel cell power plant (FCP) subsystem, and a power reactant storage and distribution (PRSD) subsystem. There are three FCPs, each providing power at 27.5V to 32.5V DC over a power range of 2-12kW and each connected to one of the three main DC buses; these supply the primary in-flight electrical power used by the Shuttle, generated through the chemical combination and conversion of cryogenic oxygen and hydrogen. In the PRSD subsystem, the cryogenic oxygen and hydrogen tanks are defined as a tank set. The tank sets installed are dependent upon specific flight requirements; up to five sets can be accommodated. Westinghouse remote power control system and master timing unit. Honeywell four channel fly by wire electrical flight control subsystem for operation of all control surfaces and main engine controls. APU subsystem consists of three Sundstrand independent APUs (each 100.7 kW; 135 shp), deriving their energy from the decomposition of hydrazine (N_2H_4).

AVIONICS AND EQUIPMENT: Fully fail-operational/fail-safe guidance, navigation and control system, including three Singer-Kearfott KT-70/SKN-2600 type inertial measuring units; triplex Ku-band microwave scan beam landing system, by the AIL Division of Eaton Corpn; head-up displays (HUD); three Northrop rate gyro assemblies; three Hoffman L-band Tacan; three Bendix accelerometer assemblies; two Honeywell C-band radar altimeters; four AiResearch air data transducers; three SIADS Inc attitude director indicators; two Collins horizontal situation indicators; two Honeywell alpha/ Mach indicators; two Bendix/King altitude/vertical velocity indicators; two Bendix/King surface position indicators; two Honeywell barometric altimeters; and two Honeywell ATC transponders. Communications and tracking equipment includes one (optionally two) Ku-band rendezvous radar/satellite com on starboard side of cargo bay; two Ball star trackers; two 100W Watkins-Johnson S-band TWT amplifiers; two P-band UHF for EVA/ATC com; Conrac S-band FM for

NASA/Rockwell International shuttle spacecraft
(Michael A. Badrocke)

Orbiter/ground and Orbiter/payload com; and Ku-band radio for Orbiter/ground com and Ku band for rendezvous. Central data processing is by means of five IBM Advanced System/4 Pi Model AP-101 digital computers and two mass memory units. Four of the computers are interconnected to process guidance, navigation and control inputs and to relay commands to FBW flight control systems; the fifth is provided for independent backup and systems management.

DIMENSIONS, EXTERNAL:

Wing span	23.79 m (78 ft 0.68 in)
Wing aspect ratio	2.265
Wing mean aerodynamic chord	12.06 m (39 ft 6.81 in)
Length overall	37.19 m (122 ft 0.2 in)
Height overall	17.25 m (56 ft 7 in)

DIMENSIONS, INTERNAL:

Payload bay: Length	18.29 m (60 ft 0 in)
Diameter	4.57 m (15 ft 0 in)
Crew module: Volume	74.33 m³ (2,625 cu ft)

AREAS:

Wings, gross	249.91 m² (2,690 sq ft)
Elevons (total)	38.38 m² (413.14 sq ft)
Rudder/speed brake	9.03 m² (97.15 sq ft)
Vertical tail surfaces (total)	38.39 m² (413.25 sq ft)
Body flap	12.61 m² (135.75 sq ft)

WEIGHTS:

Weight dry: *Discovery* (1988)	77,754 kg (171,419 lb)
Weight, incl cargo, at booster ignition (STS-26)	
	115,416 kg (254,449 lb)
Max landing weight	104,328 kg (230,000 lb)

PERFORMANCE:

Orbital speed	
	approx 15,285 knots (28,325 km/h; 17,600 mph)
Nominal touchdown speed (unpowered)	
	180 knots (334 km/h; 208 mph) EAS

ROGERSON

ROGERSON HILLER CORPORATION
(Subsidiary of Rogerson Aircraft Corporation)
William R. Fairchild International Airport, Port Angeles, Washington 98362
PRESIDENT: Gerald J. Tobias
VICE-PRESIDENT, INTERNATIONAL MARKETING:
Victor Milner Jr,
2201 Alton Avenue, Irvine, California 92714
Telephone: 1 (714) 660 0666
Telex: (910) 595 2843

This company was formed in January 1973, as Hiller Aviation Inc, to acquire from Fairchild Industries the design rights, production tooling and spares of the Hiller 12E series of light helicopters. Initially, it provided product support for helicopters of this type in worldwide service, before restarting production of piston engined and turbine powered versions in three-seat and four-seat configurations. The five-seat FH-1100 was added following purchase from Fairchild in 1980.

In April 1984, Hiller Aviation became a wholly owned subsidiary of Rogerson Aircraft Corporation, which manufactures aircraft control system parts, fuel tanks, composite materials and components for the aerospace industry. It was renamed Hiller Helicopters, resuming deliveries of the UH-12E and redesignated RH-1100 in July 1984, and has since been renamed Rogerson Hiller Corporation.

In November 1985 Rogerson Hiller occupied a new 13,006 m² (140,000 sq ft) manufacturing facility at William R. Fairchild International Airport, Port Angeles, Washington. In September 1985 the company acquired L.O.M. Corporation, manufacturer of helicopter rotor blades, and renamed the latter company Aerobond. Production of rotor blades is undertaken at the Port Angeles factory.

HILLER RH-1100
The original FH-1100 was a refined development of the OH-5A designed for the US Army's LOH (Light Observation Helicopter) competition. A total of 246 FH-1100s had been built when production ended in 1974.

The current, improved, RH-1100 has a more powerful engine and main rotor blades of 76 mm (3 in) greater chord, together with a larger diameter tail rotor and a new drive coupling between the engine and the main rotor transmission, to allow operation at a higher gross weight and increased maximum speed. Production aircraft will incorporate composite materials in their structure in place of some aluminium components.

The prototype of a multi-mission military variant of the helicopter, designated **RH-1100M Hornet**, made its debut at the 1985 Paris Air Show. The RH-1100M can carry interchangeable weapons systems including two 2.75 in folding fin rocket pods, 7.62 mm machine-guns, 0.50 calibre machine-guns and four TOW missiles. The RH-1100M has provision for an autopilot, forward looking infra-red anti-missile warning systems, air-to-air missile system capability, and chin or roof mounted sight. Hiller believes the RH-1100M's primary markets would be in South America, Africa and parts of Asia.

By early 1988 the company had delivered single examples of the FH-1100 to Sri Lanka, Taiwan and Venezuela, and expected to make first customer deliveries of the new RH-1100 in March 1989, since when no new information has been received.

The following description applies to the standard civil RH-1100, except where indicated:
TYPE: Five-seat utility helicopter.
ROTOR SYSTEM: Two-blade semi-rigid main rotor of all-metal construction. Blade section NACA 63₂015. Each blade attached to rotor head by single main retention bolt and drag link. Droop stops standard. The main rotor blades each have a rolled stainless steel leading-edge spar bonded to an aluminium trailing section with a honeycomb core. Two-blade tail rotor of stainless steel and honeycomb construction. Main rotor blades fold. Rotor brake optional. Electrically controlled trim system.
ROTOR DRIVE: Mechanical drive through single-stage bevel and two-stage planetary main transmission, with intermediate and tail rotor gearboxes. Main rotor/engine rpm ratio 1:16.30. Tail rotor/engine rpm ratio 1:2.47.

Prototype RH-1100M Hornet with civilian RH-1100 in background

FUSELAGE: Aluminium alloy semi-monocoque structure of pod and boom type.
TAIL UNIT: Vertical fin, and fixed horizontal surface, both of aluminium alloy and honeycomb construction. Tubular guard to protect rotor in tail-down landing.
LANDING GEAR: Skid type with torsion tube suspension, with choice of standard or extended support struts. Extended struts necessary with optional inflatable float installation. Ground handling wheels standard.
POWER PLANT: One 313 kW (420 shp) Allison 250-C20B turboshaft, derated to 204 kW (274 shp). Single bladder fuel tank in bottom of centre-fuselage with usable capacity of 259 litres (68.5 US gallons; 57 Imp gallons). Refuelling point on starboard side of rear fuselage. Oil capacity 2.6 litres (0.7 US gallon; 0.6 Imp gallon).
ACCOMMODATION: Pilot and co-pilot side by side with three passengers to rear, or pilot and four passengers. Four forward hinged doors, two on each side of cabin, with removable centre door post for cargo loading. Dual internal stretcher kit optional. Baggage compartment to rear of cabin, capacity 0.30 m³ (10.5 cu ft). Accommodation ventilated. Cabin heater and windscreen defroster optional.
SYSTEMS: Hydraulic system for cyclic and collective pitch controls. Electrical system includes a 28V 60A DC starter/generator and nickel-cadmium battery.
AVIONICS: A range of nav/com systems is available to customer's requirements.
EQUIPMENT: Standard equipment includes clock, engine hour meter, outside air temperature gauge, fuel filter warning system, night lighting system including two rotating beacons, edge-lit instrument panel, seatbelts, shoulder harness on front seats, sliding rear windows, tinted windows, hardpoint for optional external cargo hook, external power socket, and choice of exterior paint schemes and interior trim. Optional equipment includes stability augmentation system, dual controls, rear seat shoulder harness, cabin fire extinguisher, first aid kit, strobe lights, engine auto relight, reverse scoop intake, heated pitot, loudspeaker/siren, quick-release cargo hook, cargo racks, ambulance kit, dual litter kit, searchlight and Simplex agricultural spraygear.

DIMENSIONS, EXTERNAL:

Main rotor diameter	10.80 m (35 ft 5 in)
Tail rotor diameter	1.83 m (6 ft 0 in)
Distance between rotor centres	6.29 m (20 ft 7½ in)
Main rotor blade chord	0.33 m (13 in)
Length overall, rotors turning	12.57 m (41 ft 3 in)
Length of fuselage	9.08 m (29 ft 9½ in)
Width, rotors folded	1.32 m (4 ft 4 in)
Height overall	2.83 m (9 ft 3½ in)
Skid track	2.20 m (7 ft 2¾ in)

AREAS:

Main rotor disc	91.0 m² (979.0 sq ft)
Tail rotor disc	2.63 m² (28.3 sq ft)

WEIGHTS (A: RH-1100, B: RH-1100M):

Weight empty: A	687 kg (1,515 lb)
B (TOW)	1,048 kg (2,310 lb)
B (Scout)	726 kg (1,600 lb)
Max payload: A	462 kg (1,020 lb)
Max standard fuel weight: A, B	200.5 kg (442 lb)
Max T-O weight: A	1,292 kg (2,850 lb)
B	1,406 kg (3,100 lb)

PERFORMANCE (at max T-O weight, A and B as above):

Max level speed at S/L:	
A, B	110 knots (204 km/h; 127 mph)
Max cruising speed at 1,525 m (5,000 ft):	
A	110 knots (204 km/h; 127 mph)
Econ cruising speed: A	106 knots (196 km/h; 122 mph)
Max rate of climb at S/L	488 m (1,600 ft)/min
Vertical rate of climb at S/L: A	244 m (800 ft)/min
Service ceiling: A	5,275 m (17,300 ft)
Hovering ceiling: IGE: A	5,180 m (17,000 ft)
OGE: A	3,660 m (12,000 ft)
Range at 1,525 m (5,000 ft) with max fuel, no reserves:	
A	340 nm (629 km; 391 miles)
B (Scout)	534 nm (990 km; 615 miles)
Max endurance at 1,525 m (5,000 ft), no reserves:	
A	3 h 24 min
B	5 h 0 min

HILLER UH-12E HAULER
Rogerson Hiller has resumed delivery of the basic model UH-12E light helicopter. Customers include the government of India, to which deliveries of Haulers equipped for agricultural work began in May 1986.
TYPE: Three-seat utility helicopter.
ROTOR SYSTEM: Two-blade main rotor mounted universally on driveshaft, with small servo rotor; the latter is connected directly to the pilot's cyclic control stick, through a universally mounted transfer bearing and simple linkage. Movement of the control stick introduces positive or negative pitch changes to the servo rotor paddles. The resulting aerodynamic forces tilt the rotor head and produce cyclic pitch changes to the rotor blades. Main rotor blades are of bonded stainless steel, with aluminium honeycomb core, and wedge tips. Thickness/chord ratio 12%. Blades are interchangeable individually and are bolted to forks which are retained at the rotor head by tension-torsion bars. Blades do not fold. Rotor brake optional. Two-blade tail rotor of light alloy construction, mounted on port side of tailboom.
ROTOR DRIVE: Mechanical drive through two-stage planetary main transmission. Bevel gear drive to auxiliaries. Tail rotor gearbox (and fan gearbox on piston engined versions). Separate transmission oil system. Main rotor/engine rpm ratio 1 : 8.66. Tail rotor/engine rpm ratio 1 : 1.44.
FUSELAGE: Light alloy fully stressed semi-monocoque platform structure supporting the non-stressed cabin enclosure, engine mounting and landing gear. Tailboom of beaded light alloy sheet with no internal stiffeners.
TAIL UNIT: Horizontal stabiliser on starboard side of tailboom of three-seat versions, with steel tube spar, light alloy ribs and skin. Incidence ground-adjustable. Inverted V stabilising surfaces forward of tail rotor on four-seat versions.
LANDING GEAR: Wide track light alloy tube skids carried on spring steel cross members. Optional extended legs. Ground handling wheels standard. Optional 'zip-on' pontoons can be attached above the skids to permit water or land operations, but require extended landing gear.
POWER PLANT: One 253.5 kW (340 hp) Textron Lycoming VO-540-C2A flat-six engine, installed vertically and derated to 227.5 kW (305 hp). Engine muffler optional.

Single bladder fuel cell, capacity 174 litres (46 US gallons; 38 Imp gallons), mounted in lower portion of rear fuselage, beneath engine. Two optional auxiliary fuel tanks, mounted in fuselage on each side of engine; capacity 76 litres (20 US gallons; 16.6 Imp gallons) each. Oil capacity 12.5 litres (3.3 US gallons; 2.7 Imp gallons).

ACCOMMODATION: Three persons side by side on bench seat. Seat belts for all occupants; provision for shoulder harness. Dual controls optional. Forward-hinged door on each side, with sliding window. Baggage compartment immediately aft of engine. Heater/defroster optional.

SYSTEM: Electrical system includes a 72A alternator, nickel-cadmium battery, and battery temperature monitor.

AVIONICS AND EQUIPMENT: A range of optional avionics is available. Standard equipment includes engine hour meter, edge-lit instrument panel, outside air temperature gauge, eight-day clock, electrically controlled trim system, tinted glazing, cargo hook hardpoint, external power socket, and polyurethane paint finish. Optional equipment includes Mason cyclic control grip, fire extinguisher, first aid kit, night lighting equipment including two rotating beacons, strobe lights, 454 kg (1,000 lb) capacity quick-release cargo hook, twin heavy duty cargo racks, agricultural spray equipment, loudspeaker/siren, searchlight, and tropical doors. Agricultural equipment includes Simplex Model 3300 system with 9.75 m (32 ft) folding spraybooms and two glassfibre tanks, with total capacity of 416 litres (110 US gallons; 91 Imp gallons) or 530 litres (140 US gallons; 116 Imp gallons), designed for quick change to dry system; or Simplex Model 4500 system with single tank, capacity 530 litres (140 US gallons; 116 Imp gallons) and folding booms.

DIMENSIONS, EXTERNAL:
Main rotor diameter	10.80 m (35 ft 5 in)
Main rotor blade chord (constant)	0.33 m (1 ft 1 in)
Servo rotor diameter	3.05 m (10 ft 0 in)
Tail rotor diameter	1.68 m (5 ft 6 in)
Distance between rotor centres	6.17 m (20 ft 3 in)
Length: overall, rotors turning	12.41 m (40 ft 8½ in)
fuselage	8.69 m (28 ft 6 in)
Height to top of rotor head	3.08 m (10 ft 1¼ in)
Skid track	2.29 m (7 ft 6 in)
Cabin doors (standard, each):	
Height	1.13 m (3 ft 8½ in)
Max width	0.81 m (2 ft 8 in)
Height to sill	0.58 m (1 ft 11 in)

New production Hiller UH-12E with Simplex cropspraying system

DIMENSIONS, INTERNAL:
Cabin: Length	1.52 m (5 ft 0 in)
Max width	1.50 m (4 ft 11 in)
Max height	1.35 m (4 ft 5 in)
Floor area	1.16 m² (12.5 sq ft)

AREAS:
Tail rotor blades (each)	0.094 m² (1.01 sq ft)
Main rotor disc	91.97 m² (990.0 sq ft)
Tail rotor disc	2.57 m² (27.7 sq ft)

WEIGHTS AND LOADINGS:
Weight empty	798 kg (1,759 lb)
Max T-O weight	1,406 kg (3,100 lb)
Max disc loading	15.28 kg/m² (3.13 lb/sq ft)
Max power loading	6.18 kg/kW (10.16 lb/hp)

PERFORMANCE (at max T-O weight, except where indicated):
Never-exceed and max level speed	
	83 knots (154 km/h; 96 mph)
Cruising speed	78 knots (145 km/h; 90 mph)
Max rate of climb at S/L	393 m (1,290 ft)/min

Vertical rate of climb at S/L	225 m (740 ft)/min
Service ceiling:	
at AUW of 1,270 kg (2,800 lb)	4,575 m (15,000 ft)
at max T-O weight	2,255 m (7,400 ft)
Hovering ceiling IGE:	
at AUW of 1,270 kg (2,800 lb)	3,170 m (10,400 ft)
at max T-O weight	2,315 m (7,600 ft)
Hovering ceiling OGE:	
at AUW of 1,270 kg (2,800 lb)	2,070 m (6,800 ft)
at max T-O weight	1,155 m (3,800 ft)
Range, 30 min reserves:	
standard fuel	150 nm (278 km; 173 miles)
auxiliary fuel	316 nm (585 km; 364 miles)
Endurance with auxiliary fuel, 30 min reserves	
	4 h 1 min

SABRELINER
SABRELINER CORPORATION
6161 Aviation Drive, St Louis, Missouri 63134
Telephone: 1 (314) 731 2260
Telex: 44-7227
OTHER WORKS: Perryville Municipal Airport, Missouri
CHAIRMAN AND CHIEF EXECUTIVE OFFICER:
F. Holmes Lamoreux
VICE-PRESIDENT, GOVERNMENT OPERATIONS:
Reuben D. Best
VICE-PRESIDENT, COMMERCIAL MARKETING:
Karl R. Childs
VICE-PRESIDENT, ENGINEERING:
Bob D. Hanks

Sabreliner Corporation was formed in July 1983 as a subsidiary of the New York merchant banking company Wolsey & Co, following the latter's purchase of the Sabreliner Division of Rockwell International Corporation.

The main activities of Sabreliner Corporation are to provide product support for Sabreliner models currently in service, a total of about 600 aircraft, and refurbishment and upgrading of Lockheed T-33 and AT-33 aircraft for resale,

primarily to operators in Central and South America. Deliveries have included two Sabreliner Model 40R executive transports and 24 AT-33s to the Ecuadorian Air Force. The company also offers a modification programme for Sabreliner Model 40 and Model 60 aircraft which involves the installation of extended life Pratt & Whitney JT12 engines, Collins EFIS displays, interior and exterior refurbishing and zero-timed engines. In early 1985 Sabreliner Corporation was awarded a logistics support contract for US Navy Grumman TC-4C aircraft based at Whidbey Island (Washington), Oceana (Virginia), and Cherry Point (North Carolina). In September 1987 it was awarded a five-year contract for worldwide support of US Navy and US Marine Corps CT-39 Sabreliner aircraft. Under a service life extension programme (SLEP), it is making structural repairs and modifications to ten USAF Sabreliners (two T-39As and eight T-39Bs), the first of which was re-delivered in the Spring of 1988.

In early 1989 Sabreliner Corporation introduced its Excalibur programme for Sabreliner Model 40 and Model 60 aircraft, aimed at those airframes approaching 10,000 flying hours. The aircraft are stripped of paint, de-mated,

inspected, modified and reassembled as the Sabreliner 40EX and 60EX respectively. The Excalibur programme extends airframe life by 5,000 hours. Sabreliner also offers 30,000 hour/15,000 mission and 30,000 hour/30,000 mission airframe modifications for these models.

In August 1989 Sabreliner Corporation was awarded a contract to develop and manufacture service life extension kits for up to 644 Cessna T-37B jet trainers for the USAF's Air Training Command. The modifications will include replacement of fuselage/wing carry-through structures, lower front wing spars, tail mounting structures and horizontal tail surfaces. Sabreliner is modifying three test aircraft and will subsequently supply SLEP kits for installation by the Air Force Logistics Command.

Sabreliner has also been awarded contracts to rebuild Textron Lycoming T53 turboshafts for US Army Bell UH-1 helicopters, and to support airborne and ground-based training systems for the US Navy's Undergraduate Naval Flight Officer (UNFO) programme at NAS Pensacola, Florida.

SADLER
SADLER AIRCRAFT COMPANY
8225 East Montebello, Scottsdale, Arizona 85253
Telephone: 1 (602) 994 4631
Telex: 285776 VAMP UR
Fax: 1 (602) 481 0574
PRESIDENT: William G. Sadler
MARKETING DIRECTOR: F. Brent Stewart

Sadler Aircraft Company (formerly American Microflight Inc), whose Vampire microlight aircraft is listed in the Sport Aircraft section of this edition, has developed a series of low cost ground support and patrol/reconnaissance aircraft from this design.

SADLER A-22 LASA
The A-22 LASA (Light Armed Surveillance Aircraft) is externally similar to the Vampire, but has a watercooled 224 kW (300 hp) modified Chevrolet V-6 engine with heavy duty reduction drive, strengthened airframe, increased fuel capacity, optional retractable landing gear, and bullet resistant fuselage pod and cockpit canopy providing protection for the pilot, engine and fuel system. Provision is made for the installation of a single 7.62 mm machine gun in the leading-edge of each inboard wing section, with

ammunition storage to the rear, and for the carriage of up to 454 kg (1,000 lb) of stores, including 2.75 in rocket launching pods and bombs, on a total of four underwing hardpoints. Also under development in conjunction with McDonnell Douglas Helicopter's Ordnance Division is installation of the ASP-30 30 mm automatic cannon. Development of the A-22 LASA began during 1985. Rollout of a prototype (N22AB) was made in July 1987, with first flight on 8 October 1989. Customer demonstrations were due to begin in May 1990 after flight testing had been completed. Fixed and retractable landing gear versions are available under the designations A-22-300F and A-22-300R respectively. A two-seat version was expected to become available in mid-1990.

TYPE: Single-seat lightweight ground attack and patrol aircraft.

WINGS: Cantilever shoulder-wing monoplane of constant chord. NACA 66-A218 laminar flow wing section. Single aluminium alloy main spar, stamped ribs and flush riveted skin of aluminium alloy sheet. Aluminium alloy ailerons and four-position trailing-edge flaps. Outer wings fold upward in two hinged sections for transportation and storage.

FUSELAGE: Bullet resistant Kevlar fuselage pod and twin aluminium alloy tailbooms.

TAIL UNIT: Twin fins and rudders, interconnecting tailplane and elevator of similar construction to wings.

LANDING GEAR: Tricycle type, with trailing link suspension. Retractable landing gear optional. Fully swivelling nosewheel with steering through differential braking of mainwheels.

POWER PLANT: One 224 kW (300 hp) watercooled Chevrolet V-6 all-aluminium fuel injected engine, modified for aircraft use, with custom forged crankshaft, stainless steel forged connecting rods, forged aluminium pistons, stainless steel inlet and exhaust valves, and a heavy duty reduction drive to a two- or four-blade composites pusher propeller. Standard fuel capacity 75.7 litres (20 US gallons; 16.6 Imp gallons). Turbocharged version available for high altitude operations.

ACCOMMODATION: Pilot only, in enclosed cockpit, with bullet resistant Lexan canopy.

DIMENSIONS, EXTERNAL:
Wing span	6.70 m (22 ft 0 in)
Wing chord (constant)	1.27 m (4 ft 2 in)
Wing aspect ratio	5.28
Length overall	4.78 m (15 ft 8 in)
Height overall	1.14 m (3 ft 9 in)
Height, wings folded	2.13 m (7 ft 0 in)

Sadler A-22 LASA with wings folded

Prototype Sadler A-22 LASA single-seat lightweight ground attack aircraft

Width, wings folded	2.24 m (7 ft 4 in)
Propeller diameter	1.42 m (4 ft 8 in)
AREA:	
Wings, gross	8.51 m² (91.6 sq ft)
WEIGHTS:	
Weight empty	386 kg (850 lb)
Max payload	454 kg (1,000 lb)
Max T-O weight	975 kg (2,150 lb)

PERFORMANCE (estimated, at AUW of 975 kg; 2,150 lb, at S/L. A: A-22-300F, B: A-22-300R):

Max level speed at S/L:	
A	152 knots (282 km/h; 175 mph)
B	165 knots (306 km/h; 190 mph)
Stalling speed, flaps down:	
A, B	62 knots (115 km/h; 72 mph)
Max rate of climb at S/L: A	549 m (1,800 ft)/min
B	610 m (2,000 ft)/min
T-O run: A, B	153 m (500 ft)
Landing run: A, B	183 m (600 ft)
Range with standard fuel: A	239 nm (442 km; 275 miles)
B	260 nm (483 km; 300 miles)

SADLER OPV SERIES

Sadler Aircraft Corporation has also developed several low-cost OPV (optionally piloted vehicle) versions of the Vampire, and since 1987 has conducted manned and unmanned tests with autopilot, command uplink and autonomous guidance via Global Positioning System satellite navigation. The OPV series has been designed for patrol and observation roles and can carry payloads, in addition to pilot and fuel, of between 45-181 kg (100-400 lb). Four models are available: **OPV18-50** and **OPV18-100** with wing span 5.49 m (18 ft 0 in); and **OPV22-50** and **OPV22-100** with wing span 6.71 m (22 ft 0 in), each available with either a 38 kW (51 hp) Bombardier-Rotax 532.2V two-stroke or 71 kW (95 hp) Teledyne Continental GR-36 twin-rotor Wankel-type power plant driving two-, three- or four-blade composite propellers. Standard fuel capacity is 42 litres (11 US gallons; 9 Imp gallons).

The description for the A-22 LASA applies also to the OPV series, except as follows:

WINGS: Outer wings fold upward in single hinged sections.

DIMENSIONS, EXTERNAL:

Wing span: OPV18	5.49 m (18 ft 0 in)
OPV22	6.71 m (22 ft 0 in)
Wing aspect ratio: OPV18	4.32

AREA:	
Wings, gross: OPV18	6.97 m² (75.0 sq ft)

WEIGHTS (A: OPV18-50, B: OPV22-50, C: OPV18-100, D: OPV22-100):

*Max payload: A	45 kg (100 lb)
B	91 kg (200 lb)
C	136 kg (300 lb)
D	181 kg (400 lb)
Max T-O weight: A	329 kg (725 lb)
B	397 kg (875 lb)
C	454 kg (1,000 lb)
D	521 kg (1,150 lb)

PERFORMANCE (at max T-O weight):

Max level speed at S/L:	
A	100 knots (185 km/h; 115 mph)
B	102 knots (189 km/h; 117 mph)
C	130 knots (241 km/h; 150 mph)
D	128 knots (237 km/h; 147 mph)
Stalling speed, flaps down:	
A	47 knots (87 km/h; 54 mph)
B	40 knots (74 km/h; 46 mph)
C	56 knots (104 km/h; 65 mph)
D	46 knots (86 km/h; 53 mph)
Max rate of climb at S/L: A	183 m (600 ft)/min
B	213 m (700 ft)/min
C	229 m (750 ft)/min
D	244 m (800 ft)/min
T-O run: A	244 m (800 ft)
B	213 m (700 ft)
C	176 m (575 ft)
D	153 m (500 ft)
Landing run: A	213 m (700 ft)
B	176 m (575 ft)
C	244 m (800 ft)
D	122 m (400 ft)
Range with standard fuel:	
A	282 nm (523 km; 325 miles)
B	325 nm (603 km; 375 miles)
C	260 nm (482 km; 300 miles)
D	304 nm (563 km; 350 miles)

Drone versions can carry additional 45-68 kg (100-150 lb) payload

Sadler OPV18-50 manned/unmanned patrol and surveillance aircraft

SCALED
SCALED COMPOSITES INC
(Division of Wyman-Gordon Company)

Hangar 78, Mojave Airport, Mojave, California 93501
Telephone: 1 (805) 824 4541
Fax: 1 (805) 824 4174
PRESIDENT: Elbert L. (Burt) Rutan

VICE-PRESIDENT AND GENERAL MANAGER:
Herbert A. Iversen

Scaled Composites Inc, which had been acquired by Beech Aircraft Corporation in June 1985, was sold back to its founder, Mr 'Burt' Rutan, in November 1988 as part of a joint venture between Mr Rutan and the Wyman-Gordon Company of Worcester, Massachusetts. Scaled will design and manufacture composite aerospace structures for Wyman-Gordon, and continues to provide research and development facilities to individuals and companies requiring assistance with advanced aeronautical concepts.

Aircraft to which it contributed in the past were the NASA AD-1 oblique-wing research aircraft, for which detail design was carried out by Mr Rutan (see 1981-82 *Jane's*); the Fairchild/Ames 62% scale NGT, for which Mr Rutan completed the detail scaling from Fairchild's NGT lofting drawings (see 1982-83 *Jane's*); the M115-6.85 SCAT 1 85% scale demonstrator of the Beech Model 2000

Starship 1 (see Beech Aircraft Corporation in this section); a prototype of the Aviation Composites Mercury canard microlight (see Sport Aircraft section in 1987-88 *Jane's*); the Model 120-9E proof-of-concept Predator 480 agricultural aircraft, (described under the ATAC entry in the 1985-86 *Jane's*); the Rutan Model 81 Catbird (described under Scaled entry in 1989-90 *Jane's*); the full scale demonstrator of California Microwave Inc's CM-44 manned RPV (described and illustrated under that company's heading in the RPVs and Targets section of the 1987-88 *Jane's*); and the short production run of the Teledyne Ryan Aeronautical Scarab Mach 0.8 ground launched reconnaissance RPV.

Scaled's 2,787 m² (30,000 sq ft) facility at Mojave Airport, which is literally next door to Rutan Aircraft Factory, is well equipped for the construction of one or two prototypes of a particular design concept, and facilities include a large hangar, instrumentation and flight test departments, a short run production shop, plus a small machine shop. Future programmes are expected to involve commercial and military projects of a proprietary nature. In early 1986 a new 1858 m² (20,000 sq ft) composites fabrication facility was added to the existing plant.

Under the terms of the sale agreement with Beech, Scaled acquired rights to several projects which Mr Rutan had developed for that company. Details of these, and of other known projects on which Scaled was working in 1990, follow:

SCALED COMPOSITES MODEL 133-4.62 POC ADVANCED TECHNOLOGY TACTICAL TRANSPORT (AT³)

Under a $2.5 million Defense Advanced Research Projects Agency (DARPA) contract Scaled Composites Inc has designed, built and test flown a scale proof of concept (POC) version of an Advanced Technology Tactical Transport (AT³) intended to fill the void in military airlift capability between the Lockheed C-130 and large helicopters.

The AT³ proof of concept prototype (N133SC), designed by Scaled's President, Mr Burt Rutan, made a public 'commemorative' first flight from Mojave Airport, California on 20 January 1988, although it had flown for the first time on 29 December 1987. The aircraft is 62 per cent scale size with an airframe of composite glassfibre/foam and carbonfibre construction. To fulfil design goals of STOL performance and advanced aerodynamics, the aircraft features a 'trimaran' configuration with tandem high aspect ratio wings connected by long engine nacelles each housing a 559 kW (750 shp) Pratt & Whitney Canada PT6A-135A turboprop and the main units of the retractable tricycle-type landing gear. The forward wing has dihedral, the rear wing anhedral. Eight fast-acting electrically actuated flaps are extended aft, but not lowered, for the start of take-off roll, then rapidly lowered (full deflection takes about 1.5 s) to increase lift as rotation speed is reached, enhancing STOL capability. All fuel is contained in wings and engine nacelles, leaving the fuselage free for cargo. As originally flown the AT³ had conventional cruciform tail surfaces with sweptback fin and two-segment rudder. Small end plate fins were added subsequently. In late 1988 the aircraft was grounded for major modifications which involved removal of the tail surfaces to permit installation of a rear loading door and ramp and extension of the engine nacelles rearwards to support twin vertical fins and a high-mounted tailplane, similar in configuration to that of the Rockwell OV-10 Bronco. Wingtip extensions were also added at this time. The DARPA-funded flight test programme resumed in Spring 1989 and was completed on 27 July after the AT³ had made 65 flights totalling 150 hours.

The project may lead to full scale development of an AT³ able to carry a payload of 14 troops and 2,268 kg (5,000 lb) of cargo at 326 knots (604 km/h; 375 mph) over a low-altitude unrefuelled range of 2,400 nm (4,448 km; 2,764 miles), while operating from unimproved airstrips 305 m (1,000 ft) long. Maximum gross weight of the full size AT³ would be in the 22,680 kg (50,000 lb) class.

DIMENSIONS, EXTERNAL (final configuration):
Wing span	16.21 m (53 ft 2 in)
Foreplane span	11.48 m (37 ft 8 in)
Length overall	13.67 m (44 ft 10 in)
Height overall	4.29 m (14 ft 1 in)

AREAS:
Wings, gross	16.67 m² (179.48 sq ft)
Foreplane, gross (total)	10.97 m² (118.08 sq ft)

WEIGHTS:
Max demonstrated T-O weight	5,216 kg (11,500 lb)
Max design T-O and landing weight	5,896 kg (13,000 lb)

PERFORMANCE:
Max level speed	170 knots (315 km/h; 196 mph)
Min single-engine control speed (V_{MC})	
	63 knots (117 km/h; 73 mph)

RUTAN MODEL 143 TRIUMPH

Design work on this twin-turbofan aircraft was started in 1985, and construction began in 1986. The Model 143 was developed initially for Beech Aircraft as a proof of concept prototype for a projected range of rotary-, turboprop- and turbofan-powered six/eight-seat cabin class business aircraft which would have used a common airframe. The prototype (N143SC) made its first flight from Mojave Airport on 14 July 1988. It features composites construction and has a three-surface configuration with swept foreplane incorporating pitch control surfaces, swept wings with ailerons and trailing-edge flaps, a T tail with rearward swept tailplane, elevators and forward swept fin, and a ventral fin. Power plant is two 8.00 kN (1,800 lb st) Williams FJ44 turbofans mounted in pods above the wings. Fuel is contained in four cells in the wing strakes and outboard wings, with a combined capacity of 1,360 kg (3,000 lb).

After initial flight test the aircraft was modified to incorporate a cabin pressurisation system, maximum differential 0.52 bars (7.5 lb/sq in). No production plans have been announced. The prototype is used by Scaled as a flight test chase aircraft.

DIMENSIONS, EXTERNAL:
Wing span	14.63 m (48 ft 0 in)
Wing aspect ratio	11.55
Foreplane span	3.11 m (10 ft 2½ in)
Length overall	11.89 m (39 ft 0 in)
Fuselage diameter	approx 1.52 m (5 ft 0 in)
Height overall	3.32 m (10 ft 10¾ in)
Tailplane span	3.11 m (10 ft 2½ in)

DIMENSIONS, INTERNAL:
Cabin: Length	5.92 m (19 ft 5 in)
Max width	1.42 m (4 ft 8 in)
Height	1.32 m (4 ft 4 in)

AREA:
Wings, gross	18.49 m² (199.0 sq ft)

WEIGHTS AND LOADING:
Weight empty, equipped	approx 2,268 kg (5,000 lb)
Max usable fuel weight	1,356 kg (2,990 lb)
Max T-O weight	4,082 kg (9,000 lb)
Max wing loading	220.2 kg/m² (45.1 lb/sq ft)

PERFORMANCE (at max T-O weight, ISA, except where indicated):
Max operating speed:	
below 7,620 m (25,000 ft)	
	300 knots (556 km/h; 345 mph)
above 7,620 m (25,000 ft)	Mach 0.75
Max level speed at 10,670 m (35,000 ft)	
	400 knots (741 km/h; 460 mph)
Econ cruising speed at 10,670 m (35,000 ft)	
	340 knots (630 km/h; 392 mph)
Stalling speed, power off	75 knots (139 km/h; 87 mph)
Max rate of climb at S/L	1,370 m (4,500 ft)/min
Rate of climb at S/L, one engine out	
	305 m (1,000 ft)/min
Time to 10,670 m (35,000 ft)	13 min
Service ceiling	12,500 m (41,000 ft)
T-O run	381 m (1,250 ft)
T-O balanced field length	976 m (3,200 ft)
Landing run	671 m (2,200 ft)
Range with NBAA IFR reserves	
	1,600 nm (2,965 km; 1,842 miles)

Scaled Composites AT³ in final configuration with rear loading ramp, twin fins and wingtip extensions

Rutan Triumph light business jet prototype (two Williams FJ44 turbofans)

Photograph and three-view drawing *(Jane's/Mike Keep)* of the Rutan Model 151 ARES turbofan powered agile combat aircraft

RUTAN MODEL 151

Mr Burt Rutan began design of his Model 151 ARES (Agile Response Effective Support) all-composite light military combat aircraft in 1985. Construction of the prototype started in 1986 and this aircraft (N151SC) made its first flight from Mojave on 19 February 1990.

The aircraft, the general configuration of which can be seen in an accompanying photograph and three-view drawing, has been developed as a private venture with no outside funding, and is intended for export, particularly to Pacific Rim nations. Emphasis has been placed on agility for the anti-helicopter role, with close air support as an important secondary mission. Turning rate in combat configuration is predicted to be 36°/s. Border patrol, forward air control, drug interdiction and special operations may also be undertaken.

The Model 151 ARES has been designed to accommodate an internal GAU-12/U 25 mm cannon mounted in a 'focussed depression' on the starboard side of the fuselage below and to the rear of the cockpit and at the aircraft centre of gravity, so that gun recoil and muzzle blast reactions are balanced. To avoid ingestion of gun gases by the single Pratt & Whitney Canada JT15D-5 turbofan, the power plant is mounted at an angle several degrees to the left of the fuselage centreline, with a jet efflux pipe which curves to realign its thrust vector with the fuselage axis, and has single inlet in the port side of the fuselage to the rear of the cockpit area. Low-observable and IR-suppression technologies have not been incorporated for fear of hindering US export licensing. However, the curved engine air intake does mask the high radar-reflectivity of turbine fan blades.

When first flown, the Model 151 ARES was not fitted with a fire control system or military avionics, but after initial handling tests it was due to be equipped with a limited avionics suite for survivability/detectability trials.

TYPE: Single-seat low cost anti-helicopter and close air support aircraft.

WINGS: Composite structure of carbonfibre/epoxy over foam/PVC cores. Inner sections sweptback approximately 50°; outboard sections, incorporating 'spoiler-flaps', sweptback approximately 15°.

FOREPLANE: Forward-swept (approximately 10°) surface of composite carbonfibre/epoxy/foam/PVC construction, incorporating elevators for pitch control.

FUSELAGE: Composite structure of glassfibre/epoxy over foam/PVC core. Fuselage offset 76 mm (3 in) to starboard of wing centreline. 'Focussed depression' in gun muzzle area to shield canopy from shock loads and harness gun gas pressure for damping of yaw caused by recoil.

TAIL UNIT: Independent booms supporting two vertical surfaces, of similar construction to wings.

LANDING GEAR: Hydraulically retractable tricycle type, with single wheel on each unit. Main units retract rearward into tailbooms, nosewheel forward into fuselage.

POWER PLANT: One 13.12 kN (2,950 lb st) Pratt & Whitney JT15D-5 turbofan with electronic fuel control unit, offset 8° to port of centreline with thrust line corrected by curved jetpipe. Curved air intake on port side of centre fuselage only. Maximum internal fuel capacity 771 kg (1,700 lb). Provision for external fuel tank, capacity 227 kg (500 lb).

ACCOMMODATION: Pilot only, on Universal Propulsion Company SIIS-3ER ejection seat. Canopy hinged at rear. Two-seat version planned for training missions.

SYSTEM: Oxygen system standard.

ARMAMENT: One internal 25 mm General Electric GAU-12/U five-barrel rapid-firing cannon on starboard side of fuselage, with 220 rounds. Provision for carriage of two AIM-9L Sidewinder or four AIM-92 Stinger air-to-air missiles on external stores hardpoints.

DIMENSIONS, EXTERNAL:
Wing span	10.67 m (35 ft 0 in)
Wing aspect ratio	6.5
Foreplane span	5.84 m (19 ft 2 in)
Foreplane aspect ratio	10.7
Length overall	8.97 m (25 ft 5¼ in)
Height overall	3.00 m (9 ft 10 in)

AREAS:
Wings, gross	17.49 m² (188.3 sq ft)
Foreplane (total)	3.19 m² (34.3 sq ft)

WEIGHTS:
Weight empty, unarmed	1,308 kg (2,884 lb)
Max internal fuel weight	771 kg (1,700 lb)
Max T-O weight: unarmed	2,179 kg (4,804 lb)
with GAU-12/U and 220 rds	2,767 kg (6,100 lb)

PERFORMANCE (estimated):
Never-exceed speed	Mach 0.65
Max level speed at 10,670 m (35,000 ft)	
	375 knots (695 km/h; 432 mph)

POND RACER PR-01

Scaled is building for Mr Robert J. Pond of Minnesota a twin-engined all-composites racing aircraft designed by Mr Burt Rutan. The aircraft is of twin-boom configuration, similar to the Lockheed P-38 Lightning, with tapered forward-swept wings featuring aeroelastic tailoring. A cockpit nacelle mounted between the booms is supported by the rear surface of the wing centre-section and the tailplane. The tail unit is of three-fin configuration, with a central fin integral with the fuselage pod, while each tailboom has a sweptback, outward canted 'butterfly' fin and a small dorsal finlet. The area of the 'butterfly' fins will be progressively reduced during flight testing to optimum size. A retractable tailwheel type landing gear is fitted. The airframe is of carbonfibre/foam construction. Power plant comprises two 596/746 kW (800/1,000 hp) Electromotive/Nissan VG-30 liquid-cooled, turbocharged and intercooled V-6 automobile piston engines mounted ahead of the wing leading-edge, each driving a specially developed four-blade advanced technology propeller via reduction gearing. Methanol fuel is contained in six integral tanks, three in each nacelle boom. Wing span is 7.71 m (25 ft 3½ in); max T-O weight is expected to be about 1,500 kg (3,300 lb).

The Pond Racer, which was structurally complete in the Summer of 1989 pending delivery of its engines and gearboxes, has been designed to compete in Unlimited class air racing and is expected to be capable of maximum speeds of up to 521 knots (966 km/h; 600 mph). Test pilot for the aircraft is Dick Rutan, brother of the designer and pilot of the round-the-world Voyager aircraft. The Pond Racer was expected to make its racing debut at the National Championship Air Races at Reno, Nevada, in September 1990. Mr Pond has also announced his intention to use the aircraft for attempts to set new speed records for piston-engined aircraft in all categories.

SCHAFER
SCHAFER AIRCRAFT MODIFICATIONS INC

Route 10, Box 301, Madison Cooper Airport, Waco, Texas 76708
Telephone: 1 (817) 753 1551
Telex: 795902 SCHAFER CFTO
Fax: 1 (817) 753 8416
PRESIDENT: Earl Schafer
EXECUTIVE VICE-PRESIDENT AND DIRECTOR OF MARKETING:
R. B. Stevens

Mr Earl Schafer established this company during 1977. Initially, work was concentrated on the design and manufacture of auxiliary fuel tanks and the embodiment of modifications in Cessna business aircraft of the 300 and 400 series. Since 1979 the company has developed aircraft modification programmes of its own concept, of which details follow:

SCHAFER COMANCHERO

The Comanchero is a conversion of the Piper Pressurised Navajo with 559 kW (750 shp) Pratt & Whitney Canada PT6A-135 turboprops, flat rated at 462 kW (620 shp), replacing the standard 317 kW (425 hp) Textron Lycoming TIGO-541-E1A piston engines. This increases the useful load by 345 kg (760 lb) and offers a considerably longer max range. Max fuel capacity is increased to 1,363 litres (360 US gallons; 300 Imp gallons). The company received an FAA STC for the Comanchero in January 1981. A dual camera port installation for high altitude aerial photography is available optionally.

SECA, a subsidiary of Aerospatiale of France, has been appointed sole modification and service centre for Schafer Comanchero modifications for Europe, the Middle East and Africa.

WEIGHTS AND LOADINGS:
Weight empty	2,177 kg (4,800 lb)
Max baggage weight	218 kg (480 lb)
Max T-O weight	3,538 kg (7,800 lb)
Max wing loading	176.9 kg/km² (36.24 lb/sq ft)
Max power loading	4.07 kg/kW (6.7 lb/shp)

PERFORMANCE: As for Pressurised Navajo except:
Max cruising speed at 6,100 m (20,000 ft)	
	282 knots (522 km/h; 325 mph)
Max rate of climb at S/L	1,067 m (3,500 ft)/min
Rate of climb at S/L, one engine out	
	250 m (820 ft)/min
Service ceiling	more than 11,280 m (37,000 ft)
Service ceiling, one engine out	6,860 m (22,500 ft)
T-O to 15 m (50 ft)	533 m (1,750 ft)
Landing from 15 m (50 ft)	564 m (1,850 ft)
Max range at 8,840 m (29,000 ft), 45 min reserves	
	1,530 nm (2,835 km; 1,761 miles)

Schafer Comanchero 500 conversion of Piper Chieftain

SCHAFER COMANCHERO 500

The Comanchero 500 is a conversion of the Piper Chieftain which, basically, replaces the standard piston engines with turboprops of greater power. Design originated in mid-1980, and the prototype began flight testing in late August 1981.

Conversion of the Chieftain to **Comanchero 500B** standard involves replacement of its 261 kW (350 hp) Textron Lycoming TIO-540-J2BD piston engines by two 533 ekW (715 ehp) Pratt & Whitney Canada PT6A-27 turboprops, each flat rated at 431 ekW (578 ehp). Optionally, customers can select **Comanchero 500A** standard, with lower cost 410 kW (550 shp) PT6A-20s installed, if they do not require the hot day/high altitude performance offered by the flat rated PT6A-27s. In addition to turboprop engines, the conversion adds a 132 litre (35 US gallon; 29 Imp gallon) supplementary fuel tank in each engine nacelle, increases max T-O weight, and includes as standard an inspection of the airframe and replacement, if necessary, of such items as control surface and system bearings and bushings, landing gear bushings, and hydraulic components. Options include special interiors, avionics to customers' requirements, a detachable underfuselage cargo pod with capacity of 0.44 m³ (15.5 cu ft), and 341 litre (90 US gallon; 75 Imp gallon) supplementary nacelle tanks in lieu of the standard installation.

In early 1984 Schafer contracted with Embraer of Brazil for the licence manufacture of 50 Comanchero 500Bs in Brazil, where the aircraft is known as the Neiva NE-821 Carajá and has 410 kW (550 shp) derated PT6A-34 engines.

Two modification kits were supplied by Schafer; the remainder were manufactured locally by Neiva Indústria Aeronáutica SA.

WEIGHT:
Max T-O weight	3,629 kg (8,000 lb)

PERFORMANCE (A, Comanchero 500A, B, Comanchero 500B):
Max cruising speed: A, B at 3,660 m (12,000 ft)	
	240 knots (445 km/h; 276 mph)
Max rate of climb at S/L: A	853 m (2,800 ft)/min
B	732 m (2,400 ft)/min
Rate of climb at S/L, one engine out:	
A, B	259 m (850 ft)/min
Service ceiling: A	8,840 m (29,000 ft)
Service ceiling, one engine out: A, B	4,725 m (15,500 ft)
T-O to 15 m (50 ft): A	759 m (2,490 ft)
Landing from 15 m (50 ft): A	724 m (2,375 ft)
Range with pilot and ten passengers, 13.6 kg (30 lb) baggage allowance per passenger, and 45 min reserves, with standard fuel:	
A, B	500 nm (926 km; 575 miles)
Range with pilot and 181 kg (400 lb) payload:	
B	1,300 nm (2,410 km; 1,500 miles)

SCHAFER COMANCHERO 750

Schafer gained an STC during May 1981 for this re-engined version of the Piper Cheyenne II. This modification involves replacement of the standard 462 ekW (620 ehp) Pratt & Whitney Canada PT6A-28 turboprops by

Schafer/AMI Douglas DC-3-65TP Cargomaster conversion with Pratt & Whitney Canada PT6A-65AR turboprops

PT6A-135s flat rated at 559 kW (750 shp). A dual camera port installation for high altitude aerial photography is available optionally.

PERFORMANCE:
Max cruising speed at 7,620 m (25,000 ft)
278 knots (515 km/h; 320 mph)
Max rate of climb at S/L   869 m (2,850 ft)/min
Rate of climb at S/L, one engine out   198 m (650 ft)/min
Max range, econ cruising power, at 8,840 m (29,000 ft)
1,630 nm (3,020 km; 1,877 miles)

SCHAFER/AMI DOUGLAS DC-3-65TP CARGOMASTER

Schafer, in conjunction with Aero Modifications International of Fort Worth, Texas, has developed a turboprop conversion for the Douglas DC-3 which involves replacing the aircraft's piston engines with two Pratt & Whitney Canada PT6A-65AR turboprops. The conversion also includes a fuselage stretch forward of the wingroot to maintain the aircraft's centre of gravity envelope. The hydraulic system is modified and fuel capacity increased.

Design work on the modification, which is known as the Schafer/AMI DC-3-65TP Cargomaster, began in January 1985. The prototype (N70BF) made its first flight on 1 August 1986. Work began on the first production conversion in September 1986. By early 1989 Cargomasters were operating in South America, South Africa and the United States, and had been demonstrated to the US Air Force, US Navy and representatives of other US Government agencies at Andrews AFB, Washington, DC, on 22 February 1989. AMI anticipates a market for some 100 Cargomaster conversions over the next three years.

FUSELAGE: As for standard DC-3 but with 1.02 m (3 ft 4 in) plug forward of wingroot. Plug section can incorporate one additional cabin window on each side if required for passenger operation.

TAIL UNIT: As for DC-3 but with minor changes to horizontal tail surfaces for improved stability.

POWER PLANT: Two 1,062 kW (1,424 shp) Pratt & Whitney Canada PT6A-65AR turboprops, each flat rated at 917 kW (1,230 shp) and driving a Hartzell five-blade feathering and reversing propeller with de-icing. Engines have inertial separators and hot lip intake de-icing. One

additional fuel tank, usable capacity 447 litres (118 US gallons; 98.25 Imp gallons), in each engine nacelle. One forward auxiliary fuel tank, usable capacity 765 litres (202 US gallons; 168 Imp gallons), and one rear auxiliary fuel tank, usable capacity 753 litres (199 US gallons; 166 Imp gallons), in each inboard wing, giving total usable fuel capacity of 3,930 litres (1,038 US gallons; 864 Imp gallons). Oil capacity 9.5 litres (2.5 US gallons; 2.1 Imp gallons).

SYSTEMS: Two engine driven 250A starter/generators. Redesigned electrical system with dual batteries providing simultaneous engine start capability.

DIMENSIONS, EXTERNAL: As for standard DC-3, except:
Length overall	20.34 m (66 ft 9 in)
Propeller diameter	2.79 m (9 ft 2 in)
Baggage door: Height	1.42 m (4 ft 8 in)
Width	2.13 m (7 ft 0 in)

DIMENSIONS, INTERNAL:
Cabin: Length	12.50 m (41 ft 0 in)
Max width	2.18 m (7 ft 2 in)
Max height	1.95 m (6 ft 5 in)
Floor area	26.72 m² (287.6 sq ft)
Volume	48.85 m³ (1,725 cu ft)

WEIGHTS AND LOADINGS:
Basic operating weight	7,167 kg (15,800 lb)
Max fuel weight	3,154 kg (6,954 lb)
Max T-O and landing weight	12,202 kg (26,900 lb)
Max zero-fuel weight	11,793 kg (26,000 lb)
Max wing loading	132.8 kg/m² (27.2 lb/sq ft)
Max power loading	6.65 kg/kW (10.9 lb/shp)

PERFORMANCE:
Never-exceed speed
187 knots (346 km/h; 215 mph) IAS
Max level speed at 3,050 m (10,000 ft)
217 knots (402 km/h; 250 mph)
Max cruising speed at 3,050 m (10,000 ft)
196 knots (363 km/h; 226 mph)
Econ cruising speed at 3,050 m (10,000 ft)
185 knots (343 km/h; 213 mph)
Stalling speed, flight idle power
52 knots (96 km/h; 60 mph) IAS
Max rate of climb at S/L   610 m (2,000 ft)/min
Rate of climb at S/L, one engine out   137 m (450 ft)/min
Service ceiling   7,620 m (25,000 ft)
Service ceiling, one engine out   3,685 m (12,100 ft)
T-O run   1,051 m (3,450 ft)
T-O to 15 m (50 ft)   1,122 m (3,680 ft)
Landing from 15 m (50 ft)   670 m (2,200 ft)
Range: with max fuel and 2,268 kg (5,000 lb) payload
1,300 nm (2,409 km; 1,497 miles)
with 4,536 kg (10,000 lb) payload
100 nm (185 km; 115 miles)

SCHWEIZER
SCHWEIZER AIRCRAFT CORPORATION
PO Box 147, Elmira, New York 14902
Telephone: 1 (607) 739 3821
Telex: 932459 SCHWEIZER BIGF
Fax: 1 (607) 796 2488
PRESIDENT: Paul H. Schweizer
EXECUTIVE VICE-PRESIDENTS:
Leslie E. Schweizer
W. Stuart Schweizer
VICE-PRESIDENT: Michael D. Oakley
MARKETING DIRECTORS:
Larry A. Brooks
Truman C. Kosier
COMMUNICATIONS: Barbara J. Tweedt

Schweizer Aircraft Corporation was established in 1939 to design and manufacture sailplanes. Its current sailplane products are described in the appropriate section of this edition.

From mid-1957 until 1979 Schweizer also produced the Grumman (later Gulfstream American) Ag-Cat agricultural aircraft under subcontract. In January 1981 it purchased all rights to the Ag-Cat design, and deliveries of Schweizer Ag-Cat Super-Bs began in October 1981, since supplemented by a new turboprop version. All marketing and support for the Ag-Cat is undertaken from the Elmira facility.

It was announced on 13 July 1983 that Schweizer was to take over, under licence, sole US manufacture of the Hughes Model 300 series light helicopter, which had been in production by Hughes Helicopters since the late 1950s. Schweizer also became responsible for providing product support for Model 300s already in service, including the TH-55A military training version. Production tooling was shipped to Schweizer during the Summer of 1983, and the first Elmira built Model 300C was completed in June 1984. On 21 November 1986 Schweizer purchased all US manufacturing rights to the Model 300C from McDonnell Douglas Helicopter Corporation.

Schweizer is well known also as an aircraft subcontractor and is engaged currently in work for Bell Helicopter, Boeing, Sikorsky and other companies. It is engaged in contractual design and prototyping, and in projects to develop heavy lift vehicles, aerial applicators for pheromones, centrifuges, and spatial disorientation trainers.

Schweizer RG-8A two-seat drug interdiction aircraft of the US Coast Guard (*Ivo Sturzenegger*)

SCHWEIZER SA 2-37A
US military designation: RG-8A

The SA 2-37A is a modified version of Schweizer's SGM 2-37 motor glider (see Sailplanes section), developed primarily for use as a special purpose aircraft for law enforcement, border surveillance and other selected military applications. The wings are of slightly greater span, with modified leading-edges to improve stalling characteristics; and the SA 2-37A has a much more powerful engine, fitted with mufflers (long exhaust on each side of cowling) and driving a three-blade 'quiet' propeller. The aircraft is certificated under FAR Pt 23 for day and night VFR and IFR operations, and has a very low acoustic signature. Requiring only approximately 38.8 kW (52 hp) from the 175 kW (235 hp) IO-540 engine to maintain altitude in the quiet mission mode, it is said to be inaudible from the ground when flying at 'quiet mode' speed at 610-915 m (2,000-3,000 ft).

Standard fuel capacity is more than trebled compared with the motor glider, and can be increased further by use of an optional auxiliary tank. Behind the new bulged cockpit canopy is a 1.84 m³ (65 cu ft) payload bay designed to accept various sensor pallets such as low light level TV, infra-red imaging systems, standard cameras, or other payloads specified by customers. The pallet can be removed

quickly for replacement or maintenance, and a removable underfuselage skin and rear hatch doors provide access to the entire rear section of the aircraft. Other power plants and larger payload versions of the SA 2-37A are possible, both for specific surveillance applications and for such alternative roles as basic and advanced training, mission operator training, glider and banner towing and priority cargo delivery.

First flight of the SA 2-37A prototype (N9237A, a modified SGM 2-37) was made in 1986. Three RG-8As (85-0047, 85-0048 and 86-0404) were acquired by the US Army. The second of these was lost in an accident; the other two have since been transferred to the US Coast Guard. The prototype is fitted with a Hughes AN/AAQ-16 thermal imaging system.

TYPE: Two-seat special missions aircraft.

AIRFRAME: Generally similar to that of SGM 2-37 motor glider (which see), with wings extended in span and having Wortmann root and tip sections of FX-61-163 and FX-60-126 (modified) respectively. Leading-edges have chord extended by cuffs on portions of outer panels to improve stall characteristics. Fuselage slightly longer, and modified in forward areas to accommodate change of engine and enlarged canopy. Centre-section, outer wing panels and horizontal tail surface removable for storage and transportation. Speed fairings and hydraulic parking brakes on mainwheels.

POWER PLANT: One 175 kW (235 hp) Textron Lycoming IO-540-W3A5D flat-six engine, driving a McCauley three-blade constant-speed propeller with spinner. Standard fuel capacity of 196.8 litres (52 US gallons; 43.3 Imp gallons), increasable optionally to 253.6 litres (67 US gallons; 55.8 Imp gallons).

ACCOMMODATION: Seats for two persons side by side under two-piece upward opening canopy, hinged on centreline. Dual controls, seat belts and inertia reel harnesses standard. Compartment aft of seats enlarged to accommodate pallet containing up to 340 kg (750 lb) of sensors or other equipment.

SYSTEMS: 28V DC electrical system standard, with 100A alternator. A 300A generator and 110/120V 400Hz AC inverter are optional. Other options include air-conditioning and 1.81 m³ (64 cu ft) Scott oxygen system.

AVIONICS AND EQUIPMENT: Litton inertial navigation system. Standard Bendix/King avionics comprise dual KX 155 nav/com (one with VOR/ILS, one with VOR indicator) and single KG 258 artificial horizon, KEA 129 encoding altimeter, KR 87 ADF with indicator, KT 76 transponder, KR 21 marker beacon receiver, and KMA 24H audio control panel. Flight and engine instrumentation includes compass, ASI, rate of climb indicator, altimeter, fuel pressure and quantity gauges, oil temperature and pressure gauges, tachometer and voltmeter. Other standard equipment includes directional gyro, turn and bank indicator, exhaust gas and cylinder head temperature gauges, vacuum system, two David Clark headsets, digital clock, dual engine mufflers with resonator quiet kit, navigation/strobe/landing lights, interior post lights, flood/map light, and static wicks. Optional avionics and equipment include Bendix/King KNS 80 R/Nav, KCS 55A compass system, KFC 150 autopilot (requiring KCS 55A slave compass), and KRA 10A radar altimeter; Loran system; Stormscope WX-11; Shadin fuel flow system; 56.8 litre (15 US gallon; 12.5 Imp gallon) auxiliary fuel tank; 10 in tailwheel; armour seat protection; tinted glass; and lighting compatible with night vision goggles.

DIMENSIONS, EXTERNAL:

Wing span	18.745 m (61 ft 6 in)
Wing aspect ratio	19.0
Fuselage length	8.46 m (27 ft 9 in)
Height overall (tail down)	2.36 m (7 ft 9 in)
Tailplane span	3.24 m (10 ft 7½ in)
Wheel track	2.79 m (9 ft 2 in)
Wheelbase	5.99 m (19 ft 8 in)
Propeller diameter	2.18 m (7 ft 2 in)
Propeller ground clearance (tail up)	0.55 m (1 ft 9.7 in)

AREAS:

Wings, gross	18.52 m² (199.4 sq ft)
Ailerons (total)	1.01 m² (10.90 sq ft)
Airbrakes (total)	0.82 m² (8.79 sq ft)
Vertical tail surfaces (total)	1.62 m² (17.43 sq ft)
Horizontal tail surfaces (total)	2.13 m² (22.95 sq ft)

WEIGHTS AND LOADINGS:

Weight empty	918 kg (2,025 lb)
Max mission payload	340 kg (750 lb)
Max T-O weight	1,587 kg (3,500 lb)
Max wing loading	85.65 kg/m² (17.55 lb/sq ft)
Max power loading	9.06 kg/kW (14.89 lb/hp)

PERFORMANCE (at max T-O weight):

Max permissible diving speed	
	176 knots (326 km/h; 202 mph) CAS
Cruising speed at 1,525 m (5,000 ft):	
75% power	138 knots (256 km/h; 159 mph)
65% power	129 knots (239 km/h; 148 mph)
Approach speed	117 knots (217 km/h; 135 mph) CAS
Quiet mode speed	
	70-80 knots (130-148 km/h; 80-92 mph)
Optimum climbing speed	
	77 knots (142 km/h; 88 mph) CAS
Stalling speed:	
airbrakes open	71 knots (132 km/h; 82 mph)
airbrakes closed	67 knots (124 km/h; 77 mph)
Max rate of climb at S/L	292 m (960 ft)/min
Service ceiling	5,490 m (18,000 ft)
T-O run (S/L, ISA): hard surface	387 m (1,270 ft)
grass	533 m (1,750 ft)
T-O to 15 m (50 ft) (S/L, ISA):	
hard surface	612 m (2,010 ft)
grass	759 m (2,490 ft)
Landing from 15 m (50 ft) (S/L, ISA):	
hard surface	680 m (2,230 ft)
grass	732 m (2,400 ft)
Best glide ratio	20
g limits	+6.6/−3.3

SCHWEIZER AG-CAT SUPER-B and AG-CAT TURBINE

The prototype of the original (Grumman designed) Ag-Cat agricultural biplane flew for the first time on 27 May 1957. First deliveries were made in 1959 and 2,455 Ag-Cats (1,730 G-164A, 659 G-164B, 44 G-164C and 22 G-164D) were built by Schweizer under subcontract. Schweizer resumed production in October 1981 with two

Schweizer Ag-Cat Super-B/600 agricultural aircraft

versions of an improved G-164B known as the Ag-Cat Super-B. It has also developed the turboprop powered Ag-Cat Super-B Turbine. Details of current models are as follows:

Ag-Cat Super-B/600 (G-164B). This is the basic Schweizer Ag-Cat, with a 447.5 kW (600 hp) Pratt & Whitney R-1340 nine-cylinder radial aircooled engine, driving a Pacific Propeller Type 12D40/AG100 two-blade constant-speed metal propeller. Improvements incorporated in the Super-B include a hopper with 40 per cent greater capacity (1.51 m³; 53.5 cu ft) than that of earlier models, a 0.97 m (3 ft 2 in) wide stainless steel gatebox and bottom loader valve as standard equipment, plus numerous equipment and airframe improvements. The upper wing is raised 20 cm (8 in) to improve the pilot's view, and increase load carrying capability, operating speed and climb performance.

Ag-Cat 450B (G-164B). This alternative version of the Super-B is generally similar to the basic model, but is powered instead by a 335.5 kW (450 hp) Pratt & Whitney R-985 nine-cylinder radial aircooled engine. Usable fuel capacity is 242 litres (64 US gallons; 53.3 Imp gallons). The 450B has a 1.23 m³ (43.5 cu ft) hopper, capacity 1,230 litres (325 US gallons; 271 Imp gallons). It is available only to special order.

Ag-Cat Super-B Turbine (G-164B). Generally similar to the basic Ag-Cat Super-B, but powered by a Pratt & Whitney Canada PT6A turboprop. Alternative power plants available for this version are the 373 kW (500 shp) PT6A-11AG, 507 kW (680 shp) PT6A-15AG, and 559 kW (750 shp) PT6A-34AG. Nine Ag-Cat Super-B Turbines had been manufactured under licence by Ethiopian Airlines' Technical Services Division at Addis Ababa (which see) by early 1990. The first was completed in December 1986.

The following description applies generally to all three production models, except where indicated:

TYPE: Single-seat agricultural biplane.

WINGS: Single-bay staggered biplane. NACA 4412 (modified) wing section. Dihedral 3°. Incidence 6°. Aluminium alloy (6061-T6) two-spar structure with 6061-T6 skins on entire top surface, around leading-edge and back to front spar on undersurface. Remainder of undersurface fabric covered. Each D leading-edge is made of five separate sections to facilitate replacement if damaged. Glassfibre wingtips. N type interplane struts. Light alloy ailerons on all four wings, with ground adjustable tab on lower port aileron. No flaps.

FUSELAGE: Welded 4130 chrome-molybdenum steel tube structure, covered with duralumin sheet. Removable side panels.

TAIL UNIT: Welded 4130 chrome-molybdenum steel tube structure, covered with fabric and wire braced. Cable deflector wire from tip of fin to top of cockpit canopy. Controllable trim tab in port elevator. Ground adjustable tabs on rudder and starboard elevator.

LANDING GEAR: Non-retractable tailwheel type. Cantilever spring steel legs. Cleveland wheels with tyres size 8.50-10, 8-ply, pressure 2.42 bars (35 lb/sq in). Steerable tailwheel with tyre size 12.4-4.5, pressure 3.45 bars (50 lb/sq in). Cleveland heavy duty aircooled hydraulic disc brakes. Parking brake.

POWER PLANT: One Pratt & Whitney nine-cylinder aircooled radial engine with Pacific Propeller constant-speed propeller, or Pratt & Whitney Canada PT6A turboprop, as detailed in model listings. Fuel tanks in upper wing with combined usable capacity of 302 litres (80 US gallons; 66.6 Imp gallons). Single-point refuelling on upper surface of upper wing centre-section. Oil capacity 32.2 litres (8.5 US gallons; 7.1 Imp gallons).

ACCOMMODATION: Single seat in enclosed cockpit. Reinforced fairing aft of canopy for turnover protection. Canopy side panels open outward and down, canopy top upward and to starboard, to provide access. Baggage

compartment. Cockpit pressurised against dust ingress and ventilated by ram air. Safety padded instrument panel. Air-conditioning by J.B. Systems optional.

SYSTEMS: Hydraulic system for brakes only. Optional electrical system with 24V alternator, navigation lights and/or strobe lights, external power socket, and electric engine starter.

EQUIPMENT: Radio optional. Standard equipment includes control column lock, instrument glareshield, seat belt and shoulder harness, tinted windscreen, stall warning light, refuelling steps and assist handles, tiedown rings, and urethane paint external yellow finish.

AGRICULTURAL EQUIPMENT: Forward of cockpit, over CG, is a 1.51 m³ (53.5 cu ft) glassfibre hopper, capacity 1,514 litres (400 US gallons; 333 Imp gallons), for agricultural chemicals (dry or liquid) with distributor beneath fuselage. Low-volume, ULV or high-volume spray system, with leading- or trailing-edge booms. Emergency dump system for hopper load; can be used also for water bomber operations.

DIMENSIONS, EXTERNAL (A: Super-B/600, B: Super-B Turbine, C: 450B):

Wing span:	12.93 m (42 ft 5 in)
B: upper	12.92 m (42 ft 4½ in)
lower	12.36 m (40 ft 6¾ in)
Wing chord (constant)	1.47 m (4 ft 10 in)
Wing aspect ratio: upper wing	8.7
biplane, effective mean	5.5
Length overall: A	7.44 m (24 ft 5 in)
B	8.41 m (27 ft 7¼ in)
C	7.54 m (24 ft 9 in)
Height overall: A, C	3.51 m (11 ft 6 in)
B	3.68 m (12 ft 1 in)
Tailplane span	3.96 m (13 ft 0 in)
Wheel track	2.44 m (8 ft 0 in)
Wheelbase	5.59 m (18 ft 4 in)
Propeller diameter (max)	2.74 m (9 ft 0 in)
Propeller ground clearance: A	0.27 m (10.8 in)
B	0.37 m (1 ft 2¾ in)
Cockpit door: Height	0.53 m (1 ft 9 in)
Width	0.64 m (2 ft 1 in)
Height to sill	0.71 m (2 ft 4 in)

DIMENSIONS, INTERNAL:

Cockpit: Length	1.27 m (4 ft 2 in)
Max width	0.76 m (2 ft 6 in)
Max height	1.14 m (3 ft 9 in)

AREAS:

Wings, gross	36.48 m² (392.7 sq ft)
Ailerons (total)	2.92 m² (31.4 sq ft)
Fin	1.67 m² (17.97 sq ft)
Rudder	1.12 m² (12.0 sq ft)
Tailplane	2.12 m² (22.8 sq ft)
Elevators	2.06 m² (22.2 sq ft)

WEIGHTS AND LOADINGS:

Weight empty equipped, spray and duster versions:	
A	1,656 kg (3,650 lb)
B	1,429 kg (3,150 lb)
C	1,508 kg (3,325 lb)
Certificated AUW	2,358 kg (5,200 lb)
Max T-O weight (CAM.8)	3,184 kg (7,020 lb)
Max wing loading	87.42 kg/m² (17.91 lb/sq ft)
Max power loading: A	7.12 kg/kW (11.71 lb/hp)
B	5.70-8.54 kg/kW (9.36-14.04 lb/shp)
C	9.49 kg/kW (15.6 lb/hp)

PERFORMANCE (A: Super-B/600, B: Super-B Turbine with PT6A-15AG engine, C: 450B):

Never exceed speed	136 knots (252 km/h; 157 mph)
Working speed: A, C	100 knots (185 km/h; 115 mph)
B	113 knots (209 km/h; 130 mph)
Stalling speed, power off	56 knots (103 km/h; 64 mph)
T-O run	120 m (394 ft)
T-O to 15 m (50 ft) at 2,358 kg (5,200 lb) certificated	
AUW: A	320 m (1,050 ft)

Schweizer Model 300C Sky Knight light utility helicopter of the Minnesota State Patrol

Prototype Schweizer Model 330 (Allison 250-C20 turboshaft)

B	274 m (900 ft)
C	396 m (1,300 ft)
Landing from 15 m (50 ft)	407 m (1,333 ft)
Landing run	157 m (513 ft)
Range with max fuel	172 nm (318 km; 198 miles)
Design g limits, all versions	+4.2/−1

SCHWEIZER MODEL 300C

The early history of this helicopter can be found under the Hughes Helicopters entry in previous editions of *Jane's*, and a detailed description of the basic Model 300 in the 1976-77 edition. Hughes built more than 2,800 of all versions, including the TH-55A Osage for the US Army, before transferring production to Schweizer in July 1983. In November 1986, Schweizer purchased the Model 300 programme in its entirety.

The current Model 300C is a developed version, with improvements to allow a 45 per cent increase in payload. The prototype made its first flight in August 1969, followed by the first Hughes production model in December 1969. FAA certification was received in May 1970. The first production Schweizer Model 300C flew in June 1984 and was delivered on 29 June. In late 1985 the US Army awarded Schweizer a $4.9 million contract for the supply of 30 Model 300Cs and spare parts. In March 1986 Schweizer began delivery of 24 TH-300C training versions to the Royal Thai Army, which ordered a further 24 TH-300Cs, delivery of which was completed by mid-1989. The 250th Schweizer built Model 300C was delivered in late 1989. Schweizer manufactured 82 Model 300Cs in 1989.

The specially equipped 300C **Sky Knight** available for police patrol has safety mesh seats with inertia reel shoulder harness, ballistic glassfibre armour beneath each seat, a high power public address/siren system, a high intensity controllable searchlight system, an integrated communications system based on the Bendix/King KY 195 VHF transceiver, a heavy duty 28V 100A electrical system, cabin heater, night lights with strobe beacons, cabin utility light, external power socket, fire extinguisher, first aid kit and mapcase. Recent deliveries include two to the Cleveland Police Department and one to the Minnesota State Patrol.

TYPE: Three-seat light utility helicopter.
ROTOR SYSTEM: Fully articulated metal three-blade main rotor. Fully interchangeable blades of bonded construction, with constant section extruded aluminium spar, wraparound skin and a trailing-edge section. Blade section NACA 0015. Tracking tabs on blades at three-quarters radius. Elastomeric dampers. Electric cyclic trim. Two-blade teetering tail rotor, each blade comprising a steel tube spar with glassfibre skin. Limited blade folding. No rotor brake.
ROTOR DRIVE: Combination V-belt/pulley and reduction gear drive system. Main rotor and tail rotor gearbox have spiral bevel right-angle drive. Main rotor/engine rpm ratio 1 : 6.8. Tail rotor/engine rpm ratio 1.97 : 1.03.
FUSELAGE: Welded steel tube centre structure, with light alloy, stainless steel and Plexiglas cabin and one-piece light alloy tube tailboom.
TAIL UNIT: Horizontal and vertical fixed stabilising surfaces, made of light alloy ribs and skins.
LANDING GEAR: Skids carried on oleo-pneumatic shock absorbers. Replaceable skid shoes. Two ground handling wheels with 0.25 m (10 in) balloon tyres, pressure 4.14-5.17 bars (60-75 lb/sq in). Available optionally on floats made of polyurethane coated nylon fabric, 4.70 m (15 ft 5 in) long and with a total installed weight of 27.2 kg (60 lb).
POWER PLANT: One 168 kW (225 hp) Textron Lycoming HIO-360-D1A flat-four engine, derated to 142 kW (190 hp), mounted horizontally aft of seats. Two aluminium fuel tanks, total capacity 185.5 litres (49 US gallons; 40.8 Imp gallons) mounted externally aft of cockpit. Crash resistant fuel tank optional. Oil capacity 9.5 litres (2.5 US gallons; 2.1 Imp gallons).
ACCOMMODATION: Three persons side by side on sculptured and cushioned bench seat, with shoulder harness, in Plexiglas enclosed cabin. Carpet and tinted canopy standard. Forward hinged, removable door on each side. Dual controls optional. Baggage capacity 45 kg (100 lb). Exhaust muff heating and ventilation kits available.
SYSTEM: Standard electrical system includes 24V 70A alternator, 24V battery, starter and external power socket.

AVIONICS AND EQUIPMENT: Optional avionics include Collins VHF-253 or Bendix/King KY 196 com transceiver and headsets, and ADF650A or KR 86 ADFs, TDR 950 or KT 76A transponders. Standard equipment includes mapcase, first aid kit, fire extinguisher, engine hour meter, and main rotor blade tiedown kit. Optional equipment includes amphibious floats, litter kits, cargo racks with combined capacity of 91 kg (200 lb), external load sling of 408 kg (900 lb) capacity, Simplex Model 5200 agricultural spray or dry powder dispersal kits, Sky Knight law enforcement package, instrument training package, throttle governor, start-up overspeed control unit, night flying kit, dual controls, all-weather cover, heavy duty skid plates, single or dual exhaust mufflers, door lock, dual oil coolers, and tinted glass for cabin windows.

DIMENSIONS, EXTERNAL:	
Main rotor diameter	8.18 m (26 ft 10 in)
Main rotor blade chord	0.171 m (6¾ in)
Tail rotor diameter	1.30 m (4 ft 3 in)
Distance between rotor centres	4.66 m (15 ft 3½ in)
Length overall, rotors turning	9.40 m (30 ft 10 in)
Height over rotor head	2.66 m (8 ft 8⅝ in)
Width, rotor partially folded	2.44 m (8 ft 0 in)
Height to top of cabin	2.19 m (7 ft 2 in)
Cabin width	1.30 m (4 ft 3 in)
Skid track	1.99 m (6 ft 6½ in)
Length of skids	2.51 m (8 ft 3 in)
Passenger doors (each): Height	1.09 m (3 ft 7 in)
Width	0.97 m (3 ft 2 in)
Height to sill	0.91 m (3 ft 0 in)
AREAS:	
Main rotor blades (each)	0.70 m² (7.55 sq ft)
Tail rotor blades (each)	0.08 m² (0.86 sq ft)
Main rotor disc	52.5 m² (565.5 sq ft)
Tail rotor disc	1.32 m² (14.2 sq ft)
Fin	0.23 m² (2.5 sq ft)
Horizontal stabiliser	0.246 m² (2.65 sq ft)
WEIGHTS AND LOADING:	
Weight empty	474 kg (1,046 lb)
Max T-O weight: Normal category	930 kg (2,050 lb)
external load	975 kg (2,150 lb)
Max disc loading	17.67 kg/m² (3.62 lb/sq ft)
PERFORMANCE (at max Normal T-O weight, ISA):	
Never-exceed speed at S/L	
	91 knots (169 km/h; 105 mph)
Max cruising speed	82 knots (153 km/h; 95 mph)
Speed for max range, at 1,220 m (4,000 ft)	
	67 knots (124 km/h; 77 mph)
Max rate of climb at S/L	229 m (750 ft)/min
Service ceiling	3,110 m (10,200 ft)
Hovering ceiling: IGE	1,800 m (5,900 ft)
OGE	840 m (2,750 ft)
Range at 1,220 m (4,000 ft), 2 min warm-up, max fuel, no reserves	194 nm (360 km; 224 miles)
Max endurance at S/L	3 h 24 min

SCHWEIZER MODEL 330

At the 1987 Airborne Law Enforcement Association convention in Sacramento, California, Schweizer Aircraft displayed a mockup of its three/four-seat turbine engined Model 330. This helicopter, a prototype of which (N330TT) made its first flight in public on 14 June 1988, was designed to meet specifications for the US Army's New Training Helicopter (NTH) requirement as well as to meet overseas needs for a state-of-the-art military training and light observation helicopter. The Model 330C is powered by a 313.2 kW (420 shp) Allison 250-C20 turboshaft (derated to 149 kW; 200 shp) and uses most of the systems, controls, rotors and dynamic components of the piston engined Model 300C. Main rotor speed is 471 rpm. The integrated avionics are supplied by Honeywell.

A new forward fuselage provides an increase in cabin length of some 0.61 m (2 ft 0 in) and an increase in width of 0.43 m (1 ft 5 in) and incorporates an aerodynamically improved transparency. The centre passenger seat has been raised and moved rearward in the training version, enabling it to be used by a second, observing, student. Flight controls can be provided at all three seat positions. A new pedestal mounted instrument console incorporates an IFR flight panel with dual multi-function CRT displays. Max fuel capacity is 189 litres (50 US gallons; 41.6 Imp gallons). Streamlined fairings have been added to the rear fuselage and tailboom.

Schweizer expects to receive FAA certification of the Model 330 by the end of 1990, and to make initial production deliveries to commercial customers shortly thereafter. Launch customer for the helicopter is Crescent Airways Inc of West Hollywood, Florida, which has ordered five for use in tuna fish spotting operations. Schweizer held orders for more than 20 Model 330s in early 1990, by which time the prototype had completed some 350 flying hours in 400 flights. The Model 330 will be marketed for a variety of roles including law enforcement, scout/observation, aerial photography, light utility, agricultural spraying and personal transportation.

DIMENSIONS, EXTERNAL:	
Main rotor diameter	8.18 m (26 ft 10 in)
Tail rotor diameter	1.30 m (4 ft 3 in)
Length overall, rotors turning	9.40 m (30 ft 10 in)

Height overall	2.64 m (8 ft 8 in)	Max T-O weight: Normal category	930 kg (2,050 lb)	Max range at 1,220 m (4,000 ft), no reserves	
Skid track	1.98 m (6 ft 6 in)	external load	975 kg (2,150 lb)		221 nm (410 km; 255 miles)
DIMENSIONS, INTERNAL:		PERFORMANCE (at Normal T-O weight):		Max endurance, no reserves	3 h 6 min
Cabin: Width at seat	1.72 m (5 ft 7½ in)	Max cruising speed	100 knots (185 km/h; 115 mph)		
Height at seat	1.35 m (4 ft 5¼ in)	Normal cruising speed	91 knots (169 km/h; 105 mph)		
WEIGHTS:		Hovering ceiling: IGE	5,485 m (18,000 ft)		
Weight empty	476 kg (1,050 lb)	OGE	4,265 m (14,000 ft)		

SEAPLANES INC — *see Turbotech*

SIERRA
SIERRA INDUSTRIES INC
Garner Municipal Airport, PO Box 5184, Uvalde, Texas 78802-5184
Telephone: 1 (512) 278 4381
Telex: 9102402612
Fax: 1 (512) 278 7649
PRESIDENT: Mark Huffstutler

On 24 September 1986 Sierra Industries Inc acquired the assets of the former R/STOL Systems Inc, including some 100 supplemental type certificates for STOL and performance modifications to 40 aircraft types, as detailed in this entry.

Sierra Industries holds an FAA Supplemental Type Certificate covering the installation of RCA WeatherScout I radar inside the leading-edge of the starboard wing of a number of aircraft including the Cessna 182, 206F, T206F, TU206G, U206G and 210 series. WeatherScout I is basically a weather radar, but provides limited ground mapping capability. The truncated 13 × 30 cm (5 × 12 in) antenna is housed inside a leading-edge cutaway, with the receiver/transmitter built integrally at the back of the antenna. The wing structure is reinforced around the cutaway. A reinforced epoxy/glassfibre radome encloses the opening. Total system weight is 10.5 kg (23.1 lb).

SIERRA INDUSTRIES CESSNA AUXILIARY FUEL SYSTEMS
Sierra Industries has developed an auxiliary fuel system for Cessna Model 180, 182, 185, 206 and 207 aircraft which increases the total fuel capacity of the aircraft by 204 litres (54 US gallons; 45 Imp gallons). The modification involves the installation of three vulcanised rubber fuel bladders in each wing panel outboard of the aircraft's standard wing fuel tank. Installation is accomplished in approximately 50 man hours, and is FAA certificated to FAR Pt 23 requirements.

SIERRA INDUSTRIES CESSNA 210 LANDING GEAR DOOR MODIFICATION
Sierra Industries has developed an FAA approved modification kit for Cessna Model 210, T210 and P210 Centurions manufactured between 1970 and 1978 (c/ns 21059200-21062954 inclusive), which enables the main landing gear doors to be removed. The conversion involves the substitution of prefabricated metal fairings to close gaps left by the door removal. Claimed advantages of the modification are an 8.6 kg (19 lb) increase in useful load, reduced maintenance, reduced landing gear retraction and extension times, elimination of possible door-fouling problems and enhanced appearance comparable to that of 1979 and later model Centurions.

SIERRA/BEECH, SIERRA/CESSNA and SIERRA/PIPER SAFETY and PERFORMANCE CONVERSIONS
Continuous improvement has been made on Sierra's line of Hi-Lift systems for Beech, Cessna and Piper single-engined and smaller twin-engined aircraft. The Sierra modification, first applied to a Cessna 182, comprises full span wing leading-edge and trailing-edge high-lift systems which greatly reduce the take-off and landing distances normally required by such aircraft.

The existing ailerons are used as an integral part of the full span trailing-edge flap system. When the conventional inboard flaps are lowered for take-off or landing, the ailerons droop with them, virtually doubling the wing lift at low speeds. The ailerons retain their differential operation for roll control when drooped.

In addition, the wing is fitted with a full span distributed-camber leading-edge to provide an optimum spanwise lift distribution for maximum cruise efficiency. The cambered leading-edge also reduces the aerofoil leading-edge pressure peak at high angles of attack, to impart maximum resistance to stall and to provide highly responsive manoeuvrability at low airspeeds. Some types of Cessna single-engined aircraft built since 1972 include this leading-edge as a standard production feature.

The full span flap system, in combination with conical cambered wingtips, dorsal and ventral fins, belly mounted vortex generators, and flap/elevator automatic trim system, is applied to various models to offer increased performance.

To improve controllability at low speeds, stall fences are provided between flaps and ailerons, and to complete the

Sierra/Cessna T210, showing clearly the high differential aileron droop Hi-Lift system

Beechcraft A36 Bonanza as certificated with Sierra Hi-Lift system, including full span flaps

Sierra conversion of the Piper Seneca II features full span trailing-edge flaps, with wing upper surface spoilers for roll control

Hi-Lift modification the aileron gap is sealed with a strip of aluminium sheet or rubberised canvas. These modifications permit safe STOL landings and take-offs by even novice pilots, and cruising speed and range are increased by 2-4 per cent.

Maximum gross weight increases have accompanied the certification of modifications of twin-engined aircraft such as the Cessna Super Skymaster and Piper Twin Comanche. This is due primarily to their increased climb performance and slower take-off and landing speeds.

Development of a Hi-Lift system for the Cessna 400 series of twin-engined business aircraft entailed complete redesign of the wings from the rear spar aft to allow installation of 100 per cent Fowler flaps and flap actuated drooping ailerons. This system, in combination with an automatic pitch trim system and double hinged rudder, led to FAA certificated take-off and landing field lengths of approximately 40 per cent.

In 1974, the FAA certificated the Sierra equipped Piper Seneca I, with wing upper surface spoilers for roll control, full span slotted flaps, cambered wingtips and an anti-servo rudder tab. These modifications allow shorter take-off and landing distances; minimum control speed is reduced by 16 per cent, the best rate of climb speed is lowered by 19 per

cent, single-engine service ceiling is raised by 213 m (700 ft) and roll response is increased greatly at all speeds and configurations. A similar modification of the Seneca II was certificated during 1976.

More recent activities have entailed fitting full span trailing-edge flaps and spoilers for roll control on a Piper Cherokee SIX; and developing a high differential aileron droop Hi-Lift system for high performance single-engined aircraft, such as the Cessna Model P210 Pressurised Centurion. In this application a new and improved control mechanism droops both ailerons symmetrically to 15° when the trailing-edge flaps are extended to 20° for take-off. For roll control the ailerons travel up and down in high ratio differential: thus, with the control wheel fully to starboard, the starboard aileron moves up 42° to act as a spoiler (27° up from its normal faired position); at the same time the port aileron is deflected downward an additional 12° to a total of 27°. Ailerons are also drooped symmetrically by 15° when the trailing-edge flaps are extended to 30° for approach and landing.

Benefits from this advanced Hi-Lift system include a greatly reduced adverse yaw tendency in turns, and a high

continued on page 505

SIERRA VERSIONS OF CESSNA MODELS

	Weight empty equipped	Weight gross	Max level speed	Max cruising speed	Stalling speed, wheels and flaps down	Max rate of climb at S/L	Single-engine rate of climb at S/L	Service ceiling	T-O run	T-O to 15 m (50 ft)	Landing from 15 m (50 ft)	Landing run	Max range**	Min control speed
	kg (lb)	kg (lb)	knots (km/h; mph)	knots (km/h; mph)	knots (km/h; mph)	m (ft)/ min	m (ft)/ min	m (ft)	m (ft)	m (ft)	m (ft)	m (ft)	nm (km; miles)	knots (km/h; mph)
Model 150 and Commuter	449 (990)	725 (1,600)	110 (204; 127)	105 (195; 121)	26 (48.3; 30)	213 (700)		3,930 (12,900)	A 129 (422) B 161 (527)	A 248 (815) B 273 (895)	A 193 (632) B 230 (755)	A 90 (295) B 106 (348)	790 (1,464; 910)	
Model 172 and Skyhawk	572 (1,263)	1,043 (2,300)	126 (233; 145)	118 (219; 136)	28 (51.5; 32)	206 (675)		4,150 (13,600)	A 140 (460) B 175 (575)	A 274 (900) B 302 (990)	A 223 (730) B 267 (875)	A 92 (302) B 109 (356)	738 (1,367; 850)	
Model 172 and Skyhawk floatplane*	646 (1,425)	1,007 (2,220)	97 (180; 112)	94 (174; 108)	28 (51.5; 32)	191 (625)		3,765 (12,350)	A 256 (840) B 320 (1,050)	A 405 (1,330) B 451 (1,480)	A 267 (875) B 296 (970)	A 145 (475) B 171 (560)	477 (885; 550)	
Model 180 Skywagon	707 (1,560)	1,270 (2,800)	152 (282; 175)	144 (267; 166)	32.2 (60; 37)	364 (1,195)		6,215 (20,400)	A 110 (360) B 137 (450)	A 216 (710) B 239 (785)	A 207 (680) B 254 (835)	A 88 (290) B 104 (342)	1,098 (2,035; 1,265)	
Model 180 Skywagon floatplane	850 (1,875)	1,338 (2,950)	142 (264; 164)	133 (246; 153)	32.2 (60; 37)	332 (1,090)		5,425 (17,800)	A 245 (805) B 307 (1,006)	A 369 (1,210) B 402 (1,320)	A 254 (832) B 308 (1,010)	A 145 (475) B 171 (560)	1,063 (1,971; 1,225)	
Model 182 and Skylane	725 (1,599)	1,338 (2,950)	150 (278; 173)	143 (266; 165)	33 (62; 38)	288 (945)		5,610 (18,400)	A 131 (430) B 164 (537)	A 248 (815) B 270 (885)	A 237 (777) B 280 (920)	A 99 (325) B 117 (384)	1,050 (1,947; 1,210)	
Model 182 RG	800 (1,764)	1,412 (3,112)	187 (347; 215)	173 (321; 199)	42 (80; 48)	317 (1,040)		6,100 (20,000)	A 133 (435)	A 248 (815)	A 237 (777)	A 119 (389)	1,030 (1909; 1,186)	
Model 185 Skywagon	721 (1,590)	1,519 (3,350)	159 (295; 183)	149 (277; 172)	34 (63; 39)	320 (1,050)		5,440 (17,850)	A 114 (375) B 143 (469)	A 233 (763) B 265 (870)	A 230 (755) B 271 (890)	A 95 (310) B 111 (365)	972 (1,802; 1,120)	
Model 185 Skywagon floatplane	866 (1,910)	1,505 (3,320)	149 (277; 172)	140 (259; 161)	34 (63; 39)	311 (1,020)		5,210 (17,100)	A 182 (596) B 227 (745)	A 332 (1,090) B 364 (1,195)	A 265 (870) B 326 (1,070)	A 146 (480) B 173 (566)	903 (1,673; 1,040)	
Model 188 Ag Wagon 230	836 (1,844)	1,723 (3,800)	124 (230; 143)	116 (214; 133)	38.5 (71; 44)	245 (805)		4,330 (14,200)	A 207 (680) B 259 (850)	A 338 (1,110) B 431 (1,420)	A 186 (610) B 256 (840)	A 94 (308) B 111 (363)	303 (563; 350)	
Model A188 Ag Wagon 300†	843 (1,859)	1,814 (4,000)	135 (251; 156)	127 (235; 146)	40 (74; 46)	302 (990)		4,905 (16,100)	A 183 (600) B 229 (750)	A 293 (960) B 381 (1,250)	A 186 (610) B 256 (840)	A 94 (308) B 111 (363)	390 (724; 450)	
Model 206 Stationair 6†	785 (1,732)	1,633 (3,600)	155 (288; 179)	148 (274; 170)	36 (66; 41)	296 (970)		4,695 (15,400)	A 147 (482) B 184 (603)	A 302 (990) B 352 (1,155)	A 226 (740) B 270 (885)	A 92 (301) B 108 (355)	916 (1,697; 1,055)	
Model 206 Stationair 6 floatplane	943 (2,080)	1,587 (3,500)	144 (267; 166)	136 (253; 157)	36 (66; 41)	276 (905)		4,450 (14,600)	A 248 (815) B 311 (1,019)	A 454 (1,490) B 486 (1,595)	A 280 (917) B 343 (1,125)	A 148 (485) B 174 (572)	833 (1,544; 960)	
Model T206 Turbo Stationair 6	831 (1,832)	1,633 (3,600)	178 (330; 205)	163 (303; 188)	36 (66; 41)	322 (1,055)		8,260 (27,100)	A 148 (485) B 185 (606)	A 303 (995) B 358 (1,175)	A 226 (740) B 270 (885)	A 92 (301) B 108 (355)	963 (1,786; 1,110)	
Model T206 Turbo Stationair 6 floatplane	979 (2,160)	1,633 (3,600)	164 (304; 189)	148 (274; 170)	36 (66; 41)	311 (1,020)		7,650 (25,100)	A 241 (790) B 301 (987)	A 442 (1,450) B 475 (1,560)	A 283 (928) B 344 (1,130)	A 151 (495) B 178 (584)	911 (1,690; 1,050)	
Model 207 Skywagon and Stationair 7	862 (1,902)	1,723 (3,800)	150 (278; 173)	142 (264; 164)	38.5 (71; 44)	262 (860)		4,205 (13,800)	A 155 (510) B 194 (637)	A 332 (1,090) B 390 (1,280)	A 244 (800) B 298 (975)	A 97 (318) B 114 (375)	829 (1,536; 955)	
Model T207 Turbo Skywagon and Turbo Stationair 7	908 (2,002)	1,723 (3,800)	168 (312; 194)	156 (290; 180)	38.5 (71; 44)	277 (910)		7,650 (25,100)	A 155 (510) B 194 (637)	A 332 (1,090) B 390 (1,280)	A 244 (800) B 298 (975)	A 97 (318) B 114 (375)	812 (1,504; 935)	
Model 210 Centurion II	953 (2,102)	1,723 (3,800)	178 (330; 205)	167 (309; 192)	38.5 (71; 44)	274 (900)		4,905 (16,100)	A 155 (510) B 194 (637)	A 326 (1,070) B 376 (1,232)	A 239 (783) B 293 (960)	A 93 (305) B 110 (360)	1,137 (2,108; 1,310)	
Model T210 Turbo Centurion II	998 (2,202)	1,723 (3,800)	204 (378; 235)	192 (356; 221)	38.5 (71; 44)	293 (960)		9,020 (29,600)	A 160 (525) B 200 (656)	A 328 (1,075) B 401 (1,318)	A 239 (783) B 293 (960)	A 93 (305) B 110 (360)	1,133 (2,100; 1,305)	

A, B, *, **, †, see notes at end of Cessna table.

CESSNA MODELS—continued

	Weight empty equipped	Weight gross	Max level speed	Max cruising speed	Stalling speed, wheels and flaps down	Max rate of climb at S/L	Single-engine rate of climb at S/L	Service ceiling	T-O run	T-O to 15 m (50 ft)	Landing from 15 m (50 ft)	Landing run	Max range**	Min control speed
	kg (lb)	kg (lb)	knots (km/h; mph)	knots (km/h; mph)	knots (km/h; mph)	m (ft)/ min	m (ft)/ min	m (ft)	m (ft)	m (ft)	m (ft)	m (ft)	nm (km; miles)	knots (km/h; mph)
Model P210 Pressurised Turbo Centurion II	1,008 (2,222)	1,723 (3,800)	204 (378; 235)	192 (356; 221)	49 (91; 57)	293 (960)		9,020 (29,600)	200 (656)	401 (1,318)	293 (960)	110 (360)	1,133 (2,100; 1,305)	
Model P210 Pressurised Centurion	1,064 (2,345)	1,822 (4,016)	206 (381; 237)	††	55 (102; 63)	283 (930)		7,010 (23,000)	366 (1,200)	607 (1990)	271 (890)	424 (1,390)	925 (1,714; 1,065)	
Model 310R	1,701 (3,750)	2,495 (5,500)	237 (439; 273)	223 (414; 257)	64 (119; 74)	518 (1,700)	119 (390)	8,350 (27,400)	B 290 (950)	B 448 (1,470)	B 355 (1,165)	B 219 (720)	1,242 (2,301; 1,430)	69 (129; 80) CAS
Model 337 Super Skymaster	1,196 (2,638)	2,100 (4,630)	177 (328; 204)	168 (312; 194)	39 (72.5; 45)	369 (1,210)	99 (325)	6,125 (20,100)	A 130 (428) / B 163 (535)	A 265 (870) / B 322 (1,055)	A 273 (895) / B 323 (1,060)	A 105 (343) / B 123 (405)	†† / ††	
Model T337 Turbo Super Skymaster	1,289 (2,843)	2,131 (4,700)	204 (378; 235)	200 (370; 230)	40 (74; 46)	353 (1,160)	93 (305)	9,265 (30,400)	A 136 (445) / B 169 (556)	A 280 (920) / B 332 (1,088)	A 273 (895) / B 323 (1,060)	A 107 (352) / B 126 (415)	†† / ††	
Model T337 Pressurised Super Skymaster	1,315 (2,900)	2,132 (4,700)	217 (402; 250)	208 (385; 239)	40 (74; 46)	353 (1,160)	126 (415)	6,100 (20,000)	A 126 (413) / B 157 (516)	A 280 (920) / B 332 (1,088)	A 273 (895) / B 323 (1,060)	A 107 (352) / B 126 (415)	†† / ††	
Model 340	1,878 (4,140)	2,717 (5,990)	242 (447; 278)	228 (421; 262)	61 (114; 71)	503 (1,650)	96 (315)	9,085 (29,800)					1,372 (2,542; 1,580)	75 (140; 87) CAS
Model 401/402	1,673 (3,690)	2,858 (6,300)	226 (420; 261)	208 (386; 240)	65.5 (121; 75)	491 (1,610)	69 (225)	7,980 (26,180)	A 240 (786) / B 300 (983)	A 378 (1,240) / B 472 (1,550)	A 354 (1,160) / B 442 (1,450)	A 155 (510) / B 183 (600)	†† / ††	72 (134; 83) / 72 (134; 83)
Model 402C	1,849 (4,076)	3,107 (6,850)	††	††	65 (121; 75)	442 (1,450)	91 (300)	9,145 (30,000)	329 (1,080)	533 (1,750)	427 (1,400)	259 (850)	1,220 (2,261; 1,405)	74 (137; 85)
Model 414	1,872 (4,126)	2,880 (6,350)	††	††	67 (124; 77)	457 (1,500)	61 (200)	7,925 (26,000)	A 278 (912) / B 347 (1,140)	A 381 (1,250) / B 465 (1,525)	A 340 (1,115) / B 425 (1,395)	A 183 (600) / B 276 (905)	†† / ††	72 (134; 83) / 72 (134; 83)
Model 414A	1975 (4,354)	3,062 (6,750)	††	††	65 (121; 75)	480 (1,575)	88 (290)	9,145 (30,000)	329 (1,080)	533 (1,750)	405 (1,330)	238 (780)	1,300 (2,409; 1,497)	73 (135; 84)
Model 421A	1932 (4,260)	3,102 (6,840)	240 (444; 276)	224 (414; 258)	69 (128; 79)	512 (1,680)	88 (290)	8,230 (27,000)	A 307 (1,008) / B 384 (1,260)	A 443 (1,452) / B 553 (1,815)	A 419 (1,375) / B 524 (1,720)	A 208 (683) / B 245 (804)	1,488 (2,756; 1,713) / ††	83 (153; 95) / 83 (153; 95)
Model 421B	2,011 (4,435)	3,379 (7,450)	245 (454; 282)	230 (426; 265)	71 (132; 82)	564 (1,850)	93 (305)	9,450 (31,000)	A 313 (1,028) / B 365 (1,196)	A 428 (1,403) / B 535 (1,754)	A 427 (1,400) / B 534 (1,752)	A 134 (440) / B 158 (517)	1,490 (2,762; 1,716) / ††	78 (145; 90) / 78 (145; 90)
Model 421C	2,173 (4,790)	3,379 (7,450)	256 (475; 295)	240 (444; 276)	71 (132; 82)	591 (1,940)	107 (350)	9,200 (30,200)	B 396 (1,300)	B 558 (1,830)	B 518 (1,700)	B 317 (1,040)	1,487 (2,755; 1,712)	77 (143; 89) CAS

A: STOL operation.   B: normal operation.   *Available also with engines of increased horsepower.
**With optional long-range tanks fitted, if available.
†Leading-edge already installed by Cessna on current models.   †† No change from standard aircraft.

SIERRA VERSIONS OF PIPER MODELS

	Weight empty equipped	Weight gross	Max level speed	Max cruising speed	Stalling speed, wheels and flaps down	Max rate of climb at S/L	Single-engine rate of climb at S/L	Service ceiling	T-O run	T-O to 15 m (50 ft)	Landing from 15 m (50 ft)	Landing run	Max range**	Min control speed
	kg (lb)	kg (lb)	knots (km/h; mph)	knots (km/h; mph)	knots (km/h; mph)	m (ft)/ min	m (ft)/ min	m (ft)	m (ft)	m (ft)	m (ft)	m (ft)	nm (km; miles)	knots (km/h; mph)
PA-28-140 Cherokee	558 (1,232)	975 (2,150)	126 (223; 145)	120 (222; 138)	29 (53.2; 33)	206 (675)		4,480 (14,700)	A 171 (560) / B 189 (620)	A 354 (1,160) / B 404 (1,325)	A 192 (630) / B 221 (725)	A 94 (310) / B 110 (360)	†† / ††	
PA-28-160 Cherokee	576 (1,270)	997 (2,200)	128 (237; 147)	121 (224; 139)	31 (56.5; 35)	216 (710)		4,970 (16,300)	A 152 (500) / B 177 (580)	A 341 (1,120) / B 390 (1,280)	A 204 (670) / B 226 (740)	A 104 (340) / B 114 (375)	†† / ††	
PA-28-180 Cherokee	638 (1,406)	1,111 (2,450)	129 (238; 148)	122 (227; 141)	36 (66; 41)	221 (725)		4,313 (14,510)	A 165 (540) / B 186 (610)	A 351 (1,150) / B 399 (1,310)	A 238 (780) / B 262 (860)	A 131 (430) / B 146 (480)	596 (1,104; 686) / ††	

A, B, **, †† see notes at end of Piper table.

PIPER MODELS—continued

	Weight empty equipped	Weight gross	Max level speed	Max cruising speed	Stalling speed, wheels and flaps down	Max rate of climb at S/L	Single-engine rate of climb at S/L	Service ceiling	T-O run	T-O to 15 m (50 ft)	Landing from 15 m (50 ft)	Landing run	Max range**	Min control speed
	kg (lb)	kg (lb)	knots (km/h; mph)	knots (km/h; mph)	knots (km/h; mph)	m (ft)/ min	m (ft)/ min	m (ft)	m (ft)	m (ft)	m (ft)	m (ft)	nm (km; miles)	knots (km/h; mph)
PA-28R-180 Cherokee Arrow II	611 (1,349)	1,134 (2,500)	149 (275; 171)	142 (262; 163)	35 (64.5; 40)	270 (885)		4,695 (15,400)	A 171 (560) B 195 (640)	A 347 (1,140) B 396 (1,300)	A 259 (850) B 299 (980)	A 145 (475) B 168 (550)	911 (1,690; 1,050)	
PA-28R-200 Cherokee Arrow II	693 (1,528)	1,202 (2,650)	152 (282; 175)	143 (266; 165)	37 (69; 43)	274 (900)		4,570 (15,000)	A 175 (575) B 198 (650)	A 344 (1,130) B 393 (1,290)	A 283 (930) B 319 (1,045)	A 168 (550) B 187 (615)	782 (1,448; 900)	
PA-28-235 Cherokee 235	712 (1,570)	1,361 (3,000)	140 (259; 161)	132 (245; 152)	39 (72; 45)	244 (800)		3,660 (12,000)	A 168 (550) B 191 (625)	A 265 (870) B 302 (990)	A 274 (900) B 312 (1,025)	A 149 (490) B 171 (560)	926 (1,716; 1,066)	
PA-32-260 Cherokee SIX	783 (1,726)	1,542 (3,400)	144 (267; 166)	137 (254; 158)	38 (71; 44)	259 (850)		4,420 (14,500)	A 180 (590) B 238 (780)	A 317 (1,040) B 341 (1,120)	A 247 (810) B 267 (875)	A 155 (510) B 171 (560)	964 (1,786; 1,110)	
PA-32-300 Cherokee SIX	825 (1,819)	1,542 (3,400)	151 (280; 174)	146 (270; 168)	38 (71; 44)	320 (1,050)		4,955 (16,250)	A 171 (560) B 226 (740)	A 299 (980) B 320 (1,050)	A 247 (810) B 267 (875)	A 158 (520) B 168 (550)	921 (1,706; 1,060)	
PA-24-180 Comanche	694 (1,530)	1,157 (2,550)	149 (277; 172)	143 (266; 165)	35 (64; 40)	293 (960)		5,850 (19,200)	A 183 (600) B 302 (990)	A 324 (1,065) B 475 (1,560)	A 262 (860) B 326 (1,070)	A 128 (420) B 149 (490)	868 (1,609; 1,000)	
PA-24-250 Comanche	776 (1,710)	1,315 (2,900)	168 (311; 193)	161 (298; 185)	35.5 (66; 41)	427 (1,400)		6,310 (20,700)	A 187 (615) B 290 (950)	A 296 (970) B 389 (1,275)	A 256 (840) B 347 (1,140)	A 140 (460) B 213 (700)	1,537 (2,848; 1,770)	
PA-24-260 Comanche	812 (1,792)	1,451 (3,200)	174 (322; 200)	164 (304; 189)	36 (66; 41)	410 (1,345)		6,355 (20,850)	A 200 (655) B 302 (990)	A 338 (1,110) B 401 (1,315)	A 268 (880) B 360 (1,180)	A 152 (500) B 226 (740)	1,137 (2,108; 1,310)	
PA-24-260 Turbo Comanche	821 (1,810)	1,451 (3,200)	213 (394; 245)	201 (372; 231)	36 (66; 41)	410 (1,345)		7,620 (25,000)	A 200 (655) B 302 (990)	A 338 (1,110) B 401 (1,315)	A 268 (880) B 360 (1,180)	A 152 (500) B 226 (740)	1,306 (2,422; 1,505)	
PA-24-400 Comanche	966 (2,130)	1,633 (3,600)	196 (364; 226)	189 (351; 218)	39 (72; 45)	506 (1,660)		6,155 (20,200)	A 126 (415) B 168 (550)	A 233 (765) B 271 (890)	A 303 (995) B 379 (1,245)	A 184 (605) B 216 (710)	1,568 (2,905; 1,805)	
PA-30 Twin Comanche*	1,022 (2,253)	1,724 (3,800)	158 (293; 182)	153 (283; 176)	45 (84; 52)	427 (1,400)	79 (260)	6,100 (20,000)	B 206 (675)	B 341 (1,120)	B 355 (1,165)	B 186 (610)	1,481 (2,744; 1,705)	69 (129; 80)
PA-30 Turbo Twin Comanche*	1,088 (2,399)	1,724 (3,800)	213 (394; 245)	197 (365; 227)	45 (84; 52)	427 (1,400)	69 (225)	7,620 (25,000)	B 206 (675)	B 341 (1,120)	B 355 (1,165)	B 186 (610)	1,528 (2,832; 1,760)	69 (129; 80)
PA-39 Twin Comanche C/R*	1,022 (2,253)	1,724 (3,800)	181 (336; 209)	174 (322; 200)	45 (84; 52)	445 (1,460)	79 (260)	6,100 (20,000)	B 206 (675)	B 320 (1,050)	B 355 (1,165)	B 186 (610)	1,468 (2,720; 1,690)	65 (121; 75)
PA-39 Turbo Twin Comanche C/R*	1,088 (2,399)	1,724 (3,800)	212 (393; 244)	197 (365; 227)	45 (84; 52)	427 (1,400)	69 (225)	7,620 (25,000)	B 158 (520)	B 323 (1,060)	B 355 (1,165)	B 189 (620)	1,515 (2,808; 1,745)	65 (121; 75)
PA-23-235 Aztec	1,241 (2,735)	2,177 (4,800)	182 (338; 210)	175 (325; 202)	40 (74; 46)	465 (1,525)	62 (205)	5,515 (18,100)	B 210 (690)	B 331 (1,085)	B 381 (1,250)	B 195 (640)	1,090 (2,020; 1,255)	54 (98; 62)
PA-23-250 Aztec	1,339 (2,953)	2,266 (4,995)	197 (365; 227)	191 (354; 220)	41 (76; 47)	509 (1,670)	99 (325)	6,615 (21,700)	B 190 (625)	B 315 (1,035)	B 395 (1,295)	B 203 (665)	1,112 (2,060; 1,280)	56 (103; 64)
PA-23-250 Aztec	1,326 (2,925)	2,359 (5,200)	188 (348; 216)	179 (332; 206)	45.5 (84; 52)	491 (1,610)	85 (280)	6,035 (19,800)	B 195 (640)	B 323 (1,060)	B 395 (1,295)	B 203 (665)	916 (1,697; 1,055)	56 (105; 65)
PA-23-250 Turbo Aztec	1,397 (3,080)	2,359 (5,200)	222 (412; 256)	182 (388; 210)	43 (79; 49)	372 (1,220)	64 (210)	9,145 (30,000)	B 195 (640)	B 323 (1,060)	B 395 (1,295)	B 203 (665)	1,050 (1,947; 1,210)	56 (105; 65)
PA-34 Seneca I	1,160 (2,557)	1,905 (4,200)	170 (315; 196)	162 (300; 187)	58 (106; 66)	414 (1,360)	57 (190)	5,730 (18,800)	B 195 (640)	B 320 (1,050)	B 381 (1,250)	B 196 (645)	743 (1,378; 856)	57 (106; 65)
PA-34 Seneca II	1,280 (2,823)	2,073 (4,570)	195 (361; 225)	190 (352; 219)	66 (122; 76)	421 (1,380)	67 (220)	7,620 (25,000)	B 198 (650)	B 332 (1,090)	B 573 (1,880)	B 213 (700)	882 (1,633; 1,015)†	57 (106; 65)

A: STOL operation.   B: normal operation.   *Available also with engines of increased horsepower.
**With optional long-range tanks fitted, if available.
†1,192 (2,207; 1.371) with optional long-range tanks.   ††No change from standard aircraft.

Sierra/Cessna Century V Eagle, a Citation 500 conversion with advanced wing aerofoil section and JT15D-4 turbofans

roll rate for more precise control when flaps are down and speed low. Control wheel forces are significantly less than with unmodified aircraft, due to a tailoring of aerodynamic forces on the up-moving aileron and a crossover cable which minimises friction in the control runs

Four stall strips, two on each wing, retain the desirable stall characteristics common to all Sierra Hi-Lift systems. For aircraft fitted with wing leading-edge de-icing boots, rubber strips are cemented to the rubber boots; when these are not fitted, aluminium stall strips are riveted to the wing leading-edge. A strip 130 mm (5 in) long, close to the wingroot, initiates an early warning signal that the aircraft is approaching the stall. A longer strip, mounted further outboard and lower than the first, initiates the stall of the inboard and centre wing sections, while the outboard section and the wingtip are still unaffected by stall conditions. When the aircraft stalls it noses forward and down, under the complete control of ailerons which remain unstalled and effective for roll control.

The Sierra integrated high-lift and safety systems have been designed for easy field maintenance. They are designed to be applicable to almost the entire range of Cessna and Piper aircraft, and the Beechcraft Bonanza.

Full details of the basic Beech, Cessna and Piper airframes are given under the appropriate company headings in this and earlier editions of *Jane's*, and apply also to the Sierra versions, except for the added Hi-Lift systems as described. Weights and performance details of the Cessna and Piper range of Hi-Lift modifications are given in the accompanying tables. The conversions can be fitted as a retrospective modification to any of the models listed, irrespective of year.

Data for the modified Bonanzas are as follows:

WEIGHTS:
Weight empty, equipped:
V35B	987 kg (2,176 lb)
A36	1,009 kg (2,225 lb)
Max T-O weight: V35B	1,542 kg (3,400 lb)
A36	1,633 kg (3,600 lb)

PERFORMANCE:
Max level speed:
V35B	181 knots (335 km/h; 208 mph)
A36	177 knots (327 km/h; 204 mph)

Max cruising speed:
V35B	176 knots (325 km/h; 202 mph)
A36	169 knots (313 km/h; 194 mph)

Stalling speed, wheels and flaps down:
V35B	53 knots (98 km/h; 61 mph)
A36	54 knots (100 km/h; 62 mph)

Max rate of climb at S/L:
V35B	343 m (1,125 ft)/min
A36	309 m (1,015 ft)/min

Service ceiling: V35B 5,445 m (17,858 ft)
A36	4,875 m (16,000 ft)

T-O run: V35B* 239 m (785 ft)
A36	276 m (904 ft)

T-O to 15 m (50 ft): V35B* 420 m (1,377 ft)
A36	485 m (1,590 ft)

Landing from 15 m (50 ft):
V35B*	279 m (914 ft)
A36	305 m (1,000 ft)

Landing run: V35B* 146 m (478 ft)
A36	168 m (550 ft)

Max range, with optional long-range tanks:
V35B	875 nm (1,620 km; 1,007 miles)
A36	833 nm (1,543 km; 958 miles)

*Normal operation

SIERRA/CESSNA EAGLE, EAGLE SP, LONGWING and EAGLE 400B

The Sierra **Eagle** (formerly Astec Eagle and R/STOL Eagle) conversion entails modifications to the wing contours of the Cessna Citation 500 and Citation I twin-turbofan executive transport aircraft.

Changes to the basic Citation 500 wing include use of an advanced technology aerofoil section of increased thickness and length over the inboard portion of the wing; wingtip extensions of 0.51 m (1 ft 8 in); and the addition of cove seals to the trailing-edge flaps. The thickened wing and the wingtip extensions contain an additional 392 kg (865 lb) of fuel, accounting for about 75 per cent of the approximate 600 nm (1,112 km; 691 mile) increase in range over the basic Citation 500. The remainder of the increase is due to improved aerodynamic efficiency of the Eagle wing.

The Sierra **Eagle SP** conversion introduces identical modifications to the Citation 501, which is certificated under FAR Pt 23 and approved for single-pilot operation.

The **Longwing** conversion was introduced in 1983 and uses the Eagle wingtip extensions on Citation 500 aircraft, but does not include the wingroot modifications. The conversion increases fuel capacity (by approximately 54 kg; 120 lb on aircraft c/n 001-213) and provides a 10 per cent increase in range. Rate of climb is also improved, and approach speeds reduced.

The **Eagle 400B** designation applies to the Sierra Eagle with its JT15D-1 or -1A power plant replaced by more powerful JT15D-4B engines, each of 11.12 kN (2,500 lb st). In early 1990 Sierra had received orders for five Eagle 400Bs, and had completed one.

The description of the Citation I under Cessna's entry in previous editions applies also to the Eagle, except as follows:

WINGS: Thickness/chord ratio of inboard portions increased from 14% to 19%, and supercritical technology incorporated to improve wing/fuselage airflow. Span increased by comparison with Citation 500, by addition of wingtip extensions.

POWER PLANT: As for Citation 500, except increased fuel capacity provided in the thicker wing centre-section and wingtip extensions.

DIMENSIONS, EXTERNAL:
Wing span	14.35 m (47 ft 0½ in)
Wing chord: at root	2.95 m (9 ft 8⅛ in)
at tip	0.93 m (3 ft 0½ in)
Wing aspect ratio	7.92
Length overall	13.26 m (43 ft 6 in)
Height overall	4.36 m (14 ft 3¾ in)
Wheel track	3.84 m (12 ft 7⅛ in)
Wheelbase	4.78 m (15 ft 8¼ in)

WEIGHTS (A: JT15D-1, B: JT15D-1A, C: JT15D-4B power plant):
Weight empty: A, B	2,971 kg (6,550 lb)
C	3,180 kg (7,011 lb)
Max fuel weight: A, B, C	2,045 kg (4,510 lb)
Max T-O weight: A, B, C	5,670 kg (12,500 lb)
Max zero-fuel weight: A, B, C	4,309 kg (9,500 lb)
Max landing weight: A, B, C	5,148 kg (11,350 lb)

PERFORMANCE (at max T-O weight except where indicated):
Max cruising speed, AUW of 4,309 kg (9,500 lb), at 10,670 m (35,000 ft):
A	341 knots (631 km/h; 392 mph)
B	357 knots (661 km/h; 411 mph)

C (at 8,840 m; 29,000 ft)
400 knots (741 km/h; 460 mph)
Cruising speed, AUW of 4,309 kg (9,500 lb), at 12,500 m (41,000 ft): A 317 knots (587 km/h; 365 mph)
B	336 knots (623 km/h; 387 mph)

C (at 13,100 m; 43,000 ft)
375 knots (695 km/h; 432 mph)
Stalling speed at max landing weight:
A, B, C 78 knots (145 km/h; 90 mph)
Max rate of climb at S/L: C 1,220 m (4,000 ft)/min
Rate of climb at S/L, one engine out:
C	442 m (1,450 ft)/min

Max certificated altitude: A 10,670 m (35,000 ft)
B	12,500 m (41,000 ft)
C	13,105 m (43,000 ft)

Balanced T-O field length: A, B 907 m (2,975 ft)
C	892 m (2,925 ft)

FAA landing field length at max landing weight:
A, B, C 722 m (2,370 ft)
Max range, with 45 min fuel reserves:
A	1,800 nm (3,336 km; 2,073 miles)
C	1,997 nm (3,700 km; 2,300 miles)

SIKORSKY

SIKORSKY AIRCRAFT, DIVISION OF UNITED TECHNOLOGIES CORPORATION

6900 North Main Street, Stratford, Connecticut 06601-1381
Telephone: 1 (203) 386 4000
Telex: 96 4372
OTHER WORKS: Troy, Alabama; South Avenue, Bridgeport, Connecticut; Shelton, Connecticut; Sikorsky Memorial Airport, Stratford, Connecticut; Trumbull, Connecticut; West Haven, Connecticut; and Development Flight Test Center, West Palm Beach, Florida
PRESIDENT: Eugene Buckley
SENIOR VICE-PRESIDENTS:
  Robert C. Harris (Business Integration and Planning)
  H. Stephen Harvey (Finance)
  Ray D. Leoni (Engineering, Development and Assembly Operations)
VICE-PRESIDENTS, INTERNATIONAL PROGRAMMES:
  Robert M. Baxter (International Business)
  Glenn A. Olson (Japan)
  Clement C. Peterson (Middle East)
  James J. Satterwhite
VICE-PRESIDENT, RESEARCH AND ENGINEERING:
  Dr Kenneth M. Rosen
VICE-PRESIDENT, COMMERCIAL PROGRAMMES:
  Robert L. Kelly
VICE-PRESIDENT, GOVERNMENT BUSINESS DEVELOPMENT:
  Gary F. Rast

DIRECTOR OF COMMUNICATIONS: Larry Bingaman
MANAGER OF PUBLIC RELATIONS: Martin H. Moore

Founded on 5 March 1923 by the late Igor I. Sikorsky as the Sikorsky Aero Engineering Corporation, this company has been a division of United Technologies since 1929. It became involved in helicopter production in the 1940s, since which time it has produced more than 6,000 rotating-wing aircraft.

Sikorsky's company headquarters and main plant are at Stratford, Connecticut, with a secondary facility nearby at Bridgeport. Development flight test, commercial service and training centres are at West Palm Beach, Florida, where UTC subsidiary Pratt & Whitney has its military engine operation. Employment at all Sikorsky facilities totalled about 13,000 in 1989, making the company the largest helicopter manufacturer outside the Soviet Union. Current production is centred on the UH-60A Black Hawk and its derivatives, the CH-53E Super Stallion heavy lift helicopter and its derivatives, and the S-76 series.

Sikorsky and Boeing Helicopters are teamed to bid for development of the US Army's LH helicopter.

Sikorsky licensees include Westland of the UK, Agusta of Italy, Aerospatiale of France, MBB in West Germany, Mitsubishi of Japan, and Pratt & Whitney Canada Ltd. In the Summer of 1983 Sikorsky and Brazilian manufacturer Embraer signed an agreement for the transfer of technology involved in the design and manufacture of components made from composites materials. In June 1984 Sikorsky

and Construcciones Aeronáuticas SA (CASA) signed a memorandum of understanding to establish a long term helicopter industrial co-operation programme in Spain. CASA builds tail rotor pylon, tailcone and stabiliser components for the H-60 and S-70 helicopters. The first CASA manufactured S-70 components were delivered to Sikorsky in early January 1986.

On 12 February 1986 shareholders of Westland PLC (see United Kingdom section) approved a joint Sikorsky/Fiat plan involving financial and technical support and minor equity participation in the British company. Under the terms of the agreement Westland is licensed to manufacture the S-70 series of helicopters.

In February 1988 Sikorsky announced plans to establish an S-76 production line in South Korea within five years. A new company, Daewoo-Sikorsky Aerospace Ltd (DSA), has been established, with a production facility at Chang-Won in which civil and military variants of the S-76 will be manufactured. Also in 1988 Sikorsky contracted with Mitsubishi Heavy Industries for licensed production of S-70 helicopters in Japan.

SIKORSKY S-61/SH-3 SEA KING

Manufacture of the S-61 series by Sikorsky has ended, but various military and commercial models remain in production by Agusta in Italy and Westland in the UK, under whose entries they are described or listed. Production in Japan was completed in 1990.

Sikorsky CH-53E Super Stallion heavy-lift helicopter of the US Marine Corps

SIKORSKY CH-53D

In 1989, the Israel Defence Force launched an upgrade programme, known as **CH-53 2000**. Work will be undertaken by the MATA division of IAI (which see).

SIKORSKY H-53E

US Navy designations: CH-53E Super Stallion and MH-53E Sea Dragon

The **CH-53E Super Stallion** is a major development of the US Marine Corps' CH-53D Stallion twin-engined heavy duty transport helicopter, last described in the 1978-79 Jane's. The longer fuselage of the CH-53E, its different rotor system, three engines, uprated transmission and doubled lift capability make it the largest and most powerful helicopter yet put into production outside the Soviet Union.

Sikorsky received initial US Navy funding in 1973 to proceed with Phase I of the CH-53E development programme, and the first of two YCH-53E prototypes flew for the first time on 1 March 1974. The first production prototype flew on 8 December 1975, and the second in March 1976. Fourteen production CH-53Es (first flight 13 December 1980) were ordered in 1978, and deliveries to the US Marine Corps began on 16 June 1981. A total of 124 had been funded up to and including FY 1990. Total requirement is for 125 production CH-53Es.

The US Marine Corps operates the CH-53E in an amphibious assault role. Although capable of carrying up to 55 fully armed troops, its primary role is the transport of heavy equipment and armament, and retrieval of disabled aircraft. The US Navy uses it for vertical onboard delivery (VOD), transport duties, and removal of damaged aircraft from aircraft carriers. Operational use, in the Mediterranean area, began in Summer 1983.

Planned improvements for the CH-53E include all-composites tail rotor blades, uprated General Electric T64-416 power plants, Omega navigation system, ground proximity warning system, flight crew night vision system, and improvements to the internal cargo handling system. A missile alerting system, chaff/flare decoy ejectors, a nitrogen fuel inerting system and the ability to refill the hydraulic system from the cargo hold will also be incorporated. The modified CH-53Es may also be equipped with air-to-air missiles for self defence. Initial firing trials with an AIM-9 Sidewinder missile have been conducted at the Naval Air Test Center, NAS Patuxent River, Maryland.

In June 1986 Sikorsky began full scale development of a helicopter night vision system (HNVS) for the CH-53E, in co-operation with Northrop's Electro-Mechanical Division. The HNVS comprises a Martin Marietta pilot night vision system, Honeywell integrated helmet and display sighting system and equipment developed by Northrop for the Bell AH-1S surrogate trainer programme. The HNVS will permit low-level night operations in adverse weather. Ground testing of an HNVS equipped CH-53E began in 1988, with flight testing following two months later and a US Navy operational evaluation programme commencing in August 1989.

The **MH-53E Sea Dragon** is an airborne mine countermeasures (AMCM) version of the Super Stallion able to tow through the water mechanical, acoustic and magnetic hydrofoil sweeping gear. Its early history was described in the 1982-83 Jane's. The MH-53E has enlarged sponsons to carry nearly 3,785 litres (1,000 US gallons; 833 Imp gallons) more fuel; improved hydraulic and electrical systems; and minefield, navigational and AFC systems, including automatic tow couplers and automatic approach to/depart from hover features to enhance its AMCM capabilities. The first pre-production MH-53E made its initial flight on 1 September 1983. Deliveries to the US Navy began on 26 June 1986 and the MH-53E entered operational service with HM-12 at Norfolk, VA, on 1 April 1987. Another MH-53E delivered to HM-12 (now the AMCM training unit) in Spring 1987 was the 100th H-53E. The combined fleet of CH-53Es and MH-53Es had by then logged more than 90,000 flying hours. USN deliveries totalled 25 by early 1990, including those with HM-15 at Alameda, CA, for the Pacific Fleet.

Twenty-four production MH-53Es were funded in FY 1985-88 (2, 10, 4 and 8 respectively), with a further seven approved in FY 1989. Production of the CH-53E was halted for a period between October 1986 and July 1988, to concentrate entirely on the MH-53E. Japan has acquired helicopters similar to the MH-53E (see S-80 entry).

The following details refer to the CH-53E, but are generally applicable also to the MH-53E, except for the changes listed in the previous paragraphs:

TYPE: Triple-turbine heavy duty multi-purpose helicopter.

ROTOR SYSTEM AND TRANSMISSION: Fully articulated seven-blade main rotor. Blade twist 14°. Each blade has a titanium spar, Nomex honeycomb core and glassfibre epoxy composite skin. Sikorsky blade inspection method (BIM) embodied, utilising pressurised spar. Titanium and steel main rotor head. Hydraulic power folding system for main rotor blades. Four-blade aluminium tail rotor mounted on pylon canted 20° to port. Main gearbox is mounted in blister above main cabin and is rated at 10,067 kW (13,500 shp) for T-O. Rotor brake standard.

FUSELAGE: Watertight semi-monocoque primary structure of light alloy, steel and titanium. Separate cockpit section of glassfibre/epoxy composite. Extensive use of Kevlar for rotor/transmission blister and engine cowlings. Tail rotor pylon folds hydraulically to starboard side. Fuselage stressed to withstand crash force of 20g vertically and 10g laterally.

TAIL SURFACE: Strut braced stabiliser of gull-wing type on starboard side of inclined tail rotor pylon. Stabiliser and pylon made of Kevlar.

LANDING GEAR: Retractable tricycle type, with twin wheels on each unit. Main units retract into rear of sponsons on each side of fuselage. Fully castoring nosewheels.

POWER PLANT: Three General Electric T64-GE-416 turbo-shafts, each with a max rating of 3,266 kW (4,380 shp) for 10 min, intermediate rating of 3,091 kW (4,145 shp) for 30 min and max continuous power rating of 2,756 kW (3,696 shp). Self-sealing bladder fuel cell in forward part of each sponson, each with capacity of 1,192 litres (315 US gallons; 262 Imp gallons). Additional two-cell unit, with capacity of 1,465 litres (387 US gallons; 322 Imp gallons) brings total standard internal capacity to 3,849 litres (1,017 US gallons; 847 Imp gallons). (Total internal capacity of MH-53E is 12,113 litres; 3,200 US gallons; 2,664 Imp gallons.) Optional drop tank outboard of each sponson of CH-53E, total capacity 4,921 litres (1,300 US gallons; 1,082 Imp gallons). (MH-53E can carry seven internal range extension tanks, total capacity 7,949 litres; 2,100 US gallons; 1,748 Imp gallons.) Forward extendable probe for in-flight refuelling. Alternatively, aircraft can refuel by hoisting hose from surface vessel while hovering.

ACCOMMODATION: Crew of three. Main cabin will accommodate up to 55 troops on folding canvas seats along walls and in centre of cabin. Door on forward starboard side of main cabin. Hydraulically operated rear loading ramp. Typical freight loads include seven standard 1.02 × 1.22 m (3 ft 4 in × 4 ft) pallets. Single-point central hook for slung cargo, capacity 16,330 kg (36,000 lb).

Sikorsky CH-53E Super Stallion, with lower side view and lower front view of MH-53E Sea Dragon (Pilot Press). **See page 516 for details of S-80 export versions**

First Sikorsky MH-53E Sea Dragon airborne mine countermeasures helicopter delivered to US Navy

SYSTEMS: Hydraulic system, with four pumps, for collective, cyclic pitch, roll, yaw and feel augmentation flight control servo mechanisms; engine starters; landing gear actuation; cargo winches; loading ramp; and blade and tail pylon folding. System pressure 207 bars (3,000 lb/sq in), except for engine starter system which is rated at 276 bars (4,000 lb/sq in). (Separate hydraulic system in MH-53E to power AMCM equipment.) Electrical system includes three 115V 400Hz 40-60kVA AC alternators, and two 28V 200A transformer-rectifiers for DC power. Solar APU.

AVIONICS AND EQUIPMENT: Hamilton Standard automatic flight control system, using two digital onboard computers and a four-axis autopilot. Equipment in MH-53E includes Westinghouse AN/AQS-14 towed sonar, AN/AQS-17 mine neutralisation device, AN/ALQ-141 electronic sweep, and Edo AN/ALQ-166 towed hydrofoil sled for detonating magnetic mines.

DIMENSIONS, EXTERNAL (CH-53E and MH-53E):

Main rotor diameter	24.08 m (79 ft 0 in)
Main rotor blade chord	0.76 m (2 ft 6 in)
Tail rotor diameter	6.10 m (20 ft 0 in)
Length: overall, rotors turning	30.19 m (99 ft 0½ in)
rotor and tail pylon folded	18.44 m (60 ft 6 in)
fuselage	22.35 m (73 ft 4 in)
Width: fuselage	2.69 m (8 ft 10 in)
rotor and tail pylon folded:	
CH-53E	8.66 m (28 ft 5 in)
MH-53E	8.41 m (27 ft 7 in)
Height: to top of main rotor head	5.32 m (17 ft 5½ in)
tail rotor turning	8.97 m (29 ft 5 in)
rotor and tail pylon folded	5.66 m (18 ft 7 in)
Wheel track (c/l of shock struts)	3.96 m (13 ft 0 in)
Wheelbase	8.31 m (27 ft 3 in)

DIMENSIONS, INTERNAL (CH-53E and MH-53E):

Cabin:

Length (rear ramp/door hinge to fwd bulkhead)	9.14 m (30 ft 0 in)
Max width	2.29 m (7 ft 6 in)
Max height	1.98 m (6 ft 6 in)

AREAS (CH-53E and MH-53E):

Main rotor disc	455.38 m² (4,901.7 sq ft)
Tail rotor disc	29.19 m² (314.2 sq ft)

WEIGHTS:

Weight empty: CH-53E	15,072 kg (33,228 lb)
MH-53E	16,482 kg (36,336 lb)
Internal payload (100 nm; 185 km; 115 miles radius):	
CH-53E	13,607 kg (30,000 lb)
External payload (50 nm; 92.5 km; 57.5 miles radius):	
CH-53E	14,515 kg (32,000 lb)
Max external payload: CH-53E	16,330 kg (36,000 lb)
Useful load, influence sweep mission:	
MH-53E	11,793 kg (26,000 lb)
Max T-O weight (CH-53E and MH-53E):	
internal payload	31,640 kg (69,750 lb)
external payload	33,340 kg (73,500 lb)

PERFORMANCE (CH-53E and MH-53E, ISA, at T-O weight of 25,400 kg; 56,000 lb):

Max level speed at S/L	170 knots (315 km/h; 196 mph)
Cruising speed at S/L	150 knots (278 km/h; 173 mph)
Max rate of climb at S/L, 11,340 kg (25,000 lb) payload	762 m (2,500 ft)/min
Service ceiling at max continuous power	5,640 m (18,500 ft)
Hovering ceiling at max power:	
IGE	3,520 m (11,550 ft)
OGE	2,895 m (9,500 ft)
Self-ferry range, unrefuelled, at optimum cruise condition for best range:	
CH-53E	1,120 nm (2,075 km; 1,290 miles)

SIKORSKY MH-53J PAVE LOW III ENHANCED

As one element of a programme to upgrade the combat rescue and recovery fleet of the USAF Special Operations Forces, 33 HH-53Bs, HH-53Cs and CH-53Cs are being converted at NAS Pensacola, FL, to MH-53J Pave Low III Enhanced standard. Configuration is similar to 11 HH-53H Pave Low III conversions produced earlier, of which eight survivors will eventually be upgraded to MH-53Js. Changes include a nose-mounted FLIR, an INS, Doppler, a computer-projected map display, GPS/Navstar, titanium armour plating, a Collins AIC-3 intercom, and Texas Instruments AN/APQ-158 terrain-following/-avoidance radar in an offset nose radome. Provision is made for three machine-guns of 7.62 mm or 0.5 in calibre to be fired through windows on each side and from the open rear ramp. Chaff/flare dispensers are installed, and a Loral AN/ALQ-157 IR jammer positioned on each outrigger pylon. Crew comprises two pilots, two flight engineers and two air gunners. Two 2,935 kW (3,936 kW) General Electric T64-GE-7A turboshaft engines are fitted.

Deliveries began in mid-1987 of 15 MH-53Js to the 20th SOS at Hurlburt Field, FL, and in the following year of six to the 21st SOS at RAF Woodbridge, UK. A further four were issued in 1989 to the 1550th Combat Crew Training Wing at Kirtland AFB, NM. (At the same time, the unit received four **TH-53A**s from the US Marines.)

SIKORSKY S-70A

US Army designations: UH-60A Black Hawk, EH-60C and MH-60K
US Air Force designation: UH-60A, MH-60G Pave Hawk
US Marine Corps designation: VH-60A

A detailed account of the development and early history of the S-70/UH-60A can be found in the 1982-83 and earlier editions of *Jane's*. The helicopter was designed to meet the US Army's Utility Tactical Transport Aircraft System (UTTAS) requirement for an aircraft capable of carrying all the elements of an 11-man infantry squad, to replace the UH-1 Iroquois. The first of three Sikorsky YUH-60A prototypes flew for the first time on 17 October 1974. After fly-off evaluation against prototypes of a Boeing Vertol competitor, the Sikorsky design was declared the winner on 23 December 1976.

The initial, and major, production version is:

UH-60A Black Hawk. Assault transport version for the US Army. First production example flown in October 1978. Designed primarily to carry 11 fully equipped troops plus a crew of three. Large cabin enables it also to be used without modification for medical evacuation, reconnaissance, command and control purposes or troop resupply. For external lift missions its cargo hook has a capacity of up to 3,630 kg (8,000 lb). Design is compact, so that the helicopter itself can be airlifted over long ranges. One can be carried in a C-130 Hercules, two in a C-141 StarLifter and six in a C-5 Galaxy, using Sikorsky developed air transportability kits. In January 1988 Sikorsky was awarded a third multi-year contract for 252 UH-60As, bringing the total contracted to 1,107. The US Army anticipates a total procurement of 1,621 aircraft. The 1,000th was accepted on 17 October 1988, and by 1 January 1990 deliveries of all versions totalled 1,112. By that time

Sikorsky MH-53J Pave Low III Enhanced combat helicopter of the 21st Special Operations Squadron at RAF Woodbridge *(Paul Jackson)*

Sikorsky MH-60G Pave Hawk special operations helicopter

US Army Black Hawks had logged more than 1 million flight hours and 985 UH-60As had been delivered.

The UH-60A is deployed with the regular US Army; with US forces in Hawaii, Korea, Panama and West Germany; and with Army National Guard and Army Reserve aviation units. Medical evacuation kits for installation in Black Hawks were delivered to the US Army from 1981.

Improvements to self-defence armaments and passive defence systems are included in the **Enhanced Black Hawk,** produced by the Corpus Christi Army Depot, TX, from 1989 onwards by retrofit of new-built UH-60A/Ls. Additional equipment comprises a Tracor AN/ARN-148 Omega area navigation system, Motorola AN/LST-5B satellite UHF communications transceiver, Bendix/King AN/ARC-199 HF/SSB and an AEL AN/APR-44(V)3 specific threat RWR complementing the existing AN/APR-39 general threat RWR. An M134 Minigun may be fitted on each of the two pintle mounts, replacing the M60 weapon. First 15 delivered to the US Army in South Korea, gaining IOC in November 1989. Further conversions are to follow for US-based units.

Twelve US Army UH-60As are on loan to the US Coast Guard for use in anti-narcotics smuggling operations, augmenting four purchased directly by the agency.

Non-US operators include the governments of Australia, Brunei, Colombia, Egypt, Japan, Jordan, the Philippines, the People's Republic of China, Saudi Arabia and Turkey.

A hover infra-red suppressor subsystem (HIRSS), which cools the engine exhaust so that it no longer presents a target for heat-seeking missiles, is installed on current production aircraft and will be retrofitted to earlier UH-60s. The system does not require the helicopter to be in forward motion for effectiveness, as earlier IR suppressing systems did. By June 1987 Sikorsky had completed missile qualification for the Hellfire anti-armour missile which had been launched from UH-60As in forward, rearward and sideways flight, in the hover at night, and with the pilot wearing night vision goggles. Test firings had also been completed to evaluate the Airborne Target Handover System (ATHS) which allows for digital burst communications between a designating aircraft and the firing aircraft. Exterior and interior lighting systems compatible with night vision goggles have been incorporated on production UH-60As since November 1985 and have been retrofitted to earlier production aircraft. Testing of a Honeywell Volcano multiple delivery mine system was completed in early 1987, and US Army development testing of the system began in July 1987. Volcano dispenses up to 960 Gator anti-tank and anti-personnel mines from externally mounted expendable canisters on each side of the fuselage.

A usage monitor, which measures certain rotor loadings, is being installed on 30 UH-60As to enable the US Army and Sikorsky to determine optimum replacement times for dynamic components. During 1987 a wire strike protection system and an accident data recorder system were tested on the UH-60A. Data recorders were to be incorporated on UH-60As and EH-60As during the course of the year.

The basic design of the UH-60A has proved suitable for a number of derivatives, as follows:

Minor variants of the UH-60A include at least seven **JUH-60A** temporary trials helicopters; at least nine **GUH-60A** airframes grounded for technical training, and one **HH-60D** Night Hawk (82-23718) prototype of the abandoned USAF combat rescue variant.

EH-60C. In October 1980, Sikorsky received a US Army contract to prepare a YEH-60C prototype for the installation of 816 kg (1800 lb) of Quick Fix IIB electronic countermeasures equipment designed to intercept, locate, monitor and jam enemy battlefield communications. Prime contractor for the AN/ALQ-151 ECM kit was Electronic Systems Laboratories, a subsidiary of TRW, but installation in the EH-60C was by Tracor Aerospace Inc. The equipment includes four dipole antennae mounted on the fuselage together with a deployable whip antenna, and a data bank in the cabin. A hover infra-red suppressor subsystem (HIRSS) is standard. The YEH-60C flew for the first time on 24 September 1981. In October 1984 Tracor Aerospace Group was awarded a $51 million contract for the conversion of an initial quantity of 40 UH-60As to EH-60C ECM/ESM configuration. Tracor produced, integrated and installed the ECM/ESM systems, and flight tested the converted helicopters. The first production EH-60C was delivered on 28 July 1987, as an element of the US Army's special electronics mission aircraft (SEMA) programme. Sixty-six had been funded by FY 1987. The programme was completed in 1989.

MH-60A. Some 30 UH-60As modified to provide airlift capability for Army's 160th Special Operations Aviation Regiment, based at Fort Campbell, Kentucky and (3rd Battalion) Hunter AAF, Savannah, GA. Believed to be equipped with FLIR, Omega/VLF, multi-function display instrument panels, auxiliary fuel tanks and door-mounted 7.62 mm Minigun.

VH-60A. Nine aircraft for US Marine Corps, derived from UH-60A, to replace Bell VH-1Ns of the Executive Flight Detachment of Marine Helicopter Squadron One (HMX-1) at Quantico, Virginia. First delivered 30 November 1988. Enhancements include improved durability gearbox, weather radar, SH-60B type flight control system and ASI, cabin soundproofing, VIP configured interior, cabin radio operator's station, electromagnetic pulse hardening and extensive avionics upgrades.

MH-60G Pave Hawk. Designation for 20 aircraft (including 10 delivered originally as UH-60As), which began to enter service with USAF's 55th Aerospace Rescue and Recovery Squadron at Eglin AFB, Florida, in 1982-83 as an interim remedy for a shortfall in rescue helicopters. The USAF has contracted Sikorsky Support Services Inc of Troy, Alabama, to modify these to MH-60G Pave Hawks to incorporate an aerial refuelling probe, 443 litre (117 US gallon; 97.5 Imp gallon) internal auxiliary fuel tank and a fuel management panel. All will be fitted eventually with Doppler/INS, an electronic map display, Tacan, RDR-14 lightweight weather/ground mapping radar, secure HF and Satcom, 0.50 in machine-guns and Pave Low III FLIR, as installed in the MH-53H/J. The Pave Hawk programme replaces that for the HH-60A Night Hawk (see 1987-88 *Jane's*), which did not receive DoD funding. MH-60Gs will be operated by the 106th ARS (ANG) at Suffolk County A/P, NY, 129th ARS (ANG) at Moffett Field NAS, CA, 210th ARS (ANG) at Kulis, AK, 301st ARS (AFRes) at Homestead AFB, FL, 304th ARS (AFRes) at Portland, OR, 56th ARS at Keflavik, Iceland, and new squadrons at Misawa, Japan, and Nellis AFB, NV. Additional procurement will be required to equip these squadrons.

MH-60K. In January 1988 Sikorsky received a contract from the US Army to build and test fly a prototype MH-60K special operations aircraft (SOA) based on the Black Hawk. Due to fly in June 1990, the helicopter features twin 870.5 litre (230 US gallon; 191.5 Imp gallon) external fuel tanks, provision for two internal 700 litre (185 US gallon; 154 Imp gallon) fuel tanks, air-to-air refuelling capability, integrated avionics system with CRT cockpit displays, Hughes AN/AAQ-16 FLIR, Texas Instruments AN/APQ-174 terrain following/terrain avoidance radar, uprated engines and gearbox, an external rescue hoist, wire strike protection, rotor brake, tiedown points, T700-GE-701C engines, AFCS (similar to SH-60B), folding tailplane, strengthened pintle mounts for two 0.50 in

Sikorsky UH-60A Black Hawk with underslung 105 mm light howitzer and ammunition

machine-guns, and provision for Stinger air-to-air missiles. Other combat survivability aids include an AN/AAR-47 missile warner, AN/ALQ-136 pulse radio frequency jammer, AN/ALQ-162 continuous wave radio frequency jammer, AN/APR-39A and -44 pulse/continuous receivers, AN/AVR-2 laser detector, M-130 chaff/flare dispensers and AN/ALQ-144 IR jammer. An initial procurement of 23 MH-60Ks is anticipated by the US Army, with options for a further 38. The first production contract, for 11 conversions from UH-60A, has been placed with Sikorsky, delivery to the 160th Special Operations Aviation Regiment being due in November 1991, followed by IOC in September 1992.

SH-60B Seahawk. US Navy ASW/ASST helicopter, described separately.

SH-60F Ocean Hawk. US Navy 'CV-Helo' version to replace SH-3H Sea King. See Seahawk entry.

HH-60H and HH-60J. Search and rescue/special warfare helicopters. See Seahawk entry.

UH-60L. Upgraded version of the US Army Black Hawk with General Electric T700-GE-701C turboshaft engines and improved durability gearbox. First flight 22 March 1989. Replaced UH-60A in production from October 1989. Initial deliveries began on 7 November 1989 to Texas ANG.

UH-60M. Proposed enhanced version for US Army. Cancelled in early 1989 in favour of UH-60L production.

S-70A. Tactical utility version of UH-60A, in production for the export market. Two **S-70A-5s** have been delivered to the air force of the Philippines. The Royal Australian Air Force ordered 39 **S-70A-9s**, to replace Bell UH-1s, with deliveries commencing in October 1987 and continuing at the rate of two per month until late 1990. These have General Electric T700-GE-701A-1 turboshafts, a modified SH-60B flight control system, external rescue hoist, main rotor brake, folding tail pylon, special communications and navigation equipment and ESSS. The first S-70A-9 completed by Sikorsky at Stratford flew on 11 September 1987 and was delivered to No. 9 Squadron, based at Townsville, Queensland, on 22 February 1988. Assembly and testing of the remaining 38 aircraft are being performed in Australia by Hawker de Havilland. The Black Hawks were transferred to the Royal Australian Army commencing February 1989, although the RAAF continues to be responsible for their maintenance. In July 1988 five Black Hawks were delivered to the Colombian Air Force for anti-narcotics operations, and sale of a further five was approved in February 1989. In May 1988 the US Army awarded Sikorsky an FMS contract for 13 S-70A helicopters for Saudi Arabia, modified to **Desert Hawk** configuration and including one with a VIP interior. The Desert Hawk has 15 troop seats, a blade erosion protection system consisting of polyurethane tape and a spray-on coating, and is equipped with Racal Jaguar 5 frequency-hopping radio. The aircraft also have provision for searchlights, internal auxiliary fuel tanks and an external hoist. Delivery took place between January and April 1990 to a squadron based at King Khaled Military City. In September 1988 the Turkish Jandarma (national police) ordered six **S-70A-17s**, delivery of which was completed in December 1988. These aircraft feature a new high-density 20-seat interior layout. Two VIP Black Hawks were to be supplied to Egypt in 1990.

S-70C. Commercial version, described separately.

WS-70. One helicopter supplied in kit form and assembled by Westland in the UK (which see) as a demonstrator.

The following description applies to the standard UH-60A, except where indicated:

TYPE: Twin-turbine combat assault squad transport.

ROTOR SYSTEM: Four-blade main rotor. Sikorsky SC-1095 blade section, with thickness/chord ratio of 9.5%. Middle section has leading-edge droop and trailing-edge tab to overcome vortex impingement from preceding blade in cruising flight. Blade twist 18°. Blade tips sweptback 20°. Each blade consists of a hollow oval titanium spar, Nomex honeycomb core, graphite trailing-edge and root, covered with glassfibre/epoxy, with glassfibre leading-edge counterweight, titanium leading-edge sheath and Kevlar tip. Blades are tolerant to 23 mm gunfire damage, and are pressurised and equipped with gauges providing fail-safe confirmation of blade structural integrity. Electrically heated de-icing mat in leading-edge of each blade of both main and tail rotors. Forged titanium one-piece rotor head with elastomeric bearings which require no lubrication, reducing rotor head maintenance by 60 per cent. Bifilar self-tuning vibration absorber on rotor head. Manual blade folding. Canting of tail rotor (20° to port) increases vertical lift and allows greater CG travel. 'Cross beam' four-blade tail rotor of composite materials, eliminating all rotor head bearings.

ROTOR DRIVE: Conventional transmission system with both turbines driving through freewheeling units to main gearbox. This is of modular construction to simplify maintenance. Transmission can operate for 30 min following total oil loss. Intermediate and tail rotor gearboxes oil lubricated. Main rotor shaft can be lowered for storage or air transport.

FUSELAGE: Conventional semi-monocoque light alloy structure, designed to retain 85 per cent of its passenger and

Sikorsky VH-60A VIP transport helicopter of the US Marine Corps

Sikorsky UH-60A Black Hawk combat assault helicopter *(Pilot Press)*

flight deck space in a vertical crash at 11.5 m (38 ft)/s, a lateral crash at 9.1 m (30 ft)/s and a longitudinal crash at 12.2 m (40 ft)/s. It can also withstand a combined force of 20g forward and 10g downward. Composite materials, including glassfibre and Kevlar, are used for the cockpit doors, canopy, fairings and engine cowlings. Glassfibre/Nomex floors.

TAIL UNIT: Pylon structure with port-canted tail rotor mounted on starboard side. Tail pylon design permits normal forward flight and roll-on landing if tail rotor is destroyed. Large variable incidence tailplane has a control system which senses airspeed, collective lever position, pitch attitude rate and lateral acceleration. Tailplane is set at about +34° incidence in the hover, and −6° for autorotation. Tailplane moved by dual electric actuators, with manual backup. Tailboom folds (to starboard) immediately forward of tail pylon for transport and storage.

LANDING GEAR: Non-retractable tailwheel type with single wheel on each unit. Energy absorbing main gear with a tailwheel which gives protection for the tail rotor in taxying over rough terrain or during a high-flare landing. Axle assembly and main gear oleo shock absorbers by General Mechatronics. Mainwheel tyres size 26 × 10.00-11, pressure 8.96-9.65 bars (130-140 lb/sq in); tailwheel tyre size 15 × 6.00-6, pressure 6.21-6.55 bars (90-95 lb/sq in).

POWER PLANT: Two 1,151 kW (1,560 shp) General Electric T700-GE-700 turboshafts; combined transmission rating 2,109 kW (2,828 shp). From late 1989 (UH-60L), two T700-GE-701C engines, each developing 1,385 kW (1,857 shp). (T700-GE-701A engines have max T-O rating of 1,285 kW; 1,723 shp optional in export models.) Two crashworthy, bulletproof fuel cells, with combined usable capacity of 1,361 litres (360 US gallons; 299.5 Imp gallons), aft of cabin. Single-point pressure refuelling; or gravity refuelling via point on each tank. Auxiliary fuel can be carried internally in one of several optional arrangements, or externally by the ESSS system.

ACCOMMODATION: Two-man flight deck, with pilot and co-pilot on armour protected seats. A third crew member is stationed in the cabin at the gunner's position adjacent to the forward cabin windows. Forward hinged jettisonable door on each side for access to flight deck area. Main cabin open to cockpit to provide good communication with flight crew and forward view for squad commander. Accommodation for 11 fully equipped troops, or 14 in high density configuration. Eight troop seats can be removed and replaced by four litters for medevac missions, or to make room for internal

cargo. An optional layout is available to accommodate a maximum of six litter patients. Cabin heated and ventilated. External cargo hook, having a 3,630 kg (8,000 lb) lift capability, enables UH-60A to transport a 105 mm howitzer, its crew of five and 50 rounds of ammunition. Rescue hoist of 272 kg (600 lb) capacity optional. Large rearward sliding door on each side of fuselage for rapid entry and exit. Electric windscreen de-icing. (Executive interiors for 7-12 passengers available for the S-70A.)

SYSTEMS: Solar 67 kW (90 hp) T-62T-40-1 APU; Garrett engine start system. An optional winterisation kit provides a second hydraulic accumulator installed in parallel with the APU hydraulic start accumulator, maintaining engine start capability at low ambient temperatures; Bendix 30/40kVA and 20/30kVA electrical power generators; 17Ah nickel-cadmium battery. Engine fire extinguishing system. Rotor blade de-icing system standard on US Army aircraft, optional for export.

AVIONICS: Com equipment comprises E-Systems AN/ARC-186 VHF-FM, GTE Sylvania AN/ARC-115 VHF-AM, Magnavox AN/ARC-164 UHF-AM, Collins AN/ARC-186(V) VHF-AM/FM, Bendix AN/APX-100 IFF transponder, Magnavox TSEC/KT-28 voice security set, and intercom. Nav equipment comprises Emerson AN/ARN-89 ADF, Bendix AN/ARN-123(V)1 VOR/marker beacon/glideslope receiver, Honeywell AN/ASN-43 gyro compass, Singer Kearfott AN/ASN-128 Doppler, and Honeywell AN/APN-209(V)2 radar altimeter. E-Systems Melpar/Memcor AN/APR-39(V)1 radar warning receiver and Sanders AN/ALQ-144 infra-red countermeasures set. Hamilton Standard AFCS with digital three-axis autopilot. Additional avionics and self-protection equipment installed in Enhanced Black Hawk, as described on previous page.

ARMAMENT AND OPERATIONAL EQUIPMENT: New production UH-60As from c/n 431 onward incorporate hardpoints for an external stores support system (ESSS). This consists of a combination of fixed provisions built into the airframe and four removable external pylons from which fuel tanks and a variety of weapons can be suspended. Able to carry more than 2,268 kg (5,000 lb) on each side of the helicopter, the ESSS can accommodate two 870 litre (230 US gallon; 191.5 Imp gallon) fuel tanks outboard, and two 1,703 litre (450 US gallon; 375 Imp gallon) tanks inboard. This allows the UH-60A to self deploy 1,200 nm (2,220 km; 1,380 miles) without refuelling. The ESSS also enables the Black Hawk to carry Hellfire laser-guided anti-armour missiles, gun or M56 mine dispensing pods, ECM packs, rockets and motorcycles. Up to 16 Hellfires can be carried externally

Sikorsky SH-60B Seahawk LAMPS Mk III helicopter with parent ship USS *Crommelin* **(FFG-37)**

Sikorsky SH-60B Seahawk twin-turbine ASW/ASST helicopter *(Pilot Press)*

on the ESSS, with another 16 in the cabin to provide the capability to land and reload. (Laser designation provided by Bell OH-58 helicopter or ground troops.) Infra-red jamming flares and Tracor XM130 chaff dispenser. Two pintle mounts in cabin, adjacent to forward cabin windows on each side, can each accommodate a 0.50 in calibre General Electric GECAL 50 or 7.62 mm six-barrel Minigun.

DIMENSIONS, EXTERNAL:

Main rotor diameter	16.36 m (53 ft 8 in)
Main rotor blade chord	0.53 m (1 ft 8¾ in)
Tail rotor diameter	3.35 m (11 ft 0 in)
Length: overall, rotors turning	19.76 m (64 ft 10 in)
rotors and tail pylon folded	12.60 m (41 ft 4 in)
fuselage:	
UH-60A/MH-60G, excl flight refuelling probe	15.26 m (50 ft 0¾ in)
MH-60G, incl retracted refuelling probe	17.38 m (57 ft 0¼ in)
Fuselage: Max width: UH-60A	2.36 m (7 ft 9 in)
MH-60G with auxiliary tanks	5.46 m (17 ft 11 in)
Max depth	1.75 m (5 ft 9 in)
Height: overall, tail rotor turning	5.13 m (16 ft 10 in)
to top of rotor head	3.76 m (12 ft 4 in)
in air transportable configuration	2.67 m (8 ft 9 in)
Tailplane span	4.38 m (14 ft 4½ in)
Wheel track	2.705 m (8 ft 10½ in)
Wheelbase	8.83 m (28 ft 11¾ in)
Tail rotor ground clearance	1.98 m (6 ft 6 in)
Cabin doors (each): Height	1.37 m (4 ft 6 in)
Width	1.75 m (5 ft 9 in)

DIMENSION, INTERNAL:

Cabin: Volume	11.61 m³ (410.0 cu ft)

AREAS:

Main rotor blades (each)	4.34 m² (46.70 sq ft)
Tail rotor blades (each)	0.41 m² (4.45 sq ft)
Main rotor disc	210.05 m² (2,261 sq ft)
Tail rotor disc	8.83 m² (95.0 sq ft)
Tailplane	4.18 m² (45.0 sq ft)
Vertical stabiliser	3.00 m² (32.3 sq ft)

WEIGHTS:

Weight empty: UH-60A	5,118 kg (11,284 lb)
Mission T-O weight: UH-60A	7,708 kg (16,994 lb)
Max alternative T-O weight:	
UH-60A, S-70A	9,979 kg (22,000 lb)

PERFORMANCE (UH-60A at mission T-O weight, except where indicated):

Max level speed at S/L	160 knots (296 km/h; 184 mph)
Max level speed at max T-O weight	158 knots (293 km/h; 182 mph)
Max cruising speed at 1,220 m (4,000 ft) and 35°C (95°F)	145 knots (268 km/h; 167 mph)
Single-engine cruising speed at 1,220 m (4,000 ft), and 35°C (95°F)	105 knots (195 km/h; 121 mph)
Vertical rate of climb at S/L	over 137 m (450 ft)/min
Service ceiling	5,790 m (19,000 ft)
Hovering ceiling IGE at 35°C	2,895 m (9,500 ft)
Hovering ceiling OGE: ISA	3,170 m (10,400 ft)
at 35°C	1,705 m (5,600 ft)

Range with max internal fuel at max T-O weight, 30 min reserves 324 nm (600 km; 373 miles)
Range with external fuel tanks on ESSS pylons:
with two 870 litre (230 US gallon; 191.5 Imp gallon) tanks 880 nm (1,630 km; 1,012 miles)
with two 870 litre (230 US gallon; 191.5 Imp gallon) and two 1,703 litre (450 US gallon; 375 Imp gallon) tanks 1,200 nm (2,220 km; 1,380 miles)

Endurance: UH-60A	2 h 18 min
MH-60G with max fuel	4 h 51 min

SIKORSKY S-70B

US Navy designations: SH-60B Seahawk, SH-60F Ocean Hawk, and HH-60H
US Coast Guard designation: HH-60J
Spanish Navy designation: HS.23

The US Navy's LAMPS (light airborne multi-purpose system) programme was initiated in 1970, when the Kaman SH-2D Seasprite won the contract for the LAMPS Mk I aircraft. In 1974, IBM Federal Systems Division was selected as prime contractor for LAMPS Mk III, the proposed Mk II having been cancelled. Fly-off tests of competitive airframes from Boeing and Sikorsky were conducted in 1977, each manufacturer submitting a developed version of the aircraft it had built for the US Army's UTTAS competition. Sikorsky was selected to supply the LAMPS Mk III airframe, and General Electric to supply a navalised version of the T700 engine.

A key factor in selection of the Sikorsky S-70B was its promise of reduced development costs, due to the high degree of commonality with the Army's UH-60A Black

Hawk. The designation **SH-60B** and name **Seahawk** were allocated to the Navy model, which embodies changes to integrate the mission equipment and to provide shipboard compatibility. These changes include the addition of chin mounted pods for ESM equipment, pylons for two torpedoes or auxiliary fuel tanks, and a pylon for MAD equipment on the starboard side; installation of more powerful navalised engines; addition of a sensor operator's station and port side launcher for 25 sonobuoys in the cabin; increased fuel capacity; a rescue hoist; automatic main rotor folding system; main rotor brake; folding tail rotor pylon; modified, shorter-wheelbase landing gear; a DAF Indal RAST (recovery assist, secure and traversing) device to haul down the helicopter in rough seas on to a small deck, and to stow it in the ship's hangar; a sliding cabin door; hover in-flight refuelling system; and buoyancy features. The pilot's and co-pilot's seats are not armoured.

The first of five SH-60B prototypes (BuAer number 161169) flew on 12 December 1979, and details of subsequent development and operational testing can be found in the 1982-83 *Jane's*. Production of a first batch of 18 SH-60Bs was authorised in FY 1982, followed by 27 more in FY 1983. Total planned requirement by the US Navy is 260 aircraft. The first production Seahawk flew on 11 February 1983, and deliveries to the Navy continue at the rate of two per month, with a total of 85 delivered by June 1987. First USN squadron was HSL-41, at NAS North Island, San Diego, California. Operational deployment began in 1984 and by March 1990, 10 US Navy squadrons were operational (HSLs -41, -43, -45, -47 and -49 at NAS North Island, and -40, -42, -44, -46 and -48 at NAS Mayport, Florida). Mission capability of 97 per cent has been recorded by the USN's SH-60B fleet.

US Navy SH-60Bs will be deployed on a total of 95 'Oliver Hazard Perry' (FFG-7) class frigates, 'Spruance' class and Aegis equipped destroyers, and 'Ticonderoga' class guided missile cruisers. They will provide all-weather capability for detection, classification, localisation and interdiction of surface vessels and submarines. Compared with the LAMPS Mk I, range, loiter time and endurance are increased significantly. ASW listening time is increased by 57 min, ASST (anti-ship surveillance and targeting) loiter time by 45 min. The helicopter interfaces with its mother ship via a data link, but can also operate independently. Secondary missions include search and rescue (SAR), vertical replenishment (vertrep), medical evacuation (medevac), fleet support and communications relay.

Some SH-60Bs have been modified, and others will receive upgrades. For operations in the Arabian Gulf during closing stages of the Iran-Iraq war (1987-88) 25 helicopters were outfitted with two Sanders AN/ALQ-144 IR jammers (above and below), Tracor AN/ALE-39 chaff/flare dispensers, Honeywell AN/AAR-47 electro-optical missile warning equipment and a single 7.62 mm machine-gun in the cabin door, at a total weight penalty of 168 kg (369.5 lb). A subsequent modification to seven Seahawks was a Ford Aerospace AN/AAS-38 FLIR on the port weapons pylon with instantaneous relay to the parent vessel. Trials of the first Block 1 update SH-60B began in May 1989, the equipment being introduced with Lot 9 production. Provision is made for the NFT AGM-119 Penguin anti-ship missile, Mk 50 Advanced Lightweight Torpedo, a Rospatch AN/ARR-84 99-channel sonobuoy receiver (replacing ARR-75), Chelton AN/ARC-182 VHF/ UHF/FM radio and Rockwell/Collins Class 3A GPS/ Navstar. (USN will obtain 115 Penguin-capable Seahawks by retrofitting back to Lot 5 helicopters.) Development is due to begin in 1991 for 1999 installation of Block II upgrades including airborne low frequency sonar and inverse synthetic aperture radar.

Under a US Navy contract with Sikorsky and Rolls-Royce Turbomeca, an SH-60B began initial flight tests on 3 April 1987 re-engined with 1,566 kW (2,100 shp) RTM 322 turboshafts. A US Navy flight evaluation involving some 60 hours of flight testing followed at Sikorsky's West Palm Beach facility and at the Naval Air Test Center, NAS Patuxent River. No use of RTM 322s in US Navy H-60 series helicopters is currently contemplated.

Japan has selected the SH-60B to replace the SH-3A/Bs of the JMSDF. Two Sikorsky built Seahawk airframes, designated **XSH-60J**, were delivered to Mitsubishi at Nagoya for installation of Japanese electronics and mission equipment under a $27 million contract from the Japan Defence Agency's Technical Research and Development Institute. The first of these helicopters flew on 31 August 1987, and was followed in early October, beginning a two-year testing programme. The SH-60J Seahawk will be built by Mitsubishi (which see), and is scheduled to enter service with the JMSDF in the early 1990s, with replacement of SH-3s completed by the middle of the decade. The JASDF is to obtain an SAR version designated **UH-60J**.

On 9 October 1984 the Royal Australian Navy confirmed an initial order for eight Seahawks for its full-spectrum ASW requirement, and ordered a further eight in May 1986. These Seahawks, designated **S-70B-2** RAWS (role adaptable weapon system), will operate from the RAN's 'Adelaide' (FFG-7) class guided missile frigates. The first RAN Seahawk (N7265H) flew from Sikorsky's West Palm Beach facility on 4 December 1987. Initial plans called for fourteen of the S-70B-2 RAWS to be assembled in Australia by Hawker de Havilland, but in late 1988 it was announced that Sikorsky would manufacture the first eight, and a decision that ASTA in Australia (which see) would manufacture the remainder was taken in early 1989. The first was handed over at Stratford on 12 September 1989. Formal acceptance by HS-816 squadron at Nowra of the second took place on 4 October 1989, although software problems were expected to delay IOC until mid-1991. The RAN helicopters are equipped with MEL Super Searcher radar and Collins advanced integrated avionics including cockpit controls and displays, navigation receivers and communications transceivers, an airborne target off-hand data link, and a tactical data system (TDS). The Spanish Navy took delivery of six S-70Bs in December 1988, for operation from four FFG-7 frigates by Esquadrilla 010 at Rota.

Specialist variants of the Seahawk family are:

SH-60F Ocean Hawk. On 6 March 1985 Sikorsky received a \$50.9 million contract for full scale development and production options for a 'CV-Helo' version designated SH-60F and known officially as the CV Inner Zone ASW helicopter. Intended as a replacement for the SH-3H Sea King, this helicopter operates from aircraft carriers to protect the inner zone of a carrier battle group from submarine attack, with a mission endurance of four hours. The SH-60F differs from the SH-60B in having all LAMPS Mk III avionics, sensors and pneumatic sonobuoy launcher equipment removed, together with the cargo hook, RAST system main probe, and tail probe and control panel, although installation provisions will be retained. An integrated ASW mission avionics suite is installed, comprising a MIL-STD-1553B tactical data management system with dual Teledyne Systems AN/ASN-150 tactical navigation computers and AN/ASM-614 avionics support equipment, a redundant digital databus, a tactical data link to other aircraft, a communications control system, and multi-function keypads and display units for each of the four crew members. Seahawk prototype 161170 was modified as the SH-60F test aircraft.

Additional equipment in the SH-60F includes an Allied Signal (Bendix Oceanics) AN/AQS-13F dipping sonar system, internal/external auxiliary fuel system and an additional weapons station on an extended pylon on the port side of the fuselage. Armament includes three Mk 50 acoustic homing torpedoes. Modifications include rearrangement of the cabin interior, removal of external sensor fairings, and improvements to the automatic flight control system to permit increased rates of deceleration on automatic approaches, in addition to automatic coupled sonar cable angle hover or coupled Doppler hover. Provision is made for a chaff/sonobuoy launcher system, an attitude/heading reference system and GPS/Navstar, with future growth potential for a fatigue monitoring system, surface search radar, FLIR, night vision equipment, passive ESM, MAD, air-to-surface missile capability, a sonobuoy data link, and an increase in max T-O weight to 10,659 kg (23,500 lb). Secondary missions will include SAR and standby during launch and recovery of the carriers' fixed-wing aircraft to provide a rescue service in case of ditching.

The US Navy requirement is for 175 SH-60Fs. The initial contract provided production options for 76 helicopters in five lots, four of which (for 7, 18, 18 and 18) have so far been funded. The first SH-60F flew on 19 March 1987 and, together with a second, was used for Navy operational evaluation. Five more were delivered between 22 June and September 1989, entering service with HS-10 squadron at NAS North Island, California, followed by HS-2. Sixteen SH-60Fs had been delivered by May 1990. Initial fleet deployment in USS *Nimitz*, is due in 1991.

HH-60H. In September 1986, the US Navy awarded Sikorsky a contract for an initial production increment of five (since increased to 18) strike-rescue/special warfare support (HCS) helicopters for the Navy, designated HH-60H. The HH-60H/J is a close derivative of the SH-60F, with the same T700-401C engines as those installed in current production SH-60B/Fs. The HH-60H is equipped with an AN/APR-39 radar warning receiver, AN/ALE-39 chaff dispenser, AN/ALQ-144 infra-red jammer, night vision goggle compatible lighting, infra-red suppressors, and M60D machine-guns. It will be required to operate from the decks of FFG-7, DD-963, CG-47 and larger class vessels, as well as from unprepared sites. It is expected that all 18 will serve with the Naval Air Reserve. The first HH-60H made its initial flight on 17 August 1988, was accepted by the USN on 30 March 1989 and entered service with HCS-5 squadron at point Mugu, NAS, CA, on 5 August 1989. HCS-4 at Norfolk, VA, received its first HH-60H in January 1990. In its strike-rescue role, the HH-60H is able to recover the four-man crew of a shot-down aircraft at up to 250 nm (463 km; 288 miles) from the helicopter's launch-point. Supporting special forces, it can fly 200 nm (371 km; 230 miles) and airdrop eight SEALs from 914 m (3,000 ft).

HH-60J. Like the HH-60H, with which it has been ordered in parallel, the HH-60J is related to the SH-60F, but is optimised for service with the US Coast Guard in the medium-range recovery (MRR) role. When fitted with three 455 litre (120 US gallon; 120 Imp gallon) external tanks, it is able to attend an incident up to 300 nm (556 km;

Sikorsky SH-60F Ocean Hawk CV-Helo lowering its sonar during US Navy operational evaluation

Sikorsky HH-60H combat strike-rescue/special warfare support helicopter

345 miles) from base; spend 45 min on the scene and return with six survivors in addition to the four-man crew. Further duties include law enforcement, drug interdiction, logistics, aids to navigation, environmental protection and military readiness. It is compatible with the decks of Hamilton and Bear class USCG cutters, having a 1 h 30 min loiter time at 300 nm (556 km; 345 miles) from the vessel when investigating possible smugglers and fitted with three external tanks.

By 1990, 24 HH-60Js were on order and options held for a further 11 to complete the USCG requirement. The first was flown on 8 August 1989 and accepted by the USCG in March 1990. Equipment includes Bendix RDR-1300 search/weather radar, AN/ARN-147 ILS/VOR, KDF 806 direction finder, Tacan, VOR/ILS, VHF/UHF ADF, TACNAV, dual UHF/VHF/FM radios, HF radio, IFF VHF/UHF/HF/IFF crypto computers, and provision for GPS/Navstar. Cockpit lighting is compatible with NVGs. Rescue hoist and external cargo hook as SH-60B.

The following description applies to the SH-60B:

TYPE: Twin-turbine ASW/ASST (anti-ship surveillance and targeting) helicopter.

ROTOR SYSTEM: As for UH-60A, except that main rotor blades can be folded by electrical power, and a rotor brake is provided.

AIRFRAME: Identical to UH-60A in construction. Wheelbase is shortened by 46.6 per cent, with twin wheels on tail unit, tyre size 17.5 × 6.00-6. Multiple disc brakes on mainwheels. Landing gear structure is less complex since the SH-60B's vertical impact requirement is 71.5 per cent below that of the UH-60A.

POWER PLANT: Two 1,260 kW (1,690 shp) General Electric T700-GE-401 turboshafts in early aircraft; 1,417 kW (1,900 shp) T700-401C turboshafts introduced in 1988 and on HH-60H/J. Internal fuel capacity 2,233 litres (590 US gallons; 491 Imp gallons). Hovering in-flight refuelling capability. Two 455 litre (120 US gallon; 100 Imp gallon) auxiliary fuel tanks on fuselage pylons optional. (Three on HH-60J.) Hover infra-red suppressor subsystem (HIRSS) exhaust cowling fitted to HH-60H.

ACCOMMODATION: Pilot and airborne tactical officer/backup pilot in cockpit, sensor operator in specially equipped station in cabin. Dual controls standard. Sliding door with jettisonable window on starboard side. Accommodation is heated, ventilated and air-conditioned.

Sikorsky HH-60J rescue and law enforcement helicopter for the US Coast Guard

SYSTEMS: Generally as for UH-60A.

AVIONICS AND EQUIPMENT: Com equipment comprises Collins AN/ARC-159(V)2 UHF and AN/ARC-174(V)2 HF, Hazeltine AN/APX-76A(V) and Bendix/King AN/APX-100(V)1 IFF transponders, TSEC/KY-75 voice security set, TSEC/KG-45(E-1) com security, Telephonics OK-374/ASC com system control group and Sierra Research AN/ARQ-44 data link and telemetry. Nav equipment comprises Collins AN/ARN-118(V) Tacan, Honeywell AN/APN-194(V) radar altimeter, Teledyne Ryan AN/APN-217 Doppler, and Collins AN/ARA-50 UHF DF. Mission equipment includes Sikorsky sonobuoy launcher, Edmac AN/ARR-75 and R-1651/ARA sonobuoy receiving sets, Texas Instruments AN/ASQ-81(V)2 MAD (CAE AN/ASQ-504(V) internal MAD in Australian Seahawks), Raymond MU-670/ASQ magnetic tape memory unit, Astronautics IO-2177/ASQ altitude indicator, Fairchild AN/ASQ-164 control indicator set and AN/ASQ-165 armament control indicator set, Texas Instruments AN/APS-124 search radar (under front fuselage), IBM AN/UYS-1(V)2 Proteus acoustic processor and CV-3252/A converter display, Control Data AN/AYK-14 (XN-1A) digital computer, and Raytheon AN/ALQ-142 ESM (in chin mounted pods). External cargo hook (2,722 kg; 6,000 lb) and rescue hoist (272 kg; 600 lb) standard.

ARMAMENT: Includes two Mk 46 torpedoes and (from 1989) NFT AGM-119B Penguin Mk 2 Mod 7 anti-shipping missiles. HH-60H: two pintle-mounted M60D machine-guns.

DIMENSIONS, EXTERNAL: As UH-60A except:

Length overall (rotors and tail pylon folded:	
SH-60B	12.47 m (40 ft 11 in)
HH-60H	12.51 m (41 ft 0⅝ in)
HH-60J	13.13 m (43 ft 0⅞ in)
Length of fuselage: HH-60J	15.87 m (52 ft 1 in)
Width (rotors folded)	3.26 m (10 ft 8½ in)
Height: to top of rotor head	3.79 m (12 ft 5⅜ in)
overall, tail rotor turning	5.18 m (17 ft 0 in)
overall, pylon folded	4.04 m (13 ft 3¼ in)
Wheelbase	4.83 m (15 ft 10 in)
Tail rotor ground clearance	1.83 m (6 ft 0 in)
Main/tail rotors clearance	6.6 cm (2⅝ in)

AREAS: as UH-60A

WEIGHTS:

Empty: SH-60B ASW	6,191 kg (13,648 lb)
HH-60H	6,114 kg (13,480 lb)
HH-60J	6,086 kg (13,417 lb)
Useful load: HH-60J	3,551 kg (7,829 lb)
Internal payload: HH-60H	1,860 kg (4,100 lb)
Mission gross weight:	
SH-60B ASW	9,182 kg (20,244 lb)
SH-60B ASST	8,334 kg (18,373 lb)
Max gross weight:	
SH-60B Utility and HH-60H	9,926 kg (21,884 lb)
HH-60J	9,637 kg (21,246 lb)

PERFORMANCE:

Cruising speed at S/L:	
HH-60H	147 knots (272 km/h; 169 mph)
HH-60J	146 knots (271 km/h; 168 mph)
Dash speed at 1,525 m (5,000 ft), tropical day:	
SH-60B	126 knots (234 km/h; 145 mph)
Vertical rate of climb at S/L, 32.2°C (90°F):	
SH-60B	213 m (700 ft)/min
Vertical rate of climb at S/L, 32.2°C (90°F), one engine	
out: SH-60B	137 m (450 ft)/min

SIKORSKY S-70C

The S-70C is a commercial variant of the H-60 helicopter series which can be configured for a range of utility missions including heavy construction, external lift, maritime and environmental survey, mineral exploration, forestry and conservation. It uses the H-60 airframe, dynamics and systems, but is powered by two General Electric CT7-2C or -2D engines. Options available include a de-icing kit for the

main and tail rotors, 3,630 kg (8,000 lb) capacity external cargo hook, cabin mounted rescue hoist, aeromedical evacuation kit, and a winterisation kit. The S-70C is certificated under FAR Pt 21.25. Delivery of 24 with undernose radar to the People's Republic of China was completed in December 1985. Fourteen have been ordered by the Chinese Nationalist Air Force, Taiwan. Other export sales include two to Brunei, three to Jordan, two to the Philippines, four for the Royal Flight of the Royal Thai Air Force and one each to Rolls-Royce and Westland PLC in the United Kingdom.

An S-70C (G-RRTM) is being used by Rolls-Royce in the UK as a flying testbed for the Rolls-Royce Turbomeca RTM 322 turboshaft engine.

The Sikorsky S-70C is generally similar to the UH-60A, except as follows:

TYPE: Twin-turbine utility helicopter.

POWER PLANT: Two 1,212 kW (1,625 shp) General Electric CT7-2C or 1,285 kW (1,723 shp) CT7-2D turboshafts. Combined transmission rating (continuous) 2,334 kW (3,130 shp). Maximum fuel capacity 1,370 litres (362 US gallons; 301 Imp gallons).

ACCOMMODATION: Flight deck crew of two, with provision for 12 passengers in standard cabin configuration and up to 19 passengers in high density layout. Forward hinged door on each side of flight deck for access to cockpit area. Large rearward sliding door on each side of main cabin.

DIMENSIONS, INTERNAL:

Cabin: Length	3.84 m (12 ft 7 in)
Max width	2.34 m (7 ft 8 in)
Max height	1.37 m (4 ft 6 in)
Floor area	8.18 m² (88.0 sq ft)
Volume	10.96 m³ (387.0 cu ft)
Baggage compartment volume	0.52 m³ (18.5 cu ft)

WEIGHTS:

Weight empty	4,607 kg (10,158 lb)
Max external load	3,630 kg (8,000 lb)
Max T-O weight	9,185 kg (20,250 lb)

PERFORMANCE (ISA, at max T-O weight):

Never-exceed speed	195 knots (361 km/h; 224 mph)
Max level speed at S/L	157 knots (290 km/h; 180 mph)
Cruising speed at S/L	145 knots (268 km/h; 167 mph)
Max rate of climb at S/L	615 m (2,020 ft)/min
Service ceiling	4,360 m (14,300 ft)
Service ceiling, one engine out	1,095 m (3,600 ft)
Hovering ceiling OGE	1,204 m (3,950 ft)
Range at 135 knots (250 km/h; 155 mph) at 915 m (3,000 ft) with max standard fuel, 30 min reserves	255 nm (473 km; 294 miles)
Range, max fuel, no reserves	297 nm (550 km; 342 miles)

Sikorsky S-70C commercial derivative of the UH-60 series

Sikorsky S-76 Mark II eight/twelve-passenger commercial transport helicopter, with lower side view and scrap detail of S-76B (*Pilot Press*)

SIKORSKY S-76 MARK II

The 12-passenger twin-turbine commercial S-76 was announced on 19 January 1975 as the first stage of a programme intended to give the company a bigger share of the civil aircraft market. Construction of four prototypes began in May 1976, and the first flight was made, by the No. 2 aircraft (N762SA), on 13 March 1977. FAR Pt 29 certification was received in November 1978 and deliveries began in early 1979.

The S-76 benefits from work carried out on the dynamic system of the UH-60A Black Hawk. The main rotor, for example, is a scaled-down version of that developed for the UH-60A. The helicopter conforms with FAR Pt 29 Category A IFR. Offshore oil support, corporate executive transport, medical care and general utility operations are its primary markets.

All aircraft delivered since 1 March 1982 have been designated **S-76 Mark II** and embody more than 40 standard improvements, including a new cabin ventilation system to provide ample fresh air with no performance penalty; refinements in the major dynamic components; and an increased number of fuselage access panels, these latter features being intended to improve reliability and simplify maintenance. Kits incorporating the Mark II refinements are available to update earlier S-76 aircraft to this standard, most of them without charge.

On 18 February 1982, Sikorsky announced the availability of three quick-change medical kits to convert any S-76 to an ambulance configuration. These include an air medical evacuation system (AMES) kit for operators placing primary emphasis on air ambulance operations, providing maximum intensive care for two patients treated by two attendants; a quick-change single-stretcher kit for use where intensive care transport may be needed quickly on a standby basis; and a kit for the installation of three stretchers, when the S-76 is to be used more specifically as a civil defence or SAR type ambulance. In late 1986 Sikorsky announced a new Emergency Medical Service configuration which includes built-in redundant systems for medical gases, suction and electrical power. Many S-76s are now in aeromedical service in the USA and Canada.

The special Allison turboshaft fitted in the Mark II, designated Allison 250-C30S (for Sikorsky), has a 5 per cent higher take-off rating of 485 kW (650 shp), and contingency rating of 522 kW (700 shp) for 2½ min. Allison is developing a new version of this engine, designated 250-C34, to provide a further 10 per cent increase in power. A digital computerised fuel control system is being developed by Hamilton Standard to complement this engine. When equipped with the 250-C34 the S-76 Mark II will be certificated at a maximum T-O weight of 4,989 kg (11,000 lb) and have an uprated transmission to handle the increased power.

Between 4-9 February 1982 a production S-76 Mark II, without special modification, was used to establish 12 records in FAI classes E1d and E1e. Details of these have been given in the 1987-88 and previous editions of *Jane's*.

In the Spring of 1985 Sikorsky began testing an experimental higher harmonic control (HHC) system in an S-76 which has demonstrated a vibration reduction of up to 90 per cent over the standard S-76. In the HHC system, one rod in each of the three channels of the main rotor mechanical control system is replaced with an HHC actuator which drives the corresponding main hydraulic servo mechanism to produce a vibration-cancelling motion of the rotor blades. In a production system the actuators would probably be built into the main servos. The benefits of higher harmonic control include improved crew and passenger comfort, better systems reliability, improved fatigue life, greater stability for weapons aiming and firing, and a potential reduction in weight compared to current generation 'passive' vibration absorbers. Sikorsky has also been developing a composite rotor head and all-composite main rotor blades with graphite-glassfibre spars for the S-76, together with an ice protection kit weighing 68 kg (150 lb), of which 45 kg (100 lb) is removable during the Summer months.

Sikorsky delivered 17 S-76s (14 S-76Bs and three S-76A + s) in 1989 and expected to deliver 21 during 1990.

The following versions of the S-76 had been announced by early 1990:

S-76. Original general purpose all-weather transport, generally as described below for the S-76 Mark II, and covering aircraft delivered prior to 1 March 1982.

S-76 Mark II. Current production version from 1 March 1982, as described in detail.

S-76A+. With Turbomeca Arriel 1S turboshafts; described separately.

S-76B. With Pratt & Whitney Canada PT6B-36 power plant; described separately.

S-76C. With Turbomeca Arriel 1S1 turboshafts; described separately.

S-76 Utility. More basic version of the S-76 Mark II, for a variety of roles. Sliding doors on each side of the cabin, dual controls, and a cabin floor designed for cargo loadings of up to 976 kg/m² (200 lb/sq ft) are standard. Optional features include non-retractable landing gear with low pressure tyres, to increase rough terrain ground clearance, crash resistant fuel tanks, a similar auxiliary tank of 416 litres (110 US gallons; 91.5 Imp gallons) capacity for installation in the baggage compartment, armoured crew

Sikorsky S-76 Mark II general purpose helicopter in service with the Royal Jordanian Air Force
(Ivo Sturzenegger)

seats, removable troop seats, cargo hook, rescue hoist, engine air particle separators and provisions for stretcher installation. The Philippine Air Force received 17 military S-76 Utility helicopters, of which 12 are **AUH-76s** configured for COIN, troop/logistic support and medevac duties. Two others are configured for SAR, one with a 12-passenger utility cabin, and two with an 8-passenger cabin.

H-76 Eagle. Military development of the S-76B; described separately.

H-76N. Naval development of the H-76; described separately.

The following description and specification details apply to the standard S-76 Mark II, with Allison engines, except where indicated:

TYPE: Twin-turbine general purpose all-weather helicopter.
ROTOR SYSTEM: Four-blade main rotor, with Sikorsky SC-1095 blade section. Each blade consists of a hollow oval titanium spar, titanium and nickel leading-edge abrasion strips, and glassfibre composite outer covering over Nomex honeycomb core. Blades have swept tips of Kevlar (30° on leading-edges, 10° on trailing-edges). Fully articulated aluminium rotor head, with elastomeric bearings which need no lubrication. Hydraulic lead-lag dampers and bifilar vibration absorbers on rotor head. Cross-beam four-blade tail rotor of composite materials. Rotor brake optional.
ROTOR DRIVE: Conventional transmission system, with both turbines driving through freewheeling units to main gearbox. Intermediate and tail rotor gearboxes are oil lubricated. Max continuous rating of main transmission 969 kW (1,300 shp).
FUSELAGE: Composite structure, comprising glassfibre nose, light alloy honeycomb cabin, semi-monocoque light alloy tailcone and Kevlar doors and fairings.
TAIL UNIT: Pylon structure with tail rotor on port side. All-moving tailplane, which serves also to protect passengers or ground crew from contact with tail rotor.
LANDING GEAR: Hydraulically retractable tricycle type, with single wheel on each unit. Nosewheel retracts rearward, main units inward into rear fuselage; all three units are enclosed by wheel doors when retracted. Mainwheel tyres size 14.5 × 5.5-6, pressure 11.38 bars (165 lb/sq in); nosewheel tyre size 13 × 5.00-4, pressure 9.31 bars (135 lb/sq in). Hydraulic brakes; hydraulic mainwheel parking brake. Non-retractable tricycle gear, with low pressure tyres, optional on Utility version.
POWER PLANT: Two 485 kW (650 shp) Allison 250-C30S turboshafts, with max continuous rating of 415 kW (557 shp), intermediate rating of 522 kW (700 shp) for 2½ min, mounted above the cabin aft of the main rotor shaft. Standard fuel system has a capacity of 1,064 litres (281 US gallons; 234 Imp gallons). Extended range fuel tanks, capacity 401 litres (106 US gallons; 88 Imp gallons), optional.
ACCOMMODATION: Pilot and co-pilot plus a maximum of 12 passengers. In this configuration passengers are seated on three four-abreast rows of seats, floor mounted at a pitch of 79 cm (31 in). A number of executive layouts are available, including a four-passenger 'office in the sky' configuration. Executive versions have luxurious interior trim, full carpeting, special soundproofing, radio telephone, and co-ordinated furniture. Dual controls optional. Two large doors on each side of fuselage, hinged at their forward edges; sliding doors are available optionally. Baggage hold aft of cabin, with external access door on each side of the fuselage. Cabin heated and ventilated. Windscreen demisting and dual windscreen wipers. Windscreen heating and external cargo hook optional.
SYSTEMS: Hydraulic system at pressure of 207 bars (3,000 lb/sq in) supplied by two pumps driven from main gearbox. Hydraulic system maximum flow rate 15.9 litres (4.2 US gallons; 3.5 Imp gallons) per minute. Bootstrap reservoir. Pump head pressure 3.45 bars (50 lb/sq in). In VFR configuration, electrical system comprises two 200A DC starter/generators and a 24V 17Ah nickel-cadmium battery. In IFR configuration, system comprises gearbox driven 7.5kVA generator, and a 115V 600VA 400Hz static inverter for AC power. 34Ah battery optional. Engine fire detection and extinguishing system.

AVIONICS AND EQUIPMENT: Wide range of optional avionics available, according to configuration, including Honeywell SPZS-7000 single-pilot digital AFCS with EFIS, Hamilton Standard AFCS, VHF nav receivers, transponder, compass system, weather radar, flight director system, radar altimeter, ADF, DME, VLF nav system, and ELT and sonic transmitters. Standard equipment includes provisions for dual controls; cabin fire extinguishers; cockpit, cabin, instrument, navigation and anti-collision lights; landing light; external power socket; first aid kit; and utility soundproofing. Collins VHF-20 com transceiver and intercom system standard. Optional equipment includes air-conditioning, cargo hook, rescue hoist, emergency flotation gear, engine air particle separators, full IFR instrumentation and litter installation.

DIMENSIONS, EXTERNAL (A: Mark II, B: Mark II Utility):

Main rotor diameter	13.41 m (44 ft 0 in)
Main rotor blade chord	0.39 m (1 ft 3½ in)
Tail rotor diameter	2.44 m (8 ft 0 in)
Tail rotor blade chord	0.16 m (6½ in)
Length overall, rotors turning	16.00 m (52 ft 6 in)
Fuselage: Length	13.22 m (43 ft 4½ in)
Max width	2.13 m (7 ft 0 in)
Max depth	1.83 m (6 ft 0 in)
Height overall, tail rotor turning:	
A	4.41 m (14 ft 5¾ in)
B	4.52 m (14 ft 9¾ in)
Tailplane span: A	3.05 m (10 ft 0 in)
B	3.15 m (10 ft 4 in)
Wheel track: A	2.44 m (8 ft 0 in)
B	2.54 m (8 ft 4 in)
Wheelbase	5.00 m (16 ft 5 in)
Tail rotor ground clearance	1.97 m (6 ft 5¾ in)

DIMENSIONS, INTERNAL:

Cabin: Length	2.46 m (8 ft 1 in)
Max width	1.93 m (6 ft 4 in)
Max height	1.35 m (4 ft 5 in)
Floor area	4.18 m² (45.0 sq ft)
Volume	5.78 m³ (204.0 cu ft)
Baggage compartment volume	1.08 m³ (38.0 cu ft)

AREAS:

Main rotor disc	141.21 m² (1,520 sq ft)
Tail rotor disc	4.67 m² (50.27 sq ft)
Tailplane	2.00 m² (21.5 sq ft)

WEIGHTS AND LOADINGS:

Weight empty, standard equipment	2,540 kg (5,600 lb)
Max fuel weight: standard	861 kg (1,898 lb)
auxiliary	325 kg (716 lb)
Max payload	2,132 kg (4,700 lb)
Max external load	1,497 kg (3,300 lb)
Max T-O weight	4,672 kg (10,300 lb)
Max disc loading	33.07 kg/m² (6.77 lb/sq ft)
Max power loading	4.82 kg/kW (7.92 lb/shp)

PERFORMANCE (A: at gross weight of 4,536 kg; 10,000 lb, B: at gross weight of 3,810 kg; 8,400 lb):

Never-exceed speed	155 knots (286 km/h; 178 mph)
Max cruising speed: A	145 knots (269 km/h; 167 mph)
B	155 knots (286 km/h; 178 mph)
Cruising speed for max range:	
A	125 knots (232 km/h; 144 mph)
Max rate of climb at S/L	411 m (1,350 ft)/min
Service ceiling: A	4,575 m (15,000 ft)
Service ceiling, one engine out: A	1,890 m (6,200 ft)
B	3,445 m (11,300 ft)
Hovering ceiling IGE: A	1,890 m (6,200 ft)
B	3,415 m (11,200 ft)
Range with 12 passengers, standard fuel, 30 min reserves	404 nm (748 km; 465 miles)
Range with 8 passengers, auxiliary fuel and offshore equipment	600 nm (1,112 km; 691 miles)

SIKORSKY S-76A+

In 1987 an S-76A (F-WZSA) was fitted with 522 kW (700 shp) Turbomeca Arriel 1S turboshafts for test flying that led to FAA certification in April 1988. Since then the Turbomeca power plant has been available as a retrofit option or as a new aircraft alternative to the Allison or Pratt & Whitney Canada power plants, under the designation S-76A+. Claimed advantages of the installation are

Sikorsky S-76A+, with Turbomeca Arriel 1S turboshafts

1,064 litres (281 US gallons; 234 Imp gallons); auxiliary tank capacity 208 litres (55 US gallons; 46 Imp gallons).

DIMENSION, EXTERNAL:
Fuselage: Length	13.43 m (44 ft 0¾ in)

WEIGHTS AND LOADINGS:
Weight empty	3,019 kg (6,656 lb)
Max T-O weight	5,307 kg (11,700 lb)
Max external load	1,497 kg (3,300 lb)
Max disc loading	36.62 kg/m² (7.50 lb/sq ft)
Max power loading	3.61 kg/kW (5.94 lb/shp)

PERFORMANCE (ISA, at max T-O weight):
Never-exceed speed	155 knots (287 km/h; 178 mph)
Max cruising speed	145 knots (269 km/h; 167 mph)
Econ cruising speed	131 knots (243 km/h; 151 mph)
Max rate of climb at S/L	503 m (1,650 ft)/min
Rate of climb at S/L, one engine out	160 m (525 ft)/min
Service ceiling	4,575 m (15,000 ft)
Service ceiling, one engine out	2,375 m (7,800 ft)
Hovering ceiling OGE	1,145 m (3,750 ft)
Range at 139 knots (241 km/h; 150 mph) at 915 m (3,000 ft), with standard fuel:	
no reserves	358 nm (663 km; 412 miles)
with 30 min reserves	288 nm (533 km; 331 miles)

improved engine reliability, and increased hovering, climb and cruise performance at high temperatures and high altitudes. The S-76A+ is also certificated in Australia, France, Japan, the United Kingdom and West Germany.

In April 1989 the Hong Kong government ordered eight S-76s (six S-76A+s and two S-76Cs), with options on four more, for use by the Royal Hong Kong Auxiliary Air Force. All of these aircraft will be equipped with sliding doors of new design, and rescue hoists. The first three S-76A+s, delivered in April and May 1990, are otherwise standard, as will be the two S-76Cs scheduled for delivery in 1991 and 1992. The remaining S-76A+s, to be delivered in the Autumn of 1990, are configured for search and rescue, and are equipped with a Honeywell SPZ-7600 SAR system comprising SPZ-7000 dual digital AFCS, EDZ-705 EFIS, and integrating software providing automatic search, approach to hover and Doppler-coupled hover under IFR conditions. Other equipment includes Racal 91 Doppler, chin-mounted GEC Sensors, TICM II FLIR, Primus 701 ground mapping/weather radar, and NightSun searchlight. The first SAR-equipped S-76A+ for the RHKAAF (N76004) made its first flight in January 1990 and began a 100-150 h flight test and systems development programme expected to lead to FAA certification and delivery in October.

Bond Helicopters of Aberdeen, Scotland, ordered one new S-76A+ and announced that it would retrofit six S-76As with Turbomeca engines. Bond's new-build S-76A+ was retained by the manufacturer for a six-month flight test programme leading to certification by the Federal Aviation Administration and UK Civil Aviation Authority at the end of 1989 of the S-76A+ at an increased max T-O weight of 4,899 kg (10,800 lb). Other customers include Heli-Union of France, KK Marumasu Sangyo, Honda Airways and Seibu Shoji Company Ltd of Japan, and Wiking Helikopters of West Germany.

Turbomeca is proceeding with development of a growth version of the engine, designated 1S1, which will provide power and performance increases of three/five per cent. Sikorsky has chosen the Arriel 1S1 for installation in a new production aircraft designated **S-76C**.

The description of the S-76 Mark II applies also to the S-76A+ except as follows:

POWER PLANT: Two Turbomeca Arriel 1S turboshafts, with a max continuous rating of 508 kW (681 shp) and contingency rating of 544 kW (729 shp) for 2½ min.

WEIGHTS:
Weight empty, equipped	2,778 kg (6,126 lb)
Max T-O weight	4,898 kg (10,800 lb)

PERFORMANCE (at max T-O weight, S/L, ISA, except where indicated):
Max level speed	155 knots (287 km/h; 178 mph)
Max cruising speed	145 knots (269 km/h; 167 mph)
Max rate of climb at S/L	503 m (1,650 ft)/min
Service ceiling	4,318 m (14,167 ft)
Service ceiling, one engine out	1,370 m (4,500 ft)
Hovering ceiling, OGE	564 m (1,850 ft)
Range at 135 knots (250 km/h; 155 mph) at 915 m (3,000 ft), with standard fuel:	
no reserves	465 nm (861 km; 535 miles)
with 30 min reserves	397 nm (735 km; 457 miles)

SIKORSKY S-76B

The Sikorsky S-76B is a version of the S-76 Mark II with Pratt & Whitney Canada PT6B-36 turboshafts. Development installation began in October 1983, when a ground test airframe was modified for a 200 hour ground test programme which ended on 7 April 1984. A second PT6B-36 powered S-76B (N3123U) began flight testing on 22 June 1984, and was joined by the ground test machine in February 1985. FAA Cat A certification was granted in

early 1987. The PT6B-36 engines provide the S-76B with a 48 per cent increase in take-off power, resulting in a 51 per cent increase in useful load under hot and high conditions. Maximum take-off weight is increased by 635 kg (1,400 lb), and the main transmission rating is increased to 1,118 kW (1,500 shp). Other modifications include a 15 per cent reduction in tail rotor pylon area, and reconfigured engine exhaust fairings.

Sikorsky S-76Bs are operating in China, Japan, the Netherlands, South Korea, the United Kingdom, the USA and West Germany. Flight testing for UK certification began on 2 July 1987. An increase in max T-O weight to 5307 kg (11,700 lb) received FAA approval in June 1988. Sikorsky delivered a total of 14 S-76Bs in 1988. Recent orders included two emergency medical service (EMS) aircraft for the State of New Jersey. These aircraft, the first EMS-configured S-76Bs, are equipped with a multiple position and pivoting primary patient litter, a second litter, track mounted seats for up to four medical attendants, forward and rear medical oxygen systems, total capacity 4,000 litres (141 cu ft), floor mounts for an airborne isolette, datascope or Kaat balloon pump, and dual outlets for access to external power sources during ground operations.

The description of the S-76 Mark II applies also to the S-76B, except as follows:

POWER PLANT: Two 716 kW (960 shp) Pratt & Whitney Canada PT6B-36 turboshafts, maximum continuous power rating 649 kW (870 shp). Standard fuel capacity

SIKORSKY S-76C

At the Paris Air Show in June 1989 Sikorsky Aircraft announced details of this new version of the S-76, powered by two Turbomeca Arriel 1S1 turboshafts, each rated at 591 kW (793 shp) with a maximum continuous rating of 533 kW (715 shp). The S-76C employs the basic airframe and drivetrain of the S-76B. Initial certification at a max T-O weight of 5,171 kg (11,400 lb) will provide a useful load 342 kg (754 lb) greater than that of the S-76A while retaining its range capability. An S-76C in typical offshore support configuration to meet UK CAA IFR requirements would be able to carry 12 passengers over a range of 220 nm (407 km; 253 miles) with 45 min reserves, or 10 passengers over 320 nm (593 km; 368 miles) with the same reserves. Flight tests were due to begin during 1990 of an S-76B airframe powered by Arriel 1S1 engines. First deliveries of S-76Cs are scheduled for April 1991. Two aircraft have been ordered by the Royal Hong Kong Auxiliary Air Force.

WEIGHTS:
Weight empty, equipped	2,756 kg (6,076 lb)
Max T-O weight	5,171 kg (11,400 lb)

PERFORMANCE (at max T-O weight, ISA):
Max level speed at S/L	155 knots (287 km/h; 178 mph)
Cruising speed at S/L	145 knots (269 km/h; 167 mph)
Max rate of climb at S/L	492 m (1,614 ft)/min
Service ceiling	3,505 m (11,500 ft)
Service ceiling, one engine out	610 m (2,000 ft)
Range with max fuel, 138 knots (256 km/h; 159 mph) at 915 m (3,000 ft):	
with 30 min reserves	402 nm (745 km; 463 miles)
no reserves	436 nm (808 km; 502 miles)

Artist's impression of Sikorsky S-76C twin-turboshaft helicopter

Sikorsky S-76B with 716 kW (960 shp) Pratt & Whitney Canada PT6B-36 turboshafts

SIKORSKY H-76 EAGLE

The H-76 Eagle is a military development of the S-76B. The prototype (N3124G), which made its first flight in February 1985, incorporated the optional armoured crew seats, sliding cabin doors and heavy duty floor of that version, and introduced a wide range of optional items that include weapon pylons, an optical sight mounted above the instrument panel, self-sealing high strength fuel tanks, and provisions for door mounted weapons. The main transmission is upgraded, as are the intermediate and tail rotor gearboxes. The main rotor hub and shaft are strengthened, chord of the horizontal tail surface increased, dual spars employed in the vertical fin, and tail rotor blade chord increased. Fuselage skin thickness is increased to withstand the blast of weapons launch. The H-76 can be equipped for troop transport/logistic support, as a gunship, and for roles including airborne assault, air observation post, combat SAR, evacuation, ambulance, and conventional SAR.

The Eagle can be equipped with either a mast mounted (MMS) or roof mounted sight (RMS). Further planned developments include a version with air-to-air missiles, of which the helicopter could carry up to 16, although a more likely weapons load would be eight AAMs and two cannon pods; head-up display; laser rangefinder; integrated armament management system; self-protection systems including a radar warning receiver, infra-red jammer and chaff/flare dispensers; high-clearance landing gear; and a Honeywell SPZ-7000 automatic flight control system.

In early 1987 the H-76 prototype successfully completed weapons firing tests on a four-station pitch-compensated armament pylon (PCAP) at Mojave, California. The PCAP, which has a faired leading-edge, permits a speed increase of 3-4 knots over previously installed pylons and was tested with a GIAT M261 20 mm cannon pod, 7.62 mm and 12.7 mm machine-gun pods, the VS-MD-H mine dispenser and 70 mm rockets. The pod is one of several integrated improvements to the H-76's weapons systems, which include operation of the integrated armament management system (IAMS) from the collective pitch lever as well as from the panel, and provision of system-ready signals and a sideslip trim ball on the head-up display.

Sikorsky and Daewoo Industries of South Korea have formed Daewoo-Sikorsky Aerospace Ltd and are proposing the H-76 Eagle for the Republic of Korea's medium helicopter requirement. If successful, a production rate of 24 per year is anticipated to meet the ROK's 150-175 aircraft requirement.

The description of the S-76 Mark II applies also to the H-76, except as follows:

TYPE: Twin-turbine armed utility helicopter.
ROTOR SYSTEM, ROTOR DRIVE, FUSELAGE, TAIL UNIT and LANDING GEAR: Generally as for UH-60A. Strobex rotor blade tracker optional.
POWER PLANT: As for S-76B, except fuel is contained in two high strength, optionally self-sealing, tanks located below the rear cabin, with a total capacity of 993 litres (262.4 US gallons; 218.4 Imp gallons). Gravity refuelling point on each side of fuselage. Engine ice protection by bleed air anti-icing system. Engine fire detection and extinguishing systems. Engine air particle separator optional.
ACCOMMODATION: Pilot and co-pilot, plus varying troop/passenger loads according to role. Armoured pilot seats optional. Ten fully armed troops can be transported, or seven troops when configured as an airborne assault vehicle with multi-purpose pylon system (MPPS) and one 7.62 mm door gun installed. For evacuation use the cabin can be equipped with 12 seats or, in emergency, all seats can be removed and 16 persons can be airlifted sitting on the cabin floor. For SAR use the cabin will accommodate three patients on litters, or six persons lying prone on the floor and on the rear cabin raised deck. The standard medevac layout provides for three litters and a bench seat for two medical attendants.
SYSTEMS: Generally as for S-76B, except electrical system has a 17 or optional 34Ah battery.
AVIONICS AND EQUIPMENT: Typical avionics include VHF-20A VHF transceiver, AN/ARC-186 VHF-AM/FM com, 719A UHF com, ADF-60A ADF, DF-301E UHF DF, VIR-30A VOR with ILS, glideslope and marker beacon receivers, DME-40 DME, TDR-90 transponder and dual RMI-36 RMI, all by Collins, course deviation indicators, ELT, Andrea A301-61A intercom, cabin speaker system and loudhailer. Typical equipment includes dual controls and instrumentation, stability augmentation system, dual 5 in VGIs, Allen RCA-26 standby self-contained attitude indicator, Collins ALT-50A radio altimeter, soundproofing, 'Fasten seat belt—No smoking' sign, first aid kit, two cabin fire extinguishers, external power socket, provisions for optional emergency flotation system, and provisions for installation of cargo hook with certificated capacity of 1,497 kg (3,300 lb) and rescue hoist of 272 kg (600 lb) capacity. Standard lighting includes cockpit, cabin and instrument lights, navigation lights, anti-collision strobe light, and a battery operated self-contained cabin emergency light.
ARMAMENT: One 7.62 mm machine-gun can be pintle mounted in each doorway and fired with or without the MPPS system installed. Pintles incorporate field of fire limiters and will accept FN Herstal or Maramount

Sikorsky H-76 Eagle military utility helicopter (Pratt & Whitney Canada PT6B-36 turboshafts)

M60D machine-guns. The MPPS can be installed on the cabin floor, providing the capability to carry and deploy pods containing single or twin 7.62 mm machine-guns, 0.50 in machine-guns, 2.75 in and 5 in rocket pods, Mk 66 2.75 in rockets, Oerlikon 68 mm rockets, Hellfire, TOW, Sea Skua and Stinger missiles, and Mk 46 torpedoes. Targeting equipment can include FLIR, Saab-Scania reticle sight, TOW roof sight or TOW mast mounted sight and laser rangefinder.
DIMENSIONS, EXTERNAL AND INTERNAL, AND AREAS:
Generally as for S-76B
WEIGHTS:

Weight empty	2,545 kg (5,610 lb)
Weight empty, equipped (typical)	3,030 kg (6,680 lb)
Max fuel weight	792 kg (1,745 lb)
Max T-O weight	5,171 kg (11,400 lb)

PERFORMANCE:
Similar to S-76B, but range highly variable according to loading and mission

SIKORSKY H-76N

In February 1984 Sikorsky announced development of an H-76N naval version of the H-76, designed for anti-ship surveillance and targeting, anti-submarine warfare, surface attack, search and rescue, and utility missions, operating from frigate sized ships. Over-the-horizon targeting (OTHT) and anti-ship (ASV) variants will be available with Ferranti Seaspray 3 and MEL Super Searcher radars in mounted pods. The ASV H-76N will be armed with two BAe Sea Skua air-to-surface missiles. The anti-submarine warfare version will have a dipping sonar, processing suite and two Gould Mk 46 or Marconi Sting Ray torpedoes. Other developments planned for the H-76N include a dual digital AFCS-coupled hover capability, target information data link, a tactical navigation system, hover in-flight refuelling system, roof-or mast-mounted FLIR system, ECM pod, chaff/flare dispensers on the tailboom, strengthened landing gear providing greater ground/deck clearance, folding main rotor blades, and provision for deck securing.

The H-76N will be offered with a choice of Allison 250-C34S or Pratt & Whitney Canada PT6B-36 engines. Provisional specifications include an estimated empty weight (all versions) of 2,812 kg (6,200 lb) and max T-O weights of 4,473 kg (9,861 lb) for the OTHT variant, 4,968 kg (10,953 lb) for the ASV version and 4,754 kg (10,481 lb) for an H-76N equipped with a 136 kg (300 lb) ECM pod for secondary role jamming. Total fuel capacity for all proposed variants is 999 litres (264 US gallons; 210 Imp gallons).

SIKORSKY S-76 SHADOW

In 1985 Sikorsky modified an S-76 helicopter to have a new single-pilot cockpit attached to the forward fuselage, to test advanced automated cockpit concepts for the US Army's Advanced Rotorcraft Technology Integration (ARTI) programme. Known as the Sikorsky Helicopter Advanced Demonstrator of Operator Workload (SHADOW), it features large window areas which can be partially or totally covered during testing to evaluate cockpit visibility impact on pilot workload and effectiveness. The SHADOW made its first flight on 24 June 1985, with the single-pilot cockpit unmanned. After an initial 15-hour flight test programme it was fitted with advanced equipment, including fly by wire sidearm control stick, voice interactive system, remote map reader, FLIR, a programmable symbol generator feeding a head-up display,

Artist's impression of Sikorsky H-76N naval helicopter with MEL Super Searcher radar and torpedoes

Sikorsky Helicopter Advanced Demonstrator of Operator Workload (SHADOW), based on an S-76

a visually coupled helmet mounted display, and dual CRT displays with touch-sensitive screens. Standard flight deck controls are retained in the main cabin, to permit a safety pilot to monitor testing. Initial flight trials of the fully instrumented evaluation cockpit began in the Spring of 1986. It currently has upgraded engines and dynamic components, night vision compatible cockpit and cabin, a reconfigurable evaluation cockpit, and new high-visibility paint, to equip it for night and NOE flying.

Sikorsky's partners in the SHADOW programme include Bendix, Kaiser, Litton, Northrop, Pacer Systems, Rockwell Collins, Singer Kearfott and United Technologies Hamilton Standard division.

SIKORSKY S-72X1 X-WING PROJECT

Early in 1984 Sikorsky was awarded a contract valued at $77 million to modify one of NASA's two S-72 Rotor Systems Research Aircraft (RSRA: see 1979-80 *Jane's*) into a concept demonstrator for the NASA/Defense Advanced Research Projects Agency (DARPA) X-Wing rotor programme.

Sikorsky designed the X-Wing to replace the conventional rotor on the other S-72 (N741NA/NASA 741), which was rolled out on 19 August 1986 and subsequently moved to NASA's Ames-Dryden Flight Research Facility at Edwards Air Force Base, California, where, after a 16-second pre-planned lift-off during high-speed taxi tests on 13 November 1987, it made a 38-minute first flight (without the X-Wing) on 2 December 1987. After three further flights, however, the original contract funding expired and Sikorsky suspended all work on the X-Wing programme, and the aircraft was placed in storage at Edwards AFB.

A full description of the S-72X1 can be found in the 1987-88 *Jane's*.

SIKORSKY S-80

The S-80 is an export version of the USN/USMC CH-53E heavy duty helicopter. It is available in two forms: the **S-80E** is the basic heavy transport helicopter equivalent to the CH-53E; the **S-80M** is the export form of the airborne mine countermeasures MH-53E.

In its simplest configuration, the S-80E has a single-point cargo hook and operates in VFR conditions. Customers can enhance its capability with a variety of optional extras, including troop seats, cabin soundproofing, an internal cargo winch, external hoist of 272 kg (600 lb) capacity, two-point external cargo attachment, automatic blade and tail folding, two 2,460.5 litre (650 US gallon; 541 Imp gallon) drop tanks, ground to air and/or in-flight refuelling capability, engine air particle separators, and a wide range of com/nav equipment.

Japan authorised funding for 10 S-80Ms: four in FY 1986, two in FY 1987 and four in FY 1989. A final two will be requested in FY 1991. The first S-80M-1 (8623) was delivered on 13 January 1989 and handed over to the Japan Defence Agency on 30 November 1989.

BOEING HELICOPTERS/SIKORSKY LH

Details of the Boeing Helicopters/Sikorsky team's submission for the US Army's LH requirement may be found under the Boeing Helicopters entry in this section.

SIKORSKY S-2K

Sikorsky Aircraft has begun feasibility studies for a very large civil transport (VLCT) helicopter which could carry up to 100 passengers. The year 2000 is the target date for introduction of such a helicopter, known as Sikorsky Project S-2K. Sikorsky believes that development work being undertaken for a new Army Advanced Cargo Aircraft should produce refinements in helicopter rotor drive and other systems which would satisfy civil requirements for reliability, comfort, operating economics and safety in large passenger carrying helicopters.

SKYTRADER
SKYTRADER CORPORATION

SKYTRADER ST1700 CONESTOGA/ST1700 MD EVADER

A prototype Skytrader 800 was built by Dominion Aircraft Corporation Ltd, a Canadian company with facilities at Renton, Washington. Much of the design work was undertaken by former Boeing Company employees. This aircraft (N800ST) made its first flight on 21 April 1975, and was last described in the 1979-80 edition of *Jane's*.

Dominion Aircraft ceased trading in 1979, and the project lay dormant until 1983 when Mr John J. Dupont acquired it and formed Skytrader Aircraft. In mid-1984, Mr Dupont and Mr James F. Hudson co-founded Skytrader Corporation, which became a publicly-owned company in September of that year. In October 1984 first details were announced of the planned **Skytrader ST1700 Conestoga** which, although based on the Skytrader 800 design, differed in detail. At the 1985 convention of the Army Aviation Association of America in St Louis, the **Skytrader ST1700 MD** (military derivative) **Evader** was revealed.

In April 1989 Skytrader Corporation filed for protection under Chapter 11 of the US bankruptcy laws, to avoid an unwanted take-over bid. In September 1989 a bankruptcy judge ordered the liquidation of the company. A description and photograph of the Skytrader NV/STOL and details of the proposed Model 1400 Commuterliner, may be found in the 1989-90 edition of *Jane's*. Details of the Conestoga and Evader were contained in the 1988-89 edition.

SNOW
SNOW AVIATION INTERNATIONAL INC

2228 South Third Street, Columbus, Ohio 43207
Telephone: 1 (614) 443 2711
Fax: 1 (614) 443 3106
PRESIDENT: Harry T. Snow Jr.
EXECUTIVE VICE-PRESIDENT: William G. Ferguson
VICE-PRESIDENT, ENGINEERING: Arthur E. Eckles
VICE-PRESIDENT, SALES: Emil E. Kluever

SNOW AVIATION SA-204C and SA-210AT

Snow Aviation is developing the SA-200 STOL C/AT (short take-off and landing cargo/air transport) series of twin-turboprop utility aircraft to fulfil military tactical assault/logistics and civilian cargo, combi and commuter transport roles. Two versions are planned:

SA-204C. Commercial variant, accommodating up to 50 passengers in four-abreast seating with 0.76 m (2 ft 6 in) seat pitch. Palletised passenger seat system permits quick-change to combi or all-cargo operation.

SA-210AT. Military variant, known as the STOL C/AT cargo/assault transport, accommodates up to 61 combat equipped ground troops, or 38 paratroops, or 40 casualty litters and seven medical attendants. In all-cargo configuration the SA-210AT will accommodate four 463L military pallets, or two army high mobility multi-purpose wheeled vehicles (HMMWV), or a single HMMWV with attached M-119 howitzer, or two F100/F110 turbofans on standard A3000 trailers. The SA-210AT is suitable for special missions and can be reconfigured from modular/palletised special missions equipment to cargo role in under one hour and from cargo to troop transport role in less than 30 min. As an assault aircraft it can operate from unimproved and soft surfaces with an LCN or CBR 4.

Design work began in February 1986, and construction of the first of two prototypes commenced in February 1990. First flight was anticipated late in that year, with FAA certification expected in 1991. The first prototype is an SA-204C; the second will be an SA-210AT. Snow expects to manufacture a total of 321 aircraft in the first five years of production, at a maximum rate of two/three per week. Final assembly will take place at a new 11,613 m² (125,000 sq ft) facility at the former Rickenbacker AFB near Columbus, Ohio.

The description applies to the SA-210AT unless otherwise stated.

TYPE: Twin-turboprop STOL utility transport.
WINGS: Cantilever high-wing monoplane, with constant chord centre-section and tapered outer panels with sweepback on leading-edges. Aerofoil section NACA 64$_3$A418 at root, NACA 63$_2$A615 at tip. Incidence 3° at root, 0° at tip. Construction is of conventional 2024 aluminium alloy riveted to form torsion box from front and rear spars, ribs and skin. All-metal electrically controlled and hydraulically actuated double slotted trailing-edge flaps. Mechanically actuated ailerons, each with servo and trim tab. Downward-canted wingtips. Pneumatic de-icing system on leading-edges.
FUSELAGE: All-metal structure of constant cross-section in cargo/cabin area.
TAIL UNIT: Cantilever all-metal structure of cruciform configuration. Unswept vertical fin/rudder with dorsal fin. Fixed tailplane with elevators. Control surfaces are mechanically actuated, each with servo and trim tab. Pneumatic de-icing system on leading-edges.
LANDING GEAR: Retractable tricycle type with twin wheels on all three units. Steerable nosewheel, max steering angle 90° either side of centreline. Oleo-pneumatic shock absorption. Main units retract rearwards, nose unit forwards. Mainwheel tyres size 36 × 13, max pressure 7.93 bars (115 lb/sq in), low pressure for soft field operation 2.76 bars (40 lb/sq in); nosewheel tyres size 24 × 9, max pressure 5.52 bars (80 lb/sq in), low pressure for soft field operation 2.76 bars (40 lb/sq in). Hydraulic brakes with anti-skid system.
POWER PLANT: Two 1,978 kW (2,653 shp) Pratt & Whitney Canada PW120A turboprops, each driving a Hamilton Standard six-blade constant-speed fully-feathering and reversing composite propeller with electric anti-icing. Fuel contained in six integral wing tanks, giving maximum capacity of 5,897 litres (1,558 US gallons; 1,297 Imp gallons). Single point pressure refuelling receptacle in fuselage port side under wing, overwing refuelling point in upper surface of each outboard wing section. Oil capacity 21 litres (5.5 US gallons; 4.6 Imp gallons). Heated engine inlet lips for anti-icing by engine oil.
ACCOMMODATION: Crew of two, plus observer's seat and provision for fourth seat on flight deck. Dual controls standard. Cabin/cargo compartment has seven seat tracks to facilitate configuration changes, provision for

Artist's impression of Snow Aviation SA-210AT STOL-C/AT Cargo/Assault Transport

integral rollers for cargo handling, and reinforced treadways for wheeled vehicle loading. Single split crew door, hinged top and bottom, on port side to rear of cockpit. SA-210AT has inward-opening paratroop doors on each side at rear of cargo compartment. Flight openable full-width hydraulically actuated rear cargo door/loading ramp. Hydraulic cargo stabilisation jacks standard. Accommodation is heated and air-conditioned.
SYSTEMS: Hydraulic systems for operation of flaps, landing gear, brakes, nosewheel steering and cargo ramp, max system pressure 207 bars (3,000 lb/sq in). Electrical system comprises a 28V DC starter/generator on each engine, and two 24V lead-acid batteries. APU optional. External power receptacle on port side of nose. Pneumatic de-icing system for wing and tail leading-edges, electric anti-icing for propellers and windscreen.
AVIONICS AND EQUIPMENT: Integrated flight system comprising dual nav/com and VOR/ILS. Engine indicating and crew alerting system (EICAS) and cockpit voice, engine and flight data recorders standard. Colour weather radar with ground mapping and turbulence avoidance modes; Loran C; Omega/VLF; HF com; FMS; AFCS; and dual laser ring gyro INS optional.
ARMAMENT: Modular palletised 25 mm gun platform, gunsights, laser systems, ECM, ECCM, chaff/flare dispensers and reconnaissance systems optional on SA-210AT.
DIMENSIONS, EXTERNAL (A: SA-210AT, B: SA-204C):

Wing span	30.48 m (100 ft 0 in)
Wing chord: at root	3.71 m (12 ft 2 in)
at tip	2.18 m (7 ft 2 in)
Wing aspect ratio	9.54
Length overall	27.33 m (89 ft 8 in)
Height overall	10.26 m (33 ft 8 in)
Tailplane span	13.21 m (43 ft 4 in)
Wheel track	7.92 m (26 ft 0 in)
Wheelbase	8.71 m (28 ft 7 in)

Propeller diameter	4.19 m (13 ft 9 in)
Propeller ground clearance	1.52 m (5 ft 0 in)
Fuselage ground clearance	0.84 m (2 ft 9 in)
Crew door: Height	1.52 m (5 ft 0 in)
Width	0.76 m (2 ft 6 in)
Height to sill	1.09 m (3 ft 7 in)
Rear cargo door: Height: A	2.57 m (8 ft 5 in)
B	2.58 m (8 ft 5½ in)
Width	2.54 m (8 ft 4 in)

DIMENSIONS, INTERNAL:

Cabin, excl flight deck:	
Length	12.98 m (42 ft 7 in)
Max width	2.54 m (8 ft 4 in)
Max height: A	2.57 m (8 ft 5 in)
B	2.58 m (8 ft 5½ in)
Floor area	32.98 m² (355 sq ft)
Volume: A	84.58 m³ (2,987 cu ft)
B	85.01 m³ (3,002 cu ft)

AREAS:

Wings, gross	97.40 m² (1,048.45 sq ft)
Ailerons (total)	5.75 m² (61.88 sq ft)
Trailing-edge flaps (total)	16.12 m² (173.56 sq ft)
Fin	11.94 m² (128.5 sq ft)
Rudder, incl tab	8.55 m² (92.0 sq ft)
Tailplane	22.93 m² (246.8 sq ft)
Elevators, incl tabs	8.46 m² (91.11 sq ft)

WEIGHTS AND LOADINGS (SA-200C and SA-210TA):

Weight empty	11,163 kg (24,610 lb)
Max payload	8,800 kg (19,400 lb)
Max fuel weight	4,742 kg (10,455 lb)
Max T-O weight	23,060 kg (50,841 lb)
Max ramp weight	23,080 kg (50,886 lb)
Max zero-fuel weight	19,960 kg (44,010 lb)
Max landing weight	21,320 kg (47,000 lb)
Max wing loading	236.9 kg/m² (48.53 lb/sq ft)
Max power loading	5.83 kg/kW (9.59 lb/shp)

PERFORMANCE (estimated):

Never-exceed speed	265 knots (491 km/h; 305 mph)
Max level and max cruising speed at 3,050 m (10,000 ft)	
	245 knots (454 km/h; 282 mph)
Econ cruising speed at 3,050 m (10,000 ft)	
	192 knots (356 km/h; 221 mph)
Min single engine control speed (VMC)	
	79 knots (147 km/h; 91 mph)
Stalling speed:	
flaps down, power off	75 knots (139 km/h; 87 mph)
Max rate of climb at S/L	396 m (1,300 ft)/min
Rate of climb at S/L, one engine out	91 m (300 ft)/min
Service ceiling	8,170 m (26,800 ft)
Service ceiling, one engine out	2,070 m (6,800 ft)
Min ground turning radius, about nosewheel	
	7.92 m (26 ft 0 in)

T-O run:

at 20,610 kg (45,441 lb) T-O weight	
	317 m (1,040 ft)
at max T-O weight	662 m (2,170 ft)
T-O to 15 m (50 ft):	
at 20,610 kg (45,411 lb) T-O weight	519 m (1,700 ft)
at max T-O weight	833 m (2,730 ft)
Landing from 15 m (50 ft):	
at 20,610 kg (45,441 lb) without reverse thrust	
	580 m (1,900 ft)
at max landing weight	610 m (2,000 ft)
Landing run:	
at 20,610 kg (45,441 lb) without reverse thrust	
	397 m (1,300 ft)
at max landing weight	427 m (1,400 ft)
Range with max fuel, 45 min reserves at 3,050 m	
(10,000 ft)	1,290 nm (2,390 km; 1,485 miles)
Range with max payload, 45 min reserves at 3,050 m	
(10,000ft)	770 nm (1,427 km; 886 miles)

OPERATIONAL NOISE LEVELS (FAR Pt 36, estimated):

T-O	less than 82 EPNdB
Sideline	86.5 EPNdB
Approach	less than 94 EPNdB

SOLOY

SOLOY CONVERSIONS LTD

450 Pat Kennedy Way SW, Olympia, Washington 98502
Telephone: 1 (206) 754 7000
Fax: 1 (206) 943 7659
PRESIDENT: Joe I. Soloy
SALES MANAGER: J. T. Koester
ENGINEERING MANAGER: Nicholas R. Parkinson
MARKETING GROUP MANAGER: R. K. Furtick

Soloy Conversions has long been known for its turbine engine conversions of Bell 47G and Hiller UH-12E series helicopters. It is now devoting its major effort to work on its Turbine Pac specialised turboprop conversion scheme, development of which is being shared by the Allison Gas Turbine Division of General Motors Corporation (which see, in this section). The Turbine Pac can be produced in 16 configurations, ranging from 313 to an eventual 548 kW (420-735 shp).

SOLOY TURBINE PAC CONVERSIONS

The Turbine Pac is a specialised turboprop conversion unit that can be used to update and improve the performance of a variety of fixed-wing aircraft. In its current form it is built around a 313 kW (420 shp) Allison 250-C20S, a 373 kW (500 shp) Allison 250-C28C, or a 485 kW (650 shp) Allison 250-C30 turboshaft, with a separate shaft driven 1,800 rpm reduction gearbox to provide the propeller drive. This gearbox is rated at more than 522 kW (700 shp) to allow for future growth versions of the engine.

Flight testing of the Turbine Pac began on 23 November 1981, using a Cessna Model 185 (N5010Y) and an Allison 250-C20 engine. Details of the subsequent development programme can be found in the 1987-88 and earlier editions of *Jane's.* Three models (Cessna 206, Cessna 207 and Beechcraft A36 Bonanza) are STC approved and in production. The Soloy Turbine Pac Cessna 185 and Allison/Soloy Beechcraft T-34 are available to government agencies and others able to use non-certificated aircraft; a Cessna Model 185/U-17 with Soloy Turbine Pac power plant has been evaluated by the Royal Thai Army. Soloy Turbine Pac Cessnas have been delivered to the US Drug Enforcement Administration and the Government of Costa Rica. Several Jet-Prop A36 Bonanzas have been sold for private and business use; this conversion is described under the Tradewind heading. Under development is an adaptation of the more powerful Allison Series IV turboshaft for single- and twin-engined aircraft. Soloy has also completed the installation of a 485 kW (650 shp) Allison 250-C30M in an Aerospatiale Astar 350D helicopter, certification of which was granted in early 1986. A prototype installation of the 313 kW (420 shp) Allison 250-B17 in the Chilean ENAER Aucán prototype (1987–88 *Jane's*) made its first flight on 12 February 1986, prior to returning to Chile for evaluation. In early 1989 Soloy was developing a new Dual Pac system, which combines the power section of two Allison 250-C20R or 250-C30 turboprops with a Soloy gearbox, each engine providing independent drive to a single Hartzell propeller through a separate reduction system. Soloy believes the Dual Pac, which can operate on a single power section for fuel economy during extended flight, will provide power redundancy for twin-engined centreline thrust aircraft operating under FAR Pt 135 IFR passenger carrying requirements, and improve the safety of twin-engined aircraft in the event of engine failure, while offering a cleaner installation than that afforded by wing-mounted engines.

Soloy has also carried out a turboprop conversion of the Piper Navajo Chieftain using two 380 kW (510 shp) Teledyne Continental TP-500E turboprops. Flight testing began in 1989 with certification by FAA supplemental type certificate anticipated in late 1990.

Soloy Turbine Pac installation in a Cessna 206 with PK amphibious floats

Soloy Conversions modification of the Piper Navajo Chieftain with two Teledyne Continental TP-500E turboprops

Military version of Cessna Model 206 with Soloy Turbine Pac power plant and high flotation landing gear

SOLOY CESSNA 206 TURBINE PAC

The Soloy Turbine Pac conversion for the Cessna 206 received FAA certification on 22 May 1984 and is in production, with converted aircraft delivered to customers in Australia, Bolivia, Switzerland and the United States. The aircraft is approved for operation on Wipline and PK floats, and EDO 3500 amphibious floats. A military version of this aircraft, intended primarily for liaison and observation missions, is equipped with 'super flotation' landing gear with oversize low pressure tyres for operation off unprepared terrain, and an extended range fuel system in the wings. Soloy had delivered a total of 36 Cessna 206 Turbine Pacs by February 1989, since when no information has been received.

POWER PLANT: One 313 kW (420 shp) Soloy Model 763 Turbine Pac/Allison 250-C20S turboprop, driving a Hartzell three-blade constant-speed fully-feathering propeller. Fuel capacity 230-348 litres (61-92 US gallons; 51-77 Imp gallons), depending on airframe model. Extended range fuel tanks, total usable capacity 189 litres (50 US gallons; 42 Imp gallons), optional on military model. Oil capacity 7.1 litres (1.9 US gallons; 1.6 Imp gallons).

WEIGHTS:
Weight empty   866 kg (1,910 lb)
Max T-O weight   1,633 kg (3,600 lb)

PERFORMANCE (at max T-O weight):
Never-exceed speed
                   148 knots (274 km/h; 170 mph) IAS
Max level speed and max cruising speed at 3,050 m
 (10,000 ft)   163 knots (302 km/h; 188 mph)
Econ cruising speed at 6,100 m (20,000 ft)
                        142 knots (263 km/h; 164 mph)
Stalling speed, power off:
 flaps up   58 knots (107 km/h; 67 mph) CAS
 flaps down   52 knots (96 km/h; 60 mph) CAS
Max rate of climb at S/L   594 m (1,950 ft)/min
Service ceiling   6,100 m (20,000 ft)
T-O run   174 m (570 ft)
T-O to 15 m (50 ft)   324 m (1,063 ft)
Landing from 15 m (50 ft)   334 m (1,094 ft)
Landing run   168 m (553 ft)
Range with 333 litres (88 US gallons; 73 Imp gallons)
 usable fuel, max range power at 6,100 m (20,000 ft)
                        882 nm (1,635 km; 1,016 miles)

SOLOY CESSNA 207 TURBINE PAC

Prototype installation of a 313 kW (420 shp) Soloy Turbine Pac/Allison 250-C20S turboprop in a Cessna Model 207 (N21190) was flown for the first time on 14 January 1984. A second Cessna 207 joined the test programme in Spring 1985, and certification was achieved in early 1986. A total of nine Cessna 207 Turbine Pacs had been delivered by February 1989.

WEIGHTS:
Weight empty   893 kg (1,969 lb)
Max T-O weight   1,814 kg (4,000 lb)

PERFORMANCE:
Max level speed:
 at 1,525 m (5,000 ft)   157 knots (291 km/h; 181 mph)
 at 3,050 m (10,000 ft)   164 knots (304 km/h; 189 mph)
Stalling speed:
 flaps up, power off
                   59 knots (109 km/h; 68 mph) CAS
 flaps down, power off
                   53 knots (98 km/h; 61 mph) CAS
Max rate of climb at S/L   500 m (1,640 ft)/min
Service ceiling   7,620 m (25,000 ft)
T-O run   224 m (736 ft)
Range with 303 litres (80 US gallons; 67 Imp gallons)
 usable fuel, max range power at 3,050 m (10,000 ft)
                        558 nm (1,034 km; 642 miles)

STODDARD-HAMILTON

STODDARD-HAMILTON AIRCRAFT INC

18701 58th Avenue NE, Arlington, Washington 98223.
Telephone: 1 (206) 435 8533
Fax: 1 (206) 435 9525

STODDARD-HAMILTON T-9 STALKER

Stoddard-Hamilton Aircraft Inc is developing this turboprop version of the Glasair III all-composite home-built aircraft described in the Sport Aircraft section of this edition. The aircraft is powered by a 313 kW (420 shp) Allison 250-B17D turboprop and will be marketed as a low cost, high performance fully aerobatic military trainer adaptable to combat roles such as ground support, patrol, air defence, and search and rescue. The prototype T-9 Stalker (N253LC) made its first flight on 24 July 1988, but was destroyed in a fatal crash at Auburn Opelika Airport, Alabama on 23 May 1989.

TYPE: Two-seat turboprop powered training aircraft.
WINGS: Cantilever low-wing monoplane. Wing section LS(1)-0413 series. All-composite structure with glassfibre single-piece main spar, ribs and rear spar. Electrically operated flaps of composite construction. Composite ailerons with integral trim system.
FUSELAGE: Composite sandwich monocoque moulded in two half-shells.
TAIL UNIT: Conventional cantilever tail unit of composite construction, as for wings. Fixed sweptback fin, integral with moulded fuselage. Elevators and rudder manually operated.
LANDING GEAR: Hydraulically retractable tricycle type; nosewheel retracts rearward, mainwheels inward into wingroots. Oleo-pneumatic shock absorber in each unit.
POWER PLANT: One 313 kW (420 shp) Allison 250-B17D turboprop, driving a three-blade McCauley constant-speed reversing metal propeller. Fuel contained in integral glassfibre tanks in wings, max capacity 333 litres (88 US gallons; 73 Imp gallons). Wing surfaces treated with Thorstrand aluminised coating to protect fuel system from lightning strikes.
ACCOMMODATION: Crew of two side by side in enclosed cabin with zero/zero pilot extraction system and dual controls. Control system response can be adjusted to varying degrees of sensitivity.

Prototype Stoddard-Hamilton T-9 Stalker tactical trainer, since destroyed *(J.M.G. Gradidge)*

AVIONICS AND EQUIPMENT: Full IFR avionics with gunsight and armament management equipment. All antennae integral with airframe structure to reduce drag and installation weight.
ARMAMENT: Two hardpoints, each with max load of 125 kg (275 lb), beneath wings outboard of main landing gear can carry a variety of stores including 7- or 19-tube rocket launchers, practice bomb racks, machine-gun pods, cartridge launchers and rescue pods.

DIMENSIONS, EXTERNAL:
Wing span   7.10 m (23 ft 3½ in)
Length overall   6.64 m (21 ft 9½ in)
Height overall   2.21 m (7 ft 3 in)
Propeller diameter   2.03 m (6 ft 8 in)
DIMENSION, INTERNAL:
Cabin:
 Max width   1.07 m (3 ft 6¼ in)
AREA:
Wings, gross   7.54 m² (81.2 sq ft)
WEIGHTS AND LOADINGS:
Weight empty   680 kg (1,500 lb)
Max fuel weight   261 kg (576 lb)
Max T-O weight   1,225 kg (2,700 lb)
Max wing loading   162.46 kg/m² (33.25 lb/sq ft)
Max power loading   3.91 kg/kW (6.43 lb/shp)

PERFORMANCE (estimated, at max T-O weight unless otherwise indicated):
Never-exceed speed   350 knots (649 km/h; 403 mph)
Max level speed: at S/L   300 knots (556 km/h; 345 mph)
 at 3,050 m (10,000 ft)   331 knots (613 km/h; 381 mph)
Cruising speed at 7,620 m (25,000 ft)
                           318 knots (589 km/h; 366 mph)
Stalling speed   61 knots (113 km/h; 70 mph)
Max rate of climb at S/L, at T-O weight of 1,089 kg
 (2,400 lb)   1,013 m (3,325 ft)/min
Service ceiling   11,280 m (37,000 ft)
Max operating altitude   7,620 m (25,000 ft)
T-O run   160 m (525 ft)
T-O to 15 m (50 ft)   267 m (875 ft)
Landing from 15 m (50 ft) with propeller reversal
                           206 m (675 ft)
Landing run with propeller reversal   110 m (360 ft)
Range with max fuel: at cruising speed of 236 knots (437
 km/h; 272 mph) at 4,575 m (15,000 ft), 30 min fuel
 reserves   1,378 nm (2,554 km; 1,587 miles)
at cruising speed of 318 knots (589 km/h; 366 mph) at
 7,620 m (25,000 ft), reserves as above
                           1,200 nm (2,224 km; 1,382 miles)
g limits   +6.9/-4

SUMMIT

SUMMIT AVIATION INC

Summit Airport, Middletown, Delaware 19709

Telephone: 1 (302) 834 5400
Telex: 83-5499

SUMMIT SENTRY O2-337

Summit Aviation developed this version of the Cessna Model T337 for a wide range of military missions. No news of recent deliveries has been received. A description and photograph may be found in the 1989-90 and earlier editions of *Jane's*.

SUPER 580

SUPER 580 AIRCRAFT COMPANY

2192 Palomar Airport Road, Carlsbad, California 92008
Telephone: 1 (619) 438 3600
Telex: 140414
Fax: 1 (619) 753 1531
PRESIDENT: Ted Vallas
SENIOR VICE-PRESIDENT: James Coleman

This company, a division of Flight Trails Inc, has the licence for a turboprop conversion and remanufacturing programme for the Convair 340/440/580 series of passenger/cargo transports, known as the Super 580, from the Allison Gas Turbine Division of General Motors Corporation.

SUPER 580 AIRCRAFT SUPER 580

The Super 580 conversion employs two Allison 501-D22G turboprops, each flat rated at 2,983 kW (4,000 shp), and driving a Hamilton Standard 54H60-77 four-blade, constant-speed feathering and reversing propeller, replacing the Pratt & Whitney R-2800 radial piston engines of the Convair 340/440 or the earlier Allison 501-D13 turboprops of the Convair 580. Compared with the Convair 580, of which some 170 were converted by Convair, the Super 580 is claimed to offer a 2.5 per cent improvement in specific fuel consumption, improved engine-out performance, greater reliability, a 13 per cent increase in range, a 40 per cent increase in hot-day payload capability, cruising speeds up to 325 knots (602 km/h; 374 mph), and a 40 per cent reduction in operating costs.

The Allison 501-D22G engine conversion has been designed as a quick-change nacelle/engine module, manufactured by subcontractor Jay Dee Aircraft Supply Co of Santa Monica, California. Standard fuel capacity is 6,738 litres (1,780 US gallons; 1,482 Imp gallons), with 7,790 litres (2,058 US gallons; 1,714 Imp gallons) or 11,008 litres (2,908 US gallons; 2,421 Imp gallons) available optionally. A Garrett 95.90 APU is installed in the starboard engine nacelle, and a new fire extinguisher system is standard. A tail-mounted APU is optional.

The Super 580 remanufacturing programme includes a redesigned flight deck with a Bendix/King Gold Crown Series 3 avionics package and two Honeywell flight directors. A Rockwell Collins flight director system, incorporating an EFIS display and two digital flight directors, is optional. All electrical wiring is replaced, but the aircraft's existing DC electrical system is retained. An AC system may be introduced at a later date, either as standard equipment or as an option. The Super 580's passenger cabin, pressurised at 0.29 bars (4.16 lb/sq in), is configured for 50 passengers in airline seats with 0.91 m (36 in) pitch, and features upgraded soundproofing, lavatory and galley facilities, 0.12 m³ (4.4 cu ft) capacity overhead baggage bins, indirect fluorescent lighting and individual reading lights and air vents.

Three cabin baggage compartments are provided: a 1.44 m³ (50.9 cu ft) forward compartment with a capacity of 227 kg (500 lb); a 5.64 m³ (199.2 cu ft) aft compartment, capacity 816 kg (1,800 lb); and a stowage area for carry-on baggage and garment bags. A 2.20 m³ (77.8 cu ft) belly compartment can accommodate 453 kg (1,000 lb) of cargo.

Piston engined Convair 340/440 aircraft undergoing remanufacture as Super 580s also require modifications to their tail surfaces. A 0.30 m (1 ft 0 in) fin extension and a larger rudder with an additional 1.11 m² (12.0 sq ft) of surface area are added, fin/rudder attachment points strengthened, and horizontal tail surfaces increased in span by 0.51 m (1 ft 8 in) at each tip, with an additional 1.58 m² (17.0 sq ft) of elevator added. An anti-skid braking system is available optionally.

The first Super 580 conversion was performed by Hamilton Aviation, Tucson, Arizona. First flown after conversion on 21 March 1984, it was configured for quick-change corporate/commuter operations and delivered to The Way International of New Knoxville, Ohio, in June 1984 after receiving FAA approval to CAR 4b by means of a Supplemental Type Certificate.

DIMENSIONS, EXTERNAL:

Wing span	32.08 m (105 ft 3 in)
Length overall	24.84 m (81 ft 6 in)
Height overall	8.89 m (29 ft 2 in)

DIMENSIONS, INTERNAL:

Cabin: Length	15.75 m (51 ft 8 in)
Max height	1.98 m (6 ft 6 in)
Max width	2.69 m (8 ft 10 in)

WEIGHTS:

Basic operating weight	14,742 kg (32,500 lb)
Max fuel weight	5,421 kg (11,951 lb)
Max ramp and max T-O weight	26,383 kg (58,165 lb)
Max landing weight:	
without anti-skid	23,587 kg (52,000 lb)
with anti-skid	24,040 kg (53,000 lb)
Max zero-fuel weight	22,680 kg (50,000 lb)

Super 580 turboprop conversion of a Convairliner

PERFORMANCE:

Never-exceed speed	349 knots (647 km/h; 402 mph)
Max cruising speed:	
at S/L	280 knots (519 km/h; 322 mph)
at 3,050 m (10,000 ft)	
	310 knots (574 km/h; 357 mph)
Stalling speed	75-93 knots (139-173 km/h; 86-107 mph)
Max rate of climb at S/L	872 m (2,860 ft)/min
Rate of climb at S/L, one engine out	
	258 m (848 ft)/min
Service ceiling	7,620 m (25,000 ft)
Service ceiling, one engine out	6,860 m (22,500 ft)
Range with 18 passengers	
	1,920 nm (3,558 km; 2,211 miles)
Max range, FAR domestic reserves	
	2,000 nm (3,706 km; 2,303 miles)

SUPER 580 AIRCRAFT SUPER 580 ST

In 1984 the Convair Division of General Dynamics Corporation, under subcontract to Allison Division of General Motors, conducted feasibility studies for a stretch of existing Convair 340/440, CV-580 and CV-640 airframes to permit increased payloads of up to 78 passengers or 9,525 kg (21,000 lb) of cargo, typically in nine LD3 containers or on up to seven 2.2 × 2.7 m (88 × 108 in) pallets. Super 580 Aircraft has applied for FAA Supplemental Type Certification for the conversion, to be known as the Super 580 ST (Stretch). Tooling design for the conversion has been completed by San Diego Aircraft Engineering. Super 580 Aircraft estimates that some 270 Convair airframes are potential candidates for Super 580 ST conversion.

DIMENSIONS, EXTERNAL and INTERNAL (preliminary):

Length overall	29.18 m (95 ft 9 in)
Cabin: Volume	87.7 m³ (3,096 cu ft)
Floor area	48.1 m² (518.0 sq ft)

WEIGHTS (provisional):

Weight empty: passenger	16,951 kg (37,370 lb)
cargo	14,968 kg (33,000 lb)
Baggage: standard	201 kg (444 lb)
optional	228 kg (502 lb)
Max T-O weight	28,576 kg (63,000 lb)
Max landing weight	26,308 kg (58,000 lb)
Max zero-fuel weight	24,948 kg (55,000 lb)

SWEARINGEN

SWEARINGEN ENGINEERING AND TECHNOLOGY INC

Suite A, 1234 99th Street, San Antonio, Texas 78214
Telephone: 1 (512) 921 1208
Fax: 1 (512) 921 0198
PRESIDENT AND CHIEF EXECUTIVE OFFICER: E. J. Swearingen
VICE-PRESIDENTS:
O. L. Anderson (Marketing)
Marion J. Dees Jr (Engineering)
A. G. Hutto (Manufacturing)

Well known as the designer of the Merlin and Metro series of twin turboprop executive transports and commuter airliners, and for engineering such aircraft as the Piper Twin Comanche and Lockheed 731 JetStar II, Mr 'Ed' J. Swearingen is designing and constructing the prototype of a light turbofan-powered business jet.

JAFFE/SWEARINGEN SA-32T TURBO TRAINER

Swearingen, in conjunction with Jaffe Aircraft Corporation of San Antonio, Texas, is developing a two-seat turboprop powered training aircraft, designated SA-32T, powered by an Allison 250-B17D engine. General appearance is shown in the accompanying three-view drawing. The airframe is similar to that of Mr Swearingen's SX300 two-seat light aircraft, described and illustrated in the Sport Aircraft section of the 1987-88 *Jane's*, but with skin thickness increased by 50 per cent to cater for higher performance, a new canopy design, and larger wheels, tyres and brakes. The canopy has a miniature detonating cord with either a rocket extraction system or Martin-Baker lightweight ejection seats for emergency egress. The NASA designed laminar-flow wing section is claimed to produce the handling characteristics of a jet aircraft, and Jaffe is considering development of a single-seat anti-helicopter combat version with increased performance. Forward air control and reconnaissance are also seen as possible roles for the SA-32T.

The prototype (N6Y) made its first flight on 31 May 1989, and was displayed subsequently at the Paris Air Show after a 15 h ferry flight across the North Atlantic.
TYPE: Two-seat training aircraft.
WINGS: Cantilever low-wing monoplane, of tapered planform and mainly single-spar metal construction, including ailerons and hydraulically actuated trailing-edge flaps. Aerofoil section NASA NLF 0416. Wingtips and wing/fuselage fairings of composite materials. Ailerons have electric trim.

Prototype Jaffe SA-32T Turbo Trainer *(J. M. G. Gradidge)*

FUSELAGE: Conventional all-metal stressed skin primary structure. Tailcone and engine cowling panels of composites construction.
TAIL UNIT: Metal structure, comprising sweptback fin and rudder, non-swept tailplane and elevators. Fin and tailplane tips are of composite materials. Electrically operated trim tab in elevator.
LANDING GEAR: Hydraulically retractable tricycle type, with single wheel and oleo-pneumatic shock absorber on each unit. Manual hydraulic pump for emergency extension, and gas-spring powered secondary emergency extension. Steerable nose unit, with shimmy damper. Mainwheel tyres size 6.00-6, nosewheel tyre size 5.00-5 (all three 6-ply). Hydraulic disc brakes and parking brake.
POWER PLANT: One 313 kW (420 shp) Allison 250-B17D turboprop, driving a three-blade constant-speed propeller with spinner. Inlet anti-iced by engine bleed air. Fuel in two integral wing tanks (each 128.5 litres; 34 US gallons; 28 Imp gallons usable) and a 72 litre (19 US gallon; 16 Imp gallon) fuselage header tank, giving total usable capacity of 329 litres (87 US gallons; 72 Imp gallons).
ACCOMMODATION: Side by side seats for instructor and pupil, with full-shoulder inertia reel safety harness for each occupant. Dual controls standard. Hydraulically actuated 'omnivision' canopy, with windscreen demisting. Baggage space aft of seats (no external access). Accommodation heated (by engine bleed air) and ventilated.
SYSTEMS: Hydraulic system for actuation of flaps, landing gear and mainwheel brakes. Electrical system (28V DC), with lead-acid battery and 70A alternator, provides power for engine start, aileron and elevator trim, hydraulic pumps, navigation, strobe, landing and cockpit lights.

DIMENSIONS, EXTERNAL:

Wing span	7.43 m (24 ft 4½ in)
Wing aspect ratio	8.3
Length overall	6.86 m (22 ft 6 in)
Height overall	2.37 m (7 ft 9¼ in)

DIMENSION, INTERNAL:

Cockpit: Max width	1.04 m (3 ft 5 in)

AREA:

Wings, gross reference	6.64 m² (71.5 sq ft)

WEIGHTS:

Average weight empty, equipped	707 kg (1,560 lb)
Fuel weight (usable)	264 kg (583 lb)

Baggage (max)   32 kg (70 lb)
Max T-O and landing weight   1,179 kg (2,600 lb)

PERFORMANCE (estimated, at max T-O weight except where indicated):

Never-exceed speed	348 knots (644 km/h; 400 mph)
Max level speed at S/L	288 knots (534 km/h; 332 mph)
Max manoeuvring speed	207 knots (383 km/h; 238 mph)
Normal cruising speed at 6,100 m (20,000 ft), 75% power	274 knots (508 km/h; 315 mph)
Max gear extension speed	170 knots (314 km/h; 195 mph)
Max full flap extension speed	135 knots (250 km/h; 155 mph)

Stalling speed at 1,134 kg (2,500 lb) AUW:

gear and flaps up	86 knots (160 km/h; 100 mph)
gear and flaps down	66 knots (122 km/h; 76 mph)
Max rate of climb at S/L, at 1,134 kg (2,500 lb) AUW	1,128 m (3,700 ft)/min
Service ceiling	more than 7,620 m (25,000 ft)
T-O run	427 m (1,400 ft)
T-O to 15 m (50 ft)	518 m (1,700 ft)
Landing from 15 m (50 ft)	701 m (2,300 ft)
Landing run	335 m (1,100 ft)
Max range at normal cruising speed, no reserves	960 nm (1,779 km; 1,105 miles)
g limits	±6

Jaffe/Swearingen SA-32T side by side two-seat turboprop powered trainer *(Pilot Press)*

SWEARINGEN/JAFFE SJ30

On 30 October 1986 Swearingen announced its intention to design and build an advanced technology light twin-jet aircraft, then known as the SA-30 Fanjet. In October 1988 Gulfstream Aerospace, Williams International and Rolls-Royce plc announced that they were joining Swearingen in developing the aircraft, which was renamed Gulfstream SA-30 Gulfjet. However, on 1 September 1989 Gulfstream withdrew from the project. Its place was taken by the Jaffe Group of San Antonio, Texas, and the aircraft was redesignated Swearingen/Jaffe SJ30.

By February 1990 construction of the prototype SJ30 was 80 per cent complete, with a first flight expected mid-year and FAA certification for single-pilot operation and first customer deliveries anticipated before the end of 1992. The Ishida Group and Toyota Tsusho of Japan have been appointed to provide marketing and service support for the SJ30 for the Asia-Oceania region.

TYPE: Twin-turbofan executive transport.

WINGS: Cantilever low-wing monoplane, of all-metal fail-safe construction. Sweptback, tapered planform, and advanced technology computer-designed section. Main wing box forms integral fuel tanks. Double-slotted Fowler trailing-edge flaps and leading-edge slats for low landing speeds. Lateral control by ailerons. Three-segment airbrakes/lift dumpers on upper surface of each wing, forward of flaps. Flaps and slats are mechanically synchronised, and positioned by electrically operated screwjacks; spoilers are actuated electro-hydraulically; ailerons are actuated mechanically, and have electrically actuated trim tabs. Leading-edges are de-iced with a TKS system.

FUSELAGE: Pressurised all-metal (aluminium alloy) semi-monocoque structure of basically circular section, with chemically milled skins.

TAIL UNIT: Cantilever all-metal T tail, with sweepback on all surfaces. All-moving tailplane is positioned by electrically actuated pitch trim actuators. Rudder is mechanically actuated, and fitted with an electrically actuated trim tab. TKS de-icing of tailplane leading-edges. Twin ventral fins under tailcone.

LANDING GEAR: Retractable tricycle type, with twin wheels on each unit. Trailing-link type oleo-pneumatic suspension on main units. Hydraulic actuation, main units retracting inward and rearward into fuselage, nose unit forwards. Hydraulically steerable nose unit retracts forward.

POWER PLANT: Two 8.01 kN (1,800 lb st) Williams International FJ44 turbofans, pod-mounted on pylons on sides of rear fuselage. Inlets de-iced by engine bleed air. Fuel in three integral tanks, one in each wing and one in rear fuselage, with combined capacity of 1,893 litres (500 US gallons; 416 Imp gallons). Single-point refuelling of all three tanks.

ACCOMMODATION: Pilot and one passenger (or co-pilot) on flight deck. Main cabin, separated by a bulkhead, is fitted as standard with four chairs in facing pairs, each with adjustable reclining backs and retractable armrests, plus two foldaway tables and an optional refreshment centre at front, with toilet, washbasin and storage cabinets at rear. Other layouts, and additional seating, available optionally. Airstair passenger door at front on port side. Baggage compartment aft of main cabin, with external access via port-side door aft of wing. Two-piece wraparound windscreen, birdproof and electrically heated.

SYSTEMS: Cabin pressurised to 0.69 bars (10.0 lb/sq in), and heated by engine bleed air; cooled by a freon-cycle system. Hydraulic system for actuation of spoilers, landing gear extension/retraction and nosewheel steering. Electrical DC power supplied by two 300A engine driven starter/generators, with all necessary AC provided by

Artist's impression and three-view drawing *(Pilot Press)* **of Swearingen/Jaffe SJ30 business jet**

static inverters. Redundant frequency-wild alternators provide power for windscreen heating.

AVIONICS: Bendix/King Gold Crown III dual avionics standard, including com, nav, marker beacon receivers, glideslopes, audios, HSIs, plus ADF, DME, transponder, dual inverters, compass, colour weather radar and autopilot/flight director.

DIMENSIONS, EXTERNAL:

Wing span	11.07 m (36 ft 4 in)
Wing aspect ratio	8.0
Length overall	12.90 m (42 ft 4 in)
Height overall	3.94 m (12 ft 11 in)

DIMENSIONS, INTERNAL:
Cabin: Length:

between pressure bulkheads	4.97 m (16 ft 3½ in)
passenger section	3.41 m (11 ft 2½ in)
Max width	1.43 m (4 ft 8½ in)
Max height	1.31 m (4 ft 3½ in)
Volume	8.49 m³ (300.0 cu ft)

AREA:

Wings, gross	15.33 m² (165.0 sq ft)

WEIGHTS:

Weight empty, equipped	2,585 kg (5,700 lb)
Fuel weight	1,519 kg (3,350 lb)
Max ramp weight	4,490 kg (9,900 lb)
Max zero-fuel weight	3,447 kg (7,600 lb)
Max T-O weight	4,468 kg (9,850 lb)
Max landing weight	4,309 kg (9,500 lb)

PERFORMANCE (estimated, at max T-O weight except where indicated):

Max operating speed	Mach 0.82 (470 knots; 871 km/h; 541 mph)

Max cruising speed	445 knots (824 km/h; 512 mph)
Long-range cruising speed	
	413 knots (765 km/h; 475 mph)
Stalling speed at max landing weight	
	80 knots (149 km/h; 93 mph)

Max rate of climb at S/L	1,195 m (3,920 ft)/min
Max operating altitude	12,500 m (41,000 ft)
FAA T-O balanced field length	1,015 m (3,330 ft)
FAA landing distance	762 m (2,500 ft)
Range at Mach 0.72 (413 knots; 765 km/h; 475 mph):	

NBAA VFR reserves	
	2,076 nm (3,847 km; 2,390 miles)
NBAA IFR reserves	
	1,730 nm (3,206 km; 1,992 miles)

TAYLORCRAFT
TAYLORCRAFT AIRCRAFT CORPORATION
PO Drawer 3350, 165 Scott Avenue, Suite 102, Morgantown, West Virginia 26505
Telephone: 1 (304) 291 2376
Fax: 1 (304) 292 1902
FACTORY:
820, East Bald Eagle Street, Lock Haven, Pennsylvania 17745
PRESIDENT: Darus H. Zehrbach
CHIEF ENGINEER: Darrel C. Romick
GENERAL MANAGER: Lee Anne Demus

Taylorcraft Aircraft Corporation, which was re-formed on 1 April 1968 primarily to provide product support, also put into production a two-seat trainer/sporting aircraft designated Model F-19 Sportsman 100, based on the well known Taylorcraft Model B of Second World War origin.

In early 1980, the Model F-19 (see 1979-80 *Jane's*) was taken out of production, and the company certificated a higher powered verson designated F-21. This was supplemented by a new Model F-21A for 1983, but the latter model was replaced by the F-21B (see 1989-90 *Jane's*) during 1985.

On 9 July 1985 the company was acquired by a group of former Piper Aircraft Company employees, and the production facility was moved to the Piper Memorial Airport at Lock Haven, Pennsylvania. The first production aircraft from the new assembly line was rolled out on 9 January 1986. In early 1986 Taylorcraft acquired manufacturing rights for Edo floats.

Production ceased in August 1986 after 16 aircraft had been manufactured. Taylorcraft filed for protection under Chapter 11 of the US bankruptcy laws in late 1986.

In November 1989 the company was acquired by Aircraft Acquisition Corporation (see also New Technik Corporation in this section and Taylor Kits Corporation in the Sport Aircraft section), which has taken over the Lock Haven facility. Six models have been announced, as detailed below, all employing the same basic airframe with a choice of power plant, landing gear configuration and accommodation.

In addition, Taylorcraft has announced plans to develop new models with single-strut wings, fully cantilever wings and composite wing and fuselage skins, and an entirely new low-wing design, within the next five years.

TAYLORCRAFT F-22A CLASSIC 118
Taylorcraft began construction of the first of two prototype Model F-22As on 29 December 1989 and rolled out the aircraft in mid-January 1990. The aircraft is similar in general appearance to the Taylorcraft F-21B (described in the 1989-90 *Jane's*) but incorporates a number of improvements including trailing-edge flaps, larger door, new exhaust system and choice of tailwheel or tricycle landing gear. By early March 1990 Taylorcraft had received orders for 75 Model F-22As, of which 12 had been built, excluding the prototypes.
TYPE: Two- or three-seat trainer/sporting aircraft.
WINGS: Braced high-wing monoplane with V bracing struts each side. Wing section NACA 23012. Dihedral 1°. Composite structure with aluminium I beam spars, stamped metal ribs and Dacron covering. Frise wide-span ailerons and plain trailing-edge flaps of similar construction. No trim tabs.
FUSELAGE: Welded structure of 4130 steel tube with aluminium skinned underside and Dacron covering elsewhere.
TAIL UNIT: Wire braced welded steel tube structure with Dacron covering. Trim tab in port elevator.
LANDING GEAR: Non-retractable tailwheel type; tricycle optional. Two side Vs and half-axles. Mainwheels fitted with 6.00-6 4-ply tyres; swivelling tailwheel has 8 in pneumatic tyre as standard. Nosewheel has 5.00 × 5 4-ply tyre. Dual Cleveland hydraulic toe brakes standard. Wheel fairings optional. Edo or Aqua aluminium floats and Aero M1500 or M2000 skis optional.
POWER PLANT: One 88 kW (118 hp) Textron Lycoming O-235-L2C flat-four engine, driving a Sensenich 72CK-O-50 two-blade fixed-pitch metal propeller with spinner. One fuel tank in each wing, with combined capacity of 159 litres (42 US gallons; 35 Imp gallons), of which 151 litres (40 US gallons; 33.3 Imp gallons) are usable. Oil capacity 5.7 litres (1.5 US gallons; 1.2 Imp gallons).
ACCOMMODATION: Two adjustable seats, with shoulder harness, side by side in enclosed cabin. Folding rear seat optional, to accommodate one passenger. Dual controls standard. Metal door with sliding window each side. Standard equipment includes door locks and window latches, carpeted floor and cargo tiedown straps. Baggage compartment aft of seats, standard capacity 91 kg (200 lb), and side windows. Accommodation heated and ventilated.

Taylorcraft Model F-22A Classic 118 two/three-seat light aircraft

SYSTEMS: Electrical system powered by 12V 35A engine driven alternator, with 12V storage battery. Wiring provisions for navigation lights. Engine driven vacuum pump when optional blind-flying instrumentation installed.
AVIONICS AND EQUIPMENT: Standard avionics include single com tranceiver, transponder with Mode C encoder and intercom. Full blind flying instrumentation, Bendix/King and Narco IFR avionics and II Morrow Loran C optional. Skylight and transparent doors optional.

DIMENSIONS, EXTERNAL:
Wing span	10.99 m (36 ft 1 in)
Wing chord (constant)	1.60 m (5 ft 3 in)
Length overall	6.90 m (22 ft 8½ in)
Height overall	1.98 m (6 ft 6 in)
Tailplane span	3.05 m (10 ft 0 in)
Wheel track	1.98 m (6 ft 6 in)
Propeller diameter	1.83 m (6 ft 0 in)
Passenger door: Height	0.95 m (3 ft 1½ in)
Width	0.76 m (2 ft 5¾ in)
Height to sill	0.60 m (1 ft 11½ in)

DIMENSIONS, INTERNAL:
Cabin: Length	2.68 m (8 ft 9½ in)
Max width	1.01 m (3 ft 3¾ in)
Max height	1.17 m (3 ft 10¼ in)
Floor area	2.14 m² (23.0 sq ft)
Volume	2.47 m³ (87.4 cu ft)
Baggage compartment:	
Volume	1.36 m³ (48.1 cu ft)

AREAS:
Wings, gross	17.07 m² (183.71 sq ft)
Ailerons (total)	1.86 m² (20.0 sq ft)
Trailing-edge flaps (total)	3.72 m² (40.0 sq ft)
Fin	0.49 m² (5.3 sq ft)
Rudder	0.59 m² (6.3 sq ft)
Tailplane	1.21 m² (13.0 sq ft)
Elevators (total, incl tab)	0.99 m² (10.66 sq ft)

WEIGHTS AND LOADINGS:
Weight empty	494 kg (1,090 lb)
Max T-O weight: Normal	794 kg (1,750 lb)
Utility	626 kg (1,380 lb)
Max wing loading	46.48 kg/m² (9.52 lb/sq ft)
Max power loading	9.02 kg/kW (14.83 lb/hp)

PERFORMANCE (at max T-O weight except where indicated):
Never-exceed speed	128 knots (238 km/h; 148 mph)
Max level speed	108 knots (201 km/h; 125 mph)
Max cruising speed at 2,745 m (9,000 ft)	
	102 knots (188 km/h; 117 mph)
Econ cruising speed at 3,810 m (12,500 ft)	
	95 knots (175 km/h; 109 mph)
Stalling speed: flaps up	42 knots (78 km/h; 48 mph)
flaps down	36 knots (66 km/h; 41 mph)
Max rate of climb at S/L	229 m (750 ft)/min
Service ceiling	5,485 m (18,000 ft)
T-O run	220 m (720 ft)
T-O to 15 m (50 ft)	348 m (1,140 ft)
Landing from 15 m (50 ft)	221 m (725 ft)
Landing run	149 m (487 ft)
Range, 75% power with 30 min reserves	
	555 nm (1,028 km; 639 miles)
g limits:	
Normal category, max T-O weight	+3.8/−1.52
Utility category at 626 kg (1,380 lb) AUW	
	+4.4/−1.76

TAYLORCRAFT MODEL AA-23 STOL 180 and AA-23A1 RANGER
Construction of the prototype Model **AA-23 STOL 180** began on 2 January 1990, with first flight on 23 February and certification scheduled for April. By early March 1990

Taylorcraft held orders for 35 STOL 180s, of which six had been built.

The Model **AA-23A1 Ranger** is a police/patrol version of the STOL 180, one prototype of which has been built.

The description for the Model F-22A Classic 118 applies also to these models except as follows:
TYPE: Two/three-seat light utility aircraft.
WINGS: Ranger has provision for three external stores racks under each wing.
LANDING GEAR: Fixed tailwheel or tricycle type. Edo 1800 floats, and skis, optional.
POWER PLANT: One 134 kW (180 hp) Textron Lycoming O-360 driving a Sensenich two-blade fixed-pitch metal propeller. Standard fuel capacity as for Classic 118; two auxiliary wing tanks optional, bringing total fuel capacity to 318 litres (84 US gallons; 70 Imp gallons). Oil capacity 7.6 litres (2 US gallons; 1.67 Imp gallons).
ACCOMMODATION: Pilot and observer in Ranger, with removable seats. Kevlar ballistic armour and bullet-resistant clear doors optional.
AVIONICS AND EQUIPMENT: VHF and police band transceivers optional. Kevlar armour, underwing dispensers for riot control agents, loudspeaker system, and searchlights, optional.

DIMENSIONS, EXTERNAL:
| Propeller diameter | 1.93 m (6 ft 4 in) |
| Propeller ground clearance | 0.25 m (10 in) |

PERFORMANCE:
Never-exceed speed	128 knots (238 km/h; 148 mph)
Max level speed	124 knots (230 km/h; 143 mph)
Max cruising speed	119 knots (220 km/h; 137 mph)
Max rate of climb at S/L	
	more than 457 m (1,500 ft)/min
Service ceiling	5,485 m (18,000 ft)
T-O run	45 m (146 ft)
T-O to 15 m (50 ft)	65 m (213 ft)

TAYLORCRAFT MODEL AA-23B AEROBAT and AA-23B1 RS
Taylorcraft began construction of the first of two prototype Model **AA-23B Aerobats** in December 1989 and first flew the aircraft in March 1990. The Aerobat shares the 134 kW (180 hp) Textron Lycoming O-360 power plant of the STOL 180, but features a wing of semi-symmetrical section and reduced span, revised cowling design with ram air cooling intake, transparent cockpit doors with quick-release mechanisms, and dual bracing wires on the tail surfaces.

The Model **AA-23B1 RS** (RennSport) is a limited edition aerobatic development of the Aerobat featuring napa leather interior, custom seats and Bendix/King IFR avionics package.

The description of the STOL 180 applies also to the Aerobat and RS except as follows:
TYPE: One/two-seat sport and competition aerobatic aircraft.
WINGS: 'Clipped' wings, section NACA 230.
TAIL UNIT: Two trim tabs, one servo, and one anti-servo.
LANDING GEAR: Tailwheel type only in Aerobat, tailwheel or nosewheel type in RS.
POWER PLANT: One 134 kW (180 hp) Textron Lycoming O-360-A1F6, driving a Hartzell or McCauley three-blade constant-speed metal propeller. Auxiliary fuel tanks not available.
ACCOMMODATION: One/two-seat, interchangeable, in Aerobat, two/three seats in RS. Transparent cockpit doors, with quick release mechanisms.
AVIONICS: Bendix/King IFR package comprising dual nav/com, ADF, DME, glideslope receiver, audio panel and II Morrow 604TCA or 618 Loran C standard in RS.

PERFORMANCE:

Never-exceed speed	160 knots (297 km/h; 185 mph)
Max level speed	156 knots (290 km/h; 180 mph)
Max cruising speed	152 knots (282 km/h; 175 mph)
Econ cruising speed	139 knots (257 km/h; 160 mph)
Max rate of climb at S/L	701 m (2,300 ft)/min
Service ceiling	5,485 m (18,000 ft)
T-O run	77 m (252 ft)
T-O to 15 m (50 ft)	107 m (350 ft)

TAYLORCRAFT AGCRAFT

Taylorcraft is developing an agricultural variant of the STOL 180 designed for ultra-low volume aerial application and known as the Agcraft. The aircraft will have a redesigned cockpit to provide additional pilot protection and will feature hands-on-throttle-and-stick (HOTAS) controls. FAA certification was anticipated in September 1990.

Taylorcraft Model AA-23B Aerobat 'clipped wing' aerobatic aircraft

TCM

TELEDYNE CONTINENTAL MOTORS

PO Box 90, Mobile, Alabama 36601
Telephone: 1 (205) 438 3411

Teledyne Continental Motors has developed Voyager liquid-cooled engine retrofit programmes for Beechcraft Bonanza and Piper Navajo Chieftain aircraft. The Bonanza conversion can be carried out on late-production Model A36 and all Model B36TC Bonanzas and involves replacing the standard 212.5 kW (285 hp) Teledyne Continental IO-520-BB or 224 kW (300 hp) IO-550-B/TSIO-520-UB power plant with a turbocharged liquid-cooled 224 kW (300 hp) Voyager T-550 engine with single-lever power control, driving a new three-blade McCauley propeller. The modification includes a new front cowling with single air inlet below the spinner, and moves the propeller arc forward by about 7.6 cm (3 in). TCM flew a prototype installation in a Model A36 Bonanza (N9127Q) during the Summer of 1989. Certification by Supplemental Type Certificate and first customer conversions were expected in the third quarter of 1990. Claimed performance improvements include a 20 knot (37 km/h; 23 mph) increase in high altitude cruising speed.

The Navajo Chieftain conversion replaces the aircraft's 261 kW (350 hp) Textron Lycoming TIO-540 engines with 298 kW (400 hp) liquid-cooled turbocharged and intercooled TCM Voyager GT-550 power plants in new cowlings with single air inlets. Certification was scheduled for late 1990. Claimed improvements include an increased TBO of 2,000 h, enhanced cruising speed and a 75 per cent increase in engine-out climb performance.

TELEDYNE RYAN

TELEDYNE RYAN AERONAUTICAL

PO Box 85311, San Diego, California 92186-5311
Telephone: 1 (619) 291 7311
Telex: 910 335 1180 TDYRYN SDG
Fax: 1 (619) 260 5400
PRESIDENT: Robert A. Mitchell
VICE-PRESIDENT, ENGINEERING: Darrel L. Hirsch
VICE-PRESIDENT, MARKETING: R. A. Johnson

For many years the major production items of Teledyne Ryan Aeronautical have been the Firebee series of jet powered targets and special purpose vehicles (pre-programmed and remotely piloted) for various types of reconnaissance mission. The most recent of these is the Model 410.

TELEDYNE RYAN MODEL 410

The Model 410 was designed for long-range or long-endurance reconnaissance/surveillance (manned or unmanned), and related unmanned missions such as electronic countermeasures. A prototype (N53578) was completed in the Autumn of 1987 and made its first (manned) flight on 27 May 1988. An initial test programme, comprising seven flights and 36 take-offs and landings, has been completed.

Ability to stay aloft with a 45.4 kg (100 lb) payload for 24 hours, and to use unimproved airstrips or short stretches of roadway, are features of the design. Maximum equipment load, in unmanned form, is 227 kg (500 lb), allowing the use of standard sized rather than specially miniaturised sensors. The Model 410's exceptionally long endurance permits either great range or extended loiter capability, or combinations of the two, conferring considerable potential for cost-effective military reconnaissance as well as civilian surveillance of coastlines, borders or other sensitive areas. As initially configured, with a 2:1 turbocharger ratio, it can fly at an altitude of more than 9,150 m (30,000 ft). In unmanned form, the Model 410 can be equipped to fly autonomous (pre-programmed) missions beyond the range of ground controllers, or can be flown as an RPV with a direct data link, carrying frame or video cameras. Also claimed are all-weather and day/night operation.

AIRFRAME: Cantilever high-wing monoplane, of pod-and-twin-boom configuration, fitted with wing trailing-edge flaps and conventional three-axis control surfaces (ailerons, elevator and rudders). Main structure is built using glassfibre/epoxy skins with an infill of high-density structural foam plastics. Wings have graphite/epoxy spars and can be detached for transportation and storage. Tricycle landing gear has non-retractable mainwheels mounted on cantilever self-sprung legs of graphite/epoxy;

Teledyne Ryan Model 410 on manned flight test

nosewheel can be fully retracted rearward to avoid interference with forward looking sensors. For manned flight test phase, prototype was fitted with a single-seat cockpit under a sideways opening teardrop canopy.

POWER PLANT: One 119 kW (160 hp) Textron Lycoming TIO-320-C1B flat-four turbocharged engine, mounted in rear of fuselage pod and driving a three-blade pusher propeller with spinner. All fuel is carried in integral tanks in wings.

AVIONICS AND EQUIPMENT: Flight control system can store multiple mission programmes, and can be re-programmed in flight or controlled from a base station when aircraft is within range. Data link range can be supplemented by relaying data via land, sea or air vehicles, including other Model 410s. Both real-time data transmission and onboard data recording are standard. Ground control centre permits a two-person crew to monitor eight Model 410s and their sensors via a two-way long-range data link.

DIMENSIONS, EXTERNAL:

Wing span	9.55 m (31 ft 4 in)
Width, wings removed	2.03 m (6 ft 8 in)
Length overall	6.60 m (21 ft 8 in)
Propeller diameter	1.60 m (5 ft 3 in)

DIMENSIONS, INTERNAL:

Payload compartment volume	0.68 m³ (24.0 cu ft)

WEIGHTS:

Max payload	227 kg (500 lb)
Max T-O weight	816.5 kg (1,800 lb)

PERFORMANCE:

Max level speed	174 knots (322 km/h; 200 mph)
Typical operating speed range	85-140 knots (157-259 km/h; 98-161 mph)
Service ceiling	9,150 m (30,000 ft)
T-O run	275 m (900 ft)
Max endurance at 3,050 m (10,000 ft)	
with 45.4 kg (100 lb) payload	22 h
with 136 kg (300 lb) payload	14 h

TRADEWIND

TRADEWIND TURBINES

PO Box 31930, Amarillo, Texas 79120

Telephone: 1 (806) 376 5203

Fax: 1 (806) 376 9725

PRINCIPAL: Joe C. Boyd

TRADEWIND PROP-JET BONANZA

Allison Gas Turbine Division, in conjunction with Soloy Conversions Ltd (which see), obtained FAA certification of a turboprop conversion of the Beechcraft Model A36 Bonanza, known initially as the Allison Prop-Jet Bonanza. The STC for the conversion was subsequently sold to Tradewind Turbines, which continues to manufacture and market the aircraft. The conversion involves replacement of the Bonanza's standard 212.5 kW (285 hp) Teledyne Continental IO-520-BB piston engine with an Allison 250-B17C turboprop rated at 313 kW (420 shp) and driving a three-blade metal fully-feathering and reversing Hartzell propeller.

During the course of conversion two additional support spars are added to the bottom of the aircraft's fuselage for added strength, and the lighter Allison engine is installed

0.53 m (1 ft 9 in) further forward than the original power plant, to maintain the aircraft's centre of gravity position. A new engine mount and cowlings are provided. The resulting space behind the engine installation is available for baggage stowage, maximum capacity 54 kg (120 lb). Other standard modifications include new engine and propeller controls, new fuel lines with a Shadin fuel flow monitor, Osborne wingtip tanks, (each of 75.7 litres; 20 US gallons; 16.6 Imp gallons capacity, bringing total usable fuel capacity to 424 litres; 112 US gallons; 93 Imp gallons) each incorporating a small sweptback outward canted winglet on the upper surface, a 24V electrical system with Gill lead-acid battery and 150A starter/generator, dual actuators for the elevator trim tabs, audible V_{NE} overspeed warning, Casey cabin heating system, nosecowl mounted landing light, and Goodrich propeller de-icing system. Optional equipment includes an oxygen system, air-conditioning and alternative instrument air supply. The conversion is available for post-1979 Model A36 and A36TC Bonanzas, but not the F33. Allison had received orders for 18 Prop-Jet Bonanzas, of which 17 had been completed, by February 1989.

DIMENSIONS, EXTERNAL:
Wing span, between tips of winglets	10.20 m (33 ft 5½ in)
Length overall	8.89 m (29 ft 2 in)
Height overall	2.62 m (8 ft 7 in)
Tailplane span	3.71 m (12 ft 2 in)
Wheel track	2.92 m (9 ft 7 in)
Propeller diameter	2.29 m (7 ft 6 in)
Propeller ground clearance	0.18 m (7¼ in)

WEIGHTS:
Weight empty	1,089 kg (2,400 lb)
Max ramp weight	1,746 kg (3,849 lb)
Max T-O weight	1,739 kg (3,833 lb)
Max landing weight	1,656 kg (3,650 lb)

PERFORMANCE:
Max level speed	210 knots (389 km/h; 242 mph)
Cruising speed:	
at 4,575 m (15,000 ft)	200 knots (370 km/h; 230 mph)
at 6,100 m (20,000 ft)	195 knots (361 km/h; 224 mph)
Stalling speed, flight idle power:	
flaps up	65 knots (120 km/h; 75 mph)
flaps down	57 knots (106 km/h; 66 mph)

Tradewind Prop-Jet Bonanza conversion of the Beechcraft Model A36 Bonanza

Max rate of climb at S/L, at max T-O weight	579 m (1,900 ft)/min
Service ceiling	above 7,620 m (25,000 ft)
T-O run, 15° flap	177 m (580 ft)
T-O to 15 m (50 ft), 15° flap	244 m (800 ft)
Landing from 15 m (50 ft), 30° flap	160 m (525 ft)
Landing run, 30° flap	99 m (325 ft)

Range, with max fuel, allowances for start, taxi, T-O, climb and 45 min reserves at max cruising power:
at 3,050 m (10,000 ft)	820 nm (1,520 km; 944 miles)
at 4,575 m (15,000 ft)	985 nm (1,825 km; 1,134 miles)
at 6,100 m (20,000 ft)	1,065 nm (1,974 km; 1,226 miles)

TRIDAIR
TRIDAIR HELICOPTERS INC
3000 Airway Avenue, Costa Mesa, California 92626
Telephone: 1 (714) 540 3000
PRESIDENT: Douglas Daigle

TRIDAIR MODEL 206L-3ST GEMINI ST
This company is developing a twin-engined conversion of the Bell 206L LongRanger helicopter which involves replacing the standard 485 kW (650 shp) Allison 250-C30P turboshaft with two 324 kW (435 shp) 250-C20Rs, each with a maximum continuous rating of 276 kW (370 shp). Fuel capacity will be 416 litres (110 US gallons; 91.6 Imp gallons). Soloy Conversions Ltd is developing the engine installation and combining gearbox. The prototype Gemini ST was expected to make its first flight in late 1990, with certification anticipated during 1991. Tridair expects to have converted 50 aircraft by the end of 1993 and is establishing approved installation centres throughout the United States to carry out the conversions.
The following data are provisional:

WEIGHTS:
Weight empty	1,175 kg (2,590 lb)
Max external load	907 kg (2,000 lb)
Max T-O weight	2,018 kg (4,450 lb)

PERFORMANCE (estimated):
Never-exceed speed	130 knots (241 km/h; 150 mph)
Max cruising speed	117 knots (217 km/h; 135 mph)
Max rate of climb at S/L	408 m (1,340 ft)/min
Service ceiling	6,100 m (20,000 ft)
Hovering ceiling: IGE	5,030 m (16,500 ft)
OGE	2,285 m (7,500 ft)

TURBOTECH
TURBOTECH INC
Pearson Air Park, 1115 E 5th Street, PO Box 61586, Vancouver, Washington 98666
Telephone: 1 (206) 694 6287
PRESIDENT: L. W. Soukup

Turbotech Inc (formerly Seaplanes Inc) is carrying out performance improvements to a variety of lightplanes. Performance increases result largely from replacing the original power plant with an engine of increased power and reliability. In addition to more than 30 multiple Supplemental Type Certificates produced during the company's 18-year life, Turbotech has completed many engine model changes and add-on turbo packages on a one-time basis, all thoroughly tested and certificated by the FAA. Most recent of these endeavours has been the installation of 261 kW (350 hp) Textron Lycoming engines on a Grumman Widgeon.

Turbotech obtained development multiple Supplemental Type Certificates during 1982 for two engine modifications on the Cessna 185. These cover the installation of a 261 kW (350 hp) Textron Lycoming TIO-540-J2BD, and the introduction of a Garrett turbocharger for the 224 kW (300 hp) Continental IO-520-D of the standard Cessna 185. The conversions give the aircraft full performance to a service ceiling of 7,620 m (25,000 ft) and 7,315 m (24,000 ft) respectively. The Cessna 206 has also been approved with the 261 kW (350 hp) Textron Lycoming TIO-540-J2BD turbocharged engine. A gross weight increase of 93 kg (250 lb) with installation of wingtip tanks was approved in July 1983.
Other developments include the installation of a turbocharger on a 224 kW (300 hp) Teledyne Continental IO-520-D for the Cessna 180, and an add-on turbocharger modification on the Gulfstream American AA-5B Tiger powered by a 134 kW (180 hp) Textron Lycoming O-360-A4K flat-four engine.
Power plant replacements also include removal of the existing engine from Cessna 170, 172 and 175, and Stinson 108 aircraft, and the installation of a 164 kW (220 hp) Franklin flat-six engine and constant-speed propeller. The 186 kW (250 hp) turbocharged Franklin, also with constant-speed propeller, can be installed in the Cessna 172 and 175, Stinson 108 and Waco Vela. This power plant is used for installation in the Maule M-5 Lunar Rocket in lieu of a 156 kW (210 hp) Teledyne Continental or 164 kW (220 hp) Franklin engine. The 172 kW (230 hp) Teledyne Continental O-470 is also available for the Stinson 108. Feasibility studies are in progress for engine conversions for the Cessna 207, 210, 182 and 180.

TWIN COMMANDER
TWIN COMMANDER AIRCRAFT CORPORATION
19003 59th Drive N. E., Arlington, Washington 98223
Telephone: 1 (206) 435 9797
Fax: 1 (206) 435 1112

PRESIDENT: Dan Montgomery
In December 1989 this company acquired from Gulfstream Aerospace Corporation product support, manufacturing and marketing rights for the Commander series of twin piston-engined and turboprop business aircraft, production of which was suspended in 1984. Initially Twin Commander Aircraft will manufacture and distribute spare parts for the existing Commander fleet, but in early 1990 was also negotiating with groups outside the United States for possible production of new aircraft.

USAF
UNITED STATES AIR FORCE SYSTEMS COMMAND
Aeronautical Systems Division, Wright-Patterson AFB, Dayton, Ohio 45433-6503
Telephone: 1 (513) 255 3334

PUBLIC AFFAIRS OFFICER: Capt Jamie S. Scearse

ATF PROGRAMME DIRECTOR: Colonel James A. Fain Jr

USAF ADVANCED TACTICAL FIGHTER (ATF)
US Air Force designations: YF-22A and YF-23A
The Advanced Tactical Fighter (ATF) programme is intended to meet a United States Air Force requirement for a new air superiority fighter to replace the McDonnell Douglas F-15 Eagle in the 1990s. The ATF programme also includes development of an advanced technology engine for the aircraft. Concept definition study contracts were awarded in September 1983 to Boeing, General Dynamics, Grumman, Lockheed, McDonnell Douglas, Northrop and Rockwell. These companies submitted their prototype design proposals to the USAF on 28 July 1986.
On 31 October 1986 the USAF announced the selection of Lockheed-Burbank and Northrop to begin the demonstration/validation phase of the ATF programme. Under respective designations YF-22A and YF-23A, each contractor is building two flying prototypes and a ground based avionics testbed for demonstration and validation purposes, leading to selection of the successful ATF contender in May 1991, when the full scale development phase will begin. The prototypes were expected to fly in

mid-1990, and the first of 24 FSD ATFs in FY 1994. The timetable was delayed when, on 11 October 1989, the USAF announced a six-month extension to the evaluation phase. A draft request for full-scale development proposals was re-scheduled for April 1990; a final request was to follow in October of the same year, and announcement of the winner in May 1991. On this schedule, deliveries will begin in 1996 and peak at 48 in 2001.

Engines for the ATF are being developed from ground demonstrator power plants which began testing in 1987. Pratt & Whitney's PW5000-derived prototype engine is designated YF119 and General Electric's YF120. The YF119 will fly first in the YF-23A, and the YF120 in the YF-22A, but each of the prototype aircraft will be required to fly with GE and P&W engines.

Design goals for the ATF include greatly improved reliability and maintainability, with high sortie generation rates, increased survivability achieved through 'first-look, first-kill' opportunities using low observable 'stealth' techniques and passive sensors. Compared to current front-line fighters the ATF will have significantly reduced T-O and landing distances, increased supersonic cruise (Mach 1.5 without afterburning) and manoeuvrability performance, and greatly increased combat radius on internal fuel.

Airframe design draws on the most recent advances in flight control, including the use of fibre optics and digital flight control for stability and handling, and widespread use of composite materials. Technologies being evaluated include low-observable 'stealth' techniques, conformal sensors and hydraulically actuated weapons racks. The ATF is designed to carry existing and planned air-to-air weapons including AMRAAM, AIM-9 Sidewinder and ASRAAM, and will be equipped with an internal long-barrel 20 mm M61A1 gun. Power plant technologies under evaluation include integrated flight/propulsion controls, STOL capability and two-dimensional convergent/divergent engine nozzles. Flat panel CRT displays, extra-wide field of view HUDs, techniques for enhanced *g* load tolerance, and advanced display processing, are among technologies which may be incorporated in the ATF's advanced cockpit concept.

The USAF stated a requirement for up to 750 ATFs, but this may be reduced. The US Navy is also evaluating the ATF as a possible replacement for the Grumman F-14 Tomcat as a fleet air defence interceptor at the end of this century.

C-27

The USAF's C-27 requirement is for a twin-turboprop STOL transport, with a rear-loading ramp/door, for the intra-theatre airlift of troops and cargo (payload capacity 4,536 kg; 10,000 lb) using short and/or impaired runways. Initial plans were to order ten C-27s in FY 1988 and 1989, with option for a further eight to be funded in FY 1990, but deletion of funds for the first five from the 1988 budget resulted in the programme being deferred for re-definition of the requirement. C-27 was revived in 1989 for projected FY 1990 issue of a request for proposals and a subsequent order for 10 of the chosen aircraft to serve US Southern Command from FY 1992 onwards. Likely candidates are Boeing Canada Dash 8, Aeritalia G222 and Airtech CN-235.

TTTS

Early in 1990, the USAF selected the Beechjet 400 (which see) to meet the TTTS (Tanker/Transport Training System) requirement. Name and designation will be T-1A Jayhawk.

STRATEGIC RECONNAISSANCE AIRCRAFT

According to early 1988 press reports, US Defense Department officials have confirmed that a new long-range

Artist's impression of a possible configuration for the USAF's Advanced Tactical Fighter

F-111G (68-0286) following conversion from FB-111A, but still temporarily with SAC's 380th BW in 1989, pending transfer to TAC *(Paul Jackson)*

reconnaissance aircraft is being developed to replace the USAF's SR-71. The only details given were that the new aircraft is being designed for speeds of up to 3,300 knots (6,100 km/h; 3,800 mph) and altitudes of above 30,500 m (100,000 ft), will have in-flight refuelling capability, and will employ the latest low-observables 'stealth' design techniques and materials. It is generally believed that Lockheed's Burbank division is the prime contractor and that the programme is codenamed 'Aurora'.

The SR-71, meanwhile, was retired from USAF service in December 1989, although three will continue to fly in service with NASA and three others have been placed in storage in case of future need.

GENERAL DYNAMICS F-111G

Under a programme initiated after the signing of the INF Treaty in 1988, the US Air Force's Air Logistics Center at Sacramento, California, is modifying Strategic Air Command General Dynamics FB-111A aircraft for dual-role service with units of the Tactical Air Command under the designation **F-111G**. Under the modification programme, the FB-111A's short range attack missile

(SRAM) system for stand-off nuclear delivery is retained, and a conventional weapons release system is installed to provide dual-role capability. Other improvements include Have Quick UHF radio and a new ECM system. It is thought that the F-111G will be deployed initially with SRAM and later with AGM-131A SRAM II missiles. The first two F-111G conversions were completed in early 1989. The programme is due to continue until 1994, at the rate of approximately 12 aircraft per year. F-111Gs and FB-111As will be transferred from SAC to TAC between June and December 1990. Deployment in Europe was considered, but the aircraft will now be added to the 27th TFW at Cannon AFB, NM, (augmenting F-111Ds) following the 1990-91 disbandments of SAC's 509th BW at Pease AFB, NH, and 380th BW at Plattsburgh AFB, NY. The USAF has 62 FB-111s/F-111Gs.

A request for proposals was expected early in 1990 for an EF-111A upgrade known as the System Improvement Program (SIP) and including a new signal processor and replacement of the exciters which generate modulation for jamming.

Details of other current F-111 programmes will be found under the Rockwell heading.

VALSAN
VALSAN PARTNERS

99 Washington Street, Norwalk, Connecticut 06854
Telephone: 1 (203) 866 6051
Telex: 6714726 DALAU UW
Fax: 1 (203) 855 0362
PRESIDENT: Robert E. Wagenfeld
VICE-PRESIDENT, MARKETING: Walter H. Johnson

VALSAN 727RE 'QUIET 727'

Valsan has developed a programme for re-engining the Boeing 727-200 to enable the aircraft to meet the more stringent noise regulations of FAR Pt 36 Stage 3 and ICAO Annex 16 Chapter 3. Conversion of a Sterling Airways 727-200A 'prototype' (OY-SAS) began in late 1987 and was completed in June 1988, with first flight following on 12 July and award of a Supplemental Type Certificate granted in October 1988. This aircraft entered service with Sterling Airways in November 1988. The modification, carried out by Rockwell International, Palmdale, California, and Sterling Airways, involves acoustic treatment of the centre engine, and removal of its thrust reverser, and replacement of the outer pair of engines with two Pratt & Whitney

Valsan Partners 'Quiet 727' conversion of the Boeing 727-200RE for Federal Express

JT8D-217C turbofans. Empty weight is increased by 1,542 kg (3,400 lb); zero-fuel weight by 1,361 kg (3,000 lb); max landing weight reduced by 907 kg (2,000 lb). Performance improvements include 24 per cent increase in max rate of climb at S/L; 27 per cent improvement in T-O distances; and a 300 nm (556 km; 345 miles) increase in range. In January 1990 Valsan reported 71 firm orders and 139 options for this modification, and had completed five aircraft.

Flight testing of a 727 with added winglets was expected to begin in March 1990 and to have achieved certification by June. Other future modifications being considered include stretched cargo and passenger versions of the 727-200, with plugs of 2.54 m (8 ft 4 in) forward of the wing and 2.03 m (6 ft 8 in) aft; and a two-person 'glass cockpit' with EICAS (electronic engine instrument and crew alerting system) and dual computers and CRT displays. Valsan has also launched a programme to achieve certification of its engine retrofit for the Boeing 727-100. Modification of the first customer aircraft began in February 1990 with certification expected in June. When re-engined, the executive configuration aircraft was expected to have a range in excess of 4,000 nm (7,412 km; 4,606 miles).

OPERATIONAL NOISE LEVELS (727-200RE):

T-O	95.6 EPNdB
Approach	98.3 EPNdB
Sideline	97.4 EPNdB

VARDAX

VARDAX CORPORATION

3025 Eldridge Avenue, Bellingham, Washington 98225
Telephone: 1 (206) 671 7817
Fax: 1 (206) 671 7820
PRESIDENT: Dara Wilder

Vardax Corporation is responsible for marketing a turboprop conversion of the DHC-3 Otter known as the Vazar Dash 3. The prototype conversion was performed by Serv-Aero Engineering Inc of Salinas, California, and received a multiple Supplemental Type Certificate from the FAA.

VARDAX VAZAR DASH 3

The Dash 3 is a DHC-3 Otter re-engined with a 559 kW (750 shp) Pratt & Whitney Canada PT6A-135 turboprop, which provides improved performance and a 331 kg (730 lb) increase in useful load. The prototype (N9707B), completed in 1986, is shown in an accompanying illustration. By January 1990 Vardax had received orders for 10 Vazar Dash 3 conversions, of which five had been completed. Conversion time is approximately six weeks. The aircraft is certificated for operation on wheel and ski landing gear, and on Edo 7170 floats and Edo 7490 amphibious floats. Full details of the standard DHC-3 can be found in the 1967-68 *Jane's*.

DIMENSIONS, EXTERNAL:
As for standard DHC-3, except:
Length overall   14.02 m (46 ft 0 in)

Prototype Vardax Vazar Dash 3 turboprop conversion of a DHC-3 Otter STOL transport

WEIGHTS:			
Weight empty	3,770 kg (8,201 lb)	Max rate of climb at S/L	365 m (1,200 ft)/min
Max T-O weight	3,630 kg (8,000 lb)	Service ceiling, as tested by July 1988	4,875 m (16,000 ft)
PERFORMANCE (at max T-O weight):		T-O run	171 m (560 ft)
Max cruising speed at 3,050 m (10,000 ft)		T-O to 15 m (50 ft)	278 m (910 ft)
	144 knots (267 km/h; 166 mph)	Landing from 15 m (50 ft)	183 m (600 ft)
Stalling speed: flaps up	63 knots (117 km/h; 73 mph)	Landing run	95 m (310 ft)
flaps down	50 knots (93 km/h; 58 mph)	Endurance	5 h 18 min
		Range	649 nm (1,203 km; 748 miles)

VAT

VERTICAL AVIATION TECHNOLOGIES INC

1732 Hangar Road, Sanford, Florida 32771
Telephone: 1 (407) 322 9488
PRESIDENT: Bradley G. Clark
VICE-PRESIDENT: Ronald Mander
CONSULTANT ENGINEER: Ralph Alex

VAT S-52-3

Vertical Aviation Technologies was formed to develop and market improved and updated versions of the Sikorsky S-52 four-seat helicopter, which will be offered in kit form. A prototype (N9329R), fitted with a reconfigured glassfibre nosecone, new windscreen, restyled vertical tail surfaces and electric trim system, was first flown in February 1988 and is being tested for compliance with FAA Supplemental Type Certificate requirements. Vertical Aviation has replaced the S-52's standard 183 kW (245 hp) Franklin O-425-1 piston engine with a 231 kW (310 hp) watercooled Ford V-6 power plant. Fuel capacity is 216 litres (57 US gallons; 47 Imp gallons); oil capacity 11 litres (3 US gallons; 2.5 Imp gallons). Main rotor/engine rpm ratio 1:9.909. Tail rotor/engine rpm ratio 1:1.785. Assembly time for the helicopter is estimated at 1,000 man hours.

DIMENSIONS, EXTERNAL:
Main rotor diameter	10.06 m (33 ft 0 in)
Main rotor blade chord	0.26 m (10¼ in)
Tail rotor diameter	1.75 m (5 ft 9 in)
Length: overall, rotors turning	12.11 m (39 ft 9 in)
fuselage	9.27 m (30 ft 5 in)

Prototype Vertical Aviation Technologies S-52-3 conversion of Sikorsky S-52 helicopter

Height: to top of rotor hub	2.62 m (8 ft 7 in)	WEIGHTS:	
overall	2.87 m (9 ft 5 in)	Weight empty	771 kg (1,700 lb)
Wheel track	2.49 m (8 ft 2 in)	Max T-O weight	1,225 kg (2,700 lb)
Wheelbase	1.88 m (6 ft 2 in)	PERFORMANCE (at S/L):	
DIMENSIONS, INTERNAL:		Never-exceed speed	95 knots (176 km/h; 109 mph)
Cabin: Length	2.67 m (8 ft 9 in)	Cruising speed	85 knots (157 km/h; 98 mph)
Width	1.24 m (4 ft 1 in)	Max rate of climb	335 m (1,100 ft)/min
AREAS:		Service ceiling	3,350 m (11,000 ft)
Main rotor disc	79.46 m² (855.3 sq ft)		
Tail rotor disc	2.15 m² (23.2 sq ft)		

VERILITE

VERILITE AIRCRAFT COMPANY INC
(a subsidiary of De Vore Aviation Corporation)

6104B Kircher Boulevard NE, Albuquerque, New Mexico 87109
Telephone: 1 (505) 345 8713
Telex: 660436
Fax: 1 (505) 344 3835
PRESIDENT: Gilbert De Vore
DIRECTOR OF MARKETING: Jonathan Bent

Founded in 1954, De Vore Aviation specialised initially in consultancy and contract engineering services for aircraft manufacturers. In 1969 it acquired manufacturing rights to the PK range of seaplane and amphibian floats, and was appointed exclusive supplier of Aerojet General aircraft standby rocket engines (formerly known as JATO). In 1970 De Vore developed its Tel-Tail aircraft vertical tail floodlighting system, and in 1976 began development of a single-box airport visual approach aid, the pulsed light approach slope indicator (PLASI) which has been FAA approved for fixed- and rotating-wing aircraft. In October 1983 De Vore formed Verilite Aircraft Company Inc and announced its entry into light aircraft manufacturing.

VERILITE MODEL 100 SUNBIRD

The design goal for the Sunbird 'Affordable Airplane' was to produce a light aeroplane to sell for approximately 35-50 per cent less than comparable two-seat training aircraft. Detail design work began in the Spring of 1985 and was followed by wind tunnel tests of a one-sixth scale model at NASA Langley and flight tests of an instrumented one-quarter scale radio controlled model.

Taxying trials of the prototype took place at Albuquerque in February 1987, in the course of which the aircraft was accidentally damaged. After rebuilding and the incorporation of some small improvements a so-called second prototype (N100VL) flew successfully on 5 October 1987 and had completed some 25 hours of flight testing by February 1989, at which time it was being rebuilt to incorporate an increase in wing angle of incidence and a new engine cowling design. Static testing of the composite wing, flap and aileron structures was completed in December 1988. NASA Langley co-operated in the tunnel testing of the partially drooped leading-edge which gives the Sunbird 'unspinnable' flying characteristics.

TYPE: Two-seat single-engined light aircraft.

WINGS: Strut braced high-wing monoplane. Wing section NACA 64₁212 Mod B inboard, with extended drooped leading-edge from 54% semi-span outboard. Dihedral 2°. Incidence 4° at root, 2° at tip. No sweepback. Single bracing strut on each side. Structure of foam core sandwich with pre-preg glassfibre faces. Plain flaps and ailerons of same construction as wings. Ailerons have internal spring trim.

FUSELAGE: Aluminium keel and bulkheads, with skins of pre-preg glassfibre/foam core sandwich.

TAIL UNIT: Cantilever structure of pre-preg glassfibre/foam core sandwich. Elevators and rudder have internal spring trim system.

LANDING GEAR: Non-retractable tricycle type. Bungee suspension on nosewheel leg; aluminium spring struts on main units. Tyre size (all) 5.00-5; pressure 2.14 bars (31.0 lb/sq in). Brakes on mainwheels.

POWER PLANT: One 52.2 kW (70 hp) Emdair CF-092B two-cylinder four-stroke engine, driving a two-blade fixed-pitch pusher propeller. Single fuel tank in centre-section, capacity 49 litres (13 US gallons; 10.8 Imp gallons).

ACCOMMODATION: Two seats, side by side, in fully enclosed cabin. Canopy slides forward for access. Baggage area behind seats, capacity 22.7 kg (50 lb). Ram air ventilation.

SYSTEM: Generator/battery electrical system for engine starting, minimum avionics and navigation lights.

AVIONICS: Nav/com optional. VOR standard.

DIMENSIONS, EXTERNAL:

Wing span	10.39 m (34 ft 1 in)
Wing chord: at root	1.25 m (4 ft 1¼ in)
at tip	1.29 m (4 ft 2¾ in)
Wing aspect ratio	8.26

Length overall	7.21 m (23 ft 7¾ in)
Height overall	2.54 m (8 ft 4 in)
Tailplane span	3.28 m (10 ft 9 in)
Wheel track	2.08 m (6 ft 10 in)
Wheelbase	2.44 m (8 ft 0 in)
Propeller diameter	1.78 m (5 ft 10 in)
Passenger door: Height	0.86 m (2 ft 10 in)
Width	1.11 m (3 ft 8 in)
Height to sill	0.63 m (2 ft 1 in)

DIMENSIONS, INTERNAL:

Cabin: Length	1.73 m (5 ft 8 in)
Max width	1.01 m (3 ft 4 in)
Max height	1.14 m (3 ft 9 in)
Floor area	1.58 m² (17.0 sq ft)
Volume	approx 1.42 m³ (50.0 cu ft)

AREAS:

Wings, gross	13.08 m² (140.8 sq ft)
Ailerons (total)	0.98 m² (10.59 sq ft)
Trailing-edge flaps (total)	1.81 m² (19.50 sq ft)
Fin	0.80 m² (8.60 sq ft)
Rudder	0.59 m² (6.30 sq ft)
Tailplane	1.58 m² (17.00 sq ft)
Elevators (total)	1.12 m² (12.10 sq ft)

WEIGHTS:

Weight empty	345 kg (760 lb)
Max T-O weight	567 kg (1,250 lb)

PERFORMANCE:

Never-exceed speed at S/L	
	132 knots (245 km/h; 152 mph)
Max level speed at S/L	111 knots (206 km/h; 128 mph)
Max cruising speed (75% power) at S/L	
	100 knots (185 km/h; 115 mph)
Stalling speed: flaps up	46 knots (86 km/h; 53 mph)
flaps down	40 knots (74 km/h; 46 mph)
Max rate of climb at S/L	204 m (670 ft)/min
Range with max fuel and max payload	
	400 nm (741 km; 461 miles)

Verilite Model 100 Sunbird 'second' prototype

VOLPAR
VOLPAR AIRCRAFT CORPORATION
7701 Woodley Avenue, Van Nuys, California 91406
Telephone: 1 (818) 994 5023
Telex: 651482 VOLPAR B VAN
PRESIDENT AND CHIEF EXECUTIVE OFFICER:
  Carl G. Hokanson
VICE-PRESIDENTS:
  Robert C. Dunigan (Maintenance and Engineering)
  Frank V. Nixon (Development)
  In early 1990 Volpar Aircraft Corporation was acquired by Gaylord Holdings of Switzerland.

VOLPAR FALCON PW300-F20
At the 1989 Paris Air Show Volpar Aircraft Corporation announced plans to replace the General Electric CF700 power plants of Dassault Mystère-Falcon 20 business jets with 23.24 kN (5,225 lb st) Pratt & Whitney Canada PW305 turbofans. The conversion will include Rohr Industries thrust reversers as standard, and will feature variable inlet guide vanes for improved power at altitude. The modified aircraft will meet FAA FAR Pt 36 Stage 3 noise requirements and will provide a 50 knot (93 km/h; 58 mph) increase in cruising speed at 12,500 m (41,000 ft), and an estimated maximum IFR range, with NBAA reserves, of 2,600 nm (4,818 km; 2,994 miles). The Falcon PW300-F20 will be marketed by Advanced Falcon Aircraft Partnership of Greenwich, Connecticut. First flight of the prototype conversion was scheduled for July 1990, with FAA certification anticipated by the end of the year.

VOLPAR T-33V
Volpar Aircraft Corporation's Packaged Power turbo-prop re-engining programme for a variety of utility aircraft was described in the 1987-88 and earlier editions of *Jane's*. In collaboration with William F. Chana Associates, the company is currently developing an upgrade programme for the Lockheed T-33 two-seat jet trainer which would involve replacing the aircraft's Allison J33 turbojet engine

Artist's impression of the Volpar Falcon PW300-F20

with a Pratt & Whitney Canada PW300 turbofan, flat rated at 21.13 kN (4,750 lb st), which would reduce the aircraft's empty weight by approximately 499 kg (1,100 lb) and cut fuel burn by up to two-thirds. The modified aircraft would be known as the T-33V. Volpar anticipates a market for some 250 modified T-33Vs, and would also supply engine and airframe modification kits to existing operators of the T-33, of which approximately 1,000 are believed to remain in service worldwide.

VULCAN
VULCAN AIRCRAFT CORPORATION
Houston, Texas
DIRECTOR: Robert T. Clifton
This company has announced plans to develop the **V2000 Starfire** six-seat V/STOL fan-in-wing business aircraft, the general configuration of which can be seen in the accompanying artist's impression. As projected, the Starfire would be powered by two coupled 1,119 kW (1,500 shp) turboshaft engines which would drive vertical lift fans mounted in stub wings during take-off, hovering and landing, and two non-vectorable fans mounted in pods at the rear of the fuselage for cruising flight. The lift fans would have collective pitch change for vertical control and variable blade pitch for lateral control in VTOL mode. Conventional elevons and flaps on the cranked rear wing,

Artist's impression of the Vulcan Aircraft V2000 Starfire twin-turboshaft V/STOL business aircraft

and elevators on the forward canard surface, would be used for control in forward flight. The aircraft would have a max T-O weight of around 2,948 kg (6,500 lb). Projected performance includes: cruising speed 304 knots (565 km/h; 350 mph); hovering ceiling 1,525 m (5,000 ft); service ceiling 4,575-6,100 m (15,000-20,000 ft); range (VTOL) 434 nm

(804 km; 500 miles), (STOL) 868 nm (1,609 km; 1,000 miles).

By late 1989 some 40 hours of wind tunnel testing had been completed at Texas A&M University using a one-quarter scale model of the Starfire. Vulcan Aircraft was then said to be discussing development of a full-scale

prototype with a major aircraft manufacturer in the United States, and hoped to fly this aircraft by early 1993, with certification and first customer deliveries anticipated in 1995. An armed military variant of the Starfire with fly by wire controls, and a small commuter airliner using the same fan-in-wing configuration, are also planned.

WIPAIRE

WIPAIRE INC
South End Doane Trail, Inver Grove Heights, Minnesota 55075
Telephone: 1 (612) 451 1205
Telex: 297051
PRESIDENT: Robert Wiplinger

WIPAIRE BEAVER CONVERSIONS
This company, well known for its range of Wipline floats and amphibious floats for light and utility aircraft, has developed a modification programme for de Havilland DHC-2 Beaver aircraft. Modifications to customer's aircraft, which are available individually or as a package, include extension of the rear cabin area by 0.71 m (2 ft 4 in); installation of a 0.85 m × 0.27 m (33½ in × 10½ in) baggage door; additional 'panaview' side windows (two per side); forward skylight windows (tinted); articulating Cessna or Piper pilot's and co-pilot's seats with inertia reel shoulder harnesses; a removable sling rear seat with three seatbelts; a three-seat centre bench, forward- or rear-facing, with under-seat stowage; 3M cabin soundproofing, and door hold-open catches. In addition Wipaire offers electrically actuated trailing-edge flaps; a customised IFR instrument panel with modern switches, circuit breakers and instrument post lights; optional Digiflow fuel metering system; 3M Stormscope; S-Tech Series 50 autopilot with electric trim, altitude hold and flight director system; a Jasco alternator to replace the standard Beaver's generator; new engine firewall battery location; Cessna electric fuel pump/primer, and a Hartzell three-blade constant-speed metal propeller with spinner replacing the standard two-blade Hamilton Standard unit.

All of these features are incorporated in Wipaire's own remanufactured **Super Beavers**, which are based on surplus DHC-2 or L-20 airframes which are completely dismantled, stripped and inspected using dye penetrant tests on all structural attachment points. Damaged panels are replaced and internal and external surfaces treated with epoxy primer before reassembly using all new nuts, bolts, stainless steel cables, pulleys, rod ends, wiring and electrical

Wipaire Super Beaver amphibian, converted from a former Army Air Corps aircraft *(Ian Burnett)*

components. New or overhauled components such as the oil cooler, fuel tanks, senders and pumps, instruments, windscreen, windows and engine accessories for the 335.5 kW (450 hp) Pratt & Whitney R-985 power plant are installed, and the engine given an extensive overhaul. Avionics and Executive or Bush interiors are installed to customers' specifications, and the exterior finished in a customised IMRON paint scheme. Wipline 6000 floats or amphibious floats complete the Super Beaver conversion, most elements of which can also be applied to DHC Turbo Beavers. Wipaire has recently acquired a number of former British Army Air Corps Beavers for conversion to Super Beaver standard.

WIPAIRE AMPHIBIOUS AZTEC
Wipaire Inc has obtained FAA certification for an amphibious version of the Piper PA-23-250 Aztec using the company's Wipline 6000A amphibious floats. The conversion involves airframe and wing spar strengthening for float attachment and provision of an entrance door on the port side of the cabin in addition to the Aztec's standard starboard door. The Amphibious Aztec has a useful load of 680 kg (1,500 lb) and a cruising speed of 122-126 knots (225-233 km/h; 140-145 mph). Future conversions may also feature two 223.7 kW (300 hp) engines in place of the standard 186.4 kW (250 hp) Textron Lycoming O-540-A1D5 power plants.

WTA

WTA INC
Lubbock International Airport, Route 3, Box 48A, Lubbock, Texas 79401
Telephone: 1 (806) 765 7242
Telex: 744439
VICE-PRESIDENT: Larry T. Neal

WTA Inc acquired from Piper Aircraft Corporation marketing rights to the PA-18-150 Super Cub and the PA-36 Brave agricultural aircraft, and renamed the latter as the New Brave in versions with 279 kW (375 hp) and 298 kW (400 hp) engines. The PA-18-150 has now been restored to production by Piper (which see); deliveries by WTA totalled 250.

No recent information has been received, and there is no evidence that the New Brave remains in production. Descriptions and specifications of the New Brave 375 and New Brave 400 may be found in the 1989-90 and earlier editions of *Jane's*.

YUGOSLAVIA

SOKO

VAZDUHOPLOVNA INDUSTRIJA SOKO
88 000 Mostar
Telephone: 38 (88) 22-121, 33-831, 35-244, 35-541, 37-943, 55-120
Telex: 46-180 YU SOKOMO
GENERAL MANAGER: Dipl Oec N. Djurica
ASSISTANT GENERAL MANAGER: Dipl Ing B. Rogonja
DIRECTOR, COMMERCIAL: Dipl Oec N. Milović
DIRECTOR, ENGINEERING AND DEVELOPMENT:
Dipl Ing F. Dizdarević
Founded in 1951, this company manufactures aircraft of its own design and is participating, with Romania, in developing and producing the Orao/IAR-93 strike aircraft described under the SOKO/CNIAR heading in the International section.

SOKO also continues to build under licence the Aerospatiale SA 342L Gazelle helicopter, on behalf of the Yugoslav government.

SOKO HELICOPTER PROJECT
A Yugoslav source reports that Soko is planning a new small helicopter based on the dynamic system of its licence-built Aerospatiale Gazelle.

SOKO G-4 SUPER GALEB (SEAGULL)
This light attack and training aircraft was designed to replace the earlier G2-A Galeb and Lockheed T-33 in basic and advanced training units of the Yugoslav Air Force. The two Super Galeb prototypes (23004 and 23005) flew on 17 July 1978 and 18 December 1979, followed by the first of a

small batch of pre-production aircraft (23601) on 17 December 1980. The production Super Galeb, for which the Yugoslav Air Force placed a substantial order, differs from the pre-production model in having an all-moving tailplane with considerable anhedral, instead of the original conventional horizontal tail surfaces with elevators and no anhedral. Super Galebs are operated by the Vojno-Vazduhoplovna Adakemija (Air Force Academy) at Zadar; an advanced training school at Pula; and (from 1990) the Academy's Letece Zvezde (Shooting Stars) aerobatic team. Deliveries totalled at least 132 by September 1989, from up to 200 on order.

Two prototypes are due to fly early. in 1991 of the developed **G-4M**, featuring new avionics and nav/attack systems, but retaining (after consideration of a more modern turbofan) the Viper power plant. Addition is planned of a gyro platform, IFF, flight data recorder, an indigenous electronic sight, HUD, multi-function displays and wingtip missile rails. Weapon carrying capability will increase from 1,280 kg (2,822 lb) to 1,680 kg (3,704 lb) normal, or 1,800 kg (3,968 lb) overload. Production deliveries are due in 1992. The G-4M is intended to extend the training syllabus into areas currently covered by two-seat versions of front-line aircraft, and also to provide an improved anti-helicopter capability in wartime.

TYPE: Two-seat basic trainer and light attack aircraft.
WINGS: Cantilever low-wing monoplane. No dihedral. Sweepback at quarter-chord 22°; leading-edge sweep increased near wingroots. One-piece two-spar all-metal structure, with integrally machined skin panels inboard and chemically milled skin towards wingtips. Shallow boundary layer fence on upper surface of each wing,

forward of inboard end of aileron. Wings attached to fuselage at six points. Entire trailing-edge made up of conventional all-metal sealed ailerons and flaps. Ailerons actuated by hydraulic servo jacks, with artificial feel, flaps by electrically controlled hydraulic actuators. No slats or tabs.
FUSELAGE: All-metal semi-monocoque structure, with air intake trunk blended into each side. Rear portion, complete with tail surfaces, detachable for access to engine. Door type airbrake under rear fuselage. Landing light in nose, forward of large equipment bay. Some composite materials in secondary structure of G-4M.
TAIL UNIT: Conventional cantilever all-metal structure, with all surfaces sweptback. All-moving horizontal surfaces have 10° anhedral, and are actuated by hydraulic servo jacks, with artificial feel. Mechanically actuated rudder. Dorsal fin. Ground adjustable tab on rudder. Two ventral strakes under jetpipe.
LANDING GEAR: Hydraulically retractable tricycle type, with single wheel on each unit. Nosewheel retracts forward, main units inward into wings. Oleo-pneumatic shock absorber in each leg. Hydraulically steerable nose unit optional (not on current aircraft). Trailing link main units. Mainwheels fitted with Dunlop tyres size 615 × 225-10, pressure 4.4 bars (64 lb/sq in), and hydraulic brakes. Nosewheel has Dunlop tyre size 6.50-5.5 TC, pressure 3.0 bars (43.5 lb/sq in). Brake parachute container at base of rudder. Provision for attaching two assisted take-off rockets under centre-fuselage.
POWER PLANT: One Rolls-Royce Viper Mk 632 turbojet, rated at 17.8 kN (4,000 lb st). Fuel in three flexible bag tanks in centre-fuselage and an integral tank between the

spars of each inner wing. Total internal fuel capacity 1,720 litres (454.4 US gallons; 378.5 Imp gallons). Provision for two underwing auxiliary tanks, on inboard pylons, total capacity 625 litres (165.1 US gallons; 137.5 Imp gallons). Max fuel capacity 2,345 litres (619.5 US gallons; 516 Imp gallons). Gravity refuelling system standard.

ACCOMMODATION: Crew of two in tandem on Martin-Baker zero/zero Mk J10 ejection seats (zero height/90 knot Mk J8 optional, but not on current aircraft), with ejection through the individual sideways hinged (to starboard) canopy over each seat. Rear seat raised by 25 cm (10 in) to give occupant forward view over front seat occupant. Cockpit pressurised and air-conditioned.

SYSTEMS: Engine compressor bleed air used for pressuris-ation, air-conditioning, anti-g suit and windscreen anti-icing systems, and to pressurise fuel tanks. Dual hydraulic systems, pressure 210 bars (3,045 lb/sq in), for flying control servos, flap and airbrake actuators, landing gear retraction and extension, and wheel brakes. Hydraulic system flow rate 45 litres (12 US gallons; 10 Imp gallons)/min for main system, 16 litres (4.2 US gallons; 3.5 Imp gallons)/min for flight control system. Electrical system supplied by 9kW 28V DC generator, with nickel-cadmium battery for ground/emergency power and self contained engine starting. Two static inverters, total output 600VA, provide 115V 400Hz AC power. Gaseous oxygen system adequate for two crew for 2 h 30 min.

AVIONICS AND EQUIPMENT: Dual controls and full blind-flying instrumentation in each cockpit. Standard nav/com equipment comprises EAS type ER4.671D or RC E163 Kondor VHF com radio, GEC Avionics AD 370B or Iskra VARK-01 ADF, Collins VIR-30 VOR/ILS, Iskra 75R4 VOR marker beacon receiver, Collins DME 40 and TRT AHV-6 radio altimeter. Optional UHF or V/UHF com, gyro platform and other equipment to customer's specification. INS optional in G-4M.

ARMAMENT AND OPERATIONAL EQUIPMENT: Removable ven-tral gun pod containing 23 mm GSh-23L twin-barrel rapid fire cannon with 200 rds. Two attachments under each wing, with capacity of 500 kg (1,102 lb) inboard and 350 kg (772 lb) outboard. Total weapon load capability, with centreline gun pod, 1,280 kg (2,822 lb), or 1,800 kg (3,968 lb) for G-4M. In addition to standard high explosive bombs and napalm pods, typical Yugoslav stores include S-8-16 cluster bombs, each with eight 16 kg fragmentation munitions; KPT-150 expendable con-tainers, each with up to 40 anti-personnel or 54 anti-tank bomblets; L-57-16MD pods, each with sixteen 57 mm rockets; L-128-04 pods, each with four 128 mm rockets; adaptors for twin 5 in HVAR rockets, single 57 mm VRZ-57 training rockets; SN-3-050 triple carriers for 50 kg bombs; SN-3-100 triple carriers for 100 kg bombs; KM-3 pods each containing a single 12.7 mm (0.50 in) gun; SAM Z-80 towed target system; and auxiliary fuel tanks on the inboard pylon attachments. Ferranti D282 gyro gunsight standard. Other types of fire control system optional. Development of a photo reconnaissance/infra-red linescan pod and night illumination system, and selection of an alternative off-the-shelf reconnaissance pod, have been deferred pending identification of customer requirement.

DIMENSIONS, EXTERNAL:

Wing span	9.88 m (32 ft 5 in)
Wing aspect ratio	5.0
Length overall	11.86 m (38 ft 11 in)
Height overall	4.28 m (14 ft 0½ in)
Tailplane span	3.97 m (13 ft 0¼ in)
Wheel track	3.49 m (11 ft 5½ in)
Wheelbase	4.15 m (13 ft 7½ in)

SOKO G-4 Super Galeb jet training and light attack aircraft *(Ivo Sturzenegger)*

SOKO G-4 Super Galeb (Rolls-Royce Viper Mk 632 turbojet) *(Pilot Press)*

AREAS:

Wings, gross	19.5 m² (209.9 sq ft)
Ailerons (total)	1.358 m² (14.62 sq ft)
Trailing-edge flaps (total)	3.340 m² (35.95 sq ft)
Airbrake	0.438 m² (4.71 sq ft)
Fin	3.130 m² (33.69 sq ft)
Rudder	0.689 m² (7.42 sq ft)
Horizontal tail surfaces (total)	4.669 m² (50.26 sq ft)

WEIGHTS:

Weight empty, equipped	3,250 kg (7,165 lb)
Max fuel weight: internal	1,305 kg (2,877 lb)
external	500 kg (1,102 lb)
T-O weight: training mission	4,760 kg (10,495 lb)
normal combat mission, with 1,350 kg (2,975 lb) of weapons	6,110 kg (13,470 lb)
Max T-O weight, combat overload	6,330 kg (13,955 lb)

PERFORMANCE (at AUW of 4,760 kg; 10,495 lb, except where indicated):

Never-exceed speed	Mach 0.866
Max level speed at 6,000 m (19,680 ft)	491 knots (910 km/h; 565 mph)
Landing speed	89 knots (165 km/h; 103 mph)
Max rate of climb at S/L:	
AUW as above	1,800 m (5,905 ft)/min
with 50% internal fuel (AUW of 3,890 kg; 8,575 lb)	2,330 m (7,645 ft)/min
Time to 8,000 m (26,240 ft)	6 min
Absolute ceiling	15,000 m (49,200 ft)
T-O run	532 m (1,745 ft)
T-O to 15 m (50 ft)	850 m (2,790 ft)
Landing from 15 m (50 ft) at landing weight of 3,800 kg (8,375 lb)	750 m (2,460 ft)
Landing run at above landing weight	550 m (1,805 ft)

Combat radius, with gun pack and full internal fuel, 10% reserves:

with four BL755 cluster bombs:		
	lo-lo-lo	208 nm (386 km; 240 miles)
	hi-lo-hi	260 nm (483 km; 300 miles)
with two BL755 and two aux fuel tanks:		
	lo-lo-lo	321 nm (595 km; 370 miles)
	hi-lo-hi	438 nm (812 km; 504 miles)

Range at 11,000 m (36,000 ft), with two aux fuel tanks, 10% reserves	1,420 nm (2,630 km; 1,635 miles)
Endurance at 11,000 m (36,000 ft), with two aux fuel tanks	4 h 20 min
g limits	+8/−4.2

NOVI AVION

Under the Novi Avion (New Aircraft) programme, Yugoslavia has undertaken to produce an indigenous successor to the MiG-21 multi-role fighter. By early 1990, design definition had been completed at the Vazduhoplovno Tehnicki Institut (Defence Technical Insitute) at Zarkovo, near Belgrade, with assistance from several Western aviation companies, notably Dassault. European and US firms have held discussions concerning collaborative airframe development and possible use of Rolls-Royce, General Electric or Pratt & Whitney power plants. Production is expected to be the responsibility of SOKO.

The Novi Avion is currently seen as a single-engined, cranked-wing tail-less delta with movable canards and

SOKO-manufactured SA 342L Gazelle, armed with AT-3 'Sagger' and SA-7 'Grail' missiles

separate ventral air intakes resembling those of the Rafale. Design requirements include a thrust:weight ratio in excess of unity; speeds of Mach 1.1+ at sea level, Mach 1.4-1.6 at 4 g at 6,100 m (20,000 ft), and Mach 1.8 at 11,000 m (36,100

ft); an instantaneous 24 °/s or sustained 13-15°/s turn rate at 3,050 m (10,000 ft); and a sustained 4 g capability at Mach 0.7 at 3,050 m (10,000 ft).

A decision on the future of the Novi Avion was

reportedly due to have been made at the end of 1989, but no announcement has been forthcoming. The critical condition of the Yugoslav economy is seen as a major obstacle to the programme.

UTVA
UTVA—SOUR METALNE INDUSTRIJE, RO FABRIKA AVIONA

Jabučki Put BB, 26 000 Pančevo
Telephone: 38 (13) 512584
Telex: 13250 FA UTVA YU
GENERAL MANAGER: Dipl Ing Milan Soso
MANAGER OF AIRCRAFT DEVELOPMENT:
Dipl Ing Petar Stamatov
CHIEF DESIGNER: Dipl Ing Dragoslav Dimić

UTVA-75A21

The UTVA-75A21 is a side by side two-seat training, glider towing and utility lightplane, which was projected, designed and built in partnership by UTVA-Pančevo, Prva Petoletka-Trstenik, Vazduhoplovno Tehnicki Institut and Institut Masinskog Fakulteta of Belgrade. Design was started in 1974, to the requirements of FAR Pt 23 (Utility category). Construction of two prototypes was undertaken in 1975; the first of these flew for the first time on 19 May 1976 and the second on 18 December 1976. Series production began immediately and is continuing. A total of 136 UTVA-75A21s had been delivered to civilian flying clubs, others to the Yugoslav Air Force, by March 1989.

TYPE: Two-seat light aircraft.

WINGS: Cantilever low-wing monoplane, with short span centre-section and two constant chord outer panels. Wing section NACA 65_2415. Dihedral 0° on centre-section, 6° on outer panels. Conventional all-metal two-spar structure. Ailerons and flaps, with fluted skin, along entire trailing-edge of outer panels, except for tips. Flettner trim tab on each aileron.

FUSELAGE: Conventional all-metal semi-monocoque structure.

TAIL UNIT: Cantilever all-metal structure, with sweptback vertical surfaces. Fluted skin on fin, rudder and elevator. Rudder and elevator horn balanced. Controllable tab on elevator; ground adjustable tab on rudder.

LANDING GEAR: Non-retractable tricycle type, with single wheel on each unit, and small tail bumper. Prva Petoletka-Trstenik oleo-pneumatic shock absorbers. Dunlop tyres, size 6.00-6, pressure 2.2 bars (32 lb/sq in) on mainwheels; size 5.00-5, pressure 2.0 bars (29 lb/sq in) on nosewheel. Prva Petoletka-Trstenik hydraulic brakes.

POWER PLANT: One 134 kW (180 hp) Textron Lycoming IO-360-B1F flat-four engine, driving a Hartzell HC-C2YK-1BF/F7666A two-blade variable-pitch metal propeller. Two integral fuel tanks in wings, total capacity 160 litres (42.3 US gallons; 35 Imp gallons). Provision for carrying two 100 litre (26.4 US gallon; 22 Imp gallon) drop tanks under wings, raising max total capacity to 360 litres (95.1 US gallons; 79 Imp gallons). Oil capacity 10 litres (2.6 US gallons; 2.2 Imp gallons).

ACCOMMODATION: Two seats side by side in enclosed cabin, with large upward opening jettisonable canopy door over each seat, hinged on centreline. Dual stick type controls standard. Cabin heated and ventilated.

SYSTEMS: Dual hydraulic systems for brakes. 14V DC electrical system, with 35Ah battery, navigation lights, rotating beacon and landing lights as standard equipment.

AVIONICS AND EQUIPMENT: Bendix/King KY 195B radio optional. Standard equipment includes radio compass.

ARMAMENT AND MILITARY EQUIPMENT: Two fittings for light weapon loads underwing on military UTVA-75s. Each can carry a bomb, 100 kg (220 lb) cargo container, two-round rocket launcher or machine-gun pod.

DIMENSIONS, EXTERNAL:

Wing span	9.73 m (31 ft 11 in)
Wing chord (constant)	1.55 m (5 ft 1 in)
Wing aspect ratio	6.5
Length overall	7.11 m (23 ft 4 in)
Height overall	3.15 m (10 ft 4 in)
Tailplane span	3.80 m (12 ft 5½ in)
Wheel track	2.58 m (8 ft 5½ in)
Wheelbase	1.99 m (6 ft 6¼ in)
Propeller diameter	1.93 m (6 ft 4 in)
Propeller ground clearance	0.295 m (11¾ in)

AREAS:

Wings, gross	14.63 m² (157.5 sq ft)
Ailerons (total)	1.38 m² (14.85 sq ft)
Flaps (total)	1.61 m² (17.33 sq ft)
Vertical tail surfaces (total)	1.78 m² (19.16 sq ft)
Horizontal tail surfaces (total)	3.34 m² (35.95 sq ft)

WEIGHTS:

Weight empty, equipped	685 kg (1,510 lb)
Max crew/military load/baggage	210 kg (463 lb)
Max fuel: standard	103 kg (227 lb)
with drop tanks	256 kg (564 lb)
Max T-O weight	960 kg (2,116 lb)

PERFORMANCE (at max T-O weight):

Max level speed	116 knots (215 km/h; 133 mph)
Max cruising speed	100 knots (185 km/h; 115 mph)

UTVA-75A21 two-seat trainer with underwing pylons for light weapon loads

Econ cruising speed	89 knots (165 km/h; 102 mph)

Stalling speed, engine idling:

flaps up	52 knots (95 km/h; 59 mph)
25° flap	45 knots (82 km/h; 51 mph)
Max rate of climb at S/L	270 m (885 ft)/min
Service ceiling	4,000 m (13,125 ft)
T-O run	125 m (410 ft)
T-O to 15 m (50 ft)	250 m (820 ft)
Landing from 15 m (50 ft)	340 m (1,115 ft)
Landing run	100 m (328 ft)
Range: with max standard fuel	
	432 nm (800 km; 497 miles)
with drop tanks, no reserves	
	1,080 nm (2,000 km; 1,242 miles)
g limits	+6/-3

UTVA-75A41

The UTVA-75A41 is a four-seat version of the UTVA-75A21 for training, glider towing and utility operations. Design and construction were started in 1984 in partnership Vazduhoplovno Tehnicki Institut and Institut Masinskog Fakulteta of Belgrade, to the requirements of FAR Pt 23 (Normal category). The prototype flew for the first time in 1986, and preparations began immediately to produce a pre-series of 10 UTVA-75A41s, in parallel with continued manufacture of the two-seat UTVA-75A21. Deliveries were expected to begin in 1987.

TYPE: Four-seat light utility and training aircraft.

WINGS, FUSELAGE, TAIL UNIT, LANDING GEAR, POWER PLANT AND SYSTEMS: As for UTVA-75A21.

ACCOMMODATION: Four seats in pairs in enclosed cabin, with large upward opening jettisonable canopy door over each fore and aft pair of seats, hinged on centreline. Dual stick type controls standard. Cabin heated and ventilated.

AVIONICS AND EQUIPMENT: Bendix/King equipment standard, including dual KY 197 720-channel VHF com transceivers; KR 87 digitally tuned ADF with integral electronic flight timer and pushbutton elapsed timer; panel mounted R/Nav system comprising a KNS 81 200-channel nav, 40-channel glideslope indicator and 9-waypoint digital R/Nav computer, combined with a KI 525A pictorial nav indicator; KI 229 RMI; KN 53 200-channel VHF nav with integral 40-channel glideslope indicator and KI 525A indicator; KN 62A 200-channel DME with digital distance, ground speed and time-to-station; KT 79 all solid state digital transponder featuring cross-check readout of encoded altitude and automatic VFR code selection; and KMA 24 audio control console with integral marker beacon receiver.

ARMAMENT: None.

DIMENSIONS, EXTERNAL, and AREAS:
As for UTVA-75A21

WEIGHTS:

Weight empty, equipped	700 kg (1,544 lb)
Max payload	310 kg (683 lb)
Max fuel: standard	103 kg (227 lb)
with drop tanks	256 kg (564 lb)
Max T-O weight	1,163 kg (2,564 lb)

PERFORMANCE (at max T-O weight):

Max level speed	113 knots (210 km/h; 130 mph)
Max cruising speed	97 knots (180 km/h; 112 mph)
Econ cruising speed	86 knots (160 km/h; 99 mph)

Stalling speed, engine idling:

flaps up	57 knots (105 km/h; 65 mph)
25° flap	49 knots (90 km/h; 56 mph)
Max rate of climb at S/L	264 m (866 ft)/min
Service ceiling	4,000 m (13,125 ft)
T-O run	200 m (656 ft)
T-O to 15 m (50 ft)	400 m (1,312 ft)
Landing from 15 m (50 ft)	340 m (1,115 ft)
Landing run	180 m (590 ft)
Range:	
with max standard fuel	
	432 nm (800 km; 497 miles)
	1,080 nm (2,000 km; 1,242 miles)
g limits	+3.8/-2.2

UTVA-75AG11

The UTVA-75AG11 is an agricultural aircraft with an airframe almost identical to that of the UTVA-75A21 except for changes associated with the installation of a chemical hopper forward of a high-set single-seat cabin in the centre-fuselage. The landing gear is upgraded to cope with operations at a higher gross weight, from grass surfaces; and a more powerful engine is fitted. Although unsuccessful in a government design competition for agricultural aircraft, the UTVA-75AG continues to be offered as a private venture.

Design of the UTVA-75A11 was started on 20 December 1986. Construction of the prototype (YU-XAF) began on 15 June 1987 and the first flight took place on 3 March 1989. Differences by comparison with the UTVA-75A21 are as follows:

TYPE: Single-seat agricultural aircraft.

FUSELAGE: Basically as for UTVA-75A21, but greater use of composites, particularly for pilot's cabin. Chemical hopper, capacity 870 litres (230 US gallons; 191 Imp gallons), forward of cabin.

TAIL UNIT: Cantilever all-metal structure, with sweptback vertical surfaces. Fluted skin on fin and rudder. Elevator horn balanced. Tab on rudder and controllable tab on elevator, operated electrically by Teleflex actuator.

LANDING GEAR: Tyres size 7.00-8 on mainwheels, 6.00-6 on nosewheel.

POWER PLANT: One 224 kW (300 hp) Textron Lycoming IO-540-L1A5D flat-six engine, driving a Hartzell HC-C2YK-1BF/F8475D-4 propeller. Two fuel tanks in wings, with total capacity of 160 litres (42.3 US gallons; 35 Imp gallons). Provision for two 150 litre (39.6 US gallon; 33 Imp gallon) underwing tanks.

ACCOMMODATION: Pilot only, in high-set cabin. Downward hinged canopy/door on each side. Cabin heated and ventilated.

SYSTEMS: Electrical system is 24V 60A DC, with a 19Ah nickel-cadmium battery. Vacuum system standard.

AVIONICS AND EQUIPMENT: Prototype has Rudičajevec VHF radio, blind-flying instrumentation, navigation and landing lights, and rotating beacon.

DIMENSIONS, EXTERNAL:
As for UTVA-75A21 except:

Length overall	7.21 m (23 ft 8 in)
Propeller diameter	2.03 m (6 ft 8 in)
Propeller ground clearance	0.47 m (1 ft 6 in)

WEIGHTS:

Weight empty, equipped	820 kg (1,808 lb)

Max chemical load	900 kg (1,984 lb)
Max fuel, internal	103 kg (227 lb)
Max T-O weight	1,800 kg (3,968 lb)
Max landing weight	1,400 kg (3,086 lb)

PERFORMANCE (at max T-O weight, estimated):

Never-exceed speed	173 knots (320 km/h; 199 mph)
Max level speed	135 knots (250 km/h; 155 mph)
Max cruising speed	116 knots (215 km/h; 134 mph)
Econ cruising speed	89 knots (165 km/h; 102 mph)
Stalling speed: flaps down	54 knots (100 km/h; 62 mph)
Max rate of climb at S/L	300 m (984 ft)/min
Service ceiling	4,000 m (13,120 ft)
T-O run	340 m (1,115 ft)
T-O to 15 m (50 ft)	630 m (2,067 ft)
Landing from 15 m (50 ft)	540 m (1,772 ft)
Landing run	250 m (820 ft)
Range:	
with max internal fuel	162 nm (300 km; 186 miles)
with underwing tanks	442 nm (820 km; 510 miles)

Prototype of UTVA-75AG11 single-seat agricultural aircraft

UTVA LASTA (SWALLOW)

First shown publicly in model form at the 1985 Paris Air Show, the Lasta was designed by the Vazduhoplovno Tehnicki Institut at Zarkovo, near Belgrade, as a primary trainer for the Yugoslav Air Force, to the requirements of FAR Pt 23. Although similar in configuration and purpose to the French Epsilon, and with the same power plant, it is a larger and heavier aircraft. Pupil pilots are intended to progress from the Lasta directly to the SOKO G-4 Super Galeb jet basic trainer, and the cockpits of the two aircraft are fundamentally similar. The Lasta is intended to be suitable for basic, aerobatic, navigation, instrument and night flying training, for basic training in gunnery, rocket firing and bombing, for formation flying and combat manoeuvres.

Manufacture of the Lasta is being undertaken by Fabrika Aviona UTVA at Pančevo. Design began in 1982 and the first of two prototypes flew for the first time on 2 September 1985, followed by the second in 1986. Tooling was being prepared at that time for a pre-series of ten production Lastas. Between October 1988 and May 1989, 25 were delivered to the air force from a total requirement of approximately 100. The Lasta is employed as a lead-in trainer to the Super Galeb (which see).

TYPE: Tandem two-seat primary trainer and light attack aircraft.

WINGS: Cantilever low-wing monoplane of conventional light alloy two-spar stressed-skin construction, with plastics wingtips. Wing section NACA 64_2215 at root, NACA 64_1212 at tip. Dihedral 4° from roots. All-metal balanced ailerons and hydraulically-operated flaps over full span. Trim and servo tab in port aileron; servo tab in starboard aileron.

FUSELAGE: Conventional light alloy semi-monocoque structure.

TAIL UNIT: Cantilever light alloy stressed-skin structure. Fixed incidence tailplane. Horn balanced rudder. Long dorsal fin and shallow ventral fin. Electrically-actuated trim tab in rudder and starboard elevator.

LANDING GEAR: Hydraulically retractable tricycle type of Prva Petoletka-Trstenik design and manufacture, with single wheel on each unit. Nosewheel retracts rearward, main units inward. Oleo-pneumatic shock absorbers. Nosewheel steerable ±30°, via rudder pedals. Dunlop tyres: size 6.00-6 (8PR), pressure 3.2 bars (46.5 lb/sq in), on mainwheels; size 5.00-5 (8PR), pressure 4.2 bars (61 lb/sq in), on nosewheel. Hydraulic disc brakes.

POWER PLANT: One 224 kW (300 hp) Textron Lycoming AEIO-540-L1B5D flat-six engine, driving a Hoffmann HO-V-123K-V three-blade constant-speed propeller with spinner. Two integral fuel tanks in wings, total capacity 200 litres (53 US gallons; 44 Imp gallons). For ferrying, a 100 litre (26.5 US gallon; 22 Imp gallon) tank can be installed in second cockpit. Refuelling point in top surface of each wing. Oil capacity 18 litres (4.75 US gallons; 4 Imp gallons).

ACCOMMODATION: Two seats in tandem, with rear seat raised 76 mm (3 in). Separate jettisonable canopy over each seat, sideways hinged to starboard.

SYSTEMS: Hydraulic system with geared pump, flow rate 14 litres (3.7 US gallons; 3 Imp gallons)/min at pressure of 80 bars (1,160 lb/sq in), for actuating landing gear, wheel brakes and flaps. Auxiliary hand pump. 28V DC electrical system, with 2kW alternator and 22Ah nickel-cadmium battery. Full night lighting.

AVIONICS: Standard equipment will include VHF, VOR, ILS, marker beacon receiver and intercom. Blind-flying instrumentation standard.

ARMAMENT: Two underwing hardpoints for bombs of up to 100 kg, seven-tube rocket packs, and pods containing twin 7.62 mm machine-guns, with total external load of up to 240 kg (530 lb). Semi-automatic gyro gunsight.

DIMENSIONS, EXTERNAL:

Wing span	8.34 m (27 ft 4½ in)
Wing chord: at root	1.706 m (5 ft 7¼ in)
at tip	0.938 m (3 ft 1 in)
Wing aspect ratio	6.3
Length overall	8.04 m (26 ft 4½ in)
Height overall	2.965 m (9 ft 8¾ in)
Tailplane span	3.25 m (10 ft 8 in)

Prototype UTVA Lasta primary trainer and light attack aircraft

UTVA Lasta (Textron Lycoming AEIO-540-L1B5D engine) *(Pilot Press)*

Wheel track	2.63 m (8 ft 7½ in)
Wheelbase	2.04 m (6 ft 8¼ in)
Propeller diameter	2.00 m (6 ft 6¾ in)
Propeller ground clearance	0.29 m (11½ in)

AREAS:

Wings, gross	11.0 m² (118.4 sq ft)
Ailerons (total)	1.92 m² (20.67 sq ft)
Trailing-edge flaps (total)	1.70 m² (18.30 sq ft)
Fin	1.15 m² (12.38 sq ft)
Rudder, incl tab	0.44 m² (4.74 sq ft)
Ventral fin	0.19 m² (2.05 sq ft)
Tailplane	2.106 m² (22.67 sq ft)
Elevators, incl tab	0.78 m² (8.40 sq ft)

WEIGHTS:

Weight empty, equipped	1,060 kg (2,337 lb)
Max fuel weight: standard	150 kg (330 lb)
with ferry tank	220 kg (485 lb)
Max T-O and landing weight	1,630 kg (3,593 lb)

PERFORMANCE (at 1,340 kg; 2,955 lb AUW):

Never-exceed speed	302 knots (560 km/h; 348 mph)
Max level speed	179 knots (332 km/h; 206 mph)
Max cruising speed (75% power)	160 knots (297 km/h; 184 mph)
Econ cruising speed (65% power)	142 knots (263 km/h; 163 mph)
Max rate of climb at S/L	444 m (1,456 ft)/min
Service ceiling	5,200 m (17,060 ft)
T-O run	320 m (1,050 ft)
T-O to 15 m (50 ft)	720 m (2,363 ft)
Landing from 15 m (50 ft)	490 m (1,608 ft)
Landing run	250 m (820 ft)
Range with max fuel	577 nm (1,070 km; 665 miles)
g limits	+6/−3

Scale models of the Type 'S' (left) and Type 'D' agricultural aircraft designed by Professor Dragoljub Stanojević *(Aerosvet)*

UNIDENTIFIED DESIGNS

Development of agricultural spraying aircraft has been assigned the comparatively high priority of third in the government's 'Strategy of technological development of Yugoslavia to 2000', studies having indicated that local requirements can be met by two types of aircraft with payloads of 900 kg (1,984 lb) and 1,900 kg (4,189 lb). Early in 1990, construction was in hand of a prototype of each aircraft. These designs were winners of an official competition, to which the UTVA-75AG11 was unsuccessfully tendered.

Both designed by Professor Dragoljub Stanojević, DSc, these are of modular concept, and share a common cockpit, instrumentation, equipment, power plant (with ducted propeller), landing gear and wing construction. Unusually for an agricultural aircraft, both seat the pilot well forward, to provide a good view and eliminate chemical and exhaust fume penetration into the cockpit.

From a report appearing as this page went to press, it appeared that the likely manufacturer was a company called EMIND, whose factory is at Erevik in southern Yugoslavia.

AGRICULTURAL AIRCRAFT TYPE 'S'

The smaller of the two designs, identified only by the concocted registration 'YU-AGS' applied to a model, is a twin-boom pusher aircraft, also available as a light transport with a cabin in place of the chemical hopper. The prototype was due to have flown before the end of July 1990, and a pre-production example before 30 September 1991.

POWER PLANT: One Turbomeca TP-319 turboprop, derated to 310 kW (416 shp), driving a ducted propeller.

DIMENSIONS, EXTERNAL:

Wing span	12.28 m (40 ft 3½ in)
Wing chord, constant	1.83 m (6 ft 0 in)
Wing aspect ratio	6.7

AREA:

Wings, gross	22.50 m² (349.8 sq ft)

WEIGHTS:

Payload	900 kg (1,984 lb)
Max T-O weight	2,100 kg (4,630 lb)

PERFORMANCE:

Never-exceed speed	151 knots (280 km/h; 174 mph)
Max cruising speed	130 knots (240 km/h; 149 mph)
Normal operating speed	
	65-97 knots (120-180 km/h; 75-112 mph)
Min flying speed, flaps down:	
at 1,200 kg (2,646 lb)	37 knots (68 km/h; 42 mph)
at 1,875 kg (4,134 lb)	46 knots (85 km/h; 53 mph)

AGRICULTURAL AIRCRAFT TYPE 'D'

The larger of Professor Stanojević's designs is a twin-engined, tricycle landing gear aircraft with a conventional fuselage and tail surfaces. A stretched version with a passenger cabin is projected. Completion of the Type 'D' prototype was due prior to 31 July 1990, and of the pre-production aircraft before 31 December 1991.

Type 'S' single-engined agricultural aircraft *(Jane's/Mike Keep)*

Type 'D' twin-engined agricultural aircraft *(Jane's/Mike Keep)*

POWER PLANT: Two Turbomeca TP-319 turboprops, each derated to 310 kW (416 shp), driving ducted propellers.

DIMENSIONS, EXTERNAL:

Wing span	16.96 m (55 ft 7¾ in)
Wing chord, constant	1.83 m (6 ft 0 in)
Wing aspect ratio	9.3

AREA:

Wings, gross	31.04 m² (334.1 sq ft)

WEIGHTS:

Payload	1,900 kg (4,189 lb)
Max T-O weight	4,000 kg (8,818 lb)

PERFORMANCE:

Never-exceed speed	167 knots (310 km/h; 193 mph)
Max cruising speed	135 knots (250 km/h; 155 mph)
Normal operating speed	
	76-103 knots (140-190 km/h; 86-118 mph)
Min flying speed, flaps down:	
at 2,100 kg (4,630 lb)	42 knots (78 km/h; 48 mph)
at 3,525 kg (7,771 lb)	55 knots (102 km/h; 63 mph)

SPORT AIRCRAFT
(incorporating Homebuilt and Microlight Aircraft)

AUSTRALIA

HUGHES
HOWARD HUGHES ENGINEERING PTY LTD
PO Box 89, 11 Smith Drive, Ballina, NSW 2478
Telephone: 61 (66) 86 3148

HUGHES LIGHTWING GA55
The prototype LightWing first flew in June 1986, and 60 LightWings conforming to ANO 95-25 requirements had been built by January 1990. Approval was sought to sell kits under homebuilt or CAO 101-28 regulations, in non-retractable tailwheel and twin-float configurations. Ten kits have been completed. Construction of a prototype five-seater under CAO 101-31 is planned.

TYPE: Two-seat microlight, ARV and homebuilt.

AIRFRAME: Strut braced wings of 6061-T6 aluminium alloy construction, and welded steel tube fuselage and tail unit, all Ceconite fabric covered. Modified Clark Y wing section. Glassfibre engine cowling. Three-axis control. Non-retractable tailwheel landing gear, with optional twin floats or skis.

POWER PLANT: One 47 kW (63 hp) Rotax 532, with 2.58 : 1 reduction gear. Fuel capacity 40 litres (10.5 US gallons; 8.8 Imp gallons).

DIMENSIONS, EXTERNAL:
Wing span	9.70 m (31 ft 10 in)
Length overall	5.80 m (19 ft 0½ in)
Height overall	1.90 m (6 ft 2¾ in)
Propeller diameter	1.68 m (5 ft 6 in)

AREA:
Wings, gross	14.55 m² (156.61 sq ft)

WEIGHTS:
Weight empty	216 kg (476 lb)
Max pilot weight	100 kg (220 lb)
Baggage capacity	11.3 kg (25 lb)
Max T-O weight	450 kg (992 lb)

PERFORMANCE:
Max level speed at 915 m (3,000 ft)	80 knots (148 km/h; 92 mph)
Econ cruising speed	60 knots (111 km/h; 69 mph)
Stalling speed	32 knots (60 km/h; 37 mph)
Max rate of climb at S/L	366 m (1,200 ft)/min
Service ceiling (CAO 101-55)	915 m (3,000 ft)
T-O run	31 m (100 ft)
Landing run	92 m (300 ft)
Range	150 nm (278 km; 172 miles)
g limits	+6/−3

HUGHES LIGHTWING AEROPOWER GA-55
The Aeropower GA-55 is available in ready assembled and kit forms and produced under CAO 101-28 and 101-55 regulations, but with no microlight version. The prototype first flew in March 1987 and a kit-built aircraft flew in the following year. By January 1990 60 assembled Aeropower GA-55s had been delivered (of 65 ordered), together with six kits (two built by that date). Airframe details are similar to those for the Rotax-engined LightWing GA55.

TYPE: Two-seat homebuilt.

POWER PLANT: One 58.2 kW (78 hp) Aeropower or Limbach. Fuel capacity 60 litres (15.9 US gallons; 13.2 Imp gallons).

DIMENSIONS, EXTERNAL:
Wing span	9.11 m (29 ft 10½ in)
Length overall	5.70 m (18 ft 8½ in)
Height overall	1.90 m (6 ft 2¾ in)
Propeller diameter	1.63 m (5 ft 4 in)

WEIGHTS:
Weight empty	275 kg (606 lb)
Max pilot weight	90 kg (198 lb)
Max T-O weight	500 kg (1,102 lb)

PERFORMANCE:
Max level speed	95 knots (176 km/h; 109 mph)
Max and econ cruising speed	87 knots (161 km/h; 100 mph)
Stalling speed	35 knots (65 km/h; 40 mph)
Service ceiling	3,050 m (10,000 ft)
T-O run	92 m (300 ft)
Landing run	121 m (400 ft)
Range	217 nm (402 km; 250 miles)
Endurance	3 h 30 min
g limits	+6/−3

CALAIR
CALAIR CORPORATION
Caloundra

Calair, a public limited company listed on the Brisbane Stock Exchange in October 1989, is currently marketing a modified version of the US Denney Kitfox, known as the Skyfox. Future plans envisage production of a single-seat and a four-seat aircraft.

CALAIR SKYFOX
The Skyfox first flew on 15 September 1989. The prototype was nearing certification in early 1990 under CAO 101-55 regulations. By then the company held orders for 35 aircraft and production was soon to begin, with manufacture of five units a month initially but doubling to ten by the close of the year.

Compared to the Kitfox, the Skyfox is said to have approximately 30 modifications. A 58.2 kW (78 hp) Aeropower engine driving a wooden propeller provides power. The V bracing struts are attached further along the wings, and wing dihedral is increased. The height of the tailfin is increased, the rudder is also taller and with greater chord, and the elevators also have increased chord. Fuel capacity is 50 litres (13.2 US gallons; 11 Imp gallons). Options include long-range fuel tanks and an underfuselage cargo pod.

PERFORMANCE (provisional):
Never-exceed speed	112 knots (207 km/h; 129 mph)
Cruising speed	80 knots (148 km/h; 92 mph)
Stalling speed	24 knots (45 km/h; 28 mph)

SKYTEK
SKYTEK AUSTRALIA PTY LTD
PO Box 238, Willetton, Western Australia 6155
Telephone: 61 (9) 310 3351
Fax: 61 (9) 332 3680
DESIGNER: Graham Swannell

SKYTEK MAVERICK
This aerobatic and cross-country homebuilt first flew as a prototype on 24 December 1987. Although it is being marketed, by January 1990 only the single prototype had been built.

TYPE: Single-seat homebuilt.

AIRFRAME: Constructed mainly of glassfibre, epoxy resins, carbonfibre and foam, with fuselage built as self-jigging sandwich structure. Non-retractable tailwheel landing gear.

POWER PLANT: One 74.5 kW (100 hp) Ellison conversion of a Teledyne Continental O-200 in prototype. Options include an 85.75 kW (115 hp) engine for unlimited aerobatics. Christen inverted fuel and oil system allows 3 min inverted flight. Fuel capacity 111 litres (29 US gallons; 24.5 Imp gallons).

DIMENSIONS, EXTERNAL:
Wing span	5.79 m (19 ft 0 in)
Length overall	5.41 m (17 ft 9 in)
Height overall	1.83 m (6 ft 0 in)
Propeller diameter	1.63 m (5 ft 4 in)

AREA:
Wings, gross	5.61 m² (60.4 sq ft)

WEIGHTS:
Weight empty	300 kg (661 lb)
Baggage capacity	22.7 kg (50 lb)
Max T-O weight	476 kg (1,050 lb)

PERFORMANCE:
Max level speed at S/L	165 knots (306 km/h; 190 mph)
Max cruising speed at 3,050 m (10,000 ft)	150 knots (278 km/h; 173 mph)
Econ cruising speed at 3,050 m (10,000 ft)	130 knots (241 km/h; 150 mph)
Stalling speed	51 knots (95 km/h; 59 mph)
Max rate of climb at S/L	366 m (1,200 ft)/min
Range	600 nm (1,112 km; 691 miles)
Endurance with 45 min reserves	4 h 30 min
g limits, design: at 408 kg (900 lb) AUW	+6/−3
at max T-O weight	+4.4/−2.2

THRUSTER
THRUSTER AIRCRAFT (AUSTRALIA) PTY LTD
458 The Boulevarde, Kirrawee, NSW 2232

Telephone: 61 (2) 542 1990
Telex: AA 73953
Fax: 61 (2) 542 3004
GENERAL MANAGER: Ken Asplin

In addition to its T300 and T500 microlights (see Microlight tables), Thruster began development of the T-88 two-seat lightplane. This is not being manufactured; details plus an illustration can be found in the 1989-90 *Jane's*.

BELGIUM

EPERVIER AVIATION SA—*See Microlight tables*

EURONEF—*See Microlight tables*

SCWAL
SCWAL SA
77 Avenue Brugmann, 1060 Brussels
Telephone: 32 (2) 375 38 93
Telex: 65892 GRYF B
MANAGING DIRECTOR: Charles Rifon

SCWAL, with offices in Brussels and a 186 m² (2,000 sq ft) manufacturing plant at Baileux, was established in 1985. In addition to producing its own SCWAL 101 light aircraft, it began manufacture and sale in September 1987 of improved versions of the American Aircraft Falcon, under licence from Sonaca (see Microlight tables).

SCWAL 101
The SCWAL 101 was designed to be a fully certificated light aircraft fitting between microlights and conventional light aeroplanes. Design goals were easy maintenance, road transportability, and the ability to use non-aviation fuel. Applications include civil and military training,

Hughes LightWing GA55 in twin-float and landplane configurations

SCWAL 101 two-seat light aircraft

Circa Reproductions Nieuport 12 prototype (38.8 kW; 52 hp Snowmobile engine)

Skytek Maverick single-seat aerobatic aircraft (Greg Meggs)

---

surveillance, crop dusting and other work in addition to sport flying. A twin-engined version may follow. The first flight was achieved on 26 April 1984. Certification was expected in 1989 but no more recent news has been received.

TYPE: Side by side two-seat monoplane; conforms to FAR Pt 23 normal category.

AIRFRAME: Bolted aluminium/steel tubular mainframe. All aluminium wing and tail surfaces. Wortmann wing section. Three-axis control, including flaps. Optional enclosed Perspex transparent cockpit pod with two doors. Non-retractable tricycle landing gear.

POWER PLANT: One 67 kW (90 hp) BMW converted motorcycle engine. Fuel capacity 60 litres (16 US gallons; 13.2 Imp gallons).

DIMENSIONS, EXTERNAL:
Wing span	11.00 m (36 ft 1 in)
Length overall	5.50 m (18 ft 0½ in)

AREA:
Wings, gross	13.75 m² (148.0 sq ft)

WEIGHTS:
Weight empty	280 kg (617 lb)
Max T-O weight	520 kg (1,146 lb)

PERFORMANCE:
Max level speed	75 knots (140 km/h; 87 mph)
Stalling speed: flaps up	38 knots (70 km/h; 44 mph)
flaps down	33 knots (60 km/h; 38 mph)
Max rate of climb at S/L	162 m (530 ft)/min
T-O run	125 m (410 ft)
Endurance	8 h
g limits	+5.7/−2.85 ultimate

CANADA

CIRCA
CIRCA REPRODUCTIONS
8027 Argyll Road, Edmonton, Alberta T6C 4A9
Telephone: 1 (403) 469 2692 and 477 0024
DESIGNER PROPRIETOR: Graham R. Lee

Circa Reproductions markets plans of ⅞th scale reproductions of First World War fighters.

CIRCA REPRODUCTIONS NIEUPORT 11
The prototype Nieuport 11 reproduction first flew on 25 July 1984. Plans, including drawings for a wooden replica Lewis gun, are available, and by January 1990 a total of 600 sets had been sold. About 150 aircraft are reportedly under active construction and 18 have flown. A prefabricated engine cowling and fuel tank are available from the designer for the Experimental/microlight versions, plus an engine cowling and engine mount for the French ULM model (see below). Estimated building time is 600 working hours.

The Nieuport 11 is capable of meeting both Canadian and US ultralight regulations, and a version to conform to French ULM requirements was expected to become available in May/June 1990 (prototype ULM model first flew in October 1989), though the company prefers that it be built as an Experimental category aircraft with a weight that makes it a homebuilt. If preferred the homebuilder can complete the aircraft as a Nieuport 16, 17, 24, 24*bis* or 27, the 17 onwards having a greater wing area of about 11.6 m² (125 sq ft), or as a German Siemens-Schuckert D.I.

TYPE: Single-seat replica fighter microlight or homebuilt; conforms as microlight to FAR Pt 103, Canadian regulations, and French ULM requirements.

AIRFRAME: Tubular 6061-T6 aluminium alloy structure, with 2024-T3 duralumin gussets and covered with Ceconite and aluminium sheet. Three-axis control. Non-retractable tailskid or tailwheel landing gear. Skis optional.

POWER PLANT: One 22.4 kW (30 hp) Cuyuna ULII-02. Optional engines of up to 30 kW (40 hp). French ULM version has one 31.3 kW (42 hp) Rotax 447 with 2.58 : 1 reduction gear as standard. Fuel capacity 48 litres (12.7 US gallons; 10.5 Imp gallons) or 19 litres (5 US gallons; 4.2 Imp gallons), according to US/Canadian regulation requirements; 30 litres (7.9 US gallons; 6.6 Imp gallons) for French ULM requirements.

DIMENSIONS, EXTERNAL:
Wing span	6.55 m (21 ft 6 in)
Length overall	4.98 m (16 ft 4 in)
Height overall	2.29 m (7 ft 6 in)
Propeller diameter	1.83 m (6 ft 0 in)

AREAS:
Wings, gross: standard	10.59 m² (114.0 sq ft)
French ULM	11.92 m² (128.3 sq ft)

WEIGHTS:
Weight empty: standard	115 kg (254 lb)
French ULM	119 kg (262 lb)
Max pilot weight	88.5 kg (195 lb)
Max T-O weight: standard	249 kg (550 lb)
French ULM	250 kg (551 lb)

PERFORMANCE (at 211 kg; 465 lb AUW):
Max level speed:
with 18.6 kW (25 hp) engine	67 knots (124 km/h; 77 mph)
French ULM	62 knots (115 km/h; 71 mph)
Econ cruising speed	43 knots (80 km/h; 50 mph)

Stalling speed:
standard	23 knots (42 km/h; 26 mph) IAS
French ULM	22.5 knots (41 km/h; 25.5 mph)
Max rate of climb at S/L	137 m (450 ft)/min
T-O run: standard	76 m (250 ft)
French ULM	61 m (200 ft)
Landing run: standard	61 m (200 ft)
French ULM	61 m (200 ft)

Range with max fuel: standard
more than 173 nm (322 km; 200 miles)
Endurance: standard	4 h 45 min
g limits: standard	+5.5/−3.5
French ULM	+5/−3

CIRCA REPRODUCTIONS NIEUPORT 12
Plans of this ⅞th scale reproduction of the two-seat Nieuport 12C-2 are available, and 19 sets had been sold by January 1990; four aircraft were then under active construction. The prototype made its first flight in May 1989 on the power of a 38.8 kW (52 hp) Snowmobile engine.

TYPE: Two-seat replica homebuilt aircraft; conforms to US and Canadian Experimental regulations.

AIRFRAME: Braced sesquiplane, with UA-81 University of Alberta wing section. Sheet aluminium upper wing spars and oval tube lower spar. Remainder of airframe constructed of 6061-T6 aluminium alloy tubing, with aluminium gussets and fabric covering. Three-axis control. Non-retractable tailskid landing gear. Optional tailwheel.

POWER PLANT: One engine in 48.5-63.4 kW (65-85 hp) range preferred. Engines can include 38.8 kW (52 hp) Rotax 503 or a Teledyne Continental C65 or C85 of up to 63.4 kW (85 hp). Fuel capacity 50 litres (13.2 US gallons; 11 Imp gallons).

DIMENSIONS, EXTERNAL:
Wing span: upper	8.08 m (26 ft 6 in)
lower	6.93 m (22 ft 9 in)
Length overall	6.55 m (21 ft 6 in)
Height overall	2.59 m (8 ft 6 in)
Propeller diameter (prototype)	2.13 m (7 ft 0 in)

AREA:
Wings, gross	17.62 m² (189.7 sq ft)

WEIGHTS (prototype):
Weight empty	243 kg (536 lb)
Max T-O weight	454 kg (1,000 lb)

PERFORMANCE (Rotax 503 at 340 kg; 750 lb AUW):
Max level speed	56 knots (105 km/h; 65 mph)
Econ cruising speed	48 knots (89 km/h; 55 mph)
Stalling speed, flaps up, engine idling	29 knots (53 km/h; 33 mph)
Max rate of climb at S/L	137 m (450 ft)/min
T-O run	122 m (400 ft)
Landing run	153 m (500 ft)
Endurance	2 h-4 h 15 min
g limits	+5.7/−3

CIRCA REPRODUCTIONS SOPWITH TRIPLANE
A prototype of the ⅞th scale Sopwith Triplane has not yet been completed. Plans to allow amateur construction will become available in due course.

TYPE: Single-seat replica microlight; conforms to Canadian microlight regulations and Experimental aircraft category.

AIRFRAME: Structural materials, control and landing gear (with ski gear option) as for Nieuport 11 replica.

POWER PLANT: Prototype has one 30 kW (40 hp) Volkswagen modified motorcar engine. Max fuel capacity estimated at 45.5 litres (12 US gallons; 10 Imp gallons).

DIMENSIONS, EXTERNAL:

Wing span	7.06 m (23 ft 2 in)
Length overall	5.03 m (16 ft 6 in)
Height overall	2.82 m (9 ft 3 in)
Propeller diameter	1.83-2.01 m (6 ft 0 in-6 ft 7 in)

AREA:

Wings, gross	18.30 m² (197.0 sq ft)

WEIGHT:

Weight empty	147 kg (325 lb)

COWAN
PETER COWAN
132 Fenn Avenue, New York, Ontario M2P 1X6
Telephone: 1 (416) 224 5473

COWAN CEKADY
First flown as a prototype in 1983, the Cekady is a STOL utility monoplane using the wings, tail unit, boot cowl, landing gear legs and windscreen of a Cessna 170 or 172 married to a new steel tube fuselage. The prototype was fitted with a Textron Lycoming O-360 engine driving a constant-speed propeller and has flown on wheels, floats and wheel/ski landing gears. It embodies a Horton STOL kit, and uses manual flaps (although electrically actuated can be chosen in conjunction with suitable wings).

Plans became available in 1989. Eventually, the design may be expanded to include Cessna 150 and 182 off-shoots with 74.5-186.4 kW (100-250 hp) engines.

ELMWOOD
ELMWOOD AVIATION
RR 4 Elmwood Drive, Belleville, Ontario K8N 4Z4
Telephone: 1 (613) 967 1853
DESIGNER/PROPRIETOR: Ronald B. Mason

ELMWOOD CA-05 CHRISTAVIA Mk I
The prototype Christavia Mk I (C-GENC) first flew on 3 October 1981. Elmwood Aviation is offering plans, and considers the aircraft suitable for the type of flying carried out by professional organisations like Mission Aviation Fellowship. By early 1990, more than 300 Christavia Mk Is were under construction; about 40 had flown. Those under construction include several for the mission field.

TYPE: Tandem two-seat homebuilt.

AIRFRAME: Braced two-spar wing structure of Sitka spruce, with truss ribs and Dacron covering. Aluminium can be used alternatively to fabricate spars and ribs. Computer designed wing section. Frise ailerons of wooden construction with Dacron covering. Fuselage of welded 4130 and 1025 steel tube, Dacron covered. Wire-braced tail unit of steel tube, with mild steel plate ribs, Dacron covered. Non-retractable tailwheel landing gear. Optional floats or skis.

POWER PLANT: Prototype has a 48.5 kW (65 hp) Teledyne Continental A65. Engines of 37.25 to 112 kW (50 to 150 hp) can be fitted. Main fuel tank, capacity 57 litres (15 US gallons; 12.5 Imp gallons), in fuselage aft of firewall; auxiliary tank, capacity 23 litres (6 US gallons; 5 Imp gallons), in each wing.

DIMENSIONS, EXTERNAL:

Wing span	9.91 m (32 ft 6 in)
Length overall	6.30 m (20 ft 8 in)
Height overall	2.13 m (7 ft 0 in)
Propeller diameter	1.83 m (6 ft 0 in)

AREA:

Wings, gross	13.59 m² (146.25 sq ft)

WEIGHTS (48.5 kW; 65 hp engine, 15 US gallons fuel):

Weight empty	338 kg (745 lb)
Max T-O weight	590 kg (1,300 lb)

PERFORMANCE (at max T-O weight, engine and fuel as above):

Max level speed at S/L	104 knots (193 km/h; 120 mph)
Cruising speed at 610 m (2,000 ft), 45% power	74 knots (137 km/h; 85 mph)
Stalling speed: power off	37 knots (68 km/h; 42 mph)
power on	31 knots (57 km/h; 35 mph)
Rate of climb at S/L	259 m (850 ft)/min
Service ceiling	3,960 m (13,000 ft)
T-O run	107 m (350 ft)
Landing from 15 m (50 ft)	198 m (650 ft)
Range with standard fuel, 45% power	382 nm (708 km; 440 miles)
g limits	+4.5/−2.8

ELMWOOD CH-8 CHRISTAVIA Mk 4
This four-seat development of the Christavia Mk I first flew on 3 January 1986. Plans and an information kit are available, and about 50 were under construction in early 1990.

TYPE: Four-seat homebuilt cabin monoplane.

AIRFRAME: Similar to Christavia Mk I.

POWER PLANT: One 112 kW (150 hp) Textron Lycoming O-320 or converted motorcar engine. Fuel capacity 136.4 litres (36 US gallons; 30 Imp gallons).

DIMENSIONS, EXTERNAL:

Wing span	10.67 m (35 ft 0 in)
Length overall	7.01 m (23 ft 0 in)
Height overall	1.98 m (6 ft 6 in)
Propeller diameter	1.78 m (5 ft 10 in)

AREA:

Wings, gross	16.26 m² (175.0 sq ft)

WEIGHTS (112 kW; 150 hp engine):

Weight empty	522 kg (1,150 lb)
Max T-O weight	1,043 kg (2,300 lb)

PERFORMANCE:

Max level speed at 610 m (2,000 ft)	111 knots (206 km/h; 128 mph)
Econ cruising speed, 65% power	102 knots (188 km/h; 117 mph)
Stalling speed: flaps up	35 knots (65 km/h; 40 mph)
12° flap	31 knots (57 km/h; 35 mph)
Max rate of climb at S/L	244 m (800 ft)/min
Service ceiling	5,485 m (18,000 ft)
T-O run	91 m (300 ft)
Landing run	152 m (500 ft)
Range with max fuel	548 nm (1,017 km; 632 miles)

HUSKY
HUSKY MANUFACTURING LTD
Corman Air Park, Saskatchewan
PRESIDENT: Brian Heslin
VICE-PRESIDENT: Robert Ayres

HUSKY NORSEMAN
The Norseman, according to Husky's President, was designed for cropspraying and hard utility work from rough field strips. Mr Heslin was formerly the President of Sylvaire Manufacturing Ltd, producers of the Bushmaster ultralight described in the Sport Aircraft section of the 1987-88 *Jane's*, and the Norseman is based extensively on experience with that aircraft, the objective being to develop an aircraft with the low weight of an ultralight but the added strength needed for a robust working aeroplane.

The prototype Norseman flew for the first time in June 1987, and production began six months later in a 1,022 m² (11,000 sq ft) factory at Corman Air Park, Saskatchewan. The aircraft is available in both single-seat (Norseman I) and two-seat (Norseman II) forms, and is produced in both kit and ready to fly forms. The factory built Norseman conforms to FAR Pt 23 (Utility Category) requirements, and can be supplied for cropspraying with a 113.5 litre (30 US gallon; 25 Imp gallon) tank and accompanying spraygear.

Initial orders, including one from an unnamed US customer for 250 kits and another (for 50 aircraft) from the Aero Club of India, are said to be sufficient to ensure a production run of up to 600 aircraft. Deliveries to Canadian customers and to India began in 1988.

TYPE: Single-seat or two-seat lightweight utility aircraft.

AIRFRAME: Strut braced high-wing monoplane of constant chord, with two parallel streamline section struts each side and short jury struts. Slight dihedral. Wings constructed of Sitka spruce and glassfibre, with bonded Ceconite covering and polyurethane exterior finish. Full span differentially operating ailerons; no flaps or tabs. Riveted fuselage structure of aluminium alloy, with strong roll cage, covered with bonded Ceconite and polyurethane exterior finish. Conventional fin/rudder/tailplane/elevators, of similar construction to fuselage. Ground adjustable elevator trim. Non-retractable tailwheel landing gear; floats optional. Steerable tailwheel.

POWER PLANT: One 35 kW (47 hp) Rotax 503 two-cylinder two-stroke engine, with 2.58:1 geared reduction drive to a two-blade wooden fixed-pitch propeller. Three-blade propeller optional. Fuel capacity (petrol/oil mixture) 36.3 litres (9.6 US gallons; 8 Imp gallons).

ACCOMMODATION: Single upholstered glassfibre seat (adjustable fore and aft), or (Norseman II) two seats side by side with dual controls, in fully enclosed cabin. Large wrap-around windscreen. Reinforced transparent door on each side.

DIMENSIONS, EXTERNAL:

Wing span	10.26 m (33 ft 8 in)
Length overall	6.07 m (19 ft 11 in)
Height overall	2.01 m (6 ft 7 in)
Propeller diameter (two-blade)	1.73 m (5 ft 8 in)

AREA:

Wings, gross	14.07 m² (151.5 sq ft)

WEIGHTS (Norseman I, agricultural configuration):

Weight empty, equipped	144 kg (318 lb)
Fuel weight	26.1 kg (57.6 lb)
Max T-O weight	454 kg (1,000 lb)

PERFORMANCE (Norseman I at max T-O weight, agricultural configuration, hard runway, ISA at S/L):

Max level speed	89 knots (166 km/h; 103 mph)
Cruising speed, 75% power	78 knots (145 km/h; 90 mph)
Climbing speed:	
best climb angle	39 knots (72 km/h; 45 mph)
best climb speed	43 knots (80 km/h; 50 mph)
Stalling speed:	
power on	25 knots (45 km/h; 28 mph)
power off	29 knots (54 km/h; 33 mph)
T-O run	46 m (150 ft)
T-O to 15 m (50 ft)	76 m (250 ft)
Landing from 15 m (50 ft)	214 m (700 ft)
Endurance at 56 knots (105 km/h; 65 mph)	3 h
g limits	+6/−3

KESTREL
KESTREL SPORT AVIATION
PO Box 1808, Brockville, Ontario K6V 6K8
Telephone: 1 (613) 342 8366
Fax: 1 (613) 345 3567

KESTREL HAWK
Designed in several versions, the Hawk comes under ultralight and amateur-built regulations and is suited to sport flying and primary flight training, offering a fighter style cockpit and low operating costs. It is said to be capable of basic aerobatic manoeuvres such as loops and rolls.

Development began in about 1985 and an initial batch of 10 production aircraft was constructed that included four prototypes. The factory assembled ultralight is known simply as the Hawk, while the amateur-built version is the Kit Hawk. Both use a Rotax 503 engine. The amateur-built Sport Hawk and Float Hawk are versions with Rotax 532 engines for the US market, the latter featuring glassfibre amphibious floats. Delivery of Kit Hawks to customers in Canada was followed, from November 1988, by delivery of Sport Hawks and Float Hawks to US customers. Partial kits are also available. Construction from a kit takes between 300 and 400 working hours.

TYPE: Tandem two-seat ultralight and homebuilt biplane.

AIRFRAME: Equal-span biplane, with I interplane and diagonal struts. Pod and boom configuration, with conventional tail unit and controls. Homebuilt versions are all-metal construction; ultralight versions feature Tedlar polyurethane sheet wing skins. Semi-retractable landing gear with central monowheel, steerable tailwheel and balancer wheels beneath each lower wing.

POWER PLANT: Hawk and Kit Hawk use one 38.8 kW (52 hp) Rotax 503. Sport Hawk and Float Hawk use one 47.7 kW (64 hp) Rotax 532LC. Two-blade pusher propeller. Design reportedly capable of accepting alternative engines of up to 93.2 kW (125 hp).

DIMENSIONS, EXTERNAL (all versions):

Wing span	7.47 m (24 ft 6 in)
Length overall	7.25 m (23 ft 9½ in)
Height overall	1.68 m (5 ft 6 in)
Propeller diameter	1.52 m (5 ft 0 in)

AREA (all versions):

Wings, gross	15.93 m² (171.5 sq ft)

Prototype Cowan Cekady light aircraft using Cessna 170/172 components
(Geoffrey P. Jones)

Kestrel Hawk two-seat biplane *(Geoffrey P. Jones)*

Elmwood Aviation CH-8 Christavia Mk 4 four-seat homebuilt

Macair Merlin two-seat microlight/homebuilt

Mountain Valley Air Arrow two-seat light aircraft *(Peter M. Bowers)*

Husky Norseman I single-seat utility aircraft *(Canadian Aviation)*

WEIGHTS (A: Kit Hawk, B: Float Hawk):			
Weight empty: A	179 kg (395 lb)	Cruising speed, 75% power: A, B	
B	261 kg (575 lb)		71-74 knots (132-137 km/h; 82-85 mph)
Max T-O weight: A	376 kg (830 lb)	Stalling speed: A	33 knots (61 km/h; 38 mph)
B	476 kg (1,050 lb)	B	37 knots (68 km/h; 42 mph)
PERFORMANCE (A and B as above):		Max rate of climb at S/L: A, B	183 m (600 ft)/min
Max level speed at S/L: A, B		T-O run: A	69 m (225 ft)
	87 knots (161 km/h; 100 mph)	B	92 m (300 ft)
		B, from water	229 m (750 ft)

Landing run: A, B	107 m (350 ft)
B, on water	153 m (500 ft)
g limits: A	+6/−4
B	+4/−2

MACAIR

MACAIR INDUSTRIES INC

PO Box 1000, Baldwin, Ontario L0E 1A0
Telephone: 1 (416) 722 3411

MACAIR MERLIN

The Merlin is available in microlight and homebuilt versions, as a complete kit, in a series of partial kits, or ready assembled. The M50 version is available in Canada only and uses a Rotax 503 engine, while the Sport 65 uses the higher rated Rotax 532.

TYPE: Side by side two-seat microlight and homebuilt.
AIRFRAME: Strut braced wings with aluminium D-cell and reinforced foam ribs, Ceconite 103 covered. Welded 4130 steel tube fuselage and tail unit, Falconar fabric covered.

Glassfibre engine cowling. Non-retractable tailwheel landing gear. Three-axis control.
POWER PLANT: M50: one 37.3 kW (50 hp) Rotax 503. Sport 65: one 48.5 kW (65 hp) Rotax 532. Fuel capacity 19 litres (5 US gallons; 4.2 Imp gallons) and 38 litres (10 US gallons; 8.4 Imp gallons) respectively.

DIMENSIONS, EXTERNAL (A: M50, B: Sport 65):

Wing span: A, B	9.75 m (32 ft 0 in)
Length overall: A, B	6.10 m (20 ft 0 in)
Height overall: A, B	1.85 m (6 ft 1 in)
Propeller diameter: A	1.63 m (5 ft 4 in)
B	1.73 m (5 ft 8 in)

AREA:

Wings, gross: A, B	14.59 m² (157.0 sq ft)

WEIGHTS:

Weight empty: A	188 kg (415 lb)
B	193 kg (426 lb)

Max T-O weight: A	454 kg (1,000 lb)
B	499 kg (1,100 lb)

PERFORMANCE (two crew):
Max level speed:

A	65-69 knots (121-129 km/h; 75-80 mph)
B	69-74 knots (129-137 km/h; 80-85 mph)

Cruising speed, 55% power:

A	39-43 knots (72-80 km/h; 45-50 mph)
B	48-52 knots (89-97 km/h; 55-60 mph)

Stalling speed, power off:

A, B	21 knots (39 km/h; 24 mph)
T-O run: A	46-61 m (150-200 ft)
B	34-46 m (110-150 ft)
Landing run: A, B	76 m (250 ft)
g limits	+6/−3

MOUNTAIN VALLEY

MOUNTAIN VALLEY AIR

Box 102, Lillooet, British Columbia V0K 1V0
Telephone: 1 (604) 256 4697

MOUNTAIN VALLEY AIR ARROW

This side by side two-seat Piper Cub look-alike is available as a Lazair conversion or as a complete kit offering new advanced wings with flaps. The fuselage has a 6061-T6 aluminium alloy structure of patented extrusion

fittings, and the aircraft is finished in Hipec except for the engine cowling, which is constructed of glassfibre. The crew sit on bush style safari seats in the semi-enclosed cabin and have a dual control stick and 'sun roof' opening. Power is provided by a 40.3 kW (54 hp) Rotax 503 engine with dual carburettors, reduction gear and electric starting. Fuel capacity is 22.7 litres (6 US gallons; 5 Imp gallons). The tailwheel of the non-retractable landing gear is of castoring type.

DIMENSIONS, EXTERNAL:

Wing span	11.89 m (39 ft 0 in)
Length of fuselage	5.94 m (19 ft 6 in)

Height overall	approx 2.03 m (6 ft 8 in)
Propeller diameter	1.73 m (5 ft 8 in)

WEIGHTS:

Weight empty	172 kg (380 lb)
Max T-O weight	385 kg (850 lb)

PERFORMANCE:

Cruising speed	56 knots (105 km/h; 65 mph)
Stalling speed:	
power off	22-24 knots (41-44 km/h; 25-27 mph)
power on	17-18 knots (31-32 km/h; 19-20 mph)
Max rate of climb at S/L	244 m (800 ft)/min
T-O run	76 m (250 ft)

MURPHY

MURPHY AVIATION LTD

8880-C Young Road South, Chilliwack, British Columbia
V2P 4P5
Telephone: 1 (604) 792 5855
Fax: 1 (604) 792 7006
PRESIDENT: Darryl Murphy

In addition to the Renegade II and Renegade Spirit,
Murphy has developed a new three-seat aircraft as the
Rebel. This can be built as a homebuilt or ARV, or as a
microlight in Europe and Asia.

MURPHY RENEGADE II

The prototype Renegade II first flew in May 1985. Ready
assembled aircraft, plans and kits are available, the latter in
four standards ranging from a partial parts kit to a
300-400 working hour quick build kit with all parts
pre-manufactured plus partly assembled fuselage, wings
and engine mounting. By 19 January 1990 a total of six
assembled aircraft, 61 kits and 92 sets of plans had been
delivered. Two plans-built and 25 kit-built aircraft had by
then been completed.
TYPE: Two-seat dual-control ARV and homebuilt biplane;
also conforms to microlight regulations in Canada and
some European countries.
AIRFRAME: Strut and wire braced biplane of fabric covered
all-metal construction. NACA 23012 wing section. Frise
ailerons on lower only or all four wings. Optional
extended wings with rounded tips. Non-retractable
tailwheel landing gear. Optional floats, skis, agricultural
spraygear and parachute.
POWER PLANT: One 35.8 kW (48 hp) Rotax 503 standard;
39.5 kW (53 hp) twin-carburettor Rotax 503.2V optional.
Alternative engines include Rotax 532 and Teledyne
Continental O65, O75 and O85. Fuel in two 29.5 litre (7.8
US gallon; 6.5 Imp gallon) tanks.

DIMENSIONS, EXTERNAL:

Wing span: upper	6.48 m (21 ft 3 in)
lower	6.05 m (19 ft 10 in)
Length overall	5.61 m (18 ft 5 in)
Height overall	2.08 m (6 ft 10 in)
Propeller diameter	1.73 m (5 ft 8 in)

AREA:

Wings, gross	14.29 or 15.61 m² (153.8 or 168.0 sq ft)

WEIGHTS:

Weight empty	163-181 kg (360-400 lb)
Max T-O weight	408 kg (900 lb)

PERFORMANCE (Rotax 503 engine and 2 crew, unless stated
otherwise):

Max level speed at 305 m (1,000 ft)	
	69 knots (129 km/h; 80 mph)
Econ cruising speed	61 knots (113 km/h; 70 mph)
Stalling speed, power off	33 knots (61 km/h; 38 mph)
Max rate of climb at S/L	183 m (600 ft)/min
Service ceiling	3,660 m (12,000 ft)
T-O and landing run	61 m (200 ft)
Range with max payload	195 nm (362 km; 225 miles)
Endurance	4 h 30 min
g limits: pilot only	+10/-6
dual	+8.25/-4.5

MURPHY RENEGADE SPIRIT

The Renegade Spirit has the 47.7 kW (64 hp) Rotax 532
as its standard power plant, in a radial type cowling, and
introduces a number of other internal and external
refinements. The Rotax 912 flat-four and Norton rotary
engines can be fitted. The prototype (C-IJLW) first flew on
6 May 1987. By 19 January 1990 a total of 10 assembled
aircraft, 146 kits and 120 sets of plans had been delivered.
Two plans-built and 40 kit-built aircraft had by then been
completed.
DIMENSIONS, EXTERNAL AND WEIGHTS: As for Renegade II
PERFORMANCE (two crew):

Max level speed	78-82 knots (145-153 km/h; 90-95 mph)
Econ cruising speed	65 knots (120 km/h; 75 mph)
Stalling speed, power off	33 knots (62 km/h; 38 mph)
Max rate of climb at S/L	274 m (900 ft)/min
Service ceiling	3,660 m (12,000 ft)
T-O run	53 m (175 ft)
Landing run	61 m (200 ft)
Range with max payload	195 nm (362 km; 225 miles)
Endurance	4 h 30 min
g limits: pilot only	+10/-6 ultimate
dual	+8.25/-4.5

MURPHY REBEL

The new Rebel is a three-seat high-wing cabin monoplane, suited to recreational, training, cross country, border
patrol and other roles. Construction of the prototype began
in October 1989 and the prototype was expected to fly in
April 1990. It has been designed to conform with FAR Pt 23
and JAR 22 Utility regulations at a gross weight of 385 kg
(850 lb). Estimated building time is 300-400 hours. The
microlight version is being marketed in Europe and Asia.
Thirty-two Rebels had been ordered by April 1990, with
delivery of kits due to start in October-November that year.
TYPE: Three-seat dual-control homebuilt, ARV and microlight monoplane.
AIRFRAME: Strut braced high-wing monoplane, with aluminium alloy structure; aluminium covered fuselage.
Microlight version has fabric covered wings and control
surfaces; Experimental version has aluminium covered
wings. Modified NACA 4415 wing section. Conventional
three-axis control; full span flaperons will become
available later. Non-retractable tailwheel landing gear,
with brakes. Floats and skis optional.
POWER PLANT: One 59.7 kW (80 hp) Rotax 912 engine, with
2.58 : 1 reduction gear. Engines of 38.8-71.6 kW (52-96
hp) can be fitted, with options including Rotax 503, 532
and 582; 67 kW (90 hp) Norton P62; and 71.6 kW (96 hp)
Cam 90. Fuel capacity 109 litres (28.8 US gallons; 24 Imp
gallons).

DIMENSIONS, EXTERNAL:

Wing span	9.75 m (32 ft 0 in)
Length overall	approx 6.40 m (21 ft 0 in)
Height overall	1.83 m (6 ft 0 in)
Propeller diameter	1.78 m (5 ft 10 in)

AREA:

Wings, gross	14.86 m² (160.0 sq ft)

WEIGHTS:

Weight empty	204 kg (450 lb)
Baggage capacity	45.5-68 kg (100-150 lb)
Max T-O weight	476 kg (1,050 lb)

PERFORMANCE (estimated, with Rotax 912):

Max level speed	87 knots (161 km/h; 100 mph)
Max cruising speed	78 knots (145 km/h; 90 mph)
Stalling speed	26 knots (49 km/h; 30 mph)
Service ceiling	3,960 m (13,000 ft)
T-O run	77 m (250 ft)
Landing run	92 m (300 ft)
g limits	+7/-4

NOVADYNE

NOVADYNE AIRCRAFT INC

RR 2, Kettleby, Ontario L0G 1J0
Telephone: 1 (416) 939 2348
PRESIDENT: Lorry R. Smith

NOVADYNE TOUCAN SERIES II

The Toucan resembles an ARV version of the Cessna
Skymaster, with an engine mounted in the nose and another
at the rear of the fuselage pod. It has full single engine flight
capability.

The prototype flew for the first time in September 1983
and the first production aircraft in January 1986. The
Toucan is available in kit and ready assembled forms.
TYPE: Two-seat ARV, suited to recreational flying, pilot
training, agricultural spraying, surveillance and aerial
photography.
AIRFRAME: Strut braced rigid wing of aluminium alloy, with
UV resistant skins and glassfibre wingtips. Three-axis
control, plus flaps. Semi-monocoque fuselage of welded
4130 chrome-molybdenum steel, with twin tailbooms.
Non-retractable tricycle landing gear. Floats optional.
Recovery parachute standard.
POWER PLANT: Two 30.5 kW (41 hp) Rotax 447 engines in
'push and pull' configuration. Fuel capacity 68 litres (18
US gallons; 15 Imp gallons). Optional 23 litre (6 US
gallon; 5 Imp gallon) auxiliary tank.

DIMENSIONS, EXTERNAL:

Wing span	11.74 m (38 ft 6 in)
Length overall	6.10 m (20 ft 0 in)
Height overall	2.85 m (9 ft 4 in)
Propeller diameter	1.52 m (5 ft 0 in)

AREA:

Wings, gross	17.34 m² (186.6 sq ft)

WEIGHTS:

Weight empty	218 kg (480 lb)
Crew weight range	45.5-136 kg (100-300 lb)
Max T-O weight	476 kg (1,050 lb)

PERFORMANCE (at max T-O weight):

Max level speed at 610 m (2,000 ft)	
	68 knots (126 km/h; 78 mph)
Econ cruising speed at 610 m (2,000 ft)	
	52 knots (97 km/h; 60 mph)
Stalling speed, flaps up, engine idling	
	26 knots (49 km/h; 30 mph)
Max rate of climb at S/L	244 m (800 ft)/min
Service ceiling	3,050 m (10,000 ft)
T-O run	46 m (150 ft)
Landing run	31 m (100 ft)
Range with max payload	173 nm (321 km; 200 miles)
Endurance	4 h 30 min
g limits	+6/-3

REPLICA PLANS

REPLICA PLANS

14752 90th Avenue, Surrey, British Columbia V3R 1A4

Details of the Replica Plans S.E.5A Replica, and an
illustration, can be found in the 1988-89 *Jane's.*

SEAWIND

SEAWIND INTERNATIONAL INC

PO Box 878, Haliburton, Ontario K0M 1S0
Telephone: 1 (705) 457 1438
PRESIDENT: Leonard R. Creelman

SEAWIND INTERNATIONAL SEAWIND 2500

The production prototype Seawind (C-GFNL) flew for
the first time on 23 August 1982. An illustration can be
found in the 1987-88 *Jane's.* The Seawind 2500 is the much
refined version of which kits are available, each containing
pre-moulded components that are supplied as complete
subassemblies where possible. Assembly takes about 1000
working hours.
TYPE: Four-seat dual-control homebuilt amphibian; exceeds
FAR Pt 23 minimum performance requirements.
AIRFRAME: Wing section NLF(1)-0215F. Built-up GFRP
wing spar and PVC foam ribs, covered with GFRP skins.
Ailerons, plain flaps, wingtip floats and single-step
flying-boat hull all of GFRP/PVC foam construction.
GFRP tail unit. Hydraulically retractable tricycle landing
gear.
POWER PLANT: One 186.5 kW (250 hp) Textron Lycoming
engine. Two integral fuel cells in wings; total capacity 302
litres (80 US gallons; 66.6 Imp gallons).

DIMENSIONS, EXTERNAL:

Wing span	10.67 m (35 ft 0 in)
Length overall	8.23 m (27 ft 0 in)
Height overall	2.90 m (9 ft 6 in)
Propeller diameter	1.93 m (6 ft 4 in)

AREA:

Wings, gross	14.59 m² (157.0 sq ft)

WEIGHTS:

Weight empty	771 kg (1,700 lb)
Max T-O weight: from water	1,270 kg (2,800 lb)
from land	1,360 kg (3,000 lb)

PERFORMANCE:

Max level speed at S/L	152 knots (281 km/h; 175 mph)
Cruising speed, 75% power	
	143 knots (266 km/h; 165 mph)
Stalling speed: flaps up	52 knots (97 km/h; 60 mph)
flaps and landing gear down	
	47 knots (87 km/h; 54 mph)
Max rate of climb at S/L	320 m (1,050 ft)/min
Service ceiling	5,180 m (17,000 ft)
T-O run: land	259 m (850 ft)
water	366 m (1,200 ft)
Landing run	366 m (1,200 ft)
Range with max standard fuel	
	1,129 nm (2,092 km; 1,300 miles)

SEVILLE

SEVILLE AIRCRAFT INC

The address given in the 1988-89 *Jane's* is no longer
current. Details of the Seville Two Place, and an illustration,
can be found in that edition.

Murphy Renegade Spirit two-seat biplane *(Geoffrey P. Jones)*

Murphy Rebel three-seat cabin monoplane

Novadyne Toucan 'push and pull' twin-engined ARV

Seawind four-seat homebuilt amphibian *(J.M.G. Gradidge)*

Ultimate Aircraft 10 Dash 100 *(J.M.G. Gradidge)*

THOR
THOR AIR

The address given in the 1988-89 *Jane's* is no longer current. Details of the Thor T-1, T-2 and Juno, and an illustration, can be found in that edition.

ULTIMATE
ULTIMATE AIRCRAFT CORP
Guelph Airpark, Guelph, Ontario N1H 6H8
Telephone: 1 (519) 836 8622
PRESIDENT: Gordon Price

ULTIMATE AIRCRAFT 10 DASH 100/300
Ultimate Aircraft is offering sets of plans, kits and ready assembled examples of three closely related single-seat biplanes of the 10 Dash series. The basic model is the **10 Dash 100**, designed to be an affordable sporting biplane with a 74.5 or 134 kW (100 or 180 hp) engine. Power plants between these ratings can be installed at the customer's option. A typical power plant is a 74.5 kW (100 hp) Teledyne Continental O-200. The prototype 10 Dash 100 flew for the first time on 6 October 1985.

The **10 Dash 200** was designed as a modern competition aerobatic aircraft, utilising a 134-149 kW (180-200 hp) engine with Ellison throttle body injector and a constant-speed Hoffmann or MT composites propeller. The final model in the range is the **10 Dash 300**, a state of the art competition aircraft, with longer-span wings, incorporating full-span symmetrical ailerons; a longer fuselage; and a 224 kW (300 hp) or 261 kW (350 hp) Textron Lycoming engine, driving a three-blade Hoffmann propeller.

TYPE: Single-seat homebuilt sporting and aerobatic biplane.
AIRFRAME: Braced biplane, with Ceconite covered wooden wings. Near symmetrical wing section. Upper and lower full-span ailerons of aluminium alloy. 'Macro flap'

control (5° aileron droop with 30° 'up' elevator). Welded steel tube fuselage structure, aluminium alloy and Ceconite covered. Aluminium alloy turtledeck. Glassfibre nose cowlings. Braced steel tube tail unit, Ceconite covered. Non-retractable tailwheel landing gear.
POWER PLANT: See introduction. 10-100 has fuel capacity of 83 litres (22 US gallons; 18.3 Imp gallons). Optional 57 litre (15 US gallon; 12.5 Imp gallon) strap-on centre-section tank. Inverted fuel system.

DIMENSIONS, EXTERNAL:

Wing span: 10-100, 10-200	4.83 m (15 ft 10 in)
10-300	5.95 m (19 ft 6 in)
Length overall: 10-100	5.33 m (17 ft 6 in)
10-200	5.49 m (18 ft 0 in)
10-300	6.40 m (21 ft 0 in)
Height overall: 10-100, 10-200	1.68 m (5 ft 6 in)

AREAS:

Wings, gross: 10-100, 10-200	8.92 m² (96.0 sq ft)
10-300	11.15 m² (120.0 sq ft)

WEIGHTS:

Weight empty: 10-100	358 kg (790 lb)
10-200	420 kg (925 lb)
10-300	522 kg (1,150 lb)
Max T-O weight: 10-100, 10-200	612 kg (1,350 lb)
10-300	748 kg (1,650 lb)

PERFORMANCE:

Max level speed:	
10-100	165 knots (306 km/h; 190 mph)
10-200	191 knots (354 km/h; 220 mph)
10-300	217 knots (402 km/h; 250 mph)
Cruising speed, 75% power:	
10-100	122 knots (225 km/h; 140 mph)

10-200	148 knots (273 km/h; 170 mph)
10-300	165 knots (305 km/h; 190 mph)
Stalling speed:	
10-100: power off	46 knots (86 km/h; 53 mph)
power on	44 knots (81 km/h; 50 mph)
Max rate of climb at S/L: 10-100	350 m (1,150 ft)/min
10-300	915 m (3,000 ft)/min
T-O run: 10-100	180 m (590 ft)
Landing run: 10-100	155 m (510 ft)
Range: 10-100	564 nm (1,046 km; 650 miles)
10-200	434 nm (804 km; 500 miles)
10-300	520-781 nm (965-1,448 km; 600-900 miles)
Rate of roll: 10-200	360°/sec
g limits: all	+7/-5 operating

ULTIMATE AIRCRAFT 20 DASH 300
The Ultimate Aircraft 20 Dash 300 is identical to the 10 Dash 300 except for having two seats in tandem under a one-piece bubble canopy. It offers the same choice of Textron Lycoming engines and other options, and is available in two forms: the **20 Dash 300T** is a two-seat aerobatic training aircraft; the **20 Dash 300E** is the exhibition model.

DIMENSIONS, EXTERNAL:
As for 10-300
WEIGHTS:

Weight empty	545 kg (1,200 lb)
Max T-O weight	907 kg (2,000 lb)

PERFORMANCE:

Max level speed	217 knots (402 km/h; 250 mph)

Cruising speed, 75% power
165 knots (305 km/h; 190 mph)
Range   434-608 nm (804-1,126 km; 500-700 miles)

ULTIMATE AIRCRAFT (PITTS) SPECIAL

The standard Pitts S-1 and S-2 Specials are mentioned under the Christen heading in the main US Aircraft section of this edition. Basic feature of the Ultimate versions of these aircraft is the use of new wings with larger control surfaces and significantly increased strength of construction. These make it possible to roll at 360°/s at normal flying speeds and 240°/s at low speeds, and to perform five vertical rolls on take-off. The wings are jig built to fit any Pitts Special without modification. Other features include low-profile glassfibre engine cowlings and Plexiglas cockpit canopy, and the option to build the fuselage up to 21 cm (8½ in) longer to increase comfort.

POWER PLANT: Conformal auxiliary fuel tanks, filled with Explosafe explosion-proof metal foil, strapped above centre-section of top wing. Capacity 34 or 57 litres (9 or 15 US gallons; 7.5 or 12.5 Imp gallons) for S-1; 68 litres (18 US gallons; 15 Imp gallons) for S-2.
DIMENSION, EXTERNAL (S-1):
Wing span (upper and lower)   4.77 m (15 ft 8 in)

ULTRAVIA
ULTRAVIA AERO INC

The address given in the 1989-90 *Jane's* is no longer current. Details of the Pelican Club, and an illustration, can be found in that edition.

WESTERN
WESTERN AIRCRAFT SUPPLIES

623 Markerville Road North-East, Calgary, Alberta T2E 5X1
Telephone: 1 (403) 276 3087
DIRECTOR: Jean J. Peters

WESTERN PGK-1 HIRONDELLE

The prototype Hirondelle first flew on 27 June 1976. Plans and wood kits are available, as well as some preformed components.
TYPE: Side by side two-seat, dual-control homebuilt aircraft.
AIRFRAME: Wing section NACA 23012. All wooden structure, with Dacron covering on wings and rear fuselage. Glassfibre cabin top. Non-retractable tailwheel landing gear.
POWER PLANT: One 86 kW (115 hp) Textron Lycoming O-235-C1B. Two fuel tanks, each 54.5 litres (14.4 US gallons; 12 Imp gallons) capacity.
DIMENSIONS, EXTERNAL:

Wing span	7.92 m (26 ft 0 in)
Length overall	6.27 m (20 ft 7 in)
Height overall	2.29 m (7 ft 6 in)
Propeller diameter	1.68 m (5 ft 6 in)
AREA:	
Wings, gross	10.96 m² (118.0 sq ft)
WEIGHTS:	
Weight empty, equipped	428 kg (944 lb)
Max T-O weight	669 kg (1,475 lb)
PERFORMANCE (at max T-O weight):	
Max level speed	123 knots (228 km/h; 142 mph)
Max cruising speed	117 knots (217 km/h; 135 mph)
Stalling speed	53 knots (97 km/h; 60 mph)
Max rate of climb at S/L	over 305 m (1,000 ft)
Service ceiling	3,840 m (12,600 ft)
T-O run	approx 228 m (750 ft)
Endurance, with 45 min reserves	3 h 36 min

ZENAIR
ZENAIR AIRCRAFT LTD

Huronia Airport, Midland, Ontario L4R 4K8
Telephone: 1 (705) 526 2871
Fax: 1 (705) 526 8022
PRESIDENT AND DESIGNER: Christophe Heintz
MARKETING MANAGER: Sebastien C. Heintz

Zenair began by marketing the Zénith two-seat homebuilt aircraft, and by early 1990 there were more than 600 Zenair aircraft flying in 42 different countries.

ZENAIR MONO Z-CH 100

The single-seat Mono Z-CH 100 is of generally similar construction to the two-seat Zénith, but is smaller and less powerful. The prototype (C-GNYM) made its first flight on 8 May 1975.
Construction drawings and manual, materials, parts and complete kits are available. Building time is estimated at under 600 working hours.
TYPE: Single-seat homebuilt aircraft.
AIRFRAME: All-metal semi-monocoque construction. Wing section GAW-1 (modified). Non-retractable tricycle or, optionally, tailwheel landing gear.
POWER PLANT: One 41 kW (55 hp) 1,700 cc converted Volkswagen engine in prototype. Engines from 33.5 kW (45 hp) 1,600 cc Volkswagen to 74.5 kW (100 hp) Teledyne Continental O-200 optional. Fuel capacity 55 litres (14.4 US gallons; 12 Imp gallons).
DIMENSIONS, EXTERNAL:

Wing span	6.71 m (22 ft 0 in)
Length overall	5.94 m (19 ft 6 in)
Height overall	1.98 m (6 ft 6 in)
Propeller diameter	1.47 m (4 ft 10 in)
AREA:	
Wings, gross	8.50 m² (91.5 sq ft)
WEIGHTS (48.5 kW; 65 hp engine):	
Weight empty	286 kg (630 lb)
Baggage capacity	11.3 kg (25 lb)
Max T-O weight	435 kg (960 lb)
PERFORMANCE (engine as above):	
Max level speed	109 knots (200 km/h; 125 mph)
Cruising speed (75% power)	95 knots (177 km/h; 110 mph)
Stalling speed	42 knots (77 km/h; 48 mph)
Max rate of climb at S/L	250 m (820 ft)/min
Service ceiling	over 3,660 m (12,000 ft)
T-O and landing run	168 m (550 ft)
Range with max fuel	350 nm (645 km; 400 miles)
g limits	±9 ultimate

ZENAIR ACRO-ZÉNITH CH 150

Developed from the Mono Z-CH 100, the CH 150 is intended for aerobatic training and competition flying. The prototype first flew on 19 May 1980. Kits, complete except for engine, are available to amateur constructors. All of the more critical parts, such as wing spars and ribs, are premanufactured.
TYPE: Single-seat homebuilt aircraft.
AIRFRAME: All-metal semi-monocoque construction. Wing section NACA 0015. Non-retractable tailwheel landing gear. Skis optional.
POWER PLANT: One 112 kW (150 hp) Textron Lycoming O-320 standard. Engines of 74.5-134 kW (100-180 hp) can be fitted. Fuel capacity 55 litres (14.4 US gallons; 12 Imp gallons). Can be increased to 136 litres (36 US gallons; 30 Imp gallons) by use of ferry tank. Fuel and oil systems equipped for inverted flight.
DIMENSIONS, EXTERNAL:

Wing span	6.15 m (20 ft 2 in)
Length overall	6.17 m (20 ft 3 in)
Height overall	1.52 m (5 ft 0 in)
Propeller diameter	1.78 m (5 ft 10 in)
AREA:	
Wings, gross	7.83 m² (84.3 sq ft)
WEIGHTS (112 kW; 150 hp O-320 engine). Wooden propeller and ferry tank fitted. No electrics):	
Weight empty	331 kg (730 lb)
Typical aerobatic T-O weight	440 kg (970 lb)
Baggage capacity	20 kg (44 lb)
Max T-O weight	522 kg (1,150 lb)
PERFORMANCE (conditions as above):	
Max level speed at S/L	156 knots (290 km/h; 180 mph)
Econ cruising speed at 915 m (3,000 ft)	126 knots (233 km/h; 145 mph)
Stalling speed	48 knots (89 km/h; 55 mph)
Max rate of climb at S/L	670 m (2,200 ft)/min
Service ceiling	over 4,875 m (16,000 ft)
T-O run	213 m (700 ft)
Landing run	183 m (600 ft)
Range with standard fuel	260 nm (483 km; 300 miles)
Range at 55% power, with ferry fuel	660 nm (1,223 km; 760 miles)
Endurance with standard fuel	2 h
g limits	±12 ultimate

ZENAIR SUPER ACRO-ZÉNITH CH 180

The first Super Acro-Zénith CH 180 (C-GZEN) was an unlimited aerobatic aircraft, powered by a 171.5 kW (230 hp) Textron Lycoming IO-360 engine. It differed from the Acro-Zénith CH 150 in several respects, apart from engine, the most obvious external changes being a revised tail unit and wings without dihedral. The front fuel tank capacity is 45.5 litres (12 US gallons; 10 Imp gallons) and the rear, with header, 77 litres (20.4 US gallons; 17 Imp gallons). Construction time is 800 working hours. Engines of up to 149 kW (200 hp) can be fitted.
DIMENSIONS, EXTERNAL:

Wing span	6.15 m (20 ft 2 in)
Length overall	6.17 m (20 ft 3 in)
Height overall	1.65 m (5 ft 5 in)
AREA:	
Wings, gross	7.90 m² (85.0 sq ft)
WEIGHTS:	
Weight empty	363 kg (800 lb)
Max T-O weight	521 kg (1,150 lb)
PERFORMANCE (149 kW; 200 hp engine):	
Cruising speed (75% power)	165 knots (305 km/h; 190 mph)
Stalling speed	42 knots (77 km/h; 48 mph)
Max rate of climb at S/L	915 m (3,000 ft)/min
Max rate of roll	270°/s
Range with max fuel, 55% power	565 nm (1,046 km; 650 miles)
g limits:	±8 normal
	±12 ultimate

ZENAIR ZÉNITH-CH 200

The prototype Zénith-CH 200 flew for the first time on 22 March 1970. Sets of plans and a constructional manual are available to amateur builders, together with materials, parts and complete kits. Many hundreds of kits and plans have been sold to customers in 44 countries.
The following description applies to the standard Zénith-CH 200.
TYPE: Side by side two-seat, dual-control homebuilt aircraft.
AIRFRAME: All-metal semi-monocoque construction, except for glassfibre engine cowling and fairings. NACA 64A515 (modified) wing section. Plans show rudder only, with no fin. Conventional fin and rudder can be fitted if desired. Non-retractable tricycle or, optionally, tailwheel landing gear. Floats and skis optional.
POWER PLANT: Design suitable for engines from 63.5 kW (85 hp) to 119 kW (160 hp). Fuel capacity 90 litres (24 US gallons; 20 Imp gallons). Optional fuel tanks in wing leading-edges, total capacity 72.5 litres (19.2 US gallons; 16 Imp gallons).
DIMENSIONS, EXTERNAL:

Wing span	7.00 m (22 ft 11¾ in)
Length overall	6.25 m (20 ft 6 in)
Height overall	2.11 m (6 ft 11 in)
Propeller diameter	1.83 m (6 ft 0 in)
AREA:	
Wings, gross	9.80 m² (105.9 sq ft)
WEIGHTS (93 kW; 125 hp engine):	
Weight empty	422 kg (930 lb)
Baggage capacity	35 kg (77 lb)
Max T-O weight	680 kg (1,500 lb)
PERFORMANCE (at max T-O weight. 93 kW; 125 hp engine):	
Max level speed at S/L	131 knots (243 km/h; 151 mph)
Cruising speed (75% power) at S/L	122 knots (227 km/h; 141 mph)
Stalling speed, flaps down	47 knots (87 km/h; 54 mph)
Max rate of climb at S/L	335 m (1,100 ft)/min
T-O and landing run	244 m (800 ft)
Range with max fuel	391 nm (724 km; 450 miles)
g limit	+9 ultimate

ZENAIR ZÉNITH-CH 250

The Zénith-CH 250 is a de luxe version of the Zénith-CH 200 with two 65 litre (16.8 US gallon; 14 Imp gallon) fuel tanks in the wings and a 0.71 m³ (25 cu ft) baggage area. A forward sliding canopy and rear windows similar to those of the Tri-Z CH 300 are fitted. Recommended engines are in the 86-119 kW (115-160 hp) range. A tailwheel or float landing gear can be fitted as alternatives to the standard tricycle type.
WEIGHTS (112 kW; 150 hp engine):

Weight empty	449 kg (990 lb)
Max T-O weight	730 kg (1,610 lb)
PERFORMANCE (engine as above):	
Max level speed	144 knots (267 km/h; 166 mph)
Cruising speed (75% power)	130 knots (241 km/h; 150 mph)
Stalling speed	45 knots (84 km/h; 52 mph)
Max rate of climb at S/L	518 m (1,700 ft)/min
T-O and landing run	198 m (650 ft)
Range with standard fuel	469 nm (869 km; 540 miles)

ZENAIR TRI-Z CH 300

The three-seat Tri-Z CH 300 is a stretched version of the two-seat CH 200, with an enlarged cabin to provide room for a rear bench seat able to carry a third adult, two children or 95 kg (210 lb) of baggage. Electrically actuated slotted flaps are fitted. Recommended power is in the 93-134 kW (125-180 hp) range. Fuel is carried in two 65 litre (16.8 US

Prototype Western PGK-1 Hirondelle two-seat light aircraft

Zenair Zénith-CH 200 with float landing gear

Zenair STOL CH 701 in landplane form

Zenair Zodiac CH 600 with tricycle landing gear

Zenair Mono Z-CH 100 with optional tailwheel landing gear
(Neil A. Macdougall)

Super Acro-Zénith CH 180 unlimited aerobatic aircraft *(Neil A. Macdougall)*

gallon; 14 Imp gallon) wing tanks. Extra fuel can be carried in further wing tanks. The prototype made its first flight on 9 July 1977.

Sets of plans and a constructional manual are available to amateur builders, as are materials, prefabricated component parts and complete kits. Construction from kits takes 1,000 working hours on average.

DIMENSIONS, EXTERNAL:

Wing span	8.10 m (26 ft 6¾ in)
Length overall	6.85 m (22 ft 5¾ in)
Height overall	2.08 m (6 ft 10 in)

AREA:

Wings, gross	12.00 m² (129.2 sq ft)

WEIGHTS (93 kW; 125 hp engine):

Weight empty	476 kg (1,050 lb)
Max T-O weight	816 kg (1,800 lb)

PERFORMANCE (engine as above):

Max level speed	130 knots (241 km/h; 150 mph)
Econ cruising speed	109 knots (201 km/h; 125 mph)
Stalling speed, flaps down	45 knots (82 km/h; 51 mph)
Max rate of climb at S/L	244 m (800 ft)/min
Range (75% power)	521 nm (965 km; 600 miles)
g limits	±5.7 ultimate

ZENAIR ZODIAC CH 600

The first flight of the CH 60 was achieved in June 1984. Plans and a kit of component parts (45 per cent premanufactured) for the improved CH 600 are available to amateur builders. Construction from a kit takes about 400 working hours. It is suited to the first time builder.

TYPE: Side by side two-seat, dual-control homebuilt aircraft.

AIRFRAME: All-metal construction. No fixed fin. Wing section NACA 65018. Non-retractable tricycle or tail-wheel landing gear. Skis and floats optional.

POWER PLANT: One 63.4 kW (85 hp) Rotax 912, with reduction gear, 47.7 kW (64 hp) Rotax 532, 48.5-74.5 kW (65-100 hp) Teledyne Continental, 37.3 kW (50 hp) VW without electric starting or 52 kW (70 hp) VW engine. Fuel capacity 60 litres (16 US gallons; 13.3 Imp gallons).

DIMENSIONS, EXTERNAL:

Wing span	8.20 m (26 ft 10¾ in)
Length overall	5.65 m (18 ft 6½ in)
Height overall	1.90 m (6 ft 2¾ in)
Propeller diameter	1.52 m (5 ft 0 in)

AREA:

Wings, gross	12.1 m² (130.2 sq ft)

WEIGHTS:

Weight empty, equipped	268 kg (590 lb)
Max T-O weight	476 kg (1,050 lb)

PERFORMANCE (at max T-O weight):

Max level speed at S/L	109 knots (201 km/h; 125 mph)
Econ cruising speed	100 knots (185 km/h; 115 mph)
Stalling speed	39 knots (71 km/h; 44 mph)
Max rate of climb at S/L	366 m (1,200 ft)/min
Service ceiling	6,100 m (20,000 ft)
T-O run	107 m (350 ft)
Landing run	138 m (450 ft)
Range with max fuel, 75% power	364 nm (676 km; 420 miles)
Endurance	4 h
g limits	±6.9

ZENAIR STOL CH 701

The prototype of this Experimental category aircraft was flown for the first time in Summer 1986. The CH 701 is a strut braced high-wing cabin monoplane, capable of being completed with a tricycle or tailwheel landing gear, and with floats, amphibious and ski gears as options. Power is provided by a 37.3 kW (50 hp) Rotax 503 engine in the prototype, but a 63.4 kW (85 hp) Rotax 912, 47.7 kW (64 hp) Rotax 532, 44.7-52 kW (60-70 hp) VW, or 48.5-67 kW (65-90 hp) Teledyne Continental engine are optional; fuel capacity is 42 litres (11 US gallons; 9.2 Imp gallons). To achieve STOL performance, full span leading-edge flaps are fitted to the near constant chord wings. An agricultural version is available with a Micro AG spraying/dusting system. Aircraft are assembled by Zenair's Colombian subsidiary, Agricopteros Ltda (which see). Reports suggest that about 120 CH 701s have been sold in the Americas.

DIMENSIONS, EXTERNAL:

Wing span	8.23 m (27 ft 0 in)
Length overall	6.10 m (20 ft 0 in)
Propeller diameter	1.73 m (5 ft 8 in)

AREA:

Wings, gross	11.33 m² (122.0 sq ft)

WEIGHTS:

Weight empty	192 kg (424 lb)
Max T-O weight	429 kg (946 lb)

PERFORMANCE (48.5 kW; 65 hp engine, at max T-O weight):

Max level speed at S/L	69 knots (129 km/h; 80 mph)
Cruising speed	over 52 knots (97 km/h; 60 mph)
Stalling speed	23 knots (42 km/h; 26 mph)
Max rate of climb at S/L	250 m (820 ft)/min
Service ceiling	3,660 m (12,000 ft)
Max rate of climb at S/L	366 m (1,200 ft)/min
T-O run	30-40 m (98-132 ft)
Landing run	28 m (90 ft)
Range	160 nm (296 km; 184 miles)
Endurance	1 h 40 min
g limits	±6

ZENAIR SUPER STOL CH 801

Suitable for surveillance, patrol, training, crop spraying, light transport and other roles, the Super STOL CH 801 was designed as a light utility aircraft and carries the designation CH 801-M in military form. Construction of the first prototype began in January 1988 and first flight was expected in mid-1990. By January 1990 the two prototypes plus 18 production aircraft had been ordered but general marketing had not begun.

TYPE: Four-seat Experimental monoplane.

AIRFRAME: All-metal strut braced high-wing monoplane, with steel tube fuselage structure and aluminium alloy wing structure, the whole skinned with aluminium alloy. Ailerons, flaps, fixed leading-edge slats, rudder and elevators. Non-retractable tricycle landing gear, with brakes. Optional floats, amphibious floats or skis.

POWER PLANT: One 112 kW (150 hp) Textron Lycoming O-320 standard. Optional engines in the 74.5-149 kW

(100-200 hp) range. Two fuel tanks in wings, total capacity 75 litres (20 US gallons; 16.7 Imp gallons).

DIMENSIONS, EXTERNAL:
Wing span	9.40 m (30 ft 10 in)
Length overall	7.06 m (23 ft 2 in)
Height overall	2.70 m (8 ft 10¼ in)

AREA:
Wings, gross	15.00 m² (161.45 sq ft)

WEIGHTS:
Weight empty	460 kg (1,014 lb)
Max T-O weight	890 kg (1,962 lb)

PERFORMANCE:
Max level speed at 915 m (3,000 ft)	100 knots (185 km/h; 115 mph)
Econ cruising speed	89 knots (165 km/h; 103 mph)
Stalling speed, flaps down	34 knots (62 km/h; 39 mph)
Max rate of climb at S/L	320 m (1,050 ft)/min
Service ceiling	more than 6,100 m (20,000 ft)
T-O run	55 m (181 ft)
Landing run	47 m (155 ft)
Range	400 nm (741 km; 460 miles)
Endurance	5 h
g limits	+6/−3

ZENAIR ZÉNITH CH 2000

Fitting into the Zenair range as a side by side two-seat and smaller span derivative of the Tri-Z CH 300, the Zénith CH 2000 was designed to conform to Canadian Recreational category regulations, but is aimed at the primary training market.

AIRFRAME: All-metal construction. Wing section LS (1) 0417 (mod). Non-retractable tricycle landing gear, with optional floats and skis.

POWER PLANT: One 74.5 kW (100 hp) Teledyne Continental O-200. Fuel capacity 100 litres (26.4 US gallons; 22 Imp gallons) standard, 200 litres (52.8 US gallons; 44 Imp gallons) optional.

DIMENSIONS, EXTERNAL:
Wing span	7.60 m (24 ft 11¼ in)
Length overall	6.85 m (22 ft 5¾ in)
Height overall	2.30 m (7 ft 6½ in)
Propeller diameter	1.83 m (6 ft 0 in)

AREA:
Wings, gross	11.00 m² (118.4 sq ft)

WEIGHTS (A: aerobatic category, B: standard):
Max payload: A	180 kg (396 lb)
B, with baggage	230 kg (507 lb)
Max T-O weight: A	630 kg (1,389 lb)
B	680 kg (1,499 lb)

PERFORMANCE (estimated):
Max level speed	124 knots (230 km/h; 143 mph)
Econ cruising speed	103 knots (190 km/h; 118 mph)
Stalling speed	42 knots (78 km/h; 49 mph)
Max rate of climb at S/L	259 m (850 ft)/min
Service ceiling	more than 3,660 m (12,000 ft)
T-O run	213 m (700 ft)
Landing run	183 m (600 ft)
Range with max standard and optional fuel:	
B	928 nm (1,720 km; 1,068 miles)
Range with max payload and standard fuel:	
B	464 nm (860 km; 534 miles)

CHINA, PEOPLE'S REPUBLIC

SAP
SHIJIAZHUANG AIRCRAFT PLANT
PO Box 164, Shijiazhuang, Hebei
Telephone: 86 Shijiazhuang 744251
Telex: 26236 HBJXC CN

Details of the Qingting W5 series (Dragonfly 5) of microlights can be found in the tables that follow this section.

SAP QINGTING W6 (DRAGONFLY 6)

The Qingting W6 is a three-axis control single-seat homebuilt of more refined design than the W5 series of microlights. The structure is said to be all-metal. Power is provided by a Limbach L-2400 engine.

DIMENSIONS, EXTERNAL:
Wing span	9.802 m (32 ft 2 in)
Length overall	6.676 m (21 ft 10¾ in)
Height overall	1.74 m (5 ft 8½ in)

AREA:
Wings, gross	11.52 m² (124.0 sq ft)

WEIGHTS:
Weight empty	253 kg (558 lb)
Max T-O weight	500 kg (1,102 lb)

PERFORMANCE:
Max level speed	70 knots (130 km/h; 81 mph)
Normal cruising speed	51 knots (95 km/h; 59 mph)
Max rate of climb at S/L	180 m (590 ft)/min
Service ceiling	2,500 m (8,200 ft)
T-O run	118 m (388 ft)
Landing run	87 m (285 ft)
Range	162 nm (300 km; 186 miles)

FRANCE

AÉRODIS
AÉRODIS SARL
Notaire, Allée de la Ronce, 10340 Les Riceys
Telephone: 33 25 29 30 34
Telex: 830 607F
EXECUTIVE: Alain Carsenti

GRINVALDS G-802 ORION

The original version of the Orion was the G-801, the prototype of which flew for the first time on 2 June 1981. A prototype of the developed G-802 first flew on 4 November 1983. Plans and kits of this version are marketed.

The following description applies to the standard kit version of the G-802:

TYPE: Four-seat, dual-control homebuilt aircraft.

AIRFRAME: Wing and tail unit structures of glassfibre reinforced locally with Kevlar and carbonfibre. Wing section NACA 43015 at root, NACA 43012 at tip.

Composites fuselage of glassfibre/epoxy resin, Kevlar and graphite reinforced. Retractable tricycle landing gear.

POWER PLANT: One 134 kW (180 hp) Textron Lycoming IO-360 in first Orion, driving a 'tail-pusher' propeller. Suited to engines of 112-149 kW (150-200 hp). Two fuel tanks, total capacity 220 litres (58 US gallons; 48.4 Imp gallons). Long-range tanks available when flown with pilot and one passenger only, capacity 400 litres (106 US gallons; 88 Imp gallons), or 490 litres (129 US gallons; 108 Imp gallons) with pilot only.

DIMENSIONS, EXTERNAL:
Wing span	9.00 m (29 ft 6½ in)
Length overall	6.85 m (22 ft 5½ in)
Height overall	2.50 m (8 ft 2½ in)
Propeller diameter	1.50 m (4 ft 11 in)

AREA:
Wings, gross	11.22 m² (120.8 sq ft)

WEIGHTS (134 kW; 180 hp engine):
Weight empty, equipped	610 kg (1,345 lb)
Baggage capacity	30 kg (66 lb)
Max T-O weight	1,050 kg (2,315 lb)

PERFORMANCE (134 kW; 180 hp engine):
Max level speed at 2,440 m (8,000 ft)	178 knots (330 km/h; 205 mph)
Econ cruising speed at 2,440 m (8,000 ft)	135 knots (250 km/h; 155 mph)
Stalling speed: flaps up	54 knots (100 km/h; 63 mph)
20° flap	49 knots (90 km/h; 56 mph)
Max rate of climb at S/L	270 m (885 ft)/min
Service ceiling	4,500 m (14,775 ft)
T-O to 15 m (50 ft)	600 m (1,970 ft)
Landing run	200 m (655 ft)
Range at cruising speed, standard fuel	809 nm (1,500 km; 932 miles)
Max range with long range fuel tanks (65% power)	1,618 nm (3,000 km; 1,864 miles)

AVIASUD
AVIASUD ENGINEERING SA
Zone Industrielle la Palud, 83600 Fréjus
Telephone: 33 94 53 94 00
Telex: 461 172F AVIASUD
GENERAL MANAGER: Bernard d'Otreppe

In addition to marketing the Sirocco and Mistral, Aviasud distributes the Marco J-5 in the West (see Hewa-Technics in German part of this section).

AVIASUD SIROCCO

The first flight of the Sirocco was achieved in July 1982.

TYPE: Single-seat microlight aircraft; conforms to FAR Pt 103.

AIRFRAME: Mostly aluminium wing structure, with glassfibre front D spar, 6005A-T6 aluminium rear spar and ribs, and double surface Dacron covering. MacCready TK 7315 (modified) wing section. Fuselage boom of Kevlar reinforced glassfibre; fuselage pod of moulded glassfibre and polyester, with epoxy resin. Three-axis control. Integral tail fin stiffened with Klégécel PVC foam ribs. Non-retractable tricycle landing gear. Floats and skis optional.

POWER PLANT: One 26 kW (35 hp) Rotax 377, 17 kW (23 hp) König 430RD, 22.4 kW (30 hp) KFM 107ER or 19.4 kW (26 hp) JPX PUL 425. Fuel capacity 20 litres (5.3 US gallons; 4.4 Imp gallons) standard, 40 litres (10.6 US gallons; 8.8 Imp gallons) optional.

DIMENSIONS, EXTERNAL:
Wing span	10.12 m (33 ft 2½ in)
Length overall	5.85 m (19 ft 2¼ in)
Height overall	2.80 m (9 ft 2¼ in)
Propeller diameter (Rotax engine)	1.45 m (4 ft 9 in)

AREA:
Wings, gross	13.80 m² (148.5 sq ft)

WEIGHTS:
Weight empty	114-130 kg (251-286 lb)
Pilot weight range	55-120 kg (121-264 lb)
Baggage capacity	30 kg (66 lb)
Max T-O weight	250 kg (551 lb)

PERFORMANCE:
Max level speed	62 knots (115 km/h; 71 mph)
Econ cruising speed	43 knots (80 km/h; 50 mph)
Stalling speed, engine idling	21 knots (40 km/h; 25 mph)
Max rate of climb at S/L	300 m (985 ft)/min
Service ceiling	6,500 m (21,325 ft)
T-O run	35 m (115 ft)
Landing run	30-50 m (98-164 ft)
Range with standard fuel	162 nm (300 km; 186 miles)
Range with max fuel	270 nm (500 km; 310 miles)
Endurance with max standard fuel	4 h
g limits	+6.7/−3.6

AVIASUD MISTRAL 532

The Mistral is designed for recreational flying but is also suited to professional activities normally performed by high-cost conventional aeroplanes and helicopters, such as pilot training, aerial photography, TV and surveillance, banner towing, and cropspraying. It is sold in ready to fly form. An agricultural example sold to a Spanish operator has a 125 litre (33 US gallon; 27.5 Imp gallon) underfuselage chemical tank.

TYPE: Side by side two-seat microlight and ARV aircraft; designed to FAR Pt 23.

AIRFRAME: Braced biplane, with NACA 23012 wing section. Duralumin wing spars and wooden ribs, double surface covered; tail unit similarly constructed. Glassfibre/carbonfibre/epoxy and polyester semi-monocoque fuselage. Three-axis control. Non-retractable tricycle landing gear, with optional floats and skis.

POWER PLANT: One 47 kW (63 hp) Rotax 532. Fuel capacity 68 litres (18 US gallons; 15 Imp gallons).

DIMENSIONS, EXTERNAL:
Wing span	9.40 m (30 ft 10 in)
Length overall	5.90 m (19 ft 4 in)
Height overall	2.20 m (7 ft 2½ in)
Propeller diameter	1.70 m (5 ft 7 in)

AREA:
Wings, gross	17.90 m² (192.7 sq ft)

WEIGHTS:
Weight empty	174 kg (383 lb)
Baggage capacity	20 kg (44 lb)
Max T-O weight	400 kg (882 lb)

PERFORMANCE (at max T-O weight):
Max level speed at S/L	81 knots (150 km/h; 93 mph)
Econ cruising speed	54 knots (100 km/h; 62 mph)
Stalling speed:	
power on	30 knots (55 km/h; 34.5 mph)
power off	33 knots (60 km/h; 38 mph)

SAP Qingting W6 homebuilt aircraft

Aviasud Mistral in new twin-engined configuration for aerial advertising work

The first Grinvalds G-802 Orion all-plastics homebuilt aircraft

Centrair Parafan II
two-seat parawing
microlight

Max rate of climb at S/L	240 m (785 ft)/min
Service ceiling	4,000 m (13,125 ft)
T-O and landing run	80 m (262 ft)
Range	270 nm (500 km; 310 miles)
Endurance	8 h
g limits	+4/–2 design
	+6/–3 ultimate

AVIASUD MISTRAL 462

Also in production is this later version of the Mistral, which offers improved economy. A superlight version, with an empty weight of 149.9 kg (330 lb), has been developed for the West German market.

POWER PLANT: One 37.3 kW (50 hp) Rotax 462. Fuel capacity 33 litres (8.7 US gallons; 7.3 Imp gallons).
PERFORMANCE (two crew of 75 kg; 165 lb each, full fuel):

Max level speed	70 knots (130 km/h; 81 mph)
Max cruising speed	49 knots (90 km/h; 56 mph)
Stalling speed: power on	30 knots (55 km/h; 34 mph)
power off	32 knots (58 km/h; 36 mph)
Max rate of climb at S/L	180 m (590 ft)/min
Service ceiling	3,000 m (9,850 ft)
T-O run	100 m (330 ft)
Landing run	80 m (262 ft)
Range	162 nm (300 km; 186 miles)
Endurance	4 h
g limits	+4/–2 limit
	+6/–3 ultimate

AVIASUD MISTRAL (TWIN-ENGINED)

Developed specially for aerial advertising work, this is a standard Mistral fitted with either a Rotax 462 or 532 engine forward and carrying a Rotax 503 in pusher configuration above the upper wing. Fuel capacity is 68 litres (18 US gallons; 15 Imp gallons).
DIMENSION, EXTERNAL:

Wing span	9.60 m (31 ft 6 in)

WEIGHTS:

Weight empty	199-230 kg (439-507 lb)
Max T-O weight	450 kg (992 lb)

PERFORMANCE:

Max rate of climb at S/L	216 m (710 ft)/min

CENTRAIR
SA CENTRAIR
Aérodrome Le Blanc, BP 44, 36300 Le Blanc
Telephone: 33 54 37 07 96
Telex: 750 272 F

CENTRAIR PARAFAN

Development of this parawing microlight was started in November 1984. Many Parafans have been delivered, some to the armed forces of France and foreign countries. This aircraft offers pendulum stability in flight, and can be landed safely power-off. The maximum acceptable wind speed on the ground for take-off is a steady 12 knots (22 km/h; 14 mph), without major gusting.
TYPE: Single-seat parawing microlight.
AIRFRAME: Welded AG3 aluminium alloy trike unit, suspended under an eleven-cell NASA type ram air sports parachute wing (manufactured by PF and Aerazur) by two clusters of steering cables. Two-axis control. Non-retractable tricycle landing gear.

POWER PLANT: One 29.4 kW (39.4 hp) Rotax 447. Fuel capacity 20 litres (5.3 US gallons; 4.4 Imp gallons).
DIMENSIONS, EXTERNAL:

Parawing span	10.10 m (33 ft 1¾ in)
Trike: length	2.40 m (7 ft 10½ in)
width	1.70 m (5 ft 7 in)
height	1.70 m (5 ft 7 in)

AREA:

Parawing, gross	31.40 m² (338.0 sq ft)

WEIGHTS:

Weight empty	105 kg (231 lb)
Max payload	100 kg (220 lb)

PERFORMANCE:

Cruising speed	22-24 knots (40-45 km/h; 25-28 mph)
Max rate of climb	90-120 m (295-395 ft)/min
Theoretical ceiling	3,500 m (11,480 ft)
T-O run (no wind):	
with ground assistance	20-40 m (66-131 ft)
without ground assistance	30-50 m (98-164 ft)
Landing run (no wind)	0-20 m (0-66 ft)

CENTRAIR PARAFAN II

This is a two-seat version of the Parafan, powered by a 34 kW (45.6 hp) Rotax 503 or 38 kW (51 hp) Rotax 462 engine. Fuel capacity remains the same.
DIMENSIONS, EXTERNAL:

Parawing span	10.00 m (32 ft 9¾ in)
Trike: length	2.70 m (8 ft 10¼ in)
width	1.70 m (5 ft 7 in)
height	1.80 m (5 ft 11 in)

AREA:

Parawing, gross	44.0 m² (473.6 sq ft)

WEIGHTS:

Weight empty	140 kg (309 lb)
Max payload	200 kg (441 lb)

PERFORMANCE:

Cruising speed	27-31 knots (50-58 km/h; 31-36 mph)
Max rate of climb	90-240 m (295-785 ft)/min
Theoretical ceiling	3,500 m (11,480 ft)
T-O run (no wind):	
with ground assistance	20-40 m (66-131 ft)
without ground assistance	30-50 m (98-164 ft)

COLOMBAN
MICHEL COLOMBAN
37bis, rue Lakanal, 92500 Rueil-Malmaison
Telephone: 33 47 51 88 76

COLOMBAN MC 15 CRICRI

The MC 10 Cricri prototype was first flown on 19 July 1973. Early amateur-built Cricris were designated MC 12 and used Valmet SM 160J engines. The current model is the JPX powered MC 15. Plans are available in the French and English languages, with European standard metric dimensions; 494 sets had been sold by early 1990 to amateur builders in France and neighbouring countries, and 70 aircraft were then flying. Three are flown at air displays by the Brittany Ferries aerobatic team, whose leader, Yves

Duval, set two new international records for aircraft weighing less than 300 kg in a Cricri on 7 June 1988; he averaged 126.39 knots (234.226 km/h; 145.55 mph) over a 3 km course, and 121.98 knots (226.05 km/h; 140.46 mph) over 15/25 km.
TYPE: Single-seat light homebuilt aircraft.
AIRFRAME: Entire basic structure is of light alloy, except for Klégécel ribs in wings and tail unit, and Klégécel stringers in fuselage. Laminar-flow aerofoil derived from a Wortmann section. Full span auxiliary aerofoil wing flaps operate collectively as high-lift devices and differentially as ailerons. Non-retractable tricycle landing gear.
POWER PLANT: Two JPX PUL 212 engines, each rated at 11 kW (15 hp). Fuel capacity 23 litres (6 US gallons; 5 Imp gallons).

DIMENSIONS, EXTERNAL:

Wing span	4.90 m (16 ft 0¾ in)
Length overall	3.91 m (12 ft 10 in)
Height overall	1.20 m (3 ft 11¼ in)
Propeller diameter	0.695 m (2 ft 3½ in)

AREA:

Wings, gross	3.10 m² (33.4 sq ft)

WEIGHTS:

Weight empty	80 kg (176 lb)
Max T-O and landing weight	170 kg (375 lb)

PERFORMANCE (MC 15 at max T-O weight):

Max speed measured in dive	159 knots (295 km/h; 183 mph)
Max cruising speed (75% power)	108 knots (200 km/h; 124 mph)

Stalling speed:
flaps up   50 knots (93 km/h; 58 mph)
flaps down   39 knots (72 km/h; 45 mph)
Max rate of climb at S/L   390 m (1,280 ft)/min
Service ceiling   5,000 m (16,400 ft)
T-O run   100 m (330 ft)
Landing run   150 m (495 ft)

Range with max fuel   215 nm (400 km; 248 miles)
g limits   +9/−4.5 ultimate

COLOMBAN MC 100

M Michel Colomban was still working on the prototype of a new side by side all-metal two-seater, known as the MC 100, in 1990. It is similar in construction to the Cricri, lightweight, and capable of being dismantled in three minutes for transport on a trailer. Power is provided by a Rotax 912 engine. It has a T tail unit and non-retractable tricycle landing gear. Aims are to be economical to operate, while offering good performance and aerobatic capability.

COUPÉ-AVIATION

JACQUES COUPÉ

La Trute, Azay-sur-Cher, 37270 Montlouis sur Loire
Telephone: 33 47 50 41 84

COUPÉ-AVIATION JC-01

The prototype JC-01 was flown for the first time on 16 March 1976. Plans are available to amateur constructors, together with plans of the more powerful JC-2.

TYPE: Two-seat, dual-control homebuilt sporting aircraft.
AIRFRAME: All-wood structure, with fabric covered wings, rear fuselage, and flying control surfaces. Non-retractable tailwheel landing gear.
POWER PLANT: One 48.5 kW (65 hp) Teledyne Continental A65-8F. Fuel capacity 60 litres (15.9 US gallons; 13 Imp gallons).
DIMENSIONS, EXTERNAL:
Wing span   8.35 m (27 ft 4¾ in)
Length overall   6.40 m (21 ft 0 in)
AREA:
Wings, gross   11.69 m² (125.83 sq ft)

WEIGHTS:
Weight empty   330 kg (728 lb)
Max T-O weight   580 kg (1,279 lb)
PERFORMANCE (as originally flown, at max T-O weight):
Max level speed   108 knots (200 km/h; 124 mph)
Econ cruising speed   76 knots (140 km/h; 87 mph)
T-O speed   27 knots (50 km/h; 31 mph)
Stalling speed   25 knots (45 km/h; 28 mph)
T-O run   90 m (295 ft)

COUPÉ-AVIATION JC-2

The JC-2 is generally similar to the JC-01 but has a more powerful engine and tricycle landing gear. The prototype first flew in May 1981. At least six JC-2s are under construction by amateurs or have flown, with 74.5 kW (100 hp) engines. It was intended to market the JC-2 also in kit form.

TYPE: Side by side two-seat homebuilt aircraft.
AIRFRAME: All-wood structure, with Dacron covered wings, ailerons, flaps, rear fuselage, elevators and rudder. Wing section NACA 23012. Non-retractable tricycle landing gear.

POWER PLANT: One 67 kW (90 hp) Teledyne Continental engine in prototype. Fuel capacity 90 litres (23.8 US gallons; 19.75 Imp gallons).
DIMENSIONS, EXTERNAL:
Wing span   8.35 m (27 ft 4¾ in)
Length overall   6.40 m (21 ft 0 in)
AREA:
Wings, gross   11.70 m² (126.0 sq ft)
WEIGHTS:
Weight empty   500 kg (1,103 lb)
Baggage capacity   20 kg (44 lb)
Max T-O weight   750 kg (1,653 lb)
PERFORMANCE (with 67 kW; 90 hp engine):
Max level speed   108 knots (200 km/h; 124 mph)
Econ cruising speed   86 knots (160 km/h; 99 mph)
Stalling speed: flaps up   27 knots (50 km/h; 31 mph)
flaps down   24 knots (45 km/h; 28 mph)

COUPÉ-AVIATION JC-3

The JC-3 differs from the JC-01 primarily in having a sweptback fin and a 51 kW (68 hp) Volkswagen 1,700 cc converted motorcar engine.

CROSES

EMILIEN CROSES

63 route de Davayé (Aérodrome), 71000 Charnay les Macon
Telephone: 33 85 38 07 31

CROSES EAC-3 POUPLUME

The Pouplume single-seat tandem-wing biplane has a fixed rear wing and a pivoted forward wing which dispenses with the need for ailerons and elevators. Construction is of wood, with fabric covered wings, and a non-retractable tailwheel landing gear is fitted. The prototype has a 7.8 kW (10.5 hp) Moto 232 cc motorcycle engine; fuel capacity is 10 litres (2.6 US gallons; 2.2 Imp gallons).

The EAC-3-01 Pouplume flew for the first time in June 1961. It was followed, in 1967, by a second prototype (EAC-3-02) with a 20 cm (8 in) longer fuselage. Plans are available.

A version known as the **Pouplume Sport** differs in having a 1,500 cc Volkswagen engine and reduced span of 6.40 m (21 ft 0 in).

The following data apply to the standard Moto-powered Pouplume:
DIMENSIONS, EXTERNAL:
Wing span: forward wing   7.80 m (25 ft 7 in)
rear wing   7.00 m (23 ft 0 in)

Length overall   4.70 m (15 ft 3 in)
Height overall   1.80 m (5 ft 11 in)
AREA:
Wings, gross   16.02 m² (172.2 sq ft)
WEIGHTS:
Weight empty   110-140 kg (243-310 lb)
Max T-O weight   220-260 kg (485-573 lb)
PERFORMANCE (A: 7.8 kW; 10.5 hp engine, B: 13.4 kW; 18 hp engine):
Max level speed: A   38 knots (70 km/h; 43 mph)
B   65 knots (120 km/h; 75 mph)
Econ cruising speed: A   27 knots (50 km/h; 31 mph)
B   38 knots (70 km/h; 43 mph)
T-O run: A   60 m (200 ft)
B   40 m (131 ft)
Landing run: A   24 m (80 ft)

CROSES EC-6 CRIQUET (LOCUST)

The Criquet is a side by side two-seater, using the same tandem-wing formula as the Pouplume. The EC-6-01 prototype flew for the first time on 6 July 1965. Plans are available.

TYPE: Side by side two-seat tandem-wing homebuilt aircraft.
AIRFRAME: Wings have wooden structure, with plywood leading-edge, overall fabric covering and some components of glassfibre. NACA 23012 (modified) wing section. Wooden fuselage, covered with plywood. Glass-fibre engine cowling. Plywood covered spruce fin and rudder. Non-retractable tailwheel landing gear.

POWER PLANT: One 67 kW (90 hp) Teledyne Continental engine. Fuel capacity originally 60 litres (15.9 US gallons; 13 Imp gallons); planned to be increased to 90 litres (23.8 US gallons; 19.75 Imp gallons).
DIMENSIONS, EXTERNAL:
Wing span: forward wing   7.80 m (25 ft 7 in)
rear wing   7.00 m (22 ft 11½ in)
Length overall   4.65 m (15 ft 3 in)
AREA:
Wings, gross   16.02 m² (172.2 sq ft)
WEIGHTS:
Weight empty   290 kg (639 lb)
Max T-O weight   550 kg (1,213 lb)
PERFORMANCE (officially certificated, at max T-O weight):
Max level speed at S/L
   115 knots (213 km/h; 132 mph)
Econ cruising speed   86 knots (160 km/h; 99 mph)
Will not stall
Time to 2,000 m (6,560 ft)   6 min 14 s

CROSES EC-8 TOURISME

This three-seat touring aircraft is generally similar to the standard wooden Criquet but can have an 'all-terrain' landing gear comprising two tandem pairs of mainwheels.

HYDROPLUM

HYDROPLUM SARL

Fior di Linu, Pietranera, 20200 Bastia, Corsica
Telephone: 33 95 31 67 67

M Claude Tisserand designed two amphibians: the single-seat Hydroplum monoplane and two-seat Hydroplum II sesquiplane. The Hydroplum II was purchased by SMAN in 1987 and is currently marketed in kit and ready assembled forms as the Petrel (which see).

TISSERAND HYDROPLUM

The Hydroplum first flew in September 1983. Plans are available.

TYPE: Single-seat amphibian; conforms to microlight and Experimental regulations.
AIRFRAME: Plywood construction. Wing section NACA 2415. Three-axis control with water rudder attached to heel of single-step hull. Retractable taildragger landing gear.
POWER PLANT: One 30 kW (40 hp) 440 cc Hirth. Fuel capacity 40 litres (10.6 US gallons; 8.8 Imp gallons).
DIMENSIONS, EXTERNAL:
Wing span   9.25 m (30 ft 4¼ in)
Length overall   5.90 m (19 ft 4¼ in)
Height overall   1.40 m (4 ft 7 in)
Propeller diameter   1.40 m (4 ft 7 in)
AREA:
Wings, gross   13.00 m² (139.93 sq ft)

WEIGHTS:
Weight empty   145 kg (319 lb)
Pilot weight range   60-90 kg (133-198 lb)
Max T-O weight   260 kg (573 lb)
PERFORMANCE (at max T-O weight):
Max level speed   59 knots (110 km/h; 68 mph)
Econ cruising speed   43 knots (80 km/h; 50 mph)
Stalling speed   30 knots (55 km/h; 34 mph)
Max rate of climb at S/L   300 m (985 ft)/min
T-O run: on land   80 m (262 ft)
on water   100 m (328 ft)
Landing run: on land   80 m (262 ft)
on water   50 m (164 ft)
Range with max standard fuel
   145 nm (270 km; 167 miles)

JODEL

AVIONS JODEL SA

HEAD OFFICE: 37 Route de Seurre, 21200 Beaune
DESIGN OFFICE: 21-Darois
PRESIDENT-DIRECTOR GENERAL: Jean Delemontez

Jodel designs have been built both commercially and by amateurs, and more than 5,000 aircraft of Jodel type have flown throughout the world.

JODEL D.9 BÉBÉ SERIES

The prototype Bébé flew for the first time in January 1948. Construction can take as little as 500 working hours. An illustration can be found in the 1988-89 *Jane's*.

TYPE: Single-seat homebuilt aircraft.

AIRFRAME: All-wood construction, except for fabric covering on the wings, rudder and elevators. Non-retractable tailwheel or tailskid landing gear.
POWER PLANT: One modified Volkswagen engine is standard, but other engines of 18.6 to 48.5 kW (25 to 65 hp) may be fitted. Fuel capacity 25 litres (6.6 US gallons; 5.5 Imp gallons).
DIMENSIONS, EXTERNAL:
Wing span   7.00 m (22 ft 11 in)
Length overall   5.45 m (17 ft 10½ in)
AREA:
Wings, gross   9.0 m² (96.8 sq ft)
WEIGHTS:
Weight empty   190 kg (420 lb)
Max T-O weight   320 kg (705 lb)
PERFORMANCE (30 kW; 40 hp engine, at max T-O weight):
Max level speed at S/L   87 knots (160 km/h; 100 mph)

Cruising speed   74 knots (137 km/h; 85 mph)
Stalling speed   35 knots (65 km/h; 40 mph)
Max rate of climb at S/L   180 m (590 ft)/min
T-O run   110 m (360 ft)
Landing run   100 m (330 ft)
Range with max fuel   217 nm (400 km; 250 miles)

JODEL D.11 and D.119

The original D.11, with 33.6 kW (45 hp) Salmson engine, was the basic model in the series of Jodel two-seaters for amateur and commercial production. The version for amateur construction with 67 kW (90 hp) Teledyne Continental engine is designated D.119.

The wing is of wood, covered with Dacron, the fuselage and tail unit of wood covered with glassfibre. The following details refer to a D.11 which spans 8.23 m (27 ft 0 in), has an

Colomban MC 15 Cricri built by Mr Peter Fabish of Cambridge, England

Croses EAC-3 Pouplume light aircraft (Moto engine)

Croses EC-6 Criquet built by M Tissot of Beaune *(Geoffrey P. Jones)*

Hydroplum amphibian, designed by M Claude Tisserand

Coupé-Aviation JC-01 two-seat lightplane

First Jodel D.19 with tricycle landing gear, built by M Vion *(Geoffrey P. Jones)*

---

empty weight of 340 kg (750 lb) and loaded weight of 562 kg (1,240 lb), and is powered by a 48.5 kW (65 hp) Teledyne Continental A65-8 flat-four engine:

PERFORMANCE:

Max level speed at S/L	93 knots (173 km/h; 108 mph)
Cruising speed	86 knots (161 km/h; 100 mph)
Max rate of climb at S/L	152 m (500 ft)/min
Service ceiling	4,875 m (16,000 ft)
T-O run	152 m (500 ft)
Landing run	244 m (800 ft)
Range with max fuel	260 nm (482 km; 300 miles)

JODEL D.112 CLUB and D.113

The D.112 is a two-seat dual-control version of the D.9. Except for increased overall dimensions, a wider fuselage and enclosed side by side cockpit, the D.112 conforms in layout and structure to the D.9, but is fitted normally with a 48.5 kW (65 hp) Teledyne Continental flat-four engine. Fuel capacity is 60 litres (15.9 US gallons; 13 Imp gallons).

The version built in Sweden as the D.113 differs from the D.112 in several minor respects.

DIMENSIONS, EXTERNAL:

Wing span	8.20 m (26 ft 10 in)
Length overall	6.36 m (20 ft 10 in)

AREA:

Wings, gross	12.72 m² (136.9 sq ft)

WEIGHTS:

Weight empty	270 kg (600 lb)
Max T-O weight	520 kg (1,145 lb)

PERFORMANCE (at max T-O weight):

Max level speed at S/L	102 knots (190 km/h; 118 mph)
Econ cruising speed	81 knots (150 km/h; 93 mph)
Stalling speed	38 knots (70 km/h; 43 mph)
Max rate of climb at S/L	193 m (632 ft)/min
T-O run	137 m (450 ft)
Landing run	120 m (395 ft)
Range with max fuel	323 nm (600 km; 373 miles)

JODEL D.18

The 1981-82 *Jane's* contained details of the Delemontez-Cauchy DC-1. No plans of this are available, but M Delemontez is marketing plans of a slightly modified version, known as the Jodel D.18, with a different wing section, revised ailerons, all-moving tailplane and other changes. It has a typical Jodel light wooden airframe, with coarse dihedral on the tapered outer wing panels. Installation of a 43 kW (58 hp) 1,600 cc Volkswagen engine, instead of the usual Teledyne Continental, has resulted in a streamlined cowling and improved performance. Fuel capacity is 65 litres (17 US gallons; 14.3 Imp gallons).

The prototype D.18 was flown for the first time on 21 May 1984.

DIMENSIONS, EXTERNAL:

Wing span	7.50 m (24 ft 7¼ in)
Length overall	5.70 m (18 ft 8½ in)

AREA:

Wings, gross	9.83 m² (105.8 sq ft)

WEIGHTS:

Weight empty	230-250 kg (507-551 lb)
Max T-O weight	460 kg (1,014 lb)

PERFORMANCE:

Max level speed	135 knots (250 km/h; 155 mph)
Cruising speed	92 knots (170 km/h; 105 mph)
Stalling speed	39 knots (72 km/h; 45 mph)
Max rate of climb at S/L	180 m (590 ft)/min
T-O to 15 m (50 ft)	260 m (853 ft)
Landing from 15 m (50 ft)	450 m (1,477 ft)
Endurance	5 h

JODEL D.19

This is the designation of D.18s constructed with tricycle landing gear. An example built by M Vion is illustrated.

JURCA
MARCEL JURCA

2 rue des Champs Philippe, 92250 La Garenne-Colombes
Telephone: 33 (1) 45 94 01 38

M Marcel Jurca is the designer of a series of high-performance light aircraft of which plans have been supplied to other constructors on a purely amateur non-profit making basis. More recently, he has produced plans for representations of Second World War fighters, which were fully detailed in earlier editions of *Jane's*.

For builders in North America, Australia and New Zealand, Jurca plans are available from Mr Ken Heit, 1733 Kansas, Flint, Michigan 48506, USA (telephone: 1 313 232 5395). Mr Simon Richards, a Briton living in France and builder of the M.J.100 prototype, supplies plans to UK builders (Ecorsaint, 21150 Les Laumes, France), while Claus Colling Ltd (Priel 5A, 8051 Gammelsdorf, Federal Republic of Germany) manufactures all metal components, landing gears and flight controls for the Jurca representations of Second World War fighters.

JURCA M.J.2 and M.J.22 TEMPÊTE

The prototype **M.J.2** Tempête was flown for the first time on 27 June 1956. At least 45 Tempêtes are now flying.

The type of engine fitted to a particular aircraft is indicated by a suffix letter in its designation. Suffix letters are A for the 48.5 kW (65 hp) Teledyne Continental A65, B for the 56 kW (75 hp) Teledyne Continental A75, C for the 63.5 kW (85 hp) Teledyne Continental C85, D for the 67 kW (90 hp) Teledyne Continental C90-8/C90-14F, E for the 74.5 kW (100 hp) Teledyne Continental O-200-A, F for the 78.5 kW (105 hp) Potez 4 E-20, G for the 86 kW (115 hp) Potez 4 E-30, H for the 78.5-86 kW (105-115 hp) Textron Lycoming O-235, I for the 93 kW (125 hp) Textron Lycoming O-290-G, K for the 101-104 kW (135-140 hp) Textron Lycoming O-290-D2, N for the 112 kW (150 hp) Textron Lycoming or Teledyne Continental, P for the 119 kW (160 hp) Textron Lycoming or Teledyne Continental, and R for the 134 kW (180 hp) Textron Lycoming or Teledyne Continental. The standard version is the M.J.2A. The M.J.2D cruises at 105 knots (195 km/h; 121 mph) and climbs to 1,000 m (3,280 ft) in 3 minutes. It can also perform aerobatics without loss of height.

A version known as the **M.J.22** has a 112 kW (150 hp) engine and strengthened airframe.

The Tempête is basically a single-seat aircraft, but the 112 and 134 kW (150 and 180 hp) versions have provision for carrying behind the pilot on cross-country flights a second person weighing not more than 55 kg (121 lb). This is not permitted by the DGAC in France. The suffix 'A' is added to the aircraft designation in two-seat configuration.

The following details apply generally to all basic single-seat M.J.2 models:

TYPE: Single-seat homebuilt aircraft.

AIRFRAME: All-wood construction, except for fabric covering on the wings, ailerons, elevators and rudder. NACA 23012 wing section. Non-retractable tailwheel (or tailskid) landing gear.

POWER PLANT: See introduction. Fuel capacity 60 litres (15.9 US gallons; 13.2 Imp gallons).

DIMENSIONS, EXTERNAL:
Wing span	6.00 m (19 ft 8 in)
Length overall	5.855 m (19 ft 2½ in)
Height overall	2.40 m (7 ft 10 in)

AREA:
Wings, gross	7.98 m² (85.9 sq ft)

WEIGHTS (48.5 kW; 65 hp engine):
Weight empty	90 kg (639 lb)
Max T-O weight	430 kg (950 lb)

PERFORMANCE (48.5 kW; 65 hp engine):
Max level speed	104 knots (193 km/h; 120 mph)
Cruising speed	89 knots (165 km/h; 102 mph)
Max rate of climb at S/L	170 m (555 ft)/min
Service ceiling	3,500 m (11,500 ft)
T-O run	250 m (820 ft)
Endurance	3 h 20 min

JURCA M.J.3 DART and M.J.4 SHADOW

These are versions of the basic M.J.2 Tempête design.

JURCA M.J.5 SIROCCO

The M.J.5 Sirocco is a tandem two-seat development of the M.J.2 Tempête. It is fully aerobatic when flown as a two-seater. The prototype M.J.5 flew for the first time on 3 August 1962, powered by a 78.5 kW (105 hp) Potez 4 E-20 engine. A factory built model was awarded subsequently a certificate of airworthiness in the Utility category.

The version of the Sirocco for amateur construction is generally similar to the factory built version, with non-retractable or retractable landing gear, including optional retractable tailwheel. The type of engine fitted to a particular aircraft is indicated by a suffix letter in its designation. Suffix letters are A for the 67 kW (90 hp) Teledyne Continental C90-8 or -14F, B for the 74.5 kW (100 hp) Teledyne Continental O-200-A, C for the 78.5 kW (105 hp) Potez 4 E-20, D for the 86 kW (115 hp) Potez 4 E-30, E for the 78.5 kW (105 hp) Hirth, F for the 93 kW (125 hp) Textron Lycoming, G for the 100.5 kW (135 hp) Regnier, H for the 119.5 kW (160 hp) Textron Lycoming, K for the 134 kW (180 hp) Textron Lycoming and L for the 149 kW (200 hp) Textron Lycoming. Addition of the numeral 1 indicates a non-retractable landing gear; the numeral 2 indicates a retractable main landing gear; 2A indicates that the tailwheel also retracts.

One aircraft has a 119 kW (160 hp) PRV modified motorcar engine and P-51 Mustang type underbelly airscoop.

The details which follow refer to a Sirocco with an 86 kW (115 hp) Textron Lycoming O-235-C2B engine and 1.85 m (6 ft 0¾ in) diameter propeller, and a modified rudder of reduced height and greater chord:

DIMENSIONS, EXTERNAL:
Wing span	7.00 m (23 ft 0 in)
Length overall	6.15 m (20 ft 2 in)
Height overall, tail up:	
with modified rudder	2.60 m (8 ft 6¼ in)
standard rudder	2.80 m (9 ft 2¼ in)

AREA:
Wings, gross	10.00 m² (107.64 sq ft)

WEIGHTS:
Weight empty	430 kg (947 lb)
Max T-O weight	680 kg (1,499 lb)

PERFORMANCE (at max T-O weight):
Max level speed	127 knots (235 km/h; 146 mph)
Cruising speed	116 knots (215 km/h; 134 mph)
Stalling speed	44 knots (80 km/h; 50 mph)
Time to 1,000 m (3,280 ft)	4 min
Service ceiling	5,000 m (16,400 ft)
T-O run	250 m (820 ft)
Landing run	200 m (655 ft)
Endurance	4 h 20 min

JURCA M.J.5 SIROCCO (SPORT WING)

A special version of the Sirocco, with 86 kW (115 hp) engine and increased span, has been developed for the New Zealand and Australian market. The wing of this aircraft, known as a 'Sport' wing, embodies one additional rib and inter-rib bay each side. The modification is available in the English language set of Sirocco plans.

JURCA M.J.14 FOURTOUNA

The M.J.14 is an easy to build single-seat sport training aircraft of wooden construction. It uses an M.J.7 wing, has retractable landing gear, and is powered by a 119 kW (160 hp) Textron Lycoming engine. The prototype is under construction by M Yves Beliard of Coutances; a photograph of the Fourtouna under construction appeared in the 1989-90 Jane's.

JURCA M.J.51 SPEROCCO

The tandem two-seat Sperocco (the name being a contraction of 'Special Sirocco') is intended for high performance aerobatic and competition flying and incorporates features of the M.J.5 and M.J.7. The fuselage is of completely new design, with a basically triangular cross-section, but is of similar construction to that of the M.J.5. Landing gear is of the M.J.5 type and is fully retractable.

Any horizontally opposed engine of 112-179 kW (150-240 hp) may be installed. Fuel is contained in two wing tanks, each of 55 litres (14.5 US gallons; 12 Imp gallons) capacity, and one fuselage tank of 45 or 100 litres (11.9 or 26.4 US gallons; 10 or 22 Imp gallons) capacity.

The first M.J.51, powered by a 149 kW (200 hp) Textron Lycoming AIO-360 engine, is being constructed by M Serge Brillant at Melun.

DIMENSIONS, EXTERNAL:
Wing span	7.623 m (25 ft 0 in)
Length overall	7.24 m (23 ft 9 in)

AREA:
Wings, gross	11.00 m² (118.4 sq ft)

WEIGHT:
Max T-O weight	730 kg (1,653 lb)

PERFORMANCE (estimated, with 112 kW; 150 hp Textron Lycoming engine):
Max level speed	149 knots (275 km/h; 171 mph)
Max cruising speed (75% power)	
	135 knots (250 km/h; 155 mph)
Stalling speed	49 knots (90 km/h; 56 mph)
Time to 1,000 m (3,280 ft)	1 min 30 s

JURCA M.J.52 ZÉPHYR

The all-wooden M.J.52 Zéphyr is a very light two-seat monoplane, based on the M.J.5 Sirocco but using a converted Volkswagen motorcar engine or Teledyne Continental engine in the 30-48.5 kW (40-65 hp) range. It can have a non-retractable or retractable landing gear.

Plans of the M.J.52 have been available since Spring 1985, and a prototype is under construction. It has been designed to conform to FAR Pt 23 Utility category requirements, yet to be simple to construct in a garage or similar building and inexpensive in terms of materials and working hours.

DIMENSIONS, EXTERNAL:
Wing span	9.06 m (29 ft 8¾ in)
Length overall	6.28 m (20 ft 7¼ in)

AREA:
Wings, gross	13.50 m² (145.3 sq ft)

WEIGHTS:
Weight empty	333 kg (734 lb)
Max T-O weight	517 kg (1,140 lb)

PERFORMANCE (37.3 kW; 50 hp engine):
Max level speed	59 knots (110 km/h; 68 mph)
Stalling speed	22 knots (40 km/h; 25 mph)
Endurance	5 h
g limits	+8/-4 ultimate

JURCA M.J.53 AUTAN

The M.J.53 is a side by side two-seat version of the Sirocco. Two prototypes are under construction in Arles. It is suited to aerobatics in addition to touring.

POWER PLANT: One 134 kW (180 hp) Textron Lycoming flat-four. Fuel capacity 160 litres (42.3 US gallons; 35 Imp gallons) for touring and 80 litres (21.1 US gallons; 17.6 Imp gallons) for aerobatics.

DIMENSIONS, EXTERNAL:
Wing span	7.60 m (24 ft 11¼ in)
Length overall	6.50 m (21 ft 4 in)

AREA:
Wings, gross	11.20 m² (120.6 sq ft)

WEIGHTS:
Weight empty	600 kg (1,323 lb)
Max T-O weight, aerobatic	844 kg (1,860 lb)

PERFORMANCE:
Cruising speed, 75% power	
	130 knots (240 km/h; 149 mph)
Stalling speed	49-54 knots (90-100 km/h; 56-62 mph)
Max rate of climb at S/L	300 m (985 ft)/min
Endurance at 75% power	4 h

JURCA M.J.7 and M.J.77 GNATSUM

The Gnatsum is a precise scale replica, for amateur construction, of the North American P-51D Mustang single-seat fighter of the Second World War. Its name 'Gnatsum' is 'Mustang' reversed. Drawings of two versions are available, the two-thirds scale M.J.7 and three-quarters scale M.J.77, the latter offering seating for two crew of up to 80 kg (176 lb) each. A reinforced model has a gross weight of 1,500 kg (3,307 lb). Engine options include a 313 kW (420 hp) supercharged Gipsy or 388-410 kW (520-550 hp) inverted Ranger. Specification details, and an illustration, can be found in the 1988-89 Jane's. Three are under construction in France, and one has flown in the USA with a 410 kW (550 hp) Double Ranger V12 engine (built by Ken Bard of Elmhurst, Wheeling, Illinois).

JURCA M.J.70

Full-size representation of the North American P-51 Mustang, currently at the design stage.

JURCA M.J.8 and M.J.80 1-NINE-OH

The M.J.8 is a single-seat sporting aircraft which was designed by M Jurca by scaling down to three-quarters of the original dimensions the airframe of the Focke-Wulf Fw 190A fighter. The M.J.80 is similar but is designed to full scale. One is under construction in Austria. Specification details, and an illustration, can be found in the 1988-89 Jane's.

JURCA M.J.9 ONE-OH-NINE

Three-quarter scale representation of the Messerschmitt Bf 109 fighter of the Second World War. The prototype is under construction.

JURCA M.J.90

This is a full-size representation of a Bf 109G, to which it is dimensionally the same. Its method of construction is similar to that of the M.J.9. Plans are available, and one is under construction in West Germany and two in France.

JURCA M.J.10 SPIT

The M.J.10 is a single-seat, three-quarter scale representation of the Supermarine Spitfire that can also be completed as a two-seater. Specification details, and an illustration, can be found in the 1988-89 Jane's.

JURCA M.J.100

Plans are available for a full-size representation of the Supermarine Spitfire, known as the M.J.100. Four are under construction in France, two in South Africa and one in the USA. The latter is of glassfibre construction, being built by Mr Allen Salberman with a 447 kW (600 hp) SNECMA 12T engine. Specification details can be found in the 1988-89 Jane's.

JURCA M.J.12 PEE-40

The M.J.12 is a three-quarter scale representation of the Curtiss P-40 single-seat fighter of the Second World War. Brief details can be found in the 1988-89 Jane's.

LEDERLIN
FRANÇOIS LEDERLIN
2 rue Charles Peguy, 38000 Grenoble

This aircraft was derived from the Mignet HM-380, but retains little of the original except for the wing section. First flight was made on 14 September 1965.

Plans of the 380-L, annotated in English and with both English and metric measurements, are available to amateur constructors.

LEDERLIN 380-L

TYPE: Side by side two-seat homebuilt aircraft.

AIRFRAME: Tandem-wing biplane. Wing section 3.40-13. Wooden wings, with plywood leading-edge and overall fabric covering. Variable incidence front wing. No ailerons or flaps. Welded steel tube fuselage, covered with light alloy to front of cabin and with fabric on rear fuselage, over wooden formers. Wooden tail unit with fabric covering. Non-retractable tailwheel landing gear.

POWER PLANT: One 67 kW (90 hp) Teledyne Continental C90-14F. Fuel capacity 85 litres (22.5 US gallons; 18.75 Imp gallons).

DIMENSIONS, EXTERNAL:
Wing span: forward	7.92 m (26 ft 0 in)
rear	6.00 m (19 ft 8¼ in)
Length overall	4.77 m (15 ft 7¾ in)
Height overall	2.08 m (6 ft 10 in)
Propeller diameter	1.83 m (6 ft 0 in)

Jurca M.J.5L2 Sirocco with a retractable tailwheel, built by M Yves Guillou of Bretagne

Lucas L5 with retractable tailwheel landing gear

Jurca M.J.2N Tempête built by Mr Thomas Fahr of Gottmadingen, West Germany (112 kW; 150 hp engine)

Lendepergt LP-01 Sibylle amphibian (IO-360-1A1 engine driving an MTV 18B variable pitch propeller)

Lucas L10 four-seat lightplane

Lederlin 380-L two-seat light aircraft (Teledyne Continental C90-14F engine) *(Peter J. Bish)*

AREAS:
Wings, gross: forward	9.92 m² (106.8 sq ft)
rear	7.43 m² (80.0 sq ft)

WEIGHTS:
Weight empty	360 kg (794 lb)
Max T-O weight	600 kg (1,323 lb)

PERFORMANCE (at max T-O weight):
Max level speed at 305 m (1,000 ft)	
	109 knots (201 km/h; 125 mph)
Econ cruising speed at 610 m (2,000 ft)	
	87 knots (161 km/h; 100 mph)
Stalling speed, power off	26 knots (49 km/h; 30 mph)

Max rate of climb at S/L	275 m (900 ft)/min
Service ceiling	over 3,660 m (12,000 ft)
T-O run	122 m (400 ft)
Landing run	153 m (500 ft)
Range at econ cruising speed	
	477 nm (885 km; 550 miles)

LENDEPERGT
PATRICK LENDEPERGT
112 rue de la Jarry, 94300 Vincennes
Telephone: 33 (1) 43 65 61 95

LENDEPERGT LP-01 SIBYLLE
The prototype of this amphibian was first flown in July 1984. It is available in kit form, and possibly ready assembled. In addition to sport flying, it can be adapted for surveillance (with nose mounted EAS ATAL TV system), stretcher carrying and other uses.
TYPE: Four-seat amphibious homebuilt aircraft.
AIRFRAME: All-composites, of pre-moulded carbonfibre, Kevlar and epoxy. Laminar flow wings. Single-step hull. Retractable tricycle landing gear, with water rudder.

POWER PLANT: Standard engine is now one 149 kW (200 hp) Textron Lycoming IO-360-1A1. Fuel capacity 290 litres (76.6 US gallons; 63.8 Imp gallons) standard; optional 80 litre (21 US gallon; 17.6 Imp gallon) auxiliary tank.
DIMENSIONS, EXTERNAL:
Wing span	9.40 m (30 ft 10 in)
Length overall	6.60 m (21 ft 8 in)
Height overall	2.50 m (8 ft 2½ in)
Propeller diameter	1.62 m (5 ft 3¾ in)

AREA:
Wings, gross	12.40 m² (133.5 sq ft)

WEIGHTS:
Weight empty	600 kg (1,323 lb)
Max T-O weight	1,300 kg (2,866 lb)

PERFORMANCE:
Max level speed	151 knots (280 km/h; 174 mph)

Econ cruising speed	130 knots (240 km/h; 149 mph)
Stalling speed:	
flaps up	49 knots (90 km/h; 56 mph)
flaps down	41 knots (75 km/h; 47 mph)
Max rate of climb at S/L	120 m (363 ft)/min
Service ceiling	5,000 m (16,400 ft)
T-O run:	
from land	600 m (1,970 ft)
from water	750 m (2,460 ft)
Landing run, on land	150 m (492 ft)
Range with max fuel	1,080 nm (2,000 km; 1,240 miles)
Endurance	8 h
g limits	+4/−3

LUCAS
EMILE LUCAS
Corbonod, 01420 Seyssel
Telephone: 33 50 59 27 54

LUCAS L5
The prototype L5 was first flown on 13 August 1976. Plans are available to amateur builders, and more than 35 L5s are known to be flying or under construction, in three basic versions, as follows:
L5. Two/three-seat model, similar to prototype.

L5 200. Airframe generally similar to L5, but three seats standard. Suitable power plants include 70 kW (94 hp) Rolls-Royce Continental O-200-E and Textron Lycoming O-320. Fuel capacity 123 litres (32.5 US gallons; 27 Imp gallons). Accommodation for three persons and no baggage, or two persons and 65 kg (143 lb) baggage.
L5 360. As basic L5, but with four seats in pairs. Prototype has 134 kW (180 hp) Textron Lycoming O-360. One fuel tank in fuselage, capacity 80 litres (21.1 US gallons; 17.6 Imp gallons) and two in wings, each 50 litres (13.2 US gallons; 11 Imp gallons). Space for 30 kg (66 lb) of baggage when carrying three persons.

The following details apply to the basic L5 but the airframe description is generally applicable to all versions:
TYPE: Two/three-seat homebuilt monoplane.
AIRFRAME: All-metal airframe of light alloy. Wing section NACA 23015 (mod). Non-retractable tricycle or retractable tailwheel landing gear.
POWER PLANT: Prototype had one 85.75 kW (115 hp) Textron Lycoming O-235. Basic L5s built to plans can have an engine of between 93 and 134 kW (125-180 hp). Fuel capacity 75 or 115 litres (19.8 or 30.4 US gallons; 16.5 or 25.3 Imp gallons) in L5; see model listings for other versions.

DIMENSIONS, EXTERNAL:
Wing span	9.20 m (30 ft 2¼ in)
Length overall	6.30 m (20 ft 8 in)
Height overall	2.10 m (6 ft 10¾ in)
Propeller diameter	1.70 m (5 ft 7 in)

AREA:
Wings, gross	11.90 m² (128.1 sq ft)

WEIGHTS (prototype):
Weight empty, equipped	505 kg (1,113 lb)
Max T-O weight	746 kg (1,644 lb)

PERFORMANCE (prototype):
Max level speed:	
with retractable landing gear	
	146 knots (270 km/h; 168 mph)
with non-retractable gear	
	127 knots (235 km/h; 146 mph)
Econ cruising speed:	
with retractable landing gear	
	116 knots (215 km/h; 134 mph)
with non-retractable gear	
	97 knots (180 km/h; 112 mph)
Max rate of climb at S/L	300 m (985 ft)/min
T-O to 15 m (50 ft)	280 m (920 ft)
Landing from 15 m (50 ft)	380 m (1,245 ft)
Range with max fuel	539 nm (1,000 km; 621 miles)

LUCAS L6

Design of this tandem two-seat light aircraft was started in 1981. Two prototypes have been built, one with a retractable tricycle and one with a retractable tailwheel landing gear. By adding wingtip extensions, it can be flown as a motor glider (see Sailplanes section). It will be marketed in the form of plans and kits.

TYPE: Two-seat homebuilt aircraft.
AIRFRAME: All-metal airframe of aluminium alloy. Wing section NACA 65₃618. Retractable tailwheel or tricycle landing gear.
POWER PLANT: One 62 kW (83 hp) Limbach. Optionally one 112 kW (150 hp) Textron Lycoming O-320 for aerobatic training. Fuel capacity 50 litres (13.2 US gallons; 11 Imp gallons).

DIMENSIONS, EXTERNAL (Sport aircraft):
Wing span	9.50 m (31 ft 2 in)
Length overall	7.00 m (22 ft 11½ in)
Height overall	1.85 m (6 ft 1 in)
Propeller diameter	1.61 m (5 ft 3½ in)

AREA (Sport aircraft):
Wings, gross	13.0 m² (140.0 sq ft)

WEIGHTS (Sport aircraft, Limbach engine):
Weight empty	350 kg (772 lb)
Max T-O weight	530 kg (1,168 lb)

PERFORMANCE (Sport aircraft, Limbach engine, estimated):
Max cruising speed	205 knots (380 km/h; 236 mph)
Econ cruising speed	180 knots (333 km/h; 207 mph)
T-O run	200 m (657 ft)
Landing run	160 m (525 ft)

LUCAS L7

The L7 is a cantilever high-wing cabin monoplane, offering side by side seating for two persons with dual controls. Construction is all-metal, with the conventional control surfaces including an all-moving tailplane. Power is provided by an engine in the 44.7-112 kW (60-150 hp) range. Fuel capacity in the two wing tanks is 80 litres (21 US gallons; 17.6 Imp gallons). A non-retractable tricycle landing gear is fitted, possibly with a retractable nosewheel unit.

DIMENSIONS, EXTERNAL:
Wing span	10.60 m (34 ft 9½ in)
Length overall	9.30 m (30 ft 6 in)

AREA:
Wings, gross	12.00 m² (129.17 sq ft)

WEIGHTS:
Weight empty	285 kg (628 lb)
Max T-O weight	495 kg (1,091 lb)

PERFORMANCE (44.7 kW; 60 hp engine):
Max cruising speed	100 knots (185 km/h; 115 mph)
Endurance	5 h

LUCAS L10

The prototype L10 is under construction as a four-seat cabin lightplane of all-metal construction, to use two 71 kW (95 hp) Saüer engines mounted on the cantilever low wings. The tricycle landing gear is fully retractable.

DIMENSIONS, EXTERNAL:
Wing span	10.65 m (34 ft 11¼ in)
Length overall	8.32 m (27 ft 3½ in)

AREA:
Wings, gross	13.63 m² (146.71 sq ft)

WEIGHTS:
Weight empty	620 kg (1,367 lb)
Max T-O weight	1,050 kg (2,315 lb)

PERFORMANCE:
Cruising speed, 70% power	
	119 knots (220 km/h; 137 mph)
Max rate of climb at S/L	288 m (945 ft)/min
T-O run	450 m (1,477 ft)
Range	539 nm (1,000 km; 621 miles)

NICKEL & FOUCARD
RUDY NICKEL & JOSEPH FOUCARD
106 Avenue Château-Fleury, 26100 Romans

NICKEL & FOUCARD 001 ASTERIX

This unusually configured Experimental homebuilt aircraft has been designed to conform to FAR Pt 23 regulations. Construction of a prototype began in 1982 and the first flight was achieved in 1987. Plans are available, and three sets had been sold by early 1990.

TYPE: Tandem two-seat homebuilt monoplane.
AIRFRAME: Pod and boom type fuselage of wooden construction, providing enclosed accommodation. The strut braced pivoting parasol wing has a wooden structure, fabric and wood covered, and is foldable, with sweptback leading- and sweptforward trailing-edges, winglets of Araldite/Styrofoam construction, and small area triangular ailerons. The T tail has a steel tube structure, fabric covered, with an all-moving wire-braced tailplane. Non-retractable tailwheel landing gear.

POWER PLANT: One 27 kW (36 hp) Citroën Visa converted motorcar engine. Optional 650 cc BMW engine. Fuel capacity 28 litres (7.4 US gallons; 6.2 Imp gallons).

DIMENSIONS, EXTERNAL:
Wing span	7.50 m (24 ft 7¼ in)
Length overall	5.15 m (16 ft 10¾ in)
Height overall	2.10 m (6 ft 10¾ in)
Propeller diameter	1.24 m (4 ft 0¾ in)

AREA:
Wings, gross	12.30 m² (132.4 sq ft)

WEIGHTS:
Weight empty	200 kg (441 lb)
Pilot weight range	50-90 kg (110-198 lb)
Max T-O weight	374 kg (824 lb)

PERFORMANCE (two crew):
Max level speed	78 knots (145 km/h; 90 mph)
Cruising speed	67-70 knots (125-130 km/h; 78-81 mph)
Econ cruising speed	
	59-62 knots (110-115 km/h; 68-71 mph)
Stalling speed	30-33 knots (55-60 km/h; 35-38 mph)
Max rate of climb at S/L	150 m (492 ft)/min
Service ceiling	3,000 m (9,840 ft)
T-O run	150 m (492 ft)
Landing run	70-150 m (230-493 ft)
Range	280 nm (520 km; 323 miles)
Endurance	4 h

NICOLLIER
AVIONS H. NICOLLIER
13 rue de Verdun, 25000 Besançon
Telephone: 33 81 53 57 01

NICOLLIER HN 433 MENESTREL

The prototype of this single-seat aircraft flew for the first time on 25 November 1962. Wing spars and kits of materials are available from the Siravia company, of Pons. Moulded canopies, cowlings and wheel fairings, together with plans, are available from Avions H. Nicollier.

TYPE: Single-seat homebuilt aircraft.
AIRFRAME: All-wood structure, with some plywood covering and Dacron overall. Non-retractable tailwheel landing gear.
POWER PLANT: One 22.4-37.3 kW (30-50 hp) converted Volkswagen motorcar engine; prototype adopted a 1,300 cc engine. Recommended are Rectimo-VW models.

DIMENSIONS, EXTERNAL:
Wing span	7.00 m (22 ft 11½ in)
Length overall	5.30 m (17 ft 4½ in)
Height overall	1.48 m (4 ft 10¼ in)

AREA:
Wings, gross	8.20 m² (88.26 sq ft)

WEIGHTS:
Weight empty	201 kg (443 lb)
Max T-O weight	330 kg (727 lb)

PERFORMANCE (with 29 kW; 39 hp VW-Rectimo engine, at max T-O weight):
Max level speed at S/L	103 knots (190 km/h; 118 mph)
Max cruising speed	92 knots (170 km/h; 106 mph)
Stalling speed:	
engine idling	26 knots (48 km/h; 30 mph)
power on	22 knots (40 km/h; 25 mph)
Max rate of climb at S/L	180 m (590 ft)/min
Service ceiling	3,800 m (12,475 ft)
T-O run	120 m (395 ft)
Max range	259-278 nm (480-515 km; 298-320 miles)
g limits	+4.4/-2.2

NICOLLIER HN 434 SUPER-MENESTREL

A completely redesigned version of the Menestrel has been developed as the HN 434 Super-Menestrel, plans of which are available to amateur constructors. A 1,500 cc or 1,600 cc Volkswagen modified motorcar engine gives improved performance, although a 1,300 cc (22.4 kW; 30 hp) engine can be fitted, with which an 86 knots (160 km/h; 99 mph) cruising speed can be achieved. Fuel capacity is increased. Pilot comfort is improved. The Super-Menestrel is also simpler to construct.

NICOLLIER HN 700 MENESTREL II

This is basically a two-seat development of the HN 434, employing a 59.7 kW (80 hp) Limbach engine as standard but suitable for 1,600 cc to 2,000 cc Volkswagen converted motorcar engines.

DIMENSIONS, EXTERNAL:
Wing span	7.80 m (25 ft 7 in)
Length overall	5.30 m (17 ft 4¾ in)
Height overall	1.47 m (4 ft 10 in)

AREA:
Wings, gross	9.80 m² (105.49 sq ft)

WEIGHTS:
Weight empty	282 kg (622 lb)
Max T-O weight	500 kg (1,102 lb)

PERFORMANCE:
Max cruising speed	101 knots (187 km/h; 116 mph)

Stalling speed	43 knots (80 km/h; 50 mph)
Max rate of climb at S/L:	
pilot only	420 m (1,380 ft)/min
dual	390 m (1,280 ft)/min
Range, with reserves for 45 nm (83 km; 52 miles)	
	539 nm (1,000 km; 621 miles)

NICOLLIER HN 600 WEEK-END

The HN 600 Week-end is a single-seat light aircraft, designed for economical construction and operation by amateurs. The structure is simple, of wood and fabric, with some components of Klégécel foam. Plans became available in 1981. A number of major components, such as the wing spar, ribs, cowlings and canopy, were to be made available in completed form from the Siravia company of Pons. Recommended power plant is a converted Volkswagen 1,500 cc motorcar engine.

DIMENSIONS, EXTERNAL:
Wing span	7.00 m (22 ft 11½ in)
Length overall	5.25 m (17 ft 2¾ in)

AREA:
Wings, gross	8.20 m² (88.26 sq ft)

WEIGHTS:
Weight empty	185 kg (408 lb)
Max T-O weight	310 kg (683 lb)

PERFORMANCE (estimated, at max T-O weight):
Max level speed	108 knots (200 km/h; 124 mph)
Max cruising speed	92 knots (170 km/h; 106 mph)
Stalling speed	33 knots (60 km/h; 38 mph)
Max rate of climb at S/L	210 m (688 ft)/min
Range with max fuel at 86 knots (160 km/h; 99 mph)	
	345 nm (640 km; 397 miles)

PARENT
NORBERT PARENT
Le Mistral E5, 06150 La Bocca

PARENT NP2 BALADIN

Plans are on sale to construct this conventional side by side two-seat light homebuilt aircraft. It is a cantilever low-wing monoplane, with conventional control surfaces, and carries wingtip tanks. Cruising speed with a 67 kW (90 hp) engine is 124 knots (230 km/h; 143 mph).

Nickel & Foucard 001 Asterix two-seat homebuilt monoplane

Piel C.P.150 Onyx with non-standard glassfibre fuselage *(Geoffrey P. Jones)*

Nicollier HN 700 Menestrel II

Piel C.P. 751 Beryl two-seat homebuilt *(Geoffrey P. Jones)*

PIEL

AVIONS CLAUDE PIEL

Le Mas de Darnetz, 19300 Egletons
Telephone: 33 55 93 09 79
PROPRIETOR: Mme Claude Piel

The authorised distributor for plans of Piel designs available to amateur constructors is:

D. **Trivisonno**, 10426 Parc Georges Blvd, Montreal, Quebec H1H 4Y3, Canada.

PIEL EMERAUDE and SUPER EMERAUDE

More than 425 sets of plans of the Emeraude and Super Emeraude have been sold, and several versions have been factory-built. Current versions are as follows:

C.P.301. With 67 kW (90 hp) Teledyne Continental C90-12F engine.

C.P.304. With 63.4 kW (85 hp) Teledyne Continental C85-12F engine and wing flaps.

C.P.305. With 86 kW (115 hp) Textron Lycoming engine.

C.P.308. With 56 kW (75 hp) Teledyne Continental engine.

C.P.320. With Super Emeraude wings, a 74.5-85.75 kW (100-115 hp) Teledyne Continental engine and alternative tailwheel or tricycle landing gear.

C.P.320A. As C.P.320, but with sweptback fin.

C.P.321. As C.P.320, with 78.5 kW (105 hp) Potez engine.

C.P.323A. With 112 kW (150 hp) Textron Lycoming engine and sweptback fin. **C.P.323AB** has tricycle landing gear.

C.P.324 Emeraude Club. With 56 kW (75 hp) JPX 2100 engine.

TYPE: Side by side two-seat, dual-control homebuilt.

AIRFRAME: All-wood airframe, fabric covered except for wooden skins on tailplane. NACA 23012 wing section. Non-retractable tailwheel landing gear. Some aircraft have non-standard retractable gear.

POWER PLANT: Engine as in model listings. Fuel capacity 80 litres (21.1 US gallons; 17.6 Imp gallons). Provision for auxiliary tank, capacity 40 litres (10.6 US gallons; 8.8 Imp gallons).

DIMENSIONS, EXTERNAL:

Wing span	8.04 m (26 ft 4½ in)
Length overall: C.P.301	6.30 m (20 ft 8 in)
C.P.320	6.45 m (21 ft 2 in)
Height overall: C.P.301	1.85 m (6 ft 0¾ in)
C.P.320	1.90 m (6 ft 2¾ in)
Propeller diameter: C.P.301	1.80 m (5 ft 11 in)
C.P.320	1.78 m (5 ft 10 in)

AREA:

Wings, gross	10.85 m² (116.7 sq ft)

WEIGHTS:

Weight empty: C.P.301	380 kg (838 lb)
C.P.320	410 kg (903 lb)

Max T-O weight: C.P.301		650 kg (1,433 lb)
C.P.320		700 kg (1,543 lb)

PERFORMANCE (at max T-O weight):

Max level speed:

C.P.301	110 knots (205 km/h; 127 mph)
C.P.320	124 knots (230 km/h; 143 mph)

Econ cruising speed (65% power) at 1,200 m (3,940 ft):

C.P.301	101 knots (187 km/h; 116 mph)
C.P.320	110 knots (205 km/h; 127 mph)

Stalling speed, flaps up:

C.P.301	51 knots (92 km/h; 58 mph)
C.P.320	53 knots (97 km/h; 61 mph)

Stalling speed, flaps down:

C.P.301	46 knots (85 km/h; 53 mph)
C.P.320	49 knots (90 km/h; 56 mph)

Max rate of climb at S/L: C.P.301	168 m (551 ft)/min
C.P.320	240 m (787 ft)/min
Service ceiling: C.P.301	4,000 m (13,125 ft)
C.P.320	4,300 m (14,100 ft)
T-O run: C.P.301	250 m (820 ft)
C.P.320	230 m (755 ft)
Landing run: C.P.301	250 m (820 ft)
C.P.320	260 m (853 ft)

Range at econ cruising speed:

C.P.301, C.P.320	538 nm (1,000 km; 620 miles)

PIEL C.P.1320

Designed to combine the general characteristics of the Super Emeraude with the Super Diamant's three-seat cabin and fuel tanks in the wings, the C.P.1320 can be fitted with engines of 112 kW (150 hp) to 149 kW (200 hp). More than 40 sets of plans sold in France; others by Mr Trivisonno.

TYPE: Three-seat homebuilt.

AIRFRAME: Wooden construction. NACA 23012 wing section. Retractable tailwheel landing gear.

POWER PLANT: Prototype has one 119 kW (160 hp) Textron Lycoming engine. Fuel capacity 140 litres (37 US gallons; 30.8 Imp gallons).

DIMENSIONS, EXTERNAL:

Wing span	7.90 m (25 ft 11 in)
Length overall	6.60 m (21 ft 8 in)
Height overall	1.80 m (5 ft 11 in)
Propeller diameter	1.80 m (5 ft 11 in)

AREA:

Wings, gross	11.10 m² (119.48 sq ft)

WEIGHTS:

Weight empty	470 kg (1,036 lb)
Max T-O weight	800 kg (1,764 lb)

PERFORMANCE:

Max level speed	162 knots (300 km/h; 186 mph)

Econ cruising speed (65% power)

	132 knots (245 km/h; 152 mph)
Stalling speed: flaps up	54 knots (100 km/h; 62 mph)
flaps down	52 knots (95 km/h; 59 mph)
Max rate of climb at S/L	600 m (1,968 ft)/min

Service ceiling	5,000 m (16,400 ft)
T-O run	200 m (657 ft)
Landing run	300 m (984 ft)

Range with max fuel (65% power)

	593 nm (1,100 km; 683 miles)
g limits: normal	+5/–2.5

aerobatic (two occupants, max T-O weight 720 kg; 1,585 lb) +6/–3

PIEL SUPER DIAMANT

The Super Diamant is essentially a three/four-seat version of the Emeraude, of which more than 50 sets of plans have been sold. Current versions are as follows:

C.P.604. Prototype flown in Summer of 1964, with a 108 kW (145 hp) Teledyne Continental engine. Current version has swept vertical tail surfaces.

C.P.605. Much-modified four-seat ('2+2') version, with 112 kW (150 hp) Textron Lycoming O-320-E2A engine. Fully certificated for commercial production, as well as for amateur construction. Details in 1973-74 *Jane's*.

C.P.605B. Version of C.P.605 with retractable tricycle landing gear.

TYPE: Three/four-seat homebuilt.

AIRFRAME: All-wood airframe, fabric covered except for fixed tail surfaces which are plywood covered. Wing section NACA 23012. C.P.604 has non-retractable tailwheel landing gear. C.P.605B has retractable tricycle landing gear.

POWER PLANT: One flat-four engine (typically 119 kW; 160 hp Textron Lycoming IO-320-B1A or O-360-D1C). Fuel capacity 85 litres (22.5 US gallons; 18.7 Imp gallons). Provision for additiona' tankage to give total capacity of 160 litres (42.3 US gallons; 35 Imp gallons).

DIMENSIONS, EXTERNAL (C.P.605B):

Wing span	9.20 m (30 ft 2¼ in)
Length overall	7.00 m (22 ft 11¾ in)
Height overall	2.00 m (6 ft 6¾ in)
Propeller diameter	1.80 m (5 ft 11 in)

AREA:

Wings, gross	13.30 m² (143.2 sq ft)

WEIGHTS (C.P.605B):

Weight empty	520 kg (1,146 lb)
Max T-O weight	850 kg (1,873 lb)

PERFORMANCE (C.P.605B, at max T-O weight):

Max level speed	141 knots (260 km/h; 162 mph)

Econ cruising speed (65% power) at 1,200 m (3,940 ft)

	124 knots (230 km/h; 143 mph)
Stalling speed: flaps up	49 knots (90 km/h; 56 mph)
flaps down	45 knots (82 km/h; 51 mph)
Max rate of climb at S/L	330 m (1,082 ft)/min
Service ceiling	5,000 m (16,400 ft)
T-O run	160 m (525 ft)
Landing run	270 m (886 ft)

Range at econ cruising speed

	620 nm (1,150 km; 714 miles)

PIEL C.P.70, C.P.750 and C.P.751 BERYL

The **C.P.70 Beryl** combines the wing of the C.P.30 Emeraude, virtually unchanged, with a fuselage containing two seats in tandem, and non-retractable tricycle landing gear. It is powered by a 48.5 kW (65 hp) Teledyne Continental C65-8F engine. Plans of this version are not available from Mr Trivisonno of Canada.

Intended for aerobatic flying, the **C.P.750 Beryl** is also similar in general appearance to the Emeraude but has a longer, steel tube fuselage seating two persons in tandem, slightly reduced span, and other changes. The C.P.750 has been built principally by amateur constructors in Canada.

A further variant, the **C.P.751**, introduced several new design features and has a 134 kW (180 hp) Textron Lycoming O-360-A engine. Several are under construction or flying in Canada and the USA.

The following details refer to the C.P.750 Beryl:

TYPE: Two-seat homebuilt aerobatic monoplane.
AIRFRAME: All-wood wings, with fabric covering. Wing section NACA 23012. Fabric covered welded steel tube fuselage. Wooden tail unit; fixed surfaces plywood covered, control surfaces fabric covered. Non-retractable tailwheel landing gear.
POWER PLANT: One 112 kW (150 hp) Textron Lycoming O-320-E2A. Fuel capacity 70 litres (18.5 US gallons; 15.4 Imp gallons), with provision for two auxiliary tanks to give total capacity of 140 litres (37 US gallons; 30.75 Imp gallons).

DIMENSIONS, EXTERNAL (C.P.750):

Wing span	8.04 m (26 ft 4½ in)
Length overall	6.90 m (22 ft 7¾ in)
Height overall	2.10 m (6 ft 10¾ in)
Propeller diameter	1.80 m (5 ft 11 in)

AREA (C.P.750):

Wings, gross	11.00 m² (118.4 sq ft)

WEIGHTS:

Weight empty	480 kg (1,058 lb)
Max T-O weight	760 kg (1,675 lb)

PERFORMANCE (C.P.750, at max T-O weight):

Max level speed	151 knots (280 km/h; 174 mph)
Econ cruising speed (65% power) at 1,200 m (3,940 ft)	135 knots (250 km/h; 155 mph)
Stalling speed: flaps up	54 knots (100 km/h; 63 mph)
flaps down	52 knots (95 km/h; 59 mph)
Max rate of climb at S/L	390 m (1,280 ft)/min
Service ceiling	5,200 m (17,060 ft)
T-O run	190 m (623 ft)
Landing run	280 m (919 ft)
Range at econ cruising speed	593 nm (1,100 km; 683 miles)

PIEL C.P.80

The C.P.80 was designed as a single-seat racing aircraft for amateur construction. Details, and an illustration, can be found in the 1988-89 *Jane's*.

PIEL C.P.90 PINOCCHIO

The C.P.90 Pinocchio is essentially a smaller, single-seat development of the Emeraude, intended for aerobatic and general sporting flying.

AIRFRAME: All-wood, fabric covered. Wing section NACA 23012. Non-retractable tailwheel landing gear.
POWER PLANT: One 74.5 kW (100 hp) Teledyne Continental O-200. Fuel capacity 60 litres (15.9 US gallons; 13.2 Imp gallons).

DIMENSIONS, EXTERNAL:

Wing span	7.20 m (23 ft 7½ in)
Length overall	6.00 m (19 ft 8¼ in)
Height overall	1.80 m (5 ft 11 in)
Propeller diameter	1.80 m (5 ft 11 in)

AREA:

Wings, gross	9.65 m² (103.9 sq ft)

WEIGHTS:

Weight empty	335 kg (738 lb)
Max T-O weight	500 kg (1,102 lb)

PERFORMANCE (estimated, at max T-O weight):

Max level speed	141 knots (260 km/h; 162 mph)
Econ cruising speed (65% power) at 1,200 m (3,940 ft)	124 knots (230 km/h; 143 mph)
Stalling speed	41 knots (75 km/h; 47 mph)
Max rate of climb at S/L	480 m (1,575 ft)/min
Service ceiling	6,000 m (19,685 ft)
T-O run	180 m (590 ft)
Landing run	160 m (525 ft)
Range at econ cruising speed	296 nm (550 km; 341 miles)

PIEL C.P.150 ONYX

The Onyx was the last aircraft designed by the late M Claude Piel, and plans are currently available only from Mme Piel, in France. Construction of at least 110 Onyx is known to have been started, and several have flown.

TYPE: Single-seat tandem-wing microlight.
AIRFRAME: All-wood construction standard, except for Klégécel ribs in wings, fins and rudders, which are all Tergal fabric covered. Forward wing is pivoted for variable incidence. Rear wings have tip mounted fins and rudders, and inset ailerons. Elevator in centre-section of forward wing. Non-retractable tricycle landing gear. Alternative glassfibre fuselage being utilised by some builders.
POWER PLANT: One 8.8 kW (12 hp) Solo.

DIMENSIONS, EXTERNAL:

Wing span	7.30 m (23 ft 11½ in)
Length overall	3.53 m (11 ft 7 in)

AREAS:

Wings, gross: rear wing	9.10 m² (97.95 sq ft)
front wing	3.70 m² (39.83 sq ft)

WEIGHTS:

Weight empty	70 kg (154 lb)
Max T-O weight	180 kg (397 lb)

PERFORMANCE: No details received

POTTIER

JEAN POTTIER

4 rue de Poissy, 78130 les Mureaux
Telephone: 33 99 13 85

Details of the Pottier P.80S, P.100TS, P.110TS and P.105TS can be found in the 1987-88 *Jane's*, and of the P.50 Bouvreuil racing aircraft in the 1988-89 *Jane's*. Plans are available for the following types, plus the Bouvreuil:

POTTIER P.70S

TYPE: Single-seat homebuilt sporting aircraft.
AIRFRAME: All-metal, of 2024 alloy. Wing section NACA 4415. Non-retractable tricycle landing gear.
POWER PLANT: One 30-44.7 kW (40-60 hp) Volkswagen converted motorcar engine. Fuel capacity 40 litres (10.6 US gallons; 8.75 Imp gallons).

DIMENSIONS, EXTERNAL:

Wing span	5.85 m (19 ft 2¼ in)
Length overall	5.15 m (16 ft 10¾ in)
Height overall	1.60 m (5 ft 3 in)
Propeller diameter	1.30 m (4 ft 3¼ in)

AREA:

Wings, gross	7.20 m² (77.5 sq ft)

WEIGHTS:

Weight empty, equipped	215 kg (474 lb)
Max T-O and landing weight	325 kg (716 lb)

PERFORMANCE (A: standard P.70S with 30 kW; 40 hp engine, B: 44.7 kW; 60 hp engine, at max T-O weight except where indicated):

Max level speed at S/L:

A	97 knots (180 km/h; 112 mph)
B	116 knots (215 km/h; 133 mph)

Econ cruising speed at S/L:

A	65 knots (120 km/h; 75 mph)

Stalling speed, flaps down:

A, B	38 knots (70 km/h; 44 mph)
Max rate of climb at S/L: A	150 m (490 ft)/min
B	330 m (1,080 ft)/min
Service ceiling: A	4,500 m (14,775 ft)
T-O run: A	350 m (1,150 ft)
B	200 m (657 ft)
Range: A, B	215 nm (400 km; 248 miles)
g limit: A, B	+9 ultimate

POTTIER P.170S

The P.170S is a tandem two-seat version of the P.70S. It is of all-metal construction and has a retractable tricycle landing gear. Engine is a 37.3-52 kW (50-70 hp) Volkswagen.

TYPE: Two-seat sporting homebuilt.

DIMENSIONS, EXTERNAL:

Wing span	5.95 m (19 ft 6¼ in)
Length overall	5.70 m (18 ft 8½ in)
Height overall	1.65 m (5 ft 5 in)

AREA:

Wings, gross	7.40 m² (79.65 sq ft)

WEIGHTS:

Weight empty	230 kg (507 lb)
Max T-O weight	445 kg (981 lb)

PERFORMANCE (A: 37.3 kW; 50 hp engine, B: 52 kW; 70 hp engine):

Max level speed: A	95 knots (175 km/h; 109 mph)
B	108 knots (200 km/h; 124 mph)
Max cruising speed: A	84 knots (155 km/h; 96 mph)
B	102 knots (190 km/h; 118 mph)
Stalling speed: A, B	41 knots (75 km/h; 47 mph)
Max rate of climb at S/L: A	150 m (490 ft)/min
B	300 m (980 ft)/min
T-O run: A	380 m (1,250 ft)
B	220 m (722 ft)
Landing from 15 m (50 ft): A, B	350 m (1,150 ft)
Range with standard 50 litres (11 Imp gallons) of fuel, 45 min reserves: A, B	215 nm (400 km; 248 miles)
g limit: A, B	+6.6 ultimate

POTTIER P.180S

The P.180S is a side by side two-seat sporting aircraft, of all-metal construction and with a non-retractable tricycle landing gear. Power plant is a 41-67 kW (55-90 hp) Volkswagen.

TYPE: Two-seat sporting aircraft.

DIMENSIONS, EXTERNAL:

Wing span	6.50 m (21 ft 4 in)
Length overall	5.35 m (17 ft 6½ in)
Height overall	1.70 m (5 ft 7 in)

AREA:

Wings, gross	7.80 m² (83.96 sq ft)

WEIGHTS:

Weight empty	240 kg (529 lb)
Max T-O weight	470 kg (1,036 lb)

PERFORMANCE (estimated, 41 kW; 55 hp engine):

Max level speed	97 knots (180 km/h; 112 mph)
Max cruising speed	89 knots (165 km/h; 102 mph)
Stalling speed	41 knots (75 km/h; 47 mph)
Max rate of climb at S/L	168 m (550 ft)/min
T-O run	330 m (1,080 ft)
Landing from 15 m (50 ft)	350 m (1,150 ft)
Range	270 nm (500 km; 310 miles)
g limit	+5.7 ultimate

S.M.A.N.

SOCIÉTÉ MORBIHANNAISE D'AÉRO NAVIGATION

Anse de Mané Braz, Saint-Philibert, 56470 La Trinité-Sur-Mer
Telephone: 33 97 55 1063
Telex: 740 043
Fax: 33 97 55 17 15

GENERAL MANAGER: André Wydauw

Rights to M. Claude Tisserand's two-seat Hydroplum II amphibian were purchased by S.M.A.N. in 1987, the prototype having first flown on 1 November 1986. S.M.A.N. markets kits to build the amphibian, known as the Petrel, requiring about 500 working hours to assemble. Ready to fly Petrels are also available.

S.M.A.N. PETREL

TYPE: Side by side two-seat microlight amphibian.
AIRFRAME: Wings have aluminium alloy tubular main spar, glassfibre/epoxy leading-edge and glassfibre/foam/epoxy ribs, with Dacron covering. Wing section NACA 2412. Three-axis control. Moulded monocoque single step hull of glassfibre/epoxy, with Kevlar reinforcement; carbonfibre/epoxy tailboom with water rudder at heel. Boom supports tail unit of wood with fabric covering on fin and control surfaces. Retractable tricycle landing gear. Optional fully enclosed cockpit.
POWER PLANT: One 47.7 kW (64 hp) Rotax 532. Four-stroke engine of same power can be installed for operation in homebuilt category. Fuel capacity 50 litres (13.2 US gallons; 11 Imp gallons).

DIMENSIONS, EXTERNAL:

Wing span: upper	8.90 m (29 ft 2½ in)
Length overall	5.90 m (19 ft 4¼ in)
Height overall	1.80 m (5 ft 11 in)
Propeller diameter	1.56 m (5 ft 1½ in)

AREA:

Wings, gross	17.30 m² (186.22 sq ft)

WEIGHTS:

Weight empty, equipped	195 kg (430 lb)
Min pilot weight	75 kg (166 lb)
Max T-O weight	400 kg (882 lb)

PERFORMANCE (at max T-O weight):

Max level speed	97 knots (180 km/h; 112 mph)
Cruising speed	81 knots (150 km/h; 93 mph)
Stalling speed	30 knots (55 km/h; 34 mph)
Max rate of climb at S/L	300 m (985 ft)/min
T-O run: on land	50 m (164 ft)
on water	100 m (328 ft)
Landing run: on land	70 m (230 ft)
on water	50 m (164 ft)
Endurance	4 h 10 min
g limits	+6/-3

Pottier P.180S two-seat sporting aircraft *(M.J. Hooks)*

S.M.A.N. Petrel with optional cockpit canopy

Pottier P.70S with standard tricycle landing gear *(M.J. Hooks)*

The SB1 Antarès designed and built in Baugé, France, by M Claude Soyer and M Jean Barritault

Stern ST 80 single-seat homebuilt aircraft with wings folded *(M.J. Hooks)*

SOYER/BARRITAULT
CLAUDE SOYER and JEAN BARRITAULT
Claude Soyer: BP 19, 49160 Longue-Jumelles
Jean Barritault: 10 rue G. Clémençeau, 49150 Baugé

SOYER/BARRITAULT SB1 ANTARÈS
The SB1 Antarès first flew on 24 May 1984. Plans available to amateur builders show an airframe of more simple design, a three-seat cabin with two side by side front seats and a rear bench, a non-retractable tricycle landing gear, and 89.5 kW (120 hp) engine. The following description applies to the prototype:

TYPE: Tandem two-seat touring homebuilt.
AIRFRAME: Mostly all-wooden, with Dacron covering overall. Alternate wood and Klégécel wing nose ribs. Large polyester fairings over wing/fuselage junctions. Wing section NACA 4417. Retractable tricycle landing gear.
POWER PLANT: One 119 kW (160 hp) Textron Lycoming O-320-D2A. Fuel capacity 300 litres (79.25 US gallons; 66 Imp gallons).
DIMENSIONS, EXTERNAL:
Wing span   9.88 m (32 ft 5 in)

Length overall	7.20 m (23 ft 7½ in)
Height overall	1.90 m (6 ft 3 in)
AREA:	
Wings, gross	12.20 m² (131.3 sq ft)
WEIGHTS:	
Weight empty	642 kg (1,415 lb)
Max T-O weight	1,012 kg (2,231 lb)
PERFORMANCE:	
Cruising speed	135 knots (250 km/h; 155 mph)
Range with max fuel, 45 min reserves	
	1,215 nm (2,250 km; 1,398 miles)

STERN
RENÉ STERN
10 rue du Château, 57730 Folschviller

STERN ST 80 BALADE
The ST 80 flew for the first time on 17 July 1983. Plans are available to amateur builders, together with kits containing major component parts.
TYPE: Single-seat homebuilt.

AIRFRAME: All-wood with fabric covering, except for fuselage which has wooden skins. Wing section NACA 43015 at root, NACA 43012 at tip. Non-retractable tricycle type.
POWER PLANT: One 45 kW (60 hp) Limbach 1,700 cc in prototype. Alternative Volkswagen modified motorcar engine in 1,600 cc to 2,000 cc range. Fuel capacity 32 litres (8.5 US gallons; 7 Imp gallons).
DIMENSIONS, EXTERNAL:
Wing span	6.40 m (21 ft 0 in)
Length overall	4.90 m (16 ft 0¾ in)
Propeller diameter	1.40 m (4 ft 7 in)

AREA:	
Wings, gross	7.0 m² (75.35 sq ft)
WEIGHTS:	
Weight empty	230 kg (507 lb)
Max T-O weight	340 kg (750 lb)
PERFORMANCE:	
Max level speed	
	97-108 knots (180-200 km/h; 112-124 mph)
Max cruising speed	86 knots (160 km/h; 99 mph)
Stalling speed	44 knots (80 km/h; 50 mph)
Max rate of climb at S/L	240 m (785 ft)/min

GERMANY, WEST

AKAFLIEG MÜNCHEN
FLUGTECHNISCHE FORSCHUNGSGRUPPE an der TECHNISCHEN UNIVERSITÄT MÜNCHEN

Arcisstrasse 21, Postfach 202420, 8000 Munich 2

Although construction of the prototype Mü 30 Schlacro tandem two-seat aerobatic and towing aircraft began in 1985, it is not expected to fly until 1991. The wing span is now quoted as 8.82 m (28 ft 11¼ in), and max level speed is expected to be 216 knots (400 km/h; 248 mph). Details, and an illustration, appeared in the 1988-89 *Jane's*.

COSY
COSY EUROPE

Ahornstrasse 10, D-8901 Ried b. Augsburg
Telephone: 49 82 33/6 05 94
Fax: 49 82 33/2 01 50
OWNERS: Uli and Linda Wolters

Co Z Europe (now Cosy Europe) purchased the design rights to the Cozy side by side development of the Rutan Long-EZ in 1987, from the Co Z Development Corporation of the USA. Plans were made available but more recently Cosy Europe has undertaken some redesign of the aircraft, which is now named Classic. Plans, available since January 1990, are offered worldwide, with the exception of the USA. The company also has an aircraft supply and import service, supporting homebuilders and general aviation.

COSY CLASSIC

The prototype of the original Cozy flew for the first time on 19 July 1982. Uli and Linda Wolters built and flew the first plans-built Cozy on 19 July 1985. The new Classic has a wider fuselage to provide more shoulder room, a larger canopy with more headroom, new turtleback with improved streamlining, R1145 rain canard as standard equipment, and the options of a fixed pitch or constant speed/variable pitch propeller.

The following modified details refer to the new Classic.
TYPE: Two/three-seat sporting homebuilt.
AIRFRAME: Wing and foreplane structures of unidirectional glassfibre with rigid styrofoam core. Modified Eppler wing section; foreplane has a GU (Glasgow University) section or can use the Roncz section. Composite fuselage comprising sheets of PVC foam, with wood strips as corner fillers, in a sandwich using internal and external covering of unidirectional glassfibre. Light alloy or steel extrusions used for engine mount. Tricycle landing gear, with retractable nosewheel.
POWER PLANT: One 112-119 kW (150-160 hp) Textron Lycoming O-320 or IO-320 engine. Fuel capacity 196 litres (51.8 US gallons; 43 Imp gallons).
DIMENSIONS, EXTERNAL:

Wing span	7.96 m (26 ft 1¼ in)
Length overall	5.12 m (16 ft 9½ in)
Height overall	2.30 m (7 ft 6½ in)
Propeller diameter	1.60 or 1.62 m (5 ft 3 in or 5 ft 3¾ in)

AREA:

Wings, gross	8.88 m² (95.6 sq ft)

WEIGHTS:

Weight empty, basic	410 kg (904 lb)
Max front seat load	160 kg (352 lb)
Max T-O weight	800 kg (1,763 lb)

PERFORMANCE:

Max level speed at S/L	165 knots (306 km/h; 190 mph)
Cruising speed (75% power) at 2,440 m (8,000 ft)	162 knots (300 km/h; 186 mph)
Econ cruising speed at 3,660 m (12,000 ft)	124 knots (230 km/h; 143 mph)
Stalling speed	53 knots (97 km/h; 60 mph)
Max rate of climb at S/L: solo	457 m (1,500 ft)/min
dual	305 m (1,000 ft)/min
Service ceiling: solo	7,620 m (25,000 ft)
dual	6,100 m (20,000 ft)
T-O run: solo	250 m (821 ft)
dual	450 m (1,477 ft)
Landing run: solo	300 m (985 ft)
dual	450 m (1,477 ft)
Range, 45 min reserves:	
at 45% power	1,025 nm (1,900 km; 1,180 miles)
at 75% power	863 nm (1,600 km; 994 miles)

HEWA-TECHNICS
HEWA-TECHNICS

AIRCRAFT DIVISION: Dorfstrasse 77, 8939 Markt Wald
Telephone: 49 8262 1868
Telex: 539625 HEWAT D
GENERAL MANAGER: Heinz Wagenseil

The original J-5 composites light aircraft was designed in Poland by Mr Jaroslaw Janowski. An aircraft branch of the Marko-Elektronic Company was established in that country to offer for export kits of component parts to construct the J-5. Hewa-Technics of West Germany markets the aircraft in kit and ready-assembled forms, under the name of Marco J-5. The kit is claimed to take approximately 600 working hours to assemble.

HEWA-TECHNICS MARCO J-5
TYPE: Single-seat homebuilt.
AIRFRAME: Built entirely of glassfibre and epoxy, except for the flaperons which are glassfibre and duralumin. Wortmann FX 67-K170/17 wing section. Three-axis control. Landing gear comprises retractable mainwheel, non-retractable tailwheel and wingtip balancers. Polish-assembled example illustrated has new non-retractable conventional tailwheel gear.
POWER PLANT: One 22.4 kW (30 hp) KFM 107ER. Fuel capacity 25 litres (6.6 US gallons; 5.5 Imp gallons).
DIMENSIONS, EXTERNAL:

Wing span	8.10 m (26 ft 7 in)
Length overall	4.70 m (15 ft 5 in)
Height overall	1.40 m (4 ft 7¼ in)
Propeller diameter	1.15 m (3 ft 9¼ in)

AREA:

Wings, gross	6.50 m² (70.0 sq ft)

WEIGHTS:

Weight empty	140 kg (309 lb)
Pilot weight range	60-95 kg (132-209 lb)
Max T-O weight	260 kg (575 lb)

PERFORMANCE:

Max level speed	113 knots (210 km/h; 130 mph)
Econ cruising speed	81 knots (150 km/h; 93 mph)
Stalling speed	42 knots (78 km/h; 49 mph)
Max rate of climb at S/L	150 m (490 ft)/min
Service ceiling	5,000 m (16,400 ft)
T-O run	200 m (656 ft)
Landing run	150 m (490 ft)
Range with max fuel	378 nm (700 km; 435 miles)
g limits	+4/–3

IRAQ

CMI
RPV Department of CMI
Al Faris factory, Al Faris

CMI SAJA
As can be seen from the accompanying illustration, the Saja closely resembles the CFM Shadow tandem two-seat microlight (see UK part of Sport Aircraft section), and appears to be the modified Shadow II version marketed by ASVEC (UK) Ltd as a manned aerial surveillance system. Stated roles are oil pipeline inspection and real-time video monitoring; a TV or thermal imaging package can be carried under the fuselage pod. Two examples had been completed by early 1989. Of pod and boom configuration, other features include a braced high-mounted wing, conventional tail unit comprising a tailplane and one-piece elevator, ventral fin and rudder, and a non-retractable nosewheel landing gear. Power is provided by a 47.7 kW (64 hp) Rotax 532 engine driving a three-blade pusher propeller; fuel load is 42 kg (92 lb).

DIMENSIONS, EXTERNAL:

Wing span	8.61 m (28 ft 3 in)
Length overall	6.40 m (21 ft 0 in)

WEIGHTS:

Weight empty	176 kg (388 lb)
Max T-O weight	408 kg (899 lb)

PERFORMANCE:

Max level speed	110 knots (204 km/h; 127 mph)
Service ceiling	7,010 m (23,000 ft)
Endurance	4 h 30 min
Range for videoing	108 nm (200 km; 124 miles)

ISRAEL

SCICRAFT
SCICRAFT LTD
(Subsidiary of Cyclone Aviation Products Ltd)

PO Box 114, Carmiel 20-100
Telephone: 972 (4) 960701
Telex: 471684 CYCLV
Fax: 972 (4) 962220
PRESIDENT: Gideon Goren
MARKETING: Baruch Lavanon

SCICRAFT GAMBIT
The Gambit, of which three models are available in kit form, is aimed mainly at private recreational pilots and training markets, though amphibious, agricultural and military applications are planned. Construction takes about 200 working hours. It was designed to FAR Pt 23 requirements, and is expected to gain full certification during the 1990s. Construction of a prototype began in 1986, and this flew in the following year. By January 1990 three prototypes and three ready assembled aircraft had been completed.
TYPE: Side by side two-seat homebuilt.

AIRFRAME: Wings have aluminium alloy leading-edges, composites cambered tips and winglets, and optional Tedlar or Ceconite skins. Composites ailerons on wings. Composites foreplane of glassfibre/graphite/foam core sandwich. Elevators on foreplane. Rudder on each winglet, deflecting outward only. Composites fuselage of glassfibre/Kevlar/graphite/foam core sandwich. Non-retractable tricycle landing gear, with brakes. Dual wheel controls.
POWER PLANT: Available as **Gambit 600** with 47.7 kW (64 hp) Rotax 582, **Gambit 700** with 56 kW (75 hp) Hewland, or **Gambit 900** with 59 kW (79 hp) Rotax 912 or 63.4 kW (85 hp) Norton rotary engine. Fuel capacity 60 litres (16 US gallons; 13.2 Imp gallons) standard; optional 30 litre (8 US gallon; 6.6 Imp gallon) auxiliary tank.
DIMENSIONS, EXTERNAL:

Wing span	10.01 m (32 ft 10 in)
Foreplane span	3.86 m (12 ft 8 in)
Length overall	5.13 m (16 ft 10 in)
Height overall	2.44 m (8 ft 0 in)
Propeller diameter	1.52 m (5 ft 0 in)

AREAS:

Wings, gross	13.65 m² (147.0 sq ft)
Foreplanes, gross	1.77 m² (19.1 sq ft)

WEIGHTS (A: Gambit 600, B: Gambit 900):

Weight empty: A	289 kg (637 lb)
B	299 kg (660 lb)
Max baggage: A	16 kg (35 lb)
B	25 kg (55 lb)
Max T-O weight: A	476 kg (1,050 lb)
B	506 kg (1,115 lb)

PERFORMANCE (A and B as above):

Max level speed: A	87 knots (161 km/h; 100 mph)
B	113 knots (209 km/h; 130 mph)
Max cruising speed: A	78 knots (145 km/h; 90 mph)
B	100 knots (185 km/h; 115 mph)
Stalling speed: A	41 knots (76 km/h; 47 mph)
B	42 knots (78 km/h; 48 mph)
Max rate of climb at S/L: A	183 m (600 ft)/min
B	259 m (850 ft)/min
T-O run: A	119 m (390 ft)
Range with standard fuel:	
A	217 nm (402 km; 250 miles)
B	347 nm (643 km; 400 miles)
Endurance: A	3 h
g limits: A	+7/–2.64
B	+6.6/–2.64

First plans-built Cosy Europe Cozy, built by Uli and Linda Wolters

Dallach Sunrise II single/two-seat ultralight aircraft (see microlight tables)

Ritec Delta-Dart microlight canard-delta (see microlight tables)

Funk FK9 two-seat light aircraft (see microlight tables) *(Martin Fricke)*

Polish-assembled Marco J-5 with non-retractable tailwheel landing gear
(Martin Fricke)

CMI Saja two-seat oil pipeline inspection microlight
(Jane's Defence Weekly/Tony Banks)

Dedalus Poppy single-seat cabin monoplane *(Avio Data)*

Prototype SciCraft Gambit two-seat homebuilt

ITALY

DEDALUS
DEDALUS Srl
Viale Campania 29, 20133 Milan
Telephone: 39 (2) 71 63 41
GENERAL MANAGER: Marco Baggi

DEDALUS POPPY
The prototype Poppy flew for the first time in May 1984. Kits are available, requiring about 300 working hours to assemble. Many completed aircraft are flying.
TYPE: Single-seat homebuilt.
AIRFRAME: Airframe is geodetic structure of Sitka spruce,

with Dacron fabric covering, although aluminium alloy bracing struts are used and the engine cowling can be of glassfibre. Wing section Rhode St Genese 34. Non-retractable tailwheel landing gear.
POWER PLANT: One 18.6 kW (25 hp) KFM 107E. Fuel capacity 20 litres (5.3 US gallons; 4.4 Imp gallons).
DIMENSIONS, EXTERNAL:

Wing span	10.60 m (34 ft 9¼ in)
Length overall	5.90 m (19 ft 4¼ in)
Height overall	1.90 m (6 ft 2¾ in)
Propeller diameter	1.40 m (4 ft 7 in)

AREA:

Wings, gross	15.00 m² (161.5 sq ft)

WEIGHTS:

Weight empty	114 kg (252 lb)
Max T-O weight	210 kg (463 lb)

PERFORMANCE:

Max level speed	54 knots (100 km/h; 62 mph)
Econ cruising speed	43 knots (80 km/h; 50 mph)
Stalling speed	22 knots (40 km/h; 25 mph)
Max rate of climb at S/L	183 m (600 ft)/min
Service ceiling	3,050 m (10,000 ft)
T-O to 15 m (50 ft)	50 m (164 ft)
Landing from 15 m (50 ft)	100 m (328 ft)
Range with max fuel	108 nm (200 km; 124 miles)

IANNOTTA

DOTT ING ORLANDO IANNOTTA

Via Nicolardi 254, 80131 Naples

Telephone: 39 (81) 741 9324

In addition to the San Francesco, the 940 Zefiro microlight is available (see Microlight tables).

IANNOTTA I-66L SAN FRANCESCO

Plans to build the San Francesco are available; three are known to be flying.

TYPE: Two-seat, dual-control homebuilt motor glider.

AIRFRAME: All wood wings, with plywood leading-edges and fabric covering overall. Wing section NACA 23012. Fabric covered steel tube fuselage structure, with wooden formers. Wire braced tail unit of welded steel tube, fabric covered. Non-retractable tailwheel landing gear.

POWER PLANT: One 51 kW (68 hp) Limbach SL 1700E. Fuel capacity 70 litres (18.5 US gallons; 15.4 Imp gallons).

DIMENSIONS, EXTERNAL:

Wing span	9.34 m (30 ft 7¾ in)
Length overall	6.60 m (21 ft 8 in)
Propeller diameter	1.45 m (4 ft 9 in)

AREA:

Wings, gross	13.61 m² (146.5 sq ft)

WEIGHTS:

Weight empty	268 kg (591 lb)
Max T-O weight	462 kg (1,018 lb)

PERFORMANCE, POWERED:

Max level speed	81 knots (150 km/h; 93 mph)
Cruising speed at S/L	70 knots (130 km/h; 81 mph)
Landing speed	35 knots (65 km/h; 41 mph)
Max rate of climb at S/L	210 m (690 ft)/min
Service ceiling	3,800 m (12,470 ft)
Range with max fuel	378 nm (700 km; 435 miles)

PERFORMANCE, UNPOWERED:

Best glide ratio at 50 knots (93 km/h; 58 mph)	14
Min rate of sink at 48 knots (88 km/h; 55 mph)	
	84 m (275 ft)/min

NIKE

NIKE AERONAUTICA SRL

Via Ferrarese 10, 40013 Castelmaggiore, Bologna

Details of the Italzair, and an illustration, can be found in the 1988-89 *Jane's*.

LUXEMBOURG

WOLFF

ATELIERS PAUL WOLFF

1 Rue des Romains, L-8284 Kehlen

Telephone: 352 309 954

In addition to the Flash-3, this company has designed the four-seat Sky-Wolff, which is being built in the USA by Wolff Aircraft Engineering Ltd.

WOLFF FLASH-3

The Flash-3 was exhibited at the 1985 RSA meeting at Brienne in France, before it had made its first flight. It is offered in the form of a series of component kits, with an estimated construction time of 650 to 750 hours.

TYPE: Three-seat homebuilt aircraft.

AIRFRAME: Entire airframe constructed of vinylester and resin composites, partially strengthened with carbonfibre. Wing section NACA 43012₅ at root, 43010 at tip. Retractable tricycle landing gear.

POWER PLANT: One 112 kW (150 hp) Textron Lycoming O-320. Other engines of up to 194 kW (260 hp) can be fitted. Fuel capacity: standard tank 261 litres (69 US gallons; 57.4 Imp gallons); long range tank 541 litres (143 US gallons; 119 Imp gallons); long range tank with tip tanks 641 litres (169.3 US gallons; 141 Imp gallons).

DIMENSIONS, EXTERNAL:

Wing span, over tip tanks	8.53 m (27 ft 11¾ in)
Length overall	7.93 m (26 ft 0¼ in)
Height overall	2.11 m (6 ft 11 in)
Propeller diameter	1.93 m (6 ft 4 in)

AREA:

Wings, gross	10.00 m² (107.64 sq ft)

WEIGHTS:

Weight empty	508 kg (1,120 lb)
Baggage capacity	120 kg (264 lb)
Max T-O weight: without tip tanks	996 kg (2,196 lb)
with tip tanks	1,066 kg (2,350 lb)

PERFORMANCE (at max T-O weight):

Max level speed at S/L	197 knots (365 km/h; 227 mph)
Econ cruising speed at 3,050 m (10,000 ft)	
	180 knots (334 km/h; 207 mph)
Stalling speed, flaps down	44 knots (81 km/h; 50 mph)
Max rate of climb at S/L	366 m (1,200 ft)/min
Service ceiling	5,430 m (17,820 ft)
T-O run	230 m (755 ft)
Landing run	210 m (689 ft)
Range with standard fuel, two occupants and baggage	
	1,776 nm (3,291 km; 2,045 miles)

WOLFF SKY-WOLFF

The Sky-Wolff represents a redesign of the earlier Flash-3, offering seating for four adults in the larger fuselage. Assembly of this all-composites aircraft takes approximately 600 working hours. Cruising speed is 186 knots (346 km/h; 215 mph) IAS, and a range of up to 3,647 nm (6,759 km; 4,200 miles) can be achieved with 640 litres (169.3 US gallons; 141 Imp gallons) of fuel. A separate lock-up luggage compartment is provided, and the wings are removable for trailering.

NORWAY

LUNDS TEKNISKE

LUNDS TEKNISKE

Vikaveien 2, N-8600 Mo

Telephone: 47 87 52 100

Fax: 47 87 55 065

OWNER/MANAGER: Arne Lund

Rights to the Silhouette homebuilt aircraft were purchased from the US Silhouette Aircraft Inc, and Lunds Tekniske currently offers kits. The original prototype Silhouette first flew in the USA on 3 July 1984. By January 1990, 42 Silhouette kits had been sold, of which 15 had been assembled. Bolt-on wingtip extensions allow the Silhouette to be flown as a motor glider.

LUNDS TEKNISKE SILHOUETTE

TYPE: Single-seat sport/recreational homebuilt and motor glider; designed and tested to FAR Pt 23 standards.

AIRFRAME: Wings have glassfibre spars, pre-cut styrofoam cores, glassfibre/epoxy skins and pre-moulded wingtips. Basic wings have half span ailerons of styrofoam/glassfibre construction. Flaps will eventually be available. Provision for bolt-on wingtip extensions for use as motor glider. Centreline dive brake optional. Fuselage of glassfibre and Nomex honeycomb, pre-moulded in halves with integral tail fin, around plywood/styrofoam/glassfibre bulkheads. Tail surfaces of foam and glassfibre. Non-retractable tricycle landing gear, with brakes.

POWER PLANT: One 30 kW (40 hp) Rotax 447 or 37.3 kW (50 hp) Rotax 503. Fuel capacity with standard wing 45 litres (12 US gallons; 10 Imp gallons).

DIMENSIONS, EXTERNAL:

Wing span: standard	9.75 m (32 ft 0 in)
with optional wing extensions	12.50 m (41 ft 0 in)
Length overall	5.87 m (19 ft 3 in)
Height overall	2.03 m (6 ft 8 in)
Propeller diameter	1.47 m (4 ft 10 in)

AREAS:

Wings, gross: standard	7.06 m² (76.0 sq ft)
with extensions	8.36 m² (90.0 sq ft)

WEIGHTS:

Weight empty: standard wings	262 kg (578 lb)
Max T-O weight	374 kg (824 lb)

PERFORMANCE (standard wings):

Max level speed	122 knots (225 km/h; 140 mph)
Cruising speed	104 knots (193 km/h; 120 mph)
Stalling speed	45 knots (84 km/h; 52 mph)
Max rate of climb at S/L	244 m (800 ft)/min
Service ceiling	4,265 m (14,000 ft)
T-O run	244 m (800 ft)
Landing run	183 m (601 ft)
Range with max fuel, no reserves	
	390 nm (724 km; 450 miles)
g limits	+4.2/−2

POLAND

ORLIŃSKI

ROMAN ORLIŃSKI

ul Lesna 4, 82-200 Malbork

ORLIŃSKI RO-7 ORLIK (EAGLET)

The prototype Orlik was flown for the first time on 22 February 1987. Plans are available to amateur builders. Some glassfibre wing and fuselage components became available in 1989.

TYPE: Single-seat homebuilt.

AIRFRAME: Wing section NACA 23012. Wings of mostly wood construction, with plywood D-section leading-edge and fabric covering aft of spar. Welded steel tube forward fuselage; wooden semi-monocoque rear fuselage. Non-retractable tailwheel landing gear.

POWER PLANT: One 48.5 kW (65 hp) Walter Mikron III. Fuel capacity 30 litres (7.9 US gallons; 6.6 Imp gallons).

DIMENSIONS, EXTERNAL:

Wing span	7.60 m (24 ft 11¼ in)
Length overall	5.50 m (18 ft 0½ in)
Height overall	1.95 m (6 ft 4¾ in)
Propeller diameter	1.45 m (4 ft 9 in)

AREA:

Wings, gross	8.75 m² (94.18 sq ft)

WEIGHTS:

Weight empty	220 kg (485 lb)
Max T-O weight	320 kg (705 lb)

PERFORMANCE:

Max level speed at S/L	81 knots (150 km/h; 93 mph)
Econ cruising speed at S/L	49 knots (90 km/h; 56 mph)
Stalling speed	39 knots (71 km/h; 45 mph)
Max rate of climb at S/L	300 m (985 ft)/min
T-O run	100 m (328 ft)
Landing run	200 m (656 ft)
Range, 20 min reserves	215 nm (400 km; 248 miles)
Endurance, 20 min reserves	4 h 40 min

SPAIN

UHIA

MARTIN UHIA

36970 Portonoro, Pontevedra

Telephone: 34 (986) 723078

DIRECTOR: Martin Uhia Lima

UHIA CANELAS RANGER

Brief details of this two-seat microlight can be found in the Microlights tables of this edition. An illustration is published in this section.

Iannotta 940 Zefiro microlight (foreground) and I-66L San Francesco homebuilt

Janowski J-2 Polonez built by Mr Josef Leniec (see microlight tables)
(Andrzej Glass)

Uhia Canelas Ranger two-seat microlight (see microlight tables)

Andreasson BA-4B single-seat fully aerobatic homebuilt biplane
(Geoffrey P. Jones)

Orliński RO-7 single-seat homebuilt aircraft *(Tomasz Szulc)*

Wolff Sky-Wolff homebuilt aircraft, designed in Luxembourg and manufactured in kit form in the USA *(Geoffrey P. Jones)*

Long-wing Lunds Tekniske Silhouette motor glider (foreground) and version with standard wings (rear) *(Howard Levy)*

SWEDEN

ANDREASSON
BJÖRN ANDREASSON
Collins Väg 22B, 23600 Höllviksnäs

In addition to the aircraft described here, Mr Andreasson's BA-12 Slandan and BA-14 are detailed under the MFI heading in the Microlight tables.

ANDREASSON BA-4B
Plans to build the BA-4B are available.

TYPE: Single-seat fully aerobatic homebuilt biplane.

AIRFRAME: Braced biplane. Alternative all-metal wings, or all-wood wing structure covered with heavy plywood skin. Ailerons, of simplified sheet metal construction, on lower wings only. Provision for detachable plastics wingtips. Sheet metal fuselage and tail unit. Turtledeck either sheet metal or reinforced plastics. Non-retractable tailwheel landing gear.

POWER PLANT: Prototype has 74.5 kW (100 hp) Rolls-Royce Continental O-200-A. Provision for other engines, including Volkswagen conversions. Standard fuel capacity 50 litres (13.2 US gallons; 11 Imp gallons). Provision for external 'bullet' tank of 50 litres (13.2 US gallons; 11 Imp gallons) capacity under fuselage.

DIMENSIONS, EXTERNAL:
Wing span: upper	5.34 m (17 ft 7 in)
lower	5.14 m (16 ft 11 in)
Length overall	4.60 m (15 ft 0 in)

AREA:
Wings, gross	8.30 m² (89.3 sq ft)

WEIGHT:
Max T-O weight	375 kg (827 lb)

PERFORMANCE (prototype, at max T-O weight):
Max level speed	122 knots (225 km/h; 140 mph)
Max cruising speed	104 knots (193 km/h; 120 mph)
Min flying speed	35 knots (64 km/h; 40 mph)
Max rate of climb at S/L	610 m (2,000 ft)/min
T-O and landing run	less than 100 m (330 ft)
Range with standard fuel	152 nm (280 km; 175 miles)

ANDREASSON MFI-9 HB

The prototype BA-7 made its first flight on 10 October 1958. It entered production, and was followed by the MFI-9 version which also went into production.

Plans for the MFI-9 HB, a redrawn version of the MFI-9 for amateur builders, are currently available and the description and data refer to this version. Kits of component parts were also made available from the Cana Aircraft Company in Singapore.

TYPE: Side by side two-seat, dual control homebuilt; conforms to FAR Pt 23 in Utility category.

AIRFRAME: All-metal construction, except for glassfibre reinforced plastics wingtips. Wing section NACA 23009, modified to have leading-edge droop. Non-retractable tricycle landing gear. Optional floats or skis.

POWER PLANT: One 74.5 kW (100 hp) Teledyne Continental O-200-A. Other engines of similar weight and power rating can be used. Fuel capacity 80 litres (21 US gallons; 17.6 Imp gallons).

DIMENSIONS, EXTERNAL:

Wing span	7.43 m (24 ft 4½ in)
Length overall	5.85 m (19 ft 2¼ in)
Height overall	2.00 m (6 ft 6¾ in)

AREA:

Wings, gross	8.70 m² (93.65 sq ft)

WEIGHTS:

Weight empty	340 kg (750 lb)
Baggage capacity	20 kg (44 lb)
Max T-O weight	575 kg (1,267 lb)

PERFORMANCE:

Max level speed	130 knots (240 km/h; 149 mph)
Econ cruising speed at S/L	113 knots (210 km/h; 130 mph)
Stalling speed, power off	44 knots (80 km/h; 50 mph)
Max rate of climb at S/L	270 m (885 ft)/min
Service ceiling	4,500 m (14,775 ft)
T-O run, on grass	150 m (492 ft)
Landing run	130 m (427 ft)
Range with max payload	431 nm (800 km; 497 miles)

EKSTRÖM
STAFFAN W. EKSTRÖM

Details, and an illustration, of the Humlan autogyro can be found in the 1988-89 *Jane's*.

MFI
MALMÖ FORSKNINGS & INNOVATIONS AB
(Malmö Research & Development Ltd)

Smedstorpsgatan, S-212 28 Malmö
Telephone: 46 (40) 18 07 05
Telex: 12442 FOTEX S
TECHNICAL MANAGER: Bjorn Andreasson

This company's BA-12 Slandan and BA-14 can be found in the Microlight tables.

SWITZERLAND

BRÄNDLI
MAX BRÄNDLI

Höheweg 2, CH-2553 Safnern
Telephone: 41 (32) 55 18 23

BRÄNDLI BX-2 CHERRY

The prototype Cherry made its first flight on 24 April 1982. Plans (written in German) are available, and 117 sets had been sold by early 1990. The canopy and main spar are available in prefabricated form.

TYPE: Two-seat homebuilt.

AIRFRAME: Wings and tail unit have wood spars and Styrofoam skins covered with glassfibre. Wing section NACA 747A15. Ailerons and flaps of foam and glassfibre construction. Optional folding wings and

all-moving tailplane. Wood fuselage structure, plywood and glassfibre covered. Retractable tricycle landing gear, with brakes.

POWER PLANT: One 48.5 kW (65 hp) Teledyne Continental A65. Alternative engines include Limbach L 2400, Teledyne Continental A75 or C90-8F, or Rotax 912. Fuel capacity 84 litres (22.2 US gallons; 18.5 Imp gallons).

DIMENSIONS, EXTERNAL:

Wing span	7.00 m (22 ft 11½ in)
Length overall	5.25 m (17 ft 2½ in)
Height overall	2.05 m (6 ft 8½ in)
Propeller diameter	1.60 m (5 ft 3 in)

AREA:

Wings, gross	8.50 m² (91.5 sq ft)

WEIGHTS:

Weight empty, equipped	310 kg (683 lb)
Max payload	190 kg (419 lb)

Max baggage	40 kg (88 lb)
Max T-O and landing weight	550 kg (1,212 lb)

PERFORMANCE (with A65 engine, at max T-O weight, except where indicated):

Max level speed at 915 m (3,000 ft)	121 knots (225 km/h; 140 mph)
Max cruising speed at 915 m (3,000 ft)	113 knots (210 km/h; 130 mph)
Stalling speed, flaps down, engine idling, at AUW of 510 kg (1,125 lb)	45 knots (84 km/h; 52 mph)
Max rate of climb at S/L	180 m (590 ft)/min
Service ceiling	4,200 m (13,775 ft)
T-O run	300 m (985 ft)
Landing run	150 m (492 ft)
Range with max fuel	539 nm (1,000 km; 621 miles)
Endurance	6 h
g limits	+3.8/-1.9

BRÜGGER
MAX BRÜGGER

CH-1724 Zénauva
Telephone: 41 (37) 33 29 20

BRÜGGER MB-2 COLIBRI 2

The prototype Colibri 2 flew for the first time on 1 May 1970. Plans are available, and about 250 Colibri 2s are under construction or flying in Europe.

TYPE: Single-seat homebuilt.

AIRFRAME: All-wood construction, except for fabric covering on wings and ailerons. No fixed fin. Wing section NACA 23012. Non-retractable tailwheel landing gear.

POWER PLANT: One 30 kW (40 hp) 1,600 cc Volkswagen engine (Brügger modification). Fuel capacity 33 litres (8.7 US gallons; 7.25 Imp gallons).

DIMENSIONS, EXTERNAL:

Wing span	6.00 m (19 ft 8¼ in)
Length overall	4.80 m (15 ft 9 in)
Height overall	1.60 m (5 ft 3 in)
Propeller diameter	1.38 m (4 ft 6⅓ in)

AREA:

Wings, gross	8.20 m² (88.25 sq ft)

WEIGHTS:

Weight empty	215 kg (474 lb)
Max T-O and landing weight	330 kg (727 lb)

PERFORMANCE (at max T-O weight):

Max speed at 1,000 m (3,280 ft)	97 knots (180 km/h; 111 mph)
Econ cruising speed (70% power) at 1,000 m (3,280 ft)	86 knots (160 km/h; 99 mph)
Stalling speed	33 knots (60 km/h; 38 mph)
Max rate of climb at S/L	180 m (590 ft)/min
Service ceiling	4,500 m (14,760 ft)
T-O and landing run	200 m (656 ft)
Range with max fuel	270 nm (500 km; 310 miles)

UNITED KINGDOM

AMF
AMF MICROFLIGHT LTD

Membury Airfield, Lambourn, Berkshire RG16 7TJ
Telephone: 44 (488) 72224
Telex: 848507 MIFLI
Fax: 44 (488) 72224
MANAGING DIRECTOR: Angus M. Fleming

AMF MICROFLIGHT CHEVVRON 2-32

The Chevvron was first flown in 1983. Production began in 1987, and by January 1990 19 of 24 Chevvrons ordered had been delivered in ready assembled form.

TYPE: Side by side two-seat microlight/trainer; conforms to BCAR Section S.

AIRFRAME: Airframe of glassfibre/carbonfibre/Kevlar and

foam construction. Wortmann wing section. Three-axis control. Non-retractable tricycle landing gear, with brakes. Optional floats.

POWER PLANT: One 24 kW (32 hp) König SD 570; at least one seaplane powered by a 35.8 kW (48 hp) Köing engine. Standard fuel capacity 30 litres (7.9 US gallons; 6.6 Imp gallons). One auxiliary fuel tank optional, either of 30 litres or 20 litres (5.3 US gallons; 4.4 Imp gallons) capacity.

DIMENSIONS, EXTERNAL:

Wing span	13.41 m (44 ft 0 in)
Length overall	7.01 m (23 ft 0 in)
Height overall	1.52 m (5 ft 0 in)
Propeller diameter	1.52 m (5 ft 0 in)

AREA:

Wings, gross	17.56 m² (189.0 sq ft)

WEIGHTS:

Weight empty	175 kg (386 lb)
Pilot weight range	50-180 kg (110-396 lb)
Max T-O weight	382 kg (842 lb)

PERFORMANCE:

Max level and cruising speed	65 knots (120 km/h; 75 mph)
Econ cruising speed	55 knots (102 km/h; 63 mph)
Stalling speed	30 knots (56 km/h; 35 mph)
Max rate of climb at S/L	128 m (420 ft)/min
Service ceiling	3,050 m (10,000 ft)
T-O run	91 m (300 ft)
Landing run	137 m (450 ft)
Range with standard fuel	200 nm (370 km; 230 miles)
Endurance	3 h
g limits	+4/-2

CFM
COOK FLYING MACHINES
(trading as CFM Metal-Fax Ltd)

Unit 2D, Eastlands Industrial Estate, Leiston, Suffolk IP16 4LL

Telephone: 44 (728) 832353/833076
Telex: 9877703 CHACOM G
Fax: 44 (728) 832 498

MANAGING DIRECTOR: David G. Cook

CFM SHADOW SERIES B and B-D

The Shadow first flew as a prototype in 1983. It has been in continuous production since 1984. Type approval to BCAR CAP 482 Section S was gained in May 1985. The current standard Shadow is designated Series B, with the B-D having dual controls.

MFI-9B (Andreasson) built in Sweden by Malmö

Brügger MB-2 Colibri 2 built by Nadal Patrick (*Geoffrey P. Jones*)

Brändli BX-2 Cherry two-seat homebuilt aircraft

AMF Microflight Chevvron 2-32 two-seat microlight trainer

CFM Shadow two-seat microlight

Fulton Aircraft FA-1 two-seat microlight trainer

ULV cropspraying trials demonstrated the suitability of the Shadow in this role. A multi-function surveillance fit for photography, video recording, and closed-circuit TV microwave transmission to a command vehicle/station is also available.

TYPE: Tandem two-seat microlight; conforms to FAI and UK CAA requirements.

AIRFRAME: Wings constructed of aluminium alloy and wood, with foam/glassfibre ribs, plywood covering on forward section and polyester fabric aft. Wing design allows no 'defined stall' and will not permit spin. Fuselage pod of Fibrelam; aluminium tube tailboom. Three-axis control. Non-retractable tricycle landing gear, with brakes. Overseas options include floats, agricultural spraygear and other specialised equipment.

POWER PLANT: One 28.3 kW (38 hp) 437 cc Rotax 447. Standard fuel capacity 23 litres (6 US gallons; 5 Imp gallons). Overseas options include a 43 litre (11.4 US gallon; 9.5 Imp gallon) auxiliary fuel tank.

DIMENSIONS, EXTERNAL:
Wing span	10.03 m (32 ft 11 in)
Length overall	6.40 m (21 ft 0 in)
Height overall	1.75 m (5 ft 9 in)
Propeller diameter	1.30 m (4 ft 3 in)

AREA:
Wings, gross	15.0 m² (162.0 sq ft)

WEIGHTS:
Weight empty	150 kg (331 lb)
Pilot weight range	55-90 kg (121-198 lb)

Max passenger/payload weight	90 kg (198 lb)
Max T-O weight	348 kg (767 lb)

PERFORMANCE (at max T-O weight):
Max level speed	82 knots (153 km/h; 95 mph)
Econ cruising speed	56 knots (105 km/h; 65 mph)
Min flying speed	22 knots (41 km/h; 25 mph)
Max rate of climb at S/L:	
pilot only	299 m (980 ft)/min
dual	195 m (640 ft)/min
Service ceiling	6,100 m (20,000 ft)
T-O run from metalled surface	90 m (295 ft)
Landing run, with braking	75 m (246 ft)
Range, with reserves	113 nm (209 km; 130 miles)
Endurance, with reserves: standard fuel	1 h 45 min
optional fuel	8 h
g limits	+6/-3 static, ultimate

CFM STREAK SHADOW

This new derivative version of the Shadow is designated a microlight in Europe and an Experimental homebuilt in the USA. It has a new wing design, light airframe weight and a 47.7 kW (64 hp) Rotax 532 engine to improve performance. The wing design continues to allow no 'defined stall' and is spin resistant. Total fuel capacity is 54.6 litres (14.4 US gallons; 12 Imp gallons). Dual controls are standard. Options are electric trim and a 43 litre (11.4 US gallon; 9.5 Imp gallon) auxiliary fuel tank.

DIMENSIONS, EXTERNAL:
Wing span	8.53 m (28 ft 0 in)

Length overall	6.40 m (21 ft 0 in)
Height overall	1.75 m (5 ft 9 in)
Propeller diameter	1.32 m (4 ft 4 in)

AREA:
Wings, gross	13.01 m² (140.0 sq ft)

WEIGHTS:
Weight empty	176 kg (388 lb)
Max T-O weight	408 kg (900 lb)

PERFORMANCE:
Max level speed	105 knots (195 km/h; 121 mph)
Cruising speed:	
80% power	87 knots (161 km/h; 100 mph)
50% power	65 knots (121 km/h; 75 mph)
Min flying speed	27 knots (50 km/h; 31 mph)
Max rate of climb at S/L:	
pilot only	488-549 m (1,600-1,800 ft)/min
dual	335-396 m (1,100-1,300 ft)/min
Service ceiling	8,840 m (29,000 ft)

CFM SHADOW II

This is a specialised single-seat version of the Shadow, which was marketed by ASVEC as a manned surveillance system aircraft for day and night use (two ordered by a NATO country in 1988, with six more on option). Uses one 44.7 kW (64 hp) Rotax 532 engine, and has a wing span of 8.53 m (28 ft 0 in). Further details can be found in *Jane's Battlefield Surveillance Systems*. See also Iraq in this section.

FULTON
FULTON AIRCRAFT LTD
Fulton House, Wood Wharf Business Park, Prestons Road, London Docklands, London E14 9SF
Telephone: 44 (71) 538 0751
Telex: 887951 FULCOL G
Fax: 44 (71) 538 4743
CHAIRMAN: A. Fulton

FULTON FA-1
Development of the FA-1 took place in Canada, where the prototype first flew in August 1985. A production prototype was built in the UK.

TYPE: Side by side two-seat, dual-control microlight trainer; conforms to FAI/CAA requirements, and to CAP 482 Section S.

AIRFRAME: Constructed of rigid composite materials (glassfibre, epoxy and PVC foam plastics). Three-axis control. Non-retractable tricycle landing gear.

POWER PLANT: One 38.7 kW (52 hp) Rotax 503 2V. Fuel capacity 36.5 litres (9.6 US gallons; 8 Imp gallons).

DIMENSIONS, EXTERNAL:
Wing span	9.375 m (30 ft 9 in)
Length overall	6.08 m (19 ft 11 in)

Height overall	2.29 m (7 ft 6 in)	Crew weight range	50-180 kg (110-396 lb)	Max rate of climb at S/L	225 m (740 ft)/min
Propeller diameter	1.65 m (5 ft 5 in)	Max T-O weight	360 kg (794 lb)	Endurance with max fuel, with reserves	2 h
AREA:		PERFORMANCE (at max T-O weight):		g limits	+6/−3
Wings, gross	15.0 m² (161.5 sq ft)	Max level speed	70 knots (129 km/h; 80 mph)		
WEIGHTS (open cockpit version):		Max cruising speed	65 knots (120 km/h; 75 mph)		
Weight empty	148 kg (326 lb)	Stalling speed	25 knots (46 km/h; 29 mph)		

ISAACS

JOHN O. ISAACS
23 Linden Grove, Chandler's Ford, Hampshire SO5 1LE
Telephone: 44 (703) 260885

Details of the Isaacs Fury II and Spitfire, and illustrations, can be found in the 1988-89 *Jane's.*

NIPPER

NIPPER KITS AND COMPONENTS LTD
Foxley, Blackness Lane, Keston, Kent BR2 6HL
Telephone: 44 (689) 58351
CHAIRMAN: D. P. L. Antill
DIRECTOR: A. F. Ayles

NIPPER Mk IIIb
This light aircraft was developed and manufactured originally by Avions Fairey in Belgium. Plans, kits of component parts and an advisory service are available. Approximately 60 Nippers are flying worldwide, with three under construction in early 1990. All non-wooden components are available prefabricated.
TYPE: Single-seat aerobatic homebuilt.
AIRFRAME: Wooden wing, aileron, tailplane and elevator structures, and welded steel tube fuselage and rudder structures, all fabric covered except for glassfibre

underfuselage fairing and wood skins on tailplane and elevators. No fin. Modified NACA 43012A wing section. Non-retractable tricycle landing gear.
POWER PLANT: One 41 kW (55 hp) Rollason Ardem XI. Alternatively, Nipper recommends the 48.5 kW (65 hp) Barry Smith aerobatic engine of 1,834 cc, with fuel and oil systems for inverted flight. Fuel capacity 34 litres (9 US gallons; 7.5 Imp gallons). Provision for two 16.5 litre (4.3 US gallon; 3.6 Imp gallon) wingtip fuel tanks.
DIMENSIONS, EXTERNAL:

Wing span: without tip tanks	6.00 m (19 ft 8 in)
with tip tanks	6.25 m (20 ft 6 in)
Length overall	4.56 m (15 ft 0 in)
Height overall	1.91 m (6 ft 3 in)
AREA:	
Wings, gross	7.50 m² (80.70 sq ft)
WEIGHTS (Ardem engine):	
Weight empty	210 kg (465 lb)

Max T-O weight: Aerobatic	310 kg (685 lb)
Normal	340 kg (750 lb)
PERFORMANCE (Ardem engine at max T-O weight, unless stated otherwise):	
Max level speed at S/L:	
without tip tanks	93 knots (173 km/h; 107 mph)
Barry Smith engine	113 knots (209 km/h; 130 mph)
Econ cruising speed at S/L	78 knots (145 km/h; 90 mph)
Stalling speed, power off	33 knots (61 km/h; 38 mph)
Max rate of climb at S/L:	198 m (650 ft)/min
Barry Smith engine	305 m (1,000 ft)/min
Service ceiling	3,660 m (12,000 ft)
T-O run	85 m (280 ft)
Landing run	110 m (360 ft)
Range with tip tanks	390 nm (720 km; 450 miles)
g limits	+6/−3

NOBLE HARDMAN

NOBLE HARDMAN AVIATION LTD
Details of the Noble Hardman Aviation Snowbird, and an illustration, appeared in the 1989-90 edition of *Jane's.*

PFA

THE POPULAR FLYING ASSOCIATION
Terminal Building, Shoreham Airport, Shoreham-by-Sea, West Sussex BN4 5FF
Telephone: 44 (273) 461616

Fax: 44 (273) 463390
VICE-CHAIRMAN AND CHIEF EXECUTIVE: F. I. V. Walker
The PFA markets plans of the Currie Wot, Druine D31 Turbulent and Luton L.A.4a Minor, plus the Isaacs Fury, Evans VP-1 and VP-2, and Pazmany PL-4 detailed under

their designers' names in this section. Details of the Wot, Turbulent and Minor, plus illustrations, can be found in the 1988-89 *Jane's.*

TAYLOR

T. TAYLOR
79 Springwater Road, Eastwood, Essex SS9 5BW
Telephone: 44 (702) 521484

TAYLOR J.T.1 MONOPLANE
The prototype J.T.1 Monoplane first flew on 4 July 1959. Plans are available and by early 1990 about 800 sets had been sold. Approximately 110 plans-built Monoplanes have flown. Wood kits are available in Canada and the USA.
TYPE: Single-seat aerobatic homebuilt.
AIRFRAME: All-wood structure, with fabric covering part of wings, elevators and rudder, the remainder plywood covered. Wing section RAF 48. Non-retractable tailwheel landing gear standard.
POWER PLANT: One 30 kW (40 hp) Volkswagen 1,500 cc modified motorcar engine. Other engines fitted by constructors include a 30 kW (40 hp) Aeronca E 113, 48.5 kW (65 hp) Teledyne Continental A65, 48.5 kW (65 hp) Textron Lycoming, and a 53.7 kW (72 hp) McCulloch. Aircraft with the 48.5 kW (65 hp) engines have a 10 cm (4 in) longer nose and 25 cm (10 in) longer rear fuselage to maintain the correct CG position. Fuel capacity 32 litres (8.4 US gallons; 7 Imp gallons).
DIMENSIONS, EXTERNAL:

Wing span	6.40 m (21 ft 0 in)
Length overall	4.57 m (15 ft 0 in)
Height over tail	1.47 m (4 ft 10 in)
Propeller diameter	1.14 m (3 ft 9 in)
AREA:	
Wings, gross	7.06 m² (76.0 sq ft)

WEIGHTS:	
Weight empty	195 kg (430 lb)
Baggage capacity	4.5 kg (10 lb)
Max T-O weight	299 kg (660 lb)
PERFORMANCE:	
Max level speed at S/L	100 knots (185 km/h; 115 mph)
Econ cruising speed	87 knots (161 km/h; 100 mph)
Stalling speed, power off:	
flaps up	35 knots (65 km/h; 40 mph)
flaps down	31 knots (57 km/h; 35 mph)
Max rate of climb at S/L	305 m (1,000 ft)/min
Service ceiling	4,115 m (13,500 ft)
T-O to 15 m (50 ft)	107 m (350 ft)
Landing from 15 m (50 ft)	229 m (750 ft)
Range	252 nm (466 km; 290 miles)
Endurance	3 h
g limits	±6

TAYLOR J.T.2 TITCH
The prototype Titch first flew on 4 January 1967. Plans are available and by early 1990 about 500 sets had been sold. Approximately 32 plans-built aircraft have flown. Wood kits are available in Canada and the USA.
TYPE: Single-seat homebuilt.
AIRFRAME: All-wood structure. Wings plywood and fabric covered. Fuselage and fixed tail surfaces plywood covered, except for aluminium cockpit side panels. Rudder and elevators fabric covered. Taylor modified NACA 23012 wing section. Non-retractable tailwheel landing gear.

POWER PLANT: One 63.5 kW (85 hp) Teledyne Continental C85. Plans-built Titches fitted with engines ranging from 33.6 kW (45 hp) Volkswagen 1,600 cc modified motorcar engine to 78.3 kW (105 hp) Textron Lycoming O-235. Fuel capacity 45.5 litres (12 US gallons; 10 Imp gallons). (1,834 cc VW engined version has 32 litre; 8.4 US gallon; 7 Imp gallon fuel tank.)
DIMENSIONS, EXTERNAL:

Wing span	5.72 m (18 ft 9 in)
Length overall	5.05 m (16 ft 7 in)
Height overall	1.42 m (4 ft 8 in)
Propeller diameter	1.52 m (5 ft 0 in)
AREA:	
Wings, gross	6.60 m² (71.0 sq ft)
WEIGHTS (Teledyne Continental C85 engine):	
Weight empty	229 kg (505 lb)
Baggage capacity	4.5 kg (10 lb)
Max T-O weight	345 kg (760 lb)
PERFORMANCE (engine as above):	
Max level speed	174 knots (322 km/h; 200 mph)
Max and Econ cruising speed	135 knots (250 km/h; 155 mph)
Stalling speed, power off:	
flaps up	51 knots (94 km/h; 58 mph)
flaps down	44 knots (81 km/h; 50 mph)
Service ceiling	5,485 m (18,000 ft)
Max rate of climb at S/L	488 m (1,600 ft)/min
T-O to 15 m (50 ft)	107 m (350 ft)
Landing from 15 m (50 ft)	274 m (900 ft)
Range	330 nm (611 km; 380 miles)
g limits	±6

UNITED STATES OF AMERICA

ACE

ACE AIRCRAFT COMPANY
05-134th Street, Chesapeake, West Virginia 25315
Telephone: 1 (304) 949 3098
OWNER: Denny Meadows

The Ace Aircraft Company offers plans, material kits and some pre-welded components for the Baby Ace Model D and Jr Ace Model E (see also Acro-Sport Corben Jr Ace).

BABY ACE MODEL D
The prototype of the redesigned Baby Ace Model D flew for the first time on 15 November 1956. About 350 have since been built by amateurs.
TYPE: Single-seat homebuilt.
AIRFRAME: Wing section Clark Y (modified). Wooden wings and ailerons, and welded steel tube fuselage and tail unit, all fabric covered. Non-retractable tailwheel landing gear. Optional floats.

POWER PLANT: One Teledyne Continental A65, A85, C65 or C85 engine of 48.5 or 63.5 kW (65 or 85 hp). Fuel capacity 63.6 litres (16.8 US gallons; 14 Imp gallons).
DIMENSIONS, EXTERNAL:

Wing span	8.05 m (26 ft 5 in)
Length overall	5.40 m (17 ft 8¾ in)
Height overall	2.02 m (6 ft 7¾ in)
AREA:	
Wings, gross	10.43 m² (112.3 sq ft)

Nipper Mk IIIb single-seat light aircraft *(Tim Griffith)*

Baby Ace Model D with optional wheel spats and headrest fairing

Acro Sport I owned by Mr Sylvester Heller of Avis, Pennsylvania

Taylor J.T.1 Monoplane owned by Mr A. C. Dove *(PFA)*

Mainair Cropstar agricultural microlight (see microlight tables)

WEIGHTS (landplane, unless stated otherwise):

Weight empty, equipped	261 kg (575 lb)
Baggage capacity	4.5 kg (10 lb)
Max T-O weight: 48.5 kW (65 hp)	431 kg (950 lb)
63.5 kW (85 hp) landplane or seaplane	
	522 kg (1,150 lb)

PERFORMANCE (48.5 kW; 65 hp landplane, at max T-O weight):

Max level speed at S/L	96 knots (177 km/h; 110 mph)
Max cruising speed	
	87-91 knots (161-169 km/h; 100-105 mph)
Stalling speed	30 knots (55 km/h; 34 mph)
Max rate of climb at S/L	365 m (1,200 ft)/min
Service ceiling	4,875 m (16,000 ft)
T-O and landing run	76 m (250 ft)
Range with max fuel	304 nm (560 km; 350 miles)

JUNIOR ACE MODEL E

The Junior Ace Model E differs from the Baby Ace Model D in being a side by side two-seater. It is powered usually by a 63.5 kW (85 hp) Teledyne Continental C85, and the details refer to a typical aircraft with this power plant that also has a cockpit 7.5 cm (3 in) wider and 10 cm (4 in) deeper than that of the standard Model E, a full electrical system and increased fuel capacity of 85 litres (22.5 US gallons; 18.75 Imp gallons).

DIMENSIONS, EXTERNAL:

Wing span	7.92 m (26 ft 0 in)
Length overall	5.50 m (18 ft 0 in)
Height overall	2.00 m (6 ft 7 in)

WEIGHTS:

Weight empty	367 kg (809 lb)
Max T-O weight	606 kg (1,335 lb)

PERFORMANCE:

Max level speed at S/L	113 knots (209 km/h; 130 mph)
Cruising speed	91 knots (169 km/h; 105 mph)
Landing speed	57 knots (105 km/h; 65 mph)
Service ceiling	3,050 m (10,000 ft)
T-O run	122 m (400 ft)
Landing run	183 m (600 ft)
Range with max fuel	304 nm (560 km; 350 miles)

ACRO SPORT

ACRO SPORT INC

PO Box 462, Hales Corners, Wisconsin 53130
Telephone: 1 (414) 529 2609
PRESIDENT: LaFonda Jean Kinnaman

The Acro Sport I, Super Acro Sport, Acro Sport II and Pober Pixie were all designed by Mr Paul H. Poberezny, President of the entirely separate Experimental Aircraft Association.

ACRO SPORT I

The Acro Sport I was designed specifically for construction by school students as a pupils' project. First flight of the prototype (N1AC) was made on 11 January 1972. Plans and construction manuals are available to homebuilders, and more than 1,300 sets had been sold by early 1990. More than sixty Acro Sport Is were then flying.

The following details apply to the prototype:
TYPE: Single-seat aerobatic homebuilt biplane.
AIRFRAME: Wooden wings and ailerons (on all four wings), fabric covered. Wing section Munk M-6. Glassfibre wingtips. Fuselage of welded steel tube, with wooden stringers, fabric covered. Glassfibre nose cowl and light alloy engine cowlings. Welded steel tube tail unit, with fabric covering. Non-retractable tailwheel landing gear, with main gear modified from Piper J-3 components.
POWER PLANT: Prototype has 134 kW (180 hp) Textron Lycoming engine. Basic power plant is a 74.5 kW (100 hp) Teledyne Continental O-200. Fuel capacity 104 litres (20 US gallons; 16.7 Imp gallons).

DIMENSIONS, EXTERNAL:

Wing span: upper	5.97 m (19 ft 7 in)
lower	5.82 m (19 ft 1 in)
Length overall	5.33 m (17 ft 6 in)
Height overall	1.83 m (6 ft 0 in)
Propeller diameter	1.93 m (6 ft 4 in)

AREA:

Wings, gross	10.73 m² (115.5 sq ft)

WEIGHTS:

Weight empty, equipped	335 kg (739 lb)
Baggage capacity	16 kg (35 lb)
Max T-O and landing weight	534 kg (1,178 lb)

PERFORMANCE (at max T-O weight):

Max level speed	132 knots (245 km/h; 152 mph)
Econ cruising speed	91 knots (169 km/h; 105 mph)
Stalling speed	44 knots (81 km/h; 50 mph)
Max rate of climb at S/L	518 m (1,700 ft)/min
T-O run	46 m (150 ft)
Landing run	244 m (800 ft)
Range with max fuel	304 nm (563 km; 350 miles)

SUPER ACRO SPORT

The Super Acro Sport prototype first flew on 21 March 1973. The aircraft is intended for unlimited International Class aerobatic competition at world championship level.

The differences by comparison with the standard Acro Sport I are covered in a supplement to the basic plans available from Acro Sport Inc. The description of the Acro Sport I applies also to the Super Acro Sport, except as follows:
TYPE: Single-seat homebuilt aerobatic biplane.

AIRFRAME: As for Acro Sport I, except wing section NACA 23012.

POWER PLANT: Prototype has 149 kW (200 hp) Textron Lycoming IO-360-A2A.

DIMENSIONS, EXTERNAL: As for Acro Sport I, except:

Length overall	5.30 m (17 ft 4½ in)

WEIGHTS:

Weight empty	401 kg (884 lb)
Max T-O weight	612 kg (1,350 lb)

PERFORMANCE (at max T-O weight):

Max level speed at S/L	135 knots (251 km/h; 156 mph)
Max cruising speed	117 knots (217 km/h; 135 mph)
Stalling speed	44 knots (81 km/h; 50 mph)
Max rate of climb at S/L	549 m (1,800 ft)/min
Service ceiling	4,575 m (15,000 ft)
T-O run	38 m (125 ft)
Landing run	244 m (800 ft)
Range with max fuel	260 nm (482 km; 300 miles)

ACRO SPORT II

The Acro Sport II is a two-seat aerobatic biplane derived from the Acro Sport I, for the pilot with only a low number of flying hours to his credit. The first flight was achieved on 9 July 1978. Plans are available to homebuilders and more than 2,000 sets had been sold by early 1990. More than 40 Acro Sport IIs are flying.

TYPE: Tandem two-seat homebuilt aerobatic biplane.

AIRFRAME: As for Acro Sport I.

POWER PLANT: Prototype has 134 kW (180 hp) Textron Lycoming O-360-A4B. Can be powered by engines of 74.5-149 kW (100-200 hp). Fuel capacity 98.4 litres (26 US gallons; 21.6 Imp gallons).

DIMENSIONS, EXTERNAL:

Wing span: upper	6.60 m (21 ft 8 in)
lower	6.32 m (20 ft 9 in)
Length overall	5.75 m (18 ft 10¼ in)
Height overall	2.03 m (6 ft 7¾ in)

AREA:

Wings, gross	14.12 m² (152.0 sq ft)

WEIGHTS:

Weight empty	397 kg (875 lb)
Baggage capacity	13.6 kg (30 lb)
Max T-O weight	689 kg (1,520 lb)

PERFORMANCE (prototype):

Max cruising speed	107 knots (198 km/h; 123 mph)
Stalling speed	46 knots (86 km/h; 53 mph)
Max rate of climb at S/L	457 m (1,500 ft)/min
T-O run	91 m (300 ft)
g limits	+6.5/-4.5

POBER P-9 PIXIE

The prototype Pixie made its first flight in July 1974, with a Volkswagen engine. Some Pixies currently flying use the 48.5 kW (65 hp) Teledyne Continental engine.

Plans are available to amateur constructors, and more than 1,100 sets had been sold by early 1990.

TYPE: Single-seat sporting homebuilt.

AIRFRAME: Wooden wing structure, plywood and fabric covered. Clark Y wing section. Welded fuselage of 4130 chrome molybdenum steel tubing with wood formers and fabric covering. Tail unit of welded 4130 chrome molybdenum steel tubing, fabric covered. Non-retractable tailwheel landing gear standard.

POWER PLANT: One 44.5 kW (60 hp) Limbach SL 1700 EA. Equally suited to other Volkswagen and 48.5 kW (65 hp) engines. Fuel capacity 46.6 litres (12.3 US gallons; 10.2 Imp gallons).

DIMENSIONS, EXTERNAL:

Wing span	9.09 m (29 ft 10 in)
Length overall	5.26 m (17 ft 3 in)
Height overall	1.88 m (6 ft 2 in)
Propeller diameter	1.35 m (4 ft 5 in)

AREA:

Wings, gross	12.47 m² (134.25 sq ft)

WEIGHTS:

Weight empty	246 kg (543 lb)
Baggage capacity	9 kg (20 lb)
Max T-O weight	408 kg (900 lb)

PERFORMANCE (at max T-O weight):

Max level speed at S/L	89 knots (166 km/h; 103 mph)
Max cruising speed	72 knots (134 km/h; 83 mph)
Stalling speed	26 knots (49 km/h; 30 mph)
Max rate of climb at S/L	213 m (700 ft)/min
Service ceiling	3,810 m (12,500 ft)
T-O and landing run	91 m (300 ft)
Range with max fuel	251 nm (466 km; 290 miles)

COUGAR MODEL 1

This aircraft was designed by Mr Robert E. Nesmith, to encourage aviation among teenage boys. More than 100 Cougars have been built from plans.

TYPE: Side by side two-seat homebuilt.

AIRFRAME: All-wood wings, using modified NACA 4900-series section. Ailerons of 4130 steel tubing with aluminium trailing-edges. Welded steel tube fuselage and tail unit, with fabric covering. Glassfibre nose cowling and light alloy engine cowlings. Non-retractable tailwheel landing gear.

POWER PLANT: Suitable engines range from 48.5 to 93.2 kW (65-125 hp), including the Teledyne Continental C65, C85 and O-200; and Textron Lycoming O-235 and O-290. Fuel capacity 11.4 kg (25 lb).

DIMENSIONS, EXTERNAL:

Wing span	6.25 m (20 ft 6 in)
Length overall	5.77 m (18 ft 11 in)
Height overall	1.68 m (5 ft 6 in)
Propeller diameter	1.63 m (5 ft 4 in)

AREA:

Wings, gross	7.62 m² (82.0 sq ft)

WEIGHTS:

Weight empty: standard	283 kg (624 lb)
with folding wings	312 kg (689 lb)
Max T-O weight	567 kg (1,250 lb)

PERFORMANCE (at max T-O weight):

Max level speed	152 knots (281 km/h; 175 mph)
Econ cruising speed	104 knots (193 km/h; 120 mph)
Stalling speed	46 knots (86 km/h; 53 mph)
Max rate of climb at S/L	396 m (1,300 ft)/min
T-O run	152 m (500 ft)
Landing run	183 m (600 ft)
Range with max fuel	521 nm (965 km; 600 miles)

POBER Jr ACE

The original Corben Jr Ace was designed by Mr O. G. Corben in the 1920s. The following details apply to the plans marketed by Acro Sport of an extensively modified and larger development (see also Ace Aircraft Company):

TYPE: Side by side two-seat homebuilt.

AIRFRAME: Wooden wings and ailerons, fabric covered. Wing section Clark Y. Fuselage structure of welded steel tube and wooden stringers, fabric covered. Light alloy engine cowling. Fabric covered steel tube tail unit. Non-retractable tailwheel landing gear.

POWER PLANT: One 33.6 kW (45 hp) Szekely, Aeromarine AR-350, Teledyne Continental C65 or similar engine. Fuel capacity 38 litres (10 US gallons; 8.3 Imp gallons).

DIMENSIONS, EXTERNAL:

Wing span	10.35 m (33 ft 11½ in)
Length overall	5.73 m (18 ft 9½ in)
Height overall	2.29 m (7 ft 6 in)
Propeller diameter	1.93 m (6 ft 4 in)

AREA:

Wings, gross	15.61 m² (168.0 sq ft)

WEIGHTS:

Weight empty	255 kg (563 lb)
Max T-O weight	442 kg (975 lb)

PERFORMANCE (at max T-O weight):

Max level speed at S/L	74 knots (137 km/h; 85 mph)
Econ cruising speed	61 knots (113 km/h; 70 mph)
Stalling speed	31 knots (57 km/h; 35 mph)
Max rate of climb at S/L	152 m (500 ft)/min
Service ceiling	over 3,960 m (13,000 ft)
T-O and landing run	46 m (150 ft)
Range with max fuel	173 nm (322 km; 200 miles)

POBER SUPER ACE

This single-seat homebuilt parasol-wing monoplane is a significantly modernised derivative of an aircraft designed by Mr O. G. Corben in the 1920s. It is powered by a 48.5 kW (65 hp) Teledyne Continental C65 engine. Weights and performance were not available in January 1990, as the aircraft had still to fly.

AIRFRAME: Strut braced wooden wing and ailerons, fabric covered. Fuselage of steel tubing with wooden stringers, with an aluminium engine cowling and glassfibre nose bowl. Non-retractable tailwheel landing gear.

DIMENSIONS, EXTERNAL:

Wing span	9.82 m (32 ft 2¾ in)
Length overall	5.61 m (18 ft 5 in)

ADVANCED AVIATION
ADVANCED AVIATION INC

323 North Ivey Lane, PO Box 16716, Orlando, Florida 32811

Telephone: 1 (407) 298 2920

MARKETING MANAGER: Angel Matos

The Advanced Aviation range of aircraft includes the Sierra sailplane (see Sailplanes section).

ADVANCED AVIATION COBRA

The current standard model is the **B377 Cobra B**, which qualifies mainly under microlight regulations. The basically similar but more powerful **B447 Cobra VIP** is in the Experimental category, as is the **B532 AG Cobra** that is equipped for cropspraying. Many hundreds of Cobra kits have been sold. See Microlight tables.

ADVANCED AVIATION B532 KING COBRA B

This two-seat Experimental version of the Cobra is powered normally by a 48.5 kW (65 hp) Rotax 532, with optional engines of 32 kW (43 hp), 34.3 kW (46 hp) and 37.3 kW (50 hp). Fuel capacity is approximately 19 litres (5 US gallons; 4.2 Imp gallons). It flew for the first time in 1983 and is similar in construction to the single-seat Cobras.

DIMENSION, EXTERNAL:

Wing span	10.74 m (35 ft 3 in)

AREA:

Wings, gross	15.05 m² (162.0 sq ft)

WEIGHTS:

Weight empty	147 kg (325 lb)
Crew weight range	50-190 kg (110-420 lb)
Max T-O weight	351 kg (775 lb)

PERFORMANCE (Cuyuna RR 430 cc engine):

Max level speed	55 knots (101 km/h; 63 mph)
Econ cruising speed	43 knots (80 km/h; 50 mph)
Stalling speed	27 knots (50 km/h; 31 mph)
Max rate of climb at S/L	137 m (450 ft)/min
Service ceiling	3,660 m (12,000 ft)
T-O run	76-107 m (250-350 ft)
Landing run	76 m (250 ft)
Range	65 nm (120 km; 75 miles)
Endurance	1 h 30 min

ADVANCED AVIATION COBRA CARRERA

This is a single-seat land based-only derivative of the Buccaneer, with a non-retractable tricycle or tailwheel landing gear and elongated nose; with tricycle gear it is known as the **Carrera 150**. It is offered with four engine options, the models with a 20 kW (27 hp) Rotax 277, a 26 kW (35 hp) Rotax 377 and 30 kW (40 hp) Rotax 447 meeting FAR Pt 103-7 microlight requirements or coming under Experimental regulations, and the 34 kW (45.6 hp) Rotax 503 model being classified as an Experimental category type only. All have a fuel capacity of 19 litres (5 US gallons; 4.2 Imp gallons). Construction time is 50 h.

The following details refer to the Rotax 377-engined model:

DIMENSIONS, EXTERNAL:

Wing span	8.43 m (27 ft 8 in)
Length overall	6.22 m (20 ft 5 in)
Height overall	1.68 m (5 ft 6 in)
Propeller diameter	1.52 m (5 ft 0 in)

AREA:

Wings, gross	12.45 m² (134.0 sq ft)

WEIGHTS (Rotax 377 or 447 engine):

Weight empty	120 kg (265 lb)
Max pilot weight	113 kg (250 lb)
Max T-O weight	249 kg (550 lb)

PERFORMANCE (Rotax 377 and 77 kg; 170 lb pilot):

Max level speed	55 knots (101 km/h; 63 mph)
Cruising speed	48 knots (89 km/h; 55 mph)
Stalling speed	22 knots (41 km/h; 25 mph)
Max rate of climb at S/L	305 m (1,000 ft)/min
Service ceiling	4,265 m (14,000 ft)
T-O and landing run	46 m (150 ft)
g limits	+6/-3

ADVANCED AVIATION CARRERA 180

Deliveries were expected to begin in late 1989 of this two-seat version of the Cobra Carrera. The prototype first flew in February 1989.

ADVANCED AVIATION XA/650 BUCCANEER II

This side by side two-seat Experimental category derivative of the Buccaneer amphibian flew for the first time on 14 March 1986. The landing gear is retracted via a cockpit lever. Power plant is a 48.5 kW (65 hp) Rotax 532. Fuel capacity is 45 litres (12 US gallons; 10 Imp gallons). Kits are available.

DIMENSIONS, EXTERNAL:

Wing span	10.88 m (35 ft 8½ in)
Length overall	6.81 m (22 ft 4 in)
Height overall	2.06 m (6 ft 9 in)
Propeller diameter	1.73 m (5 ft 8 in)

AREA:

Wings, gross	15.89 m² (171.0 sq ft)

WEIGHTS:

Weight empty	249 kg (550 lb)
Max crew weight	190 kg (420 lb)
Max T-O weight	465 kg (1,025 lb)

PERFORMANCE (preliminary, crew weight 154 kg; 340 lb):

Max level speed at S/L	65 knots (120 km/h; 75 mph)
Econ cruising speed at S/L	50 knots (92 km/h; 57 mph)
Stalling speed: power off	29 knots (53 km/h; 33 mph)
Max rate of climb at S/L	183 m (600 ft)/min
T-O run: on land	77 m (250 ft)
on water	153 m (500 ft)

Acro Sport Pober P-9 Pixie owned by Mr Mario Chabot of Drummondville, Quebec

Advanced Aviation Cobra Carrera single-seat landplane (*Howard Levy*)

Pober Super Ace under construction

Cougar Model 1 owned by Mr Charles Warren Cronce of Florida

Two-seat Advanced Aviation King Cobra (*Brian M. Service*)

Aerocar Sooper-Coot Model A amphibian (*Peter M. Bowers*)

Buccaneer II two-seat homebuilt amphibian, marketed by Advanced Aviation (*Howard Levy*)

AEROCAR
AEROCAR INC

PO Box 1171, Longview, Washington 98632
Telephone: 1 (206) 423 8260
PRESIDENT AND GENERAL MANAGER: Moulton B. Taylor

In February 1948 Aerocar Inc began developing a flying automobile designed by Mr M. B. Taylor. The prototype Aerocar, with a Textron Lycoming O-290 engine, was completed in October 1949. Design and theoretical work continue on the concept, now in its CRX fourth generation form. Aerocar anticipates developing a kit-built version in the near future if financing can be found. Having a span of 10.36 m (34 ft), the CRX is expected to cruise at 150 knots (278 km/h; 173 mph) on the power of its 313 kW (420 hp) Allison turbine engine.

Fully active Aerocar programmes are detailed in this entry; separate entries for Brown and Holcomb cover other aircraft originated by Mr Taylor.

AEROCAR SOOPER-COOT MODEL A

The prototype Sooper-Coot flew for the first time in February 1971. Its 'float-wing' configuration permits rough-water operation and, since the close proximity of the wings to the water forms a 'pressure wedge', unusually low take-off and landing speeds are possible without recourse to flaps or other lift enhancing devices.

The structure is basically of wood, but the tailboom and tail unit can be of steel tube and fabric, wood monocoque or all-metal construction. Wing section is NACA 4415. The fabric covered ailerons are of metal construction. A manually retractable tricycle landing gear is standard, but an alternative powered retraction system is shown on the plans.

Recommended power plant for the Sooper-Coot is a Franklin of either 134 or 164 kW (180 or 220 hp). However, other engines of 112-168 kW (150-225 hp) can be fitted. Many builders are using a 157 kW (210 hp) Teledyne Continental IO-360. To minimise expenditure, others are fitting Textron Lycoming O-320 and O-320-B engines of 119 kW (160 hp). Fuel capacity is 170 litres (45 US gallons; 37.5 Imp gallons).

Certain component parts (including the glassfibre engine cowls, glassfibre hull shell, foredeck, instrument panel, tail fairings, engine cooling fan blades and spring steel main landing gear legs), and plans, are available to amateur constructors. Many hundreds of Sooper-Coots are under construction, and more than 130 are known to be flying.

DIMENSIONS, EXTERNAL:

Wing span	10.97 m (36 ft 0 in)
Length overall	6.10 to 6.71 m (20 ft 0 in to 22 ft 0 in)
Height overall	2.44 m (8 ft 0 in)

AREA:

Wings, gross	16.72 m² (180.0 sq ft)

WEIGHTS:

Weight empty	658 kg (1,450 lb)
Max T-O weight	975 kg (2,150 lb)

PERFORMANCE (134 kW; 180 hp engine, at max T-O weight):

Max cruising speed	113 knots (209 km/h; 130 mph)
Econ cruising speed at 50% power	95 knots (177 km/h; 110 mph)
Max rate of climb at S/L	381 m (1,250 ft)/min
T-O run (land)	61 m (200 ft)

AEROCAR MINI-IMP

The Mini-Imp is a single-seat version of the Aerocar Imp, to which it is generally similar (see 'Brown' entry). Features include an inverted V tail, tail pusher propeller, new NASA wing section with spoilers/flaps, and a retractable tricycle landing gear. The basic structure is all metal. Plans are available, together with parts kits. More than 250 amateur-built Mini-Imps are being constructed, and several are flying. Average time taken for construction is about 1,000 working hours.

The description of the Imp applies also to the Mini-Imp, except as follows:

TYPE: Single-seat sporting homebuilt.

POWER PLANT: Recommended engine is a 47 kW (63 hp) Rotax 532. Alternative engines in the 44.5-74.5 kW (60-100 hp) range may be installed. Fuel capacity 45.4 litres (12 US gallons; 10 Imp gallons), plus tip tanks, each of 34 litres (9 US gallons; 7.5 Imp gallons) capacity.

DIMENSIONS, EXTERNAL:

Wing span	7.62 m (25 ft 0 in)
Length overall	4.88 m (16 ft 0 in)
Height over fuselage	1.22 m (4 ft 0 in)
Propeller diameter	1.45 m (4 ft 9 in)

WEIGHTS:

Weight empty	227 kg (500 lb)
Baggage capacity	23 kg (50 lb)
Max T-O weight	385 kg (850 lb)

PERFORMANCE (51 kW; 68 hp Limbach 1,900 cc engine, except where indicated):

Max cruising speed at S/L	more than 130 knots (241 km/h; 150 mph)
Max cruising speed (Revmaster engine, estimated)	over 173 knots (322 km/h; 200 mph)
Stalling speed	44 knots (81 km/h; 50 mph)
Max rate of climb at S/L	305 m (1,000 ft)/min
T-O run	183 m (600 ft)
Range	over 434 nm (804 km; 500 miles)
g limits	±9

AEROCAR MICRO-IMP

The single-seat Micro-Imp is of similar configuration to the Mini-Imp, but is constructed primarily of glassfibre reinforced paper known as TPG (Taylor Paper Glass). The prototype made its first flight in the Summer of 1981. Drawings to allow amateur constructors to build the

Micro-Imp are almost complete, but the programme has been delayed pending the availability of a suitable engine. A description appeared in the 1989-90 *Jane's*.

TAYLOR BULLET 2100

Following the success of the TPG method of construction for the Micro-Imp, Aerocar designed a two-seat counterpart also utilising TPG. It is known as the Taylor Bullet 2100, because of its similarity in configuration to the Gallaudet Bullet of 1912. The prototype was completed in February 1985.

Plans to allow amateur construction of the Bullet 2100 are not yet available, but are expected to be offered eventually, together with some difficult to fabricate component parts. A description appeared in the 1989-90 *Jane's*.

AERO COMPOSITE

AERO COMPOSITE TECHNOLOGY INC

Rt 3, Box 107B, Somerset, Pennsylvania 15501

Telephone: 1 (814) 445 8608

OWNERS: William D. Forrest and Tom Wright

AERO COMPOSITE SEA HAWKER

Under the original owners, Aero Gare, design of the Sea Hawker began in 1981 and a prototype flew for the first time in July 1982. Aero Composite Technology Inc purchased the Sea Hawker from Aero Composites Inc in July 1987. Kits are marketed, comprising 22 pre-moulded components and all raw materials, with cadmium plating on all welded or machined parts. Average construction time from kits is between 1,400 and 1,600 working hours. Plans are also available. Several hundred Sea Hawkers are flying or under construction.

The Sea Hawker's amphibious rough-field landing gear permits landings on water, asphalt, grass, snow, mud, and rough fields. The glassfibre covered rubbing strips on the hull allow a safe gear-up emergency landing on hard surfaces.

TYPE: Side by side two-seat homebuilt amphibious biplane.

AIRFRAME: NASA wing section. Composite wings of glassfibre and carbonfibre. Full-span slotted ailerons on lower wings deflect with slotted flaps on upper wings for take-off and landing. Single-step hull of Kevlar, glassfibre and carbonfibre, with integral fin. Retractable tricycle landing gear. Water rudder under fin.

POWER PLANT: One 112 kW (150 hp) Textron Lycoming O-320 recommended. Two fuel tanks, each with 132.5 litre (35 US gallon; 29 Imp gallon) capacity.

DIMENSIONS, EXTERNAL:

Wing span	7.32 m (24 ft 0 in)
Length overall	6.55 m (21 ft 6 in)
Height overall	2.29 m (7 ft 6 in)
Propeller diameter	1.63 m (5 ft 4 in)

AREA:

Wings, gross	10.96 m² (118.0 sq ft)

WEIGHTS (112 kW; 150 hp engine):

Weight empty	386 kg (850 lb)
Max T-O weight	726 kg (1,600 lb)

PERFORMANCE (112 kW; 150 hp engine):

Max level and cruising speed at S/L	129 knots (238 km/h; 148 mph)
Econ cruising speed	120 knots (222 km/h; 138 mph)
Stalling speed, flaps down	37 knots (68 km/h; 42 mph)
Max rate of climb at S/L	335 m (1,100 ft)/min
Service ceiling	5,475 m (18,000 ft)
T-O run: from land	153 m (500 ft)
from water	305 m (1,000 ft)
Landing run: on land	213 m (700 ft)
on water	183 m (600 ft)
Range with max fuel, 45 min reserves	1,042 nm (1,931 km; 1,200 miles)
g limits	+5/-3

AERO DESIGNS

AERO DESIGNS INC

635 Blakeley, San Antonio, Texas 78209

Telephone: 1 (512) 650 3398

PRESIDENT: Mark Brown

MANAGER: Phil Durieux

AERO DESIGNS PULSAR

Aero Designs is marketing the Pulsar in kit form, including engine. It is basically a side by side two-seat version of the Star-Lite, designed also by Mr Mark Brown. The prototype first flew on 3 April 1988. Construction takes about 1,000 working hours. By February 1990, 75 kits had been ordered, of which 62 had been delivered and three had flown.

AIRFRAME: Construction similar to Star-Lite (see Star-Lite Aircraft Inc in 1989-90 *Jane's*). Wing section MSI-0313. Non-retractable tricycle landing gear.

POWER PLANT: One 47.7 kW (64 hp) Rotax 532. Fuel capacity 60 litres (16 US gallons; 13.3 Imp gallons).

DIMENSIONS, EXTERNAL:

Wing span	7.62 m (25 ft 0 in)
Length overall	5.79 m (19 ft 0 in)
Height overall	1.68 m (5 ft 6 in)
Propeller diameter	1.37 m (4 ft 6 in)

AREA:

Wings, gross	7.43 m² (80.0 sq ft)

WEIGHTS:

Weight empty	195 kg (430 lb)
Baggage capacity	18 kg (40 lb)
Max T-O weight	408 kg (900 lb)

PERFORMANCE:

Max level speed	122 knots (225 km/h; 140 mph)
Econ cruising speed at 1,525 m (5,000 ft)	87 knots (161 km/h; 100 mph)
Stalling speed, engine idling:	
flaps up	39 knots (71 km/h; 44 mph)
flaps down	37 knots (68 km/h; 42 mph)
Max rate of climb at S/L	244 m (800 ft)/min
Service ceiling	4,570 m (15,000 ft)
T-O and landing run	244 m (800 ft)
Range	347 nm (644 km; 400 miles)
g limits	+4/-2

AERO DYNAMICS

AERO DYNAMICS LTD

19131 59th Drive North-East, Arlington Airport, Arlington, Washington 98223

Telephone: 1 (206) 435 8558

AERO DYNAMICS SPARROW HAWK Mk II

Four separate kits are available to construct the Sparrow Hawk Mk II.

TYPE: Side by side two-seat homebuilt.

AIRFRAME: All-metal wings, ailerons and tailplane. All-composites fuselage and rudders of Kevlar/foam sandwich construction. Twin tailbooms of Kevlar, with carbonfibre reinforcement. Non-retractable tricycle landing gear.

POWER PLANT: One 47 kW (63 hp) Rotax 532. Optional two- or four-stroke engine of between 44.7 and 74.5 kW (60-100 hp). Fuel capacity 53 litres (14 US gallons; 11.7 Imp gallons) standard; optionally 60 litres (16 US gallons; 13.3 Imp gallons).

DIMENSIONS, EXTERNAL:

Wing span	10.49 m (34 ft 5 in)
Length overall	5.44 m (17 ft 10 in)
Height overall	2.11 m (6 ft 11 in)

AREA:

Wings, gross	13.29 m² (143.0 sq ft)

WEIGHTS:

Weight empty	318 kg (700 lb)
Max T-O weight	635 kg (1,400 lb)

PERFORMANCE:

*Max level speed	91-113 knots (169-209 km/h; 105-130 mph)
*Cruising speed	82-104 knots (153-193 km/h; 95-120 mph)
Stalling speed	32 knots (58 km/h; 36 mph)
Max rate of climb at S/L: dual	229 m (750 ft)/min
solo	335 m (1,100 ft)/min
Service ceiling	6,100 m (20,000 ft)
T-O run	76 m (250 ft)
Landing run	91 m (300 ft)
*Range	312-608 nm (579-1,125 km; 360-700 miles)
g limits	+6/-4

*Depending on power plant options

AERO FLIGHT

AERO FLIGHT

The Miller Air Sports Inc Texas Gem 260 is now thought to be handled by Aero Flight. Kit production may be temporarily on hold.

AEROLITES

AEROLITES INC

Route 1, Box 187, Welsh, Louisiana 70591

Telephone: 1 (318) 734 3865

Telex: 6503079915 (via WUI)

PRESIDENT: Daniel J. Roché

In October 1986 the manufacturing rights to the Bearcat homebuilt aircraft were purchased from Litecraft by AeroLites Inc. A side by side two-seat version is currently under development.

AEROLITES BEARCAT

First flown in 1984, the Bearcat bears a close external resemblance to the Piper Cub. Kits are available. Estimated building time is 100-120 working hours.

TYPE: Single-seat homebuilt or microlight; conforms to Canadian and European microlight regulations.

AIRFRAME: Strut braced parasol-wing monoplane. Wing section Clark Y. Wings and fuselage constructed of aluminium alloy and 4130 chrome-molybdenum steel tubing respectively, and covered with Dacron (double surface on wings), polyester and glassfibre. Non-retractable tailwheel landing gear. Options include full cockpit enclosure, ballistic parachute, Spray Miser Ag

system (with Rotax 532 engine only), hydraulic disc brakes, electric starter and high flotation tyres.

POWER PLANT: One 31.3 kW (42 hp) Rotax 447; 47.7 kW (64 hp) Rotax 532 available optionally. Fuel capacity 19 litres (5 US gallons; 4.2 Imp gallons).

DIMENSIONS, EXTERNAL:

Wing span	9.36 m (30 ft 8½ in)
Length overall	5.64 m (18 ft 6 in)
Height overall	1.96 m (6 ft 5 in)
Propeller diameter	1.73 m (5 ft 8 in)

AREA:

Wings, gross	14.86 m² (160.0 sq ft)

WEIGHTS:

Weight empty	136 kg (300 lb)

Aero Dynamics Sparrow Hawk Mk II two-seat light aircraft

Model of the proposed Aerocar CRX flying automobile

Canadian built Aero Composite Sea Hawker amphibian *(Peter M. Bowers)*

Aerocar Mini-Imp single-seat sporting monoplane

Aero Designs Pulsar two-seat homebuilt

AeroLites Ag Bearcat homebuilt agricultural aircraft

Aero Mirage TC-2 all-composites lightplane

Pilot weight range	45.5-136 kg (100-300 lb)
Baggage capacity	13.6 kg (30 lb)
Max T-O weight	340 kg (750 lb)

PERFORMANCE (at max T-O weight):

Max level speed at 305 m (1,000 ft)	
	61 knots (113 km/h; 70 mph)
Econ cruising speed at 305 m (1,000 ft)	
	48 knots (89 km/h; 55 mph)
Stalling speed: power on	23 knots (42 km/h; 26 mph)
power off	24 knots (44 km/h; 27 mph)
Max rate of climb at S/L	213 m (700 ft)/min
Service ceiling	3,050 m (10,000 ft)
T-O run	31 m (100 ft)
Landing from 15 m (50 ft)	137 m (450 ft)
Landing run	46 m (150 ft)
Range with max standard fuel	
	104 nm (193 km; 120 miles)
Endurance	2 h 10 min
g limits	+6/-4

AEROLITES AG BEARCAT

The Ag Bearcat was created jointly by AeroLites and Louisiana AgriLites. Only slight modification was required to the airframe to accept the Spray Miser Ag system. The standard engine is a 47 kW (63 hp) Rotax 532; fuel capacity is 38 litres (10 US gallons; 8.3 Imp gallons). Alternative Sadler radial engines of 33.6-48.5 kW (45-65 hp). Full span trailing-edge ailerons help to improve pilot control. Standard equipment includes a 12V high volume electric pump capable of flow rates of over 30.3 litres (8 US gallons; 6.7 Imp gallons)/min at 1.38 bars (20 lb/sq in), a 91 litre (24 US gallon; 20 Imp gallon) glassfibre underbelly chemical tank with emergency dump, and welded aluminium 'wet' booms, offering a swath width of 9-30 m (30-100 ft). Options include a ballistic parachute, high flotation tyres and Mylar coated fabric.

DIMENSIONS, EXTERNAL:

Wing span	9.25 m (30 ft 4 in)
Length overall	5.64 m (18 ft 6 in)

Height overall	1.96 m (6 ft 5 in)
Propeller diameter	1.73 m (5 ft 8 in)

AREA:

Wings, gross	14.77 m² (159.0 sq ft)

WEIGHTS:

Weight empty	172 kg (380 lb)
Max T-O weight	408 kg (900 lb)

PERFORMANCE (ISA, S/L with 88 kg; 195 lb pilot, except where indicated):

Max level speed	78 knots (145 km/h; 90 mph)
Cruising and spraying speed	
	56 knots (105 km/h; 65 mph)
Stalling speed, power on	31 knots (57 km/h; 35 mph)
Max rate of climb at S/L	259 m (850 ft)/min
Service ceiling	6,400 m (21,000 ft)
T-O run at max T-O weight	168 m (550 ft)
Landing run	46 m (150 ft)
Range with max fuel	152 nm (282 km; 175 miles)
Endurance with max fuel	2 h 30 min
g limits	+4.5/-2.5

AERO MIRAGE

AERO MIRAGE INC

3009 North-East 20th Way, Gainesville, Florida 32609
Telephone: 1 (904) 377 4146

AERO MIRAGE TC-2

The prototype of this high performance commuter homebuilt first flew on 16 May 1983 and the TC-2 is available in kit form to amateur builders.

The following details refer to the prototype, unless stated otherwise:

TYPE: Side by side two-seat homebuilt.

AIRFRAME: Wing and tailplane spars of glassfibre reinforced plastics with foam core webs. Remainder of airframe constructed of Kevlar, Klégécel, S glass and vinylester resin. Wing section NACA 64415. Retractable tricycle landing gear.

POWER PLANT: One 74.5 kW (100 hp) Teledyne Continental O-200-A. Other engines recommended as suitable up to

74.5 kW (100 hp), though both a Textron Lycoming O-235 and O-290 are being fitted to Mirages. Standard fuel capacity 95 litres (25 US gallons; 20.8 Imp gallons); capacity with auxiliary tanks 144 litres (38 US gallons; 31.6 Imp gallons).

DIMENSIONS, EXTERNAL:

Wing span	6.40 m (21 ft 0 in)
Length overall	5.05 m (16 ft 7 in)

Height overall	1.78 m (5 ft 10 in)
Propeller diameter	1.57 m (5 ft 2 in)

AREA:

Wings, gross	5.95 m² (64.0 sq ft)

WEIGHTS (with 48.5 kW; 65 hp engine):

Weight empty	238 kg (525 lb)
Baggage capacity	18 kg (40 lb)
Max T-O weight	431 kg (950 lb)

PERFORMANCE (engine as above, unless stated otherwise):

Max level speed at S/L	157 knots (291 km/h; 181 mph)
Cruising speed, 75% power, at S/L	
	142 knots (264 km/h; 164 mph)
Stalling speed, prototype:	
flaps up	55 knots (102 km/h; 63 mph)
flaps down	50 knots (92 km/h; 57 mph)
Landing run	137 m (450 ft)

AEROSPORT
AEROSPORT LTD
Box 278, Holly Springs, North Carolina 27540
Telephone: 1 (919) 552 6375
PRESIDENT: E. B. Trent

AEROSPORT SCAMP A
The prototype Scamp flew for the first time on 21 August 1973. The Scamp A can be used for limited aerobatics; and emphasis has been placed on simple construction techniques to make it an easy project for the homebuilder.

Plans and parts are available to amateur constructors. A total of well over 900 sets of plans had been sold by 1990. More than 40 have flown, and some examples of an agricultural version, known as Scamp B, were assembled in South America (see under Colombia in main Aircraft section of the 1984-85 *Jane's*).

TYPE: Single-seat homebuilt biplane.

AIRFRAME: All-metal construction, with light alloy semi-monocoque fuselage. Wing section NACA 23012. Non-retractable tricycle landing gear.

POWER PLANT: Prototype has 44.5 kW (60 hp) 1,834 cc Volkswagen modified motorcar engine. Design suitable for Volkswagen engines of up to 2,100 cc, though Aerosport recommends 1,834 cc as optimum. Fuel capacity 30.5 litres (8 US gallons; 6.66 Imp gallons).

DIMENSIONS, EXTERNAL:

Wing span	5.33 m (17 ft 6 in)
Length overall	4.27 m (14 ft 0 in)
Height overall	1.69 m (5 ft 6½ in)
Propeller diameter	1.42 m (4 ft 8 in)

AREA:

Wings, gross	9.75 m² (105.0 sq ft)

WEIGHTS:

Weight empty	236-249 kg (520-550 lb)
Max T-O weight	348-362 kg (768-798 lb)

PERFORMANCE (1,834 cc engine):

Max level speed	91 knots (169 km/h; 105 mph)
Cruising speed	78 knots (145 km/h; 90 mph)
Stalling speed	39 knots (73 km/h; 45 mph)
Service ceiling (estimated)	3,660 m (12,000 ft)
T-O and landing run	122 m (400 ft)
Range at cruising speed	108 nm (201 km; 125 miles)
g limits	+6/-3

AERO VISIONS
AERO VISIONS INTERNATIONAL
Route 2, Box 282, South Webster, Ohio 45682
Telephone: 1 (614) 778 3185
Fax: 1 (614) 778 3185
PRESIDENT: Michael E. Fisher

Aero Visions markets the Culex and Culite, which were formerly products of the related but now ended Fisher Flying Products company, plus the new Celebrity biplane.

AERO VISIONS CULITE
The Culite is a development of the Culex, designed to use high power-to-weight ratio Rotax engines and a lighter airframe, with fabric covered wooden geodetic fuselage. Unlike the Culex, the Culite is available only with a non-retractable tricycle landing gear.

POWER PLANT: Two 35.8 kW (48 hp) Rotax 503s. Fuel capacity 60.5 litres (16 US gallons; 13.3 Imp gallons). Optional tankage of 121 litres (32 US gallons; 26.6 Imp gallons).

DIMENSIONS, EXTERNAL: As for Culex, except:

Wing span	8.53 m (28 ft 0 in)

AREA:

Wings, gross	13.00 m² (140.0 sq ft)

WEIGHTS:

Weight empty	249 kg (550 lb)
Max T-O weight	522 kg (1,150 lb)

PERFORMANCE (estimated):

Cruising speed (75% power)	
	104 knots (193 km/h; 120 mph)
Stalling speed: flaps up	37 knots (68 km/h; 42 mph)
flaps down	30 knots (55 km/h; 34 mph)
Max rate of climb at S/L	366 m (1,200 ft)/min
T-O run	76 m (250 ft)
Landing run	107 m (350 ft)

AERO VISIONS CULEX
The Culex is powered by two 59.6 kW (80 hp) Limbach L2000 engines, and has a fuel capacity of 174 litres (46 US gallons; 38.3 Imp gallons). Airframe is an all-wood semi-monocoque structure, plywood skinned. A choice of landing gears is offered: non-retractable tailwheel or tricycle, or retractable tailwheel type.

The Culex is offered in plans form, as partial or complete airframe kits, or in a number of separate prefabricated subassembly kits.

TYPE: Tandem two-seat homebuilt.

DIMENSIONS, EXTERNAL:

Wing span	9.40 m (30 ft 0 in)
Length overall	6.20 m (20 ft 4 in)
Height overall	1.93 m (6 ft 4 in)
Propeller diameter	1.60 m (5 ft 3 in)

AREA:

Wings, gross	13.94 m² (150.0 sq ft)

WEIGHTS:

Weight empty	454 kg (1,000 lb)
Payload with max fuel	215 kg (474 lb)
Max T-O weight: aerobatic	680 kg (1,500 lb)
utility	794 kg (1,750 lb)

PERFORMANCE (estimated, at utility T-O weight):

Max level speed	130 knots (241 km/h; 150 mph)
Cruising speed (75% power)	
	121 knots (225 km/h; 140 mph)
Stalling speed: clean	52 knots (97 km/h; 60 mph)
wheels and flaps down	42 knots (77 km/h; 48 mph)
Max rate of climb at S/L	457 m (1,500 ft)/min
Rate of climb at S/L, one engine out	107 m (350 ft)/min
T-O run	92-107 m (300-350 ft)
Landing run	76-92 m (250-300 ft)
Range with max fuel	651 nm (1,207 km; 750 miles)
g limits	+6.5/-3

AERO VISIONS CELEBRITY
This biplane is marketed in full, quick-build and partial kit forms, and optional prefabricated components are a J-3 type cowling, engine mount, mechanical or hydraulic brakes, and wheel fairings; plans are not sold separately.

TYPE: Tandem two-seat homebuilt and ARV biplane.

AIRFRAME: Strut and wire braced biplane of fabric-covered wooden construction. NACA 23012 wing section. Conventional controls, with ailerons on upper and lower wings. Non-retractable tailwheel landing gear.

POWER PLANT: One 48.5-63.4 kW (65-85 hp) Teledyne Continental or 48.5-67 kW (65-90 hp) Volkswagen modified motorcar engine. Fuel capacity 45.4 litres (12 US gallons; 10 Imp gallons).

DIMENSIONS, EXTERNAL:

Wing span	6.71 m (22 ft 0 in)
Length overall	5.33 m (17 ft 6 in)
Height overall	1.83 m (6 ft 0 in)
Propeller diameter	1.83-1.88 m (6 ft 0 in-6 ft 2 in)

AREA:

Wings, gross	16.35 m² (176.0 sq ft)

WEIGHTS:

Weight empty	238 kg (525 lb)
Baggage capacity	6.8 kg (15 lb)
Max T-O weight	453 kg (1,000 lb)

PERFORMANCE:

Max level speed	82 knots (153 km/h; 95 mph)
Econ cruising speed	69 knots (129 km/h; 80 mph)
Stalling speed, power off	35 knots (65 km/h; 40 mph)
Service ceiling	4,115 m (13,500 ft)
T-O run	107 m (350 ft)
Landing run	92 m (300 ft)
Range	208 nm (386 km; 240 miles)
Endurance	3 h
g limits	+6.5/-3.5

AIR COMMAND
AIR COMMAND MANUFACTURING INC
Liberty Landing Airport, Route 3, Box 197A, Liberty, Missouri 64068
Telephone: 1 (816) 781 9313
Fax: 1 (816) 781 9366
PRESIDENT: Dennis Fetters

Details of the 447 Commander and 447 Commander Sport can be found in the Microlight tables.

AIR COMMAND 503 COMMANDER and 503 COMMANDER SPORT
This gyroplane uses the same airframe as the 447 Commander, but has a 35 kW (47 hp) Rotax 503 engine as standard. It conforms to FAR Pt 103.

WEIGHTS:

Weight empty	122 kg (270 lb)
Max T-O weight	267 kg (590 lb)

PERFORMANCE (A: Commander, B: Commander Sport):

Max level speed: A	65 knots (121 km/h; 75 mph)
B	72 knots (134 km/h; 83 mph)
Econ cruising speed: A, B	43 knots (80 km/h; 50 mph)
Max rate of climb at S/L: A	274 m (900 ft)/min
B	290 m (950 ft)/min
Ceiling: A, B	3,050 m (10,000 ft)

T-O run, with pre-rotation: A, B	18 m (60 ft)
without pre-rotation: A, B	152 m (500 ft)
Range: A, B	87 nm (161 km; 100 miles)
Endurance: A, B	2 h
g limit	+9

AIR COMMAND 532 COMMANDER ELITE and 532 COMMANDER ELITE SPORT
The 532 Commander Elite became available in kit form in Spring 1985. It has the same airframe as the 447 Commander, but uses the 47.7 kW (64 hp) Rotax 532 engine as standard, with a three-blade propeller. It conforms to FAA Experimental homebuilt requirements, and as such the kit is less than 50 per cent completed. Options include a partial enclosure.

WEIGHTS:

Weight empty	125 kg (275 lb)
Max T-O weight	340 kg (750 lb)

PERFORMANCE:

Max level speed:	
Commander	82 knots (153 km/h; 95 mph)
Commander Sport	91 knots (169 km/h; 105 mph)
Econ cruising speed	61 knots (113 km/h; 70 mph)
Max rate of climb at S/L	366 m (1,200 ft)/min
Service ceiling	3,050 m (10,000 ft)

AIR COMMAND 532 COMMANDER ELITE TWO-SEATER
By means of a simple bolt-on conversion kit, a standard 532 Commander Elite can be modified into a side by side two-seater under homebuilt regulations. Fitting a second control stick makes it suitable for training purposes. A rotor of 7.62 m (25 ft) diameter is employed. A military version has also been developed.

WEIGHTS:

Weight empty	141 kg (310 lb)
Max T-O weight	340 kg (750 lb)

PERFORMANCE (two persons):

Max level speed	78 knots (145 km/h; 90 mph)
Cruising speed	48 knots (89 km/h; 55 mph)
Max rate of climb at S/L	152 m (500 ft)/min
T-O run: with pre-rotation	46 m (150 ft)
without pre-rotation	214 m (700 ft)
Landing run	0-1.5 m (0-5 ft)

T-O run: with pre-rotation	18 m (60 ft)
without pre-rotation	152 m (500 ft)
Landing run	0-1.5 m (0-5 ft)
Endurance	1 h 30 min
g limit	+9

Aerosport Scamp A biplane built by Mr Jack Stafford of Greenville, South Carolina

Air Command 532 Commander Elite two-seater in military form

Aero Visions Culex twin-engined homebuilt

Aircraft Designs (Hollmann) HA-2M Sportster two-seat gyroplane
(J. M. G. Gradidge)

Aero Visions Celebrity homebuilt biplane

Aircraft Designs (Hollmann) Bumble Bee microlight gyroplane

AIRCRAFT DESIGNS
AIRCRAFT DESIGNS INC
25380 Boots Road, Monterey, California 93940
Telephone: 1 (408) 649 6212
PRESIDENT: Martin Hollmann

HOLLMANN HA-2M SPORTSTER
The Sportster prototype first flew in October 1974. Plans, materials and component parts are available.
TYPE: Side by side two-seat homebuilt gyroplane.
ROTOR SYSTEM: Two-blade rotor of NACA 8-H-12 section. Metal blades, each made up of a leading-edge extrusion, aluminium formed ribs and Alclad skin, riveted and bonded together. Pre-rotator and rotor brake standard.
AIRFRAME: All aluminium alloy construction, except for glassfibre fairings and tail unit tips. Non-retractable tricycle landing gear.
POWER PLANT: One 97 kW (130 hp) Franklin Sport 4B on prototype. Most aircraft powered by a 112 kW (150 hp) Textron Lycoming O-320. Fuel capacity 45.4 litres (12 US gallons; 10 Imp gallons).
DIMENSIONS, EXTERNAL:
Rotor diameter 8.53 m (28 ft 0 in)
Length overall 3.66 m (12 ft 0 in)
Height to top of rotor head 2.34 m (7 ft 8 in)
Propeller diameter 1.68 m (5 ft 6 in)

WEIGHTS (112 kW: 150 hp engine, unless stated otherwise):
Weight empty, equipped (prototype) 281 kg (620 lb)
Max T-O weight 500 kg (1,100 lb)
PERFORMANCE (112 kW; 150 hp engine, unless stated otherwise):
Max cruising speed at S/L (prototype)
65 knots (121 km/h; 75 mph)
Econ cruising speed at S/L (prototype)
52 knots (97 km/h; 60 mph)
Stalling speed (prototype) 25 knots (45 km/h; 28 mph)
Max rate of climb at S/L 274 m (900 ft)/min
Service ceiling 2,440 m (8,000 ft)
T-O run 107 m (350 ft)
Landing run 0-6 m (0-20 ft)
Range: with max fuel 78 nm (145 km; 90 miles)
with max payload 61 nm (112 km; 70 miles)

HOLLMANN BUMBLE BEE
The Bumble Bee first flew in prototype form in January 1984 and is now available in bolt together kit form or can be built from plans, using prefabricated component parts.
TYPE: Single-seat microlight gyroplane; conforms to FAR Pt 103.
AIRFRAME: Fuselage structure of square aluminium alloy tubing, with glassfibre/foam sandwich cruciform tail surfaces. Two-blade rotor of NACA 8-H-12 section, with aluminium alloy leading-edges and glassfibre/foam/epoxy trailing-edges. Rotor pre-rotator available. Non-retractable tricycle landing gear.
POWER PLANT: One 30 kW (40 hp) Rotax 447. Fuel capacity 19 litres (5 US gallons; 4.2 Imp gallons).
DIMENSIONS, EXTERNAL:
Rotor diameter 7.01 m (23 ft 0 in)
Length overall 3.35 m (11 ft 0 in)
Height overall 2.29 m (7 ft 6 in)
Propeller diameter 1.52 m (5 ft 0 in)
AREA:
Rotor disc 38.55 m² (415.0 sq ft)
WEIGHTS:
Weight empty 102 kg (225 lb)
Pilot weight range 68-113 kg (150-250 lb)
Max T-O weight 227 kg (500 lb)
PERFORMANCE:
Max level speed 56 knots (103 km/h; 64 mph)
Econ cruising speed 35 knots (64 km/h; 40 mph)
Min flying speed 4.5 knots (8 km/h; 5 mph)
Max rate of climb at S/L 366 m (1,200 ft)/min
Service ceiling 3,660 m (12,000 ft)
T-O run: without rotor pre-rotation 76 m (250 ft)
with rotor pre-rotation 30 m (100 ft)
Range with max fuel 56 nm (105 km; 65 miles)
Endurance 1 h
g limits +3.5/-1

HOLLMANN NOVA

The latest company product is the Nova, that first flew as a prototype in June 1989. Ready to fly Novas and kits (produced by Pacific Composites of Salinas, California) will become available once test flying has been completed.

TYPE: Side by side two-seat Experimental monoplane.

AIRFRAME: Cantilever mid-wing monoplane of glassfibre/Nomex honeycomb/foam core sandwich construction. Wing section NLF 0215 Modified. Foreplane with elevators, wings with ailerons and flaps, and cruciform tail unit comprising straight tailplane with elevators, sweptback dorsal fin and sweptback ventral fin with rudder. Non-retractable tricycle landing gear, with brakes.

POWER PLANT: One 48.5 kW (65 hp) Rotax 532 with 2.5 : 1 reduction gear, driving a pusher propeller at the rear of the fuselage. Fuel capacity 68 litres (18 US gallons; 15 Imp gallons).

DIMENSIONS, EXTERNAL:	
Wing span	6.10 m (20 ft 0 in)
Length overall	5.03 m (16 ft 6 in)
Height overall	2.22 m (7 ft 3½ in)
Propeller diameter	1.60 m (5 ft 3 in)
AREAS:	
Wings, gross	5.57 m² (60.0 sq ft)
Foreplane	0.28 m² (3.0 sq ft)
WEIGHTS:	
Weight empty	286 kg (630 lb)
Baggage capacity	4.5 kg (10 lb)
Max T-O weight	499 kg (1,100 lb)
PERFORMANCE:	
Max level speed	126 knots (233 km/h; 145 mph)
Econ cruising speed	78 knots (145 km/h; 90 mph)
Stalling speed, flaps down	53 knots (98 km/h; 61 mph)
Max rate of climb at S/L:	
pilot only	213 m (700 ft)/min
dual	137 m (450 ft)/min
T-O run	305 m (1,000 ft)
Landing run	275 m (900 ft)
Range: pilot only	521 nm (965 km; 600 miles)
dual	217 nm (402 km; 250 miles)
g limits	+4.4/−2.2

AIRCRAFT DYNAMICS
AIRCRAFT DYNAMICS CORPORATION

2978 East Euclid Place, Littleton, Colorado 80121
Telephone: 1 (303) 781 6121
PRESIDENT: Ernest A. Bode

AIRCRAFT DYNAMICS NUWACO T-10

Aircraft Dynamics (formerly NuWaco Aircraft Company Inc) markets plans and kits of this modernised version of the pre-war Waco 10-T taperwing biplane; by January 1990, 30 ready assembled aircraft, 10 kits and 35 sets of plans had been ordered or delivered. The prototype made its first flight on 5 May 1984.

TYPE: Three-seat homebuilt replica biplane.

AIRFRAME: Strut and wire braced structure of wood and welded steel tube construction, fabric covered. Wing section M-6. Non-retractable tailwheel landing gear. Options include floats and cockpit canopy.

POWER PLANT: Suited to engines of 164-336 kW (220-450 hp). Prototype fitted with 205 kW (275 hp) Jacobs R-755-B2 radial. Optional engines include Teledyne Continental W-670, Pratt & Whitney R-985, Wright R-975 or J5, and Jacobs R-755-A2. Fuel capacity 227 litres (60 US gallons; 50 Imp gallons). Two auxiliary fuel tanks in upper wing centre section optional, each with capacity of 66 litres (17.5 US gallons; 14.6 Imp gallons).

DIMENSIONS, EXTERNAL:	
Wing span	9.22 m (30 ft 3 in)
Length overall	6.86 m (22 ft 6 in)
Height overall	2.74 m (9 ft 0 in)
Propeller diameter: standard	2.74 m (9 ft 0 in)
optional	2.59 m (8 ft 6 in)
AREA:	
Wings, gross	21.09 m² (227.0 sq ft)
WEIGHTS:	
Weight empty	798 kg (1,760 lb)
Baggage capacity	18 kg (40 lb)
Max T-O weight	1,179 kg (2,600 lb)
PERFORMANCE (at max T-O weight, Jacobs engine):	
Max level speed at 3,050 m (10,000 ft)	123 knots (229 km/h; 142 mph)
Econ cruising speed at 3,050 m (10,000 ft), 65% power	113 knots (209 km/h; 130 mph)
Stalling speed, power off	44 knots (81 km/h; 50 mph)
Max rate of climb at S/L	564 m (1,850 ft)/min
Service ceiling	6,100 m (20,000 ft)
T-O run (224 kW; 300 hp engine)	83 m (270 ft)
Landing run (224 kW; 300 hp engine)	244 m (800 ft)
Range at 65% power	564 nm (1,046 km; 650 miles)
Endurance with max standard fuel	5 h
g limits	±10

AMERICAN AIR JET
AMERICAN AIR JET INC

710 Sunnywood Place, Woodland Park, Colorado 80863
Telephone: 1 (719) 633 5588
Fax: 1 (719) 632 8160
PRESIDENT: Stephen L. Willman

American Air Jet Inc was founded in 1987 with the purchased assets of the former Eagle Helicopter Corporation.

AMERICAN AIR JET AMERICAN

First flown in July 1988, this rotor-tip, cold air, pressure-jet helicopter is being offered initially in kit form, to be followed by ready assembled examples for export. FAA certification of production aircraft will be sought if US demand proves sufficient. The version of the American available for purchase differs in some respects from the prototype, which is detailed here:

TYPE: Tandem or side by side two-seat homebuilt helicopter.

ROTOR SYSTEM: Single rotor with two hollow glassfibre blades, controlled by mechanical swashplate system. No tail rotor.

AIRFRAME: Aluminium alloy structure, with glassfibre nosecone and steel tube engine mounting. Non-moving tail surfaces. Twin skid landing gear, with optional ground handling wheels and floats.

POWER PLANT: Prototype has 209 kW (280 hp) Wankel rotary engine, driving a centrifugal compressor to provide compressed air to thrust-jets at trailing-edge of blade tips. 'Production' engine is a 268.5 kW (360 hp) rotary turbo, with alternative turbine engine of similar rating. Standard fuel capacity 182 litres (48 US gallons; 40 Imp gallons).

DIMENSIONS, EXTERNAL:	
Rotor diameter	10.97 m (36 ft 0 in)
Fuselage length	5.49 m (18 ft 0 in)
Height overall	2.44 m (8 ft 0 in)
WEIGHTS:	
Weight empty	445 kg (980 lb)
Max T-O weight	726 kg (1,600 lb)
PERFORMANCE (estimated, with 209 kW; 280 hp engine):	
Max level speed at S/L	78 knots (145 km/h; 90 mph)
Econ cruising speed at S/L	61 knots (113 km/h; 70 mph)
Service ceiling (tested)	3,050 m (10,000 ft)
Hovering ceiling: IGE	366 m (1,200 ft)
OGE	335 m (1,100 ft)
Range at optimum speed	260 nm (483 km; 300 miles)
Endurance at 61 knots (113 km/h; 70 mph)	4 h

AUSTRALITE
AUSTRALITE INC

California
Australian Distributor:
Aeronautical Engineers Australia
Willeto, Western Australia

PRINCIPAL: Graeme Swannell

AUSTRALITE ULTRABAT

The Ultrabat, a single-seat mid-wing light aircraft designed in Australia by Mr George Markey, is marketed by this Australian-US company as an Experimental category kit. High Tech Composites of Oxnard, California, is manufacturing the components, which include an all-composites tailboom and fully enclosed cockpit. Under test for the Ultrabat has been a 67 kW (90 hp) Techtron two-cylinder engine, which drives a pusher propeller.

AVID
AVID AIRCRAFT INC

PO Box 728, 4823 Aviation Way, Caldwell, Idaho 83606
Telephone: 1 (208) 454 2600
PRESIDENT: Dean Wilson

AVID AIRCRAFT AVID FLYER

The Avid Flyer takes from 200 to 400 working hours to assemble. It is available as a single kit, or as six separate kits to spread the cost of purchase. It strongly influenced design of the Indaer-Peru Chuspi light aircraft (see under Peru in main Aircraft section).

The Avid Flyer features two forms of interchangeable wings: the original high-lift STOL wings with unique near full span auxiliary aerofoil flaperons and shorter span 'speed' wings using a new wing section. With the 'speed' wings fitted, cruising speed is increased to 95 knots (177 km/h; 110 mph) and stalling speed becomes 35 knots (65 km/h; 40 mph) at max T-O weight.

TYPE: Side by side two-seat, dual-control homebuilt.

AIRFRAME: Aluminium wing spars and plywood ribs, covered with heat shrunk Dacron. Welded fuselage, rudder, tailplane and elevators of steel tubing, Dacron covered except for fuselage nose which has pre-moulded glassfibre cowlings. Fin integral with fuselage. Non-retractable nosewheel or tailwheel landing gear. Optional floats, skis and wheel-skis.

POWER PLANT: One 48.5 kW (65 hp) Rotax 582. Fuel capacity 34 litres (9 US gallons; 7.5 Imp gallons). Optional 53 litre (14 US gallon; 11.7 Imp gallon) wing tanks.

DIMENSIONS, EXTERNAL:	
Wing span: STOL wings	9.11 m (29 ft 10½ in)
'Speed' wings	7.30 m (23 ft 11½ in)
Length overall	5.18 m (17 ft 0 in)
Height overall	1.70 m (5 ft 7 in)
Propeller diameter	1.83 m (6 ft 0 in)
AREAS:	
Wings, gross: STOL wings	11.38 m² (122.5 sq ft)
'Speed' wings	9.04 m² (97.31 sq ft)
WEIGHTS:	
Weight empty: STOL wings	154-172 kg (340-380 lb)
'Speed' wings	150-168 kg (330-370 lb)
Max T-O weight	385 kg (850 lb)
PERFORMANCE (A: STOL wings, B: 'Speed' wings, both at 385 kg; 850 lb AUW):	
Max cruising speed: A	74 knots (137 km/h; 85 mph)
B	95 knots (177 km/h; 110 mph)
Stalling speed: A	28 knots (52 km/h; 32 mph)
B	35 knots (65 km/h; 40 mph)
Max rate of climb at S/L: A	427 m (1,400 ft)/min
B	419 m (1,375 ft)/min
Service ceiling: A	5,335 m (17,500 ft)
B	4,575 m (15,000 ft)
T-O run: A	43 m (140 ft)
B	92 m (300 ft)
T-O to 15 m (50 ft): A	104 m (340 ft)
B	152 m (500 ft)
Landing run: A	46 m (150 ft)
B	183 m (600 ft)
Range with max fuel	260 nm (483 km; 300 miles)
g limits	+3.8 (+5.7 ultimate)

AVID AIRCRAFT AVID AMPHIBIAN

The Avid Amphibian first flew on 12 July 1985. Kits are available. It can be built optionally for land operation only.

TYPE: Three-seat homebuilt amphibian or landplane.

AIRFRAME: Original high lift wing section. Wing structure comprises aluminium alloy tube spars, plywood ribs, and aluminium and steel drag tubes, covered with Ceconite. Downward canted wingtips serve as stabilising floats on water. Full span trailing-edge flaperons of auxiliary aerofoil type, of similar construction to wings. Single-step flying-boat hull, with structure of steel tube, covered with glassfibre shells back to step and Ceconite over rear fuselage. Wire braced tail unit of steel tube covered with Ceconite. Retractable tailwheel landing gear.

POWER PLANT: One 48.5 kW (65 hp) Rotax 582. Fuel capacity 66 litres (17.5 US gallons; 14.6 Imp gallons).

DIMENSIONS, EXTERNAL:	
Wing span	10.97 m (36 ft 0 in)
Length overall	5.92 m (19 ft 5 in)
Height overall	1.75 m (5 ft 9 in)
Propeller diameter	1.91 m (6 ft 3 in)
AREA:	
Wings, gross	13.94 m² (150.0 sq ft)
WEIGHTS:	
Weight empty	254 kg (560 lb)
Max T-O weight	544 kg (1,200 lb)
PERFORMANCE (at max T-O weight):	
Max cruising speed	65 knots (120 km/h; 75 mph)
Stalling speed	29 knots (53 km/h; 33 mph)
Max rate of climb at S/L	286 m (940 ft)/min

Drawing of the Aircraft Designs (Hollmann) Nova two-seat homebuilt

Prototype American Air Jet American pressure-jet helicopter

Australite Ultrabat single-seat homebuilt *(J.M.G. Gradidge)*

Aircraft Dynamics NuWaco T-10 taperwing three-seat homebuilt biplane

Barnett Rotorcraft J 4B with open cockpit

Three-seat Avid Aircraft Avid Amphibian *(Anton Wettstein)*

Avid Aircraft Avid Commuter

Service ceiling	3,580 m (11,750 ft)
T-O run: on land	92 m (300 ft)
on water	230 m (756 ft)
Landing run: on land	183 m (600 ft)
on water	84 m (275 ft)

AVID AIRCRAFT AVID COMMUTER

Based on the Avid Flyer airframe and powered by a Rotax 582 CDI engine, its features include 'speed' wings as standard, electrical system, digital engine instrumentation, soundproofing, wheel fairings and hydraulic disc brakes. Deliveries began in early 1990.

BARNETT
BARNETT ROTORCRAFT

4307 Olivehurst Avenue, Olivehurst, California 95961
Telephone: 1 (916) 742 7416
PRESIDENT: K. Jerrie Barnett

Plans, materials, welded components and kits of parts are made available to construct the single-seat J 4B and two-seat J 4B-2 gyroplanes.

BARNETT J 4B and J 4B-2

The single-seat J 4B first flew in prototype form on 15 July 1968. For those wishing to construct a two-seat J 4B-2, a set of J 4B plans has to be purchased along with a set of modification plans which details the necessary changes to produce the two-seat configuration. The aluminium rotor blades, hand laid-up nacelle and engine cooling cowls are available ready fabricated.

TYPE: Single-seat (J 4B) and two-seat (J 4B-2) autogyros.
ROTOR SYSTEM: Two-blade autorotating rotor, of bonded aluminium alloy.
AIRFRAME: All-metal structure of welded 4130 chrome-molybdenum steel tubing, with fabric covered tail surfaces. Glassfibre fuselage nacelle. Non-retractable tricycle landing gear.
POWER PLANT: One 48.5-74.5 kW (65-100 hp) Teledyne Continental engine, of A65 through to O-200 type, for J 4B; 74.5 kW (100 hp) Teledyne Continental O-200 to a 134 kW (180 hp) Textron Lycoming O-360 for J 4B-2. Fuel capacity 51 litres (13.5 US gallons; 11.2 Imp gallons) in small tank or 64.4 litres (17 US gallons; 14.2 Imp gallons) in large tank.
DIMENSIONS, EXTERNAL (A: J 4B, B: J 4B-2):

Rotor diameter: A	7.01 m (23 ft 0 in)
B	7.72 m (25 ft 4 in)
Length overall, without rotor: A	3.76 m (12 ft 4 in)
B	4.17 m (13 ft 8 in)
Height overall: A	2.34 m (7 ft 8 in)
B	2.46 m (8 ft 1 in)

AREAS:

Rotor disc: A	38.70 m² (416.59 sq ft)
B	46.95 m² (505.39 sq ft)

WEIGHTS (A and B as above):

Baggage capacity: A	13.6 kg (30 lb)
B	9 kg (20 lb)
Normal T-O weight: A, no battery	333 kg (734.5 lb)
B	456 kg (1,005.5 lb)
Max T-O weight: A	363 kg (800 lb)
B	492 kg (1,085 lb)

PERFORMANCE (A and B as above):

Max level speed: A	109 knots (201 km/h; 125 mph)
B	97 knots (180 km/h; 112 mph)
Cruising speed:	
A, A65 engine	69 knots (129 km/h; 80 mph) IAS
B, O-200 engine	69-78 knots (129-145 km/h; 80-90 mph) IAS
B, O-360 engine	87-104 knots (161-193 km/h; 100-120 mph) IAS
Max rate of climb at S/L: A	457 m (1,500 ft)/min
B	152 m (500 ft)/min
Service ceiling: A	3,660 m (12,000 ft)
B	2,440 m (8,000 ft)
T-O run: A	107 m (350 ft)
B	183 m (600 ft)
Landing run: A	0-6 m (0-20 ft)
B	8 m (25 ft)

BARRACUDA
W. B. BUETHE ENTERPRISES INC
PO Box 486, Cathedral City, California 92234
Telephone: 1 (619) 324 9454
PRESIDENT: Dr William B. Buethe

BARRACUDA
The prototype Barracuda flew for the first time on 29 June 1975. Plans and kits are available, and about 25 Barracudas are believed to be flying.
TYPE: Side by side two-seat, dual-control sporting homebuilt.
AIRFRAME: Plywood covered all-wood construction, except for glassfibre used in ailerons and for tailplane tips. Wing section NACA 64,415. Retractable tricycle landing gear.
POWER PLANT: One 186 kW (250 hp) Textron Lycoming IO-540-C4B5 or other engine of 112-224 kW (150-300 hp). Fuel capacity 166.5 litres (44 US gallons; 36.6 Imp gallons). Provision for two 23 litre (6 US gallon; 5 Imp gallon) auxiliary tanks in outboard wing panels.

DIMENSIONS, EXTERNAL:
Wing span	7.54 m (24 ft 9 in)
Length overall	6.55 m (21 ft 6 in)
Propeller diameter	2.18 m (7 ft 2 in)

AREA:
Wings, gross	11.15 m² (120.0 sq ft)

WEIGHTS:
Weight empty	712 kg (1,570 lb)
Baggage capacity	27 kg (60 lb)
Max T-O weight	1,043 kg (2,300 lb)

PERFORMANCE:
Max level speed at 2,135 m (7,000 ft)	181 knots (335 km/h; 208 mph)
Cruising speed (62% power) at 2,450 m (8,050 ft)	162 knots (300 km/h; 187 mph)
Stalling speed: 'clean'	56 knots (103 km/h; 64 mph)
wheels and flaps down	54 knots (100 km/h; 62 mph)
Max rate of climb at S/L	762 m (2,500 ft)/min
Range at max T-O weight, 65% power, with auxiliary tank, 30 min reserves	800 nm (1,480 km; 920 miles)

BOAC
BARNEY OLDFIELD AIRCRAFT COMPANY
PO Box 228, Needham, Massachusetts 02192
TECHNICAL DIRECTOR: R. M. Dick Lane

OLDFIELD 'BABY' LAKES
Plans and material kits are available for this scaled-down version of the Great Lakes Sport Trainer. More than 930 sets of plans have been sold and about 100 aircraft are flying.
TYPE: Single-seat homebuilt sporting biplane.
AIRFRAME: Wooden wings, fabric covered. Wing section modified M6, tapering to USA 27 46 cm (18 in) from tips. Ailerons on lower wings only. Welded steel tube fuselage and tail unit, fabric covered. Non-retractable tailwheel landing gear.
POWER PLANT: One 63.4 kW (85 hp) Teledyne Continental. Provision for alternative engines of between 37.25 and 74.5 kW (50 and 100 hp). Fuel capacity 45 litres (12 US gallons; 10 Imp gallons).

DIMENSIONS, EXTERNAL:
Wing span: upper	5.08 m (16 ft 8 in)
Length overall	4.19 m (13 ft 9 in)
Height overall	1.37 m (4 ft 6 in)

AREA:
Wings, gross	7.99 m² (86.0 sq ft)

WEIGHTS (59.5 kW; 80 hp A80 engine):
Weight empty	215 kg (475 lb)
Max T-O weight	385 kg (850 lb)

PERFORMANCE (A80 engine, at max T-O weight):
Max level speed at S/L	117 knots (217 km/h; 135 mph)
Cruising speed at S/L	102 knots (190 km/h; 118 mph)
Stalling speed	44 knots (81 km/h; 50 mph)
Max rate of climb at S/L	610 m (2,000 ft)/min
Service ceiling	5,200 m (17,000 ft)
T-O run	91 m (300 ft)
Landing run (no brakes)	122 m (400 ft)
Max range	217 nm (400 km; 250 miles)
g limits	±9

OLDFIELD 'SUPER BABY' LAKES
The prototype 'Super Baby' Lakes flew for the first time in 1976. It was developed as a more powerful and modified variant of the 'Baby' Lakes. Plans are available.
POWER PLANT: One Textron Lycoming engine in 80.5-93 kW (108-125 hp) range. Header tank fitted.

DIMENSIONS, EXTERNAL:
As for 'Baby' Lakes, except:
Length overall	4.34 m (14 ft 3 in)

WEIGHTS:
Weight empty	218 kg (480 lb)
Max T-O weight	385 kg (850 lb)

PERFORMANCE:
Max level speed	135 knots (249 km/h; 155 mph) IAS
Cruising speed (75% power)	117 knots (217 km/h; 135 mph) IAS
Stalling speed	48 knots (89 km/h; 55 mph) IAS
Max rate of climb at S/L	915 m (3,000 ft)/min
T-O run	69 m (225 ft)
Landing run	130 m (425 ft)
Max range, with wing tanks	260 nm (483 km; 300 miles)

OLDFIELD 'BUDDY BABY' LAKES
The two-seat 'Buddy Baby' utilises standard 'Baby' wings and tail unit. To prevent a significant increase in wing loading, a 41 cm (16 in) upper wing centre-section has been introduced, together with short stub-wings built integrally with the fuselage to increase the lower span by a similar amount.

The fuselage has been widened and stretched to permit seating positions for two average-sized (77 kg; 170 lb) people in a configuration much like that of a 'buddy seat' on a motorcycle. Dual throttle, rudder pedals and brakes are provided, with a single dual-position joystick. The aircraft is flown solo from the rear seat and dual from the front position. The prototype first flew in July 1987. Plans, components, and material kits are available; by January 1990 26 material kits and 58 sets of plans had been sold. A bubble canopy is optional.
POWER PLANT: One engine in 48.5-100.7 kW (65-135 hp) range.

DIMENSIONS, EXTERNAL:
Wing span	5.49 m (18 ft 0 in)
Length overall	4.47 m (14 ft 8 in)
Height overall	1.91 m (6 ft 3 in)
Propeller diameter	1.70 m (5 ft 7 in)

AREA:
Wings, gross	8.92 m² (96.0 sq ft)

WEIGHTS:
Weight empty	243 kg (535 lb)
Max T-O weight	453 kg (1,000 lb)

PERFORMANCE (prototype with 85.75 kW; 115 hp Textron Lycoming engine and two crew):
Max level speed at 1,065 m (3,500 ft)	135 knots (249 km/h; 155 mph)
Econ cruising speed at 1,065 m (3,500 ft)	113 knots (209 km/h; 130 mph)
Stalling speed, flaps up and engine idling	48 knots (89 km/h; 55 mph)
T-O run	92 m (300 ft)
Landing run	122 m (400 ft)
Range with wing tanks	260 nm (482 km; 300 miles)
Endurance	2 h 15 min
g limits	+7/-6

BOWERS
PETER M. BOWERS
10458 16th Avenue South, Seattle, Washington 98168
Telephone: 1 (206) 242 2582

BOWERS FLY BABY 1-A
The prototype Fly Baby monoplane was produced to compete in an Experimental Aircraft Association design contest, organised to encourage the development of a simple, low-cost, easy-to-fly aeroplane that could be built by inexperienced amateurs for recreational flying. It flew for the first time on 27 July 1960. Plans are available and about 4,300 sets had been sold by early 1990. Construction of well over 700 Fly Babys is known to have been undertaken, of which about 420 have flown.

Several individual amateur builders amended the plans during 1973 to allow for construction of two-seat versions of the Fly Baby. Although Mr Bowers does not recommend this conversion, he has made some additions to the plans to cater for it.

The following description applies to the original single-seat Fly Baby 1-A.
TYPE: Single-seat homebuilt.
AIRFRAME: All-wood construction, except for Dacron covering on wings and tail unit. Wing section NACA 4412. Non-retractable tailwheel landing gear. Examples have flown with floats and skis. Cockpit canopy optional.
POWER PLANT: One 63.5 kW (85 hp) Teledyne Continental C85. Suited to modified Volkswagen engines of over 1,800 cc. Fuel capacity 60.5 litres (16 US gallons; 13.3 Imp gallons).

DIMENSIONS, EXTERNAL:
Wing span	8.53 m (28 ft 0 in)
Length overall	5.64 m (18 ft 6 in)
Height, wings folded	1.98 m (6 ft 6 in)

WEIGHTS:
Weight empty	274 kg (605 lb)
Max T-O weight	419 kg (924 lb)

PERFORMANCE (at max T-O weight):
Max level speed at S/L	over 104 knots (193 km/h; 120 mph)
Cruising speed	91-96 knots (169-177 km/h; 105-110 mph)
Landing speed	39 knots (73 km/h; 45 mph)
Max rate of climb at S/L	335 m (1,100 ft)/min
T-O and landing run	76 m (250 ft)
Range with max fuel	277 nm (515 km; 320 miles)

BOWERS FLY BABY 1-B
During 1968 Mr Bowers designed and built a set of interchangeable biplane wings for the original prototype Fly Baby and with these fitted it flew for the first time on 27 March 1969. About 18 more biplanes, designated Fly Baby 1-B, have been completed and flown. The biplane wings have the same aerofoil section and incidence as those of the monoplane version, but incorporate aluminium alloy wingtip bows. Ailerons are fitted to the lower wings only. Changeover from monoplane to biplane configuration can be accomplished by two people in approximately one hour.

The biplane is intended to use the same engines as the monoplane, for which Mr Bowers does not recommend anything heavier than the Teledyne Continental O-200. Since some biplane builders have desired to use the 93 kW (125 hp) Textron Lycoming O-290, a modification has been authorised for the biplane, whereby the wing sweep is decreased by 5° for CG reasons.
TYPE: Single-seat homebuilt biplane.

DIMENSIONS, EXTERNAL:
Wing span	6.71 m (22 ft 0 in)
Height overall	2.08 m (6 ft 10 in)

AREA:
Wings, gross	13.94 m² (150.0 sq ft)

WEIGHTS:
Weight empty	295 kg (651 lb)
Max T-O weight	440 kg (972 lb)

PERFORMANCE (at max T-O weight):
Cruising speed	75 knots (140 km/h; 87 mph)
Max rate of climb at S/L	267 m (875 ft)/min

BRISTOL
URIEL BRISTOL
PO Box 6093, Sunny Isle, St Croix, Virgin Islands 6093-00820

BRISTOL BX-200
First flown as a prototype on 15 July 1986, the BX-200 has the general appearance of an enlarged Cassutt but is an original design. Plans and kits are available; assembly time for the kit is under 1,000 working hours.
TYPE: Side by side two-seat cross-country homebuilt.
AIRFRAME: Wooden wings, with NACA 2300 laminar flow section, and Ceconite covered steel tube control surfaces. Remainder of airframe has welded steel tube structure, Ceconite covered except for glassfibre forward fuselage skins, engine cowling and canopy frame. Non-retractable tailwheel landing gear.
POWER PLANT: One 134 kW (180 hp) Textron Lycoming O-360-A4A. Fuel capacity 102 litres (27 US gallons; 22.5 Imp gallons).

DIMENSIONS, EXTERNAL:
Wing span	6.10 m (20 ft 0 in)
Length overall	5.31 m (17 ft 5 in)
Height overall	1.50 m (4 ft 11 in)
Propeller diameter	1.83 m (6 ft 0 in)

AREA:
Wings. gross	8.36 m² (90.0 sq ft)

WEIGHTS:
Weight empty	363 kg (800 lb)
Baggage capacity	22.7 kg (50 lb)
Max T-O weight	612 kg (1,350 lb)

PERFORMANCE:
Max level speed at S/L	215 knots (398 km/h; 247 mph)
Econ cruising speed at 2,135 m (7,000 ft)	190 knots (352 km/h; 219 mph)
Max rate of climb at S/L	610 m (2,000 ft)/min
Service ceiling	6,100 m (20,000 ft)
T-O and landing run	457 m (1,500 ft)
Range	500 nm (926 km; 575 miles)
Endurance	2 h 30 min
g limits	+6/-3

Barracuda two-seat sporting monoplane, built by Dr W. B. Buethe

Oldfield (BOAC) 'Buddy Baby' Lakes (*Sally Lane*)

Bowers Fly Baby 1-A (Teledyne Continental A65 engine) built by Mr Eugene Fisher of Seattle, Washington (*Peter M. Bowers*)

BX-200 cross-country homebuilt, designed by Mr Uriel Bristol

Ken Brock KB-2 Freedom Machine

Bushby/Long M-1A Midget Mustang built by Mr Lloyd Hogenson Jr of Sunnyvale, California (119 kW; 160 hp Textron Lycoming O-320 engine)

BROCK
KEN BROCK MANUFACTURING INC
(Division of Santa Ana Metal Stamping)
11852 Western Avenue, Stanton, California 90680
Telephone: 1 (714) 898 4366
Fax: 1 (714) 894 0811
    See also Microlight tables for KB-3 and Avion.

KEN BROCK KB-2 FREEDOM MACHINE
    The KB-2 prototype flew in 1970. Manufacture of kits began in 1979; several hundred have been sold.
    The KB-2 is built from eight kits of parts. Assembly of the basic airframe takes approximately 1½ hours, and the KB-2 can be assembled ready for testing in unpowered form in one weekend.

TYPE: Single-seat homebuilt autogyro.
ROTOR SYSTEM: Single two-blade semi-rigid rotor, of all-metal construction. Blade section modified Clark Y.
AIRFRAME: All-aluminium alloy construction, but with alternative wooden tail unit. Non-retractable tricycle landing gear.
POWER PLANT: One 53.7 kW (72 hp) McCulloch 4318A or Volkswagen modified motorcar engine (max power rating 74.5 kW; 100 hp). Patented seat/fuel tank, capacity 33.7 litres (8.9 US gallons; 7.4 Imp gallons).
DIMENSIONS, EXTERNAL:

Rotor diameter	6.70 m (22 ft 0 in)
Length of fuselage	3.43 m (11 ft 3 in)
Max height	2.03 m (6 ft 8 in)
Propeller diameter	1.22 m (4 ft 0 in)

AREA:

Rotor disc	35.32 m² (380.1 sq ft)

WEIGHTS:

Weight empty	109 kg (240 lb)
Max T-O weight	272 kg (600 lb)

PERFORMANCE (at max T-O weight):

Max level speed	78 knots (145 km/h; 90 mph)
Econ cruising speed	52 knots (97 km/h; 60 mph)
Min level speed	22 knots (40 km/h; 25 mph)
Max rate of climb at S/L	366 m (1,200 ft)/min
Service ceiling	3,050 m (10,000 ft)
T-O run	61 m (200 ft)
Landing run	3 m (10 ft)
Range with max fuel	130 nm (241 km; 150 miles)
Endurance	2 h

BROWN
MICHAEL BROWN
c/o Climber Aviation, 800 West Third Street, Dayton, Ohio 45407
Telephone: 1 (513) 223 8780

Details of the Brown Ascent I, and an illustration, can be found in the 1989-90 *Jane's*. Development is believed to continue.

BUSHBY
BUSHBY AIRCRAFT INC
674 Route 52, Minooka, Illinois 60447
Telephone: 1 (815) 467 2346
    The Midget Mustang and M-II Mustang II are available in plans and kit forms.

BUSHBY/LONG MM-1 and M-1A MIDGET MUSTANG
    The prototype Midget Mustang was completed in 1948 by David Long. Three basic versions have been developed by Robert Bushby from the original design, as follows:
    MM-1-85. Powered by 63.5 kW (85 hp) Teledyne

Continental C85-8FJ or -12 engine. Flew for the first time on 9 September 1959.
    MM-1-125. Powered by 101 kW (135 hp) Textron Lycoming O-290-D2 engine. Flew for first time in July 1963.
    M-1A. Recent development of the MM-1, with lowered turtledeck and bubble canopy. Suited to pilots up to 1.93 m

(6 ft 4 in) tall, and offering better visibility. No performance changes. Alterations can be retrofitted to existing aircraft.

Approximately 360 Midget Mustangs had been completed by early 1990, with 1,100 more under construction throughout the world.

TYPE: Single-seat fully aerobatic sporting homebuilt.

AIRFRAME: All-aluminium alloy flush riveted construction. Wing section NACA 64A212 at root, NACA 64A210 at tip. Non-retractable tailwheel landing gear. Some examples built with retractable gear.

POWER PLANT: See model listing. Several Midget Mustangs flying with 112 kW (150 hp) Textron Lycoming O-320. MM-1-85 fuel capacity 57 litres (15 US gallons; 12.5 Imp gallons). Optional integral wing fuel tanks, each with capacity of 57 litres (15 US gallons; 12.5 Imp gallons). Optional wingtip tanks, each with capacity of 13 litres (3.5 US gallons; 2.9 Imp gallons). MM-1-125 fuel capacity 57 litres (15 US gallons; 12.5 Imp gallons). No provision for wingtip tanks.

DIMENSIONS, EXTERNAL:

Wing span, without tip tanks	5.64 m (18 ft 6 in)
Length overall	5.00 m (16 ft 5 in)
Height overall	1.37 m (4 ft 6 in)

AREA:

Wings, gross	6.32 m² (68.0 sq ft)

WEIGHTS:

Weight empty: MM-1-85	261 kg (575 lb)
MM-1-125	268 kg (590 lb)
Baggage capacity	5.5 kg (12 lb)
Max T-O and landing weight:	
MM-1-85	397 kg (875 lb)
MM-1-125	408 kg (900 lb)

PERFORMANCE (at max T-O weight):

Max level speed at S/L:	
MM-1-85	165 knots (306 km/h; 190 mph)
MM-1-125	195 knots (362 km/h; 225 mph)
Econ cruising speed:	
MM-1-85	129 knots (238 km/h; 148 mph)
MM-1-125	143 knots (265 km/h; 165 mph)

Stalling speed, flaps down:

MM-1-85	50 knots (92 km/h; 57 mph)
MM-1-125	53 knots (97 km/h; 60 mph)
Max rate of climb at S/L:	
MM-1-85	533 m (1,750 ft)/min
MM-1-125	670 m (2,200 ft)/min
Service ceiling: MM-1-85	over 4,875 m (16,000 ft)
MM-1-125	5,790 m (19,000 ft)
T-O run: MM-1-85	137 m (450 ft)
MM-1-125	122 m (400 ft)
Landing run	152 m (500 ft)
Range with max internal fuel:	
MM-1-85	347 nm (640 km; 400 miles)
MM-1-125	325 nm (603 km; 375 miles)
Range with max internal fuel and tip tanks:	
MM-1-85	651 nm (1,200 km; 750 miles)

BUSHBY M-II MUSTANG II

This side by side two-seat derivative of the Midget Mustang flew for the first time on 9 July 1966. About 1,200 Mustang IIs were being built by amateurs in early 1990, at which time about 300 had been completed.

The description applies to the de luxe model, which is stressed for +6g. The empty weight quoted includes IFR instrumentation and nav/com equipment. The M-II can also be operated as an aerobatic aircraft in what Bushby Aircraft calls the 'Sport' configuration. This is identical to the de luxe model except that the electrical system, radio, additional IFR instrumentation, soundproofing and upholstery, wheel fairings, and some baggage capacity are deleted. The 'Sport' model has an empty weight of 340 kg (750 lb), T-O weight of 567 kg (1,250 lb) and is stressed for +9g.

TYPE: Two-seat, dual-control sporting homebuilt.

AIRFRAME: All-aluminium alloy flush riveted construction. Wing section NACA 64A212 at root, NACA 64A210 at tip. Standard version has non-retractable tailwheel landing gear. Alternative non-retractable tricycle gear.

POWER PLANT: Normally one 119 kW (160 hp) Textron Lycoming O-320. Provision for other engines including a 93 kW (125 hp) Textron Lycoming O-290. Fuel capacity 94.6 litres (25 US gallons; 21 Imp gallons). Optional integral wing fuel tanks, each with a capacity of 45 litres (12 US gallons; 10 Imp gallons). Provision for wingtip tanks.

DIMENSIONS, EXTERNAL:

Wing span	7.37 m (24 ft 2 in)
Length overall	5.94 m (19 ft 6 in)
Height overall	1.60 m (5 ft 3 in)
Propeller diameter: 93 kW (125 hp)	1.73 m (5 ft 8 in)
119 kW (160 hp)	1.83 m (6 ft 0 in)

AREA:

Wings, gross	9.02 m² (97.12 sq ft)

WEIGHTS:

Weight empty, equipped, 119 kW (160 hp) engine and tailwheel landing gear	420 kg (927 lb)
Baggage capacity	34 kg (75 lb)
*Max T-O weight	680 kg (1,500 lb)

*Except for countries that restrict max wing loading to 73.2 kg/m² (15 lb/sq ft), where T-O weight of 658 kg (1,450 lb) applies

PERFORMANCE (119 kW; 160 hp engine, tailwheel landing gear, at max T-O weight):

Max level speed at S/L	200 knots (370 km/h; 230 mph)
Max cruising speed at 2,285 m (7,500 ft)	181 knots (335 km/h; 208 mph)
Stalling speed:	
flaps up	53 knots (96 km/h; 60 mph)
flaps down	51 knots (94 km/h; 58 mph)
Max rate of climb at S/L	670 m (2,200 ft)/min
Service ceiling	6,400 m (21,000 ft)
T-O run	137 m (450 ft)
Landing run	168 m (550 ft)
Range: with standard fuel (75% power)	373 nm (692 km; 430 miles)
with optional wingtip tanks	542 nm (1,005 km; 625 miles)

CABRINHA

CABRINHA AIRCRAFT CORP

21622 Kanakoa Lane, Huntington Beach, California 92646
Telephone: 1 (714) 968 3571
DESIGNER: Richard Cabrinha

This company was formerly known as Free Spirit Aircraft Company Inc.

CABRINHA RC 412-II

The RC 412D prototype flew for the first time in July 1986. Kits are believed to be available.

TYPE: Side by side two-seat, dual-control homebuilt.

AIRFRAME: Glassfibre, graphite and honeycomb composites construction. Wing section NASA 0215. Retractable tricycle landing gear.

POWER PLANT: One 127 kW (170 hp) Textron Lycoming

IO-320. Fuel capacity 151.5 litres (40 US gallons; 33.3 Imp gallons). Provision for auxiliary tank of 57 litres (15 US gallons; 12.5 Imp gallons) capacity.

DIMENSIONS, EXTERNAL:

Wing span	8.23 m (27 ft 0 in)
Length overall	6.25 m (20 ft 6 in)
Height overall	2.13 m (7 ft 0 in)
Propeller diameter	1.83 m (6 ft 0 in)

AREA:

Wings, gross	7.25 m² (78.0 sq ft)

WEIGHTS:

Weight empty	397 kg (875 lb)
Baggage capacity:	
without auxiliary fuel tank	90 kg (200 lb)
with auxiliary fuel tank	50 kg (110 lb)
Max T-O weight	816 kg (1,800 lb)

PERFORMANCE:

Max level speed	230 knots (426 km/h; 265 mph)
Econ cruising speed at 3,660 m (12,000 ft)	195 knots (360 km/h; 224 mph)
Stalling speed: clean, solo	48 knots (89 km/h; 55 mph)
flaps and landing gear down, cowl flap open	39 knots (73 km/h; 45 mph)
Max rate of climb at S/L, solo	845 m (2,775 ft)/min
Service ceiling	6,400 m (21,000 ft)
T-O run, solo	99 m (325 ft)
Landing run	91 m (300 ft)
Range with max standard fuel	1,467 nm (2,719 km; 1,690 miles)
Range with auxiliary fuel	2,032 nm (3,765 km; 2,340 miles)
Endurance	8 h 40 min
g limits	+9/-6

CARLSON

CARLSON AIRCRAFT INC

50643 State Route 14, East Palestine, Ohio 44413
Telephone: 1 (216) 426 3934
PRESIDENT: Ernest W. Carlson

See also Microlight tables for the Sparrow.

CARLSON SPARROW SPORT SPECIAL

This Experimental category homebuilt derivative of the Sparrow design uses the same form of wing, fuselage, tail unit and landing gear structures as the basic version but is considerably heavier, due mainly to the use of a larger engine and an increase in fuel capacity. It is available in materials kit and quick build kit forms.

TYPE: Single-seat homebuilt.

POWER PLANT: One 38.8 kW (52 hp) Rotax 503. Fuel capacity 30 litres (8 US gallons; 6.66 Imp gallons).

WEIGHTS:

Weight empty	134 kg (295 lb)
Max T-O weight	272 kg (600 lb)

PERFORMANCE:

Max level speed	87 knots (161 km/h; 100 mph)
Cruising speed	74 knots (137 km/h; 85 mph)
Stalling speed	26 knots (48 km/h; 30 mph)

Max rate of climb at S/L	274 m (900 ft)/min
T-O run	30 m (99 ft)
Landing run	46 m (149 ft)
Range at cruising speed	260 nm (482 km; 300 miles)

CARLSON SPARROW II

This is basically an enlarged side by side two-seat derivative of the Sparrow Sport Special, offering dual controls, short field performance, 38 litre (10 US gallon; 8.3 Imp gallon) fuel capacity, and a baggage compartment with a 9 kg (20 lb) capacity. Options will include different engines (after testing), and ski and float landing gears. Although it is planned to offer kits, consideration was being given to certificating the aircraft for factory-built status.

TYPE: Side by side two-seat homebuilt.

DIMENSIONS, EXTERNAL:

Wing span	9.75 m (32 ft 0 in)
Length overall	5.49 m (18 ft 0 in)
Height overall	2.13 m (7 ft 0 in)

AREA:

Wings, gross	13.38 m² (144.0 sq ft)

WEIGHTS (48.5 kW; 65 hp engine):

Weight empty	177 kg (390 lb)
Max T-O weight	395 kg (870 lb)

PERFORMANCE (48.5 kW; 65 hp engine):

Max level speed	82 knots (153 km/h; 95 mph)
Cruising speed	74 knots (137 km/h; 85 mph)
Stalling speed	26 knots (47 km/h; 29 mph)
Max rate of climb at S/L	305 m (1,000 ft)/min
T-O and landing run	61 m (200 ft)
Range at cruising speed	260 nm (483 km; 300 miles)

CARLSON SKYCYCLE '87

Designed and built by Mr Neal K. Carlson, the original Skycycle first appeared in 1945. The fuselage was constructed from a Second World War drop tank. Only the prototype was built (with a 41 kW; 55 hp Textron Lycoming O-145A engine) and this was destroyed in a fire in about 1946.

The much refined Skycycle '87 may now be available in ready assembled form. The basic structure is of welded steel tubing, with glassfibre skins and a Plexiglas bubble canopy. Anticipated empty weight was 134 kg (295 lb) with a 44.7 kW (60 hp) engine installed.

The following dimensions refer to the original Skycycle, but are likely to be close to those for the Skycycle '87.

DIMENSIONS, EXTERNAL (original Skycycle prototype):

Wing span	6.10 m (20 ft 0 in)
Length overall	4.83 m (15 ft 10 in)

CHRISTEN

CHRISTEN INDUSTRIES INC

PO Box 547, Afton, Wyoming 83110
Telephone: 1 (307) 886 3151
PRESIDENT: E. H. Anderson Jnr
MARKETING DEPARTMENT: Verdean Heiner

CHRISTEN EAGLE II

The Eagle II flew for the first time in February 1977. By 1990, construction of more than 650 Eagle IIs had started

and about 300 were known to have been completed by amateur builders. Each aircraft is built from 25 parts kits, requiring 1,400-1,600 working hours to assemble.

TYPE: Two-seat unlimited class homebuilt aerobatic biplane.

AIRFRAME: Wooden wing spars and ribs; metal leading-and trailing-edges, polyester fabric covered. Symmetrical wing section. Ailerons on upper and lower wings, of similar construction to wings. Welded steel tube fuselage, covered with removable light alloy panels from firewall to back of rear seat and fabric over rear fuselage. Welded steel tube tail unit, fabric covered. Non-retractable tailwheel landing gear.

POWER PLANT: One 149 kW (200 hp) Textron Lycoming AEIO-360-A1D. Fuel capacity 98.4 litres (26 US gallons; 21.6 Imp gallons). Fuel system allows unlimited inverted flight.

DIMENSIONS, EXTERNAL:

Wing span	6.07 m (19 ft 11 in)
Length overall	5.64 m (18 ft 6 in)
Height overall	1.98 m (6 ft 6 in)
Propeller diameter	1.93 m (6 ft 4 in)

AREA:

Wings, gross	11.61 m² (125.0 sq ft)

Cabrinha two-seat homebuilt aircraft carrying previous name on fuselage
(J. M. G. Gradidge)

Carlson Sparrow II two-seat homebuilt *(Geoffrey P. Jones)*

Christen Industries Eagle II two-seat aerobatic biplane built by Mr B. H.
Grant McKay and Mr Bob Petryk of Calgary, Alberta, Canada
(Neil A. Macdougall)

First prototype Cirrus Design Corporation Cirrus VK30 four/five-seat
homebuilt aircraft

Collins Aero W-7 Dipper amphibious flying-boat

WEIGHTS:
Weight empty 465 kg (1,025 lb)
Baggage capacity 13.6 kg (30 lb)
Max T-O and landing weight 725 kg (1,600 lb)
PERFORMANCE:
Max level speed at S/L 160 knots (296 km/h; 184 mph)

Econ cruising speed at 1,825 m (6,000 ft)
137 knots (254 km/h; 158 mph)
Stalling speed 51 knots (94 km/h; 58 mph)
Max rate of climb at S/L 645 m (2,120 ft)/min
Service ceiling 5,180 m (17,000 ft)
T-O run 244 m (800 ft)

Landing from 15 m (50 ft) 480 m (1,575 ft)
Range with max fuel and max payload
330 nm (611 km; 380 miles)
g limits +9/-6

CIRRUS
CIRRUS DESIGN CORPORATION
Baraboo-Dells Airport, S3440A Highway 12, Baraboo,
Wisconsin 53913
Telephone: 1 (608) 356 3460
PRESIDENT: Alan Klapmeier

CIRRUS DESIGN CIRRUS VK30
First flown on 11 February 1988, the Cirrus is available in
prefabricated kit form and about 18 had been sold by early
1990, of which seven had been delivered. Major design
features include new laminar flow wing sections, large
Fowler flaps, and a tail mounted pusher propeller. A second
prototype was expected to fly in March 1990, featuring a
new instrument panel with moving map display. Its IO-540
engine will later be replaced by a 261 kW (350 hp) V-8.
TYPE: Four/five-seat high-performance homebuilt.

AIRFRAME: Cantilever low-wing monoplane. Wing sections
based on NASA NLF(1)-0414F. Wings constructed of
glassfibre and PVC foam, with graphite spar. Fuselage
has polyurethane foam core, graphite longerons and
glassfibre skins. Ailerons/Fowler flaps/cruise flaps are
of graphite/PVC/vinylester, and rudder/elevators of
Kevlar/PVC/vinylester. Retractable tricycle landing gear.
POWER PLANT: Usually one 216 kW (290 hp) Textron
Lycoming IO-540-G1A5; one kit built aircraft has 313
kW (420 shp) Allison 250 turboprop. Recommended
engine power 216-261 kW (290-350 hp). Fuel capacity
360 litres (95 US gallons; 79 Imp gallons). Engine options
will be researched at a later date.
DIMENSIONS, EXTERNAL:
Wing span 11.79 m (38 ft 8 in)
Length overall 7.92 m (26 ft 0 in)
Height overall 3.25 m (10 ft 8 in)
Propeller diameter 1.88 m (6 ft 2 in)

AREA:
Wings, gross 11.15 m² (120.0 sq ft)
WEIGHTS (prototype):
Weight empty 998 kg (2,200 lb)
Max T-O weight 1,565 kg (3,450 lb)
PERFORMANCE (prototype, with IO-540-G1A5 engine):
Max cruising speed 225 knots (417 km/h; 259 mph)
Cruising speed, 75% power
217 knots (402 km/h; 250 mph)
Stalling speed, flaps down, engine idling
56 knots (104 km/h; 65 mph)
Max rate of climb at S/L 457 m (1,500 ft)/min
T-O and landing run 457 m (1,500 ft)
Range, with max fuel, 75% power, with reserves
1,129 nm (2,092 km; 1,300 miles)
g limits +5/-3

COLLINS
COLLINS AERO
386 Fairville Road RD1, Chadds Ford, Pennsylvania 19317
Telephone: 1 (215) 388 2393
OWNER: Willard C. Collins

COLLINS AERO W-7 DIPPER
The Dipper prototype made its first flight on 24 August
1982. An information brochure and plans are available to
amateur constructors.

TYPE: Side by side two-seat homebuilt amphibious flying-
boat.
AIRFRAME: Uses aluminium alloy wings from a Cessna 150,
with floats added close to wingtips. Modified Cessna 150
basic fuselage, with instrument panel and windscreen
moved forward by 0.91 m (3 ft 0 in) and glassfibre
two-step boat hull and nose cowling added for water
operations. Basic Cessna 150 tail unit, but with fin of
increased height and tailplane raised by 0.46 m (1 ft 6 in).
Dorsal fin added. Retractable tricycle landing gear.

POWER PLANT: One 134 kW (180 hp) Textron Lycoming
O-360. Fuel capacity 148 litres (39 US gallons; 32.5 Imp
gallons).
DIMENSIONS, EXTERNAL:
Wing span 10.16 m (33 ft 4 in)
Length overall 7.72 m (25 ft 4 in)
Height overall 2.84 m (9 ft 4 in)
Propeller diameter 1.88 m (6 ft 2 in)
AREA:
Wings, gross 14.86 m² (160.0 sq ft)

WEIGHTS:
Weight empty, equipped	481 kg (1,060 lb)
Max T-O weight	798 kg (1,760 lb)

PERFORMANCE:
Max level speed at 2,135 m (7,000 ft)
120 knots (222 km/h; 138 mph)

Econ cruising speed	100 knots (185 km/h; 115 mph)
Stalling speed	39 knots (73 km/h; 45 mph)
Max rate of climb at S/L	427 m (1,400 ft)/min
Service ceiling	6,700 m (22,000 ft)

T-O run	122 m (400 ft)
Landing run	152 m (500 ft)
Range with max fuel	500 nm (926 km; 575 miles)

COUNTRY AIR
COUNTRY AIR INC
1230 Shepherd Street, Hendersonville, North Carolina 28739
Telephone: 1 (704) 692 7784
OWNER: Jesse D. Anglin

COUNTRY AIR J-6 KARATOO
Kits are available to amateur constructors. The following details are based on the Grover J-6 Karatoo, from which the Country Air model was derived.
TYPE: Side by side two-seat homebuilt.
AIRFRAME: Fabric covered airframe. Non-retractable tailwheel landing gear.
POWER PLANT: Powered normally by a 39 kW (52 hp) Rotax 503. A 48.5 kW (65 hp) Volkswagen engine is optional.
DIMENSIONS, EXTERNAL:
Wing span	9.91 m (32 ft 6 in)
Length overall	6.10 m (20 ft 0 in)
Height overall	1.68 m (5 ft 6 in)

AREA:
Wings, gross	13.56 m² (146.0 sq ft)

WEIGHTS (Rotax engine):
Weight empty	172 kg (380 lb)
Max T-O weight	408 kg (900 lb)

PERFORMANCE (Rotax engine):
Max level speed	74 knots (137 km/h; 85 mph)
Cruising speed	65 knots (120 km/h; 75 mph)
Max rate of climb at S/L	228 m (750 ft)/min
T-O run	46 m (150 ft)

COUNTRY AIR SPACE WALKER
The Space Walker is designed to look like Ryan monoplanes of the late 1930s and early 1940s but is built of modern materials and uses a modern engine. Drawings and component parts are available to amateur constructors. A ready assembled microlight version was to follow.
TYPE: Single-seat homebuilt.
AIRFRAME: Fabric covered wooden wings. Welded chrome-molybdenum steel tube fuselage and wire braced tail unit, also fabric covered. Non-retractable tailwheel landing gear.
POWER PLANT: One 48.5-63 kW (65-85 hp) Teledyne Continental. Fuel capacity 38 litres (10 US gallons; 8.3 Imp gallons).
DIMENSIONS, EXTERNAL:
Wing span	7.93 m (26 ft 0 in)
Length overall	5.49 m (18 ft 0 in)
Height overall	1.60 m (5 ft 3 in)

AREA:
Wings, gross	10.87 m² (117.0 sq ft)

WEIGHTS (48.5 kW; 65 hp Teledyne Continental):
Weight empty	245 kg (540 lb)
Max T-O weight	385 kg (850 lb)

PERFORMANCE (48.5 kW; 65 hp Teledyne Continental):
Max level speed at S/L	108 knots (201 km/h; 125 mph)
Cruising speed	97 knots (180 km/h; 112 mph)
Stalling speed: power off	37 knots (68 km/h; 42 mph)
power on	33 knots (61 km/h; 38 mph)
Max rate of climb at S/L	259 m (850 ft)/min
g limits	+6/–5

CVJETKOVIC
ANTON CVJETKOVIC
5324 West 121 Street, Hawthorne, California 90250
Telephone: 1 (213) 643 6931

CVJETKOVIC CA-61/-61R MINI ACE
The CA-61 can be built as a single-seat or side by side two-seat light aircraft, with any Teledyne Continental engine of between 48.5 and 63.5 kW (65 and 85 hp), and with non-retractable tailwheel landing gear or retractable gear (as the **CA-61R**). Alternatively, the single-seater can be fitted with a modified Volkswagen engine. Plans are available. Construction takes less than 1,000 h.
The following details refer specifically to the single-seat CA-61 prototype:
TYPE: Single-seat homebuilt.
AIRFRAME: All-wood construction, with fabric only over wings and ailerons. Wing section NACA 4415. Landing gear as detailed above.
POWER PLANT: Engine options as detailed above. Fuel capacity 64 litres (17 US gallons; 14.2 Imp gallons).
DIMENSIONS, EXTERNAL:
Wing span	8.38 m (27 ft 6 in)
Length overall	5.77 m (18 ft 11 in)
Height overall (in flying position)	2.08 m (6 ft 10 in)

AREA:
Wings, gross	11.75 m² (126.5 sq ft)

WEIGHTS:
Weight empty: single-seat	275 kg (606 lb)
two-seat	363 kg (800 lb)
Max T-O weight: single-seat	430 kg (950 lb)
two-seat	590 kg (1,300 lb)

PERFORMANCE:
Max level speed at S/L	104 knots (193 km/h; 120 mph)
Normal cruising speed	87 knots (161 km/h; 100 mph)

Min flying speed:
single-seat	37 knots (68 km/h; 42 mph)
two-seat	44 knots (81 km/h; 50 mph)

Range with max fuel:
single-seat	369 nm (685 km; 425 miles)
two-seat	321 nm (595 km; 370 miles)

CVJETKOVIC CA-65
The prototype CA-65 flew for the first time in July 1965. Plans are available.
TYPE: Two-seat, dual-control homebuilt.
AIRFRAME: All-wood construction, with fabric covering only on ailerons, elevators and rudder. Modified NACA 4415 wing section. Retractable tailwheel landing gear.
POWER PLANT: One 93 kW (125 hp) Textron Lycoming O-290-G. Other Textron Lycoming engines of 80.5-112 kW; (108-150 hp) can be fitted. Fuel capacity 106 litres (28 US gallons; 23.3 Imp gallons).
DIMENSIONS, EXTERNAL:
Wing span	7.62 m (25 ft 0 in)
Length overall	5.79 m (19 ft 0 in)
Height overall (in flying position)	2.24 m (7 ft 4 in)
Propeller diameter	1.73 m (5 ft 8 in)

AREA:
Wings, gross	10.03 m² (108.0 sq ft)

WEIGHTS:
Weight empty	408 kg (900 lb)
Max T-O weight	680 kg (1,500 lb)

PERFORMANCE (at max T-O weight):
Max level speed	156 knots (290 km/h; 180 mph)
Normal cruising speed	135 knots (249 km/h; 155 mph)
Stalling speed	48 knots (89 km/h; 55 mph)
Max rate of climb at S/L	305 m (1,000 ft)/min
Service ceiling	4,575 m (15,000 ft)
T-O run	137 m (450 ft)
Landing run	183 m (600 ft)
Range with max fuel	434 nm (804 km; 500 miles)
g limits	+9/–6 ultimate

CVJETKOVIC CA-65A
This is an all-metal version of the wooden CA-65.
POWER PLANT: Structure is designed to accommodate a Textron Lycoming engine of 80.5-112 kW (108-150 hp).
DIMENSIONS, EXTERNAL: As for Model CA-65 except:
Wing span	7.75 m (25 ft 5 in)
Length overall	5.99 m (19 ft 8 in)
Height overall	2.29 m (7 ft 6 in)

AREA:
Wings, gross	10.16 m² (109.4 sq ft)

PERFORMANCE (112 kW; 150 hp engine):
Max level speed	151 knots (280 km/h; 174 mph)
Normal cruising speed	130 knots (241 km/h; 150 mph)
Stalling speed	48 knots (89 km/h; 55 mph)
Max rate of climb at S/L	466 m (1,530 ft)/min
Service ceiling	4,570 m (15,000 ft)
T-O run	99 m (325 ft)
Landing run	183 m (600 ft)
Range with max fuel	460 nm (853 km; 530 miles)
g limits	+9/–6 ultimate

D 2
D 2 INC
PO Box 265, Bend, Oregon 97709
PROPRIETOR: Sidney L. Ellis
D 2 Inc acquired the designs of the Davis DA-2A and DA-5A and the Aerosport Quail, and is remarketing them.

D 2 (DAVIS) DA-2A
This two-seat homebuilt was flown for the first time on 21 May 1966. D 2 Inc offers both plans and kits of the DA-2A.
The DA-2A is of all-metal construction, with a V tail and non-retractable tricycle landing gear. Power plant in the prototype was a 48.5 kW (65 hp) Teledyne Continental A65-8, but the DA-2A is stressed for engines of up to 74.5 kW (100 hp). Fuel capacity is 75 litres (20 US gallons; 16.7 Imp gallons).
There is baggage space aft of the side by side seats or, alternatively, a child's seat may be located in this position.
DIMENSIONS, EXTERNAL:
Wing span	5.86 m (19 ft 2¾ in)
Length overall	5.44 m (17 ft 10¼ in)
Height overall	1.65 m (5 ft 5 in)

AREA:
Wings, gross	7.66 m² (82.5 sq ft)

WEIGHTS (A65-8 engine):
Weight empty	277 kg (610 lb)
Max T-O weight	510 kg (1,125 lb)

PERFORMANCE (A65-8 engine):
Max level speed at S/L	104 knots (193 km/h; 120 mph)
Cruising speed	100 knots (185 km/h; 115 mph)
Range with max fuel	390 nm (725 km; 450 miles)

D 2 (DAVIS) DA-5A
The first flight of the DA-5A was made on 22 July 1974. Plans are available to amateur constructors.
TYPE: Single-seat homebuilt aircraft.
AIRFRAME: All-metal stressed-skin construction with a V tail. Wing section Clark Y. Non-retractable tricycle landing gear.
POWER PLANT: One 48.5 kW (65 hp) Teledyne Continental A65. Fuel capacity 64.3 litres (17 US gallons; 14.2 Imp gallons).
DIMENSIONS, EXTERNAL:
Wing span	4.76 m (15 ft 7¼ in)
Length overall	4.80 m (15 ft 9 in)
Height overall	1.35 m (4 ft 5¼ in)
Propeller diameter	1.52 m (5 ft 0 in)

AREA:
Wings, gross	5.31 m² (57.2 sq ft)

WEIGHTS:
Weight empty	208 kg (460 lb)
Max T-O weight	351 kg (775 lb)

PERFORMANCE (at max T-O weight):
Max level speed at S/L	139 knots (257 km/h; 160 mph)
Econ cruising speed at S/L	104 knots (193 km/h; 120 mph)
Stalling speed	52 knots (97 km/h; 60 mph)
Max rate of climb at S/L	244 m (800 ft)/min
Service ceiling	4,420 m (14,500 ft)
T-O run	183 m (600 ft)
Landing run	183 m (600 ft)
Range with max fuel	390 nm (724 km; 450 miles)

D 2 (AEROSPORT) QUAIL
The Quail, designed by Aerosport Inc, flew for the first time in December 1971. Plans and kits are available from D 2 Inc.
TYPE: Single-seat homebuilt.
AIRFRAME: All-metal construction. Wing section NACA 23015. Non-retractable tricycle landing gear.
POWER PLANT: One 1,600 cc modified Volkswagen motorcar engine. Provision for other Volkswagen engines from 1,500 cc to 1,800 cc capacity. Fuel capacity 38 litres (10 US gallons; 8.3 Imp gallons).
DIMENSIONS, EXTERNAL:
Wing span	7.32 m (24 ft 0 in)
Length overall	4.85 m (15 ft 11 in)
Height overall	1.69 m (5 ft 6½ in)
Propeller diameter	1.37 m (4 ft 6 in)

AREA:
Wings, gross	7.8 m² (84.0 sq ft)

WEIGHTS:
Weight empty	242 kg (534 lb)
Baggage capacity	9 kg (20 lb)
Normal T-O weight	345 kg (762 lb)
Max T-O weight	359 kg (792 lb)

PERFORMANCE (at max T-O weight):
Max level speed at S/L	113 knots (209 km/h; 130 mph)
Econ cruising speed	96 knots (177 km/h; 110 mph)
Stalling speed, flaps down	42 knots (78 km/h; 48 mph)
Max rate of climb at S/L	259 m (850 ft)/min
Service ceiling (estimated)	3,660 m (12,000 ft)
T-O run	91 m (300 ft)
Landing run	122 m (400 ft)

Range with max fuel, no reserves
200 nm (370 km; 230 miles)

Country Air Space Walker homebuilt *(Geoffrey P. Jones)*

Country Air J-6 Karatoo *(J. M. G. Gradidge)*

Cvjetkovic CA-65, with extended propeller shaft and landing gear doors

D 2 (Davis) DA-2A built by Mr Wade Hammer of Augusta, Georgia
(Geoffrey P. Jones)

D 2 (Aerosport) Quail single-seat homebuilt aircraft

D 2 (Davis) DA-5A single-seat homebuilt sporting aircraft *(J. M. G. Gradidge)*

Prototype D'Apuzzo D-201 Sportwing, built by Mr Larry Stangil of Ferndale, Pennsylvania

Davis DA-7, intended for FAA certification *(Howard Levy)*

D'APUZZO
NICHOLAS E. D'APUZZO
102 Blue Rock Lane, Blue Bell, Pennsylvania 19422
Telephone: 1 (215) 646 4792

D'APUZZO D-201 SPORTWING
The D-201 is a development of the earlier PJ-260/D-260 Senior Aero Sport series. Plans and partial kits of the D-201 are available.
TYPE: Tandem two-seat homebuilt sporting biplane.
AIRFRAME: All-metal construction, except for fabric covering of the rear fuselage. Wing section NACA M-12 (modified). Non-retractable tailwheel landing gear.
POWER PLANT: One 119 kW (160 hp) Textron Lycoming IO-320-B1A. Design suitable for any Textron Lycoming engine from the 93 kW (125 hp) O-235 to the 149 kW (200 hp) O-360.
DIMENSIONS, EXTERNAL:
Wing span: upper	8.23 m (27 ft 0 in)
lower	7.86 m (25 ft 9½ in)
Length overall, tail up	6.59 m (21 ft 7½ in)
Height overall, tail down	2.34 m (7 ft 8 in)

AREA:
Wings, gross	17.14 m² (184.5 sq ft)

WEIGHTS:
Weight empty	591 kg (1,303 lb)
Design max T-O weight	862 kg (1,900 lb)

PERFORMANCE (at max T-O weight):
Max level speed at 2,135 m (7,000 ft)	115 knots (212 km/h; 132 mph)
Max cruising speed at 2,135 m (7,000 ft)	106 knots (196 km/h; 122 mph)
Stalling speed	41 knots (76 km/h; 47 mph)
Max rate of climb at S/L	320 m (1,050 ft)/min
T-O run	128 m (420 ft)
Landing run	168 m (550 ft)
Range with max fuel	313 nm (579 km; 360 miles)

DAVIS
LEEON D. DAVIS
PLANS AND PARTS: Joe Gauthier, GFG Enterprises, 9 Kowal Drive, Cromwell, Connecticut 06416
Telephone: 1 (203) 635 4058

DAVIS DA-7
The side by side two-seat DA-7 was designed for certification in the proposed Primary Aircraft category and subsequent commercial production in ready to fly form. It is of conventional light alloy construction, with a V tail. Wing section is USA 35B, and power is provided by an 86 kW (115 hp) Textron Lycoming O-235-L2C engine.
DIMENSIONS, EXTERNAL:
Wing span	6.25 m (20 ft 6 in)
Length overall	5.84 m (19 ft 2 in)

AREA:
Wings, gross	8.33 m² (89.7 sq ft)

WEIGHTS:
Weight empty	327 kg (720 lb)
Max T-O weight	576 kg (1,270 lb)

PERFORMANCE:
Max cruising speed (75% power)	126 knots (233 km/h; 145 mph)
Stalling speed	51 knots (94 km/h; 58 mph)

DAVIS WING

DAVIS WING LTD

PO Box 1103, Nampa, Idaho 83653-1103
PRESIDENT: Gilbert E. Davis

DAVIS WING STARCRUISER GEMINI

The single-seat prototype Davis Wing, known as *Alpha*, was flown for the first time on 10 June 1986. Kits are to be offered for a five-seat version, the Starcruiser Gemini.

TYPE: Five-seat homebuilt flying wing.

AIRFRAME: Majority of airframe built of pre-moulded composites, including glassfibre, Nomex honeycomb, aramid fibres, graphite fibres and various foams. Other materials include 4130 steel tubing, stainless steel and aluminium alloy. Elevons and split drag rudders. Retractable tricycle landing gear.

POWER PLANT: One 112 kW (150 hp) Textron Lycoming O-320. Fuel capacity 340 litres (90 US gallons; 75 Imp gallons) standard and 1,060 litres (280 US gallons; 233 Imp gallons) optional.

DIMENSIONS, EXTERNAL:

Wing span	12.19 m (40 ft 0 in)
Length overall	3.66 m (12 ft 0 in)
Height to top of canopy	1.52 m (5 ft 0 in)
Propeller diameter	1.73 m (5 ft 8 in)

AREA:

Wings, gross	20.09 m² (216.22 sq ft)

WEIGHTS:

Weight empty	445 kg (980 lb)
* Baggage capacity	285-517 kg (630-1,140 lb)
Max T-O weight	1,361 kg (3,000 lb)

PERFORMANCE (at max T-O weight):

Max level speed at S/L	161 knots (298 km/h; 185 mph)
Econ cruising speed at 3,660 m (12,000 ft)	
	133 knots (246 km/h; 153 mph)
Stalling speed	45 knots (84 km/h; 52 mph)
Max rate of climb at S/L	396 m (1,300 ft)/min
Max operating height	7,315 m (24,000 ft)
T-O run at normal T-O weight	137 m (450 ft)
Landing run	152 m (500 ft)
Range, max fuel, no reserves	
	1,736 nm (3,218 km; 2,000 miles)
Max endurance	15 h
g limits, normal T-O weight	+6/-3

* *Larger capacity with two people and 90 US gallons of fuel only.*

DENNEY

DENNEY AEROCRAFT COMPANY

Nampa Municipal Airport, 100 North Kings Road, Nampa, Idaho 83687
Telephone: 1 (208) 466 1711
Fax: 1 (208) 466 7194
PRESIDENT: Dan Denney

DENNEY AEROCRAFT KITFOX

The Kitfox was designed to have exceptional short-field performance. The prototype first flew on 7 May 1984. It is marketed in kit form, and by early 1990 more than 625 kits had been sold, of which more than 275 had been assembled. In addition, the aircraft is being manufactured under licence in Australia, Brazil, the Philippines (as the PAC Skyfox: see main Aircraft section), Portugal and South Africa. A specially equipped version has also been delivered for police duties.

TYPE: Side by side two-seat, dual control homebuilt.

AIRFRAME: Wings have extruded spars of aluminium alloy tubing, plywood ribs and drooped glassfibre tips, with Stits Poly-Fiber covering overall. Steel tube fuselage and tail unit, with Poly-Fiber covering. Non-retractable tailwheel landing gear, with brakes. Optional floats, amphibious floats, skis and underfuselage cargo pods.

POWER PLANT: One 48.5 kW (65 hp) Rotax 582 LC, with 2.58 : 1 reduction gear. Fuel capacity 36 litres (9.5 US gallons; 8 Imp gallons) standard. Two 22.7 litre (6 US gallon; 5 Imp gallon) or one 51 litre (13.5 US gallon; 11.25 Imp gallon) optional fuel tanks in wings.

DIMENSIONS, EXTERNAL:

Wing span	9.55 m (31 ft 4 in)
Length overall	5.38 m (17 ft 8 in)
Height overall	1.73 m (5 ft 8 in)
Propeller diameter	1.68 m (5 ft 6 in)

AREA:

Wings, gross	11.92 m² (128.3 sq ft)

WEIGHTS:

Weight empty	195 kg (430 lb)
Pilot weight range	68-113 kg (150-250 lb)
Max recommended pilot and passenger weight	
	181 kg (400 lb)
Max T-O weight	431 kg (950 lb)

PERFORMANCE (two crew, unless stated otherwise):

Max level speed	87 knots (161 km/h; 100 mph)
Cruising speed	69-74 knots (129-137 km/h; 80-85 mph)
Stalling speed	26 knots (49 km/h; 30 mph)
Max rate of climb at S/L	396 m (1,300 ft)/min
Service ceiling, pilot only	6,100 m (20,000 ft)
T-O run, pilot only	23 m (75 ft)
Landing run	46 m (150 ft)
Range	195 nm (362 km; 225 miles)
Endurance	3 h
g limits, pilot only	+6/-3

DURAND

DURAND ASSOCIATES INC

84th and McKinley Road, Omaha, Nebraska 68122
Telephone: 1 (402) 571 7058
PRESIDENT: W. H. Durand

DURAND Mk V

The prototype Durand Mk V flew for the first time on 28 June 1978. Plans are available to amateur builders, and at least 84 sets had been sold by early 1990.

TYPE: Two-seat, dual-control homebuilt biplane.

AIRFRAME: All-metal (light alloy) construction, with negative wing stagger. Full span flaps on upper wing. Anti-servo trim tabs on tailplane. Wing section NACA 23012. Non-retractable tricycle landing gear.

POWER PLANT: One 112-119 kW (150-160 hp) Textron Lycoming O-320. Fuel capacity 93 litres (24.5 US gallons; 20.4 Imp gallons). Two auxiliary wing tanks optional, each 15 litres (4 US gallons; 3.33 Imp gallons).

DIMENSIONS, EXTERNAL:

Wing span, both	7.47 m (24 ft 6 in)
Length overall	6.17 m (20 ft 3 in)
Height overall	2.03 m (6 ft 8 in)
Propeller diameter	1.83 m (6 ft 0 in)

AREA:

Wings, gross	13.38 m² (144.0 sq ft)

WEIGHTS:

Weight empty	549 kg (1,210 lb)
Baggage capacity	58 kg (128 lb)
Max T-O weight	834 kg (1,840 lb)

PERFORMANCE (at max T-O weight):

Max cruising speed at 2,285 m (7,500 ft)	
	117 knots (217 km/h; 135 mph)
Econ cruising speed at 2,285 m (7,500 ft)	
	109 knots (201 km/h; 125 mph)
Max rate of climb at S/L	366 m (1,200 ft)/min
Absolute ceiling, estimated	4,575 m (15,000 ft)
T-O run	168 m (550 ft)
Landing run	137 m (450 ft)
Range, no reserves:	
standard fuel	347 nm (644 km; 400 miles)
max optional fuel	451 nm (837 km; 520 miles)
g limits:	+3.8/-1.52
	+5.7/-2.28 ultimate design

DYKE

DYKE AIRCRAFT

2840 Old Yellow Springs Road, Fairborn, Ohio 45324
Telephone: 1 (513) 878 9832
DESIGNER: John W. Dyke

DYKE AIRCRAFT JD-2 DELTA

Plans of the JD-2 are available to amateur constructors, and a total of about 360 were thought to be under construction in early 1990. Hardware and tubing kits are available.

TYPE: Delta-winged four-seat homebuilt.

AIRFRAME: Delta wing of modified NACA 63012 and 66015 section. Wings, fuselage and tail unit have welded steel tube structures. Wings use stainless steel capstrips to which laminated glassfibre skins are secured by pop rivets (optional aluminium skins). Fuselage similar except for steel tube capstrips and Poly-Fiber covering on undersurface. Elevons and tail unit Poly-Fiber covered. Optional all-moving T tail of all-metal construction for improved low-speed trim with heavier engine. Retractable tricycle landing gear.

POWER PLANT: Prototype has one 134 kW (180 hp) Textron Lycoming O-360. 149 kW (200 hp) engine installation optional. Fuel capacity 178 litres (47 US gallons; 39.1 Imp gallons), with pilot and two passengers. Fuel capacity reduced to 117 litres (31 US gallons; 26 Imp gallons) as a four-seat aircraft.

DIMENSIONS, EXTERNAL:

Wing span	6.87 m (22 ft 2½ in)
Length overall	5.79 m (19 ft 0 in)
Height overall	1.68 m (5 ft 6 in)
Propeller diameter	1.88 m (6 ft 2 in)

AREA:

Wings, gross	16.07 m² (173.0 sq ft)

WEIGHTS (with 134 kW; 180 hp or 149 kW; 200 hp engine):

Weight empty: basic equipped	481 kg (1,060 lb)
IFR equipped	490 kg (1,080 lb)
Baggage capacity	45.4 kg (100 lb)
Max T-O weight	884 kg (1,950 lb)

PERFORMANCE (at max T-O weight with 134 kW; 180 hp engine, except where indicated):

Max level speed at 2,285 m (7,500 ft), constant-speed propeller	174 knots (322 km/h; 200 mph)
Econ cruising speed at 2,285 m (7,500 ft)	
	135 knots (249 km/h; 155 mph)
Max rate of climb at S/L	610 m (2,000 ft)/min
Service ceiling	4,420 m (14,500 ft)
T-O run	213 m (700 ft)
Landing run	244-305 m (800-1,000 ft)
Range: with max fuel and pilot only, at 66% power	
	755 nm (1,400 km; 870 miles)
with max payload	576 nm (1,067 km; 663 miles)

EARTHSTAR

EARTHSTAR AIRCRAFT INC

Route 313, Santa Margarita, California 93453
Telephone: 1 (805) 438 5235
DESIGNER AND PRESIDENT: Mark H. Beierle

EARTHSTAR LAUGHING GULL and LAUGHING GULL II

The first of five prototype Laughing Gulls flew in 1976. The single-seat model is available in ready assembled **LG1** form with a Rotax 277 engine, or as an **LG1H** microlight or homebuilt kit with engine options of up to 30 kW (40 hp). The two-seat **T2** Laughing Gull II is fitted with dual controls as a trainer, and **T2H** homebuilt kits are available with engine options of up to 47 kW (63 hp). A cropduster model is also available. Construction time is estimated at 160-190 working hours for the LG1H, and 180-250 for the T2H.

TYPES: Single-seat (Laughing Gull) and two-seat (Laughing Gull II) single-engined microlight and homebuilt aircraft; conform to FAR Pt 103/7 in LG1 and T2 forms and FAA Experimental requirements in LG1H and T2H homebuilt forms.

AIRFRAME: Welded steel tube fuselage; fully enclosed cockpit with glassfibre nosecone. Airframe structure, other than fuselage, of aluminium alloy. Double surface wings with Dacron covering. Three-axis control. Non-retractable tricycle, or optionally tailwheel, landing gear.

POWER PLANT: *Laughing Gull:* standard engine is 20 kW (27 hp) Rotax 277. Homebuilt version can have engine of up to 30 kW (40 hp). Fuel capacity 38 litres (10 US gallons; 8.3 Imp gallons). *Laughing Gull II:* standard engine is 47 kW (63 hp) Rotax 532. *Homebuilt* version can have engine of up to 47 kW (63 hp). Optional engines include a conversion of the Honda Civic motorcar engine, or a Chevrolet Sprint. Fuel capacity 38 litres (10 US gallons; 8.3 Imp gallons).

DIMENSIONS, EXTERNAL (A: LG1, B: T2):

Wing span: A		9.14 m (30 ft 0 in)
B		9.75 m (32 ft 0 in)
Length overall: A		5.72 m (18 ft 9 in)
B		6.10 m (20 ft 0 in)
Height overall: A		2.13 m (7 ft 0 in)
B		2.29 m (7 ft 6 in)
Propeller diameter: A		1.52 m (5 ft 0 in)

AREAS (A and B as above):

Wings, gross: A	13.94 m² (150.0 sq ft)
B	14.86 m² (160.0 sq ft)

WEIGHTS (A and B as above):

Weight empty: A	113 kg (250 lb)
B	156.5 kg (345 lb)
Max T-O weight: A	227 kg (500 lb)
B	363 kg (800 lb)

PERFORMANCE (A: LG1, B: T2H, unless stated otherwise):

Max level speed: A	55 knots (101 km/h; 63 mph)
B	91 knots (169 km/h; 105 mph)
Cruising speed:	
A	48-52 knots (89-97 km/h; 55-60 mph)
B	74-78 knots (137-145 km/h; 85-90 mph)
Stalling speed: A	22 knots (41 km/h; 25 mph)
B	28 knots (52 km/h; 32 mph)
Max rate of climb at S/L: A	274 m (900 ft)/min
B	244 m (800 ft)/min
Service ceiling: A, B	4,420 m (14,500 ft)

Modified Dyke Delta built by Mr Bernie Schaknowski (Textron Lycoming O-360 engine) *(Peter M. Bowers)*

Durand Mk V all-metal two-seat biplane *(Howard Levy)*

Davis Wing Starcruiser Gemini

Earthstar Laughing Gull II built by Mr Danny Romo *(John Wegg)*

Denney Kitfox owned by Mr Brian Davies in England *(Aviation Picture Library)*

Earthstar Ultra Gull U1 aircraft

Eich JE-2 Gyroplane (C85 engine) with pre-rotation gear fitted

T-O run: A	30 m (100 ft)
B	55 m (180 ft)
Landing run: A	30 m (100 ft)
B	61 m (200 ft)
Range with max fuel: A	132 nm (244 km; 152 miles)
g limits: A, B	+6/−4
Laughing Gull homebuilt	+7/−5
Laughing Gull II	+5.5/−3.8

EARTHSTAR THUNDER GULL

The Thunder Gull is similar to the Laughing Gull but is smaller and uses a 30 kW (40 hp) Rotax 447 engine.

DIMENSION, EXTERNAL:
Wing span	8.53 m (28 ft 0 in)

AREA:
Wings, gross	13.10 m² (141.0 sq ft)

WEIGHTS:
Weight empty	115 kg (253 lb)
Max T-O weight	227 kg (500 lb)

PERFORMANCE:
Max level speed	55 knots (101 km/h; 63 mph)
Cruising speed	52 knots (97 km/h; 60 mph)
Stalling speed	24 knots (44 km/h; 27 mph)

EARTHSTAR ULTRA GULL

The Ultra Gull has a special arrangement of high lift

devices allowing it to be so small that no rigging is necessary before flying (as it is trailered fully assembled). The tandem wing and vertical stabiliser arrangement controls the wingtip vortices, giving the aircraft extra stability and better performance.

Two versions are available: the basic ready assembled Ultra Gull **U1** microlight, with conventional three-axis control and a 20 kW (27 hp) Rotax 277 engine; and the kit-built Ultra Gull Homebuilt **U1H** with any Rotax engine of 20-44.7 kW (27-60 hp).

TYPES: U1: Single-seat microlight. U1H: Single-seat homebuilt.

AIRFRAME: Aluminium skinned wings, with tubular spar and foam core. Welded steel fuselage. Three-axis control. Landing gear as for Laughing Gull.

POWER PLANT: See introduction. U1 fuel capacity 19 litres (5 US gallons; 4.2 Imp gallons); U1H 38 litres (10 US gallons; 8.4 Imp gallons).

DIMENSIONS, EXTERNAL (A: U1, B: U1H):
Wing span: A	7.32 m (24 ft 0 in)
B	6.10 m (20 ft 0 in)
Length overall: A, B	3.20 m (10 ft 6 in)
Height overall: A, B	1.83 m (6 ft 0 in)
Propeller diameter: A	1.52 m (5 ft 0 in)
B	1.47 m (4 ft 10 in)

AREAS (A: U1, B: U1H):
Wings, gross: A	11.15 m² (120.0 sq ft)
B	9.29 m² (100.0 sq ft)

WEIGHTS (A: U1, B: U1H):
Weight empty: A	102 kg (225 lb)
B	more than 105 kg (232 lb)
Max pilot weight: A, B	100 kg (220 lb)
Max T-O weight: A, B	227 kg (500 lb)

PERFORMANCE (A: U1, B: U1H with 44.7 kW; 60 hp engine):
Max level speed: A	55 knots (101 km/h; 63 mph)
B	130 knots (241 km/h; 150 mph)
Cruising speed: A	52 knots (97 km/h; 60 mph)
B	122 knots (225 km/h; 140 mph)
Stalling speed: A	24 knots (44 km/h; 27 mph)
B	28 knots (52 km/h; 32 mph)
Max rate of climb at S/L: A	274 m (900 ft)/min
B	472 m (1,550 ft)/min
Service ceiling: A, B	4,420 m (14,500 ft)
T-O run: A	31 m (100 ft)
B	43 m (140 ft)
Landing run: A	37 m (120 ft)
B	40 m (130 ft)
Range with max fuel:	
A	over 147 nm (273 km; 170 miles)
B	over 260 nm (482 km; 300 miles)
g limits: A, B	±6

EICH
JAMES P. EICH
1820 West Grand Avenue, Alhambra, California 91801
Telephone: 1 (818) 289 1983

EICH JE-2 GYROPLANE
The prototype JE-2 first flew in 1977. Detailed drawings and instructions for building the aircraft are available from: Tech Man Company, 8525 E Duarte Road, San Gabriel, California 91775. At least 40 sets of plans have been sold.

The following details apply specifically to the prototype:
TYPE: Tandem two-seat, dual-control light autogyro.
ROTOR SYSTEM: Two-blade aluminium teetering rotor, with pre-rotation system.
AIRFRAME: Square section welded steel-tube girder fuselage,

covered with Dacron. Dacron fin integral with fuselage covering. Stabiliser and rudder of sheet aluminium. Non-retractable tricycle landing gear.

POWER PLANT: One 63.5 kW (85 hp) Teledyne Continental C85. Optional engines from A65 to O-200. Fuel capacity 64.5 litres (17 US gallons; 14.2 Imp gallons).

DIMENSIONS, EXTERNAL:

Main rotor diameter	7.92 m (26 ft 0 in)
Length of fuselage	4.27 m (14 ft 0 in)
Height overall	2.59 m (8 ft 6 in)
Propeller diameter	1.78 m (5 ft 10 in)

WEIGHTS:

Weight empty	211 kg (465 lb)
Max T-O weight	417 kg (920 lb)

PERFORMANCE (with current rotor blades):

Max level speed at 915 m (3,000 ft)	70 knots (129 km/h; 80 mph)
Econ cruising speed at 915 m (3,000 ft)	48 knots (89 km/h; 55 mph)
Min flying speed (no stall)	39 knots (73 km/h; 45 mph)
Max rate of climb at 915 m (3,000 ft)	91 m (300 ft)/min

T-O run with pre-rotation	153 m (500 ft)
Landing run	15 m (50 ft)
Range with max fuel and max payload	156 nm (290 km; 180 miles)

EVANS

EVANS AIRCRAFT

PO Box 744, La Jolla, California 92038

Designed for easy building and safety to fly, the single-seat Evans VP-1 is available in plans form. Those for European customers are supplied through the Popular Flying Association (PFA) in the UK (which see). VP-2 plans are no longer available. Details of this aircraft, and an illustration, can be found in the 1988-89 *Jane's*.

EVANS VP-1

TYPE: Single-seat homebuilt.

AIRFRAME: Virtually all-wood structure, with fabric covered wings and tail unit, and plywood covered fuselage with glassfibre fairing aft of pilot's seat. Wing section NACA 4412. Non-retractable tailskid landing gear. Enclosed cockpit optional.

POWER PLANT: One 30 kW, 39.5 kW or 44.5 kW (40 hp, 53 hp or 60 hp) modified Volkswagen motorcar engine. Fuel capacity 30 litres (8 US gallons; 6.7 Imp gallons).

DIMENSIONS, EXTERNAL:

Wing span	7.32 m (24 ft 0 in)
Length overall	5.49 m (18 ft 0 in)
Height overall	1.56 m (5 ft 1½ in)
Propeller diameter	1.37 m (4 ft 6 in)

AREA:

Wings, gross	9.29 m² (100.0 sq ft)

WEIGHTS:

Weight empty	200 kg (440 lb)
Max T-O weight	295-340 kg (650-750 lb)

PERFORMANCE (30 kW; 40 hp engine, at T-O weight of 295 kg; 650 lb):

Max level speed	82 knots (153 km/h; 95 mph)
Cruising speed	65 knots (121 km/h; 75 mph)
Stalling speed	35 knots (65 km/h; 40 mph)
Max rate of climb at S/L	122 m (400 ft)/min
T-O run (average breeze)	137 m (450 ft)
Landing run (average breeze)	61 m (200 ft)

FIRST STRIKE

FIRST STRIKE AVIATION INC

4 Wade Avenue, Piggott, Arkansas 72454

Telephone: 1 (501) 598 5126

PRESIDENT: Bobby Baker

FIRST STRIKE BOBCAT and SUPER CAT

The first flight of the prototype Bobcat was achieved in May 1984. Kits and plans are available, together with those for the Experimental and stronger Super Cat. Estimated building time of a Bobcat and Super Cat is 150-200 and 300 working hours respectively. Individual component parts are available to builders using plans only.

TYPES: Single-seat microlight (Bobcat) and homebuilt (Super Cat) aircraft.

AIRFRAME: Fuselage uses spruce longerons and plywood bulkheads, the wings have spruce capped foam ribs with plywood D section leading-edges, all Ceconite 7600

fabric covered. Glassfibre engine cowling. Non-retractable tailwheel landing gear.

POWER PLANT: *Bobcat:* one 20 kW (27 hp) Rotax 277. *Super Cat:* one 26 kW (35 hp) Rotax 377; optional Rotax 447. Fuel capacity 19 litres (5 US gallons; 4.2 Imp gallons) in Bobcat, 30 litres (8 US gallons; 6.66 Imp gallons) in Super Cat.

DIMENSIONS, EXTERNAL:

Wing span	8.43 m (27 ft 8 in)
Length overall	4.65 m (15 ft 3 in)
Height overall	1.83 m (6 ft 0 in)
Propeller diameter: Bobcat	1.52 m (5 ft 0 in)
Super Cat	1.73 m (5 ft 8 in)

AREAS:

Wings, gross: Bobcat	10.41 m² (112.0 sq ft)
Super Cat	11.15 m² (120.0 sq ft)

WEIGHTS (A: Bobcat, B: Super Cat):

Weight empty: A	114 kg (251 lb)
B	150 kg (330 lb)
Max T-O weight: A	226 kg (500 lb)
B	283 kg (625 lb)

PERFORMANCE (A: Bobcat, B: Super Cat):

Max level speed: A	55 knots (101 km/h; 63 mph)
B	74 knots (137 km/h; 85 mph)
Max cruising speed:	
A	39-43 knots (72-80 km/h; 45-50 mph)
B	56 knots (105 km/h; 65 mph)
Stalling speed: A	24 knots (44 km/h; 27 mph)
B	32 knots (60 km/h; 37 mph)
Max rate of climb at S/L: A	213 m (700 ft)/min
B	259 m (850 ft)/min
T-O run: A	38 m (125 ft)
B	23 m (75 ft)
Landing run: A	61 m (200 ft)
g limits: A	+4
B	+5.5/−4.5

FISHER FLYING PRODUCTS INC — *See Aero Visions International.*

Details of the former FP-404 Classic, Classic II and FP-606 Sky Baby homebuilts, and FP-101, FP-202 Koala, Super Koala, FP-303 and FP-505 Skeeter microlights can be found in the 1989-90 Jane's.

FLIGHTWORKS

FLIGHTWORKS CORPORATION

311-D East St Elmo Road, Austin, Texas 78745

Telephone: 1 (512) 441 8844

FLIGHTWORKS CAPELLA

Kits are being marketed to construct the Capella. Two wing spans are available, offering high manoeuvrability or short-field operation.

TYPE: Single-seat homebuilt; conforms to FAR Pt 23.

AIRFRAME: All-aluminium alloy wing. Welded steel tube fuselage structure, the upper portion covered with aluminium alloy skins and the remainder with Dacron.

Non-retractable tricycle or tailwheel landing gear. Floats optional.

POWER PLANT: One 30 kW (40 hp) Rotax 447. Fuel capacity 26.5 litres (7 US gallons; 5.8 Imp gallons).

DIMENSIONS, EXTERNAL:

Wing span:	
long span	9.52 m (31 ft 3 in)
short span	8.31 m (27 ft 3 in)
Length overall	5.28 m (17 ft 4 in)
Height overall	1.73 m (5 ft 8 in)

AREAS:

Wings, gross:	
long span	11.52 m² (124.0 sq ft)
short span	10.03 m² (108.0 sq ft)

WEIGHTS (short span wings):

Weight empty	151 kg (332 lb)
Max T-O weight	261 kg (575 lb)

PERFORMANCE (short span wings):

Max level speed	80 knots (148 km/h; 92 mph)
Cruising speed, 75% power	71 knots (132 km/h; 82 mph)
Stalling speed: flaps up	33 knots (61 km/h; 38 mph)
flaps down	27 knots (50 km/h; 31 mph)
Max rate of climb at S/L	244 m (800 ft)/min
T-O run	46 m (150 ft)
Landing run	31 m (100 ft)

FLSZ

FLIGHT LEVEL SIX-ZERO INC

PO Box 9980, Colorado Springs, Colorado 80932

FLSZ DER KRICKET DK-1

The prototype Der Kricket DK-1 first flew on 19 September 1978. Plans are available.

TYPE: Single-seat homebuilt sporting biplane.

AIRFRAME: Wing section NACA 4412. Wings and tail surfaces have light alloy structure, with pop riveted light alloy skins. Tips of Styrofoam covered with glassfibre. Ailerons on lower wings only. Basic fuselage structure of bolted and riveted light alloy angle, covered by light alloy skins. Non-retractable tailwheel landing gear.

POWER PLANT: Modified Volkswagen motorcar engine of 37.3-48.5 kW (50-65 hp). Fuel capacity 30.3 litres (8 US gallons; 6.66 Imp gallons).

DIMENSIONS, EXTERNAL:

Wing span (both)	4.88 m (16 ft 0 in)
Length overall	4.88 m (16 ft 0 in)
Height overall	1.68 m (5 ft 6 in)
Propeller diameter	1.37 m (4 ft 6 in)

AREA:

Wings, gross	8.92 m² (96.0 sq ft)

WEIGHTS:

Weight empty	249 kg (550 lb)
Max T-O weight	354 kg (780 lb)

PERFORMANCE (at max T-O weight):

Max level speed	91 knots (169 km/h; 105 mph)
Econ cruising speed	74 knots (137 km/h; 85 mph)
Stalling speed, power off	46 knots (84 km/h; 52 mph)
Max rate of climb at S/L	229 m (750 ft)/min
Absolute ceiling	3,660 m (12,000 ft)
T-O run	213 m (700 ft)
Landing run	198 m (650 ft)
Range with max fuel	173 nm (322 km; 200 miles)

FLSZ VAGRANT II

This new side by side two-seat monoplane will use the same pop riveted light alloy form of construction as Der Kricket, and can be powered by either an 1,835 cc (or larger) Volkswagen modified motorcar engine or a standard aircraft engine of up to 85.75 kW (115 hp).

In configuration the Vagrant II is a cantilever low-wing

cabin monoplane, with a GAW-2 wing section and conventional control surfaces. The landing gear is of non-retractable tailwheel type. The prototype had been expected to fly in early 1988, but no news has been received.

The following data apply to the Vagrant II with an 1,835 cc VW engine:

DIMENSIONS, EXTERNAL:

Wing span	6.40 m (21 ft 0 in)
Length overall	5.03 m (16 ft 6 in)

AREA:

Wings, gross	8.73 m² (94.0 sq ft)

WEIGHTS:

Weight empty	227 kg (500 lb)
Max T-O weight	431-454 kg (950-1,000 lb)

PERFORMANCE (estimated):

Max level speed	122 knots (225 km/h; 140 mph)
Cruising speed	113 knots (209 km/h; 130 mph)
Stalling speed: flaps down	44 knots (81 km/h; 50 mph)
flaps up	48 knots (89 km/h; 55 mph)
Max rate of climb at S/L	244 m (800 ft)/min

Evans VP-1 built by Dr Don Gerner of Kimball, Nebraska, with non-standard cockpit canopy, engine cowling and wheel fairings

First Strike Super Cat homebuilt cabin monoplane *(Geoffrey P. Jones)*

Unfinished Flightworks Capella prototype *(Geoffrey P. Jones)*

Grega GN-1 Aircamper (Teledyne Continental A80 engine) built by Dr Samuel Meredith of West Memphis, Arkansas

FLSZ Der Kricket DK-1 single-seat sporting biplane

Freedom Master Air Shark I four-seat homebuilt amphibian *(Joel Rieman)*

FREEDOM MASTER
FREEDOM MASTER CORPORATION
700B South Plumosa, Merritt Island, Florida 32952
Telephone: 1 (305) 453 4678
PRESIDENT: Ronald A. Lueck

FREEDOM MASTER FM-2 AIR SHARK I
The prototype Air Shark flew for the first time on 5 April 1985. Kits of pre-moulded parts are available.
TYPE: Four-seat homebuilt sporting amphibian.
AIRFRAME: Wing section NASA NLF-0215-F. Wing spar caps of S-2 glassfibre or Kevlar rovings. All aerofoils are vacuum moulded. Wing upper shell and upper fuselage of glassfibre/epoxy and Clark foam plastics sandwich construction, with wing lower surfaces of Kevlar/epoxy. Hull and control surfaces of Kevlar/epoxy with Nomex

honeycomb cores. Winglets of glassfibre/epoxy. Tail unit construction similar to wings. Retractable tricycle landing gear.
POWER PLANT: One 149 kW (200 hp) Textron Lycoming IO-360C1C. Alternative Porsche PFM 3200, Allison C250-B17 or Teledyne Continental IO-360 engine. Fuel capacity 227 litres (60 US gallons; 50 Imp gallons).
ARMAMENT: Hardpoints for weapons and other stores optional.

DIMENSIONS, EXTERNAL:
Wing span	9.96 m (32 ft 8 in)
Length overall	6.93 m (22 ft 9 in)
Height overall	2.49 m (8 ft 2 in)
Propeller diameter	1.83 m (6 ft 0 in)

AREA:
Wings, gross	12.31 m² (132.5 sq ft)

WEIGHTS:
Weight empty	680 kg (1,500 lb)
Baggage capacity	54 kg (120 lb)
Max T-O weight	1,270 kg (2,800 lb)

PERFORMANCE (at max T-O weight):
Max level speed at 2,285 m (7,500 ft)	
	178 knots (330 km/h; 205 mph)
Econ cruising speed at 2,285 m (7,500 ft)	
	148 knots (274 km/h; 170 mph)
Stalling speed: power off	55 knots (102 km/h; 63 mph)
Max rate of climb at S/L	380 m (1,250 ft)/min
Service ceiling	5,640 m (18,500 ft)
T-O run	488 m (1,600 ft)
Landing run	305 m (1,000 ft)
Range	1,736 nm (3,218 km; 2,000 miles)
Endurance	11 h 48 min
g limits	+10/–4

FRIEDMAN
JOSEPH FRIEDMAN
12912 Woodbridge Street, No. 101, Studio City, California 91604
Telephone: 1 (818) 784 5638

Mr Friedman is believed to market pre-formed all-metal kits under homebuilt regulations to construct the Andreasson MFI-9 (see Sweden).

GREGA
JOHN W. GREGA
355 Grand Boulevard, Bedford, Ohio 44146
In addition to the standard Aircamper design, of which plans are available from Mr Don Pietenpol (see 1988-89 *Jane's*), a modernised version has been developed by Mr John Grega. Plans of this are available to homebuilders, and by 1990 about 2,600 sets had been sold.

GN-1 AIRCAMPER
The prototype GN-1 Aircamper flew for the first time in

November 1965. Builders can choose wood or steel tube fuselage construction.
TYPE: Tandem two-seat homebuilt.
POWER PLANT: One 48.5 kW (65 hp) Teledyne Continental A65-8. Other engines of up to 63.5 kW (85 hp) can be installed. Fuel capacity 68 litres (18 US gallons; 15 Imp gallons).
DIMENSIONS, EXTERNAL:
Wing span	8.84 m (29 ft 0 in)
Length overall	5.51 m (18 ft 1 in)
Height overall	2.06 m (6 ft 9 in)

AREA:
Wings, gross	13.94 m² (150.0 sq ft)

WEIGHT:
Max T-O weight	499 kg (1,100 lb)

PERFORMANCE (at max T-O weight):
Max level speed at S/L	100 knots (185 km/h; 115 mph)
Max cruising speed at S/L	78 knots (145 km/h; 90 mph)
Stalling speed	31 knots (56 km/h; 35 mph)
Max rate of climb at S/L	152 m (500 ft)/min
T-O run	122 m (400 ft)
Landing run	76 m (250 ft)
Range with max fuel	347 nm (640 km; 400 miles)

GYRO

GYRO 2000
1416 4th Street, Santa Fe, New Mexico 87501
Telephone: 1 (505) 988 7188
PROPRIETOR: David Gittens

The 1987-88 *Jane's* described and illustrated the Wind Dancer proof of concept gyroplane. The same company, now known as Gyro 2000, has developed the DAKI 530Z/Ikenga, Ikenga/Cygnus 21T and Ikenga/Cygnus 21P. It is also developing a Kawasaki-powered autogyro with enclosed accommodation that was expected to appear in June 1990.

GYRO 2000 DAKI 530Z/IKENGA

First flown in February 1988, this gyroplane is available in kit form for light utility, surveillance, photography, commuter/courier and recreational uses; production of a series of 700 kits began in early 1989. Under development are a full cockpit enclosure, cargo pod, medical pod, surveillance pod, cropspraying equipment and provision for an additional passenger. The present pre-rotator is to be superseded by a 'jump' capability rotor head. Fuel tank seat.

TYPE: Single-seat autogyro.
ROTOR SYSTEM: Two-blade Skywheels composites rotor. Parsons offset gimbal rotor head and Kawasaki electric pre-rotator. Parsons jump capability rotor head to be optional.
AIRFRAME: Structure of aluminium alloy and steel tubing. Glassfibre cockpit fairing.
POWER PLANT: One 71 kW (95 hp) Suzuki 530 engine, driving a ground adjustable Precision propeller. Fuel tank bucket seat, capacity 59 litres (15.5 US gallons; 13 Imp gallons).
DIMENSIONS, EXTERNAL:

Rotor diameter	7.01 m (23 ft 0 in)
Length overall	3.71 m (12 ft 2 in)
Height overall	2.26 m (7 ft 5 in)
Propeller diameter	1.42 m (4 ft 8 in)

WEIGHTS:

Useful load	252 kg (555 lb)
Max T-O weight	399 kg (880 lb)

PERFORMANCE (estimated):

Cruising speed	81 knots (150 km/h; 93 mph)
Min level speed	13 knots (24 km/h; 15 mph)
Max rate of climb at S/L	427 m (1,400 ft)/min
Service ceiling	4,265 m (14,000 ft)
T-O run	107 m (350 ft)
T-O run with pre-rotator	46 m (150 ft)
Range	315 nm (583 km; 362 miles)

GYRO 2000 IKENGA/CYGNUS 21P

This recreational autogyro is kit-assembled, and was developed for distribution in Japan by Sumitomo Heavy Industries. The fairing and wheel covers can be retrofitted to Benson and Brock autogyros.

TYPE: Single-seat autogyro.
ROTOR SYSTEM: Two-blade Rotordyne rotor of bonded aluminium. Parsons offset gimbal rotor head.
AIRFRAME: Structure of 6061-T6 aluminium alloy tubing, with aluminium tail unit and composites fairings. Non-retractable tricycle landing gear.
POWER PLANT: One 71 kW (95 hp) Suzuki 530 engine, driving a three-blade Precision propeller. Brock 30 litre (8 US gallon; 6.7 Imp gallon) seat/fuel tank.
DIMENSIONS, EXTERNAL:

Rotor diameter	7.01 m (23 ft 0 in)
Length overall	3.35 m (11 ft 0 in)
Height overall	2.39 m (7 ft 10 in)
Propeller diameter	1.37 m (4 ft 6 in)

WEIGHTS:

Useful load	254 kg (560 lb)
Max T-O weight	399 kg (880 lb)

PERFORMANCE:

Max level speed	100 knots (185 km/h; 115 mph)
Cruising speed	78 knots (145 km/h; 90 mph)
Min flying speed	13 knots (24 km/h; 15 mph)
Rate of climb at S/L	427 m (1,400 ft)/min
Service ceiling	4,420 m (14,500 ft)
T-O run	77 m (250 ft)
T-O with pre-rotator	46 m (150 ft)
Range	143 nm (265 km; 165 miles)

GYRO 2000 IKENGA/CYGNUS 21T

This is a kit-assembled microlight autogyro with a tractor-mounted engine. The tail surfaces are of Tedlar.

TYPE: Single-seat microlight autogyro.
ROTOR SYSTEM AND AIRFRAME: Similar rotor system and materials to Cygnus 21P, except for Tedlar tail surfaces, but different configuration (see illustrations).
POWER PLANT: One 71 kW (95 hp) Suzuki 530 engine, driving a five-blade Arrowprop or Precision tractor propeller. Hamilton 59 litre (15.5 US gallon; 13 Imp gallon) seat/fuel tank.
DIMENSIONS, EXTERNAL:

Rotor diameter	7.01 m (23 ft 0 in)
Length overall	3.12 m (10 ft 3 in)
Height overall	2.26 m (7 ft 5 in)
Propeller diameter: Arrowprop	1.22 m (4 ft 0 in)
Precision	1.37 m (4 ft 6 in)

WEIGHTS:

Useful load	290 kg (640 lb)
Max T-O weight	399 kg (880 lb)

PERFORMANCE: As for Cygnus 21P except:

Range	315 nm (583 km; 362 miles)

HAPI

HAPI ENGINES INC
Eloy Municipal Airport, RR 1 Box 1000, Eloy, Arizona 85231
Telephone: 1 (602) 466 9244

In October 1983 HAPI Engines acquired the rights to market Captain A. M. Sisler's Cygnet SF-2A. Plans and pre-welded airframe kits are available. Also, in 1987, HAPI purchased the rights in the former INAV Sonerai, which it is marketing. It is a dealer for the Viking Dragonfly, quick-assembly 'Snap' Dragonfly, and Corby CJ-1 Starlet.

CYGNET SF-2A

TYPE: Two-seat homebuilt.
AIRFRAME: Wooden geodetic wing structure, with overall Dacron covering. Wing section NACA 3413. Welded chrome molybdenum steel tube fuselage and strut braced tail unit, Dacron covered. Non-retractable tailwheel landing gear. A float gear is under development.
POWER PLANT: One 44.7, 56 or 61 kW (60, 75 or 82 hp) HAPI converted Volkswagen 1,600, 1,834 or 2,200 cc motorcar engine. Fuel capacity 57 litres (15 US gallons; 12.5 Imp gallons).
DIMENSIONS, EXTERNAL:

Wing span	9.14 m (30 ft 0 in)
Length overall	5.79 m (19 ft 0 in)
Height overall	1.78 m (5 ft 10 in)
Propeller diameter	1.47 m (4 ft 10 in)

AREA:

Wings, gross	11.60 m² (124.8 sq ft)

WEIGHTS:

Weight empty	265 kg (585 lb)
Baggage capacity	23 kg (50 lb)
Max T-O weight	499 kg (1,100 lb)

PERFORMANCE (at max T-O weight):

Max level speed	94 knots (174 km/h; 108 mph)
Cruising speed at 2,440 m (8,000 ft)	87 knots (161 km/h; 100 mph)
Stalling speed: power off	42 knots (78 km/h; 48 mph)
power on	37 knots (68 km/h; 42 mph)
Max rate of climb at S/L	177 m (580 ft)/min
Service ceiling	3,660 m (12,000 ft)
T-O to and landing from 15 m (50 ft)	213 m (700 ft)

Range	304 nm (563 km; 350 miles)
g limit	+4

HAPI SONERAI I

The first flight by the prototype Sonerai was made in July 1971. Plans and certain components are available to amateur constructors, and the estimated building time is 800 working hours when a pre-welded fuselage and tail are not used. More than 400 Sonerai Is are under construction or flying.

TYPE: Single-seat homebuilt Formula V racing aircraft.
AIRFRAME: Wings of aluminium alloy construction, with NACA 64212 section. Full span aluminium alloy ailerons. Welded steel tube fuselage and tail unit, fabric covered except for glassfibre engine cowlings. Non-retractable tailwheel landing gear.
POWER PLANT: One 44.7, 56 or 61 kW (60, 75 or 82 hp) Volkswagen 1,600, 1,834 or 2,200 cc modified motorcar engine. Fuel capacity 38 litres (10 US gallons; 8.3 Imp gallons).
DIMENSIONS, EXTERNAL:

Wing span	5.08 m (16 ft 8 in)
Length overall	5.08 m (16 ft 8 in)
Height overall	1.52 m (5 ft 0 in)
Propeller diameter	1.27 m (4 ft 2 in)

AREA:

Wings, gross	6.97 m² (75.0 sq ft)

WEIGHTS:

Weight empty	199 kg (440 lb)
Max pilot weight	113 kg (250 lb)
Utility max T-O weight	340 kg (750 lb)
Max T-O weight	454 kg (1,000 lb)

PERFORMANCE (at max T-O weight):

Max level speed at S/L	148 knots (273 km/h; 170 mph)
Econ cruising speed	109 knots (201 km/h; 125 mph)
Stalling speed	35 knots (65 km/h; 40 mph)
Max rate of climb at S/L	305 m (1,000 ft)
T-O and landing run	183 m (600 ft)
Range, with reserves	217-260 nm (402-482 km; 250-300 miles)
g limits	±6g

HAPI SONERAI II, IIL, II-LT and II-LTS

The prototype of the tandem two-seat Sonerai II made its first flight in July 1973 and at least 500 have since been built and flown. Many components, complete kits for fuselage, tail and wings, and materials, are available to amateur constructors. Estimated building time is 850 working hours.

One variant, first flown in June 1980, is the **Sonerai IIL**, with low-wing instead of mid-wing configuration and 3° of dihedral. Another variant, first flown in January 1983, is the **Sonerai II-LT**, which is similar to the Sonerai IIL but has a 2,200 cc VW engine as standard, a tricycle landing gear and larger front cockpit for a taller pilot. A retrofit kit has been produced to allow existing Soneraies to be fitted with the tricycle gear. The **Sonerai II-LTS** is basically a stretched version of the Sonerai II-LT, first flown in June 1984.

The description of the Sonerai I applies also to Sonerai II, IIL, II-LT and II-LTS except as follows:

TYPE: Two-seat, dual-control sporting homebuilt.
POWER PLANT: One 44.7, 56 or 61 kW (60, 75 or 82 hp) HAPI converted Volkswagen 1,600, 1,834 or 2,200 cc motorcar engine. The 2,200 cc version is standard for the Sonerai II-LT and II-LTS. Fuel capacity 38 litres (10 US gallons; 8.3 Imp gallons) for all versions except Sonerai II-LTS, which has standard capacity of 68 litres (18 US gallons; 15 Imp gallons).
DIMENSIONS, EXTERNAL: As Sonerai I, except:

Wing span	5.69 m (18 ft 8 in)
Length overall:	
all except Sonerai II-LTS	5.74 m (18 ft 10 in)
Sonerai II-LTS	6.20 m (20 ft 4 in)
Propeller diameter	1.32 to 1.37 m (4 ft 4 in to 4 ft 6 in)

AREA:

Wings, gross	7.80 m² (84.0 sq ft)

WEIGHTS (Sonerai II):

Weight empty	227 kg (500 lb)
Utility max T-O weight	431 kg (950 lb)
Max T-O weight	521 kg (1,150 lb)

PERFORMANCE (Sonerai II/IIL with 1,700 cc engine):

Max level speed at S/L	139 knots (257 km/h; 160 mph)
Econ cruising speed at S/L	113 knots (209 km/h; 130 mph)
Stalling speed	38 knots (71 km/h; 44 mph)
Max rate of climb at S/L	152 m (500 ft)/min
T-O run	274 m (900 ft)
Landing run	152 m (500 ft)
Range, with reserves	304 nm (563 km; 350 miles)
g limits: pilot only, aerobatic	±6
max T-O weight, utility	±4.4

HATZ

HATZ AIRPLANE SHOP
Details of the Hatz CB-1 Biplane, and an illustration, appeared in the 1989-90 *Jane's*.

HIPP'S

HIPP'S SUPERBIRDS INC
PO Box 266, I-26 Exit 28, Ozone Drive, Saluda, North Carolina 28773
Telephone: 1 (704) 749 9134 and 749 3986

In addition to the J-3 Kitten, Reliant and J-4 Sportster microlights, Hipp's Superbirds offers Experimental derivatives as follows:

HIPP'S SUPERBIRDS RELIANT II

This two-seat Experimental version of the Reliant strut braced cabin monoplane is powered by a 47.7 kW (64 hp) Rotax 532 or, optionally, a 48.5 kW (65 hp) Teledyne Continental. The prototype has flown, and kits will be made available.

DIMENSIONS, EXTERNAL:

Length overall	6.10 m (20 ft 0 in)
Height overall	2.08 m (6 ft 10 in)

Gyro 2000 DAKI 530Z/Ikenga single-seat autogyro

Gyro 2000 Ikenga/Cygnus 21P autogyro

Cygnet SF-2A, designed by Captain A. M. Sisler and marketed by HAPI Engines *(J. M. G. Gradidge)*

Gyro 2000 Ikenga/Cygnus 21T microlight autogyro

HAPI Sonerai II built by Butch Mankovich of Clifton, New Jersey, USA *(Howard Levy)*

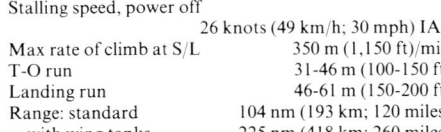

Hipp's Superbirds Reliant SX homebuilt

HIPP'S SUPERBIRDS RELIANT SX

The Reliant SX is an Experimental version of the Reliant, retaining the single-seat accommodation of the microlight. Kits are available.

TYPE: Single-seat cabin homebuilt.

AIRFRAME: Strut braced high wings, of fabric covered wooden construction (detachable). Fabric covered fuselage and tail unit have 4130 steel tube structures. Non-retractable tailwheel landing gear.

POWER PLANT: One 30 kW (40 hp) Rotax 447. Fuel capacity 19 litres (5 US gallons; 4.2 Imp gallons). Optional wing tanks.

DIMENSIONS, EXTERNAL:
Wing span	9.14 m (30 ft 0 in)
Length overall	4.98 m (16 ft 4 in)
Height overall	1.63 m (5 ft 4 in)
Propeller diameter	1.52 m (5 ft 0 in)

AREA:
Wings, gross	11.15 m² (120.0 sq ft)

WEIGHTS:
Weight empty	129 kg (285 lb)
Max T-O weight	272 kg (600 lb)

PERFORMANCE:
Max level speed	87 knots (161 km/h; 100 mph)
Econ cruising speed	63 knots (117 km/h; 73 mph)
Stalling speed, power off	26 knots (49 km/h; 30 mph) IAS
Max rate of climb at S/L	350 m (1,150 ft)/min
T-O run	31-46 m (100-150 ft)
Landing run	46-61 m (150-200 ft)
Range: standard	104 nm (193 km; 120 miles)
with wing tanks	225 nm (418 km; 260 miles)

HIPP'S SUPERBIRDS SUPER KITTEN

This is an Experimental derivative of the Kitten microlight. Kits are available.

AIRFRAME: As for Reliant SX. Wheel fairings.

POWER PLANT: As for Reliant SX. Fuel capacity 49 litres (13 US gallons; 10.8 Imp gallons).

DIMENSIONS, EXTERNAL: As for Reliant SX.

AREA:
Wings, gross	10.41 m² (112.0 sq ft)

WEIGHTS:
Weight empty	129-131 kg (285-290 lb)
Pilot weight range	55-131 kg (120-290 lb)
Max T-O weight	272 kg (600 lb)

PERFORMANCE:
Max level speed	87 knots (161 km/h; 100 mph)
Cruising speed	65 knots (121 km/h; 75 mph)
Stalling speed	27 knots (50 km/h; 31 mph)
Max rate of climb at S/L	274 m (900 ft)/min
T-O to 15 m (50 ft)	153 m (500 ft)
Range	104-225 nm (193-418 km; 120-260 miles)

HIPP'S SUPERBIRDS SUPER SPORTSTER

This is an Experimental derivative of the J-4 Sportster microlight. Kits are available.

AIRFRAME, POWER PLANT AND DIMENSIONS, EXTERNAL: As for Reliant SX.

WEIGHTS:
Weight empty	125-129 kg (275-285 lb)
Pilot weight range	55-131 kg (120-290 lb)

PERFORMANCE:
Max level speed	87 knots (161 km/h; 100 mph)
Range	104-225 nm (193-418 km; 120-260 miles)

HOLCOMB

JERRY HOLCOMB

Perigee Associates, 1010 North-East 122nd Avenue, Vancouver, Washington 98684
Telephone: 1 (206) 892 7732

HOLCOMB PERIGEE

The Perigee (originally Ultra Imp) was conceived as a single-seat tail-pusher aircraft, utilising the TPG form of construction described under the Aerocar heading in this section. The prototype flew for the first time on 4 April 1987.

The Perigee is no longer offered in plans form, but component parts are still available. Currently the Perigee is undergoing modification to the wings, and a new engine will be installed. Details of the Perigee, and an illustration, appeared in the 1989-90 *Jane's*.

HUTCHINSON

HUTCHINSON AIRCRAFT COMPANY

The address given in the 1989-90 *Jane's* is no longer current. Details of the Ag Master and an illustration can be found in that edition.

JAVELIN

JAVELIN AIRCRAFT COMPANY INC

Municipal Airport, Augusta, Kansas 67010
Telephone: 1 (316) 733 1011
PRESIDENT AND CHIEF ENGINEER: David D. Blanton

JAVELIN WICHAWK

The prototype Wichawk first flew on 24 May 1971. Plans and some components are available; by January 1990, 254 Wichawks were under construction and 30 were flying.
TYPE: Two/three-seat, dual-control homebuilt sporting biplane.
AIRFRAME: Wing section NACA 23015. Each wing has two wooden spars and light alloy ribs, fabric covered. Ailerons on lower wings only. Welded fuselage and tail unit of steel tube, with light alloy tubular fuselage stringers, fabric covered. Non-retractable tailwheel landing gear.
POWER PLANT: Prototype has 134 kW (180 hp) Textron Lycoming O-360. Provision for alternative horizontally opposed or radial engines from 112 kW (150 hp) to 224 kW (300 hp). Fuel capacity 151.5 litres (40 US gallons; 33.5 Imp gallons).

DIMENSIONS, EXTERNAL:

Wing span (upper)	7.32 m (24 ft 0 in)
Length overall	5.87 m (19 ft 3 in)
Height overall	2.18 m (7 ft 2 in)
Propeller diameter	1.93 m (6 ft 4 in)

AREA:

Wings, gross	17.2 m² (185.0 sq ft)

WEIGHTS (A: prototype with 134 kW; 180 hp engine, B: three-seat version with six-cylinder engine):

Weight empty: A		582.5 kg (1,284.5 lb)
B		635 kg (1,400 lb)
Baggage capacity		54.4 kg (120 lb)
*Max T-O weight: A		907 kg (2,000 lb)
B		978 kg (2,156 lb)

Max T-O weight is increased to 998 kg (2,200 lb) with high-powered engines

PERFORMANCE (prototype with 134 kW; 180 hp engine):

Max level speed at S/L	121 knots (225 km/h; 140 mph)
Max cruising speed	110 knots (204 km/h; 127 mph)
Stalling speed	50 knots (92 km/h; 57 mph) IAS
Max rate of climb at S/L	518 m (1,700 ft)/min
T-O run	46 m (150 ft)
g limits	+12/-6

KELLY

DUDLEY R. KELLY

Route 4, Versailles, Kentucky 40383
Telephone: 1 (606) 873 5253

KELLY-D

The prototype Kelly-D first flew on 20 December 1981. Plans are available.
TYPE: Tandem two-seat homebuilt aerobatic biplane.
AIRFRAME: Wing section NACA 4412. Wooden wings, with wooden ailerons on lower wings only. Welded steel tube fuselage and wire braced tail unit. All fabric covered. Non-retractable tailwheel landing gear.
POWER PLANT: One 86 kW (115 hp) Textron Lycoming O-235. Fuel capacity 91 litres (24 US gallons; 20 Imp gallons).

DIMENSIONS, EXTERNAL:

Wing span (both)	8.03 m (26 ft 4 in)
Length overall	5.87 m (19 ft 3 in)
Height overall	2.36 m (7 ft 9 in)
Propeller diameter	1.88 m (6 ft 2 in)

AREA:

Wings, gross	19.54 m² (210.38 sq ft)

WEIGHTS:

Basic operating weight empty	431 kg (950 lb)
Baggage capacity	18 kg (40 lb)
Max T-O and landing weight	726 kg (1,600 lb)

PERFORMANCE:

Cruising speed	78 knots (145 km/h; 90 mph)
Stalling speed	39 knots (73 km/h; 45 mph)
Max rate of climb at S/L, pilot only	274 m (900 ft)/min
Range with max fuel, 20 min reserves	
	243 nm (450 km; 280 miles)

KELLY-DII

This aircraft has been discontinued.

KENNEDY

KENNEDY AIRCRAFT COMPANY INC

2405 North Coolidge Street, Orlando, Florida 32804
PRESIDENT: Edward Kennedy

KENNEDY SKYCYCLE and FLYCYCLE

First flown as a prototype in 1960, the developed Skycycle autogyro is now marketed in plans and kit forms, in single and tandem two-seat versions. A lightweight variant is also available as the Flycycle. All are covered under Experimental regulations, while the Flycycle can also meet microlight requirements.
ROTOR SYSTEM: Rotor of aluminium alloy construction, with two McCutchin Sky Wheel blades for Skycycles. Lightweight Rotordyne rotor for Flycycle. Pre-rotator fitted.
AIRFRAME: Basic structure of bolted square light alloy tubing, with plywood fairing on single-seat Skycycle, aluminium on two-seater, and no fairing on Flycycle. Non-retractable tricycle landing gear.
POWER PLANT: Skycycle single-seater and Flycycle have 35 kW (47 hp) Rotax 503. Fuel capacity 19 litres (5 US gallons; 4.2 Imp gallons). Skycycle two-seater has 48.5 kW (65 hp) Rotax 532. Fuel capacity 23 litres (6 US gallons; 5 Imp gallons) standard; 49 litres (13 US gallons; 10.8 Imp gallons) optional.

DIMENSIONS, EXTERNAL:

Rotor diameter: single-seaters	7.01 m (23 ft 0 in)
two-seater	7.62 m (25 ft 0 in)
Length of fuselage:	
single-seat Skycycle	3.35 m (11 ft 0 in)
two-seater	3.66 m (12 ft 0 in)
Height overall	2.13 m (7 ft 0 in)

WEIGHTS:

Weight empty: single-seat Skycycle	121 kg (267 lb)
two-seater	141 kg (310 lb)
Max pilot weight: single-seaters	113 kg (250 lb)
Max T-O weight: two-seat Skycycle	317 kg (700 lb)

PERFORMANCE:

Max level speed:	
single-seat Skycycle	69 knots (129 km/h; 80 mph)
two-seater	100 knots (185 km/h; 115 mph)
Cruising speed: two-seater	
	61-65 knots (113-121 km/h; 70-75 mph)
Min forward speed: single-seaters	
	7-9 knots (13-16 km/h; 8-10 mph)
T-O run, with pre-rotator: single-seaters	
	30.5-61 m (100-200 ft)
Endurance with standard fuel: two-seater	2 h

KIMBREL

MICHAEL G. KIMBREL

1333 Garrard Creek Road, Oakville, Washington 98568
Telephone: 1 (206) 273 9203

Details of the Kimbrel Butterfly and Banty can be found in the Microlight tables. Details of the Bathtub Mk 1 and an illustration can be found in the 1988-89 *Jane's*.

KOLB

KOLB COMPANY INC

RD 3, Box 38, Phoenixville, Pennsylvania 19460
Telephone and Fax: 1 (215) 948 4136
PRESIDENT: Homer Kolb

The Ultrastar is no longer available; details and an illustration can be found in the 1988-89 *Jane's*. Details of the Firestar can be found in the Microlight tables. The latest aircraft is the Laser.

KOLB TWINSTAR MARK II

The original TwinStar first flew as a prototype in August 1984. The current model is the Mark II, differing mainly in having a wider FireStar type enclosed cockpit and canopy. Kits are available and by January 1990 110 had been ordered.
TYPE: Side by side two-seat homebuilt.
AIRFRAME: Welded steel cage structure and aluminium boom. Quick-folding wings have aluminium tube spar with aluminium ribs, double surface Stits Dacron covered. Three-axis control. Non-retractable tailwheel landing gear, with brakes. Options include ballistic recovery parachute, floats and skis.
POWER PLANT: One 35 kW (47 hp) Rotax 503, with 2.58 : 1 reduction gear. Fuel capacity 19 litres (5 US gallons; 4.2 Imp gallons).

DIMENSIONS, EXTERNAL:

Wing span	9.15 m (30 ft 0 in)
Length overall	6.38 m (20 ft 11 in)
Height overall	1.73 m (5 ft 8 in)
Propeller diameter	1.68 m (5 ft 6 in)

AREA:

Wings, gross	14.86 m² (160.0 sq ft)

WEIGHTS:

Weight empty, without fairing	132 kg (292 lb)
Max T-O weight	328 kg (725 lb)

PERFORMANCE (at max T-O weight):

Max level speed	61 knots (113 km/h; 70 mph)
Econ cruising speed at S/L	48 knots (89 km/h; 55 mph)
Stalling speed at S/L	26 knots (49 km/h; 30 mph)
Max rate of climb at S/L	213 m (700 ft)/min
Service ceiling	3,660 m (12,000 ft)
T-O run, on grass	77 m (250 ft)
Landing run, on grass	54 m (175 ft)
Range	61 nm (112 km; 70 miles)
Endurance	1 h 30 min
g limits	+4/-2

KOLB LASER

The new Laser was to be made available in kit form in 1990. Intended to fit between very fast homebuilts and microlights, design goals included low weight, low landing speed, good visibility and easy portability; set-up and take-down takes five minutes. Construction of the prototype began in 1989.
TYPE: Two-seat homebuilt monoplane.
AIRFRAME: Cantilever low-wing monoplane. Aluminium alloy and welded 4130 steel-tube structure, with Stits fabric covering. Conventional control surfaces. Non-retractable tailwheel landing gear, with brakes.
POWER PLANT: One 48.5 kW (65 hp) Rotax 582 with

Javelin Wichawk built by Mr Bill Taylor of Sydney, Australia

Kelly-D two-seat aerobatic biplane

Kennedy Skycycle autogyro in single- and two-seat forms *(Geoffrey P. Jones)*

Kolb TwinStar Mark II

Kolb Laser two-seat homebuilt *(Jane's/Mike Keep)*

Laven LACO-145 two-seat light biplane

reduction gear. Fuel capacity 38 litres (10 US gallons; 8.3 Imp gallons). Design suited to Volkswagen converted motorcar engines.

DIMENSIONS, EXTERNAL:

Wing span	6.71 m (22 ft 0 in)
Length overall	5.73 m (18 ft 9½ in)
Height overall	1.42 m (4 ft 8 in)

AREA:

Wings, gross	9.29 m² (100.0 sq ft)

WEIGHTS:

Weight empty	159 kg (350 lb)
Max T-O weight	385 kg (850 lb)

PERFORMANCE:

Max level speed	104 knots (193 km/h; 120 mph)
Max cruising speed	87 knots (161 km/h; 100 mph)
Stalling speed	33 knots (61 km/h; 38 mph)
Service ceiling	5,180 m (17,000 ft)
T-O run	92 m (300 ft)
Landing run	77 m (250 ft)
Range	173 nm (321 km; 200 miles)
g limits	+6/−4

LAVEN

JOE LAVEN

PO Box 415, Desert Hot Springs, California 92240
Telephone: 1 (619) 329 9354

LAVEN LACO-125, LACO-145 and SPECIAL

The original **LACO-125** prototype first flew on 29 May 1977. It was followed by the more powerful **LACO-145**. Plans for both models are available. The **Special** is a version of the LACO-145 being built to test minor structural changes for possible future inclusion on plans (including removable rear canopy). The main aim of these changes is to reduce the cost of construction.

TYPE: Two-seat homebuilt biplane.
AIRFRAME: Wing section NACA 2412. Wing structure has wooden spars and ribs, aluminium leading- and trailing-edges, and steel fittings. Modified Frise ailerons on lower wings only. Welded Warren truss fuselage of steel tubing, with wooden formers and stringers. Braced tail unit of welded steel tubing. Entire airframe fabric covered. Non-retractable tailwheel landing gear.
POWER PLANT: LACO-125: One 93 kW (125 hp) Teledyne Continental C-125-2. LACO-145: One 108 kW (145 hp) Teledyne Continental C-145. Fuel capacity 91 litres (24 US gallons; 20 Imp gallons).

DIMENSIONS, EXTERNAL:

Wing span: upper	6.93 m (22 ft 8¾ in)
lower	6.29 m (20 ft 7½ in)
Length overall	5.94 m (19 ft 6 in)
Height overall	2.18 m (7 ft 2 in)
Propeller diameter: LACO-125	1.83 m (6 ft 0 in)
LACO-145	1.93 m (6 ft 4 in)

AREA:

Wings, gross	13.94 m² (150.0 sq ft)

WEIGHTS:

Weight empty	390 kg (860 lb)
Max T-O weight	635 kg (1,400 lb)

PERFORMANCE (A: LACO-125, B: LACO-145):		B	104 knots (193 km/h; 120 mph)		B	42 knots (78 km/h; 48 mph)
Max level speed: A	108 knots (200 km/h; 124 mph)	Stalling speed:			Max rate of climb at S/L: A	274 m (900 ft)/min
B	115 knots (212 km/h; 132 mph)	power off: A, B	49 knots (90 km/h; 56 mph)		B	366 m (1,200 ft)/min
Max cruising speed: A	98 knots (182 km/h; 113 mph)	power on: A	44 knots (81 km/h; 50 mph)		Range with max fuel	282 nm (523 km; 325 miles)

LEADER'S

LEADER'S INTERNATIONAL INC

212 North Mecklenburg Avenue, South Hill, Virginia 23970
Telephone: 1 (804) 447 4919
PRESIDENT: Dr Rolf Brand

LEADER'S INTERNATIONAL JB-1000

The JB-1000 is available in plan, kit and ready assembled forms.
TYPE: Single-seat microlight; conforms to FAR Pt 103.
AIRFRAME: Constructed of carbonfibre and Kevlar. Three-axis control. Non-retractable tailwheel landing gear.

POWER PLANT: One 20 kW (27 hp) Rotax 277. Fuel capacity 19 litres (5 US gallons; 4.2 Imp gallons).

DIMENSIONS, EXTERNAL:

Wing span	9.14 m (30 ft 0 in)
Length overall	6.10 m (20 ft 0 in)
Height overall	1.78 m (5 ft 10 in)
Propeller diameter	1.52 m (5 ft 0 in)

AREA:

Wings, gross	13.47 m² (145.0 sq ft)

WEIGHTS:

Weight empty	113 kg (250 lb)
Pilot weight range	63.5-100 kg (140-220 lb)
Max T-O weight	238 kg (525 lb)

PERFORMANCE:

Max level speed	52 knots (97 km/h; 60 mph)
Econ cruising speed	36 knots (68 km/h; 42 mph)
Stalling speed: power on	22 knots (41 km/h; 25 mph)
power off	24 knots (44 km/h; 27 mph)
Max rate of climb at S/L	122 m (400 ft)/min
Service ceiling	3,660 m (12,000 ft)
T-O run	29 m (95 ft)
Landing run	30 m (100 ft)
g limits	+4/-2

LIGHT MINIATURE

LIGHT MINIATURE AIRCRAFT INC

Building 411, Opa-Locka Airport, Opa-Locka, Florida 33054
Telephone: 1 (305) 681 4068
PRESIDENT: Fred F. McCallum

LIGHT MINIATURE AIRCRAFT LM-1

This is basically a single-seat three-quarter scale Piper J-3 Cub replica. The prototype first flew on 15 July 1983.
Plans for the LM-1 are available. Estimated building time from plans is 600 working hours. Complete kits, partial kits and component parts for the LM-1 are available from Wicks Aircraft Supply, Highland, Illinois 62249.
TYPE: Single-seat homebuilt.
AIRFRAME: Wing section NACA 4412 modified. Dacron-covered all-wood airframe, except for aluminium alloy wing and aileron ribs. Non-retractable tailwheel landing gear.
POWER PLANT: One 22.4 kW (30 hp) Cuyuna 430RR. Fuel capacity 21 litres (5.5 US gallons; 4.6 Imp gallons).

DIMENSIONS, EXTERNAL:

Wing span	8.23 m (27 ft 0 in)
Length overall	5.38 m (17 ft 8 in)
Height overall	1.70 m (5 ft 7 in)
Propeller diameter	1.27 m (4 ft 2 in)

AREA:

Wings, gross	11.29 m² (121.5 sq ft)

WEIGHTS:

Weight empty	156 kg (345 lb)
Max T-O and landing weight	272 kg (600 lb)

PERFORMANCE:

Max level speed and max cruising speed at 610 m (2,000 ft)	56 knots (105 km/h; 65 mph)
Econ cruising speed	43 knots (80 km/h; 50 mph)
Stalling speed, engine idling	21 knots (39 km/h; 24 mph)
Max rate of climb at S/L	137 m (450 ft)/min
T-O run	61 m (200 ft)
Landing run	91-107 m (300-350 ft)
Range with 30 min reserves	139 nm (257 km; 160 miles)

LIGHT MINIATURE AIRCRAFT LM-1U and LM-1X

The prototype **LM-1U** microlight variant of the LM-1 flew for the first time on 7 April 1985. Kits are available, together with kits of an Experimental category homebuilt version, known as the **LM-1X**, which is identical except for having a 26 kW (35 hp) Rotax 377 engine and increased empty weight.
The following details refer to the LM-1U:
TYPE: Single-seat microlight: conforms to FAR Pt 103.
AIRFRAME: Wing section Göttingen 387 modified. Aluminium alloy airframe, except for wooden wing spars and overall Dacron covering. Three-axis control. Non-retractable tailwheel landing gear. Ballistic parachute and floats optional.
POWER PLANT: One 20 kW (27 hp) Rotax 277. Fuel capacity 20.4 litres (5.4 US gallons; 4.5 Imp gallons).

DIMENSIONS, EXTERNAL:

Wing span	9.14 m (30 ft 0 in)
Length overall	5.44 m (17 ft 10 in)
Height overall	1.70 m (5 ft 7 in)
Propeller diameter	1.52 m (5 ft 0 in)

AREA:

Wings, gross	10.87 m² (117.0 sq ft)

WEIGHTS (LM-1U):

Weight empty	114 kg (252 lb)
Pilot weight range	62-102 kg (135-225 lb)
Max baggage capacity	11.3 kg (25 lb)
Max T-O weight	238 kg (525 lb)

PERFORMANCE (LM-1U):

Max level speed at 305 m (1,000 ft)	61 knots (113 km/h; 70 mph)
Econ cruising speed at 305 m (1,000 ft)	47 knots (87 km/h; 54 mph)
Stalling speed, engine idling	23 knots (42 km/h; 26 mph)
Max rate of climb at S/L	168 m (550 ft)/min
T-O run	61 m (200 ft)
Landing run	91 m (300 ft)
Range, with 15 min reserves	156 nm (289 km; 180 miles)

LIGHT MINIATURE AIRCRAFT LM-3U and LM-3X

Identical except for engine and empty weight, the microlight **LM-3U** and Experimental category homebuilt **LM-3X** are three-quarter scale representations of the Aeronca 7AC Champ light aircraft. Kits to build the LM-3U and LM-3X include the appropriate Rotax engine. The prototype LM-3 flew for the first time in July 1986.

TYPES: Single-seat microlight (LM-3U) and homebuilt (LM-3X); LM-3U conforms to FAR Pt 103 and LM-3X to Experimental category regulations.
AIRFRAME: Wing section Göttingen 387. Ceconite covered wings, with wooden spars, stamped aluminium ribs and glassfibre leading-edges. Aluminium alloy fuselage longerons, uprights and cross members, with wooden formers and stringers, Ceconite covered. Glassfibre engine cowling. Three-axis control. Non-retractable tailwheel landing gear. Optional floats and recovery parachute.
POWER PLANT: LM-3U: One 20 kW (27 hp) Rotax 277. LM-3X: One 26 kW (35 hp) Rotax 377. Fuel capacity 19 litres (5 US gallons; 4.2 Imp gallons). LM-3X has option of two 20.4 litre (5.4 US gallon; 4.5 Imp gallon) auxiliary fuel tanks fitted in wingroots.
AVIONICS: Hand-held radio.

DIMENSIONS, EXTERNAL:

Wing span	9.14 m (30 ft 0 in)
Length overall	5.33 m (17 ft 6 in)
Height overall	1.70 m (5 ft 7 in)
Propeller diameter: LM-3U	1.52 m (5 ft 0 in)
LM-3X	1.63 m (5 ft 4 in)

AREA:

Wings, gross: both	11.15 m² (120.0 sq ft)

WEIGHTS (A: LM-3U, B: LM-3X):

Weight empty: A	114 kg (252 lb)
B	147 kg (325 lb)
Pilot weight range: A, B	61.5-102 kg (135-225 lb)
Baggage capacity	11.3 kg (25 lb)
Max T-O weight: A	249 kg (550 lb)
B	272 kg (600 lb)

PERFORMANCE (A and B as above):

Max level speed: A, B	65 knots (121 km/h; 75 mph)
Econ cruising speed: A, B	48 knots (89 km/h; 55 mph)
Stalling speed: A, B	19-24 knots (36-44 km/h; 22-27 mph)
Max rate of climb at S/L: A	168 m (550 ft)/min
B	183 m (600 ft)/min
T-O run: A, B	46-61 m (150-200 ft)
Landing from 15 m (50 ft): A, B	76-91 m (250-300 ft)
Range, standard fuel, with reserves:	
A	130 nm (241 km; 150 miles)
B	95 nm (177 km; 110 miles)
Endurance: A	3 h
B	2 h
g limits: A, B	+5/-4.5

LOEHLE

LOEHLE ENTERPRISES

'The Aviation Valley', Shipmans Creek Road, Wartrace, Tennessee 37183
Telephone: 1 (615) 857 3419
Fax: 1 (615) 857 3908
PRESIDENT: Michael Loehle
MARKETING MANAGER: Ms Sandy Burgess

Loehle Enterprises no longer produces microlight aircraft. Details of the Ritz Standard Model A, UFM of KY Aeroplane XP and The Fun Machine can be found in the 1989-90 and earlier editions of *Jane's*. The 5151 Mustang is categorised now as an Experimental aircraft, and by February 1990 a total of 125 kits were under construction. A series of eleven partial kits are now also available to help spread costs.

LOEHLE ENTERPRISES 5151 MUSTANG

This is an approximate ¾-scale representation of a Second World War North American P-51 Mustang fighter, offered in kit form under the Experimental category regulations. Construction time is approximately 400-500 working hours.
The prototype flew for the first time on 30 January 1986. Two versions are offered, one with a fixed landing gear and the 5151RG with a retractable gear.
TYPE: Single-seat homebuilt aircraft.
AIRFRAME: Cantilever low-wing monoplane. Constructed primarily of wood, with both conventional and geodetic structures. The whole assembly is glued together, using a T-88 epoxy, and is fabric covered. Non-retractable or retractable landing gear. Optional brakes, electric start, ballistic parachute and more.
POWER PLANT: One 34 kW (46 hp) Rotax 503 on 5151 Mustang; Rotax 503, 532 or 582 on 5151RG Mustang. Fuel capacity 19 litres (5 US gallons; 4.2 Imp gallons), or optional 49 litres (13 US gallons; 10.8 Imp gallons).

DIMENSIONS, EXTERNAL:

Wing span	8.36 m (27 ft 5 in)
Length overall	6.96 m (22 ft 10 in)
Propeller diameter: standard	1.73 m (5 ft 8 in)

AREA:

Wings, gross	12.54 m² (135.0 sq ft)

WEIGHTS (A: 5151, B: 5151RG):

Weight empty: A	233 kg (513 lb)
B	238 kg (525 lb)
B, with full options	266 kg (588 lb)
Max pilot weight: A, B	100 kg (220 lb)
Max T-O weight	401 kg (885 lb)

PERFORMANCE (A and B as above; Rotax 503 engine):

Cruising speed	65-74 knots (121-137 km/h; 75-85 mph)
Stalling speed	26 knots (49 km/h; 30 mph)
Max rate of climb at S/L	244-305 m (800-1,000 ft)/min
T-O run	46 m (150 ft)
Landing run	77 m (250 ft)
Range: A, with 5 US gallons	100 nm (185 km; 115 miles)
A, with 13 US gallons	258 nm (478 km; 297 miles)
B, with 5 US gallons	108 nm (201 km; 125 miles)
B, with 13 US gallons	273 nm (507 km; 315 miles)
g limits for wings	+4/-4

LUNDY

BRIAN LUNDY

1257 East Shadowridge Drive 11J, Midvale, Utah 84047

LUNDY GRAFLITE

Mr Brian Lundy and Mr Steve Kotula, both mechanical engineers in composite construction, designed the Graflite with the first-time builder in mind. The prototype first flew on 11 July 1987 and kits became available in late 1988. An aerobatic version is optional.
The following details refer to the prototype. The kit-built version has as standard a Textron Lycoming O-360 engine and fuel capacity of 170 litres (45 US gallons; 37.5 Imp gallons).
TYPE: Side by side two-seat homebuilt.
AIRFRAME: Moulded and vacuum bagged components

Loehle Enterprises 5151RG Mustang homebuilt

Light Miniature Aircraft LM-3X homebuilt aircraft

Lundy Graflite all-composites homebuilt aircraft

Leader's International JB-1000 microlight aircraft

MacFam marketed Jungster I built by Mr Dave Clark of Renton, Washington

of graphite/epoxy/core sandwich construction. Wing section NACA 64212.5. Winglets standard. Retractable tricycle landing gear.

POWER PLANT: One 112 kW (150 hp) Textron Lycoming O-320-A2B. Fuel capacity 129 litres (34 US gallons; 28.3 Imp gallons).

DIMENSIONS, EXTERNAL:
Wing span over winglets	7.67 m (25 ft 2 in)
Length overall	6.32 m (20 ft 9 in)
Height overall	1.88 m (6 ft 2 in)
Propeller diameter	1.70 m (5 ft 7 in)

WEIGHTS:
Weight empty	449 kg (989 lb)
Max crew weight	154 kg (340 lb)
Baggage weight	41 kg (90 lb)
Max T-O weight	726 kg (1,600 lb)

PERFORMANCE:
Max level speed at S/L	180 knots (333 km/h; 207 mph)
Econ cruising speed at 2,440 m (8,000 ft)	156 knots (290 km/h; 180 mph)
Stalling speed, engine idling	56 knots (103 km/h; 64 mph)
Max rate of climb at S/L	457 m (1,500 ft)/min
Service ceiling	5,790 m (19,000 ft)
Range with max fuel	547 nm (1,014 km; 630 miles)
Endurance	3 h 30 min
g limits	+4.4/-3

MACFAM
MACFAM
Box 788, Great Falls, Montana 59403-0788
Telephone: 1 (403) 235 6331

Readopting an earlier name, MacFam (formerly McAsco) offers plans for its Cavalier range of homebuilts, plus the Jungsters designed by Mr Rim Kaminskas.

MACFAM SA 102.5 CAVALIER
The prototype SA 102.5 Cavalier was being reworked and refurbished in an effort to reduce empty weight from the original 477 kg (1,051 lb) to 408 kg (900 lb). Fitted with a Teledyne Continental O-200 engine and a new wooden propeller, it was anticipated that a true air speed of 139 knots (257 km/h; 160 mph) could be achieved at 2,450 rpm, at a maximum weight of about 658-680 kg (1,450-1,500 lb). This prototype was also to receive a front hinged 'swing up' windshield and canopy with a composites frame and new wing flaps. The flaps were expected to offer up to a 15 per cent increase in cruising speed. Both these innovations are shown on plans.

TYPE: Side by side two-seat homebuilt.

AIRFRAME: All-wood airframe except for Dacron covered outer wing panels, rear top decking and tail unit, plus glassfibre cockpit canopy frame and doors. Wing section NACA 23015 at root, NACA 23012 at tip. Non-retractable tricycle landing gear, with optional floats or skis.

POWER PLANT: Wide choice of four-cylinder engines, including 63.5, 67 or 74.5 kW (85, 90 or 100 hp) Teledyne Continental, 93-97 kW (125-130 hp) Franklin Sport 4A, 80.5 or 86 kW (108 or 115 hp) Textron Lycoming O-235, or 93 or 101 kW (125 or 135 hp) Textron Lycoming O-290. Wingtip fuel tanks, total capacity 151 litres (40 US gallons; 33.5 Imp gallons).

DIMENSIONS, EXTERNAL:
Wing span over tip tanks	8.33 m (27 ft 4 in)
Length overall	6.71 m (22 ft 0 in)
Height overall	2.23 m (7 ft 4 in)

AREA:
Wings, gross	10.87 m² (117.0 sq ft)

WEIGHTS:
Basic operating weight empty	408 kg (900 lb)
Baggage weight	56 kg (125 lb)
Max T-O weight	680 kg (1,500 lb)

PERFORMANCE (at max T-O weight, 93 kW; 125 hp Textron Lycoming engine):
Max level speed at 2,135 m (7,000 ft)	160 knots (297 km/h; 185 mph)
Econ cruising speed	134 knots (249 km/h; 155 mph)
Stalling speed:	
flaps up	44 knots (81 km/h; 50 mph) IAS
flaps down	35 knots (65 km/h; 40 mph) IAS
Max rate of climb at S/L	over 518 m (1,700 ft)/min
Service ceiling	4,875 m (16,000 ft)
T-O run	107 m (350 ft)
Landing run	183 m (600 ft)
Max range, no reserves	720 nm (1,335 km; 830 miles)

MACFAM JUNGSTER I
The primary design requirements of this aircraft were to duplicate as closely as possible the performance and flight characteristics of the Bücker Jungmeister. The prototype flew for the first time in October 1962. Sets of plans have been available to amateur constructors for many years, with several hundred sets sold.

TYPE: Single-seat sporting homebuilt.

AIRFRAME: Braced biplane with wood structure, plywood and fabric covered except for aluminium alloy engine cowling. Wing section NACA 4413. Non-retractable tailwheel landing gear.

POWER PLANT: Options include 63.4-74.5 kW (85-100 hp) Teledyne Continental C85, C90 or O-200; 93-97 kW (125-130 hp) Franklin Sport 4, 4A or 4B; 80.5-86 kW (108-115 hp) Textron Lycoming O-235-C or -C1; 93-100.6 kW (125-135 hp) Textron Lycoming O-290-D or -D2; 104.5-112 kW (140-150 hp) Textron Lycoming O-320; or European engines in the same weight/power class. Fuel capacity 62 litres (16.5 US gallons; 13.7 Imp gallons); optional 26 litre (7 US gallon; 5.8 Imp gallon) tank in upper wing centre-section, increasing total capacity to 88 litres (23.5 US gallons; 19.5 Imp gallons).

DIMENSIONS, EXTERNAL (prototype):
Wing span	5.08 m (16 ft 8 in)
Length overall	4.88 m (16 ft 0 in)
Propeller diameter	1.73 m (5 ft 8 in)

AREA:
Wings, gross	7.43 m² (80.0 sq ft)

WEIGHTS:
Weight empty	275 kg (606 lb)
T-O weight, aerobatic	385 kg (850 lb)
Max T-O weight	455 kg (1,000 lb)

PERFORMANCE (prototype, at max T-O weight, Textron Lycoming O-235 engine):
Max level speed at S/L	109 knots (201 km/h; 125 mph) IAS
Max cruising speed at S/L	103 knots (192 km/h; 119 mph)
Stalling speed	45 knots (84 km/h; 52 mph) IAS

Max rate of climb at S/L	455 m (1,500 ft)/min
Service ceiling	3,960 m (13,000 ft)
T-O run	91 m (300 ft)
Landing run	152 m (500 ft)
Range with max fuel (incl centre-section tank)	
	260 nm (482 km; 300 miles)
g limits	+9/−6

MACFAM JUNGSTER II

The prototype of this strut braced parasol monoplane flew for the first time in March 1966. Plans are available.

TYPE: Single-seat sporting homebuilt.

AIRFRAME: All-wood structure, plywood and fabric covered. Wing section NACA 2412. Non-retractable tailwheel landing gear.

POWER PLANT (prototype): One 134 kW (180 hp) Textron Lycoming O-360. Fuel capacity 75 litres (20 US gallons; 16.7 Imp gallons). Other engines available optionally include those listed under Jungster I description, plus 119 kW (160 hp) Textron Lycoming O-320 and 134 kW (180 hp) Textron Lycoming O-360.

DIMENSIONS, EXTERNAL:

Wing span	6.81 m (22 ft 4 in)
Length overall (tail up)	5.16 m (16 ft 11 in)
Height to top of wings (tail up)	2.06 m (6 ft 9 in)
Propeller diameter	1.68 m (5 ft 6 in)

MARQUART
ED MARQUART
PO Box 3032, Riverside, California 92519
Telephone: 1 (714) 683 9582

MARQUART MA-4 LANCER

Available in plans form only, the Lancer is a single-seat biplane powered by an engine in the 48.5-93.2 kW (65-125 hp) range. Construction is of wood, steel tube and fabric.

DIMENSIONS, EXTERNAL:

Wing span	6.10 m (20 ft 0 in)
Length overall	5.03 m (16 ft 6 in)
Height overall	1.98 m (6 ft 6 in)
AREA:	
Wings, gross	10.78 m² (116.0 sq ft)
WEIGHTS:	
Weight empty	295 kg (650 lb)
Max T-O weight	454 kg (1,000 lb)

PERFORMANCE (93.2 kW; 125 hp engine):

Max level speed	113 knots (209 km/h; 130 mph)
Cruising speed	104 knots (193 km/h; 120 mph)
Stalling speed	48 knots (89 km/h; 55 mph)
Max rate of climb at S/L	488 m (1,600 ft)/min
Service ceiling	3,050 m (10,000 ft)
T-O run	91 m (300 ft)
Landing run	244 m (800 ft)
Range	325 nm (603 km; 375 miles)

MARQUART MA-5 CHARGER

Plans and component parts of this popular homebuilt biplane are available.

TYPE: Two-seat homebuilt sporting biplane.

AIRFRAME: Wooden wings and steel tube fuselage, all fabric covered. Non-retractable tailwheel landing gear.

POWER PLANT: One engine of 74.6-134 kW (100-180 hp); typically, a 134 kW (180 hp) Textron Lycoming O-360-A1G6. Fuel capacity 98.4 litres (26 US gallons; 21.6 Imp gallons).

DIMENSIONS, EXTERNAL:

Wing span	7.32 m (24 ft 0 in)
Length overall	5.94 m (19 ft 6 in)
Height overall	2.29 m (7 ft 6 in)
AREA:	
Wings, gross	15.8 m² (170.0 sq ft)
WEIGHTS:	
Weight empty	454 kg (1,000 lb)
Baggage capacity	11.3 kg (25 lb)
Max T-O weight	703 kg (1,550 lb)

PERFORMANCE (134 kW; 180 hp engine):

Max level speed	126 knots (233 km/h; 145 mph)
Max cruising speed	117 knots (217 km/h; 135 mph)
Stalling speed	37 knots (68 km/h; 42 mph)
Max rate of climb at S/L	549 m (1,800 ft)/min
Service ceiling	4,260 m (14,000 ft)
T-O run	122 m (400 ft)
Landing run	244 m (800 ft)
Range with max fuel	390 nm (724 km; 450 miles)

MAXAIR
MAXAIR AIRCRAFT CORPORATION
3855 Highway 27 North, Lake Wales, Florida 33853
Telephone: 1 (813) 676 0771
Telex: 4996511
Fax: 1 (813) 676 5701
DIRECTOR OF MARKETING AND SALES: Donald Jones

MAXAIR DRIFTER SERIES

In addition to the five versions of the Drifter of which details follow, new cable braced models of the XP503 and MU532 became available in August 1988. Each has a single chrome molybdenum steel tube strut each side and stamped aluminium alloy ribs, plus full-span flaperons for STOL performance. Kits of all models are available; by February 1990 a total of 1,796 Drifter kits had been delivered.

DR277. Original single-seat model with Rotax 277 engine, introduced in early 1983 and the only version available also in ready assembled form. Conforms to FAR Pt 103 requirements.

DR377. More powerful single-seater with Rotax 377 engine.

XP503. Tandem two-seat, dual control version of the basic Drifter. Higher weight makes it an Experimental category homebuilt aircraft.

MU532. Tandem two-seat, dual control utility counterpart of XP503, suitable for heavy duty applications such as floatplane operation and agricultural spraying. Strengthened wings and landing gear permit a 245 kg (540 lb) useful load. Rotax 532 engine.

DR532 Rocket. High-performance single-seat version with Rotax 532, shorter wing span and wide-chord full span ailerons for quick roll response. Classed as Experimental category homebuilt.

TYPES: DR277 and DR377 conform to FAR Pt 103, other models to FAA Experimental requirements.

AIRFRAME: Braced mainframe of steel and aluminium alloy tube. Wings and tail surfaces have double surface Dacron/Stits Aerothane covering. Three-axis control. Non-retractable tailwheel landing gear. Options include skis, floats, amphibious gear and nose fairings.

POWER PLANT: DR277: One 20 kW (27 hp) Rotax 277. DR377: One 26 kW (35 hp) Rotax 377. XP503: One 34 kW (46 hp) Rotax 503. MU532 and DR532: One 47.7 kW (64 hp) Rotax 532. Alternative engines are 44.7 and 67 kW (60 and 90 hp) AMWs. Fuel capacity 19 litres (5 US gallons; 4.2 Imp gallons) standard; 38 litres (10 US gallons; 8.3 Imp gallons) optional.

ARMAMENT: Military versions may be camouflaged and can reportedly carry machine-guns or Sidewinder air-to-air missiles.

DIMENSIONS, EXTERNAL (A: DR277, B: XP503, C: MU532, and D: DR532):

Wing span: A, B, C	9.14 m (30 ft 0 in)
D	7.01 m (23 ft 0 in)
Length overall: A, B, C, D	5.79 m (19 ft 0 in)
Height overall: A	2.67 m (8 ft 9 in)
B, C	2.82 m (9 ft 3 in)
D	2.79 m (9 ft 2 in)
Propeller diameter: A, B, C, D	1.52 m (5 ft 0 in)
AREAS:	
Wings, gross: A, B, C	14.12 m² (152.0 sq ft)
D	10.87 m² (117.0 sq ft)
WEIGHTS (A, B, C and D as above):	
Weight empty: A	109 kg (240 lb)
B, D	156.5 kg (345 lb)
C	166 kg (365 lb)
Max pilot weight: A	104 kg (230 lb)
B, C	109 kg (240 lb)
D	104 kg (230 lb)
Max T-O weight: A	227 kg (500 lb)
B	356 kg (785 lb)
C	408 kg (900 lb)
D	272 kg (600 lb)

PERFORMANCE (A and D with 79 kg; 175 lb pilot, B and C with two 79 kg; 175 lb crew):

Max level speed: A	55 knots (101 km/h; 63 mph)
B	65 knots (120 km/h; 75 mph)
C, D	82 knots (153 km/h; 95 mph)
Econ cruising speed: A	35 knots (64 km/h; 40 mph)
Stalling speed: A	23 knots (42 km/h; 26 mph)
B	27 knots (50 km/h; 31 mph)
C	31 knots (57 km/h; 35 mph)
D	32 knots (60 km/h; 37 mph)
Max rate of climb at S/L: A, B	183 m (600 ft)/min
C	244 m (800 ft)/min
D	427 m (1,400 ft)/min
Service ceiling: A	3,050 m (10,000 ft)
T-O run: A	46-84 m (150-275 ft)
B	76-107 m (250-350 ft)
C	46-107 m (150-350 ft)
D	79 m (260 ft)
Landing run with brakes: A	69 m (225 ft)
B, D	76 m (250 ft)
C	91 m (300 ft)
Range, 65% power: A	104 nm (193 km; 120 miles)
B	87 nm (161 km; 100 miles)
C	74 nm (136 km; 85 miles)
D	69 nm (129 km; 80 miles)
Endurance with max fuel: A	2 h 30 min
g limits: A	+6/−3.3
B	+4.2 limit
B	+6/−3 ultimate

MIRAGE
MIRAGE AIRCRAFT CORPORATION
3936 Austin Street, Klamath Falls, Oregon 97603
Telephone: 1 (503) 884 4011
PRESIDENT: Larry Burton

MIRAGE CELERITY

The prototype Celerity flew for the first time on 18 May 1985. It has since undergone considerable development, and now has retractable landing gear, as shown on plans available from Mirage Aircraft. An inexperienced builder could take more than 3,000 working hours to build a Celerity from plans. Various kits and upholstery patterns to cut working time are available via Wicks Aircraft Supply (410 Pine Street, Highland, Illinois 62249).

TYPE: Side by side two-seat homebuilt.

AIRFRAME: Wing section NACA 23015 at root, NACA 23010 at tip. Airframe structure of wood, with composite skins of foam, glassfibre and epoxy resin. Retractable tailwheel landing gear.

POWER PLANT: One 119 kW (160 hp) Textron Lycoming O-320-B1A. Fuel capacity 114 litres (30 US gallons; 25 Imp gallons). Two auxiliary tip tanks, each of 38 litres (10 US gallons; 8.3 Imp gallons) capacity. Engines of 74.5-134 kW (100-180 hp) optional.

DIMENSIONS, EXTERNAL:

Wing span over tip tanks	7.01 m (23 ft 0 in)
Length overall	6.55 m (21 ft 6 in)
Height overall	1.68 m (5 ft 6 in)
Propeller diameter	1.93 m (6 ft 4 in)

AREA:

Wings, gross	8.36 m² (90.0 sq ft)
WEIGHTS:	
Weight empty	530 kg (1,169 lb)
Baggage capacity	27 kg (60 lb)
Max T-O weight	828 kg (1,825 lb)

PERFORMANCE (at max T-O weight):

Econ cruising speed	165 knots (306 km/h; 190 mph)
Stalling speed	46 knots (86 km/h; 53 mph)
Max rate of climb at S/L	549 m (1,800 ft)/min
T-O run	244 m (800 ft)
Landing run	305 m (1,000 ft)
Range with max standard fuel	
	781-868 nm (1,448-1,609 km; 900-1,000 miles)

MITCHELL WING
MITCHELL AEROSPACE COMPANY
1900 South Newcomb, Porterville, California 93257
Telephone: 1 (209) 781 8100
DIRECTOR: James M. Meade

Details of the B-10, U-2 Superwing and A-10 Silver Eagle microlights can be found in the Microlight tables.

MITCHELL WING P-38 LIGHTNING

The P-38 was designed to be assembled by four people in one day. It flew for the first time in late 1980 and is available in plans and kit forms. Assembly time for the kit is quoted as 100 man-hours.

An **AG-38A Terrier** agricultural version, with a 12V battery, 53 litre (14 US gallon; 11.7 Imp gallon) ULV spraytank, two Beeco Mist sprayheads and an electric spraypump, is also available.

The following description applies to the standard P-38:

TYPE: Single-seat microlight; does not conform to FAR Pt 103.

AIRFRAME: Main structure of aluminium, with quick-fit ribs and Dacron covered wing and tail surfaces. Wing section NACA 23015. Three-axis control. Non-retractable tricycle landing gear. Optional cockpit 'podule', floats and skis.

POWER PLANT: One 22 kW (30 hp) 250 cc Cuyuna 430. Fuel

Jungster II monoplane owned by Mr Ed Sullivan of Fresno, California
(John Wegg)

Marquart MA-5 Charger built by Mr Remo Galeazzi of Petaluma, California
(John Wegg)

Maxair Drifter DR532 Rocket

Maxair Drifter MU532 with agricultural spraygear

Demonstration of Mitchell Wing AG-38 cropsprayer in China

Mirage Celerity (Textron Lycoming O-320) *(Peter M. Bowers)*

---

capacity 5.7 litres (1.5 US gallons; 1.25 Imp gallons). Options include 15 litre (4 US gallon; 3.33 Imp gallon) auxiliary fuel tank.

DIMENSIONS, EXTERNAL:
Wing span	8.53 m (28 ft 0 in)
Length overall	5.49 m (18 ft 0 in)
Height overall	1.52 m (5 ft 0 in)

AREA:
Wings, gross	11.52 m² (124.0 sq ft)

WEIGHTS:
Weight empty	136 kg (300 lb)
Max pilot weight	136 kg (300 lb)
Max T-O weight: standard	249 kg (550 lb)
Restricted category	340 kg (750 lb)

PERFORMANCE (at max standard T-O weight):
Max level speed	52 knots (97 km/h; 60 mph)
Max cruising speed	48 knots (88 km/h; 55 mph)
Stalling speed	28 knots (51 km/h; 32 mph)
Max rate of climb at S/L	76-91 m (250-300 ft)/min
T-O run	68 m (225 ft)
Landing run	61 m (200 ft)

Range: with max standard fuel   43 nm (80 km; 50 miles)
with auxiliary fuel   434 nm (805 km; 500 miles)
g limits   ±6

MITCHELL WING AG-38-A WAR EAGLE

The AG-38-A War Eagle is an enlarged military version of the P-38/AG-38 series, with a more powerful engine, increased fuel and provision for a variety of operational equipment. An illustration appeared in the 1987-88 *Jane's*.

POWER PLANT: One 29.4 kW (39.4 hp) Rotax 447. Standard fuel capacity 24 litres (6.5 US gallons; 5.4 Imp gallons). Optional long-range fuel tank, capacity 151 litres (40 US gallons; 33.3 Imp gallons).

OPERATIONAL EQUIPMENT: Optional items include two M60 machine-gun mounts; four Strem 89 rocket mounts; wind-driven agricultural spraypump with full-span 25 nozzle spray system and 151 litre (40 US gallon; 33.3 Imp gallon) hopper capacity; ballistic parachute; radios; video camera, transmitter and antenna; Kevlar pilot protection and night vision goggles.

DIMENSIONS, EXTERNAL:
Wing span	10.36 m (34 ft 0 in)
Length overall	5.79 m (19 ft 0 in)
Height overall	2.11 m (6 ft 11 in)
Propeller diameter	1.47 m (4 ft 10 in)

AREA:
Wings, gross	14.86 m² (160.0 sq ft)

WEIGHTS:
Weight empty	168 kg (370 lb)
Max pilot weight	104 kg (230 lb)
Max T-O weight: Normal	363 kg (800 lb)
Restricted category	476 kg (1,050 lb)

PERFORMANCE (Normal category, 77 kg; 170 lb pilot):
Best cruising speed	60 knots (111 km/h; 69 mph)
Stalling speed, power off	30 knots (56 km/h; 35 mph)
Max rate of climb at S/L	152 m (500 ft)/min
T-O run	61 m (200 ft)
Endurance with max fuel	1 h 40 min

MOSHIER

MOSHIER TECHNOLOGIES

334 State Street, Suite 106 (Dept KP1), Los Altos, California 94022

MOSHIER MANX

Moshier Technologies currently offers a two-seat, highly streamlined, coaxial twin-rotor homebuilt helicopter known as the Manx. It can achieve 130 knots (241 km/h; 150 mph) and a range of 521 nm (965 km; 600 miles).

MOSLER

MOSLER INC

140 Ashwood Road, Hendersonville, North Carolina 28739
Telephone: 1 (704) 692 7713
PRESIDENT: John W. Martin

MOSLER N3 PUP, SUPER PUP and N3-2 PUP

Mosler's N3 Pup is a microlight representation of the Piper Cub, available in ready to fly and kit forms. Average construction time is 200 working hours. The Super Pup conforms to Experimental and ARV regulations and has clipped wings, wheel fairings, brakes, a 45.5 litre (12 US gallon; 10 Imp gallon) fuel capacity and higher cruising speed.

The N3-2 is a tandem two-seat version of the N3, with 45 litres (12 US gallons; 10 Imp gallons) fuel capacity. The N3-2 kit comes under Experimental regulations. Max T-O weight of the N3-2 is 363 kg (800 lb), and cruising speed is 61 knots (113 km/h; 70 mph).

The following details refer to the Pup microlight:
TYPE: Single-seat microlight; conforms to FAR Pt 103.
AIRFRAME: Strut braced, with stamped aluminium alloy wing ribs, aluminium alloy spars, welded steel tube fuselage and overall Stits Dacron covering. Glassfibre engine cowling. Three-axis control. Non-retractable tailwheel landing gear. Options include floats, skis and ballistic parachute.
POWER PLANT: One 26 kW (35 hp) Mosler MM-CB engine. Fuel capacity 15.9 litres (4.2 US gallons; 3.5 Imp gallons).
DIMENSIONS, EXTERNAL:
Wing span	9.14 m (30 ft 0 in)
Length overall	5.08 m (16 ft 8 in)
Height overall	1.57 m (5 ft 2 in)
Propeller diameter	1.42 m (4 ft 8 in)

AREA:
Wings, gross	11.43 m² (123.0 sq ft)

WEIGHTS:
Weight empty	112 kg (248 lb)
Max T-O weight	242 kg (535 lb)

PERFORMANCE:
Max level speed	55 knots (101 km/h; 63 mph)
Max cruising speed	50 knots (93 km/h; 58 mph)
Stalling speed	22 knots (41 km/h; 25 mph)
Max rate of climb at S/L	198 m (650 ft)/min
Service ceiling	1,525 m (5,000 ft)
T-O run	38 m (125 ft)
Landing run	61 m (200 ft)
Range with max fuel	173 nm (322 km; 200 miles)
Endurance with max fuel	3 h
g limits	+6/−3

NEICO

NEICO AVIATION INC

403 South Ojai Street, Santa Paula, California 93060
Telephone: 1 (805) 933 2747
Fax: 1 (805) 933 2093

NEICO AVIATION LANCAIR 200 and 235

The prototype Lancair 200 first flew in June 1984. The **Lancair 235** is offered in kit form with an 88 kW (118 hp) O-235 engine and 0.40 m³ (14.0 cu ft) baggage area. Glassfibre is replaced by Kevlar in the latest form. Cruising speed compared to the Lancair 200 is increased to 187 knots (346 km/h; 215 mph) at 75 per cent power, and empty weight is reportedly 399 kg (880 lb).

Approximately 400 Lancair kits of all versions had been delivered to customers in 18 countries by early 1990.

The following details refer mainly to the Lancair 200:
TYPE: Side by side two-seat sporting and cross-country homebuilt.

AIRFRAME: Wing section NLF 0215F. Composite airframe of glassfibre, Nomex honeycomb, Polyimide Rohacell foam and epoxy resin. Retractable tricycle landing gear.
POWER PLANT: Originally one 74.6 kW (100 hp) Teledyne Continental O-200. Currently advertised with 88 kW (118 hp) O-235. Fuel capacity 106-114 litres (28-30 US gallons; 23.3-25 Imp gallons).
DIMENSIONS, EXTERNAL:
Wing span	7.16 m (23 ft 6 in)
Length overall	5.99 m (19 ft 8 in)
Width, wings folded	2.54 m (8 ft 4 in)
Height overall	1.85 m (6 ft 1 in)
Propeller diameter	1.47-1.52 m (4 ft 10 in-5 ft 0 in)

AREA:
Wings, gross	7.06 m² (76.0 sq ft)

WEIGHTS:
Weight empty	295 kg (650 lb)
Max T-O weight	578 kg (1,275 lb)

PERFORMANCE (100 hp engine):
Max level speed at S/L	185 knots (343 km/h; 213 mph)
Econ cruising speed	165 knots (306 km/h; 190 mph)
Stalling speed, engine idling	48 knots (89 km/h; 55 mph)
Max rate of climb at S/L	457 m (1,500 ft)/min
Service ceiling	5,485-6,100 m (18,000-20,000 ft)
T-O and landing run	183 m (600 ft)
Range with max fuel	868 nm (1,609 km; 1,000 miles)

NEICO LANCAIR 320

This latest version has a 119 kW (160 hp) engine which allows a speed and max range of 217 knots (402 km/h; 250 mph) and 1,215 nm (2,253 km; 1,400 miles) respectively to be achieved. Layout remains similar although it is 'all new', providing a larger cockpit. ACT in the Philippines is producing advanced composite structural components for the Lancair 320.

NUWACO — *See Aircraft Dynamics Corporation*

OSPREY

OSPREY AIRCRAFT

3741 El Ricon Way, Sacramento, California 95864
Telephone: 1 (916) 483 3004

PEREIRA GP3 OSPREY II

Developed from the Osprey I flying boat, the prototype Osprey II amphibian first flew from water in April 1973. Sets of plans, as well as material and component kits, are available to amateur constructors. By early 1990, more than 1,300 sets of plans had been sold to potential builders in 50 countries, and at least 175 Ospreys had flown.
TYPE: Side by side two-seat, dual-control homebuilt amphibian.
AIRFRAME: Wing section NACA 23012. All-wood wings, except for fabric covering aft of spar. Wingtip stabilising floats of polyurethane foam covered with glassfibre. All-wood hull covered with marine plywood. Hull undersurface contours formed from sculptured polyurethane foam, protected by several layers of glassfibre cloth bonded with resin. All-wood tail unit. Water rudder. Retractable tricycle landing gear.
POWER PLANT: One 112 kW (150 hp) Textron Lycoming O-320. Usable fuel capacity 98.4 litres (26 US gallons; 21.6 Imp gallons). Wing tanks available to replace standard fuselage tank, allowing increased baggage area.
DIMENSIONS, EXTERNAL:
Wing span	7.92 m (26 ft 0 in)
Length overall	6.25 m (20 ft 6 in)
Height overall (wheels down)	1.83 m (6 ft 0 in)
Propeller diameter	1.68 m (5 ft 6 in)

AREA:
Wings, gross	12.08 m² (130.0 sq ft)

WEIGHTS:
Weight empty	440 kg (970 lb)
Baggage capacity	41 kg (90 lb)
Max T-O weight	707 kg (1,560 lb)

PERFORMANCE (at max T-O weight except where indicated):
Max cruising speed at 75% power	113 knots (209 km/h; 130 mph)
Econ cruising speed at 55% power	94 knots (175 km/h; 109 mph)
Stalling speed	53 knots (97 km/h; 60 mph)
Max rate of climb at S/L, with pilot only	365 m (1,200 ft)/min
Rate of climb at S/L	305 m (1,000 ft)/min
T-O run: land	122 m (400 ft)
water	159 m (520 ft)
Range with wing tanks	313 nm (579 km; 360 miles)

PEREIRA GP4

This aircraft flew for the first time in 1984. Plans to construct the GP4 are available. In addition, pre-moulded glassfibre components and an airframe materials kit are available to reduce construction time.

TYPE: Two-seat cross-country homebuilt.
AIRFRAME: All-wood construction except for foam and glassfibre used in cowling and fairings. Wing section Laminar 63 series. Retractable tricycle landing gear.
POWER PLANT: One 149 kW (200 hp) Textron Lycoming IO-360. Fuel capacity 204 litres (54 US gallons; 45 Imp gallons).
DIMENSIONS, EXTERNAL:
Wing span	7.52 m (24 ft 8 in)
Length overall	6.55 m (21 ft 6 in)
Propeller diameter	1.83 m (6 ft 0 in)

AREA:
Wings, gross	9.66 m² (104.0 sq ft)

WEIGHTS:
Weight empty	566 kg (1,248 lb)
Baggage capacity	34 kg (75 lb)
Max T-O weight	900 kg (1,985 lb)

PERFORMANCE:
Cruising speed, 75% power	208 knots (386 km/h; 240 mph)
Stalling speed, clean	57 knots (105 km/h; 65 mph)
Max rate of climb at S/L:	
2 crew, 50% fuel	670 m (2,200 ft)/min
max T-O weight	457 m (1,500 ft)/min
Range: 75% power	955 nm (1,770 km; 1,100 miles)
60% power (195 knots; 362 km/h; 225 mph)	1,085 nm (2,011 km; 1,250 miles)
g limits, at max T-O weight	+8/−6

PARAPLANE

PARAPLANE CORPORATION

5801 Magnolia Avenue, Pennsauken, New Jersey 08109
Telephone: 1 (609) 663 2234
PRESIDENT: Steve Snyder

PARAPLANE PM-2

The ParaPlane utilises a sport parachute as its 'wing', attached to a 'powered trike' airframe. The aerofoil section parachute can be held open by two ground assistants before ground roll begins, though this is not necessary. It takes about five seconds to deploy as the lifting surface. Recreational flying is not recommended in winds in excess of 13 knots (24 km/h; 15 mph). Many hundreds have been sold.
TYPE: Single-seat microlight.
AIRFRAME: Aircraft's 'wing' is an inherently stable ram air sport parachute, made of F-111 ripstop nylon and having single-axis control through steering lines. Airframe consists of a T frame of aluminium alloy. Non-retractable tricycle landing gear.
POWER PLANT: Two 11.2 kW (15 hp) Solo 210 cc engines, driving counter-rotating pusher propellers on concentric shafts. Fuel capacity 17 litres (4.5 US gallons; 3.75 Imp gallons).

DIMENSIONS, EXTERNAL:
Parachute span	9.30 m (36 ft 6 in)
Airframe: Length	1.73 m (5 ft 8 in)
Height	1.70 m (5 ft 7 in)
Propeller diameter (each)	1.29 m (4 ft 3 in)

AREA:
Parachute	37.16 m² (400.0 sq ft)

WEIGHTS:
Weight empty	74.5 kg (164 lb)
Max pilot weight	84 kg (185 lb)
Max T-O weight	193 kg (425 lb)

Mosler N3 Pup *(Geoffrey P. Jones)*

Neico Aviation Lancair 235 *(John Wegg)*

UK registered Pereira Osprey II two-seat amphibian *(Peter J. Bish)*

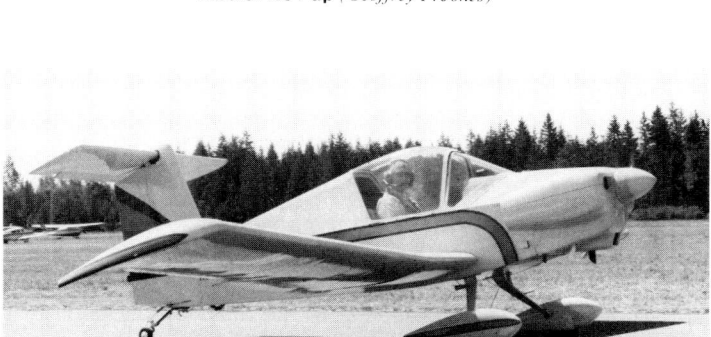

Pazmany PL-4A single-seat homebuilt *(Peter M. Bowers)*

Pereira GP4 prototype two-seat homebuilt cross-country aircraft
(Scott Kemper)

ParaPlane in flight *(Howard Levy)*

PERFORMANCE:				
Max level and cruising speed	Glide speed, engine idling	18 knots (34 km/h; 21 mph)	T-O run	30-46 m (100-150 ft)
	Max rate of climb	150 m (495 ft)/min	Range	43 nm (80 km; 50 miles)
22 knots (41 km/h; 26 mph)	Service ceiling	more than 1,525 m (5,000 ft)	Endurance	1 h 30 min

---

PARSONS
BILL PARSONS
PO Box 532, Lake Monroe, Florida 32747
Telephone: 1 (305) 323 9440

PARSONS TANDEM TRAINER
Kits are available for a tandem two-seat, dual-control autogyro known simply as the Tandem Trainer. It is of conventional configuration and metal tube construction, with a two-blade glassfibre rotor, a three-blade pusher propeller powered by a Rotax 532 or McCulloch engine, and a non-retractable tricycle landing gear.

PAZMANY
PAZMANY AIRCRAFT CORPORATION
PO Box 80051, San Diego, California 92138
Telephone: 1 (714) 276 0424
PROPRIETOR: Ladislao Pazmany

PAZMANY PL-2
The PL-2 was developed from the PL-1 (see 1979-80 *Jane's*), first flying on 4 April 1969. Plans are available. Aircraft built and flown include several examples for evaluation and use by foreign military training centres.
TYPE: Side by side two-seat, dual-control homebuilt.
AIRFRAME: All-aluminium alloy construction, except for glassfibre wingtips (including wingtip fuel tanks), wing fillets, tailcone, engine cowling, and the tips of the fin and tailplane. Wing section NACA 63₂615. Semi-monocoque fuselage has only flat or single-curvature skins. Non-retractable tricycle landing gear.
POWER PLANT: Recommended Textron Lycoming power plants include the 80.5 kW (108 hp) O-235-C1, 93 kW (125 hp) O-290-G (ground power unit), 101 kW (135 hp) O-290-D2B or 112 kW (150 hp) O-320-A. Some PL-2s are

fitted with O-360 engines. Fuel capacity 95 litres (25 US gallons; 20.8 Imp gallons). Some PL-2s built with additional integral wing tanks, total capacity 94 litres (25 US gallons; 21 Imp gallons).
DIMENSIONS, EXTERNAL:
Wing span	8.53 m (28 ft 0 in)
Length overall	5.90 m (19 ft 3½ in)
Height overall	2.44 m (8 ft 0 in)

AREA:
Wings, gross	10.78 m² (116.0 sq ft)

WEIGHTS (with 93 kW; 125 hp engine):
Weight empty	408 kg (900 lb)
Baggage capacity	18 kg (40 lb)
Max T-O weight	655 kg (1,445 lb)

PERFORMANCE (with 93 kW; 125 hp engine, at max T-O weight):
Max level speed at S/L	125 knots (232 km/h; 144 mph)
Econ cruising speed	111 knots (206 km/h; 128 mph)
Stalling speed (flaps down)	47 knots (87 km/h; 54 mph)
Max rate of climb at S/L	457 m (1,500 ft)/min
Range at econ cruising speed	422 nm (780 km; 486 miles)
Endurance	4 h 6 min

PAZMANY PL-4A
The prototype of this economical single-seater flew for the first time on 12 July 1972. Sets of plans, kits of prefabricated components, glassfibre wingtips and fuel tank, and transparent cockpit canopy are available to amateur constructors.
TYPE: Single-seat sporting homebuilt.
AIRFRAME: All-aluminium alloy construction, except for glassfibre cambered wingtips, fairings, engine cowling, spinner, elevator trim kit and fuel tank. Wing section NACA 63₃418. Non-retractable tailwheel landing gear.
POWER PLANT: One 1,600 cc modified Volkswagen motorcar engine, developing approximately 37.5 kW (50 hp). Optional Volkswagen engine conversions from Revmaster, Limbach and others, of up to 2,100 cc, or Continental A65 or C80. Fuel capacity 45 litres (12 US gallons; 10 Imp gallons).
DIMENSIONS, EXTERNAL:
Wing span	8.13 m (26 ft 8 in)
Length overall	5.04 m (16 ft 6½ in)
Height overall	1.73 m (5 ft 8 in)
Propeller diameter	1.73 m (5 ft 8 in)

AREA:
Wings, gross	8.27 m² (89.0 sq ft)

WEIGHTS:

Weight empty	262 kg (578 lb)
Baggage capacity	9 kg (20 lb)
Max T-O and landing weight	385 kg (850 lb)

PERFORMANCE (37.5 kW; 50 hp engine, at max T-O weight):

Max level speed at S/L	109 knots (201 km/h; 125 mph)
Econ cruising speed at S/L	78 knots (145 km/h; 90 mph)
Stalling speed:	
power on	40 knots (74 km/h; 46 mph)
power off	42 knots (78 km/h; 48 mph)
Max rate of climb at S/L	198 m (650 ft)/min
Service ceiling	3,960 m (13,000 ft)
T-O run	148 m (486 ft)
Landing run	133 m (436 ft)
Range with max fuel, no allowances	295 nm (545 km; 340 miles)
Endurance	3 h 48 min

PHOENIX

PHOENIX AVIATION INC

The address quoted in the 1989-90 *Jane's* is no longer current. Details of the Phoenix kit-built homebuilt and an illustration can be found in that edition.

PIETENPOL

DONALD PIETENPOL

215, 21st Street SE, Rochester, Minnesota 55904

Details of the B4 Aircamper, and an illustration, can be found in the 1988-89 *Jane's*.

PITTS — *see Christen Industries in main Aircraft section*

POLLIWAGEN

POLLIWAGEN INC

The address quoted in the 1989-90 *Jane's* is no longer current. Details of the Polliwagen homebuilt, and an illustration, can be found in that edition.

PRESCOTT

PRESCOTT AERONAUTICAL CORPORATION

The address quoted in the 1989-90 *Jane's* is no longer current. Details of the Pusher homebuilt aircraft, and an illustration, can be found in that edition.

PROWLER

PROWLER AVIATION INC

3707 Meadow View Drive, Redding, California 96002
Telephone: 1 (916) 365 4524
PRESIDENT: George Morse Jr

PROWLER AVIATION (MORSE 364P) PROWLER

The prototype Prowler, reminiscent of a Supermarine Spitfire, made its first flight on 17 March 1985. Prowler Aviation offers kits to allow amateur construction of the aircraft; the original F-85 engine has now been discontinued, to be replaced by a new 261 kW (350 hp) engine.

TYPE: Tandem two-seat high-performance homebuilt.
AIRFRAME: Aluminium alloy construction. Wing section NACA 64A-212 at roots, NACA 64A-210 at tips. Retractable tailwheel landing gear, with brakes.

POWER PLANT: One 261 kW (350 hp) modified motorcar engine based on a Chevrolet Rodeck block, with 1.67 : 1 reduction gear, under development for future kits. Originally fitted with 164 kW (220 hp) Auto Aviation modified Oldsmobile F-85 motorcar engine (discontinued for kits). Fuel capacity 227 litres (60 US gallons; 50 Imp gallons). Two external auxiliary fuel tanks possible.

DIMENSIONS, EXTERNAL:

Wing span	7.62 m (25 ft 0 in)
Length overall	6.40 m (21 ft 0 in)
Height overall	2.21 m (7 ft 3 in)
Propeller diameter	1.98 m (6 ft 6 in)

AREA:

Wings, gross	9.66 m² (104.0 sq ft)

WEIGHTS:

Weight empty	618 kg (1,362 lb)
Baggage capacity	22.7 kg (50 lb)
Max T-O weight	975 kg (2,150 lb)

PERFORMANCE (at max T-O weight, F-85 engine):

Max level speed at S/L	191 knots (354 km/h; 220 mph) IAS
Econ cruising speed at 2,135 m (7,000 ft)	148 knots (274 km/h; 170 mph)
Stalling speed, flaps up, power off	48 knots (89 km/h; 55 mph) IAS
Max rate of climb at S/L	549 m (1,800 ft)/min
Service ceiling	5,180 m (17,000 ft)
T-O and landing run	457 m (1,500 ft)
Landing from 15 m (50 ft)	610 m (2,000 ft)
Range:	
with max standard fuel	1,042 nm (1,931 km; 1,200 miles)
with auxiliary fuel	1,302 nm (2,414 km; 1,500 miles)

PT

PROTECH AIRCRAFT INC

11903 Westheimer Road, Houston, Texas 77077
Telephone: 1 (713) 589 0628

PROTECH PT-2 SASSY

The ProTech PT-2 is available in kit form, requiring about 300 working hours to assemble.

TYPE: Side by side two-seat, dual-control homebuilt STOL aircraft.
AIRFRAME: Wings have preformed aluminium alloy ribs, spars and skins. Glassfibre wingtips, wingroot fillets, rear cabin fairing and engine cowlings. Steel tube and aluminium flaperons. Welded steel tube fuselage and tail surfaces, Ceconite covered. Non-retractable tailwheel landing gear.

POWER PLANT: One 56 kW (75 hp) Revmaster. Standard fuel capacity 53 litres (14 US gallons; 11.7 Imp gallons). Optional auxiliary fuel tanks of similar capacity.

DIMENSIONS, EXTERNAL:

Wing span	9.68 m (31 ft 9 in)
Length overall	5.33 m (17 ft 6 in)
Propeller diameter	1.52 m (5 ft 0 in)

AREA:

Wings, gross	13.75 m² (148.0 sq ft)

WEIGHTS:

Weight empty	295 kg (650 lb)
Baggage weight	27 kg (60 lb)
Max T-O weight	569 kg (1,254 lb)

PERFORMANCE (pilot only):

Max level speed	100 knots (185 km/h; 115 mph)
Cruising speed	91 knots (169 km/h; 105 mph)
Stalling speed	26 knots (47 km/h; 29 mph)
T-O and landing run	61 m (200 ft)
Normal range at cruising speed, no reserves	364 nm (675 km; 420 miles)
g limits	+6/-4 computer evaluated

QUAD CITY

QUAD CITY ULTRALIGHT AIRCRAFT CORPORATION

3610 Coaltown Road, Moline, Illinois 61265
Telephone: 1 (309) 764 3515
Telex: 468556 CHALLENGER MOLINE
Fax: 1 (309) 797 4900
PRESIDENT: Dave Goulet

Details of the Challenger and Challenger II can be found in the Microlight tables.

QUAD CITY CHALLENGER SPECIAL and CHALLENGER II SPECIAL

These are higher performing versions of the Challenger and Challenger II microlights, with streamline wing struts, and landing gears, shortened wings covered with Stits Poly-Fiber or Ceconite, flaperons, Lexan door kits, and higher-powered Rotax engines as standard, to give a higher cruising speed and improved rate of roll. Kits are available. Construction time for the Challenger II Special is 150 working hours.

TYPE: Single-seat (Challenger Special) and tandem two-seat (Challenger II Special) homebuilts.

POWER PLANT: Challenger Special: One 31.3 kW (42 hp) Rotax 447, with 19 litres (5 US gallons; 4.2 Imp gallons) fuel. Challenger II Special: One 38.8 kW (52 hp) Rotax 503, with 38 litres (10 US gallons; 8.3 Imp gallons) fuel.

DIMENSIONS, EXTERNAL: As for Challenger, except:

Wing span	7.92 m (26 ft 0 in)
Length overall:	
Challenger II Special	6.32 m (20 ft 9 in)
Propeller diameter:	
Challenger Special	1.35 m (4 ft 5 in)
Challenger II Special	1.37 m (4 ft 6 in)

AREAS (A: Challenger Special, B: Challenger II Special):

Wings, gross: A	11.15 m² (120.0 sq ft)
B	13.29 m² (143.0 sq ft)

WEIGHTS (A and B as above):

Weight empty: A	118 kg (260 lb)
B	158 kg (350 lb)
Pilot weight range: A	63.5-104 kg (140-230 lb)
Max T-O weight: A	245 kg (540 lb)
B	385 kg (850 lb)

PERFORMANCE (A and B as above):

Max level speed: A	78 knots (145 km/h; 90 mph)
B	82 knots (153 km/h; 95 mph)
Cruising speed: A	69 knots (129 km/h; 80 mph)
B	74 knots (137 km/h; 85 mph)
Stalling speed:	
A, flaperons up	29 knots (53 km/h; 33 mph)
B, flaperons up	32 knots (60 km/h; 37 mph)
A, flaperons down	24 knots (44 km/h; 27 mph)
B, flaperons down	28 knots (52 km/h; 32 mph)
Max rate of climb at S/L: A, B	305-427 m (1,000-1,400 ft)/min
Service ceiling: A, B	4,265 m (14,000 ft)
T-O and landing run: A	31-46 m (100-150 ft)
B	61 m (200 ft)
Range with max fuel: A	130 nm (241 km; 150 miles)
B	191 nm (354 km; 220 miles)
Endurance: A	1 h 45 min
g limits: A	+8/-4 ultimate
B	+6/-4

Prowler Aviation Prowler all-metal two-seat homebuilt aircraft, with original engine

Pazmany PL-2 built in Sweden by Mr Hans Nielsen

ProTech PT-2 Sassy two-seat homebuilt aircraft (*J. M. G. Gradidge*)

Two-seat Quad City Challenger II Special

Questair M20 Venture sporting and cross-country monoplane

Rand Robinson KR-1 (44.75 kW; 60 hp HAPI 1,835 cc engine) built by Mr George Q. Johnson of Graham, Washington (*Peter M. Bowers*)

QUESTAIR
QUESTAIR INC
PO Box 18946, Greensboro, North Carolina 27419
Telephone: 1 (919) 668 7890 or (800) 852 3889
Fax: 1 (919) 668 7960
PRESIDENT: James E. Griswold
DIRECTOR, SALES AND MARKETING: C. S. Haupt

QUESTAIR M20 VENTURE
The prototype Venture flew for the first time on 1 July 1987. The aircraft is now available for purchase in a series of four kits of component parts, which include the engine and propeller, or as a single kit.
TYPE: Side by side two-seat, dual-control sporting and cross-country homebuilt.

AIRFRAME: Wing sections 23017 at root and 23010 at tip. All-metal construction. Retractable tricycle landing gear.
POWER PLANT: One 209 kW (280 hp) Teledyne Continental IO-550-G. Fuel capacity 212 litres (56 US gallons; 46.6 Imp gallons).
DIMENSIONS, EXTERNAL:

Wing span	8.38 m (27 ft 6 in)
Length overall	4.95 m (16 ft 3 in)
Height overall	2.35 m (7 ft 8½ in)
Propeller diameter	1.73 m (5 ft 8 in)

AREA:

Wings, gross	6.76 m² (72.75 sq ft)

WEIGHTS:

Weight empty	544 kg (1,200 lb)
Max T-O weight	907 kg (2,000 lb)

PERFORMANCE:

Max cruising speed at S/L	
	250 knots (463 km/h; 288 mph)
Max cruising speed at 3,660 m (12,000 ft)	
	240 knots (445 km/h; 276 mph)
Stalling speed	61 knots (113 km/h; 71 mph)
Max rate of climb at S/L	762 m (2,500 ft)/min
T-O run	275 m (900 ft)
Landing run	305 m (1,000 ft)
Service ceiling	8,840 m (29,000 ft)
Range at 205 knots (380 km/h; 236 mph), at 3,660 m (12,000 ft), 45 min reserves	
	1,000 nm (1,853 km; 1,151 miles)
Endurance	4 h
g limits: solo	+6/−3
at max T-O weight	+5/−3

RAND ROBINSON
RAND ROBINSON ENGINEERING INC
15641 Product Lane, Suite A-5, Huntington Beach, California 92649
Telephone: 1 (714) 898 3811

RAND ROBINSON KR-1
The KR-1 prototype flew for the first time in February 1972. Plans are available to amateur constructors; many thousands of sets have been sold and at least 200 KR-1s are known to be flying.
TYPE: Single-seat sporting homebuilt.
AIRFRAME: Wings have wooden spars and polyurethane foam ribs, polyurethane foam slab filling between ribs and Dynel reinforced epoxy covering. Pre-moulded wing skins are available. Wing section RAF 48. Ailerons of polyurethane foam, with Dynel reinforced epoxy covering; tail unit similar, with wooden spars. Lower half of fuselage of wooden construction, upper surface of carved Styrofoam covered with Dynel epoxy. Retractable (optionally non-retractable) tailwheel landing gear.
POWER PLANT: One Volkswagen modified motorcar engine.

Prototype has a Rajay turbocharged 67 kW (90 hp) 2,074 cc VW. Fuel capacity with this engine is 190 litres (50 US gallons; 41.6 Imp gallons).

DIMENSIONS, EXTERNAL:

Wing span	5.18 m (17 ft 0 in)
Length overall	3.89 m (12 ft 9 in)
Height overall	1.07 m (3 ft 6 in)
Propeller diameter	1.35 m (4 ft 5 in)

AREA:

Wings, gross	5.76 m² (62.0 sq ft)

WEIGHTS (67 kW; 90 hp VW engine):

Weight empty, equipped	218 kg (480 lb)
Max T-O weight	408 kg (900 lb)

PERFORMANCE (67 kW; 90 hp VW engine, at max T-O weight):

Max level speed at S/L	191 knots (354 km/h; 220 mph)
Econ cruising speed at 5,485 m (18,000 ft)	
	217 knots (402 km/h; 250 mph)
Stalling speed	39 knots (73 km/h; 45 mph)
Max rate of climb at S/L	457 m (1,500 ft)/min
Service ceiling	9,145 m (30,000 ft)
T-O run	122 m (400 ft)
Landing run	152 m (500 ft)
Range with max fuel	2,600 nm (4,825 km; 3,000 miles)

RAND ROBINSON KR-2

The KR-2 is a slightly larger side by side two-seat version of the KR-1, to which it is generally similar in construction. The prototype flew for the first time in July 1974. More than 7,000 sets of plans and a great many kits have been sold; at least 350 KR-2s are known to be flying.

TYPE: Side by side two-seat sporting homebuilt.

POWER PLANT: Airframe designed to accept Volkswagen modified motorcar engines of 1,600 to 2,200 cc. Fuel capacity 144 litres (38 US gallons; 31.6 Imp gallons).

DIMENSIONS, EXTERNAL:

Wing span	6.30 m (20 ft 8 in)
Length overall	4.42 m (14 ft 6 in)
Height overall	1.07 m (3 ft 6 in)
Propeller diameter	1.32 m (4 ft 4 in)

AREA:

Wings, gross	7.43 m² (80.0 sq ft)

WEIGHTS (prototype, with turbocharger):

Weight empty, equipped with IFR and electrics	
	263 kg (580 lb)
Max T-O and landing weight	499 kg (1,100 lb)

PERFORMANCE (prototype, with turbocharger):

Max level speed at S/L	161 knots (298 km/h; 185 mph)
Max cruising speed at 5,485 m (18,000 ft)	
	191 knots (354 km/h; 220 mph)
Stalling speed, prototype without turbocharger	
	39 knots (73 km/h; 45 mph)
Max rate of climb at 5,485 m (18,000 ft)	
	244 m (800 ft)/min

Service ceiling	7,925 m (26,000 ft)
T-O run	122 m (400 ft)
Landing run	152 m (500 ft)
Range with max fuel	1,735 nm (3,215 km; 2,000 miles)

RAND ROBINSON KR-100

This is an entirely new single-seater of wood, foam and glassfibre construction, with a non-retractable tailwheel landing gear and powered in prototype form by a Teledyne Continental O-200 engine. Kits are to be made available, containing mostly moulded components of composites sandwich construction.

DIMENSIONS, EXTERNAL:

Wing span	5.79 m (19 ft 0 in)
Length overall	4.72 m (15 ft 6 in)

WEIGHT (estimated):

Weight empty	249 kg (550 lb)

PERFORMANCE (estimated):

Max level speed	208 knots (386 km/h; 240 mph)
Cruising speed	182 knots (338 km/h; 210 mph)
Stalling speed, flaps down	45 knots (84 km/h; 52 mph)

RANS

RANS INC

1104 East Highway 40 By-Pass, Hays, Kansas 67601
Telephone: 1 (913) 625 6346
Fax: 1 (913) 625 2795
PRESIDENT: Randy Schlitter

Details of the S-4 Coyote and S-6 Coyote II can be found in the Microlight tables, although both can also conform to Experimental homebuilt regulations.

RANS S-7 COURIER

RANS is offering standard kits (300-500 working hours to assemble) or a quick-build kit (150 working hours, approximately) for the Courier. Following the general configuration of the Coyote, the Courier is fitted with dual controls and is therefore suited to training, in addition to recreational flying and such utility tasks as agricultural spraying. The prototype first flew in October 1985. Estimated building time from the kit is 500 hours.

TYPE: Two-seat STOL homebuilt aircraft.

AIRFRAME: Fabric covered structure, with aluminium alloy wings, and welded steel fuselage and tail unit. Glassfibre engine cowling. Non-retractable tailwheel landing gear. Optional floats and skis.

POWER PLANT: One 48.5 kW (65 hp) Rotax 532, with 2.58 : 1 reduction gear. Fuel capacity 49 litres (13 US gallons; 10.8 Imp gallons).

DIMENSIONS, EXTERNAL:

Wing span	8.92 m (29 ft 3 in)
Length overall	6.40 m (21 ft 0 in)
Height overall	1.91 m (6 ft 3 in)
Propeller diameter	1.73 m (5 ft 8 in)

AREA:

Wings, gross	14.03 m² (151.0 sq ft)

WEIGHTS:

Weight empty, equipped	204 kg (450 lb)
Max T-O weight	420 kg (925 lb)

PERFORMANCE (two persons):

Cruising speed	69 knots (129 km/h; 80 mph)
Stalling speed, power off:	
flaps up	31 knots (57 km/h; 35 mph)
flaps down	26 knots (49 km/h; 30 mph)
Max rate of climb at S/L	229 m (750 ft)/min
Service ceiling	4,115 m (13,500 ft)
T-O run	49 m (160 ft)
Landing run to safe turn speed	93 m (303 ft)
Range	208 nm (386 km; 240 miles)
Endurance	3 h
g limits	+6/−3

RANS S-9 CHAOS

The S-9 is currently offered only in Experimental category form. Construction from the kits is estimated to take 200-300 working hours.

TYPE: Single-seat aerobatic homebuilt aircraft.

AIRFRAME: Strut braced aluminium alloy wings with full-span ailerons, and pre-welded 4130 steel tube fuselage and tail unit (wire braced), Cooper Super-Flite fabric covered. Optional flaperons. Pre-moulded engine cowling. Three-axis control. Non-retractable tailwheel landing gear. Optional brakes.

POWER PLANT: One 35 kW (47 hp) Rotax 503 standard; optional 48.5 kW (65 hp) Rotax 532. Fuel capacity 25 litres (6.5 US gallons; 5.4 Imp gallons). Optional 49 or 66.6 litre (13 or 17.6 US gallon; 10.8 or 14.7 Imp gallon) capacity.

DIMENSIONS, EXTERNAL:

Wing span	6.71 m (22 ft 0 in)
Length overall	4.78 m (15 ft 8 in)
Height overall	1.47 m (4 ft 10 in)
Propeller diameter	1.63 m (5 ft 4 in)

AREA:

Wings, gross	8.50 m² (91.5 sq ft)

WEIGHTS (with Rotax 503):

Weight empty	145 kg (320 lb)
Max T-O weight	304 kg (670 lb)

PERFORMANCE (with Rotax 503):

Max cruising speed	82 knots (153 km/h; 95 mph)
Econ cruising speed (50% power)	
	65 knots (121 km/h; 75 mph)
Stalling speed:	
power on	18 knots (33 km/h; 20 mph)
power off	26 knots (47 km/h; 29 mph)
Max rate of climb at S/L	305 m (1,000 ft)/min
Service ceiling	4,725 m (15,500 ft)
T-O run	61 m (200 ft)
Landing run, no brakes	122 m (400 ft)
Endurance	2 h
g limits	+9/−6

RANS S-10 SAKOTA

The S-10 is basically a larger two-seat derivative of the S-9, with a welded steel fuselage and tail unit and aluminium alloy wings, fabric covered. Full span ailerons standard. Pre-moulded engine cowling. In addition to the kit, options available include flaperons and glassfibre wingtips.

TYPE: Side by side two-seat homebuilt.

POWER PLANT: One 48.5 kW (65 hp) Rotax 532, with 2.58 : 1 reduction gear. Fuel capacity 49 litres (13 US gallons; 10.8 Imp gallons).

DIMENSIONS, EXTERNAL:

Wing span	7.32 m (24 ft 0 in)
Length overall	5.44 m (17 ft 10 in)
Height overall	1.47 m (4 ft 10 in)
Propeller diameter	1.63 m (5 ft 4 in)

AREA:

Wings, gross	8.83 m² (95.0 sq ft)

WEIGHTS:

Weight empty	191 kg (420 lb)
Max T-O weight	397 kg (875 lb)

PERFORMANCE:

Cruising speed:	
full power	95 knots (177 km/h; 110 mph)
50% power	56 knots (105 km/h; 65 mph)
Stalling speed, flaps down:	
power off	33 knots (61 km/h; 38 mph)
power on	23 knots (42 km/h; 26 mph)
Service ceiling	4,265 m (14,000 ft)
Max rate of climb at S/L	305 m (1,000 ft)/min
T-O run	92 m (300 ft)
Landing run, no brakes	152 m (500 ft)
g limits	+6/−3

RANS S-11 PURSUIT

This single-seater is entirely different from previous RANS aircraft, having cantilever low-mounted wings blended into the streamline fuselage, a bubble cockpit canopy, and a twin fin/rudder tail unit. Welded 4130 chromoly steel cockpit cage, aluminium alloy tail unit, composite ribs, and pre-moulded wing skins and engine cowling. Retractable tricycle landing gear, with brakes. Power plant options are a 48.5 kW (65 hp) Rotax 532 or 59.7 kW (80 hp) Rotax 912. Fuel capacity is 76 litres (20 US gallons; 16.6 Imp gallons); inverted system is standard. Estimated building time 400 hours.

DIMENSIONS, EXTERNAL:

Wing span	6.10 m (20 ft 0 in)
Length overall	5.49 m (18 ft 0 in)
Height overall	1.63 m (5 ft 4 in)

WEIGHTS (Rotax 912):

Weight empty	193 kg (425 lb)
Baggage capacity	13.6 kg (30 lb)
Max T-O weight	374 kg (825 lb)

PERFORMANCE (Rotax 912):

Max level speed	143 knots (266 km/h; 165 mph)
Cruising speed (50% power)	
	96 knots (177 km/h; 110 mph)
Stalling speed:	
power on	26 knots (49 km/h; 30 mph)
power off	35 knots (65 km/h; 40 mph)
Max rate of climb at S/L	610 m (2,000 ft)/min
Service ceiling	5,485 m (18,000 ft)
T-O run	61 m (200 ft)
Landing run	153 m (500 ft)
g limits	±12

R.D.

R.D. AIRCRAFT

PO Box 107, Mayville, New York 14757
Telephone: 1 (716) 753 2111
PRESIDENT: Robert G. Dart
ENGINEER: Emerson W. Stevens

Details of the Skycycle, Skycycle II and Skycycle Gypsy series can be found in the Microlight tables.

R.D. LITTLE DIPPER REPLICA

Construction of a prototype of this reproduction of the Lockheed Little Dipper (illustrated in 1947 *Jane's*) began in February 1988.

TYPE: Single-seat ARV and homebuilt; conforms to FAR Pt 23.

AIRFRAME: Aluminium alloy construction, with some use of glassfibre. Wing section NACA 4415. Three-axis control, plus flaps. Non-retractable tricycle landing gear. Options will include cockpit canopy.

POWER PLANT: One 30 kW (40 hp) Rotax 447FA. Fuel capacity 30 litres (8 US gallons; 6.7 Imp gallons). Rotax 503 optional.

DIMENSIONS, EXTERNAL:

Wing span	7.42 m (24 ft 4 in)
Length overall	5.49 m (18 ft 0 in)
Height overall	2.21 m (7 ft 7¼ in)
Propeller diameter	1.73 m (5 ft 8 in)

AREA:

Wings, gross	9.48 m² (102.0 sq ft)

WEIGHTS:

Weight empty	201 kg (443 lb)
Max T-O weight	300 kg (661 lb)

PERFORMANCE:

Max level speed at S/L	87 knots (161 km/h; 100 mph)
Stalling speed, power off	32 knots (58 km/h; 36 mph)
Max rate of climb at S/L	229 m (750 ft)/min
T-O run	76 m (250 ft)
Range	456 nm (845 km; 525 miles)
g limits	+4.6/−2.6

Prototype RANS S-10

RANS S-7 Courier homebuilt aircraft

R.D. Little Dipper Replica *(Jane's/Mike Keep)*

RANS S-9 Chaos homebuilt aircraft

Rotec Panther 2 Plus *(Geoffrey P. Jones)*

ROTEC
ROTEC ENGINEERING INC
PO Box 380220, Duncanville, Texas 75138
Telephone: 1 (214) 298 2505
Telex: 288777 ROTEC DCVL
Fax: 1 (214) 296 9614
PRESIDENT: William W. Adaska

Rotec's aircraft are available in kit and/or ready to fly forms. Details of its military Ground Troop Army Trainers can be found in the 1987-88 *Jane's*. Details of the Rally 2B, Rally 3, Rally Sport, Rally Champ and Panther can be found in the Microlight tables.

ROTEC PANTHER PLUS and SEA PANTHER

Rotec's follow-on aircraft to the Panther, the Panther Plus, is not a microlight but is covered by the FAA's Experimental homebuilt category. Construction from the optional kit takes about 40 hours.

The standard **Panther Plus** employs many features of the Panther, but has a fully enclosed cabin and a 31.3 kW (42 hp) Rotax 447. A twin-float variant of the Panther Plus is the **Sea Panther**, with foam core glassfibre floats of 3.45 m (11 ft 4 in) length. The Sea Panther has a maximum speed of 69 knots (129 km/h; 80 mph), a cruising speed of 65 knots (121 km/h; 75 mph), a range of 152 nm (281 km; 175 miles), and a useful load of 152 kg (335 lb). Military versions of the Panther have been proposed.

The description of the Panther in the Microlight tables applies also to the Panther Plus, except as detailed above and below.
AIRFRAME: As Panther but with fully enclosed cabin.
DIMENSIONS, EXTERNAL:
Wing span   10.36 m (34 ft 0 in)

Length overall   4.88 m (16 ft 10 in)
Height overall   2.06 m (6 ft 9 in)
Propeller diameter   1.52 m (5 ft 0 in)
AREA:
Wings, gross   13.75 m² (148.0 sq ft)
WEIGHTS:
Weight empty   134 kg (295 lb)
Pilot weight range   63.5-111 kg (140-245 lb)
Baggage capacity   18 kg (40 lb)
Max T-O weight   286 kg (630 lb)
PERFORMANCE:
Max level speed   65 knots (121 km/h; 75 mph)
Econ cruising speed   52 knots (97 km/h; 60 mph)
Stalling speed: full power   19 knots (34 km/h; 21 mph)
   power off   23 knots (42 km/h; 26 mph)
Max rate of climb at S/L   244 m (800 ft)/min
Service ceiling   more than 3,050 m (10,000 ft)
T-O run   28 m (90 ft)
Landing run   23 m (75 ft)
Range with max fuel   152 nm (281 km; 175 miles)
Endurance   2 h 30 min
g limits   +3.5/−1.5

ROTEC PANTHER 2 PLUS

The Panther 2 Plus is basically a Panther Plus with a lengthened cabin to provide tandem seating for a pilot and passenger. The Rotax 447 engine remains the standard power plant; options are the 35.8 kW (48 hp) Rotax 503 and a 48.5 kW (65 hp) Rotax. An auxiliary 13.25 litre (3.5 US gallon; 2.9 Imp gallon) fuel tank is offered to supplement the standard 19 litre (5 US gallon; 4.2 Imp gallon) tank. Options include floats (**as Sea Panther 2 Plus**), skis, wheel fairings, dual controls and agricultural spraying equipment.

TYPE: Tandem two-seat cabin homebuilt; conforms to FAA Experimental category.
DIMENSIONS, EXTERNAL:
Wing span   10.36 m (34 ft 0 in)
Length overall   5.59 m (18 ft 4 in)
Height overall   2.13 m (7 ft 0 in)
Propeller diameter   1.65 m (5 ft 5 in)
AREA:
Wings, gross   17.09 m² (184.0 sq ft)
WEIGHTS:
Weight empty   179 kg (395 lb)
Pilot and passenger weight range (combined)
        136-208 kg (300-460 lb)
Max T-O weight   422 kg (930 lb)
PERFORMANCE (standard aircraft, except where indicated):
Max level speed   69 knots (129 km/h; 80 mph)
Econ cruising speed   56 knots (105 km/h; 65 mph)
Stalling speed: power on   21 knots (39 km/h; 24 mph)
   power off   25 knots (47 km/h; 29 mph)
Max rate of climb at S/L: 2 crew   167 m (550 ft)/min
   pilot only   more than 274 m (900 ft)/min
   Sea Panther   152 m (500 ft)/min
Service ceiling   more than 3,050 m (10,000 ft)
T-O run   54 m (175 ft)
T-O run, Sea Panther   106 m (350 ft)
Landing run   38 m (125 ft)
Range with max fuel   173 nm (322 km; 200 miles)
Endurance   2 h 30 min
g limits   +3.5/−1.5

ROTORWAY
ROTORWAY AIRCRAFT INC
300 South 25th Avenue, Phoenix, Arizona 85009
Telephone: 1 (602) 278 1199
Telex: 683 5059
Fax: 1 (602) 278 5887
MARKETING: John Wolven

ROTORWAY EXEC
RotorWay Aircraft currently offers Exec component kits for final construction by amateur builders, powered by the company's own RW-152D engine. The Exec has as standard the latest high lift asymmetrical aerofoil section, all-metal rotor blades, and elastomeric bearing rotor hub systems. RotorWay offers complete flight orientation and maintenance training, and a comprehensive customer service programme. It is currently marketed in the United States and in 33 foreign countries.

TYPE: Side by side two-seat homebuilt helicopter.
ROTOR SYSTEM: Asymmetrical aerofoil section two-blade main rotor. All-metal aluminium alloy blades are attached to aluminium alloy teetering rotor hub by retention straps. Teetering tail rotor, with two blades each comprising a steel spar and aluminium alloy skin. Dual push/pull cable controlled swashplate for cyclic pitch control. Elastomeric bearing rotor hub system.
AIRFRAME: Basic 4130 steel tube structure, with wraparound glassfibre fuselage enclosure. Aluminium alloy monocoque tailboom. Basic twin skid landing gear. Ground handling wheels, dual controls, luggage compartment and skid fairings among options.

POWER PLANT: One 113.3 kW (152 hp) RotorWay RW-152D. Standard fuel capacity 64.4 litres (17 US gallons; 14.2 Imp gallons).

DIMENSIONS, EXTERNAL:
Main rotor diameter	7.72 m (25 ft 4 in)
Length of fuselage	6.53 m (21 ft 5 in)
Height to top of main rotor	2.13 m (7 ft 0 in)

WEIGHTS:
Weight empty	376 kg (830 lb)
Crew weight	172 kg (380 lb)
Max T-O weight	599 kg (1,320 lb)

PERFORMANCE (at max T-O weight):
Never-exceed and max level speed	100 knots (185 km/h; 115 mph)
Normal cruising speed	82 knots (153 km/h; 95 mph)
Max rate of climb at S/L	366 m (1,200 ft)/min
Service ceiling	3,660 m (12,000 ft)
Hovering ceiling, with two persons:	
IGE	2,285 m (7,500 ft)
OGE	1,370 m (4,500 ft)
Range with max fuel at optimum cruising power	174 nm (323 km; 201 miles)

ROTORWAY ELETE
RotorWay Aircraft has recently introduced Elete model helicopter component kits designed for final construction by amateur builders. Again powered by the RW-152D engine, the Elete is the first configuration of a new generation of RotorWay helicopters. Component and bearing lifetimes are extended, and performance is improved. It comes equipped with all-metal, high-lift asymmetrical aerofoil section rotor blades and elastomeric bearing rotor hub systems. As with the Exec, RotorWay offers complete flight orientation and maintenance training and a comprehensive customer service programme.

TYPE: Side by side two-seat homebuilt helicopter.
ROTOR SYSTEM AND AIRFRAME: As for Exec. Options include ground handling wheels, dual controls, and a fully welded airframe.

POWER PLANT: As for Exec. Fuel capacity 75.7 litres (20 US gallons; 16.6 Imp gallons).

DIMENSIONS, EXTERNAL:
Main rotor diameter	7.72 m (25 ft 4 in)
Length of fuselage	6.83 m (22 ft 5 in)
Height overall	2.44 m (8 ft 0 in)

WEIGHTS:
Weight empty	376 kg (830 lb)
Crew weight	181 kg (400 lb)
Max T-O weight	612 kg (1,350 lb)

PERFORMANCE:
Never-exceed speed	113 knots (209 km/h; 130 mph)
Normal cruising speed	98 knots (182 km/h; 113 mph)
Max rate of climb at S/L	366 m (1,200 ft)/min
Service ceiling	3,660 m (12,000 ft)
Hovering ceiling, with two persons:	
IGE	2,285 m (7,500 ft)
OGE	1,370 m (4,500 ft)
Range with max fuel at optimum cruising power	225 nm (418 km; 260 miles)

SEQUOIA
SEQUOIA AIRCRAFT CORPORATION
2000 Tomlynn Street, PO Box 6861, Richmond, Virginia 23230
Telephone: 1 (804) 353 1713
Fax: 1 (804) 359 2618
PRESIDENT: Alfred P. Scott

SEQUOIA MODEL 300 SEQUOIA
This aircraft is available in plan and kit forms.
TYPE: Side by side two-seat utility and aerobatic homebuilt.
AIRFRAME: Wing section NACA 64₂A215 at root, NACA 64A210 at tip. Wings, ailerons, slotted flaps and tail unit of flush riveted aluminium alloy construction. Wings have glassfibre tips. Welded steel tube fuselage, covered entirely with lightweight shell of glassfibre/PVC foam/glassfibre sandwich, attached to tubing with glassfibre and epoxy resin. Retractable tricycle landing gear.
POWER PLANT: One 224 kW (300 hp) Textron Lycoming TIO-540-S1AD. Other Textron Lycoming engines of 175-224 kW (235-300 hp) may be used. Fuel capacity 291.5 litres (77 US gallons; 64 Imp gallons). Provision for tip tanks of approximately 75 litres (20 US gallons; 16.7 Imp gallons) capacity each; and two underwing attachment points for additional fuel tanks, radar or stores of up to 272 kg (600 lb) combined weight.

DIMENSIONS, EXTERNAL:
Wing span	9.14 m (30 ft 0 in)
Length overall	7.62 m (25 ft 0 in)
Height overall	2.90 m (9 ft 6 in)
Propeller diameter	2.03 m (6 ft 8 in)

AREA:
Wings, gross	12.08 m² (130.0 sq ft)

WEIGHTS:
Weight empty	816 kg (1,800 lb)

Baggage capacity	45 kg (100 lb)
Max T-O weight: utility	1,270 kg (2,800 lb)
aerobatic	1,088 kg (2,400 lb)

PERFORMANCE (estimated):
Max level speed at S/L	195 knots (362 km/h; 225 mph)
Max cruising speed at 2,440 m (8,000 ft)	185 knots (343 km/h; 213 mph)
Stalling speed: clean	75 knots (139 km/h; 86 mph)
flaps and wheels down	60 knots (111 km/h; 69 mph)
Max rate of climb at S/L	664 m (2,180 ft)/min
Service ceiling	7,620 m (25,000 ft)
T-O run	457 m (1,500 ft)
Landing run	548 m (1,800 ft)
Range at max cruising speed, with 45 min reserves	868 nm (1,609 km; 1,000 miles)

SEQUOIA MODEL 302 KODIAK
The Kodiak is a four-seat development of the Model 300 Sequoia with gull-wing doors to provide access to the enclosed cabin. It was designed to be fully aerobatic and is available in plan and kit forms (latter does not include prepared fuselage).

Power plant is in the 186-224 kW (250-300 hp) Textron Lycoming IO-540/TIO-540-S1AD range. Empty weight will be 839 kg (1,850 lb); max T-O weight 1,451 kg (3,200 lb); fuel capacity 341 litres (90 US gallons; 75 Imp gallons).

SEQUOIA FALCO F.8L
Sequoia Aircraft markets plans and kits to build an improved version of the Falco F.8L high-performance monoplane, designed in Italy by Ing Stelio Frati of General Avia and first flown on 15 June 1955. By February 1990, a total of 610 sets of plans had been sold and 26 Falcos had flown.

TYPE: Side by side two-seat, dual control homebuilt. Provision for child's seat in baggage space.
AIRFRAME: Entire airframe has plywood covered wood structure, with overall fabric covering and glassfibre wing fillets. Optional metal control surfaces. NACA 64₂212.5 wing section at root, NACA 64₂210 at tip. Retractable tricycle landing gear.
POWER PLANT: One 119 kW (160 hp) Textron Lycoming IO-320-B1A is standard for kit-built aircraft. Optional engines for which Sequoia offers installation kits are the 112 kW (150 hp) IO-320-A1A and 134 kW (180 hp) IO-360-B1E. Fuel capacity 151 litres (40 US gallons; 33.3 Imp gallons). Optional 7.6 litre (2 US gallon; 1.7 Imp gallon) header tank to permit inverted flight.

DIMENSIONS, EXTERNAL:
Wing span	8.00 m (26 ft 3 in)
Length overall	6.50 m (21 ft 4 in)
Height overall	2.29 m (7 ft 6 in)

AREA:
Wings, gross	10.00 m² (107.6 sq ft)

WEIGHTS (119 kW; 160 hp engine):
Weight empty	550 kg (1,212 lb)
Payload with max fuel	194 kg (428 lb)
Baggage capacity	40 kg (88 lb)
Max aerobatic weight	748 kg (1,650 lb)
Max T-O weight	853 kg (1,880 lb)

PERFORMANCE (119 kW; 160 hp engine):
Max level speed at S/L	184 knots (341 km/h; 212 mph)
Cruising speed at 1,830 m (6,000 ft), 75% power	165 knots (306 km/h; 190 mph)
Stalling speed, flaps and wheels down	54 knots (100 km/h; 62 mph)
Max rate of climb at S/L	347 m (1,140 ft)/min
Service ceiling	5,790 m (19,000 ft)
Range at econ cruising speed	868 nm (1,609 km; 1,000 miles)

SILHOUETTE — *See Lunds Tekniske of Norway*

SMITH
S & H AIRCRAFT
1300 Rosney, Bloomington, Illinois 61701
Telephone: 1 (309) 829 4656

SMITH TERMITE
Plans and an airframe kit are thought to be offered to construct this all-wooden parasol-wing monoplane. Advertising material has stated that more than 300 are flying worldwide.

SMYTH
JERRY SMYTH
ADDRESS FOR PLANS: Wicks Aircraft Supply, 410 Pine Street, Highland, Illinois 62249
Telephone: 1 (618) 654 7447
Fax: 1 (618) 654 6253

SMYTH MODEL 'S' SIDEWINDER
The prototype Sidewinder first flew on 21 February 1969. Plans and component parts are available. The following description applies to the prototype:
TYPE: Side by side two-seat limited aerobatic homebuilt.
AIRFRAME: Aluminium alloy wings, ailerons and tail unit; wings filled with epoxy. Wing section NACA 64-612 at root, NACA 64-210 at tip. Welded steel tube fuselage, with aluminium formers and skin. Electrically operated speed brake may be fitted on lower fuselage. Non-

retractable tricycle landing gear. Aircraft have been completed with retractable landing gear (see 1975-76 *Jane's*) and tailwheel type landing gear (see 1980-81 *Jane's*).
POWER PLANT: Provision for installation of engines from 67 to 134 kW (90-180 hp). Prototype has a 93 kW (125 hp) Textron Lycoming O-290-G. Fuel capacity 66.2 litres (17.5 US gallons; 14.6 Imp gallons). Provision for wingtip tanks.

DIMENSIONS, EXTERNAL:
Wing span	7.57 m (24 ft 10 in)
Length overall	5.89 m (19 ft 4 in)
Height overall	1.66 m (5 ft 5½ in)
Propeller diameter	1.70 m (5 ft 7 in)

AREA:
Wings, gross	8.92 m² (96.0 sq ft)

WEIGHTS:
Weight empty	393 kg (867 lb)

Baggage capacity	41 kg (90 lb)
Max T-O and landing weight	657 kg (1,450 lb)

PERFORMANCE (at max T-O weight):
Max level speed at S/L	152 knots (282 km/h; 175 mph)
Max cruising speed, 75% power at 610 m (2,000 ft)	139 knots (257 km/h; 160 mph)
Stalling speed, flaps up	48 knots (89 km/h; 55 mph)
Max rate of climb at S/L: at 0°C	366 m (1,200 ft)/min
at 24°C	274 m (900 ft)/min
Service ceiling	4,575 m (15,000 ft)
T-O run	244 m (800 ft)
Landing run	457 m (1,500 ft)
Range with max fuel, no reserves	369 nm (684 km; 425 miles)
g limit	+9 design

RotorWay Exec two-seat homebuilt helicopter

RotorWay Elete two-seat homebuilt helicopter

Model 300 Sequoia two-seat utility and aerobatic aircraft, with additional (lower) side view of Model 302 Kodiak (*Pilot Press*)

Smyth Sidewinder (Textron Lycoming IO-320 engine) built 20% oversize by Mr G. Walker of Renton, Washington (*Peter M. Bowers*)

Sorrell SNS-9 EXP II sport/trainer (*Peter M. Bowers*)

Sequoia Falco F.8L homebuilt aircraft

Sorrell SNS-7 Hiperbipe two-seat aerobatic biplane (*Peter M. Bowers*)

SORRELL
SORRELL AIRCRAFT COMPANY LTD
16525 Tilley Road South, Tenino, Washington 98589
Telephone: 1 (206) 264 2866

Details of the SNS-8 Hiperlight and SNS-10 Intruder can be found in the Microlight tables.

SORRELL SNS-2 GUPPY
In 1967 the late Mr Hobie Sorrell flew his SNS-2 Guppy cabin biplane for the first time, powered by a 13.5 kW (18 hp) OMC Cushman Model 200 engine. Plans for this 'back staggered' non-aerobatic single-seater are available from Sorrell Aircraft Company and/or from Mr Michael Kimbrel (which see). Sorrell is also believed to offer a kit of component parts which includes a Rotax 377 engine.
TYPE: Single-seat homebuilt cabin biplane.
AIRFRAME: Modified Grant X wing section. Wooden wings and fuselage, except for steel tube wingtips, aluminium fittings and wing drag member; Dacron covered. Full span ailerons on lower wings only, of aluminium tubing with riveted aluminium skins. Steel tube engine mounting, interplane struts and Dacron covered tail unit. Non-retractable tailwheel landing gear.
POWER PLANT: Engines of up to 27 kW (36 hp) can be fitted, including Volkswagen modified motorcar engines. Sorrell kit includes 24 kW (32 hp) Rotax 377. Fuel capacity 23 litres (6.5 US gallons; 5.4 Imp gallons).
DIMENSIONS, EXTERNAL:
Wing span	6.48 m (21 ft 3 in)
Length overall	4.70 m (15 ft 5 in)
Height overall	1.57 m (5 ft 2 in)
AREA:
Wings, gross	11.98 m² (129.0 sq ft)

WEIGHTS (prototype with Cushman engine):
Weight empty	159 kg (350 lb)
Max T-O weight	272 kg (600 lb)
PERFORMANCE (prototype with Cushman engine):
Max level speed	69 knots (129 km/h; 80 mph)
Cruising speed	61 knots (113 km/h; 70 mph)
Stalling speed, power off	26 knots (49 km/h; 30 mph)
Max rate of climb at S/L	91 m (300 ft)/min
Absolute ceiling	3,110 m (10,200 ft)
T-O run	91 m (300 ft)
Landing from 15 m (50 ft)	91 m (300 ft)
Range	182 nm (338 km; 210 miles)
g limit	+4 recommended

SORRELL SNS-7 HIPERBIPE
The Hiperbipe made its initial flight as the SNS-6 prototype in March 1973. According to reports, the SNS-7 version is on sale in plans form, with component parts available upon request.
TYPE: Side by side two-seat, dual control homebuilt aerobatic biplane.
AIRFRAME: Modified NACA 0012 wing sections. Welded steel interplane struts. Fabric-covered all-wood back-staggered wings, but with centre-section of upper wing skinned with transparent plastics to allow improved view for aerobatics. Cambered wingtips. Four full span flaperons of pop-riveted aluminium alloy. Fuselage and tail unit of welded steel tube, fabric covered. Glassfibre engine cowling. Non-retractable tailwheel landing gear.
POWER PLANT: One 134 kW (180 hp) Textron Lycoming IO-360-B1E. Fuel capacity 147.5 litres (39 US gallons; 32.5 Imp gallons).
DIMENSIONS, EXTERNAL:
Wing span	6.96 m (22 ft 10 in)
Length overall	6.35 m (20 ft 10 in)
Height overall	1.80 m (5 ft 10¾ in)
Propeller diameter	1.93 m (6 ft 4 in)
AREA:
Wings, gross (projected)	13.9 m² (150.0 sq ft)
WEIGHTS:
Weight empty	561 kg (1,236 lb)
Baggage capacity	36 kg (80 lb)
Max T-O weight: aerobatic	766 kg (1,690 lb)
normal	867 kg (1,911 lb)
PERFORMANCE (at max T-O weight):
Max level speed at S/L	149 knots (277 km/h; 172 mph)
Econ cruising speed	130 knots (241 km/h; 150 mph)
Stalling speed:	
flaperons up	51 knots (94 km/h; 58 mph)
flaperons down	43 knots (79 km/h; 49 mph)
Max rate of climb at S/L	457 m (1,500 ft)/min
Service ceiling, estimated	6,100 m (20,000 ft)
T-O run	122 m (400 ft)
Landing run	181 m (595 ft)
Range	436 nm (807 km; 502 miles)

SORRELL SNS-9 EXP II
First flown on 22 May 1985, the SNS-9 EXP II is a side by side two-seat sport/trainer, with dual controls and basic instrumentation as standard. Like other recent Sorrell designs, it is a small back-staggered biplane. The wings are made of pop riveted aluminium alloy, covered with Stits Poly-Fiber. The welded steel tube fuselage is also Poly-Fiber covered. Power for the prototype is provided by a 31.3 kW (42 hp) Rotax 447. Standard fuel capacity is 34 litres (9 US gallons; 7.5 Imp gallons). Assembly from pre-welded component kits is said to require 300 hours of work.
TYPE: Two-seat homebuilt cabin biplane.

DIMENSIONS, EXTERNAL:		WEIGHTS:			
Wing span	7.11 m (23 ft 4 in)	Weight empty	162 kg (356 lb)	Max rate of climb at S/L	183 m (600 ft)/min
Length overall	5.49 m (18 ft 0 in)	Max T-O weight	367 kg (810 lb)	T-O and landing run on grass	92 m (300 ft)
Height overall	1.63 m (5 ft 4 in)	PERFORMANCE (estimated at max T-O weight):		Range with max standard fuel	
AREA:		Max cruising speed	74 knots (136 km/h; 85 mph)		221 nm (410 km; 255 miles)
Wings, gross	13.75 m² (148.0 sq ft)	Stalling speed	34 knots (63 km/h; 39 mph)	g limits	+3.8/−1.9

SPENCER

SPENCER AMPHIBIAN AIRCRAFT INC

PO Box 327, Kansas, Illinois 61933
Spencer Amphibian Air Car Inc was sold on 15 July 1988 to Mr Robert F. Kerans.

SPENCER AMPHIBIAN AIRCRAFT MODEL S-12-E

This latest version of the S-12 series is available in plan and kit forms, while plans and certain glassfibre mouldings and metal assemblies for the differently powered and earlier S-12-D may also be available.

TYPE: Four-seat, dual control homebuilt amphibian.

AIRFRAME: Specially designed STOL (modified NACA 4415) wing section. Wing structure of wood, steel and glassfibre. Wooden ailerons and trailing-edge flaps. Glassfibre stabilising float on strut beneath each wing.

Single-stepped hull with wood frames, longerons and skin, sheathed in glassfibre and Kevlar. Welded steel tube structure to provide wing and engine mountings and attachment points for the retractable tricycle landing gear. Retractable water rudder.

POWER PLANT: One 224 kW (300 hp) Teledyne Continental Tiara 6-285. Also recommended is 224 kW (300 hp) Teledyne Continental IO-520. Development under way in 1988 to install a Ford 351-W converted motorcar engine. Fuel capacity 360 litres (95 US gallons; 79 Imp gallons).

DIMENSIONS, EXTERNAL:
Wing span	11.38 m (37 ft 4 in)
Length overall	7.92 m (26 ft 0 in)
Height overall, landing gear down	3.58 m (11 ft 9 in)
Propeller diameter	2.13 m (7 ft 0 in)

AREA:
Wings, gross	17.1 m² (184.0 sq ft)

WEIGHTS:
Weight empty	993 kg (2,190 lb)
Max T-O weight	1,451 kg (3,200 lb)

PERFORMANCE (at max T-O weight):
Max level speed at 2,440 m (8,000 ft)	135 knots (249 km/h; 155 mph)
Econ cruising speed at 3,050 m (10,000 ft)	109 knots (201 km/h; 125 mph)
Stalling speed, flaps down, power off	39 knots (73 km/h; 45 mph)
Max rate of climb at S/L	320 m (1,050 ft)/min
Service ceiling	4,875 m (16,000 ft)
T-O run from calm water	213 m (700 ft)
Landing run	213 m (700 ft)
Range, 65% power at 2,315 m (7,600 ft), 20 min reserves	695 nm (1,285 km; 800 miles)
Endurance	7 h

SPORT

SPORT AIRCRAFT INC

104 East Avenue, K4 Unit G, Lancaster, California 93535
Telephone: 1 (805) 949 2312

SPORT AIRCRAFT (SUNDERLAND) S-18

Originating from the Thorp T-18 Tiger, the modified S-18 was offered in plans form by Sunderland Aircraft, while Sport Aircraft Inc made kits and prefabricated components available. Following the closure of Sunderland Aircraft, Sport Aircraft has taken over the sale of plans also. More than 1,400 sets have been sold, and over 500 T-18s and S-18s have flown.

TYPE: Side by side two-seat, dual-control homebuilt; provision for child's jump seat.

AIRFRAME: Aluminium alloy construction. Wing section LDS-4-212. Non-retractable tailwheel landing gear.

POWER PLANT: One Textron Lycoming engine in 100-134 kW (135-180 hp) category. Optional Ford V6 motorcar engine modification by Blanton. Fuel capacity 110 litres (29 US gallons; 24.1 Imp gallons). Optional integral tank in wing leading-edge.

DIMENSIONS, EXTERNAL:
Wing span	6.35 m (20 ft 10 in)
Length overall	5.77 m (18 ft 11 in)
Height overall	1.55 m (5 ft 1 in)
Propeller diameter	1.68 m (5 ft 6 in)

AREA:
Wings, gross	8.0 m² (86.0 sq ft)

WEIGHTS (104.4 kW; 140 hp engine):
Weight empty	390 kg (860 lb)
Max T-O weight	670 kg (1,478 lb)

PERFORMANCE (112 kW; 150 hp Textron Lycoming):
Max level speed at S/L	174 knots (322 km/h; 200 mph)
Max cruising speed (75% power) at 2,590 m (8,500 ft)	166 knots (307 km/h; 191 mph)
Stalling speed	53 knots (97 km/h; 60 mph)
Max rate of climb at S/L	366 m (1,200 ft)/min
Service ceiling	6,100 m (20,000 ft)
Range with max fuel	460 nm (853 km; 530 miles)
Endurance	3 h 45 min

STARFIRE

STARFIRE AVIATION INC

3000 South Palo Verde Road, Buckeye, Arizona 85326
Telephone: 1 (602) 386 5019
PRESIDENT: H. G. McKenzie

FIREBOLT CONVERTIBLE

First flown on 15 May 1987, the Firebolt Convertible incorporates Skybolt features but is longer to give more cockpit room. Plans, kits, steel components and assemblies are available, and by early 1990 25 kits and 80 sets of plans, plus one ready assembled aircraft, had been sold; five plans-built aircraft had then flown.

In addition to the standard Model A, as detailed below, the Model B has symmetrical ailerons (upper and lower) and elevator horns, and the Model C features a new fin and rudder shape, with dynamic balance to the rudder.

TYPE: Tandem two-seat aerobatic homebuilt biplane.

AIRFRAME: Wire braced wooden wings, steel tube Warren truss fuselage structure and steel tube tail unit, all Stits Poly-Fiber covered except for metal-skinned tail unit and nose cowlings. Wing section NACA 63₂A015 on upper wing; NACA 0012 on lower wings. Non-retractable tailwheel landing gear, with brakes.

POWER PLANT: Prototype has one 134 kW (180 hp) Textron Lycoming IO-360-B1B. Fuel capacity 148 litres (39 US gallons; 32.5 Imp gallons). Optional 224 kW (300 hp) Textron Lycoming IO-540-K1A5 engine.

DIMENSIONS, EXTERNAL:
Wing span, both	7.32 m (24 ft 0 in)
Length overall	6.10 m (20 ft 0 in)
Height overall	2.18 m (7 ft 2 in)
Propeller diameter: 180-200 hp	1.88 m (6 ft 2 in)
300 hp	1.98 m (6 ft 6 in)

AREA:
Wings, gross	13.94 m² (150.0 sq ft)

WEIGHTS:
Weight empty	556 kg (1,225 lb)

Pilot weight range	68-113 kg (150-250 lb)
Baggage capacity	18 kg (40 lb)
Max T-O weight	907 kg (2,000 lb)

PERFORMANCE (134 kW; 180 hp engine, at 782 kg; 1,725 lb aerobatic weight):
Max level speed at S/L	143 knots (266 km/h; 165 mph) IAS
Max cruising speed at 1,980 m (6,500 ft)	148 knots (274 km/h; 170 mph) TAS
Econ cruising speed	109 knots (201 km/h; 125 mph)
Stalling speed, power off	51 knots (94 km/h; 58 mph)
Max rate of climb at S/L	548 m (1,800 ft)/min
Service ceiling	4,575 m (15,000 ft)
T-O run	138 m (450 ft)
Landing run	199 m (650 ft)
Range	521 nm (965 km; 600 miles)
Endurance	4 h 35 min
g limits	±6

STAR-LITE

STAR-LITE AIRCRAFT INC

The Star-Lite SL-1 is out of production. Details and an illustration can be found in the 1989-90 *Jane's*.

STODDARD-HAMILTON

STODDARD-HAMILTON AIRCRAFT INC

18701 58th Avenue North-East, Arlington, Washington 98223
Telephone: 1 (206) 435 8533
Fax: 1 (206) 435 9644
PRESIDENT: Theodore E. Setzer
MARKETING AND SALES MANAGER: Bill Sprague

Approximately 1,100 kits for all models of the Glasair had been sold by early 1990, when about 300 were flying. The Glasair I and II have been superseded by the II-S and III. Details of the Glasair I can be found in the 1989-90 *Jane's*.

STODDARD-HAMILTON GLASAIR II-S

The Glasair II-S (stretched) is available in RG (retractable landing gear), FT (non-retractable tricycle gear) and TD (taildragger) forms to supersede the earlier Glasair series. Seventy-five kits had been sold by early 1990, of which 50 had been delivered.

TYPE: Side by side two-seat, dual control homebuilt.

AIRFRAME: Glassfibre and foam composite construction, coated with Gelcoat. Wing section NASA LS(I)-0413. Upswept Hoerner style trailing-edges. Three types of landing gear, as detailed above. Brakes.

POWER PLANT: One 119-134 kW (160-180 hp) Textron Lycoming O-360 series engine. Fuel capacity 182 litres (48 US gallons; 40 Imp gallons). Auxiliary tanks of 42 litres (11 US gallons; 9.2 Imp gallons) capacity in optional wingtip extensions.

DIMENSIONS, EXTERNAL:
Wing span, standard	7.10 m (23 ft 3½ in)
Length overall	6.16 m (20 ft 2½ in)
Height overall	2.07 m (6 ft 9½ in)

AREA:
Wings, gross	7.55 m² (81.3 sq ft)

WEIGHTS (A: RG, B: FT, C: TD):
Weight empty: A	499 kg (1,100 lb)
B	454 kg (1,000 lb)
C	431 kg (950 lb)
Baggage capacity	36 kg (80 lb)
Max T-O weight: A	816 kg (1,800 lb)
B	771 kg (1,700 lb)
C	726 kg (1,600 lb)

PERFORMANCE (A: RG with 180 hp engine, B: FT with 160 hp, C: TD with 180 hp):
Max level speed at S/L	
A	217 knots (402 km/h; 250 mph)
B	207 knots (383 km/h; 238 mph)
C	208 knots (385 km/h; 239 mph)
Econ cruising speed at 2,440 m (8,000 ft):	
A	189 knots (351 km/h; 218 mph)
B	178 knots (330 km/h; 205 mph)
C	179 knots (332 km/h; 206 mph)
Stalling speed, flaps down, power off:	
A	52 knots (95 km/h; 59 mph)
B, C	51 knots (94 km/h; 58 mph)
Service ceiling: all versions	approx 5,790 m (19,000 ft)
Max rate of climb at S/L:	
all versions	732 m (2,400 ft)/min
Range:	
A, standard fuel	1,125 nm (2,085 km; 1,296 miles)
A, with auxiliary fuel	1,383 nm (2,563 km; 1,593 miles)
B, C, standard fuel	1,042 nm (1,931 km; 1,200 miles)
B, C, with auxiliary fuel	1,281 nm (2,373 km; 1,475 miles)
g limits at AUW of 708 kg (1,560 lb):	
all versions	+6/−4 limit
	+9/−6 ultimate

Spencer Amphibian four-seat amphibious homebuilt *(Aviation Picture Library)*

Sport Aircraft S-18 built by the late Mr Luther D. Sunderland

Top to bottom: Stoddard-Hamilton Glasair TD, FT, RG and Glasair III
(Jim Larsen)

Starfire Aviation Firebolt Convertible two-seat aerobatic homebuilt

Stolp SA-500 Starlet built in England by Mr S. S. Miles *(PFA)*

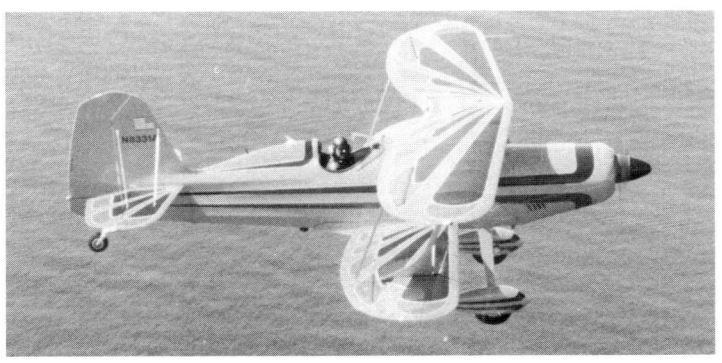

Stolp SA-300 Starduster Too owned by Mr John Remquist of Southern California

STODDARD-HAMILTON GLASAIR III

The Glasair III is a recent addition to the company's range, retaining a similar configuration to the earlier models but designed to offer exceptional performance, constructional simplicity and economical kit price. The landing gear is retractable. Construction takes approximately 1,800 working hours.

The Glasair III has a longer and wider fuselage for increased baggage space, payload capacity and comfort, also improving the longitudinal and directional stability and thereby making it a better cross-country and IFR aircraft. It features a thicker windscreen to improve protection against bird strikes at its higher speeds, and has additional glassfibre laminates, integral longerons, and a lay-up schedule which provides a structurally stronger and torsionally stiffer fuselage. The Glasair III wing uses the LS(I)-0413 section, is strengthened, and carries more fuel than previous models. NACA style air vents provide cabin ventilation.

POWER PLANT: One 224 kW (300 hp) Textron Lycoming IO-540-K1H5. Fuel capacity in wings 201 litres (53 US gallons; 44 Imp gallons). Fuselage header tank, capacity 30 litres (8 US gallons; 6.7 Imp gallons). Optional tanks in wingtip extensions, total capacity 41.6 litres (11 US gallons; 9.2 Imp gallons). Optional engine installation may be a 194 kW (260 hp) IO-540 eventually.

DIMENSIONS, EXTERNAL:
Wing span, standard	7.10 m (23 ft 3½ in)
Length overall	6.52 m (21 ft 4¾ in)
Height overall	2.29 m (7 ft 6 in)

AREA:
Wings, gross	7.55 m² (81.3 sq ft)

WEIGHTS:
Weight empty	703 kg (1,550 lb)
Baggage capacity	45 kg (100 lb)
Max T-O weight, without wingtip extensions	
	1,089 kg (2,400 lb)

PERFORMANCE (standard wings, except where indicated):
Max level speed at S/L	255 knots (473 km/h; 294 mph)
Cruising speed: 75% power at 2,440 m (8,000 ft)	
	247 knots (457 km/h; 284 mph)
50% power at 5,335 m (17,500 ft)	
	219 knots (406 km/h; 252 mph)
Stalling speed: pilot only, flaps and wheels up	
	65 knots (119 km/h; 74 mph)
flaps down, at max T-O weight	
	70 knots (129 km/h; 80 mph)
Max rate of climb at S/L	732 m (2,400 ft)/min
Service ceiling	approx 7,315 m (24,000 ft)
Range at 55% power:	
standard fuel	1,112 nm (2,061 km; 1,281 miles)
with tip tanks	1,313 nm (2,433 km; 1,512 miles)
g limits at AUW of 962 kg (2,120 lb)	+6/−4 limit
	+9/−6 ultimate

STODDARD-HAMILTON T-9 STALKER

Stoddard-Hamilton developed a low-cost military trainer version of the Glasair III, powered by an Allison turboprop engine. Details can be found in the main Aircraft section of this edition.

STOLP

STOLP STARDUSTER CORPORATION

4,301 Twining Flabob Airport, Riverside, California 92509
Telephone: 1 (714) 686 7943
PRESIDENT AND GENERAL MANAGER: William C. Clouse Jr

Stolp Starduster Corporation continues to market plans, kits and materials for the two-seat Starduster Too (well over 2,000 sets of plans sold), single-seat Starlet, aerobatic V-Star, and Acroduster Too. The latest biplane is known as the Super Starduster.

Stolp has also taken over design and marketing rights for the Steen Skybolt, of which a new Mk II version has been developed.

STOLP SA-300 STARDUSTER TOO

TYPE: Tandem two-seat homebuilt sporting biplane.
AIRFRAME: Wing section M-6 modified. All-wood wing and aileron structures, fabric covered. Welded steel tube fuselage and tail unit, with fabric covering. Glassfibre turtleback. Non-retractable tailwheel landing gear.
POWER PLANT: Prototype has a 134 kW (180 hp) Textron Lycoming O-360-A1A. Horizontally opposed or radial engines of 93-194 kW (125-260 hp) may be fitted.

DIMENSIONS, EXTERNAL:
Wing span: upper	7.32 m (24 ft 0 in)
lower	6.22 m (20 ft 5 in)
Length overall	6.63 m (21 ft 9 in)
Height overall	2.21 m (7 ft 3 in)

AREA:
Wings, gross	15.05 m² (162.0 sq ft)

WEIGHTS (typical; with 149 kW; 200 hp engine):
Weight empty	517 kg (1,139 lb)
Max T-O weight	907 kg (2,000 lb)

PERFORMANCE (typical; with 149 kW; 200 hp engine):
Max level speed	174 knots (322 km/h; 200 mph)
Econ cruising speed	100 knots (185 km/h; 115 mph)
Stalling speed	51 knots (94 km/h; 58 mph)
Sustained rate of climb, with pilot only	
	548 m (1,800 ft)/min

STOLP SA-500 STARLET

The prototype Starlet flew for the first time on 1 June 1969.
TYPE: Single-seat parasol wing homebuilt.
AIRFRAME: Dacron covered all-wood wings. Clark YH wing section. Welded steel tube fuselage and tail unit

structures, Dacron covered. Non-retractable tailwheel landing gear.

POWER PLANT: Prototype has 1,500 cc Volkswagen converted motorcar engine. Other engines of 63.5-93 kW (85-125 hp) may be fitted, the 80.5 kW (108 hp) Textron Lycoming being recommended.

DIMENSIONS, EXTERNAL:

Wing span	7.62 m (25 ft 0 in)
Length overall	5.18 m (17 ft 0 in)
Height overall	2.03 m (6 ft 8 in)

AREA:

Wings, gross	7.71 m² (83.0 sq ft)

WEIGHT (prototype):

Max T-O weight	340 kg (750 lb)

PERFORMANCE (prototype, at max T-O weight):

Cruising speed	78 knots (145 km/h; 90 mph)
Landing speed	48-52 knots (89-97 km/h; 55-60 mph)

STOLP SA-750 ACRODUSTER TOO

The SA-750 is a two-seat aerobatic biplane generally similar to the Starduster Too. It has symmetrical wings. A 149 kW (200 hp) Textron Lycoming IO-360 engine is fitted to the prototype. The front cockpit is open and has a small windscreen, while the bubble canopy for the rear cockpit is faired to the turtledeck.

DIMENSIONS, EXTERNAL:

Wing span: upper	6.53 m (21 ft 5 in)
Length overall	5.64 m (18 ft 6 in)
Height overall	2.08 m (6 ft 10 in)

AREA:

Wings, gross	12.1 m² (130.0 sq ft)

PERFORMANCE (at max T-O weight):

Cruising speed	139 knots (257 km/h; 160 mph)
Stalling speed	61 knots (113 km/h; 70 mph)
Max rate of climb at S/L	701 m (2,300 ft)/min
g limits	±9

STOLP SA-900 V-STAR

To meet the demand for low cost, low horsepower aircraft with aerobatic capability, Stolp introduced the SA-900 V-Star, which is essentially a biplane version of the SA-500 Starlet. The prototype has a 48.5 kW (65 hp) Teledyne Continental engine, but engines of 44.5-93 kW (60-125 hp) may be installed.

DIMENSIONS, EXTERNAL:

Wing span: upper	7.01 m (23 ft 0 in)
Length overall	5.23 m (17 ft 2 in)
Height overall	2.26 m (7 ft 5 in)

AREA:

Wings, gross	13.1 m² (141.0 sq ft)

PERFORMANCE (prototype, at max T-O weight):

Cruising speed	65 knots (121 km/h; 75 mph)
Stalling speed	31 knots (57 km/h; 35 mph)
Max rate of climb at S/L	183 m (600 ft)/min
g limits	±9

STOLP SUPER STARDUSTER

The Super Starduster is the first of a new series of special aerobatic aircraft for unlimited class aerobatic competition. The prototype, first flown on 1 April 1983, features a unique linkage between the ailerons and flaps, allowing the former to serve as flaps (down) with stick back, or flaps (up) with stick forward for outside loops.

TYPE: Single-seat homebuilt aerobatic biplane.

AIRFRAME: Osborne A-1 symmetrical wing section (modified). Dacron covered wooden wings and ailerons, the latter (on upper and lower wings) serving also as flaps during normal and inverted flight. Welded steel tube fuselage and tail unit, the former covered with fabric, aluminium alloy and glassfibre, and the latter with fabric. Non-retractable tailwheel landing gear.

POWER PLANT: One 149 kW (200 hp) Textron Lycoming IO-360-A1A. Fuel capacity 113.5 litres (30 US gallons; 25 Imp gallons).

DIMENSIONS, EXTERNAL:

Wing span	5.94 m (19 ft 6 in)
Length overall	4.88 m (16 ft 0 in)
Height overall	2.13 m (7 ft 0 in)
Propeller diameter	1.88 m (6 ft 2 in)

AREA:

Wings, gross	9.75 m² (105.0 sq ft)

WEIGHTS:

Basic operating weight empty	426 kg (940 lb)
Max T-O weight	680 kg (1,500 lb)

PERFORMANCE:

Max level speed at 2,440 m (8,000 ft)	156 knots (289 km/h; 180 mph) IAS
Econ cruising speed at 2,440 m (8,000 ft)	122 knots (225 km/h; 140 mph) IAS
Stalling speed, power off	48 knots (89 km/h; 55 mph) IAS
Max rate of climb at S/L	914 m (3,000 ft)/min
Service ceiling	3,810 m (12,500 ft)
T-O run	61 m (200 ft)
Landing run	335 m (1,100 ft)
Range with max fuel	440 nm (816 km; 507 miles)

STOLP (STEEN) SKYBOLT

Mr Lamar Steen designed a two-seat fully aerobatic biplane named Skybolt, which was built as a class project in a school. Simplicity of construction was a primary aim. The prototype first flew in October 1970. Plans are available, together with fuselage and wing kits; more than 3,500 sets of plans had been sold before the design was taken over by Stolp.

The following description applies to the original prototype with a 134 kW (180 hp) Textron Lycoming engine:

TYPE: Two-seat homebuilt aerobatic biplane.

AIRFRAME: Fabric covered wooden wings and ailerons (on upper and lower wings). Wing sections: upper wing NACA 63₂A015, lower wings NACA 0012. Welded steel tube fuselage and tail unit, with fabric covering. Non-retractable tailwheel landing gear.

POWER PLANT: One 134 kW (180 hp) Textron Lycoming HO-360-B1B. Provision for alternative engines of 93-194 kW (125-260 hp). Fuel capacity 110 litres (29 US gallons; 24 Imp gallons). Optional tank of 38 litres (10 US gallons; 8.3 Imp gallons) capacity can be installed in centre-section of upper wing.

DIMENSIONS, EXTERNAL:

Wing span: upper	7.32 m (24 ft 0 in)
lower	7.01 m (23 ft 0 in)
Length overall	5.79 m (19 ft 0 in)
Height overall	2.13 m (7 ft 0 in)
Propeller diameter	1.88 m (6 ft 2 in)

AREA:

Wings, gross	14.2 m² (152.7 sq ft)

WEIGHTS:

Weight empty	490 kg (1,080 lb)
Baggage capacity	13.6 kg (30 lb)
Max T-O weight	748 kg (1,650 lb)

PERFORMANCE (at max T-O weight):

Max level speed	126 knots (233 km/h; 145 mph)
Cruising speed	113 knots (209 km/h; 130 mph)
Max rate of climb at S/L	762 m (2,500 ft)/min
Service ceiling	5,500 m (18,000 ft)
T-O run	122 m (400 ft)
Range with max fuel	390 nm (720 km; 450 miles)
g limits	+12/−10

STOLP SUPER SKYBOLT

Mr William Clouse Jr and Mr Eric Shilling developed a refined version of the Skybolt biplane. Brief details, and an illustration, can be found in the 1987-88 *Jane's*.

STRIPLIN
STRIPLIN AIRCRAFT CORPORATION

PO Box 2001, Lancaster, California 93539-2001
Telephone: 1 (805) 256 2270
PRESIDENT: Kenneth Striplin

STRIPLIN LONE RANGER and SKY RANGER SERIES

The only microlight in this series is the single-seat **Lone Ranger Ultralight**; the remaining versions of the Lone Ranger and the **Sky Ranger** are Experimental homebuilt aircraft offered in **Silver Cloud STOL** form, with a tricycle landing gear; non-STOL **Silver Cloud X** form, with a tricycle landing gear and conventional inset ailerons, for higher-speed cross-country flying; and **Silver Cloud Husky STOL** form, with a tailwheel landing gear.

TYPES: Single-seat microlight and homebuilt (Lone Ranger) or two-seat homebuilt (Sky Ranger).

AIRFRAME: Wings constructed of wood, glassfibre and foam, with glassfibre skin on leading-edge and Dacron covering overall. NASA wing section. Full span flaperons on trailing-edges, of glassfibre/foam construction on all versions except the Silver Cloud X, which has in-wing ailerons. Pod and boom fuselage, the forward portion having base frame of unidirectional glassfibre, impregnated with epoxy resin, with moulded outer shell of glassfibre. At top of pod is U shaped channel, in which is buried a lightweight metal tube to which the wings are bolted and which also supports rear fuselage and tail unit. Tailboom is triangular section glassfibre and foam sandwich structure; tail surfaces of similar construction to wings. Removable fuselage side panels optional. Recovery parachute standard on all models. Non-retractable tricycle landing gear on all models except

Husky which has tailwheel type. Tailwheel, float and ski landing gears optional on all models.

POWER PLANT: *Lone Ranger Ultralight:* One 20 kW (27 hp) Rotax 277. Fuel capacity 19 litres (5 US gallons; 4.2 Imp gallons). *Lone Ranger Silver Cloud STOL:* One 33.6 kW (45 hp) Rotax 503, 48.5 kW (65 hp) Rotax 532 or 48.5 kW (65 hp) Volkswagen 1,834 cc modified motorcar engine. *Lone Ranger Silver Cloud X* and *Husky STOL* have similar options to Silver Cloud STOL but with addition of 56 kW (75 hp) Volkswagen engine. *Sky Ranger* series all have same engine options as for Lone Ranger Silver Cloud STOL, plus 41 kW (55 hp) Volkswagen 1,600 cc engine. Fuel capacity for Lone Rangers (other than Ultralight) and Sky Rangers 38 litres (10 US gallons; 8.3 Imp gallons).

DIMENSIONS, EXTERNAL (A: Lone Ranger Ultralight, B: Lone Ranger STOL with Rotax 503, C: Lone Ranger Husky STOL with 75 hp VW, D: Sky Ranger Silver Cloud X with Rotax 532):

Wing span: A, B, C	10.36 m (34 ft 0 in)
D	10.67 m (35 ft 0 in)
Length overall: A, B, C	4.78 m (15 ft 8 in)
D	4.88 m (16 ft 0 in)
Height overall: D	2.13 m (7 ft 0 in)

AREAS (A, B, C, D as above):

Wings, gross: A, B, C	12.45 m² (134.0 sq ft)
D	10.22 m² (110.0 sq ft)

WEIGHTS (A, B, C, D as above):

Weight empty: A with parachute	125 kg (275 lb)
B	163 kg (360 lb)
C	200 kg (440 lb)
D	222 kg (490 lb)
Max T-O weight: A	272 kg (600 lb)
B	363 kg (800 lb)
C, D	454 kg (1,000 lb)

PERFORMANCE (A, B, C, D as above):

Max level speed: A	54 knots (100 km/h; 62 mph)
B	73 knots (135 km/h; 84 mph)
C	89 knots (164 km/h; 102 mph)
D	95 knots (177 km/h; 110 mph)
Cruising speed: A	48 knots (89 km/h; 55 mph)
B	65 knots (121 km/h; 75 mph)
C	78 knots (145 km/h; 90 mph)
D	87 knots (161 km/h; 100 mph)
Stalling speed:	
A, flaps down	22 knots (41 km/h; 25 mph)
A, flaps up	26 knots (49 km/h; 30 mph)
B, flaps down	25 knots (45 km/h; 28 mph)
B, flaps up	30 knots (55 km/h; 34 mph)
C, flaps down	25 knots (47 km/h; 29 mph)
C, flaps up	32 knots (58 km/h; 36 mph)
D, flaps down	37 knots (68 km/h; 42 mph)
D, flaps up	42 knots (78 km/h; 48 mph)
Max rate of climb at S/L: A	183 m (600 ft)/min
B	305 m (1,000 ft)/min
C	427 m (1,400 ft)/min
D	244 m (800 ft)/min
Service ceiling: A	2,895 m (9,500 ft)
B	3,505 m (11,500 ft)
C	4,265 m (14,000 ft)
D	3,810 m (12,500 ft)
T-O run: A	54 m (175 ft)
B	46 m (150 ft)
C	34 m (110 ft)
D	191 m (625 ft)
Range, no reserves:	
A, B, C	217 nm (402 km; 250 miles)
D	234 nm (434 km; 270 miles)

SUN AEROSPACE
SUN AEROSPACE GROUP INC

PO Box 317, Nappanee, Indiana 46550
Telephone: 1 (219) 773 3220
PRESIDENT: Russell A. McDonald

SUN AEROSPACE SUN RAY 100

The prototype of the **Sun Ray 100** made its first flight on 4 September 1983. Kits available for purchase are estimated to take 500 working hours to assemble. Thought to have been under development are an amphibious version and a two-seat model known as the **Sun Ray 200**.

TYPE: Single-seat homebuilt.

AIRFRAME: Wings are spruce reinforced, with a pre-moulded glassfibre leading-edge, aluminium alloy trailing-edge, and glassfibre wrapped ribs, covered overall with Ceconite or Stits Poly-Fiber. Wing section Roncz 1104. Aluminium alloy ailerons. Twin fins and rudders of aluminium alloy tubing. Foreplane with pre-moulded skins has Roncz 1104 section. Full span elevators of similar construction on foreplane. Fuselage structure of welded aluminium alloy tubing, over which are fitted three pre-moulded glassfibre shells. Non-retractable tricycle landing gear.

POWER PLANT: One 38.8 kW (52 hp) Rotax 503. Fuel capacity 45 litres (12 US gallons; 10 Imp gallons).

DIMENSIONS, EXTERNAL:

Wing span	9.75 m (32 ft 0 in)
Length overall	3.96 m (13 ft 0 in)
Height overall	1.83 m (6 ft 0 in)
Propeller diameter	1.52 m (5 ft 0 in)

AREA:

Wings, gross (incl foreplane)	14.59 m² (157.0 sq ft)

WEIGHTS:

Weight empty	249 kg (550 lb)
Pilot weight range	46-92 kg (100-200 lb)
Baggage capacity	9 kg (20 lb)
Max T-O weight	386 kg (850 lb)

Stolp SA-750 Acroduster Too owned by Mr Gary Alpert of State College, Pennsylvania

Striplin Lone Ranger Husky STOL homebuilt

Sun Aerospace Group Sun Ray 100 *(Howard Levy)*

Sunrise Ultralight Aircraft Manufacturing Spitfire II Elite

Taylor TA-2 Bird homebuilt

Sunrise Ultralight Aircraft Manufacturing Clipper in single-seat ultralight/ Super Sport form (see microlight tables)

PERFORMANCE (estimated):				
Max level speed	87 knots (161 km/h; 100 mph)	Max rate of climb at S/L	244 m (800 ft)/min	Range	369 nm (684 km; 425 miles)
Econ cruising speed	74 knots (136 km/h; 85 mph)	Service ceiling	4,115 m (13,500 ft)	g limit	+4
Stalling speed	39 knots (71 km/h; 44 mph)	T-O run	92 m (300 ft)		
		Landing run	46 m (150 ft)		

SUNRISE

SUNRISE ULTRALIGHT AIRCRAFT MANUFACTURING COMPANY
Rt 4, Box 336, New Caney, Texas 77357
Telephone: 1 (713) 354 1348
PRESIDENT: Kim A. Zorzi
Details of the Spitfire ultralight, Spitfire Super Sport, Sonic Spitfire, Spitfire II ultralight trainer vehicle, Clipper ultralight and Clipper Super Sport can be found in the Microlights tables in this edition. By early 1990 a total of 430 kits of all versions, including the Experimental models detailed here, had been delivered.

SUNRISE SPITFIRE II ELITE
This is basically a two-seat homebuilt version of the Spitfire I microlight and Spitfire II UTV. Construction from the kit takes 60 working hours.
TYPE: Side by side two-seat homebuilt; conforms to FAI/CAA Experimental aircraft category.
AIRFRAME: Strut or, optionally, wire braced high-wing monoplane, with optional kingpost. Aluminium alloy structure, with double skinned wing and tail surfaces using Dacron fabric. Glassfibre cockpit fairing and wheel fairings. Three-axis control, with flaps. Non-retractable tricycle landing gear, with brakes. Agricultural crop-spraying equipment and ballistic parachute optional.
POWER PLANT: One 48.5 kW (65 hp) Rotax 532. Fuel capacity 38 litres (10 US gallons; 8.3 Imp gallons). Optional auxiliary fuel tank of 17.4 litres (4.6 US gallons; 3.8 Imp gallons) capacity.

DIMENSIONS, EXTERNAL:
Wing span	9.14 m (30 ft 0 in)
Length overall	5.44 m (17 ft 10 in)
Height overall	2.29 m (7 ft 6 in)
Propeller diameter	1.68 m (5 ft 6 in)

AREA:
Wing, gross	14.12 m² (152.0 sq ft)

WEIGHTS:
Weight empty	175 kg (385 lb)
Pilot weight range	45.4-113 kg (100-250 lb)
Max T-O weight	378 kg (835 lb)

PERFORMANCE:
Max level speed	74 knots (137 km/h; 85 mph)
Econ cruising speed	48 knots (89 km/h; 55 mph)
Stalling speed: flaps up	24 knots (44 km/h; 27 mph)
40% flap	19.5 knots (36 km/h; 22 mph)
Max rate of climb at S/L	244 m (800 ft)/min
Service ceiling	3,810 m (12,500 ft)
T-O run	31 m (100 ft)
Landing run	38 m (125 ft)
Range with max fuel	165 nm (305 km; 190 miles)
Endurance	3 h
g limits	+6/-4

SUNRISE CLIPPER II
This is an Experimental category derivative of the single-seat Clipper ultralight and Super Sport, with side by side seating for two persons with dual controls. Rotax 532 engine, hydraulic brakes and bush tyres. Specifications were not available in early 1990, although they will be generally similar to the single-seaters. Kit price was also not quoted, perhaps indicating that availability had not then been achieved. Clipper II two-seaters may also be made available in ultralight and Super Sport models.

TAYLOR

TAYLOR AERO INC
5855 State Route 40, Tipp City, Ohio 45371
Telephone: 1 (513) 845 1226
PRESIDENT: Col Robert H. Taylor

TAYLOR TA-2/3 BIRD
Plans and additional data are available to homebuilders, who can complete the Taylor Bird in **TA-2** form, with non-retractable tailwheel landing gear, or **TA-3** form, with non-retractable tricycle gear. Optional floats and skis. Partial assembly kits are also available to amateur builders (fin, rudder, tailplane and elevators); difficult to fabricate components, such as the main load-bearing member and

pre-formed glassfibre fairings, can be purchased. Engine and propeller reduction drawings are available as a set of separate plans, plus a propeller reduction kit and plans for constructing a clamp-on towbar.

TYPE: Tandem two-seat homebuilt.

AIRFRAME: Wings have aluminium alloy structure, with pop riveted Alclad T3 skin and plastics composite root section. Wing section NACA 23015. Full span slotted metal ailerons. Main load-bearing member of fuselage comprises a 150 mm (6 in) diameter aluminium alloy tube, to which are bolted two pylons for the cabin/landing gear/engine/wing group and the tail unit assembly. All fairings, including cabin enclosures, of glassfibre. Cantilever T tail has aluminium alloy spars and ribs, covered with Alclad T-3 skins.

POWER PLANT: One 53.7 or 84.3 kW (72 or 113 hp) watercooled Subaru 1,600 cc or 1,800 cc converted motorcar engine. Optional Volkswagen modified motorcar engine. Fuel capacity 57 litres (15 US gallons; 12.5 Imp gallons).

DIMENSIONS, EXTERNAL:
Wing span	7.92 m (26 ft 0 in)
Length overall	5.59 m (18 ft 4 in)
Height overall	1.68 m (5 ft 6 in)
Propeller diameter	1.52 m (5 ft 0 in)

AREA:
Wings, gross	10.07 m² (108.42 sq ft)

WEIGHTS:
Weight empty	277 kg (610 lb)
Max T-O weight	526 kg (1,160 lb)

PERFORMANCE:
Max level speed	113 knots (209 km/h; 130 mph)
Econ cruising speed	82 knots (153 km/h; 95 mph)
Stalling speed	39 knots (73 km/h; 45 mph)
Service ceiling	4,265 m (14,000 ft)
T-O run	137 m (450 ft)
Landing run	122 m (400 ft)
Range, with max fuel, no reserves	
	295 nm (547 km; 340 miles)

TAYLOR
TAYLOR KITS CORPORATION
PO Drawer 3350, 165 Scott Ave, Suite 102, Morgantown, West Virginia 26505
Telephone: 1 (304) 291 2376
Fax: 1 (304) 292 1902
PRESIDENT: Darus H. Zehrbach
CHIEF ENGINEER: Michael E. Renforth
GENERAL MANAGER: Lee Anne Demus

Aircraft Acquisition Corporation, owners of Helio Aircraft Corporation, Taylorcraft Aircraft Corporation and New Technik Corporation, formed the Taylor Kits Corporation in February 1990 to market aircraft, registered under the FAA 51 per cent owner built rule, based on the original C. G. Taylor designs.

Taylor Kits has drawn on the engineering, design and testing experience available through its parent corporation to produce kits which are equal to certificated production aircraft. The aircraft are manufactured to production specifications with a quality control system established.

All Taylor Kits use a 'Modular Mode' construction sequence, in which parts of the four major subassemblies are shipped in a staggered sequence based on the builder's available time and level of experience. This keeps construction and storage space to a minimum and helps ensure the proper order of assembly.

The first aircraft offered by Taylor Kits was based on the former Taylorcraft Model F21B. Although having the same basic structure as the Taylorcraft, the kit has replaced many of the original hard to fabricate parts with glassfibre and advanced composites components. The glassfibre nose cowling has been augmented with an optional glassfibre/Kevlar unit, which has been shown to have better vibration damping and energy absorption characteristics and a slightly decreased weight. As the original aircraft was designed to operate with a 48.5 kW (65 hp) Franklin engine, the kit has been made available with engine options ranging from 67 to 93.2 kW (90 to 125 hp). A prototype has been flown with each engine.

An updated version of this same aircraft has been designed for those requiring higher levels of performance. This aircraft has slightly redesigned wing and tail surfaces as well as a more streamlined fuselage shape, offering speed increases of between 7 and 10 per cent over the original for a given engine installation.

Taylor Kits Corporation also began the design in January 1990 of a light twin-engined aircraft, construction of a prototype being scheduled to start in April of that year. Known as the Twin-T, kits could be available in 1991.

TAYLOR KITS T-CRAFT
TYPE: Side by side two-seat cabin homebuilt.

AIRFRAME: Strut braced high-wing monoplane. Fabric covered wings have wood and glassfibre/Kevlar spars, and aluminium ribs. Modified Frise type ailerons. NACA 23012 wing section. Warren truss fuselage structure of 4130 steel tubing, with aluminium alloy and fabric covering. Glassfibre nose cowling. Wire braced tail unit of steel tube and fabric construction. Trim tab on port elevator. Non-retractable tailwheel landing gear, with hydraulic disc brakes and optional mainwheel fairings and floats.

POWER PLANT: One engine of 67-119 kW (90-160 hp), with Rotax and Textron Lycoming engines recommended. Fuel capacity 91-152 litres (24-40 US gallons; 20-33.3 Imp gallons).

DIMENSIONS, EXTERNAL:
Wing span	10.97 m (36 ft 0 in)
Length overall	6.78 m (22 ft 3 in)
Height overall	2.08 m (6 ft 10 in)

WEIGHTS (88 kW; 118 hp engine):
Weight empty	476 kg (1,050 lb)
Max payload	312 kg (687.5 lb)
Max T-O weight	794 kg (1,750 lb)

PERFORMANCE (88 kW; 118 hp engine):
Max level speed at 1,145 m (3,750 ft)	
	108 knots (200 km/h; 124 mph)
Econ cruising speed at 1,525 m (5,000 ft)	
	89 knots (164 km/h; 102 mph)
Stalling speed, power off	39 knots (71 km/h; 44 mph)
Max rate of climb at S/L	230 m (756 ft)/min
Service ceiling	5,335 m (17,500 ft)
T-O run	116 m (380 ft)
Landing run	122 m (400 ft)
Range, no reserves	943 nm (1,747 km; 1,086 miles)

TAYLOR KITS TWIN-T
TYPE: Two/three-seat twin-engined homebuilt.

AIRFRAME: Strut braced high-wing monoplane. Fabric covered wings have glassfibre spars and aluminium ribs. Modified Frise type ailerons and slotted Fowler trailing-edge flaps, both of aluminium/glassfibre. NACA 23012 wing section. Warren truss 4130 steel tube fuselage structure with non-structural glassfibre skins. 4130 steel tube tail unit with glassfibre skins. Trim tabs on port elevator and rudder. Non-retractable tricycle landing gear, with hydraulic disc brakes and glassfibre wheel fairings.

POWER PLANT: Two engines of 67-119 kW (90-160 hp) each. Four fuel tanks, total capacity 182-303 litres (48-80 US gallons; 40-66.6 Imp gallons).

DIMENSIONS, EXTERNAL:
Wing span	10.97 m (36 ft 0 in)
Length overall	7.51 m (24 ft 7½ in)
Height overall	3.07 m (10 ft 1 in)

AREA:
Wings, gross	17.19 m² (185.0 sq ft)

WEIGHTS (two 119 kW; 160 hp engines):
Weight empty	639.5 kg (1,410 lb)
Max payload	373 kg (823 lb)
Max T-O weight	1,020 kg (2,250 lb)

PERFORMANCE (estimated, with two 88 kW; 118 hp engines):
Max level speed at 1,525 m (5,000 ft)	
	129 knots (240 km/h; 149 mph)
Econ cruising speed at 1,525 m (5,000 ft)	
	109 knots (201 km/h; 125 mph)
Stalling speed, flaps down, power off	
	37 knots (68 km/h; 42 mph)
Max rate of climb at S/L	511 m (1,675 ft)/min
Service ceiling	6,100 m (20,000 ft)
T-O run	70 m (227 ft)
Landing run	60 m (196 ft)
Range with max fuel, with IFR reserves	
	661 nm (1,224 km; 761 miles)

TERATORN
TERATORN AIRCRAFT INC
1604 South Shore Drive, Clear Lake, Iowa 50428
Telephone: 1 (515) 357 7161
Fax: 1 (515) 357 7592
PRESIDENT: Dale Kjellsen

TERATORN TIERRA I
The Tierra single-seat microlight can be converted to a two-seater operated in the US Experimental category, with the centrally positioned single-pilot seat moved sideways to accommodate the second occupant.

Three models are currently offered, using Rotax 277, 377 and 447 engines. In other respects they are almost identical.

TYPE: Single-seat microlight conforming to FAR Pt 103, or two-seat Experimental category aircraft.

AIRFRAME: Aluminium alloy and Mylar coated Dacron construction, with double surface covering. Three-axis control. Non-retractable tailwheel landing gear. Optional floats, skis, amphibious gear combining floats with retractable wheels, and semi-enclosed or fully enclosed cockpit.

POWER PLANT: Three engine choices: 20 kW (27 hp) Rotax 277 with 19 litre (5 US gallon; 4.2 Imp gallon) fuel capacity; 26 kW (35 hp) Rotax 377 with 23 litres (6 US gallons; 5 Imp gallons) fuel; or 29.4 kW (39.4 hp) Rotax 447 with 23 litres (6 US gallons; 5 Imp gallons) of fuel.

DIMENSIONS, EXTERNAL:
Wing span	9.45 m (31 ft 0 in)
Length overall	5.49 m (18 ft 0 in)
Height overall	1.68 m (5 ft 6 in)

AREA:
Wings, gross	14.31 m² (154.0 sq ft)

WEIGHTS (Rotax 377 engine):
Weight empty	125 kg (275 lb)
Pilot weight range	55-113 kg (120-250 lb)
Max T-O weight	238 kg (525 lb)

PERFORMANCE (engine as above):
Max level speed at 762 m (2,500 ft)	
	61 knots (113 km/h; 70 mph)
Econ cruising speed at 762 m (2,500 ft)	
	52 knots (97 km/h; 60 mph)
Stalling speed	25 knots (45 km/h; 28 mph)
Max rate of climb at S/L	244 m (800 ft)/min
Service ceiling	3,050 m (10,000 ft)
T-O run	23 m (75 ft)
Landing run	46 m (150 ft)
Range with max fuel	104 nm (193 km; 120 miles)

TERATORN TIERRA II
This is a two-seat Tierra, with a Rotax 532 engine, wing flaps, enclosed cabin with rigid Lexan doors, and breakaway steerable tailwheel. Options include floats, skis and agricultural spraying equipment.

TYPE: Side by side two-seat, dual-control homebuilt; conforms to Experimental regulations.

POWER PLANT: One 48.5 kW (65 hp) Rotax 532. Fuel capacity 45.4 litres (12 US gallons; 10 Imp gallons).

DIMENSIONS, EXTERNAL:
Wing span	11.20 m (36 ft 9 in)
Length overall	5.69 m (18 ft 8 in)
Height overall	1.85 m (6 ft 1 in)
Propeller diameter	1.78 m (5 ft 10 in)

AREA:
Wings, gross	17.65 m² (190.0 sq ft)

WEIGHTS:
No data received, except:
Crew weight range	55-204 kg (120-450 lb)

PERFORMANCE:
Max level speed at 762 m (2,500 ft)	
	61 knots (113 km/h; 70 mph)
Econ cruising speed at 762 m (2,500 ft)	
	48 knots (89 km/h; 55 mph)
Stalling speed	27 knots (50 km/h; 31 mph)
Max rate of climb at S/L	183 m (600 ft)/min
Service ceiling	3,050 m (10,000 ft)
T-O run	38 m (125 ft)
Landing run	54 m (175 ft)
Range with max fuel	208 nm (386 km; 240 miles)

THURSTON
THURSTON AEROMARINE CORPORATION
24 Ledge Road, Cumberland Foreside, Maine 04110
Telephone: 1 (207) 829 6108
PRESIDENT: David B. Thurston

THURSTON TA16 TROJAN
The TA16 Trojan four-seat amphibian was conceived originally for the homebuilt market and plans became available from Thurston Aeromarine. A production version became the TA16 Seafire. The Trojan and Seafire are identical and the details of the Seafire given under the International Aeromarine Corporation entry in the main Aircraft section of this edition apply equally to the Trojan. By February 1990, a total of 63 Trojans was under construction in Brazil, Canada, Norway and the USA. No new orders are being taken.

Prototype Taylor Kits Corporation T-Craft (88 kW; 118 hp Textron Lycoming engine)

Taylor Kits Corporation Twin-T homebuilt *(Jane's/Mike Keep)*

The two-seat Teratorn Tierra II homebuilt aircraft *(Geoffrey P. Jones)*

Thurston TA16 Trojan owned by Mr Billy Johnson *(Billy Johnson)*

T.E.A.M. TA-3 two-seat monoplane; details in microlight tables
(Geoffrey P. Jones)

Tandem two-seat V-8 Special *(Howard Levy)*

TURNER
TURNER AIRCRAFT INC
Route 4, Box 115AB3, Grandview, Texas 76050
Telephone: 1 (817) 783 5350
PRESIDENT: Eugene L. Turner
The original Turner T-40 first flew on 3 April 1961. Plans of the T-40, T-40A and Super T-40A are available to

homebuilders; many hundreds of sets have been sold. Details can be found in the 1982-83 *Jane's*. In addition, development of the T-80 amphibian is to be completed once the first plans-built T-40 and the original T-40B have been restored (see 1982-83 *Jane's*). Also, Turner Aircraft has developed the T-100D Mariah (see Microlight tables) and the T-110.

TURNER T-110
This high-performance Experimental derivative of the T-100D is powered by a 32 kW (43 hp) engine. A prototype has been flight tested. Brief details and an illustration can be found in the 1987-88 *Jane's*.

V-8 SPECIAL
PLANS AND KITS FROM: Mizell Enterprises, 15749 Harvest Mile Road, Brighton, Colorado 80601
Telephone: 1 (303) 654 0049
The V-8 Special was first flown on 22 September 1978. Following the death of its designer, Mr Chris Beachner, rights in the aircraft were purchased by Mr Bill Mizell, who currently offers plans, kits, engine conversion plans and ready converted V-8 engines. Mr Mizell is also offering plans and kits of the **V-8 Special SXS**, a side by side seating model with optional non-retractable tricycle or tailwheel landing gear, or fully retractable gear.
The following details apply to the standard V-8 Special:

V-8 SPECIAL
TYPE: Tandem two-seat sporting homebuilt.

AIRFRAME: Wings, ailerons and tail unit of glassfibre/epoxy resin and polyurethane foam construction. Welded steel tube fuselage structure, covered with a shell of glassfibre/epoxy over a polyurethane foam core. Non-retractable or retractable tailwheel landing gear.
POWER PLANT: One 93.2 kW (125 hp) modified Buick watercooled motorcar engine. Alternatively, other engines in 93.2-186.4 kW (125-250 hp) range. Fuel capacity 132.5 litres (35 US gallons; 29 Imp gallons).
DIMENSIONS, EXTERNAL:

Wing span	7.32 m (24 ft 0 in)
Length overall	5.64 m (18 ft 6 in)
Propeller diameter	1.45 m (4 ft 9 in)

AREA:

Wings, gross	8.92 m² (96.0 sq ft)

WEIGHTS:

Weight empty	381 kg (840 lb)
Baggage capacity	18 kg (40 lb)
Max T-O weight	588 kg (1,296 lb)

PERFORMANCE:

Max cruising speed	more than 174 knots (322 km/h; 200 mph)
Cruising speed (50% power)	128 knots (238 km/h; 148 mph) IAS
Stalling speed: landing gear and flaps up	56 knots (103 km/h; 64 mph) IAS
flaps down	35 knots (65 km/h; 40 mph)
*Max rate of climb at S/L	over 762 m (2,500 ft)/min

Depending on engine rating

VANCRAFT
VANCRAFT COPTERS
7246 North Mohawk Avenue, Portland, Oregon 97203
Telephone: 1 (503) 286 5462
Details of the Lightning Sport Copter microlight autogyro can be found in the Microlight tables.

VANCRAFT COPTERS VANCRAFT
Kits to build this autogyro are available.
TYPE: Tandem two-seat autogyro.
ROTOR SYSTEM: Two-blade rotor, with steel spar, wooden core, and bonded and riveted aluminium alloy skins. Patented rotor head with no springs. Hydraulic pre-rotator.

AIRFRAME: Basic structure of 2 in square steel tubing, bolted and welded. Small horizontal stabiliser, fin, large-area rudder and mast supports constructed of circular-section tubing. Glassfibre cabin shell. Non-retractable tricycle landing gear.
POWER PLANT: One 74.6 kW (100 hp) SCAT modified

Volkswagen 2,180 cc motorcar engine. Fuel capacity 34 litres (9 US gallons; 7.5 Imp gallons).

DIMENSIONS, EXTERNAL:

Rotor diameter	8.53 m (28 ft 0 in)
Length overall	3.96 m (13 ft 0 in)
Height overall	2.29 m (7 ft 6 in)
Propeller diameter	1.42 m (4 ft 8 in)

WEIGHTS:

Weight empty	204 kg (450 lb)
Payload	159-181 kg (350-400 lb)

PERFORMANCE:

Max level speed	87 knots (161 km/h; 100 mph)
Cruising speed	56-65 knots (105-121 km/h; 65-75 mph)
Max rate of climb at S/L	366 m (1,200 ft)/min

T-O run	15-61 m (50-200 ft)
Range	261-304 nm (483-563 km; 300-350 miles)
Endurance	3 h 30 min

VAN'S
VAN'S AIRCRAFT INC
PO Box 160, North Plains, Oregon 97133
Telephone: 1 (503) 647 5117
PRESIDENT: Richard VanGrunsven

VAN'S RV-3
More than 1,100 sets of plans of the RV-3 have been sold, with at least 200 aircraft under construction and over 150 RV-3s flying.

TYPE: Single-seat sporting homebuilt.
AIRFRAME: Built of light alloy, with glassfibre wing and tail unit tips and engine cowling. Wing section NACA 23012. Non-retractable tailwheel landing gear.
POWER PLANT: One 93 kW (125 hp) Textron Lycoming O-290-G (GPU). Fuel capacity 91 litres (24 US gallons; 20 Imp gallons).

DIMENSIONS, EXTERNAL:

Wing span	6.07 m (19 ft 11 in)
Length overall	5.79 m (19 ft 0 in)
Height overall	1.55 m (5 ft 1 in)
Propeller diameter	1.73 m (5 ft 8 in)

AREA:

Wings, gross	8.36 m² (90.0 sq ft)

WEIGHTS:

Weight empty	315 kg (695 lb)
Max T-O weight	476 kg (1,050 lb)

PERFORMANCE (at max T-O weight):

Max level speed at S/L	169 knots (314 km/h; 195 mph)
Econ cruising speed at 3,050 m (10,000 ft)	139 knots (257 km/h; 160 mph)
Stalling speed: flaps up	46 knots (84 km/h; 52 mph)
flaps down	42 knots (78 km/h; 48 mph)
Max rate of climb at S/L	579 m (1,900 ft)/min
Service ceiling	6,400 m (21,000 ft)
T-O run	61 m (200 ft)
Landing run	91 m (300 ft)
Range, no reserves	520 nm (965 km; 600 miles)

VAN'S RV-4
The two-seat RV-4 is some 20 per cent larger than the RV-3 and there is no commonality of airframe components, although the configuration is unchanged. The first flight of the prototype was made on 21 August 1979. Plans and kits are available to homebuilders. By early 1990, over 2,500 sets of plans had been sold, with about 1,000 aircraft under construction and more than 260 RV-4s flying.

TYPE: Tandem two-seat sporting homebuilt.
AIRFRAME: As for RV-3, except wing section Van's Aircraft 135.
POWER PLANT: One 112 kW (150 hp) Textron Lycoming O-320-E1F. Fuel capacity 121 litres (32 US gallons; 26.6 Imp gallons).

DIMENSIONS, EXTERNAL:

Wing span	7.01 m (23 ft 0 in)
Length overall	6.21 m (20 ft 4½ in)
Height overall	1.60 m (5 ft 3 in)
Propeller diameter	1.73 m (5 ft 8 in)

AREA:

Wings, gross	10.22 m² (110.0 sq ft)

WEIGHTS:

Weight empty	404 kg (890 lb)
Baggage capacity	13.6 kg (30 lb)
Max T-O weight	680 kg (1,500 lb)

PERFORMANCE (at max T-O weight, and prior to prototype's aerodynamic clean-up):

Max level speed at S/L	175 knots (323 km/h; 201 mph)
Econ cruising speed (55% power at 2,440 m; 8,000 ft)	142 knots (264 km/h; 164 mph)
Stalling speed	47 knots (87 km/h; 54 mph)
Max rate of climb at S/L	503 m (1,650 ft)/min
Service ceiling	5,945 m (19,500 ft)
T-O run	137 m (450 ft)
Landing run	130 m (425 ft)
Range with max fuel (55% power)	695 nm (1,287 km; 800 miles)

VAN'S RV-6
This is basically a side by side two-seat derivative of the RV-4. The prototype first flew in June 1986. Plans and kits are available. By early 1990, more than 900 sets of plans had been sold, with more than 750 aircraft under construction and nine flying.

TYPE: Side by side two-seat sporting homebuilt.
AIRFRAME: Similar to RV-4.
POWER PLANT: One 119.3 kW (160 hp) Textron Lycoming O-320. Fuel capacity 140 litres (37 US gallons; 30.8 Imp gallons).

DIMENSIONS, EXTERNAL:

Wing span	7.01 m (23 ft 0 in)
Length overall	6.16 m (20 ft 2½ in)
Height overall	1.60 m (5 ft 3 in)
Propeller diameter	1.73 m (5 ft 8 in)

AREA:

Wings, gross	10.22 m² (110.0 sq ft)

WEIGHTS:

Weight empty	431 kg (950 lb)
Baggage capacity	27.2 kg (60 lb)
Max T-O weight	726 kg (1,600 lb)

PERFORMANCE (at max T-O weight):

Max level speed at S/L	175 knots (323 km/h; 201 mph)
Econ cruising speed (55% power) at 2,440 m (8,000 ft)	146 knots (270 km/h; 168 mph)
Stalling speed	47 knots (87 km/h; 54 mph)
Max rate of climb at S/L	503 m (1,650 ft)/min
Service ceiling	5,945 m (19,500 ft)
T-O run	160 m (525 ft)
Landing run	153 m (500 ft)
Range with max fuel (55% power)	803 nm (1,488 km; 925 miles)

VAN'S RV-6A
The RV-6A is a tricycle landing gear variation of the RV-6. Fuel capacity is 144 litres (38 US gallons; 31.6 Imp gallons). The prototype first flew in July 1988. Plans and kits are available. AIEP of Nigeria is constructing RV-6As as Air Beetle military trainers.

DIMENSIONS, EXTERNAL:

Wing span	7.01 m (23 ft 0 in)
Length overall	6.07 m (19 ft 11 in)
Height overall	2.13 m (7 ft 0 in)

AREA:

Wings, gross	10.22 m² (110.0 sq ft)

WEIGHTS:

Weight empty	451 kg (995 lb)
Baggage capacity	27.2 kg (60 lb)
Max T-O weight	726 kg (1,600 lb)

PERFORMANCE (two persons):

Max level speed	174 knots (322 km/h; 200 mph)
Econ cruising speed (55% power) at 2,440 m (8,000 ft)	144 knots (267 km/h; 166 mph)
Stalling speed	48 knots (89 km/h; 55 mph)
Max rate of climb at S/L	427 m (1,400 ft)/min
Service ceiling	4,970 m (16,300 ft)
T-O run	92 m (300 ft)
Landing run	153 m (500 ft)
Range (55% power) at 2,440 m (8,000 ft)	760 nm (1,408 km; 875 miles)

VELOCITY
VELOCITY AIRCRAFT
200 West Airport Drive, Sebastian, Florida 32958

VELOCITY AIRCRAFT VELOCITY
The prototype Velocity made its debut at the 1985 Sun 'n Fun meeting. Velocity Aircraft offers it in kit form, with the glassfibre components pre-moulded.

TYPE: Two-plus-two homebuilt.
AIRFRAME: Built of foam cores, unidirectional/biaxial-triaxial glassfibre and epoxy resin. Rear mounted wings use modified Eppler aerofoil section. Three Roncz 'vortillons' under leading-edge of each wing. Endplate fins and rudders. Speed brake under fuselage. Foreplanes on nose, of original section and with near full-span elevators. Non-retractable main landing gear. Retractable nosewheel.
POWER PLANT: Any Textron Lycoming engine of 112 to 149 kW (150 to 200 hp) or Teledyne Continental IO-360. Prototype has one 134 kW (180 hp) Textron Lycoming HIO-360. Fuel capacity of 277 litres (73 US gallons; 60.8 Imp gallons).

DIMENSIONS, EXTERNAL:

Wing span	8.72 m (28 ft 7½ in)
Length overall	5.49 m (18 ft 0 in)
Height overall	2.44 m (8 ft 0 in)
Propeller diameter	1.73 m (5 ft 8 in)

AREA:

Wings, gross	8.92 m² (96.0 sq ft)

WEIGHTS:

Weight empty	499 kg (1,100 lb)
Max T-O weight	1,020 kg (2,250 lb)

PERFORMANCE (prototype, at max T-O weight):

Max cruising speed at 610 m (2,000 ft)	191 knots (354 km/h; 220 mph)
Max rate of climb at S/L	305 m (1,000 ft)/min
Range with max fuel	1,736 nm (3,218 km; 2,000 miles)

VIKING
VIKING AIRCRAFT LTD
RR No. 1, PO Box 1000V, Eloy, Arizona 85231
Telephone: 1 (602) 466 7538
PRESIDENT: Rex Taylor

VIKING DRAGONFLY
The prototype Dragonfly first flew on 16 June 1980. Plans are available, together with a pre-formed engine cowling and canopy. Also, kits of prefabricated component parts, requiring no complex jigging or tooling, are available. In this form the aircraft is known as the 'Snap' Dragonfly. It is estimated that the kits save the builder more than 700 working hours.

In its original configuration, with the non-retractable mainwheels at the tips of the foreplane, the aircraft was designated **Dragonfly Mark I**. In parallel production, for operation from unprepared strips and narrow taxiways, was the **Dragonfly Mark II**. This has its main landing gear in the form of short non-retractable cantilever units under the wings, with individual hydraulic toe brakes, and increased foreplane and elevator areas. In 1985 a **Dragonfly Mark III** version, with non-retractable tricycle landing gear, underwent flight trials.

TYPE: Side by side two-seat, dual control sporting homebuilt.
AIRFRAME: Composites wing, foreplane and tail unit structures of styrene foam, glassfibre, carbonfibre and epoxy. Wing section Eppler 1213. Foreplane of GU25 section. Semi-monocoque fuselage, formed (not carved) from 12.5 mm (½ in) thick urethane foam, with strips of 18 mm (¾ in) foam bonded along edges to allow large-radius external corners. Fuselage covered with glassfibre inside and out. (See introduction for landing gears.)
POWER PLANT: One 44.5 kW (60 hp) HAPI 1,835 cc modified Volkswagen motorcar engine; 1,600 cc engine, rated at 33.5 kW (45 hp), optional. Fuel capacity 56.8 litres (15 US gallons; 12.5 Imp gallons).

DIMENSIONS, EXTERNAL:

Wing span	6.71 m (22 ft 0 in)
Length overall	5.79 m (19 ft 0 in)
Height overall: Mk I	1.22 m (4 ft 0 in)
Propeller diameter	1.32 m (4 ft 4 in)

AREA:

Wings, gross	4.51 m² (48.5 sq ft)

WEIGHTS (Dragonfly Mk I with 1,835 cc engine):

Weight empty	274 kg (605 lb)
Max payload	184 kg (405 lb)
Max T-O weight	488 kg (1,075 lb)

PERFORMANCE (Dragonfly Mk I with 1,835 cc engine):

Max level speed at S/L	146 knots (270 km/h; 168 mph) IAS
Econ cruising speed at 2,285 m (7,500 ft)	121 knots (225 km/h; 140 mph)
Stalling speed, power on	39 knots (73 km/h; 45 mph) IAS
Max rate of climb at S/L	259 m (850 ft)/min
Service ceiling	5,640 m (18,500 ft)
T-O run	137 m (450 ft)
Landing run	213 m (700 ft)
Range with max fuel, 30 min reserves	434 nm (804 km; 500 miles)
g limits	+4.4/-2

Van's RV-6 side by side two-seat homebuilt aircraft

First Velocity all-composites four-seat aircraft built from a kit by
Mr Neil Hunter *(Howard Levy)*

Viking Aircraft Dragonfly Mark I built in West Germany as the Schneider
TC-1 Dragonfly *(Geoffrey P. Jones)*

Volmer VJ-22 Sportsman two-seat homebuilt amphibian

UK registered Wag-Aero Acro Trainer *(PFA)*

VOLMER
VOLMER AIRCRAFT
Box 5222, Glendale, California 91201
Telephone: 1 (818) 247 8718
PRESIDENT: Volmer Jensen

Details of the VJ-23E Swingwing and VJ-24W Sunfun can be found in the Microlight tables.

VOLMER VJ-22 SPORTSMAN
The prototype Sportsman flew for the first time on 22 December 1958. Plans are available to amateur constructors. Over 800 sets had been sold by early 1989 and more than 100 Sportsman amphibians are flying. Some have tractor propellers, but this modification is not recommended by Mr Jensen.

TYPE: Side by side two-seat, dual-control homebuilt amphibian.
AIRFRAME: Wings are standard Aeronca Chief or Champion assemblies with wooden spars, light alloy ribs and fabric covering, and carry stabilising floats under the tips. Plans of specially designed wing, with wooden ribs and spars, available. Flying-boat hull of wooden construction, coated with glassfibre. Steel tube tail unit, fabric covered. Retractable tailwheel landing gear. Water rudder.
POWER PLANT: One 63.5 kW (85 hp) Teledyne Continental C85, 67 kW (90 hp) or 74.5 kW (100 hp) Teledyne Continental O-200-B. Fuel capacity 76 litres (20 US gallons; 16.7 Imp gallons).
DIMENSIONS, EXTERNAL:
Wing span	11.12 m (36 ft 6 in)
Length overall	7.32 m (24 ft 0 in)
Height overall	2.44 m (8 ft 0 in)

AREA:
Wings, gross	16.3 m² (175.0 sq ft)

WEIGHTS (63.5 kW; 85 hp):
Weight empty	454 kg (1,000 lb)
Max T-O weight	680 kg (1,500 lb)

PERFORMANCE (63.5 kW; 85 hp, at max T-O weight):
Max level speed at S/L	83 knots (153 km/h; 95 mph)
Max cruising speed	74 knots (137 km/h; 85 mph)
Stalling speed	39 knots (72 km/h; 45 mph)
Max rate of climb at S/L	183 m (600 ft)/min
Service ceiling	3,960 m (13,000 ft)
Range with max fuel, no reserves	
	260 nm (480 km; 300 miles)

WAG-AERO
WAG-AERO INC
PO Box 181, 1216 North Road, Lyons, Wisconsin 53148
Telephone: 1 (414) 763 9586
PRESIDENT: Richard H. Wagner
MARKETING SUPERVISOR: Mary Pat Henningfield

WAG-AERO SPORT TRAINER
Wag-Aero plans and kits offer homebuilders the choice of four different modern versions of the Piper J-3.

Known as the **Sport Trainer**, the basic two-seat sporting aircraft follows the original design, but the wing has a wooden main spar and ribs, light alloy leading-edge and fabric covering. The fuselage and tail unit are of welded steel tube with fabric covering. The Sport Trainer can be powered by any flat-four Continental, Franklin or Textron Lycoming engine of between 48.5 and 93 kW (65 and 125 hp).

Also available are the **Acro Trainer**, which differs from the standard version by having a strengthened fuselage, shortened wings (8.23 m; 27 ft), modified lift struts, improved wing fittings and rib spacing, and a new leading-edge; the **Observer**, which is a replica L-4 military liaison aircraft; and the **Super Sport**, with structural modifications to accept engines of up to 112 kW (150 hp), making it suitable for glider towing, bush operations, or for operation as a floatplane.

The Sport Trainer first flew on 12 March 1975. The following details refer to this version:
DIMENSIONS, EXTERNAL:
Wing span	10.73 m (35 ft 2½ in)
Length overall	6.82 m (22 ft 4½ in)
Height overall	2.03 m (6 ft 8 in)

AREA:
Wings, gross	16.58 m² (178.5 sq ft)

WEIGHTS:
Weight empty	327 kg (720 lb)
Max T-O weight	635 kg (1,400 lb)

PERFORMANCE (at max T-O weight):
Max level speed at S/L	89 knots (164 km/h; 102 mph)
Cruising speed	82 knots (151 km/h; 94 mph)
Stalling speed	34 knots (63 km/h; 39 mph)
Max rate of climb at S/L	149 m (490 ft)/min
Service ceiling	over 3,660 m (12,000 ft)
T-O run	114 m (375 ft)

Range: at cruising speed with standard fuel (45.5 litres; 12 US gallons; 10 Imp gallons)
191 nm (354 km; 220 miles)
with auxiliary fuel (98.5 litres; 26 US gallons; 21.6 Imp gallons) 395 nm (732 km; 455 miles)

WAG-AERO WAG-A-BOND
The name Wag-A-Bond applies to a replica of the Piper PA-15 Vagabond, known as the **Classic**, and the **Traveler**. The latter is a modified and updated version of the Piper Vagabond with port and starboard doors, overhead skylight window, extended sleeping deck (conversion from aircraft to camper interior taking about two minutes and accommodating two persons), extended baggage area, engine of up to 85.7 kW (115 hp), and provision for a full electrical system.

The prototype Wag-A-Bond was completed by Wag-Aero in May 1978. The following details apply to both versions, unless stated otherwise:

TYPE: Side by side two-seat homebuilt.

AIRFRAME: All-wood wing and aluminium alloy aileron structures. Welded steel tube and flat plate fuselage structure, and steel tube tail unit. Complete airframe is fabric covered. Non-retractable tailwheel landing gear. Optional skis.

POWER PLANT: Traveler can be powered by a Textron Lycoming engine of 80.5-85.7 kW (108-115 hp). Classic can be powered by a Teledyne Continental engine of 48.5-74.5 kW (65-100 hp). Fuel capacity: Traveler 98.5 litres (26 US gallons; 21.6 Imp gallons), Classic 45.5 litres (12 US gallons; 10 Imp gallons).

DIMENSIONS, EXTERNAL:
Wing span	8.32 m (29 ft 3½ in)
Length overall	5.66 m (18 ft 7 in)
Height overall	1.83 m (6 ft 0 in)

AREA:
Wings, gross	13.70 m² (147.5 sq ft)

WEIGHTS (A: Traveler, B: Classic):
Weight empty: A	329 kg (725 lb)
B	290 kg (640 lb)

Baggage capacity:
A	27 kg (60 lb)
B	18 kg (40 lb)
Max T-O weight: A	658 kg (1,450 lb)
B	567 kg (1,250 lb)

PERFORMANCE (A: Traveler, B: Classic):
Max level speed: A	118 knots (219 km/h; 136 mph)
B	91 knots (169 km/h; 105 mph)
Cruising speed: A	108 knots (200 km/h; 124 mph)
B	83 knots (153 km/h; 95 mph)
Stalling speed: A, B	39 knots (73 km/h; 45 mph)
Max rate of climb at S/L: A	259 m (850 ft)/min
B	190 m (625 ft)/min

WAG-AERO 2+2 SPORTSMAN

The 2+2 Sportsman is based on the Piper PA-14 Family Cruiser. It is a true four-seater, with the option of a hinged rear fuselage decking to provide access to the baggage and rear seat areas. The rear seat itself can be removed so that cargo or a stretcher can be carried.

Plans and material kits are available for the 2+2 Sportsman. A pre-welded fuselage structure is also available.

TYPE: Four-seat homebuilt.

AIRFRAME: Similar construction to Wag-A-Bond, with glassfibre tips. Alternatively, drawings and materials provided to modify standard PA-12, PA-14 or PA-18 wings. Upper and lower spoilers.

POWER PLANT: Engine of 93-149 kW (125-200 hp). Usable fuel capacity 148 litres (39 US gallons; 32.5 Imp gallons).

DIMENSIONS, EXTERNAL:
Wing span	10.90 m (35 ft 9 in)
Length overall	7.12 m (23 ft 4½ in)
Height overall	2.02 m (6 ft 7½ in)

AREA:
Wings, gross	16.18 m² (174.12 sq ft)

WEIGHTS:
Weight empty	490 kg (1,080 lb)
Max T-O weight	998 kg (2,200 lb)

PERFORMANCE (typical; actual data depend on engine fitted):
Max level speed	112 knots (207 km/h; 129 mph)
Cruising speed	108 knots (200 km/h; 124 mph)
Stalling speed	33 knots (62 km/h; 38 mph)
Max rate of climb at S/L	244 m (800 ft)/min
Service ceiling	4,510 m (14,800 ft)
Range at cruising speed	582 nm (1,078 km; 670 miles)

RICHARD WARNER
RICHARD WARNER AVIATION INC
Thunderhill Aerodrome, 82341 Highway 1129, Covington, Louisiana 70433
Telephone: 1 (504) 892 3721
OWNER: Capt. Richard M. Warner

RICHARD WARNER (ANDERSON) W-1 SUPER KINGFISHER

The prototype EA-1 Kingfisher amphibian was designed and built by Mr Earl Anderson. The first flight was made on 24 April 1969. Plans were made available to amateur constructors via Anderson Aircraft Corporation; all rights to the Kingfisher have since been transferred to Richard Warner Aviation.

The latest version is the W-1 Super Kingfisher, the prototype of which first flew on 25 December 1988. By late December 1989 a total of 250 sets of plans for the EA-1 Kingfisher and W-1 Super Kingfisher had been sold, and 75 plans-built aircraft were then flying. In comparison to the Kingfisher, the Super Kingfisher has two doors, adjustable seats, extended water rudder, skylight, greater fuel capacity, larger spray rails, an O-320 engine, and larger baggage area. The following details refer to the Super Kingfisher:

TYPE: Side by side two-seat homebuilt amphibian.

AIRFRAME: Standard J3, PA-11, PA-12, Super Cub or homebuilt wing with aluminium alloy spars and ribs, and Ceconite covering; plans include alternative wood wing. Wing section USA 35B modified. Wing stabilising floats and flying-boat hull of wooden construction, covered with plywood and coated with glassfibre. Strut braced tail unit of steel tubing, fabric covered. Retractable tailwheel landing gear, with brakes.

POWER PLANT: One 112 kW (150 hp) Textron Lycoming O-320-A2B in prototype. Fuel capacity 153 litres (40.5 US gallons; 33.7 Imp gallons).

DIMENSIONS, EXTERNAL:
Wing span	11.00 m (36 ft 1 in)
Length overall	7.16 m (23 ft 6 in)
Height overall	2.51 m (8 ft 3 in)
Propeller diameter	1.88 m (6 ft 2 in)

AREA:
Wings, gross	17.19 m² (185.0 sq ft)

WEIGHTS (O-320-A2B engine):
Weight empty	512 kg (1,129 lb)
Baggage capacity	22.7 kg (50 lb)
Max T-O weight	816 kg (1,800 lb)

PERFORMANCE (with O-320-A2B engine, at max T-O weight):
Max level speed	109 knots (201 km/h; 125 mph)
Econ cruising speed at 305 m (1,000 ft)	74 knots (137 km/h; 85 mph)
Stalling speed, flaps down, power on	33 knots (61 km/h; 38 mph)
Max rate of climb at S/L	305 m (1,000 ft)/min
Service ceiling	3,660 m (12,000 ft)
T-O run	92 m (300 ft)
Landing run	153 m (500 ft)
Range	369 nm (684 km; 425 miles)
Endurance	5 h 15 min

WATSON
WATSON WINDWAGON COMPANY
Route 1, Box 51, Newcastle, Texas 76372

Telephone: 1 (817) 862 5615
OWNER: Gary Watson

Details of the GW-1 Windwagon, and an illustration, can be found in the 1988-89 *Jane's.* Plans remain available.

WHATLEY
VASCOE WHATLEY Jr
PO Box 474, Allendale, South Carolina 29810
Telephone: 1 (803) 584 2691

Details of the Whatley Special, and an illustration, can be found in the 1988-89 *Jane's.* Plans remain available.

WHEELER
WHEELER AIRCRAFT COMPANY
Dept 27, Tacoma-Narrows Airport, Gig Harbor, Washington 98335
Telephone: 1 (206) 851 5793
Fax: 1 (206) 851 5916
PRESIDENT: Ken Wheeler

WHEELER EXPRESS

The Express was CAD designed as a high speed cross-country kitplane, with the unusual seating arrangement of one forward and one aft facing seat in the rear, behind two front seats with dual controls. The prototype, built from a kit of pre-moulded parts, flew for the first time on 28 July 1987. The first larger, production line Express demonstrator flew for the first time in May 1990. It is powered by a Teledyne Continental engine. Kits are available.

TYPE: Four-seat, dual-control cross-country homebuilt; conforms to FAR Pt 23.

AIRFRAME: Constructed of composites sandwich material, comprising polyurethane foam core, glassfibre, unidirectional glassfibre tape and vinylester resin. Wing section NASA NFL-1 0215-F (laminar flow). Non-retractable tricycle landing gear. Retractable gear optional.

POWER PLANT: Demonstrator fitted with 156.6 kW (210) Teledyne Continental engine; 119 or 134 kW (160 or 180 hp) Textron Lycoming engine optional. Fuel capacity 197 litres (52 US gallons; 43.3 Imp gallons); optional 348 litres (92 US gallons; 76.6 Imp gallons).

DIMENSIONS, EXTERNAL:
Wing span	9.45 m (31 ft 0 in)
Length overall	7.62 m (25 ft 0 in)
Height overall	2.13 m (7 ft 0 in)

AREA:
Wings, gross	11.71 m² (126.0 sq ft)

WEIGHTS:
Weight empty	567 kg (1,250 lb)
Baggage capacity, with four 77 kg (170 lb) persons	29 kg (64 lb)
Max T-O weight	1,043 kg (2,300 lb)

PERFORMANCE (149 kW; 200 hp engine, retractable landing gear):
Max level speed at S/L	204 knots (378 km/h; 235 mph)
Max cruising speed at S/L (75% power)	182 knots (338 km/h; 210 mph)

Stalling speed at max T-O weight:
flaps up	55 knots (101 km/h; 63 mph)
flaps down	50 knots (92 km/h; 57 mph)
Max rate of climb at S/L	488 m (1,600 ft)/min
Range at 55% power, no reserves	1,042 nm (1,931 km; 1,200 miles)
g limits	+4.4/-2.2
	+8.8/-4.4 ultimate

WHITE
E. MARSHALL WHITE
Meadowlark Airport, 5141 Warner Avenue, Huntington Beach, California 92649
Telephone: 1 (714) 846 2409

Details of the WW-1 Der Jäger D.IX, and an illustration, can be found in the 1988-89 *Jane's.* Plans, kits and some components remain available.

WHITE LIGHTNING
WHITE LIGHTNING AIRCRAFT CORPORATION
Box 497, Walterboro, South Carolina 29488-0497
Telephone: 1 (803) 538 3999
PRESIDENT: Nick Jones

WHITE LIGHTNING AIRCRAFT WHITE LIGHTNING

The first prototype White Lightning flew initially on 8 March 1986. In the same year it established several world speed records in Classes C1b and C1c.

Kits are available, and 28 had been delivered by January 1990, by which time nine aircraft had flown. Construction takes under 1,000 working hours for the first-time builder and about 600 hours for the experienced builder.

TYPE: Four-seat homebuilt.

AIRFRAME: Wing section NACA 66₂-215. Wings have graphite tubular 'wet' main spar, and glassfibre/epoxy

Richard Warner Aviation (Anderson) W-1 Super Kingfisher amphibian

First production Wheeler Express four-seat homebuilt

Prototype White Lightning Aircraft White Lightning four-seat composites homebuilts

WindRyder Engineering Hurricane single-seat composites autogyro

front and rear spars and ribs, all pre-cast in the lower glassfibre/epoxy skin. Fowler flaps. Glassfibre/epoxy fuselage moulded in upper and lower halves. Tail unit has spars and ribs of fin and tailplane pre-cast into one skin of each. Retractable tricycle landing gear. Options include electrical kit and engine installation kit.

POWER PLANT: Prototype has 156.6 kW (210 hp) Teledyne Continental IO-360 CB. Usable fuel capacity 257 litres (68 US gallons; 56.6 Imp gallons).

DIMENSIONS, EXTERNAL:
Wing span	8.43 m (27 ft 8 in)
Length overall	7.11 m (23 ft 4 in)
Height overall	2.18 m (7 ft 2 in)
Propeller diameter	1.85 m (6 ft 1 in)

AREA:
Wings, gross	8.27 m² (89.0 sq ft)

WEIGHTS:
Weight empty	635 kg (1,400 lb)
Max baggage capacity	154 kg (340 lb)
Max T-O weight	1,088 kg (2,400 lb)

PERFORMANCE (at max T-O weight):
Max level speed at S/L	243 knots (450 km/h; 280 mph)
Econ cruising speed at 3,350 m (11,000 ft)	221 knots (410 km/h; 255 mph)
Stalling speed: flaps up	78 knots (145 km/h; 90 mph)
flaps down	58 knots (108 km/h; 67 mph)
Max rate of climb at S/L	579 m (1,900 ft)/min
Service ceiling	7,010 m (23,000 ft)
T-O run, full flap	381 m (1,250 ft)
Landing run	397 m (1,300 ft)
Range with max fuel	1,389 nm (2,575 km; 1,600 miles)
Endurance	6 h 10 min
g limits:	+6/−4 aerobatic
	+4.4/−2 utility

WINDRYDER
WINDRYDER ENGINEERING INC
555 Alter Street, Unit 15, Broomfield, Colorado 80020
Telephone: 1 (303) 466 6669
Fax: 1 (303) 469 2801
PRESIDENT: Jim McCutchen

WINDRYDER ENGINEERING HURRICANE
The first of two prototype Hurricane autogyros flew initially in August 1985. Kits are available. Construction takes about 100 working hours.

The Hurricane was demonstrated to the US Army, in Florida, in April 1987. Possible non-sport uses include surveillance, liaison and re-supply.

TYPE: Single-seat autogyro.

ROTOR SYSTEM: Skywheels two-blade rotor of 8H12 section, constructed of unwoven bi-directional S-glass in a vinylester matrix, with an extruded aluminium alloy spar bonded inside the leading-edge. Unwoven bi-directional S-glass pylon, manufactured in two halves, with tubular D section forward half carrying most loads. 'Tilt spindle' rotor head. Pre-rotator.

AIRFRAME: Monocoque fuselage of pre-moulded inner and outer shells, factory bonded, using bi-directional unwoven S-glass and graphite in a polyester resin matrix, completed by installation of composite seat/fuel tank. Dihedral tailplane, three fins and large central rudder. Tail surfaces have NACA 0012 section. Non-retractable tricycle landing gear.

POWER PLANT: One 47.7 kW (64 hp) Rotax 532. Optional 74.5 kW (100 hp) Teledyne Continental O-200. Fuel capacity in seat tank 66 litres (17.5 US gallons; 14.6 Imp gallons). Optional 82 kW (110 hp) Hirth F30 engine.

DIMENSIONS, EXTERNAL:
Rotor diameter	8.84 m (29 ft 0 in)
Length overall (excl rotor)	3.38 m (11 ft 1 in)
Height overall	2.57 m (8 ft 5 in)
Propeller diameter	1.68 m (5 ft 6 in)

AREA:
Rotor disc	61.3 m² (660.0 sq ft)

WEIGHTS:
Weight empty	204 kg (450 lb)
Max payload	159 kg (350 lb)
Max T-O weight	363 kg (800 lb)

PERFORMANCE:
Max level speed at S/L	100 knots (185 km/h; 115 mph)
Econ cruising speed at S/L	69 knots (129 km/h; 80 mph)
Max rate of climb at S/L	305 m (1,000 ft)/min
Service ceiling	3,050 m (10,000 ft)
T-O run	46 m (150 ft)
Landing run	15 m (50 ft)
Range	173 nm (322 km; 200 miles)
Endurance	2 h
g limit	+3

WINDRYDER ENGINEERING HURRICANE 100
This is a high performance version of the Hurricane, with an 83.5 kW (112 hp) Arrow engine. The airframe is similar, except that carbonfibre replaces S-glass for the rotor and fuselage skins, and that the main landing gear units use compression struts and the nosewheel has a trailing arm for suspension. Standard fuel capacity is 64.4 litres (17 US gallons; 20.4 Imp gallons). Optional cargo pod.

DIMENSIONS, EXTERNAL:
Rotor diameter	8.84 m (29 ft 0 in)
Length overall (excl rotor)	3.56 m (11 ft 8 in)
Height overall	2.82 m (9 ft 3 in)
Propeller diameter	1.68 m (5 ft 6 in)

AREA:
Rotor disc	61.3 m² (660.0 sq ft)

WEIGHTS:
Weight empty	227 kg (500 lb)
Max T-O weight	499 kg (1,100 lb)

PERFORMANCE:
Max level speed	96 knots (177 km/h; 110 mph)
Econ cruising speed	69 knots (129 km/h; 80 mph)
Max rate of climb at S/L	305 m (1,000 ft)/min
Service ceiling	3,660 m (12,000 ft)
T-O run	31 m (100 ft)
Landing run	none
Range	173 nm (322 km; 200 miles)
Endurance	2 h
g limit	+3

WITTMAN
S. J. WITTMAN
7200 South-East 85th Lane, Ocala, Florida 32672

WITTMAN TAILWIND MODEL W-8
The prototype W-8 was built in 1952-53. Sets of plans and prefabricated components are available, and more than 350 Tailwinds have flown. Some Tailwinds have been built with tricycle landing gear, retractable mainwheels and other design changes.

TYPE: Side by side two-seat cabin homebuilt.

AIRFRAME: Wing section is a combination of NACA 4309

(upper surface) and NACA 0006 (lower surface). Wooden wing structure with plywood and fabric covering. Ailerons, flaps and tail unit of steel and stainless steel construction. Steel tube fuselage, fabric covered. Non-retractable tailwheel landing gear standard.

POWER PLANT: Normally one 67 kW (90 hp) Teledyne Continental C90-12F. Alternative engines include the 63.5 kW (85 hp) Teledyne Continental C85, 74.5 kW (100 hp) Teledyne Continental O-200, 86 kW (115 hp) Textron Lycoming O-235 and 104.5 kW (140 hp) Textron Lycoming O-290. Fuel capacity 94.5-132.5 litres (25-35 US gallons; 20.8-29.1 Imp gallons).

DIMENSIONS. EXTERNAL:
Wing span	6.86 m (22 ft 6 in)
Length overall	5.87 m (19 ft 3 in)
Height overall	1.73 m (5 ft 8 in)
Propeller diameter	1.63 m (5 ft 4 in)

AREA:
Wings, gross	8.36 m² (90.0 sq ft)

WEIGHTS (74.5 kW; 100 hp Teledyne Continental O-200 engine):
Weight empty	318 kg (700 lb)
Baggage capacity	27 kg (60 lb)
Max T-O weight	590 kg (1,300 lb)

PERFORMANCE (74.5 kW; 100 hp Teledyne Continental O-200 engine at max T-O weight):
Max level speed at S/L	143 knots (265 km/h; 165 mph)
Econ cruising speed	113 knots (209 km/h; 130 mph)
Landing speed:	
flaps up	57 knots (105 km/h; 65 mph)
flaps down	48 knots (89 km/h; 55 mph)
Max rate of climb at S/L	275 m (900 ft)/min
Service ceiling	more than 4,875 m (16,000 ft)
T-O run	245 m (800 ft)
Landing run	183 m (600 ft)

Range with max payload at 3,050 m (10,000 ft), no reserves:
at 139 knots (257 km/h; 160 mph)	
	521 nm (965 km; 600 miles)
at 122 knots (225 km/h; 140 mph)	
	607 nm (1,125 km; 700 miles)

WITTMAN TAILWIND MODEL W-10

Revisions to the Tailwind plans (available as a separate package) produced a version known as the Model W-10. This is basically a W-8 with a 112 kW (150 hp) Textron Lycoming O-320, 108 kW (145 hp) Teledyne Continental, or aluminium block Oldsmobile F85 or Buick V-8 engine. Fuel capacity is 114 litres (30 US gallons; 25 Imp gallons). Airframe improvements include a new and more efficient wingtip design and round spring steel landing gear legs with wood and fabric fairings. Empty and max T-O weights of this version, with Teledyne Continental O-300 engine, are 413 kg (910 lb) and 680 kg (1,500 lb) respectively.

PERFORMANCE (Teledyne Continental O-300 engine):
Max level speed at S/L	182 knots (338 km/h; 210 mph)
Econ cruising speed	156 knots (290 km/h; 180 mph)
Stalling speed: flaps up	38 knots (70 km/h; 43 mph)
flaps down	35 knots (65 km/h; 40 mph)
Service ceiling	4,875 m (16,000 ft)
T-O run	366 m (1,200 ft)

WOLF
DONALD S. WOLF
17 Chestnut Street, Huntington, New York 11743
Telephone: 1 (516) 427 9678

Details of the W-11 Boredom Fighter, and an illustration, can be found in the 1988-89 *Jane's*. Plans remain available.

WOOD WING
WOOD WING SPECIALTY
PO Box 1258, Tehachapi, California 93561

PLUMB CJ-3D CRACKER JACK
The prototype Cracker Jack made its first flight on 6 October 1982. In addition to plans, Wood Wing Specialty offers four prefabricated components, comprising a glass-fibre nose cowling, wingtips, windscreen and propeller.

TYPE: Single-seat homebuilt.

AIRFRAME: Fabric covered all-wood airframe structure, except for aluminium alloy tubing used for elevator and rudder curves. Wing section NACA 4413. Glassfibre nose cowling. Non-retractable tailwheel landing gear. Optional cockpit side windows.

POWER PLANT: One 28.3 kW (38 hp) Aero-DAF 95 950 cc converted motorcar engine. Main fuel tank capacity 17 litres (4.5 US gallons; 3.7 Imp gallons), plus header tank of 3.8 litres (1 US gallon; 0.83 Imp gallon) capacity. Optional half-Volkswagen converted motorcar engine (950-1,000 cc).

DIMENSIONS. EXTERNAL:
Wing span	8.53 m (28 ft 0 in)
Length overall	5.33 m (17 ft 6 in)
Propeller diameter	1.32 m (4 ft 4 in)

AREA:
Wings, gross	9.29 m² (100.0 sq ft)

WEIGHTS:
Weight empty	159 kg (350 lb)
Recommended max pilot weight	91 kg (200 lb)
Baggage capacity	9 kg (20 lb)
Max T-O weight	272 kg (600 lb)

PERFORMANCE:
Max level speed at S/L	74 knots (137 km/h; 85 mph)
Max and econ cruising speed at S/L	
	65 knots (121 km/h; 75 mph)
Stalling speed	34 knots (63 km/h; 39 mph)
Max rate of climb at S/L	244 m (800 ft)/min
Service ceiling	3,050 m (10,000 ft)
T-O and landing run	91 m (300 ft)
Range	173 nm (321 km; 200 miles)
Endurance	2 h 42 min
g limits	+6/-4

Wood Wing Specialty CJ-3D Cracker Jack

Wittman Tailwind W-10 (inverted 93 kW; 125 hp 3,500 cc Oldsmobile F85 engine)

MICROLIGHTS

Company & Address	Model	Wing span/ Rotor diameter m/ft in	Length overall m/ft in	Airframe F = flexwing R = rigid wing B = braced S = single surface fabric D = double surface fabric C = conventional fuselage O = open fuselage structure P = fuselage pod	Power plant	Weight empty kg/lb	Pilot weight range kg/lb	Max speed knots (km/h; mph)	Max range or endurance nm (km; miles)	Accom	Forms/Remarks K = kits P = plans A = assembled
ARGENTINA Pampa's Bull SA San Martin 969, piso 1°, 1004 Buenos Aires	AgStar, AviaStar and FlightStar	9.14/ 30-0 AgStar	5.02/ 16-5½ AgStar	R, B, D, P	FlightStar: one 30 kW (40 hp) Rotax 447. AgStar and AviaStar: 38.8 kW (52 hp) Rotax 503	n.k.	n.k.	78 (144; 89) AgStar	n.k.	Pilot in FlightStar and AgStar. Two seats in AviaStar	AgStar is agricultural model of FlightStar, with 106 litre (28 US gallon; 23.3 Imp gallon) chemical hopper and Micron X ultra low volume spray system.
AUSTRALIA Blue Max Ultralight PO Box 42, Nagambie, Victoria 3608	Blue Max	8.53/ 28-0	5.49/ 18-0	R, B, D, O, P	One 33.6 kW (45 hp) Rotax 447 or 21 kW (28 hp) König 570	115/254	95/210 max	59 (109; 68) with Rotax	2 h with Rotax	Pilot	A. Hirth engine fitted to one aircraft in early 1990.
Eastwood Aircraft Pty Ltd Stevens Road, PO Box 445 Goolwa, Currency Creek, South Australia 5214	Tyro Mk 2	8.90/ 29-2	5.33/ 17-6	R, B, D, O, P	One 20 kW (27 hp) Rotax 277 or 32 kW (43 hp) Rotax 447	113/250 with Rotax 277	54.4-91/ 120-200	69 (129; 80)	130 (241; 150)	Pilot	Materials K, P. Conforms to CAO 95-10. 105 sold by December 1989.
Gareth J. Kimberley 211 Fowler Road, Illawong, New South Wales 2234	Sky-Rider	9.86/ 32-4	5.74/ 18-10 without elevator trim tab	R, B, S, O	One 13.4 kW (18 hp) 250 cc Fuji Robin or 8.9 kW (12 hp) McCulloch MC 101 or Rotax	95/210	91/200 max	43 (80; 50)	35 (64; 40)	Pilot	P. Conforms to CAO 95-10 and FAR Pt 103.
Robert Labahan 6 Victoria Street, Seville, Victoria 3139	Hitchiker	8.05/ 26-5	4.80/ 15-9	R, B, O and optional P	One 20 kW (27 hp) Rotax 277	100/220	n.k.	61 (113; 70)	156 (290; 180)	Pilot	A. Conforms to CAO 95-10.
Ligeti Aeronautical Pty Ltd 44 Wirraway Road, Essendon Airport 3041, Victoria 3104	Stratos	5.36/ 17-7	2.49/ 8-2	R, D, P	Prototype: one 21 kW (28 hp) König SD 570. Optional engines up to 37.3 kW (50 hp)	78/172	55-83/ 121-183	108 (200; 124)	388 (720; 447)	Pilot	Conforms to CAO 95-10. All-composites construction. Joined tandem wing configuration. Business offered for sale or partnership.
Graham J. Percy PO Box 135, 50 Baxter-Tooradin Road, Pearcedale, Victoria 3912	Maya	8.48/ 27-10	5.33/ 17-6	R, B, D, C	One 21 kW (28 hp) König SD 570 or other two-stroke engine	112.5/248	91/200 max	55 (101; 63)	n.k.	Pilot	P. Conforms to CAO 95-10.
Skywise Ultraflight Pty Ltd PO Box 226, Hornsby, New South Wales 2077	Sadler Vampire SV-2	7.00/ 22-11½	5.14/ 16-10½	R, D, P	One 30.6 kW (41 hp) Rotax 447	166.5/367	91/200	88 (163; 101) IAS	n.k.	Pilot	Manufactured in Australia to US design. Fully enclosed pod and twin boom aircraft. New Skywise Vampire SV-200 two-seat aircraft was expected to enter production in 1989.
SV Aircraft Pty Ltd PO Box 85, Nagambie, Victoria 3608	SV 11B Farmate	8.00/ 26-3	5.30/ 17-4¾	R, B, D, P	One 20 kW (27 hp) Rotax 277	150/331	75-95/ 165-209	80 (148; 92)	180 (333; 207)	Pilot	A. Glassfibre skins. No news received of SV 14 two-seat microlight.

Company & Address	Model	Wing span/ Rotor diameter m/ft in	Length overall m/ft in	Airframe F = flexwing R = rigid wing B = braced S = single surface fabric D = double surface fabric C = conventional fuselage O = open fuselage structure P = fuselage pod	Power plant	Weight empty kg/lb	Pilot weight range kg/lb	Max speed knots (km/h; mph)	Max range or endurance nm (km; miles	Accom	Forms/Remarks K = kits P = plans A = assembled
AUSTRALIA *Contd.*											
Thruster Aircraft (Australia) Pty Ltd 458 The Boulevarde, Kirrawee, New South Wales 2232	T300	9.60/ 31-6	5.50/ 18-0	R, B, D, O, P	One 43.25 kW (58 hp) Rotax 503. Optional 47.7 kW (64 hp) Rotax 532	180/396	50-100/ 110-220	70 (130; 81)	195 (362; 226)	Two seats	K, A. T300 is current designation of TST microlight. Conforms to CAO 95-25, CASO 19 and BCAR Section S.
Thruster Aircraft (Australia) Pty Ltd	T500	As for T300	As for T300	R, B, D, C	As for T300	200/441	As for T300	As for T300	270 (500; 310)	Two seats	Version of T300 with enclosed rear fuselage, 55 litre (14.5 US gallon; 12 Imp gallon) fuel tank, electric starting and full instrument package.
Ron Wheeler Aircraft (Sales) Pty Ltd 152 Bellevue Parade, Carlton, New South Wales 2218	Scout Mk III	8.69/ 28-6 nominal	5.20/ 17-0¾	R, B, O	Mk III RN: one 13.4 kW (18 hp) Fuji Robin EC 25. Mk III RX: one 26 kW (35 hp) Rotax 337	Mk III RN: 68/150 Mk III RX: 82/181	79/175 max	57 (105; 65)	48 (90; 56)	Pilot	A. Several hundred Scouts sold in Mk I, II and III forms.
Scott Winton c/o J & P Heard, North Creek Road, Ballina, New South Wales 2478	Sapphire	8.84/ 29-0	4.93/ 16-2	R, D, P	Sapphire 10: one 26 kW (35 hp) Rotax 377. Sapphire LSA: one 30 kW (40 hp) Rotax 447	Sapphire 10: 104/230 Sapphire LSA: 141/310	n.k.	80 (148; 92)	n.k.	Pilot	Sapphire 10: K, A. Sapphire LSA: A.
BELGIUM											
Dynali SA 24 rue A. Delporte, 1050 Brussels	Chickinox	9.50/ 31-2	5.00/ 16-5	Semi-rigid, B, S, O, P	One 33.6 kW (45 hp) Rotax	155/342	n.k.	49 (90; 56) cruising	n.k.	Two seats	Side by side or tandem seating. Indian Air Force to receive 25 for training.
Epervier Aviation SA Rue Delfosse, 1 bis, 1400 Nivelles	Epervier	11.15/ 36-7	6.82/ 22-4½	R, B, D, C	One 37 kW (50 hp) Rotax 503-2V Optional Rotax 582 and 912, or Limbach SL 1700 engines	175/386	n.k.	189/ (165; 103)	n.k.	Two seats	A. Side by side cabin monoplane of conventional layout. Construction of carbonfibre/ glassfibre/Nomex honeycomb/epoxy. Microlight model initially in production.
Euronef SA Chaussée de Grammont 79-B7860, Lessines	ATTL-1	12.11/ 59-8¾	6.45/ 21-2	R, B, D, C	One 38.8 kW (52 hp) Rotax	175/386	n.k.	65 (120; 75)	n.k.	Two seats	CAD designed. Constructed of carbonfibre/glassfibre/ Kevlar. Suited to agricultural and other roles. Can use electronic flight guidance display.
SCWAL SA 77 Avenue Brugmann, 1060 Brussels	Falcon B.1	10.97/ 36-0	5.30/ 17-4¾	R, B, D, P	One 20 kW (27 hp) Rotax 277 or 26 kW (35 hp) Rotax 377. Optionally other Rotax or Göbler-Hirth	113/249	40-100/ 88-222	63 (116; 72)	108 (200; 124) standard fuel	Pilot	A.
SCWAL SA	Falcon B.2	10.97/ 36-0	5.30/ 17-4¾	R, B, D, P	One 34.3 kW (46 hp) Rotax 503	174/384	100-200/ 220-441 crew	80 (148; 92)	270 (500; 310) standard fuel	Two seats	A. First production aircraft built in 1989.

Company & Address	Model	Wing span/ Rotor diameter m/ft in	Length overall m/ft in	Airframe F = flexwing R = rigid wing B = braced S = single surface fabric D = double surface fabric C = conventional fuselage O = open fuselage structure P = fuselage pod	Power plant	Weight empty kg/lb	Pilot weight range kg/lb	Max speed knots (km/h; mph)	Max range or endurance nm (km; miles)	Accom	Forms/Remarks K = kits P = plans A = assembled
CANADA Airtech Canada PO Box 415, Peterborough Municipal Airport, Peterborough, Ontario K9J 6Z3	Skylark	10.97/ 36-0	5.49/ 18-0	R, B, D, O, P	One 21 kW (28 hp) König	129/284	n.k.	51 (95; 59)	n.k.	Pilot	K, A. Conforms to FAR Pt 23.
Aces High Light Aircraft RR1, London, Ontario	Cuby I	9.75/ 32-0	n.k.	R, B, D, C	One 20 kW (27 hp) Rotax 277	113/250	n.k.	82 (153; 95)	n.k.	Pilot	K.
Aces High Light Aircraft	Cuby II	10.21/ 33-6	n.k.	R, B, D, C	One 35.8 kW (48 hp) Rotax 503	163/360	n.k.	87 (161; 100)	n.k.	Two seats	K.
Beaver RX Enterprises Ltd 3-9531 192nd Street, Surrey, British Columbia V3T 4W2	RX-35 and RX-35 Floater	9.45/ 31-0	5.38/ 17-8	R, B, D, O, P	One 26 kW (35 hp) Rotax 377	RX-35: 121.5/ 268 Floater: 149/328	RX-35: 59-118/ 130-260 Floater: 59-102/ 130-225	RX-35: 56 (103; 64) Floater: 52 (97; 60)	RX-35: 78 (145; 90) Floater: 69 (128; 80)	Pilot	K. Conform to BCAR Section S and JAR 22. Floater has amphibious landing gear. Optional full enclosure.
Beaver RX Enterprises Ltd	RX-550, RX-550 Floater and RX-550SP	10.67/ 35-0	6.30/ 20-8	R, B, D, O, P	RX-550: one 35.8 kW (48 hp) Rotax 503. Floater and RX-550SP: one 47.7 kW (64 hp) Rotax 532	179/395	54-104/ 120-130	69 (129; 80)	156 (290; 180) standard fuel	Two seats	K, A. Conform to BCAR Section S and JAR 22. Optional full enclosure.
Beaver RX Enterprises Ltd	RX-650	9.45/ 31-0	6.63/ 21-9	R, B, D, P	One 35.8 kW (48 hp) Rotax 503 or 47.7 kW (64 hp) Rotax 532 standard; 67 kW (90 hp) Norton or Rotax 912 optional	150/330 estimated	50-113/ 110-250	104 (193; 120) design Vd	217 (402; 250)	Two seats	Conforms to BCAR Section S and JAR 22. Suitable for training, cropspraying and other roles. Optional amphibious floats. Tandem seats in enclosed cabin pod.
Birdman Enterprises 1986 Ltd, Box 609, 702 12th Avenue, Nisku, Alberta T0C 2G0.	Chinook 1-S	10.67/ 35-0	5.34/ 17-6	R, B, P	One 20 kW (27 hp) Rotax 277 or 26.8 kW (36 hp) Rotax 377	113/250	50-113/ 110-250	52 (97; 60)	130-173 (241-321; 150-200)	Pilot	K.
Birdman Enterprises 1986 Ltd	Chinook 2-S	11.28/ 37-0	5.46/ 17-11	R, B, P	One 30 kW (40 hp) Rotax 447 or 35 kW (47 hp) Rotax 503	n.k.	n.k.	n.k.	n.k.	Two seats	K.
Circa Reproductions (see main Sport section)	Nieuport 11										
Falconar Aviation 19 Airport Road, Edmonton, Alberta T5G 0W7	HM-290E Flying Flea	6.10/ 20-0	n.k.	R, B, D, C	One 22.4 kW (30 hp) Hirth	109/240	n.k.	55 (101; 63)	n.k.	Pilot	K.
Kestrel Sport Aviation (see main Sport section)	Hawk and Kit Hawk										

Company & Address	Model	Wing span/ Rotor diameter m/ft in	Length overall m/ft in	Airframe F = flexwing R = rigid wing B = braced S = single surface fabric D = double surface fabric C = conventional fuselage O = open fuselage structure P = fuselage pod	Power plant	Weight empty kg/lb	Pilot weight range kg/lb	Max speed knots (km/h; mph)	Max range or endurance nm (km; miles)	Accom	Forms/Remarks K = kits P = plans A = assembled
CANADA *Contd.*											
Macair Industries Inc (see main Sport section)	Merlin										
Magal Holdings Ltd 19 Pensville Road South East, Calgary, Alberta T2A 4K3 (see 1989-90 *Jane's*)	Cuby I and II										
Snowbird Aviation 12624-124 Street, Edmonton, Alberta T5L 0N7	Bushmaster I Mk 2	10.21/ 33-6	n.k.	R, B, D, C	One 30 kW (40 hp) Rotax 447	115/253	n.k.	69 (129; 80)	n.k.	Pilot	K.
Thor Air (see 1988-89 edition)	Thor T-1, T-2 and Juno										
CHINA											
Beijing University of Aeronautics & Astronautics PO Box 85, 37 Xue Yuan Road, Haidian District, Beijing 100083	Mifeng-2 (Bee-2)	10.00/ 32-9¾	5.05/ 16-7	R, B, S, P	One 19.4 kW (26 hp)	100/220	65-80/ 143-176	40 (75; 47)	97 (180; 112)	Pilot	K, A.
Beijing University of Aeronautics & Astronautics	Mifeng-3 (Bee-3)	10.00/ 32-9¾	6.14/ 20-1¾	R, B, S, P	One 31.3 kW (42 hp) Rotax 447	150/331	65-80/ 143-176	51 (95; 59)	88 (163; 101)	Two seats or pilot and 70-100 kg (154-220 lb) payload	K, A. Sesquiplane development of Mifeng-2; first flight July 1983. Conforms to BCAR Section S-CAP 482. Used for agricultural, touring, training, forest protection and photography roles.
Beijing University of Aeronautics & Astronautics	Mifeng-3C (Bee-3C)	8.60/ 28-2½	6.10/ 20-0¼	R, B, S, P	One 31.3 kW (42 hp) Rotax 447	150/331	n.k.	65 (120; 75)	296 (550; 341)	Two seats	Derived from the Mifeng-3, but with increased speed, higher g limit, more flexibility and easier to assemble. Three flew in formation over a distance of 2,750 nm (5,100 km; 3,170 miles).
Beijing University of Aeronautics & Astronautics	Mifeng-4 and 4A (Bee-4 and 4A)	Mifeng-4: 10.44/ 34-3	6.15/ 20-2¼	R, B, D, P	One 31.3 kW (42 hp) Rotax 447	180/397	65-80/ 143-176	Mifeng-4: 54 (100; 62)	Mifeng-4: 86 (159; 99)	Two seats	K, A. Mifeng-4A has shorter wing span.
Beijing University of Aeronautics & Astronautics	Mifeng-5 (Bee-5)	n.k.	n.k.	R, B, D	n.k.	n.k.	n.k.	n.k.	n.k.	Three seats or pilot and 140 kg (309 lb) payload	First flown in September 1985, as light multi-purpose aircraft.
Shijiazhuang Aircraft Plant PO Box 164, Shijiazhuang, Hebei	W-5 and W-5A Qingting (Dragonfly)	10.55/ 34-7½	5.36/ 17-7	R, B, O. W-5A has P	One 22.4 kW (30 hp) engine	W-5: 123/271 W-5A: 135/298	n.k.	W-5: 47 (88; 54) W-5A: 42 (77; 48)	W-5: 56 (104; 64); W-5A: 46 (86; 53)	W-5: Pilot. W-5A: Two seats	W-5 has small nose fairing. W-5A has side by side seats.
Shijiazhuang Aircraft Plant	W-5B Qingting (Dragonfly)	10.62/ 34-10	5.75/ 18-10½	R, B, O, P	One 33.6 kW (45 hp) Rotax 447	150/331	n.k.	54 (100; 62)	65 (120; 74)	Two seats	Seating in tandem.

Company & Address	Model	Wing span/ Rotor diameter m/ft in	Length overall m/ft in	Airframe F = flexwing R = rigid wing B = braced S = single surface fabric D = double surface fabric C = conventional fuselage O = open fuselage structure P = fuselage pod	Power plant	Weight empty kg/lb	Pilot weight range kg/lb	Max speed knots (km/h; mph)	Max range or endurance nm (km; miles)	Accom	Forms/Remarks K = kits P = plans A = assembled
CZECHOSLOVAKIA —	SP-1 Spunt	10.60/ 34-9¼	5.68/ 18-7¾	F, B, D, P	One 22 kW (29.5 hp) Trabant	175/386	n.k.	48 (90; 56)	n.k.	Pilot	High wing monoplane, with pod (open) and boom fuselage. Designed and built by a team of enthusiasts.
Rudy Letov Beranovych 65, 19902 Prague 9, Letnany	LK-2 Sluka	9.20/ 30-2¼	5.10/ 16-8¾	Semi-rigid, B, D, P	One 26 kW (35 hp) Rotax 447	150/331	55-90/ 121.5-198	54 (100; 62)	81 (150; 193)	Pilot	First factory-built microlight from Czechoslovakia. Suited for sport and working roles. Optional P65/66 or Rotax 503-2V engines. Ten production aircraft built by January 1990.
FRANCE Aermas (Automobiles Martini SA) ZI, 58470 Magny-Cours	Aermas 386	11.16/ 36-7½	7.20/ 23-7½	R, B, D, P	One 38 kW (51 hp) Rotax 462	174/384	n.k.	65 (120; 75) cruising	n.k.	Two seats	Conforms to FAR Pt 23, Normal category.
Aéronautic 2000 52 rue Galande, 75005 Paris	Baroudeur	10.90/ 35-9¼	5.60/ 18-4½	R, B, D, P	One 38 kW (51 hp) Rotax 462 or 37.3 kW (50 hp) Fuji Robin	175/385	n.k.	54 (100; 62)	54-151 (100-280; 62-174)	Two seats	20 or 40 litre fuel tank. Can be armed with 89 mm rocket launchers in military form.
Air Creation Aérodrome de Lanas, 07200 Aubenas	Fun GT 447	10.00/ 32-9¾	2.70/ 8-10¼	F, B, D (30%), O. Optional P	One 31.3 kW (42 hp) Rotax 447	137/302	40-120/ 88-264 with Quartz 18 flexwing	46 (85; 53)	n.k.	Two seats	A. Many hundreds of Fun GT 447/Quartz/ SX GT two-seaters sold (see entries below), combining two-seat Safari GT BI trikes with various Rotax engines and Fun 18, Quartz 18 and SX 16 flexwings. Optional 38 litre fuel tank.
Air Creation	Quartz GT 503	10.00/ 32-9¾	2.70/ 8-10¼	F, B, D (80%), O. Optional P	One 38.8 kW (52 hp) Rotax 503	142/313	As above	57 (105; 65)	n.k.	Two seats	A. More than 600 sold.
Air Creation	Quartz GT 462	10.00/ 32-9¾	2.70/ 8-10¼	F, B, D (80%), O. Optional P	One 38.8 kW (52 hp) Rotax 462	142/313	As above	57 (105; 65)	n.k.	Two seats	A.
Air Creation	SX GT 462 and SX GT 503	10.00/ 32-9¾	2.70/ 8-10¼	F, B, D (90%), O. Optional P	SX GT 462: one 38.8 kW (52 hp) Rotax 462. SX GT 503: one Rotax 503	145/320	As above	65 (120; 75)	n.k.	Two seats	A. SX GT 462 is quiet version with low fuel consumption.
Air Creation	SX Racer and Fun Racer	10.00/ 32-9¾	2.50/ 8-2½	F, B, D, O. Optional P	One 31.3 kW (42 hp) Rotax 447	110/242 with SX 12 flexwing	50-120/ 110-265 with SX 12 flexwing	49 (90; 56) Fun Racer. 65 (120; 75) SX Racer	243 (450; 279) with SX 12 flexwing	Pilot	A. Combines Racer trikes with Fun 14 and SX 12 flexwings. Fun Racer 40% double surface. Optional 38 litre fuel tank.
Air International Service (A.I.R's SA) 26 rue des Roses, 75018 Paris	Allegro	9.00/ 29-6¼	5.50/ 18-0½	R, B, D, O, P	One 26 kW (35 hp) Rotax 377 or 38 kW (51 hp) Rotax	125/276	n.k.	75 (140; 87)	1 h 45 min	Pilot	A.
Air International Service (A.I.R's SA)	Maestro	10.50/ 34-5½	5.50/ 18-0½	R, B, D, O, P	One 34 kW (45.6 hp) Rotax 503. Optional 38 kW (51 hp) Rotax or 47 kW (63 hp) Rotax 532	167/368	n.k.	59 (110; 68)	1 h 30 min	Two seats	A. Agricultural version uses Rotax 532 engine.

Company & Address	Model	Wing span/ Rotor diameter m/ft in	Length overall m/ft in	Airframe F = flexwing R = rigid wing B = braced S = single surface fabric D = double surface fabric C = conventional fuselage O = open fuselage structure P = fuselage pod	Power plant	Weight empty kg/lb	Pilot weight range kg/lb	Max speed knots (km/h; mph)	Max range or endurance nm (km; miles	Accom	Forms/Remarks K = kits P = plans A = assembled
FRANCE *Contd.*											
ASL Club d'Avions Supers Légers du Cher 45 rue Guilbeau, 18000 Bourbes	ASL 18 La Guêpe	7.86/ 25-9½	6.24/ 20-5¾	R, B, D, C	One 37.3 kW (50 hp) 1,600 cc converted Volkswagen motorcar engine	175/386	50-90/ 110-198	76 (140; 87)	135 (250; 155)	Two seats	P. Biplane with pivoting lower wings for roll control. Can also be built as an Experimental homebuilt.
Aviasud Engineering SA (see main Sport section)	Sirocco and Mistral										
Bernard Broc Enterprise Route de Freycenet, Borne, 43350 St Paulien	Papillon	10.00/ 32-9¾	2.90/ 9-6¼	R, B, D, P	Two 17.9 kW (24 hp) König radials	170/375	n.k.	65 (120; 75) max cruising	323 (600; 372)	Pilot	Tandem wing aircraft with aluminium alloy wings (forward wings sweptback) and glassfibre fuselage pod.
SA Centrair Aérodrome Le Blanc, BP 44, 36300 Le Blanc (see main Sport section)	Parafan										
Yves Chasle 8 Lotissement-Concorde, Odos, 65310 Laloubére	YC-100/ 101/110/ 111 Hirondelle (Swallow)	8.30/ 27-2¾ for YC-100	5.43/ 17-9¾	R, B, D, C	One 16.4 kW (22 hp) JPX PUL 425/503 or 18 kW (24 hp) König SC 430 in YC-100	110/243 for YC-100	n.k.	70 (130; 80) for YC-100	n.k.	Pilot	P. YC-101 and YC-111 have 9.35 m (30 ft 8½ in) wing spans, and YC-110 has 8.25 m (27 ft 0¾ in) span. All higher powered models.
Ets D. Lascaud 41 rue de Crussol, 07500 Granges-les-Valence	Bifly	6.19/ 20-3¾	3.25/ 10-8	R, D, C	One 15 kW (20 hp) J-C-V 274 cc	65/143	n.k.	59 (110; 68)	89 (165; 102)	Pilot	K, A. Tandem wings, with rudder-only tail unit.
Société d'Exploitation des Aéronefs Henri Mignet Logis des Pierrières, Saint-Romain de Benêt, 17600 Saujon	HM-1000 Balerit	7.30/ 23-11½	5.00/ 16-5	R, B, D, O, P	One 34.3 kW (46 hp) Rotax 503 or 44.7 kW (60 hp) Rotax 532	175/386 with Rotax 503	110/ 242	57 (105; 65) with Rotax 503	215 (400; 248)	Two seats	Tandem wings. Pivoting forward wing and rudder control. Cannot spin or stall. Side by side seating. Suited to sport and working roles.
Ets Nion Aéronautiques RN 85, Châteauvieux, 05130 Tallard	Sirius	12.00/ 39-4½	5.90/ 19-4¼	R, B, D, P	One 13.4 kW (18 hp) JPX 425 or 17.9 kW (24 hp) König 430	135/298	100/220 max	62 (115; 71) with König engine	75.5 (140; 87)	Pilot	K, P, A. Microlight pod and boom motor glider.
GERMANY, WEST											
Dallach Flugzeuge GmbH Stauferstrasse 10, 7076 Wissgoldingen	Sunrise II	13.10/ 42-11¾	5.30/ 17-4¾	R, C	One 30 kW (40 hp) KKHD	150/330	n.k.	81 (150; 93)	143 (266; 165)	Pilot or two seats	K, A. Conventional low-wing monoplane.
Otto and Peter Funk Im Steigert 5, 6737 Böhl-Iggelheim	FK 9	11.80/ 38-8½	6.00/ 19-8¼	R, B, C	One 28.3 kW (38 hp) Rotax 462	150/330	n.k.	70 (130; 81) cruising	442 (820; 509)	Two seats	Production model will have smaller wing span and more engine power.
HFL-Flugzeug-bau GmbH Hohenhorststrasse 1B, 2120 Lüneburg	Stratos 300	12.60/ 41-4	6.30/ 20-8	R, D, P	One 17.9 kW (24 hp) König SC 430	150/330	n.k.	70 (130; 81)	216 (400; 248)	Pilot	Pod and twin boom motor glider.

Company & Address	Model	Wing span/ Rotor diameter m/ft in	Length overall m/ft in	Airframe F = flexwing R = rigid wing B = braced S = single surface fabric D = double surface fabric C = conventional fuselage O = open fuselage structure P = fuselage pod	Power plant	Weight empty kg/lb	Pilot weight range kg/lb	Max speed knots (km/h; mph)	Max range or endurance nm (km; miles)	Accom	Forms/Remarks K = kits P = plans A = assembled
Ikarus Deutschland Comco GmbH Tannenweg 20, 7042 Aidlingen/Württ	C22	10.40/ 34-1½	6.25/ 20-6	R, B, D, O, P	One 28.3 kW (38 hp) Rotax 462. Optional 38.8 kW (52 hp) Rotax or 30 kW (40 hp) Citroën Visa	170/374	65-200/ 143-441	59 (110; 68) max cruising	about 189 (350; 217)	Two seats	A. Side by side two-seat version of former Fox-D. High tailboom. 398 sold by January 1990.
Ikarus Deutschland Comco GmbH	C22HP	10.40/ 34-1½	6.40/ 21-0	R, B, D, C	One 28.3 kW (38 hp) Rotax 447, 38.8 kW (52 hp) Rotax 462 or 30 kW (40 hp) Citroën Visa	185/408	65-185/ 143-408	62 (115; 71) max cruising	about 243 (450; 280)	Two seats	A. Side by side seating. Fully enclosed cabin. High Performance (HP).
Ikarusflug Bodensee Mennwanger Strasse 3, 7777 Salem-Altenbeuren	BA 83 Mistral II	9.40/ 30-10	5.88/ 19-3½	R, B, S, O, P	One 21 kW (28 hp) König SD 570	114/251	70-117/ 154-258	46 (85; 53)	102 (190; 118)	Pilot	Conforms to West German national standards.
Konsuprod GmbH & Co KG Gwinnerstrasse 13, 6000 Frankfurt am Main	ULM-1B Moskito	10.40/ 34-1½	5.85/ 19-2¼	R, B, D, P	One 17 kW (23 hp) König SC 430	123/271	55-95/ 122-209	49 (90; 56) with two-blade propeller	140 (260; 161)	Pilot	K, A. Pod and boom design, built mainly of composites.
Leichtflugzeug GmbH & Co KG Osemundstrasse 22, 5982 Neuenrade	Sky Walker II	10.15/ 33-3½	5.70/ 18-8½	R, B, D, O	One 26.8 kW (36 hp) Göbler Hirth 2702 or 38.8 kW (52 hp) Göbler Hirth 2703 or 38.8 kW (52 hp) Rotax 462 or 503	168/370	65-110/ 144-242	54 (100; 62)	n.k.	Two seats	K, A. Can be used for photographic, banner towing and spraying work.
Ritec GmbH Jörg-Syrlin Strasse 39, 7900 Ulm/ Donau	Delta-Dart	6.24/ 20-5¾	4.58/ 15-0¼	R, D, P	One 32 kW (43 hp) Rotax	150/331	n.k.	135 (250; 155)	755 (1,400; 870)	Pilot (in bicycle sitting position)	First flown in early 1989. GFRP canard delta, with special wing section and winglet/rudders. Retractable landing gear. Suited also to agricultural and military purposes.
Saurier Flugservice LtB Bohmte/Bad Essen, LBA Nr II-A 328	Vagabond	7.55/ 24-9¼	6.70/ 21-11¾	R, B, D, C	One 22.4 kW (30 hp) Citroën	150/331	n.k.	59 (110; 68)	n.k.	Two seats	Wood and fabric biplane of conventional layout.
Tandem Aircraft KG Blumen Strasse 10, Postfach 1169, 7301 Deizisau	Sunny	7.00/ 22-11½	3.75/ 12-3½	R, B, D, O	One 28.3 kW (38 hp) Rotax 447 or 38.8 kW (52 hp) Rotax 462	150/331	n.k.	43-54 (80-100; 50-62) cruising	n.k.	Two seats	Biplane, with swept upper wing and interplane vertical surfaces at wingtips.
Ultraleicht-Fluggerätebau GmbH Twist 9, 4455 Wietmarschen	Wildente	10.50/ 34-5½	6.10/ 20-0	R, B, D, O	One 16.4 kW (22 hp) Göbler-Hirth F263	145/320	n.k.	54 (100; 62)	140 (260; 162)	Pilot	
Ultraleicht-Fluggerätebau GmbH	Wildente 2	11.00/ 36-1	7.10/ 23-3½	R, B, D, O	One 28 kW (38 hp) Göbler-Hirth F2702R	150/331	n.k.	n.k.	n.k.	Two seats	

Company & Address	Model	Wing span/ Rotor diameter m/ft in	Length overall m/ft in	Airframe F = flexwing R = rigid wing B = braced S = single surface fabric D = double surface fabric C = conventional fuselage O = open fuselage structure P = fuselage pod	Power plant	Weight empty kg/lb	Pilot weight range kg/lb	Max speed knots (km/h; mph)	Max range or endurance nm (km; miles	Accom	Forms/Remarks K = kits P = plans A = assembled
GERMANY, WEST *Contd.*											
UPM GmbH Postfach 2013, 6095 Ginsheim 2	Funplane I	10.50/ 34-5½	n.k.	Open trike unit and wing	One 28.3 kW (38 hp) Rotax 462	138/304	n.k.	40-54 (75-100; 47-62)	n.k.	Two seats	In production.
UPM GmbH	Omega	10.90/ 35-9¼	n.k.	Trike unit and wing	One 30 kW (40 hp) Sauer 1750	180/397	n.k.	40-54 (75-100; 47-62)	n.k.		In production. Four sold to Royal Netherlands Army for special forces trials.
UPM GmbH	Omega II	10.90-11.00/ 35-9¼-36-1	n.k.	Trike unit and wing	One 43.25 kW (58 hp) Mathes 1000	180/397	n.k.	54-75 (100-140; 62-87)	n.k.		
Helmut Vogt Mörikestrasse 20, 7982 Baienfurt	LO-120	12.00/ 39-4½	7.00/ 22-11½	R, D, O	One 28.3 kW (38 hp) Rotax 337	150/331	60-130/ 132-286 crew	54 (100; 62)	215 (400; 248)	Two seats	K. Twin boom design, with inverted V tail.
Helmut Vogt	LO-150	15.00/ 49-2½	n.k.	R, D, P	One 28.3 kW (38 hp) or 38.8 kW (52 hp) Rotax	150/331	n.k.	81 (150; 93)	n.k.	Two seats	K. Twin boom design, with inverted V tail unit. Differs from LO-120 mainly in having fuselage pod and larger tapered wings.
Vulcan UL-Aviation Kiefernweg 13, 8011 Zorneding bei München	Albatros	9.60/ 31-6	6.00/ 19-8¼	R, B, D, O, P	One 28.3 kW (38 hp) Rotax 462 or 47 kW (63 hp) Rotax 532 for export floatplanes	150/331	n.k.	62 (115; 71)	162 (300; 186)	Two seats	
Heinrich Zettl Vor der Pfanne, 6293 Loehnberg	Götz 50	10.90/ 35-9¼	6.15/ 20-2¼	R, B, D, C	One 17.2 kW (23 hp) Göbler-Hirth F263	145/ 320 estimated	n.k.	54 (100; 62)	n.k.	Pilot	
HUNGARY Air Service PO Box 1502, Kóérberki út 36, H-1112 Budapest XI PF. 56	KSML-P1 Nemere	n.k.	n.k.	R, B, D, O	n.k.	n.k.	n.k.	n.k.	n.k.	Pilot	
Air Service	KSML-P2 Nyírség	10.20/ 33-5½	5.90/ 19-4¼	R, B, D, O	One 29.4 kW (39.4 hp) Rotax 447	150/331	n.k.	37 (68; 42) cruising	n.k.	Two seats	Suited to sport flying, training, agricultural spraying, etc.
Air Service	KSML-1M Nyírség-2	10.08/ 33-1	6.20/ 20-4	R, B, D, O	One 35 kW (47 hp) Rotax 503-2V	199/439	n.k.	40 (75; 47) cruising	n.k.	Two seats	Tandem seating for sport, training, spraying, survey, etc.
Hlamot Design Városmajor út 32, 1122 Budapest	Hlamot-M	10.60/ 34-9¼	1.90/ 6-2¾	F, B, D, O	One 34 kW (45.6 hp) Rotax 503E	110/243	250/551 max crew	32 (60; 37)	48.5 (90; 56)	Two or three seats	Can be used for navigation training.
ITALY Aeroservice Italiana Srl Frazione Masio 103, Valle Masio, 10046 Poirino (To)	Eagle XL	10.67/ 35-0	4.57/ 15-0	F, B, O	One 26 kW (35 hp) Rotax 337	102/225	n.k.	43 (80; 50)	78 (145; 90)	Pilot	Three-axis version of US designed Eagle. Conforms to FAR Pt 103.
Aeroservice Italiana Srl	Eagle XL Country	10.67/ 35-0	4.57/ 15-0	F, B, O	One 38.8 kW (52 hp) Rotax 462 or 44.7 kW (60 hp) Arrow GT-500	145/320	n.k.	46 (85; 53)	1 h 30 min	Pilot	Agricultural version of the Eagle XL. 80 litre (21 US gallon; 17.6 Imp gallon) chemical tank.
Aeroservice Italiana Srl	Eagle 2 PLC	n.k.	n.k.	F, B, O	One 34.3 kW (46 hp) Rotax 503	137/302	n.k.	49 (90; 56)	1 h 30 min	Two seats	Two-seat version of the Eagle XL.

Company & Address	Model	Wing span/ Rotor diameter m/ft in	Length overall m/ft in	Airframe F = flexwing R = rigid wing B = braced S = single surface fabric D = double surface fabric C = conventional fuselage O = open fuselage structure P = fuselage pod	Power plant	Weight empty kg/lb	Pilot weight range kg/lb	Max speed knots (km/h; mph)	Max range or endurance nm (km; miles	Accom	Forms/Remarks K = kits P = plans A = assembled
Aeroservice Italiana Srl	F2-Foxcat	10.97/ 36-0	4.33/ 14-2½	R, B, D, P	One 20 kW (27 hp) Rotax 277 or other engine of 18.6-22.4 kW (25-30 hp)	115/254	n.k.	65 (120; 75)	over 162 (300; 186)	Pilot	All-composites version of American Aircraft Falcon. High wing and canard.
Aeroservice Italiana Srl	F2-Foxcat 2 PLC	10.97/ 36-0	5.63/ 18-5¾	R, B, D, P	One 34 kW (45.6 hp) Rotax	150/331	n.k.	86 (160; 99)	over 270 (500; 310)	Two seats	Two-seat version of F2-Foxcat.
Aliferrari Zona Industriale 24, 45026 Lendinara (RO)	Cormorano	10.20/ 33-5½	6.00/ 19-8¼	R, B, D, O, P	One 47 kW (63 hp) Rotax 532	165/364	n.k.	59 (110; 68)	n.k.	Two seats	Enclosed helicopter type cabin.
Aviazione Ultraleggera Italiana (AUI) Via Sempione 9, 28040 Marano Ticino (NO)	T7 Leone	9.40/ 30-10	6.40/ 21-0	R, B, D, P	One 22.4 kW (30 hp) KFM 107ER	115/254	n.k.	65 (120; 74)	4 h	Pilot	A.
Centro Ultraleggeri Partenopeo (CUP) Via S. Maria de Pianto 42, 80143 Naples	F-3	9.55/ 31-4	5.06/ 16-7¼	R, D, C	One 18.6 kW (25 hp) KFM 107ER	115/254	60-91/ 133-200 crew	55 (102; 63)	3 h	Pilot	K, A (to experienced pilots).
Centro Ultraleggeri Partenopeo (CUP)	BF-3	10.40/ 34-1½	5.45/ 17-10½	R, D, C	One 28 kW (37.5 hp) Rotax 462	150/331	57-150/ 126-331 crew	n.k.	n.k.	Two seats	K, A?
EPA Costruzioni Aeronautiche 50037, S Piero A Sieve, FI	Sky Ranger	9.76/ 32-0½	6.44/ 21-1½	R, B, D, C	One 59.7 kW (80 hp) Limbach L2000 or 40.3 kW (54 hp) Rotax 532	41/90	n.k.	102 (190; 118) pilot only, Limbach engine	5 h pilot only, Limbach engine	Two seats	Kevlar/carbonfibre/ glassfibre construction. Suited to training (dual controls), surveillance, search and rescue, photography, cargo dropping, first aid/ambulance, and armed military roles with 150 kg (331 lb) of stores.
General Gliders Via Stadera a Poggioreale, 62 80143 Naples	940A Zefiro	11.22/ 36-9¾	6.20/ 20-4	R, B, D, O	One 22.4 kW (30 hp) KFM 107 ER MAXI	115/254	50-100/ 110-220	59 (110; 68)	108 (200; 124)	Pilot	P. Conforms to FAR Pt 103 and FAR 23; certificated as a homebuilt in Italy. See also Sailplanes.
Hobbystica Avio Via Migliara 52/5, 04014 Pontinia (Latina)	A-2-S Barracuda	8.20/ 26-10¾	6.02/ 19-9	R, B, D, C	One 30 kW (40 hp) 521 cc Hirth	130/287	n.k.	73 (135; 84)	188 (350; 217)	Pilot	A.
Hobbystica Avio	A-2-2 Barracuda	10.05/ 32-11¾	n.k.	R, B, D, C	One 48.5 kW (65 hp) Arrow	165/364	n.k.	70 (130; 81)	n.k.	Two seats	A.
Polaris Srl Valdichiascio -Gubbio (PG)	Cross-Country	n.k.	n.k.	F, B, O	One 35.8 kW (48 hp) Rotax 503	64/141	n.k.	n.k.	n.k.	Pilot or two seats	Forty built by early 1989, when last news received.
Polaris Srl	Lomac Trick	10.60/ 34-9½	n.k.	F, B, O	One 35.8 kW (48 hp) Rotax 503	130/287	60-180/ 133-397 crew	43 (80; 50)	3 h	Two seats	K. Convertible landplane/ flying-boat/boat using inflatable boat/hull.
Technologia Europea Divisione Aeronautica Srl (TEDA) Via Canova 8, 20145 Milan	Lucky	10.11/ 33-2	5.83/ 19-1½	R, B, D, C	One 22.4 kW (30 hp) KFM 107	114/251	110/242 max	54 (100; 62)	n.k.	Pilot	
Technologia Europea Divisione Aeronautica Srl (TEDA)	Ranger	10.40/ 34-1	6.24/ 20-5¾	R, B, D, C	One 35.8 kW (48 hp) Rotax 503	150/331	160/353 max	54 (100; 62)	n.k.	Two seats	Two-seat version of Lucky.

Company & Address	Model	Wing span/ Rotor diameter m/ft in	Length overall m/ft in	Airframe F = flexwing R = rigid wing B = braced S = single surface fabric D = double surface fabric C = conventional fuselage O = open fuselage structure P = fuselage pod	Power plant	Weight empty kg/lb	Pilot weight range kg/lb	Max speed knots (km/h; mph)	Max range or endurance nm (km; miles	Accom	Forms/Remarks K = kits P = plans A = assembled
SOUTH KOREA											
Korean Air (Institute of Aeronautical Technology) CPO Box 864, 41-3 Seosomun-Dong, Chung-Ku, Seoul	Blue Sky	n.k.	n.k.	n.k.	n.k.	n.k.	n.k.	n.k.	n.k.	n.k.	—
POLAND											
Instytut Lotnictwa (Aviation Institute) Al. Krakowska 110/114, 02-256 Warszawa-Okecie	Zem-90	11.60/ 38-0¾	3.60/ 11-9¾	Semi-rigid, B, D, P	One 37.3 kW (50 hp) Rotax 503-2V	150/331	n.k.	59 (110; 68) cruising	539 (1,000; 621)	Two seats	Control by dorsal fin above Dacron-covered hang glider wing. Semi or fully enclosed trike.
Jaroslaw Janowski ul Nowomiejska 2 m 29, 91-061 Lodz	J-2 Polonez	7.00/ 23-0	4.84/ 15-10½	R, D, C	One 22.5 kW (30 hp) Trabant motorcar engine. Other engine of 18.5-30 kW (25-40 hp) may be fitted	105/231	n.k.	86 (160; 99)	3 h	Pilot	All-wood construction, except for fabric covering on wings, ailerons, tailplane and rudder.
SPAIN											
Martin Uhia 36970 Portonoro, Pontevedra	Canelas Ranger	11.53/ 34-6½	5.70/ 18-8½	R, B, D, P	One 38.8 kW (52 hp) Rotax 462 or 48.5 kW (65 hp) Rotax 912	190/419	150/331	78 (145; 90)	269 (500; 310)	Two seats	Composites construction. Pod and boom fuselage.
SWEDEN											
Malmö Forsknings & Innovations AB (MFI) Smedstorpsgatan, S-212 28 Malmö	Andreasson BA-12 Slandan (Dragonfly)	10.00/ 32-9¾	5.00/ 16-4¾	R, B, D, P	One 21 kW (28 hp) König or 26 kW (35 hp) Rotax 447	135/298	n.k.	54 (100; 62) cruising	108 (200; 124) with König engine	Pilot	K, A. All-composites construction.
Malmö Forsknings & Innovations AB (MFI)	Andreasson BA-14	11.40/ 37-4¾	n.k.	R, B, D, C	One Textron Lycoming O-235 or Rotax 532 or Rotax 912	n.k.	n.k.	86 (159; 99) cruising	4 h	Two seats	Combines features of the BA-12 and Andreasson side by side two-seat lightplanes.
SWITZERLAND											
Swiss Aerolight CP444, Pt Lancy 1, 1213 Geneva	Fun Fly	11.20/ 36-9	5.50/ 18-0½	R, B, D, O	One 39.5 kW (53 hp) Rotax 503	175/386	200/441	65 (120; 74)	215 (400; 248)	Two seats	K, P, A.
Swiss Aerolight	Observer	10.00/ 32-9¾	5.50/ 18-0½	R, B, D, O	Two 39.5 kW (53 hp) Rotax 503s	180/397	200/441	76 (140; 87)	162 (300; 186)	Pilot	P. Twin engines. Prone pilot's position.
UNION OF SOVIET SOCIALIST REPUBLICS											
Peter Almurzin Kuibyshev	Crystall	n.k.	n.k.	R, B, D, P	One 26 kW (35 hp)	n.k.	n.k.	76 (142; 88)	n.k.	Pilot	Pod and boom monoplane with conventional controls.
Antonov	Slavutitch M-1	8.80/ 28-10½	4.40/ 14-5¼	F, B, O	One 17.2 kW (23 hp) Neptun	74.5/164	87.5/ 193 max	35 (65; 40)	16 (30; 18.5)	Pilot	Trike and hang glider.
	T-4	10.40/ 34-1½	n.k.	F, B, P	One 22.4 kW (30 hp)	85/187	n.k.	38 (70; 43) cruising	1 h 30 min	Pilot	Trike and hang glider. Can be used also for forestry, agricultural and transport work.
Alexander Beliovkin, Jury Pribylsky and Nikolai Kuleshow Riga	Delta Agro	n.k.	n.k.	F, B, D, P	One 22.4 kW (30 hp)	145/319	n.k.	41 (76; 47)	n.k.	Pilot	Has ducted fan at rear of trike pod. May have agricultural uses.

Company & Address	Model	Wing span/ Rotor diameter m/ft in	Length overall m/ft in	Airframe F = flexwing R = rigid wing B = braced S = single surface fabric D = double surface fabric C = conventional fuselage O = open fuselage structure P = fuselage pod	Power plant	Weight empty kg/lb	Pilot weight range kg/lb	Max speed knots (km/h; mph)	Max range or endurance nm (km; miles	Accom	Forms/Remarks K = kits P = plans A = assembled
Litovskaya Aviatsionnaya Konstruktsiya (LAK) Prenaisk, Litovsk, Lithuania	BROK-1M Garnys	8.20/ 26-11	5.40/ 17-8½	R, B, D, C	One 18.4 kW (25 hp) Zuzycie	128/282	82.5/ 182	75 (140; 87)	n.k.	Pilot	Microlight version of the Oshkinis BRO-23KR Garnys glider.
Kintautas Yuodinas Shiauliai, Lithuania	Medvegalis	n.k.	n.k.	R, B, O, P	One 37.3 kW (50 hp) 450 cc	n.k.	n.k.	54 (100; 62) cruising	n.k.	Two seats	Fabric covered tubular wings and conventional tail surfaces.
UNITED KINGDOM Aerotech International Ltd Hinton in the Hedges Aerodrome, Steane, Brackley, Northants NN13 5NS	MW5K Sorcerer										Aerotech offers assembled examples of the Whittaker MW5B Sorcerer. Plans are offered by Mr Whittaker (which see).
AMF Microflight Ltd (see main Sport section)	Chevvron 2-32										
Cook Flying Machines (CFM) (see main Sport section)	Shadow and Shadow II										
Fulton Aircraft Ltd (see main Sport section)	FA-1										
Hornet Microlights Ltd Perseverance Mills, Mill Street, Wibsey, Bradford BD6 3HR	Hornet R	10.60/ 34-9¼	3.50/ 11-5¾	F, B, D, P	One 38.8 kW (52 hp) Rotax 462	171/377	55-180/ 122-396	66 (122; 76)	225 (418; 260)	Two seats	Conforms to BCAR Section S. Side by side seating.
Hornet Microlights Ltd	Hornet RS	10.60/ 34-9¼	3.50/ 11-5¾	F, B, D, P	One 47.4 kW (64 hp) Rotax 532	173/381	55-180/ 122-396	66 (122; 76)	225 (418; 260)	Two seats	Conforms to BCAR Section S. Initially developed at request of Skylink Systems Ltd (parent company) for commercial applications.
Hornet Microlights Ltd	Hornet RSE	10.60/ 34-9¼	3.50/ 11-5¾	F, B, D, P	One Rotax 582	175/386	55-180/ 122-396	66 (122; 76)	234 (434; 270)	Two seats	Conforms to BCAR Section S. Luxury model. Includes 720 channel radio interfaced into two-way crew helmet intercom system.
Mainair Sports Ltd, Unit 2, Alma Industrial Estate, Regent Street, Rochdale, Lancashire OL12 0HQ	Cropstar	10.60/ 34-9½	3.83/ 12-6¾	F, B, D, O, P	One 47.7 kW (64 hp) Rotax 532	198/436	90/198 max	61 (113; 70)	69 (128; 80)	Pilot. Optional second seat by removing agricultural spraygear	Not available yet in UK. Flexwing and trike agricultural microlight.
Mainair Sports Ltd	Gemini Flash 2 Alpha	10.60/ 34-9½	3.83/ 12-6¾	F, B, D, O, P	One 34.3 kW (46 hp) Rotax 503, 38.8 kW (52 hp) Rotax 462 or 47.7 kW (64 hp) Rotax 532	147-150/ 324-331	55-180/ 122-396	65 (121; 75)	69-138 (128-257; 80-160)	Two seats	A. Conforms to BCAR Section S. Flexwing and trike type. An RPV version is the Sky Ranger.
Mainair Sports Ltd	Scorcher	9.20/ 30-2	2.88/ 9-9½	F, B, D, O, P	One 34.3 kW (46 hp) Rotax 503	132/291	50-90/ 110-198	65 (121; 75)	130-260 (241-482; 150-300)	Pilot	A. Conforms to BCAR Section S. Flexwing and trike type.

Company & Address	Model	Wing span/ Rotor diameter m/ft in	Length overall m/ft in	Airframe F = flexwing R = rigid wing B = braced S = single surface fabric D = double surface fabric C = conventional fuselage O = open fuselage structure P = fuselage pod	Power plant	Weight empty kg/lb	Pilot weight range kg/lb	Max speed knots (km/h; mph)	Max range or endurance nm (km; miles)	Accom	Forms/Remarks K = kits P = plans A = assembled

UNITED KINGDOM *Contd.*

Company & Address	Model	Wing span/ Rotor diameter	Length overall	Airframe	Power plant	Weight empty	Pilot weight range	Max speed	Max range	Accom	Forms/Remarks
Medway Microlights Burrows Lane, Middle Stoke, Rochester, Kent	Hybred R	10.97/ 36-0	n.k.	F, B, D, O, P	One 29.4 kW (39.4 hp) Rotax 447	149/328	n.k.	69 (129; 80)	130 (241; 150)	Two seats	A. Flexwing and trike type.
Microflight Aircraft Ltd Hangar 6, Shobdon Airfield, Herefordshire HR6 9NR	Spectrum	11.88/ 39-0	5.94/ 19-6	R, B, D, P	One 34.3 kW (46 hp) Rotax 503	170/375	55-90/ 122-198	58 (107; 67)	120 (222; 138)	Two seats	A. Conforms to FAI/CAA requirements.
Noble Hardman Aviation Ltd (see main Sport section)	Snowbird Mk IV										
Pegasus Transport Systems Ltd 56 George Lane, Marlborough, Wiltshire SN8 4BY	Pegasus Q	10.36/ 34-0	2.59/ 8-6	F, B, D, O, P	One 30 kW (40 hp) Rotax 447 or 35.8 kW (50 hp) Rotax 462LC	148/326	55-180/ 122-396	65 (121; 75) with Rotax 462LC	217 (402; 250) with Rotax 462LC	Two seats	A. Cross-country flexwing/trike type, with speed range of 22-65 knots (40-121 km/h; 25-75 mph). All new airframe.
Pegasus Transport Systems Ltd	Pegasus XL-R	10.36/ 34-0	n.k.	F, B, D (50%), O, P	One 30 kW (40 hp) Rotax 447 or 38.8 kW (52 hp) Rotax 462	145/320	180/396 max crew	43 (80; 50) cruising	approx 86 (161; 100)	Two seats	A. Conforms to FAI/CAA definitions and built to BCAR Section S standards.
J. Romain & Sons 111 Burnham Green Road, Burnham Green, Welwyn, Hertfordshire	Cobra Mk I	5.69/ 18-8	4.42/ 14-6	R, B, D, C	One 22.4 kW (30 hp) KFM	70/154	76/168 max	78 (145; 90)	87 (161; 100)	Pilot	Prototype only. Conventional biplane. Conforms to BCAR Section S-CAP 482.
Michael W. J. Whittaker Dawlish Cottage, Pincots Lane, Wickwar, Wotton-under-Edge, Gloucestershire GL12 8NY	MW5 Sorcerer	9.16/ 30-0½	4.80/ 15-9	R, B, D, O, P	One 37.3 kW (50 hp) Fuji Robin EC44 PM02, or Rotax 377 or 447, or other engine	140/308 with 44.7 kW (60 hp) engine	55-100/ 122-220	65 (120; 75) with 33.6 kW (45 hp) engine	150 (278; 172) with 33.6 kW (45 hp) engine	Pilot	P. Conforms to FAI/CAA requirements.
Michael W. J. Whittaker	MW6 Merlin	9.75/ 32-0	5.33/ 17-6	R, B, D, O, P	One 37.3 kW (50 hp) Fuji Robin EC44PM, or Rotax 503 or 532	150/331	46-181/ 100-400 crew	55 (102; 63)	78 (144; 90)	Two seats	P. Microlight or homebuilt aircraft.
Michael W. J. Whittaker	MW7	6.71/ 22-0	4.57/ 15-0	R, B, D, O, P	One 47.7 kW (64 hp) Rotax 532	145/320	100/220 max	100 (185; 115)	220 (407; 253)	Pilot	P. Microlight or homebuilt. First flown in August 1988.

UNITED STATES OF AMERICA

Company & Address	Model	Wing span/ Rotor diameter	Length overall	Airframe	Power plant	Weight empty	Pilot weight range	Max speed	Max range	Accom	Forms/Remarks
Advanced Aviation Inc 323 North Ivey Lane, Orlando, Florida 32811	Cobra B	10.57/ 34-8	5.46/ 17-10¾	R, B, D, O	One 30 kW (40 hp) Rotax 447. AG Cobra: one 48.5 kW (65 hp) Rotax 532LC (optional for Cobra VIP)	112-120/ 247-265	50-102/ 110-225	48-52 (88-97; 55-60)	78 (145; 90)	Pilot	K. Cobra B is a microlight, conforming to FAR Pt 103. Cobra VIP and AG Cobra conform to Experimental homebuilt category.
Advanced Aviation Inc (see main Sport section)	Cobra Carrera										K.

Company & Address	Model	Wing span/ Rotor diameter m/ft in	Length overall m/ft in	Airframe F = flexwing R = rigid wing B = braced S = single surface fabric D = double surface fabric C = conventional fuselage O = open fuselage structure P = fuselage pod	Power plant	Weight empty kg/lb	Pilot weight range kg/lb	Max speed knots (km/h; mph)	Max range or endurance nm (km; miles	Accom	Forms/Remarks K = kits P = plans A = assembled
Advanced Aviation Inc	(Highcraft) Buccaneer	10.21/ 33-6	5.84/ 19-2 as amphibian	R, B, D, C	One 26 kW (35 hp) Rotax 377. Optional 20 kW (27 hp) Rotax 277 in Model XA/280 or 30 kW (40 hp) Rotax 447 in Model XA/430	144/318 with Rotax 377	50-113/ 100-250 with Rotax 377	55 (101; 63) with Rotax 377	88 (162; 101) with Rotax 377	Pilot	K. Conforms to FAR Pt 103. Amphibious microlight, or can be built as a landplane.
Advanced Aviation Inc	Buccaneer SX	8.43/ 27-8	6.22/ 20-5	R, B, D, C	One 30 kW (40 hp) Rotax 447, 34 kW (45.6 hp) Rotax 503 or 48.5 kW (65 hp) Rotax 532	144/318	n.k.	69 (129; 80)	n.k.	Pilot	New amphibian, reportedly to supersede the earlier model. Carrera airframe but with hull and wing floats. Microlight or Experimental homebuilt.
Aerolights Route 1, Box 187, Welsh, Louisiana 70591	Air Master	8.74/ 28-8	n.k.	R, B, D, C	One 48.5 kW (65 hp) Rotax 532	159/350	n.k.	78 (145; 90)	n.k.	Pilot	K. Low-wing monoplane.
Aerolights (see main Sport section)	Bearcat										
Air Command Manufacturing Inc Liberty Landing Airport, Route 3, Box 197A, Liberty, Missouri 64068	447 Commander and 447 Commander Sport	7.01/ 23-0	Commander: 3.25/10-8 Commander Sport: 3.51/ 11-6	Gyroplane with P (optional)	One 30 kW (40 hp) Rotax 447	114/252	55-136/ 120-300	Commander: 55 (101; 63) Commander Sport: 63 (117; 73)	87 (161; 100)	Pilot	K (more than 900 sold). Conforms to FAR Pt 103.
Aircraft Designs Inc (see main Sport section)	Bumble Bee										
Aircraft Development Inc 1326 North Westlink Boulevard, Wichita, Kansas 67212	EZ-1	9.45/ 31-0	5.33/ 17-6	R, D	One 15 kW (20 hp) Zenoah G25B-1	106/234	45-102/ 100-225	43 (80; 50)	67 (124; 77)	Pilot	Conforms to FAR Pt 103. Composites and aluminium construction, using self-adhesive 'Scotch-A-Frame' bonding technique.
American Aircraft Inc 650 Sacramento Street, San Francisco, California 94111	Falcon	10.97/ 36-0	4.34/ 14-3	R, D, P	One 20 kW (27 hp) Rotax 277	113/250	50-95/ 110-210	55 (101; 63)	105 (194; 121)	Pilot	A. Conforms to FAR Pt 103. Much use of composites. Foreplane forward and high-mounted swept rear main wings.
Brutsche Aircraft Corporation (BAC) 1800 West 1887 South, Woods Cross, Utah 84087	Freedom 28	8.48/ 27-10	5.31/ 17-5	R, B, D, C	One 20 kW (27 hp) Rotax 277	115/254	n.k.	55 (102; 63) cruising	2 h-3 h 30 min	Pilot	K. Homebuilt version with a Rotax 503 engine is the Freedom 48.
Ken Brock Manufacturing Inc 11852 Western Avenue, Stanton, California 90680	Avion	8.84/ 29-0	4.72/ 15-6	R, B, D, O	One 20 kW (27 hp) Rotax 277	109/240	59-95/ 130-210	45 (84; 52)	121 (225; 140)	Pilot	K. Conforms to FAR Pt 103 and AC 103-7.
Ken Brock Manufacturing Inc	KB-3	6.70/ 22-0	3.35/ 11-0	Autogyro, O	One 48.5 kW (65 hp) Rotax 532	113/250	n.k.	55 (101; 63)	65 (120; 75)	Pilot	K. Microlight version of the KB-2. Conforms to FAR Pt 103.

Company & Address	Model	Wing span/ Rotor diameter m/ft in	Length overall m/ft in	Airframe F = flexwing R = rigid wing B = braced S = single surface fabric D = double surface fabric C = conventional fuselage O = open fuselage structure P = fuselage pod	Power plant	Weight empty kg/lb	Pilot weight range kg/lb	Max speed knots (km/h; mph)	Max range or endurance nm (km; miles)	Accom	Forms/Remarks K = kits P = plans A = assembled
UNITED STATES OF AMERICA *Contd.*											
Carlson Aircraft Inc 50643 State Route 14, East Palestine, Ohio 44413	Sparrow	9.21/ 30-2⅜	5.11/ 16-9	R, B, D, C	One 20 kW (27 hp) Rotax 277	115/254	n.k.	55 (101; 63)	173 (321; 200)	Pilot	K. Conforms to FAR Pt 103.
Carlson Aircraft Inc (see main Sport section)	Sparrow Sport Special										
CGS Aeronautics PO Box 32336, Cleveland Ohio 44132	Hawk	8.79/ 28-10	6.30/ 20-8	R, B, D, P	One 35 kW (47 hp) Rotax 503	115/254	n.k.	74 (137; 85)	n.k.	Pilot	K.
CGS Aeronautics	Hawk Tandem	8.84/ 29-0	n.k.	R, B, D, P	One 35 kW (47 hp) Rotax 503	152/335	n.k.	78 (145; 90)	n.k.	Two seats	K.
Chuck's Aircraft Company 11845 Loop 107, Adkins, Texas 78101	Texan Chuck Bird	7.77/ 25-6	4.57/ 16-0	R, B, D, C	One 30 kW (40 hp) Chaparral	n.k.	n.k.	n.k.	n.k.	n.k.	K, A.
Coldfire Systems Inc 2235 First Street, Route 107, Simi Valley, California 93065	Ascender II +	10.06/ 33-0	5.08/ 16-8	R, B, D, O	One 26 kW (35 hp) Rotax 377	107/235	45.5-136/ 100-300	52 (97; 60)	87 (161; 100)	Pilot or two seats	Formerly marketed by Freedom Fliers Inc. Conforms to FAR Pt 103 with 5 US gallon fuel tank and pilot only.
Coldfire Systems Inc	Buckeye	10.21/ 33-6	n.k.	Parawing microlight with open trike	Probably one 26 kW (35 hp) Rotax 377	81/179	38.5-84/ 85-185	Probably 22 (42; 26) constant speed	Probably 43 (80; 50)	Pilot	Formerly marketed by Freedom Fliers Inc.
Diehl Aero-Nautical 1855 North Elm, Jenks, Oklahoma 74037	XTC Hydrolight	9.75/ 32-0	4.62/ 15-2	R, D, P	One 18.6 kW (25 hp) 294 cc KFM 107ER or 20 kW (27 hp) Rotax 277 or 32 kW (43 hp) Rotax 447	136/300	45-90/ 100-200	52 (97; 60) with KFM engine	130 (241; 150) with KFM engine	Pilot	K. Microlight or homebuilt landplane or amphibian. Conforms to FAR Pt 103 as microlight.
Earthstar Aircraft Inc (see main Sport section)	Laughing Gull, Laughing Gull II, Thunder Gull and Ultra Gull										Microlights and homebuilts.
Flightworks (see main Sport section)	Capella										
Gemini International 20 Barnes Street, Daleville, Alabama 36322	Humming-bird 103	10.97/ 36-0	n.k.	R, B, D, O	Two 215 cc Solos	95/210	n.k.	48; (89; 55)	n.k.	Pilot	K.
Gemini International	Humming-bird Longwing	12.50/ 41-0	n.k.	R, B, D, O	Two 215 cc Solos	100/220	n.k.	43 (80; 50)	n.k.	Pilot	K.
Golden Circle Air 11691 North-West 46th Avenue, Grimes, Iowa 50111	T-Bird	9.45/ 31-0	n.k.	R, B, D, O	One 21 kW (28 hp) Rotax 277	115/253	n.k.	54 (100; 62)	n.k.	Pilot	K.

Company & Address	Model	Wing span/ Rotor diameter m/ft in	Length overall m/ft in	Airframe F = flexwing R = rigid wing B = braced S = single surface fabric D = double surface fabric C = conventional fuselage O = open fuselage structure P = fuselage pod	Power plant	Weight empty kg/lb	Pilot weight range kg/lb	Max speed knots (km/h; mph)	Max range or endurance nm (km; miles	Accom	Forms/Remarks K = kits P = plans A = assembled
Golden Circle Air	T-Bird II	10.97/ 36-0	n.k.	R, B, D, O	One 47.7 kW (64 hp) Rotax 532	175/385	n.k.	65 (120; 75)	n.k.	Two seats	K.
Hipp's Superbirds Inc PO Box 266, I-26 Exit 28, Ozone Drive, Saluda, North Carolina 28773	J-3 Kitten	9.14/ 30-0	4.98/ 16-4	R, B, D, C	One 21 kW (28 hp) Rotax 277	114/252	55-113/ 120-250	55 (101; 63)	104 (193; 120)	Pilot	K, P, A. Conforms to FAR Pt 103.
Hipp's Superbirds Inc	Reliant	9.14/ 30-0	4.98/ 16-4	R, B, D, C	One 21 kW (28 hp) Rotax 277	115/254	55-113/ 120-250	55 (101; 63)	104 (193; 120)	Pilot	K, A. Conforms to FAR Pt 103.
Hipp's Superbirds Inc	J-4 Sportster	8.53/ 28-0	4.98/ 16-4	R, B, D, C	One 21 kW (28 hp) Rotax 277	113/248	55-113/ 120-250	55 (101; 63)	104 (193; 120)	Pilot	K, P, A. Parasol wing. Conforms to FAR Pt 103.
Howland Aero Designs Box 233, Maryland, New York 12116	H-3 Pegasus	7.62/ 25-0	n.k.	R, D, C	One 21 kW (28 hp) Rotax 277	114/252	n.k.	52 (97; 60)	n.k.	Pilot	K. Conforms to FAR Pt 103.
Robert W. Hovey Aircraft Specialties Co PO Box 1074, Canyon County, California 91351	Beta Bird	7.77/ 25-6	5.03/ 16-6	R, B, D, open P	One 33.5 kW (45 hp) Volkswagen motorcar engine	184/405	n.k.	74 (137; 85)	113 (209; 130)	Pilot	P. Pod and boom type.
Robert W. Hovey	Delta Bird	7.32/ 24-0	4.60/ 15-1	R, B, D, C	One 22.5 kW (30 hp) Cuyuna 430R	99/218	95/210 max	48 (88; 55)	61 (112; 70)	Pilot	K, P. Conforms to FAR Pt 103. Biplane.
Robert W. Hovey	Delta Hawk and Super Hawk	7.32/ 24-0	4.75/ 15-7	R, B, D, C	Delta Hawk: one 28.7 kW (38.5 hp) 440 cc Kawasaki 440 Super Hawk: Rotax	Delta Hawk: 112/248 Super Hawk: 113/250	54-100/ 120-220	55 (101; 63)	65 (120; 75)	Pilot	P, A. Conform to FAR Pt 103. Super Hawk has all-metal skin. Biplanes.
Robert W. Hovey	Whing Ding II (WD-II)	5.69/ 18-8	4.27/ 14-0	R, B, open P	One 10.5 kW (14 hp) McCulloch MC-101A	55/120	84/185 max	43 (80; 50)	17 (32; 20)	Pilot	P. Conforms to FAR Pt 103. Open pod and boom type biplane. Wing warping control.
Kennedy Aircraft Company Inc (see main Sport section)	Flycycle										
Michael G. Kimbrel 1333 Garrard Creek Road, Oakville, Washington 98568	Banty	9.75/ 32-0	5.74/ 18-10	R, B, D, C	One 20 kW (27 hp) Rotax 277	108/237	50-102/ 110-225	43 (80; 50) cruising	n.k.	Pilot	P.
Michael G. Kimbrel	Butterfly	11.13/ 36-6	6.55/ 21-6	R, B, D, P	One 20 kW (27 hp) Rotax 277	90/198	93/205 max	39 (72; 45) cruising	78 (145; 90)	Pilot	P. Conforms to FAR Pt 103.
Kolb Aircraft Inc RD3, Box 38, Phoenixville, Pennsylvania 19460	Firestar	8.43/ 27-8	6.17/ 20-3	R, B, D, P	One 26 kW (35 hp) Rotax 377	120/264	64-118/ 140-260	61 (113; 70)	95 (177; 110)	Pilot	K. Conforms to FAR Pt 103-7.
Kopy Kat 5453 East Airport Road, Mount Pleasant, Michigan 48858	Kopy Kat	n.k.	n.k.	R, B, D, C	One 20 kW (27 hp) Rotax 277	n.k.	n.k.	n.k.	n.k.	Pilot	K, P, A. Conforms to FAR Pt 103. Estimated building time 350 hours. Microlight version of a conventional single-seat biplane.
Leader's International Inc (see main Sport section)	JB-1000										

Company & Address	Model	Wing span/ Rotor diameter m/ft in	Length overall m/ft in	Airframe F = flexwing R = rigid wing B = braced S = single surface fabric D = double surface fabric C = conventional fuselage O = open fuselage structure P = fuselage pod	Power plant	Weight empty kg/lb	Pilot weight range kg/lb	Max speed knots (km/h; mph)	Max range or endurance nm (km; miles)	Accom	Forms/Remarks K = kits P = plans A = assembled
UNITED STATES OF AMERICA *Contd.*											
Leading Edge Air Foils 331 South 14th Street, Colorado Springs, Colorado 80904	Nieuport 11	6.55/ 21-6	n.k.	R, B, D, C	One 30 kW (40 hp) Rotax 447	114/252	n.k.	55 (101; 63)	n.k.	Pilot	K.
Leading Edge Air Foils	Nieuport 12	8.08/ 26-6	n.k.	R, B, D, C	One 47.7 kW (64 hp) Rotax 532	243/536	n.k.	74 (137; 85)	n.k.	Two seats	K.
Light Miniature Aircraft Inc Building 411, Opa-Locka Airport, Opa-Locka, Florida 33054 (see main Sport section)	LM-1U and LM-3U										
Magnum Industries 9815 Lemona Avenue, Sepulveda, California 91343	Honcho II and Super-Honcho	9.80/ 32-2	Honcho II: 5.35/ 17-6½ Super-Honcho: 5.46/ 17-11	R, B, D, P	Honcho II: one 20 kW (27 hp) Rotax 277 Super-Honcho: one 37.3 kW (50 hp) Rotax 503	Honcho II: 108/239 Super-Honcho: 110/243	n.k.	Honcho II: 50 (93; 58) CAS. Super-Honcho: 55 (101; 63) CAS	Honcho II: 139 (257; 160) Super-Honcho: 121 (225; 140)	Pilot	
Magnum Industries	Nomad II	11.00/ 36-1	5.75/ 18-10½	R, B, D, P	One 20 kW (27 hp) Rotax 277	97/214	n.k.	49 (90; 56) CAS	139 (257; 160)	Pilot	
Maxair Aircraft Corporation (see main Sport section)	Drifter series										
Mc² Box 73415, Puyallup, Washington 98373	Chaser S	8.10/ 26-7	n.k.	F, B, O	One 26 kW (35 hp) Rotax 377	100/220	n.k.	80 (148; 92)	n.k.	Pilot	K.
Mitchell Aerospace Company (Mitchell Wing) 1900 South Newcomb, Porterville, California 93257	A-10 Silver Eagle	10.46/ 34-4	2.59/ 8-6	R, D, P	One 17.2 kW (23 hp) Zenoah	113/250	54.5-129/ 120-285	55 (101; 63)	131 (243; 151)	Pilot	A. Conforms to all FAA ultralight regulations, including FAR Pt 103.
Mitchell Aerospace Company (see main Sport section)	AG-38-A War Eagle, AG-38A Terrier and P-38 Lightning										
Mitchell Aerospace Company	B-10	10.36/ 34-0	n.k.	R, B, D, O and P (optional)	One 15 kW (20 hp) Honda	91/200	136/300 max	56 (105; 65)	35-434 (64-805; 40-500) standard or auxiliary fuel	Pilot	K, P, A. Conforms to FAR Pt 103. B-10F is foot-launched version; B-10 has tricycle landing gear.
Mitchell Aerospace Company	TU-10 Double Eagle	n.k.	n.k.	n.k.	One 29.4 kW (39.4 hp) Rotax 447	n.k.	n.k.	n.k.	n.k.		Two-seat version of the A-10 Silver Eagle.
Mitchell Aerospace Company	U-2 Superwing	10.36/ 34-0	2.84/ 9-4	R, D, P	One 15 kW (20 hp) Honda	136/300	136/300 max	74 (137; 85)	39-434 (72-805; 45-500) standard or auxiliary fuel	Pilot	K, P. Does not conform to FAR Pt 103.

Company & Address	Model	Wing span/ Rotor diameter m/ft in	Length overall m/ft in	Airframe F = flexwing R = rigid wing B = braced S = single surface fabric D = double surface fabric C = conventional fuselage O = open fuselage structure P = fuselage pod	Power plant	Weight empty kg/lb	Pilot weight range kg/lb	Max speed knots (km/h; mph)	Max range or endurance nm (km; miles)	Accom	Forms/Remarks K = kits P = plans A = assembled
Pago Jet North America PO Box 5147, Poughkeepsie, New York 12602	Pago Jet	9.22/ 30-3	n.k.	Parawing microlight	One 17 kW (23 hp) König	22/48	n.k.	22 (40; 25) cruising	n.k.	Pilot	K.
Paraplane Corporation (see main Sport section)	PM-2										
Phantom Sport Airplane Corporation Box 145, Southern Pines, North Carolina 28387	Phantom	8.69/ 28-6	5.11/ 16-9	R, B, D, O, P	One 26 kW (35 hp) Rotax 377	114/252	41-97/ 90-215	54 (100; 62)	126 (233; 145)	Pilot	K. Conforms to FAR Pt 103.
Phantom Sport Airplane Corporation	Phantom F II	n.k.	n.k.	R, B, D, O, P	One 35 kW (47 hp) Rotax 503DC	n.k.	n.k.	n.k.	n.k.	Two seats	K. New two-seat version of the Phantom.
Pinaire Engineering Inc 1313 Newton Avenue, Evansville, Indiana 47715	Ultra-Aire I	7.92/ 26-0	4.32/ 14-2	R, B, O	One 26 kW (35 hp) Cuyuna ULII-02	109/240	n.k.	55 (101; 63)	n.k.	Pilot	K, A. Conforms to FAR Pt 103.
Powercraft Corporation 513 North 21st Avenue, Suite C, Yakima, Washington 98902	Parascender	10.49/ 34-6	n.k.	Parawing microlight with trike	One 31.3 kW (42 hp) Rotax 447	104/230	n.k.	23 (42; 26)	n.k.	n.k.	K.
Quad City Ultralight Aircraft Corporation 3610 Coaltown Road, Moline, Illinois 61265	Challenger	9.60/ 31-6	5.64/ 18-6	R, B, D, C	One 20 kW (27 hp) Rotax 277 or optional Rotax 377, 447 or 503	107/235	n.k.	55 (101; 63) with Rotax 277	130 (241; 150)	Pilot	K. Conforms to FAR Pt 103 with Rotax 277 engine. With larger engine, becomes Experimental homebuilt. Challenger Special version has clipped wings.
Quad City Ultralight Aircraft Corporation	Challenger II	9.60/ 31-6	6.10/ 20-0	R, B, D, C	One 31.3 kW (42 hp) Rotax 447 or optionally Rotax 503	136/300	68-136/ 150-300	74 (137; 85)	121 (225; 140) with two crew	Two seats	K. Microlight trainer to FAR Pt 103 or Experimental homebuilt. Challenger II Special version has clipped wings.
Quicksilver Enterprises Inc PO Box 1572, 42143 Avenita Alvarado, Temecula, California 92390	Quicksilver GT	9.14/ 30-0	6.20/ 20-4	R, B, D, O and P (optional)	One 38 kW (51 hp) Rotax 462	139/306	n.k.	51 (96; 60)	n.k.	Pilot	K, A.
Quicksilver Enterprises Inc	Quicksilver MXL and MXL II	9.14/ 30-0 for MXL	5.51/ 18-1 for MXL	R, B, D, O and P (optional)	One 26 kW (35 hp) Rotax 377 for MXL	112/247 for MXL	54-109/ 120-240 for MXL	53 (98; 61) for MXL	99 (183; 114) for MXL	MXL: Pilot MXL II: Two seats	MXL conforms to FAR Pt 103 and FAI requirements. MXL II has larger wing area.
RANS Inc 1104 East Highway 40 By-Pass, Hays, Kansas 67601	S-4 Coyote	8.99/ 29-6	5.18/ 17-0	R, B, D, C	One 31.3 kW (42 hp) Rotax 447	125/276	n.k.	55 (101; 63)	n.k.	Pilot	A and K. Conforms to FAR Pt 103-7 as a microlight.
RANS Inc	S-6 Coyote II	9.45/ 31-0	6.10/ 20-0	R, B, D, C	One 35 kW (47 hp) Rotax 503 or 48.5 kW (65 hp) Rotax 532	172-191/ 380-420	n.k.	68-74 (126-137; 78-85) cruising	n.k.	Two seats	K. Microlight or Experimental categories.

Company & Address	Model	Wing span/ Rotor diameter m/ft in	Length overall m/ft in	Airframe F = flexwing R = rigid wing B = braced S = single surface fabric D = double surface fabric C = conventional fuselage O = open fuselage structure P = fuselage pod	Power plant	Weight empty kg/lb	Pilot weight range kg/lb	Max speed knots (km/h; mph)	Max range or endurance nm (km; miles)	Accom	Forms/Remarks K = kits P = plans A = assembled
UNITED STATES OF AMERICA *Contd.*											
R. D. Aircraft PO Box 211, Mayville, New York 14757	Skycycle	9.65/ 31-8	5.99/ 19-8	R, B, D, C	One 15 kW (20 hp) Snowmobile (or similar), Zenoah, 16.4 kW (22 hp) Yamaha 246 cc, or 18.6 kW (25 hp) KFM 107SR	112.5/248	50-118/ 110-260	48 (90; 56)	174 (322; 200)	Pilot	P, A and components. Conforms to FAR Pt 103.
R. D. Aircraft	Skycycle II	9.65/ 31-8	5.99/ 19-8	R, B, D, C	One 26 kW (35 hp) Cuyuna ULII-02 or 28.3 kW (38 hp) Kawasaki TA440 or 26 kW (35 hp) Rotax 377	n.k.	n.k.	n.k.	n.k.	Two seats	P, A and components. Microlight trainer.
R. D. Aircraft	Skycycle Gypsy, Skycycle Gypsy II, Skycycle Cabin Gypsy, and Wood Gypsy	9.65/ 31-8 Gypsy	6.20/ 20-4 Gypsy	R, B, D, C	One 15 kW (20 hp) Snowmobile (or other engine as for Skycycle). One 20 kW (27 hp) Rotax 277 also optional or (for Cabin Gypsy) standard	112/246 Gypsy	50-118/ 110-260 Gypsy	49 (90; 56) Gypsy	174 (322; 200) Gypsy	Pilot	P, A and components. Derived from Skycycle. Conform to FAR Pt 103. Gypsy II has tubular V bracing struts instead of kingpost, Cabin Gypsy has enclosed cabin and is smaller, and Wood Gypsy is constructed of wood.
R. D. Aircraft	Gypsy Trainer	9.35/ 30-8	6.17/ 20-3	R, B, D, C	One 30 kW (40 hp) Rotax 447	159/350	55-154/ 120-340	61 (113; 70)	174 (322; 200)	Two seats	First flown in 1989.
Roberts Ultralight Aircraft Jacksonville, Florida	RB-2	n.k.	n.k.	R, B, D, C	One Honda	n.k.	n.k.	n.k.	n.k.	Pilot	Conventional strut braced high-wing cabin monoplane.
Rotec Engineering Inc PO Box 380220, Duncanville, Texas 75138	Panther	10.36/ 34-0	5.13/ 16-10	R, B, D, P	One 20 kW (27 hp) Rotax 277 or Rotax 377 or 447	113/250	45-91/ 100-200	50 (93; 58) cruising	149 (277; 172)	Pilot	K, A. Pod and boom type.
Rotec Engineering Inc	Rally 2B	9.45/ 31-0	5.13/ 16-10	R, B, S, O	One 28.3 kW (38 hp) Rotax 377	98/216	100/220 max	35 (64; 40) cruising	73 (135; 84)	Pilot	K, A. Conforms to FAR Pt 103.
Rotec Engineering Inc	Rally 3	11.58/ 38-0	5.28/ 17-4	R, B, S, O	One 35.8 kW (48 hp) Rotax 503	129/285	195/430 max crew	35 (64; 40) cruising	87 (161; 100)	Two seats	K, A. Two-seat version of Rally 2B.
Rotec Engineering Inc	Rally Champ	9.45/ 31-0	5.13/ 16-10	R, B, S, O and optional P	One 20 kW (27 hp) Rotax 277	92/202	55-91/ 120-200	35 (64; 40) cruising	74 (136; 85)	Pilot	K, A. Low cost version of Rally 2B.
Rotec Engineering Inc	Rally Sport	8.23/ 27-0	5.05/ 16-7	R, B, S, O and optional P	One 35.8 kW (48 hp) Rotax 503	112/248	45.5-100/ 100-220	52 (96; 60)	72 (133; 83)	Pilot	K, A. Version of Rally capable of aerobatic manoeuvres.
Saphir America PO Box 2343, New York, New York 10009	The Minimum	n.k.	n.k.	F, B, O	n.k.	n.k.	n.k.	n.k.	n.k.	Pilot	Flexwing hang glider and trike.

Company & Address	Model	Wing span/ Rotor diameter m/ft in	Length overall m/ft in	Airframe F = flexwing R = rigid wing B = braced S = single surface fabric D = double surface fabric C = conventional fuselage O = open fuselage structure P = fuselage pod	Power plant	Weight empty kg/lb	Pilot weight range kg/lb	Max speed knots (km/h; mph)	Max range or endurance nm (km; miles)	Accom	Forms/Remarks K = kits P = plans A = assembled
Sorrell Aircraft Company Ltd 16525 Tilley Road South, Tenino, Washington 98589	SNS-8 Hiperlight and Hiperlight EXP	6.71/ 22-0	4.72/ 15-6	R, B, D, C	Hiperlight: one 20 kW (27 hp) Rotax 277. Hiperlight EXP: one 26.8 kW (36 hp) Rotax 377	111.5/ 246 Hiperlight	104/230 Hiperlight	55 (101; 63) Hiperlight	174 (322; 200) Hiperlight	Pilot	K. Conforms to FAR Pt 103. Cabin biplane.
Sorrell Aircraft Company Ltd	SNS-10 Intruder	4.57/ 15-0	n.k.	R, B, D, C	n.k.	n.k.	n.k.	n.k.	n.k.	Pilot	Believed to be a strengthened version of Hiperlight for limited aerobatics.
Sport Flight Engineering Inc PO Box 2164, Grand Junction, Colorado 81502	Sky Pup	9.45/ 31-0	4.85/ 15-11	R, D, C	One 20 kW (27 hp) Rotax 277 or other engines in 13.5-20 kW (18-27 hp) range	91/200	86/190 max	53 (98; 61)	104 (193; 120)	Pilot	P. Conforms to FAR Pt 103.
Star Flight Aircraft Liberty Landing Airport, Route 3, Box 197, Liberty, Missouri 64066	XC series (data for XC 280 Stiletto)	8.69/ 28-6	5.18/ 17-0	R, B, D, O and P (optional)	One 24 kW (32 hp) Rotax 377 or 20 kW (27 hp) Rotax 277	107/235	59-113/ 130-250	42 (77; 48)	78 (145; 90)	Pilot or two seats	K, P and components? Conform to FAR Pt 103. Series includes XC 320 with larger wing, two-seat XC 2000 with larger wing and Rotax 447, and AgLite agricultural version of XC 2000.
Striplin Aircraft Corporation (see main Sport section)	Lone Ranger Ultralight										
Sunrise Ultralight Aircraft Manufacturing Company Route 4, Box 336, New Caney, Texas 77357	Clipper Ultralight and Clipper Super Sport	9.14/ 30-0	5.44/ 17-10	R, B, D, C	Clipper Ultralight: one 26 kW (35 hp) Rotax 377. Clipper Super Sport: one 38.8 kW (52 hp) Rotax 503	114/252 Clipper Ultralight. 122/270 Clipper Super Sport	46-113/ 100-250	52 (97; 60) Clipper Ultralight. 74 (136; 85) Clipper Super Sport	104 (193; 120) Clipper Ultralight. 165 (305; 190) Clipper Super Sport	Pilot	K. Conforms to FAR Pt 103. Conventional aeroplane layout.
Sunrise Ultralight Aircraft Manufacturing Company	Spitfire Ultralight, Spitfire Super Sport and Sonic Spitfire	9.14/ 30-0	5.44/ 17-10	R, B, D, O, P	Spitfire Ultralight: one 26 kW (35 hp) Rotax 377. Spitfire Super Sport and Sonic Spitfire: one 38.8 kW (52 hp) Rotax 503	114/252 Spitfire Ultralight. 122/270 Spitfire Super Sport	46-113/ 100-250 Spitfire Ultralight and Spitfire Super Sport	52 (97; 60) Spitfire Ultralight. 74 (136; 85) Spitfire Super Sport	104 (193; 120) Spitfire Ultralight. 165 (305; 190) Spitfire Super Sport	Pilot	K. Conform to FAR Pt 103. Sonic Spitfire has twice the fuel capacity (10 US gallons).
Sunrise Ultralight Aircraft Manufacturing Company	Spitfire II UTV	9.14/ 30-0	5.44/ 17-10	R, B, D, O, P	Spitfire II UTV: one 38.8 kW (52 hp) Rotax 503	159/350 Spitfire II UTV	46-113/ 100-250	52 (97; 60) Spitfire II UTV	86 (161; 100) Spitfire II UTV	Two seats	K.
Tennessee Engineering and Manufacturing Inc (T.E.A.M.) State Route 53 and Ivy Bluff Road, Route 1, Box 338C, Bradyville, Tennessee 37026	Hi-MAX	7.62/ 25-0	4.72/ 15-6	R, B, D, C	One 20 kW (27 hp) Rotax 277	113/250	n.k.	52 (97; 60)	n.k.	Pilot	K, P. High wing and enclosed cabin version of miniMAX.

Company & Address	Model	Wing span/ Rotor diameter m/ft in	Length overall m/ft in	Airframe F = flexwing R = rigid wing B = braced S = single surface fabric D = double surface fabric C = conventional fuselage O = open fuselage structure P = fuselage pod	Power plant	Weight empty kg/lb	Pilot weight range kg/lb	Max speed knots (km/h; mph)	Max range or endurance nm (km; miles	Accom	Forms/Remarks K = kits P = plans A = assembled
UNITED STATES OF AMERICA *Contd.*											
Tennessee Engineering and Manufacturing Inc (T.E.A.M.)	miniMAX	7.62/ 25-0	4.72/ 15-6	R, B, D, C	One 20 kW (27 hp) Rotax 277	109/240	104/230	52 (97; 60)	95.5 (177; 110)	Pilot	K, P. Microlight to FAR Pt 103 or homebuilt to Experimental regulations. Low-wing monoplane.
Tennessee Engineering and Manufacturing Inc (T.E.A.M.)	TA-3	n.k.	n.k.	R, B, D, C	One 35.8 kW (48 hp) Rotax 503 or 48.5 kW (65 hp) Rotax 532	181/400	n.k.	87 (161; 100)	n.k.	Two seats	K. Side by side two-seater with enclosed cockpit. (See illustration in Sport section.)
Turner Aircraft Inc Route 4, Box 115AB3, Grandview, Texas 76050	T-100D Mariah	9.75/ 32-0	5.18/ 17-0	R, D, P	Prototype: One 15 kW (20 hp) Cuyuna 215. Production model: KFM 105ER or Ultra	114/251	100/220 max	53 (98; 61)	3 h 35 min	Pilot	P, A. Conforms to FAR Pt 103. Pod and boom type.
Two Wings Aviation 821 3rd Street, Farmington, Minnesota 55024	Fury	8.64/ 28-4	3.96/ 13-0	R, B, D, C	See 'Forms'	115/254	46-113/ 100-250	over 52 (97; 60) cruising	n.k.	Pilot	K, A. Microlight with 30 kW (40 hp) Rotax 447; Experimental homebuilt with 37.3 kW (50 hp) Rotax. Biplane.
Two Wings Aviation	Mariner	9.55/ 31-4	5.92/ 19-5	R, B, D, C amphibious hull	One 30 kW (40 hp) Rotax 447 as microlight	138/304	up to 136/300	82 (153; 95)	n.k.	Pilot or two seats	K, A. Amphibious biplane. All-metal below waterline. Can be built as Experimental homebuilt using 37.3 kW (50 hp) or 47.7 kW (64 hp) Rotax engine, requiring 600-800 hours to assemble from 51% kit.
Ultra Efficient Products Inc 1637 7th Street, Sarasota, Florida 34236	Demoiselle	8.23/ 27-0	6.40/ 21-0	R, D, O	One 15 kW (20 hp) Zenoah G25B	111/245	59-95/ 130-210	43 (80; 50)	86 (161; 100)	Pilot	P and some components.
Ultra Efficient Products Inc	Invader Mk III-B	9.45/ 31-0	5.49/ 18-0	R, D, P	One 20 kW (27 hp) Rotax 277	111/245	59-95/ 130-210	52 (97; 60)	217 (402; 250)	Pilot	P and components. Conforms to FAR Pt 103. Pod and boom type with shoulder wings and V tail.
Ultra Efficient Products Inc	Penetrater	7.32/ 24-0	4.88/ 16-0	R, D, P	One 15 kW (20 hp) Zenoah	79.5/175	59-81/ 130-180	52 (97; 60)	217 (402; 250)	Pilot	P. Pilot lays prone on boom type fuselage.
Ultralight Aircraft Inc 39416-264th Avenue, South East Enumclaw, Washington 98022	Sno-Bird	n.k.	n.k.	Autogyro	Rotax	n.k.	n.k.	n.k.	n.k.	Pilot	A?
Ultra Sail Inc 225 East Side Avenue, Mattituck, New York 11952	Cloud Dancer	12.19/ 40-0	5.41/ 17-9	R, D, P	One 20 kW (27 hp) Rotax 277	115/253	50-100/ 110-220	55 (101; 63)	173 (322; 200)	Pilot	K, A. Pod and boom low wing monoplane with V tail.
Vancraft Copters 7246 North Mohawk Avenue, Portland, Oregon 97203	Lightning Sport Copter	7.01 or 8.53/ 23-0 or 28-0	3.63/ 11-11	Autogyro	One 34.3 kW (46 hp) Rotax 503	114/252	68-100/ 150-220	55 (101; 63)	69-95 (128-177; 80-110)	Pilot	Conforms to FAR Pt 103. Semi-enclosed accommodation.
Volmer Aircraft Box 5222, Glendale, California 91201	VJ-23E Swingwing	9.93/ 32-7	5.31/ 17-5	R, B, D, O	One 7.5 kW (10 hp) McCulloch	54.5/120	45.5-91 (100-200)	n.k.	n.k.	Pilot	P. Foot launched powered sailplane.
Volmer Aircraft	VJ-24W Sunfun	11.13/ 36-6	5.64/ 18-6	R, B, D, O, P	One 11.2 kW (15 hp) Yamaha	95/210	n.k.	24 (45; 28) cruising	n.k.	Pilot	P.

SAILPLANES

AUSTRALIA

SCHNEIDER
EDMUND SCHNEIDER PTY LTD
Details of the Schneider ES 65 Platypus can be found in the 1989-90 and previous editions of *Jane's*.

AUSTRIA

HB-AIRCRAFT INDUSTRIES — *See main Aircraft Section*

HOFFMANN — *See Germany, West*

BELGIUM

ARPLAM
ALL REINFORCED PLASTIC MOULDINGS
Sint-Eloois-Winkel, Flanders

ARPLAM LEUVENSE L-1
The L-1 was designed by students of the Leuvense University Aero Club, and its construction was assisted financially by the Flemish regional government and the

Belgian Department of Science. Two flying prototypes and a ground test airframe of the L-1 were built by Arplam. No recent news has been received. Further details and a three-view drawing can be found in the 1989-90 *Jane's*.

BRAZIL

Aeromot AMT-100 Ximango side by side two-seat motor glider

AEROMOT
AEROMOT-INDÚSTRIA MECÁNICO-METALÚRGICA Ltda
Av Das Indústrias 1210, Porto Alegre, RS
Telephone: 55 (512) 42 3132
Telex: (051) 1991
Fax: 55 (512) 43 3655
PRESIDENT: Claudio Miguel Barreto Viana
OPERATIONAL AND SPECIAL PROGRAMMES MANAGER:
Sílvio Barreto Viana

AEROMOT AMT-100 XIMANGO
The Ximango is the current production version of the French Aérostructure (Fournier) RF-10 motor glider.

First flown on 6 March 1981, the original RF-10 was generally similar to the Fournier RF-9 (1981-82 *Jane's*) but of plastics construction and having a carbonfibre main spar. A more powerful engine was fitted, fuel capacity increased, all control surfaces balanced, and the main landing gear had larger wheels. Two prototypes were built by Fournier Aviation in 1981, with low-set tailplanes, but a T tail was adopted for the production version, which first flew on 10 May 1984.

By the time French certification was granted on 23 October 1984 a total of 11 RF-10s had been completed, and by early 1985 orders from French production totalled 30, of which 13 had been delivered to customers in Brazil, France and Portugal.

The French company sold all production rights to Aeromot in July 1985. Brazilian CTA certification of the renamed AMT-100 Ximango was granted on 5 June 1986. The Civilian Aeronautical Department ordered 100 Ximangos. One of the first two produced was certificated with a Brazilian Retimotor RM-2000A version of the Limbach/Volkswagen engine. Other sales and deliveries of the AMT-100 have been made, to private customers in Brazil, Argentina and France. The AMT-100 is also being produced for military purposes, such as observation, patrol and counter-insurgency. The basic military version has two side windows below the canopy and carries an underfuselage pod for 100 kg (220 lb) of weapons or equipment (avionics, cameras, etc). By January 1990 the Brazilian military police had received three military examples for patrol and ecological observation against forest fires, and a further 12 aircraft were then on option for other police forces.

TYPE: Side by side two-seat training and sporting motor glider.
AIRFRAME: Cantilever low-wing monoplane, of glassfibre construction with a carbonfibre main spar. NACA 64₃618 section unswept wings, with 2° 30′ dihedral from roots. Ailerons of GFRP; light alloy Schempp-Hirth upper surface airbrakes. Wings can be detached from fuselage for transportation; outer portion of each wing can be folded inward for stowage, without disconnecting aileron controls. Semi-monocoque glassfibre fuselage, slightly swept fin and rudder, and fixed incidence T tailplane with elevator. Entire tail unit of GFRP. Mechanically retractable mainwheels (tyre size 330 × 130), with hydraulic suspension and JPX hydraulic disc brakes; steerable tailwheel with size 210 × 65 tyre. One-piece cockpit canopy opens upward and rearward. Dual controls standard.
POWER PLANT: One 59.5 kW (80 hp) Limbach L 2000 EO1 flat-four engine, driving a Hoffmann two-blade three-position variable-pitch propeller. Fuel in two main tanks in wings, combined capacity 90 litres (23.8 US gallons; 19.75 Imp gallons). Electric starter and 12V 30A alternator.

DIMENSIONS, EXTERNAL:
Wing span	17.47 m (57 ft 3¾ in)
Wing aspect ratio	16.3
Width, wings folded	10.15 m (33 ft 3½ in)
Length overall	7.89 m (25 ft 10¾ in)
Height over tail	1.93 m (6 ft 4 in)

AREA:
Wings, gross	18.70 m² (201.3 sq ft)

WEIGHTS AND LOADINGS:
Weight empty	600 kg (1,323 lb)
Max T-O weight	800 kg (1,764 lb)
Max wing loading	42.78 kg/m² (8.77 lb/sq ft)
Max power loading	13.42 kg/kW (22.05 lb/hp)

PERFORMANCE, UNPOWERED (at max T-O weight):
Best glide ratio at 54 knots (100 km/h; 62 mph)	30
Min rate of sink at 49 knots (90 km/h; 56 mph)	0.96 m (3.15 ft)/s
Stalling speed	39 knots (72 km/h; 45 mph)
Max speed (smooth air)	133 knots (245 km/h; 153 mph)
Max speed (rough air)	97 knots (180 km/h; 112 mph)
g limits	+5.3/−2.65

PERFORMANCE, POWERED (at max T-O weight):
Max cruising speed	108 knots (200 km/h; 124 mph)
Econ cruising speed	97 knots (180 km/h; 112 mph)
Stalling speed	39 knots (72 km/h; 45 mph)
Max rate of climb at S/L	150 m (492 ft)/min
Service ceiling	5,000 m (16,400 ft)
Range with max fuel	728 nm (1,350 km; 839 miles)
Max endurance	7 h 30 min

CETEC
CENTRAL TECHNICAL FOUNDATION OF MINAS GERAIS
Belo Horizonte

PROJECT LEADER: Claudio Pinto de Barros
Brief details of the CETEC CB-7 Vesper motor glider can be found in the 1989-90 *Jane's*.

IPE
INDÚSTRIA PARANAENSE DE ESTRUTURAS Ltda
Rua Jerônimo Durski 357, Caixa Postal 7931, 80430 Curitiba, Paraná

MANAGER: Eng J. C. Boscardin

IPE KW 1 b 2 QUERO-QUERO II
Brazilian Air Force designation: Z-16
Four prototypes (first flight 1 October 1972) and 154 production examples of the Quero-Quero were built, of which about 110 remained fully airworthy in 1989. US certification was not gained due to a lack of resources.

Details of the Quero-Quero II can be found in the 1989-90 and previous editions of *Jane's*.

IPE KW 1 GB
This 15 metre Class version of the Quero Quero was constructed of wood and glassfibre. Two examples were built (one with water ballast). IPE has sent an application to the FAI for the World Class Glider Contest, for a version without winglets and water ballast. Further brief details can be found in the 1987-88 *Jane's*.

IPE-02b NHAPECAN II
Brazilian Air Force designation: TZ-14

The IPE-02 Nhapecan I first prototype (PP-ZQL) flew for the first time on 24 May 1979, and was described and illustrated in the 1983-84 *Jane's*.

The second prototype, known as the IPE-02b Nhapecan II, was considerably redesigned, with different dimensions and a more modern wing section based on the work of the Brazilian engineer Francisco Leme Galvão. As a result, performance was noticeably improved, and initial certification was followed by delivery of 15 to the Brazilian Air Force Academy. These were subsequently retrofitted with rudder and elevator mass balances. Final certification was granted and production resumed, but production was halted in November 1989 after the 79th sailplane. The next example has been constructed as the prototype of a modified version, with a 1° 30′ increase in wing leading-edge sweep, elimination of ballast and other modifications. Production will resume after these changes have been approved.

The following details refer to the Nhapecan II before the most recent modifications:

TYPE: Tandem two-seat training sailplane.

AIRFRAME: Shoulder-wing monoplane with Galvão BR-JKNA 3511/04 wing section. Ailerons and upper/lower surface spoilers. Wooden wings and tail surfaces; steel tube (4130) fuselage with glassfibre skin. Non-retractable monowheel, in streamline fairing, and tailwheel.

DIMENSIONS, EXTERNAL:
Wing span	16.60 m (54 ft 5½ in)
Wing aspect ratio	16.0
Length overall	8.54 m (28 ft 0¼ in)
Height over tail	1.90 m (6 ft 2¾ in)

AREA:
Wings, gross	17.20 m² (185.1 sq ft)

WEIGHTS AND LOADING:
Weight empty	340 kg (749 lb)
Max T-O weight	560 kg (1,234 lb)
Max wing loading	32.56 kg/m² (6.67 lb/sq ft)

PERFORMANCE (at max T-O weight):
Best glide ratio at 48 knots (88 km/h; 55 mph)	better than 32
Min rate of sink at 38 knots (70 km/h; 43 mph):	
single-seat	0.65 m (2.13 ft)/s
two-seat	0.75 m (2.46 ft)/s
Stalling speed	37 knots (68 km/h; 43 mph)
Max speed (smooth air)	108 knots (200 km/h; 124 mph)

IPE-04
This designation now applies to a two-seat aerobatic training sailplane. The first prototype was fitted with a 134 kW (180 hp) Textron Lycoming IO-320 engine as a motor glider in February 1990, and further work is in this form.

IPE-05 QUERO-QUERO III
This is a new high performance 15 m sailplane, developed from the KW 1 b 2 Quero-Quero. Construction is of wood and plastics. The first prototype was expected to fly in August-September 1990. Like the Quero-Quero, it has upper/lower surface spoilers.

TYPE: Single-seat glider.

DIMENSIONS, EXTERNAL:
Wing span	15.00 m (49 ft 2½ in)
Length overall	6.70 m (21 ft 11¾ in)

AREA:
Wings, gross	10.50 m² (113.0 sq ft)

WEIGHTS AND LOADING:
Weight empty	120 kg (265 lb)
Max T-O weight	240 kg (529 lb)
Max wing loading	22.86 kg/m² (4.68 lb/sq ft)

PERFORMANCE (estimated):
Best glide ratio	38
Min rate of sink at 42 knots (78 km/h; 48 mph)	0.69 m (2.26 ft)/s
Stalling speed	38 knots (70 km/h; 44 mph)
Max speed	151 knots (280 km/h; 174 mph)

CHINA, PEOPLE'S REPUBLIC

Sailplane development in China began in 1958, when a number of Polish gliding instructors were invited into the country to train air force cadets. Since that time the Chinese industry has manufactured more than 1,000 gliders of various types. The X prefix in designations stands for Xiangji, the Chinese word for glider.

CHENGDU AIRCRAFT CORPORATION
PO Box 800, Chengdu, Sichuan
Telephone: 86 (28) 669629
Telex: 60132 CCDAC CN
Fax: 86 (28) 69816

CHENGDU X-7 JIAN FAN (SWORD POINT)
The X-7 was flown for the first time in October 1966. A total of 130 had been built by the beginning of 1980; present production status is not known, although it is believed the X-7 remains a current type (perhaps now built at Shenyang).

TYPE: Tandem two-seat basic training glider.

AIRFRAME: High-wing monoplane, braced by single I strut on each side. Wing section Göttingen 535 (modified). Dihedral from roots. Single-spar constant chord wings, comprising a glassfibre/honeycomb/epoxy sandwich torsion box, fabric covered aft of spar. Glassfibre ailerons and upper surface airbrakes. Semi-monocoque glassfibre pod and boom fuselage, moulded in two halves and joined at centreline. Fabric covered glassfibre cruciform tail unit; fin built integrally with fuselage. Non-retractable monowheel, nose-skid and tailskid. Tandem open cockpits, with windscreen.

DIMENSIONS, EXTERNAL:
Wing span	13.07 m (42 ft 10½ in)
Wing aspect ratio	9.5
Length overall	7.06 m (23 ft 2 in)
Height over tail	1.60 m (5 ft 3 in)

AREA:
Wings, gross	18.00 m² (193.75 sq ft)

WEIGHTS AND LOADING:
Weight empty	220 kg (485 lb)
Max T-O weight	370 kg (816 lb)
Max wing loading	20.55 kg/m² (4.21 lb/sq ft)

PERFORMANCE (at max T-O weight):
Best glide ratio at 34 knots (63 km/h; 39 mph)	12
Min rate of sink at 32 knots (60 km/h; 37 mph)	1.40 m (4.59 ft)/s
Stalling speed	25 knots (45 km/h; 28 mph)
Max speed (smooth air)	81 knots (150 km/h; 93 mph)
Max speed (rough air)	54 knots (100 km/h; 62 mph)
Max winch-launching speed	43 knots (80 km/h; 50 mph)
g limits	+4/−2

SHENYANG SAILPLANE FACTORY
Shenliao Zhong Road 1-5, Shenyang, Liaoning
Telex: 804007 MIECS CN
GENERAL MANAGER: Zhu Ri Xie
CHIEF ENGINEER: Li Ji Jung

SHENYANG X-9 JIAN FAN (SWORD POINT)
Used extensively in the Chinese People's Republic, the X-9 is a tandem two-seat training glider, said to have flying characteristics similar to those of the Schweizer SGS 2-33 (see US section). It is a braced high-wing monoplane (wing section Göttingen 535), of wood and aluminium construction. Design and first flight took place in 1977, and approx 150 had been built by the Autumn of 1980. The X-9 is thought still to be in production.

DIMENSIONS, EXTERNAL:
Wing span	14.42 m (47 ft 3¾ in)
Wing aspect ratio	11.0
Length overall	7.335 m (24 ft 0¾ in)
Height over tail	2.32 m (7 ft 7¼ in)

AREA:
Wings, gross	18.90 m² (203.4 sq ft)

WEIGHTS AND LOADING:
Weight empty	230 kg (507 lb)
Max T-O weight	380 kg (837 lb)
Max wing loading	20.10 kg/m² (4.12 lb/sq ft)

PERFORMANCE (at max T-O weight):
Best glide ratio at 36 knots (67 km/h; 42 mph)	17
Min rate of sink at 32 knots (60 km/h; 37 mph)	0.96 m (3.15 ft)/s
Stalling speed	25 knots (45 km/h; 28 mph)
Max speed (smooth air)	81 knots (150 km/h; 93 mph)
Max speed (rough air)	54 knots (100 km/h; 62 mph)
Max aero-tow speed	65 knots (120 km/h; 75 mph)
Max winch-launching speed	54 knots (100 km/h; 62 mph)

SHENYANG X-10 QIAN JIN (FORWARD)
This single-seat high performance club sailplane is a licence built version of the Polish SZD-8/14 Jaskolka, modernised to utilise both wood and glassfibre construction (wing section NACA 43012A modified). It has been built in large numbers, and is probably the most widely used single-seater in China. Production status is unknown, although production is thought to be continuing.

DIMENSIONS, EXTERNAL:
Wing span	16.00 m (52 ft 6 in)
Wing aspect ratio	18.63
Length overall	7.625 m (25 ft 0¼ in)
Height over tail	1.605 m (5 ft 3¼ in)

AREA:
Wings, gross	13.74 m² (147.90 sq ft)

WEIGHTS AND LOADING:
Weight empty	252 kg (556 lb)
Max T-O weight	342 kg (754 lb)
Max wing loading	24.9 kg/m² (5.10 lb/sq ft)

PERFORMANCE (at max T-O weight):
Best glide ratio at 38 knots (70 km/h; 43 mph)	26
Min rate of sink at 37 knots (68 km/h; 42 mph)	0.75 m (2.46 ft)/s
Stalling speed	32-33 knots (58-60 km/h; 36-38 mph)
Max speed (smooth air)	135 knots (250 km/h; 155 mph)
Max speed (rough air)	97 knots (180 km/h; 112 mph)
Max aero-tow speed	81 knots (150 km/h; 93 mph)
Max winch-launching speed	59 knots (110 km/h; 68 mph)

SHENYANG HU-2 PETREL 650B
Superseding the earlier two-seat Petrel 550 and three-seat Petrel 650, the latest Petrel 650B cabin motor glider is a highly improved three-seater which gained its Certificate of Airworthiness of CAAC and has been in substantial production. It may continue to use the 60.4 kW (81 hp) Limbach L 2000 EO1 engine. It has strut braced high mounted wings of Göttingen 535 section, and introduces a conventional tailwheel landing gear.

DIMENSIONS, EXTERNAL:
Wing span	14.92 m (48 ft 11½ in)
Wing aspect ratio	11.3
Length overall	7.02 m (23 ft 0½ in)
Height overall	2.14 m (7 ft 0¼ in)

AREA:
Wings, gross	19.63 m² (211.29 sq ft)

WEIGHTS AND LOADING:
Weight empty	445 kg (981 lb)
Max T-O weight	715 kg (1,576 lb)
Max wing loading	36.42 kg/m² (7.46 lb/sq ft)

PERFORMANCE:
Stalling speed	33 knots (60 km/h; 38 mph)
Max level speed	73 knots (135 km/h; 84 mph)
Cruising speed	54 knots (100 km/h; 62 mph)
Max rate of climb	144 m (472 ft)/min
Service ceiling, powered	3,850 m (12,625 ft)
Max range, powered	323 nm (600 km; 372 miles)
Endurance	6 h

SHENYANG HU-1 SEAGULL
The HU-1 Seagull is a fairly new side by side two-seat motor glider, intended primarily for aerial survey, aerial photography and forest patrol work, having a camera hatch below one seat. Future development calls for a training version and a four-seat version. Certification in China was gained in July 1988.

TYPE: Side by side two-seat motor glider.

AIRFRAME: Cantilever shoulder-wing monoplane. Wing section E603. Dihedral 1°. Incidence 2°. Aluminium alloy semi-monocoque construction, except for glassfibre and wood used for some non-load bearing structures and fabric covering elevator and rudder. Single spar wing structure. Non-retractable monowheel main landing gear unit, with low pressure tyre size 480 × 200. Steerable tailwheel size 200 × 80 below cantilever T tail on boom. Balancer wheels at wingtips. Cockpit canopy opens upward and backward. Starboard seat may be removed to make room for special equipment when used for agricultural, industrial or other purposes.

POWER PLANT: One 88 kW (118 hp) Textron Lycoming O-235-N2A flat-four engine, driving a pusher propeller.

IPE Nhapecan II sailplane in latest modified form

IPE-05 Quero-Quero III *(Jane's/Mike Keep)*

Shenyang X-10 Qian Jin single-seat sailplane

Chengdu X-7 Jian Fan two-seat glassfibre training glider *(Charles M. Gyenes)*

Shenyang HU-1 Seagull two-seat motor glider carrying aerial survey equipment

Shenyang X-9 two-seat training glider, with enclosed cockpits
(Charles M. Gyenes)

Shenyang HU-2 Petrel 650B cabin motor glider

DIMENSIONS, EXTERNAL:		Max T-O weight: A	1,050 kg (2,315 lb)	PERFORMANCE, POWERED:	
Wing span	17.00 m (55 ft 9¼ in)	B	900 kg (1,984 lb)	Max permissible speed	121 knots (225 km/h; 140 mph)
Wing aspect ratio	16.4	Max wing loading: A	59.39 kg/m² (12.16 lb/sq ft)	Cruising speed	86 knots (160 km/h; 99 mph)
Length overall	7.62 m (25 ft 0 in)	B	50.90 kg/m² (10.43 lb/sq ft)	Stalling speed, flaps up	46 knots (85 km/h; 53 mph)
Height overall	1.73 m (5 ft 8 in)	Max power loading: A	11.93 kg/kW (19.62 lb/hp)	Max rate of climb at S/L	240 m (787 ft)/min
Propeller diameter	1.76 m (5 ft 9¼ in)	B	10.23 kg/kW (16.81 lb/hp)	Service ceiling	4,500 m (14,765 ft)
AREA:		PERFORMANCE, UNPOWERED:		T-O run	173 m (568 ft)
Wings, gross	17.68 m² (190.3 sq ft)	Best glide ratio	20	Range	485 nm (900 km; 559 miles)
WEIGHTS AND LOADINGS (A: normal, B: utility categories):		Min rate of sink at 43 knots (80 km/h; 50 mph)		Endurance	5 h
Weight empty: A, B	600 kg (1,323 lb)		1.50 m (4.92 ft)/s	g limits	+3.8/–1.9

CZECHOSLOVAKIA

AEROTECHNIK

AEROTECHNIK

Podnik ÚV Svazarmu, 68604 Uherské Hradiště-Kunovice
Telephone: 42 (632) 5122
Telex: 60380
HEAD OF TECHNICAL DEPARTMENT: Ing E. Parma

In addition to the overhaul and re-engining of Zlin 226s and 326s, Aerotechnik is producing for Czech aeroclubs the L-13SE Vivat, a motor glider version of the Let L-13 Blaník that has superseded the previous L-13SW model (83 built, including three prototypes).

AEROTECHNIK L-13SE VIVAT

The L-13SE is a modernised version of the L-13SW Vivat, first flown on 27 September 1989. Forty-five have been ordered by Czechoslovak aeroclubs.

The Vivat, which features side by side seating instead of the tandem layout of the Blaník sailplane on which it is based, has been optimised for both elementary and advanced training. Authorised manoeuvres include sharp turns and stalls up to 60°, slips, skids, and unlimited spinning.

The following description applies to the initial production version:

TYPE: Side by side two-seat motor glider.

AIRFRAME: Cantilever mid-wing monoplane. NACA wing sections: 63₂A615 at root, 63₂A612 at tip. Dihedral 3°. Incidence 4° at root, 1° at tip. Sweepforward 5° at quarter-chord. All-metal single-spar wings, with light alloy riveted skin and wingtip 'salmons'. Fabric covered light alloy ailerons and slotted area-increasing flaps. DFS type light alloy airbrakes in upper and lower surfaces. Oval section fuselage, forward portion being a welded metal tube structure with glassfibre skin, rear portion a riveted light alloy semi-monocoque. Light alloy fin and fixed incidence tailplane; fabric covered rudder and elevators. Trim tab in each elevator. Horizontal tail

surfaces fold upward for transportation. Mechanically semi-retractable rubber sprung monowheel, with size 350 × 135-125 mm tyre (pressure 3.2 bars; 46.4 lb/sq in); non-retractable rubber sprung controllable tailwheel, with size 200 × 50-90 mm tyre (pressure 1.2 bars; 17.4 lb/sq in); and retractable outrigger wheels in wingtip 'salmons'. Moravan n.p. mechanical brake on monowheel. One-piece Plexiglas bubble canopy, raised upwards and rearwards on struts to permit access to cockpit. Tesla LS 5 VHF or Becker AR-3201 com radio, and standard VFR instrumentation.

POWER PLANT: One 48.5 kW (65 hp) Aerotechnik Mikron III AE or Mikron III SE in-line engine with electric starting, driving an Aeron Brno V 218 fixed-pitch or Hoffmann HO-V-62R two-blade wooden propeller with spinner. Welded light alloy fuel tank in centre-fuselage, max capacity 50 litres (13.2 US gallons; 11 Imp gallons).

DIMENSIONS, EXTERNAL:

Wing span   16.705 m (54 ft 9¾ in)

Wing aspect ratio	13.8
Length overall	8.30 m (27 ft 2¾ in)
Height overall	2.30 m (7 ft 6½ in)

AREA:

Wings, gross	20.20 m² (217.4 sq ft)

WEIGHTS AND LOADINGS:

Weight empty, equipped	470 kg (1,036 lb)
Max T-O weight	700 kg (1,543 lb)
Max wing loading	34.65 kg/m² (7.10 lb/sq ft)
Max power loading	14.43 kg/kW (23.74 lb/hp)

PERFORMANCE, UNPOWERED (at max T-O weight with propeller feathered. A: V 218, B: HO-V-62R):

Best glide ratio:

A at 48 knots (90 km/h; 56 mph)	21
B at 53 knots (98 km/h; 61 mph)	24

Min rate of sink:

A at 43 knots (80 km/h; 50 mph)	1.20 m (3.94 ft)/s
B at 46 knots (85 km/h; 53 mph)	1.05 m (3.44 ft)/s
Stalling speed: A, B	34 knots (62 km/h; 39 mph)

Max speed (smooth air):

A, B	124 knots (230 km/h; 143 mph)

Max speed (rough air):

A, B	86 knots (160 km/h; 99 mph)
g limits: A, B	+5/-2.65

PERFORMANCE, POWERED (at max T-O weight; A and B as above):

Max cruising speed:

A	94 knots (175 km/h; 109 mph)
B	100 knots (185 km/h; 115 mph)
Econ cruising speed: A	84 knots (155 km/h; 96 mph)
B	86 knots (160 km/h; 99 mph)
Stalling speed: A, B	33 knots (60 km/h; 37 mph)
Max rate of climb at S/L: A	140 m (460 ft)/min
B	198 m (650 ft)/min
Service ceiling: A, B	4,000 m (13,125 ft)
T-O run: A	200 m (655 ft)
B	110 m (361 ft)
T-O to 15 m (50 ft): A	430 m (1,410 ft)
B	370 m (1,214 ft)
Landing from 15 m (50 ft): A, B	370 m (1,214 ft)
Landing run: A, B	110 m (361 ft)

Range (depending on weight of crew):

A, B, 30 litres (7.9 US gallons; 6.6 Imp gallons) fuel	205 nm (380 km; 236 miles)
A, B, 50 litres (13.2 US gallons; 11 Imp gallons) fuel	345 nm (640 km; 398 miles)

AEROTECHNIK XL-113

Illustrations in the east European press have shown an L-13SW Vivat equipped with spraygear. The designation of this prototype is XL-113. Power plant has been increased to 58 kW (78 hp), and a tricycle landing gear with fixed main units has been used. Other changes include a fin extension and increased cockpit glazing. Max T-O weight is quoted as 890 kg (1,962 lb), and max level speed at 108 knots (200 km/h; 124 mph).

LET

LET KONCERNOVÝ PODNIK (Let Concern Enterprise)

Uherské Hradiště-Kunovice
Telephone: 42 (5) 411111
Telex: 060387 and 060388
OFFICERS: see Aircraft section

LET L-23 SUPER BLANÍK

Well known as the source of the L-13 Blaník sailplane (1984-85 and earlier *Jane's*), Let designed the L-23 version to meet the requirements of OSTIV 1986 and the Utility category of JAR 22. Design of the Super Blaník started in 1986 and construction of a prototype began in 1987. This (OK-926) first flew on 13 May 1988. Production began in 1989.

A total of 2,649 examples of the L-13 were built. Major design changes in the L-23 include improved cockpit comfort and view, no wing flaps, and the introduction of a T tail unit.

TYPE: Tandem two-seat training and performance soaring sailplane.

AIRFRAME: Cantilever shoulder-wing monoplane. NACA wing sections: 63₂A-615 at root, 63₂A-612 at tip. Dihedral 3°. Incidence 4°. Sweepforward 5° at quarter-chord. All-metal wings, with three-point attachment to fuselage each side. Single main spar forms rigid torsion box with leading-edge. Ailerons are of fabric covered light alloy. DFS type upper and lower surface airbrakes.

Downturned wingtips are of GFRP. All-metal semi-monocoque oval section fuselage, forward portion comprising a frame of longerons and bulkheads with stressed skin; rear portion consists of two semi-monocoque halves, riveted to reinforcing bulkheads. Sweptback fin and rudder; non-swept, fixed incidence T tailplane with elevators. Fin (integral with fuselage) and tailplane are all-metal; rudder and elevators are of fabric covered light alloy. Trim tab in each elevator. Single mainwheel, with Let oleo-pneumatic shock absorber and mechanical drum brake, is fitted with Rudy Rijen Otrokovice Barum tyre, size 350 × 135 mm, pressure 2.5 bars (36 lb/sq in), and can be semi-retracted manually by lever mechanism. Non-retractable rubber sprung tailwheel is fully castoring and spring centred. Small undersno skid. Aero-tow hook forward of this, ahead of first fuselage bulkhead; CG towing hook optional. Winch towing coupling each side at fourth fuselage bulkhead. Tandem seating for one or two occupants, with dual controls, upholstered seat cushions, GFRP backrests and four-point harnesses standard. Forward backrest adjustable for length and inclination; both backrests shaped for back type parachutes. Space for 20 kg (44 lb) of baggage. Separate Plexiglas canopies, the forward one (which is jettisonable from either seat) opening sideways to starboard; rear canopy is hinged at rear and opens upward. Both cockpits are ventilated, and have provision for radio, oxygen equipment and an artificial horizon.

DIMENSIONS, EXTERNAL:

Wing span	16.20 m (53 ft 1¾ in)
Wing aspect ratio	13.7

Length overall	8.50 m (27 ft 10¾ in)
Height over tail	1.90 m (6 ft 2¾ in)

AREA:

Wings, gross	19.15 m² (206.1 sq ft)

WEIGHTS AND LOADINGS (A: single-seat, B: two-seat):

Weight empty: A, B	310 kg (683 lb)
Max T-O weight: A	420 kg (926 lb)
B	510 kg (1,124 lb)
Max wing loading: A	21.93 kg/m² (4.49 lb/sq ft)
B	26.63 kg/m² (5.45 lb/sq ft)

PERFORMANCE (estimated at max T-O weight, A and B as above):

Best glide ratio:

A at 43 knots (80 km/h; 50 mph) IAS	28
B at 46 knots (85 km/h; 53 mph) IAS	28

Min rate of sink:

A at 40 knots (75 km/h; 47 mph) IAS	0.73 m (2.40 ft)/s
B at 43 knots (80 km/h; 50 mph)	0.82 m (2.69 ft)/s
Stalling speed: A	30 knots (55 km/h; 34 mph) IAS
B	33 knots (60 km/h; 38 mph) IAS

Max speed (smooth air):

A, B	135 knots (250 km/h; 155 mph) IAS

Max speed (rough air):

A, B	86 knots (160 km/h; 99 mph)

Max aero-tow speed:

A, B	81 knots (150 km/h; 93 mph)

Max winch-launching speed:

A, B	64 knots (120 km/h; 74 mph)
g limits: A	+6/-3
B	+5.3/-1.5

VSO

VYVOJOVÁ SKUPINA ORLIČAN

c/o Orlican Státni Podnik, 56537 Choceň
Telephone: 42 (468) 952
Telex: 0 196 210

This group was formed by members of the former VSB (1973-74 *Jane's*) and some of the design staff of the Orličan National Works. Its first product is the VSO 10.

VSO 10 GRADIENT

Design of the VSO 10 began in March 1972. Construction of three prototypes (one for structural test and two for flight test) began in 1975, and the first flight took place on 26 October 1976. Series production began in December 1978. By the beginning of 1990 a total of 221 had been delivered to Czechoslovak aeroclubs, including 12 of the VSO 10C Club Class version with non-retractable monowheel.

TYPE: Single-seat Standard and Club Class sailplane.

AIRFRAME: Cantilever shoulder-wing monoplane, with Wortmann wing sections: FX-61-163 at root, FX-60-126

at tip. Dihedral 3°. All-wood single-spar forward-swept wings with glassfibre sandwich skin. All-metal DFS airbrakes on upper surfaces. All-wood slotted ailerons. Glassfibre monocoque front and centre fuselage sections, latter reinforced by steel tube frame. Monocoque rear fuselage of aluminium alloy sheet. Metal T tail with fabric covered elevators and rudder. Fixed incidence tailplane. Retractable rubber sprung monowheel (tyre pressure approx 2.45 bars; 35.5 lb/sq in), with drum brake. Semi-recessed unsprung tailwheel. Detachable cockpit canopy. Provision for 56 litres (14.8 US gallons; 12.3 Imp gallons) water ballast.

DIMENSIONS, EXTERNAL:

Wing span	15.00 m (49 ft 2½ in)
Wing aspect ratio	18.75
Length overall	7.00 m (22 ft 11¾ in)
Height over tail	1.38 m (4 ft 6¼ in)

AREA:

Wings, gross	12.00 m² (129.2 sq ft)

WEIGHTS AND LOADING (both versions):

Weight empty	250 kg (551 lb)

Max T-O weight	380 kg (837 lb)
Max wing loading	31.67 kg/m² (6.49 lb/sq ft)

PERFORMANCE (at max T-O weight):

Best glide ratio:

10 at 49 knots (90 km/h; 56 mph)	36
10C at 51 knots (95 km/h; 59 mph)	34

Min rate of sink:

10 at 39 knots (73 km/h; 45 mph)	0.64 m (2.10 ft)/s
10C at 43 knots (79 km/h; 49 mph)	0.72 m (2.36 ft)/s
Stalling speed: 10	37 knots (68 km/h; 43 mph)
10C	38 knots (70 km/h; 44 mph)

Max speed (smooth air):

10, 10C	135 knots (250 km/h; 155 mph)

Max speed (rough air), and max aero-tow speed:

10, 10C	86 knots (160 km/h; 99 mph)

Max winch-launching speed:

10, 10C	65 knots (120 km/h; 75 mph)
g limits: 10, 10C	+5.3/-3.5

FRANCE

AÉRONAUTIQUE

AÉRONAUTIQUE SERVICE

Aérodrome Le Blanc, BP 44, 36300 Le Blanc
Telephone: 33 54 37 06 91 and 37 07 96
Telex: 750272 F

In 1988 Aéronautique Service took over SA Centrair, the latter having been founded in January 1970 by M Marc Ranjon, an ex-Aéronavale pilot and a flying and gliding instructor. Centrair had a covered factory space of 7,000 m² (75,347 sq ft).

AÉRONAUTIQUE SERVICE 101 and PÉGASE

The following versions are believed to be available:

101 Club. Basic version, with non-retractable mono-

wheel, no water ballast and no instrumentation. First flown November 1981, certificated June 1982.

Pégase A. As 101, but with retractable monowheel. Prototype (F-WFRA), first flown on 20 November 1981, was of this version. Certificated June 1982; winglet version first flown May 1982. Total of well over 300 built.

Pégase B. Identical to Pégase A except standard water ballast capacity of 160 litres (42.3 US gallons; 35.2 Imp gallons). First flown May 1984.

Pégase D. Definitive competition version, embodying experience gained with Pégase BC. Certificated by DGAC on 3 November 1986.

TYPE: Single-seat Standard or Club Class sailplane.

AIRFRAME: Cantilever shoulder-wing monoplane, constructed of Conticell sandwich and epoxy resin, with glassfibre roving spar. Onera wing sections: COAP 1 at root, COAP

2 at tip. Dihedral 2° 18'. Double plate upper surface airbrakes. Turned-down wingtips. Glassfibre/epoxy resin monocoque fuselage (reinforced with carbonfibre on all except 101). Cantilever T tailplane, with elevator. All control surfaces mass balanced. Retractable (all Pégase variants) or non-retractable (101 Club) unsprung monowheel (size 5.00-5, pressure 3.5 bars; 50.75 lb/sq in), with drum brake (hydraulic disc brake on Pégase B from September 1985); rubber tail bumper, with metal skid or recessed wheel. Nosewheel on 101 Club. Nose or CG towing hook. One-piece cockpit canopy, hinged at front and opening upward. Pégase B and D have two 80 litre (21.1 US gallon; 17.6 Imp gallon) leading-edge water ballast tanks as standard.

DIMENSIONS, EXTERNAL (all versions):

Wing span	15.00 m (49 ft 2½ in)

Aerotechnik L-13SE Vivat, a powered version of the original Blaník sailplane
(J. Vychodsky)

Let L-23 Super Blaník two-seat training sailplane

Prototype Aéronautique Service Marianne two-seat training
and aerobatic sailplane

VSO 10C Club Gradient single-seat Club Class sailplanes

Aéronautique Service Pégase B single-seat Standard Class sailplane
(Peter F. Selinger)

Wing aspect ratio	21.4
Length overall	6.82 m (22 ft 4½ in)
Height over tail	1.42 m (4 ft 8 in)

AREA:

Wings, gross (all versions)	10.50 m² (113.0 sq ft)

WEIGHTS AND LOADINGS:

Weight empty, equipped: 101	245 kg (540 lb)
Pégase A	251 kg (553 lb)
Pégase B	256 kg (564 lb)
Pégase D	252 kg (556 lb)
Max T-O weight: 101, Pégase A	455 kg (1,003 lb)
Pégase B, D	505 kg (1,113 lb)
Max wing loading:	
101, Pégase A	43.3 kg/m² (8.87 lb/sq ft)
Pégase B, D	48.1 kg/m² (9.86 lb/sq ft)

PERFORMANCE (at max T-O weight):

Best glide ratio:		
101 at 50 knots (92 km/h; 57 mph)		38
Pégase A at 53 knots (98 km/h; 61 mph)		40
Pégase B at 55 knots (102 km/h; 63 mph)		40
Pégase D at 57 knots (105 km/h; 65 mph)		42.5
Min rate of sink:		
101 at 39 knots (72 km/h; 45 mph)	0.65 m (2.13 ft)/s	
Pégase A at 43 knots (80 km/h; 50 mph)		
	0.67 m (2.20 ft)/s	
Pégase B at 45 knots (83 km/h; 51 mph)		
	0.65 m (2.13 ft)/s	
Pégase D at 46 knots (85 km/h; 53 mph)		
	0.62 m (2.03 ft)/s	
Max speed (smooth air):		
all versions	135 knots (250 km/h; 155 mph)	
Max speed (rough air):		
all versions	97 knots (180 km/h; 112 mph)	
Max aero-tow and max winch-launching speed:		
all versions	86 knots (160 km/h; 99 mph)	

AÉRONAUTIQUE SERVICE 2001 MARIANNE

The Marianne is a tandem two-seat sailplane for training and aerobatics. All structural calculations were made by Dassault Aviation, and the programme receives financial assistance from the French government. The Marianne was the winner of an FFVV competition, and 250 are expected to be acquired for use by French aero clubs.

First flight by prototype F-WGMA was made on 19 September 1985. Certification was granted on 29 January 1987.

AIRFRAME: Cantilever shoulder-wing monoplane. Onera laminar flow aerofoil sections: COAP 1 at root, COAP 2 at tip. Laminated wings, of Klégécel/glassfibre/epoxy resin construction with glassfibre roving spar. Dihedral 3°. Ailerons of similar construction. No flaps. Double plate aluminium upper surface airbrakes. Laminated fuselage of Klégécel, glassfibre and epoxy. Cantilever T tailplane, with elevator; construction of glassfibre and epoxy. Non-retractable 5.00-5 monowheel, tyre pressure 3.5 bars (50.75 lb/sq in), with hydraulic disc brake; non-retractable 3.00-3 nosewheel. Two seats in tandem under separate canopies: front canopy opens forward, rear canopy sideways to starboard. No water ballast. Aero-tow and winch-launching hooks.

DIMENSIONS, EXTERNAL:

Wing span	18.55 m (60 ft 10¼ in)
Wing aspect ratio	19.9
Length overall	9.00 m (29 ft 6½ in)
Height over tail	1.55 m (5 ft 1 in)

AREA:

Wings, gross	17.185 m² (185.0 sq ft)

WEIGHTS AND LOADING:

Weight empty, equipped	430 kg (948 lb)
Max T-O weight	650 kg (1,433 lb)
Max wing loading	37.82 kg/m² (7.75 lb/sq ft)

PERFORMANCE (at max T-O weight):

Best glide ratio at 57 knots (105 km/h; 65 mph)		40
Min rate of sink at 46 knots (85 km/h; 53 mph)		
	0.65 m (2.13 ft)/s	
Stalling speed	37 knots (67 km/h; 42 mph)	
Max speed (smooth air)	135 knots (250 km/h; 155 mph)	
Max speed (rough air), and max aero-tow speed		
	92 knots (170 km/h; 105 mph)	
Max winch-launching speed		
	70 knots (130 km/h; 81 mph)	
g limits	+4.3/-1.5 ultimate	

AÉRONAUTIQUE SERVICE 2001M MARIANNE M

The 2001M Marianne M motor glider airframe is identical to the sailplane but has underwing balancer wheels for take-off and landing.

POWER PLANT: One 45 kW (60 hp) Volkswagen engine (JPX modification), driving a two-blade fixed-pitch propeller and mounted in a detachable pod which also accommodates a 15 litre (4 US gallon; 3.3 Imp gallon) fuel tank.

WEIGHTS AND LOADINGS:

Weight empty, equipped	500 kg (1,102 lb)
Max T-O weight	725 kg (1,598 lb)
Max wing loading	42.15 kg/m² (8.64 lb/sq ft)
Max power loading	16.21 kg/kW (26.64 lb/hp)

PERFORMANCE, POWERED (estimated at max T-O weight):

Max cruising speed	108 knots (200 km/h; 124 mph)	
Econ cruising speed	84 knots (155 km/h; 96 mph)	
Stalling speed	49 knots (90 km/h; 56 mph)	
Best glide ratio at 54 knots (100 km/h; 62 mph)		31
Min rate of sink at 52 knots (96 km/h; 60 mph)		
	1.00 m (3.28 ft)/s	

FOURNIER

AVIONS RENÉ FOURNIER

Aérodrome d'Athée-Nitray, 37270 Montlouis-sur-Loire
Telephone: 33 47 50 68 30
Telex: 751 236 F
DIRECTOR: René Fournier
PRODUCTION: Coparavia SA, Beas de Segura (Jaen), Andalucia, Spain

M René Fournier re-established this company to put back into series production his RF 5 motor glider, of which more than 200 were delivered to customers in about 30 countries. All manufacturing and assembly is now done by partner company Coparavia SA in Spain, with the French company acting solely as marketer and distributor for the aircraft. New production began in May 1987, and the RF 5 is available in both kit form and ready to fly. The co-production agreement provides also for re-introduction of the Fournier RF 4.

FOURNIER RF 5

TYPE: Tandem two-seat motor glider.
AIRFRAME: Cantilever low-wing monoplane. NACA wing sections: 23015 at root, 23012 at tip. Dihedral 3° 15' at main spar centreline. Incidence 4° at root, 0° at tip. No sweepback. All-wood single-spar wings, with plywood and fabric covering. Fabric covered wooden ailerons. Three-section metal skinned spoilers on each upper surface. Outer wing panels fold inward for transportation and storage. All-wood oval section fuselage of bulkheads and stringers, plywood and fabric covered. Conventional all-wood tail unit, plywood and fabric covered, is detachable for transportation. Fixed incidence tailplane; Flettner tab in port elevator. Spring assisted, manually retractable Tost monowheel, with twin oleo-pneumatic shock absorbers. Dunlop tyre, size 6.00-6, pressure 1.96 bars (28.4 lb/sq in). Manually operated mainwheel brake. Tailwheel, also with shock absorber, is steerable by rudder pedals. Outrigger wheel beneath each wing just inboard of fold line. Adjustable tandem seats for pilot and passenger, with dual controls, under one-piece sideways opening canopy. Adjustable rudder pedals and canopy emergency release standard. Space for 10 kg (22 lb) of baggage aft of rear seat. Cockpits heated and ventilated.
POWER PLANT: One 59 kW (80 hp) Limbach L 2000 EOI flat-four engine, driving a Hoffmann HO-V-62-R/160 two-blade fixed-pitch propeller with spinner. Fuel in two wingroot leading-edge metal tanks, total capacity 60 litres (15.9 US gallons; 13.2 Imp gallons). Refuelling point on top of port wing.

DIMENSIONS, EXTERNAL:
Wing span	13.74 m (45 ft 1 in)
Width, wings folded	8.60 m (28 ft 2½ in)
Wing aspect ratio	12.5
Length overall	7.80 m (25 ft 7¼ in)
Height overall, tail down	1.96 m (6 ft 5 in)

AREA:
Wings, gross	15.12 m² (162.8 sq ft)

WEIGHTS AND LOADINGS:
Weight empty	420 kg (926 lb)
Max T-O weight	650 kg (1,433 lb)
Max wing loading	42.8 kg/m² (8.77 lb/sq ft)
Max power loading	10.9 kg/kW (17.91 lb/hp)

PERFORMANCE, POWERED (at max T-O weight):
Never-exceed speed	135 knots (250 km/h; 155 mph)
Max cruising speed	113 knots (210 km/h; 130 mph)
Stalling speed, clean configuration	43 knots (78 km/h; 49 mph)
Max rate of climb at S/L	195 m (640 ft)/min
T-O and landing run	200 m (655 ft)
Range with max fuel	378-485 nm (700-900 km; 435-559 miles)
Best glide ratio	20
g limits	+6/-3

ISSOIRE

ISSOIRE-AVIATION SA (Groupe Siren)

Aérodrome d'Issoire-le-Broc (Puy-de-Dôme), BP No.1, 63501 Issoire Cédex
Telephone: 33 73 89 01 54
Telex: 990 185 F ISSAVIA
PRESIDENT/DIRECTOR GENERAL: Xavier Laguette
TECHNICAL DIRECTOR: Xavier Lauras

This company is one of three forming the Siren group, the others being Siren SA and Aéro Berry.

Issoire is responsible for the PIK-20E2F and PIK-30 self-launching sailplanes.

ISSOIRE PIK-20E2F

Details of the PIK-20 sailplane can be found under the Eiri heading in the Finnish sections of the 1979-80 and previous editions of *Jane's*.

The prototype of the PIK-20E powered version flew for the first time on 2 October 1976 and was described in the 1977-78 *Jane's*. The production prototype made its first powered flight on 18 March 1978, and series production began in late 1978. Approx 50 were delivered by Eiri before production in Finland ended in 1980. A description can be found in the 1980-81 *Jane's*. The French built version has a Rotax 505 (instead of 501) engine and is designated PIK-20E2F.

As part of a programme to collect airflow data on flight at low Reynolds numbers, NASA's Dryden Research Center used a PIK-20 as a testbed to develop wing profiles appropriate to high-altitude low-speed flight. Further details of this programme appeared in the 1989-90 *Jane's*.

The following description applies to the standard production PIK-20E2F:
TYPE: Single-seat self-launching 15 metre Class sailplane.
AIRFRAME: Cantilever shoulder-wing monoplane with T tail. Wortmann wing sections: FX-67-K-170 at root, FX-67-K-150 at tip. Dihedral 3°. Sweepback 1° 21.6'. Glassfibre/epoxy/PVC foam sandwich wings. Spars of carbonfibre reinforced epoxy. Schempp-Hirth airbrakes standard. Plain flaps (flaperons) function as both flaps and ailerons. Provision for 80 litres (21.1 US gallons; 17.5 Imp gallons) of water ballast. Glassfibre/epoxy monocoque fuselage, reinforced with ribs and carbonfibre. T tail of similar construction to wings. Fixed incidence tailplane, with one-piece elevator. Retractable sprung Tost monowheel with drum brake. Steerable rubber sprung tailwheel. Non-retractable wingtip wheels. Forward hinged one-piece cockpit canopy. Optional Tost towing hook.
POWER PLANT: One 32 kW (43 hp) Rotax 505 two-cylinder two-stroke engine, with reduction drive to a Hoffmann two-blade fixed-pitch wooden propeller and retracting manually into fuselage aft of cockpit when not in use. Electric starter. Kevlar fuel tank, capacity 30 litres (7.9 US gallons; 6.6 Imp gallons).

DIMENSIONS, EXTERNAL:
Wing span	15.00 m (49 ft 2½ in)
Wing aspect ratio	22.5
Length overall	6.53 m (21 ft 5 in)
Height over tail	1.47 m (4 ft 10 in)

AREA:
Wings, gross	10.00 m² (107.6 sq ft)

WEIGHTS AND LOADINGS:
Weight empty	310 kg (683 lb)
Max water ballast	80 kg (176 lb)
Max T-O weight	470 kg (1,036 lb)
Max wing loading	47.0 kg/m² (9.63 lb/sq ft)
Max power loading	14.62 kg/kW (24.03 lb/hp)

PERFORMANCE, UNPOWERED (at max T-O weight, engine retracted):
Best glide ratio at 63 knots (117 km/h; 73 mph)	41
Min rate of sink at 47 knots (88 km/h; 55 mph)	0.70 m (2.30 ft)/s
Stalling speed	41 knots (75 km/h; 47 mph)
Max speed (smooth air)	154 knots (285 km/h; 177 mph)
Max speed (rough air)	119 knots (220 km/h; 136 mph)
Max aero-tow speed	105 knots (195 km/h; 121 mph)
Max winch-launching speed	67 knots (125 km/h; 78 mph)

PERFORMANCE, POWERED (at max T-O weight except where indicated):
Cruising speed (75% power) at 370 kg (816 lb) AUW	73 knots (135 km/h; 84 mph)
Stalling speed	41 knots (75 km/h; 47 mph)
Max rate of climb at S/L	162 m (531 ft)/min
Service ceiling	5,200 m (17,050 ft)
T-O to 15 m (50 ft)	less than 500 m (1,640 ft)
Landing run	300 m (985 ft)
Range with max fuel	156 nm (290 km; 180 miles)

ISSOIRE PIK-30

Construction of this aircraft, which is basically a 17 metre Open Class version of the PIK-20E2F, started in 1983. The prototype first flew in April 1984, followed by a second aircraft, to production standard, in December 1984. French certification was awarded in September 1985. PIK-30s have been ordered by customers in France, New Zealand, UK and USA. Production is at the rate of one per month.

The PIK-30 incorporates removable, 1 metre long, glassfibre wingtips, enabling it to qualify also in the FAI 15 m Class if desired.
POWER PLANT: As for PIK-20E2F, plus automatic system for vertical positioning of propeller when engine is stopped. Fuel capacity 29 litres (7.7 US gallons; 6.4 Imp gallons).

DIMENSIONS, EXTERNAL: As PIK-20E2F except:
Wing span	17.00 m (55 ft 9¼ in)
Wing aspect ratio	27.2

AREA:
Wings, gross	10.63 m² (114.42 sq ft)

WEIGHTS AND LOADINGS:
Weight empty	310 kg (683 lb)
Max T-O weight	460 kg (1,014 lb)
Max wing loading	43.27 kg/m² (8.86 lb/sq ft)
Max power loading	14.38 kg/kW (23.58 lb/hp)

PERFORMANCE, UNPOWERED (at max T-O weight):
Best glide ratio at 59 knots (110 km/h; 68 mph)	45
Min rate of sink at 41 knots (75 km/h; 47 mph)	0.54 m (1.77 ft)/s
Stalling speed	38 knots (70 km/h; 44 mph)
Never-exceed speed	140 knots (260 km/h; 162 mph)
Max speed (rough air), and max aero-tow speed	102 knots (190 km/h; 118 mph)
Max winch-launching speed	67 knots (125 km/h; 78 mph)
g limits	+5.3/-2.65

PERFORMANCE, POWERED (at max T-O weight):
Max cruising speed	73 knots (135 km/h; 84 mph)
Econ cruising speed	65 knots (120 km/h; 75 mph)
Stalling speed	38 knots (70 km/h; 44 mph)
Max rate of climb at S/L	240 m (785 ft)/min
T-O run	280 m (920 ft)
Landing run	300 m (985 ft)
Range with max fuel	162 nm (300 km; 186 miles)

LA MOUETTE

SARL LA MOUETTE

1 rue de la Petite Fin, 21121 Fontaine les Dijon
Telephone: 33 80 56 66 47
Telex: 350 053 F
Fax: 33 80 55 42 01

In addition to the Atlas and Compact hang gliders detailed in the hang glider tables (which see), La Mouette has available two motor gliders as the Atlas 21M (first flown in 1987 and at least 1,200 ordered) and the Chronos (first flown in 1988 and 1,000 built).

LA MOUETTE ATLAS 21M

Construction of 2017AT3 aluminium alloy.

DIMENSIONS, EXTERNAL:
Wing span	10.60 m (34 ft 9¼ in)
Wing aspect ratio	5.2

AREA:
Wings, gross	21.5 m² (231.4 sq ft)

WEIGHTS:
Weight empty	42 kg (93 lb)
Max T-O weight	350 kg (771 lb)

PERFORMANCE, UNPOWERED:
Best glide ratio	6
Min rate of sink	1.80 m (5.91 ft)/s
Stalling speed	21 knots (38 km/h; 24 mph)
Max speed (smooth air)	65 knots (120 km/h; 74 mph)

PERFORMANCE, POWERED:
Max cruising speed	35 knots (65 km/h; 40 mph)
Stalling speed	20 knots (36 km/h; 23 mph)
Max rate of climb at S/L	300 m (985 ft)/min
T-O run	20 m (66 ft)
Landing run	30 m (99 ft)

LA MOUETTE CHRONOS

Construction of 2017AT3 aluminium alloy with single surface fabric covering on wings. Pendular control. Tricycle landing gear. One 47.7 kW (64 hp) engine; fuel capacity 24 litres (6.3 US gallons; 5.3 Imp gallons).

DIMENSIONS, EXTERNAL:
Wing span	10.00 m (32 ft 9¾ in)
Wing aspect ratio	7.1
Propeller diameter	1.68 m (5 ft 6 in)

AREA:
Wings, gross	14.0 m² (150.7 sq ft)

WEIGHTS:
Weight empty	130 kg (287 lb)
Max T-O weight	300 kg (661 lb)

PERFORMANCE, UNPOWERED:
Best glide ratio at 33 knots (60 km/h; 38 mph)	8
Min rate of sink	1.6 m (5.25 ft)/s
Stalling speed	25 knots (45 km/h; 28 mph)
Max speed (smooth air)	70 knots (130 km/h; 80 mph)

PERFORMANCE, POWERED:
Max cruising speed	65 knots (120 km/h; 75 mph)
Econ cruising speed	38 knots (70 km/h; 43 mph)
Stalling speed	25 knots (45 km/h; 28 mph)
Max rate of climb at S/L	300 m (985 ft)/min
T-O and landing run	30 m (99 ft)
g limits	+6/-4

Fournier RF 5 tandem two-seat motor glider

Akaflieg Berlin B 13 side by side two-seat Open Class motor glider before completion

Akaflieg Berlin B 13 side by side two-seat Open class motor glider
(Jane's/Mike Keep)

Issoire built PIK-30 self-launching sailplane, with power plant extended

STRALPES Aéro ST-11 prototype Club Class sailplane

STRALPES AÉRO
STRALPES AÉRO SARL
BP 14, Aérodrome RN6, 73190 Challes-les-Eaux
Telephone: 33 79 70 49 27
DIRECTOR: Christian Brondel

STRALPES Aéro (Société de Traitement, Réparation, Approvisionnement, Livraison de Pièces En Stratifié) was formed in March 1979. It is a distributor and maintenance centre for Glaser-Dirks sailplanes, and developed the ST-11 and other designs of its own.

STRALPES AÉRO ST-11
Objective of the ST-11's designers was to produce a low cost sailplane for club and personal use, with a wing span of less than 15 m and built of composite materials. The prototype (F-WBCB) made its first flight on 29 August 1982. General appearance is shown in the accompanying photograph. An **ST-11M** powered version was also designed (see 1986-87 edition).

TYPE: Single-seat Club Class sailplane.
AIRFRAME: Cantilever mid-wing monoplane, with cruciform tail unit, non-retractable semi-recessed monowheel and tailskid. Wings have a STRALPES Aéro (modified Wortmann) section, with thickness/chord ratio of 15% at root and 12.6% at tip. Carbonfibre main spar, upper surface airbrakes, and glassfibre/epoxy sandwich skin. One-piece cockpit canopy. No water ballast.

DIMENSIONS, EXTERNAL:
Wing span	11.60 m (38 ft 0¾ in)
Wing aspect ratio	20.6
Length overall	5.55 m (18 ft 2½ in)
Height over tail	1.135 m (3 ft 8¾ in)

AREA:
Wings, gross	6.54 m² (70.4 sq ft)

WEIGHTS AND LOADING:
Weight empty	110 kg (243 lb)
Max T-O weight	230 kg (507 lb)
Max wing loading	35.17 kg/m² (7.20 lb/sq ft)

PERFORMANCE (at wing loading of 29 kg/m²; 5.94 lb/sq ft):
Best glide ratio at 54 knots (100 km/h; 62 mph)	35
Min rate of sink at 43 knots (80 km/h; 50 mph)	0.65 m (2.13 ft)/s
Stalling speed	37 knots (68 km/h; 42 mph)
Max speed (rough and smooth air)	124 knots (230 km/h; 143 mph)
Max aero-tow speed	89 knots (165 km/h; 102 mph)
Max winch-launching speed	70 knots (130 km/h; 80 mph)
g limits (JAR 22)	+5.3/-2.65

STRALPES AÉRO ST-15
The prototype of this 15 metre Class sailplane (F-WBCD) flew for the first time on 23 August 1986. It has a Horstmann-Quast wing section, aspect ratio of 22.9 and best glide ratio of 41.5.

WEIGHTS:
Weight empty	240 kg (529 lb)
Max T-O weight:	
without water ballast	350 kg (772 lb)
with water ballast	440 kg (970 lb)

GERMANY, WEST

AKAFLIEG BERLIN
AKADEMISCHE FLIEGERGRUPPE BERLIN eV
Technische Universität Berlin, Strasse des 17 Juni 135, 1000 Berlin 12
Telephone: 49 (30) 314 24995
INFORMATION: Holm Friedrich

Akaflieg Berlin comprises a group of students concerned with the development and construction of sailplanes. Flying is done from an airfield at Ehlershausen-Grosses Moor, near Celle, where six other sailplanes are also flown by the group.

AKAFLIEG BERLIN B 13
The B 13 is a motor glider but without self-launching capability. The Rotax engine is carried within the front of the fuselage and is fixed, driving a five-blade folding propeller developed by Professor Claus Oehler (a member of Akaflieg Berlin) via a belt-driven shaft.

Design of the B 13 began in 1982, with construction of the prototype starting in the following year. The first flight was expected to be made in Summer 1990.

TYPE: Side by side two-seat Open class motor glider.
AIRFRAME: Cantilever mid-wing monoplane with a T tail. Wings of Stemme S 10 type, designed by Akaflieg Berlin members and modified to have wider carry-through structure in fuselage. Wing section HQ 41. Dihedral 1° 18'. Incidence 0°. Wings and ailerons constructed of CFRP and GFRP, with CFRP flaps. Schempp-Hirth airbrakes, constructed of AFRP and GFRP. Water ballast now deleted. Fuselage of CFRP/AFRP sandwich construction, with stringers. T tail of similar materials to fuselage, with rudder and elevators. Landing gear of modified ASH 25 type. Two seats side by side under front-hinged one-piece canopy.

POWER PLANT: One 24 kW (32 hp) Rotax 377 two-cylinder piston engine, driving an Oehler folding five-blade propeller. One fuel tank, capacity 25 litres (6.6 US gallons; 5.5 Imp gallons).

DIMENSIONS, EXTERNAL:

Wing span	23.20 m (76 ft 1½ in)
Wing aspect ratio	28.5
Length overall	8.30 m (27 ft 2¾ in)
Height overall	1.90 m (6 ft 2¾ in)
Propeller diameter	0.86 m (2 ft 10 in)

AREA:

Wings, gross	18.90 m² (203.44 sq ft)

WEIGHTS AND LOADING:

Weight empty	520 kg (1,146 lb)
Max T-O weight	800 kg (1,763 lb)
Max wing loading	42.33 kg/m² (8.67 lb/sq ft)

PERFORMANCE, UNPOWERED (calculated):

Best glide ratio at 57 knots (105 km/h; 65 mph)	49
Min rate of sink at 40 knots (75 km/h; 47 mph)	0.55 m (1.80 ft)/s
Stalling speed	38 knots (70 km/h; 44 mph)
Max speed (smooth air)	151 knots (280 km/h; 174 mph)
Max speed (rough air)	108 knots (200 km/h; 124 mph)
Max aero-tow speed	75 knots (140 km/h; 87 mph)
Max winch-launching speed	64 knots (120 km/h; 74 mph)
g limits	+5.3/−2.65

AKAFLIEG BRAUNSCHWEIG
AKADEMISCHE FLIEGERGRUPPE BRAUNSCHWEIG eV

Flughafen Akafliegheim, 3300 Braunschweig
Telephone: 49 (531) 350312

AKAFLIEG BRAUNSCHWEIG SB-13
Construction of the prototype SB-13 began in 1985, and the first flight was made on 18 March 1988.

TYPE: Standard Class sailplane.

AIRFRAME: Cantilever mid-wing 'flying wing' monoplane with Horstmann-Quast HQ-34N aerofoil section at root, HQ-36K at tip. Dihedral 4°. Incidence −1° 48′ at mid span, −0° 48′ at tip. Wings have compound sweepback (15° max, 12° mean, at quarter-chord), are turned up at tips to form winglets/fins and rudders, and are built of carbonfibre (HT and HM) reinforced plastics, with two tanks in each wing for a total of 115 litres (30.4 US gallons; 25.3 Imp gallons) of water ballast. Two carbonfibre elevons on each trailing-edge, carbon Schempp-Hirth airbrakes in upper surface. Fuselage is a load-bearing shell of GFRP. Size 300 × 100 mm sprung monowheel, tyre pressure 3.2 bars (46 lb/sq in), and 260 × 85 mm non-steerable sprung nosewheel, tyre pressure 2.6 bars (38 lb/sq in), both fully retractable; brake on monowheel. Single seat under one-piece Plexiglas canopy which opens sideways to starboard. Rescue system comprising three parachutes, allowing a descent rate of 300 m (985 ft)/min.

DIMENSIONS, EXTERNAL:

Wing span	15.00 m (49 ft 2½ in)
Wing aspect ratio	19.4
Length of fuselage	3.02 m (9 ft 11 in)
Height over tail	1.96 m (6 ft 5¼ in)

AREA:

Wings, gross	11.60 m² (124.86 sq ft)

WEIGHTS AND LOADING:

Weight empty, incl rescue system	285 kg (628 lb)
Max T-O weight	425 kg (937 lb)
Max wing loading	36.6 kg/m² (7.50 lb/sq ft)

PERFORMANCE (at wing loading of 31 kg/m²; 6.35 lb/sq ft):

Best glide ratio at 56 knots (103 km/h; 64 mph)	41.5
Min rate of sink at 42 knots (78 km/h; 48 mph)	0.58 m (1.90 ft)/s
Stalling speed at AUW of 350 kg (770 lb)	40 knots (74 km/h; 46 mph)
Max speed (rough and smooth air)	above 113 knots (210 km/h; 130 mph)
Max aero-tow speed	91 knots (170 km/h; 105 mph)
Max winch-launching speed	81 knots (150 km/h; 93 mph)
g limits (JAR 22)	+5.3/−2.65

AKAFLIEG DARMSTADT
AKADEMISCHE FLIEGERGRUPPE DARMSTADT eV

Technische Hochschule, Magdalenenstrasse 8, 6100 Darmstadt
Telephone: 49 (6151) 24720

The Fliegergruppe of Darmstadt University has been designing, building and flying sailplanes since 1920. Its postwar products have been described in several previous editions of *Jane's*. The latest is the D-41.

AKAFLIEG DARMSTADT D-41
Design began in 1987 and construction of a prototype started in 1988.

TYPE: Side by side two-seat sailplane.

AIRFRAME: Cantilever mid-wing monoplane with T tail-plane. LS-6 wing section. Dihedral 3°. Incidence 2° 12′. No sweepback or sweepforward. Wings constructed of carbonfibre/aramid. Ailerons and trailing-edge flaps of aramid. Schempp-Hirth airbrakes. Wing water ballast 200 litres (53 US gallons; 44 Imp gallons). Fuselage and tail unit of carbonfibre/aramid/glassfibre construction. Retractable tailwheel landing gear, with 5.00-5 mainwheels, pressure 2.7 bars (39 lb/sq in). Brakes. Canopy hinged at front.

DIMENSIONS, EXTERNAL:

Wing span	20.00 m (65 ft 7½ in)
Wing aspect ratio	28.6
Length overall	8.30 m (27 ft 2¾ in)
Height over canopy	0.85 m (2 ft 9½ in)

AREA:

Wings, gross	14.00 m² (150.7 sq ft)

WEIGHTS AND LOADING:

Weight empty	360 kg (794 lb)
Water ballast	200 kg (441 lb)
Pilot weight range	100-200 kg (221-441 lb)
Max T-O weight	750 kg (1,653 lb)
Max wing loading	53.57 kg/m² (10.97 lb/sq ft)

PERFORMANCE:

g limits	+5.3/−1.7

AKAFLIEG HANNOVER
AKADEMISCHE FLIEGERGRUPPE HANNOVER eV

Welfengarten 1a, 3000 Hannover 1
Telephone: 49 (41051 1) 762 6422 or 70 30 32
PROJECT MANAGER, AFH 24: Uwe Kradt
PUBLIC RELATIONS MANAGER: Jörg Burmeister

AKAFLIEG HANNOVER AFH 24
Features of the AFH 24 single-seat Standard Class sailplane include a forward-sliding nose section for cockpit access instead of a hinged canopy. General configuration is that of a shoulder-wing monoplane, with a minimal diameter rear fuselage supporting a T tail; landing gear comprises a retractable monowheel and small tailwheel. The wings, fitted with upper surface spoilers, are essentially those of a Glaser-Dirks DG-300, but have a modified HQ (Horstmann-Quast) aerofoil section. The tail unit is of new design, but the elevators are of Schleicher ASW 24 type. Construction is mainly of GFRP, CFRP and AFRP composites.

Design of the AFH 24 began in 1982; fabrication of the complicated front section to meet JAR 22 requirements caused some delay in completion of the sailplane, further hindered by the need to reconstruct the hangar following a fire. The first flight is now anticipated in 1990.

DIMENSIONS, EXTERNAL:

Wing span	15.00 m (49 ft 2½ in)
Wing aspect ratio	21.8
Fuselage: Max width	0.64 m (2 ft 1¼ in)
Max depth	0.81 m (2 ft 8 in)

AREA:

Wings, gross	10.30 m² (110.9 sq ft)

WEIGHTS AND LOADING:

Weight empty	225 kg (496 lb)
Max T-O weight	475 kg (1,047 lb)
Max wing loading	46.12 kg/m² (9.45 lb/sq ft)

PERFORMANCE (estimated):

Max speed (smooth air)	146 knots (270 km/h; 168 mph)

AKAFLIEG KARLSRUHE
AKADEMISCHE FLIEGERGRUPPE KARLSRUHE eV

Akademische Fliegergruppe an der Universität Karlsruhe eV, Kaiserstrasse 12, 7500 Karlsruhe 1
Telephone: 49 (721) 608 2044
SECRETARY: Wolfgang Lieff

AKAFLIEG KARLSRUHE AK-5
Design of this single-seat FAI Standard Class sailplane began in August 1984, with the objective of providing group members with experience in designing and building sailplanes using composite materials. The AK-5 is expected to have a performance comparable with such other German types as the Glaser-Dirks DG-300, Rolladen-Schneider LS4, Schempp-Hirth Discus and Streifeneder Falcon. Flight testing began in early 1990.

TYPE: Single-seat Standard Class sailplane.

AIRFRAME: Cantilever mid-wing monoplane with T tailplane and separate elevator. Horstmann-Quast HQ-21 wing section from root to tip. Dihedral 3°. Incidence 1°. Sweepforward approx 0° 18′ at quarter-chord. Entire airframe built of GFRP composites. Schempp-Hirth airbrakes in upper surface. Tanks in wings for 160 litres (42.3 US gallons; 35.2 Imp gallons) of water ballast; trim tank for 7 litres (1.85 US gallons; 1.54 Imp gallons) of water in tail. Retractable monowheel, with brake; non-retractable tailwheel. Canopy hinged at front, opening upward.

DIMENSIONS, EXTERNAL:

Wing span	15.00 m (49 ft 2½ in)
Wing aspect ratio	21.1
Length overall	6.80 m (22 ft 3¾ in)
Height over tail	1.45 m (4 ft 9 in)

AREA:

Wings, gross	10.656 m² (114.7 sq ft)

WEIGHTS AND LOADING:

Weight empty, equipped	245 kg (540 lb)
Max water ballast	160 kg (353 lb)
Max T-O weight	485 kg (1,069 lb)
Max wing loading	45.51 kg/m² (9.32 lb/sq ft)

PERFORMANCE (calculated, at wing loading of 35 kg/m²; 7.17 lb/sq ft):

Best glide ratio at 51 knots (95 km/h; 59 mph)	41
Min rate of sink at 45 knots (84 km/h; 52 mph)	0.60 m (1.97 ft)/s
Stalling speed	38 knots (70 km/h; 44 mph)
Max speed (smooth air)	146 knots (270 km/h; 168 mph)
Max speed (rough air), and max aero-tow speed	105 knots (195 km/h; 121 mph)
Max winch-launching speed	81 knots (150 km/h; 93 mph)
g limits	+5.3/−2.65

AKAFLIEG STUTTGART
AKADEMISCHE FLIEGERGRUPPE STUTTGART eV

Pfaffenwaldring 35, 7000 Stuttgart 80

Telephone: 49 (711) 685 2443

PRESIDENT: Markus Dibon

AKAFLIEG STUTTGART Fs-32
This new single-seat 15 metre Class sailplane is under construction, and building is planned to continue into 1991. General appearance is shown in an accompanying three-view drawing.

Main features of the Fs-32 are the Fowler type high lift slotted flaps, which are in two segments on each wing. With the ailerons, they occupy the entire trailing-edge. The wings, which are of Wortmann FX-81-K-144/20 section, will be constructed of carbonfibre and other composite materials, and will have upper surface airbrakes. Dihedral angle is 3°. The carbon/glassfibre fuselage is modified from that of a Schempp-Hirth Ventus b, and has an improved version of the Ventus T tail. Landing gear comprises a retractable monowheel and semi-recessed tailwheel. The flapped wings are expected to permit a reduction in stalling speed

Akaflieg Braunschweig SB-13 prototype

Akaflieg Karlsruhe AK-5 all-plastics Standard Class sailplane

Akaflieg Darmstadt D-41 two-seat sailplane *(Jane's/Mike Keep)*

The 15 metre Class Akaflieg Stuttgart Fs-32 *(Jane's/Mike Keep)*

Akaflieg Hannover's Standard Class AFH 24 sailplane

Hänle (Doktor Fiberglas) H 101 Salto *(Peter F. Selinger)*

---

compared with other 15 m Class sailplanes, and to bring about a considerable improvement in all-round handling and performance.

DIMENSIONS, EXTERNAL:

Wing span	15.00 m (49 ft 2½ in)
Wing aspect ratio	22.6
Length overall	6.62 m (21 ft 8½ in)

AREA:

Wings, gross	9.94 m² (107.0 sq ft)

WEIGHTS (estimated):

Weight empty	260 kg (573 lb)
Max T-O weight	500 kg (1,102 lb)

PERFORMANCE (estimated):

Best glide ratio at 57 knots (105 km/h; 65 mph)	43

Min rate of sink at 46 knots (85 km/h; 53 mph)
0.60 m (1.97 ft)/s
Stalling speed approx 33 knots (60 km/h; 38 mph)
Max speed (smooth air) 135 knots (250 km/h; 155 mph)

DOKTOR FIBERGLAS
DOKTOR FIBERGLAS (URSULA HÄNLE)
Postfach 1112, 5438 Westerburg
Telephone: 49 (2663) 3420
DIRECTOR: Ursula Hänle

HÄNLE H 101 SALTO
This single-seat Standard and Club Class sailplane was produced originally by the Start + Flug company, which delivered 60 before its closure in the Spring of 1978.

The Salto is based on the Glasflügel Standard Libelle, from which it differs chiefly in having a V tail. It first flew in 1971, and is certificated by the LBA and FAA for both

Utility and Aerobatic category flying. In the latter category it is fitted with the standard span (13.30 m; 43 ft 7½ in) wings; in the Utility category it is available either with 13.30 m wings or with detachable tips which extend the span to 15.50 m (50 ft 10¼ in)

TYPE: Single-seat Standard and Club Class sailplane.

AIRFRAME: Cantilever mid-wing monoplane. Wings have Conticell sandwich shell and HH type glassfibre spar caps, and detachable tip extensions (except in Aerobatic category). Dihedral 3° from roots. Glassfibre ailerons and four flush-fitting airbrakes on trailing-edges. Glassfibre monocoque fuselage. Cantilever V tail (included angle 99°), with glassfibre fixed surfaces and glassfibre/honeycomb sandwich balanced ruddervators. Non-retractable semi-recessed monowheel, size 300 × 100 mm, with glassfibre shock absorption and internally

expanding brake. Non-retractable semi-recessed tailwheel. Brake parachute attachment standard on all versions. Canopy opens sideways to starboard.

DIMENSIONS, EXTERNAL (A: Aerobatic, U: Utility):

Wing span: A	13.30 m (43 ft 7½ in)
U (optional)	15.50 m (50 ft 10¼ in)
Wing aspect ratio: A	20.6
U (optional)	26.4
Length overall	5.70 m (18 ft 8½ in)
Height over tail	0.80 m (2 ft 7½ in)

AREAS:

Wings, gross: A	8.58 m² (92.4 sq ft)
U (optional)	9.10 m² (98.0 sq ft)

WEIGHTS AND LOADINGS:

Weight empty: A	182 kg (401 lb)
U	187 kg (412 lb)

Max T-O weight: A	280 kg (617 lb)
U	310 kg (683 lb)
Max wing loading: A	32.6 kg/m² (6.68 lb/sq ft)
U (13.3 m)	36.1 kg/m² (7.40 lb/sq ft)
U (15.5 m)	34.0 kg/m² (6.97 lb/sq ft)

PERFORMANCE (at max T-O weight except where indicated):
Best glide ratio at 51 knots (94 km/h; 58 mph):

A	34.5
U	37

Min rate of sink at 39 knots (72 km/h; 45 mph):
A, U (15.5 m), at AUW of 280 kg (617 lb)
    0.70 m (2.30 ft)/s
A, U (15.5 m), at AUW of 250 kg (551 lb)
    0.60 m (1.97 ft)/s
U (13.3 m), at AUW of 250 kg (551 lb)
    0.55 m (1.80 ft)/s

Stalling speed: A	38 knots (70 km/h; 44 mph)
U	34 knots (62 km/h; 39 mph)

Max speed (rough and smooth air):

A	151 knots (280 km/h; 174 mph)
U	135 knots (250 km/h; 155 mph)

Max aero-tow speed:

A, U	81 knots (150 km/h; 93 mph)

Max winch-launching speed:

A, U	70 knots (130 km/h; 81 mph)
g limits: A	+7/−4.9

GLASER-DIRKS
GLASER-DIRKS FLUGZEUGBAU GmbH

Im Schollengarten 19-20, Postfach 41 47, 7520 Bruchsal 4
Telephone: 49 (7257) 890
Telex: 7822410 GL DG D
Fax: 49 (7257) 8922
DIRECTORS: Gerhard Glaser and Dipl-Ing Wilhelm Dirks

Glaser-Dirks was formed in 1973; its 1,000th aircraft (including Elan licence production) was completed in 1987. The company designed, and remains the type certificate holder for, the DG-101 and DG-300 sailplanes, now manufactured by Elan in Yugoslavia (which see). Glaser-Dirks' main current activity concerns production of the DG-400, DG-500 and DG-600.

GLASER-DIRKS DG-400

The DG-400 is a self-launching development of the DG-202 (1984-85 *Jane's*), from which it differs principally in having a slightly deeper rear fuselage to accommodate the power plant when retracted. As with the unpowered versions, the DG-400 has 15 m span wings with add-on tips which increase the span to 17 m. The prototype (D-KOLL) flew for the first time on 1 May 1981. Deliveries began in June 1982; a total of 260 had been delivered by the end of 1989.

TYPE: Single-seat self-launching sailplane.
AIRFRAME: Cantilever shoulder-wing monoplane. Wing section Wortmann FX-67-K-170-17 at root, FX-67-K-170 (15 m span) or FX-60-K-126 (17 m span) at tip. Dihedral 3° from roots. Incidence −1°. Carbonfibre roving main spar, wing skin, flaps and ailerons. Schempp-Hirth aluminium airbrakes on upper surfaces. All-glassfibre semi-monocoque fuselage, fin and rudder. Glassfibre/foam sandwich T tailplane, with carbonfibre elevator. Manually retractable monowheel, size 5.00-5, tyre pressure 3.0 bars (43.5 lb/sq in), with Tost drum brake; size 200 × 50 tailwheel, tyre pressure 2.0 bars (29 lb/sq in). One-piece cockpit canopy, hinged at front to open upwards. Water ballast tank in each wing, combined capacity 90 litres (23.8 US gallons; 19.8 Imp gallons).
POWER PLANT: One 32 kW (43 hp) Rotax 505 two-stroke engine, pylon-mounted on fuselage aft of wing trailing-edge and driving a Hoffmann two-blade fixed-pitch propeller. Installation retracts, electrically, rearward into fuselage when not in use. Single fuselage fuel tank standard, capacity 20 litres (5.3 US gallons; 4.4 Imp gallons). Optional 15 litre (4 US gallon; 3.3 Imp gallon) tank in each wing, in lieu of water ballast, raising total fuel capacity to 50 litres (13.2 US gallons; 11 Imp gallons).

DIMENSIONS, EXTERNAL:

Wing span: 15 m	15.00 m (49 ft 2½ in)
17 m	17.00 m (55 ft 9¼ in)
Wing aspect ratio: 15 m	22.5
17 m	27.3
Length overall	7.00 m (22 ft 11¾ in)
Height over tail	1.40 m (4 ft 7 in)
Propeller diameter	1.29 m (4 ft 2¾ in)

AREAS:

Wings, gross: 15 m	10.00 m² (107.6 sq ft)
17 m	10.57 m² (113.8 sq ft)

WEIGHTS AND LOADINGS:

Weight empty	305 kg (672 lb)
Max T-O weight: 15 m	480 kg (1,058 lb)
17 m	460 kg (1,014 lb)
Max wing loading: 15 m	48.0 kg/m² (9.84 lb/sq ft)
17 m	43.5 kg/m² (8.91 lb/sq ft)
Max power loading: 15 m	14.9 kg/kW (24.6 lb/hp)
17 m	14.0 kg/kW (23.1 lb/hp)

PERFORMANCE, UNPOWERED (at max T-O weight):
Best glide ratio at 59 knots (110 km/h; 68 mph):

15 m	41
17 m	44

Min rate of sink at 43 knots (80 km/h; 50 mph):

15 m	0.60 m (1.97 ft)/s
17 m	0.50 m (1.64 ft)/s
Stalling speed: 15 m	35 knots (65 km/h; 41 mph)
17 m	34 knots (63 km/h; 40 mph)

Max speed (smooth air)
    146 knots (270 km/h; 168 mph)
Max speed (rough air), and max aero-tow speed
    102 knots (190 km/h; 118 mph)
Max winch-launching speed
    70 knots (130 km/h; 81 mph)

g limits	+6/−4

PERFORMANCE, POWERED (at max T-O weight):

Max cruising speed	76 knots (140 km/h; 87 mph)
Econ cruising speed	70 knots (130 km/h; 81 mph)
Stalling speed: 15 m	35 knots (65 km/h; 41 mph)
17 m	34 knots (63 km/h; 40 mph)
Max rate of climb at S/L	234 m (768 ft)/min
Service ceiling	5,000 m (16,400 ft)
T-O run at 15°C	170 m (558 ft)
Landing run	50 m (164 ft)

Range with max fuel:

level cruise	215 nm (400 km; 248 miles)
'saw-tooth' cruise/soar	404 nm (750 km; 466 miles)

GLASER-DIRKS DG-500 ELAN

The DG-500 is a two-seat sailplane/motor glider, produced by Glaser-Dirks, with airframe components manufactured by Elan in Yugoslavia. The **DG-500M** motor glider prototype (D-KMDG) made its first flight on 19 March 1987, with a Rotax 535C power plant installation similar to that of the DG-400 but uprated to 44.7 kW (60 hp). Production of the DG-500M began in Spring 1988. The other production versions are the **DG-500/22 Elan** (first flown 8 June 1989) and **DG-500 Elan Trainer** (first flown 27 April 1989), both generally similar to the DG-500M but without the engine. By the end of 1989 five DG-500Ms and two DG-500/22 Elans had been delivered.

The Elan Trainer has a reduced wing span, no flaps, either retractable (standard) or non-retractable (optional) mainwheel, and full controls in each cockpit. Only the prototype had been built by the end of 1989. It is to be certificated for all aerobatic manoeuvres necessary to obtain an aerobatic licence.

The following details refer to the DG-500M prototype, unless stated otherwise:

TYPE: Two-seat motor glider.
AIRFRAME: Cantilever mid-wing monoplane. Wortmann wing sections: FX-73-K-170/20 at root, -170/22 at tip. Dihedral 3°. Incidence 0°. Sweepforward 0° 36′ at quarter-chord. Four-piece wings built of CFRP/GFRP/Conticell foam sandwich, with CFRP spar. CFRP/Divinicell foam interconnected ailerons and trailing-edge flaps. Schempp-Hirth two-plate upper surface airbrakes. Fuselage of GFRP, the rear boom being of honeycomb construction. T tail unit, with fixed incidence tailplane, is also all-GFRP/foam. Fully retractable steel sprung monowheel (tyre size 380 x 150.5, pressure 3.0 bars; 43.5 lb/sq in), with brake; semi-recessed 260 x 85 nosewheel (steerable option on DG-500M) and 200 x 50 tailwheel. Tanks for water ballast in wings: 100 litres (26.4 US gallons; 22 Imp gallons) for DG-500M and 160 litres (42.3 US gallons; 35.2 Imp gallons) for DG-500/22 Elan. Tandem seats for two persons; canopies open sideways to starboard.
POWER PLANT: One 44.7 kW (60 hp) Rotax 535C two-cylinder two-stroke engine, mounted on pylon aft of rear cockpit and driving an MT Propeller MT 158R 125-1A two-blade propeller. Installation retracts into fuselage when not in use. Single 40 litre (10.6 US gallon; 8.8 Imp gallon) fuselage fuel tank standard; optional 20 litre (5.3 US gallon; 4.4 Imp gallon) tank in each wing, raising total fuel capacity to 80 litres (21.1 US gallons; 17.6 Imp gallons).

DIMENSIONS, EXTERNAL (A: DG-500M prototype, B: DG-500/22 Elan, C: Elan Trainer):

Wing span: A, B	22.00 m (72 ft 2 in)
C	18.00 m (59 ft 0¾ in)
Wing aspect ratio: A, B	26.5
C	19.52
Length overall: A, B, C	8.66 m (28 ft 5 in)
Height overall: A	1.80 m (5 ft 11 in)
B, C	1.665 m (5 ft 5½ in)
Propeller diameter: A	1.58 m (5 ft 2¼ in)

AREAS (A, B and C as above):

Wings, gross: A, B	18.29 m² (196.9 sq ft)
C	16.60 m² (178.7 sq ft)

WEIGHTS AND LOADINGS (A, B and C as above):

Weight empty: A	525 kg (1,157 lb)
B	445 kg (981 lb)
C	390 kg (860 lb)
Max water ballast: A	100 kg (220 lb)
B	160 kg (353 lb)
Max T-O weight: A	825 kg (1,819 lb)
B	750 kg (1,653 lb)
C	615 kg (1,356 lb)
Max wing loading: A	45.08 kg/m² (9.23 lb/sq ft)
B	41.00 kg/m² (8.40 lb/sq ft)
C	37.05 kg/m² (7.59 lb/sq ft)
Max power loading: A	18.45 kg/kW (30.31 lb/hp)

PERFORMANCE, UNPOWERED (A, B and C as above):

Best glide ratio: A, B, at 59 knots (110 km/h; 68 mph)		47
C		40

Min rate of sink at 41 knots (75 km/h; 47 mph):

B	0.51 m (1.68 ft)/s
Stalling speed: A	46.5 knots (85.5 km/h; 53.5 mph)
B	31.5 knots (58 km/h; 36 mph)
C at 470 kg (1,036 lb) AUW	
	35 knots (65 km/h; 41 mph)

Max speed (smooth air):

A, B, C	145 knots (270 km/h; 167 mph)

Max speed (rough air):

A, C	110 knots (205 km/h; 127 mph)
B	106 knots (197 km/h; 122 mph)

Max aero-tow speed:

B	106 knots (197 km/h; 122 mph)
C	110 knots (205 km/h; 127 mph)

Max winch-launching speed:

A, B	75 knots (140 km/h; 87 mph)
g limits: A	+5.3/−2.65
B	+5.64/−3.64
C	+7/−5

PERFORMANCE, POWERED (DG-500M, at 750 kg; 1,653 lb AUW):

Cruising speed	76-81 knots (140-150 km/h; 87-93 mph)
Max rate of climb at S/L	156 m (512 ft)/min
Service ceiling	5,000 m (16,400 ft)
T-O run	260 m (854 ft)

Range: max standard fuel 129 nm (240 km; 149 miles)
with wing tanks 259 nm (480 km; 298 miles)
'saw-tooth' cruise, standard fuel
    296 nm (550 km; 341 miles)
'saw-tooth' cruise, with optional tanks
    593 nm (1,100 km; 683 miles)

GLASER-DIRKS DG-600

The prototype DG-600 (D-8600) made its first flight on 15 April 1987, design having started some two years earlier. It is intended for the 15 metre Class, but standard add-on wingtip panels can extend the span to 17 m.

Features include a new thin-section wing of CFRP construction and with single-piece flaperons; a fuselage based on that of the DG-400, but with a slimmer tailboom; a DG-300/400 one-piece canopy; and a new horizontal tail. Production began in 1988, and 40 had been delivered by the end of 1989.

On 11 November 1989 the new **DG-600M** motor glider version first flew, based on the DG-600 but with a retractable 18.6 kW (25 hp) Rotax 275 engine with reduction gear and driving an MT Propeller MT 180 L97-1B propeller. Weight empty for the 15 m and 17 m versions are 305 kg (672 lb) and 310 kg (683 lb) respectively. Performance data had not been determined by the close of 1989.

TYPE: 15 metre Class sailplane.
AIRFRAME: Cantilever mid-wing monoplane with T tail. Wing sections HQ-35 (for 15 m span), HQ-37 (for wingtip add-on panels for 17 m span). Dihedral 2° 30′. Incidence −1°. Sweepforward 0° 5′ 24″ at quarter-chord. Wings, and full span flaperons, are all-composites sandwich structures of CFRP and PVC foam, except for their Schempp-Hirth aluminium upper surface airbrakes. Fuselage is a GFRP shell; tail unit is similarly constructed, but with elevator and rudder of GFRP and PVC foam sandwich. Single retractable steel-sprung mainwheel (tyre size 5.00-5, pressure 3.3 bars; 48 lb/sq in), with brake. Fixed tailwheel, tyre size 200 × 50 mm, pressure 2.0 bars (29 lb/sq in). Single seat under one-piece canopy which is hinged at front and opens upward. Wing tanks for 180 litres (47.6 US gallons; 39.6 Imp gallons) of water ballast, plus small amount in vertical fin.

DIMENSIONS, EXTERNAL:

Wing span: 15 m	15.00 m (49 ft 2½ in)
17 m	17.00 m (55 ft 9¼ in)
Wing aspect ratio: 15 m	20.5
17 m	24.9
Length overall	6.83 m (22 ft 5 in)
Height over tail	1.35 m (4 ft 5¼ in)

AREAS:

Wings, gross: 15 m	10.95 m² (117.9 sq ft)
17 m	11.59 m² (124.75 sq ft)

WEIGHTS AND LOADINGS (DG-600):

Weight empty, equipped: 15 m	255 kg (562 lb)
17 m	260 kg (573 lb)
Max water ballast (both): wings	180 kg (397 lb)
vertical fin	7 kg (15.4 lb)
Max T-O weight (both)	525 kg (1,157 lb)

Glaser-Dirks DG-600M motor glider

Glaser-Dirks DG-400 self-launching sailplane

Glaser-Dirks DG-500 Elan Trainer

Grob G 103C Twin III

RAF Grob G 109B Vigilant T. Mk 1 *(Paul Jackson)*

Max wing loading: 15 m	47.94 kg/m² (9.82 lb/sq ft)	Min rate of sink: 15 m	0.56 m (1.84 ft)/s	Max rough air and aero-tow speed	
17 m	45.30 kg/m² (9.28 lb/sq ft)	17 m	0.50 m (1.64 ft)/s		108 knots (200 km/h; 124 mph)
PERFORMANCE (DG-600, estimated at max T-O weight):		Stalling speed	35 knots (64 km/h; 40 mph)	Max winch-launching speed	
Best glide ratio: 15 m	44.5	Max speed (smooth air)	146 knots (270 km/h; 168 mph)		81 knots (150 km/h; 93 mph)
17 m	48.5			*g* limits	+5.8/−3.8

GROB

BURKHART GROB LUFT- UND RAUMFAHRT GmbH & Co KG (Division of Grob-Werke GmbH & Co KG)

Postfach 1257, 8948 Mindelheim
Telephone: 49 (8268) 9980
Telex: 5 39 623
Fax: 49 (8268) 998-14 or 998-24
CHAIRMAN: Dr hc Dipl-Ing Burkhart Grob
DEPUTY CHAIRMAN:
Dipl-Ing Klaus Harald Fischer

This company built 200 Schempp-Hirth Standard Cirrus under licence between 1972 and 1975, before concentrating on composites sailplanes and motor gliders of its own design, all meeting JAR 22 European airworthiness requirements. However, having sold a total of approximately 3,000 aircraft, no gliders or motor gliders were built for some time. More recently, in addition to its G 115 and G 116 lightplane production (see main aircraft section), Grob constructed further G 103C Twin IIIs.

GROB G 103C TWIN III

This tandem two-seat sailplane for training and club flying is the successor to the Twin Astir I (291 built: 1979-80 *Jane's*), from which it differs mainly in having lower-mounted wings, a more streamlined fuselage, modified landing gear, improved cockpit layout and reduced weight. First flight was made in late 1979, and FAA certification was granted on 26 March 1982. Production of the **Twin II** (1986-87 *Jane's*) totalled 555 by January 1986, including Acros. The G 103C **Twin III** was introduced in 1986, and the data apply to this version.

Formal acceptance of the G 103 into service with the Royal Air Force took place on 5 October 1984 at the Air Cadet Central Gliding School, Syerston, Nottinghamshire. A total of 100 Twin II Acros was delivered to the RAF, by whom they are known as the **Viking TX. Mk 1** (97 on charge in early 1990). Four Acros were ordered by the Royal Jordanian Gliding Club in 1986.

TYPE: Tandem two-seat training and club sailplane.
AIRFRAME: Cantilever low/mid-wing monoplane. Glassfibre main spar; wings and tail surfaces have glassfibre/epoxy resin sandwich skin. Conventional ailerons are of glassfibre sandwich, with elastic gap seals. No flaps. Cantilever T tail. Non-retractable nosewheel and monowheel, both semi-recessed; plus tailwheel. Individual canopies, opening sideways to starboard. No water ballast provision.

DIMENSIONS, EXTERNAL:
Wing span	18.00 m (59 ft 0¾ in)
Wing aspect ratio	18.5
Length overall	8.18 m (26 ft 10 in)
Height over tail	1.55 m (5 ft 1 in)

AREA:
Wings, gross	17.50 m² (188.4 sq ft)

WEIGHTS AND LOADING:
Weight empty	approx 370 kg (815 lb)
Max T-O weight	600 kg (1,323 lb)
Max wing loading	34.3 kg/m² (7.03 lb/sq ft)

PERFORMANCE (at max T-O weight except where indicated):
Best glide ratio at 59 knots (109 km/h; 68 mph)   38
Min rate of sink at 38 knots (71 km/h; 44 mph)
0.57 m (1.87 ft)/s
Stalling speed (carrying pilot only)
34 knots (62 km/h; 39 mph)

Max speed (smooth air):	
Twin III	135 knots (250 km/h; 155 mph)
Acro	151 knots (280 km/h; 174 mph)
Max speed (rough air)	108 knots (200 km/h; 124 mph)
Max aero-tow speed:	
Twin III	91 knots (170 km/h; 105 mph)
Acro	100 knots (185 km/h; 115 mph)
Max winch-launching speed	
	75 knots (140 km/h; 87 mph)
g limits: Twin III	+5.3/−2.65
Acro	+7/−5

GROB G 109B

The prototype G 109 (D-KBGF), with a 56 kW (75 hp) Limbach engine, flew for the first time on 14 March 1980. Series production began in the Summer of 1981. The G 109 is certificated in 17 countries, including West Germany and the USA under JAR 22. Production of the G 109A version (see 1983-84 *Jane's*) totalled 150.

The G 109B, of which a prototype was flown in March 1983, differs mainly in having modified wings, of greater span, and a more powerful engine. The first production G 109B flew in August 1983, and 250 had been built by 1986, when production was halted. The line was re-opened in January 1990 to construct 70-100 more that year, including 53 for the RAF as **Vigilant T. Mk 1s**, to expand the Air Cadets' sailplane fleet.

TYPE: Side by side two-seat motor glider.
AIRFRAME: Cantilever low-wing monoplane with T tail. Wings of Eppler E 580 section (thickness/chord ratio 16.1%) from root to tip. Dihedral 3°. Incidence 2°. No sweepback. Construction of glassfibre (GFRP) and carbonfibre (CFRP); ailerons of GFRP. Schempp-Hirth airbrakes in upper surface only. No water ballast. Wings are foldable rearward, and have automatic connection and disconnection of aileron controls. Fuselage is a GFRP monocoque. Fixed incidence tailplane, with elevator; entire tail unit is of GFRP, except for CFRP rudder. Non-retractable tailwheel type landing gear. Mainwheels have tyres size 380 × 150 mm, pressure 2.5 bars (36.25 lb/sq in), and are fitted with hydraulic disc brakes and speed fairings; tailwheel tyre size 250 × 85 mm. Side by side seats for pilot and passenger. Centre of canopy consists of two doors, hinged on c/l to open upward. Additional viewing port in each side of fuselage, forward of wingroot. Standard instrumentation and radio. Optional equipment includes VOR, ADF, DME, transponder, and electric variometer.
POWER PLANT: One 56 kW (75 hp) Limbach engine in RAF aircraft; formerly one 67 kW (90 hp) Grob 2500 engine, driving a Hoffmann two-blade three-speed variable-pitch wooden propeller with spinner. Fuselage fuel tank, capacity 100 litres (26.4 US gallons; 22 Imp gallons).
DIMENSIONS, EXTERNAL:

Wing span	17.40 m (57 ft 1 in)
Length overall	8.10 m (26 ft 7 in)
Height over tail	1.80 m (5 ft 10¾ in)
AREA:	
Wings, gross	19.00 m² (204.5 sq ft)
WEIGHTS (Grob 2500 engine):	
Weight empty, equipped	620 kg (1,367 lb)
Max T-O weight	850 kg (1,874 lb)
PERFORMANCE, UNPOWERED (at max T-O weight):	
Best glide ratio at 62 knots (115 km/h; 71 mph)	28
Min rate of sink at 57 knots (105 km/h; 65 mph)	
	1.10 m (3.61 ft)/s
Stalling speed	40 knots (73 km/h; 46 mph)
Max speed (rough and smooth air)	
	130 knots (240 km/h; 149 mph)
g limits	+5.3/−2.65
PERFORMANCE, POWERED (Grob 2500 engine, at max T-O weight):	
Never-exceed speed	130 knots (240 km/h; 149 mph)
Max cruising speed	111 knots (205 km/h; 127 mph)
Stalling speed	40 knots (73 km/h; 46 mph)
Max rate of climb at S/L	198 m (650 ft)/min
Service ceiling	6,000 m (19,675 ft)
T-O run	196 m (645 ft)
Landing run	200 m (656 ft)
Range at 97 knots (180 km/h; 112 mph) with max fuel	
	809 nm (1,500 km; 932 miles)

HAVRDA

HORST HAVRDA
Lindenberg

HAVRDA SH-2H
TYPE: Single-seat competition sailplane.
AIRFRAME: Cantilever mid-wing monoplane. Wings use Wortmann FX-71-L-150/20 section, fitted with trailing-edge flaps/ailerons. Airbrakes on upper surfaces. Tailplane ahead of fin, with elevators. All-composites construction using glassfibre. Non-retractable monowheel and tailwheel. Canopy opens sideways.
DIMENSIONS, EXTERNAL:

Wing span	10.40 m (34 ft 1½ in)
Length overall	6.50 m (21 ft 4 in)
Height overtail	1.34 m (4 ft 4¾ in)
AREA:	
Wings, gross	11.40 m² (122.7 sq ft)
WEIGHTS AND LOADING:	
Weight empty	240 kg (529 lb)
Max T-O weight	340 kg (750 lb)
Max wing loading	29.80 kg/m² (6.10 lb/sq ft)
PERFORMANCE:	
Best glide ratio	26
Min sinking speed at 46 knots (85 km/h; 53 mph)	
	0.80 m (2.62 ft)/s
Stalling speed	35 knots (65 km/h; 41 mph)
Max speed	194 knots (360 km/h; 223 mph)
g limits	±8

HINZ

LUCIA AND BERNHARD HINZ
Bei der Kirche 17, D-7024 Filderstadt 1
Telephone: 49 (7158) 65441

HINZ BL1-KEA
First flown in 1989, this is a side by side two-seat motor glider of GFRP construction. It has cantilever low wings (wing section FX-67-K150/20), a T tail with full span elevator, and a retractable landing gear comprising a monowheel, balancer wheels at about one-quarter span and a faired (non-retractable) tailwheel.
POWER PLANT: One 70 kW (94 hp) Limbach L 2400 engine in nose, driving a Mühlbauer MTV-1-A/L160-03 two-blade propeller with spinner. Fuselage fuel tank, capacity 100 litres (26.4 US gallons; 22 Imp gallons).
DIMENSIONS, EXTERNAL:

Wing span	10.00 m (32 ft 9¾ in)
Length overall	6.75 m (22 ft 1¾ in)
AREA:	
Wings, gross	12.00 m² (129.2 sq ft)
WEIGHTS:	
Weight empty	480 kg (1,058 lb)
Max T-O weight	720 kg (1,587 lb)
PERFORMANCE:	
Max speed	146 knots (270 km/h; 168 mph)
Stalling speed	46 knots (85 km/h; 53 mph)
T-O and landing run	200 m (656 ft)
Range	863 nm (1,600 km; 994 miles)

HOFFMANN

WOLF HOFFMANN FLUGZEUGBAU KG
Sportflugplatz, 8870 Günzburg/Ulm
Telephone: 49 (8221) 1417
Telex: 531625 HOFBG D
DIRECTOR: Dipl-Ing Wolf D. Hoffmann

In addition to production of its aircraft in West Germany, including the H 40 (see main Aircraft section), the Dimona and Super Dimona have been built in Austria by Hoffmann Aircraft, NA Ottostrasse 5, A 2700 Wiener Neustadt. *Telephone:* 43 (262) 226700. *Telex:* 112820 HAC A.

HOFFMANN H 36 DIMONA
The prototype of this two-seat motor glider flew for the first time on 9 October 1980, and was followed by two further prototypes. The Dimona was awarded LBA type certification on 30 March 1982, and also has a British C of A. About 300 examples were completed.

The final version was given a strengthened main landing gear, a sprung tailwheel, modified engine cowling, improved propeller pitch control, better cockpit heating and ventilation, a redesigned instrument panel and other refinements.
TYPE: Side by side two-seat motor glider; positive aerobatics permissible.
AIRFRAME: Cantilever low/mid-wing monoplane, constructed of GFRP. Wing section Wortmann FX-63-137. Upper surface airbrakes. Wings are attached independently to fuselage by bolts, and can be folded back alongside fuselage for transportation and storage. Fuselage sidewalls and frames are strengthened with extensive GFRP rovings. Double shell in cockpit area. Cantilever T tail. Non-retractable tailwheel type landing gear, with 6 in mainwheels and sprung, steerable tailwheel. Cantilever GFRP mainwheel legs. Fairings on main legs and wheels. Cockpit canopy hinged at rear to open upward. Baggage space aft of seats.
POWER PLANT: One 59.7 kW (80 hp) Limbach L 2000 EB1C engine, driving a Hoffmann HO-V62/160 two-blade three-position propeller. Fuel tank capacity 80 litres (21.1 US gallons; 17.5 Imp gallons).
DIMENSIONS, EXTERNAL:

Wing span	16.00 m (52 ft 6 in)
Wing aspect ratio	16.8
Width, wings folded	2.10 m (6 ft 10¾ in)
Length overall	6.85 m (22 ft 5¾ in)
Length, wings folded	9.30 m (30 ft 6¼ in)
Height over tail	1.625 m (5 ft 4 in)
Propeller diameter	1.60 m (5 ft 3 in)
AREA:	
Wings, gross	15.20 m² (163.6 sq ft)
WEIGHTS AND LOADINGS:	
Weight empty	540 kg (1,190 lb)
Max T-O weight	770 kg (1,697 lb)
Max wing loading	50.7 kg/m² (10.38 lb/sq ft)
Max power loading	12.91 kg/kW (21.21 lb/hp)
PERFORMANCE, UNPOWERED (at max T-O weight):	
Best glide ratio at 56 knots (105 km/h; 65 mph)	27
Min rate of sink at 43 knots (80 km/h; 50 mph)	
	0.90 m (2.95 ft)/s
Stalling speed	39 knots (72 km/h; 45 mph)
Max speed (smooth air)	148 knots (275 km/h; 171 mph)
Max speed (rough air)	113 knots (210 km/h; 130 mph)
g limits:	+5.3/−2.65 permissible
	+9.3 ultimate
PERFORMANCE, POWERED (at max T-O weight):	
Max cruising speed	97 knots (180 km/h; 112 mph)
Econ cruising speed	95 knots (176 km/h; 109 mph)
Stalling speed	39 knots (72 km/h; 45 mph)
Max rate of climb at S/L	210 m (689 ft)/min
Service ceiling	6,000 m (19,675 ft)
T-O run	180 m (590 ft)
Landing run	150 m (492 ft)
Range with max fuel	540 nm (1,000 km; 621 miles)

HOFFMANN HK 36 SUPER DIMONA
The Super Dimona is a development of the H 36, incorporating several modifications without changing the basic design. Production has begun.

Compared to the H 36 Dimona, the Super Dimona has the fuselage of the H 40 lightplane, a Limbach EB1C, similarly rated Rotax 912A or more powerful 67 kW (90 hp) Limbach L 2400 EB engine with optional dual ignition and driving a similar HO-V62/160 or HO-V/170 (with Rotax) propeller, better access to the engine and control system by the use of completely removable cowlings, a carbonfibre wing spar and main bulkhead, increased elevator chord and trim tab for improved longitudinal stability, improved spin characteristics resulting from a modified inboard wing leading-edge and the CG range moved forward, an improved airbrake mechanism, a reinforced main landing gear with removable fairings, an improved sprung tailwheel, and a new larger canopy with new mechanism. Certain aerobatic manoeuvres are permissible.
DIMENSIONS, EXTERNAL:

Wing span	16.20 m (53 ft 1¾ in)
Wing aspect ratio	17.15
Length overall:	
Limbach engine	6.98 m (22 ft 10¾ in)
Rotax engine	7.07 m (23 ft 2¼ in)
Length, wings folded:	
Limbach engine	9.43 m (30 ft 11¼ in)
Rotax engine	9.52 m (31 ft 2¾ in)
Width, wings folded	2.15 m (7 ft 0¾ in)
AREA:	
Wings, gross	15.30 m² (164.69 sq ft)

WEIGHTS AND LOADINGS (A: Limbach L 2000 EB1C, B: L 2400 EB, C: Rotax 912A):

Weight empty: A	560 kg (1,235 lb)
B	574 kg (1,265 lb)
C	550 kg (1,213 lb)
Max T-O weight: A, B, C	770 kg (1,697 lb)
Max wing loading: A, B, C	50.33 kg/m² (10.31 lb/sq ft)
Max power loading: A, C	12.90 kg/kW (21.21 lb/hp)
B	11.49 kg/kW (18.86 lb/hp)
PERFORMANCE, UNPOWERED:	
Best glide ratio at 56 knots (105 km/h; 65 mph):	
A, B, C	27
Min rate of sink at 43 knots (80 km/h; 50 mph):	
A, B	1.16 m (3.81 ft)/s
C	1.12 m (3.67 ft)/s
Stalling speed: A, B, C	39 knots (72 km/h; 45 mph)
Max speed: A, B, C	148 knots (275 km/h; 171 mph)
PERFORMANCE, POWERED:	
Max cruising speed: A	89 knots (165 km/h; 103 mph)
B	97 knots (180 km/h; 112 mph)
C	108 knots (200 km/h; 124 mph)

Hoffmann H 36 Dimona two-seat motor glider

Rolladen-Schneider LS4 Standard Class sailplane (*Avio Data*)

Schleicher ASK 13, still in production by Jubi at Oerlinghausen
(*Peter F. Selinger*)

15 m Class Rolladen-Schneider LS6 (*Martin Fricke*)

Econ cruising speed:			T-O run: A	200 m (656 ft)	Range: A	372 nm (690 km; 428 miles)
A, B, C	95 knots (176 km/h; 109 mph)		B	185 m (607 ft)	B	350 nm (650 km; 404 miles)
Stalling speed: A, B, C	39 knots (72 km/h; 45 mph)		C	175 m (574 ft)	C	388 nm (720 km; 447 miles)
Max rate of climb at S/L: B	240 m (787 ft)/min					

JUBI

JUBI GmbH SPORTFLUGZEUGBAU

Robert-Kronfeldstrasse 2, 4811 Oerlinghausen
Telephone: 49 (5202) 72446
Jubi is the production source for the Schleicher ASK 13 two-seat sailplane.

JUBI (SCHLEICHER) ASK 13

This tandem-seat sailplane was developed by Schleicher from the K 7, which is in worldwide use by gliding clubs. The prototype first flew in July 1966.
Production by Schleicher has ended, but the ASK 13 is still manufactured, under licence, by Jubi.
TYPE: Tandem two-seat training and high-performance sailplane.
AIRFRAME: Cantilever mid-wing monoplane. Wing section developed from Göttingen 535 and 549. Sweepforward at quarter-chord 6°. Dihedral 5°. Single-spar wooden wings, with fabric covering. Wooden ailerons, with plywood covering; Schempp-Hirth metal airbrakes above and below each wing. Welded steel tube fuselage with spruce formers and fabric main covering. Nose made of glassfibre. Turtledeck aft of canopy is plywood shell. Cantilever wooden tail unit, plywood covered except for fabric covered rear portion of rudder and elevators. Flettner tab in starboard elevator. Non-retractable sprung monowheel, with Tost drum brake; skid in front of wheel; steel tailskid. Canopy opens sideways to starboard.

DIMENSIONS, EXTERNAL:
Wing span	16.00 m (52 ft 6 in)
Wing aspect ratio	14.6
Length overall	8.18 m (26 ft 9½ in)
Height over tail	1.60 m (5 ft 3 in)

AREA:
Wings, gross	17.50 m² (188.4 sq ft)

WEIGHTS AND LOADING:
Weight empty	290 kg (640 lb)
Max T-O weight	480 kg (1,060 lb)
Max wing loading	26.8 kg/m² (5.49 lb/sq ft)

PERFORMANCE (at 470 kg; 1,036 lb T-O weight):
Best glide ratio at 49 knots (90 km/h; 56 mph)	28
Min rate of sink at 38 knots (70 km/h; 43 mph)	0.80 m (2.62 ft)/s
Stalling speed	33 knots (61 km/h; 38 mph)
Max speed (smooth air)	108 knots (200 km/h; 124 mph)
Max speed (rough air), and max aero-tow speed	76 knots (140 km/h; 87 mph)
Max winch-launching speed	54 knots (100 km/h; 62 mph)
g limit (safety factor of 2)	+4

LUTZ

JÜRGEN LUTZ

Details of the Lutz Libelle lightweight sailplane, and an illustration, can be found in the 1989-90 *Jane's*.

ROLLADEN-SCHNEIDER

ROLLADEN-SCHNEIDER FLUGZEUGBAU GmbH

Postfach 1130, Mühlstrasse 10, 6073 Egelsbach/Hessen
Telephone: 49 (6103) 4126
Telex: 6103985 LSFLUG
Fax: 49 (6103) 45526
OFFICERS: Walter Schneider and Dipl-Ing Wolf Lemke
Current activities are concerned with manufacture of the LS4, LS6 and LS7. Rolladen-Schneider's 1,000th sailplane, an LS4, was completed in 1981.

ROLLADEN-SCHNEIDER LS4

Design of this Standard Class sailplane began in the Winter of 1979/80, and the prototype (D-6680) flew for the first time on 28 March 1980. In the 1983 World Championships at Hobbs, New Mexico, USA, LS4s took 13 of the first 15 places in the Standard Class, including all of the first six places.
The LS4 utilises a modified LS3-a fuselage combined with a new, thin-section wing, mid-mounted on the fuselage. The **LS4-a** is identical except for an additional rubber spring on the monowheel (introduced also on the LS4 from mid-1983), and twin water ballast bag tanks in each wing, increasing the volume to 80-85 litres (21.1-22.4 US gallons; 17.6-18.7 Imp gallons) per wing.
A total of well over 600 LS4s and LS4-as have been built.
TYPE: Single-seat Standard Class sailplane.
AIRFRAME: Cantilever mid-wing monoplane, of glassfibre/Conticell foam construction. Wings have thickness/chord ratio of 15% at root and 13% at tip (modified Wortmann sections), 3° 30′ dihedral, and 0° incidence. Schempp-Hirth upper surface airbrakes. No flaps. Provision for 140 litres (37 US gallons; 30.8 Imp gallons) water ballast in wings on LS4, 160-170 litres (42.3-44.9 US gallons; 35.2-37.4 Imp gallons) on LS4-a. Semi-monocoque fuselage. Cantilever T tailplane, with elevator. Entire structure of GFRP sandwich. Retractable Tost rubber sprung monowheel, tyre pressure 2.94 bars (43 lb/sq in); tailskid standard, 200 mm tailwheel optional. Tost Kobold brake on mainwheel. Canopy hinged at front to open upward.

DIMENSIONS, EXTERNAL:
Wing span	15.00 m (49 ft 2½ in)
Wing aspect ratio	21.4
Length overall	6.83 m (22 ft 5 in)
Height over tail	1.26 m (4 ft 1½ in)

AREA:
Wings, gross	10.50 m² (113.0 sq ft)

WEIGHTS AND LOADINGS (A: LS4, B: LS4-a):
Weight empty: A	238 kg (525 lb)
B	240 kg (529 lb)
Max T-O weight: A	472 kg (1,040 lb)
B	525 kg (1,157 lb)
Max wing loading: A	44.9 kg/m² (9.21 lb/sq ft)
B	50.0 kg/m² (10.25 lb/sq ft)

PERFORMANCE (at max T-O weight):
Best glide ratio at 54 knots (100 km/h; 62 mph)	40.5
Min rate of sink at 40 knots (75 km/h; 47 mph)	0.60 m (1.97 ft)/s
Stalling speed	37 knots (68 km/h; 43 mph)
Max speed (smooth air):	
A	146 knots (270 km/h; 168 mph)
B	151 knots (280 km/h; 174 mph)
Max speed (rough air) and max aero-tow speed:	
A	97 knots (180 km/h; 112 mph)
B	102 knots (190 km/h; 118 mph)
Max winch-launching speed:	
A	70 knots (130 km/h; 81 mph)
B	75 knots (140 km/h; 87 mph)
g limits:	
at 97 knots (180 km/h; 112 mph)	+5.3/−2.65
at 146 knots (270 km/h; 168 mph)	+4/−1.5

ROLLADEN-SCHNEIDER LS6

The LS6 is a successor to the LS3. Development had been started by the beginning of 1982, and the prototype (D-0662) flew for the first time on 1 December 1983. Series production began in August 1984. LS6s gained first, second and sixth places in the 1985 World Championships, held in Italy.

An **LS6-a** version is available with a 5.5 litre (1.45 US gallon; 1.2 Imp gallon) water tank in the fin; the **LS6-b** has carbonfibre wings, with the fin water tank as an optional extra; and the latest **LS6-17.5** is a version with a 17.5 m (57 ft 5 in) wing span. The following details refer to the 15 m span LS6:

TYPE: 15 metre Class single-seat sailplane.

AIRFRAME: Cantilever mid-wing monoplane, constructed mainly of PVC foam and glassfibre. Wings have modified Wortmann sections, 4° dihedral, no sweep (forward or back), and carbonfibre spar caps. Ailerons and flaps are of Kevlar, glassfibre and Rohacell foam sandwich. Schempp-Hirth upper surface airbrakes. Water ballast tanks in wings. Glassfibre monocoque fuselage, with integral fin of PVC foam sandwich; Kevlar rudder. Fixed incidence T tailplane with elevator, built of PVC foam sandwich, carbonfibre and glassfibre. Rubber sprung (three element) Tost monowheel, as on LS4 but with new folding-strut retraction mechanism; choice of tailskid or 200 mm tailwheel. Tost Kobold mainwheel brake. One-piece Plexiglas canopy, hinged at front and opening upward; instrument panel opens with canopy.

DIMENSIONS, EXTERNAL:
Wing span	15.00 m (49 ft 2½ in)
Wing aspect ratio	21.4
Length overall	6.65 m (21 ft 9¾ in)
Height over tail (with tailwheel)	1.30 m (4 ft 3¼ in)

AREA:
Wings, gross	10.50 m² (113.0 sq ft)

WEIGHTS AND LOADING:
Weight empty	250 kg (551 lb)
Max water ballast	180 kg (397 lb)
Max T-O weight	525 kg (1,157 lb)
Max wing loading	50.0 kg/m² (10.25 lb/sq ft)

PERFORMANCE:
Best glide ratio	more than 40
Min rate of sink	less than 0.60 m (1.97 ft)/s
Max speed (smooth air)	146 knots (270 km/h; 168 mph)
Stalling speed	36 knots (65 km/h; 41 mph)

ROLLADEN-SCHNEIDER LS7

The LS7, of which production began in April 1988, combines enhanced handling qualities with good manoeuvrability.

TYPE: 15 metre Class single-seat sailplane.

AIRFRAME: Cantilever mid-wing monoplane. Wings have new section, are double tapered, and are constructed as a carbonfibre sandwich (designed for maximum torsional stiffness for optimum performance, increased stiffness when flying with water ballast and high handling resistance). Carbonfibre roving spar caps. Kevlar sandwich ailerons. Upper surface airbrakes. Ballast bags in wings. Glassfibre fuselage shell. Carbonfibre sandwich T-mounted tailplane; Kevlar sandwich elevators. Retractable monowheel landing gear.

DIMENSIONS, EXTERNAL:
Wing span	15.00 m (49 ft 2½ in)
Wing aspect ratio	23
Length overall	6.66 m (21 ft 10¼ in)

AREA:
Wings, gross	9.74 m² (104.84 sq ft)

WEIGHTS AND LOADING:
Weight empty	235 kg (518 lb)
Max T-O weight	486 kg (1,071 lb)
Max wing loading	49.90 kg/m² (10.22 lb/sq ft)

PERFORMANCE:
Best glide ratio	43
Max speed (smooth air)	145 knots (270 km/h; 168 mph)
Stalling speed	37 knots (68 km/h; 43 mph)

SCHEIBE

SCHEIBE FLUGZEUGBAU GmbH

HEAD OFFICE AND WORKS: August-Pfaltz-Strasse 23, Postfach 1829, 8060 Dachau, near Munich
Telephone: 49 (8131) 72083 and 72084
Telex: 05 26 650
Fax: 49 (8131) 6985
MANAGERS: Dipl-Ing Egon Scheibe and Ing Christian Gad

Scheibe Flugzeugbau GmbH was founded at the end of 1951 by Dipl-Ing Scheibe; its first type produced in quantity was the Mü-13E Bergfalke I.

Subsequently, Scheibe has built many new types of sailplane, and since 1957 has been a major producer of motor gliders in the Federal Republic of Germany. Principal production model in 1990 is the SF-25C/C-2000 Falke; the SF-25E Super-Falke, SF-28A Tandem-Falke and SF-36 motor gliders, and the SF-34 sailplane, remain available, although production in recent years has been minimal.

Scheibe has built more than 2,000 aircraft of various types, in addition to many kits for home construction by amateurs. Gliders of Scheibe design are built under licence by gliding clubs as well as by foreign companies.

SCHEIBE SF-25C FALKE 90 (FALCON)

The SF-25C is an improved version of the SF-25B Falke, to which it is structurally similar. The primary difference is the use of a more powerful engine, giving an enhanced performance. Type certification was granted in September 1972.

By January 1990 several hundred SF-25C Falkes had been built by Scheibe; a further 50 were built under licence by Sportavia in Germany. Scheibe also produced 20 **SF-25C-S**, with Hoffmann feathering propellers, as detailed in earlier editions of *Jane's*.

Current models, known as **SF-25C Falke 90**, have the design improvements listed in the 1977-78 *Jane's*. With optional 59.5 kW (80 hp) Limbach engine, they are known as **SF-25C-2000**. Optional features include an additional exhaust outlet and a slower-turning propeller. With this installation the nominal noise level is reduced to less than 60 dB.

TYPE: Side by side two-seat motor glider, particularly suitable for basic and advanced training.

AIRFRAME: Cantilever low-wing monoplane. Forward swept wooden wings, with airbrakes and aerodynamically balanced ailerons. Fully folding wings optional. Fabric covered welded steel tube fuselage; forward section coated with laminated glassfibre. Wooden tail unit. Non-retractable rubber sprung monowheel with brake and aerodynamic fairing; steerable tailwheel; sprung outrigger stabilising wheel under each wing. Alternative trike landing gear with steerable nosewheel or twin-wheel main gear available optionally, with streamline wheel fairings.

POWER PLANT: One 48.5 kW (65 hp) Limbach SL 1700 EA modified Volkswagen engine (59.5 kW; 80 hp L 2000 EA in SF-25C-2000), driving a two-blade propeller. Feathering propeller optional. Electric starter. Fuel in single fuselage tank, capacity 55 litres (14.5 US gallons; 12.1 Imp gallons) standard, 80 litres (21.1 US gallons; 17.6 Imp gallons) optional.

SYSTEM: 12V electrical system.

DIMENSIONS, EXTERNAL:
Wing span	15.30 m (50 ft 2½ in)
Wing aspect ratio	13.8
Length overall	7.60 m (24 ft 11¼ in)
Height over tail	1.85 m (6 ft 0¾ in)

AREA:
Wings, gross	18.20 m² (195.9 sq ft)

WEIGHTS AND LOADINGS:
Weight empty	approx 420 kg (925 lb)
Max T-O weight	650 kg (1,433 lb)
Max wing loading	35.71 kg/m² (7.32 lb/sq ft)
Max power loading: C	13.41 kg/kW (22.05 lb/hp)
C-2000	10.89 kg/kW (17.91 lb/hp)

PERFORMANCE, UNPOWERED (at max T-O weight):
Best glide ratio	23-24
Min rate of sink	approx 1.00 m (3.28 ft)/s

PERFORMANCE, POWERED (at max T-O weight):
Max level speed: C	97 knots (180 km/h; 112 mph)
C-2000	102 knots (190 km/h; 118 mph)
Max cruising speed: C	86 knots (160 km/h; 99 mph)
C-2000	92 knots (170 km/h; 106 mph)
Stalling speed (both)	36 knots (65 km/h; 41 mph)
Max rate of climb at S/L: C	138 m (453 ft)/min
C-2000	192 m (630 ft)/min
Service ceiling: C	5,000 m (16,400 ft)
T-O run: C	approx 180 m (590 ft)
C-2000	approx 100 m (328 ft)
Landing run: C	100 m (328 ft)
Range with max fuel (both)	approx 378 nm (700 km; 435 miles)
Endurance (both)	4-5 h

SCHEIBE SF-25E SUPER-FALKE

Developed from the SF-25C-S, the Super-Falke has increased wing span and a rubber sprung monowheel; a cabin heater is standard. Production aircraft have a tailwheel and upper surface airbrakes.

A 48.5 kW (65 hp) Limbach SL 1700 EA I engine is fitted as standard, with a 59.7 kW (80 hp) Limbach L 2000 optionally, plus a 12V battery and alternator for electric engine starting. Fuel capacity is 45 litres (11.9 US gallons; 9.9 Imp gallons).

The Super-Falke was flown for the first time in the Summer of 1974; 64 had been delivered by January 1990. Details of the SF-25E can be found in the 1985-86 and earlier editions of *Jane's*.

SCHEIBE SF-28A TANDEM-FALKE

The Tandem-Falke, as its name implies, is a further development of the Falke series of motor gliders in which the two seats are arranged in tandem. Design began in 1970, and the prototype (D-KAFJ) flew for the first time in May 1971, powered by a 33.5 kW (45 hp) Stamo MS 1500 engine. Details of the production version have appeared in the 1985-86 and earlier editions of *Jane's*. Production had totalled 118 by January 1983, but only two more examples have been completed since that time.

SCHEIBE SF-34B

Design of the SF-34 sailplane began in 1978, and the prototype flew for the first time on 28 October that year. Production takes place, under licence, in Hungary; a total of 35 had been built by January 1990.

TYPE: Tandem two-seat training and sporting sailplane.

AIRFRAME: Cantilever mid-wing monoplane. Wortmann wing sections: FX-61-184 at root, FX-60-126 at tip. Glassfibre roving main spar. Wings and tail unit of GFRP honeycomb sandwich; fuselage is a GFRP shell. Schempp-Hirth airbrake in upper surface of each wing. Non-retractable semi-exposed monowheel and nosewheel, tyre sizes 5.00-5 and 260 × 85 respectively; tailskid. Tandem seats under frameless one-piece sideways opening flush canopy. Towing hooks under nose and at CG.

DIMENSIONS, EXTERNAL:
Wing span	15.80 m (51 ft 10 in)
Wing aspect ratio	16.9
Length overall	7.50 m (24 ft 7¼ in)
Height over tail	1.40 m (4 ft 7 in)

AREA:
Wings, gross	14.80 m² (159.3 sq ft)

WEIGHTS AND LOADING:
Weight empty	approx 320 kg (705 lb)
Max T-O weight	540 kg (1,190 lb)
Max wing loading	36.5 kg/m² (7.48 lb/sq ft)

PERFORMANCE (at max T-O weight):
Best glide ratio at 51 knots (95 km/h; 59 mph)	35
Min rate of sink at 41 knots (75 km/h; 47 mph)	0.70 m (2.30 ft)/s
Stalling speed	38 knots (70 km/h; 44 mph)
Max speed (rough and smooth air)	135 knots (250 km/h; 155 mph)
Max aero-tow speed	86 knots (160 km/h; 99 mph)
Max winch-launching speed	67 knots (125 km/h; 78 mph)

SCHEMPP-HIRTH

SCHEMPP-HIRTH FLUGZEUGBAU GmbH

Krebenstrasse 25, Postfach 14 43, 7312 Kirchheim unter Teck
Telephone: 49 (7021) 2441 and 45007
Telex: 7267817 HATE D
Fax: 49 (7021) 3809
DIRECTOR: Dipl-Ing Klaus Holighaus

Schempp-Hirth specialises in the production of high-performance Open Class, FAI 15 m Class, Standard Class and two-seat sailplanes and powered sailplanes. Dipl-Ing Klaus Holighaus is 100 per cent shareholder.

Production of the Schempp-Hirth Standard Cirrus was undertaken by Jastreb in Yugoslavia (see 1987-88 *Jane's*).

The Oehler system power plant installation, described under the Ventus heading, is also available for the Janus and Nimbus series.

SCHEMPP-HIRTH DISCUS

A total of more than 300 production examples of this Standard Class sailplane had been built by early 1990, in two versions. The first prototype, **Discus a** (D-6111), flew for the first time on 21 April 1984 and the second prototype, **Discus b** (D-8111), made its initial flight on 17 May 1984. The Discus a utilises the fuselage and tail unit of the 15 metre Class Ventus a. The Discus b has the longer fuselage of the Ventus b, incorporating a roomier cockpit.

Discus sailplanes of both versions took five of the first six places at the 1985 World Championships held at Rieti, Italy; first ten places at the 1986 US National Championships; first place at the Australian, Finnish, West German, Italian, Swedish and Swiss nationals in 1986; and first six places at the 1987 World Championships.

A new model flew for the first time on 18 November 1987 as the aerobatic **Discus K** (brief details in the 1989-90 *Jane's*). Only the single prototype was constructed, and this has since been modified to a standard Discus b. The Discus K will not enter production.

Another new version is the **Discus bT**, which first flew on 6 September 1988. This is a powered 'Turbo' version with a 15.3 kW (20.5 hp) Solo engine on a retractable

Rolladen-Schneider LS7 15 metre Class single-seat sailplane

Schempp-Hirth Nimbus 3/24-5 *(Peter F. Selinger)*

Scheibe SF-25C-2000 two-seat motor glider with standard landing gear

Schempp-Hirth Discus bT powered sailplane flown by the Chilean Air Force
(Kenneth Munson)

First SF-34B to be completed at Scheibe's factory in Hungary
(Peter F. Selinger)

fuselage mount (similar engine arrangement to earlier 'Turbo' powered sailplanes from Schempp-Hirth). Weight empty and max T-O weight are 275 kg (606 lb) and 450 kg (992 lb) respectively, fuel capacity is 8 litres (2.1 US gallons; 1.76 Imp gallons), and range ('sawtooth' profile) is over 160 nm (296 km; 184 miles).

The following details refer to the Discus a and b:

TYPE: Single-seat Standard Class sailplane.

AIRFRAME: Cantilever mid-wing monoplane, with 3° dihedral. No details have been released of the wing aerofoil section. Boundary layer control is achieved with lower surface turbulator strips. Kinked, sweptback leading-edges on outer sections. Centre-section is unswept, with constant chord. The wings are of GFRP with a carbonfibre main spar, and have ailerons of GFRP, plus Schempp-Hirth upper surface airbrakes. Fuselage and tail unit as described for Ventus a/b. Retractable rubber sprung monowheel (tyre size 4.00-4, pressure 4.41 bars; 64 lb/sq in), with drum brake; fixed rubber tailskid. Provision for 180 litres (47.6 US gallons; 39.6 Imp gallons) of water ballast.

DIMENSIONS, EXTERNAL:
Wing span (a, b)	15.00 m (49 ft 2½ in)
Wing aspect ratio (a, b)	21.3
Length overall: a	6.35 m (20 ft 10 in)
b	6.58 m (21 ft 7 in)
Height over tail (a, b)	1.27 m (4 ft 2 in)

AREA:
Wings, gross (a, b)	10.58 m² (113.9 sq ft)

WEIGHTS AND LOADING:
Weight empty: a	228 kg (503 lb)
b	230 kg (507 lb)
Max T-O weight (a, b)	525 kg (1,157 lb)
Max wing loading (a, b)	49.62 kg/m² (10.16 lb/sq ft)

PERFORMANCE (a, b, at max T-O weight):
Best glide ratio at 54 knots (100 km/h; 62 mph)	43
Min rate of sink at 42 knots (78 km/h; 49 mph)	0.59 m (1.94 ft)/s

Stalling speed	36 knots (66 km/h; 41 mph)
Max speed (smooth air)	135 knots (250 km/h; 155 mph)
Max speed (rough air)	108 knots (200 km/h; 124 mph)
Max aero-tow speed	97 knots (180 km/h; 112 mph)
Max winch-launching speed	81 knots (150 km/h; 93 mph)
g limits	+5.3/−2.65

SCHEMPP-HIRTH NIMBUS 3

The prototype Nimbus 3 (D-2111) flew for the first time on 21 February 1981. Production versions are the basic **Nimbus 3** and the **Nimbus 3/24.5** with add-on wingtip extensions. Nimbus 3s fitted with the Oehler power plant system (see Ventus entry) are designated **Nimbus 3T** (for Turbo). The two-seat **Nimbus 3D** versions are described separately. A total of at least 120 of all versions had been built by early 1990.

TYPE: Single-seat Open Class sailplane and powered sailplane.

AIRFRAME: Cantilever mid-wing monoplane. Four-piece (six on 3/24.5), thin section (Wortmann/Holighaus) wings, with 14% thickness/chord ratio, fitted with spoilerons, trailing-edge flaps and interconnected Schempp-Hirth upper surface airbrakes. Inboard/outboard leading-edge tanks for up to 280 litres (74 US gallons; 61.5 Imp gallons) of water ballast. Turned-down wingtips. Cantilever T tailplane, with elevators. Forward fuselage is a glassfibre shell; rear fuselage of carbonfibre, reinforced by GFRP/foam sandwich webs. Wing shells of carbonfibre/foam sandwich, with carbonfibre spar caps and GFRP/foam sandwich shear webs. Carbonfibre/GFRP/foam sandwich tailplane, with CF/GFRP elevators; CF/foam sandwich fin, with GFRP/foam sandwich rudder. Fully retractable monowheel, with shock absorption; tail bumper. One-piece canopy, opening sideways.

DIMENSIONS, EXTERNAL:
Wing span: 3	22.90 m (75 ft 1½ in)
3/24.5	24.50 m (80 ft 4½ in)

Wing aspect ratio: 3	32.2
3/24.5	35.9
Length overall	7.63 m (25 ft 0½ in)
Height over tail	1.55 m (5 ft 1 in)

AREAS:
Wings, gross: 3	16.30 m² (175.45 sq ft)
3/24.5	16.70 m² (179.76 sq ft)

WEIGHTS AND LOADINGS:
Weight empty: 3	392 kg (864 lb)
3/24.5	396 kg (873 lb)
Max T-O weight: 3, 3/24.5	750 kg (1,653 lb)
Max wing loading: 3	46.0 kg/m² (9.43 lb/sq ft)
3/24.5	44.9 kg/m² (9.19 lb/sq ft)

PERFORMANCE (at max T-O weight except where indicated):
Best glide ratio at 51 knots (95 km/h; 59 mph), wing loading of 29 kg/m² (5.94 lb/sq ft):
3	55
3/24.5	58

Min rate of sink at 40 knots (75 km/h; 47 mph):
3	0.44 m (1.44 ft)/s
3/24.5	0.41 m (1.35 ft)/s
Stalling speed: 3	33 knots (60 km/h; 38 mph)
3/24.5	32 knots (59 km/h; 37 mph)
Max speed (smooth air)	146 knots (270 km/h; 168 mph)

Max speed (rough air):
3	108 knots (200 km/h; 124 mph)
3/24.5	102 knots (190 km/h; 118 mph)
Max aero-tow speed	97 knots (180 km/h; 112 mph)
Max winch-launching speed	81 knots (150 km/h; 93 mph)
g limits at design manoeuvring speed	+5.3/−2.65

SCHEMPP-HIRTH NIMBUS 3D

A prototype of this Open Class two-seater (D-KCJC) flew for the first time on 2 May 1986. It combines a modified Janus fuselage with the long-span Nimbus 3/24.5 wing, a new wing mounting structure and a reinforced main spar, has 1° 30′ of forward sweep at the leading-edge and a small nosewheel. Two powered versions are also available which use the Oehler power plant system, namely the **3DT** with the 'Turbo' retrieve system based on a Solo engine, and the **3DM** offering full self-launching capability using a Rotax engine. The prototype 3DM flew for the first time on 17 March 1988. Thirty Nimbus 3Ds, 3DMs and 3DTs had been completed by early 1990.

TYPE: Open Class two-seat sailplane (3DT powered sailplane and 3DM self-launching sailplane).

AIRFRAME: Cantilever mid-wing monoplane. Wortmann wing sections: FX-79-K-143/17 at root, FX-77-135/20 at tip. Dihedral 3°. Incidence 1° 30'. Wings, fuselage and tail unit otherwise generally as described for Nimbus 3, except that fuselage is constructed of carbonfibre for the centre and aft sections (including fin) and carbon/Kevlar for the forward section, fairings are used at the wing-fuselage junctures, water ballast tanks (each of 84 litres; 22.2 US gallons; 18.5 Imp gallons capacity) are in outer wing panels only, and wingtips are not turned down. Retractable unsprung monowheel (tyre size 5.00-5, pressure 4.5 bars; 65 lb/sq in), with brake, plus tailskid and mini nosewheel bumper. Two seats in tandem, under one-piece canopy which opens sideways to starboard.

POWER PLANT: *Nimbus 3DT:* One 19.4 kW (26 hp) Solo 2350 auxiliary engine, installed in retractable mounting aft of cockpit and driving an OE-FL 5.88/83 propeller with five foldable blades. Retraction method as for Janus CM; extension takes 15 seconds, with an altitude loss of 80 m (265 ft). Fuel in single fuselage tank, capacity 16 litres (4.2 US gallons; 3.5 Imp gallons). *Nimbus 3DM:* One 44.7 kW (60 hp) Rotax 535C two-cylinder two-stroke engine, with 3:1 toothed belt reduction to a two-blade composites propeller, the installation retracting as for the 3DT. Fuel capacity 50 litres (13.2 US gallons; 11 Imp gallons).

DIMENSIONS, EXTERNAL:
Wing span	24.60 m (80 ft 8½ in)
Wing aspect ratio	35.9
Length overall	8.70 m (28 ft 6½ in)
Height over tail	1.39 m (4 ft 6¾ in)
Propeller diameter	0.88 m (2 ft 10¾ in)

AREA:
Wings, gross	16.85 m² (181.4 sq ft)

WEIGHTS AND LOADINGS (A: 3D, B: 3DT, C: 3DM):
Weight empty: A	485 kg (1,069 lb)
B	530 kg (1,168 lb)
C	575 kg (1,268 lb)
Max water ballast: A	168 kg (370 lb)
Max crew weight (each)	100-110 kg (220-243 lb)
Max T-O weight: A	750 kg (1,653 lb)
B, C	800 kg (1,764 lb)
Max wing loading: A	44.51 kg/m² (9.12 lb/sq ft)
B, C	47.48 kg/m² (9.73 lb/sq ft)
Max power loading: B	41.24 kg/kW (67.83 lb/hp)
C	17.90 kg/kW (29.4 lb/hp)

PERFORMANCE, UNPOWERED (at max T-O weight):
Best glide ratio at 57 knots (105 km/h; 65 mph)	57
Min rate of sink at 43 knots (80 km/h; 50 mph)	
	0.45 m (1.48 ft)/s
Stalling speed	42 knots (77 km/h; 48 mph)
Max speed (smooth air)	148 knots (275 km/h; 171 mph)
Max speed (rough air)	102 knots (190 km/h; 118 mph)
Max aero-tow speed	97 knots (180 km/h; 112 mph)
Max winch-launching speed	
	81 knots (150 km/h; 93 mph)
g limits	+5.4/−3.4

PERFORMANCE, POWERED (B and C as above at max T-O weight):
Never-exceed speed:	
B, C	148 knots (275 km/h; 171 mph)
C, under power	100 knots (185 km/h; 115 mph)
Max cruising speed: B	67 knots (125 km/h; 78 mph)
C, at 65% power	80 knots (148 km/h; 92 mph)
Stalling speed: B	43 knots (80 km/h; 50 mph)
Max rate of climb at S/L: B	33 m (108 ft)/min
C	132 m (433 ft)/min
T-O run: C	270 m (885 ft)
T-O to 15 m (50 ft): C	399 m (1,310 ft)
Range: C, cruising	190 nm (352 km; 218 miles)
C, 'sawtooth' method	280 nm (518 km; 322 miles)
Min rate of sink at 43 knots (80 km/h; 50 mph):	
B	29 m (95 ft)/min
C	31 m (102 ft)/min

SCHEMPP-HIRTH NIMBUS 4

This single-seater is currently under development to succeed the Nimbus 3. No details are yet available.

SCHEMPP-HIRTH JANUS

The Janus design was started by Dipl-Ing Holighaus in 1969, and the prototype made its first flight in the Spring of 1974.

Production began in January 1975 with the second, improved aircraft; a **Janus B** version became available in March 1978, with fixed incidence tailplane. The **Janus C** has 20 m span carbonfibre wings and a carbonfibre tailplane. At the end of 1985 Janus C sailplanes held FAI

records for distance in a straight line, distance to a fixed goal, out and return distance to a goal, and speed around triangular courses of 100 km and 300 km.

The **Janus CM** self-launching version of the C, first flown in 1978, has the same Rotax engine installation as the Nimbus 3DM, pylon mounted aft of the cockpit and retracting rearward into the top of the fuselage when not in use by means of an electric spindle drive (also used on Nimbus 3DM). Empty and max T-O weights are 480 kg (1,058 lb) and 700 kg (1,543 lb) respectively. This version established world records in FAI Class DM-2 for multi-seat motor gliders for out and return distance to a goal, and speed over triangular courses of 300 and 500 km. The **Janus CT** powered retrieve system version is similar, but has the Oehler installation described under the Ventus entry.

By early 1990 production totalled 260 Janus, Janus B, Janus C, Janus CM and Janus CT, including 30 of the CM version.

The following description applies to the standard Janus B, except where indicated:

TYPE: Tandem two-seat high-performance training sailplane.

AIRFRAME: Cantilever mid-wing monoplane. Wortmann wing sections: FX-67-K-170 at root, FX-67-K-15 at tip. Dihedral 4°. Sweepforward 2° on leading-edge. Glassfibre/foam sandwich wings, with glassfibre monocoque ailerons, trailing-edge flaps and Schempp-Hirth upper surface airbrakes. Ailerons and flaps interconnected. Glassfibre fuselage shell, with bonded-in foam bulkheads, on a welded steel tube central frame. Cantilever glassfibre/foam sandwich fixed incidence T tailplane, with elevator. Non-retractable semi-recessed monowheel (diameter 380 mm) and nosewheel. Continental tyres: pressure 2.69 bars (39 lb/sq in) on mainwheel; pressure 0.79 bars (11.5 lb/sq in) on nosewheel. Tost drum brake on mainwheel. Bumper under rear fuselage. Jettisonable tail drag-chute. One-piece canopy opens sideways to starboard. Provision for 200 kg (440 lb) of water ballast.

DIMENSIONS, EXTERNAL:
Wing span: B	18.20 m (59 ft 8½ in)
C	20.00 m (65 ft 7½ in)
Wing aspect ratio: B	20.0
C	23.0
Length overall	8.62 m (28 ft 3¼ in)
Height over tail	1.45 m (4 ft 9 in)

AREAS:
Wings, gross: B	16.60 m² (178.7 sq ft)
C	17.40 m² (187.3 sq ft)

WEIGHTS AND LOADINGS:
Weight empty: B	365 kg (805 lb)
C	355 kg (783 lb)
Max T-O weight: B	620 kg (1,366 lb)
C	700 kg (1,543 lb)
Max wing loading: B	37.0 kg/m² (7.58 lb/sq ft)
C	40.0 kg/m² (8.20 lb/sq ft)

PERFORMANCE (at max T-O weight except where indicated):
Best glide ratio at wing loading of 36.5 kg/m² (7.48 lb/sq ft) and speed of 59 knots (110 km/h; 68 mph):	
B	39.5
C	43.5
Min rate of sink at above wing loading and speed of 49 knots (90 km/h; 56 mph):	
B	0.70 m (2.30 ft)/s
C	0.60 m (1.97 ft)/s
Stalling speed at above wing loading:	
B, C	38 knots (70 km/h; 43 mph)
Max speed (rough and smooth air):	
B	118 knots (220 km/h; 136 mph)
C	135 knots (250 km/h; 155 mph)
Max aero-tow speed:	
B	91 knots (170 km/h; 105 mph)
C	97 knots (180 km/h; 112 mph)
Max winch-launching speed:	
B	65 knots (120 km/h; 75 mph)
C	81 knots (150 km/h; 93 mph)
g limits: B, C	+5.3/−2.65

SCHEMPP-HIRTH VENTUS

First flown on 3 May 1980, the Ventus (Latin for wind) features a thin section carbonfibre wing. It became available with a choice of two fuselages, the Ventus b having a slightly larger cockpit for pilots more than 1.75 m (5 ft 9 in) tall.

In 1982 Schempp-Hirth introduced the **Ventus b/16.6**, with detachable CFRP/GFRP wingtip extensions, for Open Class competition.

An Oehler retractable power plant, using a 13.5 kW (18 hp) Solo engine and 15 litre (4.0 US gallon; 3.3 Imp gallon) fuel tank, became available in 1982 on the Ventus b/16.6, which is then known as the **Ventus bT**. Engine and wingtips are readily removable for reversion to 15 metre Class flying. This installation provides a retrieve system.

In late 1987 the **Ventus c** was introduced to the range. Wingtip extensions can be fitted to the standard 15.00 m wings to provide optional spans of 16.60 m (54 ft 5½ in) or 17.60 m (57 ft 9 in). The Ventus c also has flaps that can act as additional inboard ailerons, Schempp-Hirth airbrakes, a 5 litre (1.32 US gallon; 1.1 Imp gallon) water ballast tank in

the tail fin, the options of a sprung landing gear and swing-up instrument panel, and drag-reducing wing/fuselage fairings. Mini winglets are an option for the 15 m wings. Two fuselage sizes are available for the Ventus c.

A 15.3 kW (20.5 hp) Solo-engined 'Turbo' retrieve version is the **Ventus cT**, with 17.60 m (57 ft 9 in) span. By removing the engine, battery, propeller, fuel tank and wingtip extensions, the aircraft returns to Ventus c configuration. Fuel capacity is 16 litres (4.2 US gallons; 3.5 Imp gallons).

A self-launching version of the Ventus c is also available, as the **Ventus cM**. First flown on 18 February 1988, it too has wingtip extensions to provide the full 17.60 m span. The Solo power plant is uprated to give 22 kW (29.7 hp) and is fitted with 2.3:1 belt reduction drive. The fuselage is constructed of carbonfibre/Kevlar except for aramid fibre in the cockpit area. Removal of the power plant can be performed quickly. Fuel capacity is 22 litres (5.8 US gallons; 4.8 Imp gallons).

Ventus production (all versions) totalled 460 by early 1990.

TYPE: Single-seat 15 metre Class sailplane (Ventus cT powered sailplane and cM self-launching sailplane).

AIRFRAME: *Ventus a and b:* Cantilever mid-wing monoplane, with newly developed Wortmann/Holighaus/Althaus thin-section wings of all-carbonfibre construction, including skins. Two-segment ailerons. Schempp-Hirth upper surface airbrakes. Fuselage centre frame of steel tube to carry main wing and landing gear loads. Cantilever fixed incidence T tailplane, with elevator; rudder area increased on Ventus b. Retractable monowheel; tail bumper. One-piece cockpit canopy, opening sideways to starboard. Provision for 150 kg (331 lb) of water ballast. *Ventus c, cT and cM:* See introductory paragraphs.

DIMENSIONS, EXTERNAL (A: a, B: b, C: b/16.6, D: bT, E: c, F: cT, and G: cM):
Wing span: A, B, E	15.00 m (49 ft 2½ in)
C, D, E optional	16.60 m (54 ft 5¼ in)
E optional, F, G	17.60 m (57 ft 9 in)
Wing aspect ratio: A, B, E	23.7
C, D, E with 16.60 m span	27.7
E with 17.60 m span, F, G	30.2
Length overall: A	6.35 m (20 ft 10 in)
all other versions	6.58 m (21 ft 7 in)
Height overall: all versions	1.27 m (4 ft 2 in)

AREAS:
Wings, gross: A, B, E	9.51 m² (102.4 sq ft)
C, D, E with 16.60 m span	9.96 m² (107.2 sq ft)
E with 17.60 m span, F, G	10.15 m² (109.25 sq ft)

WEIGHTS AND LOADINGS (A, B, C, D, E, F, G as above):
Weight empty: A, B, E	approx 240 kg (529 lb)
C	243 kg (535 lb)
E with 17.60 m span	244 kg (538 lb)
F	289 kg (637 lb)
G	300 kg (661 lb)
Max T-O weight: A, B, E	525 kg (1,157 lb)
C, F, G	430 kg (948 lb)
E with 17.60 m span	500 kg (1,102 lb)
Max wing loading:	
A, B, E	55.2 kg/m² (11.31 lb/sq ft)
C	43.2 kg/m² (8.85 lb/sq ft)
E with 17.60 m span, G	49.3 kg/m² (10.10 lb/sq ft)
F	42.4 kg/m² (8.68 lb/sq ft)
Max power loading:	
F	28.10 kg/kW (46.24 lb/hp)
G	19.55 kg/kW (31.92 lb/hp)

PERFORMANCE, UNPOWERED (at max T-O weight except where indicated; A, B, C, E, G as above):
Best glide ratio at wing loading of 35 kg/m² (7.17 lb/sq ft):	
A, B, E at 56 knots (105 km/h; 65 mph)	43.5
C at 51 knots (95 km/h; 59 mph)	46.5
E with 17.60 m span	49
G at 56 knots (105 km/h; 65 mph)	48-49
Min rate of sink at 41 knots (75 km/h; 47 mph):	
A, B	0.58 m (1.90 ft)/s
C	0.59 m (1.94 ft)/s
G, power plant retracted	approx 0.68 m (2.23 ft)/s
Stalling speed: A, B	36 knots (65 km/h; 41 mph)
C	35 knots (64 km/h; 40 mph)
Max speed (smooth air):	
A, B, C	135 knots (250 km/h; 155 mph)
E	145 knots (270 km/h; 167 mph)
Max speed (rough air):	
A, B, C	108 knots (200 km/h; 124 mph)
Max aero-tow speed:	
A, B, C	97 knots (180 km/h; 112 mph)
Max winch-launching speed:	
A, B, C	81 knots (150 km/h; 93 mph)
g limits at design manoeuvring speed:	
A, B, C	+5.3/−2.65

PERFORMANCE, POWERED (at max T-O weight; D and G as above):
Max speed:	
G, power plant retracted	
	146 knots (270 km/h; 168 mph)
G, power on	86 knots (160 km/h; 99 mph)
Cruising speed:	
D, F	approx 70 knots (130 km/h; 81 mph)
G	approx 76 knots (140 km/h; 87 mph)
Min speed: G	41 knots (75 km/h; 47 mph)

Schempp-Hirth Nimbus 3DM (Peter F. Selinger)

Schempp-Hirth Ventus cM self-launching sailplane (Peter F. Selinger)

Schempp-Hirth Ventus b/T with Webra engine (Peter F. Selinger)

Schempp-Hirth Janus B flown by the Chilean Air Force (Kenneth Munson)

Schleicher ASW 20 C 15 metre Class sailplane (Peter F. Selinger)

Max rate of climb: G	120 m (394 ft)/min	T-O run: G	approx 280 m (919 ft)	D	more than 108 nm (201 km; 125 miles)
Rate of climb (depending upon altitude and ambient temperature):		T-O to 15 m (50 ft): G	approx 420 m (1,378 ft)	G	approx 270 nm (500 km; 310 miles)
		Range (combining powered climbs and engine-off glides in 'sawtooth' method):		Range in cruise: G	approx 172 nm (320 km; 199 miles)
D	38-68 m (125-225 ft)/min			Max endurance: G	2 h

SCHLEICHER
ALEXANDER SCHLEICHER GmbH & Co
HEAD OFFICE AND WORKS: Postfach 60, 6416 Poppenhausen/Wasserkuppe
Telephone: 49 (6658) 225
Fax: 49 (6658) 776

This company is one of the oldest manufacturers of sailplanes in the world. Since its formation in 1927, Schleicher and its licencees have built approximately 5,200 wood/metal gliders and over 2,000 composites sailplanes and motor gliders. Those in its current range designed by Ing Rudolf Kaiser are prefixed ASK; those with ASW designations are designed by Ing Gerhard Waibel. An ASH prefix indicates the work of Schleicher's youngest designer, Martin Heide. Schleicher also manufactures and markets spare parts, constructional materials, and dust- and weatherproof covers for sailplanes.

SCHLEICHER ASK 13
Production of the ASK 13 by Schleicher, which totalled 603, has ended, but the ASK 13 is still being manufactured, under licence, by Jubi GmbH (which see).

SCHLEICHER ASW 20 B and 20 C
The ASW 20 was designed to take advantage of the March 1975 CIVV regulations for unlimited 15 metre

sailplanes, and is fitted with trailing-edge flaps as well as large upper surface spoilers. It has an additional high-drag flap range incorporating a special mechanism to eliminate pitch and airspeed changes when changing flap position.

The prototype ASW 20 made its first flight on 29 January 1977, and many hundreds of various models have been built by Schleicher, plus more under licence, including the ASW 20 BL and 20 CL, which are described separately. Current basic production models are designated **ASW 20 B** and **ASW 20 C**, the former having a reinforced wing structure enabling it to carry more water ballast in good soaring conditions. The B and C models differ from the original ASW 20 in having a modified wing undersurface with lower drag and DLR patented 'turbulators' (see ASW 22 entry for description) which smooth out the airflow in the area of the flap hinges. Other improvements include metal foil sealing of the wing control surfaces (optional), automatic elevator connection, disc (instead of drum) brake, and instrument panel hinged to open with the canopy. These modifications also apply to the BL and CL models.

In 1988 ASW 20/B/Cs gained first place in the Canadian National Championships, second places in the Pre-World Championships (Wiener Neustadt) and the German National Championships, third place in the Finnish National Championships, and second place in the Premier Open de France in Fayence.

The following details apply to the ASW 20 B and C:

TYPE: Single-seat 15 metre Class sailplane.
AIRFRAME: Cantilever mid-wing monoplane. Wing sections Wortmann FX-63-131-K (modified DLR/Horstmann-Quast) at root, Wortmann FX-60-126 at tip. Dihedral 2° 20′. No sweepforward at quarter-chord. Glassfibre roving wing main spar. Wings of GFRP/hard foam sandwich, with leading-edge bag tanks for water ballast. Schempp-Hirth metal airbrakes in upper surface. GFRP monocoque fuselage. Cantilever T tail and elevator, with new Wortmann aerofoil sections. Five-position trailing-edge wing flaps (travel –12° to +40°). Ailerons are linked with flaps, and are automatically deflected upward when 'flaps down' is selected for landing. All control surfaces are of aramid/GFRP, and are partly mass balanced. Retractable sprung monowheel, size 5.00-5, with hydraulic disc brake. Rubber tailskid with wear plate is standard; optional fit of tailskid with polyamid roller, or fixed 210 × 65 mm tailwheel with pneumatic tyre and fairing. One-piece Plexiglas canopy, hinged at front and opening upward, can be jettisoned in emergency. Tost towing hook at CG. Options include oxygen bottle, barograph, battery and headrest.
DIMENSIONS, EXTERNAL:
Wing span	15.00 m (49 ft 2½ in)
Wing aspect ratio	21.4
Length overall	6.82 m (22 ft 4½ in)
Height over tail	1.45 m (4 ft 9 in)

AREA:
Wings, gross   10.50 m² (113.0 sq ft)
WEIGHTS AND LOADINGS:
Weight empty: B   260 kg (573 lb)
    C   250 kg (551 lb)
Max water ballast: B   160 kg (352 lb)
    C   120 kg (264 lb)
Max T-O weight with water ballast:
    B   525 kg (1,157 lb)
    C   454 kg (1,001 lb)
Max wing loading: B   50.00 kg/m² (10.25 lb/sq ft)
    C   43.24 kg/m² (8.86 lb/sq ft)
PERFORMANCE (at max T-O weight except where indicated):
Best glide ratio:
    B (without ballast) at 54 knots (100 km/h; 62 mph)
        42.5
    B (with ballast) at 65 knots (120 km/h; 75 mph)   43
    C (without ballast) at 48 knots (90 km/h; 56 mph)   43
    C (with ballast) at 62 knots (115 km/h; 71 mph)   42
Min rate of sink:
    B (without ballast) at 45 knots (84 km/h; 52 mph)
        0.59 m (1.93 ft)/s
    C (without ballast) at 47 knots (87 km/h; 54 mph)
        0.57 m (1.87 ft)/s
    C (with ballast) at 52 knots (96 km/h; 60 mph)
        0.68 m (2.23 ft)/s
Stalling speed (without ballast):
    B, C   35 knots (65 km/h; 41 mph)
Max speed (smooth air):
    B   151 knots (280 km/h; 174 mph)
    C   143 knots (265 km/h; 165 mph)
Max speed (rough air):
    B   103 knots (191 km/h; 118 mph)
    C   143 knots (265 km/h; 165 mph)
Max aero-tow speed:
    B   103 knots (191 km/h; 118 mph)
    C   97 knots (180 km/h; 112 mph)
Max winch-launching speed:
    B   70 knots (129 km/h; 80 mph)
    C   67 knots (125 km/h; 78 mph)
g limits:
    B at 103 knots (191 km/h; 118 mph), C (without
    ballast) at 94 knots (174 km/h; 108 mph)
        +5.3/−2.65
    B at 151 knots (280 km/h; 174 mph), C (without
    ballast) at 143 knots (265 km/h; 165 mph)   +4/−1.5

SCHLEICHER ASW 20 BL and 20 CL

The ASW 20 L (for Lang: long), first flown in May 1977, is a version of the ASW 20 with detachable outer wing panels, increasing the span to 16.59 m (54 ft 5¼ in) for Open Class competition. Production began in late 1978. Current models are the ASW 20 BL and CL, to which the following data apply:

TYPE: Single-seat Open Class sailplane.
AIRFRAME: Generally as for ASW 20 B and C except for wings, which have detachable span-increasing outer panels. Reduced water ballast in BL, no provision for water ballast in CL.
DIMENSIONS, EXTERNAL: As ASW 20 B and C except:
Wing span   16.59 m (54 ft 5¼ in)
Wing aspect ratio   24.9
AREA:
Wings, gross   11.05 m² (118.9 sq ft)
WEIGHTS AND LOADINGS:
Weight empty: BL   265 kg (584 lb)
    CL   255 kg (562 lb)
Max water ballast: BL   50 kg (110 lb)
Max T-O weight: BL   430 kg (948 lb)
    CL   380 kg (837 lb)
Max wing loading: BL   38.91 kg/m² (7.97 lb/sq ft)
    CL   34.39 kg/m² (7.05 lb/sq ft)
PERFORMANCE (at max T-O weight except where indicated):
Best glide ratio:
    BL (without ballast) at 48 knots (90 km/h; 56 mph)   45
    CL at 49 knots (91 km/h; 57 mph)   46
Min rate of sink:
    BL at 45 knots (84 km/h; 52 mph)   0.53 m (1.74 ft)/s
Stalling speed:
    BL (without ballast) and CL
        35 knots (64 km/h; 40 mph)
Max speed (smooth air):
    BL, CL   135 knots (250 km/h; 155 mph)
Max speed (rough air):
    BL   97 knots (180 km/h; 112 mph)
    CL   89 knots (165 km/h; 103 mph)
Max aero-tow speed:
    BL   89 knots (165 km/h; 103 mph)
    CL   86 knots (160 km/h; 99 mph)
Max winch-launching speed:
    BL   70 knots (130 km/h; 80 mph)
    CL   65 knots (120 km/h; 75 mph)
g limits:
    BL at 97 knots (180 km/h; 112 mph)   +5.3/−2.65
    CL at 89 knots (165 km/h; 103 mph)   +5.3/−2.65

SCHLEICHER ASK 21

Designed by Ing Kaiser, the ASK 21 prototype flew for the first time on 6 February 1979; it received LBA

certification on 18 April 1980. A total of 450 had been built by the end of 1989, including 10 in 1983 for the UK Air Cadets, by whom they are known as the **Vanguard**.

TYPE: Tandem two-seat competition and training sailplane.
AIRFRAME: Cantilever mid-wing monoplane. Two-piece double tapered wings, primarily of GFRP/foam sandwich construction with GFRP roving spar. Wortmann wing sections: FX-S-02-196 from root to inboard of ailerons, FX-60-126 at tip. Dihedral 4°. Sweepforward at quarter-chord 1° 30′. Schempp-Hirth upper surface metal airbrakes. GFRP/tubuscore sandwich fuselage. Fixed T tailplane and separate elevator of similar construction to wings; rudder and elevator partly mass-balanced. Non-retractable semi-recessed nosewheel (size 4.00-4) and rubber sprung monowheel (size 5.00-5), the latter with hydraulic disc brake; steel shod rubber tailskid standard, pneumatic tailwheel (210 × 65 mm) optional. Front and rear canopies hinged at front and rear respectively, both opening upward.

DIMENSIONS, EXTERNAL:
Wing span   17.00 m (55 ft 9¼ in)
Wing aspect ratio   16.1
Length overall   8.35 m (27 ft 4¾ in)
Height over tail   1.55 m (5 ft 1 in)
AREA:
Wings, gross   17.95 m² (193.2 sq ft)
WEIGHTS AND LOADING:
Weight empty   360 kg (794 lb)
Max T-O weight   600 kg (1,323 lb)
Max wing loading   33.4 kg/m² (6.84 lb/sq ft)
PERFORMANCE (carrying pilot only):
Best glide ratio at 46 knots (85 km/h; 53 mph)   35
Min rate of sink at 36 knots (67 km/h; 42 mph)
        0.65 m (2.13 ft)/s
Stalling speed   34 knots (62 km/h; 39 mph)
Max speed (smooth air)   151 knots (280 km/h; 174 mph)
Max speed (rough air)   135 knots (250 km/h; 155 mph)
Max aero-tow speed   94 knots (175 km/h; 109 mph)
Max winch-launching speed
        70 knots (130 km/h; 81 mph)
g limits at 97 knots (180 km/h; 112 mph)   +6.5/−4

SCHLEICHER ASW 22 B

Extensive use is made of composite materials in the construction of this Open Class sailplane, which has combined flaps/airbrakes similar to those fitted to the ASW 20. A special feature of the wing design is the provision of about 1,000 tubular apertures ('turbulators') in the underside, over 17 m (55 ft 9¼ in) of the span, through which air can be vented to provide a form of boundary layer control and improve performance at the upper end of the speed range.

Design of the ASW 22 began in 1979, and the prototype (D-7122) flew for the first time on 4 July 1981. Production ended in July 1985, a total of 39 having been completed, all with 22 m (72 ft 2¼ in) span wings. A description can be found in the 1985-86 Jane's.

In January 1986 Schleicher began building a prototype of the ASW 22 B version, with wing span increased from 22 to 25 metres and other improvements including a new HQ-17 aerofoil section on the inner wings. This replaced the original model in production. By the end of 1989 six had been built. In 1988 ASW 22 Bs gained third and fourth places in the European Championships in Finland. The description which follows applies to the ASW 22 B:

TYPE: Single-seat Open Class sailplane.
AIRFRAME: Cantilever mid-wing monoplane. Wing sections DLR-HQ-17 at root, Delft University DU84-132 V3 at tip. Dihedral 3° 30′. Incidence 5°. Sweepback 0° 48′ on outer panels only. CFRP/foam sandwich wing skins. Trailing-edge flaps and ailerons are of AFRP/foam sandwich construction. Schempp-Hirth aluminium upper surface airbrakes. Monocoque fuselage of carbon/aramid/GFRP. Cantilever T tail with carbonfibre/epoxy sandwich tailplane, GFRP/AFRP sandwich fin, and AFRP/foam sandwich elevator and rudder. Main landing gear is a twin-wheel (size 5.00-5) retractable unit, both with rubber shock absorption and one with Cleveland hydraulic disc brake. Foam rubber tailskid, with wear plate, is standard; non-retractable tailwheel (size 210 × 65 mm) is optional. Tost CG towing hook, covered in flight by landing gear doors. Two 60 litre (15.8 US gallon; 13.2 Imp gallon) and two 50 litre (13.2 US gallon; 11 Imp gallon) water ballast tanks in wing leading-edges. One-piece jettisonable canopy, hinged at front to open upward.

DIMENSIONS, EXTERNAL:
Wing span   25.00 m (82 ft 0¼ in)
Wing aspect ratio   38.3
Length overall   8.10 m (26 ft 7 in)
Height over tail   1.66 m (5 ft 5½ in)
AREA:
Wings, gross   16.31 m² (175.6 sq ft)
WEIGHTS AND LOADING:
Weight empty, equipped   450 kg (992 lb)
Max water ballast   235 kg (518 lb)
Max T-O weight   750 kg (1,653 lb)
Max wing loading   45.98 kg/m² (9.42 lb/sq ft)
PERFORMANCE (estimated):
*Best glide ratio at 51 knots (95 km/h; 59 mph)   60

*Min rate of sink at 43 knots (80 km/h; 50 mph)
        0.41 m (1.35 ft)/s
*Stalling speed   35 knots (65 km/h; 41 mph)
Max speed (smooth air)   151 knots (280 km/h; 174 mph)
Max speed (rough air), and max aero-tow speed
        102 knots (190 km/h; 118 mph)
Max winch-launching speed
        75 knots (140 km/h; 87 mph)
g limits   +5.3/−2.65
*without ballast

SCHLEICHER ASW 22 BE

Construction of prototypes of this self-launching motor glider version of the ASW 22 B started in November 1985. First flight, by D-KKJP, took place on 22 March 1986. Eleven had been built by the end of 1989. In 1988 ASW 22 BEs gained second, sixth and seventh places in the European Motor Glider Championships in Issoudun.

AIRFRAME: As for ASW 22 B except for changes necessary to accommodate power plant, and two (instead of four) 60 litre (15.8 US gallon; 13.2 Imp gallon) water ballast tanks in wings.
POWER PLANT: One 36 kW (48 hp) Rotax 505A engine, driving a two-blade propeller. Fuel in one fuselage and two inboard wing tanks, combined capacity 70 litres (18.5 US gallons; 15.4 Imp gallons).
DIMENSIONS, EXTERNAL: As ASW 22 B, plus:
Propeller diameter   1.58 m (5 ft 2¼ in)
WEIGHTS AND LOADINGS:
Weight empty, equipped   510 kg (1,124 lb)
Max water ballast   120 kg (264 lb)
Max T-O weight   750 kg (1,653 lb)
Max wing loading   45.98 kg/m² (9.42 lb/sq ft)
Max power loading   20.83 kg/kW (34.44 lb/hp)
PERFORMANCE, UNPOWERED (estimated): As ASW 22 B, except:
*Best glide ratio at 59 knots (110 km/h; 68 mph)   60
*Min rate of sink at 46 knots (85 km/h; 53 mph)
        0.44 m (1.44 ft)/s
*Stalling speed   41 knots (76 km/h; 48 mph)
*without ballast
PERFORMANCE, POWERED:
Max speed (smooth air)   151 knots (280 km/h; 174 mph)
Max cruising speed   92 knots (170 km/h; 106 mph)
Econ cruising speed (alternate climbing/gliding profile)
        49 knots (90 km/h; 56 mph)
Stalling speed   41 knots (75 km/h; 47 mph)
Max rate of climb at S/L   132 m (433 ft)/min
T-O run   200 m (656 ft)
Range with max fuel   431 nm (800 km; 497 miles)

SCHLEICHER ASK 23

Announced in the Spring of 1981, the ASK 23 is essentially a successor to the K 8 as a single-seat training and club glider, but making use of GFRP constructional materials. Design began in November 1980; production started in October 1983.

The **ASK 23 B** version is suitable for cloud flying and aerobatic manoeuvres in accordance with JAR 22 Category U. This has empty and max T-O weights of 235 kg (518 lb) and 360 kg (793 lb); speeds and other performance data are as for the original ASK 23. A total of 145 of both models had been built by the end of 1989. The following description applies to the ASK 23:

TYPE: Single-seat training and performance sailplane.
AIRFRAME: Cantilever shoulder-wing monoplane. Wortmann wing sections: FX-61-168 at root, FX-60-126 at tip. Dihedral 2° 40′. Sweepback 0° 53′ 24″ at quarter-chord. Construction of GFRP/foam sandwich, with glassfibre roving main spar and aluminium upper surface airbrakes. GFRP honeycomb sandwich fuselage shell. Cantilever T tail, of similar construction to wings, with separate elevator. Landing gear comprises a 260 × 85 mm nosewheel, non-retractable rubber sprung 5.00-5 mainwheel (with Tost drum brake), and rubber sprung tailskid. One-piece forward opening Plexiglas canopy, with emergency jettison. Nose and CG towing hooks standard.

DIMENSIONS, EXTERNAL:
Wing span   15.00 m (49 ft 2½ in)
Wing aspect ratio   17.4
Length overall   7.05 m (23 ft 1½ in)
Height over tail   1.37 m (4 ft 6 in)
AREA:
Wings, gross   12.90 m² (138.8 sq ft)
WEIGHTS AND LOADING:
Weight empty   approx 240 kg (529 lb)
Max T-O weight   360 kg (794 lb)
Max wing loading   27.91 kg/m² (5.72 lb/sq ft)
PERFORMANCE (at 340 kg; 750 lb T-O weight):
Best glide ratio at 49 knots (90 km/h; 56 mph)   34
Min rate of sink at 40 knots (74 km/h; 46 mph)
        0.66 m (2.17 ft)/s
Stalling speed   33 knots (60 km/h; 38 mph)
Max speed (smooth air)   116 knots (215 km/h; 134 mph)
Max speed (rough air), and max aero-tow speed
        78 knots (145 km/h; 90 mph)
Max winch-launching speed
        67 knots (125 km/h; 77 mph)
g limits at 78 knots (145 km/h; 90 mph)   +5.3/−2.65

Schleicher ASK 21 tandem two-seat sailplane *(Avio Data)*

Schleicher ASW 24 Standard Class sailplane

ASH 25, designed by Schleicher's Martin Heide

Schleicher ASW 22 BE motor glider

Schleicher ASK 23 training and performance sailplane

SCHLEICHER ASW 24

The ASW 24, the prototype of which flew in 1986, was intended to be a successor to the ASW 19. An all-new design, it incorporates a wing aerofoil section developed by the Department of Aerospace Engineering at Delft University of Technology in the Netherlands. Eighty had been built by the end of 1989. The **ASW 24 E** self-launching version and the new **ASW 24 TOP** are described separately.

In 1988 ASW 24s gained fourth and fifth places in the USA Standard Class National Championships, and third, sixth, seventh and eighth places in the German Standard Class Championships.

TYPE: Standard Class sailplane.

AIRFRAME: Cantilever mid-wing monoplane, with Delft University DU84-158 aerofoil section from root to tip. Dihedral 3°. Incidence 4°. Two-piece double tapered wing, of GFRP/AFRP and hard foam sandwich construction, with carbonfibre spar caps; ailerons of AFRP/foam sandwich. Double-panelled aluminium airbrakes in upper wing surface, with spring loaded GFRP cover plates. Fuselage is a CFRP/AFRP/GFRP monocoque. Cantilever T tail: fin is GFRP sandwich, tailplane is CFRP sandwich, and elevator is AFRP/CFRP/GFRP and hard foam sandwich. Retractable rubber sprung monowheel (tyre size 5.00-5), with hydraulic disc brake, plus tailskid. Canopy hinged at front, opening upward. Wing tanks for 170 litres (44.9 US gallons; 37.4 Imp gallons) of water ballast. CG towing hook standard. Options include nose towing hook, tailwheel with 210 × 65 mm pneumatic tyre, oxygen bottle and battery.

DIMENSIONS, EXTERNAL:
Wing span	15.00 m (49 ft 2½ in)
Wing aspect ratio	22.5
Length overall	6.55 m (21 ft 6 in)
Height over tail	1.30 m (4 ft 3¼ in)

AREA:
Wings, gross	10.00 m² (107.6 sq ft)

WEIGHTS AND LOADING:
Weight empty, equipped	230 kg (507 lb)
Max water ballast	170 kg (375 lb)
Max T-O weight	500 kg (1,102 lb)
Max wing loading	50.0 kg/m² (10.24 lb/sq ft)

PERFORMANCE (estimated, at max T-O weight except where indicated):
*Best glide ratio at 57 knots (105 km/h; 65 mph)	43
Min rate of sink at 38 knots (70 km/h; 44 mph)	0.58 m (1.90 ft)/s
*Stalling speed	38 knots (70 km/h; 44 mph)
Max permissible speed (smooth air)	145 knots (270 km/h; 168 mph)
Max speed (rough air) and max aero-tow speed	110 knots (205 km/h; 127 mph)
Max winch-launching speed	75 knots (140 km/h; 87 mph)
g limits	+5.3/-2.65

*at AUW of 315 kg (694 lb)

SCHLEICHER ASW 24 E

The prototype of this self-launching version of the ASW 24 first flew in 1988, and series production began in 1989. By

the close of that year 72 had been built. It is suited to the experienced cross-country pilot. It conforms to JAR 22 category U and the preliminary LBA requirements for motor gliders of composite plastics construction. It can be used for training, competition in the Standard Class, cloud flying and semi-aerobatics.

AIRFRAME: As for ASW 24, except for changes necessary to accommodate power plant, and only 140 litres (37 US gallons; 30.8 Imp gallons) of water ballast.

POWER PLANT: One 18.6 kW (25 hp) Rotax 275 engine, driving a two-blade propeller.

DIMENSIONS, EXTERNAL: As for ASW 24 plus:
Propeller diameter	1.40 m (4 ft 7 in)

WEIGHTS AND LOADINGS:
Weight empty	275 kg (606 lb)
Max T-O weight	500 kg (1,102 lb)
Max wing loading	50.0 kg/m² (10.24 lb/sq ft)
Max power loading	26.88 kg/kW (44.08 lb/hp)

PERFORMANCE, UNPOWERED:
Best glide ratio at 59 knots (110 km/h; 68 mph)	43
Min rate of sink	0.62 m (2.03 ft)/s

PERFORMANCE, POWERED:
Max permissible speed (smooth air)	145 knots (270 km/h; 168 mph)
Stalling speed	41 knots (75 km/h; 47 mph)
Max rate of climb at S/L	138 m (453 ft)/min
T-O run	200 m (656 ft)
T-O to 15 m (50 ft)	400 m (1,312 ft)

SCHLEICHER ASW 24 TOP

Three examples of this new powered version of the ASW 24 had been built by the end of 1989, which conforms to JAR 22 category U and preliminary LBA requirements for motor gliders of composite construction. The engine can be attached or removed in minutes to make the glider self-launching or usable in competition. It retracts into the fuselage and can be extended into the airstream by electric actuator and started by electric starter. Height loss during the whole starting cycle is only 20 m (66 ft). The engine is said to run unusually smoothly and quietly.

AIRFRAME: As for ASW 24, except for changes necessary to accommodate power plant, and only 140 litres (37 US gallons; 30.8 Imp gallons) of water ballast.

POWER PLANT: One 18 kW (24 hp) König SC 430 three-cylinder radial engine, with self-folding three-blade propeller.

DIMENSIONS, EXTERNAL: As for ASW 24 plus:
Propeller diameter	1.30 m (4 ft 3¼ in)

WEIGHTS AND LOADINGS:
Weight empty	approx 270 kg (595 lb)
Max T-O weight	500 kg (1,102 lb)
Max wing loading	50.0 kg/m² (10.24 lb/sq ft)
Max power loading	27.78 kg/kW (45.9 lb/hp)

PERFORMANCE, UNPOWERED:
Best glide ratio at 59 knots (110 km/h; 68 mph)	42
Min rate of sink	0.62 m (2.03 ft)/s

PERFORMANCE, POWERED: As for ASW 24 E except:
Max rate of climb at S/L	120 m (394 ft)/min

SCHLEICHER ASH 25

Prototype construction of the ASH 25 (D-1025) started in January 1986, a year after design, by Martin Heide, began. The AS 22-2 (see 1985-86 and 1986-87 *Jane's*) was used as the basis of the design, with some fuselage modifications. First flight was made on 11 May 1986. Forty-nine had been built by the end of 1989, plus 35 ASH 25 E motor gliders (described separately).

In 1988 ASH 25s gained fifth, seventh and eighth places in the European Championships in Finland; first place in the British Open Class National Championships; first, fourth and sixth places in the German Open Class National Championships; first place in the Premier Open de France in Fayence; and first, fourth and other places in the Pre-World Championships (Wiener Neustadt). Also the sailplane was used to establish world speed records over 300 km, 500 km, 750 km and 1,000 km triangular courses in 1988, flown by Hans Werner Grosse and Karin Grosse at Alice Springs.

TYPE: Open Class tandem two-seat sailplane.

AIRFRAME: Wings and tail unit as for AS 22-2, but two 60 litre (15.8 US gallon; 13.2 Imp gallon) water ballast tanks only (in outer panels). Fuselage is a hybrid carbon/aramid FRP monocoque. Retractable rubber sprung mono-wheel, tyre size 380 × 150 mm, pressure 3.5 bars (51 lb/sq in), with brake; retractable tailwheel, tyre size 210 × 65 mm, pressure 2.5 bars (36 lb/sq in). Canopies similar to those of ASK 21.

DIMENSIONS, EXTERNAL:
Wing span	25.00 m (82 ft 0¼ in)
Wing aspect ratio	38.3
Length overall	9.00 m (29 ft 6¼ in)
Height over tail	1.67 m (5 ft 5¾ in)

AREA:
Wings, gross	16.31 m² (175.6 sq ft)

WEIGHTS AND LOADING:
Weight empty, equipped	450 kg (992 lb)
Max water ballast	220 kg (485 lb)
Max T-O weight	750 kg (1,653 lb)
Max wing loading	45.98 kg/m² (9.42 lb/sq ft)

PERFORMANCE (at max T-O weight):
Best glide ratio at 58 knots (108 km/h; 67 mph)	57
Min rate of sink at 43 knots (80 km/h; 50 mph)	0.45 m (1.48 ft)/s
Stalling speed	42-45 knots (77-84 km/h; 48-52 mph)
Max speed (smooth air)	151 knots (280 km/h; 174 mph)
Max speed (rough air) and max aero-tow speed	103 knots (190 km/h; 118 mph)
Max winch-launching speed	75 knots (140 km/h; 87 mph)

SCHLEICHER ASH 25 E

This is a motor glider version of the ASH 25, but is not capable of self-launching. For the first time with a retractable engine system, the 18.6 kW (25 hp) Rotax 277 engine drives a two-blade propeller via a reduction unit. Thirty-five had been built by the end of 1989. ASH 25 Es gained first, fifth and ninth places in the European Motor Glider Championships in Issoudun in 1988.

AIRFRAME: As for ASH 25, except for changes necessary to accommodate power plant. Water ballast remains the same.

DIMENSIONS, EXTERNAL: As for ASH 25 plus:

Propeller diameter	1.30 m (4 ft 3¼ in)

WEIGHTS AND LOADINGS:

Weight empty	475 kg (1,047 lb)
Max T-O weight	750 kg (1,653 lb)
Max wing loading	45.98 kg/m² (9.42 lb/sq ft)
Max power loading	40.32 kg/kW (66.12 lb/hp)

PERFORMANCE, UNPOWERED:

Best glide ratio	57
Min rate of sink at 44 knots (80 km/h; 50 mph)	0.45 m (1.48 ft)/s

PERFORMANCE, POWERED:

Max rate of climb at S/L	0.8 m (2.62 ft)/min

SCHLEICHER ASH 25 MB

Single custom-made motor glider, of which brief details appeared in the 1989-90 *Jane's*. No type approval and no production.

STEMME

STEMME GmbH & Co KG

Gustav Meyer Allee 25, 1000 Berlin 65
Telephone: 49 (30) 4634071/2
Telex: (17) 308145 BIG
Fax: 49 (30) 4694649
MANAGING DIRECTOR: Dr Reiner Stemme
DISTRIBUTION: Stemme GmbH & Co KG Flugzeuge und Dienstleistungen, Flughafen Lilienthalplatz, 3300 Braunschweig
Telephone: 49 (531) 351705

UK AGENTS:
Michael Jefferyes
Hermann Sommersell
Tanglewood, Fingrith Hall Road, Blackmore, Essex CM4 0RU
Telephone: 44 (277) 823066

Stemme GmbH & Co KG was formed in Berlin in November 1984 to develop a high performance two-seat motor glider designated the S 10. Its power plant is based on the concept invented by Dr Reiner Stemme.

STEMME S 10

Claimed by Stemme to be the first sailplane to incorporate a fully effective propulsion system without suffering aerodynamic penalties, the first S 10 prototype (D-KKST) made its first flight at Braunschweig on 6 July 1986. During powered phases, only the propeller blades are extended outside the aircraft, instead of the pylon structure associated with most other retractable power plant installations.

Rigorous flight testing continued into 1989, proving the capabilities of the propulsion system for take-off and cruise, and demonstrating the S 10's handling and gliding performance.

Deliveries to customers began in 1988. Ten pre-series aircraft had been completed by the end of 1989, and series production started in the newly equipped manufacturing facility in West Berlin.

Stemme is producing the S 10 for two markets, namely sport/leisure and commercial. The latter encompasses surveillance, atmospheric research, aerial reconnaissance and pollution control, the aircraft's low noise level, simple maintenance and low fuel consumption making it suitable for low cost aerial uses. A demonstrator of the Stemme S 10 gsm was shown at the Paris Air Show at Le Bourget in 1989 in co-operation with the Swiss Gepard Sensor Technologies Systems Inc. (See Addenda for further details.)

TYPE: Side by side two-seat high performance motor glider.

AIRFRAME: Cantilever shoulder-wing monoplane with T tail. High aspect ratio wings, with tapered outer panels. Wing section Horstmann & Quast HQ-41/14.35. Long-span flaps and ailerons on trailing-edges; Schempp-Hirth upper surface airbrakes. Wings are built of CFRP, in three sections, with integral fuel tanks. Inboard sections can be folded on to fuselage. Modular fuselage comprises three sections bolted together. The central load-bearing mainframe is of welded steel tube, with GFRP cladding. The cockpit is of CFRP with Kevlar lining, and the rear fuselage is also of CFRP. Tail unit incorporates a damped elevator. Landing gear comprises twin 5.00-5 mainwheels on steel tube legs, each sprung and fully retractable into its own bay, and a partially recessed 210 × 65 mm steerable tailwheel. Side by side seats, with dual controls, under one-piece canopy which is hinged at front and opens upward. 12V 44Ah battery for engine starting.

POWER PLANT: One 70 kW (94 hp) Limbach L 2400 four-cylinder four-stroke engine, mounted in centre-fuselage aft of seats and beneath wings, close to CG. Propeller, at front of fuselage, consists of an aluminium centre section and two hinged glassfibre/aramid/carbonfibre composites blades and is driven via a carbon shaft in a Kevlar tunnel between the two seats, and a five-belt gearbox, power transmission occurring, via a centrifugal clutch. Start-up is achieved by extending the nosecone forward (on the ground or in flight, by control in cockpit) with no change to trim; the propeller blades deploy from the folded position by centrifugal force. For gliding flight, the engine is stopped and the propeller blades swivel in sideways by spring loading. Once aligned the blades are concealed within fuselage by returning the nosecone to its 'glider' position to restore an aerodynamically clean nose contour. Fuel (mogas) in two integral wing tanks with combined capacity of 90 litres (23.8 US gallons; 19.8 Imp gallons) or, optionally, 120 litres (31.7 US gallons; 26.4 Imp gallons).

DIMENSIONS, EXTERNAL:

Wing span	23.00 m (75 ft 5½ in)
Wing aspect ratio	28.22
Length overall	8.42 m (27 ft 7½ in)
Height over tail	1.79 m (5 ft 10½ in)
Wheel track	1.15 m (3 ft 9¼ in)
Wheelbase	5.40 m (17 ft 8½ in)
Propeller diameter	1.61 m (5 ft 3½ in)

AREA:

Wings, gross	18.74 m² (201.7 sq ft)

WEIGHTS AND LOADINGS:

Weight empty	approx 635 kg (1,400 lb)
Max T-O weight	850 kg (1,874 lb)
Max wing loading	45.36 kg/m² (9.29 lb/sq ft)
Max power loading	12.14 kg/kW (19.94 lb/hp)

PERFORMANCE, UNPOWERED (at AUW of 850 kg; 1,874 lb, ISA):

Best glide ratio at 57 knots (105 km/h; 65 mph)	50
Min rate of sink	0.55 m (1.80 ft)/s
Stalling speed	42 knots (78 km/h; 49 mph)
Max speed (smooth air)	145 knots (270 km/h; 167 mph)
Max speed (rough air)	102 knots (190 km/h; 118 mph)

PERFORMANCE, POWERED (at AUW of 850 kg; 1,874 lb, ISA):

Max cruising speed	108 knots (200 km/h; 124 mph)
Max rate of climb at S/L	185 m (607 ft)/min
Service ceiling	5,000 m (16,400 ft)
T-O run	300 m (985 ft)
T-O to 15 m (50 ft)	450 m (1,475 ft)
Landing from 15 m (50 ft)	250 m (820 ft)
Landing run	150 m (495 ft)
Range with 90 litres (23.8 US gallons; 19.8 Imp gallons) of fuel	701 nm (1,300 km; 807 miles)

TECHNOFLUG

TECHNOFLUG LEICHTFLUGZEUGBAU GmbH

Dr-Kurt-Steim-Strasse 6, 7230 Schramberg-2
Telephone: 49 (7422) 8423
DESIGNER: Dipl Ing B. Karrais

TECHNOFLUG PICCOLO

The Piccolo is a modified and slightly larger version of the Neukom AN-20B, which first flew in prototype form in May 1986. It is now available in ready-assembled form; 60 had been sold by January 1990. It is certificated in European countries and in New Zealand.

TYPE: Single-seat microlight motor glider; conforms to JAR 22.

AIRFRAME: Wings have a single GFRP composites spar and sandwich skins, and carry upper surface spoilers. Wing section Wortmann FX-63-137. Monocoque fuselage and tail unit of GFRP construction. Three-axis control. Non-retractable tricycle landing gear.

POWER PLANT: One 17 kW (23 hp) Solo 2350B with electric starting, driving a rearward folding propeller. Fuel capacity 22 litres (5.8 US gallons; 4.8 Imp gallons).

DIMENSIONS, EXTERNAL:

Wing span	13.30 m (43 ft 7½ in)
Wing aspect ratio	16.6
Length overall	6.55 m (21 ft 6 in)
Height overall	1.02 m (3 ft 4¼ in)
Propeller diameter	1.18 m (3 ft 10½ in)

AREA:

Wings, gross	10.60 m² (114.1 sq ft)

WEIGHTS AND LOADINGS:

Weight empty	180 kg (397 lb)
Baggage weight	10 kg (22 lb)
Pilot weight range	65-110 kg (144-242 lb)
Max T-O weight	297 kg (655 lb)
Max wing loading	28.02 kg/m² (5.74 lb/sq ft)
Max power loading	17.47 kg/kW (28.48 lb/hp)

PERFORMANCE, UNPOWERED:

Best glide ratio at 42 knots (78 km/h; 48 mph)	23
Min rate of sink at 35 knots (65 km/h; 40 mph)	0.9 m (2.95 ft)/s

PERFORMANCE, POWERED:

Max level speed	74 knots (138 km/h; 86 mph)
Econ cruising speed	65 knots (120 km/h; 75 mph)
Stalling speed	30 knots (54 km/h; 34 mph)
Max rate of climb at S/L	126 m (413 ft)/min
Service ceiling	3,500 m (11,500 ft)
T-O to 15 m (50 ft): concrete	273 m (896 ft)
grass	308 m (1,011 ft)
Landing run	50 m (164 ft)
Range with max fuel approx 248 nm (460 km; 285 miles)	
Endurance	4 h
g limits	+5.3/-2.6

VALENTIN

VALENTIN FLUGZEUGBAU GmbH and Co KG

Flugplatzstrasse 18, 8728 Hassfurt
Telephone: 49 (9521) 2041
Telex: 539227 VALGMD
Fax: 49 (9521) 7317
DIRECTOR: Günter Posch
SALES MANAGER: Franz Trubert

This company is producing the Taifun two-seat motor glider and Kiwi sailplane. In July 1981 it took over the former MFB company (see 1981-82 *Jane's*) and became responsible for producing that company's Mistral-C sailplane, although this is no longer in production. Development work and construction of metal components takes place at Königsbrunn; production of GFRP components, and final assembly, are undertaken at Hassfurt.

VALENTIN TAIFUN 17 E II (TYPHOON)

The Taifun motor glider was proposed originally in two versions, the 15 m span Taifun 15 E and 17 m span Taifun 17 E, as detailed in the 1983-84 and previous editions of *Jane's*. Construction of the first prototype, to Taifun 17 E configuration, began in July 1979, and this aircraft (D-KONO) made its first flight on 28 February 1981. A second prototype was used for extended trials and development of the mechanical (instead of the original electrical) undercarriage retraction gear, a shock absorbing engine mounting, and other improvements.

In 1982, due to lack of sufficient interest in the smaller version, it was decided to begin production only of the Taifun 17 E. German certification of this version, with a 59 kW (80 hp) Limbach L 2000 EB engine, was awarded on 29 April 1983, and series manufacture began in mid-year. The current version, to which the following description applies, has a more powerful engine.

TYPE: Two-seat motor glider.

AIRFRAME: Cantilever low-wing monoplane with T tail. Wortmann FX-67-K-170/17 wing section. Dihedral 3°. Incidence 0° 48′. Sweepforward 0° 38′ 24″ at quarter-chord. Wings and ailerons of glassfibre/foam sandwich, with double T section glassfibre roving main spar booms. All-glassfibre cambered trailing-edge flaps, interconnected with ailerons at 8° setting only. Schempp-Hirth upper surface airbrakes. Wings fold back alongside fuselage for transportation and storage. Fuselage is a stressed skin structure of glassfibre and foam sandwich, reinforced with carbonfibre in the cockpit area. Fixed incidence T tailplane, with horn balanced elevator, of similar construction to wings. Flettner tab in port half of elevator. Electro-hydraulically retractable tricycle landing gear, with hydraulically damped pneumatic shock absorbers, Goodyear 5 in mainwheel tyres, pressure 2.5 bars (36 lb/sq in), and Cleveland type hydraulic mainwheel disc brakes. Single nosewheel or tailwheel. Cockpit seats two persons side by side under rearward sliding canopy.

POWER PLANT: One 67 kW (90 hp) Limbach L 2400 EB1B four-cylinder four-stroke engine, driving a Mühlbauer MTV-1-A/L160-03 two-blade variable-pitch feathering propeller. Fuel in two wing tanks, total capacity 90 litres (23.8 US gallons; 19.8 Imp gallons).

DIMENSIONS, EXTERNAL:

Wing span	17.00 m (55 ft 9¼ in)
Wing aspect ratio	16.4
Length overall	7.782 m (25 ft 6½ in)
Height over tail	2.30 m (7 ft 6½ in)
Tailplane span	3.30 m (10 ft 10 in)
Wheelbase	1.75 m (5 ft 9 in)
Propeller diameter	1.60 m (5 ft 3 in)

AREA:

Wings, gross	17.60 m² (189.4 sq ft)

WEIGHTS AND LOADINGS:

Weight empty	610 kg (1,345 lb)

Stemme/Gepard S 10 gsm aerial sensor platform with engine in use *(Gepard)*

Valentin Taifun 17 E II two-seat motor glider *(Geoffrey P. Jones)*

Valentin Kiwi with 'TOP' engine installation

Auto-Aero Góbé R-26SU two-seat training sailplane

Technoflug Piccolo motor glider

Max T-O weight	850 kg (1,874 lb)
Max wing loading	48.30 kg/m² (9.90 lb/sq ft)
Max power loading	12.67 kg/kW (20.82 lb/hp)

PERFORMANCE, UNPOWERED (at max T-O weight):

Best glide ratio at 57 knots (105 km/h; 65 mph)		30
Min rate of sink at 46 knots (85 km/h; 53 mph)		
		0.95 m (3.12 ft)/s
Stalling speed		39 knots (72 km/h; 45 mph)
Max speed (smooth air)		135 knots (250 km/h; 155 mph)
Max speed (rough air)		100 knots (185 km/h; 115 mph)
g limits		+5.3/−2.65

PERFORMANCE, POWERED (at max T-O weight):

Max cruising speed	113 knots (210 km/h; 130 mph)
Stalling speed	35 knots (64 km/h; 40 mph)
Max rate of climb at S/L	180 m (590 ft)/min
Service ceiling	5,000 m (16,400 ft)
T-O run	250 m (820 ft)
Landing run	200 m (655 ft)
Range with max fuel	593 nm (1,100 km; 683 miles)

VALENTIN KIWI

The Kiwi sailplane has an optional retractable engine package to provide self-launch capability and auxiliary power for short periods of flying. The prototype (D-KELT) flew for the first time in August 1986 and series production began in late 1988.

TYPE: Single-seat (optionally self-launching) sailplane.

AIRFRAME: Cantilever mid-wing monoplane, with Wortmann FX-61-163/FX-60-126 wing sections. Double tapered wings are of glassfibre and PVC rigid foam sandwich construction, over an I spar with carbonfibre spar caps, and are bolted to fuselage. Airbrakes on upper surface only. Fuselage comprises an all-GFRP shell at front, with a tailboom and T tail unit of glassfibre and PVC rigid foam. Non-retractable 5.00-5 sprung monowheel, with drum brake, plus 210 × 65 mm tailwheel. Cockpit has bonded-in glassfibre seat pan, and is enclosed by a one-piece, front-hinged upward opening canopy.

POWER PLANT (optional): Fully retractable F & E Fischer 'TOP' installation, comprising a 17.9 kW (24 hp) König SC 430 three-cylinder two-stroke engine driving a three-blade folding pusher propeller via a toothed belt reduction gear. Fuel tank capacity 10 litres (2.6 US gallons; 2.2 Imp gallons).

DIMENSIONS, EXTERNAL:

Wing span	15.00 m (49 ft 2½ in)
Wing aspect ratio	20.4
Length overall	6.80 m (22 ft 3¾ in)
Height over tail	1.46 m (4 ft 9½ in)
Propeller diameter	1.30 m (4 ft 3¼ in)

AREA:

Wings, gross	11.03 m² (118.7 sq ft)

WEIGHTS AND LOADINGS (A: without/B: with engine):

Weight empty: A	210 kg (463 lb)
B	250 kg (551 lb)
Max T-O weight: A	300 kg (661 lb)
B	380 kg (838 lb)
Max wing loading: A	27.2 kg/m² (5.57 lb/sq ft)
B	34.5 kg/m² (7.06 lb/sq ft)

PERFORMANCE (at max T-O weight):

Best glide ratio: A	37
B	35
Min rate of sink: A	0.58 m (1.90 ft)/s
Max cruising speed:	
B	124 knots (230 km/h; 143 mph)
Stalling speed: A, B	34 knots (62 km/h; 39 mph)
Max rate of climb at S/L: B	102 m (335 ft)/min
T-O run: B, hard surface	250 m (820 ft)
B, grass	350 m (1,150 ft)
Range	approx 108 nm (200 km; 124 miles)

HUNGARY

AUTO-AERO

AUTO-AERO KÖZLEKEDÉSTECHNIKAI VÁLLALAT (Automobile and Aeronautical Technical Establishment)

Szombathely, H-9701 Zanati u. 4
Telephone: 36 (94) 11341 and 13930
Telex: 37 346
Fax: 36 (94) 13930
SOLE IMPORTER: Louis Rotter, Byways Private Hotel, Warrington Road, Hoole, Chester CH2 3PA, England
Telephone: 44 (244) 326555

AUTO-AERO GÓBÉ R-26SU

The first of two R-26 prototypes made its initial flight on 6 May 1961, and 120 of the original version were put into production in the mid-1960s, as last described in the 1965-66 *Jane's.* The current version, to which the following details apply, is designated R-26SU (utility), which first flew on 15 December 1982. BGA certification was gained in 1989. By February 1990 a total of 180 R-26SUs had been built.

TYPE: Two-seat training sailplane.

AIRFRAME: Cantilever shoulder-wing monoplane. Constant chord wings of Göttingen 549 (modified) section, having 3° dihedral and 1° 30′ of forward sweep. Single-spar mainly aluminium alloy (dural) wings, with leading-edge torsion box covered by riveted skin; fabric covering aft of 35 per cent chord line. Schempp-Hirth perforated metal airbrakes in upper and lower surfaces. Frise type slotted ailerons, of fabric covered metal construction. Aluminium alloy fuselage, with partial linen fabric covering. Conventional tail surfaces, with tailplane mounted at intersection of fin and dorsal fin. Balanced rudder; ground adjustable tab on port elevator. All aluminium alloy construction, except for linen-covered elevator. Non-retractable, partly recessed rubber sprung 12 × 5 monowheel, pressure 1.96 bars (28.43 lb/sq in); faired castoring tailwheel under rear fuselage. Towing hook/cable release under front fuselage, forward of monowheel for winch towing; nose hook for aerial towing. Two seats in tandem under one-piece framed canopy which opens sideways to starboard.

DIMENSIONS, EXTERNAL:

Wing span	14.00 m (45 ft 11¼ in)
Wing aspect ratio	10.9
Length overall	9.00 m (29 ft 6⅓ in)
Height over tail	1.96 m (6 ft 5¼ in)

AREA:

Wings, gross	18.00 m² (193.75 sq ft)

WEIGHTS AND LOADING:

Weight empty	240 kg (529 lb)
Max T-O weight	440 kg (970 lb)
Max wing loading	24.4 kg/m² (5.00 lb/sq ft)

PERFORMANCE (at max T-O weight):

Best glide ratio at 43 knots (80 km/h; 50 mph)		23.2
Min rate of sink at 43 knots (80 km/h; 50 mph)		
		0.97 m (3.18 ft)/s
Stalling speed		34 knots (62 km/h; 39 mph)
Max speed (smooth air)		102 knots (190 km/h; 118 mph)
Max speed (rough air)		77 knots (143 km/h; 89 mph)
Max aero-tow speed		70 knots (130 km/h; 81 mph)
Max winch-launching speed		
		59 knots (110 km/h; 68 mph)
g limits		+5.3/−2.65

INDIA

CIVIL AVIATION DEPARTMENT
TECHNICAL CENTRE, CIVIL AVIATION DEPARTMENT

Civil Aviation Department, Technical Centre, Opp. Safdarjung Airport, New Delhi 110003
Telephone: 91 (11) 611504
Telex: 31 66407 NAA
DIRECTOR GENERAL: P. C. Sen
DIRECTOR (R & D): Y. P. Bawa

Since 1950 the Technical Centre of the Indian Civil Aviation Department has undertaken design and development of gliders utilising predominantly indigenous materials. The first of these gliders was flown in November 1950. Since then the Centre has built 10 types for use at gliding clubs and centres in India, many as listed in previous editions of *Jane's*. Of these, seven have been original designs. The latest design is the LT-1 light training aircraft (see Addenda).

The Technical Centre does not undertake quantity production of gliders. Drawings of designs developed at the Centre are supplied to interested organisations with permission to manufacture them in series.

ATS-1 ARDHRA

This two-seat training sailplane was designed by the team responsible earlier for the Mrigasheer, last described in the 1980-81 *Jane's*. The Ardhra prototype (VT-GEJ) made its first flight on 5 March 1979 and was certificated by the Indian DGCA on 2 November of that year.

The Ardhra has been approved for use by the National Cadet Corps and civil gliding clubs, and has been in production at the Kanpur Division of Hindustan Aeronautics Ltd. A second prototype (VT-GEN), flown for the first time on 28 June 1981, was representative of the production version, of which 61 were built (59 for the Indian Air Force). Due to a requirement for 60 more from the Indian National Air Corps (Air Wing), production is to restart. A substantial number of the earlier Ardhras were fitted with enlarged canopies. (Illustration in 1985-86 *Jane's*).
TYPE: Tandem two-seat advanced training sailplane.
AIRFRAME: Cantilever shoulder-wing monoplane. Wortmann FX-61-184 wing section from root to tip. Dihedral 3°. Incidence 3° at root. Sweepforward 3° at leading-edge; 2° washout on outer half of each wing. Two-spar wooden wings, plywood covered on leading- and trailing-edges; plain wood ailerons; wood airbrakes in upper and lower wing surfaces. Tail unit of similar construction, but with rear portions of rudder and elevator fabric covered. Horn balanced rudder; mass and horn balanced elevator. Plywood covered tab in starboard elevator. Semi-monocoque wood fuselage, with plywood covering. Nosecone of glassfibre. Non-retractable unsprung mono-

wheel, tyre size 6.00-4. Rubber sprung nose-skid, with replaceable steel shoe, and rubber sprung tailskid.

DIMENSIONS, EXTERNAL:
Wing span	16.50 m (54 ft 1½ in)
Wing aspect ratio	12.5
Length overall	8.61 m (28 ft 3 in)
Height over tail	2.464 m (8 ft 1 in)

AREA:
Wings, gross	21.83 m² (235.0 sq ft)

WEIGHTS AND LOADING:
Weight empty	328 kg (723 lb)
Max T-O weight	508 kg (1,120 lb)
Max wing loading	23.28 kg/m² (4.77 lb/sq ft)

PERFORMANCE (at max T-O weight):
Best glide ratio at 47 knots (87 km/h; 54 mph)		26
Min rate of sink at 39 knots (72 km/h; 45 mph)		
		0.78 m (2.56 ft)/s
Stalling speed	33 knots (61 km/h; 38 mph)	
Max speed (smooth air)	113 knots (210 km/h; 130 mph)	
Max speed (rough air)	69 knots (127 km/h; 79 mph)	
Max aero-tow and max winch-launching speed		
	59 knots (110 km/h; 68 mph)	
g limits		+5.3/-2.65

ITALY

GENERAL
GENERAL GLIDERS

Via Stadera a Poggioreale, 62 80143, Naples
Telephone: 39 (81) 26 53 02
Fax: 39 (81) 26 53 02

GENERAL MANAGER: Cozzolino Carlo

General Gliders began offering kits (in about March 1990) to construct the 940A Zefiro motor glider/sailplane, originally designed by Orlando Iannotta. The accompanying illustration shows its light wood and fabric construction.

Wing section is Göttingen GO 532 (modified). Max T-O weight is 230 kg (507 lb). Further details can be found in the microlight tables.

NORWAY

LUNDS TEKNISKE
LUNDS TEKNISKE

Vikaveien 2, N-8600 Mo
Telephone: 47 (87) 52 100
Fax: 47 (87) 55 065

LUNDS TEKNISKE SILHOUETTE

The Silhouette, purchased by Lunds Tekniske from Silhouette Aircraft Inc of the USA (see Sport Aircraft section), is produced in kit form in two versions, the aerobatic sport aircraft being convertible to a Utility category motor glider by the addition of bolt-on wing extensions. These result in the following changes:
TYPE: Single-seat motor glider.
AIRFRAME: As described in Sport Aircraft section, plus bolt-on wing extension panels comprising stub spars,

pre-shaped polystyrene cores and materials for glassfibre/epoxy skin. No washout in extensions.
POWER PLANT: Engine and standard fuel capacity details as for Sport Aircraft version. Motor glider has option for variable-pitch feathering propeller, but no option for larger fuel tank.

DIMENSIONS, EXTERNAL:
Wing span	12.50 m (41 ft 0 in)
Wing chord at tip	0.39 m (1 ft 3½ in)
Wing aspect ratio	18.92

AREA:
Wings, gross	8.36 m² (90.0 sq ft)

WEIGHTS AND LOADING:
Weight empty	271 kg (597 lb)
Max T-O weight	374 kg (824 lb)
Max wing loading	46.1 kg/m² (9.44 lb/sq ft)

PERFORMANCE, UNPOWERED:
Best glide ratio	almost 25

PERFORMANCE, POWERED (at max T-O weight):
Never-exceed speed	104 knots (193 km/h; 120 mph) IAS
Max cruising speed	87 knots (161 km/h; 100 mph) IAS
Econ cruising speed	57 knots (105 km/h; 65 mph) IAS

Stalling speed:
power on	40 knots (74 km/h; 46 mph) IAS
power off	44 knots (80 km/h; 50 mph) IAS
Max rate of climb at S/L	229 m (750 ft)/min
T-O run	244 m (800 ft)
Landing run	168 m (550 ft)
Endurance at max cruising speed	4 h 6 min
g limits	+3.2/-2

POLAND

PW
POLITECHNIKA WARSZAWSKA
(Warsaw University of Technology)

Institute of Aeronautics and Applied Mechanics, ul. Nowowiejska 22/24, 00-665 Warszawa
Telephone: 48 (2) 10070 965
Telex: 813307 PW PL
DIRECTOR: Dr Roman Switkiewicz

PW-2 GAPA

The PW-2 Gapa is the productionised version of the ULS (Ultralekkiego Szybowca: ultralight sailplane), which flew for the first time on 27 September 1981 and was described and illustrated in the 1984-85 *Jane's*.

Construction of three PW-2 prototypes (including one for ground tests) began in September 1984, and the first flight was made on 25 July 1985. Designed for basic training and recreation, the Gapa can be winch or bungee launched, or tow launched by an aircraft or motorcar. Its light glassfibre structure meets all requirements of JAR 22, and a novel feature are the wing strut fairings, which are hinged and can be pivoted for use as airbrakes.

The PW-2 has been available in plans and kit forms, as well as ready to fly.
TYPE: Single-seat ultra-lightweight sailplane.
AIRFRAME: Braced high-wing monoplane. Constant chord wings, of NACA 4415 constant section from root to tip. Dihedral 1°. Incidence 3°. No sweep. Single-spar wings, spar and D nose section forming a glassfibre torsion box; fabric covered glassfibre structure aft of spar. Glassfibre

ailerons, projecting aft of trailing-edge. No spoilers. Fairing behind each bracing strut pivots to act as airbrake. Keel type fuselage, of glassfibre laminate. Conventional unbraced tail unit, of similar construction to rear portion of wings. Non-retractable rubber sprung monowheel, tyre size 255 × 110 mm, pressure 1.8 bars (26 lb/sq in); no brake. Nose-skid and small tailskid. Single seat in open cockpit with windscreen.

DIMENSIONS, EXTERNAL:
Wing span	11.00 m (36 ft 1 in)
Wing aspect ratio	9.52
Length overall	5.50 m (18 ft 0¾ in)
Height over tail	2.45 m (8 ft 0½ in)

AREA:
Wings, gross	12.70 m² (136.7 sq ft)

WEIGHTS AND LOADING:
Weight empty, equipped	110 kg (243 lb)
Max T-O weight	220 kg (485 lb)
Max wing loading	17.32 kg/m² (3.55 lb/sq ft)

PERFORMANCE (at max T-O weight):
Best glide ratio at 37 knots (69 km/h; 43 mph)		16
Min rate of sink at 31 knots (58 km/h; 36 mph)		
		1.00 m (3.28 ft)/s
Stalling speed	27 knots (49 km/h; 31 mph)	
Max speed (smooth air)	81 knots (150 km/h; 93 mph)	
Max speed (rough air) and max aero-tow speed		
	64 knots (120 km/h; 74 mph)	
Max winch-launching speed		
	54 knots (100 km/h; 62 mph)	
g limits		+5.3/-2.65

PW-3 BAKCYL

The two-seat PW-3 is a progressive development of the PW-2, having inset Frise ailerons and an enclosed cabin, increasing the empty weight and improving the best glide ratio. It is particularly suited to primary training, cannot be spun, and can be launched by a bungee normally used for single-seaters. It has a composite structure, with the wings using the CAGI R-III aerofoil section.

The first PW-3 made its initial flight in August 1988, since when a full flight test programme has been completed.
TYPE: Two-seat sailplane.
DIMENSIONS, EXTERNAL:
Wing span	14.65 m (48 ft 1¾ in)
Wing aspect ratio	12.0
Length overall	7.25 m (23 ft 9½ in)
Height overall	2.50 m (8 ft 2½ in)

AREA:
Wings, gross	17.50 m² (188.37 sq ft)

WEIGHTS:
Weight empty	220 kg (485 lb)
Max T-O weight	420 kg (926 lb)

PERFORMANCE:
Best glide ratio at 49 knots (90 km/h; 56 mph)		20
Min rate of sink		1.10 m (3.61 ft)/s
Stalling speed	30 knots (55 km/h; 34.5 mph)	
Max speed (smooth air)	97 knots (180 km/h; 112 mph)	
g limits		+5.3/-2.65

PW-4

This motor glider is based on the PW-3 but has a low-mounted fuselage boom to allow for the 50 kW (67 hp)

Indian Civil Aviation Dept ATS-1 Ardhra two-seat training sailplane in Indian Air Force markings

General Gliders (Iannotta) 940A Zefiro microlight motor glider/sailplane

Politechnika Warszawska PW-2 Gapa lightweight single-seat sailplane
(Robert Senkowski)

Lunds Tekniske Silhouette in motor glider form

Politechnika Warszawska PW-3 Bakcyl two-seat sailplane

Model of the Politechnika Warszawska PW-4 motor glider

Limbach SL 1700ES engine mounted behind the wings and driving an HO11-145B75ES fixed-pitch two-blade pusher propeller. Fuel capacity is 40 litres (10.6 US gallons; 8.8 Imp gallons). The prototype was expected to make its first flight in Spring 1990.

Using the CAGI R-III wing section, construction is of glassfibre/epoxy except for fabric covering the wings and rudder. Airbrakes are fitted to the upper surfaces of the wings. The landing gear is of non-retractable tricycle type, using glassfibre/epoxy spring legs. Mainwheel tyres are size 150 × 350; the steerable tailwheel is size 125 × 300. Disc brakes are fitted to the mainwheels.

TYPE: Two-seat motor glider.

DIMENSIONS, EXTERNAL:
Wing span	16.00 m (52 ft 6 in)
Wing aspect ratio	13.6
Length overall	8.00 m (26 ft 3 in)
Height overall	2.40 m (7 ft 10½ in)

AREA:
Wings, gross	18.80 m² (202.36 sq ft)

WEIGHTS AND LOADINGS:
Weight empty	410 kg (904 lb)
Max T-O weight	670 kg (1,477 lb)
Max wing loading	35.64 kg/m² (7.30 lb/sq ft)
Max power loading	13.40 kg/kW (22.04 lb/hp)

PERFORMANCE (estimated, at max T-O weight):
Best glide ratio at 49 knots (91 km/h; 57 mph)	22
Min rate of sink at 44 knots (82 km/h; 51 mph)	1.10 m (3.61 ft)/s
Stalling speed	35 knots (65 km/h; 41 mph)
g limits	+5.3/−2.65

SZD

PRZEDSIEBIORSTWO DOŚWIADCZALNO-PRODUKCYJNE SZYBOWNICTWA (Experimental and Production Concern for Gliders) PZL-BIELSKO

HEAD OFFICE AND WORKS: Ulica Cieszyńska 325, 43-300 Bielsko-Biala 1
Telephone: 48 250 21 to 250 23
Telex: 035259 PZL PL
MANAGING DIRECTOR: Juliusz Borth
TECHNICAL DIRECTOR: Jerzy Smielkiewicz MSc
TECHNICAL INFORMATION MANAGER: Wladyslaw Korzonkiewicz
SALES REPRESENTATIVE: Pezetel, 61 Aleja Stanow Zjednoczonych (PO Box 6), 00-991 Warszawa 44
Telephone: 48 10 80 01
Telex: 813314

The Instytut Szybownictwa (Gliding Institute), formed officially in January 1946 at Bielsko-Biala, has since undergone several changes of name, as detailed in the *1977-78 Jane's.* The change to the present title took place in July 1975, but the well known designation initials SZD are retained. This organisation is responsible for the design and development of nearly all Polish sailplanes. Production plants are at Bielsko-Biala, Wroclaw and Jezów.

Between 1947 and 1 January 1990 the Polish aircraft industry produced 4,915 gliders of more than 116 different types, and SZD sailplanes have been exported all over the world in substantial numbers.

SZD-42-2 JANTAR 2B (AMBER 2B)

Designed by Dipl-Ing Adam Kurbiel, the SZD-42-2 Open Class sailplane was based on the SZD-42-1. The prototype flew for the first time on 13 March 1978, and 126

Jantar 2Bs were built before production ended on 31 December 1988.

A 22/24 m (72 ft 2¼ in/78 ft 9 in) Open Class Jantar, with detachable wingtips, was planned as a developed version of the SZD-42-2 Jantar 2B. However, initial studies revealed some disadvantages of the design and the project was abandoned.

Full details of the Jantar 2B can be found in the 1989-90 *Jane's.*

SZD-48-3 JANTAR STANDARD 3

This Standard Class sailplane is the current version of the SZD-48-1 and SZD-48-2 Jantar Standard 2, which were described in the 1983-84 *Jane's.* Production of these versions, which totalled 313, ended in March 1983.

The prototype SZD-48-3 Jantar Standard 3 was flown for the first time on 9 February 1983, and 302 of this version had been built by 1 January 1990.

TYPE: Single-seat Standard Class sailplane.
AIRFRAME: Cantilever shoulder-wing monoplane, with NN-8 wing section. Dihedral 1° 30′. Single glassfibre roving main spar, with glassfibre/foam/glassfibre moulded skins (no ribs) and plain ailerons. Glassfibre upper/lower surface airbrakes. Glassfibre fuselage, with steel tube central support structure, rear portion stiffened by half-frames and fin ribs. Cantilever T tail of similar construction to wings. Fin integral with fuselage; mass balanced rudder, with upward angled lower edge to avoid damage in tail-down landing. Mass balanced elevator, with spring trim. Retractable unsprung monowheel, tyre size 350 × 135 mm, with disc brake; semi-recessed tailwheel, diameter 200 mm. One-piece canopy, hinged at front and opening upward. Optional CG towing hook on mainwheel fork. Provision for 150 litres (39.6 US gallons; 33 Imp gallons) water ballast.

DIMENSIONS, EXTERNAL:
Wing span	15.00 m (49 ft 2½ in)
Wing aspect ratio	21.1
Length overall	6.85 m (22 ft 5¾ in)
Height over tail	1.51 m (4 ft 11½ in)

AREA:
Wings, gross	10.66 m² (114.7 sq ft)

WEIGHTS AND LOADING:
Weight empty	274 kg (604 lb)
Max T-O weight:	
without water ballast	390 kg (860 lb)
with water ballast	540 kg (1,190 lb)
Max wing loading	50.7 kg/m² (10.38 lb/sq ft)

PERFORMANCE (at max T-O weight):
Best glide ratio at 66 knots (123 km/h; 76 mph)	40
Min rate of sink at 52 knots (97 km/h; 60 mph)	
	0.77 m (2.53 ft)/s
Stalling speed	45 knots (82 km/h; 51 mph)
Max speed (smooth air)	154 knots (285 km/h; 177 mph)
Max speed (rough air)	108 knots (200 km/h; 124 mph)
Max aero-tow speed	81 knots (150 km/h; 93 mph)
Max winch-launching speed	
	67 knots (125 km/h; 77 mph)
g limits	+5.3/−2.65

SZD-50-3 PUCHACZ (EAGLE OWL)

The Puchacz, designed by Dipl-Ing Adam Meus, is a high performance sailplane intended particularly for training and performance flying. It was modified and developed from a prototype, designated SZD-50-1 Dromader, which first flew on 21 December 1976.

A second prototype made its initial flight on 20 December 1977, and the first production SZD-50-2 Puchacz (SP-3151) followed on 13 April 1979. A total of 231 had been built by 1 January 1990, with exports made to Argentina, Austria, Canada, China, Denmark, Finland, East and West Germany, Greece, Sweden, Switzerland, Turkey, the UK and the USSR. The current version of the Puchacz, designated SZD-50-3, has a larger horizontal tail situated 30 cm (11¾ in) higher on the fin, an enlarged rudder, and a fairing over the mainwheel. Inverted flight and extended aerobatic manoeuvres became permissible in 1986.
TYPE: Tandem two-seat high performance training sailplane.
AIRFRAME: Cantilever mid-wing monoplane, mainly of glassfibre sandwich construction. Wortmann wing sections. Plain ailerons. Upper/lower surface airbrakes.

Glassfibre fuselage, supported in central portion by two wooden frames, with integral fin. Glassfibre sandwich cruciform tail unit, with fabric covered glassfibre rudder. Non-retractable semi-recessed nosewheel (size 255 × 110 mm) and sprung monowheel (size 350 × 135 mm, with disc brake), and tailskid. One-piece canopy opens sideways.

DIMENSIONS, EXTERNAL:
Wing span	16.67 m (54 ft 8¼ in)
Wing aspect ratio	15.3
Length overall	8.38 m (27 ft 6 in)
Height over tail	2.04 m (6 ft 8¼ in)

AREA:
Wings, gross	18.16 m² (195.5 sq ft)

WEIGHTS AND LOADING:
Weight empty	360 kg (794 lb)
Max T-O weight	570 kg (1,256 lb)
Max wing loading	31.4 kg/m² (6.43 lb/sq ft)

PERFORMANCE (at max T-O weight):
Best glide ratio at 46 knots (85 km/h; 53 mph)	30
Min rate of sink at 40 knots (75 km/h; 47 mph)	
	0.70 m (2.30 ft)/s
Stalling speed	33 knots (60 km/h; 38 mph)
Max speed (smooth air)	116 knots (215 km/h; 133 mph)
Max speed (rough air)	86 knots (160 km/h; 99 mph)
Max aero-tow speed	81 knots (150 km/h; 93 mph)
Max winch-launching speed	
	59 knots (110 km/h; 68 mph)
g limits	+5.3/−2.65

SZD-51-1 JUNIOR

Designed in 1979 by Dipl-Ing Stanislaw Zientek, and first flown in SZD-51-0 prototype form on 31 December 1980, the Junior is a single-seat Club Class sailplane of GFRP construction. Production began at Wroclaw in 1984, and 158 Juniors had been completed by 1 January 1990.
TYPE: Single-seat Club Class sailplane.
AIRFRAME: Cantilever shoulder-wing monoplane, with FX-S-02-196 (root) and FX-S-02/1-158 (tip) wing sections. Dihedral 3° from roots. Incidence 1° 30′. No sweep. Single glassfibre I section roving main spar, with glassfibre/foam/glassfibre sandwich moulded skins (no ribs). Schempp-Hirth duraluminum upper surface airbrakes. Airbrake boxes and airbrakes, and aileron pushrod control system, suspended on main spar. Glassfibre fuselage, with steel tube central support structure; rear portion stiffened by PVC foam half-frames and foam ribs. Fin, which carries VHF aerial, is integral with fuselage; rudder fabric covered. Cantilever T tail unit, of similar construction to wings; elevators have mass balance and spring trim. Non-retractable unsprung monowheel (tyre size 350 × 135 mm), with SZD disc brake; semi-recessed tailwheel, tyre size 200 × 50 mm; auxiliary front skid. Nose and CG towing hooks. One-piece Mecaplex canopy, opening sideways to starboard.

DIMENSIONS, EXTERNAL:
Wing span	15.00 m (49 ft 2½ in)
Wing aspect ratio	18.0
Length overall	6.69 m (21 ft 11½ in)
Height over tail	1.54 m (5 ft 0⅔ in)

AREA:
Wings, gross	12.51 m² (134.7 sq ft)

WEIGHTS AND LOADING:
Weight empty	242 kg (533 lb)
Max T-O weight	355 kg (783 lb)
Max wing loading	28.4 kg/m² (5.81 lb/sq ft)

PERFORMANCE (at wing loading of 26 kg/m²; 5.33 lb/sq ft):
Best glide ratio at 43 knots (80 km/h; 50 mph)	35
Min rate of sink at 39 knots (72 km/h; 45 mph)	
	0.59 m (1.94 ft)/s
Stalling speed	33 knots (60 km/h; 38 mph)
Max speed (smooth air)	119 knots (220 km/h; 137 mph)
Max speed (rough air)	81 knots (150 km/h; 93 mph)
Max aero-tow speed	75 knots (140 km/h; 87 mph)
Max winch-launching speed	
	69 knots (128 km/h; 79 mph)
g limits	+5.3/−2.65

SZD-55

In 1985 Dipl Ing Tadeusz Labuć with the design staff of SZD began development of a new high performance single-seat Standard Class sailplane of GFRP construction, to conform to JAR 22 requirements. The first of three prototypes first flew on 15 August 1988. By January 1989 prototype testing had been completed and the Polish Certificate of Airworthiness was issued.
TYPE: Single-seat Standard Class sailplane.
AIRFRAME: Cantilever shoulder wing monoplane. NN-27 wing section. Dihedral 3°. Incidence 2° 30′. Eliptical wing planform but with a straight trailing-edge perpendicular to the plan of symmetry. Wings of glassfibre and foam sandwich construction, with integral double T spars but no ribs. Water ballast tanks in wings of 195 litre (51.5 US gallon; 43 Imp gallon) capacity; additional water ballast tank in fin, capacity 9 litres (2.4 US gallons; 2 Imp gallons). Glassfibre/foam sandwich ailerons. Aluminium alloy airbrakes on upper surfaces. Fuselage and integral fin of glassfibre/epoxy construction. T tailplane with elevator, and rudder, of glassfibre/foam sandwich construction. Retractable unsprung monowheel with tyre size 350 × 135 mm, pressure 2 bars (29 lb/sq in). Tailwheel size 200 × 50 mm, pressure 1.5 bars (22 lb/sq in), can be replaced by tailskid. Tost towing hook on front of fuselage or on main landing gear unit (retracting with it).

DIMENSIONS, EXTERNAL:
Wing span	15.00 m (49 ft 2½ in)
Wing aspect ratio	23.44
Length overall	6.85 m (22 ft 5¾ in)
Height overall	1.47 m (4 ft 10 in)

AREA:
Wings, gross	9.60 m² (103.33 sq ft)

WEIGHTS AND LOADING:
Weight empty	210 kg (463 lb)
Max T-O weight	500 kg (1,102 lb)
Max wing loading	52.0 kg/m² (10.65 lb/sq ft)

PERFORMANCE (at 50.5 kg/m²; 10.34 lb/sq ft wing loading):
Best glide ratio at 64 knots (119 km/h; 74 mph)	44.1
Min rate of sink at 54 knots (100 km/h; 62 mph)	
	0.686 m (2.25 ft)/s
Stalling speed	46 knots (84 km/h; 53 mph)
Max speed (smooth air)	137 knots (255 km/h; 158 mph)
Max speed (rough air)	105 knots (195 km/h; 121 mph)
Max winch-launching speed	
	81 knots (150 km/h; 93 mph)
g limits	+5.32/−2.65

WSK PZL-KROSNO
WYTWÓRNIA SPRZETU KOMUNIKACYJNEGO PZL-KROSNO (Transport Equipment Manufacturing Centre, Krosno)

38-400 Krosno n. Wislokiem
Telephone: 48 229 11
Telex: 065247 or 065263
Fax: 48 228 61
GENERAL MANAGER: Ing Jan Czerniecki
CHIEF DESIGNER: Ing Eugeniusz Pelczar

WSK PZL-Krosno has designed a two-seat training glider intended for widespread use by Polish aeroclubs. Known as the KR-03A Puchatek, it is Krosno's first glider design for more than 20 years.

PZL-KROSNO KR-03A PUCHATEK ('POOH')

Polish aeroclubs (Aeroklub PRL) are suffering a shortage of two-seat sailplanes suitable for basic and advanced training. Only dozens remain of the Bocian, the most popular type for more than 25 years, plus a handful of the earlier Czaplas. Their place was intended to be taken by the SZD-50 Puchacz (which see), but supplies of this aircraft were slow, due mainly to a reliance on imported composite materials which require hard currency payments and have made the cost of the Puchacz unacceptably high.

In an attempt to remedy this deficiency, PZL-Krosno designed the Puchatek ('Pooh', after A. A. Milne's famous Winnie-the-Pooh) in response to a specification issued in June 1982. This meets Aeroklub PRL requirements in terms of cost, materials and ease of maintenance, as well as providing adequate performance.

Preliminary design work, under the leadership of Ing Jerzy Krawczyk, started in March 1983, and construction of a static test aircraft began in mid-1984. The KR-03 first flying prototype (SP-P336), using the second airframe, flew for the first time on 1 August 1985. The second Puchatek prototype, which flew for the first time on 20 November 1986, differed slightly in construction and was designated KR-03A. Certification under JAR 22 was awarded on 19 December 1987, and the first five initial production KR-03A Puchateks first flew in February 1988. The head of Aeroklub PRL has said that up to 600 Puchateks may be built to meet present and future requirements. After basic training on the Puchatek, students will graduate to the SZD-51-1 Junior (which see).
TYPE: Tandem two-seat basic and advanced training, and general-purpose sailplane.
AIRFRAME: Cantilever mid-wing monoplane. Constant chord wings of Wortmann FX-S-02-158 section, set at incidence of 5°. Sweepforward 3°. Dihedral 4° from roots. Conventional structure of PA-7 duralumin main and auxiliary spars and ribs, each wing being attached to fuselage by three bolts. Forward portion of each wing is duralumin skinned, rear portion fabric covered. Two-segment slotted ailerons on each wing, of fabric covered metal construction. Ailerons, and Schempp-Hirth upper/lower surface airbrakes at mid span, actuated by pushrods. Fuselage is an all-metal semi-monocoque, reinforced with nine frames but having no longitudinal stiffening. Forward (cockpit) section consists of two riveted halves of PA-2 duralumin sheet; rear section comprises two conical sections of PA-7 duralumin sheet. Conventional T tail surfaces, fin (integral with fuselage) and fixed incidence tailplane being all-metal (PA-2/PA-7), rudder and elevators (incorporating spring trim) of fabric covered metal construction. Non-retractable 350 × 135 mm sprung monowheel, with oleo-pneumatic shock absorber and brake; rubber sprung tailskid; and rubber sprung ash nose-skid. Tandem seats for instructor (at rear) and pupil. One-piece canopy, opening sideways to starboard. Dual controls and radio standard.

DIMENSIONS, EXTERNAL:
Wing span	16.40 m (53 ft 9¾ in)
Wing chord, constant	1.20 m (3 ft 11¼ in)
Wing aspect ratio	13.7
Length overall	8.63 m (28 ft 3¾ in)
Height over tail	1.55 m (5 ft 1 in)

AREA:
Wings, gross	19.44 m² (209.25 sq ft)

WEIGHTS AND LOADING:
Weight empty	335 kg (739 lb)
Max T-O weight	540 kg (1,190 lb)
Max wing loading	27.78 kg/m² (5.69 lb/sq ft)

PERFORMANCE:
Best glide ratio	27
Min rate of sink	0.78 m (2.56 ft)/s
Stalling speed	32 knots (59 km/h; 37 mph) IAS
Max speed (smooth air)	
	108 knots (200 km/h; 124 mph) IAS
Max aero-tow speed	70 knots (130 km/h; 81 mph) IAS
Max winch-launching speed	
	67 knots (125 km/h; 77 mph) IAS
g limits	+5.3/−2.65

SZD-48-3 Jantar Standard 3 single-seat sailplane

SZD-50-3 Puchacz two-seat training sailplane

SZD-51-1 Junior Club Class sailplane

SZD-55 single-seat Standard Class sailplane

Production version of the PZL-Krosno KR-03A Puchatek sailplane

IS-28M2A two-seat motor glider

IS-28B2 tandem two-seat high performance training sailplane

ROMANIA

ICA
INTREPRINDEREA DE CONSTRUCTII AERONAUTICE (Aeronautical Construction Enterprise)

Str. Aeroportului 1, Căsuta Postală 198, 2200 Brasov
Telephone: 40 (21) 16719 and 16720
Telex: 61266
DIRECTOR: Eng Ion Georgescu

As detailed in the Aircraft section, the current activities of the Romanian aircraft industry are divided between four main centres: IAv Bucuresti, IAv Bacau, IAv Craiova and ICA Brasov. In addition to its work on powered aircraft (which see), the ICA is responsible for all sailplane development and production. The principal Romanian designer of sailplanes was Dipl Ing Iosif Silimon, who died in February 1981. His designs are prefixed with the letters IS. Details of his earlier sailplanes have appeared in many previous editions of *Jane's*.

IS-28B2

This high performance sailplane was developed from the IS-28B (1975-76 *Jane's*), which made its first flight on 26 April 1973, and the IS-28B1 (1976-77 edition). Standard version since 1976, of which more than 385 had been built by early 1990, is the IS-28B2, with Hütter (instead of DFS type) airbrakes and trailing-edge split flaps. Production is continuing, and exports have been made to about 20 countries which include Argentina, Australia, Botswana, Canada, China, Colombia, France, West Germany, Hungary, India, Norway, the UK and the USA.

TYPE: Tandem two-seat training and aerobatic sailplane.

AIRFRAME: Cantilever shoulder-wing monoplane. Wortmann wing sections: FX-61-163 at root, FX-60-126 at tip. Forward swept all-metal wings, with L section main spar booms and dural web, dural auxiliary spar, and dural ribs. Upper surface Hütter metal airbrakes. Ailerons and split trailing-edge flaps fabric covered. No tabs. All-metal semi-monocoque forward and centre fuselage. Rear fuselage is duralumin monocoque. Cantilever T tail, with moderate tailplane dihedral. Elevator trailing-edges and rudder fabric covered. Trim tab in each elevator. Semi-retractable monowheel with oleo-pneumatic shock absorber and shoe brake; non-retractable tailwheel. Canopy opens sideways (to starboard) and can be jettisoned in flight. Dual controls standard. Nose towing hook, with Tost cable release, is standard; CG towing hook optional.

DIMENSIONS, EXTERNAL:
Wing span	17.00 m (55 ft 9¼ in)
Wing aspect ratio	15.8

Length overall	8.45 m (27 ft 8¾ in)
Height over tail	1.87 m (6 ft 1½ in)

AREA:

Wings, gross	18.24 m² (196.3 sq ft)

WEIGHTS AND LOADINGS:

Weight empty	400 kg (882 lb)
Max T-O weight: single-seat	520 kg (1,146 lb)
two-seat	590 kg (1,300 lb)
Max wing loading:	
single-seat	28.51 kg/m² (5.84 lb/sq ft)
two-seat	32.34 kg/m² (6.62 lb/sq ft)

PERFORMANCE (at max T-O weight except where indicated):

Best glide ratio:	
single-seat at 51 knots (94 km/h; 58 mph)	33
two-seat at 54 knots (100 km/h; 62 mph)	33
Min rate of sink:	
single-seat at 43 knots (80 km/h; 50 mph)	
	0.74 m (2.43 ft)/s
two-seat at 46 knots (85 km/h; 53 mph)	
	0.78 m (2.56 ft)/s
Stalling speed: single-seat	37 knots (67 km/h; 42 mph)
two-seat	39 knots (72 km/h; 45 mph)
Max speed (smooth air)	124 knots (230 km/h; 143 mph)
Max speed (rough air)	91 knots (169 km/h; 105 mph)
Max aero-tow speed	76 knots (140 km/h; 87 mph)
Max winch-launching speed	
	59 knots (110 km/h; 68 mph)
g limits:	+6.5/−4 single-seat
	+5.3/−2.65 two-seat

IS-28M2A

Two motor glider versions of the IS-28B2 were developed initially, with tandem (IS-28M1) and side by side seating (IS-28M2). The former was described in the 1981-82, the latter in 1984-85 and earlier editions of *Jane's*. The IS-28M1 has since been redesignated IAR-34.

The rear fuselage is essentially the same as that of the IS-28B2, but the powered version is of low-wing configuration and has a redesigned forward fuselage, cockpit canopy and main landing gear.

The prototype (YR-1013) flew for the first time on 26 June 1976; production continues. All since c/n 41 are fitted with reinforced wings and are designated IS-28M2A. The aircraft is certificated in Australia, Japan, Norway, Portugal and the UK, and has been supplied to customers in Argentina, Australia, Canada, Denmark, Hungary, India, Israel, Norway, the Philippines, Spain, Sweden, Switzerland, the UK and the USA. Small scale manufacture continues.

TYPE: Two-seat motor glider.

AIRFRAME: Cantilever low-wing monoplane, of mainly metal construction. Wortmann wing sections: FX-61-163 at root, FX-60-126 at tip. Dihedral 2°. Sweepforward 2° 30' at quarter-chord. Single-spar wings, with aluminium ribs and skin, fabric covered metal ailerons and (optionally) all-metal split flaps on trailing-edges. Flaps can be set to a negative position. All-metal two-section Hütter airbrakes on upper surfaces. Conventional fuselage, in three parts: metal front portion, built up on two longerons and cross-frames and having glassfibre fairings and engine cowling panels; aluminium alloy monocoque centre portion; and rear portion of aluminium alloy frames and skin. Cantilever aluminium alloy T tail, with dihedral tailplane. Rudder and elevator trailing-edges fabric covered. Trim tab in each elevator. Two retractable mainwheels, with rubber disc shock absorbers and mechanically operated drum brakes, side by side under fuselage centre-section; steerable tailwheel, also with shock absorber. Side by side seats under rearward sliding canopy. Dual controls standard.

POWER PLANT: One 50.7 kW (68 hp) Limbach SL 1700 EI (optionally a 59.5 kW; 80 hp Limbach L 2000 EOI) flat-four engine, driving a Hoffmann HO-V-62R/L160T two-blade adjustable-pitch fully-feathering propeller with spinner. Single fuel tank aft of cockpit, capacity 40 litres (10.6 US gallons; 8.8 Imp gallons) standard, 60 litres (15.8 US gallons; 13.2 Imp gallons) optional.

DIMENSIONS, EXTERNAL: As IS-28B2 except:

Length overall	7.00 m (22 ft 11½ in)
Height over tail	2.15 m (7 ft 0¾ in)
Wheel track	1.36 m (4 ft 5½ in)

WEIGHTS AND LOADINGS:

Weight empty	560 kg (1,234 lb)
Max T-O weight	760 kg (1,675 lb)
Max wing loading	41.7 kg/m² (8.54 lb/sq ft)
Max power loading: 68 hp	14.7 kg/kW (24.1 lb/hp)
80 hp	12.7 kg/kW (20.9 lb/hp)

PERFORMANCE, UNPOWERED (at max T-O weight):

Best glide ratio at 54 knots (100 km/h; 62 mph)	27
Min rate of sink at 43 knots (80 km/h; 50 mph)	
	1.20 m (3.94 ft)/s
Stalling speed, flaps down	36 knots (66 km/h; 41 mph)
Max speed (smooth air)	113 knots (210 km/h; 130 mph)
Max speed (rough air)	95 knots (177 km/h; 110 mph)
g limits	+5.3/−2.65

PERFORMANCE, POWERED (at max T-O weight):

Never-exceed speed	113 knots (210 km/h; 130 mph)
Max level speed: 68 hp	97 knots (180 km/h; 112 mph)
80 hp	100 knots (185 km/h; 115 mph)
Max cruising speed	92 knots (170 km/h; 106 mph)
Econ cruising speed	70 knots (130 km/h; 81 mph)
Stalling speed	36 knots (65 km/h; 41 mph)
Max rate of climb at S/L: 68 hp	120 m (394 ft)/min
80 hp	138 m (453 ft)/min
Service ceiling: 68 hp	4,700 m (15,420 ft)
80 hp	5,000 m (16,400 ft)
T-O run (grass)	250 m (820 ft)
T-O to 15 m (50 ft) (grass): 68 hp	593 m (1,945 ft)
80 hp	430 m (1,410 ft)
Landing run	90 m (295 ft)
Range with max fuel, no reserves	
	243 nm (450 km; 280 miles)
g limits	+5.3/−2.65

IS-29D2

Descriptions can be found in the 1980-81 and earlier editions of *Jane's* of the IS-29B, D, D3, D4, E, E4, G, and IS-31(E3). None of these versions is now in production. Models current in 1990 were as follows:

IS-29D2. Current Standard Class version, with improved cockpit and controls, Hütter airbrakes, separate tailplane and elevator, and improved rigging system. Certificated in Australia, Canada, China, West Germany, Hungary, Switzerland, Turkey, the USA and elsewhere. At least 215 built by early 1990; in production.

IS-29D2 Club. Club Class version of D2, with flaps deleted and non-retractable monowheel. Certification granted. Small number built, including some for Australia; further orders placed.

The following description applies to the IS-29D2, except where indicated:

TYPE: Single-seat Standard Class (Club class) sailplane.

AIRFRAME: Cantilever shoulder-wing monoplane, with T tail. Wortmann wing sections: FX-61-163 at root, FX-61-126 at tip. All-metal wings, with main spar, false rear spar and riveted dural skin. Full span trailing-edge flaps and ailerons coupled to operate in unison, but can be disconnected for separate operation during landing. Hütter airbrake in upper surface of each wing. All-metal semi-monocoque fuselage. Detachable glassfibre nosecap. Cantilever all-metal T tail, with full span elevator. Retractable sprung monowheel, with brake; non-retractable tailwheel. Canopy hinges sideways to starboard and can be jettisoned in flight.

DIMENSIONS, EXTERNAL:

Wing span	15.00 m (49 ft 2½ in)
Wing aspect ratio	21.6
Length overall	7.30 m (23 ft 11½ in)
Height over tail	1.68 m (5 ft 6¼ in)

AREA:

Wings, gross	10.40 m² (111.9 sq ft)

WEIGHTS AND LOADING:

Weight empty	240 kg (529 lb)
Max T-O weight	360 kg (793 lb)
Max wing loading	34.62 kg/m² (7.09 lb/sq ft)

PERFORMANCE (at max T-O weight):

Best glide ratio at 50 knots (93 km/h; 58 mph): D2	37
D2 Club	36
Min rate of sink at 42 knots (78 km/h; 48 mph)	
	0.65 m (2.13 ft)/s
Stalling speed:	
D2 (flaps down)	36 knots (65 km/h; 41 mph)
D2 Club	41 knots (75 km/h; 47 mph)
Max speed (smooth air)	121 knots (225 km/h; 140 mph)
Max speed (rough air)	93 knots (172 km/h; 107 mph)
Max aero-tow speed	76 knots (140 km/h; 87 mph)
Max winch-launching speed	
	70 knots (130 km/h; 81 mph)
g limits	+5.3/−2.65

IS-30

The IS-30, which underwent flight testing in the Spring of 1978, is based on the IS-28B2. Production continued in 1990 against orders.

TYPE: Tandem two-seat sailplane.

AIRFRAME: All-metal cantilever shoulder-wing monoplane. Wortmann wing sections: FX-61-163 at root, FX-60-126 at tip. Dihedral 2°. Incidence 4°. No sweep on leading-edge. Hütter two-plate upper and lower surface metal airbrakes. All-metal ailerons; flaps optional. All-metal semi-monocoque fuselage, generally similar to IS-28B2. All-metal cantilever T tail, with full span elevator. Standard landing gear comprises a non-retractable rubber sprung 5 in Tost monowheel and 210 × 65 mm tailwheel; a semi-retractable 6 in monowheel and 280 × 85 mm nosewheel are available optionally. One-piece canopy opens sideways to starboard and can be jettisoned in flight. Dual controls standard; fully equipped front and rear instrument panels optional. Nose towing hook, with Tost cable release, standard; CG towing hook optional. No provision for water ballast.

DIMENSIONS, EXTERNAL, AND WING AREA: As IS-28B2 except:

Height over tail	2.27 m (7 ft 5½ in)

WEIGHTS AND LOADINGS: As IS-28B2

PERFORMANCE (at max T-O weight): As IS-28B2 except:

Stalling speed: single-seat	38 knots (70 km/h; 43 mph)
two-seat	41 knots (75 km/h; 47 mph)
Max speed (smooth air):	
single-seat	135 knots (250 km/h; 155 mph)
two-seat	121 knots (225 km/h; 140 mph)
Max speed (rough air)	86 knots (160 km/h; 99 mph)
Max winch-launching speed	
	67 knots (125 km/h; 78 mph)

IS-32

First shown publicly at the Paris Air Show in June 1977, the IS-32 tandem two-seat Open Class sailplane was developed from the IS-28B2. Certification to BCAR Section E. Customers to date have included those from Australia, China, the UK and the USA.

TYPE: Tandem two-seat Open Class sailplane.

AIRFRAME: All-metal cantilever shoulder-wing monoplane. Wortmann wing sections: FX-67-K-170 at root, FX-67-K-150 at tip. Dihedral 2° 30'. Incidence 2°. Sweepforward 2° on leading-edge. Hütter two-plate upper and lower surface metal airbrakes. All-metal interconnected flaps and ailerons. All-metal semi-monocoque fuselage, generally similar to IS-28B2 and IS-30. All-metal cantilever T tail, with full span elevator. Mechanically retractable Tost monowheel, size 5.00-5, with Tost double shoe brake and oleo-pneumatic shock absorber; semi-recessed 210 × 65 mm tailwheel. One-piece jettisonable canopy, opening sideways to starboard; tinted canopy optional. Dual controls standard; fully equipped front and rear instrument panels optional. Nose towing hook, with Tost cable release. No provision for water ballast.

DIMENSIONS, EXTERNAL:

Wing span	20.00 m (65 ft 7½ in)
Wing aspect ratio	27.25
Length overall	8.36 m (27 ft 5¼ in)
Height over tail	2.27 m (7 ft 5½ in)

AREA:

Wings, gross	14.68 m² (158.0 sq ft)

WEIGHTS AND LOADING:

Weight empty	400 kg (882 lb)
Max T-O weight	590 kg (1,300 lb)
Max wing loading	40.2 kg/m² (8.23 lb/sq ft)

PERFORMANCE (at max T-O weight):

Best glide ratio at 59 knots (110 km/h; 68 mph)	44.5
Min rate of sink at 49 knots (90 km/h; 56 mph)	
	0.62 m (2.03 ft)/s
Stalling speed	43 knots (78 km/h; 49 mph)
Max speed (smooth air)	105 knots (195 km/h; 121 mph)
Max speed (rough air)	87 knots (161 km/h; 100 mph)
Max aero-tow speed	76 knots (140 km/h; 87 mph)
Max winch-launching speed	
	59 knots (110 km/h; 68 mph)
g limits	+4/−1.5

IAR-35

The IAR-35 is a single-seat all-metal glider designed to JAR 22 requirements, essentially for aerobatics but also for general-purpose use. Design began in 1984, and the prototype made its first flight in May 1986. Certification was gained under JAR 22 aerobatic category regulations, and production is under way.

TYPE: Single-seat aerobatic sailplane.

AIRFRAME: Cantilever shoulder-wing monoplane, with constant chord non-swept centre-section (NACA 64-015) and tapered outer panels. Dihedral 0° on centre-section, 2° on outer panels. Incidence 1°. Three-spar wing structure, with ribs and adhesive-bonded metal-to-metal stiffened skins, each wing being attached to fuselage by two fittings each side. All-metal statically balanced ailerons occupy entire trailing-edge. Automatic tab in each aileron. All-metal DFS type upper and lower surface airbrakes. Sprung rubber balancer wheel, at each wingtip. Fuselage has all-metal semi-monocoque structure, with aluminium alloy frames and longerons, covered with duralumin skins. Sweptback fin and statically balanced rudder; fixed incidence, strut braced tailplane with statically balanced elevators. Trim tab in each elevator. Ailerons, airbrakes and elevators are actuated by pushrods; rudder and elevator tabs are cable actuated. Mechanically retractable 340 × 125 mm monowheel, with brake; semi-recessed, non-retractable 210 × 65 mm tailwheel. Single seat for pilot (adjustable for height and inclination), under one-piece detachable Plexiglas canopy.

DIMENSIONS, EXTERNAL:

Wing span	12.00 m (39 ft 4½ in)
Wing aspect ratio	13.3
Length overall	6.47 m (21 ft 2¾ in)
Height over tail	1.72 m (5 ft 7¾ in)

AREA:

Wings, gross	10.80 m² (116.2 sq ft)

WEIGHTS AND LOADING:

Weight empty	250-270 kg (551-595 lb)
Max T-O weight	380 kg (838 lb)
Max wing loading	35.19 kg/m² (7.21 lb/sq ft)

PERFORMANCE (estimated):

Best glide ratio at 56 knots (104 km/h; 65 mph)	24
Min rate of sink	0.85 m (2.79 ft)/s
Stalling speed	47 knots (86 km/h; 54 mph)
Max speed (smooth air)	205 knots (380 km/h; 236 mph)
Max speed (rough air) and design manoeuvring speed	
(V_A)	109 knots (202 km/h; 125 mph)
g limits	+7.4/−7

IS-29D2 single-seat sailplane

Prototype of the aerobatic single-seat IAR-35

Celair GA-1 aerobatic competition sailplane *(Peter F. Selinger)*

Danish registered IS-30 two-seat sailplane *(Peter F. Selinger)*

Radab Windex 1200 powered sailplane *(Michael A. Badrocke)*

ICA Brasov IS-32 Open Class sailplane *(Air Photo Supply)*

SOUTH AFRICA

CELAIR
CELAIR MANUFACTURING AND EXPORT (PTY) LTD
PO Box 77, Ermelo, Transvaal
Telephone: 27 (1341) 4059
Fax: 27 (1341) 91925

CELAIR GA-1
First flown on 8 July 1989, this competition sailplane was conceived by national power aerobatics champion Peter Celair and took just six months to design and build to prototype stage. It is certificated to JAR 22 and production was scheduled to start in 1990 (two ordered from

Switzerland by late 1989). The prototype successfully took part in the World Aerobatic Glider Championships in Hockenheim, West Germany, in August 1989.

TYPE: Single-seat aerobatic competition sailplane.

AIRFRAME: Cantilever shoulder-wing monoplane of low pressure elevated temperature (LPET) glassfibre/epoxy/aramid composites construction. Wortmann FX 71-L-150/25 wing section. No dihedral, sweepback or incidence. Full span mass balanced ailerons. Airbrakes. No water ballast. Retractable (semi-recessed) monowheel, with tailwheel.

DIMENSIONS, EXTERNAL:
Wing span	11.05 m (36 ft 3 in)
Wing aspect ratio	11.7

Length overall	6.50 m (21 ft 4 in)
Height over tail	1.70 m (5 ft 7 in)
AREA:	
Wings, gross	10.30 m² (110.87 sq ft)
WEIGHTS AND LOADING:	
Weight empty	265 kg (584 lb)
Max T-O weight	375 kg (827 lb)
Max wing loading	36.4 kg/m² (7.46 lb/sq ft)
PERFORMANCE:	
Best glide ratio	23
Stalling speed	44 knots (80 km/h; 50 mph)
Max speed (smooth air)	175 knots (324 km/h; 201 mph)
g limits	±10

SWEDEN

RADAB
AB RADAB
PO Box 81054, S-104 81 Stockholm
Telephone: 46 (8) 440610
Telex: 124 43 FOTEX S Att WINDEXRADAB
Fax: 46 (8) 404436
MANAGING DIRECTOR: Harald Undén
TECHNICAL DIRECTOR: Sven Olof Ridder

RADAB WINDEX 1200
This small single-seat motor glider was designed in 1981 to meet the requirements of JAR 22 (Aerobatic category).

Construction of the first Windex 1100 prototype (SE-XSD) started in January 1982, and this made its first flight, unpowered, on 15 March 1985. Two further prototypes were built but only one has flown under power (initially on 15 March 1985). The powered production prototype (SE-XSH) is representative of initial kit aircraft (König engine) and flight testing had almost been completed by late 1989. In addition to normal testing, full aerobatic tests that included positive and negative quick rolls as well as positive and inverted spins were demonstrated.

Initial kit aircraft have the 17.2 kW (23 hp) König engine of the powered prototype, but development continued in

1989 of the Windex 300 engine comprising three chain-saw cylinders in-line and offering 18.6 kW (25 hp).

The first prototype had hot-wire shaped wings of 11.00 m (36 ft 1 in) span, but the powered prototype and production kit aircraft, designated Windex 1200, have Nomex honeycomb moulded wings of increased span, though the wing area remains unchanged. The tailplane, originally mounted halfway up the fin, was raised to a T configuration to simplify rudder geometry and improve elevator efficiency.

TYPE: Single-seat homebuilt motor glider.

AIRFRAME: Cantilever mid-wing monoplane, with KTH-FFA (Stockholm Royal Institute of Technology) laminar flow wing section having 17% thickness/chord ratio from root to tip. Dihedral 3° 30′ from roots. Incidence 2° 35′ 24″. No sweep. Wings have a single spar of unidirectional glassfibre, with glassfibre/epoxy/Nomex honeycomb sandwich skin, and are detachable for transportation and storage. Bottom-hinged plain flaps/airbrakes, top-hinged balanced ailerons, and downswept winglets at tips, are all of similar construction, as are the fuselage, sweptback fin and rudder, and non-swept T tailplane and one-piece elevator. The engine cowling is part aluminium. Non-retractable, partially enclosed unsprung 12 in monowheel with drum brake. Landing skid forward of monowheel. Fixed tailwheel. Single moulded, reclined bucket seat under one-piece canopy, which opens upward. Ballistic parachute and water ballast tanks optional.

POWER PLANT: One 18.6 kW (25 hp) Windex 300 three-cylinder aircooled two-stroke inline engine, with V belt reduction drive to a Radab propeller which has mechanically operated variable pitch and feathering and two Kevlar/epoxy blades. Engine is mounted halfway up fin. Two aluminium fuel tanks forward of wing spar, total capacity 24 litres (6.3 US gallons; 5.3 Imp gallons).

DIMENSIONS, EXTERNAL:

Wing span	12.10 m (39 ft 8½ in)
Wing aspect ratio	19.75
Length overall	4.92 m (16 ft 1¾ in)
Height over tail	1.14 m (3 ft 9 in)
Propeller diameter	1.05 m (3 ft 5½ in)

AREA:

Wings, gross	7.41 m² (79.8 sq ft)

WEIGHTS AND LOADINGS:

Weight empty	130 kg (287 lb)
Max T-O weight: Aerobatic	250 kg (551 lb)
Utility	300 kg (661 lb)
Max wing loading:	
Aerobatic	33.74 kg/m² (6.91 lb/sq ft)
Utility	40.48 kg/m² (8.29 lb/sq ft)
Max power loading:	
Aerobatic	13.44 kg/kW (22.05 lb/hp)
Utility	16.10 kg/kW (26.45 lb/hp)

PERFORMANCE (estimated at 230 kg; 507 lb T-O weight):

Best glide ratio at 54 knots (100 km/h; 62 mph)	38
Min rate of sink at 41 knots (75 km/h; 47 mph)	
	0.61 m (2.00 ft)/s
Stalling speed	35 knots (65 km/h; 41 mph)
Max speed (rough air)	109 knots (202 km/h; 125 mph)
g limits	+7/−5

PERFORMANCE, POWERED (estimated at 230 kg; 507 lb T-O weight):

Never-exceed speed	170 knots (316 km/h; 196 mph)
Max level speed	146 knots (270 km/h; 168 mph)
Cruising speed (50% power)	
	113 knots (210 km/h; 130 mph)
Stalling speed	35 knots (65 km/h; 41 mph)
Max rate of climb at S/L	264 m (865 ft)/min
T-O run (grass)	110 m (360 ft)
T-O to 10 m (33 ft)	250 m (820 ft)
Range with max fuel, no reserves	
	485 nm (900 km; 559 miles)

UNION OF SOVIET SOCIALIST REPUBLICS

ANTONOV
OLEG K. ANTONOV DESIGN BUREAU
Kiev

JUNIOR 1
This is a very basic strut braced high-wing glider, featuring an open slab-sided fuselage pod and a low tailboom with a conventional tail unit.

TYPE: Single-seat sailplane.

DIMENSIONS, EXTERNAL:

Wing span	10.56 m (34 ft 7¾ in)
Wing aspect ratio	7.3
Length overall	5.60 m (18 ft 4½ in)
Height overall	2.10 m (6 ft 10¾ in)

AREA:

Wings, gross	15.6 m² (167.92 sq ft)

WEIGHTS AND LOADING:

Weight empty	85 kg (187 lb)
Max T-O weight	175 kg (386 lb)
Max wing loading	11.22 kg/m² (2.30 lb/sq ft)

PERFORMANCE:

Best glide ratio	16.2
Min rate of sink	0.95 m (3.12 ft)/s
Max speed (smooth air)	48 knots (90 km/h; 56 mph)

ESAG and SSAKTB
EKSPRIMENTINE SPORTINES AVICIJOS GAMYKLA (Experimental Sport Aviation Plant)
Pociūnai, Prienai, Lietuvos TSR (Lithuania)
DIRECTOR: Aleksandras Jonušas
CHIEF ENGINEER: Algimantas Zadavičius
HEAD OF PRODUCTION: Algimantas Pauža
CHIEF TEST PILOT: Algirdas Virbickas

SPECIALUS SPORTINES AVICIJOS KONSTRAVIMO — TECHNOLOGINIS BIURAS
(Special Sport Aviation Design and Technology Bureau)
DIRECTOR: Klemas Juočas
DEPUTY DIRECTOR: Vytautas Mekšriūnas
CHIEF ENGINEER: Julius Armonaitis
CHIEF DESIGNERS:
  Jonas Bankauskas
  Gintaras Sabaliauskas
  Vilhelmas Gerlichas
TEST PILOTS:
  Gintautas Nekrašius
  Vytautas Sabeckis

Lietuvišzta Aviacine Konstrukcija (Lithuanian Aero-Construction) was founded in Lithuania in 1969, with the objective of developing a plastics-construction sailplane. Its first (and the first Soviet) plastics sailplane, designed by Mr Boleslovas Karvyalis, was the BK-7 Lietuva, which was first flown on 8 December 1972 and was described and illustrated in the 1975-76 Jane's. This has undergone progressive development, the latest version being the LAK-12.

In July 1986 LAK was divided into two sections, ESAG itself and SSAKTB (at the same address). ESAG is charged with manufacture and repair, in a new building, while SSAKTB is concerned with research and design.

Current products of ESAG are the LAK-12 Lietuva and LAK-16M sailplanes, the LAK-T3 trailer/hangar and LAK-T4 universal trailer/hangar (1988 design), and the LAK-RE-303 electronic variometer. The LAK-16 was conceived by SSAKTB, as was the SL-2P flying laboratory twin-fuselage sailplane that is used for aerofoil research.

ESAG is the sole overhaul centre in the USSR for the LAK-12 and Czechoslovak L-13 Blaník sailplanes. Repairs have also been undertaken of Polish Cobra-15, German MBB Phoebus and Schleicher ASW 15 plastics sailplanes.

LAK-8
The 1987-88 Jane's detailed the LAK-5 Nemunas motor glider. Later, by removing the engine and with other minor modifications, it was converted into the LAK-8 two-seat sailplane. Dimensions, weights and performance recently quoted in a Polish magazine are similar to those given previously in Jane's for the LAK-5.

LAK-12 LIETUVA (LITHUANIA)
The Lietuva was the first all-plastics sailplane produced in the USSR, and in its latest known form is designated LAK-12. Development began in 1969; details of the BK-7/7A/7V/7S, LAK-9/9M and LAK-10 early versions can be found in the 1982-83 Jane's.

The LAK-12 became the sixth production version. Compared with the earlier versions originated by Mr Boleslovas Karvyalis, it was considerably redesigned under the leadership of Mr Kęstutis Gečhas. It is intended as a training aircraft for high class glider pilots participating in all-Soviet and international events, and for record attempts. Compared with the LAK-10 it has a more comfortable cockpit, with improved instrument layout, a better positioned control column, and a one-piece canopy. Streamlining of the airframe is enhanced, the wings are lowered to a mid position, the fuselage and horizontal tail surfaces are of completely new design, and construction makes extensive use of composite materials, including carbonfibre for the wing spars and other components.

First flight of the LAK-12 took place on 21 December 1979. Flight testing was completed in 1980, and deliveries of production aircraft began later that year.

TYPE: Single-seat Open Class sailplane.

AIRFRAME: Cantilever mid-wing monoplane. Wortmann wing sections: FX-67-K-170 from root to junction with outer panels, then tapering to FX-67-K-150 at tip. No wing fillets. Main wing spar is a carbonfibre T beam. Trailing-edge flaps and interconnected ailerons are attached to auxiliary rear spar. Airbrakes on upper surfaces only. Wings, split flaps and ailerons have a skin of three-ply glasscloth, with foam plastics infill between each layer; carbonfibre tape is used to reinforce flap construction. Fuselage, and integral fin, are of glassfibre construction, reinforced with carbonfibre tape. Slightly swept fin and rudder, and non-swept low-mounted tailplane and elevators (all of Wortmann FX-71-L-150/25 section), are of similar construction to wings. Rudder and elevators are mass balanced. Retractable monowheel, with mechanical brake and oleo-pneumatic shock absorber; non-retractable shock absorbing tail bumper. One-piece cockpit canopy. Provision for 190 litres (50 US gallons; 41.8 Imp gallons) water ballast in wing leading-edge tanks.

DIMENSIONS, EXTERNAL:

Wing span	20.42 m (67 ft 0 in)
Wing aspect ratio	28.5
Length overall	7.23 m (23 ft 8½ in)
Height over tail	1.92 m (6 ft 3½ in)

AREA:

Wings, gross	14.63 m² (157.5 sq ft)

WEIGHTS AND LOADING:

Weight empty	360 kg (794 lb)
Max T-O weight:	
without water ballast	430 kg (948 lb)
with water ballast	650 kg (1,433 lb)
Max wing loading	44.42 kg/m² (9.10 lb/sq ft)

PERFORMANCE (at max T-O weight except where indicated):

Best glide ratio at 61 knots (113 km/h; 70 mph)	48
Min rate of sink at 46 knots (85 km/h; 53 mph)	
	0.50 m (1.64 ft)/s
Stalling speed	36 knots (65 km/h; 41 mph)
Max speed (smooth air)	135 knots (250 km/h; 155 mph)
Max aero-tow speed	75 knots (140 km/h; 87 mph)
g limits	+6/−3

LAK-12 LIETUVA 2R
The LAK-12 Lietuva 2R is a two-seat Open Class version of the Lietuva, designed by Mr Antanas Rukas and Mr Algimantas Jonušas. Construction of the prototype began in 1985, and this first flew in April 1986. By March 1988, a second aircraft had been completed. Compared with the single-seater, the Lietuva 2R has a reinforced fuselage structure with a modified control system, a modified and reinforced retractable landing gear with a brake and bungee suspension, 100 litres (26.4 US gallons; 22 Imp gallons) of water ballast in wing tanks, and tandem seats in the longer fuselage.

DIMENSION, EXTERNAL:

Length overall	7.73 m (25 ft 4¼ in)

WEIGHTS AND LOADING:

Weight empty	400 kg (882 lb)
Max water ballast	100 kg (220 lb)
Max T-O weight, with water ballast	690 kg (1,521 lb)
Max wing loading	47.16 kg/m² (9.66 lb/sq ft)

PERFORMANCE:

Best glide ratio at 62 knots (115 km/h; 71 mph)	48
Min rate of sink at 43 knots (80 km/h; 50 mph)	
	0.50 m (1.64 ft)/s
Stalling speed	38 knots (70 km/h; 44 mph)
Max speed (smooth air)	135 knots (250 km/h; 155 mph)
Max speed (rough air)	94 knots (175 km/h; 108 mph)
Max aero-tow speed	75 knots (140 km/h; 87 mph)
g limits	+4/−2

LAK-15
This is a single-seat Open Class sailplane, designed for setting records.

AIRFRAME: Cantilever mid-wing monoplane of large span. Four section aerofoil. Dihedral 3°. Carbonfibre spar and three-ply glassfibre/carbonfibre skins. Airbrake, two flaps and aileron on each wing. Composites fuselage and integral fin. T tailplane. Retractable monowheel, to be fitted with brake, with shock absorber. Fixed tailwheel. Water ballast in wings.

DIMENSIONS, EXTERNAL:

Wing span	25.60 m (83 ft 11¾ in)
Wing aspect ratio	28.5
Length overall	8.20 m (26 ft 10¾ in)
Height over tail	2.19 m (7 ft 2¼ in)

AREA:

Wings, gross	17.40 m² (187.3 sq ft)

WEIGHTS AND LOADING:

Weight empty	385 kg (849 lb)
Max T-O weight	750 kg (1,653 lb)
Max wing loading	43.10 kg/m² (8.83 lb/sq ft)

PERFORMANCE:

Best glide ratio at 108 knots (200 km/h; 124 mph)	59

LAK-16
Designed by Mr Gintaras Sabaliauskas and Mr Kestutis Leonavičius as a successor to the LAK-14 Strazdas, the LAK-16 first prototype was flown initially on 6 September

LAK-12 Lietuva 2R two-seat sailplane

LAK-16 single-seat training glider *(Michael A. Badrocke)*

Oškinis BRO-23KR primary training glider (reproduced from *Krilya Rodini*)

1986 with a LAK-14 wooden wing. Production aircraft have a higher aspect ratio wing, with inset ailerons, constructed initially of fabric covered GFRP. A metal framed wing was to be introduced later, for added strength, which might be indicated by the latest designation LAK-16M. The LAK-16 is said to be less costly to produce than the Strazdas, and capable of wider application, having provisions for the future addition of such features as wing spoilers, ski landing gear and a power plant if required. It is believed that production began in 1987.

The following details refer mainly to the LAK-16M:
TYPE: Single-seat primary training glider.
AIRFRAME: Strut braced high-wing monoplane. Wings have an R-IIIA-15 aerofoil section, with dihedral from roots, and are constructed of metal or (for initial production LAK-16s) from a GFRP spar, ribs and leading-edge, both versions having fabric covering. Ailerons are of fabric covered duralumin tube. All bracing wires are covered in translucent PVC sleeves, and (with the aileron controls) can be disconnected, enabling the entire wing to

pivot and align with the fuselage for transportation and storage. Open frame fuselage is of steel tube at front, riveted duralumin tube at rear. Tail unit is of fabric covered duralumin tube, with cable controlled elevators and rudder. Tailplane strut (but not control cables) can be disconnected to stow horizontal surfaces for transportation and storage. Landing gear comprises twin mainwheels on self sprung GFRP legs, a self sprung GFRP nose-skid, and a self-centring tailwheel. Pilot sits on a GFRP seat (adjustable fore and aft) attached at three points to the lower and rear steel fuselage members, and is provided with a seat belt and headrest.

DIMENSIONS, EXTERNAL:
Wing span	9.66 m (31 ft 8¼ in)
Wing chord, constant	0.90 m (2 ft 11½ in)
Wing aspect ratio	11.6
Length overall	5.38 m (17 ft 7¾ in)

AREA:
Wings, gross	8.05 m² (86.65 sq ft)

WEIGHTS AND LOADING:
Weight empty	88 kg (194 lb)
Max T-O weight	175 kg (386 lb)
Max wing loading	21.74 kg/m² (4.45 lb/sq ft)

PERFORMANCE:
Best glide ratio at 29 knots (54 km/h; 34 mph)	12
Min rate of sink	1.20 m (3.94 ft)/s
Max speed (smooth air)	52 knots (96 km/h; 59 mph)
Stalling speed	26 knots (48 km/h; 30 mph)
g limits	+5.5/−2.75

SSAKTB SL-2P

First flown on 25 June 1987, the SL-2P is a flying laboratory for aerofoil research, joining two standard L-13 Blanik sailplanes and using an SSAKTB-designed centre wing and centre tailplane. Further details, and an illustration, can be found in the 1988-89 *Jane's*.

OŠKINIS
OŠKINIS BRO-23KR GARNYS (STORK)

Designed in 1981, the BRO-23KR is a single-seat open-cockpit primary training glider, designed to provide a successor to the BRO-11M/LAK-2, of which production was completed in 1979. Mr Oškinis was assisted in its design by pilots Ch. Kišonas and K. Rinkevičius of the Kaunas hang gliding club. Production is believed to have started in about 1983 or 1984.
AIRFRAME: Strut and steel cable braced high-wing monoplane. Constant chord slotted wings have a GA(W)-1 aerofoil section, 16% thickness/chord ratio, dihedral from roots, full span ailerons and turned-down tips. Ribs and spar are of woven glassfibre, with three-ply glasscloth skin forward of main spar. Spaces between ends of ribs filled with flat plates made of two layers of glasscloth.

Trailing fixed portion of wings is cast with epoxy filler, using longitudinal glassfibre, and covered with glasscloth. Entire ribbed surface is then covered with Lavsan film, glued in position and heat-shrunk to fit. Ailerons are of similar construction. Wingtips of textolite. GFRP fuselage, including cockpit, is built in two halves. T tail unit is of similar construction to wings. Five rubber blocks provide main landing shock absorption, to which can be fitted a wide GFRP snow skid for Winter flying; the same skid with a wheel attached for Summer use; a tricycle undercarriage for 'aeroplane landing' training; or floats for waterborne operation. Self-sprung tail bumper of glassfibre reinforced resin. Aircraft has been tested also with a small nosewheel. Open cockpit, lined with polyurethane and fitted with windscreen and foam plastics reclining seat.

DIMENSIONS, EXTERNAL:
Wing span	8.20 m (26 ft 10¾ in)
Wing aspect ratio	6.5
Length overall	6.40 m (21 ft 0 in)
Height over tail	2.20 m (7 ft 2½ in)

AREA:
Wings, gross	10.40 m² (111.9 sq ft)

WEIGHTS AND LOADING:
Weight empty	83.5 kg (184 lb)
Max T-O weight	158.5 kg (349 lb)
Max wing loading	15.2 kg/m² (3.11 lb/sq ft)

PERFORMANCE:
Best glide ratio	15
Min rate of sink	1.00 m (3.28 ft)/s
Stalling speed	23 knots (42 km/h; 27 mph)
Max speed (smooth air)	54 knots (100 km/h; 62 mph)

UNITED KINGDOM

LIGHTWING
LIGHTWING RESEARCH
68 Timberleys, Littlehampton, West Sussex BN17 6QB
Telephone: 44 (903) 722578
DESIGNER/BUILDER: John M. Lee

Details and an illustration of the Lightwing CT6 Companion can be found in the 1989-90 *Jane's*.

UNITED STATES OF AMERICA

ADVANCED AVIATION
ADVANCED AVIATION INC
323 North Ivey Lane, Orlando, Florida 32811
Telephone: 1 (305) 298 2920
Advanced Aviation is best known for its range of microlight and Experimental aeroplanes and amphibians (see Sport Aircraft section). It has now added to its range a low-cost, lightweight sailplane known as the Sierra.

ADVANCED AVIATION SIERRA

The Sierra was first flown in prototype form on 25 March 1988. In June that year it became available as a bolt-together kit, requiring approximately 80 working hours to assemble, and in ready assembled form. The prototype differed from 'production' aircraft only in having an aluminium cockpit pod instead of the now standard moulded pod. The Sierra can be air-towed, auto-towed,

winch or bungee launched, and the company's King Cobra and Caribou have already been used as towing aircraft.
TYPE: Single-seat lightweight sailplane.
AIRFRAME: Strut braced high-wing monoplane. Bolted aluminium alloy tubular structure, with Dacron covering. Moulded glassfibre cockpit pod, with side hinged canopy. Three-axis control (via ailerons, rudder and elevators). Monowheel landing gear with tailskid;

removable tailwheel dolly has been used. Swivelling permanent tailwheel is under consideration. Set up time 25 min.

DIMENSIONS, EXTERNAL:

Wing span	11.87 m (38 ft 11½ in)
Wing aspect ratio	11
Length overall	6.57 m (21 ft 6½ in)

AREA:

Wings, gross	12.17 m² (131.0 sq ft)

WEIGHTS AND LOADING:

Weight empty	70 kg (155 lb)
Max T-O weight	181 kg (400 lb)
Max wing loading	14.89 kg/m² (3.05 lb/sq ft)

PERFORMANCE (calculated; 77 kg; 170 lb pilot, ISA):

Best glide ratio	approx 20
Min rate of sink	0.86 m (2.83 ft)/s
Best glide speed	30 knots (56 km/h; 35 mph)
Stalling speed	23 knots (42 km/h; 26 mph)

MARSKE
MARSKE AIRCRAFT CORPORATION
130 Crestwood Drive, Michigan City, Indiana 46360
Telephone: 1 (219) 879 7039
PRESIDENT: James J. Marske

MARSKE MONARCH

The Monarch was designed and built by Mr Jim Marske, and made its first flight on 4 July 1974. Plans and kits are available, and 109 sets of drawings had been sold by the beginning of 1990, from which eight Monarchs had been completed.

In 1976 Mr Marske successfully test flew the Monarch prototype in self-launching form, with a 9 kW (12 hp) McCulloch engine installed behind the pilot's seat, driving a 0.635 m (2 ft 1 in) diameter pusher propeller. This did not provide sufficient power, but is thought to be adequate for the Monarch E which is at least 9.1 kg (20 lb) lighter.

The earlier Monarch B was described in the 1977-78 *Jane's*; the following description applies to the Monarch C and subsequent versions, including the D (longer span ailerons) and E (revised spoiler location, overhead window and larger rudder).

TYPE: Single-seat ultralight homebuilt glider.

AIRFRAME: Braced high-wing monoplane, with single extruded aluminium strut each side. Wing section NACA 43012A, reflexed at 75 per cent chord. Dihedral 2°. Sweepforward 3° at quarter-chord. Moulded glassfibre D leading-edge, with glassfibre front spar web and booms, corrugated glassfibre web ribs with wooden capstrips, wooden rear spar and trailing-edge, and Dacron covering. Inset transparency in centre of leading-edge on Monarch E. Ailerons (outboard) and elevators (inboard) each have single Sitka spruce spar and glassfibre/wood ribs. Fixed tab on each elevator. All control surfaces Dacron covered. Aluminium spoiler above each wing. Simple minimal beam type fuselage of laminated glassfibre, moulded in two halves and joined at centreline. Forward section supports pilot's seat, with nose fairing over instrument panel; rear section forms integral fin leading-edge. CG tow hook on each side of nose fairing. Fin and rudder, above and below level of wings. Glassfibre leading-edge (fin), wooden trailing-edge (rudder), glassfibre/wood ribs and fabric covering. No horizontal tail surfaces. Reinforced underfuselage landing skid. Single landing wheel, below and slightly behind pilot's open seat. Conventional floor-mounted control column.

DIMENSIONS, EXTERNAL:

Wing span	12.80 m (42 ft 0 in)
Wing aspect ratio	9.5
Length overall	3.71 m (12 ft 2 in)
Height over tail	2.39 m (7 ft 10 in)

AREA:

Wings, gross	17.19 m² (185.0 sq ft)

WEIGHTS AND LOADING:

Weight empty: C, D, E	100 kg (220 lb)
Pilot weight range	45-104 kg (100-230 lb)
Max T-O weight	204 kg (450 lb)
Max wing loading	11.72 kg/m² (2.40 lb/sq ft)

PERFORMANCE:

Best glide ratio at 35 knots (64 km/h; 40 mph)	19
Min rate of sink at 26 knots (48 km/h; 30 mph)	
	0.82 m (2.70 ft)/s
Stalling speed	21 knots (39 km/h; 24 mph)
Max speed (smooth air)	61 knots (113 km/h; 70 mph)
Max speed (rough air), max aero-tow and max winch-launching speed	43 knots (80 km/h; 50 mph)
T-O and landing run	12 m (40 ft) or less
*g limits	+5.3/−2.6

*Has been static loaded to +9.6g without failure

MARSKE PIONEER II

Designed some years ago as a simple, high performance sailplane for amateur construction, the Pioneer I prototype first flew in 1968. From it were developed the initial Pioneer IA, and then the smaller and lighter Pioneer II which made its first flight in July 1972.

The Pioneer II-A featured NACA 23012R/23010R wing sections and short bubble canopy, these being changed in the Pioneer II-B to a longer canopy and NACA 33012R/33010R wing sections which considerably improved low-speed performance. Improvements in the current **Pioneer II-C**, to which the following description applies, include a further refinement of the wing aerofoil section, closer spacing of the wing nose ribs, a simplified fuselage structure with lighter and more comfortable glassfibre bucket seat, reduction of 51 mm (2 in) in cockpit height and 102 mm (4 in) lower top line to the nose to improve forward view. Like the Monarch, the Pioneer is highly resistant to stalls and spins. The **Pioneer II-D** is similar to the II-C except for a sweptback tail and a modified upper surface in the wing leading-edge D tube.

By early 1990, Marske had sold 104 sets of Pioneer drawings, and 17 of these aircraft had been flown. These have accumulated more than 2,000 flying hours without a single reported accident.

TYPE: Single-seat homebuilt sailplane.

AIRFRAME: Cantilever mid-wing monoplane. Dihedral 4° 30′. Incidence 6°. Sweepforward 2° at quarter-chord. Modified NACA 33012/33010 wing sections in II-C and II-D. Wings have a single I-section spruce main spar, plywood ribs and D-tube skins; remainder fabric covered. Ailerons and inboard mounted elevators have spruce ribs and spars, with fabric covering. Upper and lower surface spoilers each consist of aluminium plate hinged at forward edge. Short, stubby fuselage has a welded steel tube frame and two-part outer shell of moulded glassfibre/epoxy. Upper half, including top-decking and fin, incorporates all necessary ribs and stiffeners bonded into place; lower half is supplied with all bulkheads bonded in. Rudder is of fabric covered wood construction. Single 30.5 cm (12 in) mainwheel, with drag brake, slightly aft of CG; 2 in castoring tailwheel. Towing hook on each side of fuselage under wing leading-edge, near CG. One-piece removable cockpit canopy.

DIMENSIONS, EXTERNAL:

Wing span	12.98 m (42 ft 7 in)
Wing aspect ratio	12.6
Length overall	3.81 m (12 ft 6 in)
Height over tail	1.98 m (6 ft 6 in)

AREA:

Wings, gross	13.38 m² (144.0 sq ft)

WEIGHTS AND LOADINGS:

Weight empty: II-C	163 kg (360 lb)
II-D	159 kg (380 lb)
Pilot weight range	57-104 kg (125-230 lb)
Max T-O weight: II-C	295 kg (650 lb)
II-D	286 kg (630 lb)
Max wing loading: II-C	22.0 kg/m² (4.51 lb/sq ft)
II-D	21.4 kg/m² (4.38 lb/sq ft)

PERFORMANCE (at max T-O weight):

Best glide ratio at 52 knots (97 km/h; 60 mph)	35
Min rate of sink at 39 knots (72 km/h; 45 mph)	
	0.70 m (2.30 ft)/s
Stalling speed	31 knots (57 km/h; 35 mph)
Max speed (rough and smooth air)	
	113 knots (209 km/h; 130 mph)
Max aero-tow speed	87 knots (161 km/h; 100 mph)
Max winch-launching speed	
	61 knots (113 km/h; 70 mph)
g limits	+5.3/−2.65

MAUPIN
JIM MAUPIN LTD
Star Route 3, Box 4300-37, Tehachapi, California 93561-9803

MAUPIN WOODSTOCK ONE

The Woodstock One was flown for the first time in early 1970. It has been flight tested to include spins (four turns) and stalls; and has been dived at 110 per cent of its never-exceed speed.

Plans, including an instructional booklet, have been available to amateur constructors, and 520 sets of plans had been sold worldwide by early 1990. Homebuilders' kits are no longer available.

TYPE: Single-seat homebuilt sailplane.

AIRFRAME: Cantilever shoulder-wing monoplane, of Douglas fir and birch construction with some fabric covering. Culver wing sections (thickness/chord ratio 18% at root, 13% at tip). Airbrakes on upper wing surfaces. Non-retractable semi-recessed monowheel. Undernose towing hook. Plans depict both open and enclosed cockpits, and a powered version with a non-retractable pylon mounted power plant aft of the cockpit.

DIMENSIONS, EXTERNAL:

Wing span	11.89 m (39 ft 0 in)
Wing aspect ratio	14.5
Length overall	5.87 m (19 ft 3 in)
Height over tail	1.30 m (4 ft 3 in)

AREA:

Wings, gross	9.73 m² (104.7 sq ft)

WEIGHTS AND LOADING:

Weight empty	106.5 kg (235 lb)
Max T-O weight	204 kg (450 lb)
Max wing loading	20.9 kg/m² (4.29 lb/sq ft)

PERFORMANCE (at max T-O weight):

Best glide ratio at 39 knots (72 km/h; 45 mph)	24
Min rate of sink at 35 knots (64 km/h; 40 mph)	
	0.79 m (2.60 ft)/s
Stalling speed	28 knots (52 km/h; 32 mph)

Max speed (smooth air)	87 knots (161 km/h; 100 mph)
Max speed (rough air)	68 knots (125 km/h; 78 mph)
Max aero-tow and max winch-launching speed	
	56 knots (105 km/h; 65 mph)
g limit	+5

MAUPIN WINDROSE

The Windrose self-launching sailplane, first flown in 1983, was made available in plans form, with instruction book. It was also intended that the sailplane would be marketed as a complete kit for homebuilding, or partial kit (eg hardware, moulded fuselage pod). Its general appearance is shown in an accompanying photograph. By early 1990, 180 sets of plans had been sold worldwide.

The first prototype was sold to a Japanese buyer, and a second, with a 30 kW (40 hp) Rotax engine, was built in 1986. The following description applies to the lower powered first prototype with a Cuyuna engine:

TYPE: Single-seat self-launching sailplane.

AIRFRAME: Cantilever shoulder-wing monoplane, of pod and boom configuration. Wings each made of five blocks of plastics foam, hot wire cut with rib pattern at each end; each piece is notched top and bottom to take spar cap, and dowel is pushed into foam between spar caps and glued in position. Unidirectional glassfibre spar caps are laid into notches in foam blocks before skinning. Flaperons (interchangeable left/right) on inboard trailing-edges. Delta shaped spoiler on wing centre-section. Basic fuselage formed by two plywood boxes, one forming tailboom, the other extending forward under pilot, joined by two boxed-in plywood slabs. One-piece balanced elevator; one-piece balanced rudder, with small ventral fin. Enclosed cockpit. Towing hook.

POWER PLANT: One 24.6 kW (33 hp) Cuyuna ULII-02 two-cylinder two-stroke engine, driving a pusher propeller. Fuel capacity 19 litres (5 US gallons; 4.2 Imp gallons).

DIMENSIONS, EXTERNAL:

Wing span	12.65 m (41 ft 6 in)
Wing aspect ratio	17.9
Length overall	6.58 m (21 ft 7 in)
Height overall	1.68 m (5 ft 6 in)
Propeller diameter	0.81 m (2 ft 8 in)

AREA:

Wings, gross	8.92 m² (96.0 sq ft)

WEIGHTS AND LOADINGS:

Weight empty	232 kg (512 lb)
Normal T-O weight	317 kg (700 lb)
Max T-O weight	335 kg (740 lb)
Wing loading:	
at normal T-O weight	35.59 kg/m² (7.29 lb/sq ft)
at max T-O weight	37.64 kg/m² (7.71 lb/sq ft)
Power loading:	
at normal T-O weight	12.89 kg/kW (21.2 lb/hp)
at max T-O weight	13.62 kg/kW (22.4 lb/hp)

PERFORMANCE, UNPOWERED (A: at normal T-O weight, B: at max T-O weight):

Best glide ratio at 45 knots (84 km/h; 52 mph): A, B	29
Min rate of sink:	
A, B at 40 knots (74 km/h; 46 mph)	0.70 m (2.30 ft)/s
Max speed (smooth air):	
A	114 knots (212 km/h; 132 mph)
B	110 knots (204 km/h; 127 mph)
Max speed (rough air):	
A	87 knots (161 km/h; 100 mph)
B	83 knots (154 km/h; 96 mph)
Manoeuvring speed: A	76 knots (142 km/h; 88 mph)
B	73 knots (135 km/h; 84 mph)

PERFORMANCE, POWERED (Cuyuna engine):

Max rate of climb at S/L	152 m (500 ft)/min
Ceiling	3,960 m (13,000 ft)
T-O run at S/L, ISA	213 m (700 ft)

MAUPIN CARBON DRAGON

The prototype of this foot launchable homebuilt glider is believed to have made its first flight in the Spring of 1987. The design objective was to bring foot launch soaring performance up into the lower performance range of sailplanes. Seventy-five sets of plans had been sold worldwide by early 1990.

Advanced Aviation Sierra single-seat sailplane *(Geoffrey P. Jones)*

Marske Pioneer II-C homebuilt sailplane

Marske Monarch E single-seat homebuilt glider

Maupin Woodstock One homebuilt sailplane

Rotax engined Maupin Windrose self-launching sailplane flying in Indonesia

Maupin Carbon Dragon foot launchable homebuilt glider

Schweizer SGS 2-33A two-seat general purpose sailplane
(Neil A. Macdougall)

TYPE: Foot launchable homebuilt glider.

AIRFRAME: Cantilever high-wing monoplane, with pod and boom fuselage and conventional tail unit. Wings have a Culver aerofoil section and are fitted with full span flaperons which occupy 30 per cent of the total chord, being operable from –5° to +15° as flaps and differentially from –5° to +25° as ailerons. They are actuated by two vertical pushrods inside the fuselage. Rudder is cable actuated from foot pedals. Pilot pod is constructed from two triangular torque boxes, faired to

an overall oval cross-section, and has a 1.52 × 0.46 m (5 ft 0 in × 1 ft 6 in) side-hinged 'landing gear' door in its floor for the pilot's legs. This door is closable after foot launch, with landing made on a monowheel. One-piece Lexan canopy.

DIMENSIONS, EXTERNAL:
Wing span	13.41 m (44 ft 0 in)
Wing aspect ratio	12.9
Length overall	approx 6.10 m (20 ft 0 in)

AREA:
Wings, gross	13.94 m² (150.0 sq ft)

WEIGHTS:
Weight empty	54.5 kg (120 lb)
Max T-O weight	136 kg (300 lb)

PERFORMANCE (estimated):
Best glide ratio	25
Min rate of sink	0.51 m (1.67 ft)/s

SCHWEIZER
SCHWEIZER AIRCRAFT CORPORATION
PO Box 147, Elmira-Corning Regional Airport, Elmira, New York 14902
Telephone: 1 (607) 739 3821
Telex: 932459
OFFICERS: see Aircraft section

Incorporated on 15 December 1939, Schweizer Aircraft Corporation has long been the leading American designer and manufacturer of sailplanes. Its current types include the SGS 2-33A, SGS 1-36 Sprite and SGM 2-37. Details of the company's other aircraft activities can be found in the main Aircraft section.

SCHWEIZER SGS 2-33A
The SGS 2-33 was developed to meet the demand for a medium priced two-seat sailplane for training and general family soaring. The prototype was first flown in the Autumn of 1966 and received FAA type approval in February 1967. Production began in January 1967, and 85 of the original **2-33** model were built. These were superseded by the **2-33A** production version, and the **2-33AK** kit version for amateur construction. Many hundreds of 2-33A and 2-33AK sailplanes have been sold, and the aircraft remain available. A more comprehensive description can be found in the 1987-88 *Jane's*.
TYPE: Tandem two-seat training sailplane.

DIMENSIONS, EXTERNAL:
Wing span	15.54 m (51 ft 0 in)
Length overall	7.85 m (25 ft 9 in)
Height over tail	2.83 m (9 ft 3½ in)

AREA:
Wings, gross	20.39 m² (219.48 sq ft)

WEIGHTS AND LOADING:
Weight empty	272 kg (600 lb)
Max T-O weight	472 kg (1,040 lb)
Max wing loading	23.14 kg/m² (4.74 lb/sq ft)

PERFORMANCE (at max T-O weight except where indicated):
Best glide ratio at 45 knots (84 km/h; 52 mph) dual, 39 knots (72 km/h; 45 mph) solo   22.25

Min rate of sink: dual at 37 knots (68 km/h; 42 mph)
0.95 m (3.10 ft)/s
solo at 33 knots (61 km/h; 38 mph) 0.79 m (2.60 ft)/s
Stalling speed: dual   31 knots (57 km/h; 35 mph)
solo   27 knots (50 km/h; 31 mph)
Max speed (rough and smooth air), and max aero-tow
speed   85 knots (158 km/h; 98 mph)
Max winch-launching speed
60 knots (111 km/h; 69 mph)
g limits   +4.67/−2.56

SCHWEIZER SGS 1-36 SPRITE

The Sprite was designed to offer modern performance, handling and appearance to up to 99 per cent of the solo glider pilots in the USA and overseas as a personal, school or club sailplane. Although a new design, it utilises some components of the 1-34 and 1-35 in its construction. The Sprite is, however, aimed at a different market from these earlier types, and is a 'one-design' class, as was the 1-26. The Sprite is also intended to fulfil a worldwide need for a single-seat Club Class sailplane.

Two versions are available:

36903-1. With forward-positioned monowheel, sprung tailwheel, and no nose-skid. One example of this version, used by NASA's Dryden Research Center, was fitted with a pivoting tailplane for flight research into aircraft controllability problems, particularly those involving deep stall situations. This tailplane can be set at approx 60° nose down.

36903-3. With monowheel further aft, unsprung tailwheel, and aluminium nose-skid. This version is recommended for school and club operation, where sturdiness and ease of ground handling are important considerations.

The prototype flew for the first time on 2 August 1979. FAA certification was received in September 1980. A more comprehensive description can be found in the 1987-88 *Jane's*.

TYPE: Single-seat multi-purpose sailplane.

DIMENSIONS, EXTERNAL:
Wing span   14.07 m (46 ft 2 in)
Length overall   6.27 m (20 ft 7 in)
Height over tail   1.45 m (4 ft 9 in)
AREA:
Wings, gross   13.07 m² (140.72 sq ft)
WEIGHTS AND LOADING:
Weight empty   215 kg (475 lb)
Max T-O weight   322 kg (710 lb)
Max wing loading   24.64 kg/m² (5.05 lb/sq ft)

PERFORMANCE (at max T-O weight):
Best glide ratio at 46 knots (85 km/h; 53 mph)   31
Min rate of sink at 36 knots (68 km/h; 42 mph)
0.68 m (2.25 ft)/s
Stalling speed   31 knots (57 km/h; 35 mph)
Max speed (rough and smooth air), and max aero-tow
speed   105 knots (195 km/h; 121 mph)
Max winch-launching speed
68 knots (126 km/h; 78 mph)
g limits   +5.33/−2.67

SCHWEIZER SGM 2-37
US Air Force designation: TG-7A

First details of this two-seat motor glider were announced in early 1982. The prototype (N36221) flew for the first time on 21 September 1982, and certification was received in the following February. At least 11 TG-7As were delivered to the USAF Academy at Colorado Springs for sailplane flight training duties. Modified versions for other roles include the more powerful **SA 2-37A** (see main Aircraft section).

TYPE: Two-seat motor glider.

AIRFRAME: Cantilever low-wing monoplane, of all-metal construction. Wortmann wing sections: FX-61-163 from root to station 246, FX-60-126 at tip. Dihedral 3° 30′ on outer panels. Leading-edges have extended chord on portions of outer panels to improve stall characteristics. Incidence 1° at root, 0° at tip. No sweepback. Aluminium airbrake in upper and lower surface of each outer panel. Aluminium alloy top-hinged ailerons; no flaps. Semi-monocoque fuselage of aluminium alloy. Slightly swept fin and rudder; non-swept all-moving tailplane, with anti-servo tab. Non-retractable mainwheels, with cantilever legs, urethane block shock absorbers, Cleveland disc brakes and 14 × 5 × 5 in tyres, pressure 2.41 bars (35 lb/sq in); non-retractable and castoring Scott tailwheel, with 6 × 2 × 3 in solid tyre (USAF aircraft have 5.00-5 mainwheels for operation from hard runways). Two seats side by side under rearward sliding canopy, with dual controls. Baggage compartment aft of seats, max capacity 45 kg (100 lb).

POWER PLANT: One 83 kW (112 hp) Textron Lycoming O-235-L2C flat-four engine, driving a Sensenich 72CK-0-50 two-blade fixed-pitch metal propeller. Optional engines include 112 kW (150 hp) Textron Lycoming O-320-E26 and 134 kW (180 hp) Textron Lycoming O-360-A series, with choice of McCauley fixed-pitch climb propeller for glider towing or Hoffmann HO-V-72 constant-speed feathering propeller for soaring. Single fuel tank in port wing standard, capacity 59 litres (15.5

US gallons; 12.9 Imp gallons), of which 54 litres (14.2 US gallons; 11.8 Imp gallons) are usable. Provision for optional similar tank, in starboard wing, increasing total capacity to 107.5 litres (28.4 US gallons; 23.6 Imp gallons).

DIMENSIONS, EXTERNAL:
Wing span   18.14 m (59 ft 6 in)
Wing aspect ratio   18.1
Length overall   8.38 m (27 ft 6 in)
Height over tail   2.37 m (7 ft 9½ in)
Wheel track   2.79 m (9 ft 2 in)
Wheelbase   5.74 m (18 ft 10 in)
Propeller diameter   1.83 m (6 ft 0 in)
DIMENSIONS, INTERNAL:
Cockpit: Max width   1.14 m (3 ft 9 in)
Baggage compartment volume   0.76 m³ (27 cu ft)
AREA:
Wings, gross   18.18 m² (195.71 sq ft)
WEIGHTS AND LOADINGS:
Weight empty   572 kg (1,260 lb)
Max T-O weight   839 kg (1,850 lb)
Max wing loading   46.14 kg/m² (9.45 lb/sq ft)
Max power loading   10.11 kg/kW (16.5 lb/hp)
PERFORMANCE, UNPOWERED (at max T-O weight):
Best glide ratio at 54 knots (100 km/h; 62 mph)   22
Min rate of sink at 52 knots (97 km/h; 60 mph)
1.16 m (3.80 ft)/s
Stalling speed   44 knots (81 km/h; 50 mph)
Max speed (smooth air)   115 knots (214 km/h; 133 mph)
Max speed (rough air)   88 knots (162 km/h; 101 mph)
g limits   +5.3/−2.67
PERFORMANCE, POWERED (at max T-O weight):
Max cruising speed at 2,285 m (7,500 ft), 75% power
99 knots (183 km/h; 114 mph)
Econ cruising speed   81 knots (150 km/h; 93 mph)
Stalling speed   44 knots (81 km/h; 50 mph)
Max rate of climb at S/L   265 m (870 ft)/min
Service ceiling   above 7,315 m (24,000 ft)
T-O run (grass)   161 m (526 ft)
T-O to 15 m (50 ft) (grass)   326 m (1,070 ft)
Landing from 15 m (50 ft) (grass)   406 m (1,331 ft)
Landing run   200 m (654 ft)
Range with standard fuel, 75% power, no reserves
213 nm (396 km; 246 miles)
Range with max optional fuel
520 nm (963 km; 598 miles)
Endurance at 50% power, no reserves   3 h 30 min
g limits   +5.3/−2.67

STROJNIK
PROF ALEX STROJNIK

2337 East Manhatton Drive, Tempe, Arizona 85282
Telephone: 1 (602) 838 1832

Mr Strojnik, a Professor of Physics at Arizona State University, has designed a homebuilt motor glider known as the S-2A.

STROJNIK S-2A

The S-2A is a single-seat motor glider, design and construction of which began in September 1977. The S-2 prototype (N8037X) was flown for the first time in November 1980, and plans for the slightly lighter S-2A are available. Compared to the prototype, the small number of changes introduced to the S-2A include a decrease in fin area. A total of about 126 sets of plans and partial kits had been sold by January 1990, and seven S-2As are believed to be flying.

On 25 July 1985 the prototype S-2 flew a controlled 300 km triangle, earning its pilot/designer a completed FAI Gold Badge with one Diamond. Mr Strojnik believes this to be the first ever Gold + Diamond achieved in a homebuilt motor glider.

TYPE: Single-seat motor glider.

AIRFRAME: Cantilever shoulder-wing monoplane, with Wortmann wing sections. Dihedral 2° on outer panels. Incidence 0°. No sweep. Carbonfibre and aluminium main spar; wing skin, ailerons and trailing-edge flaps of glassfibre. No airbrakes. Pod and boom fuselage; pod has a glassfibre skin and plywood bulkheads, boom is an aluminium tube. Glassfibre tail unit, with elevators on low-set tailplane. Non-retractable unsprung twin mainwheels in tandem, each with tyre size 10 × 3.75 in, pressure 31.86 bars (56 lb/sq in), with friction brakes. One-piece Plexiglas canopy, opening sideways to starboard. Standard sailplane instrumentation and radio. No provision for water ballast.

POWER PLANT: Prototype has one 21 kW (28 hp) Kohler K 340-2AX piston engine, mounted aft of cockpit and driving a Farrington two-blade (foldable) fixed-pitch wooden pusher propeller with spinner. The Kohler is no longer available, and most builders have chosen either a Kawasaki 440, König SD 570 or Rotax 447. Single fuselage fuel tank, capacity 7.5 litres (2 US gallons; 1.7 Imp gallons).

DIMENSIONS, EXTERNAL:
Wing span   15.00 m (49 ft 2½ in)
Wing aspect ratio   19.1
Length overall   6.88 m (22 ft 7 in)

Height over tail   1.65 m (5 ft 5 in)
Propeller diameter   0.94 m (3 ft 1 in)
AREA:
Wings, gross   11.80 m² (127.0 sq ft)
WEIGHTS AND LOADINGS (S-2):
Weight empty   280 kg (617 lb)
Max T-O weight   444 kg (980 lb)
Max wing loading   37.7 kg/m² (7.72 lb/sq ft)
Max power loading   21.14 kg/kW (35.0 lb/hp)
PERFORMANCE, UNPOWERED (S-2 at max T-O weight):
Best glide ratio at 48 knots (88 km/h; 55 mph)   34
Min rate of sink at 35 knots (64 km/h; 40 mph)
0.67 m (2.20 ft)/s
Stalling speed, flaps down   33 knots (62 km/h; 38 mph)
Max speed (smooth air)   129 knots (240 km/h; 149 mph)
Max speed (rough air)   87 knots (161 km/h; 100 mph)
g limits   +5.3/−4.2
PERFORMANCE, POWERED (S-2 at max T-O weight):
Max cruising speed   78 knots (145 km/h; 90 mph)
Econ cruising speed   43 knots (80 km/h; 50 mph)
Stalling speed   33 knots (62 km/h; 38 mph)
Max rate of climb at S/L   107 m (350 ft)/min
T-O run   610 m (2,000 ft)
Landing run   91 m (300 ft)
Range with max fuel   87 nm (161 km; 100 miles)

YUGOSLAVIA

ELAN
ELAN TOVARNA ŠPORTNEGAORODJA N.SOL.O

Begunje 1, 64275 Begunje na Gorenjskem
Telephone: 38 (64) 75 010 and 75 560
Telex: 34518
Fax: 38 (64) 74 929
DEVELOPMENT ENGINEER: Dipl Ing Marjan Žvokelj

Formed in 1944 by a group of 10 workers, Elan is well known as a manufacturer of skis, gymnastics equipment, pleasure craft, and gliders. In 1979 it started production of DG-100 series sailplanes which had been transferred to Elan from Glaser-Dirks of West Germany (which see). At present, Elan is responsible for production of the jointly designed DG-300 Elan, including the latest DG-300 Club

Elan version. Elan is also the sole production centre for the DG-500 Elan series of two-seat sailplanes (see Glaser-Dirks).

ELAN (GLASER-DIRKS) DG-101 ELAN

The basic DG-100 was a modified and lighter-weight development of the Akaflieg Darmstadt D-38. By the end of 1978 Glaser-Dirks had completed 105 DG-100s, including 16 DG-100Gs. From early 1979 production was transferred to Elan, which introduced the improved DG-101 models on to the line from c/n E58 in early 1981. By the end of 1989, when production was terminated, Elan had completed 222 DG-101s. The moulds have been kept for repairs and production of spare parts. A description of the DG-101, and an illustration, can be found in the 1989-90 *Jane's*.

ELAN/GLASER-DIRKS DG-300 ELAN

This Standard Class design, first flown on 27 April 1983, is a joint venture by Elan and Glaser-Dirks and is a developed version of the DG-101G, which it resembles closely. Design began in July 1982, and five pre-series aircraft were built by Elan. Series production began in December 1983, at which time 110 had been ordered, including the pre-series examples. By the end of 1989 a total of 402 had been ordered.

Principal differences from the DG-101G include a new low-drag, laminar flow wing section, developed by engineers of the German DLR, which incorporates a tubular boundary layer distribution system for optimum lift; larger airbrakes; location of the wings slightly further aft, with an improved wing/fuselage junction; a 20 cm (7.9 in) reduction in fuselage length; improved directional

Schweizer SGS 1-36 Sprite training and club sailplane (36903-3 version)

First homebuilt Strojnik S-2A, constructed by Mr Thomas Sweeney of Salt Lake City, Utah, USA

Schweizer TG-7A (SGM 2-37) in service with the US Air Force Academy

Elan/Glaser-Dirks DG-300 Club Elan Standard Class sailplane

Jastreb VUK-T all-plastics training sailplane

Jastreb Standard Cirrus G/81, developed from the 75-VTC

stability, resulting from an improved fin aerofoil section and reduced rudder depth; a 2 cm (0.79 in) wider and more comfortable cockpit; automatically connecting controls; and provision for an auxiliary water ballast tank in the fin.

The latest version is the **DG-300 Club Elan**, which has been in series production since January 1988. Like the DG-101(G) Club Elan version of the DG-101 (see 1989-90 *Jane's*), the DG-300 Club Elan has a non-retractable monowheel, no water ballast and no boundary layer distribution system.

The following data apply to the standard DG-300 Elan:

TYPE: Single-seat Standard Class sailplane.

AIRFRAME: Cantilever shoulder-wing monoplane, with Horstmann-Quast 300 G-D (Mod 2) aerofoil section. Incidence 3°. Sweepforward 0° 30′ at quarter-chord. Glassfibre/Conticell/foam sandwich wings, with Schempp-Hirth duralumin airbrakes in upper surface. All-glassfibre semi-monocoque fuselage. Cantilever T tailplane, with elevator and automatic self-connecting. Manually retractable sprung mainwheel (non-retractable

on Club version) with Tost drum brake and tailwheel. Tyre size 361 × 126 - 127 mm, pressure 2.5 bars (36 lb/sq in) on mainwheel; tailwheel tyre size 200 × 50 - 100 mm, pressure 2.0 bars (29 lb/sq in). One-piece cockpit canopy, hinged at nose and opening upward. Standard provision for 130 or 190 litres (34.3 or 50.2 US gallons; 28.6 or 41.8 Imp gallons) of water ballast in wings; optional tank in fin has max capacity of 5.5 litres (1.5 US gallons; 1.2 Imp gallons).

DIMENSIONS, EXTERNAL:
Wing span	15.00 m (49 ft 2½ in)
Wing aspect ratio	21.9
Length overall	6.80 m (22 ft 3¾ in)
Height over tail	1.40 m (4 ft 7 in)

AREA:
Wings, gross	10.27 m² (110.5 sq ft)

WEIGHTS AND LOADING:
Weight empty	245 kg (540 lb)
Max T-O weight	525 kg (1,157 lb)
Max wing loading	51.1 kg/m² (10.47 lb/sq ft)

PERFORMANCE (at max T-O weight except where indicated):
Best glide ratio:
at wing loading of 32 kg/m² (6.55 lb/sq ft) and speed of 54 knots (100 km/h; 62 mph) — 41
at wing loading of 50 kg/m² (10.24 lb/sq ft) and speed of 66 knots (122 km/h; 76 mph) — 42
Min rate of sink:
at wing loading of 32 kg/m² (6.55 lb/sq ft) and speed of 39 knots (72 km/h; 45 mph) — 0.59 m (1.94 ft)/s
at wing loading of 50 kg/m² (10.24 lb/sq ft) and speed of 48 knots (88 km/h; 55 mph) — 0.68 m (2.23 ft)/s
Stalling speed at wing loading of 32 kg/m² (6.55 lb/sq ft) — 35 knots (65 km/h; 41 mph)
Max speed (smooth air) 147 knots (270 km/h; 168 mph)
Max speed (rough air), and max aero-tow speed — 108 knots (200 km/h; 124 mph)
Max winch-launching speed — 70 knots (130 km/h; 80 mph)
g limits: +5.3/−2.65 (at VA)
+4/−1.5 (at VNE)

JASTREB

JASTREB FABRIKA AVIONA I JEDRILICA
(Jastreb Aircraft and Sailplanes Factory)
ul. Podrvsanska 17, 26300 Vrsac
Telephone: 38 (13) 813 639
Telex: 13193 YU JASTREB
MANAGER: Zec Predrag

Jastreb, known formerly as VTC, is the production centre for two versions of the Standard Cirrus sailplane, designed originally by Schempp-Hirth in West Germany and built subsequently under licence by VTC at Vrsac (see 1981-82 *Jane's*). It manufactures the VUK-T, designed at the University of Belgrade, and built a two-seat motor glider known as the SOLE-77 (last described in the 1987-88 *Jane's*).

JASTREB (SCHEMPP-HIRTH) STANDARD CIRRUS 75-VTC
Designed by Dipl-Ing Klaus Holighaus of Schempp-Hirth, this Standard Class version of the Cirrus entered production in Germany in the Summer of 1969, following its first flight in March 1969. By April 1977, when West German production ended, a total of 700 Standard Cirrus had been built, including 200 under licence by Grob Flugzeugbau.

Licence manufacture has been undertaken since January 1979 by VTC (now Jastreb) in Yugoslavia.

TYPE: Single-seat Standard and Club Class sailplane.

AIRFRAME: Cantilever mid-wing monoplane. Wortmann wing section. Dihedral 3°. Sweepback 1° 18′ at leading-edge. Glassfibre/foam sandwich wings, ailerons and tail

surfaces. Schempp-Hirth glassfibre airbrakes on upper surfaces. Glassfibre fuselage shell, stiffened with bonded-in foam rings. All-moving T tailplane. Retractable monowheel standard; non-retractable faired monowheel optional. Tost wheel with drum brake and Continental tyre, pressure 3.45 bars (50 lb/sq in). Canopy opens sideways to starboard. Provision for 60 kg (132 lb) of water ballast.

DIMENSIONS, EXTERNAL:
Wing span	15.00 m (49 ft 2½ in)
Wing aspect ratio	22.5
Length overall	6.41 m (21 ft 8½ in)
Height over tail	1.32 m (4 ft 4¾ in)

AREA:
Wings, gross	10.00 m² (107.6 sq ft)

WEIGHTS AND LOADINGS:

Weight empty	220 kg (485 lb)
Max T-O weight:	
without water ballast	330 kg (727 lb)
with water ballast	390 kg (860 lb)
Max wing loading:	
without water ballast	33.0 kg/m² (6.76 lb/sq ft)
with water ballast	39.0 kg/m² (7.99 lb/sq ft)

PERFORMANCE (at max T-O weight):

Best glide ratio at 49 knots (90 km/h; 56 mph)	38.5
Min rate of sink at 38 knots (70 km/h; 44 mph)	
	0.57 m (1.87 ft)/s
Stalling speed	34 knots (62 km/h; 39 mph)
Max speed (rough and smooth air)	
	119 knots (220 km/h; 137 mph)
Max aero-tow speed	81 knots (150 km/h; 93 mph)
Max winch-launching speed	
	65 knots (120 km/h; 75 mph)
g limit	+10

JASTREB STANDARD CIRRUS G/81

The Standard Cirrus G/81 was developed by Jastreb from the Standard Cirrus 75-VTC, and differs from it in the following respects:

AIRFRAME: As 75-VTC except for lack of option for non-retractable monowheel; new canopy, based on that of Schempp-Hirth Mini-Nimbus, opening sideways to starboard; roomier cockpit, able to accommodate a larger pilot; and a variable incidence T tailplane with separate elevator. CG tow hook standard, nose hook optional.

DATA: As for Cirrus 75-VTC

JASTREB VUK-T

The prototype of this single-seat all-plastics sailplane was designed and built at Belgrade University in 1976, and made its first flight in 1977. Production was started by Jastreb in January 1979.

Chief features of the VUK-T are the use of plastics stressed-skin construction and a supercritical wing section. The sailplane is designed to OSTIV airworthiness requirements, and is cleared for cloud flying, aerobatics and spinning.

TYPE: Single-seat advanced training sailplane.

AIRFRAME: Cantilever mid-wing monoplane. NASA GAW-1 supercritical wing section from root to tip, with no twist. Thickness/chord ratio 17%. Dihedral 3°. Glassfibre roving main spar, integral with the upper and lower wing skins, which are of glassfibre/Conticell foam sandwich. Auxiliary rear spar carries the top-hinged plain ailerons. Schempp-Hirth airbrakes in upper surfaces at 50 per cent chord. Fuselage is of glassfibre sandwich construction forward, glassfibre monocoque aft. Cantilever T tailplane, with separate elevator, of similar construction to wings. Retractable sprung monowheel, with brake, and non-retractable tailwheel. Semi-reclining seat under one-piece flush-fitting jettisonable canopy which opens sideways to starboard. No water ballast provision.

DIMENSIONS, EXTERNAL:

Wing span	15.00 m (49 ft 2½ in)
Wing aspect ratio	15.0
Length overall	6.50 m (21 ft 4 in)
Height over tail	1.35 m (4 ft 5¼ in)

AREA:

Wings, gross	15.00 m² (161.5 sq ft)

WEIGHTS AND LOADING:

Weight empty	245 kg (540 lb)
Max T-O weight	355 kg (782 lb)
Max wing loading	23.67 kg/m² (4.85 lb/sq ft)

PERFORMANCE (at max T-O weight):

Best glide ratio at 51 knots (95 km/h; 59 mph)	37.5
Min rate of sink at 42 knots (78 km/h; 49 mph)	
	0.65 m (2.13 ft)/s
Stalling speed	32 knots (59 km/h; 37 mph)
Max speed (smooth air)	129 knots (240 km/h; 149 mph)
Max speed (rough air)	81 knots (150 km/h; 93 mph)
Max aero-tow speed	70 knots (130 km/h; 80 mph)
Max winch-launching speed	
	65 knots (120 km/h; 75 mph)
g limits (safety factor 1.5)	+5.3/–2.65

SOKO
SOUR VAZDUHOPLOVNA INDUSTRIJA SOKO

88000 Mostar

Telephone: 38 (88) 22-121, 33-831, 35-244, 35-541, 37-943 and 55-120

Telex: 46 180 YU SOKOMO

PRESIDENT: Dipl Ing Milenko Pjescić
VICE-PRESIDENT, RESEARCH AND DEVELOPMENT:
Dipl Ing Mladen Zadro

SOKO SL-40 LISKA

Construction of the prototype Liska single-seat motor glider began at the end of 1975, and it flew for the first time on 19 February 1981. The flight test programme is running behind schedule, due to the flight test department's high workload on other projects. Full details of the Liska can be found in the 1987-88 and previous editions of *Jane's*.

HANG GLIDERS

CONTRACTORS' ADDRESSES:

Country	Company	Address	Telephone/Telex/Fax
Australia	Moyes Delta Gliders Pty Ltd	173 Bronte Road, Waverley, Sydney, NSW 2024	Tel: 61 (2) 387 5114 Telex: 10101 INTSY AA Fax: 61 (2) 387 4472
Austria	Steinbach-Delta Fun-Air GesmpH	6370 Kitzbühel/Tyrol, Achenweg 30	Tel: 43 (5356) 71233 Fax: 43 (5356) 72208
	VEGA-Drachenbau Pawel Wierzbowski	4563 Micheldorf, Hauptstrasse 43	Tel: 43 (7582) 4081
France	Aerotec SARL	68830 Oderen 21	Tel: 33 89 82 10 79
	SARL La Mouette	1 rue de la Petite Fin, 21 121 Fontaine les Dijon	Tel: 33 80 56 66 47 Telex: 350 053 F Fax: 33 80 55 42 01
West Germany	Drachen Studio Kecur GmbH	Zechenweg 9, 5603 Wülfrath	Tel: 49 (2058) 3000
	Finsterwalder Drachenflug GmbH	Pagodenburgstrasse 8, 8000 Munich 60	Tel: 49 (811) 65 28 Fax: 49 (814) 41 07
	Firebird Schweiger KG	Postfach 28, Hitzleriederstrasse 15, 8959 Seeg/Allgäu	Tel: 49 (8364) 1078/1079 Telex: 541412 Fax: 49 (8364) 1294
	Günter Rochelt	HBK, Lerchenfeld 2, 2000 Hamburg 76	Tel: 49 (40) 2984 3295 or 3233
	Thalhofer Team	Sudetenstrasse 10, 7449 Neckartenzlingen	Tel: 49 (7127) 187 95
	Wills Wing Deutschland (see USA for aircraft)	Am Burgblick 5, 7070 Schwäbisch Gmünd	Tel: 49 (7171) 40769 4945
Italy	Polaris Srl	Valdichiascio-Gubbio, (Perugia)	Tel: 39 (75) 92002930 Telex: 564006 POLARE I Fax: 39 (75) 92003435
Poland	Akademicki Ośrodek Konstrukcyjny (AOK: Academic Design Centre)	Wydzial Doświadczalny Kompozytów Polimerowych ('Kompol'), Instytut Inżynierii Materiałowej Politechniki Warszawskiej, ul. Narbutta 85, 02-524 Warszawa	Tel: 48 (22) 250633
	Instytut Lotnictwa (Aviation Institute)	Al. Krakowska 110/114, 02-256 Warszawa-Okecie	Tel: 48 (22) 460011 and 460993 Telex: 813537
Switzerland	Swiss Aerolight	PO Box 22, Pt Lancy 1, CH-1213 Geneva	Tel: 41 (22) 793 3722
Union of Soviet Socialist Republics	O. K. Antonov Design Bureau	Kiev	
	Onpo Technologia	Obninsk	
United Kingdom	Airwave Gliders Ltd	Elm Lane, Shalfleet, Newport, Isle of Wight PO30 4JY	Tel: 44 (983) 78611 Telex: 869188 GLIDER G Fax: 44 (983) 78552
	Pegasus Transport Systems Ltd/ Solar Wings Ltd	56 George Lane, Marlborough, Wiltshire SN8 4BY	Tel: 44 (672) 55066 Telex: 449 703 Fax: 44 (672) 54492
United States of America	Delta Wing Aviation	PO Box 483, Van Nuys, California 91408	Tel: 1 (818) 787 6000 Telex: 65-1425
	Pacific Airwave Inc	PO Box 4384, Salinas, California 93912	Tel: 1 (408) 422 2299 Telex: 4944863 PACWIN Fax: 1 (408) 758 3270
	Seedwings	41 Aero Camino, Santa Barbara, California 93117	Tel: 1 (805) 968 7070 Fax: 1 (805) 968 0059
	UP Inc (Ultralite Products)	PO Box 659, Temecula, California 92390	Tel: 1 (714) 676 5652 Telex: 910 332 1306
	Volmer Aircraft	PO Box 5222, Glendale, California 91201	Tel: 1 (818) 247 8718
	Wills Wing Inc	1208-H, East Walnut, Santa Ana, California 92701	Tel: 1 (714) 547 1344/6366 Fax: 1 (714) 547 0972

RIGID AND FLEXIBLE WING DATA

Manufacturer and Model	Rigid: R Flexwing: F	FAI or other class	Span: m/ft-in	Leading-edge (flexwing): m/ft-in	Length (rigid); Keel (flexwing): m/ft-in	Nose/Billow angle (flexwing): degrees
AUSTRALIA						
Moyes Delta						
Mars 150	F	1	8.84/29-0	5.10/16-9	2.54/8-4	125/0.5
Mars 170	F	1	9.45/31-0	5.51/18-1	2.62/8-7	125/0.5
Mars 190	F	1	10.06/33-0	5.87/19-3	2.74/9-0	125/0.5
GTR 148	F	1	9.75/32-0	4.80/15-9	1.98/6-6	130/0-1.5
GTR 162	F	1	10.36/34-0	5.14/16-10½	3.57/11-8½	130/0-1.5
GTR 175	F	1	10.97/36-0	5.49/18-0	2.13/7-0	130/0-1.5
GTR 210	F	1	10.97/36-0	5.49/18-0	2.90/9-6	130/0-1.5
Mission 170	F	1	9.55/31-4	5.51/18-1	2.62/8-7	125/0.5
AUSTRIA						
Steinbach-Delta Fun-Air						
Chiron 22	F	3 & 4 (DHV)	8.30/27-2¾	n.k.	n.k.	n.k.
Chiron 25	F	3 & 4 (DHV)	9.20/30-2¼	n.k.	n.k.	n.k.
Chiron 28	F	3 & 4 (DHV)	10.1/33-1½	n.k.	n.k.	n.k.
Condor 5+	F	n.k.	8.10/26-7	n.k.	3.10/10-2	n.k.
Divine 100	n.k.	n.k.	9.35/30-8	n.k.	n.k.	133/n.k.
Divine 200	n.k.	n.k.	9.35/30-8	n.k.	n.k.	135/n.k.
Euro III	F	n.k.	9.40/30-10	n.k.	n.k.	132/n.k.
Fun Air	F	n.k.	9.30/30-6¼	n.k.	n.k.	n.k.
Para Fun1	F	n.k.	9.10/29-10¼	n.k.	3.35/11-0	n.k.
Para Fun	F	n.k.	n.k.	n.k.	n.k.	n.k.
Para Safe	F	n.k.	n.k.	n.k.	n.k.	n.k.
SP	F	n.k.	10.40/34-1½	n.k.	n.k.	128/n.k.
SP Vario	F	n.k.	10.50/34-5½	n.k.	n.k.	126-130/n.k.
VEGA						
16/PR	F	DHV/SHV/BAZ	10.50/34-5½	n.k.	n.k.	132/n.k.
Alfa	F	n.k.	9.75/32-0	n.k.	n.k.	120/n.k.
MX	F	DHV/SHV/BAZ	10.50/34-5½	n.k.	n.k.	129-133/n.k.
FRANCE						
Aerotec						
Rapace 15	F	n.k.	10.30/33-9½	n.k.	n.k.	130/n.k.
Rapace 16	F	n.k.	10.80/35-5¼	n.k.	n.k.	130/n.k.
La Mouette						
Atlas 14	F	1	9.30/30-6¼	5.36/17-7	3.50/11-5¾	120/0.5
Atlas 16	F	1	9.90/32-5¾	5.70/18-8½	3.50/11-5¾	120/0.5
Atlas 18	F	1	10.50/34-5½	6.10/20-0	3.50/11-5¾	120/0.5
Compact	F	n.k.	10.00/32-9¾	6.00/19-8¼	3.50/11-5¾	—
WEST GERMANY						
Drachen						
Tropi 16	F	n.k.	10.60/34-9¼	n.k.	n.k.	130/n.k.
Tropi 17	F	n.k.	10.60/34-9¼	n.k.	n.k.	130/n.k.
Finsterwalder						
Bergfex	F	n.k.	n.k.	n.k.	n.k.	n.k.
Funfex	F	1 & 2 (DHV)	9.40/30-10	5.50/18-0½	2.40/7-10	120/0
Minifex M2	F	2 (DHV)	9.14/29-11¾	n.k.	n.k.	130/0
Superfex	F	n.k.	9.80/32-1¾	n.k.	n.k.	n.k.
Topfex	F	2 & 3 (DHV)	10.40/34-1½	5.80/19-0¼	2.00/6-6¾	130/0
Firebird						
Classic	F	2 & 3 (DHV)	10.20/33-5½	5.80/19-0¼	n.k.	132/n.k.
New Wave 15	F	3 (DHV)	10.40/34-1½	5.80/19-0¼	n.k.	132/n.k.
New Wave 16	F	3 (DHV)	11.00/36-1	5.80/19-0¼	n.k.	132/n.k.
Quattro-S	F	2 & 3 (DHV)	9.92/32-6	5.75/18-10½	n.k.	125/n.k.
Quattro-S Piccolo	F	2 (DHV)	9.35/30-8	5.40/17-8½	n.k.	125/n.k.
Uno	F	1 & 2 (DHV)	9.95/32-7¾	5.75/18-10½	n.k.	125/n.k.
Uno Jumbo	F	2 (DHV)	10.80/35-5¼	5.80/19-0¼	n.k.	125/n.k.
Uno Piccolo	F	1 & 2 (DHV)	9.35/30-8	5.40/17-8½	n.k.	120/n.k.
Rochelt						
Flair	R	n.k.	12.00/39-4½	n.k.	n.k.	—
Schneid Air	F	n.k.	9.00/29-6⅓	n.k.	n.k.	n.k.
Thalhofer						
GT	F	n.k.	10.30/33-9½	n.k.	n.k.	124/n.k.
Joker	F	n.k.	9.65/31-8	n.k.	n.k.	122/n.k.
Swing	F	n.k.	10.40/34-1½	n.k.	n.k.	127/n.k.
ITALY						
Polaris						
FR 16	F	1	10.85/35-7¼	5.60/18-4½	3.60/11-9¾	132/0
*Ares	F	1	11.15/36-7	5.50/18-0½	3.30/10-10	130/0
*Gryps	F	1	10.60/34-9¼	5.50/18-0½	3.30/10-10	130/0
*Spit	Semi-R	1	10.60/34-9¼	5.50/18-0½	3.30/10-10	130/0
Touring 13	F	1	9.60/31-6	5.23/17-2	3.50/11-5¾	120/0
Touring 15	F	1	9.60/31-6	5.23/17-2	3.50/11-5¾	120/0

*Ares, Gryps and Spit are specifically for powered flying, using trikes or other attachable units (single- or two-seat).

Manufacturer and Model	Rigid: R Flexwing: F	FAI or other class	Span: m/ft-in	Leading-edge (flexwing): m/ft-in	Length (rigid); Keel (flexwing): m/ft-in	Nose/Billow angle (flexwing): degrees
POLAND						
AOK						
SB-1 WARS	F	1	9.50/31-2	6.00/19-8¼	4.20/13-9¼	105/0
Stratus E-2C I	F	1	10.60/34-9¼	6.10/20-0¼	3.60/11-9¾	126/variable
Stratus E-2C II	F	1	11.10/36-5	6.40/21-0	3.80/12-5½	126/variable
Stratus E-3C I	F	1	10.20/33-5½	5.90/19-4¼	3.60/11-9¾	126/variable
Stratus E-3C II	F	1	10.70/35-1¼	6.15/20-2¼	3.80/12-5½	126/variable
Stratus E-4 C	F	1	9.80/32-1¾	5.65/18-6½	3.60/11-9¾	126/0
Instytut Lotnictwa						
Zeta-87	Semi-R	1	11.60/38-0¾	6.00/19-8¼	3.60/11-9¾	134/-2
SWITZERLAND						
Swiss Aerolight						
Nimbus	R	n.k.	12.50/41-0¼	n.k.	n.k.	—

n.k. = not known

Wing area: m²/sq ft	Wing aspect ratio	Weight: kg/lb	Glide ratio	Sink rate: m/ft per min	Pilot weight: kg (lb)	Stalling speed: knots (km/h; mph)	g limits
13.94/150.0	5.6	23.6/52	8.5	61/200	41-82 (90-180)	19 (34; 21)	+6/−4
15.98/172.0	5.6	28.1/62	8	61/200	57-109 (125-240)	23 (42; 26)	+6/−4
17.65/190.0	5.7	30/66.1	8	55/180	68-113 (150-250)	12 (21; 13)	+6/−4
13.75/148.0	6.9	30/66.1	10	61/200	54-100 (120-220)	14 (26; 16)	n.k.
15.05/162.0	7.2	30.8/68	10	55/180	59-104 (130-230)	15 (28; 18)	n.k.
16.26/175.0	7.4	35/77.2	10	55/180	68-113 (150-250)	13 (23; 14)	n.k.
19.51/210.0	6.2	40/88.2	10	55/180	73-118 (160-260)	11 (20; 12)	n.k.
16.16/174.0	5.8	29/63.9	9	58/190	59-95 (130-210)	11 (20; 12)	+6/−4
22.00/236.8	3.13	n.k.	7	66/216	50-75 (110-165)	12 (21; 13)	n.k.
25.00/269.1	3.38	n.k.	7	60/197	65-90 (144-198)	12 (21; 13)	n.k.
28.00/301.4	3.64	n.k.	7.1	54/177	80-115 (177-253)	11 (20; 12)	n.k.
26.00/279.9	n.k.	28/61.7	5	168/551	60-90 (132-198)	n.k.	n.k.
14.20/152.8	n.k.	28/61.7	n.k.	n.k.	60-90 (132-198)	n.k.	n.k.
14.20/152.8	n.k.	28/61.7	n.k.	n.k.	60-90 (132-198)	n.k.	n.k.
17.00/183.0	5.2	24/53	n.k.	n.k.	n.k.	n.k.	n.k.
29.00/312.2	n.k.	n.k.	5	114/374	50 (110) min	n.k.	n.k.
31.00/333.0	n.k.	32/70.5	n.k.	n.k.	60-100 (132-220)	n.k.	n.k.
29.00/312.2	n.k.	n.k.	n.k.	n.k.	n.k.	n.k.	n.k.
26.00/279.9	n.k.	n.k.	n.k.	n.k.	n.k.	n.k.	n.k.
15.80/170.1	6.85	29/63.9	n.k.	n.k.	n.k.	n.k.	n.k.
15.80/170.1	6.98	33/72.8	n.k.	n.k.	n.k.	n.k.	n.k.
16.00/172.2	6.9	31/68.3	n.k.	n.k.	56-99 (124-218)	13 (24; 15)	n.k.
15.80/170.1	6	26/57.3	n.k.	n.k.	n.k.	13 (24; 15)	n.k.
14.30/153.9	7.7	31/68.3	n.k.	n.k.	55-85 (122-187)	13 (24; 15)	n.k.
15.30/164.7	7	n.k.	n.k.	n.k.	60-90 (132-198)	12 (22; 14)	n.k.
15.80/170.1	7.2	n.k.	n.k.	n.k.	75-100 (165-220)	12 (22; 14)	n.k.
13.80/148.5	6.3	24.5/54	9	60/197	50-75 (110-165)	14 (25; 16)	+6/−4
15.80/170.0	6.2	25/55.1	9	60/197	65-95 (143-209)	14 (25; 16)	+6/−4
18.00/193.8	6.1	29/63.9	9	60/197	90-140 (198-308)	14 (25; 16)	+6/−4
14.00/150.7	7.1	n.k.	11	54/177	n.k.	14 (25; 16)	+6/−4
15.30/164.7	7.3	34/75	n.k.	n.k.	50-110 (110-242)	11 (20; 12)	n.k.
16.30/175.5	6.9	35/77.2	n.k.	n.k.	65-110 (143-242)	11 (20; 12)	n.k.
n.k.	n.k.	n.k.	n.k.	n.k.	n.k.	n.k.	n.k.
16.00/172.2	5.5	22/48.5	11	52/171	60-100 (132-220)	15 (28; 18)	n.k.
14.00/150.7	5.7	22/48.5	10	54/177	45-65 (99-143)	15 (28; 18)	n.k.
16.80/180.8	n.k.	15.8/34.8	n.k.	72/236	65-95 (143-209)	16.5 (30; 19)	n.k.
16.10/173.3	6.7	29/63.9	12	54/177	65-110 (143-242)	18 (32; 20)	n.k.
15.50/166.8	6.7	32/70.5	n.k.	n.k.	60-100 (132-220)	18 (32; 20)	+6/−3
15.00/162.5	7.21	30.5/67.25	n.k.	n.k.	60-95 (132-209)	19 (35; 22)	+6/−3
16.00/172.2	7.56	33/72.8	n.k.	n.k.	70-100 (154-220)	19 (35; 22)	+6/−3
15.80/170.1	6.4	26/57.3	n.k.	n.k.	60-118 (132-260)	16.5 (30; 19)	+6/−3
14.00/150.7	6.24	25/55.1	n.k.	n.k.	45-70 (100-155)	16.5 (30; 19)	+6/−3
15.50/166.8	6.4	24.5/54	8.5	n.k.	50-100 (110-220)	12 (22; 14)	+6/−3
17.50/188.4	6.67	28/61.7	n.k.	n.k.	70-100 (154-220)	12 (22; 14)	+6/−3
14.00/150.7	6.25	20/44.1	n.k.	n.k.	75 (165) max	14 (25; 16)	+6/−3
11.00/118.4	n.k.	48/106	30	30/98	n.k.	17 (30; 19)	±6
n.k.	n.k.	19/42	n.k.	n.k.	n.k.	n.k.	n.k.
15.80/170.1	6.71	28/61.7	11	54/177	60-100 (132-220)	14 (25; 16)	n.k.
16.50/177.6	5.64	24.5/54	9.5	52/171	50-100 (110-220)	14 (25; 16)	n.k.
15.80/170.0	6.85	29/63.9	10	52/171	55-123 (121-271)	12 (22; 14)	n.k.
15.60/167.9	7.5	32/70.5	12	n.k.	80-95 (176-209)	14 (25; 16)	n.k.
20.50/220.7	6	42/92.6	8	n.k.	240 (529) max	15 (28; 18)	n.k.
18.50/199.1	6	42/92.6	9	n.k.	240 (529)	15 (28; 18)	n.k.
13.50/145.3	8.3	43/94.8	8	n.k.	240 (529)	15 (28; 18)	n.k.
13.50/145.3	6.8	23/50.7	10	54/177	55-72 (121-159)	14 (25; 16)	n.k.
15.00/161.5	6.14	24/52.9	10	54/177	68-86 (150-189)	14 (25; 16)	n.k.
18.90/203.4	4.8	25/55.1	8	75/246	50-110 (110-242)	16 (29; 19)	+6/−3
15.30/164.7	7.34	30/66	11	54/177	55-90 (121-198)	27 (50; 31)	n.k.
16.90/181.9	7.29	33/72.8	11	54/177	75-105 (165-231)	27 (50; 31)	n.k.
15.00/162.5	6.94	29/63.9	10	57/187	55-85 (121-187)	26 (48; 30)	n.k.
16.60/178.7	6.90	31/68.3	10	57/187	70-100 (154-220)	26 (48; 30)	n.k.
15.50/166.8	6.20	27/60	8.5	66/217	55-90 (121-198)	25 (47; 29)	n.k.
16.00/172.2	7.9	30-35/66-77	11-14	48-54/157-177	50-120 (110-264)	n.k.	+6/−3
16.20/174.4	n.k.	38/84	18	45/148	50-100 (110-220)	16 (28; 18)	+8/−6

RIGID AND FLEXIBLE WING DATA

Manufacturer and Model	Rigid: R Flexwing: F	FAI or other class	Span: m/ft-in	Leading-edge (flexwing): m/ft-in	Length (rigid); Keel (flexwing): m/ft-in	Nose/Billow angle (flexwing): degrees
UNION OF SOVIET SOCIALIST REPUBLICS						
Antonov						
Slavutitch Sport	F	n.k.	10.50/34-5½	n.k.	3.90/12-9½	n.k.
Slavutitch-UT	F	n.k.	8.90/29-2½	5.72/18-9¼	4.235/13-10¾	104/1.0
Onpo Technologia						
Kompozit UT	F	n.k.	n.k.	n.k.	n.k.	n.k.
UNITED KINGDOM						
Airwave						
Calypso	F	1	9.30/30-6¼	5.30/17-4½	n.k.	120/0
Magic IV 133	F	1	8.95/29-4½	5.20/17-0¾	n.k.	n.k.
Magic IV 150	F	1	9.50/31-2	5.53/18-1¾	n.k.	n.k.
Magic IV 155	F	1	9.99/32-9¼	5.89/19-4	3.66/12-0	120/n.k.
Magic IV 166	F	1	10.40/34-1½	5.99/19-8	3.66/12-0	120/n.k.
Magic IV 177	F	1	10.64/34-11	6.21/20-4½	3.66/12-0	120/n.k.
Magic Kiss	F	1	10.39/34-1	n.k.	n.k.	132/0
Pegasus/Solar Wings						
Ace/Ace RX (small)	F	1	9.60/31-6	n.k.	n.k.	122/variable
Ace/Ace RX (medium)	F	1	9.91/32-6	n.k.	n.k.	122/variable
Ace/Ace RX (large)	F	1	10.36/34-0	n.k.	n.k.	122/variable
Ace Fun	F	n.k.	n.k.	n.k.	n.k.	n.k.
Ace Sport	F	n.k.	n.k.	n.k.	n.k.	n.k.
Ace Supersport	F	n.k.	n.k.	n.k.	n.k.	n.k.
Rumour	F	n.k.	n.k.	n.k.	n.k.	n.k.
UNITED STATES OF AMERICA						
Delta Wing						
Dream 165	F	1	9.55/31-4	n.k.	n.k.	124/1.0
Dream 175	F	1	n.k.	n.k.	n.k.	n.k.
Dream 185	F	1	10.31/33-10	n.k.	n.k.	124/1.0
Mystic 155	F	n.k.	9.96/32-8	n.k.	n.k.	n.k.
Mystic 166	F	n.k.	10.39/34-1	n.k.	n.k.	n.k.
Mystic 177	F	n.k.	10.57/34-8	n.k.	n.k.	n.k.
Streak 130	F	1	8.84/29-0	n.k.	n.k.	133/0
Streak 160	F	1	10.62/34-10	5.56/18-3	3.35/11-0	133/0
Streak 180	F	1	11.38/37-4	n.k.	n.k.	133/0
Pacific Airwave						
Genesis	F	1	8.59/28-2	5.03/16-6	3.66/12-0	122/0
Magic Kiss 154	F	1	10.36/34-0	5.56/18-3	3.66/12-0	132/0
Vision Mk IV 17	F	1	9.19/30-2	5.33/17-6	3.66/12-0	122/0
Vision Mk IV 19	F	1	9.75/32-0	5.82/19-1	3.66/12-0	122/0
Seedwings						
Sensor 510E-160 VG	F	1	10.62/34-10	n.k.	2.11/6-11	135/0
UP						
Comet 2B 165	F	1	9.96/32-8	5.86/19-2¾	2.49/8-2	120/0
Comet 2B 185	F	1	10.57/34-8	6.22/20-4¾	2.62/8-7	120/0
Gemini M 134	F	1	8.78/28-9½	5.22/17-1½	2.18/7-2	120/1.0
Gemini M 164	F	1	9.91/32-6	5.86/19-2¾	2.49/8-2	120/1.0
Gemini M 184	F	1	10.49/34-5	6.22/20-4¾	2.62/8-7	120/1.0
Glidezilla 155	F	1	10.36/34-0	5.87/19-3	2.06/6-9	126/0
Volmer						
VJ-23 Swingwing	R	n.k.	9.93/32-7	9.93/32-7	5.31/17-5	—
VJ-24 Sunfun	R	n.k.	11.13/36-6	11.13/36-6	5.54/18-2	—
Wills Wing						
Skyhawk 168	F	1	9.19/30-2	5.49/18-0	3.66/12-0	115/0
Skyhawk 188	F	1	10.01/32-10	5.94/19-6	3.66/12-0	115/0
Sport AT 150	F	1	9.60/31-6	5.54/18-2	3.45/11-4	124/0
Sport AT 167	F	1	10.21/33-6	5.94/19-6	3.45/11-4	124/0
Sport AT 180	F	1	10.50/34-5½	6.10/20-0	3.45/11-4	128/0
Sport American 167	F	1	10.21/33-6	5.94/19-6	3.45/11-4	124/0
HP AT 145	R	1	10.13/33-3	5.54/18-2¼	3.43/11-3	—
HP AT 158	R	1	10.54/34-7	5.77/18-11¼	n.k.	n.k.

n.k. = not known

Wing area: m²/sq ft	Wing aspect ratio	Weight: kg/lb	Glide ratio	Sink rate: m/ft per min	Pilot weight: kg (lb)	Stalling speed: knots (km/h; mph)	g limits
16.30/175.5	n.k.	33.5/74	10+	60/197	n.k.	14 (25; 16)	+6/–3
17.50/188.4	n.k.	25/55	7	78/256	n.k.	14 (25; 16)	+4.5
17.00/183.0	6.2	19/42	9	60/197	65-95 (143-209)	10 (18; 11.5)	+5
15.80/170.0	5.5	28/61.7	n.k.	n.k.	55-105 (121-231)	15 (28; 18) estimated	+6/–3
12.36/133.0	6.6	26/57.3	n.k.	n.k.	45-60 (100-132)	n.k.	n.k.
13.94/150.0	6.3	26/57.3	n.k.	n.k.	52-64 (115-160)	n.k.	n.k.
14.49/156.0	6.7	29/64	11	52/171	64-73 (140-160)	16 (29; 18)	n.k.
15.79/170.0	6.8	29.9/66	11	52/171	70-79 (155-175)	16 (29; 18)	n.k.
16.54/178.0	6.8	32.2/71	11	54/177	79-91 (175-200)	16 (29; 18)	n.k.
14.30/154.0	7.4	31/68.3	n.k.	n.k.	52-95 (115-210)	22 (40.5; 25) approx	+6/–3
13.94/150.0	6.1	28.6/63	n.k.	n.k.	51-83 (113-183)	n.k.	n.k.
14.86/160.0	6.6	31.8/70	n.k.	n.k.	70-89 (154-196)	n.k.	n.k.
15.79/170.0	6.8	33.6/74	n.k.	n.k.	83-100 (183-220)	n.k.	n.k.
13.94/150.0 or 14.86/160.0	n.k.	n.k.	n.k.	n.k.	n.k.	n.k.	n.k.
13.94/150.0 or 14.86/160.0 or 15.79/170.0	n.k.	n.k.	n.k.	n.k.	n.k.	n.k.	n.k.
13.94/150.0 or 14.86/160.0	n.k.	n.k.	n.k.	n.k.	n.k.	n.k.	n.k.
13.47/145.0 or 14.40/155.0	n.k.	30/66 or 32.5/72	n.k.	n.k.	n.k.	n.k.	n.k.
15.33/165.0	6.4	28.1/62	n.k.	n.k.	59-91 (130-200)	n.k.	n.k.
16.26/175.0	n.k.	n.k.	n.k.	n.k.	n.k.	n.k.	n.k.
17.19/185.0	6.2	30.8/68	n.k.	n.k.	n.k.	n.k.	n.k.
14.49/156.0	6.7	29/64	n.k.	n.k.	45-77 (100-170)	n.k.	n.k.
15.42/166.0	6.8	29.9/66	n.k.	n.k.	64-95 (140-210)	n.k.	n.k.
16.26/175.0	6.8	32.2/71	n.k.	n.k.	77-109 (170-240)	n.k.	n.k.
12.08/130.0	6.6	24.9/55	n.k.	50/165	n.k.	n.k.	+8.5/–5
14.68/158.0	7.5	32.7/72	n.k.	50/165	59-100 (130-220)	n.k.	+8.5/–5
16.72/180.0	7.6	37.2/82	n.k.	50/165	n.k.	n.k.	+8.5/–5
12.82/138.0	6.4	21.3/47	11	55/180	43-75 (95-165)	17 (31; 19)	+6/–4
14.31/154.0	7.5	30.4/67	13	52/170	59-95.3 (130-210)	17 (31; 19)	+6/–4
15.05/162.0	5.4	26.8/59	11	55/180	52.5-88.5 (115-195)	17 (31; 19)	+6/–4
16.91/182.0	5.6	29/64	11	55/180	70.5-113 (155-250)	17 (31; 19)	+6/–4
14.77/159.0	7.64	30.8/68 Model SS	12-14	49/160	n.k.	n.k.	+6/–4.5
		31.8/70 Model ER	n.k.	n.k.	66-102 (145-225)	n.k.	n.k.
		32.7/72 Model FR	n.k.	n.k.	n.k.	n.k.	n.k.
15.33/165.0	6.5	29/64	10+	55/180	59-104 (130-230)	13.5 (25; 15) IAS	+6.5/–3.5
17.19/185.0	6.6	35.4/78	10+	55/180	68-113 (150-250)	13.5 (25; 15) IAS	+6.5/–3.5
12.45/134.0	6.2	24.9/55	8.5	64/210	43-75 (95-165)	12.5 (23; 14) IAS	n.k.
15.24/164.0	6.4	28.6/63	8.5	64/210	57-91 (125-200)	12.5 (23; 14) IAS	n.k.
17.09/184.0	6.4	34/75	8.5	64/210	68-104 (150-230)	12.5 (23; 14) IAS	n.k.
14.31/154.0	7.5	32.7/72	12.5	52/170	64-104 (140-230)	13 (24; 15)	+6.5/–3.5
16.63/179.0	5.9	45.5/100	9	n.k.	45.5-91 (100-200)	13 (24; 15)	+2 normal +3 ultimate
15.14/163.0	8.2	50/110	9	n.k.	91 (200) max	13 (24; 15)	+2.57 normal +3.87 ultimate
15.42/166.0	5.5	24.5/54	8.5	69/225	52-75 (115-165)	19 (36; 22)	+6/–3
17.47/188.0	5.7	29/64	8.5	69/225	66-88 (145-195)	19 (36; 22)	+6/–3
13.94/150.0	6.6	26/57	9	64/210	50-70 (110-154)	20 (37; 23)	+7.5/–3.5
15.51/167.0	6.8	28/62	9	64/210	60-90 (133-198)	20 (37; 23)	+7.5/–3.5
16.72/180.0	6.6	32/71	9	64/210	90-140 (198-308)	20 (37; 23)	+7.5/–3.5
15.51/167.0	6.7	29.9/66	9	64/210	64-109 (140-240)	20 (37; 23)	+7.5/–3.5
13.47/145.0	7.62	29.5/65	11	64/210	59-104 (130-230)	21 (39; 24)	+9/–4.5
14.68/158.0	7.57	31.3/69	11	64/210	68-113 (150-250)	21 (39; 24)	+9/–4.5

LIGHTER THAN AIR: AIRSHIPS

AUSTRALIA

ADA
AIRSHIP DEVELOPMENTS AUSTRALIA PTY LTD

96 Rankins Road, Kensington, Victoria 3031
Telephone: 61 (3) 376 2450
DESIGNER: Bruce N. Blake, c/o Advanced Airship Corporation Ltd, Jurby, Isle of Man, England
Telephone: 44 (624) 897962

Mr Bruce Blake, a consulting engineer, initiated a series of airship designs under the name of his Airship Developments Australia company, the latest of which is the LUA four/six-seat light utility airship. To demonstrate the airworthiness of this design, at minimal cost, while generating revenue, a one-third scale drone version of the LUA, named Albatross, was built during 1985.

During 1989 Mr Blake worked under contract as Engineering Manager for US-LTA (see the US part of this section). Since January 1990 he has served as Chief Designer with Advanced Airship Corporation Ltd in the Isle of Man (see under UK).

ADA ALBATROSS

First flown on 6 November 1986, the Albatross RPMB (remotely piloted mini-blimp) introduced several innovative features, including a lifting outrigger with blown flap similar to one wind-tunnel tested in the USA for the GZ-16 non-rigid of the 1950s. Revenue is generated at outdoor displays, such as the Australian Bicentennial Air Show at Richmond AFB, near Sydney, in October 1988, and other promotional opportunities.

The full scale version of the LUA, for which preliminary design work has been completed, is known as the **ADA-1200**. Efforts to attract venture capital for this airship are continuing.

Initial flight testing of the Albatross demonstrated most of the expected performance characteristics of the full scale design. The airship can be taxied in light winds, and has shown very short take-off and landing performance. Successful flights at more than 20 per cent heaviness have been made; hands-off stability appears to be excellent, combining positive pitch stability with weathercocking yaw stability. No pitch or yaw oscillations have been observed, and roll damping is satisfactory.

The following description relates to the Albatross one-third scale prototype:
ENVELOPE: The envelope is a two-skin type, the inner (gas cell) being made from metallised laminated nylon film while the outer (load carrying) skin is of stabilised polyester fabric. Seams of the outer skin are double sewn, with heat-sealed tapes to attain full fabric strength across the seams. The inner skin, which is highly plastic and roughing tolerant, conforms to the shape of the outer skin as it stretches with use. A single spherical ballonet (volume 8.0 m³; 283 cu ft) is provided, constructed from nylon film. Automatic pressure control is achieved by the use of a pressure switch, an electric centrifugal blower (with a one-way flow valve) and an outflow valve. An overpressure valve is provided to vent helium, should envelope pressure exceed safe limits. Additionally, a remotely controlled dump valve will enable the initiation of a controlled descent in an emergency. The Albatross has an X-fin tail unit, each fin being fitted with two ruddervators for redundancy, actuated by servos, with electronic mixing, to provide control in pitch and yaw. The fins are constructed from balsa wood and covered with a heat-shrunk polyester film.

One-thirtieth scale model (1m: 3.28 ft long) of the projected ADA-1200

POWER PLANT: Two 2.6 kW (3.5 hp) Robin EY15D single-cylinder four-stroke engines, lightened in weight and each fitted with an electric starter/generator. Engines are mounted on stub-wings, each with direct drive to a two-blade wooden propeller with spinner. Single fuel tank in spine fairing, max capacity 15 litres (4 US gallons; 3.3 Imp gallons).
GONDOLA, SPINE AND WING: The cabin/spine unit is of scale size, and is an innovation of the LUA design. Past non-rigids have generally relied upon cables and catenary curtains fitted into the upper envelope to support the gondola, but by elongating the cabin/spine it is entirely practicable, with modern materials, to introduce vertical loading into the lower envelope surface. In addition, the cabin/spine configuration leads to improved stiffness, in pitch and roll, between it and the envelope, and allows the installation of tricycle landing gear, essential for ground manoeuvring. The Albatross prototype is not entirely representative of the full size ADA-1200, since the CG of the cabin/spine is aft of the appropriate position, and the two-skin envelope precludes a conventional internal suspension system. Instead, cords at the wingtips provide the missing support. Materials used in the cabin/spine are hand laid glass/epoxy/PVC foam sandwich, with aircraft plywood structural reinforcing. The wing, lifting outrigger or lift plane, attached to the rear of the spine, is constructed from light gauge aluminium alloy sheet and provides structural attachment for the engines and main landing gear units. The trailing-edge is formed by a 30 per cent chord flap, servo actuated to ±40° deflection. This provides a useful increment of aerodynamic lift control. Landing gear has gas strut shock absorption and twin wheels, with 5½ in pneumatic tyres, on each unit.
GUIDANCE AND CONTROL: A standard FM radio control unit is used for line-of-sight operation. Minor modification

was made to enable the use of a large external battery for the transmitter, with a similar improvement at the receiver. Control is provided for throttles, ruddervators, flaps and dump valve; three channels remain unused. The system provides an electronic discriminator for fail-safe operation in the event of signal interference. Advanced RPV television based guidance is a possibility for future out-of-sight operations.

DIMENSIONS, OVERALL:	
Length	12.00 m (39 ft 4½ in)
Height	4.40 m (14 ft 5¼ in)
Width	3.60 m (11 ft 9¾ in)
DIMENSIONS, ENVELOPE:	
Length	12.00 m (39 ft 4½ in)
Max diameter	3.20 m (10 ft 6 in)
Volume	76.5 m³ (2,702 cu ft)
DIMENSIONS, GONDOLA/WING:	
Gondola: Length	3.90 m (12 ft 9½ in)
Height (incl landing gear)	1.00 m (3 ft 3¼ in)
Wing span	2.10 m (6 ft 10¾ in)
Wing chord	0.60 m (1 ft 11½ in)
Wheel track	2.00 m (6 ft 6¾ in)
Wheelbase	2.50 m (8 ft 2½ in)
Propeller diameter	0.76 m (2 ft 6 in)
WEIGHTS:	
Weight empty	64 kg (141 lb)
Max fuel	11 kg (24 lb)
Max payload	11 kg (24 lb)
PERFORMANCE:	
Max level speed:	
neutral buoyancy	34 knots (63 km/h; 39 mph)
18% heavy	30 knots (55 km/h; 34.5 mph)
Min flying speed, 20% heavy	7 knots (13 km/h; 8.1 mph)
Max operating height	305 m (1,000 ft)

CHINA, PEOPLE'S REPUBLIC

BUAA
BEIJING UNIVERSITY OF AERONAUTICS AND ASTRONAUTICS (Light Aircraft Design and Research Section)

37 Xue Yuan Road, Beijing 100083
Telephone: 86 (1) 2017251
Telex: 22036 BIAAT CN
DIRECTOR AND SENIOR RESEARCH ENGINEER: Hu Jizhong

BUAA MIFENG-6 (BEE-6)

Following a number of microlight aircraft (see tables in that section), the BUAA's sixth Mifeng (Bee) design, started in September 1985, is a four-place hot-air airship. It has an envelope of lightweight high-strength nylon which can be stored in a bag with a volume of only 1.5 m³ (53 cu ft). There are two vertical fins, each with a rudder for yaw control, and two horizontal stabilisers (without elevators). The gondola has a mainframe of chrome plated steel tube, covered with sheet aluminium. The envelope is inflated by the propulsion

BUAA Mifeng-6 four-place hot-air airship

engine, two gas burners providing heat for buoyancy control. Propulsion is provided by a 31.3 kW (42 hp) Rotax 447 two-stroke engine driving a BUAA three-blade fixed-pitch pusher propeller. Fuel tank capacity is 50 litres (13.2 US gallons; 11.0 Imp gallons).

The prototype first flew on 20 December 1985. Three production Mifeng-6s had been completed by early 1990, and the airship has been used for aerial and cinema film photography, scientific experiment flights and sightseeing. One example assisted in erecting power transmission lines for the Ge-Zhou-Ba hydro-electric power station, successfully lifting the 500,000V ultra-high-voltage leading cable in this mountainous area. After appearing successfully

at the first World Hot-Air Airship Championships in Luxembourg in August 1988, one Bee-6 was sold to a customer in the UK.

DIMENSIONS:

Length overall	33.70 m (110 ft 6¾ in)
Length of gondola	3.60 m (11 ft 9¾ in)
Envelope diameter (max)	13.30 m (43 ft 7½ in)
Height overall, incl gondola	16.40 m (53 ft 9¾ in)
Horizontal stabiliser span	15.00 m (49 ft 2½ in)
Wheel track (gondola)	1.20 m (3 ft 11¼ in)
Propeller diameter	1.28 m (4 ft 2½ in)
Envelope volume, gross	2,983 m³ (105,344¼ cu ft)

WEIGHTS:

Weight empty	325 kg (716 lb)
Max T-O weight	740 kg (1,631 lb)

PERFORMANCE:

Max level speed at S/L	19 knots (35 km/h; 22 mph)
Cruising speed at S/L	13.5 knots (25 km/h; 15.5 mph)
Max rate of climb at S/L, 15°C	120 m (394 ft)/min
Min turning radius	50 m (164 ft)
Design ceiling	3,000 m (9,840 ft)
Range with max fuel	16 nm (30 km; 18.5 miles)

FRANCE

AERAZUR

AERAZUR (Member company of the Groupe Zodiac)
Division Equipements Aéronautiques
58 boulevard Galliéni, 92137 Issy-les-Moulineaux
Telephone: 33 (1) 45 54 92 80
Telex: 270 887 F
Fax: 33 (1) 45 57 99 85

CHIEF EXECUTIVE OFFICER: Jean Louis Gerondeau
INTERNATIONAL MARKETING MANAGER: Jean-Pierre Fetu

Aerazur began building lighter than air craft before the Second World War, and in the 1960s manufactured the world's largest non-rigid kite balloons (up to 15,000 m³; 529,720 cu ft), which were used for tests in the atmosphere of French nuclear weapons. It has made a series of small Vénus balloons for the French space agency CNES, as well as very large stratosphere research balloons of up to one

million m³ (35,314,720 cu ft) in volume. Recent programmes have included development of a surveillance balloon carrying a Thomson-CSF radar, and barrage balloons for anti-aircraft defence. Aerazur designs and manufactures envelopes for the Airship Industries Skyship 500 and 600 series, and is associated in designing the envelope for the Sentinel 5000 airship for the US Navy.

GERMANY, WEST

GEFA-FLUG

GEFA-FLUG GmbH
Weststrasse 14, 5100 Aachen
Telephone: 49 (241) 874026
Fax: 49 (241) 875206
MANAGING DIRECTOR: Karl Ludwig Busemeyer

Gefa-Flug has been operating advertising, filming and passenger-carrying balloons and airships since 1975. It has provided camera platforms for nationwide networks such as the BBC, WDR and ZDF. Various archaeological research projects have been undertaken in about a dozen countries including France, Germany, Italy, Oman, Pakistan, Syria and Turkey. The company currently operates seven hot-air balloons, one manned hot-air airship, and several remotely controlled LTA systems.

A leading part of Gefa-Flug's activities consists of aerial photogrammetry, in collaboration with the environmental research department of the German Mining Museum in Bochum, to obtain various kinds of data from low altitude. More than 70 of Gefa-Flug's remotely controlled balloons and airships have been sold worldwide; two of its airships used for such work were described and illustrated in the 1988-89 *Jane's*.

GEFA-FLUG AS 80 GD

Together with important international environmental research organisations, Gefa-Flug was working in 1990 on a

Gefa-Flug AS 80 GD two-seat hot-air environmental research airship

two-seat hot-air airship designated AS 80 GD, to be used worldwide in various environmental research projects. It is also expected to be a highly cost-effective advertising medium.

POWER PLANT: One 38.8 kW (52 hp) Rotax 462.

DIMENSIONS:

Length overall	36.00 m (118 ft 1¼ in)
Height overall, incl gondola	13.50 m (44 ft 3½ in)
Envelope volume	2,250 m³ (79,458 cu ft)

WEIGHT:

Max payload	100 kg (220 lb)

PERFORMANCE:

Max level speed	25 knots (46 km/h; 29 mph)
Max endurance	3 h

WDL

WESTDEUTSCHE LUFTWERBUNG THEODOR WÜLLENKEMPER KG (WDL Flugdienst GmbH and WDL Luftschiff GmbH)
Flughafen Essen-Mülheim, 4330 Mülheim/Ruhr
Telephone: 49 (208) 378080
Telex: 856810
Fax: 49 (208) 3780833 (Management)
49 (208) 3780841 (Operations)
MANAGING DIRECTOR: Theodor Wüllenkemper
CHIEF DESIGNER: Richard Gründer

Fifteen years after building its last (WDL 1) airship, WDL began airship construction again in 1987 with the first batch of a new design known as the WDL 1B. In addition to its airship activities, WDL operates and maintains six Fokker F27 transport aircraft, based in Düsseldorf and used on passenger/cargo flights within Europe.

WDL 1B

The WDL 1B, of which 10 had been completed by early 1990 (including two for Mitsui in Japan and two for customers in the USA) first flew (D-LDPF) on 30 August 1988. This airship, named *Asahi*, was delivered to Mitsui in mid-September of that year.

One of the largest non-rigid airships in the world, the WDL 1B has two ballonets (40 per cent air-filled) and carries 300 litres (79.25 US gallons; 66 Imp gallons) of water ballast. The new-design gondola, built by Gomolzig of Wuppertal, can accommodate up to eight passengers and features improved control instrumentation compared with the earlier WDL 1. Ballonet valves are actuated by a digital computer which indicates gas temperature and pressure; on *Asahi*, the coloured advertising graphics are also

WDL 1B eight-passenger non-rigid (two Continental IO-360-CD flat-six engines)

computer-controlled. This airship also carries a 9,000-bulb night sign. Later WDL 1Bs are expected to be fitted with a fly by wire flight control system, although this had not been certificated up to early 1990.

POWER PLANT: Two 157 kW (210 hp) Continental IO-360-CD flat-six engines, each driving a two-blade propeller. Total fuel capacity (two tanks) 400 litres (105.7 US gallons; 88 Imp gallons).

DIMENSIONS, ENVELOPE:

Length overall	59.90 m (196 ft 6¼ in)
Max diameter	16.40 m (53 ft 9¾ in)
Volume	6,904 m³ (243,813 cu ft)

DIMENSIONS, GONDOLA:

Length overall	7.60 m (24 ft 11¼ in)
Width: top	2.10 m (6 ft 10¾ in)
bottom	1.30 m (4 ft 3¼ in)
Height: excl landing gear	2.53 m (8 ft 3½ in)
incl landing gear	3.68 m (12 ft 1 in)

WEIGHTS:

Hull weight	2,000 kg (4,409 lb)
Max payload	1,290 kg (2,844 lb)
Weight empty	7,058 kg (15,560 lb)

PERFORMANCE:

Never-exceed speed	48 knots (90 km/h; 60 mph)
Max manoeuvring speed	35 knots (65 km/h; 40 mph)
Max endurance	22 h

ITALY

PAOLO BONANNO
BALLOONS SERVICE DI BONANNO LETTERIO

Via Volo 3/A, 12036 Revello (CN)
Telephone: 39 (175) 75666
Fax: 39 (175) 759313

Mr Bonanno's repair station for hot-air balloons and airships has been operating as a balloon homebuilder since 1980. He started co-operating with Cameron Balloons Ltd (see UK part of this section) in 1985, contributing experience in flight, construction and technology; he has since developed new products that he manufactures for Cameron, such as the Bonanno quick release device for take-off, the Bonanno modified Rego 7553 valve, and the Bonanno blast valve manifold system (the Mk 4 Super).

Mr Bonanno's AX-8 class hot-air balloon I-PAAM (see tables at the end of this section) was being used in 1989 as a testbed for a new Mk 4 Super double burner for Cameron, with hydraulic remote control and manifold valve.

BONANNO RBX-7

Mr Bonanno started work in 1988 on the prototype of a hot-air airship, known as the **RBX-7**. First flight was scheduled to take place in July 1989, but no confirmation of this had been received by Spring 1990. This two-place craft (I-AIRS) was designed as a testbed for a new system in envelope pressurisation and flight controls. All controls are electric, using a single multi-function control stick for steering, trim adjustment and propeller tilting. The burner is a special double unit with hydraulic control.

POWER PLANT: One 22.4 kW (30 hp) KFM 107 Maxi two-cylinder two-stroke engine.
DIMENSIONS, ENVELOPE:
Length	approx 34.0 m (111 ft 6½ in)
Max diameter	approx 12.0 m (39 ft 4½ in)
Volume	2,800 m³ (98,881 cu ft)

Gondola of the Bonanno RBX-7

General arrangement of the Bonanno RBX-7 hot-air airship *(Jane's/Mike Keep)*

MEXICO

SPACIAL
SERVICIOS PUBLICITARIOS AÉREOS CONSTRUCCIÓN E INGENIERÍA DE AERONAVES LIGERAS SA de CV

Margaritas 312-8, Colonia Florida, Mexico DF 01030
Telephone: 52 (5) 524 7262
CHAIRMAN: Lic Ramón González Parra
DIRECTOR GENERAL: Ing Mario Sánchez Roldán
CONSTRUCTION MANAGER: Arno Gjumlich Navarro

SPACIAL MLA-32-B TOLUCA

Research, development and design work on this unusual rigid airship (MLA is an abbreviation of the Spanish for 'lighter than air') began in 1973. The MLA-24-A prototype was nearing completion in the Spring of 1985 but was destroyed in a tornado before it could make its first flight. Details and illustrations of the MLA-24-A were published in the 1985-86 *Jane's*.

By early 1986 construction of the larger MLA-32-A (XB-RGP: see 1988-89 *Jane's*) had begun on a new site at Toluca, 64 km (40 miles) south-west of Mexico City, where the first flight was originally set for 19 December 1986. This was delayed by sabotage, but the repaired craft was ready to begin test flying in mid-March 1987, only to be damaged again by hurricane winds. The first take-off was eventually made on 12 February 1988, inadvertently, due to the Toluca breaking free from its mooring mast while final adjustments for a crewed first flight were being made to the port engine. Although damage was confined to the gondola and one split gas cell, Spacial decided to build an entirely new structure, designated MLA-32-B. This airship made its first flight on 24 June 1989.

The envelope/hull of the MLA-32-B consists of an ellipsoid frame of 6063-T6 aluminium tube and steel, with an aluminium tube structure at the equator and stamped aluminium halves forming a sandwich above and below the tubular intersections. The hull is covered with a protective layer of foam plastics and an outer skin of polyester fabric, and is of NACA 0012 aerofoil section. Inside the frame are six helium cells and a lead shot ballast system. At the rear is a tail assembly comprising three fins (the outer two with rudders), bridged at their tops by a wide span tailplane with elevator. Kevlar rope webbing is used throughout the aluminium tubing, to ensure a very strong mooring cone. Kevlar cables connect the hull to the new gondola, which is of chrome molybdenum steel tube, Styrofoam and acrylic materials with inner and outer skins of Kevlar. The gondola accommodates a pilot and three passengers, and is intended only as a control module, to which various custom-designed containers can be attached. It is equipped with two Honeywell (Sperry) inclinometers, which can be coupled to a computer for left/right and front/rear manoeuvring control.

Power plant comprises a pair of 82 kW (110 hp) Hirth two-stroke engines, which can be swivelled through 140° (120° down/20° up) to provide thrust vectoring for manoeuvring.

DIMENSIONS, EXTERNAL:
Hull diameter	32.0 m (105 ft 0 in)
Hull depth (max)	10.67 m (35 ft 0 in)
Hull volume	5,944 m³ (209,910 cu ft)
Height overall (incl gondola and wheel)	
	13.87 m (45 ft 6 in)

WEIGHTS:
Gondola, incl control and ballast system	204 kg (449 lb)
Lead ballast	184 kg (405 lb)
Total weight empty (excl ballast)	2,944 kg (6,490 lb)
Max T-O weight	6,100 kg (13,448 lb)

LIFT:
Dynamic lift (thrust)	879 kg (1,938 lb)
Useful lift (static) at 305 m (1,000 ft)	
	2,650 kg (5,842 lb)
Total vertical lift	3,422 kg (7,544 lb)
Gross lift at 4,591 m³ (162,130 cu ft) inflation	
	4,581 kg (10,099 lb)

PERFORMANCE:
Cruising speed	50 knots (93 km/h; 57.5 mph)
Rate of sink, power off	0.20 m (0.66 ft)/s

Spacial MLA-32-B Toluca elliptical hull airship, first flown in June 1989

UNION OF SOVIET SOCIALIST REPUBLICS

DEMENTYEV

Moscow
CHIEF DESIGNER: Pyotr Dementyev

DEMENTYEV DS-3

The DS-3 multi-purpose transport airship, currently under development in the USSR, is planned to make its first flight in 1992. It is a helium filled semi-rigid, with cruciform tail unit and an internally rigged envelope made of rubber coated Lavsan fabric. The gondola carries a crew of two, and can seat up to eight more people in its passenger version. As a cargo lifter, it can transport up to 3,000 kg (6,614 lb) in the cargo hold or up to 2,000 kg (4,409 lb) of externally slung bulky load. The twin engines, of unknown type, have ducted propellers, one each side of the rear of the gondola, that can be vectored 120° upward and 120° downward.

DIMENSIONS, ENVELOPE:
Length overall	62.00 m (203 ft 5 in)
Max diameter	15.00 m (49 ft 2½ in)
Volume	8,040 m³ (283,930 cu ft)

WEIGHT:
Structural weight empty	4,500 kg (9,921 lb)

PERFORMANCE (estimated):
Max level speed	54 knots (100 km/h; 62 mph)

Preliminary drawing of the Dementyev DS-3 passenger/cargo airship *(Jane's/Mike Keep)*

Max cruising speed	43 knots (80 km/h; 50 mph)
Max operating altitude	3,000 m (9,850 ft)
Range at cruising speed of 38 knots (70 km/h; 43 mph)	1,080 nm (2,000 km; 1,243 miles)

Endurance at cruising speed of 38 knots (70 km/h; 43 mph) 29 h

MAI

MOSCOW AVIATION INSTITUTE
DIRECTOR: Yuri A. Ryzhov

THERMOPLANE

Currently in the design definition stage, with a proof-of-concept (POC) vehicle scheduled to fly in 1993, the Thermoplane is the subject of an extensively funded Soviet government programme to develop a heavy-lift airship to transport bulky cargo (eg for construction, logging or mining) in remote areas. It has a disc-shaped envelope with elliptical cross-section, with a unique two-gas lift system. The centre portion of the envelope would be occupied by helium-filled spheres, while the remainder would be filled with natural gas. Hot air bled from the Thermoplane's twin turboshaft engines would be used to heat the natural gas, as required, to augment the basic lift provided by the helium spheres, while smaller engines fore and aft would generate additional lift and control in conjunction with horizontal and vertical control surfaces. Using this configuration, MAI has estimated that a full-size vehicle with a 200 m (656 ft) diameter should be able to lift a payload of some 550 t (1.1 million lb), on a cargo platform slung beneath the gondola.

The POC Thermoplane is intended to utilise two 298 kW (400 shp) Isotov GTD-350 turboshafts from an Mi-2 helicopter as its primary power plant, with the flight deck/cabin portion of the Mi-2 serving as the gondola. This testbed will have an envelope diameter of about 36-40 m (118-131 ft), and a T-O weight of 8,500 kg (18,740 lb) including a 2,150 kg (4,740 lb) payload. Performance expectations include a max speed of 43 knots (80 km/h; 50 mph) and ceiling of 2,000 m (6,560 ft).

UNITED KINGDOM

ADVANCED AIRSHIP

ADVANCED AIRSHIP CORPORATION
Airship Facility, Jurby, Isle of Man
Telephone: 44 (624) 897962
Telex: 627835 AIRSHP G
Fax: 44 (624) 897006
MANAGING DIRECTOR: John Hooper
MARKETING MANAGER: B. Begley
PUBLIC RELATIONS: Rosie Bailey

The Advanced Airship Corporation is a CAA approved company for the design and manufacture of non-rigid airships and is currently building the Advanced Non-Rigid (ANR) airship at Jurby, Isle of Man, where development and flight testing are also undertaken.

The ANR is designed to fulfil many roles in the commercial, defence and paramilitary fields. Commercial roles are essentially tourism and civil flights, and the airship's high speed capability will allow the ANR to be a contender for regular scheduled flights. Defence and paramilitary uses are mainly as surveillance and sensor platforms. Possible applications range from airborne early warning and anti-submarine warfare to coastguard patrols and fishery law enforcement. Long time on station, excellent crew cabin accommodation and low noise enhance the usefulness of the ANR for the defence and paramilitary market.

ADVANCED AIRSHIP ANR

The ANR airship is a 20/30-seat passenger airship which can also operate in many defence and paramilitary roles. It has a potential on-station endurance of 77 hours at a patrol speed of 30 knots (56 km/h; 34 mph). The envelope is manufactured by Thunder & Colt. First flight was scheduled during 1990.

TYPE: Non-rigid helium filled airship.

ENVELOPE: Conventional non-rigid ellipsoidal design, manufactured from aramid fabric coated with titanium oxide pigmented polyurethane. Four catenary curtains and 24 catenary cables terminate at four vertical load points on the gondola; 52 lateral load connections are also made to the gondola frames. Solid nose carapace replaces conventional batten arrangements at nose. One ballonet in nose and one in rear of hull, supplied by two single stage axial flow fans each capable of delivering 170 m³ (6,000 cu ft)/min.

TAIL UNIT: Four equally spaced tail fins, in X configuration, all four with ruddervators for pitch and yaw control. The fins are made from metallic honeycomb ribs with tubular spars and are fabric covered. The ruddervators are built entirely from Kevlar faced honeycomb panels.

POWER PLANT: Two 313 kW (420 shp) Allison 250-B17C turboprops, mounted on stub-wings attached to gondola and each driving a Hartzell HC-B3TF-7A/T10173 three-blade propeller. Entire wing/propulsion unit can rotate from 0° to 75° up to vector thrust. Standard fuel capacity 1,438 litres (380 US gallons; 316 Imp gallons), contained in three tanks in stub wings and a collector tank at base of equipment bay. Provision for extra fuel in removable tanks in cargo hold.

ACCOMMODATION: Crew of two on gondola flight deck. Main cabin can accommodate a variety of passenger layouts, ranging from 14 in a 7-pair twin dining alcove arrangement to 28 in a four-abreast layout, all with a central aisle, plus provision for one or two cabin attendants. Toilet and galley installations to customer's requirements. Large baggage hold at rear of gondola. All-cargo interior available optionally. For military and paramilitary use, gondola can be equipped with crew quarters and fitted out with many sensors and recording devices. Radar antennae can be mounted inside the envelope, with the display located inside the gondola.

Model of the Advanced Airship ANR; full-size version was due to fly in 1990

DIMENSIONS:
Length overall	60.96 m (200 ft 0 in)
Height overall, incl gondola	18.90 m (62 ft 0 in)
Envelope: Max diameter	15.24 m (50 ft 0 in)
Volume	7,270 m³ (256,724 cu ft)
Ballonet volume (two, total)	1,753 m³ (61,922 cu ft)
Fin area (total, net)	116.8 m² (1,257 sq ft)
Gondola: Length	13.66 m (44 ft 9½ in)
Max width	2.84 m (9 ft 4 in)
Max height	2.35 m (7 ft 8½ in)
Propeller diameter	2.29 m (7 ft 6 in)

Gondola passenger cabin:
Length of seating area	6.71 m (22 ft 0 in)
Max width	2.67 m (8 ft 9 in)
Min height	2.35 m (7 ft 8½ in)

WEIGHTS:
Weight empty	3,371 kg (7,432 lb)
Fuel: standard	1,134 kg (2,500 lb)
minimum	590 kg (1,300 lb)

Payload (typical):
26 passengers, plus cabin attendants and baggage, or max cargo, with min fuel	3,052 kg (6,728 lb)
Max T-O weight	7,167 kg (15,800 lb)

PERFORMANCE (estimated, at 915 m; 3,000 ft, ISA):
Max level speed	80 knots (148 km/h; 92 mph)
Max cruising speed	78 knots (144 km/h; 90 mph)
Lower limit speed at max heaviness	24 knots (45 km/h; 28 mph)
Max rate of climb	610 m (2,000 ft)/min

Pressure ceiling: commercial   1,525 m (5,000 ft)
    coastal patrol   1,830 m (6,000 ft)
Range with standard fuel load of 1,134 kg (2,500 lb):
    at 30 knots (56 km/h; 34 mph)
        732 nm (1,356 km; 843 miles)
    at 50 knots (93 km/h; 57 mph)
        714 nm (1,323 km; 822 miles)
    at 70 knots (130 km/h; 81 mph)
        481 nm (891 km; 554 miles)

Range with increased fuel load of 3,402 kg (7,500 lb), provisions, and second crew:
    at 30 knots (56 km/h; 34 mph)
        2,316 nm (4,292 km; 2,667 miles)
    at 50 knots (93 km/h; 57 mph)
        2,166 nm (4,014 km; 2,494 miles)
    at 70 knots (130 km/h; 81 mph)
        1,443 nm (2,674 km; 1,662 miles)

Endurance, conditions as above:
   with standard fuel:
    at 30 knots (56 km/h; 34 mph)   24 h 24 min
    at 50 knots (93 km/h; 57 mph)   14 h 16 min
    at 70 knots (130 km/h; 81 mph)   6 h 53 min
   with additional fuel:
    at 30 knots (56 km/h; 34 mph)   77 h 12 min
    at 50 knots (93 km/h; 57 mph)   43 h 19 min
    at 70 knots (130 km/h; 81 mph)   20 h 37 min

AIRSHIP INDUSTRIES
AIRSHIP INDUSTRIES (UK) LTD

No. 1 Hangar, Cardington, Bedfordshire MK42 0TF
Telephone: 44 (234) 741901
Fax: 44 (234) 742234
MANAGING DIRECTOR:
   Rear-Admiral Edward J. Hogan Jr, USN (Ret'd)
TECHNICAL DIRECTOR: Roger Munk
MILITARY MARKETING MANAGER: Graham Winterbottom
MANAGER, PUBLIC RELATIONS: Claire Baker

Airship Industries is a CAA approved company for the design, manufacture and operation of non-rigid airships. Skyship 500 and 600 series airships are intended to satisfy requirements in the civil, government agency and military fields. The prime civil applications are for aerial advertising, promotional and pleasure flight operations. The government agency roles are essentially maritime surveillance and internal security. EEZ (exclusive economic zone) patrol, search and rescue and fishery protection, are logical applications. In all of these roles the extended endurance, low noise and vibration levels, large cabin space and low operating costs render the airship a cost-effective surveillance platform. By the beginning of 1990 the company had sold six airships, including two within the government agency market.

Due to the high volume of the gondola, which can house a thorough and sophisticated communications, navigation and sensor system, and the large dimensions of the envelope for mounting internal antennae, the airship also has considerable potential in such roles as maritime surveillance, electronic warfare and mine countermeasures.

Five Skyship 500s and nine 600s had been completed by the beginning of 1990.

AIRSHIP INDUSTRIES SKYSHIP 500

The first production Skyship 500 (G-BIHN, c/n 02) made its first flight, at RAE Cardington, Bedfordshire, on 28 September 1981. Operation was under a British CAA aerial work C of A initially, with a full transport category certificate awarded on 21 November 1984, and on 23 April 1986 Skyship 500-02 inaugurated the first scheduled airship passenger service for 49 years when it took off from Leavesden Airport for the first of four daily sightseeing flights over central London. The service continued to run until 15 June 1986, and was repeated, during 1987 and 1988, using the larger Skyship 600. The standard Skyship 500 civil configuration seats a pilot and up to seven passengers on five individual seats and a three-person seat at the rear.
ENVELOPE: The airship envelope is manufactured, by the Zodiac division of Aerazur in France, from a single ply polyester fabric, coated with a titanium dioxide loaded polyurethane to reduce ultraviolet degradation, and with a polyvinylidene chloride film bonded onto an inner coating of polyurethane on the inside of the envelope to minimise loss of helium gas. Two ballonets, which together comprise 26 per cent of the envelope volume, are installed fore and aft, so that differential inflation will provide static fore and aft trim. There is a ballonet air intake aft of each propulsor unit. Four parabolic

Airship Industries Skyship 600, currently operated in the Far East for surveillance and advertising

arch load curtains carry multiple Kevlar 29 gondola suspension cables and peripheral bolt rope. The nose structure consists of a domed disc, moulded from GFRP and carrying the fitting by which the airship is moored to its mast. The tail unit is of conventional cruciform layout, each surface being attached to the envelope at its root and braced by wires on each side. All four surfaces are constructed from interlocking ribs and spars of Fibrelam and have GFRP skins: their hinged rudder and elevator control surfaces are cable operated, and each has a spring tab. A full-authority fly by light control system is also available (see Skyship 600 entry for details).
GONDOLA: One-piece moulding of Kevlar reinforced plastics, with flooring and bulkheads of Fibrelam panels; those which form the engine compartment at the rear are faced with titanium for fire protection. There is accommodation for a pilot and co-pilot, with dual controls, although the airship is designed to be flown by a single pilot. Ballast is contained in a box situated below the crew seats, and disposable water ballast is contained in tanks at the rear. On the ground, the airship rests on a single two-wheeled assembly with double tyres, mounted beneath the rear part of the gondola.
POWER PLANT: Two 152 kW (204 hp) Porsche 930/10 six-cylinder aircooled piston engines mounted in the rear of the gondola. Each drives a ducted propulsor consisting of a Hoffmann five-blade reversible-pitch propeller rotating within an annular duct constructed of GFRP, reinforced with carbonfibre. Each propulsor can be rotated about its pylon attachment to the gondola

through an arc of 210°: 90° upward and 120° downward. The vectored thrust available gives the airship a V/STOL capability, as well as in-flight hovering ability. A fuel tank is mounted at the rear of the engine compartment. Engine modifications include provision of automatic mixture control, fuel injection and electronic ignition.
SYSTEM AND AVIONICS: 28V electrical system, supplied by engine driven alternators. Avionics include Bendix/King Silver Crown series dual nav/com, ADF, Omega, VOR/ILS and weather radar.
DIMENSIONS, ENVELOPE:
Length overall	52.00 m (170 ft 7¼ in)
Max diameter	14.00 m (45 ft 11¼ in)
Height overall	18.66 m (61 ft 2½ in)
Tail fin span	17.00 m (55 ft 9 in)
Volume: gross	5,153 m³ (181,977 cu ft)
ballonets (total)	1,334 m³ (47,102 cu ft)

DIMENSIONS, GONDOLA:
Length overall	9.24 m (30 ft 3½ in)
Max width	2.41 m (7 ft 10¾ in)
Cabin: Length	4.20 m (13 ft 9½ in)
Height	1.96 m (6 ft 5 in)

WEIGHT:
Gross disposable load	1,260 kg (2,778 lb)

PERFORMANCE:
Max level speed	55 knots (101 km/h; 63 mph)
Cruising speed (50% power)	
	47 knots (87 km/h; 54 mph)
Pressure ceiling	3,050 m (10,000 ft)
Still air range at 40 knots (74 km/h; 46 mph)	
	470 nm (870 km; 541 miles)
Endurance	12 h

AIRSHIP INDUSTRIES SKYSHIP 500HL

The 500HL, first flown on 30 July 1987, is a higher lift airship which can operate with a greater payload in hotter climates and at higher altitudes than the Skyship 500. It is powered by two 152 kW (204 hp) Porsche 930 engines; fuel tank capacity is 545 litres (144 US gallons; 120 Imp gallons).
DIMENSIONS, ENVELOPE: As for Skyship 600
DIMENSIONS, GONDOLA: As for Skyship 500
WEIGHT:
Gross disposable load	2,190 kg (4,829 lb)

PERFORMANCE:
Max level speed	50 knots (93 km/h; 57 mph)
Cruising speed	up to 47 knots (87 km/h; 54 mph)
Pressure ceiling	3,050 m (10,000 ft)
Endurance at 35 knots (65 km/h; 40 mph)	17 h

AIRSHIP INDUSTRIES SKYSHIP 600

The Skyship 600, first flown on 6 March 1984, accommodates up to 13 passengers in its civil configuration, and adding turbochargers to the Porsche engines increases the available power to 190 kW (255 hp) per engine. Fuel capacity is increased to 682 litres (180 US gallons; 150 Imp gallons), and auxiliary fuel tanks are available as optional

Skyship 500HL (G-SKSB) heavy-lift airship at its Cardington base

equipment. A special category C of A was awarded by the UK CAA on 1 September 1984. Aerial work certification was received in the Spring of 1986, and on 8 January 1987 the Skyship 600 became the world's only airship with full passenger certification. This initiated the Skycruise aerial sightseeing service over London, San Francisco, Munich and Sydney in 1987, and over Paris in 1988. The first US FAA type certificate awarded to an airship for civil use was issued to the Skyship 600 in May 1989.

The world's first full-authority fly by light system, developed in conjunction with GEC Avionics, was successfully flown on 23 October 1988 on Skyship 600-04 (G-SKSF) at Airship Industries' Weeksville base in the USA. The system incorporates a digital flight control computer, and is highly resistant to electro-magnetic interference and lightning strikes, while greatly reducing pilot workload. The system will be fitted to the US Navy Sentinel 1000 and 5000 airships (see separate entries), and can be incorporated into the specification for smaller airships as required. A sidestick control is fitted in place of the original conventional yoke control.

DIMENSIONS, ENVELOPE:

Length overall	59.00 m (193 ft 7 in)
Max diameter	15.20 m (49 ft 10½ in)
Height overall	20.30 m (66 ft 7¼ in)
Tail fin span	19.20 m (63 ft 0 in)
Volume: gross	6,666 m³ (235,400 cu ft)
ballonets (total)	1,733 m³ (61,200 cu ft)

DIMENSIONS, GONDOLA:

Length overall	11.67 m (38 ft 3½ in)
Max width	2.56 m (8 ft 4¾ in)
Cabin: Length	6.89 m (22 ft 7¼ in)
Height	1.92 m (6 ft 3½ in)
Floor area (usable)	12.00 m² (130.0 sq ft)

WEIGHT (design):

Gross disposable load	2,343 kg (5,165 lb)

PERFORMANCE:

Max level speed	58 knots (107 km/h; 67 mph)
Cruising speed (70% power)	52 knots (96 km/h; 60 mph)
Pressure ceiling	3,050 m (10,000 ft)
Still air range at 40 knots (74 km/h; 46 mph), without auxiliary tanks	550 nm (1,019 km; 633 miles)

AIRSHIP INDUSTRIES SENTINEL 1000

Driven by a market requirement for a vehicle with greater payload capability, endurance, speed and flexibility to better perform such military and naval roles as mine countermeasures, airborne early warning and anti-submarine warfare, considerable progress has been made in the development of this new addition to the existing product range. A derivative of the Skyship 600, the Sentinel 1000 (or 600S as it is called in its civil variant) has an envelope capacity of just over 10,000 m³, a higher performance engine, and will be equipped with the world's first fly by light optical fibre flight control system, developed by GEC Avionics.

As, in many areas, the Sentinel 1000 represents a half-linear-scale version of the YEZ-2A under development for the US Navy (see following entry), it will provide a useful tool for development and optimisation for the US Navy programme, and as such has been designated the official trials vehicle. Until the YEZ-2A is completed the Sentinel 1000 will be the largest non-rigid airship flying, combining substantial increase in payload, improved flight control through the autopilot/autostabilisation elements of the YEZ-2A flight control system, and upgrading of the general vehicle avionics. First flight trials of the Sentinel 1000 were scheduled to take place in mid-1990.

DIMENSIONS, ENVELOPE:

Length overall	67.50 m (221 ft 5½ in)
Max diameter	16.70 m (54 ft 9½ in)
Height overall	20.20 m (66 ft 3¼ in)
Volume: gross	10,022 m³ (353,924 cu ft)
ballonets (total)	2,405 m³ (84,932 cu ft)

DIMENSIONS, GONDOLA: As for Skyship 600

DESIGN WEIGHT:

Gross disposable load	3,875 kg (8,543 lb)

PERFORMANCE (estimated):

Max level speed	57 knots (105 km/h; 65 mph)
Cruising speed (70% power)	50 knots (92 km/h; 57 mph)
Still air range at 36 knots (67 km/h; 41 mph), with long-endurance tanks	2,400 nm (4,448 km; 2,764 miles)

AIRSHIP INDUSTRIES SENTINEL 5000
US Navy designation: YEZ-2A

Six-month study contracts were placed in mid-1985 with three US companies (Boeing Military Airplanes, Goodyear and Westinghouse), to investigate the suitability of airships for use by the US Navy in an independent airborne early warning role.

The Navy requirement is for an independent airborne early warning system capable of operating with surface attack groups anywhere in the world. Primary functions were described by the Naval Air Development Center as "detection, classification, identification and tracking of surface and airborne targets, particularly those of low radar cross-section, flying at low altitude and high speed in a sea clutter environment, and communications connectivity

General configuration of the YEZ-2A Sentinel 5000, now with X configuration tail unit

Ground test vehicle for the YEZ-2A Sentinel 5000 gondola and propulsion system, at Weeksville, North Carolina

between surface ships in a battle group". The surveillance system would warn surface ships of threats beyond the range of shipboard radars, including long-range sea-skimming cruise missiles.

Because of the independent operations required of the surveillance systems, and the long endurance required to accompany a naval force, an airship was considered the only feasible solution. It would be equipped with a large, long-range radar carried internally, the size of which would largely dictate the size of the airship.

All three study contractors responded initially to the USN request for proposals issued in August 1986, but Boeing (whose design was the only rigid airship submitted) subsequently withdrew, leaving Goodyear and the Westinghouse/Airship Industries partnership as the final contenders. Award of a $168.9 million contract to WAI for an operational development model (ODM) airship, based on the Airship Industries Sentinel 5000 design, was announced by NASC on 5 June 1987. Originally, the contract envisaged the installation of an E-2C Hawkeye avionics suite, but this is now unlikely to be used. Up to early 1990 an alternative suite had still to be selected. The ODM vehicle will have an unrefuelled endurance of 2-3 days; by refuelling and replenishing from surface units within a task force, a mission capability of some 30 days is intended. Designated USN missions are surveillance and targeting, airborne early warning, and communications.

The NASC contract included options for up to five additional airships, and the potential production programme could involve up to 50 of these craft. Defence budget cuts led to stop-work orders on the naval airship programme in April 1988, but these early funding problems were resolved in the following month. First flight of the ODM prototype is now planned for November 1993, with subsequent flight and operational test programmes to be decided when more is known about the proposed avionics suite. Final assembly and initial flight testing will take place in the USA.

Based on earlier Airship Industries studies for very large airships, the Sentinel 5000 will be the largest non-rigid ever constructed, and will carry a crew of 10-15 in a multi-deck, wide-bodied and pressurised gondola. The upper deck will provide living accommodation for the crew, including double cabins, showers, separate wardroom galley, and a small gymnasium. Mission avionics, control information centre, galley, replenishment stores and refuelling equipment will occupy the lower deck. Below these two is a smaller flight deck containing the flight controls and instrumentation. The envelope will be made of a single-ply

Dacron weave material, laminated with Tedlar and Mylar and bonded with Hytrel. The X configuration tail unit will have two control surfaces per fin, each control surface having two actuators and triple hinges. The control actuation will have full autostabilisation and autopilot provided by GEC Avionics computer controlled, optically signalled fly by light system. The system, using two MIL-STD-1750A standard computers and a MIL-STD-1553B databus, will provide redundant fail-safe actuation of the movable tail surfaces via fibre-optic signalling, automatic stability and good handling characteristics throughout the flight regime, hands-off autopilot control for cruising, hovering and mooring, and automatic speed control.

An unpressurised engine room aft contains a CODAG (combined diesel and gas turbine) propulsion system, comprising an internally mounted pair of 1,394 kW (1,870 hp) ducted propulsion CRM diesel units, with thrust vectoring, plus a 1,394 kW (1,870 shp) General Electric CT7-9 turboprop, mounted on the gondola centreline at the rear, to provide additional power when a higher dash speed is required. A substantial winching bay is located between the engine room aft and pressurised accommodation section forward, from where refuelling, re-storing and personnel transfers will be conducted through a large opening in the base of the gondola.

Two preliminary design reviews (PDRs) of the ODM programme were held in late January and June 1989, and the subsequent critical design review (CDR) was held in September 1989. These briefings, on the design status of the airship, were attended by representatives of the US Navy, DARPA and the Naval Air Development Center.

DIMENSIONS, ENVELOPE:

Length overall	129.54 m (425 ft 0 in)
Max diameter	32.00 m (105 ft 0 in)
Height overall	41.15 m (135 ft 0 in)
Volume, gross	70,864 m³ (2,502,540 cu ft)

DIMENSIONS, GONDOLA:

Length	24.18 m (79 ft 4 in)
Max width	5.08 m (16 ft 8 in)
Max height	7.32 m (24 ft 0 in)

PERFORMANCE (estimated):

Max level speed (3 engines)	90 knots (167 km/h; 103 mph)
Operating height range	S/L to 3,050 m (10,000 ft)
Pressure ceiling	4,270 m (14,000 ft)
Max unrefuelled endurance at 40 knots (74 km/h; 46 mph) at 1,525 m (5,000 ft)	more than 60 h
Mission capability	30 days

CAMERON
CAMERON BALLOONS LTD

St John's Street, Bedminster, Bristol BS3 4NH
Telephone: 44 (272) 637216
Telex: 44138
Fax: 44 (272) 661168
MANAGING DIRECTOR:
  D. A. Cameron, BSc (Aero Eng), MIE, MRAeS
SALES DIRECTOR: Philip Dunnington, BA

Cameron began manufacturing hot-air balloons in 1968 and holds CAA, FAA, French CNT and West German Musterzulassungsschein type certificates for its balloons. By January 1990 it had produced some 2,300 balloons at two UK factories (Bristol and Harrogate), plus about 500 more under licence in the USA by its factory at Dexter, Michigan. Output includes more than 110 specially shaped balloons for advertising purposes. In 1986-87 the O-120, N-133, and N-145 models were introduced to cater for increasing demand for passenger carrying balloons, and in August 1987 the N-850, with a double-deck basket, achieved a new world record of 45 passengers carried in a balloon. The company developed the ULD-1 helium filled pressure balloon for Mr Nott (see 'Endeavour' entry in the 1987-88 *Jane's*), and is making the envelope (now 90 per cent complete) for the full size *Endeavour*. Cameron's current range of commercial balloons is listed in the tables at the end of this section. In 1990 the company planned to open in Moscow a new balloon factory as a joint venture with a Soviet company, with an anticipated production of 50 balloons in its first year.

Cameron Balloons Ltd also designs and produces hot-air airships, being the first company to develop a craft of this type. Production hot-air airships now include the pressurised DP series. Helium filled airships have included the DG-19 single-seater and DG-25 two-seater, both now superseded by the single-seat DG-14.

CAMERON DP SERIES

First flown in April 1986, the DP prototype (G-BMEZ) was the first of a new generation of pressurised hot-air airships, differing from earlier airships of this kind in utilising a single engine for both propulsion and pressure control. In the event of an engine failure the DP series can be flown unpressurised, and landed like a hot-air balloon. Twin silencers are fitted, to minimise the engine noise level. The DP series has a new, specially designed gondola, and is equipped with an ergonomically designed cockpit and a unique Cameron self-regulating pressure control system. The DP 60 and DP 70 can carry one or two persons, and Cameron has added the two-place DP 80 and DP 90 to the range for hot and high operation. Figures in the designations indicate approximate envelope volume in thousands of cubic feet.

By 1 January 1990 Cameron had completed, in addition to the DP 50 prototype, one DP 60 and 10 DP 70s; customer countries comprised Belgium, Chile, Luxembourg, Switzerland, the UK, the USA and Venezuela. DP 90s have been sold to customers in Australia, Brazil, West Germany and Switzerland.

GONDOLA: All-aluminium structure, seating one or two persons will full-harness seat belts. Full height polycarbonate windscreen.
POWER PLANT: One 21 kW (28 hp) König SD 570 four-cylinder two-stroke engine, driving a three-blade König shrouded pusher propeller. Fuel capacity 22.7 litres (6 US gallons; 5 Imp gallons) of 40:1 two-stroke mixture.
EQUIPMENT: Instrumentation comprises manometer, rev counter, fuel contents gauge, voltmeter, variometer, altimeter and thermistor. 12V 30Ah battery standard. Propane fuel in two Worthington, Cameron 599 or Cameron 426 tanks, according to model, with respective capacities of 77.3, 86.4 or 104.6 litres (20.4, 22.8 or 27.6 US gallons; 17, 19 or 23 Imp gallons) per tank. Manual piezo-electric or electronic ignition.

DIMENSIONS, ENVELOPE:

Length overall: DP 50	28.35 m (93 ft 0 in)
DP 60	30.48 m (100 ft 0 in)
DP 70	32.31 m (106 ft 0 in)
DP 80	33.83 m (111 ft 0 in)
DP 90	35.05 m (115 ft 0 in)
Height: DP 50	12.80 m (42 ft 0 in)
DP 60	13.72 m (45 ft 0 in)
DP 70	14.63 m (48 ft 0 in)
DP 80	15.24 m (50 ft 0 in)
DP 90	15.54 m (51 ft 0 in)
Max width: DP 50	10.67 m (35 ft 0 in)
DP 60	11.28 m (37 ft 0 in)
DP 70	11.89 m (39 ft 0 in)
DP 80	12.19 m (40 ft 0 in)
DP 90	12.80 m (42 ft 0 in)
Volume, gross: DP 50	1,415.8 m³ (50,000 cu ft)
DP 60	1,699.0 m³ (60,000 cu ft)
DP 70	1,982.2 m³ (70,000 cu ft)
DP 80	2,265.3 m³ (80,000 cu ft)
DP 90	2,548.5 m³ (90,000 cu ft)
Max display area per side: DP 50	77.02 m² (829 sq ft)
DP 60	86.96 m² (936 sq ft)
DP 70	95.97 m² (1,033 sq ft)
DP 80	91.97 m² (990 sq ft)
DP 90	99.03 m² (1,066 sq ft)

Cameron DP 90 pressurised hot-air airship, largest in the DP series

WEIGHTS:

Gondola (all models)	195 kg (430 lb)
Envelope: DP 60	146 kg (322 lb)
Useful passenger load (S/L, 15°C): DP 50	90 kg (198 lb)
DP 60	149 kg (328 lb)
DP 70	222 kg (489 lb)
DP 80	285 kg (628 lb)
DP 90	359 kg (791 lb)
Max T-O weight: DP 50	452 kg (997 lb)
DP 60: one person	469 kg (1,034 lb)
two persons	546 kg (1,204 lb)
DP 70: one person	485 kg (1,069 lb)
two persons	562 kg (1,239 lb)

PERFORMANCE:

Max speed: DP 50	19 knots (35 km/h; 22 mph)
DP 60	15 knots (28 km/h; 17 mph)
Endurance: DP 50	1 h 30 min

CAMERON D-96

A description of the D-96, the world's first hot-air airship, can be found in the 1989-90 and many earlier editions of *Jane's*. It is no longer in production.

CAMERON DG-14

Tests of the two-man helium filled **DG-19** prototype (G-BK1K) during the Summer of 1983 convinced Cameron Balloons that the design offered a new formula for a 'minimum' low-cost airship.

Two DG-19s had been built by early 1990, with a third under construction, plus one example of the 708 m³ (25,000 cu ft) **DG-25**. Data for the DG-19 were given in the 1986-87 *Jane's*, and dimensions of the DG-25 in the 1987-88 edition.

Current model, which made its first flight (G-BRDU) in October 1989, is the single-seat **DG-14**, powered by a small two-stroke engine driving a single ducted fan and small enough to pass through the doors of a standard aircraft hangar. Major use is expected to be for advertising, but the

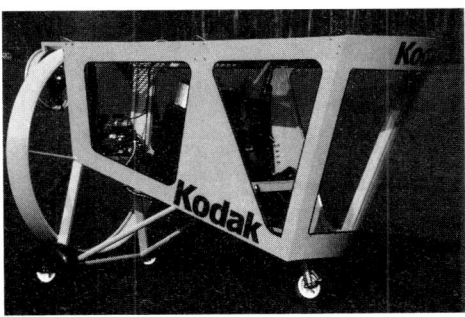

Gondola of the Cameron DP series

DG-14 could also find applications for surveillance or as a camera platform. It can be moored to a portable mast, but in adverse weather could be hangared without the loss of expensive helium that deflation would involve. British CAA certification trials were completed in November 1989.
ENVELOPE: Helium-filled, with main and tail ballonets, 0.305 m (12 in) manual gas valves, main and overpressure patch-type rip panels and ball type mast connection.
POWER PLANT: One 21 kW (28 hp) König SD 570 four-cylinder two-stroke engine, driving a six-blade ducted fan with pitch adjustment, flow straighteners and 40° thrust vectoring. Electric starting. Fuel capacity 22.7 litres (6 US gallons; 5 Imp gallons).
GONDOLA: Single-seat, with welded steel frame and aluminium skin. Three-wheeled landing gear.
DIMENSIONS:

Envelope: Length	19.00 m (62 ft 4 in)
Max diameter	6.86 m (22 ft 6 in)
Height overall, incl gondola	8.23 m (27 ft 0 in)
Volume	396.4 m³ (14,000 cu ft)
Banner area (each side): Length	9.50 m (31 ft 2 in)
Height	2.59 m (8 ft 6 in)

Newest and smallest Cameron helium airship, the single-seat DG-14

THUNDER & COLT

THUNDER & COLT LTD

Maesbury Road, Oswestry, Shropshire SY10 8HA
Telephone: 44 (691) 670644
Telex: 35503 COLT G
Fax: 44 (691) 670617
MANAGING DIRECTOR: Per Lindstrand
TECHNICAL DIRECTOR: Mark Broome
PRODUCTION DIRECTOR: Paul Dickinson
SALES AND MARKETING DIRECTOR: Chris Kirby
INFORMATION OFFICER: John Templeman

In addition to its current range of hot-air and helium airships described in this entry, Thunder & Colt was constructing in 1989 the envelope of the ANR airship described under the Advanced Airship Corporation heading in this section. Thunder & Colt also manufactures an extensive range of hot-air balloons (see details in tables at the end of this section), of which the 300A is currently the world's largest passenger-carrying balloon for regular operation. Current output totals more than 250 hot-air balloons and airships per year, of which over 80 per cent are exported. The 1987 *Virgin Atlantic Flyer*, at 60,315 m³ (2.13 million cu ft) the largest hot-air balloon ever manufactured and flown, was described in the 1987-88 *Jane's*. In a new 16,990 m³ (600,000 cu ft) high altitude balloon named *Stratoquest* the company's managing director, Mr Per Lindstrand, reached approx 19,812 m (65,000 ft) after take-off from Laredo, Texas, on 1 June 1988, a new world altitude record for hot-air balloons. In the same year, with its sister company Airborne Industries, Thunder & Colt built a new gas balloon known as the GB-1. The envelope of this balloon is tested and certificated for hydrogen/helium, methane and coal gas. Appearing for the first time at the 1988 World Gas Balloon Championships, it gained first place, crewed by Jo Starkbaum and Gert Scholz. Two weeks later, with the same crew, it won the 32nd Gordon Bennett race by the greatest margin in recent times; and won the same race again in 1989.

COLT AS 80 Mk II and AS 105 Mk II

The Colt AS 80 Mk II is currently the most popular of the Colt hot-air airships in production. It was developed and certificated in 1988, and 10 had been built by January 1990. The AS 105 Mk II uses the same gondola as the AS 80 Mk II, but has a larger envelope of 2,973.3 m³ (105,000 cu ft). An AS 80 Mk II won the Hot-Air Airship European Championships in France in 1989.

The envelope is manufactured in HTN90K high-tenacity and high temperature resistant fabric. It has a fineness ratio of 2.5, and four inflated fins in a cruciform configuration. Steering is by a single rudder on the bottom fin, operated by ropes connecting it to the gondola. The twin catenary load suspension system distributes the loads of gondola weight and power plant forces evenly into the envelope. The gondola is of aluminium panels over a stainless steel tubular spaceframe, with tricycle landing gear; pilot and passenger sit in tandem. In single-seat configuration, the passenger seat is exchanged for an extra fuel tank. The windscreen is

Colt AS 80 Mk II single/two-person thermal airship, winner of the 1989 European Championships

made from polycarbonate sheet, forming a partially enclosed cockpit.

The power plant is a 38.8 kW (52 hp) Rotax 462 two-cylinder watercooled engine driving a two-blade pusher propeller. The engine also drives a generator supplying an electric fan used to pressurise the envelope. Additional air for pressurisation of the envelope is taken from a scoop situated in the propeller slipstream. The burners are situated inside the envelope and operated electrically with a manual override. Pilot lights are fitted with electric spark and piezo-electric ignition and are specially modified to operate directly underneath the inflating fan without blowing out. Standard instrumentation comprises an altimeter, variometer, envelope temperature and pressure gauges, propane volume gauge, petrol level gauge, voltmeter, engine water temperature and engine rpm gauge. A 720-channel VHF com transceiver option, with pilot-passenger intercom, is available.

DIMENSIONS, ENVELOPE (A: AS 80 Mk II, B: AS 105 Mk II):

Length overall: A	31.00 m (101 ft 8½ in)
B	34.00 m (111 ft 6½ in)
Max diameter: A	12.40 m (40 ft 8¼ in)
B	13.87 m (45 ft 6 in)
Volume: A	2,123.8 m³ (75,000 cu ft)
B	2,973.3 m³ (105,000 cu ft)

DIMENSIONS, GONDOLA (both):

Length overall	3.84 m (12 ft 7¼ in)
Max width	1.75 m (5 ft 9 in)
Height overall	1.80 m (5 ft 11 in)
Propeller diameter	1.57 m (5 ft 2 in)

WEIGHTS (A: AS 80 Mk II, B: AS 105 Mk II):

Envelope: A	190 kg (419 lb)
B	213 kg (469 lb)
Gondola, empty: A, B	210 kg (463 lb)
Propane fuel: A, B	60-110 kg (132-242 lb)
Gross lift: A	600 kg (1,323 lb)

PERFORMANCE (A and B as above):

Max level speed: A, B	20 knots (37 km/h; 23 mph)
Max endurance: A, B	2 h 30 min

COLT AS 56

The AS 56 is the one-man hot-air airship available from Thunder & Colt. Construction largely follows the same lines as that of AS 80 Mk II, with a stainless steel tubular spaceframe and tricycle landing gear. The envelope is also of similar construction, with twin catenary curtains and cruciform tail surfaces. The power plant is a 21 kW (28 hp) König SC 570 four-cylinder two-stroke driving a two-blade pusher propeller.

Recently, the AS 56 envelope pressurisation system has been modified, and now incorporates a similar system to that used in the AS 80 Mk II, with electric fan and automatic pressure relief system. An airship of this type won the first Hot-Air Airship World Championships in Luxembourg in 1988.

DIMENSIONS, ENVELOPE:

Length overall	28.00 m (91 ft 10½ in)
Max diameter	11.20 m (36 ft 9 in)
Volume	1,585.75 m³ (56,000 cu ft)

DIMENSIONS, GONDOLA:

Length overall	2.75 m (9 ft 0¼ in)
Max width	1.50 m (4 ft 11 in)
Height overall	1.40 m (4 ft 7 in)
Propeller diameter	1.32 m (4 ft 4 in)

WEIGHTS:

Envelope	120 kg (265 lb)
Gondola	110 kg (242 lb)
Propane fuel	40 kg (88 lb)
Max T-O weight	365 kg (805 lb)

PERFORMANCE:

Max level speed	15 knots (28 km/h; 17 mph)
Max endurance	1 h 30 min

THUNDER & COLT AS 261

The largest hot-air airship ever flown, the AS 261 is also the first with cargo carrying capability. It is a scaled-up version of the AS 80 Mk II, heated by triple Colt Mk 2 burners, and has the same power plant as the GA 42 airship. The prototype, flown extensively during 1989, has seats for a further three crew, and has been operating over the jungle in French Guyana. In this operation a huge netting platform, spread over an inflatable support frame, was lowered onto the rain forest canopy to support the four-man team of scientists and their equipment without disturbing or damaging the environment. The platform and scientific payload had a total weight of 740 kg (1,631 lb).

DIMENSIONS, ENVELOPE:

Length overall	47.80 m (156 ft 10 in)
Max diameter	18.80 m (61 ft 8 in)
Height overall	20.40 m (66 ft 11 in)
Volume	7,391 m³ (261,000 cu ft)

DIMENSIONS, GONDOLA:

Length overall	3.90 m (12 ft 9½ in)
Max width	1.70 m (5 ft 7 in)
Height overall	1.80 m (5 ft 11 in)

WEIGHTS (TROPICS):

Envelope	375 kg (827 lb)
Gondola	530 kg (1,168 lb)
Max T-O weight	2,100 kg (4,630 lb)

World's largest hot-air airship, the AS 261, with netting and inflatable support platform for botanical investigation team

COLT GA 42

This helium filled dirigible is a project in which Thunder & Colt co-operates with its sister company Airborne Industries of Southend on Sea. Thunder & Colt undertook design and production of the gondola and design of the envelope; Airborne Industries was responsible for envelope manufacture.

The prototype (G-MATS) made its first flight on 2 September 1987. The type certificate was issued in May 1989 after an intensive testing and modification period. The design is certificated to BCAR CAP 471 Section Q in the aerial work category.

Four GA 42s were built and sold during 1989, and a further six were to be produced in 1990.

ENVELOPE: Helium-filled envelope of polyurethane coated polyamide, with ultra-violet blockage, hydrolysis proofed. Two air-filled ballonets (one forward, one aft), with max fill ratio of 25 per cent, inflated by an engine driven Porsche axial fan and controlled manually or (at pre-set levels) by an automatic pressure relief valve. Helium pressure relief valve operates automatically, but can be actuated manually in an emergency. Hull shape and stability maintained by two catenary curtains, which transfer weight loading to top of envelope. Four independent tail-fins, in cruciform configuration, are fabricated from GFRP composites and attached to hull by rigging wires. Movable control surface on all except upper vertical fin. Quick-release mooring by hard nose with 12 aluminium battens.

GONDOLA: All-aluminium riveted semi-monocoque structure, supported by seven catenary cables each side (three forward, four aft). Side by side bucket seats for crew of two, with full harnesses, on fully enclosed and heated flight deck; 180° single-curvature polycarbonate windscreen, plus observation window in roof for viewing airship interior. Fully castoring, rubber sprung single-wheel landing gear.

POWER PLANT: One 75 kW (100 hp) Teledyne Continental O-200-B flat-four engine, driving a Hoffmann four-blade fixed-pitch wood/composite pusher propeller. Fuel capacity 130 litres (34.3 US gallons; 28.6 Imp gallons).

SYSTEMS: Fly by wire flight control system, using three linear DC actuators; twin analog backup circuits.

Thunder & Colt GA 42 helium airships awaiting take-off on commercial advertising flights

Electrical systems powered by a 25Ah wet cell battery, charged via engine mounted alternators capable of delivering 60A at 14V DC. Ample battery power available to supply control systems for landing in the event of alternator failure.

AVIONICS: VHF nav/com, ADF, transponder, VOR, and ADF indicators. Instrument panel is roof-mounted in order not to obstruct all-round field of view.

DIMENSIONS, ENVELOPE:

Length	27.50 m (90 ft 2¾ in)
Max diameter	9.20 m (30 ft 2¼ in)
Height overall between fin-tips	11.20 m (36 ft 9 in)
Volume: gross	1,189.3 m³ (42,000 cu ft)
ballonets (total)	approx 311.5 m³ (11,000 cu ft)
Banner area (each side): Length	14.70 m (48 ft 2¾ in)
Height	7.50 m (24 ft 7¼ in)

DIMENSIONS, GONDOLA:

Length	3.44 m (11 ft 3½ in)
Max width	1.54 m (5 ft 0½ in)
Height: excl wheel	1.55 m (5 ft 1 in)
incl wheel	2.14 m (7 ft 0¼ in)

WEIGHTS:

Max static heaviness	100 kg (220 lb)
Design gross lift	1,100 kg (2,425 lb)

PERFORMANCE:

Cruising speed: max	40 knots (74 km/h; 46 mph)
normal	32 knots (60 km/h; 37 mph)
econ	27 knots (50 km/h; 31 mph)
Max rate of climb	396 m (1,299 ft)/min
Max rate of descent	456 m (1,496 ft)/min
Pressure ceiling (ISA)	2,900 m (9,515 ft)
Max endurance	7 h 30 min
Pitch angle limits	+30°/−25°

UNITED STATES OF AMERICA

ABC

AMERICAN BLIMP CORPORATION
18908 13th Place South, Seattle, Washington 98148
Telephone: 1 (206) 241 7422
PRESIDENT: James Thiele

ABC LIGHTSHIP A-50 and A-60

The Lightship series are lightweight advertising airships, designed for in the field assembly to minimise the need for expensive hangarage and long cross-country flights. They are illuminated internally for full-colour advertising displays. The four-place A-50 prototype first flew on 9 April 1988, and by the end of 1989 had flown some 700 hours, made 1,000 take-offs and landings, and carried about 500 people. A five-place A-60, of which four had been ordered by late 1989, is under development.

The envelope, made by Aerostar (Raven), is what ABC describes as "familiar Goodyear shape", having an outer structural cloth ply skin with a separate inner, disposable gas-tight bladder made of evenly extruded bare urethane film and a single urethane ballonet. All structural attachments to the sewn outer bag, such as nose mooring, fin base and guy wires, car catenary and handling lines, are made with webbing reinforcements sewn directly to the hull.

The Lightship has four fins, in cruciform configuration, identical to each other and cable controlled from the gondola with a rotational clearance of 9° during take-off. Both Lightship models use the same nose hardware, and moor to a standard mast.

The Lightship gondola is suspended by 12 cables each attached to twin external patches, eliminating the need for internal cables, gas-tight fittings and bellow sleeves. The Lightship can be inflated outdoors, without a net, by attaching the ballasted car before adding helium, and the car can be removed from an inflated Lightship without a net by ballasting the catenary cables themselves. Primary flight controls are fitted for the front left-hand seat only.

Twin 33.5 kW (45 hp) gear-reduced Rotax engines are pusher mounted to enhance propulsive efficiency and reduce noise. Standard capacity of the rear-mounted fuel tank is 197 litres (52 US gallons; 43.3 Imp gallons), but for long cross-country or special missions an auxiliary bag tank can be installed in the ballast compartment.

Apart from its advertising graphics applications, the Lightship can be equipped with a stabilised TV camera and video downlink. For news event coverage and VIP presentations, the airship normally carries three persons in addition to the pilot.

The following data apply to the A-50:

DIMENSIONS, ENVELOPE:

Length	36.58 m (120 ft 0 in)
Max diameter	9.14 m (30 ft 0 in)
Fineness ratio	3.8
Fin area (four, total)	42.74 m² (460 sq ft)
Volume	1,415.8 m³ (50,000 cu ft)

DIMENSIONS, GONDOLA:

Length overall	3.96 m (13 ft 0 in)
Width	1.52 m (5 ft 0 in)
Height overall	2.90 m (9 ft 6 in)
Propeller diameter	1.52 m (5 ft 0 in)
Cabin: Length	2.74 m (9 ft 0 in)
Height	1.83 m (6 ft 0 in)

WEIGHTS:

Total weight empty	859 kg (1,894 lb)
Max buoyancy	1,542 kg (3,400 lb)
Max dynamic lift	113 kg (250 lb)
Useful lift: ISA	431 kg (950 lb)
max	683 kg (1,506 lb)
Max gross weight	1,655 kg (3,650 lb)

PERFORMANCE:

Max level speed	50 knots (92 km/h; 57 mph)
Max range at 35 knots (65 km/h; 40 mph)	
	455 nm (843 km; 524 miles)
Max endurance at 35 knots (65 km/h; 40 mph)	13 h

ABC Lightship gondola *(Peter M. Bowers)*

American Blimp Corporation Lightship A-50 *(Peter M. Bowers)*

AEROLIFT

AEROLIFT INC

5050 Quorum Drive, Suite 215, Dallas, Texas 75240
Telephone: 1 (214) 960 0561
Fax: 1 (214) 960 8229
PRESIDENT AND CHIEF EXECUTIVE OFFICER:
 W. Larry Mahaffey
VICE-PRESIDENT, OPERATIONS: J. J. Morris
VICE-PRESIDENT, ENGINEERING: Allan Arnold
VICE-PRESIDENT, TECHNICAL SERVICES:
 Wilfred J. Eggington
PUBLIC RELATIONS: Bonnie Jones

AeroLift was founded in 1980. Now headquartered in Dallas, Texas, its operations are based in a Second World War airship hangar at Tillamook, Oregon, which is one of the world's largest timber structures. Originally funded by five major Canadian logging companies, AeroLift is now publicly owned and holds patents to develop a hybrid (aerostatic/aerodynamic) heavy lift vehicle known as the CycloCrane.

AEROLIFT CYCLOCRANE

The CycloCrane introduced a new concept for a lighter than air aircraft, combining fixed-wing and rotating-wing techniques. It has a helium filled centrebody resembling the envelope of a conventional airship. Structure within the envelope supports four external aerofoil surfaces, known as blades. These are attached at 90° intervals around its circumference, which enables them to rotate and so vary their angle of attack in relation to airflow past the vehicle. An articulated symmetrical wing surface is mounted in T form at the outer end of each blade. On the outer side of each wing is a pylon mounted pod containing a 75 kW (100 hp) Hirth F-30 two-stroke engine driving, via a 3.47 : 1 reduction gear, a 2.34 m (7 ft 8 in) three-blade propeller.

The entire centrebody rotates at a max 13 rpm about a shaft which passes longitudinally through its axis. This rotation allows an airflow over the wings of 52 knots (96 km/h; 60 mph), creating the required lift necessary for manoeuvring. At the forward end of the shaft is a cylindrical housing for control equipment; at the rear are stabilising surfaces in the form of a multi-faceted annular structure with an inverted 'Y' insert. A pilot's cabin is suspended by cables attached at each end to outer race bearings on the central shaft. The load to be airlifted is slung on cables beneath this cabin.

The structure is so designed that the net aerostatic lift of the helium is equal to the sum of all structural weight, fuel, crew, and 50 per cent of the intended sling load. The balance of lift for the sling load, and thrust for control and translation, are created by the external aerofoils.

When the CycloCrane is in a hover mode, the wings are positioned parallel to the shaft on which the centrebody rotates, providing lift via cyclic control enabling the CycloCrane to ascend and descend vertically as well as laterally. The blade aerofoils have both cyclic and collective control systems. The cyclic system allows the aircraft to pitch and yaw; the collective system allows it to move forward and backward. The wing and blade control systems, while rotating, allow the CycloCrane to maintain a position over the ground or over a load. Non-rotating forward flight is accomplished by turning the entire wing/blade assemblies. The wing/blade assemblies continue to turn as the vehicle accelerates. When optimum forward

AeroLift CycloCrane proof of concept prototype

speed is reached, all aerofoil surfaces and engines are aligned with the direction of flight and the centrebody ceases to rotate. Cruising speed is similar to that of a helicopter hauling a comparable external load.

The proof of concept vehicle has a two-ton sling load capacity. Unmanned testing in its current modified form began in August 1984, followed by initial manned test flights starting on 23 October 1984. Flight testing has ended, and data and dynamic computer model analysis have verified earlier Princeton University studies indicating that a CycloCrane should offer controllability equal to that of a helicopter of similar external lift capacity under gust and direct side wind conditions. It can be mast moored and can be designed to float hundreds of feet above the ground on a single line tether. When major storms are predicted, standard aircraft procedures would be followed and the vehicle flown out of the area of danger. The initial design was intended primarily for logging use worldwide, and its preliminary development was partially supported by the US Forest Service, the US Army, and the Defense Advanced Research Projects Agency (DARPA). It is, however, suitable for other ultra-heavy vertical lift applications where precision lifting and placement of heavy and outsize cargo are required. Commercial use of CycloCranes is expected to start in the 1990s, as soon as larger capacity vehicles have been built and certificated. Each of these is likely to have a sling load capacity of 10-35 tons; but AeroLift emphasises that the CycloRotor concept is valid for sling loads of up to at least 100 tons.

In 1987 AeroLift developed, under contract to the US Army Aviation Systems Command, a preliminary design of a 31.75-40.8 tonne (35-45 US ton) heavy lift CycloCrane for over-the-shore logistics and other missions. In addition,

AeroLift conducted an evaluation of the application of CycloCrane technology to high endurance surveillance platforms, as part of the US Strategic Defense Initiative programme during 1987.

During 1988 and 1989 AeroLift completed contracts for DARPA to conduct CycloCrane mooring tests on a 10.97 m (36 ft) model; refurbish and modify the proof of concept vehicle to enhance its capability to demonstrate military mission effectiveness; to evaluate additional military applications of the CycloCrane technology; and to develop preliminary CycloCrane designs to perform defined missions.

In 1989 AeroLift presented the government of Honduras with a proposal for ecologically sound rain forest management using the CycloCrane, and negotiations were expected to be finalised by mid-1990. Serious consideration was also given during 1989 to the use of CycloCranes in US drug interdiction activities by the Department of Defense, and a contract for work towards production craft was anticipated in the Spring of 1990.

The following data apply to the present proof of concept CycloCrane:

DIMENSIONS:

Length overall	54.25 m (178 ft 0 in)
Height overall, top centre engine nacelle to payload hook	77.73 m (255 ft 0 in)
Aerostat diameter (max)	20.73 m (68 ft 0 in)
Aerostat length	41.45 m (136 ft 0 in)
Helium volume (nominal)	9,345 m³ (330,000 cu ft)

WEIGHTS (design):

Operating weight empty (buoyant)	680 kg (1,500 lb)
Max gross weight (allowing for combined aerostatic and aerodynamic lift)	1,451 kg (3,200 lb)

BOLAND

BOLAND BALLOON

Pine Drive, RFD 2, Burlington, Connecticut 06013
Telephone: 1 (203) 673 1307
PROPRIETOR: Brian J. Boland

Mr Brian Boland has designed and built 45 hot-air balloons (see tables at the end of this section), as well as a hot-air airship named *Albatross*. A description of *Albatross* can be found in the 1985-86 and earlier editions of *Jane's*. Manufacture of a second airship, named *Rover*, began in early 1982.

BOLAND A-2 ROVER

Work to manufacture the envelope of *Rover* began in early 1982. The envelope was first inflated outdoors, at Farmington, Connecticut, on 24 November 1985 and made its first free flight on 8 September 1986. The gondola carries a crew of two seated side by side, and is suspended from exterior load tapes. It was hoped to use the 30 kW (40 hp) Rockwell JLO engine from the A-1 *Albatross* eventually, with a 0.91 m (3 ft 0 in) diameter propeller, but *Rover* is believed to be powered initially by a lighter-weight 15 kW

(20 hp) Xenoah with belt reduction drive to a slower-turning propeller.

No recent news of *Rover* has been received. All known details, and an illustration, can be found in the 1989-90 *Jane's*.

GOODYEAR

GOODYEAR AEROSPACE CORPORATION
(Division of Loral Systems Group)

1210 Massillon Road, Akron, Ohio 44315
Telephone: 1 (216) 796 4635
Telex: 986439, 810-431-2080 GDYRAERO AKRA
Fax: 1 (216) 796 7886/4242
PRESIDENT: Robert W. Clark
EXECUTIVE VICE-PRESIDENT: Raymond E. Stankard
VICE-PRESIDENT, MARKETING: Willis S. Zeigler
DIRECTOR, PUBLIC RELATIONS: Lyle Schwilling

During the past 77 years Goodyear has built over 310 airships, more than any other company in the world. Of these, over 250 were constructed under contract for the US Army and Navy.

In March 1987 Goodyear's aircraft and aerospace subsidiary for more than 60 years, Goodyear Aerospace Corporation, was sold to Loral Corporation, and continues

to operate as a Division of Loral Systems Group. It continues to provide airship manufacturing services and support to the Goodyear airship programme. Loral also continues development of the current Goodyear GZ-22 airship.

Goodyear Tire & Rubber Company currently operates three GZ-20A non-rigid airships in the USA for public relations and sales promotion activities: *America* (N3A), *Columbia* (N10A) and *Enterprise* (N1A). Details of the most recently constructed *Columbia* were given in the 1987-88 *Jane's*. In size, equipment and performance it is generally the same as the two other airships in the fleet.

GOODYEAR GZ-22

This latest airship, which flew for the first time on 9 October 1987, has a conventional envelope of typical Goodyear construction (a sandwich of Neoprene between

two layers of rubber coated polyester fabric), with tail fins set in an X configuration. After early flight trials, control surface area was increased by about 30 per cent during 1988. It is powered by two 313 kW (420 shp) Allison 250-B17C turboprops, each driving a three-blade Hartzell propeller turning within an annular duct which can be swivelled (+75°/-30°) to vector the thrust. The gondola, built by Advanced Technology and Research Inc of Clearwater, Florida, is of composite construction, with AFRP honeycomb and fabric covering over a steel frame. It has dual controls for one or two pilots, and the airship has an electronic fly by wire control system with a mechanical backup.

The GZ-22, registered N4A and named *Spirit of Akron*, is larger than the GZ-20A series, and the first to be powered by turbine engines. Vectoring of the ducted fans provides more precise control during very slow speed and ground handling manoeuvres. The cabin is bigger, with larger windows, and seats nine passengers; an improved night sign, with truer colours and greater resolution, is mounted on the envelope and is made up of 8,064 lamps.

FAA certification was awarded in September 1989, and the GZ-22 was due to be delivered to Goodyear Tire & Rubber Co in early 1990 as an advertising and camera platform replacement for GZ-20A *Enterprise* at Pompano Beach, Florida. Goodyear has no current plans to build additional GZ-22s.

DIMENSIONS, ENVELOPE:
Length overall	62.64 m (205 ft 6 in)

Height	18.34 m (60 ft 2 in)
Max diameter	14.33 m (47 ft 0 in)
Volume (helium)	7,017 m³ (247,800 cu ft)

DIMENSIONS, GONDOLA:
Length	10.59 m (34 ft 9 in)
Max width	2.44 m (8 ft 0 in)
Max depth	2.44 m (8 ft 0 in)
Propeller diameter	2.08 m (6 ft 10 in)

WEIGHTS:
Gondola	181.5 kg (400 lb)
Max payload	998 kg (2,200 lb)

Useful load	1,996 kg (4,400 lb)
Max gross weight	6,804 kg (15,000 lb)

PERFORMANCE:
Never-exceed speed	72 knots (133 km/h; 83 mph)
Max level speed	56 knots (104 km/h; 65 mph)
Normal cruising speed	48 knots (88 km/h; 55 mph)
Operating altitude	305-915 m (1,000-3,000 ft)
Pressure ceiling	3,050 m (10,000 ft)
Max range (estimated)	781 nm (1,448 km; 900 miles)
Max endurance (estimated)	24 h

MEMPHIS
MEMPHIS AIRSHIPS INC
Isle-A-Port Airport, 1720 Harbor Avenue, PO Box 13037, Memphis, Tennessee 38113
Telephone: 1 (901) 775 0386
Fax: 1 (901) 775 0917
PRESIDENT: Steve Garner
EXECUTIVE VICE-PRESIDENT: Jim Groce

Memphis Airships was formed in 1981 as a producer of small unmanned advertising airships and fan supported inflatables, and continues to manufacture such items. From 1982 it was involved with the research and development of a small air recreation vehicle known as the Ultrablimp, designed by Mr Steve Garner.

A prototype of the Ultrablimp was flown at the 1985 Sun 'n Fun and Oshkosh meetings, and was described and illustrated in the 1987-88 *Jane's*. It was followed by a second prototype (Ultrablimp II) in 1987. Details and a photograph of the one-off Dreamfinder non-rigid single-place airship appeared in the 1986-87 *Jane's*. Memphis Airships' latest designs are the two-place EXP-II and one-place Zephyr 200, described in this entry.

MEMPHIS EXP-II
First flown in 1987, the EXP-II is a two-place advertising blimp with an envelope of ripstop nylon coated material and thermoplastic urethane, coated externally with aluminium oxide paint. It has two internal ballonets, inflatable by propeller wash or auxiliary electric fan, and cruciform tail surfaces with a rudder on the lower vertical fin. In its original form, interchangeable advertising banners can be attached to the envelope sides, or displays can be painted directly on to the fabric. A lightweight illuminated display is available. Other suitable applications for the EXP-II are as a camera platform and for various observation/surveillance missions.

The gondola, supported on a single-wheel landing/ground handling gear, carries a pilot and one passenger and is equipped with standard aircraft radios.
POWER PLANT: One 48.5 kW (65 hp) Rotax 532 two-cylinder two-stroke engine, driving a two-blade ducted pusher

Memphis Airship EXP-II two-person small airship

propeller. Fuel capacity 45.4 litres (12 US gallons; 10 Imp gallons).

DIMENSIONS, ENVELOPE:
Length overall	27.67 m (90 ft 9¼ in)
Max diameter	6.51 m (21 ft 4¼ in)
Height overall: excl gondola	7.68 m (25 ft 2½ in)
incl gondola	8.80 m (28 ft 10¾ in)
Fineness ratio	4.25
Volume: envelope	613.7 m³ (21,672 cu ft)
ballonets (total)	101.9 m³ (3,600 cu ft)

WEIGHTS:
Weight empty, incl gondola	424 kg (935 lb)
Payload capacity	163-218 kg (360-480 lb)
Gross lift (94% helium effectiveness):	
ballonets full	520 kg (1,147 lb)
ballonets empty	638 kg (1,408 lb)

PERFORMANCE:
Max level speed	48 knots (88 km/h; 55 mph)
Cruising speed	33 knots (61 km/h; 38 mph)
Max rate of climb	274 m (900 ft)/min
Max rate of descent	183 m (600 ft)/min
Ceiling	1,370 m (4,500 ft)
Max endurance	3 h

MEMPHIS ZEPHYR 200
Light enough to meet FAR 103 (ultralight) criteria, the Zephyr 200 is a single-place sport/recreation airship, powered by a pair of 5.2 kW (7 hp) Honda aircooled four-stroke engines driving twin shrouded propellers aft of the gondola. The envelope is helium-filled, with valves and ballasting for full control in ascent and descent. It can be free ballooned for long periods in the event of any control or engine failure. The Zephyr 200 is not intended for commercial use. Production deliveries were expected to begin in the Spring of 1990.

DIMENSIONS, ENVELOPE:
Length overall	18.26 m (59 ft 10¾ in)
Max diameter	5.03 m (16 ft 6 in)
Height overall, incl gondola	6.55 m (21 ft 6 in)
Fineness ratio	3.70
Volume: envelope	230.3 m³ (8,134 cu ft)
ballonets (total)	15.6 m³ (550 cu ft)

WEIGHTS:
Weight empty, incl gondola	114 kg (251 lb)
Payload capacity	91-118 kg (200-260 lb)
Max gross lift (ballonets 25% full)	236 kg (520 lb)

PERFORMANCE:
Max level speed	30 knots (56 km/h; 35 mph)
Cruising speed	22 knots (42 km/h; 26 mph)
Max rate of climb	244 m (800 ft)/min
Max rate of descent	214 m (700 ft)/min
Ceiling	855 m (2,800 ft)
Max endurance	3 h

Memphis Zephyr 200 customised for use in a Japanese television commercial

SKYRIDER
SKYRIDER AIRSHIPS INC
2840 Wilderness Place (Suite E), PO Box 1158, Boulder, Colorado 80301
Telephone: 1 (303) 449 2190
Fax: 1 (303) 449 2074
PRESIDENT: Frank E. Rider

RIDER BA-3
Built in 14 months, the BA-3 prototype (N25FR) was flown for the first time on 11 May 1988. A single-passenger, non-rigid helium airship, it is powered by two small engines but can be free ballooned in the event of engine failure. It can be kept safely at its mooring mast in winds of at least 35

knots (64 km/h; 40 mph), and requires a ground crew of four or five when away from the mast.
ENVELOPE: Main envelope made of 6.5 oz methane coated nylon. Two ballonets (one forward, one aft), occupying 18 per cent of total volume and filled by onboard blowers. Three valves (air and helium), operated by automatic pressure switching system with manual backup. Tail surfaces are of fabric covered welded chromoly steel.
GONDOLA: Welded chromoly structure, with composites skin panels and Lexan windscreen, suspended from envelope by internal catenary curtains.
POWER PLANT: Two 21 kW (28 hp) Rotax 277FA flat-twin engines, each driving a 1.14 m (3 ft 9 in) diameter GSC Systems three-blade ground adjustable propeller and mounted on an electrically actuated shaft permitting

thrust to be vectored between 90° up and 45° down. Fuel capacity 41.6 litres (11 US gallons; 9.1 Imp gallons).

AVIONICS AND EQUIPMENT: 720-channel nav/com. Instrument panel includes standard flight instruments, JPI engine temperature scanner and Dwyer photohelic pressure gauge. Onboard water ballast.

DIMENSIONS, OVERALL:
Length	29.26 m (96 ft 0 in)
Width	8.23 m (27 ft 0 in)
Height	9.75 m (32 ft 0 in)

DIMENSIONS, ENVELOPE:
Length	29.26 m (96 ft 0 in)
Max diameter	7.32 m (24 ft 0 in)
Volume	849.5 m³ (30,000 cu ft)

Gondola of the Rider BA-3

Prototype of the Rider BA-3 single-passenger airship

WEIGHTS:
Weight empty	612 kg (1,350 lb)
Max T-O weight at S/L	907 kg (2,000 lb)

PERFORMANCE:
Max level speed	30 knots (56 km/h; 35 mph) IAS

Cruising speed		Typical T-O run	15-30 m (50-100 ft)
	17-22 knots (32-40 km/h; 20-25 mph) IAS	Typical landing run	less than 15 m (50 ft)
Landing speed	4.3 knots (8 km/h; 5 mph)	Endurance, with reserves	4 h
Pressure ceiling	approx 1,070 m (3,500 ft)		

THOMPSON
JAMES THOMPSON, AIAA
1700 Citizens Plaza, Louisville, Kentucky 40202
Telephone: 1 (502) 589 0130
Telex: 204335

THOMPSON AIRSHIP
Construction of this small, two-person sport and advertising airship was suspended during 1988-89, but has been resumed, and completion was expected in 1990.

The airship has a helium filled envelope, inside which are two 56.6 m³ (2,000 cu ft) capacity air ballonets that will be filled unequally to provide pitch trim. The tail unit is a fabric covered aluminium tube inverted Y structure (all three angles 120°), the elevators of which operate differentially to control rolling moment. There are no catenary curtains: cables attached to five finger patches on each side of the envelope suspend the gondola slightly forward of the centre of buoyancy, to compensate for pitch-up. The gondola itself has a steel tube frame, with glassfibre and urethane foam skin panels, and accommodates the crew, power plant and two water ballast tanks. Propulsion is provided by a 1,200 cc Honda liquid-cooled engine, with 2.2:1 toothed-belt reduction drive to a two-blade shrouded wooden pusher propeller. The gondola is stabilised by three cables attached to the propeller shroud.

Model of the Thompson two-person airship

DIMENSIONS, ENVELOPE:
Length overall	24.91 m (81 ft 9 in)
Max diameter	7.91 m (25 ft 11¼ in)

Volume: helium	695.0 m³ (24,544 cu ft)	Gondola	187 kg (412 lb)
ballonets	97.9 m³ (3,456 cu ft)	Water ballast	81.5 kg (180 lb)
design total	792.9 m³ (28,000 cu ft)	Max T-O weight	696 kg (1,534 lb)
Fineness ratio	3.15	PERFORMANCE (estimated):	
WEIGHTS:		Design speed	30 knots (55 km/h; 34 mph)
Envelope	244 kg (538 lb)		

ULITA
ULITA INDUSTRIES INC (Manufacturing Division)
PO Box 412, Sheboygan, Wisconsin 53082-0412
Telephone: 1 (414) 458 2842
PRESIDENT AND TECHNICAL ADVISER: Thomas S. Berger
VICE-PRESIDENT, MARKETING: Mark R. Forss

Ulita has three current light utility airship programmes: the UM20 and UM10, of which prototypes are under construction, and the UM30, which is in the design stage.

ULITA UM10-22 CLOUD CRUISER
Optimised for the ARV (air recreational vehicle) category, the UM10-22 was conceived and designed by Mr T. S. Berger, President and Technical Adviser of Ulita Industries Inc. It is intended as a low-cost light utility airship to appeal to a broad range of markets that larger contemporary airships cannot satisfy.

Prototype construction was nearing completion in January 1990. Certification is being considered, but in the meantime the UM10-22 is available only in kit form.

ENVELOPE: Non-rigid helium filled hull, with twin ballonets. Attached directly to the hull are two stabiliser fin roots which are located 45° below the horizontal plane of symmetry, creating an inverted V. Attached to the ends of this inverted V are two vertical stabilisers each incorporating a movable control surface which operates as a rudder. The horizontal stabilisers are also attached to the ends of the inverted V and provided with movable control surfaces which operate as elevators. This fin arrangement provides for easy assembly and maintenance. One landing wheel at base of each fin.

GONDOLA: Side by side seating, with dual control wheels, for pilot and one student/passenger. Two landing wheels, mounted on outriggers. Accommodation ventilated, but not heated.

Model of the Ulita UM10-22 air recreation vehicle airship

POWER PLANT: Two 18 kW (24 hp) König SC 340 three-cylinder two-stroke engines, each driving a three-blade fixed-pitch ducted propeller, mounted on an outrigger from gondola and capable of rotation to provide horizontal or vertical thrust. Main fuel tank is located in the control car, with provisions for auxiliary tanks on the outriggers. Maximum fuel capacity 60.6 litres (16 US gallons; 13.3 Imp gallons).

ELECTRICAL SYSTEM: 12V DC battery and alternator.
DIMENSIONS, OVERALL:
Length	25.17 m (82 ft 6.8 in)
Width	8.05 m (26 ft 4.8 in)
Height	8.88 m (29 ft 1.8 in)

DIMENSIONS, ENVELOPE:
Length	24.69 m (81 ft 0 in)
Max diameter	6.86 m (22 ft 6 in)

Volume: ballonets (total)	140.2 m³ (4,950.75 cu ft)
gross	637.23 m³ (22,503.43 cu ft)
DIMENSIONS, GONDOLA:	
Length: at top	3.12 m (10 ft 3 in)
overall	3.44 m (11 ft 3.6 in)
Width: at top	1.32 m (4 ft 4 in)
at floor	1.04 m (3 ft 4.9 in)
overall (incl propulsors)	4.33 m (14 ft 2.4 in)
Height: excl landing gear	1.71 m (5 ft 7.3 in)
incl landing gear	2.12 m (6 ft 11.4 in)
Propeller diameter (each)	1.07 m (3 ft 6 in)
WEIGHTS:	
Weight empty	380 kg (838 lb)
Fuel (standard)	32.7 kg (72 lb)
Crew of 2	63.5 kg (140 lb)
Payload	52.5 kg (116 lb)
Total gross lift	620 kg (1,366 lb)
PERFORMANCE (estimated):	
Max level speed	42 knots (78 km/h; 48 mph)
Econ cruising speed	26 knots (48 km/h; 30 mph)
Pressure ceiling	2,440 m (8,000 ft)

ULITA UM20-48

The UM20-48 (formerly LUA-1) has been designed primarily for advertising and training purposes. The prototype control car has been completed, and in early 1990 final work was being performed on the envelope and tail surfaces. The airship is due to be available, fully certificated, upon completion of flight tests by late 1991.

ENVELOPE: Non-rigid helium filled airship, with two ballonets. Tail unit, of inverted Y configuration, is a riveted aluminium truss structure with lightweight fabric covering. Trim tab on rudder and each ruddervator.

GONDOLA: Primary structure is a welded 4130 steel tube truss, with a skin of light gauge aluminium sheet riveted to aluminium angle and channel. It is fitted with a single non-retractable landing gear unit, carrying twin fully castoring and bungee sprung wheels of 244 mm (9.6 in) diameter, and has side by side seats for a pilot and one passenger. Storage space behind seats and under main cabin floor. Forward opening door on each side. Accommodation is heated and ventilated.

POWER PLANT: One 85.75 kW (115 hp) Textron Lycoming O-235-G1B flat-four engine, driving a two-blade reversible-pitch pusher propeller. Single 98 litre (26 US gallon; 21.6 Imp gallon) fuel tank standard; 38 litre (10 US gallon; 8.3 Imp gallon) auxiliary tank.

ELECTRICAL SYSTEM: 12V DC battery and alternator.

DIMENSIONS, OVERALL:	
Length	32.57 m (106 ft 10.4 in)
Width	9.33 m (30 ft 7.4 in)
Height	12.68 m (41 ft 7.1 in)
DIMENSIONS, ENVELOPE:	
Length	31.95 m (104 ft 10 in)
Max diameter	8.88 m (29 ft 1.4 in)
Volume: ballonets (two)	271.8 m³ (9,600 cu ft)
gross	1,359.2 m³ (48,000 cu ft)

DIMENSIONS, GONDOLA:	
Length overall	4.21 m (13 ft 9.6 in)
Width: at top	1.07 m (3 ft 6 in)
at floor	1.07 m (3 ft 6 in)
Height: excl landing gear	2.01 m (6 ft 7.2 in)
incl landing gear	2.81 m (9 ft 2.6 in)
WEIGHTS (estimated):	
Weight empty	974 kg (2,147 lb)
Fuel (standard)	72.5 kg (160 lb)
Payload (nominal)	83.5 kg (184 lb)
Total gross lift	1,284 kg (2,831 lb)
PERFORMANCE (estimated):	
Max level speed	43 knots (80 km/h; 50 mph)
Econ cruising speed	26 knots (48 km/h; 30 mph)
Pressure ceiling	2,745 m (9,000 ft)

ULITA UM25-64

The four-seat UM25-64 is the latest addition to Ulita's line-up of specially designed airships. Designed specifically for today's multi-media advertising market, its simple design provides for low initial investment and low operating costs. Construction of the prototype envelope is currently well under way, with fabrication of the control car and fins being completed by mid-1990. Certification is planned to be completed by early 1991, with availability of the ship to follow shortly afterward. Ulita Airship Operations intends eventually to operate five of these airships for training flight crews, advertising, and special purpose leasing operations.

ENVELOPE: Non-rigid, helium filled, with two ballonets. Tail unit, in a cruciform arrangement, is a riveted aluminium truss structure with lightweight fabric covering. Trim tab on rudder only.

GONDOLA: Primary structure is a welded 4130 steel tube truss, with a skin of light gauge aluminium sheet riveted to aluminium angle and channel. The car will incorporate a tricycle landing gear system. Shock absorption is provided by a shock cord system.

POWER PLANT: One Textron Lycoming O-320-D3G flat-four engine, rated at 119 kW (160 hp) at 2,700 rpm, mounted on back of car in pusher configuration. A twin-engined version, utilising two 59.7 kW (80 hp) Limbach engines, will also be available. Fuel is supplied from two 94.6 litre (25 US gallon; 20.8 Imp gallon) tanks and a 47.3 litre (12.5 US gallon; 10.4 Imp gallon) auxiliary tank.

ELECTRICAL SYSTEM: 24V DC battery and alternator.

DIMENSIONS, OVERALL:	
Length	35.73 m (117 ft 2.9 in)
Width	10.42 m (34 ft 2.4 in)
Height	14.41 m (47 ft 3.4 in)
DIMENSIONS, ENVELOPE:	
Length	35.05 m (115 ft 0 in)
Max diameter	9.74 m (31 ft 11.3 in)
Volume: ballonets (two)	444.4 m³ (15,692.7 cu ft)
gross	1,851.5 m³ (65,386 cu ft)
DIMENSIONS, GONDOLA:	
Length overall	5.18 m (17 ft 0 in)
Width: at top	1.83 m (6 ft 0 in)
at floor	1.37 m (4 ft 6 in)

Height: excl landing gear	2.47 m (8 ft 1.2 in)
incl landing gear	3.43 m (11 ft 3 in)
WEIGHTS (estimated):	
Weight empty	1,224 kg (2,699 lb)
Fuel (standard)	136 kg (300 lb)
Payload (nominal)	67.5 kg (149 lb)
Total gross lift	1,737 kg (3,829 lb)
PERFORMANCE (estimated):	
Max level speed	43 knots (80 km/h; 50 mph)
Econ cruising speed	36 knots (66 km/h; 41 mph)
Pressure ceiling	3,350 m (11,000 ft)

ULITA UM30-71

Still in the design stage, the UM30-71 (originally LUA-2) is a second-generation vehicle intended to offer greater payload capacity and in-flight endurance, opening up the market to such applications as harbour patrol, rescue/casevac and short-range maritime surveillance. Features will include vectored thrust propulsion, tricycle landing gear for improved ground handling, gondola accommodation for a pilot and three passengers, composite construction, and a fly by light control system with automated flight control capabilities.

POWER PLANT: One 149 kW (200 hp) Textron Lycoming IO-360 flat-four engine, driving two five-blade reversible-pitch ducted propellers with thrust vectoring. Fuel capacity (standard) 227 litres (60 US gallons; 50 Imp gallons).

DIMENSIONS, OVERALL:	
Length	41.45 m (136 ft 0 in)
Width	9.94 m (32 ft 7.3 in)
Height	13.65 m (44 ft 9.4 in)
DIMENSIONS, ENVELOPE:	
Length	41.15 m (135 ft 0 in)
Max diameter	9.87 m (32 ft 4.4 in)
Volume: ballonets (two)	404.4 m³ (14,283 cu ft)
gross	2,022.2 m³ (71,413 cu ft)
DIMENSIONS, GONDOLA:	
Length overall	7.84 m (25 ft 8.6 in)
Width: at top	1.71 m (5 ft 7.2 in)
at bottom	1.22 m (4 ft 0 in)
Height: excl landing gear	2.50 m (8 ft 2.4 in)
incl landing gear	3.05 m (10 ft 0 in)
WEIGHTS (estimated):	
Weight empty	1,386 kg (3,055 lb)
Fuel (standard)	163 kg (360 lb)
Payload	154 kg (340 lb)
Total gross lift	1,857 kg (4,095 lb)
PERFORMANCE (estimated):	
Max level speed	54 knots (100 km/h; 62 mph)
Max cruising speed	48 knots (90 km/h; 56 mph)
Econ cruising speed	43 knots (80 km/h; 50 mph)
Pressure ceiling	2,135 m (7,000 ft)
Range at econ cruising speed, standard fuel	326 nm (605 km; 376 miles)
Endurance at econ cruising speed, standard fuel	7 h 30 min

US-LTA
US LIGHTER THAN AIR CORPORATION
(A division of Aerotech)
6040 Hangar Road, Tillamook, Oregon 97141
Telephone: 1 (503) 842 3032
Fax: 1 (503) 842 7362
GENERAL MANAGER: Dix Evans
DIRECTOR OF AIRSHIP OPERATIONS: Lee Cermak
CHIEF PILOT: Hunter H. Harris

Originally known as Grace Aircraft Corporation, later (1985) as US Airship Corporation, and then (April 1986) as Aerotek Corporation, this company came under new ownership in July 1988 and is now known as US Lighter Than Air Corporation. Assets acquired by US-LTA included the prototype Aerotek USA 100 (originally Grace GAC-20) airship, which is now known as the US-LTA 138-S. Major components of this prototype were built at Eugene; final assembly took place in the former US Navy airship hangars at Tillamook, Oregon. US-LTA expected to gain FAA certification by the Summer of 1990.

US-LTA 138-S

The US-LTA 138-S is intended for commercial advertising, and as a testbed for further engineering and development of airship systems. It is designed and built in accordance with new FAA airworthiness standards for airships. First flight was made on 28 October 1987, and over 200 hours of flying had been completed by early 1990. Certification flight requirements were due to be completed by Spring 1990, with FAA certification to follow shortly afterward.

HULL: Non-rigid envelope of ellipsoidal configuration, made of polyurethane coated Dacron with a non-woven material laminated on the inside for bias stability. Seams are heat-sealed inside and out. Nose is stiffened by 16 battens to permit higher airspeeds and distribute mooring loads. Weight of gondola is supported by cables attached to two internal catenary curtains which hang from upper quarter of envelope over half of its length. Side loads and thrust from car are transmitted to envelope via the car catenary, a fabric doubler extending away from car perimeter in all directions to ensure uniform load distribution to envelope. Two air-filled ballonets within helium compartment, to compensate for variations in hull pressure and adjust in-flight trim, are made of heat sealed urethane coated nylon. Air is supplied to ballonets via ram air duct aft of propeller, with mechanically controlled valves to duct air to front or rear ballonet as required. A passive pressure relief valve is fitted to each ballonet and in the helium compartment to control and prevent accidental envelope overpressure. Manual cable control permits controlled venting of helium or air if required. Inverted Y tail unit, comprising three identical aluminium framework fins, covered with doped fabric; each fin is attached to envelope with 13 fan patches at its base and supported by three guy wires on each side.

GONDOLA: Control car is shaped as an ellipsoidal hyperbola with a circular end section, and has an exterior shell of glassfibre epoxy sandwich construction with a foam core, over a welded steel tube frame. Windows of Plexiglas. The cabin seats six persons, including the crew, in pairs, and is separated acoustically from the engine compartment at the rear. The single-wheel landing gear is of trailing link type, pivoting about a vertical axis.

POWER PLANT: One 224 kW (300 hp) Textron Lycoming IO-540-K1A5 flat-six engine, mounted aft of control car on a 4130 steel tube frame and driving a Hartzell HC-3YR-7LF three-blade constant-speed reversible-pitch pusher propeller within an annular duct. Fuel tanks at rear of car, combined capacity 386 litres (102 US gallons; 85 Imp gallons).

SYSTEMS: Electrical system is a standard light aircraft 28V 100A negative ground type, powered by an engine driven alternator. While moored, a blower system is powered by a ground based generator for automatic monitoring and control of envelope pressurisation. Flight control is cable driven and hydraulically boosted, using a conventional stick with pushrods in combination with an adjustable friction damper, hydraulic boost system and mechanical mixer for the tail surfaces. System can be flown manually in the event of hydraulic failure.

AVIONICS AND EQUIPMENT: Avionics include dual nav/com radios with VOR/ILS, Loran, ADF, transponder, and marker beacon receivers. Standard instrumentation includes ASI, VSI, attitude indicator, barometric and radar altimeters, turn co-ordinator, directional gyro, magnetic compass, engine and fuel system instruments, inside and outside air temperature gauges, ballonet and helium envelope manometers, hydraulic system temperature and pressure gauges, and clock.

DIMENSIONS, OVERALL:	
Length	48.77 m (160 ft 0 in)
Width	12.80 m (42 ft 0 in)
Height	17.37 m (57 ft 0 in)
Envelope volume	3,908 m³ (138,000 cu ft)
DIMENSIONS, GONDOLA:	
External:	
Length: incl power plant	6.55 m (21 ft 6 in)
excl power plant	approx 5.79 m (19 ft 0 in)
Max width	approx 1.83 m (6 ft 0 in)
Max height	approx 2.74 m (9 ft 0 in)
Internal (cabin):	
Length	4.07 m (13 ft 4¼ in)
Max width: at floor	1.65 m (5 ft 4¾ in)
at ceiling	1.77 m (5 ft 9½ in)
Max height	1.93 m (6 ft 4 in)
WEIGHTS:	
Weight empty	2,660 kg (5,865 lb)
Control car, empty	1,052 kg (2,320 lb)
Max fuel	278 kg (612 lb)
Payload with standard fuel	1,143 kg (2,520 lb)
Gross weight	3,804 kg (8,386 lb)
PERFORMANCE:	
Max level speed	56 knots (104 km/h; 65 mph)
Demonstrated service ceiling	2,745 m (9,000 ft)

Range with max fuel, cruising at 30 knots (56 km/h;
  35 mph)   434 nm (804 km; 500 miles)
Endurance with max fuel, speed as above   14 h 30 min

Prototype of the US-LTA 138-S

WAI
WESTINGHOUSE-AIRSHIP INDUSTRIES INC

PO Box 17193, Baltimore, Maryland 21203
Telephone: 1 (301) 379 2306
Fax: 1 (301) 379 2310
CHAIRMAN: R. M. Packard
PRESIDENT:
  Rear-Admiral Edward J. Hogan Jr, USN (Ret'd)
VICE-PRESIDENT, PROGRAMS AND OPERATIONS:
  Gordon T. Adams Sr

SENTINEL 5000

A Naval Airship Program (NAP) was initiated by Naval Air Systems Command in 1985 to investigate the suitability of airships in the AEW role. A contract award was made to WAI in June 1987 selecting the Sentinel 5000 (US Navy designation **YEZ-2A**) as the basis for an operational development model (ODM) airship. A description and illustrations of the Sentinel 5000 can be found under the Airship Industries heading in the UK part of this section.

In October 1988 the NAP evolved from an exclusively US Navy programme to one by the Defense Advanced Research Projects Agency (DARPA). The lighter than air programme still focuses on the demonstration of a long-range, long-endurance surveillance system capable of seeing low-observable sea-skimming cruise missiles. However, OTH (over the horizon) third-party targeting now appears to be an evolving requirement for the US Navy battle group. In addition, drug surveillance and interdiction functions have a need for a surveillance platform that is fundamentally non-provocative, capable of sophisticated air and sea search in the detection of drug runners, and has the ability to act as a command and control centre for other government agencies. The Sentinel 5000 is a prime candidate for this role.

LIGHTER THAN AIR: BALLOONS

CONTRACTORS' ADDRESSES:

Country	Company	Address	Telephone/Telex/Fax
Australia	Kavanagh Balloons Pty Ltd	13/10 Pioneer Avenue, Thornleigh, NSW 2120	Tel: 61 (2) 484 3193 Fax: 61 (2) 484 4915
Czechoslovakia	Aerotechnik	Letiste Kunovice, 68604 Uherské Hradiště	Tel: 42/5122 Telex: 60380
France	Ballons Chaize	48 rue Balay, 42000 Saint-Étienne	Tel: 33/77 33 43 76
Germany, West	Ballonfabrik See- und Luftausrüstung GmbH & Co KG	Postfach 101327, Austrasse 35, 8900 Augsburg 1	Tel: 49 (821) 41 50 41 Telex: 17/821810
Hungary	Repülőgépes Szolgálat (RSZ)	PO Box 56, Koérberki út 36, H 1112 Budapest XI	Tel: 36 (1) 185 1344 Telex: 22-5187 Fax: 36 (1) 166 8118
Italy	Paolo Bonanno Balloons Service	Via Volo 3/A, 12036 Revello (CN)	Tel: 39 (175) 75666 Fax: 39 (175) 759313
South Africa	Flamboyant Balloons (Pty) Ltd	PO Box 149, Lanseria 1748, Transvaal	Tel: 27 (11) 659 2687 Fax: 27 (11) 659 1451
United Kingdom	Cameron Balloons Ltd	St John's Street, Bedminster, Bristol BS3 4NH	Tel: 44 (272) 637216 Telex: 444825 GASBAG G Fax: 44 (272) 661168
	Thunder & Colt Ltd	Maesbury Road, Oswestry, Shropshire SY10 8HA	Tel: 44 (691) 670644 Telex: 35503 COLT G Fax: 44 (691) 670617
United States of America	Adams Balloon Loft Inc	Building 27, Dekalb Peachtree Airport, Atlanta, Georgia 30341	Tel: 1 (404) 452 8066
	Aerostar International Inc (subsidiary of Raven Industries)	Box 5057, Sioux Falls, South Dakota 57117-5057	Tel: 1 (605) 331 3500 Fax: 1 (605) 331 3520
	Avian Balloon Company	South 3722 Ridgeview Drive, Spokane, Washington 99206	Tel: 1 (509) 928 6847
	The Balloon Works	PO Box 827, 810 Salisbury Road, Statesville, North Carolina 28677	Tel: 1 (704) 878 9501 Fax: 1 (704) 878 9505
	Boland Balloon	Pine Drive, RFD 2, Burlington, Connecticut 06013	Tel: 1 (203) 673 1307
	Galaxy Balloons Inc	820 Salisbury Road, Statesville, North Carolina 28677	Tel: 1 (704) 878 9147 Fax: 1 (704) 878 9505

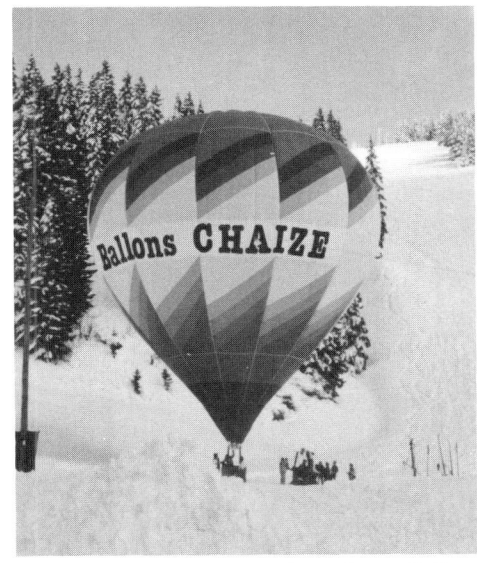

Representative hot-air balloon from Ballons Chaize

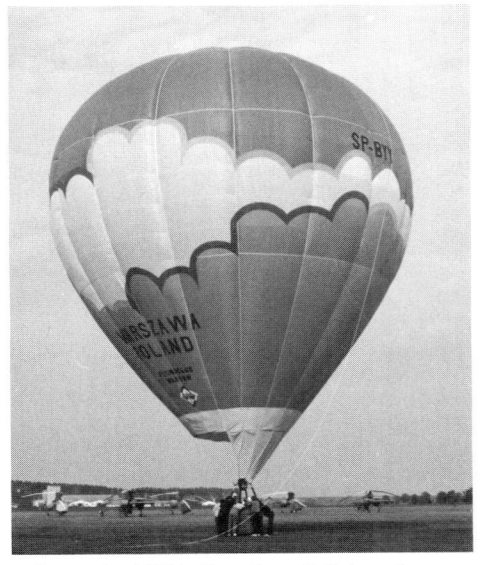

Hungarian RSZ balloon for a Polish customer

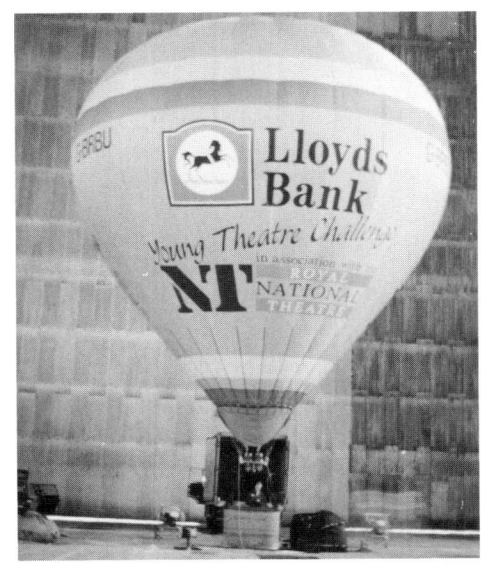

Thunder & Colt 17,000 cu ft Cloudhopper

HOT-AIR (AX) AND GAS BALLOON (AA) DATA

Country	Company	Model	Volume m³/cu ft	Gores	Diameter m/ft	Height m/ft	Max gross weight kg/lb	Crew	Basket	Fuel cylinders/ Burners
FAI CLASS AA/AX-2 (250-400 m³; 8,829-14,126 cu ft)										
USA	Aerostar	MG-300	300/10,595	?	8.78/28.8	8.23/27	?	1	Mixed structure	NA
FAI CLASS AA/AX-3 (400-600 m³; 14,126-21,189 cu ft)										
West Germany	Ballonfabrik	K 630/1-Ri	630/22,248	?	10.64/34.91	18.0/59	?	3-4	Rattan	NA
UK	Cameron	Viva-20	566.3/20,000	?	9.14/30	9.75/32	?	1	Harness seat	1/1
UK	Thunder & Colt	Cloudhopper Midi	481.4/17,000	?	9.45/31	9.45/31	?	1	Harness seat	1/1
UK	Thunder & Colt	Cloudhopper Super	594.7/21,000	?	10.06/33	10.67/35	?	1	Harness seat	1/1
FAI CLASS AA/AX-4 (600-900 m³; 21,189-31,783 cu ft)										
Czechoslovakia	Aerotechnik	AB-3	890/31,430	?	12.0/39.37	14.0/45.93	?	1	Harness seat	1/1
West Germany	Ballonfabrik	K 780/2-Ri	780/27,545	?	11.5/37.73	19.81/65	?	4	Rattan	NA
West Germany	Ballonfabrik	B 800/2-Ri	800/28,252	?	11.5/37.73	20.12/66	?	4	Rattan	NA
West Germany	Ballonfabrik	K 945/2-Ri	945/33,372	?	12.17/39.93	20.42/67	?	5-6	Rattan	NA
UK	Cameron	H-24 Skyhopper	680/24,000	?	?	?	?	1	Harness seat	1/1
UK	Cameron	N-31	890/31,430	?	12.5/41	14.63/48	?	1	Willow/Cane	2/1
UK	Cameron	O-31	890/31,430	?	12.5/41	14.63/48	?	1	Willow/Cane	2/1
UK	Cameron	Viva-31	890/31,430	?	12.5/41	14.63/48	?	1	Willow/Cane	2/1
UK	Thunder & Colt	31Z	890/31,430	?	12.19/40	14.63/48	?	1	Wicker/Cane	2/1
USA	Aerostar	S-40A	883/32,000	16	12.19/40	16.76/55	?	1	Aluminium chair	1/1
USA	Boland	Ultralight	899.5/31,765	?	11.58/38	?	?	1	?	2/1
USA	Boland	Ultralight	879/31,044	?	?	?	?	1	?	2/1
USA	Boland	*Football*	718.5/25,373	?	11.13/36.5	?	?	1	?	2/1
FAI CLASS AA/AX-5 (900-1,200 m³; 31,783-42,378 cu ft)										
West Germany	Ballonfabrik	K 1050/3-Ri	1,050/37,080	?	12.6/41.3	20.7/67.9	?	5-6	Rattan	NA
West Germany	Ballonfabrik	K 1260/3-Ri	1,260/44,496	?	13.4/44	22.25/73	?	6	Rattan	NA
South Africa	Flamboyant	AX5-40M	1,132/40,000	?	12.9/42.32	14.0/45.93	?	1	Rattan	1/1
UK	Cameron	O-42	1,190/42,024	?	14.26/46.8	12.07/39.6	?	2	Willow/Cane	2/1
UK	Thunder & Colt	42 Series 1	1,189/42,000	12	13.59/44.6	14.3/46.9	?	2	Wicker/Cane	2/1
UK	Thunder & Colt	42A	1,189/42,000	16	13.69/44.9	14.5/47.6	?	2	Wicker/Cane	2/1
USA	Adams	LD	964/34,029	?	12.95/42.5	15.54/51	?	1	Rattan	1-2/1
USA	Adams	LD-S	1,104/38,978	?	12.95/42.5	16.46/54	?	1-2	Rattan	1-2/1
USA	Aerostar	MG-1000	1,047/36,959	?	13.34/43.76	12.72/41.72	?	1-3	Rattan	NA
USA	Aerostar	S-45A	1,198/42,300	16	13.72/45	?	?	?	?	?
USA	Avian	Sparrow	1,189/42,000	?	13.41/44	16.46/54	?	1	Wicker	2/1
USA	Balloon Works	FireFly 42	1,182/41,740	?	14.02/46	14.63/48	?	1-2	Wicker	3/2
USA	Boland	*Puppy Chow*	906/32,000	?	?	?	?	1-2	?	1-4/1
FAI CLASS AA/AX-6 (1,200-1,600 m³; 42,378-56,503 cu ft)										
Australia	Kavanagh	C-56	1,586/56,000	?	15.2/49.87	17.25/56.6	?	2	Cane	1-4/1
France	Chaize	CS.1600	1,600/56,503	?	14.0/45.93	22.5/73.82	?	2	Rattan	2/1
West Germany	Ballonfabrik	K1360/4-Ri	1,360/48,028	?	13.75/45.11	25.0/82.02	?	6	Rattan	NA
West Germany	Ballonfabrik	K1680/4-Ri	1,680/59,329	?	14.78/48.5	24.4/80	?	6	Rattan	NA
South Africa	Flamboyant	AX6-56	1,586/56,000	?	15.0/49.2	18.0/59.0	?	2	Rattan	2/1
South Africa	Flamboyant	AX6-56M	1,586/56,000	?	15.0/49.2	18.0/59.0	?	2	Rattan	2/1
UK	Cameron	H-34 Skyhopper	963/34,000	?	?	?	?	1	Harness seat	1/1
UK	Cameron	O-56	1,590/56,150	?	15.24/50	17.07/56	?	3	Willow/Cane	2/1
UK	Cameron	Viva-56	1,590/56,150	?	15.24/50	17.07/56	?	3	Willow/Cane	2/1
UK	Cameron	N-56	1,590/56,150	?	15.24/50	17.07/56	?	3	Willow/Cane	2/1
UK	Thunder & Colt	GB-1	1,050/37,080	?	13.0/42.65	21.0/68.9	?	5-6	Willow/Cane	NA
UK	Thunder & Colt	56 Series 1	1,586/56,000	12	15.39/50.5	16.31/53.5	?	3	Wicker/Cane	2-3/1
UK	Thunder & Colt	56A	1,586/56,000	20 or 28	15.61/51.2	16.4/53.8	?	3	Wicker/Cane	2-3/1
USA	Adams	A50	1,557/54,985	?	15.24/50	17.68/58	?	2	Rattan	1-4/1
USA	Aerostar	S-50A	1,597/56,400	20	15.24/50	18.29/60	635/1,400	2-4	Wicker	3/1
USA	Aerostar	RX-6	1,597/56,400	12	15.24/50	17.68/58	648/1,430	2-3	Wicker	2/1
USA	Balloon Works	GadFly 56	1,576/55,660	?	15.3/50.1	16.1/52.8	?	3	Wicker	3/1
USA	Balloon Works	GadFly 560	1,576/55,660	?	15.24/50	16.46/54	?	1-3	Wicker	3/1
USA	Balloon Works	DragonFly 56	1,576/55,660	?	15.24/50	15.85/52	?	1-3	Wicker	3/1
USA	Balloon Works	DragonFly 560	1,576/55,660	?	15.24/50	15.85/52	?	1-3	Wicker	3/1
USA	Boland	*Baby Snake*	1,359/48,000	?	13.72/45	?	?	2-3	Wicker/Aluminium	2/1
USA	Boland	*Rainbow-Stars*	1,444/51,000	?	14.02/46	?	?	2	?	1-4/1
FAI CLASS AA/AX-7 (1,600-2,200 m³; 56,503-77,692 cu ft)										
Australia	Kavanagh	C-65	1,840/65,000	?	15.9/52.16	17.95/58.9	?	2-3	Cane	1-4/1
Australia	Kavanagh	C-77	2,194/77,500	?	16.8/55.12	19.05/62.5	?	3-4	Cane	1-4/1-2
Australia	Kavanagh	D-77	2,194/77,500	?	16.8/55.12	19.05/62.5	?	3-4	Cane	1-4/1-2
Czechoslovakia	Aerotechnik	AB-2	2,190/77,339	12, 20 or 28	16.0/52.49	16.0/52.49	?	4	Rattan	2/2
France	Chaize	CS.1800	1,800/63,566	?	15.0/49.2	22.5/73.8	?	2-3	Rattan	3/1
France	Chaize	CS. 2000	2,000/70,629	?	16.5/54.1	22.5/73.8	?	3	Rattan	3/1
France	Chaize	CS. 2200	2,200/77,692	?	18.0/59	22.5/73.8	?	3-4	Rattan	4/2
Hungary	RSZ	RSZ-05	2,200/77,692	?	17.0/55.77	20.7/68	?	1-3	Rattan	2-4/2
South Africa	Flamboyant	AX7-65	1,840/65,000	?	16.0/52.5	20.0/65.6	?	3	Rattan	2/1
South Africa	Flamboyant	AX7-77M	2,180/77,000	?	16.0/52.5	20.0/65.6	?	3	Rattan	2/1
UK	Cameron	Viva-65	1,840/64,980	?	16.15/53	18.0/59	?	3	Willow/Cane	2/1
UK	Cameron	O-65	1,840/64,980	?	16.15/53	18.0/59	?	3	Willow/Cane	3/1
UK	Cameron	N-65	1,840/64,980	?	16.15/53	18.0/59	?	3	Willow/Cane	3/1
UK	Cameron	Viva-77	2,190/77,339	?	17.07/56	18.9/62	?	4	Willow/Cane	2/1
UK	Cameron	O-77	2,190/77,339	?	17.07/56	18.9/62	?	4	Willow/Cane	4/1
UK	Cameron	N-77	2,190/77,339	?	17.07/56	18.9/62	?	4	Willow/Cane	4/1
UK	Thunder & Colt	65 Series 1	1,840/65,000	12	16.18/53.1	17.19/56.4	?	3	Wicker/Cane	2-3/1
UK	Thunder & Colt	69A	1,954/69,000	24 or 30	16.31/53.5	17.31/56.8	?	3	Wicker/Cane	2-3/1
UK	Thunder & Colt	77 Series 1	2,180/77,000	12	16.79/55.1	18.11/59.4	?	4	Wicker/Cane	2-3/1-2
UK	Thunder & Colt	77A	2,180/77,000	24 or 32	17.01/55.8	18.29/60	?	4	Wicker/Cane	2-3/1-2
USA	Adams	A50S	1,755/61,977	?	15.24/50	18.59/61	?	3	Rattan	1-4/1
USA	Adams	A55	2,123/74,973	?	16.76/55	19.51/64	?	3	Rattan	1-4/1
USA	Aerostar	S-52A	1,840/65,000	?	15.85/52	18.29/60	?	2-3	Wicker	2-3/1-2
USA	Aerostar	S-55A	2,195/77,500	24	16.76/55	19.2/63	651/1,435	3-4	Wicker	2-3/1-2
USA	Aerostar	RX-7	2,195/77,500	12	16.76/55	19.2/63	671/1,480	3	Wicker	2-3/1-2

NA: Not applicable (gas balloon)

HOT-AIR (AX) AND GAS BALLOON (AA) DATA *(continued)*

Country	Company	Model	Volume m³/cu ft	Gores	Diameter m/ft	Height m/ft	Max gross weight kg/lb	Crew	Basket	Fuel cylinders/ Burners
FAI CLASS AA/AX-7 (1,600-2,200 m³; 56,503-77,692 cu ft) *(continued)*										
USA	Avian	Falcon II	1,699/60,000	?	15.54/51	18.59/61	?	1-3	Wicker	2/1
USA	Balloon Works	DragonFly 65	1,840/65,000	?	17.07/56	17.68/58	?	3-4	Wicker	3/1
USA	Balloon Works	DragonFly 650	1,840/65,000	?	17.07/56	17.68/58	?	3-4	Wicker	3/1
USA	Balloon Works	DragonFly 77	2,167/76,520	?	17.07/56	17.68/58	?	3-4	Wicker	3/1
USA	Balloon Works	DragonFly 770	2,167/76,520	?	17.07/56	17.68/58	?	3-4	Wicker	3/1
USA	Balloon Works	FireFly 65	1,840/65,000	?	17.07/56	17.68/58	?	3-4	Wicker	3/1
USA	Balloon Works	FireFly 650	1,840/65,000	?	17.07/56	17.68/58	?	3-4	Wicker	3/1
USA	Balloon Works	FireFly 77	2,167/76,520	?	17.07/56	17.68/58	?	3-4	Wicker	3/1
USA	Balloon Works	FireFly 770	2,167/76,520	?	17.07/56	17.68/58	?	3-4	Wicker	3/1
USA	Boland	*MIA-POW*	1,736/61,304	?	14.63/48	?	?	2-3	Rattan/Plywood	2-4/1
USA	Boland	*Mrs Snake*	1,869/66,000	?	15.24/50	?	?	3-4	Wicker/Aluminium	2-4/1
USA	Galaxy	Galaxy 7	2,170/76,633	?	17.07/56	17.68/58	?	3-4	Rattan/Wicker	4/1-2
FAI CLASS AX-8 (2,200-3,000 m³; 77,692-105,944 cu ft)										
Australia	Kavanagh	D-84	2,378/84,000	?	17.4/57.1	19.55/64.1	?	4	Cane	1-4/1-2
Australia	Kavanagh	D-90	2,548/90,000	?	17.8/58.4	19.85/65.1	?	5	Cane	1-4/1-2
Australia	Kavanagh	D-105	2,973/105,000	?	18.7/61.4	20.95/68.7	?	6	Cane	2-4/2
Czechoslovakia	Aerotechnik	AB-8	2,950/104,178	?	18.5/60.7	18.0/59.06	?	6	Rattan	3/2
France	Chaize	CS.3000	3,000/105,944	?	19.44/63.8	25.0/82	?	5-6	Rattan	5/2
Hungary	RSZ	RSZ-03/1	3,000/105,944	?	18.7/61.35	22.9/75.13	?	5	Rattan	3-4/2
Italy	Bonanno	I-PAAM	2,950/104,178	?	19.0/62.34	22.0/72.18	?	4	Willow/Cane	4/2
South Africa	Flamboyant	AX8-85	2,407/85,000	?	18.0/59	20.0/65.6	?	4	Rattan	2/1
South Africa	Flamboyant	AX8-105	2,973/105,000	?	19.0/62.3	21.0/68.9	?	6	Rattan	3/2
UK	Cameron	O-84	2,380/84,047	?	17.68/58	19.5/64	?	4	Wicker	4/1
UK	Cameron	N-90	2,548/90,000	?	17.98/59	19.81/65	?	4-5	Wicker	6/2
UK	Cameron	A-105	2,970/104,885	?	18.9/62	20.73/68	?	6	Willow/Cane	6/2
UK	Cameron	N-105	2,970/104,885	?	18.9/62	20.73/68	?	6	Willow/Cane	6/2
UK	Cameron	O-105	2,970/104,885	?	18.9/62	20.73/68	?	6	Willow/Cane	6/2
UK	Thunder & Colt	84 Series 1	2,378/84,000	12	17.3/56.8	18.41/60.4	?	4	Wicker/Cane	2-3/1-2
UK	Thunder & Colt	90A	2,548/90,000	24	17.71/58.1	18.81/61.7	900/1,984	5	Wicker/Cane	2-4/2
UK	Thunder & Colt	90 Series 1	2,548/90,000	12	17.5/57.4	18.59/61	900/1,984	5	Wicker/Cane	2-4/2
UK	Thunder & Colt	90 Series 2	2,548/90,000	20	17.56/57.6	18.68/61.3	900/1,984	5	Wicker/Cane	2-4/2
UK	Thunder & Colt	105 Series 1	2,973/105,000	12	18.71/61.4	19.6/64.3	1,050/2,315	6	Wicker/Cane	2-6/2
UK	Thunder & Colt	105A	2,973/105,000	24	18.9/62	19.9/65.3	1,050/2,315	6	Wicker/Cane	2-6/2
UK	Thunder & Colt	105 Series 2	2,973/105,000	20	18.84/61.8	19.78/64.9	1,050/2,315	6	Wicker/Cane	2-6/2
USA	Adams	A55S	2,350/82,990	?	16.76/55	20.42/67	?	4	Rattan	1-4/1
USA	Adams	A60	2,973/105,000	?	18.59/61	22.25/73	?	5	Rattan	4/1-2
USA	Aerostar	RX-8	2,548/90,000	12	17.37/57	20.12/66	?	3-4	Wicker	2-4/1-2
USA	Aerostar	S-57A	2,548/90,000	24	17.37/57	20.12/66	660-748/ 1,455-1,650	3-4	Wicker	2-4/1-2
USA	Aerostar	S-60A	2,985/105,400	24	18.29/60	21.03/69	677-816/ 1,470-1,800	4-5	Wicker	2-4/1-2
USA	Avian	Skyhawk	2,265/80,000	?	16.76/55	20.12/66	?	1-4	Wicker	2/1
USA	Avian	Turbo 8	2,973/105,000	?	18.29/60	21.33/70	?	1-6	Wicker	4/2
USA	Balloon Works	DragonFly 90	2,600/91,818	?	17.98/59	18.75/61.5	?	3-4	Wicker	3/1
USA	Balloon Works	DragonFly 105	2,957/104,440	?	18.9/62	19.51/64	?	4-5	Wicker	6/2
USA	Balloon Works	DragonFly 900	2,600/91,818	?	17.98/59	18.75/61.5	?	3-4	Wicker	3/1
USA	Balloon Works	DragonFly 1050	2,957/104,440	?	18.9/62	19.51/64	?	4-5	Wicker	6/2
USA	Balloon Works	Firefly 8	2,965/104,708	?	19.4/63.65	20.5/67.26	1,111/2,450	5-6	Rattan/Wicker	6/2
USA	Balloon Works	FireFly 90	2,600/91,818	?	17.98/59	18.75/61.5	?	3-4	Wicker	3/1
USA	Balloon Works	FireFly 105	2,957/104,440	?	18.9/62	19.51/64	?	4-5	Wicker	6/2
USA	Balloon Works	FireFly 900	2,600/91,818	?	17.98/59	18.75/61.5	?	3-4	Wicker	3/1
USA	Balloon Works	FireFly 1050	2,957/104,440	?	18.9/62	19.51/64	?	4-5	Wicker	6/2
USA	Boland	*Levity*	2,563/90,500	?	?	?	?	4	Rattan/Plywood	4/2
USA	Galaxy	Galaxy 8	2,965/104,708	?	19.4/63.65	20.5/67.26	1,088/2,400	5-6	Rattan/Plywood	6/2
FAI CLASS AX-9 (3,000-4,000 m³; 105,944-141,259 cu ft)										
Australia	Kavanagh	E-120	3,398/120,000	?	19.3/63.3	21.75/71.4	?	7	Cane	2-4/2
Australia	Kavanagh	E-140	3,964/140,000	?	20.3/66.6	22.55/74.0	?	8	Cane/Stainless steel*	2-4/2
France	Chaize	CS.4000	4,000/141,259	?	22.0/72.2	27.5/90.2	?	8	Rattan	6/2
Hungary	RSZ	RSZ-04/1	4,000/141,259	?	20.6/67.6	24.7/81.0	?	8	Rattan	3-6/2
UK	Cameron	A-120	3,398/120,000	?	19.02/62.4	18.29/60	?	7	Stainless steel/Cane* (T)	6/2
UK	Cameron	O-120	3,398/120,000	?	20.24/66.4	17.07/56	?	7	Stainless steel/Cane* (T)	6/2
UK	Cameron	N-133	3,766/133,000	?	19.9/65.3	18.59/61	?	7	Stainless steel/Cane* (T)	6/2
UK	Cameron	A-140	3,960/139,846	?	20.73/68	21.95/72	?	8	Stainless steel/Cane* (T)	6/2
UK	Thunder & Colt	120A	3,398/120,000	24	19.51/64	21.03/69	?	7	Wicker/Cane	2-6/2
UK	Thunder & Colt	140 Series 2	3,964/140,000	20	20.48/67.2	21.3/69.9	1,200/2,645	8	Stainless steel/Cane*	2-6/2
USA	Adams	A60S	3,370/119,000	?	18.59/61	22.86/75	?	5-6	Rattan	4/2
USA	Adams	AB	3,540/125,000	?	19.51/64	23.16/76	?	6	Rattan	6/2
USA	Aerostar	S-66A	3,993/141,000	24	20.12/66	22.86/75	907-1,134/ 2,000-2,500	8	Wicker	6/2
USA	Avian	Magnum IX	3,964/140,000	?	20.12/66	23.16/76	?	1-8	Wicker	4/2
USA	Balloon Works	FireFly 140	3,964/140,000	?	20.12/66	22.86/75	?	5-6	Wicker	6-9/2
USA	Boland	*Tour d'Argent*	3,693/130,400	?	19.66/64.5	?	?	7	Rattan	6/2
USA	Galaxy	AX9	3,964/140,000	?	20.12/66	22.86/75	?	6-8	Wicker	6-8/2
FAI CLASS AX-10 (4,000-6,000 m³; 141,259-211,888 cu ft)										
Australia	Kavanagh	E-160	4,530/160,000	?	21.2/69.6	23.65/77.6	?	9	Cane/Stainless steel*	2-6/3
Australia	Kavanagh	E-200	5,663/200,000	?	22.8/74.8	25.15/82.5	?	10-11	Cane/Stainless steel*	2-6/3
Australia	Kavanagh	E-210	5,947/210,000	?	23.2/76.1	25.45/83.5	?	11	Cane/Stainless steel*	2-6/3
Czechoslovakia	Aerotechnik	AB-10	5,500/194,231	?	22.0/72.18	22.0/72.18	?	12	Rattan	4/3
South Africa	Flamboyant	AX10-150	4,248/150,000	?	21.0/68.9	22.0/72.2	?	8	Rattan	4/2
UK	Cameron	N-145	4,106/145,000	?	20.54/67.4	19.2/63	?	8	Stainless steel/Cane* (T)	6/2
UK	Cameron	O-160	4,530/160,000	?	21.0/69	22.25/73	?	8	Stainless steel/Cane* (T)	6/2
UK	Cameron	N-180	5,097/180,000	?	27.13/89	29.57/97	?	9	Stainless steel/Cane* (T)	8/3
UK	Cameron	A-210	5,947/210,000	?	23.77/78	24.99/82	?	12	Stainless steel/Cane* (T)	8/4
UK	Thunder & Colt	160 Series 1	4,530/160,000	12	21.61/70.9	22.71/74.5	1,300/2,866	9	Stainless steel/Cane*	2-8/3
UK	Thunder & Colt	160A	4,530/160,000	28	21.7/71.2	23.01/75.5	1,300/2,866	9	Stainless steel/Cane*	2-8/3
UK	Thunder & Colt	180 Series 1	5,097/180,000	12	22.48/73.75	23.62/77.5	1,300/2,866	9	Stainless steel/Cane*	2-8/3

*Partition format

HOT-AIR (AX) AND GAS BALLOON (AA) DATA *(continued)*

Country	Company	Model	Volume m³/cu ft	Gores	Diameter m/ft	Height m/ft	Max gross weight kg/lb	Crew	Basket	Fuel cylinders/ Burners
FAI CLASS AX-10 (4,000-6,000 m³; 141,259-211,888 cu ft) *(continued)*										
UK	Thunder & Colt	180A	5,097/180,000	24	23.0/75.46	24.0/78.74	1,300/2,866	10	Stainless steel/Cane*	2-9/3
USA	Aerostar	S-71A	4,955/175,000	?	21.64/71	23.77/78	?	7	Wicker/Stainless steel	4/2
USA	Aerostar	S-77A	5,975/211,000	28	23.47/77	26.52/87	1,270/2,800	9	Wicker/Stainless steel	4/2
USA	Boland	*Red Baron*	4,814/170,000	?	19.66/64.5	27.43/90	?	8	Rattan/Plywood	6/2
FAI CLASS AX-11 (6,000-9,000 m³; 211,888-317,832 cu ft)										
Australia	Kavanagh	E-240	6,796/240,000	?	23.8/78.1	26.45/86.8	?	12-13	Cane/Stainless steel*	2-6/3
Australia	Kavanagh	E-260	7,362/260,000	?	25.0/82.0	27.0/88.6	?	12-13	Cane/Stainless steel*	2-6/3
South Africa	Flamboyant	AX11-240	6,796/240,000	?	24.0/78.7	23.0/75.5	?	12	Willow/Cane	6/2
UK	Cameron	A-250	7,079/250,000	?	24.32/79.8	23.41/76.8	?	15	Stainless steel/Cane* (T)	8/3
UK	Cameron	A-300	8,495/300,000	?	25.85/84.8	24.81/81.4	?	20	Stainless steel/Cane* (double T)	8/3-4
UK	Thunder & Colt	240A	6,796/240,000	28	24.51/80.4	25.79/84.6	1,600/3,527	12	Stainless steel/Cane*	2-10/3-4
UK	Thunder & Colt	300A	8,495/300,000	28	26.46/86.8	27.19/89.2	2,200/4,850	12	Stainless steel/Cane*	2-10/3-4
USA	Boland	*Mr Gunsnook*	6,513/230,000	?	22.25/73	30.48/100	?	13	?	6/3
FAI CLASS AX-12 (9,000-12,000 m³; 317,832-423,776 cu ft)										
UK	Thunder & Colt	400A	11,327/400,000	28	29.11/95.5	29.99/98.4	2,900/6,393	16	Stainless steel/Cane*	2-10/3-4
FAI CLASS AX-13 (12,000-16,000 m³; 423,776-565,035 cu ft)										
UK	Cameron	A-530	15,008/530,000	?	31.21/102.4	29.99/98.4	?	30	Stainless steel/Cane* (2-deck)	10/3-4
FAI CLASS AX-15 (22,000 m³; 776,924 cu ft and above)										
UK	Cameron	N-850	24,069/850,000	?	37.49/123	35.05/115	?	50	Stainless steel/Cane* (2-deck)	12/6

*Partition format

A Thunder & Colt Type 31 advertising 'special shape'

Thunder & Colt 300A of Transworld Safaris, Kenya

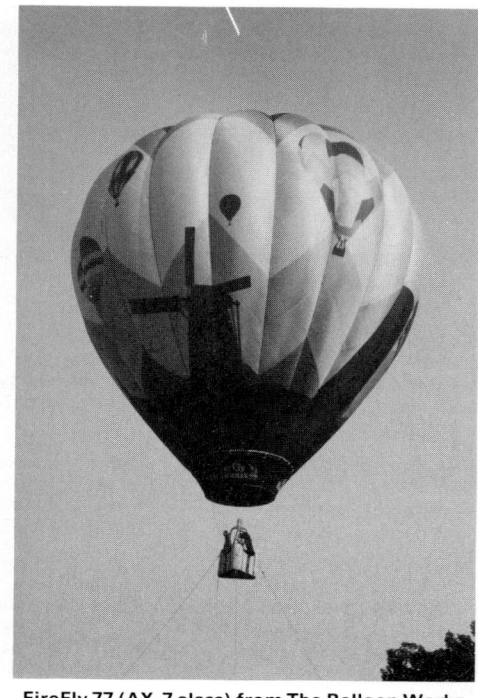

FireFly 77 (AX-7 class) from The Balloon Works

AERO ENGINES

> This section includes all available details of engines of manned aircraft, including microlights, and aerospacecraft. Rocket engines and other propulsion systems used purely for UAVs, targets, missiles and unmanned spaceflight are no longer included. Readers are referred for these subjects to *Jane's Battlefield Surveillance Systems, World Unmanned Aircraft* by Kenneth Munson, and *Interavia Space Directory*.

AUSTRALIA

HDHV
HAWKER DE HAVILLAND VICTORIA LTD
Box 779H, GPO Melbourne, Victoria 3001
Telephone: 61 (3) 647 6111
Telex: AA 30721
Fax: 61 (3) 646 3431
OFFICERS: See HDH entry in Aircraft section

HDHV makes components for engines and airframes. It makes F404 blades and seals, and assembles and tests engines for the RAAF. It makes CF6-50 and -80 rings for GE, and CMF56 rings, and supports RAAF Atar 9C and Viper engines.

AUSTRIA

ROTAX
BOMBARDIER-ROTAX GmbH
Postfach 5, A-4623 Gunskirchen
Telephone: 43 (7246) 271-0
Telex: 25 546 BRG K A
Fax: 43 (7246) 271286
PRODUCT MANAGER: Josef Fürlinger

This company is one of the world's largest producers of light piston engines. Those listed for light aircraft, microlights and gliders use 1:50 mix of oil with petrol (gasoline) of not below MON 83 or RON 90 grade. Customers have many options, including rewind manual or electric starter.

Rotax sustained an output of about 6,500 engines per year, all derived from snowmobile engines, until 1988 when it added the Model 912 that had been specially designed for aircraft.

Rotax 508UL twin-cylinder piston engine

Rotax 912 four-cylinder piston engine

ROTAX LIGHT AIRCRAFT ENGINES

Engine Model	277	377	447	503	503.2V	462	508UL	532	582	912
Layout	1 cylinder (4,7) Piston port	2 cylinder (4,7) Piston port	2 cylinder (4,7) Piston port	2 cylinder (4,7) Piston port	2 cylinder (4,7) Piston port	2 cylinder (5,7) Rotary valve	2 cylinder (4,8) Overhead valve	2 cylinder (5,7) Rotary valve	2 cylinder (5,7) Rotary valve	4 cylinder (6,8) Overhead valve
Bore/stroke mm (in)	72.0/66.0 (2.83/2.60)	62.0/61.0 (2.44/2.40)	67.5/61.0 (2.66/2.40)	72.0/61.0 (2.83/2.40)	72.0/61.0 (2.83/2.40)	69.5/61.0 (2.74/2.40)	71.0/64.0 (2.79/2.52)	72.0/64.0 (2.83/2.52)	76.0/64.0 (2.99/2.52)	79.5/61.0 (3.13/2.40)
Capacity cc (cu in)	268.7 (16.397)	368.3 (22.475)	436.5 (26.637)	496.7 (30.310)	496.7 (30.310)	462.8 (28.242)	507.0 (30.8)	521.1 (31.799)	580.7 (35.44)	1211.2 (73.912)
Weight, Dry (1) kg (lb)	19.0 (41.9)	27.5 (60.6)	27.5 (60.6)	30.2 (66.6)	30.2 (66.6)	27.0 (59.5)	38.0 (83.7)	28.0 (61.7)	28.4 (62.4)	60 (132) (9)
Weight, Dry (2) kg (lb)	24.0 (52.9)	32.5 (71.6)	32.5 (71.6)	36.2 (79.8)	36.2 (79.8)	32.0 (70.5)	48.5 (106.9)	33.0 (72.8)	33.8 (78.2)	59.9 (132.0)
Rating (3) kW (hp)	19 (25.5) 6,500 rpm	26 (34.9) 6,500 rpm	29.4 (39.4) 6,500 rpm	34 (45.6) 6,500 rpm	38 (51.0) 6,500 rpm	38 (51.0) 6,500 rpm	32.0 (43.0) 7,800 rpm	48 (64.0) 6,500 rpm	47 (63) 6,500 rpm	59 (79) 5,500 rpm

Notes: 1, Bare, unequipped; 2, with carburettor (503.2V, twin carburettors), intake silencer and exhaust system; 3, standard bare engine; 4, aircooled; 5, liquid cooled; 6, liquid cooled heads, aircooled barrels; 7, two-stroke; 8, four-stroke; 9, with accessories and exhaust.

WESTERMAYER
OSKAR WESTERMAYER
Hauptstrasse 11, A-2161 Poysbrunn
Telephone: 43 (2554) 405
Telex: 73379

This engineer has developed a piston engine with aircooled barrels but liquid-cooled heads. He claims that, compared with the Continental O-200 which was the basis for the engine, fuel consumption is reduced by 25 per cent. Compression ratio is raised to 8.6.

WESTERMAYER W 5/33
This flat-four engine has cylinder heads of cast aluminium alloy, cooled by pure ethylene glycol. The coolant pump feeds via a separate pipe to each head, and the return line passes through an air radiator. Certification to FAR 33 was completed in December 1986.

DIMENSIONS:
Length	730 mm (28.7 in)
Width	790 mm (31.1 in)
Height: carburettor	625 mm (24.6 in)
airbox	700 mm (27.6 in)

The 74.6 kW (100 hp) Westermayer W 5/33

Westermayer W 5/33 engine installation in Cessna 150

WEIGHT, DRY:
Bare	85 kg (187 lb)
With starter, alternator and silencer	102 kg (225 lb)

PERFORMANCE RATING:
T-O   74.6 kW (100 hp) at 2,750 rpm

FUEL CONSUMPTION:
T-O   25.5 litres (6.7 US gallons; 5.6 Imp gallons)/h

SPECIFIC FUEL CONSUMPTION:
T-O   71 µg/J (0.42 lb/h/hp)

682 BELGIUM/CANADA: ENGINES—FNM/P&WC

BELGIUM

FNM

FN MOTEURS SA
(Subsidiary of Fabrique Nationale Herstal)

Route de Liers 121, B-4411 Herstal
Telephone: 32 (41) 784671
Telex: B 41223 FABNA
Fax: 32 (41) 785207 (general)
        32 (41) 786739 (sales & marketing)
DIRECTOR AND GENERAL MANAGER: G. Gevers
BUSINESS DEVELOPMENT: J. C. Morin

With long experience of piston engines, FN began jet engine production in 1949. Today's activity is equally distributed in three sectors: fighter engine production, medium/large transport and space propulsion production,

and depot maintenance for air forces. FN Moteurs employs 1,650 people. Major programmes are:

FNM is responsible for the production and assembly of the P&W F100 fan and engine core modules, and for assembly and test of complete engines.

FNM is reponsible for four major parts of the GE F110: fan discs 1 and 3, the HP turbine disc, and the fan stator case.

FNM is a member of the consortium (RR, MTU, SNECMA, FNM) producing Tyne 21 and 22 engines for the Atlantique and Transall, with a 9.5 per cent share.

After having produced parts for the JT8D and JT9D-7R4, FNM signed a partnership agreement with Pratt & Whitney for a 3 per cent share in the PW4000 series. FNM is

responsible for the HP compressor case and various other components.

Since 1972, in association with SNECMA, FNM has developed and produced the lubrication modules of all CFM56 versions. FNM has increased its participation up to 10 per cent of the SNECMA share (5 per cent overall) in the -5A and -5C versions, to power respectively the Airbus A320 and A340. FNM is responsible for the lubrication and shop modules and other stator or rotor parts. FNM is also performing endurance testing of complete engines.

FNM has signed a co-operation agreement with Turbomeca, and is developing several critical parts of the TM 333.

BRAZIL

CELMA

CELMA-CIA ELECTROMECANICA

Rue Alice Hervê 356, PO Box 90341, 25669 Petrópolis, RJ
Telephone: 55 (242) 43 4962

Telex: (021) 21271
Fax: 55 (242) 42 3684
PRESIDENT: Alexandre Gonçalves Silva
TECHNICAL DIRECTOR: Carlos A. R. Pereira

This company of 1,950 people has facilities totalling 45,000 m² (485,000 sq ft) in which it overhauls many kinds of jet engine and accessories. It shares in the production of components for the Rolls-Royce Spey 807 turbofan.

IMAER

INDÚSTRIA MECÂNICA E AERONÁUTICA LTDA

HEAD OFFICE AND WORKS: Aeroporto de Botucatú, PO Box 301, 18600 Botucatú, SP
Telephone: 55 (149) 22 1908 and 22 5938

IMAER, formerly Retimotor, manufactures four-stroke reciprocating engines for light aircraft, ultralights and powered gliders.

IMAER 2000

This engine is available in two models: the **2000 M1**, with single ignition, JAR 22 certificated, and the **ME1**, with dual ignition, being certificated in 1988.
TYPE: Four-cylinder horizontally-opposed aircooled.
CYLINDERS: Bore 90.4 mm (3.56 in). Stroke 78.4 mm (3.09 in). Swept volume 2,017 cc (123.08 cu in). Compression ratio 8.7.
INDUCTION: Stromberg-Zenith 150 CD or Marvel-Schebler MA 3PA carburettor.

FUEL GRADE: Avgas 100/130.
IGNITION: Slick 4230 or Bendix S4RN21 magneto and/or Bosch electronic.
DIMENSIONS:
Length	590 mm (23.23 in)
Width	764 mm (30.08 in)
Height	447 mm (17.60 in)
WEIGHT: 78-81 kg (172-178.6 lb)
PERFORMANCE RATING: 59.7 kW (80 hp) at 3,400 rpm

IMAER 1000

Again these are two models: The **1000 M1**, with magneto single ignition, not certificated, and the **1000 E1**, with electronic single ignition, not certificated.
TYPE: Two-cylinder horizontally-opposed aircooled.
DIMENSIONS:
Length	370 mm (14.57 in)
Width	764 mm (30.08 in)
Height	410 mm (16.14 in)

IMAER 2000 M1 four-cylinder piston engine

WEIGHT: 39 kg (86 lb)
PERFORMANCE RATING: 47.6 kW (63.8 hp) at 3,600 rpm.

CANADA

CAM

CANADIAN AIRMOTIVE INC

407-5940 No. 6 Road, Richmond, BC V6V 1Z1
Telephone: 1 (604) 270 0188
Telex: 04 355779 SEI IND VCR
Fax: 1 (604) 270 6048

CAM TURBO 90

This is a three-cylinder in-line turbocharged four-stroke piston engine.

CYLINDERS: Overhead camshaft, aluminium head and block each in one piece. Bore 74 mm (2.91 in). Stroke 77 mm (3.03 in). Compression ratio 8.2. Capacity 993 cc (61 cu in).
INDUCTION: Turbocharger and carburettor with mixture control. Fuel 92 RON or 100LL.
IGNITION: Dual capacitive discharge electronic, self diagnostic.
COOLING: Water/glycol mix.
ACCESSORIES: Electric starter, 20A alternator, provision for controllable propeller.

PROPELLER DRIVE: Cam action silent chain in oil bath, normal ratio 2.23.
WEIGHT, DRY: 65 kg (144 lb)
PERFORMANCE RATING (T-O): 67 kW (90 hp) at 5,300 rpm
SPECIFIC FUEL CONSUMPTION (cruise): 64.2 µg/J (0.38 lb/h/hp)

ORENDA

HAWKER SIDDELEY CANADA INC
(Orenda Division)

3160 Derry Rd East, Mississauga, Ontario L4T 1A9
Telephone: 1 (416) 677 3250

Telex: 06-968727
Fax: 1 (416) 678 1538
VICE-PRESIDENT AND GENERAL MANAGER: R. J. Munro
DIRECTOR OF MARKETING: C. M. Hinds

Orenda has a 67,262 m² (724,000 sq ft) facility close to Toronto International Airport. It meets the maintenance needs of the Canadian Forces for General Electric J85 and F404 engines, and makes engine parts under subcontract.

P&WC

PRATT & WHITNEY CANADA (Subsidiary of United Technologies Corporation)

1000 Marie Victorin, Longueuil, Quebec J4G 1A1
Telephone: 1 (514) 677 9411
Telex: 05 267509
PRESIDENT AND CHIEF EXECUTIVE OFFICER: L. D. Caplan
EXECUTIVE VICE-PRESIDENT: G. P. Ouimet
VICE-PRESIDENTS:
  C. Lloyd (Marketing and Customer Support)
  P. Henry (Communications)
  B. H. Sanders (Engineering)

Pratt & Whitney Canada is owned 97 per cent by United Technologies Corporation, Connecticut, USA, and is the P&W Group member responsible for engines for general aviation and regional transport. P&WC employs some 10,000 persons. By 1 January 1990 it had delivered 33,458 engines.

P&WC JT15D

Designed to power business aircraft, small transports and training aircraft, the JT15D first ran on 23 September 1967.

Initial application was the twin-engined Cessna Citation. Up to 1976 Cessna used the **JT15D-1**. Late that year it announced the Citation I powered by the **JT15D-1A** and the Citation II powered by the **JT15D-4**. During 1983 the D-1A was replaced by the **D-1B**.

Other twin-engined business jets powered by the JT15D-4 are the Aerospatiale Corvette and Mitsubishi Diamond I. TBO is 3,500 h for the JT15D-1/D-1A, and 3,000 h for the JT15D-4.

The **JT15D-4B** is an altitude optimised variant for the Citation S/II.

The **JT15D-4C** has an aerobatic oil system for sustained inverted flight, and an electronic fuel control. Powers Agusta S.211.

The **JT15D-4D** is flat rated for improved hot/high performance for the Diamond IA.

The **JT15D-5** is a growth version. A new fan with higher pressure ratio and flow, plus an improved boost stage and HP compressor, are combined to produce 25 per cent more altitude cruise thrust, with a 3 per cent improvement in sfc. HP turbine blades and electronic fuel control are also improved. Powers Cessna T-47A and Diamond II.

The **JT15D-5A** has a hydromechanical fuel control. Selected for Citation V. By 1990 total deliveries of all JT15D engines had reached 3,687. Operating time totalled 11,179,919 h.

The following description relates to the JT15D-1B, except where indicated:
TYPE: Two-shaft turbofan.
FAN: Single-stage axial with 28 solid titanium blades with part-span shrouds. Mass flow, 34 kg (75 lb)/s; bypass ratio about 3.3; fan pressure ratio 1.5.
COMPRESSOR: Single stage titanium centrifugal. Overall pressure ratio about 10:1. (D-4 and D-5 have axial boost stage between fan and compressor.)
COMBUSTION CHAMBER: Annular reverse flow type. Spark igniters at 5 and 7 o'clock (viewed from rear).
FUEL SYSTEM: Pump delivering at 44.8 bars (650 lb/sq in). D-1, 4, 4B, 5A have DP-L2 hydromechanical control; 4C, 4D and 5 have JFC 118 or 119 electronic system.
FUEL GRADES: JP-1, JP-4, JP-5 to CPW 204.
TURBINE: Single-stage HP with 71 solid blades; two-stage LP, first stage cast integrally with 61 blades and second carrying 55 blades in fir tree roots.

LUBRICATION SYSTEM: Integral oil system, with gear type pump delivering at up to 5.52 bars (80 lb/sq in). Capacity, 9.0 litres (2.4 US gallons; 2.0 Imp gallons).
OIL SPECIFICATION: PWA521 Type II, CPW 202.
STARTING: Air turbine starter or electric starter/generator.
DIMENSIONS:

Diameter: JT15D-1	691 mm (27.2 in)
JT15D-4	686 mm (27.0 in)
Length overall: JT15D-1	1,506 mm (59.3 in)
JT15D-4	1,600 mm (63.0 in)

WEIGHT, DRY:

JT15D-1, -1A	232.5 kg (514 lb)
JT15D-1B	235 kg (519 lb)
JT15D-4	253 kg (557 lb)
JT15D-4B	258 kg (568 lb)
JT15D-4C	261 kg (575 lb)
JT15D-4D	255 kg (560 lb)
JT15D-5, -5A	291.5 kg (632 lb)

PERFORMANCE RATINGS:

T-O: JT15D-1, -1A, -1B	9.8 kN (2,200 lb st)
JT15D-4, -4B, -4C, -4D	11.12 kN (2,500 lb st)
JT15D-5, -5A	12.89 kN (2,900 lb st)
Max continuous:	
JT15D-1, -1A, -1B	9.3 kN (2,090 lb st)
JT15D-4, -4B, -4D	10.56 kN (2,375 lb st)
JT15D-4C	9.45 kN (2,125 lb st)
JT15D-5, -5A	12.89 kN (2,900 lb st)

SPECIFIC FUEL CONSUMPTION (T-O):

JT15D-1, -1A, -1B	15.30 mg/Ns (0.540 lb/h/lb st)
JT15D-4, -4C	15.92 mg/Ns (0.562 lb/h/lb st)
JT15D-5, -5A	15.61 mg/Ns (0.551 lb/h/lb st)

Longitudinal section of the P&WC JT15D-5 turbofan

P&WC PW305

Planned for corporate aircraft of the 1990s, this engine is aimed at US coast-to-coast flights at Mach 0.75 at 14,325 m (47,000 ft). MTU of West Germany will be responsible for the LP turbine section, as a partner sharing 25 per cent of the estimated development cost of $Can 500 million.

Certification was achieved in mid-1990. The PW305 powers the BAe 1000.
TYPE: Two-shaft turbofan.
FAN: Single-stage, overhung ahead of front bearing. Pointed rotating spinner. Bypass ratio (S/L, T-O) 4.5.
COMPRESSOR: Four axial stages followed by one centrifugal. Core pressure ratio 15.
COMBUSTION CHAMBER: Annular, fed around periphery by ring of separate curved pipes ducting air from diffuser case of centrifugal compressor.
CONTROL SYSTEM: Dowty and Smiths Industries full-authority digital, with dual channels.
HP TURBINE: Two axial stages, the first having aircooled blades.
LP TURBINE: Three axial stages joined via centre stage disc to fan shaft. Two main shaft bearings.
DIMENSIONS (estimated):

Diameter	869 mm (34.2 in)
Length	2,069 mm (81.4 in)
WEIGHT, DRY (installed):	441 kg (972 lb)

PERFORMANCE RATINGS (ISA, estimated):
T-O, S/L   23.29 kN (5,236 lb st) or flat rated at 21.13 kN (4,750 lb st) to 25°C
Cruise at Mach 0.8 at 12,200 m (40,000 ft)   4.95 kN (1,113 lb)
SPECIFIC FUEL CONSUMPTION (estimated):

T-O as above	11.50 mg/Ns (0.406 lb/h/lb st)
Cruise as above	19.12 mg/Ns (0.675 lb/h/lb)

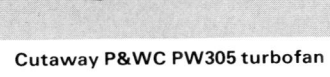

Cutaway P&WC PW305 turbofan

P&WC PW100

The PW100 is a free turbine turboprop consisting of turbomachine and reduction gearbox modules connected by a torque-measuring driveshaft and integrated structural intake case.

Flight development of the PW100 began in February 1982. Principal versions are as follows:

PW115. T-O rated at 1,256 ekW; 1,193 kW (1,685 ehp; 1,600 shp) at 1,300 propeller rpm to 44°C. Selected for Embraer EMB-120 Brasilia. Certificated December 1983.

PW118. T-O rated at 1,411 ekW; 1,342 kW (1,892 ehp; 1,800 shp) at 1,300 propeller rpm to 33°C. Selected for EMB-120 Brasilia.

PW120. T-O rated at 1,566 ekW; 1,491 kW (2,100 ehp; 2,000 shp) at 1,200 propeller rpm to 27.7°C. Selected for Boeing Canada Dash 8-100, Aerospatiale/Aeritalia ATR 42 and Snow SA-210TA. Certificated December 1983.

PW120A. T-O rated at 1,566 ekW; 1,491 kW (2,100 ehp; 2,000 shp) at 1,200 propeller rpm to 29°C. Selected for Dash 8.

PW121. T-O rated at 1,679 ekW; 1,603 kW (2,252 ehp; 2,150 shp) at 1,200 propeller rpm to 26°C.

PW123. T-O rated at 1,866 ekW; 1,775 kW (2,502 ehp; 2,380 shp) at 1,200 propeller rpm to 35°C. Selected for Dash 8-300.

PW124. Growth version, with T-O rating of 1,880 ekW; 1,790 kW (2,522 ehp; 2,400 shp) to 34.4°C. **PW124A** is identical but has higher max continuous power rating.

PW124B. PW124 with PW123 turbomachinery to suit four-blade propeller. Selected for ATR 72.

PW125B. Growth PW124 with T-O rating of 2,095 ekW; 1,864 kW (2,810 ehp; 2,500 shp) at 1,200 propeller rpm to 30°C. Powers Fokker 50.

PW126. Growth engine, max contingency 2,078 ekW; 1,978 kW (2,786 ehp; 2,653 shp) at 1,200 propeller rpm to 32.4°C. Powers BAe ATP.

PW126A. Growth 124A with T-O rating of 2,073 ekW; 1,978 kW (2,780 ehp; 2,653 shp) at 1,200 propeller rpm to 29.2°C. Selected for BAe ATP.

PW130. Growth version under study. Potential of 2,684 kW (3,600 shp) but limited to 2,238 kW (3,000 shp) with present gearbox.

By 1990 deliveries of engines of the PW100 family had reached 1,567. Operating time exceeded 4,379,414 h.

The following description applies to all PW100 series engines:
TYPE: Free turbine turboprop.
PROPELLER DRIVE: Twin-layshaft gearbox with propeller shaft offset above turbomachine. Max propeller speeds 1,300 rpm (PW115) and 1,200 rpm (PW120).
AIR INTAKE: S-bend duct. A secondary duct forms a flowing bypass to prevent foreign object ingestion.
COMPRESSOR: Two centrifugal impellers in series, each driven by its own turbine. Air guided through ring of curved pipes from LP diffuser to HP entry.
COMBUSTION CHAMBER: Annular reverse flow type, with 14 air blast fuel nozzles around periphery and two spark igniters.
FUEL SYSTEM: Hydromechanical control and electronic power management.
FUEL GRADES: JP-1, JP-4, JP-5 to PWA Spec 522.
TURBINES: Single-stage HP with 47 aircooled blades. Single-stage LP with 53 solid blades. Two-stage power turbine, first with 68 blades and second with 74, all with shrouded tips.
ACCESSORY DRIVES: Pads driven by HP compressor, for starter/generator, hydromechanical fuel control and hand turning. Pads on reduction gearbox for alternator, hydraulic pump, propeller control module, overspeed governor and electric auxiliary pump. Electric torque signal and auto power augmentation.
LUBRICATION SYSTEM: One pressure pump and two scavenge pumps, all driven off HP rotor. Integral tank, capacity 9.44 litres (2.5 US gallons, 2.08 Imp gallons).
OIL SPECIFICATION: CPW202 or PWA521 Type II.
STARTING: Electric starter/generator.
DIMENSIONS:

Length: PW115, 118	2,057 mm (81 in)
PW120, 123, 124, 124A	2,134 mm (84 in)
Width: PW115, 118, 120, 120A, 121	635 mm (25 in)
others	660 mm (26 in)
Height: all	787 mm (31 in)

WEIGHT, DRY:

PW115, 118	391 kg (861 lb)
PW120	417.8 kg (921 lb)
PW120A	423 kg (933 lb)
PW121	425 kg (936 lb)
PW123	450 kg (992 lb)
PW124, 125, 126 models	481 kg (1,060 lb)

PERFORMANCE RATINGS (S/L, static):
T-O: See under model listings
Max continuous:

PW115	1,256 ekW; 1,193 kW (1,685 ehp; 1,600 shp) at 1,300 rpm to 44°C
PW118	1,411 ekW; 1,342 kW (1,892 ehp; 1,800 shp) at 1,300 rpm to 33°C
PW120	1,333 ekW; 1,268 kW (1,787 ehp; 1,700 shp) at 1,200 rpm to 32.7°C
PW120A	1,411 ekW; 1,342 kW (1,892 ehp; 1,800 shp) at 1,200 rpm to 33°C
PW121	1,524 ekW; 1,454 kW (2,044 ehp; 1,950 shp) at 1,200 rpm to 28°C
PW123, 124	1,686 ekW; 1,603 kW (2,261 ehp; 2,150 shp) at 1,200 rpm to 45°C
PW124A	1,749 ekW; 1,663 kW (2,345 ehp; 2,230 shp) at 1,200 rpm to 42°C
PW125B	2,095 ekW; 1,603 kW (2,810 ehp; 2,150 shp) at 1,200 rpm to 45°C
PW126	1,734 ekW; 1,648 kW (2,325 ehp; 2,210 shp) at 1,200 rpm to 27.9°C

Cutaway P&WC PW100 turboprop

Max cruise:

PW115		1,178 ekW; 1,119 kW
	(1,580 ehp; 1,500 shp) at 1,300 rpm to 20°C	
PW118		1,188 ekW; 1,128 kW
	(1,593 ehp; 1,512 shp) at 1,300 rpm to 20°C	
PW120		1,271 ekW; 1,207 kW
	(1,704 ehp; 1,619 shp) at 1,200 rpm to 15°C	
PW120A		1,296 ekW; 1,231 kW
	(1,738 ehp; 1,651 shp) at 1,200 rpm to 15°C	
PW121		1,330 ekW; 1,268 kW
	(1,784 ehp; 1,700 shp) at 1,200 rpm to 15°C	
PW123, 124, 124A		1,593 ekW; 1,514 kW
	(2,136 ehp; 2,030 shp) at 1,200 rpm to 22.2°C	
PW125B		1,623 ekW; 1,513 kW
	(2,203 ehp; 2,030 shp) at 1,200 rpm to 22.2°C	
PW126		1,635 ekW; 1,553 kW
	(2,192 ehp; 2,083 shp) at 1,200 rpm to 26.3°C	
PW126A		1,632 ekW; 1,553 kW
	(2,188 ehp; 2,083 shp) at 1,200 rpm to 26.3°C	

SPECIFIC FUEL CONSUMPTION:

T-O rating:

PW115	87.2 μg/J (0.516 lb/h/ehp)
PW118	84.2 μg/J (0.498 lb/h/ehp)
PW120, 120A	82.0 μg/J (0.485 lb/h/ehp)
PW121	80.4 μg/J (0.476 lb/h/ehp)
PW123	79.4 μg/J (0.470 lb/h/ehp)
PW124, 124A	79.1 μg/J (0.468 lb/h/ehp)
PW125B, 126	78.2 μg/J (0.463 lb/h/ehp)
PW126A	76.6 μg/J (0.454 lb/h/ehp)

P&WC PT6A

US military designations: T74 (separate entry) **and T101** (PT6A-45R)

The PT6A is a free turbine turboprop, built in many versions since November 1959. By 1990 a total of 22,068 had logged over 145 million hours in 10,113 aircraft of 4,419 customers.

Current versions of the PT6A are as follows:

PT6A-11. Flat rated at 394 ekW; 373 kW (528 ehp; 500 shp) at 2,200 propeller rpm to 42°C. Fitted to Piper Cheyenne I and IA, T-1040, original Claudius Dornier Seastar and Harbin Y-12 I.

PT6A-110. Flat rated at 374 ekW; 354 kW (502 ehp; 475 shp) at 1,900 propeller rpm to 38°C. Fitted to Dornier 128-6.

PT6A-11AG. Flat rated at 394 ekW; 373 kW (528 ehp; 500 shp) at 2,200 propeller rpm to 42°C. Can use diesel fuel. Fitted to Ayres Turbo-Thrush, Schweizer Turbo Ag-Cat and Weatherly 620 TP.

PT6A-112. Flat rated at 394 ekW; 373 kW (528 ehp; 500 shp) at 1,900 rpm to 56°C. Fitted to Cessna Conquest I, Reims-Cessna F 406 Caravan II, Claudius Dornier Seastar CD2 and AAC Turbine P-210 conversion.

PT6A-114. Flat rated at 471 ekW; 447 kW (632 ehp; 600 shp) at 1,900 rpm to 54.4°C. Fitted to Cessna Caravan I, with single exhaust.

PT6A-15AG. Flat rated at 533 ekW; 507 kW (715 ehp; 680 shp) at 2,200 propeller rpm to 22°C. Can use diesel fuel. Fitted to Ayres Turbo-Thrush, Frakes Turbo-Cat, Schweizer Turbo Ag-Cat D, Air Tractor AT-400, and prototypes of ICA Brasov IAR-827TP and IAR-825TP Triumf.

PT6A-21. Flat rated at 432.5 ekW; 410 kW (580 ehp; 550 shp) at 2,200 propeller rpm to 33°C. Mates A-27 power unit with A-20A gearbox. Fitted to Beechcraft King Air C90.

PT6A-25. Flat rated at 432.5 ekW; 410 kW (580 ehp; 550 shp) at 2,200 propeller rpm to 33°C. Oil system for sustained inverted flight. Fitted to Beechcraft T-34C and Norman Firecracker.

PT6A-25A. Some castings of magnesium alloy instead of aluminium alloy. Fitted to Pilatus PC-7.

PT6A-25C. Flat rated at 584 ekW; 559 kW (783 ehp; 750 shp) at 2,200 propeller rpm to 31°C. A-25 with A-34 hot end and A-27 first stage reduction gearing. Fitted to Embraer EMB-312. Selected for production IAR-825TP Triumf.

PT6A-27. Flat rated at 553 ekW; 507 kW (715 ehp; 680 shp) at 2,200 propeller rpm to 22°C, attained by increase in

mass flow, at lower turbine temperatures than in PT6A-20. Hamilton Westwind II/III (Beech 18) conversions, Beechcraft 99 and 99A, and U-21A and U-21D, DHC-6 Twin Otter 300, Pilatus/Fairchild Industries PC-6/B2-H2 Porter, Frakes Aviation (Grumman) Mallard conversion, Let L-410A Turbolet, Saunders ST-27A conversion, Embraer EMB-110 Bandeirante (early), Harbin Y-12 II, SAC Spectrum-One, and Schafer Comanchero 500B/Neiva Carajá.

PT6A-28. Similar to PT6A-27, this has an additional cruise rating of 419 ekW (562 ehp) available to 21°C and max cruise up to 33°C. Beechcraft King Air E90 and A100, and 99A, Piper Cheyenne II, Avtek 400 and Embraer Xingu I.

PT6A-34. Flat rated at 584 ekW; 559 kW (783 ehp; 750 shp) at 2,200 propeller rpm to 31°C, this version has aircooled nozzle guide vanes. IAI 102/201 Arava, Saunders ST-28, Frakes Aviation (Grumman) Mallard conversion, Airmaster Avalon 680, Omni Turbo Titan, Spectrum-One, Embraer EMB-110P1/P2 and EMB-111, and Carajá.

PT6A-34B. Aluminium alloy replaces magnesium in major castings. Fitted to Beechcraft T-44A.

PT6A-34AG. Agricultural, certificated on diesel fuel. Frakes conversion of Ag-Cat and Ayres Turbo-Thrush. Selected for PZL-106AT/BT Turbo-Kruk, Schweizer Turbo Ag-Cat and Brooklands Fieldmaster.

PT6A-135. Flat rated at 587 ekW; 559 kW (787 ehp; 750 shp) at 1,900 rpm. Changed drive ratio to reduce noise; higher cycle temperatures. JetCrafters Taurus, Embraer 121A1 Xingu II, Piper Cheyenne IIXL, Advanced Aircraft Turbine P-210 and Regent 1500, Airmaster Avalon 680, and Schafer Comanchero/Comanchero 750 conversions.

PT6A-135A. Higher thermodynamic ratings. Avtek 400, Beech F90-1, Dornier Seastar and OMAC Laser 300.

PT6A-36. Flat rated at 586 ekW; 559 kW (786 ehp; 750 shp) at 2,200 rpm to 36°C. Similar to -34 but higher rating. Fitted to IAI 101B/202 Arava and Beechcraft C99.

PT6A-41. Higher mass flow, aircooled nozzle guide vanes and two-stage free turbine. T-O rating of 673 ekW; 634 kW (903 ehp; 850 shp) at 2,000 propeller rpm, to 41°C. Thermodynamic power 812 ekW (1,089 ehp). Beechcraft Super King Air 200 and C-12, and Piper Cheyenne III.

PT6A-41AG. For agricultural aviation. Frakes Turbo-Cat and Schweizer Turbo Ag-Cat.

PT6A-42. A-41 with increase in cruise performance. Beechcraft Super King Air B200.

PT6A-45A. A-41 with gearbox to transmit higher powers at reduced speeds. Rated at 916 ekW; 875 kW (1,229 ehp; 1,173 shp) at 1,700 rpm to 8°C, or to 21°C with water injection. Shorts 330 and Mohawk 298.

PT6A-45B. A-45A with increased water injection.

PT6A-45R. A-45B with reserve power rating and deleted water system.

T101-CP-100. A-45R for Shorts C-23A.

PT6A-50. A-41 with higher ratio reduction gear for quieter operation. T-O 875.5 ekW; 835 kW (1,174 ehp;

1,120 shp) with water up to 34°C at 1,210 propeller rpm. DHC-7.

PT6A-60. Flat rated to 522 kW (700 shp). TBM 700.

PT6A-60A. A-45B with jet flap intake and increased mass flow for high altitude cruise. Rated at 830 ekW; 783 kW (1,113 ehp; 1,050 shp) at 1,700 rpm to 25°C. Beech Super King Air 300 and OMAC Laser 300A.

PT6A-61. A-60 gas generator matched with A-41 power section with 2,000 rpm gearbox. T-O rating 673 ekW; 634 kW (903 ehp; 850 shp) to 46°C. Cheyenne IIIA.

PT6A-62. Flat rated to 708 kW (950 shp). Pilatus PC-9.

PT6A-65B. A-65R without reserve rating. Flat rated at 875.5 ekW; 820 kW (1,174 ehp; 1,100 shp) at 1,700 rpm to 51°C. Beechcraft 1900 and C-12J, and CASA Aviocar C-212P.

PT6A-65R. A-45R with four-stage compressor with jet flap intake, fuel control and fuel dump. Improved hot end and exhaust duct. Reserve power 1,087 ekW; 1,026 kW (1,459 ehp; 1,376 shp) at 1,700 rpm to 28°C. Alternative T-O at 975 ekW; 917 kW (1,308 ehp; 1,230 shp) at 1,700 rpm to 24°C. Shorts 360.

PT6A-65AR. Reserve power 1,125 ekW; 1,062 kW (1,509 ehp; 1,424 shp) at 1,700 rpm to 27.7°C. Shorts 360 and AMI DC-3.

PT6A-66. Flat rated at 674 ekW; 534 kW (905 ehp; 850 shp) at 2,000 rpm to 62.2°C. Piaggio Avanti with opposed rotation gearbox.

PT6A-67. Flat rated at 870 ekW; 820 kW (1,167 ehp; 1,100 shp) at 1,700 rpm to 60°C. Beechcraft Starship 2000 and RC-12K.

PT6A-67A. Flat rated at 948 ekW; 894 kW (1,272 ehp; 1,200 shp) at 1,700 rpm to 51°C. Powers Beech Starship 1 and 1900D.

PT6A-67AF. Flat rated at 1,125 ekW; 1,061 kW (1,509 ehp; 1,424 shp) at 1,700 rpm to 37.2°C. Powers Conair/IMP Turbo Firecat.

PT6A-67R. A-67 with reserve power rating for commuter aircraft. Flat rated at 1,125 ekW; 1,061 kW (1,509 ehp; 1,424 shp) at 1,700 rpm to 37.2°C. Powers Shorts 360-300 and Basler Turbo 67.

The following data apply generally to the PT6A series:

TYPE: Free turbine axial-plus-centrifugal turboprop.

PROPELLER DRIVE (all models up to and including PT6A-41): Two-stage planetary. Ratio 15. Higher ratio gears for A-45R, -50, -60, -65 and -67.

AIR INTAKE: Annular at rear with screen. Aircraft-supplied alcohol or inertial anti-icing.

COMPRESSOR: Three axial stages, plus single centrifugal (-65 series, four axial stages). PT6A-27: pressure ratio 6.7, mass flow 3.1 kg (6.8 lb/s). PT6A-65: pressure ratio 10, mass flow 4.3 kg (9.5 lb/s).

COMBUSTION CHAMBER: Annular reverse flow, with 14 simplex burners.

FUEL SYSTEM: Bendix DP-F2 pneumatic automatic fuel control. A-50 has DP-F3 with starting spill valve and motive flow systems; A-60 series (except -62) have Woodward 83212 hydromechanical system.

FUEL GRADE: JP-1, JP-4, JP-5, MIL-J-5624. Gasolines (MIL-G-5572) grades 80/87, 91/98, 100/130 and 115/145 for up to 150 h during any overhaul period. Agricultural use, diesel.

TURBINES: Up to A-34 two single-stage axial; HP (58 blades) drives compressor, and LP (41 shrouded blades) drives output shaft. A-41 onward have two-stage LP turbine. All blades have fir tree root.

ACCESSORIES: Pads on accessory case (rear of engine) for starter/generator, hydraulic pump, aircraft accessory drive, vacuum pump and tachometer generator. Pad on reduction gear for propeller governor, constant speed unit and tachometer.

LUBRICATION SYSTEM: One pressure and four scavenge elements driven by gas generator. Integral oil tank 8.75 litres (2.3 US gallons).

OIL SPECIFICATION: CPW202, PWA521 Type II (7.5 cs vis) (MIL-L-23699, MIL-L-7808 for military engines).

STARTING: Electric starter/generator on accessory case.

DIMENSIONS:

Max diameter	483 mm (19 in)
Length, excl accessories:	
PT6A-11 to -36	1,575 mm (62 in)

Longitudinal section of P&WC PT6A-67 turboprop

PT6A-41, 42, 61	1,701 mm (67 in)
PT6A-45, 60A	1,829 mm (72 in)
PT6A-50	2,133 mm (84 in)
PT6A-62, -66	1,778 mm (70 in)
PT6A-65B, -67	1,880 mm (74 in)
PT6A-65R, -65AR	1,905 mm (75 in)

WEIGHT, DRY:

PT6A-11	142.4 kg (314 lb)
PT6A-11AG	145.6 kg (321 lb)
PT6A-110	148.3 kg (327 lb)
PT6A-112	147.8 kg (326 lb)
PT6A-114	156.5 kg (345 lb)
PT6A-15AG	144.7 kg (319 lb)
PT6A-21	143.3 kg (316 lb)
PT6A-25	154.6 kg (341 lb)
PT6A-25A	150.1 kg (331 lb)
PT6A-25C	151.9 kg (335 lb)
PT6A-27, -28	142.4 kg (314 lb)
PT6A-34, -36	145.1 kg (320 lb)
PT6A-34B, -135, -135A	149.7 kg (330 lb)
PT6A-34AG	143.8 kg (317 lb)
PT6A-41, -42	177.3 kg (391 lb)
PT6A-41AG	181.4 kg (400 lb)
PT6A-45, -45R	196.8 kg (434 lb)
PT6A-45R	197.7 kg (436 lb)
PT6A-50	275.3 kg (607 lb)
PT6A-60A	210.9 kg (465 lb)
PT6A-61	193.2 kg (426 lb)
PT6A-62	205.9 kg (454 lb)
PT6A-65B, -65R	218.2 kg (481 lb)
PT6A-65AR	220.4 kg (486 lb)
PT6A-66	216.4 kg (477 lb)
PT6A-67, -67A	229.5 kg (506 lb)
PT6A-67AF	241.0 kg (532 lb)
PT6A-67R	233.5 kg (515 lb)

PERFORMANCE RATINGS (S/L, static):
T-O: See under model listings
Max continuous:

PT6A-110	374 ekW; 354 kW (502 ehp; 475 shp) at 1,900 rpm (to 38°C)
PT6A-11, 11AG	394 ekW; 373 kW (528 ehp; 500 shp) at 2,200 rpm (to 42°C)
PT6A-112	394 ekW; 373 kW (528 ehp; 500 shp) at 1,900 rpm (to 56°C)
PT6A-114	471 ekW; 447 kW (632 ehp; 600 shp) at 1,900 rpm (to 54.4°C)
PT6A-15AG, -27, -28	533 ekW; 507 kW (715 ehp; 680 shp) at 2,200 rpm (to 22°C)
PT6A-21	432.5 ekW; 410 kW (580 ehp; 550 shp) at 2,200 rpm (to 33°C)
PT6A-25, -25A	432.5 ekW; 410 kW (580 ehp; 550 shp) at 2,200 rpm (to 33°C)
PT6A-25C	584 ekW; 559 kW (783 ehp; 750 shp) at 2,200 rpm (to 31°C)
PT6A-34	584 ekW; 559 kW (783 ehp; 750 shp) at 2,200 rpm (to 30°C)
PT6A-135	587 ekW; 559 kW (787 ehp; 750 shp) at 1,900 rpm (-135 to 29°C, -135A to 34°C)
PT6A-36	586 ekW; 559 kW (786 ehp; 750 shp) at 2,200 rpm (to 36°C)
PT6A-41	673 ekW; 634 kW (903 ehp; 850 shp) at 2,000 rpm (to 41°C)
PT6A-42	674 ekW; 634 kW (904 ehp; 850 shp) at 2,000 rpm (to 41°C)
PT6A-45A, -45B, -45R	798 ekW; 761 kW (1,070 ehp; 1,020 shp) at 1,700 rpm (to: -45A, 26.7°C; -45B, 29°C; -45R, 33°C)
PT6A-50	762 ekW; 725.5 kW (1,022 ehp; 973 shp) at 1,210 rpm (to 32°C)
PT6A-60A	830 ekW; 783 kW (1,113 ehp; 1,050 shp) at 1,700 rpm (to 25°C)
PT6A-61	673 ekW; 634 kW (902 ehp; 850 shp) at 2,000 rpm (to 46°C)
PT6A-62	751 ekW; 708 kW (1,008 ehp; 950 shp) at 2,000 rpm (to 37°C)
PT6A-65B	875 ekW; 820 kW (1,174 ehp; 1,100 shp) at 1,700 rpm (to 45°C)
PT6A-65R	931 ekW; 875 kW (1,249 ehp; 1,173 shp) at 1,700 rpm (to 38°C)
PT6A-66	675 ekW; 634 kW (905 ehp; 850 shp) at 2,000 rpm (to 62°C)
PT6A-67	870 ekW; 820 kW (1,167 ehp; 1,100 shp) at 1,700 rpm (to 54.4°C)
PT6A-67R	965 ekW; 910 kW (1,294 ehp; 1,220 shp) at 1,700 rpm (to 48°C)

Max cruise rating:

PT6A-110	374 ekW; 354 kW (502 ehp; 475 shp) at 1,900 rpm (to 19°C)
PT6A-11	394 ekW; 373 kW (528 ehp; 500 shp) at 2,200 rpm (to 37°C)
PT6A-11AG	394 ekW; 373 kW (528 ehp; 500 shp) at 2,200 rpm (to 36°C)
PT6A-112	394 ekW; 373 kW (528 ehp; 500 shp) at 1,900 rpm (to 48°C)
PT6A-114	471 ekW; 447 kW (632 ehp; 600 shp) at 1,900 rpm (to 31.1°C)
PT6A-15AG	as PT6A-27
PT6A-21, -25, -25A	432.5 ekW; 410 kW (580 ehp; 550 shp) at 2,200 rpm (to 47.2°C; 33°C; 33°C)

PT6A-25C	545 ekW; 522 kW (731 ehp; 700 shp) at 2,200 rpm (to 19°C)
PT6A-27	486 ekW; 462 kW (652 ehp; 620 shp) at 2,200 rpm (to 21°C)
PT6A-28	486 ekW; 462 kW (652 ehp; 620 shp) at 2,200 rpm (to 33°C)
PT6A-34	545 ekW; 522 kW (731 ehp; 700 shp) at 2,200 rpm (to 19°C)
PT6A-135	548 ekW; 522 kW (735 ehp; 700 shp) at 1,900 rpm (-135 to 37°C, -135A to 41°C)
PT6A-36	548 ekW; 522 kW (735 ehp; 700 shp) at 2,200 rpm (to 19°C)
PT6A-41	673 ekW; 634 kW (903 ehp; 850 shp) at 2,000 rpm (to 28°C)
PT6A-42	674 ekW; 634 kW (904 ehp; 850 shp) at 2,000 rpm (to 33°C)
PT6A-45	749 ekW; 713 kW (1,004 ehp; 956 shp) at 1,425 rpm (to 15°C)
PT6A-50	706 ekW; 671 kW (947 ehp; 900 shp) at 1,020-1,160 rpm (to 23°C)
PT6A-60A	791 ekW; 746 kW (1,061 ehp; 1,000 shp) at 1,700 rpm (to 28°C)
PT6A-61	as max continuous but to 43.8°C
PT6A-62	712 ekW; 671 kW (955 ehp; 900 shp) at 2,000 rpm (to 32°C)
PT6A-65B, -65R	762 ekW; 713 kW (1,022 ehp; 956 shp) at 1,425 rpm (to 27°C)
PT6A-65AR	762 ekW; 713 kW (1,022 ehp; 956 shp) at 1,425 rpm (to 29°C)
PT6A-66	675 ekW; 634 kW (905 ehp; 850 shp) at 2,000 rpm (to 56°C)
PT6A-67, -67A	792 ekW; 746 kW (1,062 ehp; 1,000 shp) at 1,700 rpm (to 50°C)
PT6A-67AF	808 ekW; 760 kW (1,083 ehp; 1,020 shp) at 1,700 rpm (to 37°C)
PT6A-67R	808 ekW; 761 kW (1,083 ehp; 1,020 shp) at 1,425 rpm (to 35°C)

SPECIFIC FUEL CONSUMPTION:
At T-O rating:

PT6A-110	111.0 µg/J (0.657 lb/h/ehp)
PT6A-11, -11AG	109.4 µg/J (0.647 lb/h/ehp)
PT6A-112	107.6 µg/J (0.637 lb/h/ehp)
PT6A-114	108.2 µg/J (0.640 lb/h/ehp)
PT6A-15AG, -27, -28	101.8 µg/J (0.602 lb/h/ehp)
PT6A-21, -25, -25A	106.5 µg/J (0.630 lb/h/ehp)
PT6A-25C, -34, -34B, -34AG	100.6 µg/J (0.595 lb/h/ehp)
PT6A-135, -135A	98.9 µg/J (0.585 lb/h/ehp)
PT6A-36	99.7 µg/J (0.590 lb/h/ehp)
PT6A-41, -61	99.9 µg/J (0.591 lb/h/ehp)
PT6A-42	101.5 µg/J (0.601 lb/h/ehp)
PT6A-45A, -45B	93.5 µg/J (0.554 lb/h/ehp)
PT6A-45R	93.4 µg/J (0.553 lb/h/ehp)
PT6A-50	94.6 µg/J (0.560 lb/h/ehp)
PT6A-60A	92.6 µg/J (0.548 lb/h/ehp)
PT6A-62	95.8 µg/J (0.567 lb/h/ehp)
PT6A-65B	90.6 µg/J (0.536 lb/h/ehp)
PT6A-65R	86.5 µg/J (0.512 lb/h/ehp)
PT6A-65AR	86.0 µg/J (0.509 lb/h/ehp)
PT6A-66	104.8 µg/J (0.620 lb/h/ehp)
PT6A-67	92.4 µg/J (0.547 lb/h/ehp)
PT6A-67R	92.8 µg/J (0.549 lb/h/ehp)
PT6A-67AF, -67R	87.9 µg/J (0.520 lb/h/ehp)

OIL CONSUMPTION:
Max   0.091 kg (0.20 lb)/h

P&WC T74

T74 is a US designation for military versions of the PT6A turboprop and PT6B turboshaft.

T74-CP-700. US Army PT6A-20. More than 300 delivered to Beechcraft for 129 U-21A. Inertial separator system.

T74-CP-702. Rated at 580 ekW (778 ehp) and retrofitted in Beechcraft U-21.

The P&WC PT6B-36 turboshaft engine

P&WC PT6B/PT6C

The PT6B is the commercial turboshaft version of the PT6A and has a lower ratio reduction gear. Current versions are:

PT6B-36. Reverse drive 6,409 rpm gearbox. T-O rating 732 kW (981 shp) to 15°C, with 2½-min contingency 770 kW (1,033 shp) to 15°C. Sikorsky S-76B.

PT6B-36A. Identical to -36 but with different ratings.

PT6C. Direct drive from the power turbine.

DIMENSIONS:

Max diameter: PT6B-36, -36A	495 mm (19.5 in)
Length, excl accessories: PT6B-36, -36A,	1,504 mm (59.2 in)

WEIGHT, DRY:

PT6B-36	169 kg (372 lb)
PT6B-36A	171 kg (378 lb)

PERFORMANCE RATINGS:
T-O: See under model listings
Max cruise, continuous:

PT6B-36	640 kW (870 shp) to 15°C
PT6B-36A	652 kW (887 shp) to 15°C

SPECIFIC FUEL CONSUMPTION:
At T-O rating:

PT6B-36	100.5 µg/J (0.594 lb/h/shp)
PT6B-36A	98.2 µg/J (0.581 lb/h/shp)

OIL CONSUMPTION:
Max   0.091 kg (0.20 lb)/h

P&WC PT6T TWIN-PAC

US military designation: T400 (separate entry)

First run in July 1968, the Twin-Pac comprises two PT6 turboshaft engines side by side and driving a combining gearbox.

PT6T-3. T-O rating 1,342 kW (1,800 shp). For Bell and Agusta-Bell 212 and S-58T.

In these applications, shaft power is limited by the transmission. In the Model 212 the 1,342 kW (1,800 shp) PT6T-3 is restricted to a T-O rating of 962 kW (1,290 shp) and 843 kW (1,130 shp) for continuous power. In the S-58T the limits are 1,122 kW (1,505 shp) at T-O and 935 kW (1,254 shp) for continuous operation.

PT6T-3B. PT6T-3 with some T-6 hardware and improved single-engine performance. Bell 212 and 412.

PT6T-6. Improved compressor-turbine nozzle guide vanes and rotor blades. S-58T and AB 212. By 1989 18,448,884 equivalent PT6 hours had been flown by PT6T engines in 2,047 helicopters in 83 countries.

The following features differ from the PT6:

TYPE: Coupled free turbine turboshaft.

SHAFT DRIVE: Combining gearbox comprises three separate gear trains, two input and one output, each contained within an individual sealed compartment and all interconnected by driveshafts. Overall reduction ratio 5.

AIR INTAKES: Additional inertial particle separator to reduce ingestion. High frequency compressor noise suppressed.

FUEL SYSTEM: As PT6 with manual backup, and dual manifold for cool starts. Automatic power sharing and torque limiting.

FUEL GRADES: JP-1, JP-4 and JP-5.

ACCESSORIES: Starter/generator and tachogenerator on accessory case at front of each power section. Other drives on gearbox, including power turbine governors and tachogenerators, and provision for blowers and aircraft accessories.

OIL SPECIFICATION: PWA Spec 521. For military engines, MIL-L-7808 and -23699.

STARTING: Electrical, with cold weather starting down to −54°C.

DIMENSIONS:

Length	1,702 mm (67.0 in)
Width	1,118 mm (44.0 in)
Height	838 mm (33.0 in)

WEIGHT, DRY (standard equipment):
PT6T-3	292 kg (645 lb)
PT6T-3B, -6	298 kg (657 lb)

PERFORMANCE RATINGS:
T-O (5 min):
Total output, at 6,600 rpm:
PT6T-3, -3B	1,342 kW (1,800 shp)
PT6T-6	1,398 kW (1,875 shp) (to 21°C)

Single power section only, at 6,600 rpm:
PT6T-3, -3B	671 kW (900 shp)
PT6T-6, -3B (2½ min)	764 kW (1,025 shp)

30 min power (single power section), at 6,600 rpm:
PT6T-3B, -6	723 kW (970 shp)

Cruise A:
Total output, at 6,600 rpm:
PT6T-3, -3B	932 kW (1,250 shp)
PT6T-6	1,014 kW (1,360 shp)

Single power section only, at 6,600 rpm:
PT6T-3, -3B	466 kW (625 shp)
PT6T-6	500 kW (670 shp)

Cruise B:
Total output, at 6,600 rpm:
PT6T-3, -3B	820 kW (1,100 shp)
PT6T-6	891 kW (1,195 shp)

Single power section only, at 6,600 rpm:
PT6T-3, -3B	410 kW (550 shp)
PT6T-6	440 kW (590 shp)
Ground idle, at 2,200 rpm	44.7 kW (60 shp) max

SPECIFIC FUEL CONSUMPTION:
At 2½-min rating (single power section):
PT6T-3B	100.7 μg/J (0.596 lb/h/shp)
PT6T-6	101.6 μg/J (0.602 lb/h/shp)

OIL CONSUMPTION:
Max (for both gas generators)	0.18 kg (0.4 lb)/h

P&WC T400

Military version of the PT6T Twin-Pac; castings of aluminium instead of magnesium and minimum infra-red signature. Produced from March 1970 for Bell UH-1N, AH-1J and CH-135. Deliveries totalled 799 engines.

The T400-WV-402 is the military PT6T-6 and is used in the AH-1T; 524 were delivered.

DIMENSIONS (CP-400 and WV-402):
Length	1,659 mm (65.3 in)
Width	1,115 mm (43.5 in)
Height	828 mm (32.6 in)

WEIGHT, DRY:
T400-CP-400	324 kg (714 lb)
T400-WV-402	338 kg (745 lb)

Cutaway drawing of the P&WC PW206A free turbine turboshaft

PERFORMANCE RATINGS:
Intermediate:
T400-CP-400	1,342 kW (1,800 shp) at 6,600 rpm
T400-WV-402	1,469 kW (1,970 shp) at 6,600 rpm

Max continuous:
T400-CP-400	1,141 kW (1,530 shp) at 6,600 rpm
T400-WV-402	1,248 kW (1,673 shp) at 6,600 rpm

SPECIFIC FUEL CONSUMPTION (Intermediate rating):
T400-CP-400	100.4 μg/J (0.594 lb/h/shp)
T400-WV-402	99.9 μg/J (0.591 lb/h/shp)

P&WC PW200

In 1983 P&WC announced the development of this new engine series. The basic design is flexible and is planned to permit increased power and reduced sfc without dimensional change. The first model in the series is the **PW206A**. Certification is due at the end of 1991.

TYPE: Free-turbine turboshaft.

AIR INTAKE: Inwards amidships through mesh screen.

COMPRESSOR: Single-stage centrifugal of machined titanium. Pressure ratio 8.

COMBUSTION CHAMBER: Reverse-flow annular with 12 air blast nozzles. Two capacitor discharge igniters.

FUEL SYSTEM: Hydromechanical with digital electronics powered by dedicated alternator.

FUEL GRADE: JP-1, JP-4, JP-5 or a range of gasolines.

TURBINES: Single-stage axial compressor and power turbines with blades held in dovetail slots. Cold junction temperature sensing.

GEARBOX: Front mounted combined reduction and accessory gearbox with 6,000 rpm output. Includes phase shift torquemeter and drives for starter/generator, hydraulic pump and alternator.

DIMENSIONS:
Length	912 mm (35.9 in)
Width	500 mm (19.7 in)
Height	566 mm (22.3 in)

PERFORMANCE RATINGS:
2½ min	462 kW (619 shp)
30 min and T-O	450 kW (603 shp)
Max continuous	396 kW (531 shp)

SPECIFIC FUEL CONSUMPTION:
2½ min	93.8 μg/J (0.555 lb/h/shp)
30 min and T-O	93.9 μg/J (0.556 lb/h/shp)
Max continuous	95.8 μg/J (0.567 lb/h/shp)

CHINA, PEOPLE'S REPUBLIC

MAS
MINISTRY OF AERO-SPACE INDUSTRY
PO Box 33, Beijing
Telephone: 86 (1) 440517
Telex: 211244 MAS CN
MINISTER: Lin Zongtang

CHINA NATIONAL AERO-ENGINE CORPORATION
67 Jiao Nan Dejie, Beijing
Telephone: 86 (1) 4013322 ext 5401
Cables: 9696

INTERNATIONAL MARKETING:
CATIC (China National Aero-Technology Import and Export Corporation)
5 Liang Guo Chang Road, East City District (PO Box 1671), Beijing
Telephone: 86 (1) 445831, 442444
Telex: 22318 AEROT CN
Cables: CAID BEIJING
Fax: 86 (1) 4015381
PRESIDENT: Sun Zhaoqing
EXECUTIVE VICE-PRESIDENT: Tang Xiaoping

In the past 30 years China has enormously expanded its aero-engine industry. Today there are eight major engine manufacturing centres, five factory-managed design institutes and four engine research and design institutes. Over 48,000 engines of 25 types have been manufactured for the air force and navy, 756 engines of 10 types manufactured for CAAC, and smaller numbers for export. Not within the scope of this annual, nine types of large solid and liquid rocket engines have also been manufactured. Most factories are seeking foreign orders or partners.

The following survey is by alphabetical order in English of the design or manufacturing organisation.

CEC
CHENGDU ENGINE COMPANY
PO Box 613, Chengdu, Sichuan
Telephone: 86 (28) 442470
Cables: 4721
Telex: 60142 CET CN
Fax: 86 (28) 442470

GENERAL MANAGER: Pei Hongbin

This company was formed in October 1958, and is also known as CEF (Chengdu Aero-Engine Factory). Most of the staff and resources came from the Shenyang Overhaul Factory, and the first task was to produce the **RD-500K** (RR Derwent derivative) turbojet for a cruise missile.

Today CEC has a site area exceeding 130 ha (321.2 acres) and a workforce of over 20,000. It produces the **WP6** turbojet (see LEMC), the **WP13** turbojet (see LMC) and components for the Pratt & Whitney **JT8D** turbofan, including combustion liners.

CLXMW
CHANGZHOU LAN XIANG MACHINERY WORKS
PO Box 37, Changzhou, Jiangxi
Telephone: 86 (596) 602095, 602097
Cables: 5046

DIRECTOR: Tian Taiwu

Also known as JHEF (Jiangxi Helicopter Engine Factory), this works has a payroll of over 5,000. Its main product is the **WZ6** turboshaft and the **WZ6G** industrial derivative. Rated at 1,145 kW (1,536 shp) and with a dry

weight of 300 kg (661 lb), the WZ6 is derived from the Turbomeca Turmo IIIC. Work began in 1975, testing occupied 1980-82 and WZ6 engines first flew in a Z-8 helicopter in 1986.

DEMC
DONGAN ENGINE MANUFACTURING COMPANY
PO Box 51, Harbin, Heilongjiang
Telephone: 86 (451) 61431
Cables: 0021
Telex: 87082 HEF CN
GENERAL MANAGER: Zhang Hongbiao

Also known as HEF (Harbin Engine Factory), this establishment was founded in 1948 and employs more than

10,000. Its first product was the 1,268 kW (1,700 hp) **HS7**, a 14-cylinder radial piston engine based on the Soviet Shvetsov ASh-82V. In parallel, in 1957-59, a few ASh-21 engines were made, but only the HS7 went into production, for the Z-5 helicopter. In the late 1950s there was a need for a better engine for the Il-12, Il-14, Tu-2 and Curtiss C-46, with the main need on altitude performance. The result, produced from 1962 until 1980, was the **HS8**, which combined the main body and supercharger of the HS7 with the reduction gear of the ASh-82T. The HS8 is rated at 1,380 kW (1,850 hp).

A larger effort began in 1968 when development of the **WJ5** was transferred from ZEF. Rated at 1,901 ekW (2,550 ehp), this engine is derived from the Ivchenko AI-24A. Among problems solved were broaching of the turbine disc and welding of the annular combustion chambers. Following 5,678 test hours the WJ5 was certificated in January 1977. From 1969 an even larger project was development of the **WJ5A**, to meet the needs of the SH-5. The turbine section was almost completely redesigned, with aircooled rotor blades, and many other parts changed in design or material. The first 5A went on test in late 1970, and certification was gained in January 1980. This modernised engine is rated at 2,350 ekW (3,150 ehp) up to 30°C. In 1979 work began on modifying the original WJ5 to enable the Y-7 series of aircraft to have better hot/high

performance. The result, certificated in 1982, is the **WJ5A I**, basically a 5A flat rated at 2,162.5 ekW (2,900 ehp) to 38°C.

In 1966 Harbin was assigned the task of modifying the

WJ5 into the **WZ5** turboshaft engine for the Z-6 helicopter. After a prototype had been run this engine was transferred to ZARI (which see).

GADRI
GUIZHOU AERO-ENGINE DESIGN AND RESEARCH INSTITUTE

Supported by many companies, GADRI developed the **WP7B** fighter engine which, for convenience, is included in the main WP7 entry under LMC.

GEF — See under LMC.

HEF — See under DEMC.

JHEF — See under CLXMW.

LEMC
LIMING ENGINE MANUFACTURING CORPORATION

PO Box 424, Shenyang, Liaoning
Telephone: 86 (24) 443139
Cables: 4104
Telex: 80025 LMMCS CN
Fax: 86 (24) 732221
GENERAL MANAGER: Yan Guangwei

With site area exceeding 100 ha (247.1 acres), more than 200,000 m² (2,152,850 sq ft) covered area, and a workforce of over 20,000, Liming (Daybreak) is one of the largest and most experienced aero-engine centres in China. Alternatively known as SEF (Shenyang Aero-Engine Factory), or just as The New Factory, it was set up on the basis of the old overhaul factory in 1954-57. The first product was the **WP5** turbojet, a licensed version of the Soviet Klimov VK-1F (Rolls-Royce Nene derivative). Production of the WP5 was achieved in June 1956. By 1957 the WP5A, based on the VK-1A, was in production, but in 1963, following increased demand to power the H-5, production was transferred to XEF (see XAE).

In 1956 SADO (Shenyang Aero-Engine Design Office) was established, later being restyled SARI. This undertook the design of the first Chinese turbojet, the **PF1A**, based on the WP5 but smaller and rated at 15.7 kN (3,527 lb st) to power the JJ-1 trainer. Design was complete in 1957 and the PF1A powered the prototype JJ-1 in July 1958, but later the requirement for the JJ-1 was dropped.

In early 1958 Soviet documents arrived for licence production of the Tumansky RD-9BF-811. This supersonic axial turbojet with afterburner, with 2,521 component parts, proved a major challenge, but the Shenyang **WP6** was first tested at the end of 1958. Tests were not successful, but following improvements in quality control trial production restarted in 1961. Subsequently several thousand, with progressive upgrades, have been made for the J-6, JJ-6 and Q-5. Much further work led to the **WP6A** for the Q-5 I attack aircraft, with a variable inlet stator stage and increased turbine temperature. This engine was certificated in August 1973. A further variant was the **WP6B** for the J-12, not made in quantity.

The following is a description of the WP6A:
INLET: Cast assembly with four de-iced radial struts, one housing drive to accessory section above and projecting ahead of inlet. Central fixed bullet and front bearing.

COMPRESSOR: Welded ring construction with one row of variable inlet stators and nine rows of rotor blades. T-O airflow 46.2 kg (101.85 lb)/s. Pressure ratio 7.44.
COMBUSTION CHAMBER: Can-annular type with 12 flame tubes, each terminating in a section of turbine inlet periphery. Spill type burners. Two igniters fed from starting tank.
TURBINE: Two-stage type with blades inserted into large flat discs, driving compressor via tubular shaft.
AFTERBURNER: Constant diameter type with main starting burner in turbine rear cone and single ring of fuel nozzles and gutter flameholders around rear of cone. Ten adjustable nozzle flaps positioned by four rams.
DIMENSIONS:
Length	5,483 mm (215.9 in)
Max height	950 mm (37.4 in)
Diameter	668 mm (26.3 in)
WEIGHT, DRY: 725 kg (1,598 lb)
PERFORMANCE RATINGS (S/L, static):
Afterburner: WP6A	36.78 kN (8,267 lb st)
WP6B	39.72 kN (8,929 lb st)
Max dry: WP6A	29.42 kN (6,614 lb st)
Normal: WP6A	24.03 kN (5,401 lb st)
WP6B	24.51 kN (5,511 lb st)

The WP6A afterburning turbojet

Longitudinal section through WP6A turbojet (afterburner shown shortened)
1 variable inlet stator, 2 stator vanes, 3 compressor case, 4 air bleed band, 5 bleed actuating cylinder, 6 rear load relief cavity, 7 centre bearing, 8 starting igniter, 9 stage 1 nozzle, 10 turbine rotor, 11 stage 2 nozzle, 12 quick-release ring, 13 diffuser, 14 quick-release ring, 15 front flange, 16 case, 17 shroud, 18 bracket, 19 actuating cylinder, 20 adjustable flap flange, 21 actuator and rod heat shield, 22 nozzle adjusting ring, 23 copper plate, 24 flap, 25 centring pin, 26 cylinder cowl, 27 clamp strip, 28 rear bearing, 29 oil jet, 30 flame tube, 31 compressor, 32 front load relief cavity, 33 front bearing, 34 front case

SPECIFIC FUEL CONSUMPTION (WP6A):
Afterburner
         0.163 kg/h/N (45.24 mg/Ns; 1.597 lb/h/lb st)
Max   0.1 kg/h/N (27.76 mg/Ns; 0.980 lb/h/lb st)
Normal   0.099 kg/h/N (27.48 mg/Ns; 0.970 lb/h/lb st)

To meet the needs of the J-7 fighter programme the Shenyang factory produced the Tumansky R-11F-300 afterburning turbojet under licence. Designated WP7, this Mach 2 engine was an even greater challenge as many key Soviet documents were not supplied, and 1,097 documents had errors or omissions. Eventually, using indigenous materials, the first WP7 went on test in October 1965. Dry and afterburning ratings were 38.2 kN (8,598 lb st) and 56.4 kN (12,676 lb st) respectively. By 1970 production of this engine was transferred to LMC. Shenyang continued to

introduce design improvements, and a stall flutter problem was solved by using 24 larger blades in the first stage of the compressor instead of 31, while other changes were made to the HP turbine disc, bearing lubrication and afterburner nozzle flap design.

In 1964 a decision had to be made on how to power the J-8 fighter. No engine in the 120 kN (12 tonne) class could be produced in time, but Rong Ke, deputy director of Beijing Aeronautical Materials Institute, undertook to produce aircooled blades within a year to allow two uprated WP7 engines to be used. In May 1965 the resulting engine was authorised as the WP7A. After prolonged testing against forged blades with three large cooling holes the decision was taken to use nine-hole cast blades. Dry and afterburning ratings were established at 43.14 kN (9,698 lb st) and 59 kN (13,265 lb st), respectively. These engines powered the J-8 on its first flight in July 1969, and were

certificated in June 1982. Subsequently LMC developed the WP7B.

Also in 1964 a meeting was held to select an engine for a new indigenous fighter. The choice fell on an augmented turbofan, the WS6. Drawings were produced in 1964-66, and by 1969 two prototype engines had been made. Then the cultural revolution delayed the programme by about 10 years, but after 1978 further progress was possible. A two-spool engine with aircooled HP blades, it overcame many problems and reached design figures in 1980. Full details are not yet available, but dry and afterburning thrusts are respectively 71.3 kN (16,027 lb st) and 122.2 kN (27,470 lb st), and dry weight 2,100 kg (4,632 lb). In 1980-82 modifications were made, especially to the afterburner, to increase maximum thrust in the WS6A to 138.3 kN (31,085 lb st), giving a thrust/weight ratio close to 7. This engine is expected to power the H-7.

LMC
LIYANG MACHINERY CORPORATION

PO Box 5, Pingba, Guizhou
Telephone: 86 (34) Guiyang
Cables: 4099, 4101
Telex: 66044 LYNCG CN
GENERAL MANAGER: Hu Wenqin

With a covered area of 750,000 m² (8,073,200 sq ft), and a workforce exceeding 10,000, LMC is also known as GEF (Guizhou Aero-Engine Factory). The associated GADRI undertook the development of the WP7B afterburning turbojet, the programme being transferred to LMC because Shenyang was overloaded. The main change in the 7B concerned the structure and length of the afterburner. Severe problems were encountered with the cast aircooled turbine blades, which tended to crack, with the high reject rate of castings, and with burning of the rear fuselage caused by excessive afterburner wall temperatures. The 7B was eventually certificated in 1978 and succeeded the WP7 in production in 1980. Further changes enabled TBO to be increased from 100 h to 200 h. Guizhou then eliminated the separate petrol (gasoline) starter and its tank and supply system, which reduced weight and maintenance and improved air starting. The engine is known as the WP7B (M batch) and entered production in 1982. A further modification, in the WP7B (BM), reduces weight by 17 kg (37.5 lb), enabling the F-7M to add drop tanks. The following refers to the WP7B (BM):

TYPE: Two-shaft turbojet with afterburner.
INLET: No inlet guide vanes, first LP compressor stage overhung ahead of front roller bearing.
COMPRESSOR: Three-stage LP compressor with pressure ratio of 2.74. Three-stage HP compressor giving overall pressure ratio of 8.1. All blades inserted into discs carried on short tubular shafts.
COMBUSTION CHAMBER: Can-annular, with ten flame tubes, Nos. 1 and 6 being of a different pattern and incorporating torch igniters. Air-film liners coated on both sides with ceramic material.
TURBINES: Single-stage HP with 96 inserted shrouded blades. Single-stage LP with shrouded blades. Outlet gas temperature 1,083°K (810°C).
AFTERBURNER: Multiple gutters and double-wall liner. Multi-flap nozzle driven by four hydraulic rams. Up to 40 h operation permitted in each 200 h overhaul period.
PERFORMANCE RATINGS (S/L, static):
Max afterburner   59.82 kN (13,448 lb st)
Max dry   43.15 kN (9,700 lb st)
SPECIFIC FUEL CONSUMPTION (as above):
Max afterburner   56.37 mg/Ns (1.99 lb/h/lb st)
Max dry   28.61 mg/Ns (1.01 lb/h/lb st)

The next major production of LMC was the WP13. Though this has some features in common with the Tumansky R-13 it is a Chinese development, based on experience with the WP7. A two-spool afterburning turbojet, it was developed to power the J-7 III and J-8 II. Compared with the WP7 the airflow is increased, work per stage improved, pressure ratio raised (the HP spool having five stages) and surge margin doubled. New titanium alloys were used for the compressor discs and blades, and in a major development two more new titanium alloys were used for the cast compressor casings. WP13 development began in 1978, and it was decided to make the engine a 50/50 joint project with CEC. Both factories tested engines, and certification was gained in 1985. Further development introduced aircooled HP turbine blades and modifications to the combustion chamber and afterburner, the afterburner of the WP13A II being longer. In 1988 the WP13G and WP14 were announced, with a new annular combustion chambers, for later J-7 versions. In October 1988 SNECMA announced that it was assisting CATIC to develop the improved WP13G and WP14 for later F-7 versions. New annular combustion chambers will be produced.

WP7B(BM) afterburning turbojet for the F-7M Airguard fighter

LMC WP13A II turbojet (afterburner not fitted)

DIMENSIONS:
Length overall:
  WP13   4,600 mm (181.1 in)
  WP13A II   5,150 mm (202.75 in)
Diameter: both   907 mm (35.71 in)
Max height: WP13 1,085 mm (42.72 in)
WEIGHT, DRY:
WP13   1,211 kg (2,670 lb)
WP13A II   1,201 kg (2,648 lb)
PERFORMANCE RATINGS (S/L, static):
Max afterburner:
  WP13   64.73 kN (14,550 lb st) at 11,156 LP rpm
  WP13A II   65.9 kN (14,815 lb st)

Max dry:
  WP13   40.21 kN (9,039 lb st) at 11,156 LP rpm
  WP13A II   42.7 kN (9,590 lb st)
SPECIFIC FUEL CONSUMPTION (as above):
Max afterburner:
  WP13   63.73 mg/Ns (2.25 lb/h/lb st)
  WP13A II   62.32 mg/Ns (2.20 lb/h/lb st)
Max dry:
  WP13   27.19 mg/Ns (0.96 lb/h/lb st)
  WP13A II   28.04 mg/Ns (0.99 lb/h/lb st)
OVERHAUL LIFE:
  WP13   500 h (total service life 1,500 h)
  WP13A II   300 h (including up to 90 h in afterburner)

SAC
SHENYANG AERO-ENGINE COMPANY

This was formed in 1979 from the merger of SEF (LEMC) and SARI. Today it is part of LEMC.

SAMP

SHANGHAI AERO-ENGINE MANUFACTURING PLANT

PO Box 600, 600 Guangzhong Road, Shanghai
Telephone: 86 (21) 650644
Cables: 5834
Telex: 33136 SHAIR CN
Fax: 86 (21) 651482

DIRECTOR: Zhou Kecheng

This factory was built in 1971-74 and was originally the SAF (Shanghai Aero-Engine Factory). It has a covered area of 56,191 m² (604,855 sq ft) and workforce of 2,000. Apart from various non-aero engines and components its main development effort was the **WS8** turbofan, to power the Y-10. Work proceeded quickly and the first engine went on test in June 1975. Eight engines were built, one running a

1,000 h test, one a 150 h certification test and one was flight tested, making eight flights totalling 22 h. A front-fan engine with a short bypass duct, the WS8 was rated at 80 kN (18,000 lb st). About 17 per cent was titanium, and new techniques included Ni-Cd anti-corrosion coating, graphite varnish of titanium parts and aluminised siliconising of turbine blades. The Y-10 was not put into production and the engine had no other application.

SARI

SHENYANG AVIATION ENGINE RESEARCH INSTITUTE

PO Box 428, Shenyang, Liaoning
Telephone: 86 (24) 443910
Cables: 4391 (national), SARI (international)
Telex: 80055 SARI CN
Fax: 86 (24) 445723

Originally (August 1956) SADO, the Shenyang Aero-Engine Design Office, SARI was merged into SAC in 1979. Responsible for R&D rather than manufacture, SARI was nevertheless charged with design and development of the **PF1A** (see LEMC) and in 1962 of the **WS5**. This was to be the first Chinese turbofan, developed by adding an aft fan to a **WP6** turbojet. Work began in January 1963. Compared with the WP6 the WS5 featured variable guide vanes ahead of the first three compressor stages instead of bleed valves, a

rear fan instead of an afterburner, and other related changes. The first engine was assembled in early 1965. Great difficulty was met in developing the double-deck turbine/fan blades, and in eliminating stall flutter. Seven engines were tested, and taxi tests carried out on an H-5. Take-off thrust reached 35 kN (7,940 lb st) with sfc reduced by 30 per cent. H-5 performance would have been greatly improved, but it was decided not to re-engine the aircraft and WS5 development ceased in 1973.

SEF — *Original abbreviation of SAC (see LEMC).*

SMPMC

SOUTH MOTIVE POWER AND MACHINERY COMPLEX

PO Box 211, Zhuzhou, Hunan 412002
Telephone: 86 (733) 21151
Cables: 2820
Telex: 995002 CHENF CN
Fax: 86 (733) 24220

SAEC (South Aero-Engine Company)

Address as above
GENERAL MANAGER: Wu Shenduo

With a covered area of nearly 300,000 m² (3,230,000 sq ft) and workforce of over 10,000, SMPMC is one of the larger MAS establishments. Until 1983 its aero-engine division, SAEC, was known as ZEF (Zhuzhou Aero-Engine Factory), and in 1951 was set up as the first aero-engine factory in China. Its first product was the Soviet Shvetsov **M-11FR** radial piston engine rated at 119 kW (160 hp), the first three being completed in July 1954. Mass production followed. To meet the needs of the Y-5 (licensed An-2) ZEF began in September 1956 to work on the HS5 (licensed ASh-621R). Over 2,600 of these 746 kW (1,000 hp) radial piston engines were produced by 1986, some being installed

in CAAC Li-2s. Lacking the chosen Praga Doris B engine to power the CJ-6 trainer, the Soviet Ivchenko AI-14R radial piston engine was produced as the **HS6**. Rated at 191 kW (260 hp), the HS-6 entered production in June 1962, about 700 being produced. To improve performance, especially at altitude, ZEF increased rpm, compression ratio and supercharger gear ratio. The result, in 1963, was the **HS6A**, with T-O power increased to 212.5 kW (285 hp). About 3,000 were made by 1986. In 1975 the engine was again modified to power the Y-11; rpm was increased and the reduction gear strengthened. The resulting **HS6D**, with power of 224 kW (300 hp), was certificated in August 1980. The latest version, for an agricultural aircraft (Haiyan), the **HS6E**, has a further increased compression ratio and modifed exhaust valves and reduction gear, raising output to 261 kW (345 hp). Experimental models, in the 1963-70 period, were the turbocharged **HS6B** and the **HS6C** for helicopters, used in the 701 and Yan'an II helicopters.

Work on gas turbines began in January 1965 in support of the development by BIAA (Beijing Institute of Aeronautics and Astronautics) of the **WP11**. This simple turbojet, rated at 8.3 kN (1,874 lb st), powered the WZ-5 unmanned reconnaissance vehicle. The WP11 first ran in June 1971 and was certificated in 1980, manufacture then

being transferred to ZEF. In September 1965 ZEF was selected to develop the **WJ5** turboprop, but this was transferred in 1968 to HEF (see DEMC). In 1969 ZEF was ordered to develop the **WJ6** turboprop, based on the Soviet Ivchenko AI-20M, to power the Y-8. Testing started in 1970, but various problems delayed certification until January 1977. Further changes (for example to compressor vane angle, igniter and lubrication clearances) resulted in TBO being raised in stages from 300 h to 3,000 h. T-O power was 3,169 ekW (4,250 ehp) and weight 1,200 kg (2,645 lb). In 1977 work began on the **WJ6A** to power the Y-8 with a pressure cabin and greater payload. By using aircooled blades and raising the rpm this engine was successfully run in 1983 at 3,393 ekW (4,550 ehp).

In 1980 ZEF began the assembly and test of the **WZ8** (Turbomeca Arriel 1C) for the Z-9 helicopter. ZEF gives the output as 522 kW (700 shp) for a weight of 118 kg (260 lb). An all-Chinese WZ8 ran in 1985, and resulted in major technical upgrades at Zhuzhou (the high-voltage power unit was the only imported part). As part of the offset, 40 accessory gearboxes were supplied to France.

ZEF also produces solid rocket motors for air-to-air missiles.

XAE

XIAN AERO-ENGINE CORPORATION

PO Box 13, Xian, Shaanxi
Telephone: 86 (29) 61951, 63366
Cables: 5411
Telex: 70102 XIARO CN
GENERAL MANAGER: Yang Naishi

Construction of this factory began in August 1958, as XEF (Xian Aero-Engine Factory), and today its workforce exceeds 10,000. Its first task, undertaken in collaboration with HEF and SEF, was to develop and produce the **WP8** turbojet. Based on the Soviet Mikulin RD-3M (AM-3M), this large engine is rated at 93.17 kN (20,944 lb st) and

weighs 3,100 kg (6,834 lb). It posed the greatest challenge to the embryonic Chinese industry, especially as many questions were left unanswered by the licensor (for example, the composition and work processes for the nozzle guide vanes). In 1963 the whole WP8 programme was transferred to XEF, and the engine was certificated and put into production in January 1967.

In 1963 the increased demand for **WP5A** engines for the H-5 resulted in series production being transferred to XEF from SEF. XEF also produced engines for the HJ-5 and HZ-5. In 1965, together with Chengdu Aircraft Corporation, XEF developed the modified **WP5D** for the JJ-5 trainer. In 1966 it developed the **WP5B** and produced

it in quantity for Soviet-made MiG-15 bis fighters. In 1976 it developed and series-produced the **WP5C** to power Soviet-made MiG-17 all-weather fighters.

In 1971 Premier Zhou Enlai called for a major upgrade in Chinese aeronautical quality and technology. As a result negotiations with Rolls-Royce began in May 1972, leading to a licence to produce the Spey 202 augmented turbofan signed on 13 December 1975. The work was assigned to XEF, the engine being designated **WS9**. After a great effort, of major benefit to the industry, four WS9 engines were successfully tested in China and Britain in 1979-80, but no Chinese application has yet emerged.

ZAC

ZHUZHOU AERO-ENGINE COMPANY

This organisation, apparently an alternative or earlier title for SAEC (see SMPMC entry), was formed in 1983 by

merging ZEF and ZARI. Its main task so far has been to produce the **WJ9** turboprop to power a production version of the Y-12. This engine, rated at 507 kW (680 shp), is based on the WZ8 (Arriel 1C), but with a new reduction gear,

accessory drives and fuel and lubrication systems. The first engine ran in 1986 and met the design figures. A production WJ9 would probably also power agricultural and other special-purpose aircraft.

ZARI

ZHUZHOU AERO-ENGINE RESEARCH INSTITUTE

This organisation was established in 1968. From the start it has been tasked with R&D of shaft-drive gas-turbine

engines, starting with the **WZ5** (see DEMC). The poor payload and lack of twin-engine safety of the Z-5 and Z-6 led to a new helicopter, the Z-7, in 1970. This was powered by the twin-packaged **WZ5A**, developed at ZARI. Contingency power of each power section was 1,737 kW

(2,330 shp). Design was finished in 1971, but the cultural revolution caused a delay of eight years. The WZ5A then reached its design targets, but was cancelled upon the abandonment of the Z-7. ZARI was merged with ZEF in 1983 to form ZAC.

ZEF

ZHUZHOU AERO-ENGINE FACTORY

Established in 1951 as China's first aero-engine factory (see SMPMC entry), ZEF was amalgamated with ZARI in 1983 to form ZAC.

CZECHOSLOVAKIA

OMNIPOL

OMNIPOL FOREIGN TRADE CORPORATION

Nekázanka 11, 112 21 Prague 1
Telephone: 42 (2) 2140 111

Omnipol is responsible for exporting products of the Czechoslovak aviation industry and for supplying information on those products which are available for export.

AEROTECHNIK

68604 Uherské Hradiste 4, Kunovice
Telephone: 42 (632) 5122
Telex: 60380
TECHNICAL DEPT: Ing E. Parma

This company is now producing the long established inverted four-cylinder Walter Mikron piston engine, of 2,440 cc (149 cu in) capacity. The factory at Mor. Trebová calls it the **Mikron IIIS (A)**. It powers the Aerotechnik L-13SW Vivat motor glider. Since 1989 the **Mikron IIISE (AE)** has also been produced, with electric starter and alternator. This increases weight from 65.9 kg (145.3 lb) to 70.0 kg (154 lb).

PERFORMANCE RATINGS (both versions):
T-O	48.5 kW (65 hp) at 2,600 rpm
Cruise	35.5 kW (47.6 hp) at 2,350 rpm

Aerotechnik Mikron IIISE(AE) piston engine

AVIA

AVIA KŮNCERNOVÝ PODNIK

199 03 Prague 9, Letñany
Telephone: 42 (2) 89 51 21
Telex: Prague AVIA C 121 475

This company is at present engaged in series production of piston engines, propellers and spare parts.

AVIA M 137 A

Designed to power light aerobatic aircraft, the 134 kW (180 hp) M 137 A piston engine is a modification of the M 337 with fuel and oil systems for aerobatic operation and without a supercharger. It powers the Zlin 42 M and Z 526 F. The **M 137 AZ** is a modified version, with the air intake port at the rear so that a dust filter can be incorporated. Details are as M 337, with the following differences:

CRANKSHAFT: No oil holes for propeller control.
FUEL SYSTEM: Type LUN 5150 pump; system designed for sustained aerobatics.
STARTER: LUN 2131 electric.
DIMENSIONS:
Length	1,344 mm (52.9 in)
Width	443 mm (17.44 in)
Height	630 mm (24.80 in)
WEIGHT (incl starter):	141.5 kg (312 lb)

PERFORMANCE RATINGS:
T-O	134 kW (180 hp) at 2,750 rpm
Max continuous	119 kW (160 hp) at 2,680 rpm
Max cruise	104.5 kW (140 hp) at 2,580 rpm

SPECIFIC FUEL CONSUMPTION:
At T-O rating	91.26 µg/J (0.540 lb/h/hp)
At max cruise rating	81.96 µg/J (0.485 lb/h/hp)

AVIA M 337 A

The M 337 A six-cylinder aircooled supercharged engine powers several types of light aircraft that were built in Czechoslovakia, including the L-200D Morava, Zlin 43 and Zlin 726K. It can be supplied with hubs for fixed-pitch or controllable-pitch propellers. The **M 337 AK** is fitted to the Zlin 142.

TYPE: Six-cylinder inverted in-line aircooled, ungeared, supercharged and with direct fuel injection.

Avia M 137 A six-cylinder aircooled piston engine

CYLINDERS: Bore 105 mm (4.13 in). Stroke 115 mm (4.53 in). Swept volume 5.97 litres (364.31 cu in). Compression ratio 6.3 : 1. Steel cylinders with cooling fins machined from solid. Cylinder bores nitrided. Detachable cylinder heads are aluminium alloy castings.
PISTONS: Aluminium alloy with graphited surfaces.
CONNECTING RODS: Two split big ends bolted together.
CRANKSHAFT: Forged from chrome vanadium steel, machined all over. Nitrided crankpins.
CRANKCASE: Heat treated magnesium alloy (Elektron).
IGNITION: Shielded type. Two plugs per cylinder.
LUBRICATION: Dry sump pressure feed type. The M 337 AK has a system for sustained inverted operation.
SUPERCHARGER: Centrifugal, ratio 7.4 : 1.
FUEL SYSTEM: Low pressure injection system with nozzles in front of inlet valves. The M 337 A has a unified fuel injection pump.
FUEL GRADE: Minimum 72-78 octane.
STARTING: Electric, engaged by an electromagnet.

ACCESSORIES: One 600W 28V dynamo. Electric tachometer. Propeller control unit. Mechanical tachometer on oil pump. Hydraulic pump to special order.
PROPELLER DRIVE: Direct left hand tractor.
DIMENSIONS:
Length, excl propeller boss	1,410 mm (55.51 in)
Width	472 mm (18.58 in)
Height	628 mm (24.72 in)
WEIGHT, DRY:	148 kg (326.3 lb)

PERFORMANCE RATINGS:
T-O	157 kW (210 hp) at 2,750 rpm
Max cruise at 1,200 m (3,940 ft)	
	112 kW (150 hp) at 2,400 rpm

SPECIFIC FUEL CONSUMPTION:
At T-O rating	100.6 µg/J (0.595 lb/h/hp)
At max cruise rating at 1,200 m (3,940 ft)	
	72.7 µg/J (0.430 lb/h/hp)

MOTORLET
ENGINE DIVISION OF AERO

Prague-Jinonice
Telephone: 42 (2) 521119
GENERAL MANAGER: Ing Josef Krča

Motorlet National Corporation operates the main aero engine establishment in Czechoslovakia, based on the former Walter factory. The Walter name continues as a trademark. Motorlet's status was being decided in 1990 following Czechoslovakia's political and economic changes.

WALTER M 601

The M 601 was designed to power the L-410 transport. It drives an Avia V 508 propeller.

The first version, rated at 410 ekW (550 ehp), ran in October 1967. Development of the **M 601 B**, of increased diameter, started during 1968. The Let L-410M powered by M 601 B engines was in Aeroflot service by early 1979. The M 601B powers the L-410UVP. In 1982 a further variant, the **M 601 D**, entered production. This gives increased power and can be operated to longer TBO.

By 1985 the **M 601 Z** had entered production to power the Z 37T agricultural aircraft. It drives an auxiliary piston compressor for the spraying/dusting installation. TBO is 1,000 h. The **M 601 E** powers the L-410UVP-E and PZL Turbo Orlik. It has a TBO of 2,000 h. It drives a VJ 8.508E five-blade propeller, and an alternator for anti-icing windshields and propeller blades.

TYPE: Free turbine turboprop.
PROPELLER DRIVE: Reduction gear at front of engine with drive from free turbine. Reduction ratio 14.9.
AIR INTAKE: Annular, at rear (reverse flow engine).

Cutaway drawing of the Walter M 601 E turboprop

COMPRESSOR: Two axial stages of stainless steel, plus single centrifugal stage of titanium. Pressure ratio (601 B) 6.4, (601 D) 6.55, (601 E) 6.65, at 36,660 rpm gas generator speed. Air mass flow (601 B) 3.25 kg (7.17 lb)/s, (601 D) 3.55 kg (7.83 lb)/s, (601 E) 3.6 kg (7.94 lb)/s.
COMBUSTION CHAMBER: Annular combustor with rotary fuel injection and low-voltage ignition.
COMPRESSOR TURBINE: Single stage with solid blades; inlet temperature 952°C.
POWER TURBINE: Single stage.

FUEL SYSTEM: Low pressure regulator, providing gas generator and power turbine speed controls.
FUEL GRADE: PL4, PL5 kerosene.
LUBRICATION SYSTEM: Pressure gear-pump circulation. Integral oil tank and cooler.
OIL SPECIFICATION: B3V synthetic oil.
STARTING: LUN 2132-8 8kW electric starter/generator.
DIMENSIONS:
Length: 601 D	1,658 mm (65.27 in)
601 B, E, Z	1,675 mm (65.94 in)

Width	590 mm (23.23 in)
Height	650 mm (25.59 in)

WEIGHT, DRY:
601 B, D, E	193 kg (425.5 lb)
601 Z	197 kg (434.3 lb)

PERFORMANCE RATINGS (T-O):
601 B	515 kW (691 shp)
601 D	540 kW (724 shp)
601 E	560 kW (751 shp)
601 Z	360 kW (483 shp)

SPECIFIC FUEL CONSUMPTION (T-O):
601 B	109.55 µg/J (0.648 lb/h/ehp)
601 D	109.4 µg/J (0.647 lb/h/ehp)

WALTER M 602

This engine was developed to power the L 610, which first flew on 28 December 1988. Certification was expected in 1990.

TYPE: Three-shaft turboprop.

PROPELLER DRIVE: Double spur reduction, ratio 12.58.

AIR INTAKE: At front, S duct from chin inlet passing up behind reduction gear.

COMPRESSORS: LP centrifugal, pressure ratio 4.15 at 25,000 rpm. HP centrifugal, pressure ratio 3.133 at 31,489 rpm. Overall pressure ratio 13. Mass flow 7.33 kg (16.16 lb)/s.

COMBUSTION CHAMBER: Short annular reverse flow with 14 simplex nozzles and low-voltage semiconductor ignition.

COMPRESSOR TURBINES: Single-stage HP, single-stage LP.

POWER TURBINE: Two-stage, 16,600 rpm.

FUEL SYSTEM: LP electrohydraulic regulator and electronic limiter.

FUEL GRADE: T-1, TS-1, RT, Jet A-1.

Yakovlev Yak-40 testbed with M 601 E power plant on nose *(Letectvi + Kosmonautika/Vaclav Jukl)*

LUBRICATION SYSTEM: Pressure gear-pump circulation, integral oil tank and cooler.

OIL SPECIFICATION: B3V, AeroShell 500, 550.

STARTING: LUN 5362-8 pneumatic.

DIMENSIONS:
Length	2,669 mm (105.08 in)
Width	753 mm (29.65 in)
Height	872 mm (34.33 in)

WEIGHT, DRY (equipped):	570-580 kg (1,257-1,279 lb)

PERFORMANCE RATINGS (S/L):
T-O	1,360 kW (1,824 shp)
Max continuous	1,200 kW (1,608 shp)
Cruise	700 kW (938 shp)

SPECIFIC FUEL CONSUMPTION:
T-O	94.5 µg/J (0.559 lb/h/shp)

Cutaway drawing of the Walter M 602 turboprop

ZVL
ZÁVODY NA VÝROBU LOŽÍSK
01734 Považská Bystrica
Telephone: 42 (822) 23825
Telex: 075233, 075316
CHIEF DESIGNER: E. Jiři Bednář

ZVL is a major new design bureau which also includes the VUM research institute. It partnered the Lotarev (ZKMB) bureau in the Soviet Union (which see) in designing the DV-2.

EGYPT

AOI
AOI ENGINE FACTORY (135)
PO Box 12, Helwan
Telephone: 20 (2) 745090, 747984 and 781088
Telex: 92135 ENFAC UN

CHAIRMAN: Hassan El Gebali

Among other work, about 3,500 people are employed in assembly and test of the Larzac 04 and PT6A-25E, delivery of the first PT6 having been made in 1985. Following selection of a new fighter for the Egyptian Air Force, the factory is expected to assemble either the F100, F404 or M53-P2. Since 1980 AOI/EF has carried out complete overhaul, repair and test of Soviet APUs and the SNECMA Atar 9C and Larzac, GE T64 and Allison T56.

FRANCE

FAM
FRANCE AÉRO MOTEURS SARL
Roanne
CONTACT: Avions Pierre Robin (see Aircraft section)

This company, inaugurated on 29 April 1985, was formed on a 50/50 basis by Avions Pierre Robin and the Motorop division of Besson-Moteurs Sopart, to develop an aircraft version of the PRV (Peugeot-Renault-Volvo) V6 car engine.

It is still in the development phase. For the latest news see Robin 3000 (Aircraft section).

JPX
ATELIERS JPX
Z.I. Nord, BP 13, 72320 Vibraye
Telephone: 33 43 93 61 74
Telex: 722151 F
Fax: 33 43 93 62 71

PUL 212
The PUL 212 is a single-cylinder low-cost two-stroke, with bore of 66 mm (2.6 in), stroke of 62 mm (2.44 in) and capacity of 212 cc. Weighing 7.9 kg (17.42 lb) with pull cord inertia starter, it gives 11 kW (15 hp) at 6,000 rpm and is cleared to run at up to 6,500 rpm.

PUL 425
This is an opposed engine with two cylinders of the same size as in the PUL 212. Dry weight is 14.5 kg (32 lb), or 16.7 kg (36.8 lb) with silencer. Rated power is 16.4 kW (22 hp) at 4,600 rpm. With 0.5 reduction gear weight is 21 kg (46 lb).

JPX 4T60/A

Unlike previous JPX engines this is a four-stroke, with four opposed aircooled cylinders with bore 93.0 mm (3.66 in) and stroke 75.4 mm (2.97 in). Capacity 2,050 cc (125 cu in). Compression ratio 8.2. Overall length 650 mm (25.6 in). Width 805 mm (31.7 in). Weight, dry (without propeller hub) 73.0 kg (161 lb). Developed from the Volkswagen VW126A of smaller capacity, the 4T60/A has an electric starter and alternator, and is rated at 47.8 kW (65 hp) at 3,200 rpm, and 42.0 kW (57 hp) at 2,500 rpm. Using 4-star motor fuel or 100LL fuel, this engine was certificated by the DGAC on 9 January 1985, ready for production for the Robin ATL. The **4T60/AES** for ultralight aircraft weighs 61 kg (134 lb).

The lightweight JPX 4T60/AES

MICROTURBO
MICROTURBO SA

Chemin du Pont de Rupé, BP 2089, 31019 Toulouse Cédex
Telephone: 33 61 70 11 27
Telex: 531442
Fax: 33 61 70 75 40
MANAGEMENT:
  A. Halna du Fretay
  P. Calmels (General Manager)
  L. Pech (Deputy General Manager)
Microturbo operates as the gas turbine division of the Labinal group, in conjunction with Microturbo Ltd of Fareham, England, Microturbo North America of Bohemia, New York, USA, and Electromecanismes RFB in Paris. Total staff of the division is 800.
Details of Microturbo engines for missiles, UAVs and target drones can be found in the 1987-88 *Jane's*.

MICROTURBO TRB

Development of the TRB 13 and TRB 19 turbojets began in 1986. The former has a diameter of 230 mm (9.06 in), length of 480 mm (18.90 in), weight of 16 kg (35.3 lb) and thrust rating of 0.81 kN (182 lb st) with sfc of 32.5 mg/Ns (1.15 lb/h/lb st). The TRB 19 has a diameter of 280 mm (11.02 in), length of 580 mm (22.85 in), weight of 28 kg (61.7 lb) and thrust rating of 1.2 kN (270 lb st) with sfc of 33.0 mg/Ns (1.17 lb/h/lb st).

MICROTURBO TRS 18

This single-shaft turbojet is of modular construction. The forward module incorporates the intake, gearbox, electronic governing and start sequencing. The starter/generator is in the nose bullet. The oil tank, with submerged pump, is on the underside, and includes provision for inverted flight.
The turbine module comprises: the one-piece centrifugal compressor, with diffuser and straightener vanes; the axial turbine rotor and nozzle diaphragm; and the main frame. The aft module comprises: the turbine backplate, carrying the annular folded combustion chamber; 10 spill burners; two igniter plugs, and jetpipe.
The fuel pump is driven electrically. The lubrication system is a closed circuit, with pressure supply. The engine can be shut down and restarted in flight, and incorporates automatic fault and protection systems.
The following are current versions for piloted aircraft:
TRS 18 Model 046. Powers Bede BD-5J and various prototypes. 28V starter/generator up to 600W.
TRS 18 Model 046-1. Powers Microjet 90, A-21SJ Calif, NASA/Ames AD-1, Fairchild scaled NGT and other prototypes. 28V starter/generator up to 900W.
TRS 18-1 Models 081 and 083. Powers Microjet 200B and Caproni C-22J.
TRS 18-1 Model 202. For Caproni C-22J.
TRS 18-2. Uprated version of TRS 18-1, with unchanged dimensions.

DIMENSIONS:
Length: TRS 18	578 mm (22.75 in)
TRS 18-1	564 mm (22.20 in)
Width: TRS 18, 18-1	306 mm (12.05 in)
Height: TRS 18	349 mm (13.74 in)
TRS 18-1	339.5 mm (13.36 in)

WEIGHT, DRY:
TRS 18	37.0 kg (81.5 lb)
TRS 18-1	38.5 kg (84.9 lb)

PERFORMANCE RATINGS (T-O, ISA, S/L):
TRS 18	1.00 kN (225 lb st)
TRS 18-1	1.45 kN (326 lb st)
TRS 18-2	1.80 kN (405 lb st)

SPECIFIC FUEL CONSUMPTION (as above):
TRS 18	34.5 mg/Ns (1.22 lb/h/lb st)
TRS 18-1	33.4 mg/Ns (1.18 lb/h/lb st)

MICROTURBO TFA

Two simple turbofans have been under study since 1986. The **TFA 66**, with a diameter of 350 mm (13.78 in) and length of 1,000 mm (39.37 in), will be rated at 3.60 kN (810 lb st) with sfc of 25.28 mg/Ns (0.892 lb/h/lb st). The TFA 130, with a diameter of 440 mm (17.32 in) and length of 975 mm (38.39 in), will be rated at 3.57 kN (802 lb st) with sfc of 17.48 mg/Ns (0.617 lb/h/lb st). Projected weight for each of these engines is approx 60 kg (132 lb).

MUDRY
MOTEURS MUDRY-BUCHOUX (AVIONS MUDRY et CIE)

Aérodrome de Bernay, BP 47, 27300 Bernay
Telephone: 33 32 43 47 34
DIRECTOR: Auguste Mudry

MUDRY MB-4-80

This aircooled four-stroke flat-four incorporates some parts, such as piston rings, rocker arms, valves and springs, of standard auto industry type. Development is continuing.
CYLINDERS: Cast in pairs in light alloy with cast iron liners. Bore 93 mm (3.7 in). Stroke 92 mm (3.6 in). Capacity 2,498 cc (152.4 cu in).
VALVES: Flat cylinder heads with twin vertical overhead valves operated by pushrods.
PISTONS: Hypersilicate alloy, forming chamber in head. Three rings including U-Flex scraper.
CRANKCASE: AS7G-06 alloy divided on vertical centreline.

FUEL GRADE: 100LL or automobile gasoline.
ACCESSORIES: Generator, starter and alternator. Two 32 mm carburettors. Bendix dual ignition.
DIMENSIONS:
Length	730 mm (28.7 in)
Width	710 mm (28.0 in)
Height	420 mm (16.5 in)

WEIGHT, DRY (equipped): 83 kg (183 lb)
PERFORMANCE RATING (S/L):
Max T-O	59.7 kW (80 hp) at 2,750 rpm

RECTIMO
RECTIMO AVIATION SA

Aérodrome de Chambéry, 73420 Savoie
Telephone: 33 79 54 40 06
Telex: 980 202
DIRECTOR: André Rosselot
Rectimo has manufactured more than 500 **Type 4 AR 1200** single ignition derivatives of the Volkswagen four-cylinder aircooled car engine, which together with the larger 4 AR 1600 are used in the Sportavia RF4D motor glider and various lightweight aircraft. The 30 kW (40 hp) 4 AR 1200 engine has a 1,192 cc cubic capacity, 7 : 1 compression ratio and weighs 61.5 kg (136 lb). Fuel consumption under cruise conditions is 11 litres (2.9 US gallons; 2.4 Imp gal)/h. The 4 AR 1600 produces 45.5 kW (61 hp) at T-O and has a cubic capacity of 1,600 cc and an 8 : 1 compression ratio. Weight is 64 kg (141 lb). Both engines have a maximum speed of 3,600 rpm.

Rectimo 4 AR 1200 piston engine of 30 kW (40 hp)

SCOMA
SCOMA-ÉNERGIE

OFFICE: 11-13 rue Forest, 75018 Paris
Telephone: 33 (1) 43 87 55 79
WORKS: 58 rue de la Fosse aux Anglais, 77190 Dammarie-les-Lys (Melun)
Telephone: 33 (1) 64 37 46 17
This company, which specialises in diesel research and applications, has been flying a Cessna L-19 since June 1987 equipped with a **GMA 140 TK** geared diesel. This is a four-in-line liquid cooled engine of 2,068 cc (126 cu in) capacity, with turbocharger and geared drive. Installed weight is 180 kg (397 lb), and T-O power is 96 kW (136 hp) at 2,660 propeller rpm. At economic cruise of 2,300 propeller rpm the power is 65 kW (88 hp) and fuel consumption less than 22 litres (5.8 US gallons; 4.8 Imp gallons)/h. The engine has multi-fuel capability and is run mainly on Jet 1 or light diesel oil. Experience with this engine is being used to assist the design of a new range of engines called Comète (Comet), which are 170° V type engines with 1, 4, 6, 8, 12 or 16 cylinders each of 94 mm (3.7 in) bore and stroke. All are turbocharged and liquid cooled geared units, with ratings from 30 kW (40 hp) to 480 kW (653 hp).

**The Cessna L-19 powered by a
SCOMA GMA 140 TK diesel engine**

SNECMA
SOCIÉTÉ NATIONALE D'ÉTUDE ET DE CONSTRUCTION DE MOTEURS D'AVIATION

2 boulevard du Général Martial Valin, 75724 Paris Cédex 15
Telephone: 33 (1) 40 60 80 80
Telex: 600 700 SNECMA
Fax: 33 (1) 40 60 81 02
CHAIRMAN AND CHIEF EXECUTIVE: Louis Gallois
SENIOR VICE-PRESIDENT:
  Pierre Alesi (Engineering and Production)
VICE-PRESIDENTS:
  Jean Bonnet (Military Programmes and Marketing)
  Dominique Paris (Commercial Programme Management and Marketing)
COMMUNICATION ADVISER: Vonick Morel

More than 5,200 Atar turbojets have been produced for Mirage fighters. SNECMA is now producing the M53 turbojet and developing the M88. It is also participating in international collaborative programmes, as described hereunder.

Today, SNECMA heads about 26,000 persons formed around its major subsidiaries: SEP (rocket motors, remote sensing and composites), Hispano-Suiza (aeronautical equipment, nuclear and robotic equipment), Messier-Bugatti (landing gears) and Sochata (engine repair).

SNECMA ATAR 9K50

The Atar is a single-shaft military turbojet first run in 1946 and subsequently developed and cleared for flight at Mach numbers greater than 2. The current version is the Atar 9K50, which powers all production Mirage F1 versions, the Mirage 50 and the Atlas Cheetah.

DIMENSIONS:
Diameter	1,020 mm (40.2 in)
Length overall	5,944 mm (234 in)

WEIGHTS:
Dry, complete with all accessories	1,582 kg (3,487 lb)

PERFORMANCE RATINGS:
With afterburner	70.6 kN (15,870 lb st) at 8,400 rpm
Without afterburner	49.2 kN (11,055 lb st)

SPECIFIC FUEL CONSUMPTION:
With afterburner	55.5 mg/Ns (1.96 lb/h/lb st)
Without afterburner	27.5 mg/Ns (0.97 lb/h/lb st)

OIL CONSUMPTION: 1.5 litres (3.2 US pints; 2.64 Imp pints)/h

SNECMA M53

The M53 is a single-shaft turbofan capable of propelling fighter aircraft to Mach 2.5, without any throttle limitations over the flight envelope. Its modular construction allows easier maintenance.

It includes a three-stage fan, five-stage compressor (pressure ratio 9.8 at 10,600 rpm), annular combustion chamber, two-stage turbine and an afterburner equipped with a multi-flap variable nozzle. The control system is monitored by an ELECMA electronic computer. The following versions are in service:

M53-5. Produced in 1980-85 as the initial engine of the Mirage 2000.

M53-P2. Designed to power the Mirage 2000 from 1985; current production version.

DIMENSIONS:
Length, overall	5,070 mm (199.6 in)
Max diameter	1,055 mm (41.5 in)

WEIGHT, DRY:
M53-5	1,470 kg (3,240 lb)
M53-P2	1,500 kg (3,307 lb)

PERFORMANCE RATINGS:
Max with afterburner:
M53-5	88.2 kN (19,830 lb st)
M53-P2	95.0 kN (21,355 lb st)

Max without afterburner:
M53-5	54.4 kN (12,230 lb st)
M53-P2	64.3 kN (14,455 lb st)

SPECIFIC FUEL CONSUMPTION (without afterburner):
M53-5	24.64 mg/Ns (0.87 lb/h/lb st)
M53-P2	25.55 mg/Ns (0.90 lb/h/lb st)

SNECMA M88

The M88 is a family of advanced augmented turbofans, built around the same core, with thrust ranging from 75 kN (16,860 lb) to 105 kN (23,600 lb). In a six-year demonstration programme an uprated core with 1,850°K turbine entry temperature completed its first simulated altitude tests in February 1987.

M88-2. This is the basic engine of the family, under development since 1987 for the Rafale ACT/ACM aircraft for the French Air Force and Navy. The first engine went on test on 27 February 1989, afterburner operation began in April 1989 and one engine flew in the Rafale A in March 1990.

The following relates to the basic M88-2:
TYPE: Two-shaft augmented turbofan.
COMPRESSOR: Variable inlet guide vanes, three-stage LP (fan), six-stage HP, with three variable stator stages.

SNECMA Atar 9K50 afterburning turbojet

Longitudinal section through the SNECMA M53-P2 augmented bypass turbojet

SNECMA M53-P2 augmented bypass turbojet

Longitudinal section through SNECMA M88 augmented turbofan

SNECMA M88-2 augmented turbofan

COMBUSTOR: Annular, with aerodynamic injection.
TURBINES: Single-stage HP, single-stage LP.
ACCESSORIES: Full-authority digital control system.
DIMENSION:

Length	3,540 mm (139.0 in)

WEIGHT, DRY: 897 kg (1,970 lb)
PERFORMANCE RATINGS (installed):

With afterburner	72.9 kN (16,400 lb st)
Without afterburner	48.7 kN (10,950 lb st)

SPECIFIC FUEL CONSUMPTION:

With afterburner	49.9 mg/Ns (1.76 lb/h/lb st)
Without afterburner	24.9 mg/Ns (0.88 lb/h/lb st)

GE/SNECMA GE90

It was announced in January 1990 that SNECMA will partner General Electric on the GE90 programme described under GE of the USA.

GE/SNECMA/MTU/VOLVO/FIAT CF6

As a continuation of the CF6-50 and CF6-80A programmes, SNECMA participates in the General Electric CF6-80C2 and CF6-80E1 programmes for all applications with a share of 10 per cent.

CFM INTERNATIONAL CFM56

This programme is covered under CFM in the International part of this section.

GE/SNECMA GE36

SNECMA had a 35 per cent share in the GE36 UDF (unducted fan) programme, and was in charge of acoustic measurement during flight testing on a Boeing 727. SNECMA participated in development of an improved engine for flight test on an MD-80. Jointly with GE, SNECMA was developing an advanced gas generator, and was in charge of the HP compressor, combustor, structural casings, fuel systems and nacelle.

SNECMA/TURBOMECA LARZAC

This appears under Turbomeca-SNECMA GRTS.

RR/SNECMA/MTU/FN TYNE

Under Rolls-Royce licence, the Tyne 22 turboprop for the Transall C-160, was put back into production in October 1977. The similar Tyne 21 is in production for the Dassault Atlantique 2. These 4,549 kW (6,100 ehp) engines were last described in the 1975-76 *Jane's*.

TURBOMECA
SOCIÉTÉ TURBOMECA

64511 Bordes
Telephone: 33 59 32 84 37
Telex: 560928
Fax: 33 59 53 15 12
PARIS OFFICE: 1 rue Beaujon, 75008 Paris
Telephone: 33 (1) 40 75 01 78
Telex: 650347
Fax: 33 (1) 40 75 01 79
CHIEF EXECUTIVE OFFICER: Jacques Marchand
PRESS RELATIONS MANAGER: Jacques Millepied

By 1 January 1990 more than 27,000 Turbomeca aircraft engines had been delivered to customers in 120 countries. Approximately 14,000 more engines have been built under licence by what are today Rolls-Royce plc in the UK, Teledyne CAE in the USA, ENMASA in Spain, Hindustan Aeronautics in India, Bet-Shemesh in Israel, SMPMC in China and state factories in Romania and Yugoslavia.

A European Small Engines Co-operation Agreement signed in April 1985 joins Turbomeca, MTU of West Germany and Rolls-Royce of the UK in promoting three complementary new engines: the Turbomeca TM 333, MTU-Turbomeca-RR MTR 390 and Rolls-Royce Turbomeca RTM 322. Other European small engine makers may join the collaboration, in which each partner may share in engines sold to its own government.

In March 1989 a UK marketing company was formed, Turbomeca Ltd. Address as for Rolls-Royce Turbomeca (see International part of this section); General Manager Michel Dubarry.

Total covered floor area for Turbomeca's three plants at Bordes, Mézières and Tarnos is 136,487 m² (1,134,469 sq ft). The company employs about 4,260 people.

ROLLS-ROYCE TURBOMECA ADOUR

This turbofan appears in the International part of this section.

TURBOMECA-SNECMA LARZAC

This turbofan appears under Turbomeca-SNECMA GRTS.

TURBOMECA TM 319

This turboshaft is compact, there being no axial compressor. Initial rating is 340 kW (456 shp). The first TM 319 was run on the bench on 21 February 1983. Full authority digital electronic control is supplied by Elecma.

Production deliveries for the AS 355 began in 1987, and were continuing in 1988 at the rate of 50 per year. Certification took place in 1988. The same gas generator is used in the TP 319 turboprop.

TM 319-1. Basic version to which data below apply. Twin TM 319s at a T-O rating of 358 kW (480 shp) are an alternative power plant for the MBB BO 108.

TM 319-2. Growth version, max T-O rating 473 kW (634 shp). Selected for McDonnell Douglas MD 900.
DIMENSIONS:

Length	782 mm (30.78 in)
Width	360 mm (14.2 in)
Height	540 mm (21.26 in)

WEIGHT, DRY: 87 kg (192 lb)
PERFORMANCE RATINGS (TM 319-1, ISA, S/L):

Max contingency	408 kW (547 shp)
Max T-O	380 kW (509 shp)
Max continuous	295 kW (395 shp)

TURBOMECA TP 319

The turboprop version is fully aerobatic. The gas generator and power turbine modules are identical with those of the TM 319. The first TP 319 ran on 11 September 1985. Flight testing in an Epsilon began in November 1985, followed by a Valmet L-90 TP in December 1987. The TP 319 is flying in the Socata Oméga.
DIMENSIONS:

Length	826 mm (32.52 in)
Width	476 mm (18.74 in)
Height	590 mm (23.22 in)

WEIGHT, DRY (bare): 111 kg (245 lb)
PERFORMANCE RATINGS (ISA, S/L):

Twin T-O contingency	343 kW (460 shp)
T-O	313 kW (420 shp)
Cruise (6,100 m, 20,000 ft)	179 kW (240 shp)

TURBOMECA ARRIEL

This turboshaft powers the single-engined AS 350 and AS 550 Ecureuil, twin-engined AS 365 and AS 565 Dauphin, Agusta A 109K and Sikorsky S-76A + and S-76C.

The Arriel has modular construction. The first complete engine ran on 7 August 1974.

There are 13 qualified production versions, differing essentially only in power rating:

Arriel 1A, 1B. T-O rating 478 kW (641 shp); powers AS 350B and AS 365C.

Arriel 1C. T-O rating 492 kW (660 shp); powers AS 365N.

Arriel 1D. T-O rating 510 kW (684 shp); powers AS 350B and L₁.

Arriel 1C1, 1M, 1K, 1S. All have T-O rating of 522 kW (700 shp); power AS 365F and N₁, A 109K and S-76A +.

Arriel 1C2. T-O rating 550 kW (738 shp); powers AS 365N₂.

Arriel 1D1. T-O rating 558 kW (749 shp); powers AS 350B₂, and AS 550U₂.

Arriel 1M1. T-O rating 558 kW (749 shp); powers AS 565UA and AS 565MA.

Arriel 1S1. T-O rating 539 kW (723 shp); powers S-76C.

Arriel 2. Growth version with single-stage gas generator turbine. To provide at least 16 per cent more power than 1S. Candidate engine for P 120, Dauphin and S-76.

By 1 March 1990 a total of 2,406 Arriels had been delivered, with production continuing at the rate of 375 per year. These engines had then flown 2.9 million hours in 74 countries. These totals do not include engines produced under licence in China.

The following relates to the Arriel 1A, 1B:
TYPE: Single-shaft free turbine turboshaft.
COMPRESSOR: Single-stage axial and supersonic centrifugal. Pressure ratio 9.
COMBUSTION CHAMBER: Annular, with flow radially outwards and then inwards. Centrifugal fuel injection.
GAS GENERATOR TURBINE: Two integral cast axial stages with solid blades.
POWER TURBINE: Single axial stage with inserted blades.
REDUCTION GEAR: Light alloy gearbox, containing two stages of helical gears, giving drive at 6,000 rpm to front and rear. Hydraulic torquemeter.
ACCESSORY DRIVES: Main pad provides for optional 12,000 rpm alternator; other drives for oil pumps, tachometer generator, governor and starter.
LUBRICATION SYSTEM: Independent circuit through gear pump and metallic cartridge filter.
OIL SPECIFICATION: AIR 3512 or 3513A.
STARTING: Electric starter or starter/generator.
DIMENSIONS:

Length, excl accessories	1,090 mm (42.91 in)
Height overall	569 mm (22.40 in)
Width	430 mm (16.93 in)

WEIGHT, DRY:

With all engine accessories	120 kg (265 lb)

PERFORMANCE RATINGS: See variants list
SPECIFIC FUEL CONSUMPTION:

T-O	96.8 µg/J (0.573 lb/h/shp)

Turbomeca TM 319 free-turbine turboshaft

Turbomeca TP 319 free-turbine turboprop

Turbomeca Arriel 1S free-turbine turboshaft

Turbomeca TM 333 free-turbine turboshaft

TURBOMECA ASTAZOU TURBOPROP

The Astazou turboprop is in production in its 761 kW (1,020 ehp) Astazou XVI (AZ16) version. The XVIG, equipped for sustained inverted flight, powers the Argentine IA 58 Pucará. By 1988 deliveries of all XVI versions totalled 367, against orders for 440.

The following data refer to the XVIG:
DIMENSIONS:
Diameter over intake cowl	546 mm (21.5 in)
Overall length, incl propeller	2,047 mm (80.6 in)

WEIGHT, DRY: 228 kg (502 lb)
PERFORMANCE RATINGS:
T-O	761 ekW; 720 kW
	(1,020 ehp; 965 shp) at 43,000 rpm
Max continuous	696 ekW; 654 kW
	(934 ehp; 877 shp) at 43,000 rpm

SPECIFIC FUEL CONSUMPTION:
At T-O rating 88.7 µg/J (0.525 lb/h/shp)

TURBOMECA ASTAZOU TURBOSHAFT

This turboshaft series is derived from the Astazou II turboprop. Variants are:

Astazou IIA. Rated at 390 kW (523 shp) for SA 318C. Total of 615 built.

Astazou IIIA. Derived from IIA but with revised turbine to match power needs of SA 341G. Produced jointly by Turbomeca and Rolls-Royce, with 1,008 delivered.

Astazou XIVB and XIVF. For SA 319B; XIVB is civil and XIVF military. Flat rated to 441 kW (591 shp) (1 h) up to 4,000 m (13,125 ft) or +55°C.

Astazou XIVH. For SA 342J/L, to remove altitude and temperature limitations; 1,146 delivered.

Astazou XVIIIA. Higher gas temperature. Powers AS 360C.

Astazou XX. Fourth axial compressor stage added. Designed for operation in hot and high countries.

The following description relates to the Astazou IIIN except where indicated:
TYPE: Single-shaft axial-plus-centrifugal turboshaft.
REDUCTION GEAR: Two-stage epicyclic having helical primary and straight secondary gears. Ratio 7.039 : 1 (XIVB/F, 7.345; XVIIIA, 7.375).
COMPRESSOR: Single-stage axial (IIA, IIN, IIIN), two-stage axial (XIV, XVIII) or three-stage axial (XX) followed by single-stage centrifugal. Mass flow 2.5 kg (5.5 lb)/s.
COMBUSTION CHAMBER: Reverse flow annular with centrifugal injector using rotary atomiser. Two ventilated torch igniters.
TURBINE: Three-stage axial with blades integral with discs.
ACCESSORIES: Five drive pads on casing forming rear of air intake.
FUEL SYSTEM: Automatic constant speed control.
LUBRICATION SYSTEM: Pressure type with gear type pumps. Oil tank of 8 litre (17 US pints; 14 Imp pint) capacity.
STARTING: Electrical, automatic.
DIMENSIONS:
Length overall: Astazou IIA	1,272 mm (50.0 in)
Astazou III, XIVB/F	1,433 mm (56.3 in)
Astazou XIVH	1,470 mm (57.9 in)
Astazou XVIIIA	1,327 mm (52.2 in)
Astazou XX	1,529 mm (60.22 in)
Height: Astazou IIA	458 mm (18.0 in)
Astazou III, XIVH	460 mm (18.1 in)
Astazou XVIIIA	698 mm (27.48 in)
Astazou XX	721 mm (28.4 in)
Width: Astazou IIA	480 mm (18.8 in)
Astazou III, XIVH	460 mm (18.1 in)

WEIGHTS:
Equipped: Astazou III	147 kg (324 lb)
Astazou III (suffix 2)	150 kg (330 lb)
Astazou XIVB/F	166 kg (366 lb)
Astazou XIVH	160 kg (353 lb)
Astazou XVIIIA	155 kg (341 lb)
Astazou XX	195 kg (430 lb)

PERFORMANCE RATINGS:
Max power: Astazou IIA	390 kW (523 shp)
Astazou III	441 kW (592 shp)
Astazou III (suffix 2)	481 kW (645 shp)
Astazou XX	749 kW (1,005 shp)
One hour: Astazou XIVB/F	441 kW (591 shp)
Astazou XVIIIA	651 kW (873 shp)
	maintained at sea level to 40°C
Max continuous: Astazou IIA	353 kW (473 shp)
Astazou III	390 kW (523 shp)
Astazou III (suffix 2)	441 kW (592 shp)
Astazou XIVB/F	405 kW (543 shp)
Astazou XIVH	flat rated in SA 341 at 440.7 kW
	(591 shp) to 55°C or 4,000 m (13,125 ft)
Astazou XVIIIA	600 kW (805 shp)
Astazou XX	675 kW (905 shp)

SPECIFIC FUEL CONSUMPTION:
At max power rating:
Astazou IIA	105.3 µg/J (0.623 lb/h/shp)
Astazou III	108.7 µg/J (0.643 lb/h/shp)
Astazou III (suffix 2)	109.9 µg/J (0.650 lb/h/shp)
Astazou XIVB/F	105.5 µg/J (0.624 lb/h/shp)
Astazou XVIIIA	91.3 µg/J (0.540 lb/h/shp)
Astazou XX	85.9 µg/J (0.508 lb/h/shp)

TURBOMECA ARTOUSTE III

The Artouste IIIB is a single-shaft turboshaft with two-stage axial-centrifugal compressor and three-stage turbine. Pressure ratio 5.2. Mass flow 4.3 kg/s (9.5 lb/s) at 33,300 rpm. Built under licence in India by Hindustan Aeronautics.

The IIIB powers the SA 315B and SA 316B/C. The uprated IIID has a reduction gear giving 5,864 rpm at the driveshaft (instead of 5,773) and in revised equipment. The IIID powers the SA 316C; data are for this version. A total of 2,525 Artouste III engines had been built by 1988.
DIMENSIONS:
Length	1,815 mm (71.46 in)
Height	627 mm (24.68 in)
Width	507 mm (19.96 in)

WEIGHT, DRY: 178 kg (392 lb)
PERFORMANCE RATING (T-O, maintained up to 55°C at S/L or up to 4,000 m; 13,125 ft): 440 kW (590 shp)
SPECIFIC FUEL CONSUMPTION: 126.2 µg/J (0.747 lb/h/shp)

MTU-TURBOMECA RR MTR 390

This appears in the International part of this section.

TURBOMECA TM 333

This turboshaft was launched in July 1979 to power the AS 365 and other helicopters in the 4,000 kg (8,800 lb) class including the Indian ALH. French certification of the 1A version was obtained on 11 July 1986.

TM 333 1A. Basic version, composed of a gas generator module, free turbine module and reduction gear module.

TM 333 1M. For military AS 565.

TM 333 2B. Growth version with single crystal HP turbine, giving T-O rating of 747 kW (1,001 shp). First run 6 November 1984. Selected for HAL (India) ALH. First deliveries 1989.

The TM 333 is one of three new engines included in the European Small Engines Co-operation Agreement. Data are for the 2B:
TYPE: Free turbine turboshaft.
COMPRESSOR: Variable inlet guide vanes, two stage axial compressor, single stage centrifugal.
COMBUSTION CHAMBER: Annular, reverse flow.
GAS GENERATOR TURBINE: Single-stage with uncooled inserted blades.
POWER TURBINE: Single-stage axial with uncooled inserted blades.
GEARBOX: Two stages to give drive at 6,000 rpm to front output shaft.

LUBRICATION: Independent system. Oil passes through gear pump and metallic cartridge filter.
FUEL SYSTEM: Microprocessor numerical control.
DIMENSIONS:
Length, including accessories	1,045 mm (41.1 in)
Height overall	712 mm (28.0 in)
Width	454 mm (17.9 in)

WEIGHT, DRY: 156 kg (345 lb)
PERFORMANCE RATINGS:
Max contingency	788 kW (1,057 shp)
T-O	747 kW (1,002 shp)
Max continuous	663 kW (889 shp)

SPECIFIC FUEL CONSUMPTION:
Max contingency	88 µg/J (0.523 lb/h/shp)
T-O	89.4 µg/J (0.529 lb/h/shp)
Max continuous	91.7 µg/J (0.543 lb/h/shp)

TURBOMECA TURMO

The Turmo free turbine engine is in service in both turboshaft and turboprop versions.

Current variants are as follows:
Turmo IIIC5, IIIC6, IIIC7. For SA 321F/G/H/Ja. Total production 549.

Turmo IIIE6. Higher turbine temperature.

Turmo IVA. Civil engine derived from IIIC4, with contingency rating of 1,057 kW (1,417 shp). The IVB is a military version.
TYPE: Free turbine turboshaft.
REDUCTION GEAR: IIIC3, C5 and E3 fitted with rear mounted reduction gear; IIIC4 direct drive.
COMPRESSOR: Single-stage axial followed by single-stage centrifugal. Pressure ratio 5.9 on IIIC3. Mass flow 5.9 kg (13 lb)/s.
COMBUSTION CHAMBER: Reverse flow annular with centrifugal fuel injector using rotary atomiser. Two ventilated torch igniters.
GAS GENERATOR TURBINE: Two-stage axial.
POWER TURBINE: Two-stage axial unit in IIIC3, C5 and E3, and single stage in IIIC4.
ACCESSORIES: Pads for oil pump, fuel control, electric starter, tacho-generator and, on IIIC4, oil cooler fan.
FUEL SYSTEM: Fuel control for gas generator on IIIC3, C5 and E3, with speed limiter for power turbine on E3. Constant-speed system on IIIC4 power turbine.
FUEL GRADE: AIR 3405 for IIIC4.
LUBRICATION SYSTEM: Pressure type with oil cooler and 13 litre (27.5 US pints; 23 Imp pint) tank.
OIL SPECIFICATION: AIR 3155A, or AIR 3513, for IIIC4.
STARTING: Automatic system with electric starter motor.
DIMENSIONS:
Length:
Turmo IIIC3, C5 and E3	1,975.7 mm (78.0 in)
Turmo IIIC4	2,184 mm (85.5 in)
Turmo IIID3	1,868 mm (73.6 in)

Width:
Turmo IIIC3, C5 and E3	693 mm (27.3 in)
Turmo IIIC4	637 mm (25.1 in)
Turmo IIID3	934 mm (36.8 in)

Height:
Turmo IIIC3, C5 and E3	716.5 mm (28.2 in)
Turmo IIIC4	719 mm (28.3 in)
Turmo IIID3	926 mm (36.5 in)

WEIGHT, DRY:
Turmo IIIC3 and E3, fully equipped	297 kg (655 lb)
Turmo IIIC5, IIIC6 and IIIC7	325 kg (716 lb)
Turmo IIIC4, equipped engine	225 kg (496 lb)
Turmo IIID3, basic engine	365 kg (805 lb)

PERFORMANCE RATINGS:
T-O: Turmo IIIC3, D3 and E3	1104 kW (1,480 shp)
Turmo IIIE6	1,181 kW (1,584 shp)

Max contingency:
Turmo IIIC4 at 33,800 gas generator rpm	
	1,032 kW (1,384 shp)

Turmo IIIC$_6$ at 33,550 gas generator rpm
1,156 kW (1,550 shp)
Turmo IIIC$_7$ at 33,800 gas generator rpm
1,200 kW (1,610 shp)
Turmo IVA at 33,950 gas generator rpm
1,057 kW (1,417 shp)
Turmo IVC at 33,800 gas generator rpm
1,163 kW (1,560 shp)
T-O and intermediate contingency:
Turmo IIIC$_5$
1,050 kW (1,408 shp)
SPECIFIC FUEL CONSUMPTION:
At T-O rating:
Turmo IIIC$_3$ and E$_3$ 101.9 µg/J (0.603 lb/h/shp)
Turmo IIID$_3$ 104.1 µg/J (0.616 lb/h/shp)
At max contingency rating:
Turmo IIIC$_4$, C$_5$, C$_6$, C$_7$ and IV
106.8 µg/J (0.632 lb/h/shp)
Turmo IVA   106.3 µg/J (0.629 lb/h/shp)

Turbomeca Makila 1A free-turbine turboshaft

ROLLS-ROYCE TURBOMECA RTM 322

See International part of this section.

TURBOMECA MAKILA

This turboshaft powers the AS 332. Derived partly from the Turmo, it incorporates rapid-strip modular construction; three axial stages of compression plus one centrifugal; centrifugal atomiser; two-stage gas generator turbine with cooled blades; two-stage free power turbine; and lateral exhaust.

Makila 1A. Certificated 1980. OEI rating 1,310 kW (1,757 shp).

Makila 1A1. Certificated 1984. OEI rating 1,400 kW (1,877 shp).

Makila 1A2. Under development. OEI rating (30 s) 1,569 kW (2,103 shp), (2 min) 1,433 kW (1,921 shp).

By the end of 1989 deliveries of Makila engines had reached 923, of which 100 were delivered in 1989.

DIMENSIONS:

Length, intake face to rear face	1,395 mm (54.94 in)
Max diameter	514 mm (20.25 in)
WEIGHT, DRY: Basic	210 kg (463 lb)
Equipped	243 kg (535 lb)

PERFORMANCE RATINGS (ISA, S/L):
Max contingency: see model listings
Cruise: 1A, 1A1, 1A2   700 kW (939 shp)
SPECIFIC FUEL CONSUMPTION:
Max contingency: 1A   83.9 µg/J (0.496 lb/h/hp)
1A1   81.4 µg/J (0.481 lb/h/hp)
Cruise: 1A   97.7 µg/J (0.578 lb/h/hp)
1A1   95.0 µg/J (0.562 lb/h/hp)

TURBOMECA-SNECMA

GROUPEMENT TURBOMECA-SNECMA (GRTS)

1 rue Beaujon, BP 37-08, 75362 Paris Cédex 08
Telephone: 33 (1) 49 24 18 61

Groupement Turbomeca-SNECMA is a company formed jointly by Société Turbomeca and SNECMA to manage the Larzac turbofan launched in 1968. GRTS has no capital and comprises primarily a joint management organisation.

TURBOMECA-SNECMA LARZAC

In February 1972 the **Larzac 04** turbofan was selected for a joint Franco-German programme to provide propulsion for the Alpha Jet (see under Dassault/Dornier in International part of Aircraft section). In addition to the two French engine partners, two West German companies, MTU and KHD, shared in production and development. Complete engines were assembled in both countries.

Current versions are as follows:

Larzac 04-C6. Two-stage fan, four-stage HP compressor, annular combustion chamber, single-stage HP turbine with cooled blades and single-stage LP turbine. Maximum airflow 28 kg (62 lb)/s, pressure ratio 10.6 and BPR 1.13. First production delivery September 1977.

Larzac 04-C20. Growth version with increased mass flow compressor and higher temperature HP turbine. Thrust increased by 7 to 15 per cent according to speed and altitude. First run March 1982; first flight December 1982; production deliveries from September 1984.

DIMENSIONS:

Overall length of basic engine	1,179 mm (46.4 in)
Overall diameter	602 mm (23.7 in)
WEIGHT, DRY:	290 kg (640 lb)

Turbomeca-SNECMA Larzac 04-C20 two-shaft turbofan

T-O THRUST (S/L, static):
Larzac 04-C6   13.19 kN (2,966 lb)
Larzac 04-C20   14.12 kN (3,175 lb)

SPECIFIC FUEL CONSUMPTION:
Larzac 04   20.1 mg/Ns (0.71 lb/h/lb st)

GERMANY, WEST

F&W

FISCHER & ENTWICKLUNGEN GmbH

Sonnenring 38, D-8300 Landshut/Altdorf
Telephone: 49 (871) 32099

ASW 24 TOP

TOP stands for Take-Off Power, this three-cylinder two-stroke piston engine being packaged as a unit fitting on top of sailplanes, raised above the fuselage or retracted flush against it by a control from the cockpit. Maximum power 18 kW (24 hp) at 4,200 rpm. Installed weight 44 kg (97 lb) including 30-start battery and fuel.

HIRTH

GÖBLER HIRTHMOTOREN GmbH

Postfach 20, Max Eyth Strasse 10, 7141 Benningen
Telephone: 49 (71) 44 6074
Telex: 7 264 530 GHIR D

This company produces small piston engines for microlights and other aircraft in the range 2.61-97 kW (3.5-130 hp). Except for the F 30, all are two-cylinder upright in-line two-strokes with carburettor, Bosch magneto ignition and direct drive. In mid-1990 it was planned to introduce a new engine series of 625 cc (38.1 cu in), weighing about 29 kg (64 lb), rated at 29.8-52.2 kW (40-70 hp) at 6,500 rpm.

HIRTH F 263 R 53

Cylinders 66 mm (2.598 in) bore and 56 mm (2.205 in) stroke, giving capacity of 383 cc (23.37 cu in). Compression ratio 9.5, using 25:1 fuel mix. Weight with electric starter 24.0 kg (52.8 lb), silencer adding 2.5 kg (5.5 lb). Max power 16.2 kW (22 hp) at 3,900 rpm.

HIRTH F 22

Cylinders as F 263. Weight with electric starter 20.0 kg (44 lb), silencer adding 3 kg (6.6 lb). Max power 17 kW (23 hp) at 5,000 rpm.

HIRTH F 23A

Cylinders 72 mm (2.835 in) bore and 64 mm (2.52 in) stroke, giving capacity of 521 cc (31.79 cu in). Compression ratio 10.5, using 50:1 fuel mix. Equipped weight 24.0 kg (52 lb), silencer adding 4.5 kg (10 lb). Max power 30 kW (40 hp) at 5,500 rpm.

HIRTH 2701 R 03

Cylinders 70 mm (2.756 in) bore and 64 mm (2.52 in) stroke, giving capacity of 493 cc (30.08 cu in). Compression ratio 11, using 50:1 fuel mix. Weight with fan and recoil starter 32.8 kg (72.5 lb). Max power 32 kW (43 hp) at 6,750 rpm.

HIRTH 2702 R 03

Cylinders as F 23A. Weight with fan and recoil starter 35.0 kg (77 lb). Max power 31 kW (41.6 hp) at 5,500 rpm.

HIRTH 2703

Similar to 2702 but enlarged to 521 cc (31.8 cu in). Max power 44 kW (59 hp).

HIRTH 2704

Again enlarged, to 625 cc (38.1 cu in). Max power 38 kW (51 hp) at 4,500 rpm.

HIRTH F 30

Four-cylinder engine tested in two sizes, the smaller (1,042 cc) being a twinned 2702 but lighter. Both can have direct or geared drive, data being for the former.

1,042 cc (63.58 cu in) version: Weight dry 36.0 kg (79.4 lb). Max power 48.5 kW (65 hp) at 4,500 rpm, 82 kW (110 hp) at 6,500 rpm.

1,270 cc (77.50 cu in) version. Weight dry 35.0 kg (77 lb). Max power 59.5 kW (80 hp) at 4,500 rpm, 97 kW (130 hp) at 6,500 rpm.

Hirth F 30 flat-four piston engine

KHD

KHD LUFTFAHRTTECHNIK GmbH

Hohemark Str 60-70, Postfach 1246, D-6370 Oberursel

Telephone: 49 (61) 71 500591
Telex: 410727
Fax: 49 (61) 71 500485

The business of this company was taken over in 1990 by BMW Rolls-Royce, which see in International part of this section.

KÖNIG

KÖNIG MOTORENBAU

Friedrich-Olbricht Damm 72, 1000 Berlin 13
Telephone: 49 (30) 344 3071

This company produces small two-stroke piston engines for microlights and other aircraft. All except the SF 930 have radial cylinders of 66 mm (2.598 in) bore and 42 mm (1.654 in) stroke, with natural air cooling. A 33:1 fuel mix is used, aspirated through a single bowl carburettor and with capacitor discharge ignition. The SC 430 and SD 570 have an electric starter and are available with direct drive or with 1.75:1 Powergrip belt.

KÖNIG SC 430

This engine has three cylinders spaced at 120°, giving a capacity of 430 cc (26.24 cu in). Weight with full equipment is 16 kg (35.3 lb) and max power 18 kW (24 hp) at 4,000-4,200 rpm.

KÖNIG SD 570

This engine has four cylinders spaced at 90°, giving a capacity of 570 cc (34.78 cu in). Weight with full equipment is 18.5 kg (41 lb) and max power 21 kW (28 hp) at 4,000-4,200 rpm.

KÖNIG SF 930

Production of this larger four-cylinder radial began in April 1985. Bore and stroke are respectively 70 and 60 mm (2.756 and 2.362 in), giving a capacity of 930 cc (56.75 cu in); equipped weight is 36 kg (79.4 lb) and maximum power 35.8 kW (48 hp) at 4,000-4,200 rpm.

König SF 930 piston engine driving a four-blade propeller

LIMBACH

LIMBACH FLUGMOTOREN GmbH

Kotthausener Strasse 5, 5330 Königswinter 21, Sassenberg
Telephone: 49 (2244) 2322 and 3031
Telex: 889574 plm d
Fax: 49 (2244) 6976
In USA: **Limbach Aircraft Engines**
PO Box 1201, Tulsa, Oklahoma 74101
Telephone: 1 (918) 832 9017
Telex: 821849 LAC USA
PRESIDENT: Peter Limbach Sr

This company manufactures four-stroke and two-stroke piston engines for very light aeroplanes and powered gliders.

LIMBACH L 90E

Smallest of the company's range, this is an aircooled flat-twin two-stroke.
CYLINDERS: Bore 42 mm (1.654 in). Stroke 31 mm (1.220 in). Capacity 86 cc (5.248 cu in). Compression ratio 9.5.
INDUCTION: Twin all-attitude diaphragm carburettors.
FUEL GRADE: 96 RON plus 1:25 oil.
IGNITION: Bosch solid state, single plugs.
WEIGHT, DRY: 4 kg (8.8 lb)
PERFORMANCE RATINGS:
T-O (5 min)   4.2 kW (5.6 hp) at 8,500 rpm
Continuous   2.9 kW (3.9 hp) at 7,000 rpm

LIMBACH L 275E

This engine is intended for low cost propulsion of RPVs and microlight aircraft.
TYPE: Two-cylinder horizontally opposed two-stroke aircooled piston engine.
CYLINDERS: Cast aluminium alloy with Nicasil liner. Bore 66 mm (2.6 in). Stroke 40 mm (1.57 in). Capacity 274 cc (16.72 cu in).
INDUCTION: Two all-attitude diaphragm carburettors.

FUEL GRADE: 90 octane, mixed 25:1 with two-stroke oil.
IGNITION: 12V Bosch transistorised, one Bosch WK 175T6 plug per cylinder.
ACCESSORIES: Leistritz type turbo silencer (muffler).
DIMENSIONS:
Length overall   226 mm (8.89 in)
Width overall   390 mm (15.35 in)
Height overall   187 mm (7.36 in)
WEIGHT (with silencer):   7.5 kg (16.5 lb)
PERFORMANCE RATING: 18 kW (24 hp) at 7,300 rpm

LIMBACH L 550E

This is a four-cylinder version of the two-stroke L 275E. Capacity is thus 548 cc (33.5 cu in).
WEIGHT, DRY: 15.5 kg (34 lb)
PERFORMANCE RATING: 32 kW (43 hp) at 7,300 rpm

LIMBACH SL 1700

Several variants have been certificated by the LBA.
Limbach SL 1700D. Dual ignition. Not certificated. Fitted to Sportavia RF7.

Sportavia-Limbach SL 1700E. Fitted to Sportavia RF5 and RF5B.
Limbach SL 1700EA. Front-end starter and different induction system. Fitted to Scheibe SF-25C Falke.
Limbach SL 1700EAI. Hoffmann variable-pitch propeller. Fitted to Scheibe SF-28.
Limbach SL 1700EC. E with carburettor intake heating box.
Limbach SL 1700 ECI. EC equipped to drive variable-pitch propeller.
Sportavia-Limbach SL 1700EI. E equipped to drive variable-pitch propeller. Optional for Sportavia RF5B.

Unless otherwise stated, the following description refers to the SL 1700E:
TYPE: Four-cylinder opposed aircooled four-stroke piston engine.
CYLINDERS: Bore 88 mm (3.46 in). Stroke 69 mm (2.71 in). Capacity 1,680 cc (102.51 cu in). Compression ratio 8.
INDUCTION: Stromberg-Zenith 150CD carburettor.
FUEL GRADE: 90 octane.
IGNITION: Single Slick 4230 magneto feeding one Bosch WB 240 ERT 1 plug in each cylinder.

Limbach L 275E two-stroke piston engine

Sportavia-Limbach SL 1700E piston engine

Limbach SL 1700EA four-stroke piston engine

STARTING: One Fiat 0.37 kW (0.5 hp) starter (EA, EAI, one Bosch 0.3 kW; 0.4 hp).

ACCESSORIES: Ducellier 250W alternator; APG 17.09.001 fuel pump (EA,EAI, 17.09.001A).

DIMENSIONS:

Length overall: SL 1700D	649 mm (25.6 in)
SL 1700EA, EAI	558 mm (22.0 in)
SL 1700E, EI, EC, ECI	618 mm (24.3 in)
Width overall: SL 1700D	800 mm (31.5 in)
SL 1700EA, EAI	770 mm (30.3 in)
other variants	764 mm (30.1 in)
Height overall: SL 1700D	451 mm (17.8 in)
SL 1700EA, EAI	392 mm (15.4 in)
other variants	368 mm (14.5 in)

WEIGHT, DRY:

SL 1700E, EI	73 kg (161 lb)
SL 1700EA, EAI	70 kg (154 lb)
SL 1700EC, ECI	74 kg (164 lb)

PERFORMANCE RATINGS:

T-O: SL 1700D	48.5 kW (65 hp) at 3,600 rpm
SL 1700E, EI, EC, ECI	51 kW (68 hp) at 3,600 rpm
SL 1700EA, EAI	44.7 kW (60 hp) at 3,550 rpm
Continuous:	
SL 1700E, EI, EC, ECI	45.5 kW (61 hp) at 3,200 rpm
SL 1700EA, EAI	41.7 kW (56 hp) at 3,300 rpm

LIMBACH L 2000

This family is based on the SL 1700 with increased bore and stroke:

Limbach L 2000EO1. As 1700EI. Installed in Fournier RF-5, RF-9 and RF-10.

Limbach L 2000EA1. As 1700EAI. Installed in Scheibe SF-25C Falke 2000 and SF-36.

Limbach L 2000EB1. As 1700EBI. Installed in Grob G 109, Valentin Taifun and Hoffmann Dimona.

Details as for SL 1700, except for following:

CYLINDERS: Bore 90 mm (3.54 in). Stroke 78.4 mm (3.09 in). Capacity 1,994 cc (120.26 cu in). Compression ratio 8.7 (EAI, 8.9).

FUEL GRADE: 100L.

WEIGHT, DRY (with all accessories):

L 2000EOI	70 kg (154 lb)
L 2000EAI	69 kg (152 lb)
L 2000EBI	71.5 kg (157.5 lb)

PERFORMANCE RATINGS:

T-O: all models	59 kW (80 hp) at 3,400 rpm
Continuous:	
L 2000EOI, EAI	52 kW (70 hp) at 3,000 rpm
L 2000EBI	53 kW (72 hp) at 3,000 rpm

LIMBACH L 2400

Similar to L 2000 but has further increased dimensions.

CYLINDERS: Bore 97 mm (3.82 in). Stroke 82 mm (3.23 in). Capacity 2,424 cc (147.91 cu in). Compression ratio 8.5.

INDUCTION: Twin Stromberg-Zenith 150 CD-3 carburettors.

FUEL GRADE: Minimum 96 RON.

IGNITION: Slick 4230 or Bendix S4RN21 magneto feeding single Bosch WB 240 ERT 1 plugs.

ACCESSORIES: 1.4 kW starter, 14-V 33 or 55 A generator, fuel pump and tachometer. Provision for Hoffmann or Mühlbauer variable-pitch propeller.

WEIGHT, DRY: 82 kg (181 lb)

PERFORMANCE RATINGS:

T-O (5 min)	65 kW (87 hp) at 3,200 rpm
Continuous	63 kW (84.5 hp) at 3,000 rpm

MTU

MOTOREN- UND TURBINEN-UNION MÜNCHEN GmbH

Dachauer Str 655, Munich-Allach (Postal address, Postfach 500640, 8000 Munich 50)

Telephone: 49 (89) 1489 0

Telex: 529 500-15 MT D

Fax: 49 (89) 1502621

MTU München, a subsidiary of Deutsche Aerospace AG, is Germany's largest aero engine company. It produces engines for all classes of aircraft. In March 1990 it signed an agreement which gives Pratt & Whitney a firm foothold in Europe and makes MTU United Technologies' 'preferred partner worldwide'.

GENERAL ELECTRIC CF6

MTU has approximately a 12 per cent share in the manufacture of the CF6-50 for the A300, approximately an 8 per cent share of the CF6-80A/A1 for the A310 and 767 and a 9 per cent share of the CF6-80C2 for the A300-600, 747 and 767. MTU makes HP turbine parts.

PRATT & WHITNEY PW2000

MTU is a partner, with Fiat of Italy, in the PW2037 and 2040. It is responsible for the LP turbine, under an 11.2 per cent share.

IAE V 2500

MTU has a 12.1 per cent share in IAE (see International part of this section).

PRATT & WHITNEY JT8D-200

MTU has a 12.5 per cent share, being largely responsible for the LP turbine.

EUROJET EJ200

MTU has a 33 per cent share in this engine, described in the International part of this section.

TURBOMECA-SNECMA LARZAC

MTU has a 23 per cent share (see under France).

TURBO-UNION RB199

MTU has a 40 per cent share in this engine, described in the International part of this section.

ROLLS-ROYCE TYNE

MTU has a 28 per cent share in about 170 Tyne turboprops for the Transall. MTU supports all Tyne 21 engines (Atlantique) and Tyne 22 (Transall), as well as Tynes used by civil operators.

ALLISON 250-C20B

MTU licence built more than 700 engines, designated 250-MTU-C20B, for the PAH-1 and VBH military variants of the MBB BO 105 helicopter. MTU is converting C20Bs into C20Rs and is supporting engines used by civil operators.

MTU TURBOMECA RR MTR 390

Brief details of this three-nation helicopter engine are given in the International part of this section.

P&WC PW305

MTU has a 25 per cent share in this Canadian turbofan. One of its responsibilities is the LP turbine.

PARODI

PARODI MOTORSEGLERTECHNIK

Hauptstrasse 70, 7895 Klettgau-Erzingen

Telephone: 49 (7742) 7689

DIRECTOR: Roland Parodi

This company has developed a family of piston engines for ultralight aircraft and motor gliders. With various designations in the HP 45 and HP 60 series, these are derived from a Honda design, with a new crankcase and lubrication system.

Details were given in the 1984-85 *Jane's* of the HP 60 series engines of 44.7 kW (60 hp). These have been uprated to the 59.7 kW (80 hp) class, and are being used to support later engines for two-seat aircraft. Parodi hopes to produce two definitive engines: one with variable turbo pressure for 74.6 kW (100 hp), cruising at 55.9 kW (75 hp); and the other for 96.9 kW (130 hp), cruising at 74.6 kW (100 hp).

PIEPER

PIEPER MOTORENBAU GmbH

Postfach 1229, Viktoriastrasse 50, 4950 Minden

Telephone: 49 (571) 34088

STAMO MS 1500

Pieper manufactures the 33.5 kW (45 hp) Stamo MS 1500-1 modified Volkswagen four-cylinder aircooled piston engine, applications for which have included the Scheibe SF-25B Falke two-seat motor glider. Capacity 1,500 cc, compression ratio 7.2 : 1, length 640 mm (25 in), width 745 mm (29.3 in), height 395 mm (15.5 in) and dry weight 52 kg (115 lb). The MS 1500-1 operates on 80/86 or 90 octane fuel, and is started by a pull-cord. The MS 1500-2, has electric starter and generator. This increases weight to 60 kg (132 lb).

Pieper built Stamo MS 1500-1 four-cylinder four-stroke engine, rated at 33.5 kW (45 hp)

PORSCHE

DR ING h c F. PORSCHE AG

Postfach 1140, 7251 Weissach

Telephone: 49 (7044) 35 2743

Telex: 7 263 771

Fax: 49 (7044) 35 2555

MANAGER, DEVELOPMENT AIRCRAFT ENGINE: Dipl Ing Heinz Dorsch

PORSCHE PFM 3200

Developed from the well known 911 sports car engine, this piston engine is the first since 1955 designed for aircraft (standard 911S engines power the Airship Industries Skyships). A four-stroke flat-six, the PFM 3200 is aircooled, with a fan, and has a capacity of 3.2 litres (195 cu in) and dry sump lubrication. It has a geared drive of 0.442 ratio, single-lever control, and electronic ignition. Rated at 156 kW (209 hp), the PFM can burn Avgas or Mogas, or any mixture, and has fuel consumption 10-20 per cent lower than competitor engines.

The following versions have been announced:

N00. Derated N01, lower compression, unleaded Mogas.

N01. Basic model, in production.

N03. Uprated, higher compression, 100LL only.

T03. N03 with lower compression, different pistons, Garrett density controlled turbocharger.

Certification was completed in September 1984 by the LBA and in August 1985 by the FAA. Pilot production was initiated in August 1985. Series production started in April 1987.

CYLINDERS: Bore 95.0 mm (3.74 in). Stroke 74.4 mm (2.93 in). Capacity 3,164 cc (193 cu in). Compression ratio N01, 9.2; N03, 10.5; T03, 8.5.

FUEL SUPPLY: K-Jetronic direct injection, two electrical pumps; fuel grade 100LL or Mogas.

ACCESSORIES: Magneti Marelli electronic ignition, power/speed proportional fan cooling, two 28V alternators, two vacuum pumps.

DIMENSIONS:

Length	973 mm (38.3 in)
Width	855 mm (33.7 in)
Height (excluding exhaust system)	610 mm (24.0 in)

WEIGHT, DRY:

Bare engine	181 kg (399 lb)
N01, 03 equipped	200 kg (441 lb)
T03, equipped	220 kg (480 lb)

PERFORMANCE RATING (S/L):

T-O:

N01	156 kW (209 hp) at 5,300 rpm
N03	162 kW (217 hp) at 5,300 rpm
T03	180 kW (241 hp) to 5,500 m (18,000 ft)

Econ cruise:

N01	109 kW (146 hp) at 4,550 rpm
N03	113 kW (151.5 hp) at 4,550 rpm
T03	126 kW (169 hp) to 5,500 m (18,000 ft)

SPECIFIC FUEL CONSUMPTION (econ cruise):

N01	73.5 µg/J (0.435 lb/h/hp)
N03	70.3 µg/J (0.416 lb/h/hp)
T03	74.7 µg/J (0.442 lb/h/hp)

Porsche PFM 3200 six-cylinder piston engine

SAUER

SAUER MOTORENBAU GmbH

Nieder-Olmer Str 16, 6501 Ober Olm
Telephone: 49 (61) 36/8 9377
This company is marketing two sizes of four-cylinder four-stroke piston engine.

SAUER SS 2100 H1S

This engine can have dual Slick 4230 magnetos and runs on 100LL Avgas or Mogas. It has twin Bing 64/32 carburettors, a 12V starter and 15A alternator.
CYLINDERS: Bore 90 mm (3.54 in). Stroke 84 mm (3.31 in). Capacity 2,135 cc (130.3 cu in). Compression ratio 9.5.
WEIGHT, DRY: 76 kg (168 lb)
PERFORMANCE RATING: 59.5 kW (80 hp) at 3,000 rpm

SAUER ST 2500 H1S

Similar to SS 2100 but increased bore. It has a 45A generator.
CYLINDERS: Bore 97 mm (3.82 in). Stroke 84 mm (3.31 in). Capacity 2,481 cc (151.3 cu in).
WEIGHT, DRY: 79 kg (174 lb)
PERFORMANCE RATING: 68 kW (91.2 hp) at 3,000 rpm

Sauer SS 2100 H1S four-cylinder piston engine
(Wolfgang Wagner)

ZOCHE

MICHAEL ZOCHE

Keferstrasse 13, 8000 Munich 40
Telephone: 49 (89) 34 45 91
Telex: 523 402 ZOCHE D
Fax: 49 (89) 34 24 51
This company's diesel aero engines incorporate the latest cylinder technology as well as such refinements as tungsten counterweights and full aerobatic pressure lubrication. Both engines have a propeller governor and four accessory drive pads. The weights given include starter, alternator, governor, vacuum pump and turbocharger.

ZOCHE ZO 01A

CYLINDERS: Four, arranged at 90°. Bore 95 mm (3.74 in). Stroke 94 mm (3.70 in). Capacity 2,665 cc (162.6 cu in). Compression ratio 17.
FUEL GRADES: Diesel No. 2, JP-4 or Jet A.

DIMENSIONS:

Length	720 mm (28 in)
Height or width	530 mm (20.9 in)
Diameter	640 mm (25.2 in)

WEIGHT, DRY: 89 kg (196 lb)
PERFORMANCE RATING: 110 kW (150 hp) at 2,500 rpm
SPECIFIC FUEL CONSUMPTION (above rating): 65.0 µg/J (0.385 lb/h/hp)

ZOCHE ZO 02A

This is a double-row eight-cylinder engine using 01A cylinders. It is 825 mm (32.5 in) long, weighs under 130 kg (286 lb) and has a T-O rating of 220 kW (300 hp).

Zoche ZO 01A four-cylinder diesel engine
(Howard Levy)

INDIA

GTRE

GAS TURBINE RESEARCH ESTABLISHMENT

Suranjan Das Road, Post Bag 9302, C. V. Raman Nagar, Bangalore 560 093
Telephone: 91 (812) 570698
Telex: 0845 2438 GTRE IN
DIRECTOR: Arun Prasad
Established in 1959, the GTRE is one of 45 R&D establishments administered by the DRDO (Defence Research & Development Organisation). By far its biggest challenge is the design and development of a new engine for fighter aircraft.

GTRE GTX

This engine is planned as the power plant of the production LCA (Light Combat Aircraft). Although influenced by existing engines, the GTX is a completely Indian project, and is being developed in the following versions:

GTX37-14U. This afterburning turbojet was the first designed in India. First run in 1977, it has a three-stage LP compressor and seven-stage HP compressor, both driven by single-stage turbines. It is flat-rated to ISA +30°C at 44.5 kN (10,000 lb st) dry and 64.3 kN (14,450 lb st) with full reheat. A few engines will continue running to support later variants.

GTX37-14UB. Turbofan version with bypass ratio of 0.215. Max thrust 88.9 kN (19,990 lb st) with a larger frontal area.

GTX-35. Advanced turbojet with five-stage HP compressor, new annular combustor and increased turbine temperature. Offered required thrust for LCA, but higher fuel consumption due to higher thrust levels.

GTX-35VS. Improved turbofan planned as engine for LCA. Core to run in early 1991, engine in mid-1992.
LP COMPRESSOR: Three stages, with transonic blading. Pressure ratio 3.22.
HP COMPRESSOR: Five stages with some variable stators. Pressure ratio 6.5. Overall pressure ratio 21.
COMBUSTION CHAMBER: Annular, with air-blast atomisers.
HP TURBINE: Heavily loaded single-stage with DS cooled blades. Entry gas temperature 1,377°C. Later to have thermal barrier coating.
LP TURBINE: Single-stage, cooled.
CONTROL SYSTEM: FADEC being developed by HAL Lucknow Division, in collaboration with DSIC Ltd.
PERFORMANCE RATINGS (flat-rated to ISA +20°C, S/L):

Max: dry	50.6 kN (11,380 lb st)
with afterburning	80.07 kN (18,000 lb st)

HAL
HINDUSTAN AERONAUTICS LTD
PO Box 5150, 15/1 Cubbon Road, Bangalore 560 001
Telephone: 91 (812) 76901
OFFICERS: see Aircraft section

The Bangalore Engine and Koraput Divisions of HAL constitute the main aero engine manufacturing elements of the Indian aircraft industry.

BANGALORE COMPLEX (Engine Division)
Adour 811 engines are manufactured under Rolls-Royce Turbomeca licence. The Orpheus 701 and Dart 536-2T are manufactured under licence from Rolls-Royce. The Artouste IIIB is made under licence from Turbomeca.

KORAPUT DIVISION
This Division was established to manufacture under Soviet government licence the Tumansky R-11 afterburning turbojet. With help from the Soviet Union, the first engine

was run in early 1969. In 1977 production switched to the R-25 for the MiG-21 bis, followed in 1984 by the R-29B for the MiG-27M.

INTERNATIONAL PROGRAMMES

BMW ROLLS-ROYCE
BMW AG
Munich, West Germany
Telephone: 49 (89) 3895 4556
Rolls-Royce plc
65 Buckingham Gate, London SW1E 6AT, England
Telephone: 44 (71) 222 9020

These two companies announced in May 1990 that they were forming a joint venture company to develop and produce aircraft gas turbines. BMW Rolls-Royce has taken over the business of KHD Luftfahrttechnik, and is owned 50.5 per cent by BMW and 49.5 per cent by Rolls-Royce. The company will collaborate in the Rolls-Royce Tay and Trent programmes, and will design and develop engines of

less than 89.0 kN (20,000 lb st) for emerging airframe and re-engining requirements.

CFM
CFM INTERNATIONAL SA
2 boulevard Victor, 75015 Paris, France
Telephone: 33 (1) 40 60 81 89
CHAIRMAN AND CHIEF EXECUTIVE: J. Bilien
MARKETING DIRECTOR: Richard B. Shaffer

CFM International, a joint company, was formed by SNECMA (France) and General Electric (USA) in 1974 to provide management for the CFM56 programme and a single customer interface.

GE is responsible for design integration, the core engine and the main engine control. The core engine is derived from that of the F101 turbofan developed for the US military. SNECMA is responsible for the low-pressure system, gearbox, accessory integration and engine installation.

CFM INTERNATIONAL CFM56
US military designation: F108
In the late 1960s SNECMA and General Electric (now GE Aircraft Engines) concluded that a large market existed for a high bypass ratio engine in the ten ton class (97.9-106.8 kN; 22,000-24,000 lb st). The first CFM56 demonstrator ran at GE's Evendale plant on 20 June 1974.

The CFM56 designation covers a family of engines from 89.0 to 138.7 kN (20,000-31,200 lb st). By April 1990 a total of 3,683 engines had been delivered, against orders for more than 6,800. The following are current versions:

CFM56-2. Certificated 8 November 1979, under FAR Pt 33 and JAR-E, at 106.8 kN (24,000 lb st); but several applications use only a 97.9 kN (22,000 lb) T-O rating. CFM56-2 production was launched in 1979 to re-engine the DC-8-60 to Super 70 standard. Scheduled operations began on 24 April 1982 and 110 aircraft in service with 16 operators have logged more than 6,000,000 engine flight hours. Engine-caused shop visit rate is 0.14 and the dispatch reliability is 99.89 per cent. The CMF56-2 exists in several variants, differing by their ratings or configuration details.

CFM56-2A. Certificated 6 June 1985 at 106.8 kN (24,000 lb st), flat rated to 35°C (95°F), the CFM56-2A-2 powers the US Navy E-6 communications aircraft and the Royal Saudi Air Force E-3 advanced warning aircraft and KE-3 tanker, the E-3s for the UK and France and the Boeing E-8A. These applications require long duration oil tank, reverser and gearbox for two high capacity integrated drive generators.

CFM56-2-B. Certificated 25 June 1984 at 97.9 kN (22,000 lb st), flat rated to 32°C (90°F), the CFM56-2-B1 was selected by the US Air Force for its KC-135A tanker re-engining programme on 22 January 1980. First flight of a KC-135R took place on 4 August 1982 and production F108-CF-100 engines power KC-135R aircraft delivered from late 1983. CFM56-2-B1 also retrofits C-135FR tankers of the French Armée de l'Air.

CFM56-2C. Version of CFM56-2 for re-engining DC-8; T-O thrust of 97.9 kN (22,000 lb st), with flat rating to 30°C (86°F) in -2-C1 to -2-C6 subvariants.

CFM56-3-B1. Derivative of CFM56-2, rated at 89.00 kN (20,000 lb st), flat rated to 30°C (86°F), with smaller fan. Powers Boeing 737-300. First ran in March 1982. US and French certification granted 12 January 1984. Entered airline service November 1984. Rerated at 82.2 kN (18,500 lb st), powers 737-500.

CFM56-3B-2. Certificated at 97.90 kN (22,000 lb st), flat rated to 30°C (86°F), on 20 June 1984. For 737-300 and 737-400 with improved payload/range from short, hot, high airfields.

Features of the CFM International CFM56-5C for the Airbus A340 include advanced fan; new booster; dual schedules for variable stator; active clearance control for the compressor; modulated clearance control for the HP and LP turbines; advanced aerodynamics for the HP turbine; high efficiency HP/LP turbine interface; advanced aerodynamics, 5-stage LP turbine; new turbine frame; integrated mixer nozzle; and full authority digital electronic control

Longitudinal section of CFM56-5-A1

CFM56-3C-1. Rated at 104.5 kN (23,500 lb st) for 737-300, -400 and -500. Certificated December 1986.

By April 1990 more than 88 customers had ordered 3,800 CFM56-3 engines. Over 680 Boeing 737-300s and -400s in service had logged more than 10,000,000 engine flight hours. Engine-caused shop visit (12 month rolling averages) was 0.11, and dispatch reliability 99.96 per cent.

CFM56-5-A1. Launched September 1984, for A320. Has fan diameter of –2, with improved aerodynamics in all LP and HP components, advanced clearance control features and FADEC. Nominal rating of 111.21 kN (25,000 lb st), flat rated to 30°C (86°F). Certificated 27 August 1987.

CFM56-5A3. Rated at 117.8 kN (26,500 lb st). To meet specific airline requirements for A320.

CFM56-5B1. Rated at 133.5 kN (30,000 lb st) to power A321.

CFM56-5B2. Rated at 137.9 kN (31,000 lb st) to power A321.

CFM56-5C. With an initial T-O rating of 138.7 kN (31,200 lb st) and FADEC, this is the advanced version of the -5 selected by Airbus for the A340. This engine has growth capability to 151.2 kN (34,000 lb st), and 5 per cent better specific fuel consumption than the 5-A1.

TYPE: Two-shaft subsonic turbofan.

FAN: Single-stage axial. Forged titanium disc holding (CFM56-2) 44 titanium blades, each with a tip shroud to form a continuous ring; (CFM56-3) 38 titanium blades, each with part-span shroud; (CFM56-5) 36 titanium blades, each with part-span shroud. Mass flow (-2A-2) 370 kg (817 lb)/s, (-3B-2) 312 kg (688 lb)/s, (-5-A1) 386 kg (852 lb)/s. Bypass ratio (-2) 6, (-3) 5, (-5) 6, (-5C) 6.6.

LP COMPRESSOR: Three axial stages (4 on -5B and -5C), on titanium drum bolted to fan disc. A ring of bleed doors allows core airflow to escape into fan duct at low power settings.

HP COMPRESSOR: Nine-stage rotor with three stages of titanium blades and remainder of steel. Stator vanes are steel, with first four stators variable. Overall pressure ratio 25:1 class (-3, 22.6; -5, 26.5; -5C, climb, 37.5).

COMBUSTION CHAMBER: Machined ring, fully annular, with advanced film cooling.

HP TURBINE: Single-stage with aircooled stator and rotor airfoils, directionally solidified on -5. Entry gas temperature in 1,260°C class. HP system carried in two bearings (-5, three bearings).

LP TURBINE: Four-stage (5 on -5C) with tip shrouds.

EXHAUST UNIT (FAN): Constant diameter duct of sound-absorbent construction. Outer cowl and engine cowl form convergent plug nozzle, with airframe mounted reverser.

EXHAUST UNIT (CORE): Fixed-area with convergent nozzle, mixer on -5C.

ACCESSORY DRIVE: (CFM56-2 and -5) Gearbox in front sump transmits drive from front of HP spool to transfer gearbox on underside of fan case. Air starter at transfer gearbox (-2) or accessory gearbox (-5). (CFM56-3) Side mounted accessory drive gearbox with transfer gearbox; air starter pad on accessory gearbox.

CONTROL SYSTEM: Hydromechanical with electronic trim (-2, -3); FADEC (-5).

LUBRICATION: Non-pressure-regulated system.

DIMENSIONS:
Length, excl spinner:

CFM56-2	2,430 mm (95.7 in)
CFM56-3	2,360 mm (93.0 in)
CFM56-5-A1, -5A3	2,422 mm (95.4 in)
CFM56-5B1, -5B2	2,512 mm (98.9 in)
CFM56-5C	2,616 mm (103 in)

Fan diameter:

CFM56-2, -5A, -5B	1,735 mm (68.3 in)
CFM56-3	1,522 mm (60.0 in)
CFM56-5C	1,836 mm (72.3 in)

WEIGHT, DRY:

CFM56-2A-2	2,187 kg (4,820 lb)
CFM56-2B-1	1,846 kg (4,071 lb)
CFM56-2C series	2,102 kg (4,635 lb)
CFM56-3-B1	1,939 kg (4,276 lb)
CFM56-3B-2, -3C	1,951 kg (4,301 lb)
CFM56-5-A1	2,204 kg (4,860 lb)
CFM56-5A3	2,265 kg (4,995 lb)
CFM56-5B1, -5B2	2,381 kg (5,250 lb)
CFM56-5C	2,492 kg (5,494 lb)

PERFORMANCE RATINGS:
Max T-O: see under model listings
Cruise, installed, 10,670 m (35,000 ft), Mach 0.8, ISA:

CFM56-2A-2	25.62 kN (5,760 lb)
CFM56-2B-1	22.10 kN (4,970 lb)
CFM56-2C series	22.15 kN (4,980 lb)
CFM56-3-B1	20.67 kN (4,650 lb)
CFM56-3-B1 rerate	19.13 kN (4,300 lb)
CFM56-3B-2	22.42 kN (5,040 lb)
CFM56-3C	23.88 kN (5,370 lb)
CFM56-5-A1, -5A3	22.23 kN (5,000 lb)
CFM56-5B1, -5B2	26.96 kN (6,060 lb)
CFM56-5C (with mixer)	30.78 kN (6,920 lb)

SPECIFIC FUEL CONSUMPTION (cruise, as above):

CFM56-2A-2	18.83 mg/Ns (0.665 lb/h/lb)
CFM56-2B-1	18.57 mg/Ns (0.656 lb/h/lb)
CFM56-2C series	19.00 mg/Ns (0.671 lb/h/lb)
CFM56-3 (all)	18.54 mg/Ns (0.655 lb/h/lb)
CFM56-5-A1, -5A3, -5B1, -5B2	16.87 mg/Ns (0.596 lb/h/lb)
CFM56-5C (with mixer)	16.06 mg/Ns (0.567 lb/h/lb)

EUROJET

EUROJET TURBO GmbH

Arabellastrasse 13, D-8000 Munich 81, Federal Republic of Germany
Telephone: 49 (89) 9210050
Telex: 5212124 EJET D
Fax: 49 (89) 92100539 and 92100562
MANAGING DIRECTOR: D. A. Marsh

Formed in August 1986 by a consortium of Fiat Aviazione of Italy, MTU-München GmbH of West Germany, Rolls-Royce of the UK and Sener of Spain, this company became operational on 1 January 1987 as EUROJET Turbo GmbH. It was established to co-ordinate the design, development and manufacture of the EJ200 engine for the European Fighter Aircraft.

The workshare is proportional to the expected aircraft requirements of the four nations, and has been agreed as follows: Fiat (21 per cent), LP turbine and shaft, interstage support, reheat system, gearbox, oil system, and participation in the intermediate casing; MTU (33 per cent), LP compressor, HP compressor, participation in HP turbine, and FADEC (full authority digital electronic control) design responsibility; Rolls-Royce (33 per cent), combustion system, HP turbine, intermediate casing, and participation in LP and HP compressors, LP turbine, interstage support, reheat system and nozzle; Sener (13 per cent), nozzle, jetpipe, exhaust diffuser and bypass duct.

Engine build and test during development and production will be at each partner's facilities. Each partner will provide comprehensive support for engines of its own national air force. The initial requirement of the four nations is for nearly 800 aircraft, including about 2,000 engines. The contract for full scale development was signed in November 1988. In the same month the first Design Verification Engine began running at MTU.

EUROJET EJ200

This engine will be an advanced turbofan designed for Mach numbers of about 2. It is fully modular, and allows for on-condition maintenance with built-in engine health monitoring and test equipment. Low maintenance and life-cycle cost along with high reliability have been prime design criteria. The total number of aerofoils is only approximately 60 per cent of those used in the RB199. The EJ200 programme has achieved all technical milestones on time and cost. This includes 150 h of accelerated mission endurance testing at full temperature rating. Entry into service is expected to be in 1996.

TYPE: Two-shaft augmented turbofan.

LP COMPRESSOR: Three stages, with 3-D transonic blades of robust large-chord section. No inlet guide vanes. Third stage blisks. Overhung ahead of high-capacity ball bearing and forward roller bearing. Bypass ratio about 0.4. Pressure ratio 4-plus.

HP COMPRESSOR: Five stages, with first-stage variable inlet guide vanes and blisk rotor stage. Shaft supported between front ball and rear roller bearings. Overall pressure ratio more than 25.

EJ200 engine DV02 on test at Fiat, Turin

Longitudinal half-section through the EUROJET EJ200 two-shaft augmented turbofan

COMBUSTOR: Fully annular, with vaporising burners.

HP TURBINE: Single-stage, with powder metallurgy disc and low density aircooled single crystal blades.

LP TURBINE: Single-stage, with powder metallurgy disc and single crystal blades. Both turbine bearings in single interstage support frame.

EXHAUST SYSTEM: High efficiency augmentor of burn-then-mix type, with fully variable convergent-divergent nozzle.

ACCESSORIES: Central gearbox driven via tower shaft in interstage support. Full authority digital electronic control. Integrated health monitoring system. Rotating-tank oil system to give artificial positive gravity at all times.

DIMENSIONS: Smaller throughout than RB199.

WEIGHT: In 1,000 kg (2,000 lb) class.

PERFORMANCE RATING: In 90 kN (20,000 lb st) class.

IAE

INTERNATIONAL AERO ENGINES AG

OFFICES: Corporate Center, 628 Hebron Avenue, Glastonbury, Connecticut 06033, USA
Telephone: 1 (203) 280 1800
Telex: 4436031 INTLAERO
Fax: 1 (203) 525 1586/4966
PRESIDENT: Nicholas R. Tomassetti
EXECUTIVE VICE-PRESIDENT: J. M. S. Keen
VICE-PRESIDENT BUSINESS: D. M. Evans
VICE-PRESIDENT MARKETING: C. R. Nelson
PUBLIC RELATIONS MANAGER: Robert Nuttall

IAE is a management company set up on 14 December 1983 to direct the entire programme for the V2500 turbofan worldwide. The following shareholders signed a 30-year agreement: Rolls-Royce 30 per cent, UTC (P&W) 30 per cent, Japanese Aero Engines (IHI, KHI, MHI) 23 per cent, MTU 11 per cent and Fiat 6 per cent. Responsibility for each module is allocated according to shareholding. Overall engineering direction is delegated to Pratt & Whitney. Engines are assembled and tested by Pratt & Whitney and Rolls-Royce.

JAEC is responsible for the fan (derived from 535E4) and LP compressor, Rolls-Royce for the HP compressor, Pratt & Whitney for the combustor and HP turbine, MTU for the LP turbine and Fiat for the gearbox and turbine exhaust case. Turbines, gearbox and FADEC use PW2000 technology.

IAE V2500

V2500-A1. In service on the A320. IAE supplies the complete package, including the nacelle (by Rohr/Shorts). Testing of the engine began in December 1985. A flight programme on a Boeing 720B in Canada was completed in 35 h in Spring 1988, and every ingestion and fan-blade-off test was passed first time (believed an industry record). The first pair of propulsion systems was delivered to Airbus Industrie in March 1988, and the V2500 was certificated in June 1988.

The first V2500-powered A320 made its first flight on 28 July 1988. The aircraft entered service with Adria Airways in May 1989.

Subsequent development to higher thrust is being achieved by increasing the core airflow and aerodynamic changes. Pressure ratio of the LP compressor is increased by adding a fourth stage. All engines in the A (Airbus) and D (Douglas) series have common fans and cores, and fit into a common nacelle which for the MD-90 is modified for fuselage side mounting.

V2522-D5. Rated at 99.79 kN (22,000 lb st). Four-stage LP compressor, as in all A5 and D5 versions. Bypass ratio 4.9. Pressure ratio 24.9. For MD90-10.

V2525-A5. Flat rated at 111.25 kN (25,000 lb st). Bypass ratio 4.8. Pressure ratio 27.7. For A320.

V2525-D5. Flat rated at 111.25 kN (25,000 lb st). Bypass ratio 4.8. Pressure ratio 27.7. For MD90-30.

V2528-D5. Rated at 124.55 kN (28,000 lb st). Bypass ratio 4.7. Pressure ratio 30.4. For MD90-40.

V2530-A5. Rated at 133.4 kN (30,000 lb st). Bypass ratio 4.6. Pressure ratio 32.5. For A321.

By April 1990 the first 14 customers had specified V2500 engines for a total of 555 aircraft, comprising 229 A320s, 86 A321s and 240 MD-90s.

The primary features of the V2500-A1 are as follows:
TYPE: Two-spool subsonic turbofan.
FAN: Single-stage with wide-chord shroudless blading. Diameter 1,600 mm (63.0 in). Pressure ratio 1.70. Bypass ratio 5.42. Mass flow 355 kg (783 lb)/s.

LP COMPRESSOR: Three stages, bolted to rear of fan to boost inlet to core. (Four stages in A5 and D5 versions.)
HP COMPRESSOR: Ten stages of blading supported by a drum rotor. Inlet guide and first three vane stages variable. Overall pressure ratio 29.4.
COMBUSTOR: Annular segmented construction eliminates hoop stresses and provides low emissions and uniform exit temperatures.
HP TURBINE: Two stages of aircooled single-crystal blading in powder metallurgy discs. Active tip clearance control.
LP TURBINE: Five stages of uncooled blading in welded and bolted rotor. Active clearance control.
GEARBOX: Modular unit, fan-case mounted.
CONTROL SYSTEM: Full authority digital electronic control (FADEC) to provide command outputs for engine fuel flow, stator vane angle, bleed modulation, turbine and exhaust case cooling, oil cooling, ignition and reverser functions. Supplied by Hamilton Standard.
NACELLE: Full length nacelle with reverser. Cowl load sharing to minimise case deflections. Acoustically treated.
DIMENSIONS:

Length (flange to flange)	3,200 mm (126 in)
Fan diameter	1,600 mm (63.0 in)

WEIGHT, DRY (with original single-stage LP compressor):

Bare engine	2,242 kg (4,942 lb)
Complete power plant, incl nacelle	3,311 kg (7,300 lb)

PERFORMANCE RATINGS (installed):

T-O, S/L, ISA	111.25 kN (25,000 lb st) to ISA + 15°C
Cruise Mach 0.8, 10,670 m (35,000 ft)	21.6 kN (4,850 lb)

SPECIFIC FUEL CONSUMPTION (Cruise Mach 0.8, 10,670 m; 35,000 ft, installed) 16.29 mg/Ns (0.575 lb/h/lb)

Longitudinal section of IAE V2500-A5/D5 two-shaft turbofan

LOTAREV/ZVL

LOTAREV (ZMKB): see under USSR
ZVL: see under Czechoslovakia

The DV-2 turbofan is a joint programme by these two organisations. It is described under Lotarev.

MTR

MTU-TURBOMECA-RR GmbH

Arabellastrasse 13, D-8000 Munich 81, West Germany
Telephone: 49 (89) 910 2017
Telex: (17) 89 74 32
Fax: 49 (89) 910 1543

MTR 390

This turboshaft engine is being developed by a joint company owned equally by MTU, Turbomeca and Rolls-Royce. First application, geared to an 8,000 rpm output, will be to power the Eurocopter Tiger. The direct-drive MTR 390T (27,000 rpm output) is proposed for the JEH Tonal derivative of the Agusta A 129. All models are covered by the European Small Engines Co-operation Agreement described in the introduction to Turbomeca of France. First run took place at MTU on 19 January 1989, and flight in a Dauphin testbed was to follow in 1990.
COMPRESSOR: Two centrifugal stages. Mass flow 3.2 kg (7.05 lb)/s. Pressure ratio 13.
COMBUSTION CHAMBER: Reverse flow annular.
TURBINES: Single-stage cooled gas generator turbine. Two-stage free power turbine.

Longitudinal section through MTR 390 turboshaft

CONTROL SYSTEM: Full authority digital.
DIMENSIONS:

Length	1,078 mm (42.4 in)
Width	442 mm (17.4 in)
Height	682 mm (26.8 in)
WEIGHT:	169 kg (372.5 lb)

RATINGS (ISA, S/L):

Emergency (20 s)	1,160 kW (1,556 hp)

Preparing MTR 390 turboshaft at MTU

T-O (5 min)	958 kW (1,285 hp)
Max continuous	873 kW (1,171 hp)

SPECIFIC FUEL CONSUMPTION:

T-O	75.94 µg/J (0.450 lb/h/hp)

ROLLS-ROYCE LYULKA

ROLLS-ROYCE: see under UK
LYULKA: see under USSR

It was announced on 16 May 1990 that a preliminary agreement has been signed between Rolls-Royce, the Lyulka (Saturn) engine design bureau and the Sukhoi aircraft design bureau which is intended to lead to the joint development of an engine for a supersonic business jet. By May 1991 the two engine teams will have determined the engine configuration and main characteristics. Further progress will then depend on a business evaluation, finance, and the approval of the two governments to launch the programme.

ROLLS-ROYCE TURBOMECA
ROLLS-ROYCE TURBOMECA LIMITED
4/5 Grosvenor Place, London SW1X 7HH, England
Telephone: 44 (71) 235 3641
Telex: 918944
Fax: 44 (71) 245 6385

This joint company was formed in June 1966 to control design, development and production programmes for the Adour two-shaft turbofan.

In 1980 Rolls-Royce Turbomeca launched the RTM 321 turboshaft demonstrator, leading to the RTM 322.

Rolls-Royce Turbomeca Adour Mk 151 two-shaft turbofan

ROLLS-ROYCE TURBOMECA ADOUR
US military designation: F405

The Adour was designed for the SEPECAT Jaguar. The whole engine is simple and robust and of modular design.

Bench testing began at Derby on 9 May 1967. Engines for Jaguars were assembled at Derby (RR) and Tarnos (Turbomeca) from parts made at single sources in Britain and France. Turbomeca makes the compressors, casings and external pipework (to preserve Anglo-French parity the afterburner is subcontracted to SNECMA); Rolls-Royce makes the remainder.

Following selection of the Adour for the Mitsubishi T-2 trainer and F-1 fighter/support aircraft, Ishikawajima-Harima Heavy Industries has been producing the Adour since 1970 under a licence agreement. In 1972 a non-afterburning Adour was selected to power the British Aerospace Hawk advanced trainer. More than 2,300 engines have been produced, including licence manufacture in Japan, India and Finland. Flight hours exceed 3.3 million.

Current versions of the engine are as follows:

Mk 102. Original production engine for Jaguars in service with RAF and Armée de l'Air. Qualified in 1972.

Mk 104. Uprated RT172-26 version similar to Mk 804; RAF Mk 102 engines were converted to this standard.

Mk 151. Non-afterburning version for Hawk. Internal components and certification temperatures identical to Mk 102 and Mk 801A. Qualified in 1975.

Mk 801A. Japanese designation TF40-IHI-801A. For Mitsubishi T-2 and F-1. Qualified in 1972. (See Ishikawajima-Harima in Japanese section.)

Mk 804. Uprated engine for Jaguar International.

Mk 804. Uprated engine for Jaguar International. Rating with full afterburner at Mach 0.9 at S/L, ISA, increased by 27 per cent. Qualified in 1976.

Mk 811. Uprated version for Jaguar International. Revised compressor aerodynamics and hot-end improvements. Assembled by Hindustan Aeronautics, with increasing Indian manufactured content.

Mk 815C. Mk 804 uprated to Mk 811 performance level by conversion at overhaul.

Mk 851. Non-afterburning version of Mk 804 for export Hawk.

Mk 861. Non-afterburning version of Mk 811, first deliveries 1981.

Mk 861-49. US designation **F405-RR-400**. Derated version of Mk 861, for prototype McDD/BAe T-45A Goshawk for US Navy. Certificated 1988.

Mk 871. Uprated version for BAe Hawk Series 100 and 200. Replaces Mk 861-49 in T-45A. Certification scheduled for 1990.

The following refers to non-afterburning versions, except where indicated:

TYPE: Two-shaft turbofan for subsonic aircraft.

FAN: Two-stage. Full length bypass duct leading to afterburner. Bypass ratio, 0.75-0.80.

COMPRESSOR: Five stages. Overall pressure ratio 11 : 1.

COMBUSTION CHAMBER: Annular, with 18 air spray fuel nozzles and two igniter plugs. Lucas engine fuel system.

HP TURBINE: Single-stage, aircooled.

LP TURBINE: Single-stage. Squeeze-film bearings.

DIMENSIONS:

Length:	
Mks 102, 801A, 804, 811	2,970 mm (117 in)
Mks 151, 851, 861, 861-49, 871	1,956 mm (77 in)
Inlet diameter (all)	559 mm (22 in)
Max width (all)	762 mm (30 in)
Max height (all)	1,041 mm (41 in)

WEIGHT, DRY:

Mk 102, 801A	704 kg (1,552 lb)
Mk 104, 804	713 kg (1,571 lb)
Mk 151	553 kg (1,220 lb)
Mk 851	568 kg (1,252 lb)
Mk 861	577 kg (1,273 lb)
Mk 811	738 kg (1,627 lb)
Mk 871	603 kg (1,330 lb)

PERFORMANCE RATINGS (S/L T-O):

Mk 102, 801A	32.5 kN (7,305 lb st)*
Mk 104	35.1 kN (7,900 lb st)*
Mk 151, 851	23.1 kN (5,200 lb st)
Mk 804	35.8 kN (8,040 lb st)*
Mk 861	25.4 kN (5,700 lb st)
Mk 861-49	24.2 kN (5,450 lb st)
Mk 811	37.4 kN (8,400 lb st)*
Mk 871	26.0 kN (5,845 lb st)

*With afterburner

Rolls-Royce Turbomeca RTM 322-01 turboshaft

SPECIFIC FUEL CONSUMPTION (Mk 102):

S/L static, dry	21 mg/Ns (0.74 lb/h/lb st)
Mach 0.8, 11,890 m (39,000 ft)	27 mg/Ns (0.955 lb/h/lb st)

ROLLS-ROYCE TURBOMECA RTM 322

Rolls-Royce and Turbomeca combined their extensive experience in helicopter gas turbines to produce the RTM 322 family of engines. Since 1986, Piaggio of Italy has been a 10 per cent participant. The launch engine is the RTM 322-01 turboshaft, which is conservatively rated at 1,566 kW (2,100 shp) with easy growth potential to 2,237 kW (3,000 shp).

The family, which will include turboprop and turbofan derivatives, is configured to combine simple design, reliability, low fuel consumption, light weight and low cost of ownership. Rolls-Royce Turbomeca is studying a turboprop that uses the RTM 322-01 core. This would produce 1,193-1,491 kW (1,600-2,000 shp), with potential for growth to 2,088 kW (2,800 shp). It is therefore suitable for aircraft in the 35-70 seat range.

The turboshaft itself has full-authority digital electronic control, availability of different output drive configurations, a choice of three starting systems, and options for an inlet particle separator and infra-red suppressor. Combined with engine mounts configured for compatibility with a number of existing airframes, these features give the unit a wide range of potential civil and military applications in the 7 to 15 tonne class. Examples are: EH 101, Sikorsky Black Hawk and Seahawk series, European NH 90, Westland WS-70 and AH-64 Apache. The engine has been studied by the US Army as a potential growth power plant for the Black Hawk and Apache, and during 1987 the US Navy carried out an operability study in an SH-60B. In November 1986 Pratt & Whitney confirmed its licence rights for marketing and manufacture of the RTM 322 for sales to the US and Canadian Governments after an initial agreement made in 1985.

In 1988 a major competition was held between Rolls-Royce Turbomeca and General Electric for the production engine contract of all UK EH 101 helicopters. In September 1988 the Minister of Defence Procurement announced that Rolls-Royce Turbomeca had won this competition for approximately 500 engines, as it provided 'the best value for money'. The first flight on the EH 101 is planned for 1992.

The first complete RTM 322-01 ran on 4 February 1985. Over 1,790 kW (2,400 shp) has been demonstrated. A total of over 10,000 hours running have been completed, which includes 1,100 hours of flight development in the S-70C (from 14 June 1986) and then in the SH-60B. UK military certification was completed in October 1988, and will be followed by civil certification in early 1991.

The following particulars apply to the RTM 322-01 turboshaft:

COMPRESSOR: Three-stage axial and single-stage centrifugal.

COMBUSTOR: Annular reverse flow. Ignition by Lucas Aerospace exciter.

TURBINES: Two-stage gas generator turbine. Cooling is applied to the 1st and 2nd stage stators and 1st stage rotor. The 2nd stage rotor is made of single crystal material and is uncooled. Two-stage power turbine with drive to front or rear.

DIMENSIONS:

Length overall	1,171 mm (46 in)
Diameter	604 mm (23.8 in)

WEIGHT, DRY: 240 kg (538 lb)

PERFORMANCE RATINGS (S/L):

Max contingency	1,724 kW (2,312 shp)
Max T-O	1,566 kW (2,100 shp)
Typical cruise	940 kW (1,260 shp)

SPECIFIC FUEL CONSUMPTION:

Cruise (as above)	81 µg/J (0.48 lb/shp/h)

TURBO-UNION

TURBO-UNION LTD

PO Box 3, Filton, Bristol BS12 7QE, England
Telephone: 44 (272) 791234
Telex: 44185 RR BSLG
MUNICH OFFICE: Arabellastrasse 13, D-8000 Munich 81,
Federal Republic of Germany
Telephone: 49 (89) 9242 1
Telex: 524151 TUD
CHAIRMAN: Dr G. C. Boffetta
MANAGING DIRECTOR: Kurt Münzenmaier

Formed in 1969 as a European engine consortium comprising Rolls-Royce plc (40 per cent) of the United Kingdom, MTU Motoren- und Turbinen-Union München GmbH (40 per cent) of the Federal Republic of Germany and Fiat Avio SpA (20 per cent) of Italy. The consortium was established to design, develop, manufacture and support the RB199 turbofan for the Panavia Tornado aircraft.

Cutaway drawing of Turbo-Union RB199 Mk 104 three-shaft augmented turbofan

TURBO-UNION RB199

The RB199 is a three-spool turbofan offering low fuel consumption for long-range dry cruise and approximately 100 per cent thrust augmentation with full afterburner for combat manoeuvre and supersonic acceleration. It features an integral thrust reverser system for installation in the Tornado, but is available for other applications without it. It was the first military engine with FADEC without hydromechanical backup, available on all production versions. The present engine family comprises:

Mk 103. Standard production engine for Tornado IDS. In-service experience at low level in the most arduous conditions has proven the RB199's high resilience to FOD and birdstrike, a direct result of the three-spool layout incorporating short, rigid rotating assemblies held between small bearing spans.

Mk 104. Identical to Mk 103 but incorporates a jetpipe extended by 360 mm (14 in) to provide thrust increases up to 10 per cent as well as reduced sfc. The 104 is the standard production engine for the Tornado ADV F.3. The **104D** powers the BAe EAP. The main difference is absence of the reverser, which reduces weight by 10 per cent. The **Mk 104E** is the interim engine for EFA prototypes.

Mk 105. The Tornado ECR is powered by the Mk 105. Similar to the 103, it includes an increased pressure ratio and mass flow LP compressor, and single-crystal HP turbine blades, giving a thrust increase of 10 per cent and significant life-cycle cost reductions. This represents a major step towards an enhanced engine in the early 1990s. This will have improved IP and HP compressors, turbine NGVs and single-crystal IP turbine blades. Thrust improvements of over 20 per cent will be available, together with significant LCC reductions.

The RB199 passed one million flying hours in Summer 1988. Firm orders exist for over 2,400 engines, guaranteeing new engine production well into the 1990s.

The following refers to the Mk 105:
TYPE: Three-shaft turbofan with afterburner and reverser.

LP COMPRESSOR: Three-stage axial of titanium alloy. Casing of three bolted sections. Rotor of three discs welded together. Rotor blades secured by dovetail roots, all with snubbers. Mass flow approx 74.6 kg (164 lb)/s. Bypass ratio about 1:1.

IP COMPRESSOR: Three stages of titanium alloy. Rotor has welded discs in which blades are secured by dovetails.

HP COMPRESSOR: Six-stage; material changes from titanium at front to heat resisting alloy at rear, except stator blades are heat resisting steel throughout. Rotor discs secured by ten through-bolts, carrying blades by dovetail roots. Bevel drive to gearbox. Overall pressure ratio greater than 23.

BYPASS DUCT: Fabricated in titanium.

COMBUSTION CHAMBER: Annular flame tube fabricated from nickel alloy, bolted at rear end between outer casing, forged and chemically milled in nickel-iron alloy, and inner casing of nickel alloy. Carries 13 double-headed fuel vaporisers which give combustion without visible smoke. Two igniter plugs. Hot-streak injector for afterburner ignition.

HP TURBINE: Shrouded single stage. Entry temperature over 1,327°C. Rotor blades and stator vanes aircooled.

IP TURBINE: Shrouded single stage. Aircooled stator vanes and rotor blades.

LP TURBINE: Two-stage with shrouded hollow uncooled rotor blades.

AFTERBURNER: Front end of titanium fabricated jetpipe carries afterburner in which bypass air and core gas burn concurrently, without a mixing section. For core flow, two gutter flameholders fed by upstream atomisers. For bypass flow, reverse colander with radial extensions, each containing vaporising primary burner, between which multiple jets inject remainder of afterburner fuel. Fully modulated augmentation.

NOZZLE: Variable area, short petal, convergent nozzle operated by shroud actuated by four screwjacks, driven by fourth stage HP air motor via flexible shafting. Each of 14 master and 14 secondary petals is precision cast in cobalt alloy which minimises friction.

REVERSER: External two bucket type driven via flexible shafts by motor using HP air. In stowed position outer skins form aircraft profile. Deployment takes 1 s at any thrust setting from idle to max dry.

ACCESSORY DRIVES: Accessory gearbox on underside of intermediate casing (quick attach/detach coupling) carries hydromechanical portions of main and afterburner fuel systems, oil tank and pump, and output shaft to aircraft gearbox carrying KHD gas turbine starter/APU.

FUEL SYSTEM: Electronic main engine control unit uses signals from pilot's lever and power plant sensors. Afterburner fuel from engine driven vapour core pump.

DIMENSIONS:

Length overall: Mk 103		3,251 mm (128 in)
Mk 104		3,607 mm (142 in)
Mk 105		3,302 mm (130 in)
Intake diameter: Mk 103		719 mm (28.3 in)
Mk 104		719 mm (28.3 in)
Mk 105		752 mm (29.6 in)

WEIGHT, DRY (excl reverser):

Mk 103	965 kg (2,107 lb)
Mk 104	976 kg (2,151 lb)
Mk 105	980 kg (2,160 lb)

PERFORMANCE RATINGS (S/L, ISA):

Max dry: Mk 103	40.48 kN (9,100 lb st)
Mk 104	40.48 kN (9,100 lb st)
Mk 105	42.95 kN (9,656 lb st)
Max afterburning: Mk 103	71.17 kN (16,000 lb st)
Mk 104	72.95 kN (16,400 lb st)
Mk 105	74.73 kN (16,800 lb st)

ISRAEL

BSEL

BET-SHEMESH ENGINES LTD

Mobile Post Haela, Bet-Shemesh 99000
Telephone: 972 (2) 911661-6
Telex: 25590 BSENG IL
Fax: 972 (2) 911970 or 915117

Bet-Shemesh Engines is partly owned by the Israeli Government. Its 400 employees produce Turbomeca Marboré VI and Bet-Shemesh Sorek 4 turbojets (not included as it powers missiles and UAVs) and parts for the

F100, J52, J79 and JT8. Support is provided for the Allison 250, F100, J79, Marboré and PW1120. There is an important investment casting division.

IAI

ISRAEL AIRCRAFT INDUSTRIES LTD

Ben-Gurion International Airport, 70100
Telephone: 972 (3) 97131111
Telex: ISRAV-IL 371133
Fax: 972 (3) 972290

The Engine Overhaul Plant is part of IAI's Bedek Aviation Division. It produces J79 engines and performs extensive overhaul and maintenance of civil and military engines.

J79-IAI-J1E

The J79-IAI-J1E powers the IAI Kfir and is produced by IAI under GE licence. It is a J79-GE-19 incorporating 102 per cent engine speed at high aircraft Mach number, smokeless combustors, and a T_5 reset for fast acceleration. Accessories and gearboxes are relocated, and a titanium heatshield covers the afterburner. A Combat Plus system increases T-O thrust from 78.9 kN (17,750 lb) to 83.4 kN (18,750 lb).

Details of the J79 can be found in the 1978-79 edition of *Jane's.*

Data for the J1E include:

MASS FLOW:	77.1 kg (170 lb)/s
PRESSURE RATIO:	12.4
DIMENSIONS:	
Max diameter	995.7 mm (39.2 in)
Length	5,283 mm (208 in)
WEIGHT, DRY:	1,699 kg (3,746 lb)
MAX RATINGS (T-O, S/L):	
With augmentation	83.4 kN (18,750 lb st)
Dry	49.4 kN (11,110 lb st)

ITALY

ALFA ROMEO AVIO

ALFA ROMEO AVIO SpA

80038 Pomigliano D'Arco, Naples
Telephone: 39 (81) 8430111
Telex: 710083 ARAVIO
CHAIRMAN: Gen Fulvio Ristori
MANAGING DIRECTOR: Ing Filippo De Luca

Alfa Romeo Avio was prime contractor for the manufacture, under General Electric licence, of the J85, J79 and T58. It manufactures CF6 combustors and JT9D

components, and assembles PT6T engines for the AB 212. Under GE licence it is responsible for the hot section of the T64-P4D, co-produced with Fiat, and participates in the RB199. The company is a partner in Italian production of the Rolls-Royce Spey 807. In November 1988 it became a 6.4 per cent partner in the Rolls-Royce Tay programme.

In February 1986 it began deliveries of GE T700-401 engines for EH 101 prototypes. It supplies components for T700 engines fitted to American helicopters and is developing new versions. It is also involved, with Fiat, in the

development of the GE CT7-6, aimed at the EH 101, NH 90 and a new version of the A 129.

ALFA ROMEO AVIO AR.318

Alfa Romeo Avio is developing this simple turboprop to cover powers from 298 to 596 kW (400-800 shp). The programme draws upon Rolls-Royce under a contract for technical support. RAI (Italian civil) certification was achieved in April 1985, and production engines with FAA certification are now available.

TYPE: Single-shaft turboprop.
REDUCTION GEAR: Epicyclic, driven by muff coupling from compressor forward shaft. Accessory gear train driven from first reduction stage. Phase displacement torque-meter and torque/speed sensing unit.
COMPRESSOR: Single-stage centrifugal. Pressure ratio 5.4.
COMBUSTION CHAMBER: Annular reverse flow type, with eight T shape vaporiser tubes. Two igniters and three starter spray nozzles.
TURBINE: Two-stage axial. Each IGV row is a one-piece investment casting. Rotors and blades are integral solid castings, joined by a curvic coupling.
OIL SYSTEM: One pressure and two scavenge pumps. Provision for engine mounted tank, fuel heater and temperature/pressure transducers.
FUEL SYSTEM: Single assembly of filters, pumps, metering and overspeed protection. Optional beta control, top temperature and torque limiting, and autofeather.
FUEL GRADE: JP-1, JP-4.
DIMENSIONS:

Length	1,061 mm (41.8 in)
Width	534 mm (21.0 in)
Height	658 mm (25.9 in)

WEIGHT, DRY: 140.6 kg (310 lb)
PERFORMANCE RATINGS (S/L, ISA):

T-O (no time limit)	453 kW (608 shp)
Max continuous	420 kW (564 shp)
Cruise	394 kW (529 shp)

SPECIFIC FUEL CONSUMPTION:

T-O	97.7 µg/J (0.578 lb/h/shp)
Max continuous	99.2 µg/J (0.587 lb/h/shp)
Cruise	102.4 µg/J (0.606 lb/h/shp)

Alfa Romeo Avio AR.318 single-shaft turboprop

ARROW

ARROW snc
Via Badiaschi 25, 29100 Piacenza
Telephone: 39 (523) 41932
Telex: 530112 CC PC1
Fax: 39 (523) 34367
CHAIRMAN: Tullio Osellini
ENGINEERING MANAGER: G. Polidoro

This company produces modular aircooled piston engines for microlights and homebuilts. In 1985 Arrow powered the winners of the French ULM championship and the Grande Course for two-seat microlights.

ARROW GT250
Single-cylinder geared two-stroke. Cast light alloy cylinder with ceramic coated interior. Bore 74.6 mm (2.94 in). Stroke 57.0 mm (2.24 in). Capacity 250 cc (15.25 cu in). Induction through 36 mm Dell'Orto carburettor of 100 grade fuel mixed with 2 per cent oil. Electric starter and 12V electronic ignition with one or two plugs. Planetary reduction gear of 0.335 ratio.
DIMENSIONS:

Length	460 mm (18.12 in)
Width	370 mm (14.60 in)
Height	380 mm (15.0 in)

WEIGHT, READY TO RUN: 26.0 kg (57.26 lb)
PERFORMANCE RATING: 25.33 kW (34 hp) at 6,800 rpm
FUEL CONSUMPTION: 4 to 6 litres (1.06-1.58 US gallons; 0.88-1.32 Imp gallons)/h

ARROW GT500
This is the opposed-twin version of the GT250. A 38 mm carburettor is used.
DIMENSIONS:

Length	500 mm (19.65 in)
Width	500 mm (19.65 in)
Height	451 mm (17.70 in)

WEIGHT, READY TO RUN: 36.0 kg (79.3 lb)
PERFORMANCE RATING: 48.5 kW (65 hp) at 6,800 rpm
FUEL CONSUMPTION: 6 to 10 litres (1.58-2.64 US gallons; 1.32-2.20 Imp gallons)/h

ARROW GT1000
This is the flat-four version, using the same cylinders as in the foregoing engines. Two 38 mm carburettors are fitted.
DIMENSIONS:

Length	521 mm (20.45 in)
Width	500 mm (19.65 in)
Height	451 mm (17.70 in)

WEIGHT, READY TO RUN: 54.0 kg (119 lb)
PERFORMANCE RATING: 82 kW (110 hp) at 6,200 rpm
FUEL CONSUMPTION: 8 to 14 litres (2.11-3.70 US gallons; 1.76-3.08 Imp gallons)/h

ARROW GT654
This is a 90° V twin four-stroke based on the Moto Guzzi V65 motorcycle engine. The light alloy cylinders have Nicasil liners. Bore 80.0 mm (3.15 in). Stroke 64.0 mm (2.52 in). Capacity 650 cc (39.66 cu in). Fuel is 100 mogas fed through twin 30 mm Dell'Orto carburettors. A 12V starter is fitted, and the planetary geared drive has a ratio of 0.335.
DIMENSIONS:

Length	702 mm (27.6 in)
Width	431 mm (17.0 in)
Height	460 mm (18.12 in)

WEIGHT, READY TO RUN: 60.0 kg (132 lb)
PERFORMANCE RATING: 41.0 kW (55 hp) at 6,500 rpm
FUEL CONSUMPTION: 4 to 6 litres (1.06-1.58 US gallons; 0.88-1.32 Imp gallons)/h

Arrow GT1000 four-cylinder engine

Arrow GT250 single-cylinder engine

Arrow GT500 two-cylinder engine

Arrow GT654 V-twin engine

FIAT

FIAT AVIAZIONE SpA
Via Nizza 312, 10127 Turin
Telephone: 39 (11) 69311
Telex: 221320 FIATAV
MANAGING DIRECTOR: P. Torricelli

Fiat Aviazione's main aircraft engine programmes now concern the IAE V2500, Turbo-Union RB199, Rolls-Royce Spey 807 and Viper 600, Pratt & Whitney PW2037/2040 and PW4000, and General Electric CF6 (including CF6-80C2), CT7 and T64. It is a partner in EUROJET Turbo. Fiat Aviazione makes the FA150-Argo APU for the AMX, transmissions for Aerospatiale helicopters and many other aviation products.

EUROJET TURBO EJ200
Fiat is responsible for 21 per cent of this programme. Its duties include design, development and manufacture of the LP turbine and shaft, rear bearing support, gearbox, oil tank and pump, afterburner and some accessories including the nozzle control unit and part of the DECU software.

TURBO-UNION RB199
Fiat holds 20 per cent of the shares of Turbo-Union Ltd. Its responsibility is the LP turbine and shaft, exhaust diffuser, jetpipe and nozzle.

IAE V2500
The V2500 is being developed by the IAE consortium. Fiat is responsible for the accessory gearbox, oil tank and pumps, exhaust case and No. 5 bearing compartment.

ROLLS-ROYCE SPEY 807
This turbofan is produced under a Rolls-Royce licence to the Italian government, by Fiat (prime contractor in Italy) and CELMA (prime contractor in Brazil). The engine underwent type testing in the first half of 1987. Fiat carries out bench testing in support of the prototype aircraft, and rig testing of the engine Group-A parts.

PRATT & WHITNEY PW2037/2040 and PW4000

Since 1974 Fiat has been responsible for design and development of the accessory drive gearbox for these Pratt & Whitney engines.

GENERAL ELECTRIC CF6

Fiat produces components for the CF6 for GE and SNECMA. For GE the company supplies accessory gearboxes, inlet gearboxes and shafts. SNECMA is supplied with gearbox components and shafts for CF6-50 engines. Fiat is collaborating with GE on CF6-80C/C2 engines.

GENERAL ELECTRIC T64-P4D

This turboprop powers the Aeritalia G222. Under a licence agreement between GE and the Italian government, the engine is manufactured in Italy, with Fiat as prime contractor.

GENERAL ELECTRIC T700/CT7

Parts of the T700 are made by Fiat, while for the EH 101 helicopter the CT7-6 is being developed by GE, Fiat Aviazione and Alfa Romeo Avio.

ROLLS-ROYCE VIPER 600

Development of this turbojet was undertaken in collaboration with Rolls-Royce. For most versions, components rearward of the compressor (except turbine discs and blades) are Fiat's responsibility. However, the Mk 632-43 is licensed to Piaggio.

IAME
ITAL-AMERICAN MOTOR ENGINEERING
Via Lisbona 15, 24040 Zingonia
Telephone: 39 (35) 883022
Telex: 301205
Fax: 39 (35) 885744

IAME light piston engines are known as KFM (Komet Flight Motors). They were launched in 1981, the chief market being US homebuilders and microlight aircraft manufacturers.

KFM 107 MAXI

Two-cylinder two-stroke engine for microlights, motor gliders, UAVs and similar uses. Available as: **107E**, direct drive, with electric starter and alternator; and **107ER**, with V belt reduction gear (2 : 1).
CYLINDERS: Bore 64 mm (2.52 in). Stroke 52 mm (2.05 in). Capacity 334 cc (20.38 cu in).
DIMENSIONS:
Length	435 mm (17.13 in)
Width (over plugs)	440 mm (17.32 in)
Height	253 mm (9.96 in)

WEIGHT, DRY:
Maxi 107E	19.0 kg (41.8 lb)
Maxi 107ER	22.5 kg (49.6 lb)

PERFORMANCE RATINGS:
Max T-O	22.4 kW (30 hp) at 6,300 rpm
Max continuous	20.1 kW (27 hp) at 6,080 rpm

KFM 107E Maxi two-stroke piston engine

FUEL CONSUMPTION:
Cruise   8.3 litres (2.19 US gallons; 1.83 Imp gallons)/h

KFM 112

This is the only KFM four-stroke engine currently in production.
CYLINDERS: Bore 90 mm (3.54 in). Stroke 64 mm (2.52 in). Capacity 1,628.6 cc (99.4 cu in).
DIMENSIONS:
Length	583 mm (22.95 in)
Width	603 mm (23.74 in)
Height	380 mm (14.96 in)

KFM 112 flat-four piston engine

WEIGHT, DRY (with starter and dual ignition):
	54 kg (119 lb)

PERFORMANCE RATINGS:
Max rated (3 min)	45.63 kW (61 hp)
Max continuous	39.74 kW (54 hp)

FUEL CONSUMPTION:
Max continuous
    16.3 litres (4.3 US gallons; 3.6 Imp gallons)/h
70 per cent cruise
    11.2 litres (2.97 US gallons; 2.47 Imp gallons)/h

PIAGGIO
INDUSTRIE AERONAUTICHE E MECCANICHE RINALDO PIAGGIO SpA
Via Cibrario 4, 16154, Genoa
Telephone: 39 (10) 600 41
Telex: 270695 AERPIA I
Fax: 39 (10) 603378

WORKS AND OFFICERS: see Aircraft section

The Aero Engine Division of Piaggio manufactures the following engines under licence agreements: Rolls-Royce Viper 11, 526, 540 and 632-43 turbojets; Textron Lycoming T53-L-13, T55-L-11 and -712 turboshafts; and Rolls-Royce 1004 turboshafts. Piaggio also participates in co-production under licence of the Rolls-Royce Spey 807 turbofan and has joined Rolls-Royce Turbomeca in development and production of the RTM 322-01 turboshaft. The Engine Division also produces IR suppression devices.

VM
VM MOTORI SpA
Via Ferrarese 29, 44042 Cento (Fe)
Telephone: 39 (51) 908511
Telex: 511642
Fax: 39 (51) 908517

VM Motori specialises in high speed lightweight diesel engines. Following automotive production, the company entered the aeronautical field with a range of horizontally opposed engines. All are aircooled four-stroke compression ignition engines, cooled by a propylenic glycol mixture and burning Jet A-1, JP-4, JP-5, JP-8 or similar fuel with direct injection by camshaft-driven plunger pumps. Each engine is turbocharged for operation to 8,850 m (29,000 ft). The engines are fully modular and are being offered with an initial TBO of 3,000 h. Cylinder size is 130 mm (5.1 in) by 110 mm (4.33 in) and compression ratio 18. Specific fuel consumption (econ cruise) is 106.4 µg/J (0.63 lb/h/hp).

VM TPJ 1304HF

Four cylinders, capacity 5.84 litres (356 cu in). Weight, dry with electrical system, 185 kg (408 lb). Maximum power 154 kW (206 hp) at 2,640 rpm.

VM TPJ 1306HF six-cylinder diesel engine

VM TPJ 1306HF

Six cylinders, capacity 8.76 litres (535 cu in). Weight, dry with electrical system, 243 kg (536 lb). Maximum power 235 kW (315 hp) at 2,640 rpm.

VM TPJ 1308HF

Eight cylinders, capacity 11.68 litres (713 cu in). Weight, dry with electrical system, 298 kg (657 lb). Maximum power 316 kW (424 hp) at 2,640 rpm.

JAPAN

IHI

ISHIKAWAJIMA-HARIMA JUKOGYO KABUSHIKI KAISHA
(Ishikawajima-Harima Heavy Industries Co Ltd)

Shin Ohtemachi Bldg 2-1, Ohtemachi 2-chome, Chiyoda-ku, Tokyo 100

Aero-Engine and Space Operations (ASO):
ADDRESS: As above
Telephone: 81 (3) 244 5331
Telex: 22232 IHIHQT J
GENERAL MANAGER, ASO: Masami Hamanaka
GENERAL MANAGER, BUSINESS PLANNING & PUBLIC RELATIONS: Koichi Ichida

Under licensing agreements with GE, IHI is producing the T58 turboshaft and T64 turboprop, and under agreement with Allison it produces the T56 turboprop. By March 1988 deliveries totalled 800 T58s, 391 T64s and 190 T56s. Under licence from RR Turbomeca, IHI delivered 426 Adour turbofans designated TF40-IHI-801A.

IHI is participating in development of the V2500, described under IAE in the International part of this section. It is responsible for the fan.

IHI was nominated in 1978 as prime contractor of the Pratt & Whitney F100 for the F-15J; by March 1988 IHI had delivered 249 F100s.

In collaboration with Mitsubishi and Kawasaki, IHI built prototypes of the FJR710 (see NAL entry).

IHI F3

Development of this turbofan began in 1976, with funding by the JDA's Technical Research & Development Institute. The Phase 1 **XF3-1** form has a single-stage fan with bypass ratio of 1.9, five-stage transonic compressor, 12-burner combustor and single-stage HP and LP turbines. Rating is 11.79 kN (2,650 lb st).

In 1977 JDA contracted with IHI for the **XF3-20**, with reduced bypass ratio and higher turbine temperature to give

F3-IHI-30 two-shaft turbofan

a rating of 16.28 kN (3,660 lb st). This was followed by the **XF3-30**, which in 1982 was selected by the JASDF as the engine for the T-4 trainer. XF3-30 qualification was completed in March 1986. The engine is now redesignated **F3-IHI-30**, and the first production engine was delivered to JDA on 17 December 1987.

TYPE: Two-shaft turbofan.
FAN: Two-stage axial. No inlet guide vanes. Mass flow 34 kg (75 lb)/s. Pressure ratio 2.6. Bypass ratio 0.9.
COMPRESSOR: Five stages. First two stators variable. Overall pressure ratio 11.
COMBUSTION CHAMBER: Annular, with 12 duplex fuel nozzles.
HP TURBINE: Single-stage, aircooled rotor blades.
LP TURBINE: Two-stage, tip shrouded.
FUEL SYSTEM: Hydromechanical, with electronic supervisor.
DIMENSIONS:
Length   1,340 mm (52.76 in)
Inlet diameter   560 mm (22.0 in)
WEIGHT, DRY: 340 kg (750 lb)

PERFORMANCE RATING (T-O, S/L):
                          16.37 kN (3,680 lb st) class
SPECIFIC FUEL CONSUMPTION:
                          19.83 mg/Ns (0.7 lb/h/lb st)

IHI ITS 90

News of this pioneer all-Japanese helicopter turboshaft engine was received in May 1988. The first prototype was successfully run in March 1988. The second prototype is hoped to weigh only 130 kg (287 lb).
COMPRESSOR: Axial stage followed by centrifugal.
COMBUSTION CHAMBER: Annular reverse flow.
TURBINES: Axial gas generator turbine. Axial free power turbine.
FUEL SYSTEM: FADEC control being developed.
DIMENSIONS:
Length   750 mm (29.5 in)
Diameter   540 mm (21.3 in)
WEIGHT, DRY: 130 kg (287 lb)
PERFORMANCE RATING: 671 kW (900 shp)

KAWASAKI

KAWASAKI JUKOGYO KABUSHIKI KAISHA
(Kawasaki Heavy Industries Ltd)

1-18 Nakamachi-dori 2-chome, Chuo-ku, Kobe 650-91
Telephone: 81 (78) 341 7731
Jet Engine Division: 1-1 Kawasaki-cho, Akashi 673
Telephone: 81 (78) 923 1313
Telex: 5628 951 to 953
OFFICERS: see Aircraft section

In 1967 KHI started manufacturing T53 turboshafts. Deliveries of the resulting KT5311A, KT5313B and T53-K-13B engines totalled 285 by 1986. KHI now licence-builds the T53-K-703 for AH-1S HueyCobras and T55-K-712 for CH-47J Chinooks. Kawasaki shares in parts manufacturing for the Adour, F100 and JT8D and IHI-assembled T56. It is a member of the IAE consortium (see under International heading).

KHI is developing a helicopter turboshaft engine in the

597-746 kW (800-1,000 shp) class, but no details were known by mid-1990.

KAWASAKI KJ12

This simple low cost turbojet has been developed as the core of various future engine programmes. In its present form it is suited to UAVs and sporting aircraft. Component testing began in 1979 and the first KJ12 ran in early 1981. It has a centrifugal compressor driven by a single-stage axial turbine; the combustion chamber is annular and the control system of the electronic type.
DIMENSIONS:
Length   653 mm (25.71 in)
Max diameter   314 mm (12.36 in)
WEIGHT, DRY: 40 kg (88.2 lb)
PERFORMANCE RATINGS:
T-O   1.47 kN (331 lb st)
Cruise (9,145 m; 30,000 ft at Mach 0.9) 0.716 kN (161 lb)

Kawasaki KJ12 single-shaft turbojet

MITSUBISHI

MITSUBISHI JUKOGYO KABUSHIKI KAISHA (Mitsubishi Heavy Industries Ltd)

HEAD OFFICE: 5-1, Marunouchi 2-chome, Chiyoda-ku, Tokyo 100
NAGOYA WORKS: 10 Oye-cho, Minato-ku, Nagoya 455
Telephone: 81 (52) 611 2111
Fax: 81 (52) 611 2681

OFFICERS: see Aircraft section

Between January 1973 and June 1981, under licence agreement with Pratt & Whitney, MHI delivered 72 JT8D-M-9 turbofans. MHI entered into a risk- and revenue-sharing agreement on the JT8D-200 in 1984, and on the PW4000 in 1989.

In collaboration with IHI and Kawasaki, MHI participates in the V2500 (see IAE in the International part of this section). Like IHI and KHI, Mitsubishi is developing a turboshaft in the 597-746 kW (800-1,000 shp) class. One of these engines is expected to power the planned medium helicopter.

NAL

NATIONAL AEROSPACE LABORATORY

7-44-1 Jindaijihigashi-machi, Chofu City, Tokyo 182
Telephone: 81 (422) 47 5911
DIRECTOR: Dr Kazuyuki Takeuchi
HEAD OF AERO-ENGINE DIVISION: Hiroyuki Nouse

The NAL is a government establishment responsible for research and development. In 1971 the Ministry of International Trade and Industry (MITI) funded a high bypass ratio turbofan development programme.

MITI/NAL FJR710

NAL manages the design of the FJR710. Manufacture of development engines was contracted to IHI, Kawasaki and Mitsubishi. The first engine ran in May 1973.

Phase 2 of the programme began in 1976, and the first of three FJR710/600s had been completed by December 1978. This version was followed by the lower-rated **FJR710/600S**, rated at 47 kN (10,582 lb st), which powers the experimental Asuka QSTOL aircraft. By early 1990

FJR710/600S two-shaft turbofan

total FJR710 running time had reached 7,100 h. The following description applies to the /600 engine:
TYPE: Two-shaft turbofan.
FAN: Single-stage, with inserted titanium blades with part span shrouds. Bypass ratio 6.5.
COMPRESSOR: Twelve-stage axial with inserted blades of titanium and high nickel alloy. Five rows of variable stator blades.
COMBUSTION CHAMBER: Smokeless annular type.

TURBINE: Two-stage HP with cooled blades; gas temperature 1,250°C. Four-stage LP.
DIMENSIONS (approx):
Length (flange to flange)	2,350 mm (93 in)
Diameter (inlet)	1,240 mm (49 in)
WEIGHT, DRY: 980 kg (2,160 lb)
PERFORMANCE RATINGS (ISA):
T-O 50 kN (11,243 lb st)

Cruise at 7,600 m (25,000 ft) at Mach 0.75
13.24 kN (2,976 lb)
SPECIFIC FUEL CONSUMPTION:
T-O 10.5 mg/Ns (0.370 lb/h/lb st)
Cruise, as above 19.3 mg/Ns (0.680 lb/h/lb st)

POLAND

PZL
POLSKIE ZAKŁADY LOTNICZE
ul. Miodowa 5, 00251 Warsaw
Telephone: 48 (22) 261441
Telex: 814281

Pezetel Foreign Trade Enterprise Co:
00-991 Warsaw 44, Al. Stanów Zjednoczonych 61, PO Box 6
Telephone: 48 (22) 108001
Telex: 813314

The Polish aircraft and diesel engine industry is managed by the association of aviation and engine producers 'PZL'. Pezetel handles all exports of Polish aeronautical material and diesel engines.

IL
INSTYTUT LOTNICTWA (Aviation Institute)
HEADQUARTERS: Al. Krakowska 110/114, 02-256 Warsaw-Okecie
Telephone: 48 (22) 460993
MANAGING DIRECTOR: Dr Ing Konrad Tott
CHIEF CONSULTANT FOR SCIENTIFIC AND TECHNICAL CO-OPERATION: Dipl Ing Jerzy Grzegorzewski
CHIEF OF SCIENTIFIC, TECHNICAL AND ECONOMIC INFORMATION DIVISION: Dr Ing Tadeusz Kostia
The Aviation Institute is concerned with aeronautical research and testing. It can construct prototypes to its own design.

IL SO-3B single-shaft turbojet

IL K-15
This turbojet was announced in Summer 1988.
TYPE: Single-shaft turbojet.
COMPRESSOR: Six stages. Rotor blades and shrouded stator blades of stainless steel. Two blow-off valves. Pressure ratio 5.3. Mass flow 23 kg (50.7 lb)/s.
COMBUSTION CHAMBER: Short annular type, with 18 vaporising burners and six starting atomisers. Electric ignition.
FUEL SYSTEM: Hydromechanical, with electronic blow-off valve control and overspeed and overtemperature limiters.
FUEL GRADE: Kerosene PSM-2 or TS-1.
TURBINE: Single-stage. Disc attached by Hirth coupling.
LUBRICATION SYSTEM: Self-contained recirculatory system. Fully aerobatic.

OIL SPECIFICATION: Type SDF synthetic.
ACCESSORY DRIVES: Gearbox at bottom of intake casing driven by bevel gear from front of compressor.
STARTING: 27V starter/generator in nose bullet.
DIMENSIONS:
Length overall	1,560 mm (61.42 in)
Width	725 mm (28.54 in)
Height	892 mm (35.12 in)
WEIGHT, DRY: 350 kg (772 lb)
PERFORMANCE RATINGS:
T-O	14.7 kN (3,305 lb st) at 15,900 rpm
Max continuous	11.5 kN (2,585 lb st) at 15,025 rpm
SPECIFIC FUEL CONSUMPTION:
At T-O rating 28.49 mg/Ns (1,006 lb/h/lb st)

IL SO-1
The Aviation Institute designed the SO-1 turbojet to power the TS-11 trainer. Guaranteed overhaul life is 200 h. Production was handled by the WSK-Rzeszów, as noted in that organisation's entry.
TYPE: Single-shaft axial-flow turbojet.
COMPRESSOR: Seven-stage axial, all-steel. Stator blades bonded with resin into slots in carrier rings. Pressure ratio 4.8.
COMBUSTION CHAMBER: Annular with 24 vaporisers.
FUEL SYSTEM: Starting system has six injectors. Main system has 12 twin injectors with outlets towards the vaporisers.
FUEL SPECIFICATION: Kerosene P-2 or TS-1.
TURBINE: Single-stage axial.
LUBRICATION SYSTEM: Open type for rear compressor and turbine bearings. Closed type for all other points.
OIL SPECIFICATION: Type AP-26 (synthetic).
ACCESSORY DRIVES: Gearbox at bottom of air intake casing and driven by bevel shaft.
STARTING: 27V starter/generator.
DIMENSIONS:
Length overall	2,151 mm (84.7 in)
Width	707 mm (27.8 in)
Height	764 mm (30.1 in)
WEIGHT, DRY: 303 kg (668 lb)
PERFORMANCE RATINGS:
T-O	9.8 kN (2,205 lb st) at 15,600 rpm
Max continuous	8.7 kN (1,958 lb st) at 15,100 rpm
SPECIFIC FUEL CONSUMPTION:
At T-O rating 29.6 mg/Ns (1.045 lb/h/lb st)
OIL CONSUMPTION: 0.8 litres (1.7 US pints; 1.4 Imp pints)/h

IL SO-3
This improved SO-1 replaced the earlier type in production. Intended for tropical use, it incorporates minor changes in compressor, combustion chamber and turbine, data remaining the same as for the SO-1. The **SO-3B** is now the standard TS-11 engine, with TBO of 400h. It also powers the PZL I-22, with the designation SO-3W22. A revised vaporising burner and flame tube result in more uniform gas temperature entering the turbine. Data are as for the SO-1 except:
OIL SPECIFICATION: AW-30 synthetic.
WEIGHT, DRY: 321 kg (708 lb)
PERFORMANCE RATINGS:
T-O	10.8 kN (2,425 lb st) at 15,600 rpm
Max continuous	9.8 kN (2,205 lb st) at 15,100 rpm
OIL CONSUMPTION:
1.0-1.2 litres (2.1-2.5 US pints; 1.7-2.1 Imp pints)/h

IL K-15 single-shaft turbojet

REFRIGERATION EQUIPMENT
REFRIGERATION EQUIPMENT WORKS
ul. Metalowców 25, 39-200 Debica
Telephone: 48 (146) 2031
Telex: 066617 WUCH PL

PZL-F ENGINES
In 1975 Pezetel acquired rights to manufacture and market the entire range of aircooled piston engines formerly produced by the Franklin Engine Company (Aircooled Motors) of the USA. These engines, known as PZL-F, are being produced in Poland for light aircraft and motor gliders. Previously manufactured by WSK-PZL Rzeszów, they were transferred in 1985 to the Debica works.
Current applications include the SZD-45-2 Ogar F motor

glider (2A-120C), PZL-126 Mrówka (2A-120C), PZL-110 Koliber (4A-235B3), and PZL Mielec M-20 Mewa (6A-350C). The 2A-120C, 4A-235B3 and 6A-350C each have a Polish CACA certificate.
All models are of the horizontally opposed type, with cylinders of 117.48 mm (4.625 in) bore and 88.9 mm (3.5 in) stroke. All have direct drive and operate on 100/130 grade fuel. Accessories normally include electric starter, alternator and fuel pump. Other details are tabulated:

PZL-F 4A-235B four-cylinder piston engine

PZL-F 2A-120C two-cylinder piston engine

PZL-F 6A-350 six-cylinder piston engine

PZL-F ENGINES

Engine model	Cylinder arrangement	Capacity cc (cu in)	Compression ratio	Max T-O rating at S/L kW (hp) at rpm	Overall dimensions mm (in) length	width	height	Weight, dry kg (lb)
2A-120C	2 horiz	1,916 (117)	8.5	45 (60) at 3,200	581 (22.9)	795 (31.3)	515 (20.3)	75.8 (167)
4A-235B	4 horiz	3,850 (235)	8.5	93 (125) at 2,800	774 (30.5)	795 (31.3)	637 (25.1)	117.6 (259)
6A-350C	6 horiz	5,735 (350)	10.5	164 (220) at 2,800	952 (37.5)	795 (31.3)	641 (25.25)	167 (367)

WSK-PZL KALISZ
WYTWÓRNIA SPRZETU KOMUNIKACYJNEGO-PZL KALISZ

ul. Czestochowska 140, 62-800 Kalisz
Telephone: 48 (62) 77351
Telex: 046 384
GENERAL MANAGER: Dipl Ing Jan Kolodziej

In 1952 the Soviet Union transferred responsibility for manufacture and service support of Soviet aircooled radial piston engines to the WSK (transport equipment manufacturing centre) at Kalisz. Current production is centred on the following, plus the TVD-10B turboprop described under WSK-PZL Rzeszów.

PZL (IVCHENKO) AI-14R

The original 260 hp AI-14R version of this nine-cylinder aircooled radial engine was produced in very large quantities, in the Soviet Union, China and Poland. Subsequent versions are:

AI-14RA. Rated at 191 kW (256 hp). Piston compressor drive and pneumatic starter. For Yak-12, Yak-18, PZL-101A Gawron and PZL-104 Wilga 35.

AI-14RA-KAF. RA with carburettor further aft, for Wilga 80.

AI-14RD. Rated at 206 kW (276 hp). Electric starter. For PZL-104 Wilga.

AI-14RDP. With pneumatic starter. For PZL-104 Wilga.

K8-AA. Direct drive and pneumatic starter. Aerobatic. For PZL-130 Orlik (Vedeneyev M-14Pm).

The following description refers to the AI-14RA:
TYPE: Nine-cylinder aircooled radial.
CYLINDERS: Bore 105 mm (4.125 in). Stroke 130 mm (5.125 in). Capacity 10.16 litres (620 cu in). Compression ratio 5.9.
FUEL GRADE: 91 to 100 octane.
PROPELLER DRIVE: Planetary gears, ratio 0.787.
DIMENSIONS:
Length   956 mm (37.63 in)
Diameter   985 mm (38.78 in)
WEIGHT, DRY: 200 kg (441 lb)
PERFORMANCE RATINGS:
T-O   191 kW (256 hp) at 2,350 rpm
Rated   162 kW (217 hp) at 2,050 rpm

PZL K8-AA (M-14Pm) nine-cylinder piston engine

SPECIFIC FUEL CONSUMPTION:
T-O   95-104.3 μg/J (0.562-0.617 lb/h/hp)

PZL (SHVETSOV) ASz-62R

Power plant of the An-2 transport biplane, the ASz-62R was developed in the Soviet Union as the ASh-62. Current versions are:

ASz-62IR-16. Centrifugal oil filter. For An-2 and PZL-106 Kruk.

ASz-62IR-M18. Hydraulic airframe pump drive. For PZL M-18 Dromader.

ASz-62IR-M18/DHC-3. As M18 plus vacuum pump. For DHC-3 Otter.

K9-AA. Uprated engine designed at Kalisz, 860 kW (1,170 hp) at 2,300 rpm. Electric starter and hydraulic airframe pump. For PZL M-24 Super Dromader.
TYPE: Nine-cylinder aircooled radial.

PZL ASz-62IR nine-cylinder piston engine

CYLINDERS: Bore 155 mm (6.10 in). Stroke 174 mm (6.85 in). Capacity 29.87 litres (1,823 cu in). Compression ratio 6.4.
FUEL GRADE: 91 to 100 octane.
PROPELLER DRIVE: Planetary gears, ratio 0.687.
The following relates to the IR-16:
DIMENSIONS:
Length overall   1,130 mm (44.50 in)
Diameter   1,375 mm (54.13 in)
WEIGHT, DRY:
Without power take-off   579 kg (1,276 lb)
PERFORMANCE RATINGS:
T-O   735 kW (985 hp) at 2,200 rpm
Rated power   603 kW (809 hp) at 2,100 rpm
SPECIFIC FUEL CONSUMPTION:
T-O   112 μg/J (0.661 lb/h/hp)

WSK-PZL RZESZÓW
WYTWÓRNIA SPRZETU KOMUNIKACYJNEGO-PZL RZESZÓW

ul. Obrońców Stalingradu 120, 35-078 Rzeszów, PO Box 340
Telephone: 48 (17) 46100
Telex: 0632411
Fax: 48 (17) 46710
GENERAL MANAGER: Eng Tadeusz Cebulak

Current production at WSK Rzeszów is centred on the TVD-10 turboprop and turboshaft, and GTD-350 turboshaft, together with WR-2 reduction gear for Mi-2 helicopters; the tropicalised SO-3 turbojet for the TS-11 Iskra trainer; and the PZL-3S piston engine for agricultural aircraft. The SO-3 is described under the IL heading.

TVD-10B

The Soviet designed Glushenkov TVD-10B turboprop engine, rated at 716 kW (960 shp), is made under licence in

Glushenkov TVD-10B licensed to PZL Rzeszów

Poland for the An-28 STOL light transport built at WSK-PZL Mielec. TBO is 1,000 h.

TYPE: Free turbine turboprop.

AIR INTAKE: Three radial struts, inlet guide vanes and starter de-iced by bleed air from combustion chamber.

COMPRESSOR: Six axial stages and one centrifugal. Stage 1 has front bearing journal, bolted to stages 2 to 6 which are pinched by compressor shaft used as tie bolt. Blades in dovetail roots. Pressure ratio 7.4. Mass flow 4.6 kg (10.14 lb)/s at 29,600 rpm.

COMPRESSOR CASING: Forward upper and lower halves in titanium; rear section welded from sheet steel and containing anti-surge bleed valve and radial diffuser.

COMBUSTION CHAMBER: Annular with centrifugal burner, and two starting units each with semiconductor igniter and auxiliary burner.

FUEL SYSTEM: Comprises supply pump, filter, pump governor, acceleration control, signalling block and thermocorrector.

FUEL GRADE: T-1, T-2, TS-1 or RT.

COMPRESSOR TURBINE: Two-stage axial. Blades held by fir tree roots. Inlet guide vanes of hollow sheet with air cooling. Ceramic liner.

POWER TURBINE: Single-stage axial, blades with fir tree roots, held in front roller and rear ball bearing.

REDUCTION GEARS: Single-stage spur high speed gear to accessory box and propeller gear; under the high speed gear is the feathering pump oil tank. Accessory box drives 16kW alternator, propeller tachometer and reduction gear oil pump, with propeller brake. Upper driveshaft to single-stage planetary reduction gear.

ENGINE ACCESSORIES: Box contains oil centrifuge; and drives tachometer, oil pump, fuel pump and pump governor. The starter is on the front with a claw clutch.

OIL SYSTEM: Closed and pressurised. Gas generator and reduction gear pumps. Oil tank capacity 16 litres (3.5 Imp gallons).

OIL GRADE: Oil mixture: 25 per cent MK-22 or MS-20, 75 per cent MK-8 or MS-8p.

DIMENSIONS:

Length without airframe jetpipe	2,060 mm (81.1 in)
Width	555 mm (21.9 in)
Height	900 mm (35.4 in)

WEIGHT, DRY:

Complete engine	230 kg (507 lb)
	295 kg (650 lb)

PERFORMANCE RATINGS:

T-O	754 kW (1,011 shp)
Nominal	613 kW (823 shp)
Max cruise	547 kW (739 shp)

SPECIFIC FUEL CONSUMPTION (T-O):
95.8 µg/J (0.567 lb/h/shp)

PZL-10W

This is the helicopter version of the TVD-10B, two of which power the PZL Swidnik Sokól. It uses the same gas generator, with the following differences:

TYPE: Free-turbine turboshaft engine.

FUEL SYSTEM: Pump governor provides automatic operation at selected constant helicopter rotor speeds, as well as control of anti-surge bleed valve, maintaining constant fuel flow in starting cycle, limiting shaft speed and gas temperature and automatic switch-off of faulty engine and selection of emergency power on remaining unit.

POWER TURBINE: Single-stage axial, with blades held in fir tree roots. Speed maintained at 22,490 rpm.

OIL SYSTEM: Closed and pressurised, with one delivery and four-section scavenge pump. Oil tank airframe-mounted, normal capacity 14 litres (3.08 Imp gallons).

OIL GRADE: B-3W synthetic.

ACCESSORIES: Integral cast box drives 5kW starter, starter unit, electronic temperature limiter, vibration sensor, tachometer generator, oil pumps and centrifuge, phase torquemeter, de-icing valve, power-turbine speed limiter and operation time counter.

DIMENSIONS:

Length with jetpipe	1,875 mm (73.8 in)
Width	740 mm (29.0 in)

WEIGHT, DRY:

	141 kg (310 lb)

PERFORMANCE, RATINGS (ISA):

T-O	662 kW (900 shp)
Max contingency	846 kW (1,134 shp)
Max cruise	515 kW (691 shp)

SPECIFIC FUEL CONSUMPTION:

T-O	97 µg/J (0.575 lb/h/hp)

PZL GTD-350

The **GTD-350** is a helicopter turboshaft. In the Mi-2, the drive is taken from the rear. Though developed by the Isotov bureau in the Soviet Union, it is in production only in Poland. PZL Rzeszów has developed a new version rated at 331 kW (444 shp) and designated **GTD-350P**. Technical life of the GTD-350 is 4,000 h.

TYPE: Axial/centrifugal-flow free-turbine turboshaft.

AIR INTAKE: Stainless steel. Automatic de-icing of inlet guide vanes and bullet by air bleed.

COMPRESSOR: Seven axial stages and one centrifugal, all of steel. Pressure ratio 6.05. Mass flow 2.19 kg (4.83 lb)/s at 45,000 rpm.

Longitudinal section through PZL-10W turboshaft

COMBUSTION CHAMBER: Reverse-flow type with air supply through two tubes. Centrifugal duplex single-nozzle burner. Semiconductor igniter plug.

FUEL SYSTEM: NR-40TA pump governor; RO-40TA power turbine governor, DS-40 controlling bleed valves; and electromagnetic starting valve.

FUEL GRADE: TS-1, TS-2 or Jet A-1.

COMPRESSOR TURBINE: Single stage. Shrouded blades with fir tree roots. Temperature before turbine 940°C (GTD-350P, 985°C).

POWER TURBINE: Two-stage constant speed (24,000 rpm). Shrouded blades with fir tree roots. Discs bolted together. Turbine stators integrally cast.

REDUCTION GEARING: Two sets of gears, with ratio of 0.246 : 1, in magnesium alloy casing. Output speed 5,900 rpm.

LUBRICATION SYSTEM: Closed type. Gear type pump with one pressure and four scavenge units. Cooler and tank, capacity 12.5 litres (2.75 Imp gallons).

OIL GRADE: B3-W (synthetic), Castrol 98 or 5000, Elf Turbojet II or Shell Turbine Oil-500.

ACCESSORIES: STG3 3kW starter/generator, NR-40TA governor pump, D1 tachometer and oil pumps driven by gas generator. RO-40TA speed governor, D1 tachometer and centrifugal breather driven by power turbine.

STARTING: STG3 starter/generator suitable for operation at up to 4,000 m (13,125 ft) altitude.

DIMENSIONS:

Length overall	1,385 mm (54.53 in)
Max width	520 mm (20.47 in)
Width (with jetpipes)	626 mm (24.65 in)
Max height	630 mm (24.80 in)
Height (with jetpipes)	760 mm (29.9 in)

WEIGHT, DRY:

Less jetpipes and accessories	139.5 kg (307 lb)

PERFORMANCE RATINGS:

T-O rating (6 min) at 96% max gas generator rpm:

GTD-350	298 kW (400 shp)
GTD-350P	331 kW (444 shp)

Nominal rating (1 h) at 90% gas generator rpm:

GTD-350	238.5 kW (320 shp)
GTD-350P	261 kW (350 shp)

Cruise rating (I)
212.5 kW (285 shp) at 87.5% gas generator rpm

Cruise rating (II)
175 kW (235 shp) at 84.5% gas generator rpm

SPECIFIC FUEL CONSUMPTION:

T-O	136 µg/J (0.805 lb/h/shp)
Nominal	146 µg/J (0.861 lb/h/shp)
Cruise (I)	154 µg/J (0.913 lb/h/shp)
Cruise (II)	165 µg/J (0.978 lb/h/shp)

OIL CONSUMPTION:

Max	0.3 litres (0.63 US pints; 0.53 Imp pints)/h

PZL-3S

Derived from Soviet AI-26W via LiT-3. Applications include PZL-106A Kruk, IAR-827A and conversions of Grumman/Schweizer Ag-Cat A, B and C, Thrush Commander, DHC-2 Beaver and DHC-3 Otter.

TYPE: Seven-cylinder aircooled radial.

CYLINDERS: Bore 155.5 mm (6.12 in). Stroke 155 mm (6.1 in). Capacity 20.6 litres (1,265 cu in). Comp ratio 6.4.

PISTONS: Forged aluminium.

INDUCTION SYSTEM: Float type carburettor. Mechanically driven supercharger.

FUEL GRADE: Aviation gasoline, minimum 91 octane.

LUBRICATION: Gear type oil pump. Oil grade Aero Shell 100 or other to MIL-L-6082.

PROPELLER DRIVE: Direct. Provision for constant-speed US-132000A propeller.

ACCESSORIES: ANG 6423 Prestolite alternator and two output shafts, one 20 kW (27 hp) (26 kW; 35 hp max) for spraying pump and the other 3.7 kW (5 hp).

STARTING: Electric.

DIMENSIONS:

Diameter	1,267 mm (49.88 in)
Length	1,110 mm (43.72 in)

WEIGHT, DRY:

	411 kg (906 lb)

PERFORMANCE RATINGS:

Max T-O	447 kW (600 hp) at 2,200 rpm

Cutaway PZL-3S seven-cylinder piston engine

PZL (Isotov) GTD-350 free-turbine turboshaft

Max continuous	410 kW (550 hp) at 2,050 rpm
Cruise (75 per cent)	310 kW (415 hp) at 2,000 rpm
SPECIFIC FUEL CONSUMPTION:	
T-O, max continuous	105 µg/J (0.61 lb/h/hp)
Cruise	86 µg/J (0.51 lb/h/hp)

PZL-3SR
This is the geared version of the PZL-3S. Applications include the PZL-106AR and BR and M-21. The following are the main differences:

PROPELLER DRIVE: Planetary gear of 0.7 ratio. Provision for constant-speed propeller, Type US-133000.
DIMENSION:
Length 1,271 mm (50.06 in)
WEIGHT, DRY: 446 kg (983 lb)

ROMANIA

TURBOMECANICA
INTREPRINDEREA TURBOMECANICA BUCURESTI

c/o Centrul National Aeronautic, Bulevardul Dacia 13, Casuta Postala 22-149, R-70185 Bucharest
Telephone: 40 (0) 12 08 78
Telex: 10660 CNAER

This factory produces under licence the Rolls-Royce Spey 511-14W and Viper 632/633, and the Turbomeca Turmo IVC.

SINGAPORE

SA
SINGAPORE AEROSPACE PTE LTD
540 Airport Road, Paya Lebar, Singapore 1953

Telephone: 65 287 1111
Telex: RS 55851 SAERO
SA manufactures engine parts for General Electric and

Turbomeca. It has 2 per cent of the PW4000 programme and will be sole source of eleven high-precision parts, mainly in the compressor section.

SOUTH AFRICA

ATLAS
ATLAS AIRCRAFT CORPORATION OF SOUTH AFRICA (PTY) LTD
PO Box 11, Atlas Road, Kempton Park 1620, Transvaal

Atlas is manufacturing the Rolls-Royce Viper 540 turbojet under sublicence from Piaggio of Italy, for use in Atlas Impala attack trainers.

SPAIN

ITP
INDUSTRIA DE TURBOPROPULSION SA
Zamudio Industrial Park, Bilbao
The Spanish Government approved the establishment of this company in April 1989. Three state-owned Spanish

companies—Sener, CASA (see Aircraft section) and Bazan—hold 51 per cent of the shares. Rolls-Royce plc holds 45 per cent, and the remaining 4 per cent is held by the Banco Bilbao. The Spanish Government is providing $34 million, described as 'subsidies'.

ITP will make parts for civil and military jet engines. Its main work is expected to include a share (probably 13 per cent) in the EJ200 programme, described under Eurojet in this section.

SENER
SENER-INGENIERIA Y SISTEMAS SA
Raimundo Fernández Villaverde 65 Madrid 28003
Telephone: 34 (1) 456 7062

Sener, engaged in NATO programmes and ESA space activities, was to have been the Spanish partner in the consortium that will build the EJ200 engine of the

Eurofighter EFA. This role has now been assumed by ITP, in which Sener is a shareholder, as briefly referred to above and in the International part of this section.

SWEDEN

FLYGMOTOR
VOLVO FLYGMOTOR AB
S-461 81 Trollhättan
Telephone: 46 (520) 94000
Telex: 420 40 VOLFA S
Fax: 46 (520) 34010

Volvo Flygmotor produces turbofans, ramjets and rockets. Since 1980 it has been a risk and revenue sharing partner with General Electric on the CF6-80A and -80C for wide-body transports. Volvo Flygmotor also participates in development and production of the Garrett TFE731-5 turbofan and TPE331-14/15 turboprop. The company also has agreements with Pratt & Whitney on the JT8D-200, PW2000 and V2500, and with Rolls-Royce on the Tay, making combustors for the Tay 610-650 and compressor intermediate casings for the Mk 670.

FLYGMOTOR RM8
The RM8 is a Swedish military version of the Pratt & Whitney JT8D turbofan which Flygmotor developed to power the Saab 37 Viggen. Following the **RM8A** for the AJ 37, SF 37, SH 37 and SK 37, the **RM8B** was developed for the JA 37. The major change to improve functional stability at high altitude involved replacing the first stage of the LP compressor by a third stage on the fan. To increase thrust the RM8B has a four-nozzle burner combustion system and a new HP turbine. Delivery of RM8B engines was completed on 19 September 1988.
The following description refers to the RM8A:
TYPE: Two-spool turbofan with modulated afterburner.
FAN: Two-stage front fan. Titanium blades.
LP COMPRESSOR: Four-stage integral with fan.
HP COMPRESSOR: Seven-stages. Overall pressure ratio 16.5. Bypass ratio approximately 1. Mass flow 145 kg (320 lb)/s.
COMBUSTION CHAMBER: Cannular with nine flame tubes. Two spark plugs, each with its own igniter.
HP TURBINE: Single-stage with cast aircooled blades.
LP TURBINE: Three-stage axial flow, with cast blades.
AFTERBURNER: One hot streak igniter. Hydraulically (fuel) actuated nozzle.

CONTROL SYSTEMS: Bendix hydromechanical controls for gas generator and for afterburner and nozzle.
ACCESSORY DRIVE: Via gearbox driven from HP shaft.
DIMENSIONS:

Length overall: RM8A	6,153 mm (242.2 in)
RM8B	6,223 mm (245 in)
Max diameter (both versions)	1,349 mm (53.1 in)
Inlet diameter (both)	1,030 mm (40.55 in)
WEIGHT, DRY:	
RM8A	2,100 kg (4,630 lb)
RM8B	2,220 kg (4,894 lb)

PERFORMANCE RATINGS (ISA, S/L):

Max T-O, augmented:	
RM8A	115.6 kN (25,990 lb st)
RM8B	125 kN (28,110 lb st)
Max T-O, dry:	
RM8A	65.6 kN (14,750 lb st)
RM8B	72.1 kN (16,200 lb st)

SPECIFIC FUEL CONSUMPTION:

Max augmented:	
RM8A	70.0 mg/Ns (2.47 lb/h/lb st)
RM8B	71.4 mg/Ns (2.52 lb/h/lb st)
Max dry:	
RM8A	17.6 mg/Ns (0.63 lb/h/lb st)
RM8B	18.1 mg/Ns (0.64 lb/h/lb st)
Max continuous (both)	17.3 mg/Ns (0.61 lb/h/lb st)

Cutaway drawing of Flygmotor RM12 two-shaft augmented turbofan

FLYGMOTOR RM12
The RM12 is a version of the F404 developed jointly by General Electric and Volvo Flygmotor to power the JAS 39 Gripen. General Electric retains all rights to the design and engineering policy and supplies approximately 60 per cent by value of parts.
Volvo Flygmotor is a 20 per cent partner in all F404 single-engine applications. Volvo Flygmotor will supply parts to General Electric similar to those parts that it manufactures for the RM12.
The RM12 thrust improvement has been achieved by increasing the turbine inlet temperature by up to 105°C and by increasing fan airflow. The fan meets more stringent bird strike requirements, and this has required changes to the control system, with built-in redundancy to ensure get-home power. Increased temperature and pressure have required changes to hot section materials. RM12 testing started at GE in June 1984, and the Gripen first flew on 9 December 1988. Production deliveries are due in 1991.
The following are changes from the F404.
FAN: Variable first-stage stator. Airflow 68 kg (150 lb)/s. Bypass ratio 0.28.
WEIGHT, DRY: 1,050 kg (2,315 lb)
PERFORMANCE RATINGS:

Max T-O: dry	54 kN (12,140 lb st)
augmented	80.5 kN (18,100 lb st)

TURKEY

TEI
TUSAS ENGINE INDUSTRIES
Muttalip Mevkii Mrk, PK 610 Eskisehir
Telephone: 90 (222) 22 030
Fax: 90 (222) 22 057
MANAGING DIRECTOR: F. Monsipapa

TEI is a joint venture between US General Electric and Turkish shareholders. The factory, near Eskisehir Airbase, is in production with the F110 fighter engine, and had delivered 63 engines by the end of 1989.

UNION OF SOVIET SOCIALIST REPUBLICS

GLUSHENKOV

In 1969 this design bureau was responsible for the TVD-10 turboprops of the Be-30. Since then it has produced turboprop and turboshaft engines.

GLUSHENKOV TVD-10
Military designation: GTD-3

This free turbine engine was developed to power the Kamov Ka-25 helicopter. The civil turboshaft was licensed to Poland for production, and a description appears under WSK-PZL Rzeszów. Ka-25 engines were made in the Soviet Union, the **GTD-3F** being rated at 671 kW (900 shp) and the **GTD-3BM** at 738 kW (990 shp).

The **TVD-10B** is the turboprop version selected to power the An-28. This engine is produced in Poland as the **TVD-10S**, as described under WSK-PZL Rzeszów.

GLUSHENKOV TVD-20

This turboprop is fitted to early examples of the An-3. Its rating of 1,081 kW (1,450 shp) is sufficiently greater than that of the TVD-10 to conclude that it has a new gas generator. In the An-3 the gearbox has a particularly large reduction ratio to drive a slow-turning propeller. The exhaust stack is at the front, confirming the same back-to-front layout as in the TVD-10B.

GLUSHENKOV (NOVIKOV, RYBINSK) TVD-1500

This engine has been developed in the first instance as a turboprop to power the production An-3, but the core is seen as the basis for turbofan, turbojet, propfan and other engines. Features include modular construction, using a wide range of metals and composites, and careful attention paid to reducing both first cost and operating cost. Also

Longitudinal section of TVD-1500 turboshaft (air inlet at right)
(Jacques Marmain, Aviation Magazine International, Paris)

selected at 1,120 kW (1,500 shp) for MiG-101N and (driving pusher contraprops) Ilyushin Il-X. TVD-155 turboshaft version rated at 970 kW (1,300 shp) selected for Kamov V-62 (see Novikov).

TYPE: Free-turbine turboprop.
COMPRESSOR: Annular inlet at rear of engine. Three axial stages, with inlet guide vanes and both stators variable, followed by centrifugal. Pressure ratio 14.4.
COMBUSTION CHAMBER: Annular folded reverse flow.
TURBINES: Two-stage gas generator turbine (max entry temperature 1,227°C), two-stage power turbine.
CONTROL SYSTEM: Electronic; automatic systems for ground and flight operation.
REDUCTION GEAR: Front drive shaft in cooled tunnel through jetpipe leading to two-stage spur gears in anti-vibration mounting.

ACCESSORIES: Rear shaft from power turbine passes through compressors and drives accessories mounted on large wheelcase facing to rear. Power extracted (described as air compression) can vary up to 10 per cent of nominal power.

WEIGHT, DRY:	248 kg (547 lb)
PERFORMANCE RATINGS (S/L, 15°C):	
Max T-O	1,140 kW (1,528 shp)
Max continuous	828 kW (1,110 shp)
Cruise	597 kW (800 shp)
SPECIFIC FUEL CONSUMPTION:	
Max T-O	74.9 µg/J (0.443 lb/h/shp)
Cruise	89.4 µg/J (0.529 lb/h/shp)

ISOTOV

This bureau, headed by S. P. Isotov until his death in 1983, was responsible for the GTD-350 turboshaft which powers Mil Mi-2 helicopters. It is in production in Poland, and is described under WSK-PZL Rzeszów. In 1990 the bureau revealed that it is now entitled the Leningrad KB (design bureau) and that it also goes under the name of the Klimov KB in honour of its first General Designer. See under Klimov.

IVCHENKO

The collective at Zaporozhye, headed by A. G. Ivchenko until his death in 1968, was later headed by V. Lotarev, who has his own entry later; also see ZMKB.

The first Ivchenko engine was the 41 kW (55 hp) AI-4G piston engine used in the Ka-10 helicopter. He progressed, via the AI-14 and AI-26 piston engines, to become a leading producer of gas turbine engines. Since 1952 Soviet piston engines have been assigned to Poland (see under WSK-PZL Kalisz). Ivchenko turboprops are also produced in China (which see).

Ivchenko AI-20M single-shaft turboprop *(Aviation Magazine International, Paris)*

IVCHENKO AI-20

This turboprop was developed as the NK-4 at the Kuznetsov bureau in 1947-52, with the assistance of German engineers. Eventually preferred to the VK-2, the Zaporozhye collective was charged with refinement and production. Redesignated AI-20, it was produced from 1955, with series deliveries from late 1958.

AI-20K. Rated at 2,942 ekW (3,945 ehp). Used in Il-18V, An-10A and An-12. Produced at Shanghai as WJ-6.

AI-20M. Initial T-O rating of 3,124 ekW (4,190 ehp), later increased to 3,169 ekW (4,250 ehp). Fitted to An-12 and Il-18/20/22/38.

AI-20D. Rated at 3,124 ekW (4,190 ehp); navalised engine fitted to Beriev M-12.

AI-20DM. Rated at 3,812 ekW (5,112 ehp). Fitted to An-32. In 1985 this engine was reported to the FAI as the **AM-20.** Another designation is **AI-20D Series 5.**

The AI-20 was designed to operate from –60°C to +55°C. The rotor speed is at 12,300 rpm by automatic variation of propeller pitch. TBO is 4,000 or 4,750 h for AI-20K versions but only 1,000 h for the D family. Excluding China total deliveries exceed 19,000 engines, and these have flown well over 60 million hours.

The following description refers to the AI-20M:
TYPE: Single-shaft turboprop.

COMPRESSOR: Ten-stages. Magnesium alloy stator casing in upper and lower halves. Pressure ratio 9.45. Mass flow 20.7 kg (45.6 lb)/s.
COMBUSTION CHAMBER: Annular with ten burner cones. Pilot burners and ignition plugs at top of casing.
FUEL GRADE: T-1 or TS-1 to GOST-10227-62 (DERD.2492, JP-1 to MIL-F-5616).
TURBINE: Three stages. Rotor blades shrouded at inner and outer ends and installed in pairs in slots in aircooled discs. Entry temperature, AI-20D series 930°C, AI-20K series 850°C.
REDUCTION GEAR: Planetary type, incorporating six-cylinder torquemeter and negative-thrust transmitter (type IKM), for autofeathering AV-681 propeller. Ratio 0.08732 (input speed 12,300 rpm except ground-idle 10,400 rpm).
LUBRICATION: Pressure-feed type with full recirculation.
OIL GRADE: 75 per cent GOST 982-56 or MK-8 to GOST 6457-66 (DERD.2490 or MIL-O-6081B) and 25 per cent MS-20 or MK-22 to GOST 1013-49 (DERD.2472 or MIL-O-6082B).
STARTING: Two electric starter/generators, Type STG-12 TMO-1000, supplied from ground or TG-16 APU.

DIMENSIONS:	
Length	3,096 mm (121.89 in)
Width	842 mm (33.15 in)
Height	1,180 mm (46.46 in)
WEIGHT, DRY:	1,040 kg (2,292 lb)
PERFORMANCE RATINGS:	
T-O	3,169 ekW (4,250 ehp)
Cruise (350 knots; 650 km/h; 404 mph at 8,000 m; 26,000ft)	2,013 ekW (2,700 ehp)
SPECIFIC FUEL CONSUMPTION:	
T-O	104.3 µg/J (0.617 lb/h/ehp)
Cruise, as above	73.3 µg/J (0.434 lb/h/ehp)

IVCHENKO AI-24

This turboprop powers the An-24 and its derivatives. Production began in 1960 and the following data refer to engines of the second series, which were in production by the Spring of 1966.

The **AI-24** of 1,875 ekW (2,515 ehp) powered the An-24V Series I, and was followed by the **AI-24A** with provision for water injection; produced at DEMC (China) as the WJ5A.

The **AI-24T** of 2,103 ekW (2,820 ehp) with water injection is used in the An-26 and An-30. Vibration monitoring, automatic relief of overloads and gas temperature and autofeathering. From 1980, designated **AI-24VT** with improved fuel economy.

The AI-24 is maintained at 15,100 rpm by automatic variation of propeller pitch. The engine is flat rated to 3,500 m (11,500 ft). TBO is 3,000 h (original AI-24, 4,000 h). Deliveries, excluding Chinese production, total 14,800. Total flight time in 1988 was nearly 51 million hours.

Following the flight testing of propellers with eight blades on an An-24, a research programme has been under way on propfans, with emphasis on contra-rotating configurations. Two full scale examples have been run with an AI-24 engine. Typical configurations have 6+6, 7+7 and 8+8 blades.

TYPE: Single-shaft turboprop.

COMPRESSOR: Ten-stage axial. Pressure ratio, AI-24T 7.55, VT 7.65. Mass flow 14.4 kg (31.7 lb)/s.

COMBUSTION CHAMBER: Annular, with eight simplex burners and two starting units, each comprising a body, pilot burner and igniter plug.

FUEL GRADE: T-1, TS-1 to GOST 10227-62 (DERD.2494 or MIL-F-5616).

TURBINE: Three-stage axial with solid blades. Rotor/stator sealing effected by soft inserts mounted in grooves in nozzle assemblies. Entry temperature 797°C.

REDUCTION GEAR: Planetary type, incorporating hydraulic torquemeter and electromagnetic negative thrust transmitter for propeller autofeathering. Type AV-72 propeller (AI-24T drives AV-72T propeller). Ratio 0.08255.

LUBRICATION: Pressure circulation system.

OIL GRADE: 75 per cent GOST 982-56 or MK-8 (DERD.2490 or MIL-O-6081B) and 25 per cent MS-20 or MK-22 (DERD.2472 or MIL-O-6082B).

ACCESSORIES: Mounted on front casing are starter/generator, alternator, aerodynamic probe, ice detector, negative-thrust feathering valve, torque transmitter, oil filter, propeller speed governor and centrifugal breather. Below casing are oil unit, air separator, LP and HP fuel pumps and drives to hydraulic pump and tachometer generators.

STARTING: Electric STG-18TMO starter/generator supplied from ground power or from TG-16 APU.

DIMENSIONS:
Length overall	2,346 mm (92.36 in)
Width	677 mm (26.65 in)
Height	1,075 mm (42.32 in)

WEIGHT, DRY: 600 kg (1,323 lb)

PERFORMANCE RATINGS:
T-O: AI-24A	1,875 ekW (2,515 ehp)
AI-24VT	2,103 ekW (2,820 ehp)
Cruise rating at 243 knots (450 km/h; 280 mph) at 6,000 m (18,300 ft):	
AI-24A	1,156 ekW (1,550 ehp)
AI-24T	1,178 ekW (1,580 ehp)

SPECIFIC FUEL CONSUMPTION:
At cruise rating: AI-24A	91.3 μg/J (0.540 lb/h/ehp)
AI-24T	90.1 μg/J (0.533 lb/h/ehp)
AI-24VT	76.4 μg/J (0.452 lb/h/ehp)

OIL CONSUMPTION: 0.85 kg (1.87 lb)/h

IVCHENKO AI-25

This turbofan powers the Yak-40. Yak-40Bs of the Soviet Air Force have an AI-25 with an aircooled HP turbine and rating of 17.13 kN (3,850 lb st). The AI-25TL powers the Czech L-39 trainer but will be replaced by the Lotarev DV-2. Deliveries since 1967 have reached 9,800, flight time exceeding 40 million hours.

TYPE: Two-shaft turbofan.

FAN: Three-stage axial. Drum/disc construction with pin-jointed blades. Casing and fan duct of magnesium alloy. Pressure ratio, 1.695 at 10,750 rpm. Bypass ratio 2.

COMPRESSOR: Eight-stage axial. Drum/disc construction of titanium, with aluminium and magnesium casing.

Ivchenko AI-24 single-shaft turboprop *(Aviation Magazine International, Paris)*

Ivchenko AI-25TL two-shaft turbofan

Dovetailed blades. Peak pressure ratio, 4.68 at 16,640 rpm. Overall pressure ratio 8.

COMBUSTION CHAMBER: Annular. Inner and outer casings joined upstream to 12 burner heads with stabilisers.

FUEL GRADE: T-1, TS-1 to GOST 10227-62 (DERD.2494, MIL-F-5616).

TURBINE: Single-stage HP turbine; two-stage LP turbine. Shrouded solid rotor blades held by fir tree roots in cooled discs.

LUBRICATION: Self-contained, pressure circulating.

OIL GRADE: MK-8 to GOST 6457-66 or MK-6 to GOST 10328-63 (Western equivalents, DERD.2490 or MIL-O-6081B). Consumption 0.3 litres (0.63 US pints; 0.53 Imp pints)/h.

ACCESSORIES: All mounted on gearbox driven off HP spool. Equipment includes automatic fire extinguishing (agent can be supplied into oil-contacted labyrinth cavities), ice protection, automatic starting and control system, oil system chip detector and casing vibration monitor.

STARTING: Pneumatic. Air starter type SV-25 is supplied from ground hose or AI-9 APU or an operating engine bleed.

DIMENSIONS:
Length overall	1,993 mm (78.46 in)
Width overall	820 mm (32.28 in)
Height overall	895 mm (35.24 in)

WEIGHT, DRY:
Without accessories	290 kg (639 lb)

PERFORMANCE RATINGS:
T-O	14.71 kN (3,307 lb st)
Long-range cruise rating, 6,000 m (20,000 ft) and 296 knots (550 km/h; 342 mph)	3.49 kN (785 lb st)

SPECIFIC FUEL CONSUMPTION:
T-O	15.86 mg/Ns (0.56 lb/h/lb st)
Cruise, as above	23.71 mg/Ns (0.837 lb/h/lb st)

KHACHATUROV

See comment under Yak-41 in Aircraft section.

KKBM
KUIBYSHEV ENGINE DESIGN BUREAU

This is the bureau formerly named for N. D. Kuznetsov. Established engines are listed under Kuznetsov; the P-020 was disclosed in 1990.

KKBM P-020

The first new Soviet piston engine to be revealed for many years, the P-020 is a small but highly rated two-cylinder two-stroke opposed aircooled engine for manned and unmanned applications. T-O power 14.9 kW (20 hp) at 7,300 rpm. Sfc 133.5 μg/J (0.79 lb/h/hp). Dry weight 9 kg (19.8 lb). In production at Kuibyshev MPO named for M. V. Frunze.

KKBM P-020 flat-twin two-stroke piston engine

KLIMOV
LENINGRAD NPO IM. KLIMOV
GENERAL DESIGNER: Alexander Alexandrovich Sarkisov

The great design bureau and factory at Leningrad, the former Factory No. 117, was a major centre for high-power piston engines developed under Vladimir Yakovlyevich Klimov. In 1946 it was selected to build the Rolls-Royce Nene turbojet, later developed as the Klimov VK-1. Klimov was succeeded by his deputy, Sergei Pietrovich Isotov, who developed gas turbines mainly for helicopters but which in 1968 moved into the field of fighters. Isotov died in 1983 and today the bureau has been renamed for its founder, and is also often simply called the Leningrad bureau.

KLIMOV RD-33

This important fighter engine was designed before Isotov's death. Detail design began in 1968, meeting the requirements of the MiG-29, and the first bench run took place in 1972. Deliveries were initiated in 1976, and mass production followed in 1981. It powers all known MiG-29 versions and is offered as the engine of an upgraded MiG-21.

TYPE: Two-shaft afterburning bypass turbojet (low ratio turbofan).

LP COMPRESSOR: Four stages. Front bearing carried in four-strut nose, but no inlet guide vanes. Bypass ratio 0.4.

HP COMPRESSOR: Nine stages. Overall pressure ratio 20.

COMBUSTION CHAMBER: Annular with air-blast fuel nozzles giving generally smokeless combustion of a range of fuels.

TURBINES: Single-stage HP turbine with single-crystal cooled blades. Single-stage LP turbine.

AFTERBURNER: Combustion in both core and bypass flows. Nozzle with fully variable area and profile in primary and secondary flows. Outer nozzle has 24 flaps.

ACCESSORIES: Oil tank, hydromechanical fuel control and auxiliaries grouped above engine to reduce cross-section.

DIMENSIONS:

Length	4,127 mm (162.5 in)
Max diameter	1,000 mm (39.37 in)

WEIGHT, DRY:

Bare engine	980 kg (2,160 lb)
Complete power plant	1,217 kg (2,683 lb)

PERFORMANCE RATINGS (S/L):

Max augmented	81.4 kN (18,300 lb st)
Max dry	50.0 kN (11,240 lb st)

SPECIFIC FUEL CONSUMPTION:

Max augmented	59.48 mg/Ns (2.10 lb/h/lb st)
Max dry, S/L	21.8 mg/Ns (0.77 lb/h/lb st)

KLIMOV (ISOTOV) TV2-117

The power plant of the Mi-8 comprises two **TV2-117A** engines coupled through a VR-8A gearbox. The complete package incorporates a control system (separate from the control system of each gas generator) which maintains desired rotor speed, synchronises the power of both engines, and increases the power of the remaining engine if the other should fail.

TV2-117TG. Qualified to operate on propane or butane gas. Flown on Mi-8, ratings unchanged. A foreign production facility is sought.

TYPE: Free turbine helicopter turboshaft.

COMPRESSOR: Ten-stage axial. Inlet guide vanes and stators of stages 1, 2 and 3 are variable. Pressure ratio 6.6 at 21,200 rpm.

COMBUSTION CHAMBER: Annular, with eight burner cones.

FUEL GRADE: T-1 or TS-1 to GOST 10227-62 specification (Western equivalents, DERD.2494, MIL-F-5616).

TURBINE: Two-stage axial compressor turbine with solid blades. Two-stage free power turbine.

OUTPUT SHAFT: Conveys torque from the free turbine to the overrunning clutch of the main gearbox (VR-8A) and also to the speed governor. Max output speed 12,000 rpm; main rotor speed 192 rpm.

ACCESSORIES: Engine control system includes fuel, hydraulic, anti-icing, gas temperature restriction, engine electric supply and starting, and monitoring systems. Up to 1.8 per cent of the mass flow can be used to heat the intake and other parts liable to icing. Fire extinguishant can be released by the pilot.

LUBRICATION: Pressure circulation type. Oil is scavenged from the five main bearings by the lower pump, returned through the air/oil heat exchanger and thence to the tank.

OIL GRADE: Synthetic, Grade B-3V to MRTU 38-1-157-65 (nearest foreign substitute Castrol 98 to DERD.2487).

STARTING: The SP3-15 system comprises DC starter/generator, six storage batteries, control panel, ground supply receptacle, and control switches and relays; airframe mounted except the GS-18TP starter/generator. The ignition unit comprises a control box, two plugs, solenoid valve, and switch. The starting fuel system comprises an automatic unit on the NR-40V pump, constant-pressure valve, and two igniters.

DIMENSIONS:

Length overall	2,835 mm (111.5 in)
Width (without jetpipe)	547 mm (21.5 in)
Height	745 mm (29.25 in)

Klimov TV7-117 turboprop (test fairing on left in place of propeller)
(Jacques Marmain, Aviation Magazine International, Paris)

Klimov (Isotov) TV2-117A free-turbine turboshaft

Klimov RD-33 augmented bypass turbojet

WEIGHT, DRY:

Engine, without generator, etc	338 kg (745 lb)
VR-8A gearbox, less entrapped oil	745 kg (1,642 lb)

PERFORMANCE RATINGS:

Max	1,267 kW (1,700 shp)
T-O (S/L, static)	1,118 kW (1,500 shp)
Max continuous	895 kW (1,200 shp)
Cruise (122 knots; 225 km/h; 140 mph at 500 m; 1,640 ft)	746 kW (1,000 shp)

SPECIFIC FUEL CONSUMPTION:

T-O, as above	102.4 μg/J (0.606 lb/h/shp)
Cruise, as above	115.4 μg/J (0.683 lb/h/shp)

KLIMOV TV3-117

This second-generation turboshaft has been produced in very large numbers. Bench testing began in 1974, the first flight was in 1976 and series production began in 1978.

TV3-117BK. Electronic control. Rated at 1,618 kW (2,170 shp). Powers some Ka-27s and Ka-28.

TV3-117MT. 1,417 kW (1,900 shp). Powers Mi-8T/TB/TBK, -14, -17, -24.

TV3-117V. 1,660 kW (2,225 hp). Powers some Ka-27s, -29 and -32.

TV3-117VK. Electronic control. Rated at 1,640 kW (2,200 shp). Powers Kamov 'Hokum'.

TV3-117VM. Electronic control. Rated at 1,678 kW (2,250 shp) to 3,600 m (11,810 ft). Powers Mi-17-1VA, -25, -28 and -35.

Data below refer mainly to the MT:

TYPE: Free-turbine turboshaft.

COMPRESSOR: Ten-stage axial. Inlet guide vanes and first three stators variable. Pressure ratio 7.5.

COMBUSTION CHAMBER: Annular, improved version of TV2-117.

TURBINES: Two-stage gas generator turbine, improved from TV2-117. Two-stage power turbine.

OUTPUT: As TV2-117 but more compact jetpipe.

STARTING: BK, MT, pneumatic air turbine; V, VK, VM, electric.

DIMENSIONS:

Length	2,085 mm (82.1 in)
Width	640 mm (25.2 in)
Height	725 mm (28.5 in)

WEIGHT, DRY:

	285 kg (628 lb)

PERFORMANCE RATINGS (S/L, max T-O): See variants

SPECIFIC FUEL CONSUMPTION:

Max T-O, TV3-117V	96.3 μg/J (0.57 lb/h/shp)

KLIMOV TV7-117

Described as a third-generation engine, the TV7-117 has a modular core incorporating advanced features and materials, and envisaged as the basis for various jet and shaft engines. Its immediate application is as a turboprop to power the Il-114, produced in collaboration with Polish industry. Also selected at 1,866 kW (2,250 shp) for MiG-101M and at 2,090 kW (2,800 shp) for MiG SVB freighter driving SV-346 six-blade propellers.

TV7-117V. Turboshaft version. Flat-rated at 1,753 kW (2,350 shp) to 2,700 m (8,860 ft); OEI contingency 2,536 kW (3,400 shp) at S/L only. Powers Mi-38.

A growth core with two centrifugal stages is under development. Output will be in the 2,985 kW (4,000 shp) class.

TYPE: Free-turbine turboprop.

COMPRESSOR: Annular ram inlet around reduction gear tapers to entry to five-stage axial compressor, with variable inlet guide vanes and next two stators, followed by centrifugal stage on same shaft. Pressure ratio 16.

Longitudinal section of Klimov TV7-117V helicopter turboshaft

COMBUSTION CHAMBER: Annular folded reverse flow. Minimum pollution with wide range of fuels.

TURBINES: Two-stage gas generator turbine with cooled blades. Entry temperature 1,242°C. Two-stage power turbine.

REDUCTION GEAR: Planetary type, with new tooth profiles and anti-vibration mountings.

CONTROL SYSTEM: Full-authority electronic, with separate automatic control for ground and flight operation.

STARTING: Pneumatic air turbine, mass flow 0.2 kg (0.44 lb)/s.

DIMENSIONS:
Length	2,143 mm (84.37 in)
Width	886 mm (34.88 in)
Height	940 mm (37.0 in)

WEIGHT, DRY: 520 kg (1,146 lb)

PERFORMANCE RATINGS:
Max T-O
 1,865 kW (2,500 shp) to 35°C and 250 m (820 ft)
Cruise (6,000 m; 19,685 ft at 270 knots; 500 km/h; 311 mph)
 1,342 kW (1,800 shp)

SPECIFIC FUEL CONSUMPTION:
Cruise, as above 68.95 μg/J (0.408 lb/h/shp)

KOLIESOV

It is reported that this design bureau took over the assets of that of V. A. Dobrynin in the 1950s, and has since concentrated on powerful afterburning turbojets. It has now been renamed for its location: see under RKBM.

KOLIESOV VD-7

This large single-shaft turbojet was fitted to at least the final Myasishchev M-50 supersonic bomber (NATO reporting name 'Bounder'), with afterburners on the inner engines. Maximum thrust estimated in the 137.5 kN (30,900 lb st; 14 tonne) class. It is commonly supposed that a derived version powers the Tu-22 (NATO 'Blinder') family.

KOPTCHYENKO

This engine bureau, based at Omsk, was unknown until in late 1988 it was named as responsible for the design of the helicopter engine described below.

KOPTCHYENKO TV-O-100

This engine was developed to provide a modern core in the 537 kW (720 shp) class. Its initial application is in the single-turbine Ka-126 helicopter produced under licence in Romania. Future development of the engine to 619 kW (830 shp), with pressure ratio about 10.2 and turbine entry temperature of 1,077°C, may be carried out in collaboration with that country. A derated version (530 kW; 710 shp) is a candidate engine for the Ka-118. TsIAM, the national aero-engine research organisation, is testing a heat exchanger with which specific fuel consumption may be reduced by 15-20 per cent.

TYPE: Free-turbine turboshaft. Modular construction.

COMPRESSOR: Inlet above engine leads via large dust/sand extractor to two-stage axial compressor, with inlet and intermediate stator stages variable, and single centrifugal stage. Pressure ratio 9.2.

COMBUSTION CHAMBER: Annular folded reverse flow.

TURBINES: Single-stage gas generator turbine with uncooled blades. Turbine entry temperature 1,027°C. Single-stage power turbine.

CONTROL SYSTEM: Dual-channel electronic.

OUTPUT SHAFT: Central quill shaft drives gear train at front, with triple spur gears to output shaft at top.

WEIGHT, DRY: 156 kg (344 lb)

Cutaway drawing of Koptchyenko TV-O-100 turboshaft
(Jacques Marmain, Aviation Magazine International, Paris)

PERFORMANCE RATINGS (S/L):
Maximum	537 kW (720 shp)
Cruise	343 kW (460 shp)

SPECIFIC FUEL CONSUMPTION:
Cruise	109.2 μg/J (0.646 lb/h/shp)

KOPTCHYENKO GTE-400

This new turboshaft, rated at 298 kW (400 shp), has been selected for the twin-engined version of the Ka-118.

KUZNETSOV

GENERAL DESIGNER IN CHARGE OF BUREAU:
Nikolai Dmitrievich Kuznetsov

Kuznetsov was deputy to General V. Ya. Klimov during the Second World War. In the late 1940s his own bureau at Kuibyshev developed large turboprops and turbofans. The NK-4 was transferred to Ivchenko, and is described under that collective's heading, as the AI-20. Later engines are described here; also see KKBM.

KUZNETSOV NK-8

The NK-8 was developed through a number of variants, the most powerful of which is the NK-144. Basic versions are the 99.1 kN (22,273 lb st) **NK-8-4**, later uprated to 103 kN (23,150 lb st), which originally powered the Il-62, and the 93.2 kN (20,950 lb) **NK-8-2** which was the original engine of the Tu-154. The NK-8-4 remains in service with several Il-62 (not Il-62M) operators, including LOT. It led to the NK-86 described later.

TYPE: Two-shaft turbofan.

FAN: Two-stage axial, with anti-flutter sweptback blades on first rotor stage. Pressure ratio 2.15 at 5,350 rpm. Bypass ratio 1.02 (NK-8-2, 1.00).

COMPRESSOR: Two IP stages on fan shaft. Six-stage HP compressor. Construction almost wholly of titanium. Core pressure ratio, 10.8 at 6,950 HP rpm (NK-8-2, 10 at 6,835 rpm).

COMBUSTION CHAMBER: Annular, with 139 burners.

FUEL GRADE: T-1 and TS-1 to GOST 10227-62 or T-7 to GOST 12308-66 (equivalent to Avtur 50).

TURBINE: Single-stage HP turbine, two-stage LP turbine, all with shrouded rotor blades, aircooled discs and hollow nozzle blades (stators). Gas temperature, not over 870°C (1,143°K) ahead of turbine, not over 670°C (NK-8-2, 650°C) downstream.

JETPIPE: Mixer leads bypass flow into common jetpipe which may be fitted with blocker/cascade type reverser giving up to 48 per cent (NK-8-2, 45 per cent) reverse thrust, and noise suppressor.

LUBRICATION: Continuous pressure feed and recirculation. Pressure not less than 2.28 bars (33 lb/sq in).

OIL GRADE: Mineral oil MK-8 or MK-8P to GOST 6457-66 (DERD.2490 or MIL-O-6081B).

ACCESSORIES: These include automatic flight deck warning of vibration, ice and fire. All grouped beneath fan duct casing. RTA-26-9-1 turbine temperature controller by Smiths Industries.

STARTING: HP spool driven by constant-speed drive type PPO-62M, or started pneumatically by air from TA-6 APU from ground hose or by air bleed (NK-8-2, pneumatic only).

DIMENSIONS:
NK-8-4: Length, no reverser	5,100 mm (201 in)
NK-8-2: Length, with reverser	5,288 mm (208.19 in)
Length, no reverser	4,762 mm (187.48 in)
Diameter	1,442 mm (56.8 in)

WEIGHT, DRY:
NK-8-4: No reverser	2,100 kg (4,629 lb)
With reverser	2,400 kg (5,291 lb)
NK-8-2: No reverser	2,100 kg (4,629 lb) max
With reverser	2,350 kg (5,180 lb) max

PERFORMANCE RATINGS:
NK-8-4: T-O rating 103.0 kN (23,150 lb st)
 Cruise rating at 11,000 m (36,000 ft) and 458 knots (850 km/h; 530 mph) 27.0 kN (6,063 lb)
NK-8-2: T-O rating 93.2 kN (20,950 lb st)
NK-8-2U: T-O rating 103.0 kN (23,150 lb st)

SPECIFIC FUEL CONSUMPTION:
At cruise rating at 11,000 m (36,000 ft) and 458 knots (850 km/h; 530 mph):
NK-8-4	22.1 mg/Ns (0.78 lb/h/lb st)
NK-8-2	21.53 mg/Ns (0.76 lb/h/lb st)

KUZNETSOV NK-86

Though described by the Ilyushin aircraft bureau as a new engine, this turbofan of 127.5 kN (28,660 lb st) is closely related to the NK-8 series. Four power the Il-86 with combined reversers and noise attenuators.

KUZNETSOV NK-88

Almost certainly another derivative of the NK-8 series, the NK-88 is the engine fitted to the Tu-155 (Tu-154 development) fuelled by liquid hydrogen, which first flew on 15 April 1988. No major modification is needed for the cryogenic fuel (other than to the aircraft and engine fuel systems), nor to burn LNG (liquefied natural gas) which was expected to be used in 1988 in the same aircraft. Engine performance is unlikely to differ materially from the NK-8-2U.

KUZNETSOV NK-144

This augmented turbofan was derived from the NK-8 to power the Tu-144 SST. A version of the NK-144 is believed to be the engine of at least the first subtype of the Tupolev Tu-26 supersonic bomber known to NATO as 'Backfire'.

The NK-144 is reported to have a two-stage titanium fan, three-stage IP compressor, eleven-stage HP compressor, annular combustion chamber, single stage HP turbine and two-stage LP turbine. Aircooled blades are used in the HP turbine, and titanium is used extensively in construction of the engine. Bypass ratio is reported to be 1 : 1, maximum mass flow 250 kg (551 lb)/s, and pressure ratio 15 : 1. The jetpipe incorporates an afterburner, with hydraulically actuated variable area nozzle. Gas temperature at turbine entry is 1,050°C.

DIMENSIONS:
Length overall	5,200 mm (204.7 in)
Diameter	1,500 mm (59 in)

WEIGHT:
Without jetpipe, but with afterburner	
	2,850 kg (6,283 lb)

PERFORMANCE RATINGS:
Max: without afterburning	127.5 kN (28,660 lb st)
with afterburning	196.1 kN (44,090 lb st)

KUZNETSOV NK-12M

Designed at Kuibyshev in 1947-52 under N. D. Kuznetsov and former German engineers, the NK-12M is the most powerful turboprop in the world. The **NK-12M** developed 8,948 ekW (12,000 ehp). The **NK-12MV** is rated at 11,033 ekW (14,795 ehp) and powered the Tu-114, driving four-blade contra-rotating propellers of 5.6 m (18 ft 4 in) diameter. As the **NK-12MA**, rated at 11,185 kW (15,000 shp), it powers the An-22, with propellers of 6.2 m (20 ft 4 in) diameter. A further application is in the Tupolev Tu-95/-142 bomber and its derivatives, and Tu-126, both believed to be powered by the NK-12MV.

The NK-12M has a 14-stage axial-flow compressor. Pressure ratio varies from 9 to 13 according to altitude, and variable inlet vanes and blow-off valves are necessary. A can-annular type combustion system is used: each flame tube is mounted centrally on a downstream injector, but all tubes merge at their maximum diameter to form an annular secondary region. The single turbine is a five-stage axial. Mass flow is 65 kg (143 lb)/s.

The casing is made in four portions, from sheet steel, precision welded. An electric control for variation of propeller pitch is incorporated, to maintain constant speed.

DIMENSIONS:
Length	6,000 mm (236.2 in)
Diameter	1,150 mm (45.3 in)

WEIGHT, DRY:
	2,350 kg (5,181 lb)

PERFORMANCE RATINGS (NK-12MV):
T-O	11,033 ekW (14,795 ehp)
Nominal power	
	8,826 ekW (11,836 ehp) at 8,300 rpm
Idling speed	6,600 rpm

Kuznetsov NK-86 two-shaft turbofan (*Flight International*)

Kuznetsov NK-12MV single-shaft turboprop (*Aviation Magazine International, Paris*)

LOTAREV (ZMKB)

GENERAL DESIGNER IN CHARGE OF BUREAU:
Feodor Mikhailovich Muravtchyenko

Today the large engine bureau at Progress Works, Zaporozhye, once headed by A. I. Ivchenko and then by V. A. Lotarev, is known as the ZMKB (Zaporozhye engine design bureau). It has been kept under Lotarev's name temporarily for the convenience of readers.

LOTAREV/ZVL DV-2

This small turbofan was designed jointly with ZVL (which see, under Czechoslovakia) to replace the AI-25TL as the engine of the Aero L-39 MS trainer. The engine was designed to fit the existing engine bay, so that L39s can be re-engined.

The same core is to be used in several engines:

DV-2. Basic turbofan. The description below applies to this engine. Will power L-39 MS and selected to power Il-108 business jet.

DV-2B. Larger fan, with bypass ratio 2. T-O rating 25 kN (5,610 lb st); sfc 15.26 mg/Ns (0.539 lb/h/lb st); dry weight about 500 kg (1,102 lb).

DV-2F. Afterburning engine for supersonic applications. Bypass ratio 1.4; maximum thrust 36 kN (8,085 lb st); sfc 61.1 mg/Ns (2.16 lb/h/lb st); dry weight about 600 kg (1,323 lb).

DV-12. Turboshaft for helicopters. Large curved jetpipe to side and rear gearbox and output shaft. Max contingency power 5,480 kW (7,346 shp); sfc 68.1 μg/J (0.403 lb/h/shp); dry weight about 580 kg (1,279 lb).

DV-22. Turbofan for transport aircraft. Mass flow 122 kg (269 lb)/s; bypass ratio 5; T-O thrust 35.1 kN (7,900 lb st); sfc 11.1 mg/Ns (0.391 lb/h/lb st); dry weight 675 kg (3,062 lb). Planned for later Il-108.

DV-32. Turboshaft for helicopters. As DV-12 but front drive. Same weight.

DV-X. Projected core for pusher turboprop or propfan. T-O rating 4,425 kW (5,932 shp) plus 2.4 kN (540 lb st) to 30°C; sfc 75.4 μg/J (0.446 lb/h/shp).

Lotarev/ZVL DV-2 two-shaft turbofan (*Brian M. Service*)

TYPE: Two-shaft turbofan.
FAN: Single stage, overhung, with 15 titanium blades of large chord, without snubbers, hub/tip ratio 0.37, bypass ratio 1.46. Diameter 645 mm (25.4 in). Mass flow 49.5 kg (109 lb)/s.
LP COMPRESSOR: Two stages, rotating with fan.
HP COMPRESSOR: Seven stages. Pressure ratio 13.5.
COMBUSTION CHAMBER: Annular, giving low emissions.
HP TURBINE: Single stage, max gas temperature 1,127°C.
LP TURBINE: Uncooled, two-stage.
STARTING: Air turbine.

DIMENSIONS:
Length	1,721 mm (67.75 in)
Width	994 mm (39.1 in)
Height	1,050 mm (41.3 in)

WEIGHT, DRY:
	475 kg (1,047 lb)

PERFORMANCE RATING (S/L, T-O): 21.58 kN (4,852 lb st)
SPECIFIC FUEL CONSUMPTION: 16.7 mg/Ns (0.59 lb/h/lb st)

LOTAREV D-36

As successor to Ivchenko at Zaporozhye, Lotarev developed the turbofan that powers the An-72, An-74 and Yak-42. Bench testing began in 1971, flight testing under a Tu-16 in 1974 and series production in 1977. The D-36 has also been selected for the MiG-18-50 long range business jet. Also see D-436.

TYPE: Three-shaft turbofan. Made of 12 modules.
FAN: Single-stage; 29 inserted titanium blades with part-span shrouds (snubbers). Mass flow 260 kg (573 lb)/s. Bypass ratio 5.6. Speed (max) 5,300 rpm.
LP COMPRESSOR: Six stages with variable inlet vanes and four blow-off valves. Speed (max) 11,200 rpm.
HP COMPRESSOR: Six stages, titanium and steel. Speed (max) 14,300 rpm. Overall engine pressure ratio at T-O, S/L ISA static, 20.
COMBUSTION CHAMBER: Annular, with 28 burners and with integral inlet guide vanes to HP turbine.

HP TURBINE: Single-stage; aircooled blades. Max inlet temperature 1,177°C (1,450°K).

LP TURBINE: Single-stage. (Called IP in Western engines.)

FAN TURBINE: Two-stage. (Called LP in Western engines.)

BYPASS DUCT: Short-length, comprising forward module (fan contravane) and rear module (intermediate case). Contravane contains 49 vanes to remove twist. Provision for reverser downstream of intermediate case.

ACCESSORIES: Shaft driven units mounted on gearbox mounted around underside of intermediate case.

DIMENSIONS:
Length	3,470 mm (136.6 in)
Diameter	1,390 mm (54.7 in)

WEIGHT, DRY: 1,106 kg (2,438 lb)

PERFORMANCE RATINGS (ISA):
T-O static	63.74 kN (14,330 lb st)
Max continuous	49.0 kN (11,025 lb st)
Max cruise at 8,000 m (26,250 ft) at Mach 0.75	
	15.7 kN (3,527 lb)

SPECIFIC FUEL CONSUMPTION:
T-O	10.195 mg/Ns (0.360 lb/h/lb st)
At max cont rating	9.83 mg/Ns (0.347 lb/h/lb st)
Max cruise as above	18.4 mg/Ns (0.65 lb/h/lb st)

LOTAREV D-18T

For many years the main gap in the spectrum of available Soviet engines was a large HBPR (high bypass ratio) turbofan. In the 1970s the Lotarev bureau produced such engines in two sizes, the smaller (D-36) to an earlier timescale. The linear scale is about 2 : 1; so, in terms of airflow and thrust, the ratio is about 4 : 1.

The bigger engine is more advanced than the small one, its pressure ratio and turbine entry temperature being higher. The D-18T also has an integral fan duct reverser. It first ran in 1981 and four were fitted to the An-124 prototype which made its first flight on 26 December 1982. The D-18T has been produced in quantity for the An-124 and An-225.

TYPE: Three-shaft turbofan for large subsonic aircraft.

FAN: Single-stage with 33 inserted titanium blades with part-span shrouds. Mass flow 765 kg (1,687 lb)/s. Bypass ratio 5.7 at ISA S/L static. Speed (max) 3,300 rpm.

IP COMPRESSOR: Seven-stage axial with variable inlet vanes. Speed (max) 5,750 rpm.

HP COMPRESSOR: Seven-stage axial. Speed (max) 9,000 rpm. Overall engine pressure ratio 27.5.

COMBUSTION CHAMBER: Annular, with forged and machined outer case and 28 vaporising burners.

FUEL GRADE: T-1, TS-1 or T-7 (Avtur equivalent).

HP TURBINE: Single-stage with aircooled directionally solidified blades with tip shrouds and raised root platforms. Max inlet temperature 1,327°C (1,600°K); temperature at cruise (as below) 1,080°C (1,353°K).

IP TURBINE: Single-stage with aircooled blades with tip shrouds.

LP TURBINE: Four stages with tip shrouded blades.

BYPASS DUCT: Comprises forward module, called contra-vane, with inserted blades (vanes) to remove twist from flow, followed by rear case with six large radial struts carrying pipes and shaft drives.

REVERSER: Attached to rear fan duct case, with multiple blocker doors pulled inwards by axial movement of translating cowl section, which simultaneously opens peripheral cascade rings directing expelled air forwards.

ACCESSORIES: Oil tank and all shaft driven accessories are grouped around lower half of rear fan case.

DIMENSIONS:
Length	5,400 mm (212.6 in)
Fan diameter	2,330 mm (91.73 in)

WEIGHT, DRY: 4,100 kg (9,039 lb)

PERFORMANCE RATINGS:
T-O (S/L, ISA + 13°C)	229.5 kN (51,590 lb st)
Max cruise (11,000 m; 36,100 ft, Mach 0.75, ISA)	
	50.47 kN (11,345 lb)

SPECIFIC FUEL CONSUMPTION:
T-O	10.195 mg/Ns (0.360 lb/h/lb st)
Cruise as above	16.142 mg/Ns (0.570 lb/h/lb)

LOTAREV (ZMKB) D-136

This turboshaft was developed for the Mi-26 helicopter. Aviaexport stresses its background of over 20,000 h running prior to certification to standards which included FAR and BCAR. Bench testing started in 1979 and series production began in 1982. It is composed of nine modules, some of which are identical with those of the D-36, though the LP compressor runs faster.

TYPE: Two-spool free turbine turboshaft.

LP COMPRESSOR: Six stages, with one row of variable inlet guide vanes. Faces for bleed ducts for anti-icing the Mi-26 air inlets. Mass flow 36 kg (79.4 lb)/s. Speed (max) 11,350 rpm.

HP COMPRESSOR: Six stages, in casing with large bleed pipes and carrying main gearbox and mounting points. Speed (max) 14,300 rpm. Overall pressure ratio 18.3.

COMBUSTION CHAMBER: Annular, with 28 burners and incorporating inlet guide vanes for HP turbine.

HP TURBINE: Single-stage with aircooled blades. Max inlet temperature 1,205°C (1,478°K).

Lotarev D-36 three-shaft turbofan
(Brian M. Service)

Lotarev D-18T three-shaft turbofan with reverser *(Brian M. Service)*

Lotarev D-236 turboprop *(Jacques Marmain, Aviation Magazine International, Paris)*

LP TURBINE: Single-stage, separated from HP rotor by large intermediate case with 26 guide vanes (stators).

POWER TURBINE: Two stages forming separate module; casing with 12 long-chord radial struts. Speed (max) 8,300 rpm.

DRIVE SHAFT: Flexibly mounted shaft at rear.

ACCESSORIES: Mounted on gearbox above HP compressor.

DIMENSIONS:
Length	3,715 mm (146.26 in)
Width	1,382 mm (54.41 in)
Height	1,133 mm (44.61 in)

WEIGHT, DRY: 1,050 kg (2,315 lb)

PERFORMANCE RATINGS (ISA, S/L):
Max T-O at 8,300 rpm	8,380 kW (11,240 shp)
Max cont at 7,500 output rpm	8,280 kW (11,100 shp)

SPECIFIC FUEL CONSUMPTION:
Max T-O	73.8 µg/J (0.4365 lb/h/shp)

LOTAREV (ZMKB) D-236

This engine uses a core similar to that of the D-136 turboshaft, but it incorporates a reduction gearbox to drive a contra-rotating propfan. As exhibited in 1987, the front propeller only, with eight composite blades, weighed 380 kg (838 lb). This propeller turned at 960 rpm and demonstrated propulsive efficiency of 87 per cent at Mach 0.7, the diameter being 4.2 m (13 ft 10 in). This engine first ran in 1984 and flew in 1987, replacing one of the engines of an Il-76.

By this time the propellers had been redesigned, the front unit retaining eight blades but the rear having only six. Blades are epoxy-bonded glassfibre, without metal reinforcement along the leading-edge. Speed has increased to 1,100 rpm. The production D-236 will power a twin-engined Antonov aircraft, and a pusher version is expected to be an alternative power plant for the Tu-334.

GAS GENERATOR: Generally as D-136.

REDUCTION GEAR: Planetary, giving contra-rotating output. Drive ratio 7.5.

CONTROL SYSTEM: Hydromechanical, with electronic computer.

WEIGHT, DRY: 1,600 kg (3,527 lb) with propellers

PERFORMANCE RATINGS:
T-O, S/L	
7,459 kW (10,000 shp); 8-9 tonnes (17,635-19,840 lb st)	
Cruise thrust	1.6 tonnes (3,527 lb)

SPECIFIC FUEL CONSUMPTION:
Cruise, at height	81.97 µg/J (0.485 lb/h/shp)

LOTAREV (ZMKB) D-436

This advanced derivative of the D-36 was developed chiefly to match the requirements of the initial version of the Tu-334. The **D-436K** first ran, without reverser, in 1985. Series production was due to begin in 1989, initially for An-72 and An-74 aircraft.

The definitive engine is the **D-436T**, with a larger fan. This results in a bypass ratio of 6.5 and increased thrust ratings. This engine is expected to fly in the first Tu-334 in 1991.

The following data relate to the D-436K:

TYPE: Three-shaft turbofan.

Lotarev D-136 free-turbine turboshaft *(Brian M. Service)*

Lotarev (ZMKB) D-436K three-shaft turbofan *(Brian M. Service)*

FAN: As D-36 but with improved performance. Mass flow 285 kg (628 lb)/s. Bypass ratio 5.49. Speed (max) 5,850 rpm.

COMPRESSORS: As D-36, except seven HP stages. Overall pressure ratio 20.97.

TURBINES: As D-36 but new HP turbine based on D-18T for entry temperature increased to 1,207°C, and fan turbine has three stages and speed increased to 5,850 rpm.

REVERSER: Based on that of D-18T.

DIMENSIONS:

Length	3,030 mm (119.3 in)
Diameter	1,390 mm (54.72 in)

WEIGHT, DRY: 1,250 kg (2,756 lb)

PERFORMANCE RATINGS:

S/L, T-O	73.6 kN (16,550 lb st)
Cruise (8,000 m; 26,250 ft, Mach 0.75)	
	19.26 kN (4,330 lb)

SPECIFIC FUEL CONSUMPTION:

T-O	10.57 mg/Ns (0.373 lb/h/lb st)
Cruise, as above	18.3 mg/Ns (0.646 lb/h/lb st)

LYULKA

GENERAL DESIGNER: Viktor Chepkin

During the late 1930s A. M. Lyulka, who died in June 1984, worked on an axial turbojet that became an early war casualty. Brief details of his subsequent work have appeared in previous editions of *Jane's*. His first major success was achieved with the AL-7. Based in Moscow, the bureau is today known as the Saturn, or Saturn/Lyulka, KB.

LYULKA AL-7
Service designation: TRD-31

The first AL-7 ran on the bench in late 1952 and the first production version was cleared for use in 1954 at a design rating of 63.74 kN (14,330 lb st). The main innovation in this engine was supersonic flow through the first two stages of the compressor. In the mid-1950s the afterburning **AL-7F** powered the initial production Su-7, and the Tu-98, Il-54 and La-250. Later versions were the **AL-7RV** and **AL-7PB** without afterburner, the latter powering the Be-10. By 1963 production had been transferred to an uprated afterburning version designated **AL-7F-1** to power the Su-7BM and later versions and the Su-9 series. The final production version was the **AL-7F-2**.

TYPE: Single-shaft turbojet, with or without afterburner.

COMPRESSOR: Ten-stage axial (eight stages in original AL-7 design). First two stages widely separated axially, with variable stators ahead of first two stages. Mass flow 114 kg (251 lb)/s. Pressure ratio 9.1.

COMBUSTION CHAMBER: Annular type with perforated inner flame tube. Multiple downstream fuel injectors inserted through cups in forward face of liner.

TURBINE: Two-stage axial-flow type. Both wheels overhung behind rear bearing; front disc bolted to flange on hollow tubular driveshaft. Entry temperature 927°C.

AFTERBURNER (AL-7F): Comprises upstream diffuser and downstream combustion section. Pilot combustor includes single nozzle ring and flame holder; main spray ring and gutter flame holder assembly downstream at greater radius. Refractory liner in combustion section. Variable-area nozzle, with 24 hinged flaps.

ACCESSORIES: Fuel pump and control unit, oil pumps, hydraulic pump, electric generator, tachometer and other items grouped into quickly replaceable packages beneath compressor casing.

DIMENSIONS (AL-7F-1):

Length	6,810 mm (268 in)
Max diameter	1,250 mm (49.2 in)

WEIGHT, DRY:

AL-7F-1	2,010 kg (4,431 lb)
AL-7F-2	2,103 kg (4,636 lb)

Lyulka AL-31F sectioned display engine *(Piotr Butowski)*

Lyulka AL-21F-3 single-shaft afterburning turbojet

PERFORMANCE RATINGS:

AL-7F	63.0 kN (14,250 lb st)
AL-7F, with afterburner	88.25 kN (19,840 lb st)
AL-7PB, RV	63.74 kN (14,330 lb st)
AL-7F-1	68.65 kN (15,432 lb st)
AL-7F-1, with afterburner	90.22 kN (22,282 lb st)
AL-7F-2, with afterburner	97.08 kN (21,825 lb st)

SPECIFIC FUEL CONSUMPTION:
Al-7F-1, max continuous rating

25.49 mg/Ns (0.90 lb/h/lb st)

LYULKA AL-21

This important engine, in its **AL-21 F-3** version, has been produced in thousands for such aircraft as the MiG-23, Su-24, Su-17/20/22 and Su-15. Developed in the early 1970s, and cleared for production in 1970-74, it is noteworthy for its major advances in the design of the compressor, combustion chamber, turbine and afterburner.

COMPRESSOR: 14-stage axial. Inlet frame carries front bearing, with hot-air de-icing of fixed inlet vanes. Variable stators downstream pivoted to casing and central bullet. Variable stators ahead of stages 2, 3 and 4. Parallel HP section with independently scheduled variable stators ahead of stages 10, 11, 12, 13 and 14. Mass flow 104 kg (229 lb)/s. Pressure ratio 14.6.

COMBUSTION CHAMBER: Can-annular type, with 12 flame tubes each with duplex downstream burner.

TURBINE: Three stages with aircooled first stage blades. Entry temperature 1,112°C. Rotor assembly supported by rear bearing held in eight-strut rear frame and drives via cone coupled to rear of compressor shaft.

AFTERBURNER: Rapid combustion downstream of three injector/flameholder rings. Corrugated insulated liner with ceramic coating. Fully variable nozzle with 24 flaps driven by six rams. Full-regime control giving smooth lightup and modulated power over whole range from flight idle to max afterburner.

WEIGHT, DRY: 1,720 kg (3,792 lb)

PERFORMANCE RATINGS (S/L):

Military power	76.5 kN (17,200 lb st) at 8,400 rpm
Max afterburner	110.5 kN (24,800 lb st)

SPECIFIC FUEL CONSUMPTION (S/L):
Military power 22.6 mg/Ns (0.80 lb/h/lb st)

LYULKA AL-31

This was A. Lyulka's last and greatest engine. With afterburner, as the **AL-31 F**, it powers all known versions of the Su-27. Engines designated **R-32** (almost certainly the Service designation for all AL-31 engines) were fitted to the P-42, an Su-27 development aircraft, which set rate of climb

Lyulka AL-31 F two-shaft augmented bypass turbojet

records in 1986. A high proportion of the engine is titanium or stainless steel. Production by Salyut MMPO.

TYPE: Two-shaft augmented turbofan.

FAN: Inlet has 23 variable guide vanes. Four fan stages slotted into discs. Bypass ratio 0.4.

COMPRESSOR: Variable inlet guide vanes followed by nine-stage HP spool with first three stators variable. Overall pressure ratio 20.

COMBUSTION CHAMBER: Annular, with 24 downstream burners fed from inner manifold.

TURBINES: Single-stage HP with cooled blades. Two-stage LP.

AFTERBURNER: Two flameholder rings downstream of multiple radial spray bars. Interlinked primary and secondary multi-flap nozzles are angled about 5° downwards.

CONTROL SYSTEM: Hydromechanical full-regime control giving smooth power from flight idle to max afterburner in all manoeuvre conditions. Linked via software to Su-27 fly by wire flight control system. All accessories grouped above engine.

DIMENSIONS:

Length	4,950 mm (195 in)
Diameter	1,220 mm (48.0 in)

WEIGHT, DRY: 1,530 kg (3,373 lb)

PERFORMANCE RATINGS:

Max augmented	123.85 kN (27,560 lb st)
Max dry	79.42 kN (17,857 lb st)

SPECIFIC FUEL CONSUMPTION:
Max dry 18.98 mg/Ns (0.67 lb/h/lb st)

MIKULIN/SOYUZ

DEPUTY GENERAL DESIGNER: Alexander Girnov

A. A. Mikulin was a leading designer of engines from 1916. The large turbojet described here was designed immediately after the Second World War. The name Soyuz (Alliance) was added in 1989. In 1990 this bureau exhibited the R-27V-300 engine, but a description of this appears under Tumansky.

MIKULIN AM-3
Service designation: TRD-3

The AM-3M single-spool turbojet was developed under the leadership of P. F. Zubets from the Mikulin M-209 (civil RD-3 or AM-3) which powers the Tu-16 and early M-4 bombers and was adapted for the USSR's first jet transport, the Tu-104. Current M-4s are believed to have the AM-3D; while the usual engine of Tu-16s is the AM-3M. This engine was produced at the Xian factory in China as the WP8 (see under XAE, China).

It has a simple configuration, with an eight-stage compressor, annular combustion system with 14 flame tubes, and a two-stage turbine. The compressor casing is

made in front, centre and rear portions, the front casing housing a row of inlet guide vanes. The inlet bullet houses an S-300M gas turbine starter, developing 75 kW (100 hp) at 31,000-35,000 rpm. Pressure ratio is 6.4; temperature after turbine 720°C.

DIMENSIONS:

Length overall	5,340 mm (210.23 in)
Diameter	1,400 mm (55.12 in)

PERFORMANCE RATINGS (T-O):

AM-3	85.8 kN (19,285 lb st)
AM-3D	85.3 kN (19,180 lb st)
AM-3M, RD-3M	93.19 kN (20,950 lb st)

MKB
MOTOROSTROITELNOYE KONSTRUKTORSKOYE BURO

93 Komsomolsky Prospect (PO Box 624), Perm 614600
Telephone: 7 (83422) 452019
Cables: Perm 10 LAVA
Telex: 134135

GENERAL DESIGNER: Yuri E. Reshetnikov

This large design bureau used to be named for P. A. Soloviev (which see). Today many of its new projects are based on the core of the PS-90A turbofan. One group, beginning with the PS-90 GP-1 and GP-2, are for industrial and marine applications. Some are shaft engines for aircraft, with ratings up to 16,000 kW (21,400 shp). Another series are advanced propfans, particular attention being paid to aft-fan derivatives with contra-rotating shrouded fans with a bypass ratio in the region of 30.

MKB D-100/110

The D-100 and D-110 are turbofans for the 1990s, based on the PS-90A core. The **D-100** would have a fan with a diameter of 2,333 mm (91.85 in), the bypass ratio being between 6 and 8. Overall pressure ratio would be 35 to 45. TET 1,287°-1,327°C, dry weight 3,350-3,550 kg (7,385-7,826), T-O thrust 19-21 tonnes (186.3-205.9 kN, 41,890-46,300 lb st) and sfc (cruise, 11 km/36,000 ft, M 0.8) of 15.30 mg/Ns (0.54 lb/h/lb st).

MKB projects based on the PS-90A: from the top, D-100, D-110 and an advanced propfan

The **D-110** is a more advanced engine with a geared fan of 2,670 mm (105 in) diameter, giving a bypass ratio of 9 to 12. Overall pressure ratio would be 31 to 44, TET 1,327°C, dry weight 3,500-4,000 kg (7,716-8,820 lb), T-O thrust 20-24 tonnes (196.1-235.3 kN, 44,090-52,900 lb st) and sfc (cruise, same conditions) 14.73 mg/Ns (0.52 lb/h/lb st).

An accompanying illustration shows the two engines together with the planned next generation propfan. This has some features resembling the Garrett ATF3, with the same double reverse-flow arrangement, accessories being at the rear and the core jet being turned 180° to escape into the fan duct.

NOVIKOV
Rybinsk

In 1990 this previously unknown OKB was announced as the source of a turboshaft version of the TVD-1500 (see Glushenkov). Rated (presumably max continuous) at 970 kW (1,300 shp), it will power the Kamov V-62 twin-engined helicopter. Novikov may be responsible for the TVD-155 and TV-O-100 (see Koptchyenko).

RKBM
RYBINSK ENGINE DESIGN BUREAU

This organisation has taken over the assets of the KB named for Koliesov.

RKBM RD-36-35FVR

This is the simple lift jet fitted to the Yak-38.

TYPE: Single-shaft turbojet for operation in near vertical attitudes.
COMPRESSOR: Five stages. Part composite construction.
COMBUSTION CHAMBER: Annular, 12 burners.
TURBINE: Single stage, air impingement starting.
WEIGHT, DRY: 210 kg (463 lb)
PERFORMANCE RATING: 30 kN (6,725 lb st)

RKBM RD-36-51A

This large afterburning turbojet has no connection with the RD-36-35FVR, despite the similarity of designation. It powered the Tu-144D supersonic transport, and thus was designed to cruise at Mach 2.2. It has several features in common with the Olympus engine of Concorde.

TYPE: Two-shaft turbojet with afterburner.
LP COMPRESSOR: Six stages. Inlet guide vanes and all stator stages variable. Titanium and steel.

HP COMPRESSOR: Five stages. All stators variable. Mainly refractory steel.
COMBUSTION CHAMBER: Annular with 20 vaporising burners.
TURBINES: Single-stage HP with cooled blades, two-stage LP. TET 1,160°C.
AFTERBURNER: Close-coupled, with con/di nozzle driven by 12 hydraulic rams. Not used in cruising flight.
ACCESSORIES: Airframe mounted, driven off HP spool (see photograph).
DIMENSIONS:
Length   5,228 mm (205.8 in)
Diameter   1,486 mm (58.5 in)
WEIGHT, DRY: 4,125 kg (9,094 lb)
PERFORMANCE RATING:
T-O   196.12 kN (44,090 lb st)

SPECIFIC FUEL CONSUMPTION (Cruise, hi-alt, M 2.2):
                              24.93 mg/Ns (0.88 lb/h/lb st)

RKBM PROJECT

In 1990 RKBM revealed plans for a range of engines based on a core already developed. This single-shaft core has a nine-stage compressor driven by a single-stage turbine. Mass flow is 22.5 kg (49.6 lb)/s, pressure ratio 12.4 and TET 1,547°C. Three derived engines would be: a helicopter turboshaft rated at 4,480-5,970 kW (6,000-8,000 shp), a high bypass ratio turbofan in the 12 tonne (117.5 kN, 26,455 lb st) class, and an advanced propfan, with three core booster stages, giving a thrust of 12-15 tonnes (117.5-147.1 kN, 26,455-33,070 lb st).

Cutaway RKBM RD-36-35FVR turbojet
(Flight International)

RKBM RD-36-51A afterburning turbojet *(Flight International)*

RKBM exhibit showing future engines based on a common core *(Flight International)*

SALYUT

This name (Salute) is that of the MMPO (production factory) making the Lyulka AL-31F.

SATURN

For the time being, engines developed by this bureau will continue to be listed under Lyulka.

SHVETSOV

FOUNDER OF BUREAU: Arkadiya Dmitrievich Shvetsov

A. D. Shvetsov was responsible for the M-11 five-cylinder aircooled radial engines made in enormous numbers in 1928-59 at powers from 74.6 kW (100 hp) to 149 kW (200 hp). He later developed larger radials, the most important

being the ASh-82, which at ratings up to 1,491 kW (2,000 hp) powered Lavochkin fighters, the Tu-2 and Tu-4 bombers, Il-12 and -14 transports and Mi-4 and Yak-24 helicopters. The ASh-62 was made in large numbers at ratings in the 750 kW (1,000 hp) class for the Li-2 and An-2. The ASh-62M agricultural version, developed by Vedeneyev, and all An-2 engines after 1952, were transferred

to Poland (see WSK-PZL Kalisz and WSK-PZL Rzeszów). Another important engine was the 545 kW (730 hp) ASh-21, fitted to the Yak-11. All these have been described in earlier editions. The ASh-62 and ASh-82 have been produced under licence in China, as described in the Chinese entry in this section.

SOLOVIEV (MKB)

Engines for which Soloviev's design team was responsible include the turbofans fitted in the Il-62M, Il-76, Il-96-300, Tu-124, Tu-134, Tu-154M and Tu-204 transport aircraft, and the turboshafts which power the Mi-6 and Mi-10 helicopters. Today the bureau is known as the MKB (Perm engine design bureau), which see.

SOLOVIEV D-15

This engine was first reported, in 1959, as that fitted to the Type 201-M which gained world records for speed and altitude. This aircraft was a special Myasishchev M-4, and the engine was standard in some versions of this aircraft. Details of the D-15 are still unknown in the West, but it is probably a two-shaft turbojet. It laid the foundation upon which Soloviev's bureau produced the civil D-20 and D-30.

PERFORMANCE RATING:
T-O   128.6 kN (28,660 lb st)

SOLOVIEV D-25V

D-25V is the Soloviev designation for the turboshaft which powers the Mi-6 and Mi-10 helicopters. It is usually referred to by its official designation of **TV-2BM**.

The helicopter power plant comprises two D-25V engines, identical except for handed jetpipes, and an R-7 gearbox. The latter has four stages of large gearwheels providing an overall ratio of 69.2. The R-7 is 2,795 mm (110.04 in) high, 1,551 mm (61.06 in) wide and 1,852 mm (72.91 in) long. Its dry weight is 3,200 kg (7,054 lb).

The D-25V is flat rated to maintain rated power to 3,000 m (10,000 ft) or to temperatures up to 40°C at sea level.

The **D-25VF** is uprated to 4,847 kW (6,500 shp). These engines are believed to incorporate a zero stage on the compressor and to operate at higher turbine gas temperatures. They power the Mi-10K crane helicopter.

The following details apply to the basic D-25V:

TYPE: Single-shaft turboshaft with free power turbine.
COMPRESSOR: Nine-stage axial, with fixed inlet guide vanes and blow-off valves. Pressure ratio 5.6 at T-O power, 10,530 rpm.
COMBUSTION CHAMBER: Can-annular with 12 flame tubes.
FUEL GRADE: T-1, TS-1 to GOST 10227-62 (DERD.2494, MIL-F-5616)
TURBINE: Single-stage compressor turbine, overhung behind rear roller bearing. Two-stage power turbine, overhung on end of rear output shaft. Normal power turbine rpm, 7,800-8,300; maximum 9,000.
LUBRICATION: Pressure circulation at 3.45-4.41 bars (50-64 lb/sq in). Separate systems for gas generator and for power turbine, transmission and gearbox.
OIL GRADE: Gas generator, MK-8 to GOST 6457-66 or GOST 982-56. Power turbine and gearbox, mixture (75-25 Summer, 50-50 Winter) of MK-22 or MS-20 to GOST 1013-49 and MK-8 or 982-56.
ACCESSORIES: SP3-12TV electric supply and starting system; fuel supply to separate LP and HP systems; airframe accessories driven off upper and lower gearboxes.

**Soloviev D-30KU
two-shaft turbofan
with reverser**

STARTING: The SP3-12TV comprises an STG-12TM starter/generator on each engine, igniter unit, two spark plugs with cooling shrouds, two contactors, solenoid air valve, pressure warning, PSG-12V control panel and electro-hydraulic cutout switch of the TsP-23A centrifugal governor.
DIMENSIONS:
Length overall, bare   2,737 mm (107.75 in)
Length overall with transmission shaft
                                5,537 mm (218.0 in)
Width   1,086 mm (42.76 in)
Height   1,158 mm (45.59 in)
WEIGHT, DRY:
With engine mounted accessories   1,325 kg (2,921 lb)
PERFORMANCE RATINGS:
T-O   4,101 kW (5,500 shp)
Rated power   3,504 kW (4,700 shp)
Cruise (1,000 m; 3,280 ft, 135 knots; 250 km/h; 155 mph)   2,983 kW (4,000 shp)
SPECIFIC FUEL CONSUMPTION:
T-O, as above   108 μg/J (0.639 lb/h/shp)
Cruise, as above   118.1 μg/J (0.699 lb/h/shp)

SOLOVIEV D-30

Since about 1972 the standard engine of the Tu-134A has been the **D-30-II**, with reverser. One Tu-134 was flown with D-30 engines with a zero stage on the LP compressor; the existing ratings were obtained at reduced gas temperature and maintained to ISA + 25°C.

TYPE: Two-shaft turbofan (bypass turbojet).
FAN: Four-stage axial (LP compressor). First stage has shrouded titanium blades held in disc by pinned joints. Pressure ratio (T-O rating, 7,700 rpm, S/L, static), 2.65. Mass flow 125 kg (265 lb)/s. Bypass ratio 1.
COMPRESSOR: Ten-stage axial (HP compressor). Drum and disc construction, largely of titanium. Pressure ratio (T-O rating, 11,600 rpm, S/L, static), 7.1. Overall pressure ratio, 17.4.

COMBUSTION CHAMBER: Can-annular, with 12 flame tubes fitted with duplex burners.
FUEL GRADE: T-1 and TS-1 to GOST 10227-62 (equivalent to DERD.2494 or MIL-F-5616).
TURBINE: Two-stage HP turbine. First stage has cooled blades in both stator and rotor. LP turbine also has two stages. All blades shrouded and bearings shock mounted.
JETPIPE: Main and bypass mixer with curvilinear ducts. D-30-II engine of Tu-134A fitted with twin-clamshell reverser.
LUBRICATION: Open type, with oil returned to tank.
OIL GRADE: Mineral oil MK-8 or MK-8P to GOST 6457-66 (equivalent to DERD.2490 or MIL-O-6081B).
ACCESSORIES: Automatic ice protection system, fire extinguishing for core and bypass flows, vibration detectors on casings, oil chip detectors and automatic limitation of exhaust gas temperature to 620°C at take-off or when starting and to 630°C in flight (5 min limit). Shaft driven accessories driven via radial bevel gear shafts in centre casing, mainly off HP spool. D-30-II carries constant speed drives for alternators.
STARTING: Electric DC starting system incorporating STG-12TVMO starter/generators.
DIMENSIONS:
Overall length   3,983 mm (156.8 in)
Base diameter of inlet casing   1,050 mm (41.3 in)
WEIGHT, DRY: 1,550 kg (3,417 lb)
PERFORMANCE RATINGS:
T-O   66.68 kN (14,990 lb st)
Long-range cruise rating, 11,000 m (36,000 ft) and Mach 0.75   12.75 kN (2,866 lb)
SPECIFIC FUEL CONSUMPTION:
T-O   17.56 mg/Ns (0.62 lb/h/lb st)
Cruise, as above   21.81 mg/Ns (0.77 lb/h/lb)

SOLOVIEV D-30K

Despite its designation, this turbofan is much larger and more powerful than the D-30. The basic **D-30KU**, to which the specification details apply, replaced the NK-8-4 as power plant of the Il-62M. The **D-30KU-154-II** is configured to suit the Tu-154M and is derated to 104 kN (23,380 lb st). The **D-30KP**, rated at 117.7 kN (26,455 lb st), was the original engine of all versions of the Il-76. Clamshell reversers are fitted to all four engines of this aircraft, and to the outer engines of the Il-62M. These reversers are airframe assemblies incorporated in the nacelle. In 1980 the KP was replaced in production by the **KP-1** which maintains full power to ISA + 23°C. The **D-30KTV**, again rated at 117.7 kN (26,455 lb st) powers the Beriev A-40 Albatross, with reversers superficially resembling those of the Il-76.

TYPE: Two-shaft turbofan, with mixer and reverser.
FAN (LP COMPRESSOR): Three stages, mainly of titanium alloy. First-stage rotor blades with part-span snubbers. Mass flow, 269 kg (593 lb)/s at 4,730 rpm (87.9 per cent), with bypass ratio of 2.42.
HP COMPRESSOR: Eleven stages, first two having part-span snubbers. Guide vanes turn 30° over 7,900-9,600 rpm, while air is bled from fifth and sixth stages. Overall pressure ratio (S/L, static) 20 at HP speed of 10,460 rpm (96 per cent).
COMBUSTION CHAMBER: Can-annular type with 12 flame tubes. Each tube comprises hemispherical head and eight short sections welded with gaps for dilution air. Single swirl type main/pilot burner centred in each tube. Igniter plugs in two tubes.
FUEL GRADE: T-1, TS-1, GOST-10227-62, A-1 (D1655/63t), DERD.2494 or 2498, Air 3405/B or 3-GP-23e.
TURBINES: Two-stage HP turbine with cooled blades in both stages. Second-stage rotor blades tip shrouded. Max

Soloviev D-25V free-turbine turboshaft

Soloviev D-30 Series II two-shaft turbofan with reverser

gas temperature 1,122°C. Four-stage LP turbine with shrouded blades.

LUBRICATION: Closed type. Fuel/oil heat exchanger and centrifugal air separator with particle warning.

OIL GRADE: MK-8 or MK-8P to GOST 6467-66 (mineral) or BNII NP-50-1-4F to GOST 13076-67 (synthetic).

ACCESSORIES: Front and rear drive boxes under engine carry all shaft driven accessories. Differential constant speed drive to alternator and air turbine starter.

STARTING: Pneumatic starter fed by ground supply, APU or cross-bleed.

DIMENSIONS:

Length with reverser	5,700 mm (224 in)
Inlet diameter	1,464 mm (57.6 in)
Maximum diameter of casing	1,560 mm (61.4 in)

WEIGHT, DRY:

With reverser	2,650 kg (5,842 lb)
Without reverser	2,300 kg (5,071 lb)

PERFORMANCE RATINGS (ISA):

T-O	107.9 kN (24,250 lb st) to 21°C
Cruise at 11,000 m (36,000 ft) and Mach 0.8	
	27 kN (6,063 lb)

SPECIFIC FUEL CONSUMPTION:

At T-O rating	13.88 mg/Ns (0.49 lb/h/lb st)
Cruise, as above	19.83 mg/Ns (0.70 lb/h/lb)

SOLOVIEV PS-90A (D-90A)

This high bypass ratio turbofan is not derived from any existing engine. It is assembled from 11 modules, and is designed for long life, high reliability and low fuel burn.

Bench testing began in 1985. Flight testing was in progress in 1987 with an engine replacing a D-30KP in an Il-76. Certification was due in 1989. The PS-90A powers the Il-96-300, first flown on 28 September 1988 with engines derated to 132.4 kN (29,762 lb st), and the Tu-204, first flown on 2 January 1989 with fully rated PS-90As. This engine is the first to have a designation reflecting the name of the General Designer.

In 1990 Mr Reshetnikov stated that the sfc so far achieved is 16.85 mg/Ns (0.595 lb/h/lb), and that remedial measures include adding a third stage to the LP booster and modifying blade profiles. The improved engine is to be certificated in 1993.

TYPE: Two-shaft turbofan with mixer and fan reverser.

FAN: Single-stage, with 28 wide-chord (at root 250 mm; 9.84 in) titanium blades, without snubbers or shrouds. Hub/tip ratio 0.34. Bypass ratio (cruise) 4.8.

LP COMPRESSOR: Two-stage booster bolted to rear of fan.

HP COMPRESSOR: 13-stage spool with variable inlet guide vanes and first two stators. Overall pressure ratio (cruise) 35.5. Speed (max) 11,820 rpm.

Soloviev (MKB) PS-90A two-shaft turbofan *(Brian M. Service)*

COMBUSTION CHAMBER: Fully annular with vaporising burners and two igniters.

HP TURBINE: Two stages, with advanced aircooled blades. Entry gas temperature 1,565°K (1,292°C).

LP TURBINE: Four stages.

CONTROL SYSTEM: Full-authority digital electronic.

REVERSER: Multiple blocker doors close off fan duct as translating mid-section of cowl moves to rear, to uncover all-round reverser cascades. No core reverser.

DIMENSIONS:

Fan diameter	1,900 mm (74.8 in)
Overall length	5,329 mm (209.8 in)

WEIGHT, DRY: 2,800 kg (6,173 lb)

PERFORMANCE RATINGS (ISA):

T-O, S/L	156.9 kN (35,275 lb st) to 30°C
Cruise at 11,000 m (36,000 ft) and Mach 0.8	
	34.36 kN (7,716 lb)

SPECIFIC FUEL CONSUMPTION:

Cruise, as above	16.43 mg/Ns (0.58 lb/h/lb)

TUMANSKY

Academician Sergei Konstantinovich Tumansky, who died in 1973, was a noted designer of piston engines. His RD-9 axial turbojet went into production in 1953. On Mikulin's disgrace in 1956, Tumansky was appointed head of the bureau. Production of his subsequent engines easily exceeds that of any other family of aircraft gas turbines in the post-1955 era.

TUMANSKY RD-9

First axial turbojet of wholly Soviet design to be placed in production, this engine was designed under Tumansky in the Mikulin bureau in 1950-51 and received the TsIAM designation **AM-5**. The afterburning **AM-5F** was selected for the MiG-19 and the unaugmented engine for the Yak-25. After Mikulin's removal in 1956 the engine was redesignated **RD-9**, the afterburning type being called **RD-9B**. In 1957 the **RD-9BM** entered production, with a hydraulically actuated three-step nozzle. All variants have a nine-stage compressor, can-annular combustor and two-stage turbine; pressure ratio at take-off is 7.14. Production in the Soviet Union tapered off in 1958 in favour of the R-11. In China, production of the RD-9BM began in 1960 and has continued for the J-6 and Q-5. Diameter of all models is 813 mm (32.0 in). Maximum T-O rating of the BM is 32.36 kN (7,275 lb st).

A detailed description and drawing will be found under the designation WP6 in the Chinese (LEMC) part of this section.

TUMANSKY R-11
Service designation: TRD-37

The first R-11 turbojets (known as the R-37 series by the armed forces) ran in 1953 and entered production in 1956. The R-11 is a two-spool engine, with accessories grouped on the underside of the compressor. It was one of the first engines to have an overhung first rotor stage without inlet guide vanes. Other features include a can-annular combustion chamber with ten flame tubes, which in some versions provides large air bleed couplings for flap blowing, and, in most installations, a large afterburner with multi-flap variable nozzle. All early versions (but not the Chinese derivative) are started on petrol (gasoline) fed from a separate tank, and gaseous oxygen can be fed to the burners to increase relight altitude from 8 to 11.9 km

Tumansky R-11F2S-300 two-shaft turbojet, with afterburner removed

(26,250 to 39,000 ft). Considerably more than 20,000 of all versions have been delivered from Soviet plants, to power many types of aircraft including versions of the MiG-21 and Yak-28. Many more have been produced by Hindustan Aeronautics in India, and by the Chinese as the LEMC WP7. Known Soviet versions are:

R-11. Initial production series, rated at 38.25 kN (8,600 lb st) dry and 50.0 kN (11,240 lb st) with afterburner.

Three-stage transonic LP compressor and three-stage HP, each driven by single-stage turbine.

R-11-300. Fitted with enlarged afterburner and new nozzle. Powered speed-record Ye-66 in 1959. Dry thrust unchanged but maximum increased to 58.4 kN (13,120 lb st). Believed to power Yak-28 versions.

R-11F. Original engine uprated, with small afterburner; dry thrust unchanged, maximum 56.4 kN (12,676 lb st).

R-11FS, F2S. Suffix S signifies provision for flap blowing. Final version was the **R-11F2S-300**. According to a Polish magazine this powers not only various MiG-21s but also initial versions of the Sukhoi T-37, with dry and maximum ratings of 38.2 kN (8,588 lb st) and 60.8 kN (13,668 lb st). The F2S-300 was until at least 1986 still in production in India and China. Details will be found in the entry on the Chinese WP7.

TUMANSKY R-13

This two-spool turbojet supplanted the R-11 as the MiG-21 engine in the late 1960s, before giving way to the R-25. It has an advanced afterburner, and a new five-stage HP compressor handling a greater airflow. An unaugmented version powers the Su-25 (see R-195 below). The **PDM** fitted to the record breaking Ye-66B of 1974 may have been an R-13. The standard ratings for the **R-13-300** are 41.55 kN (9,340 lb st) dry and 64.73 kN (14,550 lb st) with afterburner. Fuller details will be found in the entry on the Chinese WP13.

TUMANSKY R-195

This tough and simple turbojet was developed from the R-13 to power the Su-25 and Su-28 family of attack and training aircraft. Originally designated **R-95**, it was further developed into the R-195 before entering production in about 1979. The entire engine was designed to offer considerable resistance to 23 mm gunfire, and to continue to operate after suffering damage in eight places.

TYPE: Two-shaft turbojet.
LP COMPRESSOR: Three stages. No inlet guide vanes or variable stators.
HP COMPRESSOR: Five stages. No variable stators, but auto bleed valves.
COMBUSTION CHAMBER: Can-annular with multiple duplex burners. Cleared for kerosene, diesel oil and MT petrol.
TURBINES: Single-stage HP, single-stage LP.
JETPIPE: No afterburner, simple fixed-area nozzle.
DIMENSIONS:
Length	3,300 mm (130 in)
Diameter	914 mm (36 in)

WEIGHT, DRY: 990 kg (2,183 lb)
PERFORMANCE RATING:
T-O   44.18 kN (9,921 lb st)

TUMANSKY R-15

In early 1990 it was announced that the engine of the MiG-25R variants is an afterburning turbojet designated **R-15BD-300**, rated at 110 kN (24,700 lb st). Presumably it is related to the R-31.

Another MiG-25 engine is the **R-15B-300** illustrated.

TUMANSKY RU-19

Service designation: TRD-29

This single-shaft turbojet has been used to power aircraft and as an APU and emergency booster (in the An-26). When used as an APU its thrust is reduced depending upon the shaft power extracted. The fully rated **RU-19-300** has a thrust of 8.83 kN (1,985 lb st). This is installed in the An-24RV and An-24RT. The **RU-19A-300** is rated at 7.85 kN (1,765 lb st) and is installed in the An-26 and An-30. When providing full electrical power the residual thrust is only 2.16 kN (485 lb st). An RU-19 was selected as the APU/booster for the MAI-Tashkent Semurg, the rating in this application being 3.1 kN (697 lb st). Another RU-19, equipped as a turbojet and fully rated, powers the La-17 target (see RPVs and Targets in 1977-78 *Jane's*). The RU-19 powered the Yak-30 and Yak-32 jet trainers.

TUMANSKY R-25

This two-spool turbojet was a new design, and its compressor of high pressure ratio confers a markedly lower sfc than the R-13. The R-25 has redesigned accessory systems but is installationally interchangeable with the R-13. The first LP compressor stage has 21 titanium blades of large chord. The afterburner has two stages (the R-11 and R-13 having one) and so can be used in combat at high altitudes. The **R-25-300** powers the MiG-21bis, with ratings of 52 kN (11,700 lb st) dry and 74.5 kN (16,755 lb st) with afterburner. No longer made, except under licence by HAL of India for MiG-21bis.

TUMANSKY R-266/R-31

The R-26 sub-type 6 is a single-shaft afterburning turbojet designed for the MiG-25. It stemmed from the P-166 fitted to the Ye-166 which set a world speed record in 1962. The P-166 had a thrust with afterburner of 98.06 kN (22,046 lb st). This was also the thrust of the original R-266, announced under its service designation of **R-31** as being fitted to prototypes of the MiG-25 (designated Ye-266).

Constructed mainly of steel, the R-266 has a five-stage compressor with T-O pressure ratio of about 7, driven by a single-stage turbine with uncooled blades. Special T-6 fuel is used, with freezing point of −62.2°C and flash point of 54.4°C. In the MiG-25, water/methanol is injected into the variable inlet duct at supersonic speeds. At Mach 3 most of

Tumansky R-195 two-shaft turbojet *(Flight International)*

Cutaway Tumansky R-15B-300 single-shaft afterburning turbojet *(Piotr Butowski)*

Tumansky R-25 two-shaft turbojet, with afterburner removed

Two views of the Tumansky R-27V-300 vectored-thrust turbojet (box above left nozzle is added for demonstration purposes)
(Flight International)

the thrust is generated by the three-ring afterburner and multi-flap variable nozzle.

RD-F. This is an uprated R-266 fitted to the Ye-266M (MiG-25 variant) which set time-to-height records in 1975. According to a Polish magazine the R-26 powers the MiG-25M, with dry and maximum ratings of 90 kN (20,230 lb st) and 138 kN (31,025 lb st). This engine may have the military designation TRD-31F.

R-31-300. This is the production engine of the MiG-25 fighter versions. Ratings are 91.18 kN (20,500 lb st) dry and 120 kN (27,010 lb st) with afterburner.

Type D. This is the only known designation of the engine of the MiG-31. It is presumed to be related to the R-15 and R-31. Dry and maximum ratings are 99.2 kN (22,300 lb st) and 137.3 kN (30,865 lb st). A non-afterburning version may power the Myasishchev M-17.

TUMANSKY R-27

This engine was a natural growth development from the R-11, -13, -25 series. It entered production in about 1970 to power the initial series versions of the MiG-23.

R-27V-300. Afterburner replaced by bifurcated nozzles each rotating through about 100° (cycle time 8 s), driven by two hydraulic motors linked by cross-shaft. Provides lift/cruise propulsion of Yak-38. Displayed 1990 by Mikulin/Soyuz bureau.

TYPE: Two-shaft turbojet.

LP COMPRESSOR: Five stages. No inlet guide vanes or variable stators.

HP COMPRESSOR: Six stages. No variable stators.

COMBUSTION CHAMBER: Annular, burners fed from inner manifold. Water injection with max afterburner.

TURBINES: Single-stage HP with aircooled blades, single-stage LP.

JETPIPE: Afterburner with profiled multi-flap primary and secondary nozzles. R-27V, plenum chamber and two vectoring nozzles.

DIMENSIONS:
Length: R-27	4,850 mm (191 in)
R-27V	3,700 mm (146 in)
Diameter	915 mm (36 in)

WEIGHT, DRY:
R-27	1,500 kg (3,300 lb)
R-27V	1,350 kg (2,976 lb)

PERFORMANCE RATINGS:
R-27 max with afterburner and water injection	100 kN (22,485 lb st)
R-27 max dry	68.65 kN (15,430 lb st)
R-27V-300 max T-O	68.0 kN (15,300 lb st)

TUMANSKY R-29

This augmented turbojet is simpler than the corresponding American F100, with fewer compressor stages and a lower pressure ratio; but it is more powerful and costs much less. Different subtypes are fitted to all current MiG-23 and MiG-27 versions for Warsaw Pact front-line use, and to the Su-22. In all these aircraft water injection is used on take-off, the MiG-23MF water tank having a capacity of 28 litres (7.4 US gallons; 6.2 Imp gallons).

The following versions have been identified:

R-29B. Original full-rated production engine for MiG-23MF and related versions.

R-29PN. This replaced the R-29B as the standard engine of non-export MiG-23 aircraft.

R-29B-300. Simplified engine with small afterburner and short two-position nozzle for subsonic low-level operation. Fitted to all MiG-27 versions, with fixed or variable inlet ducts.

R-29BS-300. This is the engine of the Su-22 (export Su-17 versions).

Tumansky R-29B built under licence by HAL (rear view with afterburner removed)

COMPRESSOR: Five-stage LP, six-stage HP. Overall pressure ratio (29B) 12.4, (29-300) 13. Mass flow (29B) 105 kg (235 lb)/s, (R-29-300) 110 kg (242.5 lb)/s.

COMBUSTION CHAMBER: Annular, vaporising burners.

TURBINES: HP has single stage with aircooled blades; max 8,800 rpm. Two-stage LP; max 8,500 rpm.

AFTERBURNER: Fuel rings with separate light-up give modulated fully variable augmentation. Fully variable nozzles differ in different installations (see variants).

DIMENSIONS (R-29-300):
Length	4,960 mm (195 in)
Max diameter	912 mm (35.9 in)

WEIGHT, DRY:
R-29B	1,760 kg (3,880 lb)
R-29-300	1,880 kg (4,145 lb)

PERFORMANCE RATINGS:
Max S/L unaugmented	78.45 kN (17,635 lb st)
Min with afterburner	97.1 kN (21,825 lb st)
Max T-O, wet (R-29B-300)	112.8 kN (25,350 lb st)
Max T-O, wet (MiG-23MF)	122.0 kN (27,500 lb st)

TUMANSKY R-35

In early 1990 it was announced that the MiG-23ML, MLA and MLD are powered by the the **R-35F-300**, rated at 127.5 kN (28,660 lb st). It is not yet known how closely this engine resembles the R-29.

VEDENEYEV

GENERAL DESIGNER IN CHARGE OF BUREAU:
Ivan M. Vedeneyev

This designer was responsible for improvement of the AI-14 piston engine designed by the Ivchenko bureau. He also developed the ASh-62M, produced in Poland as the ASz-62M, from Shvetsov's ASh-62IR.

M-14V-26

Derived from the AI-14 engines for fixed-wing aircraft, the M-14V-26 powers the Ka-26 helicopter. In this installation the stub wing carries an engine on each tip. Beneath the rotor an R-26 gearbox combines the power of the engines and distributes it equally between the two coaxial main rotors. The same engine in a revised installation powers the Mi-34 helicopter.

The engine has forced cooling by an axial fan driven via a friction clutch and extension shaft ahead of the main output bevel box at 1.452 times crankshaft speed. The planetary gearbox has a ratio of 0.309 and incorporates friction and ratchet clutches. The central R-26 gearbox has a ratio of 0.34; it also drives the generator, hydraulic pump, oil pump and tachometer generator.

DIMENSIONS:
Length	1,145 mm (45.08 in)
Diameter	985 mm (38.78 in)

WEIGHT, DRY: 245 kg (540 lb)

PERFORMANCE RATINGS:
T-O	242 kW (325 hp) at 2,800 rpm
Max continuous I	205 kW (275 hp) at 2,450 rpm
Max continuous II	142 kW (190 hp) at 2,350 rpm
Cruise I	142 kW (190 hp) at 2,350 rpm
Cruise II	108 kW (145 hp) at 2,350 rpm

SPECIFIC FUEL CONSUMPTION:
At cruise ratings 77.7 µg/J (0.46 lb/h/hp)

VEDENEYEV M-14P

For fixed-wing applications, the M-14P was used with direct drive in the original version of the OSKB-1-3PM Kwant, at a T-O rating of 242 kW (325 hp). Currently, the Kwant has an M-14 II of 268 kW (360 hp). The same rating is quoted for the M-14P fitted to the Yak-18T, -50, -52, -53 and -55 and Su-26 and -26M, all of which have a controllable-pitch propeller.

Drawing of Vedeneyev M-14V-26 radial piston engine, with cooling fan

ZMKB

For the time being, the engines of the Zaporozhye Engine Design Bureau will continue to be listed under Lotarev.

SOVIET ENGINE OF UNKNOWN DESIGN

The 1989-90 *Jane's* was the first for many years to have no entries under this heading. This year one must be added.

Tu-160 ENGINE

The Tu-160 'Blackjack' is powered by four augmented turbofans whose T-O rating is given as 245 kN (55,115 lb st).

The designation is officially given as **Type P** and also as **Type 15**.

UNITED KINGDOM

EMDAIR

EMDAIR LTD

Harbour Road, Rye, E Sussex TN31 7TH
Telephone: 44 (797) 223460
Telex: 957116 FOR EMDAIR
Fax: 44 (797) 224615

Activities centre on lightweight four-stroke flat-twin engines. These aircooled engines run on Avgas and have four-valve heads, electronic management systems, central and side spark plugs, direct injection, alternator and electric starter. They are intended to combine high specific output at low rpm with low sfc, low costs and long life. Each engine is available in A (direct drive) and B (geared, torsional damping and extension shaft) versions.

EMDAIR CF 077A

Crankshaft rotation counterclockwise, seen from the front. An exhaust muffler (silencer) is optional. Conforms to JAR 22.

CYLINDERS: Bore 95.0 mm (3.74 in). Stroke 88.9 mm (3.50 in). Capacity 1,261 cc (76.91 cu in). Compression ratio 9.5.

DIMENSIONS:
Length	400 mm (15.75 in)
Width	698 mm (27.5 in)
Height	447 mm (17.75 in)

WEIGHT, DRY (with starter): 47.27 kg (104 lb)

PERFORMANCE RATINGS:
Max	44.8 kW (60 hp) at 3,600 rpm
Max cruise	33.6 kW (45 hp) at 3,090 rpm

FUEL CONSUMPTION:
Max cruise 13.25 litres (3.5 US gallons; 2.9 Imp gallons)/h

EMDAIR CF 077B

This version powers the De Vore Sunbird, designed to FAR Pt 23. Geared output with torsional vibration damping, reducing propeller speed to 2,600 rpm.

EMDAIR CF 092A

CYLINDERS: Bore 104.0 mm (4.094 in). Stroke 88.9 mm (3.50 in). Capacity 1,511 cc (92.17 cu in). Compression ratio 9.5. The **092B** is a geared version.

DIMENSIONS:
Length	401 mm (15.8 in)
Width	698 mm (27.5 in)
Height	447 mm (17.75 in)

WEIGHT, DRY (with starter): 51.0 kg (112 lb)

PERFORMANCE RATINGS:
Max	52.2 kW (70 hp) at 3,600 rpm
75 per cent cruise	39.1 kW (52.5 hp) at 3,075 rpm

FUEL CONSUMPTION:
Max cruise 14.4 litres (3.8 US gallons; 3.2 Imp gallons)/h

EMDAIR CF 112

The **112B** has an epicyclic gearbox giving a propeller speed of 2,500 rpm at a crankshaft speed of 3,600 rpm. The following relates to the **112A**:

CYLINDERS: Bore 110 mm (4.35 in). Stroke 96.0 mm (3.78 in). Capacity 1,834 cc (112 cu in). Compression ratio 9.5.

DIMENSIONS:
Length	412.75 mm (16.25 in)
Width	711.2 mm (28.0 in)
Height	425 mm (16.75 in)

Emdair CF 092B two-cylinder piston engine

WEIGHT, DRY (with starter): 57.28 kg (128 lb)

PERFORMANCE RATINGS:
Max	63.4 kW (85.0 hp) at 3,600 rpm
75 per cent cruise	47.5 kW (63.75 hp) at 3,270 rpm

FUEL CONSUMPTION:
Max cruise 15.5 litres (4.1 US gallons; 3.4 Imp gallons)/h

NORTON

NORTON MOTORS LTD

Lynn Lane, Shenstone, Lichfield, Staffs WS14 0EA
Telephone: 44 (543) 480101
Telex: 335998 NORTON G
Fax: 44 (543) 481128
MANAGING DIRECTOR: Graham Williams
DIRECTOR OF ENGINEERING: David W. Garside
DIRECTOR OF MARKETING: Jon H. Skofic

Norton designs and manufactures gasoline-fuelled Wankel-type rotary engines from 15 to 90 kW (20 to 120 bhp). Norton claims these engines offer a power-to-weight ratio superior to a two-stroke. With sfc competitive with a four-stroke, the rotary is capable of longer missions or carrying greater payload. Radial vibration is eliminated and torsional vibration is very small. The rotary's low maintenance requirement is a further advantage.

The rotary engine offers great potential as a multi-fuel engine. Norton has already carried out preliminary work which has established the feasibility of running the rotary on jet or diesel fuels. Turbocharging the engine to maintain power at altitude forms part of future development plans for the Norton rotary.

NORTON NR642

This engine comprises a heavy-duty version of Norton's basic twin-rotor engine mated to a dedicated helical spur reduction gearbox. The rotors are aircooled by exhaust ejector. The housings are watercooled. Designed to meet BCAR Section 3/JAR-E (equivalent to FAR Pt 33). Certification was expected during 1990. In 1989 the NR642 was selected by the joint McDonnell Douglas/Developmental Sciences Corporation team as the power plant for its candidate in the US DoD's UAV-Short-Range competition. Trial installations and first flights of NR642 were made in the Shaw TwinEze (UK) and Seabird Sentinel (Australia) in 1989. It is in limited production.

DIMENSIONS:
Length	702 mm (27.6 in)
Width	457 mm (18.0 in)
Height	444 mm (17.2 in)

WEIGHT (complete, wet with accessories): 64 kg (140 lb)

PERFORMANCE RATING: 67 kW (90 bhp)

SPECIFIC FUEL CONSUMPTION:
Max rating	91 µg/J (0.54 lb/bhp/hp)
At cruise	84 µg/J (0.50 lb/bhp/hp)

Norton NR642 twin-rotor engine

Norton NR622 twin-rotor engine

NORTON NR622

Twin rotors cooled by induction air, water-cooled housings, incorporating 2:1 or 3:1 reduction gearbox. Suitable for ultralights, autogyros and light aircraft. Capacity 2 × 294 = 588 cc (35.9 cu in).

DIMENSIONS:
Length	550 mm (21.6 in)
Width	330 mm (13.0 in)
Height	350 mm (13.8 in)
WEIGHT, READY TO RUN:	52 kg (115 lb)
PERFORMANCE RATING:	61 kW (82 hp) at 7,500 rpm
SPECIFIC FUEL CONSUMPTION: As NR642	

NORTON NR602

Similar to NR622 but without gearbox. Applications include light aircraft with in-built reduction drive (for example, BD-5) and industrial roles. First units are undergoing trial installation in BD-5.

DIMENSIONS:
Length	432 mm (17 in)
Width	330 mm (13 in)
Height	305 mm (12 in)
WEIGHT, READY TO RUN:	48 kg (105 lb)
PERFORMANCE RATING:	61 kW (82 hp) at 7,500 rpm
SPECIFIC FUEL CONSUMPTION:	
Max rating	88 µg/J (0.52 lb/h/hp)
At cruise	81 µg/J (0.48 lb/h/hp)

Norton NR801 single-rotor engine

NORTON NR801

This single-rotor engine with liquid-cooled housings and without reduction gearbox has been developed for UAVs. It is anticipated that a version with revised accessories and with a reduction drive will be developed for the ultralight market.

DIMENSIONS:
Length	305 mm (12 in)
Width	325 mm (12.8 in)
Height	249 mm (9.8 in)
WEIGHT, READY TO RUN (with generator):	22.7 kg (50 lb)
PERFORMANCE RATING:	39 kW (52 bhp) at 7,500 rpm
SPECIFIC FUEL CONSUMPTION: As NR642	

NORTON NR731

This single-rotor engine with ram-air cooled housings and rotor has the highest power-to-weight ratio ever achieved by a standard production rotary engine. It is currently used for powering the Target Technology Banshee 300 (UK). With modification it could be developed as the power unit for small man-carrying aircraft or powered gliders.

Norton NR731 single-rotor engine

DIMENSIONS:
Length	190 mm (7.4 in)
Width	237 mm (9.3 in)
Height	262 mm (10.3 in)
WEIGHT, READY TO RUN:	10 kg (22 lb)
PERFORMANCE RATING:	28.3 kW (38 bhp)
SPECIFIC FUEL CONSUMPTION:	
Max rating	96 µg/J (0.57 lb/bhp/hp)
At cruise	88 µg/J (0.52 lb/bhp/hp)

NPT

NOEL PENNY TURBINES LTD

Siskin Drive, Toll Bar End, Coventry CV3 4FE
Telephone: 44 (203) 301528
Telex: 312285 PENNY G
Fax: 44 (203) 302025
CHAIRMAN AND CHIEF EXECUTIVE: R. N. Penny

NPT specialises in turbojets for low-cost manufacture. New products range from a 0.22 kN (50 lb st) turbojet, for ultra low-cost production to replace a rocket, to a 4.0 kN (900 lb st) two-shaft turbofan. NPT also produces industrial and aerospace gas turbines rated at up to 2,000 kW (2,700 shp) and 6.67 kN (1,500 lb st). Turbojets for unmanned applications include the NPT 151 (667N; 150 lb st), the NPT 171 (756N; 170 lb st), various types of NPT 301 (1.4 kN; 315 lb st class) and the NPT 401 (1.779 kN; 400 lb st).

NPT 301

The 301 family was developed for re-usable drones and target vehicles requiring thrusts in the range 1.3 to 2 kN (300

to 450 lb st) at up to 13,850 m (45,000 ft). One version, the NPT 301-3/4, has a manned aircraft application: the prototype CMC Leopard light business aircraft, first flown in January 1989.

TYPE: Single shaft turbojet.
COMPRESSOR: Centrifugal, aluminium alloy. Air mass flow 2.27 kg (5.0 lb)/s. Pressure ratio 4.5.
COMBUSTION CHAMBER: Reverse flow annular, with vaporising burners.
FUEL SYSTEM: LP pressurised inlet electric pump. Analog or digital electronic control.
FUEL GRADES: Jet A-1, JP-5.
TURBINE: Single-stage axial with integral blades.
STARTING: External air source impingement on compressor.
ACCESSORY DRIVE: Alternator, currently 2.5 kW.
LUBRICATION: Total loss pulsed oil flow.
DIMENSIONS:
Length	1,000 mm (39.6 in)
Diameter	343 mm (13.5 in)

Cutaway NPT 301 turbojet

WEIGHT, DRY:	45.4 kg (100 lb)
PERFORMANCE RATING (S/L):	1.334 kN (300 lb st)
SPECIFIC FUEL CONSUMPTION:	30.6 mg/Ns (1.08 lb/h/lb st)

ROLLS-ROYCE

ROLLS-ROYCE plc

65 Buckingham Gate, London SW1E 6AT
Telephone: 44 (71) 222 9020
Telex: 918091
Fax: 44 (71) 233 1733
MAIN LOCATIONS:
PO Box 31, Moor Lane, Derby DE2 8BJ
Telephone: 44 (332) 242424
Fax: 44 (332) 249936/7
PO Box 3, Filton, Bristol BS12 7QE
Telephone: 44 (272) 791234
Fax: 44 (272) 797575
Leavesden, Watford WD2 7BZ
Telephone: 44 (923) 674000
Fax: 44 (923) 661939
CHAIRMAN: Sir Francis Tombs
DEPUTY CHAIRMAN: Sir Ralph Robins

More than 320 million hours have been accumulated with Rolls-Royce civil and military gas turbines, which are used by over 310 airlines, over 110 armed forces and more than 700 executive customers.

The main activities are at Derby, Glasgow, Bristol, Coventry and Leavesden, where aircraft gas turbines are produced, and at Ansty, where aircraft gas turbine techniques are applied to industrial and marine uses. Employees total 64,000.

In April 1985 Rolls-Royce joined with Turbomeca and MTU in the European Small Engines Co-operation Agreement. This involves the Rolls-Royce Turbomeca RTM 322, MTU-Turbomeca RR-MTR 390, and Turbomeca TM 333. Further details are given under Turbomeca (France) and in the International part of this section. The company is a partner in IAE, EUROJET, Turbo-Union, Rolls-Royce Turbomeca and Williams-Rolls Inc. Through NEI the group designs and builds heavy capital plant and equipment.

In 1990, BMW Rolls-Royce was formed, which see in International part of this section.

ROLLS-ROYCE TURBOMECA ADOUR

See the International part of this section.

TURBO-UNION RB199

See the International part of this section.

EUROJET EJ 200

See the International part of this section.

IAE V2500

See the International part of this section.

ROLLS-ROYCE RB211

The designation RB211 applies to a family of three-shaft turbofans of high bypass ratio and high pressure ratio, with thrusts from 166 kN (37,400 lb) to 355.2 kN (80,000 lb). The engine was selected by Lockheed in March 1968 to power the L-1011 TriStar, and later by Boeing as an alternative option on the 747 and 767.

For all announced applications Rolls-Royce retains responsibility for the complete propulsion system, comprising the engine, fan airflow reverser, pod cowlings and related systems, and noise attenuation for the intake, fan cowl and turbine exhaust duct. The engine is built up of seven modules, each changed easily.

The **RB211-22B**, fitted to the L-1011-1 and -100 TriStar, is flat rated at 187 kN (42,000 lb st) to 28.9°C. Certificated in February 1973 by the CAA and in April 1973 by the FAA. Production ceased in 1982 when over 670 engines had been delivered. By 1990 engine flight hours in service exceeded 18 million.

The **RB211-524** series of engines was developed from the RB211-22B and covers a range of thrusts from 222 kN (50,000 lb) to 355.2 kN (80,000 lb). The -524 entered airline service in 1977 with the L-1011 and 747. By the beginning of 1990 more than 800 engines had been delivered, and service experience of nearly 15 million hours achieved.

The **RB211-524B**, which powers the L-1011-200, L-1011-500 and 747, is certificated at 222 kN (50,000 lb) to 28.9°C. Further developments at the same thrust but offering better fuel consumption include the **RB211-524B3**, giving a 3.5 per cent improvement over the -524B, and which entered service in May 1980; and the **RB211-524B4**, which offers up to 4.8 per cent better sfc than the 524B and entered service in February 1981. Further savings are obtained from the **524B4 Improved** and the **524B4-B**, which incorporate additional sfc and component life improvements. These engines can be installed new or by modifying existing engines in the L-1011-250.

The **RB211-524C** offers increased thrust ratings for the 747. It entered service in April 1980 with a rating of 229 kN (51,500 lb).

The **RB211-524D4** is an improved engine rated at 236 kN (53,000 lb) for the 747, and offering a 4.8 per cent better fuel consumption relative to the -524B. Certification was followed by entry into service in November 1981.

The **RB211-524D4 Upgrade** offers 2.6 per cent lower sfc than the D4 and is rated at 236 kN (53,000 lb) for the 747. This engine entered service in 1984. Variants entering service from 1987 increased the sfc improvements to around 5 per cent.

The **RB211-524G** incorporates advanced features proven on the 535E4, such as the wide-chord fan, 3-D aerodynamics, directionally solidified HP and IP turbine blades and integrated mixer nozzle. Another new feature is a full-authority digital control system. It is rated at 258 kN (58,000 lb st), with sfc 8.8 per cent lower than the D4, and was certificated in early 1988 for the 747-400, entering service in June 1989.

The **RB211-524H**, rated at 270 kN (60,600 lb st) entered service with the Boeing 767 in February 1990, and is mechanically identical to the 524G.

A higher thrust variant, the **RB211-524L**, is described separately as the Rolls-Royce Trent.

The following description relates to the RB211-524G:
TYPE: Three-shaft axial turbofan. Overall pressure ratio 33.
FAN: Single-stage overhung, driven by LP turbine. Composite nosecone, 24 hollow wide-chord blades in titanium alloy, supercritical outlet guide vanes. Aluminium casing, with Armco containment ring. Mass flow 728 kg (1,604 lb)/s. Bypass ratio 4.3.
IP COMPRESSOR: Seven-stage, driven by IP turbine. Two drums, one of titanium discs welded together and the other of welded steel discs, bolted to form one rotor, carrying titanium blades. Aluminium and steel casings carry steel stator blades. Single-stage titanium variable inlet guide vanes.
HP COMPRESSOR: Six-stage, driven by HP turbine. Welded titanium discs, single steel disc and welded nickel alloy discs bolted together carrying titanium, steel and nickel alloy blades. Steel casing carries steel and Nimonic stator blades.
COMBUSTION CHAMBER: Fully annular, with steel outer casings and nickel alloy combustor. Downstream fuel injection by 18 airspray burners with annular atomisers. High energy igniter plugs in Nos 8 and 12 burners.
HP TURBINE: Single-stage, with directionally solidified nickel alloy rotor blades, both convection and film cooled, mounted in nickel alloy disc by fir tree roots.
IP TURBINE: Single-stage, with directionally solidified nickel alloy rotor blades fir tree mounted in nickel alloy disc.
LP TURBINE: Three-stage, with nickel alloy rotor blades fir tree mounted in steel discs.
EXHAUST NOZZLE: Integrated nozzle with deep-chute forced mixer.
ACCESSORY DRIVES: Radial drive from HP shaft to gearbox on fan casing. Accessories include integrated drive generator and aircraft hydraulic pumps.
LUBRICATION SYSTEM: Continuous circulation dry sump system supplying oil to four bearing chambers with a combination of ball and roller bearings. 27 litre (57.6 US pint; 48 Imp pint) oil tank integral with gearbox.
DIMENSIONS:
Length overall:
RB211-22B, -524C2   3,033 mm (119.4 in)
RB211-524B4, -524D4   3,106 mm (122.3 in)
RB211-524G, -524H   3,175 mm (125.0 in)
Fan diameter:
RB211-22B, -524C2   2,154 mm (84.8 in)
RB211-524B4, -524D4   2,180 mm (85.8 in)
RB211-524G, -524H   2,192 mm (86.3 in)
WEIGHT, DRY:
RB211-22B   4,171 kg (9,195 lb)
RB211-524B4, B4 Improved   4,452 kg (9,814 lb)
RB211-524C2   4,472 kg (9,859 lb)
RB211-524D4, D4 Upgrade, -524G/H   4,479 kg (9,874 lb)
PERFORMANCE RATINGS:
T-O: see model listings
Cruise at 10,670 m (35,000 ft) and Mach 0.85 (uninstalled):
RB211-22B   42.2 kN (9,495 lb)
RB211-524B4, B4 Improved   48.9 kN (11,000 lb)
RB211-524C2   51.1 kN (11,490 lb)
RB211-524D4 (all models)   50.0 kN (11,230 lb)
RB211-524G, -524H   52.1 kN (11,720 lb)
SPECIFIC FUEL CONSUMPTION (cruise):
RB211-22B   17.79 mg/Ns (0.628 lb/h/lb)
RB211-524B4   17.56 mg/Ns (0.620 lb/h/lb)
RB211-524B4 Improved   17.16 mg/Ns (0.606 lb/h/lb)

Rolls-Royce RB211-524G three-shaft turbofan

Longitudinal sections of the Rolls-Royce RB211-524G (upper half) and RB211-524D4 Upgrade (lower)

RB211-524C2   18.21 mg/Ns (0.642 lb/h/lb)
RB211-524D4   17.48 mg/Ns (0.617 lb/h/lb)
RB211-524D4 Upgrade (1987)   16.68 mg/Ns (0.589 lb/h/lb)
RB211-524G, -524H   15.95 mg/Ns (0.563 lb/h/lb)

ROLLS-ROYCE TRENT

Known originally as the RB211-524L, this is the most powerful conventional aircraft engine currently under firm contract in the world. Its detail engineering design began in 1988 to meet the propulsion needs of wide-body aircraft planned for the 1990s, initially including the MD-11 and A330. Although planned as a low-risk derivative engine, the Trent does incorporate a totally new fan of increased diameter, an extra IP stage, a four-stage LP turbine and core mounting. Remarkably, thanks to advanced design techniques and materials, the Trent will be lighter than the smaller RB211-524G. The first engine was due to begin testing in 1990.

The Trent was launched in February 1989 by an order from Air Europe to power the MD-11. For this aircraft the engine will be certificated in 1993 at 300.7 kN (67,500 lb st), although initially the rating will be 289.6 kN (65,000 lb st). In April 1989 Cathay Pacific selected the Trent for its A330s. In this application the engine will be certificated in 1994 at 320.8 kN (72,000 lb st), although the initial rating will be 304.3 kN (68,400 lb st). A rating of 338.6 kN (76,000 lb st) will be established shortly afterwards. Rolls-Royce expects to certificate the Trent at ratings higher than 356.4

kN (80,000 lb st) by the year 2000. In June 1989 TWA picked the Trent to enable its fleet of A330s to carry full payloads (for example) from the US West Coast to Europe, requiring the full 320.8 kN rating.

The following description outlines major differences between the Trent and the RB211-524G/H:
FAN: Single-stage overhung, with 26 wide chord blades of hollow titanium. Blades made by superplastic forming and diffusion bonding to form integral canted spars running from root to tip. Total airflow 870 kg (1,918 lb)/s. Bypass ratio 5.1.
IP COMPRESSOR: Eight stages, to give increased core airflow. Variable inlet guide vanes and first two stator stages.
HP COMPRESSOR: New six-stage design offering greater efficiency, with improved tip clearance control based on V2500 technology. Overall pressure ratio 35.
COMBUSTION CHAMBER: Based on latest technology, optimised for reduced emissions.
HP TURBINE: Fitted with blading of latest three-dimensional design, with DS blades. Complete HP module common with 1992 524G/H.
IP TURBINE: Increased annulus design with single-crystal uncooled blades.
LP TURBINE: New four-stage design with three-dimensional blading.
REVERSER: Hurel Dubois four-door type with Lucas hydraulic actuation, governed by main engine Lucas FADEC.
MOUNTING: Entire engine mounted from the core, for enhanced rigidity, reduced distortion of the fan case and reduced weight.

DIMENSIONS:

Fan diameter	2,477 mm (97.5 in)
Length (flange to flange)	3,917 mm (154.2 in)

WEIGHT, DRY:

Bare engine	4,345 kg (9,580 lb)
Complete pod with reverser and cowls	
	6,163 kg (13,589 lb)

SPECIFIC FUEL CONSUMPTION (estimated):

Cruise	15.38 mg/Ns (0.543 lb/h/lb)

ROLLS-ROYCE 535

The **535C** was launch engine for the Boeing 757. It has an HP module based on the RB211-22B, six-stage IP compressor without variable stator vanes, and a scaled down -524 fan. Fan airflow is 18 per cent lower than that of the -22B, and core airflow 12 per cent lower. The engine runs at moderate temperatures, pressures and velocities, resulting in low noise and outstanding reliability for short-haul operation. The 535C entered service on 1 January 1983. In the seventh year of service the total engine-caused removal rate was 0.099 per 1,000 h.

The **535E4** is an advanced version offering increased thrust, together with about 10 per cent reduction in fuel consumption relative to the 535C. These stem from a new wide chord fan blade without snubbers, together with advanced compressor and turbine blading and an integrated nozzle. CAA certification was achieved in November 1983, at a T-O rating of 178 kN (40,100 lb), and revenue service began in October 1984. The E4 reliability rates are similar to those of its predecessor. In the fifth year of service the total engine-caused removal rate was 0.052 per 1,000 h. The 757 with this engine is the quietest civil aircraft with more than 100 seats. The E4 allowed 757s powered by it to be cleared for extended-range operations (EROPS) in December 1986.

An uprated 535E4 entered service in August 1989. Its T-O rating of 192 kN (43,100 lb) enables the 757 to carry heavier payloads from the most noise-sensitive airfields.

The following description relates to the 535E4:

TYPE: Three-shaft turbofan.

FAN: Single-stage, with only 22 wide chord blades, without snubbers, each of activated diffusion bonded titanium skins on titanium honeycomb core. Fan case of Rohrbond with Kevlar containment. Mass flow 522 kg (1,150 lb)/s. Bypass ratio 4.1 (535C, 4.4).

IP COMPRESSOR: Six stages of controlled diffusion design. No variable vanes.

HP COMPRESSOR: Six stages of end-bend blading, with stage -4, -5 and -6 discs in titanium super alloy. Low expansion casing for improved tip clearance control. Overall engine pressure ratio 28.5 (535C, 21.1).

COMBUSTION CHAMBER: Annular, 18 airspray nozzles, flexible liner mountings, heatshields and thermal barrier coatings.

HP TURBINE: Single-stage. Rotor blades, directionally solidified, cast with HP leading-edge cooling, HP and LP internal air cooling passages both with triple pass system. Nozzle guide vanes with curved stacking, highly cooled and with thermal barrier coating on platforms.

IP TURBINE: Single stage. Cooled NGVs with multi-lean stacking for improved airflow onto high aspect ratio blades.

LP TURBINE: Three stages. All turbine casings double wall and cooled.

JETPIPE: Core and bypass flows mixed in integrated nozzle.

REVERSER: Fan reverser only. Jacks move translating cowl to rear, blocker deals seal fan duct and uncover cascade vanes. Over expansion reduces core thrust.

GEARBOX: Mounted under fan case, driven from HP spool.

DIMENSIONS:

Length: 535C	3,010 mm (118.5 in)
535E4	2,995 mm (117.9 in)
Inlet diameter: 535C	1,877 mm (73.9 in)
535E4	1,892 mm (74.5 in)

WEIGHT, DRY:

535C	3,309 kg (7,294 lb)
535E4	3,295 kg (7,264 lb)

PERFORMANCE RATINGS (note: flexible T-O ratings involving considerable derating are used in operation):

T-O (S/L, ISA): 535C	166.4 kN (37,400 lb st)
535E4	178.4-192 kN (40,100-43,100 lb st)

Max climb (10,670 m; 35,000 ft, Mach 0.80):

535C	40.1 kN (9,023 lb)
535E4	41.4 kN (9,300 lb)

Max cruise (10,670 m; 35,000 ft, Mach 0.80):

535C	37.6 kN (8,453 lb)
535E4	38.7 kN (8,700 lb)

SPECIFIC FUEL CONSUMPTION (cruise, as above):

535C	18.30 mg/Ns (0.646 lb/h/lb)
535E4	17.19 mg/Ns (0.607 lb/h/lb)

Longitudinal section of Rolls-Royce Trent and nacelle

Longitudinal section and cutaway of Rolls-Royce 535E4

ROLLS-ROYCE RB163 CIVIL SPEY
US military designation: F113

Design of the Spey began in September 1959. The first engine ran at the end of December 1960. Civil Speys are the subject of a collaborative production programme between Rolls-Royce and the government of Romania. The **F113-RR-100** is the Mk 511-8 which powers the Gulfstream C-20A C-SAM aircraft.

The following details refer to the Spey Mk 512-14DW, as fitted to the BAe and Rombac One-Eleven Series 500, except where indicated:

TYPE: Two-spool turbofan.

COMPRESSOR: Two spools. Five-stage (four-stage on Mks 505 and 506) low pressure (LP) and 12-stage high pressure (HP). First-stage HP stator vanes variable incidence. Pressure ratio 21.2. Mass flow 94.4 kg (208 lb)/s. Bypass ratio 0.64.

COMBUSTION CHAMBER: Tubo-annular with 10 Nimonic sheet liners. Duplex downstream burners, one per chamber. High energy igniters in chambers 4 and 8.

FUEL SYSTEM: Plessey LP pump feeding through fuel cooled oil cooler and Marston Excelsior fuel heater to LP filter at inlet to Lucas GD pump.

FUEL GRADE: DERD.2482 or 2486.

WATER INJECTION SYSTEM (engines bearing 'W' suffix): Water supplied by Lucas air turbopump to injector passages in fuel spray nozzles.

TURBINES: Two two-stage. First HP aircooled. Nickel alloy blades attached by fir tree roots.

Rolls-Royce 535E4 three-shaft turbofan

REVERSER AND SUPPRESSOR: Normally internal clamshell (Gulfstream II and III target type). Five- or six-chute silencing nozzles available.

ACCESSORY DRIVES: Port gearbox, driven from LP rotor, carries LP governor and LP tacho. Starboard gearbox, driven from HP rotor, carries LP and HP fuel pumps, fuel regulator, main oil pumps, airflow control rpm signal transmitter, starter and HP tacho. Provision in starboard gearbox for aircraft ancillaries.

LUBRICATION SYSTEM: Self-contained continuous circulation. Tank capacity 6.8 litres (14.4 US pints; 12 Imp pints). Normal pressure 2.41-3.45 bars (35-50 lb/sq in).

OIL SPECIFICATION: DERD.2487.

STARTING: Plessey 220 air turbine starter.

DIMENSIONS:

Length, less tailpipe	2,911 mm (114.6 in)
Diameter	942 mm (37.1 in)

WEIGHT, DRY:

	1,168 kg (2,574 lb)

PERFORMANCE RATINGS:

Max T-O	55.8 kN (12,550 lb st)
Max continuous	51.5 kN (11,580 lb st) at 12,450 rpm
Typical cruise rating at 450 knots (834 km/h; 518 mph) at 9,750 m (32,000 ft)	13.7 kN (3,070 lb)

SPECIFIC FUEL CONSUMPTION (cruise as above)

22.7 mg/Ns (0.800 lb/h/lb)

OIL CONSUMPTION:

Max (all Marks)	0.42 litre (0.89 US pint; 0.75 Imp pint)/h

Rolls-Royce Spey Mk 807 two-shaft turbofan

ROLLS-ROYCE RB183

Developed for the Fokker F28, this derivative engine has a similar configuration to the Spey but has a four-stage LP compressor. Pressure ratio 15.4, mass flow 90.27 kg (199 lb)/s and bypass ratio 1. The following versions are in use:

Mk 555-15. Basic model, rated at 43.8 kN (9,850 lb st).
Mk 555-15H. Hot-day version, flat rated at 44.0 kN (9,900 lb st) to 29.7°C. Entered service 1973.
Mk 555-15N. Mk 555-15 with 10-lobe mixer.
Mk 555-15P. More fuel-efficient -15H with 10-lobe mixer. Entered service 1982.

The following data refer to the 555-15P:

DIMENSIONS:

Length	2,553 mm (100.5 in)
Diameter	940 mm (37.0 in)

WEIGHT, DRY:

	1,024 kg (2,257 lb)

PERFORMANCE RATINGS:

T-O: see model listings	
Cruise at 7,620 m (25,000 ft) at 440 knots (815 km/h; 507 mph)	16.59 kN (3,730 lb)

SPECIFIC FUEL CONSUMPTION:

T-O	15.9 mg/Ns (0.560 lb/h/lb st)
Cruise (as above)	22.7 mg/Ns (0.800 lb/h/lb)

ROLLS-ROYCE RB168 SPEY

The RB168 military versions of the Spey are as follows:

Mk 101. Basic engine, but with air offtake for BLC. Fitted to BAe Buccaneer.

Mk 202. Augmented engine for supersonic aircraft, with shaft/disc LP compressor and fully modulated afterburner. Fitted to Phantom FGR.2 (F-4M) and licensed to China. Phantom FG.1 (F-4K) has **Mk 203**.

Mk 250. Fully navalised. Fitted to BAe Nimrod MR.1, R.1 and MR.2.

Mk 807. Mk 101 rotors within RB183 structure, with BLC deleted and fitted with manual emergency fuel control. Produced under licence in Italy with Brazilian participation for AMX aircraft.

A new version was announced in Spring 1989, as a more powerful engine for future use in the AMX. Modular changes include use of discrete elements from the Mk 202, such as the HP compressor. The initial version is as follows:

Mk 807A. Demonstrator engine, with dry rating of 57.8 kN (13,000 lb st), was to fly in an AMX airframe in 1990 and will be available to customers in 1993.

DIMENSIONS:

Length: Mk 101	2,911 mm (114.6 in)
Mk 202	5,204 mm (204.9 in)
Mk 250, 251	2,972 mm (117.0 in)
Mk 807	2,456 mm (96.7 in)
Diameter	825 mm (32.5 in)

WEIGHT, DRY:

Mk 101	1,121 kg (2,471 lb)
Mk 202	1,857 kg (4,093 lb)
Mk 250, 251	1,243 kg (2,740 lb)
Mk 807	1,096 kg (2,417 lb)

PERFORMANCE RATINGS (max T-O):

Mk 101, 807	49.1 kN (11,030 lb st)
Mk 202: dry	54.5 kN (12,250 lb st)
augmented	91.2 kN (20,515 lb st)
Mk 250, 251	53.3 kN (11,995 lb st)

Rolls-Royce Tay two-shaft turbofan

ROLLS-ROYCE TAY

The Tay turbofan is designed around the core and external gearbox of the RB183 Mk 555. The LP system has been tailored to complement this by maintaining core inlet and outlet conditions similar to those of the original engine. The wide-chord fan and three-stage IP compressor are driven by a three-stage LP turbine which uses the latest proven technology. The cold bypass air and hot exhaust are combined in a forced mixer. The bypass duct is carbonfibre composite.

The initial production versions are the **Tay 610** and **620**. The **Tay 650** gives a 9 per cent increase in maximum take-off thrust and a 15 per cent increase in maximum continuous, climb, and cruise thrusts, achieved by a small increase in fan diameter and an advanced HP turbine.

The Tay 610 and 620 engines received certification from the CAA in June 1986, with certification of the Tay 650

Longitudinal section of Rolls-Royce Tay two-shaft turbofan

engine achieved ahead of schedule in June 1988. More than 630 Tays had been ordered in advance of the engine's entry into service in the Spring of 1987. The **Tay 670** was launched in September 1988.

The Tay easily meets all current emission standards, and enables the Fokker 100, Gulfstream IV and re-engined BAe One-Eleven to comply with FAR Pt 36 Stage 3 noise requirements. In May 1990, the Tay 650 was selected to re-engine the 727-100 fleet of up to 80 aircraft of United Parcel Service. All versions are subject to a collaborative agreement with Volvo Flygmotor of Sweden (which see).

Tay 610-8. Selected for Gulfstream IV. Certificated on 26 June 1986. All replaced by **Tay 611** (see data).

Tay 620-15. Selected for Fokker 100. Entered service April 1988.

Tay 650-14. Selected to re-engine BAe One-Eleven.

Tay 650-15. Specified for higher-performance versions of Fokker 100. Entered service October 1989.

Tay 670. Rated at 80 kN (18,000 lb st) for re-engining DC-9, 737-200 and 727.

TYPE: Two-shaft turbofan.

FAN: Single-stage with wide chord blades.

LP COMPRESSOR: New design with three stages on fan shaft.

HP COMPRESSOR: 12-stage axial (RB183 Mk 555).

COMBUSTION CHAMBER: Tubo-annular with 10 flame tubes, each with one burner.

FUEL SYSTEM: As RB183 Mk 555 but with improved fuel control unit.

HP TURBINE: All Mks except 650 and 670, two stages as RB183 Mk 555. Tay 650 and 670, advanced two-stage design.

LP TURBINE: New design with three stages.

MIXER: Forced deep chute type with 12 lobes.

DIMENSIONS:
Length	2,405 mm (94.7 in)
Inlet diameter: Tay 610/620	1,118 mm (44.0 in)
Tay 650	1,138 mm (44.8 in)
Tay 670	1,245 mm (49.0 in)

WEIGHT, DRY:
Tay 610	1,406 kg (3,099 lb)
Tay 650	1,514 kg (3,338 lb)

PERFORMANCE RATING (T-O):
Tay 610-8	55.24 kN (12,420 lb st) to 37°C
Tay 611, 620-15	61.61 kN (13,850 lb st) to 30°C
Tay 650	67.17 kN (15,100 lb st) to 30°C
Tay 670	80.1 kN (18,000 lb st) to 30°C

SPECIFIC FUEL CONSUMPTION (cruise):
Tay 610 and 611 (13,100 m; 43,000 ft, Mach 0.8)	
	20.1 mg/Ns (0.709 lb/h/lb)
Tay 620 and 650 (9,145 m; 30,000 ft, Mach 0.73)	
	19.5 mg/Ns (0.69 lb/h/lb)
Tay 670 (10,669 m; 35,000 ft, Mach 0.76)	
	19.9 mg/Ns (0.704 lb/h/lb)

ROLLS-ROYCE RB550

The RB550 is a projected new turboprop which incorporates the technology of the core of the Rolls-Royce Turbomeca RTM 322 turboshaft mated with reduction gear technology from the latest Rolls-Royce Dart engine. It will enable the company to exploit commercial opportunities in the 60/80-passenger aircraft market.

The RB550 would have greater mass flow than the RTM 322. By adopting an in-line configuration the engine has several advantages over turboprops which have a flexible chin intake duct, including much lighter and simpler mounting, improved airflow, simpler anti-icing and oil cooling, less external drag and reduced noise. For ease of maintenance the engine is intended to be assembled from seven modules.

ROLLS-ROYCE TYNE

The 4,549 ekW (6,100 ehp) Tyne two-shaft turboprop is being produced by a consortium comprising SNECMA and MTU (prime contractors carrying out assembly and test), Rolls-Royce and FN. The Mk 21 engine powers the Atlantique and the Mk 22 the Transall.

ROLLS-ROYCE RB545

Under this designation, project design studies have been carried out with BAe on the unique combined air-breathing and rocket propulsion system for the BAe HOTOL. From take-off to Mach 5 the power plant uses atmospheric oxygen with the hydrogen fuel, rocket operation then following to reach orbit. Rig testing of critical components was carried out as part of a two-year proof of concept study.

ROLLS-ROYCE VIPER

This turbojet remains in production. More than 5,000 are in civil and military operation.

Current versions are as follows:

Viper 11 (Mk 200 Series). Single-shaft seven-stage axial compressor driven by single-stage turbine. Mass flow 20 kg (44 lb)/s. Type tested at 11.12 kN (2,500 lb st) and powers Jindivik Mk 3 drone, Jet Provost T.4 and 5, SOKO Galeb and HJT-16 Kiran Mk I/IA.

A Viper 11 version, the 22-1, was built under licence in Italy by Piaggio for the Aermacchi MB-326 and by Atlas of South Africa and HDHV of Australia.

Viper 500 Series. Development with zero stage on compressor. Major applications include early HS 125 (Mks 521, 522) and PD-808 executive aircraft (Mk 526) and Strikemaster (Mk 535), MB-326 (Mk 540) and Jastreb (Mk 531) training and light combat aircraft. Mk 540 built under licence by Piaggio and Atlas.

Viper 600 Series. Eight-stage compressor driven by two-stage turbine; annular vaporising combustion chamber. Take-off rating 16.7 kN (3,750 lb st) civil and 17.8 kN (4,000 lb st) military. Agreement signed with Fiat (Italy) in July 1969 for technical collaboration (see Fiat).

The civil Viper 601 powers the BAe 125-600; the military 632 is fitted to the G-4 Super Galeb, MB-326K and MB-339. The 632-41 powers the Orao/IAR-93A and IAR-99. The 632 is built under licence in Italy, Romania and Yugoslavia. The 633 has an afterburner of the two-gutter type, with hot streak ignition; rating 22.3 kN (5,000 lb).

The **Viper 680** is the latest variant for the MB-339. It produces up to 10 per cent more thrust than the Viper 632.

The following details apply to the Viper 600 Series:

TYPE: Single-shaft axial turbojet.

COMPRESSOR: Eight-stage. Steel drum type rotor with disc assemblies. Magnesium alloy casing with blow-off valve. Pressure ratio 5.8 : 1. Mass flow 26.5 kg (58.4 lb)/s.

COMBUSTION CHAMBER: Short annular type with 24 vaporising burners and six starting atomisers. Electric ignition.

FUEL SYSTEM: Hydromechanical, with pump, barometric control and air/fuel control.

FUEL GRADE: JP-1 or JP-4.

TURBINE: Two-stage axial. Shrouded blades attached to discs by fir tree roots and locking strips.

ACCESSORY DRIVES: Gearbox driven from front of compressor by bevel gear.

LUBRICATION SYSTEM: Self contained recirculatory system. Military version fully aerobatic.

OIL SPECIFICATION: Mobil Jet 2, Shell ASTO 500 and Castrol 98.

STARTING: 24V starter/generator.

DIMENSIONS:
Length (flange to flange):	
Viper 11	1,626 mm (64.0 in)
Viper 531, 535, 540, 632	1,806 mm (71.1 in)
Max casing diameter:	
all versions	622 mm (24.5 in)

WEIGHT, DRY:
Viper 11	284 kg (625 lb)
Viper 531	345 kg (760 lb)
Viper 535	331 kg (730 lb)
Viper 540	342 kg (755 lb)
Viper 601, 632 and 680	358 kg (790 lb)

PERFORMANCE RATINGS (T-O):
Viper 11	11.12 kN (2,500 lb st)
Viper 531	13.9 kN (3,120 lb st)
Viper 535, 540	14.9 kN (3,360 lb st)
Viper 601	16.7 kN (3,750 lb st)
Viper 632	17.8 kN (4,000 lb st)
Viper 680	19.4 kN (4,360 lb st)

SPECIFIC FUEL CONSUMPTION (T-O):
Viper 11	30.3 mg/Ns (1.07 lb/h/lb st)
Viper 500 series	28.3 mg/Ns (1.00 lb/h/lb st)
Viper 601	26.6 mg/Ns (0.94 lb/h/lb st)
Viper 632	27.5 mg/Ns (0.97 lb/h/lb st)

OIL CONSUMPTION (max):
all versions	0.71 litre (1.5 US pints; 1.25 Imp pints)/h

ROLLS-ROYCE XG40

XG40 is a technology programme which encompasses rig testing, core engine running and two demonstrator engines. Launched in 1983, the programme is centred at Bristol and funded jointly by the company and MoD. Its purpose is to demonstrate the technology required for an advanced fighter engine. It provided a solid background for Rolls-Royce to contribute its share of the collaborative EUROJET EJ200 (which see in International section).

Each XG40 engine module was extensively tested in rig form, and in March 1986 the core engine first ran. The first complete demonstrator engine ran on 23 December 1986, and the second in 1987.

ROLLS-ROYCE PEGASUS
USMC designations: F402

The Pegasus is a turbofan for STOVL applications. It has two main rotating systems which rotate in opposite directions, thus minimising gyroscopic effects. Thrust vectoring is achieved by four rotatable nozzles simultaneously operated and symmetrically positioned on each side of the engine. The total thrust is divided between the four nozzles, and the resultant thrust passes through a fixed point irrespective of nozzle angle, thus minimising aircraft control problems. HP bleed air is used for aircraft stabilisation.

The Pegasus ran in August 1959. The engine entered service in the BAe Harrier in 1969 as the **Pegasus 11 Mk 103**, (US designation **F402-RR-402**). A maritime version, designated **Mk 104**, for the Sea Harrier embodies material changes to the LP and intermediate casings, sacrificial protective coatings on ferrous components, and an increased capacity gearbox.

The **Pegasus 11-21** developed for the McDonnell Douglas/BAe Harrier II has the US designation **F402-RR-406** and UK designation **Mk 105**; it includes improved HP turbine cooling, a new shrouded LP turbine, revised swan-neck intermediate casing and changes to suit the revised airframe. Delivery of Mk 105 engines began in December 1984. Since 1986 production engines for the AV-8B (designated **F402-RR-406A**) and Harrier GR.5 have been fitted with FADEC (full authority digital engine control), replacing the previous hydromechanical system.

To enhance the Harrier II's hot-day vertical landing capability, and to cater for future growth, an uprating programme began in 1983. This programme, designated **XG15**, is funded by the company and MoD. On 22 October 1986 the full-performance demonstrator engine first ran. It has the fan pressure ratio raised from 2.3 to 2.6, a new combustor and improved cooling with single-crystal turbine blades. The engine is running at thrust levels higher than those of the **Pegasus 11-61 (F402-RR-408)**, the version scheduled for production, which provides 105.9 kN (23,800 lb st), together with improved reliability and maintainability, and lower life-cycle costs. The new fan has Dunlop blade root dampers of silicone rubber, Nomex textiles and titanium.

Work is continuing on thrust augmentation by plenum chamber burning (PCB). Testing has demonstrated a thrust increase at the front nozzles of over 100 per cent, equivalent to about 50 per cent overall. High altitude PCB tests have indicated that handling and ignition are compatible with future supersonic V/STOL aircraft. A Pegasus 11 with PCB would have a thrust of 120 kN (27,000 lb st).

For future combat aircraft Rolls-Royce is studying vectored-thrust engines (with and without PCB) together with other advanced V/STOL systems such as a hybrid fan, remote augmented lift and ejector lift. The company is also studying lift fan engines for advanced transports and UAVs.

The following data apply specifically to the Pegasus 11-21 (-406A, Mk 105):

TYPE: Two-shaft vectored thrust turbofan.

FAN: Three-stage, overhung ahead of front bearing. Titanium blades with part-span snubbers. Mass flow 196 kg (432 lb)/s. Pressure ratio 2.3. Bypass ratio 1.4.

HP COMPRESSOR: Eight-stage with titanium rotor blades. Overall pressure ratio 14.

COMBUSTION SYSTEM: Annular, with LP vaporising burners.

FUEL SYSTEM: DSIC duplicated digital electronic control with emergency manual backup.

TURBINES: Two-stage HP with cooled blades and two-stage LP.

THRUST NOZZLES: Two steel zero-scarf cold nozzles and two Nimonic hot nozzles, actuated by duplicated air motors through shafts and chains under pilot command.

LUBRICATION SYSTEM: Self contained, with fuel cooled oil cooler.

Cutaway drawing of Rolls-Royce Viper 632 single-shaft turbojet

Rolls-Royce Pegasus 11-61 (F402-RR-408) vectored-thrust turbofan

STARTING: Gas turbine starter/APU on intermediate casing.
DIMENSIONS:

Length, without nozzles	2,510 mm (98.83 in)
Length, with nozzles	3,485 mm (137.2 in)
Diameter, fan casing	1,220 mm (48.05 in)

WEIGHT, DRY (without nozzles):

Mk 103	1,412 kg (3,113 lb)
Mk 104	1,442 kg (3,179 lb)
Mk 105	1,470 kg (3,240 lb)

PERFORMANCE RATINGS (ISA, S/L static):
Max lift thrust:

Mks 103, 104	95.64 kN (21,500 lb st)
All 11-21 versions	97.86 kN (22,000 lb st)

ROLLS-ROYCE TURBOMECA RTM 322
See the International part of this section.

MTU TURBOMECA RR-MTR 390
See the International part of this section.

ROLLS-ROYCE GEM
The Gem was developed at Leavesden, for the Westland Lynx helicopter. Subsequent applications are the Westland 30 and advanced Lynx versions, and Agusta A 129. The Gem 41 and 60 have been civil certificated.

Choice of a two-spool gas generator gives fast response to power demand without the need for a complex control system. There are seven major modules, each assembled, tested and released as an interchangeable unit.

Provision is made for in-flight and on-ground condition monitoring systems. Features include access ports for intrascope inspection of each LP compressor stage, HP compressor, combustor, LP turbine and power turbine, and mountings for vibration pickups.

The following versions have been announced:
Gem Mk 1001. Engine change unit for Lynx of British services and French Navy. Rated at 671 kW (900 shp).
Gem 2. Export military, rated at 671 kW (900 shp).

RR 1004. For Agusta A 129. Direct drive in place of reduction gearbox and electronic instead of hydromechanical control. Production under licence by Piaggio.
Gem 41 series. Modified compressor to increase mass flow by about 10 per cent plus small increase in TET.
Gem 42 series. Same ratings as Gem 41, but improved reliability and power retention.
Gem Mk 510. Civil Gem 41 for Westland 30.

Gem 60 series. Further increase in mass flow of approximately 26 per cent over Gem 41, derived from LP compressor incorporating new blades; TET also increased.
Gem Mk 531. Civil Gem 60 for Westland 30.
The following description relates to the Gem Mk 1001:
TYPE: Free turbine turboshaft.
SHAFT DRIVE: Single-stage double-helical reduction gear with rotating planet cage carried by ball bearing at front and roller bearing at rear. Alternative of direct drive output at 27,000 rpm or gearbox giving governed output speed of 6,000 rpm.
LP COMPRESSOR: Four-stage axial.
HP COMPRESSOR: Single-stage centrifugal, alternate inducer and radial vanes. Overall pressure ratio 12.0.
COMBUSTION CHAMBER: Annular reverse flow with air atomiser fuel sprays. High energy ignition.
HP TURBINE: Single-stage close-coupled to HP impeller.
LP TURBINE: Single-stage with shrouded blades.
POWER TURBINE: Two-stage axial with shrouded blades.
ACCESSORY DRIVES: Bevel gear on front of HP shaft drives starter/generator, fuel pump, oil cooler fan and other accessories.
FUEL SYSTEM: Plessey fluidics automatic control, and power matching for multi-engine installation. Hamilton Standard electronic control fitted to RR 1004 and Gem 60.
LUBRICATION SYSTEM: Engine mounted oil tank and cooler. Magnetic chip detectors. Oil filter in accessory wheelcase.
DIMENSIONS:

Length overall	1,099 mm (43.2 in)
Width overall	575 mm (22.6 in)
Height overall	596 mm (23.5 in)

WEIGHT, DRY:

Gem 1001, 2	178 kg (393 lb)
Gem 41, 42	183 kg (404 lb)
RR 1004	163 kg (360 lb)
Gem 60	185 kg (407 lb)

PERFORMANCE RATINGS: see table
SPECIFIC FUEL CONSUMPTION:
50 per cent max T-O:

Except Gem 60	110 µg/J (0.65 lb/h/shp)
Gem 60	103 µg/J (0.61 lb/h/shp)

ROLLS-ROYCE GNOME
Gnome is the name given to the General Electric T58 turboshaft which Rolls-Royce manufactures. More than 2,300 have been delivered in the following versions:

Cutaway drawing of Rolls-Royce Gem 60 free turbine turboshaft

GEM ENGINE RATINGS, kW (shp) ISA S/L STATIC

Designation	Date In Service	One Engine Inoperative				Normal Twin Operation		
		Emergency (20 s)	Max Contingency (2½ min)	Intermediate Contingency (60 min)	Max (T-O) (30 min)	Max (T-O) (5 min)	Max Continuous	
Gem 2, Mk 1001	1976	N/A	671 (900)	619 (830)	N/A	619 (830)	559 (750)	
RR 1004	1990	759 (1,018)	704 (944)	657 (881)	657 (881)	N/A	615 (825)	
Gem 41-1, Mk 1014	1978	N/A	835 (1,120)	790.5 (1,060)	N/A	746 (1,000)	664 (890)	
Gem 42, Mk 1017	1987	N/A	835 (1,120)	790.5 (1,060)	N/A	746 (1,000)	664 (890)	
Gem 60-3/1 Mk 530	1983	N/A	897 (1,203)	844 (1,132)	N/A	844 (1,132)	821.75 (1,102)	
Gem 60-3/3 Mk 531	1983	N/A	897 (1,203)	844 (1,132)	N/A	821.75 (1,102)	821.75 (1,102)	

N/A: Not applicable

H.1000. Initial version, rated at 783 kW (1,050 shp) for Whirlwind and Agusta-Bell 204B.

H.1200. Rated at 932 kW (1,250 shp). Used in Agusta-Bell 204B, Boeing 107 and some Kawasaki KV107-II-5s. Coupled version for Wessex comprises two H.1200s driving through a coupling gearbox.

H.1400. Rated at 1,044 kW (1,400 shp). Based on the H.1200, with modified compressor to increase airflow.

H.1400-1. Rated at 1,145 kW (1,535 shp). Increased gas generator speed and improved gas generator turbine blades. In production for Sea King and Commando.

H.1400-1T. Tropical model; turbine nozzle adjusted for better high ambient performance.

The following description refers to the H.1400-1:

TYPE: Free turbine turboshaft.

COMPRESSOR: Ten-stage axial. Variable inlet guide vanes and first three stator rows. Mass flow 6.26 kg (13.8 lb)/s.

COMBUSTION CHAMBER: Annular with 16 Simplex injectors, eight on each of two sets of manifolds. One Lodge high energy igniter.

FUEL SYSTEM: Lucas hydromechanical controlled by BAe computer.

FUEL GRADE: DERD.2452, 2453, 2454, 2486, 2494 and 2498 (NATO F44, F34, F40, F35 and F43).

GAS-PRODUCER TURBINE: Two-stage.

POWER TURBINE: Single-stage free turbine.

REDUCTION GEAR: Optional double helical gear providing reduction from nominal 19,500 rpm power turbine speed to 6,600 rpm at left or right output shaft.

ACCESSORY DRIVES: Fuel and lubrication systems mounted beneath compressor casing. Power take-off shaft up to 100 shp.

LUBRICATION: Scavenged gear pumps. Serck oil cooler.

STARTING: Rotax electric starter in nose bullet.

Cutaway drawing of Rolls-Royce Gnome H.1400-1 free turbine turboshaft

DIMENSIONS:	
Length: H.1400-1	1,392 mm (54.8 in)
Max height: H.1400-1	549 mm (21.6 in)
Max width: H.1400-1 (ungeared)	577 mm (22.7 in)
WEIGHT, DRY:	
H.1400-1 (ungeared)	148 kg (326 lb)
Reduction gearbox	52.6 kg (116 lb)
PERFORMANCE RATINGS (at power turbine shaft):	
Max contingency (2½ min; multi-engine aircraft only):	
H.1400-1	1,238 kW (1,660 shp)
H.1400-1T	1,092 kW (1,465 shp) to 45°C

Max one-hour (single engine):	
H.1400-1	1,145 kW (1,535 shp)
H.1400-1T	1,030 kW (1,380 shp) to 45°C
Max continuous:	
H.1400-1	932 kW (1,250 shp)
H.1400-1T	783 kW (1,050 shp) to 45°C
SPECIFIC FUEL CONSUMPTION:	
At max contingency rating:	
H.1400-1	102.75 μg/J (0.608 lb/h/shp)
H.1400-1T (30°C)	105.8 μg/J (0.626 lb/h/shp)

UNITED STATES OF AMERICA

AEROJET

AEROJET-GENERAL
(Subsidiary of GenCorp Inc)
10300 N Torrey Pines Road, La Jolla, California 92037
Telephone: 1 (619) 455 8500
PRESIDENT: R. I. Ramseier
VICE-PRESIDENT, PUBLIC AFFAIRS: Tom Sprague

Aerojet is a major aerospace and defence contractor with expertise in solid and liquid rocket propulsion, electronics and ordnance.

AEROJET TECHSYSTEMS CO
Sacramento, California: Development and manufacture of all liquid fuel engines for the US Air Force's Titan family of vehicles; second stage propulsion for the Japanese Space Agency (NASDA) N-II launch vehicles; and Orbiter Manoeuvring System (OMS) engines for the Space Shuttle.

AEROJET SPACE SHUTTLE OMS ENGINE
The Space Shuttle Orbiter has two Orbiter Manoeuvring System (OMS) engines, in pods each side of the vertical stabiliser (fin). They provide thrust for orbit insertion, circularisation and plane change, rendezvous and de-orbit manoeuvres. The propellants are monomethylhydrazine (MMH) and nitrogen tetroxide. At launch the basic system carries 4,087 kg (9,010 lb) of usable MMH and 6,743 kg (14,866 lb) of usable oxidiser. Fully qualified OMS engines have flown on all Shuttle missions to date. The following are chief characteristics.

THRUST (in vacuo):	26.7 kN (6,000 lb)
CHAMBER PRESSURE (in vacuo):	8.62 bars (125 lb/sq in)
SPECIFIC IMPULSE:	316 s
MIXTURE RATIO:	1.65 : 1
NOZZLE AREA RATIO (flight):	55 : 1
WEIGHT, DRY:	118 kg (260 lb)
THRUST VECTOR LIMITS:	±7°
STORAGE LIFE:	10 years
FIRING LIFE (100 missions):	15 h
NUMBER OF STARTS:	500
LONGEST SINGLE FIRING:	1,250 s

Aerojet Space Shuttle OMS rocket engine

ALLISON

ALLISON GAS TURBINE DIVISION, GENERAL MOTORS CORPORATION
Indianapolis, Indiana 46206-0420
Telephone: 1 (317) 230 2000
GENERAL MANAGER: Dr F. Blake Wallace

Allison Gas Turbine Division has 7,500 employees producing gas turbine engines and components for aircraft, vehicular and industrial/marine applications.

Collaboration on the T800 engine with Garrett is described under LHTEC on a later page. Collaboration with MTU is reported under the International heading.

ALLISON MODEL 250
US military designations: T63 and T703
The Model 250 is a small turboshaft/turboprop. Deliveries exceed 23,000, logging over 66 million hours.

A development contract for the T63 military version was received by Allison in June 1958. Details of early versions last appeared in the 1978-79 *Jane's*; the following are current models:

T63-A-720. Military turboshaft engine with hot-end improvements, increasing T-O rating to 313 kW (420 shp), for the Bell OH-58C.

T703-A-700. Military turboshaft engine corresponding to 250-C30R, for Bell OH-58D.

250-B17. Uprated version of B15 turboprop. The B17B operates at 17°C higher turbine gas temperature with hot-end improvements which maintain full power at high ambient temperatures. Produced from 1974 for Turbostar 402 conversions, Turbostar 414, ASTA Nomad N22 and 24, SIAI-Marchetti SM.1019E and various agricultural aircraft. B17C introduced improved gearbox allowing use of 313 kW (420 shp) on T-O. Produced for Nomad N22 and 24, SF.260TP and 600TP, Turbostar 402/414, Allison Bonanza, Bobby Aerostar, Par Turbine Aerostar, LoPresti Piper/Globe/Temco Swift, ASI Jet Cruzer, Glasair III, Advanced Airship, BN-2T Turbine Islander, Composite Eagle, P.68TP Viator. B17D produced for SF.260TP, Aucán, Redigo, KM-2 Fuji T-5, HTT-34, Mentor 420 and SA.32T. B17F, with new compressor as in -C20R for increased T-O power, introduced in 1985 for BN-2T, SM600TP, HX-1, Redigo and Turbine P-210, and intended for production ASI Jet Cruzer.

250-C20B. Introduced 1974, and rated at 313 kW (420 shp). For Bell and Agusta-Bell 206B JetRanger III and 206L LongRanger, MD 500D and E, Kitty Hawk, FH-1100 and UH-12E, Ka-226, RFB Fantrainer 400 and Bell 47G conversions.

250-C20F. For AS 355 Ecureuil 2/Twinstar.

250-C20J. For Bell and Agusta-Bell 206B JetRanger III.

250-C20R. Derivative of C20B with new axial-centrifugal compressor. C20R/1 with redundant overspeed system for twin-engine applications certificated September 1986 for A 109A Mk II and BO 108. C20R/2 for single-engine helicopters certificated early 1987 for MD 500ER, JetRanger III and LongRanger, and selected for MD 520N.

250-C20S. Turboprop for Soloy Turbine Pac conversions of Cessna 185, 206 and 207. Powers prototype ASI Jet Cruzer.

250-C28. Major redesign with single centrifugal compressor only, with increased airflow. Reduced noise and emissions, and minimal infra-red signature. New main gearbox. Certificated December 1977.

Allison Model 250-B17C free-turbine turboprop

Allison Model 250-C20R free turbine turboshaft

250-C28B. With particle separator; 2½-min rating of 410 kW (550 shp). Powers Bell LongRanger I.

250-C28C. Improved model with plain inlet; 2½-min rating of 410 kW (550 shp). Powers MBB BO 105 LS.

250-C30. Advanced single-stage compressor and dual ignition. Initial rating 485 kW (650 shp), with a 2½ min rating of 522 kW (700 shp). Certification completed March 1978. Produced for S-76 and MD 530G.

250-C30G. Produced for Heli-Air Bell 222.

250-C30L. With digital control, produced for Bell 406CS.

250-C30M. Produced for AS 350.

250-C30P. Produced for LongRanger III.

250-C30R. With digital control, produced for AHIP OH-58D.

250-C30S. Produced for S-76.

TYPE: Light turboshaft or turboprop.

COMPRESSOR: C20, C20B and B17B have six axial stages and one centrifugal. B17F and C20R have four axial stages and one centrifugal. Other models have single-stage centrifugal compressor only. Pressure ratio: C20B, B17, 7.2; C28B/C, C30, 8.4. Mass flow: C20B, B17C, 1.56 kg (3.45 lb)/s; C28B/C, 2.02 kg (4.45 lb)/s; C30, 2.54 kg (5.6 lb)/s.

COMBUSTION CHAMBER: Single can type at rear. Single duplex fuel nozzle in rear face. One igniter on C20B, B17C, C28B/C and C30L/M/P/R. Dual igniters on C30 and C30S; optional on C28B/C.

TURBINES: Two-stage gas producer turbine and two-stage free power turbine. Integrally cast rotor blades and wheels.

CONTROL SYSTEM: Pneumatic-mechanical system (B17C, hydromechanical; C20B, C28, C30/30M P/S, pneumatic-mechanical; C30L, C30R, supervisory electronic).

FUEL: Primary fuels are ASTM-A or A-1 and MIL-T-5624, JP-4, JP-5 and diesel fuel.

LUBRICATION: Dry sump.

OIL SPECIFICATION: MIL-L-7808 and MIL-L-23699.

DIMENSIONS:

Length: B17C	1,143 mm (45.0 in)
C20B, R	985 mm (38.8 in)
C28C	1,201 mm (47.3 in)
C30	1,041 mm (41.0 in)
Width: B17C, C20B	483 mm (19.0 in)
C28, C30	557 mm (21.94 in)
Height: B17C	572 mm (22.5 in)
C20B	589 mm (23.2 in)
C28, C30	638 mm (25.13 in)

WEIGHT, DRY:

B17C	88.4 kg (195 lb)
C20B	71.5 kg (158 lb)
C20R	76.0 kg (168 lb)
C28	99.3 kg (219 lb)
C28B, C	104 kg (230 lb)
C30	109.3 kg (240 lb)

PERFORMANCE RATINGS (S/L, ISA):

T-O:

B17C, C20B, C20J, C20S (5 min)	313 kW (420 shp)
B17F, C20R (5 min, to 26.7°C)	335 kW (450 shp)
C20F	317 kW (425 shp)
C28, 28B, 28C (30 min)	373 kW (500 shp)
C30 (5 min)	485 kW (650 shp)
Max continuous: B17C (cruise)	275 kW (369 shp)
C20B	276 kW (370 shp)
C20R	283 kW (380 shp)
C28	368 kW (494 shp)
C30	415 kW (557 shp)
Cruise B (75 per cent): B17C	206 kW (277 shp)
C20B	207 kW (278 shp)
C20R	236 kW (317 shp)
C28	274 kW (367 shp)
C30	312 kW (418 shp)

SPECIFIC FUEL CONSUMPTION:

At T-O rating: B17C	111 µg/J (0.657 lb/h/shp)
C20B	110 µg/J (0.650 lb/h/shp)
C20R	103 µg/J (0.608 lb/h/shp)
C28	102.5 µg/J (0.606 lb/h/shp)
C30	100 µg/J (0.592 lb/h/shp)

At cruise B rating: B17C	120.8 µg/J (0.715 lb/h/shp)
C20B	120 µg/J (0.709 lb/h/shp)
C20R	112.5 µg/J (0.666 lb/h/shp)
C28	112 µg/J (0.664 lb/h/shp)
C30	111 µg/J (0.657 lb/h/shp)

ALLISON T56 and MODEL 501

US military designation: T56

Current versions of the T56 are as follows:

T56-A-14. Rated at 3,661 ekW (4,910 ehp). Generally similar to T56-A-15, but seven-point suspension and detail changes. Powers the P-3B and C Orion.

T56-A-15. Rated at 3,661 ekW (4,910 ehp). Introduced aircooled turbine blades. Powers current C-130.

T56-A-423 and **A-16.** Rated at 3,661 ekW (4,910 ehp). Powers US Navy versions of the C-130.

T56-A-425. Rated at 3,661 ekW (4,910 ehp). Powers E-2C Hawkeye and C-2A Greyhound.

T56-A-427. Rated at 3,915 kW (5,250 shp), this engine provides increase in power and 13 per cent improvement in specific fuel consumption compared with the T56-A-425. It features a digital electronic supervisory control and a modified propeller drive to maintain the 1,106 rpm output with 14,239 power section rpm.

Model 501-D22A. Rated at 3,490 ekW (4,680 ehp). Commercial version of T56-A-15. Powers Lockheed L-100.

Model 501-D39. Commercial derivative of T56-A-427 with modified propeller drive to provide 1,020 rpm output with 14,239 power section rpm.

Model 501-M78. Turboprop version of YT701 incorporating modified T56-A-14 gearbox for NASA-sponsored propfan flight testing at Mach numbers to 0.8. One M78, driving a single-rotation tractor propfan, is mounted on the port wing of a Gulfstream II.

Including the Model 501 commercial engines, production of these engines reached 14,620 by 1 January 1990.

The following details apply to the T56-A-15:

TYPE: Axial-flow turboprop.

PROPELLER DRIVE: Combination spur/planetary gear type. Overall gear ratio 13.54. Power section rpm 13,820. Weight of gearbox approximately 249 kg (550 lb) with pads on rear face for accessory mounting.

COMPRESSOR: Fourteen-stage axial flow. Pressure ratio 9.5. Mass flow 14.70 kg (32.4 lb)/s. Constant speed 13,820 rpm.

COMBUSTION CHAMBER: Six stainless steel can-annular type perforated combustion liners within one-piece stainless steel outer casing. Two ignitors in diametrically opposite combustors.

FUEL SYSTEM: High pressure type. Bendix control system. Water/alcohol augmentation system available.

FUEL GRADE: MIL-J-5624, JP-4 or JP-5.

TURBINE: Four-stage. Rotor assembly consists of four stainless steel discs, with first stage having hollow aircooled blades, secured by fir tree roots. Gas temperature before turbine 1,076°C.

ACCESSORY DRIVES: Accessory pads on rear face of reduction gear housing at front end of engine.

LUBRICATION SYSTEM: Low pressure. Dry sump. Pesco dual-element oil pump. Normal oil supply pressure 3.8 bars (55 lb/sq in).

OIL SPECIFICATION: MIL-L-7808.

MOUNTING: Three-point suspension.

STARTING: Air turbine, gearbox mounted.

DIMENSIONS:

Length (all current versions)	3,708 mm (146 in)
Width (all current versions)	686 mm (27 in)
Height: A-15, A-16, A-425, D-22A	991 mm (39 in)
A-14	1,118 mm (44 in)

WEIGHT, DRY:

A-14	855 kg (1,885 lb)
A-15	828 kg (1,825 lb)
A-16	835 kg (1,841 lb)
A-425	860 kg (1,895 lb)
D22A	832 kg (1,834 lb)

PERFORMANCE RATINGS (S/L, ISA, static):

T-O: A-14, A-15, A-16, A-425	
	3,661 ekW; 3,424 kW (4,910 ehp; 4,591 shp)
501-D22A	3,490 ekW (4,680 ehp)
Normal: A-14, A-15, A-16, A-425, D22A	
	3,255 ekW; 3,028 kW (4,365 ehp; 4,061 shp)

SPECIFIC FUEL CONSUMPTION:

At max rating:	
A-14, A-15, D22A	84.67 µg/J (0.501 lb/h/ehp)
At normal rating:	
A-14, A-15	87.4 µg/J (0.517 lb/h/ehp)

OIL CONSUMPTION:

A-14, A-15	1.3 litres (0.35 US gallon; 0.29 Imp gallon)/h

ALLISON GMA 2100

US military designation: T406-AD-400

The GMA (General Motors Allison) 2100 designation covers a family of shaft, fan, propeller and jet engines covering a wide range of powers. All rest on 140 million T56 hours built into the core. The first application is as a shaft engine, the T406.

The T406-AD-400 is a free-turbine, front drive 4,588 kW (6,150 shp) turboshaft incorporating high efficiency components and reduced maintenance features required for operation in the V-22 Osprey. It features six rows of variable compressor stators, dual full-authority digital electronic fuel controls, self-contained oil system capable of engine operation in the vertical position and modular construction. The T406 has completed its flight rating tests and is being utilised in the V-22 flight test programme. Full production is scheduled for 1992.

The T406 provides a basis for turboprop, propfan and turbofan applications up to 9,694 kW (13,000 shp) and 53.38 kN (12,000 lb st), when mated with appropriate LP components. Aircraft applications currently under study include high speed turboprop and turbofan commuters, commercial tilt-rotors and regional airliners.

Allison T56-A-427 single-shaft turboprop

The first GMA 2100 turboprop went on test in June 1988, and a month later Dowty exhibited a GMA 2100 six-blade propeller. This engine is scheduled to be qualified for production in 1991, and is expected to cover the range 2,984-5,968 kW (4,000-8,000 shp). It has a completely new gearbox which saves 68 kg (150 lb) weight and has a life of 30,000 hours. Accessories are grouped on the rear face. In July 1989 this engine was selected at a rating of 3,394 kW (4,550 shp) to power the Saab 2000. The complete propulsion system began testing in December 1989 and soon demonstrated 4,550 kW (6,100 shp) under FADEC control.

The following details apply to the T406-AD-400:

TYPE: Axial flow turboshaft.

COMPRESSOR: Fourteen-stage axial flow, with variable inlet guide vanes and first five stator rows. Pressure ratio 14. Mass flow 16.1 kg (35.5 lb)/s.

COMBUSTOR: Annular convection film cooled, with 16 air-blast-type fuel nozzles providing smoke-free operation. Dual capacitor discharge ignition.

CONTROL SYSTEM: Full-authority digital, with analog backup.

FUEL GRADE: MIL-T-5624; grades JP-4, JP-5 and MIL-T-83188; JP-8.

TURBINE: Gas generator turbine has two axial stages with aircooled single-crystal blading; both stages overhung to the rear of the gas generator thrust bearing. Power turbine has two axial stages on a straddle-mounted shaft which runs the entire length of the engine. Film-damped bearings eliminate the need for a centre bearing.

OUTPUT: Power turbine forward shaft drives a torquemeter assembly which is directly coupled to the V-22 rotor gearbox. The torque tube housing serves as the main engine mount.

ACCESSORY DRIVES: An engine accessory gearcase is mounted beneath the air inlet housing. It provides for engine starter, generator, oil pump and fuel pump metering unit drives.

LUBRICATION SYSTEM: Self contained, featuring positive scavenging sumps, 3-micron filtration, quantitative

Allison T406-AD-400 free-turbine turboshaft

debris monitor and a bottom-mounted, all-attitude oil reservoir with service scuppers on each side of the engine.

OIL GRADE: MIL-L-7808 or MIL-L-23699.

DIMENSIONS:
Length overall, without gearbox	1,958 mm (77.08 in)
Length from inlet flange	1,521 mm (59.88 in)
Width	671 mm (26.40 in)
Height	864 mm (34.00 in)

WEIGHT, DRY: 440.4 kg (971 lb)

PERFORMANCE RATINGS:
Max power (S/L)   4,586 kW (6,150 shp) to 43°C
Max cont power (static 1,219 m; 4,000 ft)
                     4,391 kW (5,888 shp) to 25°C

SPECIFIC FUEL CONSUMPTION:
Max cont power   71.0 μg/J (0.42 lb/h/shp)

ALLISON GMA 3000

This designation covers a range of proposed turbofan derivatives of the T406, using the same HP core. The Rolls-Royce RB580, described in the 1989-90 *Jane's*, is not now going ahead. The first member of this family to find an application is the **GMA 3007**, announced in April 1990 as the engine selected for the Embraer EMB-145. A turbofan in the 31.14 kN (7,000 lb st) class, the 3007 will have a single-stage fan with wide-chord blades, single-crystal HP turbine blades and FADEC control. A prototype engine is to run in 1991.

ALLISON MODEL 578

This is described later under the entry for PW-Allison Engines.

ALTURDYNE

ALTURDYNE

8050 Armour Street, San Diego, California 92111
Telephone: 1 (619) 565 2131
Telex: (910) 335-2000
Fax: 1 (619) 279 4296
PRESIDENT: Frank Verbeke

This company has developed small gas turbines for UAVs and very light aircraft. It was formed in 1970 and employs 100 people.

At present it purchases the basic gas generator and incorporates this into a complete engine for various purposes. The two main products are of 112 kW (150 hp) and 157 kW (210 hp). These are based upon the Solar T62

Titan single-shaft gas turbine (last described in the 1975-76 *Jane's*). A company funded lightweight rotary combustion aircraft engine is under development in two sizes up to 186.5 kW (250 hp). The first engines were tested in December 1984. Tests are being conducted with a reduction gearbox and using diesel fuel.

AMI

AEROMOTION INC

1224 S Park Ave, Oshkosh, Wisconsin 54901
Telephone: 1 (414) 233 0773

This company has produced a light two-cylinder opposed piston engine tailored to light aircraft. It uses some off the shelf automotive parts. The first AeroMotion Twin ran in April 1982 and has shown high reliability since then. Pre-production engines flew in a Heath Parasol in March 1984 and in a Ken Brock autogyro a month later.

AEROMOTION TWIN

TYPE: Two-cylinder opposed four-stroke aircooled piston engine.

CYLINDERS: Bore 104.8 mm (4.125 in). Stroke 95.25 mm (3.75 in). Capacity 1,650 cc (100 cu in).

IGNITION: Twin Slick magnetos, dual plugs.

DIMENSIONS:
Length	451 mm (17.75 in)
Width	787 mm (31.0 in)
Height	470 mm (18.5 in)

WEIGHT, DRY (equipped): 45 kg (100 lb)

PERFORMANCE RATING (S/L):
                     37-39.5 kW (50-53 hp) at 3,100 rpm

AeroMotion Twin two-cylinder piston engine

CFE

CFE COMPANY

111 South 34th Street, PO Box 5274, Phoenix, Arizona 85010
Telephone: 1 (602) 231 3285
Fax: 1 (602) 231 7722

This company was formed jointly by Garrett Engine Division and General Electric in June 1987. It is managing all phases of the development, manufacture, marketing and support of the CFE738 turbofan.

CFE738

This turbofan is being developed to power regional airliners and large business jet aircraft. The CFE738 is being designed to the latest airline standard technology, with modular construction for 'on wing' maintenance. Its core is essentially that of the GE27, developed under the US Army's MTDE (Modern Technology Demonstrator Engine) programme since 1983 and part of the T407/GLC38 programme. This core is designed to have an initial time between overhauls of 5,000 hours. Cores will be shipped to Garrett complete with the engine control system. Garrett is responsible for the new fan and LP turbine, and for engine assembly and test. Complete engine testing for certification programmes will be shared equally by the two partners. Deliveries of the first version, CFE738-1, are due in 1992 after 6,000 hours of testing.

Full-scale model of CFE738 two-shaft turbofan

In April 1990 the CFE738 was selected to power the Dassault Falcon 2000. The thrust was announced as 26.69 kN (6,000 lb).

The following data relate to the CFE738-1. Growth versions are planned with thrust ratings exceeding 31.1 kN (7,000 lb).

TYPE: Two-shaft subsonic turbofan.

FAN: Single stage with 30 inserted titanium blades with part-span snubbers and rotating pointed spinner. Front end of LP shaft held in large-capacity ball bearing. Mass flow 109 kg (240 lb)/s. Pressure ratio 1.7. Bypass ratio 5.3.

HP COMPRESSOR: Five axial stages followed by one centrifugal. First three stator stages variable. Overall pressure ratio 30.

COMBUSTION CHAMBER: Centrifugal diffuser leads into annular chamber with 16 burners.

HP TURBINE: Two stages with cooled blades.

LP TURBINE: Three stages.

JETPIPE: Fixed mixer assembly with 14 chutes for combining the hot and cold flows from core and bypass duct. Provision for reverser.

DIMENSIONS:
Overall diameter	889 mm (35 in)
Length	1,829 mm (72 in)

WEIGHT, DRY:	558 kg (1,230 lb)
PERFORMANCE RATINGS (ideal installation):	
S/L, T-O	24.87 kN (5,600 lb st) to 30°C (86°F)
Cruise, 12,200 m (40,000 ft), Mach 0.8	
	5.83 kN (1,310 lb)
SPECIFIC FUEL CONSUMPTION:	
S/L, T-O	10.54 mg/Ns (0.372 lb/h/lb st)
Cruise (as above)	18.27 mg/Ns (0.645 lb/h/lb)

CSD

CHEMICAL SYSTEMS DIVISION (A division of United Technologies Corporation)

PO Box 49028, San Jose, California 95161-9028
Telephone: 1 (408) 281 1122
DIVISION EXECUTIVE VICE-PRESIDENT AND GENERAL MANAGER:
David E. Lee

In 1986 CSD joined the Booster Production Company (BPC) and a newly formed unit, Space Flight Systems (SFS), to create Space Transportation Systems, an operating unit of UTC's Defense & Space Group. CSD is formed into four units: Strategic and SDI Booster Systems; Space Launch Booster Systems; Space Maneuvering Systems; and Tactical Systems; as well as an Advanced Propulsion Technology group. Its only current product with a manned application is the Shuttle booster separation motor. Many of its activities are now covered by other *Jane's* publications.

CSD AIR-BREATHING PROPULSION

CSD spearheads the efforts of its parent, United Technologies Corporation, in the research and development of ramjet propulsion systems. In 1973 it was awarded a contract by the US Navy to develop an integral rocket/ramjet (IRR) which operates as a solid rocket booster until it reaches supersonic speeds. At that point, through a series of mechanical changes, it becomes a ramjet. These changes involve the opening of air inlets, an increase in the nozzle diameter and a switch to the burning of liquid fuel and air in the combustion chamber.

EMG

EMG ENGINEERING COMPANY

PO Box 1368, Hesperia, California 92345
Telephone: 1 (714) 247 8519

Eugene M. Gluhareff, a pioneer of ultra-lightweight rotorcraft, has been developing a simple air-breathing jet engine for rotor tip drive. The first model is the G8-2, which was designed in 1955 and developed for tip drive or sailplane auxiliary propulsion. Production has been hard pressed to keep up with demand, a fast growing market being radio controlled flight vehicles. Manned platforms, hang gliders and small helicopters are also proving to be a large market for EMG engines.

GLUHAREFF G8-2

The design is based on propane. Tank pressure delivers the fuel, via a needle valve throttle, to the burner. The fuel is vaporised in a heat exchanger. Vapour passes to the injector where its residual pressure is converted to kinetic energy. The high velocity gas jet induces air through three 'supercharger' intakes, each synchronised to the internal flow, which gives the correct fuel/air ratio for the combustion chamber. Here the mixture is initially ignited by a spark plug and thereafter burns continuously.

Since 1979 four more models have been available, the G8-2-20, -80, -130 and -700, rated respectively at 0.09, 0.36, 0.58 and 3.11 kN (20, 80 130 and 700 lb st). The best sfc has

been reduced dramatically from 170 mg/Ns (6 lb/h/lb st) to only 21.8 mg/Ns (0.77 lb/h/lb st). Some, such as the G8-2-130R, are used for rotor tip drive. The biggest unit (-700) weighs 36.3 kg (80 lb).

The units are manufactured by Gluhareff's subsidiary EMG Engineering Co. Customers have the option of buying plans, a construction package, an assembly kit or finished engine.

FISHER

FISHER RESEARCH CORPORATION

Two Cairn Street, Rochester, New York 14611-2476
Telephone: 1 (716) 235 5993
Fax: 1 (716) 328 1984

This organisation has developed an aircraft engine, the Fisher Tornado, based on the automotive Ford 3.8 litre V-6, using a Kevlar-reinforced toothed belt giving a choice of two reduction ratios. Changes include: fitting forged pistons, regrinding the camshaft, fitting a twin-throat downdraught carburettor, fitting harder aluminium main and camshaft bearings and adding a second electronic ignition module. The Tornado is being flight tested in a PA-28-140 Cherokee, with the 50/50 water/glycol coolant piped to a radiator in the rear fuselage fed through NACA inlets in the fuselage sides. Fuel can be premium automotive or 100LL. Engine dry weight is 177 kg (390 lb) and S/L performance includes: T-O, 205 kW (275 hp) at 5,000 rpm (propeller 3,125 or 2,500 rpm) with consumption of 57 litres (15 US gallons; 12.5 Imp gallons)/h, and 75 per cent cruise, 155 kW (206 shp) at 4,200 rpm with consumption of 29 litres (7.7 US gallons; 6.4 Imp gallons)/h. Converted engines will have TBO of over 1,500 h and a factory warranty.

GARRETT

GARRETT ENGINE DIVISION (a division of Allied Signal Aerospace Company)

Sky Harbor Airport, 111 South 34th Street, PO Box 5217, Phoenix, Arizona 85010
Telephone: 1 (602) 231 1000
Fax: 1 (602) 231 7722
PRESIDENT: Malcolm E. Craig

Garrett Engine Division has been called the world's largest producer of small gas turbines.

At the end of 1984 Garrett announced its collaboration with Allison on the T800-LHT-800 turboshaft for the LH helicopter programme. This is mentioned under LHTEC.

The CFE738 turbofan, being developed jointly by Garrett and General Electric, is to be found under CFE.

GARRETT ATF3

US military designation: F104-GA-100

The ATF3 was the first engine to combine three-spool design with a reverse-flow combustion system and turbines, and mixed-flow exhaust.

The arrangement of components allows the fan design to be determined largely independently of the gas generator, and permits operation at optimum fan speed. Omission of inlet guide vanes, mixing of the exhaust with the fan airflow, and double reversal of the airflow, enable the ATF3 to offer reductions in noise and IR signature.

In May 1976 it was announced that the **ATF3-6A** had been selected by Dassault to power the Falcon 200 business jet. FAA certification was achieved on 24 December 1981, and Falcon 200 deliveries began in 1983. It also powers the HU-25A Guardian.

TYPE: Three-shaft axial-flow turbofan.

LOW PRESSURE (FAN) SYSTEM: Single-stage titanium fan, driven by three-stage IP turbine. Bypass ratio 2.8 at take-off. Mass flow 73.5 kg (162 lb)/s.

INTERMEDIATE PRESSURE SYSTEM: Five-stage titanium compressor, driven by two-stage LP turbine. Airflow is delivered to rearward facing HP compressor via eight tubes feeding into annular duct. Core airflow 18.15 kg (40 lb)/s.

Cutaway drawing of Garrett ATF3-6A three-shaft turbofan

HIGH PRESSURE SYSTEM: Single titanium centrifugal compressor, driven by single-stage HP turbine. IP airflow enters the impeller from the rear. Overall pressure ratio (T-O) 21, (high altitude cruise) 25.

COMBUSTION SYSTEM: Reverse-flow annular type.

TURBINES: Single-stage HP, three-stage IP and two-stage LP turbines drive, respectively, the HP, fan (LP) and IP compressors. IP and LP turbines have shrouded blades. Aircooled HP rotor blades. Exhaust gases turned 180° through eight sets of cascades to mix with fan bypass flow.

FUEL SYSTEM: Electromechanical, incorporating solid state computer. Manual emergency backup system.

ACCESSORY DRIVES: Three drive pads on rear-mounted gearbox driven by HP shaft, providing for hydraulic pump, starter/generator and one spare.

EXHAUST SYSTEM: Mixed fan and turbine exhaust discharged via annular nozzle surrounding combustion section.

LUBRICATION SYSTEM: Hot tank integral with gearbox.

STARTING: Electric or pneumatic.

DIMENSIONS:
Length	2,591 mm (102.0 in)
Max diameter	853 mm (33.6 in)
WEIGHT, DRY:	510 kg (1,125 lb)
PERFORMANCE RATINGS (uninstalled):	
T-O (ISA, S/L, static)	24.20 kN (5,440 lb st)
Cruise (12,200 m; 40,000 ft at Mach 0.8)	
	4.69 kN (1,055 lb)
SPECIFIC FUEL CONSUMPTION:	
At T-O rating (S/L, ISA static)	
	14.33 mg/Ns (0.506 lb/h/lb st)
At cruise (as above)	23.51 mg/Ns (0.83 lb/h/lb)

GARRETT TFE109
US military designation: F109-GA-100

Based on the core of the T76/TPE331 turboprops, with performance improvements, this turbofan was selected in July 1982 as the engine of the US Air Force's Fairchild T-46A. This was subsequently cancelled.

TFE109-1. Basic engine, as described below. Powers first Jet Squalus.

TFE109-2. Rated at 6.7 kN (1,500 lb st). Selected for twin-engined Promavia ATTA 3000.

TFE109-3. Uprated to 7.12 kN (1,600 lb st). Powers second Jet Squalus.

The core of the TFE109 is used in the T800 helicopter engine, described under LHTEC.

TYPE: Two-shaft turbofan.

FAN: Single-stage, with 28 blades with part-span shrouds (snubbers) inserted in self-de-icing rotating spinner.

COMPRESSOR: Tandem two-stage centrifugal with titanium impellers. LP and HP bleeds.

COMBUSTION CHAMBER: Annular reverse flow type, with piloted air blast nozzles for low emissions.

HP TURBINE: Two-stage axial, with single pass cooling.

LP TURBINE: Two-stage axial, with tip shrouds.

CONTROL SYSTEM: Full-authority digital with hydro-mechanical backup.

ACCESSORIES: Mounted on one-piece gearbox, under intermediate case, with drive from HP shaft taken through one of five main aerofoil struts spaced at 72°.

DIMENSIONS:
Length	1,089 mm (42.89 in)
Diameter	588 mm (23.15 in)

WEIGHT, DRY:
	199 kg (439 lb)

PERFORMANCE RATINGS (ISA):
T-O	5.92 kN (1,330 lb st)
Max continuous (9,145 m; 30,000 ft, Mach 0.5)	1.78 kN (400 lb)

SPECIFIC FUEL CONSUMPTION:
Max T-O as above	11.10 mg/Ns (0.392 lb/h/lb st)

Cutaway drawing of Garrett TFE109-1 two-shaft turbofan

GARRETT TFE731

Announced in April 1969, the TFE731 is a two-spool geared turbofan designed for business jet aircraft. Use of a geared fan confers flexibility in operation and yields optimum performance at up to 15,545 m (51,000 ft).

Deliveries for the Falcon 10 took place in August 1972, and for the JetStar II in 1974. The **TFE731-3** was also selected for the Learjet 54/56, Cessna Citation III, Dassault Falcon 50, BAe 125-700, IAI Westwind 1 and 2 and Astra, Rockwell International's Sabreliner 65A, CASA C-101 and Argentine IA 63.

In 1980 the **731-5** was announced, to offer higher thrust and reduced noise, while maintaining low smoke characteristics. The -5 has a higher bypass ratio fan driven by a new LP turbine.

This version was certificated in November 1983. Its first applications are the BAe 125-800 and the CASA C-101. The **TFE731-5A**, with a mixer nozzle reducing sfc and raising standard thrust to that of the APR rating, was certificated in December 1984. It powers the Dassault Falcon 900, and is offered as a retrofit for the Falcon 20. Volvo Flygmotor has a 5.6 per cent share of the 731-5 production programme.

TYPE: Turbofan with two shafts and geared front fan.

FAN: Single-stage axial titanium fan, with inserted blades. The fan shaft is connected directly to the planetary gearbox ring gear. Mass flow, sea level static, TFE731-2, 51.25 kg (113 lb)/s; -3, 53.7 kg (118.3 lb)/s; -5, 64.86 kg (143 lb)/s. Bypass ratio, -2, 2.66; -3, 2.80; -5, 3.48.

COMPRESSOR: Four-stage LP, followed by centrifugal HP on separate shaft running at higher speeds. Overall pressure ratio (S/L, static): -2, 14.0; -3, 14.6.

COMBUSTION CHAMBER: Annular reverse flow type, with 12 nozzles injecting tangentially. Meets EPA/FAA emission requirements.

FUEL SYSTEM: Hydro-electronic, with single lever control.

TURBINES: Single-stage HP and three-stage LP. Average HP inlet gas temperature, S/L, max T-O, -2, 860°C; -3, 907°C; -5, 952°C.

ACCESSORY DRIVES: Pads provided for hydraulic pump, starter/generator or starter motor and alternators. Pads on back side of drive fuel control and oil pump.

DIMENSIONS:
Length overall:
-2, -3	1,520 mm (59.83 in)
-3A, -3B	1,440 mm (59.70 in)
-5	1,665 mm (65.54 in)
-5A	2,314 mm (91.10 in)
Intake diameter	716 mm (28.20 in)

Width:
-2, -3, -3A, -3B	869 mm (34.20 in)
-5, -5A	858 mm (33.79 in)

Height overall:
-2, -3, -3A, -3B	1,000 mm (39.36 in)
-5, -5A	1,029 mm (40.52 in)

WEIGHT, DRY:
-2	332 kg (730 lb)
-3	337 kg (742 lb)
-3A	345 kg (758 lb)
-3B	346 kg (760 lb)
-5	387 kg (852 lb)
-5A	402 kg (884 lb)

PERFORMANCE RATINGS:
Max T-O (S/L, 24.4°C):
-2	15.57 kN (3,500 lb st)
-3, -3A	16.46 kN (3,700 lb st)
-3B	16.24 kN (3,650 lb st)
-5	19.15 kN (4,304 lb st)
-5A	20.02 kN (4,500 lb st)

Max T-O (APR, auto performance reserve):
-3, -3A, -3B	17.13 kN (3,850 lb st)
-5, -5A	20.02 kN (4,500 lb st)

Cruise (12,200 m; 40,000 ft at Mach 0.8):
-2	3.36 kN (755 lb)
-3	3.64 kN (817 lb)
-3A	3.73 kN (838 lb)
-3B	3.75 kN (844 lb)
-5	4.25 kN (955 lb)
-5A	4.39 kN (986 lb)

SPECIFIC FUEL CONSUMPTION:
Cruise (as above):
-2	23.08 mg/Ns (0.815 lb/h/lb)
-3	23.65 mg/Ns (0.835 lb/h/lb)
-3A	23.30 mg/Ns (0.823 lb/h/lb)
-3B	23.11 mg/Ns (0.816 lb/h/lb)
-5	22.72 mg/Ns (0.802 lb/h/lb)
-5A	21.84 mg/Ns (0.771 lb/h/lb)

Longitudinal section of TFE731-5 (top half) and TFE731-3 (bottom half) geared turbofans

GARRETT TFE1042/1088
US military designation: F124-GA-100

This derivative of the TFE731 was launched in 1978 as a co-operative programme with Volvo Flygmotor of Sweden. Details last appeared in the 1982-83 *Jane's*, when it was described as a family of related engines, with lower bypass

Garrett TFE1042/1088 two-shaft augmented turbofan

ratio than the TFE731. The TFE1042-7, with afterburner, was stated to have dry and maximum augmented ratings of 21.44 kN (4,820 lb st) and 37.1 kN (8,340 lb st) respectively.

The engine was then withdrawn from our pages, even after it had been announced as the power plant of the Taiwanese AIDC Ching-kuo indigenous defence fighter. But at the 1989 Paris Air Show Garrett showed the engine and revealed that it had been working on it with Taiwan since 1982. Fully modular, it is based on the TFE731 but has now matured as a family of engines to be marketed by Garrett as the TFE1088. The basic engine, the 1042-70/1088-11, had by May 1989 completed over 6,000 hours of testing. Initial flight release was achieved in February 1989, with full qualification testing due in April 1990. Garrett claim the basic engine as "the most reliable and efficient in this power class".

The following are existing and planned versions:

TFE1042-70. Basic version, fitted to Ching-kuo IDF. Description below applies to this version.

TFE1088-11. USAF F124-GA-101. Similar to TFE1042-70. Being marketed by Garrett at 29.49 kN (6,630 lb st) intermediate thrust and 43.15 kN (9,700 lb st) maximum.

TFE1088-12. Growth version for 1994. Turbine inlet 1,454°C; maximum rating 54.49 kN (12,250 lb st).

TFE1088-13. Growth engine for 1997. Turbine inlet 1,566°C; maximum thrust 62.28 kN (14,000 lb st).

TFE1088-16. Fully rated dry version, with USAF designation F124-GA-100. Details as below except: length 1,511 mm (59.5 in); dry weight 454 kg (1,001 lb); corrected airflow 43 kg (94.8 lb)/s; maximum thrust 29.8 kN (6,700 lb st).

TFE1088-17. F124 growth engine for 1994. Turbine inlet 1,454°C; maximum thrust 36.12 kN (8,120 lb st).

TFE1088-18. F124 dry growth engine for 1998. Turbine inlet 1,566°C; maximum thrust 43.82 kN (9,850 lb st).

TYPE: Two shaft augmented turbofan.

FAN: Three stages with rotating spinner. Maximum airflow 43.29 kg (95.4 lb)/s. Bypass ratio 0.3.

COMPRESSOR: Four axial stages followed by one centrifugal.

COMBUSTION CHAMBER: As TFE731.

TURBINES: Single-stage HP and LP turbine. HP entry gas temperature 1,343°C.

AUGMENTOR: Reheat in bypass and core flows. Three fuel-pressure rams drive 10-flap variable nozzle.

DIMENSIONS:

Inlet diameter	605 mm (23.8 in)
Length	2,880 mm (134.0 in)
Maximum nozzle diameter	782 mm (30.8 in)

WEIGHT, DRY: 603 kg (1,330 lb)

PERFORMANCE RATINGS:

Intermediate	22.24 kN (5,000 lb st)
Maximum augmented	37.14 kN (8,350 lb st)

SPECIFIC FUEL CONSUMPTION:
TFE1042-70 (intermediate) 23.79 mg/Ns (0.84 lb/h/lb st)

GARRETT TPE331
US military designation: T76

Based upon experience with APUs, this was the first Garrett engine for aircraft propulsion. By January 1988 deliveries of all versions had passed 11,000.

The following are major versions:

TPE331 series I, II. FAA certificated in February 1965. Rated at 451 ekW; 429 kW plus 0.33 kN (605 ehp; 575 shp plus 75 lb st). Redesignated **TPE331-25/61** and **-25/71** and produced until 1970. Powers MU-2 (A to E models), Porter, Jet Liner, Super Turbo 18, FU-24, Hawk Commander and 680, and Turbo Beaver.

TPE331-1 series. Certificated December 1967 at 526 ekW; 496 kW plus 0.44 kN (705 ehp; 665 shp plus 100 lb st). Powers MU-2 (F and G), Turbo-Porter and AU-23A Peacemaker, CJ600, Turboliner, Interceptor 400, Turbo Commander and (customer option) Thrush Commander, Merlin IIB and Fletcher 1284, Turbo Thrush and Turbo Ag-Cat.

TPE331-2 series. Certificated in December 1967 at 563 ekW; 533 kW plus 0.45 kN (755 ehp; 715 shp plus 102 lb st). Powers Skyvan, CASA 212 pre-series, Turbo Goose and Turbo Beaver.

TPE331-3 series. Certificated in March 1970 at 674 ekW; 626 kW plus 0.71 kN (904 ehp; 840 shp plus 159 lb st). Uprated gas generator with increased airflow and pressure ratio, but same turbine temperature as in original TPE331. Powers Merlin III, IV and Metro, and Jetstream III.

TPE331-5/6 series. The -5 was certificated in March 1970; this matches the gas generator of the -3 with the 715 shp gearbox, and is flat rated to 2,135 m (7,000 ft). Powers MU-2, King Air B100 (-6), CASA 212 (-5), Dornier 228 (-5), and Commander 840/900. The -5 designation indicates output speed of 1,591 rpm; the -6 has an output speed of 2,000 rpm.

TPE331-8. Matches compressor and gearbox of -3 with new turbine section. Thermodynamic power of 676 ekW; 645 kW (905 ehp; 865 shp) plus 0.47 kN (105 lb st), but flat rated at 533 kW (715 shp) to 36°C. Certification was received in November 1976. Powers Conquest II.

TPE331-9. Thermodynamic rating 645 kW (865 shp).

TPE331-10. Rated at 746 kW (1,000 shp). Certificated January 1978. Powers Marquise and Solitaire, Commander 980/1000, Merlin IIIC, CASA 212-200 and Jetstream 31.

Cutaway drawing of Garrett TPE331-14 turboprop

TPE331-11. Certificated 1979. Higher gearbox limit; wet rating 820 kW (1,100 shp). Powers Metro III.

TPE331-12. Same size as -10 but offers 834 kW (1,119 shp). Certificated December 1984. Powers Jetstream Super 31 and Metro V. The **TPE331-12B**, powers the Shorts Tucano. Rolls-Royce makes 30 per cent by value of engines for Shorts, and supports RAF engines in service.

TPE331-14/15. Scaled-up models, with thermodynamic power in the 1,227 kW (1,645 shp) class. The -14 was certificated in April 1984 and is flat rated at 746 kW (1,000 shp) for the Cheyenne 400. In the Metro VI it is rated at 932 kW (1,250 shp).

TPE331-14GR/HR (clockwise/anti-clockwise) handed engine, flat rated at 1,119 kW (1,500 shp) to 35°C, selected for Jetstream 41.

T76. Military engine, with gas generator similar to TPE331-1 but with front end inverted, to give inlet above spinner. All models power OV-10 Bronco.

Except for the TPE331-14, all versions are of similar frame size, and the following data apply generally to all:

TYPE: Single-shaft turboprop.

PROPELLER DRIVE: Two-stage reduction gear, one helical spur and one planetary, with overall ratio of 20.865 or 26.3.

COMPRESSOR: Tandem two-stage centrifugal made from titanium. Mass flow, 2.61 kg (5.78 lb)/s for -25/61, -25/71, 2.81 kg (6.2 lb)/s for -1, 2.80 kg (6.17 lb)/s for -2 and T76, 3.52 kg (7.75 lb)/s for -5 and 3.54 kg (7.8 lb)/s for -3. Pressure ratio 8.0 for -25/61, -25/71, 8.34 for -1, 8.54 for -2 and T76, 10.37 for -5 and -3.

COMBUSTION CHAMBER: Annular, with capacitor discharge igniter plug on turbine plenum.

FUEL SYSTEM: Woodward or Bendix control with Beta propeller control. Max fuel pressure 41.4 bars (600 lb/sq in).

FUEL GRADE (TPE331): ASTM designation D1655-64T types Jet A, Jet B and Jet A-1; MIL-F-5616-1, Grade JP-1.

TURBINE: Three-stage axial. In early models, blades cast integrally with disc. In -10, -11, -12 first-stage disc with inserted blades. In -14/15 inserted blades in all three stages. Inlet gas temperature, 987°C for -25/61, -25/71, 993°C for T76, 1,005°C for all other models.

ACCESSORIES: AND 20005 Type XV-B tachometer generator, AND 20002 Type XII-D starter/generator, AND 20010 Type XX-A propeller governor and AND 20001 Type XI-B hydraulic pump.

LUBRICATION SYSTEM: Medium pressure dry sump system. Normal oil supply pressure 6.90 bars (100 lb/sq in).

OIL SPECIFICATION: MIL-L-23699-(1) or MIL-L-7808.

STARTING: Pad for 399A starter/generator.

DIMENSIONS (approx):

Length overall:	
TPE331	1,092 to 1,333 mm (43-52.5 in)
T76	1,118 mm (44 in)
Width: TPE331	533 mm (21 in)
T76	483 mm (19 in)
Height: TPE331	660 mm (26 in)
T76	686 mm (27 in)

WEIGHT, DRY:

TPE331-25/61, 71	152 kg (335 lb)
TPE331-1, -2	152.5 kg (336 lb)
T76	155 kg (341 lb)
TPE331-3	161 kg (355 lb)
TPE331-5	163 kg (360 lb)
TPE331-8	168 kg (370 lb)
TPE331-10	172 kg (380 lb)
TPE331-11	182 kg (400 lb)
TPE331-12	176 kg (387 lb)
TPE331-14/15	256 kg (565 lb)

PERFORMANCE RATINGS:

T-O   see under model listings

Military (30 min): T76-G-410/411
533 kW; 563 ekW (715 shp; 755 ehp)

Normal: T76-G-410/411
485 kW; 514.5 ekW (650 shp; 690 ehp)

Max cruise (ISA, 3,050 m; 10,000 ft and 250 knots; 463 km/h; 288 mph):

TPE331-25/61, 71	332 kW (445 shp)
TPE331-1	404 kW (542 shp)
TPE331-2, T76	430 kW (577 shp)
TPE331-3, -5	530 kW (710 shp)

SPECIFIC FUEL CONSUMPTION:
At T-O rating:

TPE331-25/61, 71	111.5 µg/J (0.66 lb/h/shp)
TPE331-1	102.2 µg/J (0.605 lb/h/shp)
TPE331-2	99.4 µg/J (0.588 lb/h/shp)
TPE331-3	99.7 µg/J (0.59 lb/h/shp)
TPE331-5	105.8 µg/J (0.626 lb/h/shp)
TPE331-8	96.7 µg/J (0.572 lb/h/shp)
TPE331-10	94.6 µg/J (0.560 lb/h/shp)
TPE331-11	94.3 µg/J (0.558 lb/h/shp)
TPE331-12	92.8 µg/J (0.549 lb/h/shp)

Longitudinal section of Garrett TPF351-20 free-turbine pusher turboprop

TPE331-14/-15	84.8 µg/J (0.502 lb/h/shp)
T76-G-410/411	101.4 µg/J (0.60 lb/h/shp)

OIL CONSUMPTION:
Max 0.009 kg (0.02 lb)/h

GARRETT TPF351

This is Garrett's first free-turbine turboprop. It is being developed initially as the **TPF351-20** for pusher installation in the Embraer/FAMA CBA-123. The engine is modular, and arranged for clockwise (CW) or counter-clockwise (CCW) propeller rotation (both forms of gearbox are shown in the drawing).

TYPE: Free-turbine pusher turboprop.

AIR INLET: Ram inlet at front of nacelle with duct passing above accessory gearbox.

COMPRESSOR: Tandem two-stage centrifugal. Mass flow 6.35 kg (14.0 lb)/s. Pressure ratio 13.3.

COMBUSTION CHAMBER: Annular reverse flow with dual-channel ignition system.

FUEL SYSTEM: FADEC with mechanical backup fuel control unit and integral electrical shutoff valve.

TURBINES: Two-stage gas generator turbine. Three-stage power turbine; inter-turbine temperature 805°C (1,481°F), EGT 571°C (1,061°F).

JET PIPE: Bifurcated with diagonal outlet on each side (depicted in drawing as above and below).

PROPELLER DRIVE: Epicyclic with drive to auxiliary gearbox.

DIMENSIONS:

Length overall	1,954 mm (76.94 in)
Width	606 mm (23.84 in)
Height	838 mm (33.0 in)

WEIGHT, DRY:

CW	340.2 kg (750.1 lb)
CCW	347.0 kg (765.1 lb)

PERFORMANCE RATING (ISA, S/L, T-O):
Thermodynamic 1,566 kW (2,100 shp), torque-limited to 1,081 kW (1,450 shp)

SPECIFIC FUEL CONSUMPTION (T-O):
83.66 µg/J (0.495 lb/h/shp)

GENERAL ELECTRIC
GE AIRCRAFT ENGINES

Neumann Way, Evendale, Ohio 45215
Telephone: 1 (513) 243 2000
Telex: 212078 GEAEG UR
Fax: 1 (513) 243 0613/0614
1000 Western Avenue, Lynn, Massachusetts 01910
Telephone: 1 (617) 594 0100
Telex: 6817065
Fax: 1 (617) 594 1611

SENIOR VICE-PRESIDENT AND GROUP EXECUTIVE: B. H. Rowe

Current products of GE Aircraft Engines include the F103, F110, F118, F120, F404, F412, T407, T64, T700 and TF34 for military use, and the GE90, CF6, CF34, CT7 and GLC38 for the commercial and general aviation market. A new turbofan is being developed in partnership with Garrett and appears under CFE. In partnership with SNECMA of France a company was formed to develop and market the CFM56 turbofan, as described in the International part of this section under CFM International.

Details of the CF700, CJ610, F101, J79, J85, T58 and TF39 engines, which are no longer in production, can be found in earlier editions of *Jane's.*

GENERAL ELECTRIC F404

In May 1975 the US Navy selected the McDonnell Douglas/Northrop team to develop its F/A-18 Hornet, powered by two F404-GE-400 engines.

First F404 engine test took place in December 1976. Preliminary flight rating test took place in May 1978, first F/A-18 flight in November 1978 and MQT (model qualification test) in July 1979. The first production delivery took place in December 1979.

The following are current versions of the F404:

F404-GE-400. Original production engine for all F/A-18 models. Also powers the Grumman X-29, Dassault Rafale and Rockwell/MBB X-31. Max rating 71.2 kN (16,000 lb st).

F404-GE-402. Enhanced Performance Engine (EPE) in the 79 kN (17,700 lb st) class; combines a 2,000-h hot section with a 10 to 20 per cent increase in thrust, achieving this performance through improved design and materials in the turbines and afterburner. Designed to replace the F404-GE-400, the EPE will be supplied for all US Navy F/A-18 aircraft procured beginning in October 1992. Also selected for F/A-18s for Kuwait, Switzerland and Republic of South Korea.

F404-GE-100D. A 49 kN (11,000 lb st) non-afterburning derivative of the F404-GE-400 powering the Singapore Air Force A-4 Super Skyhawk.

F404-GE-F1D2. A non-afterburning turbojet derivative of the F404-GE-400 powering the US Air Force F-117A.

F404/RM12. An 80 kN (18,100 lb st) F404 derivative. Fan handles five per cent greater airflow and has increased resistance to foreign-object damage. Increased turbine inlet temperature provides operating margin for lower right hand corner of flight envelope. Modified control system for single-engined JAS 39 Gripen. Interim engine for Indian Light Combat Aircraft and proposed for re-engining Chinese F-7 and J-8. Candidate for Yugoslav Novi Avion and other programmes. See Volvo Flygmotor, Sweden.

F404-GE-400D. Unaugmented version of F404-GE-400 rated at 48.0 kN (10,800 lb st). Powered Grumman A-6F prototype.

The following description applies to the F404-GE-402:

TYPE: Two-shaft augmented low bypass ratio turbofan (turbojet with continuous bypass bleed).

FAN: Three-stage. Bypass ratio 0.27. Mass flow 66.2 kg (146 lb)/s.

HP COMPRESSOR: Seven-stage. Overall pressure ratio, 26 : 1 class.

COMBUSTION CHAMBER: Single-piece annular.

HP TURBINE: Single-stage with aircooled blades.

LP TURBINE: Single-stage.

EXHAUST SYSTEM: Close coupled afterburner. Convergent-divergent exhaust nozzle with hydraulic actuation.

CONTROL SYSTEM: Electrical-hydromechanical.

DIMENSIONS:

Length overall	4,030 mm (158.8 in)
Max diameter	880 mm (34.8 in)

WEIGHT, DRY: 1,016 kg (2,240 lb)

PERFORMANCE RATING:
Max T-O 79 kN (17,700 lb st)

General Electric F404-GE-100D unaugmented turbofan

GENERAL ELECTRIC F412

GE is developing the F412-GE-400 engine for the US Navy's A-12 aircraft programme. It may be expected to be an advanced turbofan, suitable for a Stealth attack aircraft.

GENERAL ELECTRIC TF34

This turbofan won a 1965 US Navy competition. In August 1972 the **TF34-GE-2**, the initial variant for the Lockheed S-3A Viking, completed its model qualification test (MQT) and entered fleet service in February 1974. In January 1975 GE began shipment of the **TF34-GE-400A/B**, which replaced the GE-2 as S-3A engine. In 1970 the TF34 was selected to power the A-10A attack aircraft as the **TF34-GE-100**, with a long fan duct and side mountings.

In 1974 a third version was selected to provide auxiliary (thrust) power for the Sikorsky S-72 research aircraft.

TYPE: Two-shaft high bypass ratio turbofan.

FAN: Single-stage fan has blades forged in titanium. Mass flow (TF34-400A/B) 153 kg (338 lb)/s at 7,365 rpm with pressure ratio 1.5. Bypass ratio 6.2.

COMPRESSOR: 14-stage axial on HP shaft. Inlet guide vanes and first five stators variable. First nine rotor stages titanium, remainder high nickel alloy. Performance at max S/L rating, core airflow 21.3 kg (47 lb)/s at 17,900 rpm with pressure ratio 14 : 1, overall pressure ratio 21.

COMBUSTION CHAMBER: Annular Hastelloy liner and front dome, with 18 carburetting burners.

TURBINE: Two-stage HP; four-stage LP with tip-shrouded blades. EGT 1,225°C maximum.

FUEL SYSTEM: Hydromechanical with electronic amplifier. Fuel grade JP-4 or JP-5.

DIMENSIONS:
Max diameter:

TF34-GE-400A/B	1,321 mm (52.0 in)
TF34-GE-100	1,245 mm (49.0 in)
Basic length (both)	2,540 mm (100.0 in)

WEIGHT, DRY:

TF34-GE-400A/B	670 kg (1,478 lb)
TF34-GE-100	653 kg (1,440 lb)

PERFORMANCE RATING (max T-O; S/L static):

TF34-GE-400A/B	41.3 kN (9,275 lb st)
TF34-GE-100	40.3 kN (9,065 lb st)

SPECIFIC FUEL CONSUMPTION (max T-O, S/L static):

TF34-GE-400A/B	10.3 mg/Ns (0.363 lb/h/lb st)
TF34-GE-100	10.5 mg/Ns (0.370 lb/h/lb st)

General Electric CF34-3A two-shaft turbofan

Features of General Electric CF6-80C2 two-shaft turbofan

(Diagram labels:)
Aluminum/Kevlar Containment
HPT
• DS Stg. 1 Blade
• Improved Flow Path and Airfoils
• Active Clearance Control
5½ Stage LPT
Retwisted/ Recambered Airfoils
Aerodynamic Struts
93" Recambered Fan Blade
Stiffened Bore Cooled Rotor
4 Stage Orthogonal Booster

GENERAL ELECTRIC CF34

The CF34-3A is a commercial adaptation of the TF34. Total airflow at take-off power with automatic power reserve (APR) is 151 kg (332 lb)/s. Bypass ratio is 6.3. Certificated in August 1982, the CF34-1A powers the Challenger 601-1A and the CF34-3A1 the Challenger 601-3A and Canadair RJ.

DIMENSIONS:
Length (overall)	2,616 mm (103.0 in)
Max diameter (at mounts)	1,245 mm (49.0 in)

WEIGHT, DRY:
	739 kg (1,625 lb)

PERFORMANCE RATINGS (S/L, static):
T-O (APR)	41.0 kN (9,220 lb st)
T-O (Normal)	38.8 kN (8,729 lb st)

SPECIFIC FUEL CONSUMPTION (as above):
T-O (Normal)	10.11 mg/Ns (0.357 lb/h/lb st)

GENERAL ELECTRIC GE90

On 16 January 1990 General Electric announced it is developing a high-bypass turbofan with thrust in the range 333-422 kN (75,000-95,000 lb st) capable of powering all new and derivative widebody aircraft that may enter the market in the mid-1990s.

The GE90 is scheduled for certification at 355.5 kN (80,000 lb st) in May 1994, and entry into service at 311-333 kN (70,000-75,000 lb st) on the Boeing 777 in mid-1995.

This new design is based on a compressor scaled directly from GE's Energy Efficient Engine programme, a joint GE/NASA-funded project aimed at establishing a technology base for engines of the 1990s. It will feature the largest fan yet built, with composite wide-chord blades.

The large fan diameter increases the bypass ratio to 10, higher than that of any engine yet developed. The higher bypass ratio will help achieve a 10 per cent improvement in specific fuel consumption compared to today's large turbofan engines, while providing reduced noise levels.

Improvements to the combustor design will result in significantly improved emissions (oxides of nitrogen).

The engine will feature a composite, structural, load-sharing nacelle, integrating the design of the engine and the nacelle. As a result, a complete propulsion system will be provided, incorporating substantial weight savings, improved performance retention, and reduced airline maintenance costs.

The compressor permits a shorter, lighter, stiffer engine with a high overall cycle pressure ratio that also contributes to the significantly improved specific fuel consumption. The double-dome combustor was designed specifically for low NO_x emissions. Under low thrust, the outer combustor nozzles are used; as thrust is increased, the inner set of main nozzles begins operation. The high-pressure turbine will feature single-crystal blades, and the turbine discs are boltless, with smooth side plates for low windage losses.

GE's partners will include SNECMA of France. Among the GE90's features are:

FAN: Low speed, low pressure ratio with bypass ratio of approximately 10; composite, unshrouded wide-chord rotor blades; structural outlet guide vanes. Blade/vane quantities and spacing optimised for low acoustics.

LP COMPRESSOR: Three stages; low speed; moderate pressure ratio; low noise features.

HP COMPRESSOR: Ten stages; pressure ratio 23; derived from GE/NASA Energy Efficient Engine (E^3) technology demonstrator. Overall pressure ratio over 40.

COMBUSTOR: Double annular design for low NO_x emissions; derived from E^3 technology demonstrator.

HP TURBINE: Two stages with monocrystal blades and powdered metal discs.

LP TURBINE: Seven stages with relatively low stage loading for improved efficiency, low noise features.

FUEL SYSTEM: FADEC control of fuel flow, variable geometry and active clearance control systems.

DIMENSIONS:
Fan diameter	3,048 mm (120 in)
Length, flange to flange	4,775 mm (188 in)

GENERAL ELECTRIC CF6
US military designation (CF6-50E): F103-GE-100

On 11 September 1967 General Electric announced the commitment of corporate funding for development of the CF6 turbofan for wide-body transports. The CF6-6D for the DC-10-10 was selected by United and American on 25 April 1968. Details of this and other early versions appeared in the 1987-88 *Jane's*. The following are current versions:

CF6-50C2/E2. Rated 233.5 kN (52,500 lb st) to 30°C. Certification 1978. Military -50C2 powers KC-10; -50E2 powers Boeing E-4.

CF6-80A/A3. Improved sfc and performance retention, with length and weight reduced by elimination of turbine mid frame and reduction in combustor and diffuser length. Engine rated at 213.5 kN (48,000 lb) as the -80A/A1, and 222.4 kN (50,000 lb) as the -80A2/A3. Fitted to 767 and A310. Programme launched November 1977, first engine ran October 1979 and certification October 1981. About 9 per cent built by Volvo Flygmotor. The -80A and -80C2 on the 767 were first to receive FAA approval (January 1989) for 180 min EROPS operations.

CF6-80C2. Described separately.

The following data relate to the CF6-50C2/E2, with -80 differences noted:

TYPE: Two-shaft high bypass ratio turbofan.

FAN: Single-stage with three-stage LP compressor both driven by LP turbine. The 38 fan rotor blades have anti-vibration shrouds at two-thirds span. Blades, discs, spool of titanium; exit guide vanes of aluminium; fan frame and shaft of steel; spinner and fan case of aluminium alloy. Total airflow 591 kg (1,303 lb)/s, bypass ratio 5.7. CF6-80A/A1 has better efficiency and bird strike resistance, with Kevlar containment in fan case. Fan diameter 2,195 mm (86.4 in). Mass flow, CF6-80A/A1, 651 kg (1,433 lb)/s; -80A2/A3, 663 kg (1,460 lb)/s. Bypass ratio, -80A/A1, 4.7; -80A2/A3, 4.6.

LP COMPRESSOR: Three core booster stages; 12 bypass doors maintain flow matching between fan/LP and core by opening at low power settings, closed during take-off and cruise.

HP COMPRESSOR: Fourteen-stage with inlet guide vanes and first six stator rows having variable incidence. Core airflow 125 kg (276 lb)/s. CF6-80A series incorporate bore cooling for blade/casing clearance control, and one-piece steel casing with insulated aft stages and short diffuser section. Overall pressure ratio (T-O), 29.13 (-50C), 30.1 (-50E), 28.0 (-80A/A1), 29.0 (-80A2/A3).

COMBUSTOR: Fully annular. CF6-80A has rolled ring combustor, 152 mm (6.0 in) shorter, mounted at aft flange.

HP TURBINE: Two-stage aircooled, TET 1,330°C. CF6-80A has no turbine mid-frame and eliminates one main bearing, and HP case has active clearance control.

LP TURBINE: Four-stage constant tip diameter with nominal 871°C inlet temperature. Rotor blades tip-shrouded and not aircooled. CF6-80A, new turbine with active clearance control.

THRUST REVERSER (FAN): Rear portion of fan outer cowl translates aft on rotating ballscrews to uncover cascade vanes. Blocker doors (16) flush-mounted in cowl on link arms hinged in inner cowl, rotate inwards to expose cascade vanes and block fan duct. CF6-80A1/A3 (A310) similar; 767 reverser by Boeing.

ACCESSORY DRIVE: Inlet gearbox in forward sump transfers energy from the core. Transfer gearbox on bottom of fan frame with starter, fuel pump, main engine control, lubrication pump and tachometer. Pads for aircraft hydraulic pumps, constant speed drive and alternator. CF6-80A gearbox in environmental enclosure on core; -80A1 on fan case.

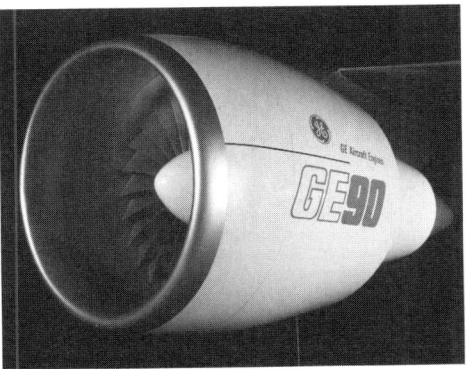

General Electric GE90 nacelle mockup

General Electric CF6-80C2 two-shaft turbofan

FUEL SYSTEM: Hydromechanical, schedules acceleration and deceleration fuel flow, variable stator vane position and LP compressor variable bypass doors. CF6-80, electronic trimming.

FUEL GRADES: Fuels conforming to ASTM-1655-65T, Jet A, Jet A1 and Jet B, and MIL-T-5624G2 grades JP-4 or JP-5 are authorised, but Jet A is primary specification.

LUBRICATION SYSTEM: Dry sump centre-vented nominal pressure is 2.07-6.21 bars (30-90 lb/sq in).

STARTING: Air turbine starter mounted on the front of the accessory gearbox at the through shaft.

NOISE SUPPRESSION: Acoustic panels integrated with fan casing, fan front frame and thrust reverser.

DIMENSIONS:
Max height (over gearbox)	2,675 mm (105.3 in)

Length overall (cold):
CF6-50 series	4,394 mm (173.0 in)
CF6-80A	3,998 mm (157.4 in)

WEIGHT, DRY:

Basic engine:
CF6-50C2	3,960 kg (8,731 lb)
CF6-50E, -E1	3,851 kg (8,490 lb)
CF6-50E2	3,977 kg (8,768 lb)
CF6-80A, -80A2	3,854 kg (8,496 lb)
CF6-80A3	3,819 kg (8,420 lb)

Reverser:
CF6-50E	962 kg (2,121 lb)

PERFORMANCE RATINGS:

Max T-O, uninstalled, ideal nozzle: See under model listings

Max cruise thrust at 10,670 m (35,000 ft), Mach 0.85, flat rated to ISA + 10°C, uninstalled, real nozzle:
CF6-50C2, -E2	50.3 kN (11,300 lb)
CF6-80A, -80A1	45.9 kN (10,320 lb)

SPECIFIC FUEL CONSUMPTION:

At T-O thrust, as above:
CF6-50E	10.65 mg/Ns (0.376 lb/h/lb st)
CF6-50C2, -E2	10.51 mg/Ns (0.371 lb/h/lb st)
CF6-80A	9.74 mg/Ns (0.344 lb/h/lb st)

OIL CONSUMPTION: 0.9 kg (2.0 lb)/h

GENERAL ELECTRIC CF6-80C2

This engine is a major redesign for higher thrust and improved sfc, based on the CF6-80A1/A3 but with a 2,362 mm (93 in) diameter fan. It has a four-stage LP compressor and LP turbine redesigned aerodynamically with 5½ stages. The first CF6-80C2 ran in May 1982, and exceeded 276 kN (62,000 lb) corrected thrust. Flight test on an A300 took place between August and December 1984, leading to certification on 28 June 1985. The engine entered revenue service on 5 October 1985, and now powers also many Boeing 747-400s.

Programme sharing agreements have been signed with SNECMA of France, MTU of Germany, Volvo Flygmotor of Sweden and Fiat Aviazione of Italy. Applications are shown in table on this page.

The CF6-80C2 differs from earlier CF6 engines in the following features:

FAN: Single-stage, with integrally mounted four-stage booster (LP compressor). Mainly titanium except for steel mid-fan shaft, aluminium spinner and blade-containment shroud of layers of Kevlar around aluminium case. Eighty composite exit guide vanes canted for better aerodynamic efficiency. Mass flow 802 kg (1,769 lb)/s; bypass ratio 5.05.

LP COMPRESSOR: Four stages with blades and vanes mounted orthogonally, with dovetail offset from centre of pressure to reduce bending.

HP COMPRESSOR: 14-stage, with inlet guide vanes and first five stator rows with variable incidence. Blades in stages 1-5 titanium, 6-14 steel; vanes all steel. One-piece steel casing with insulated aft stages. Core airflow 154 kg (340 lb)/s. Overall pressure ratio 30.4.

COMBUSTOR: Annular, rolled ring construction, aft-mounted with film cooling.

HP TURBINE: Two-stage. Stage one blades directionally solidified. Casing with active and passive clearance control. No midframe.

LP TURBINE: Five stages, with cambered struts in rear frame to reduce exit swirl, effectively producing another half-stage. Rear hub heated by exhaust gas to reduce thermal stress.

FUEL SYSTEM: FADEC or hydromechanical fan speed control with electronic supervision; one throttle position corresponds to each engine rating in all flight conditions.

DIMENSION:
Length	4,087 mm (160.9 in)

WEIGHT, DRY: 4,144 kg (9,135 lb)

PERFORMANCE RATINGS (uninstalled, ideal nozzle):
Max T-O	See table
Max cruise (10,670 m; 35,000 ft, Mach 0.85)	50.4 kN (11,330 lb)

SPECIFIC FUEL CONSUMPTION:
T-O, as above	9.32 mg/Ns (0.329 lb/h/lb st)

GENERAL ELECTRIC CF6-80E1

This engine is a major redesign for higher thrust and improved sfc, based on the CF6-80C2 but with a 2,438 mm (96 in) diameter fan. It has a four-stage LP compressor and

CF6-80C2 and -80E1 MODELS

Model	Thrust Ideal nozzle	Real nozzle	Application
CF6-80C2A2	238 kN (53,500 lb)	233.5 kN (52,460 lb) to 43.9°C	A310-200, -300
CF6-80C2A3	268 kN (60,200 lb)	262 kN (58,950 lb) to 30°C	A300-600
CF6-80C2A5	272.5 kN (61,300 lb)	267.5 kN (60,100 lb) to 30°C	A300-600R
CF6-80C2B1	252 kN (56,700 lb)	249 kN (55,980 lb) to 30°C	747-200, -300
CF6-80C2B1F	258 kN (58,000 lb)	254 kN (57,160 lb) to 32.2°C	747-400
CF6-80C2B2	233.5 kN (52,500 lb)	231 kN (51,950 lb) to 32.2°C	767-200ER, -300ER
CF6-80C2B2F	234.5 kN (52,700 lb)	231.5 kN (52,010 lb) to 32.2°C	767-300ER
CF6-80C2B4	257.5 kN (57,900 lb)	254.5 kN (57,180 lb) to 32.2°C	767-200ER, -300ER
CF6-80C2B4F	258 kN (58,100 lb)	255 kN (57,280 lb) to 32.2°C	767-300ER
CF6-80C2B6	270 kN (60,800 lb)	267 kN (60,070 lb) to 30°C	767-300ER
CF6-80C2B6F	270 kN (60,800 lb)	267 kN (60,070 lb) to 30°C	767-300ER
CF6-80C2D1F	273.5 kN (61,500 lb)	268 kN (60,240 lb) to 30°C	MD-11
CF6-80E1A1	287 kN (64,500 lb)	281.5 kN (63,290 lb) to 30°C	A330
CF6-80E1A2	292.5 kN (65,800 lb)	287 kN (64,530 lb) to 30°C	A330
CF6-80E1A3	309 kN (69,500 lb)	303.5 kN (68,240 lb) to 30°C	A330

LP turbine redesigned aerodynamically with 5½ stages. The first CF6-80E1 was to run in October 1990 at 67,500 lb st corrected thrust. Flight test on an A300 is planned for late 1991 and early 1992, leading to certification in December 1992. The engine will enter revenue service in 1993 on the A330.

The CF6-80E1 development is being shared with SNECMA of France, MTU of Germany, Volvo Flygmotor of Sweden, and Fiat Aviazione of Italy.

The CF6-80E1 differs from the CF6-80C2 in the following features:

FAN: Diameter increased; number of blades reduced from 38 to 34.

LP COMPRESSOR: Flow capacity increased 9 per cent at a 12 per cent increased pressure ratio.

HP COMPRESSOR: High-temperature alloys in last stage. Overall pressure ratio: E1A1, 32; E1A2, 32.6; E1A3, 34.6.

COMBUSTOR: No change.

HP TURBINE: High-temperature alloys and improved cooling.

LP TURBINE: High-temperature alloys, improved cooling changes and aerodynamic changes.

FUEL SYSTEM: Surface-mounted FADEC; a higher-capacity system with an externally valved staging system (50 per cent of nozzles can be turned off) for low thrust operability.

DIMENSIONS:
Length: Engine	4,405 mm (173.5 in)
Propulsion system	7,356 mm (289.6 in)

WEIGHT, DRY:
Engine	4,818 kg (10,600 lb)
Propulsion system	6,532 kg (14,400 lb)

PERFORMANCE RATINGS: See table

SPECIFIC FUEL CONSUMPTION (Max T-O):
E1A1	9.18 mg/Ns (0.324 lb/h/lb st)
E1A2	9.26 mg/Ns (0.327 lb/h/lb st)
E1A3	9.63 mg/Ns (0.340 lb/h/lb st)

GENERAL ELECTRIC F110

The **F110** (previously F101 DFE) is a fighter engine derivative of the F101. The first ran in late 1979. In early 1984 the USAF selected the F110 to power future F-16 aircraft.

The following are current versions of the F110:

F110-GE-100. Initial USAF engine, also selected by Israel (100 engines) and Turkey (177 engines). Other orders have been received from Bahrain, Egypt and Greece. Delivery of production F-16C/D aircraft with F110 engines began in mid-1986. The US Navy selected the Dash-100 to power its F-16Ns for the adversary role in its Top Gun programme.

F110-GE-400. Powers F-14A (Plus) and F-14D Tomcat for the US Navy. First production aircraft with this engine

delivered to Navy in November 1987. Tomcats powered with this engine show a significant improvement in fuel consumption and the ability to catapult launch without use of an afterburner, resulting in a 61 per cent time-to-climb reduction and a 62 per cent improvement in mission range. Ratings are: maximum 120.2 kN (27,000 lb st), dry 71.2 kN (16,000 lb st).

F110-GE-129. Rated at 129 kN (29,000 lb st), the GE IPE (Improved Performance Engine) is the successor to the F110-GE-100. Through the use of improved design and materials, higher operating temperatures, speeds and pressures, the GE IPE increases thrust levels by as much as 30 per cent in certain areas of the flight envelope, while retaining more than 80 per cent parts commonality. The IPE's digital electronic control has 50 per cent fewer parts than previous controls, and offers substantially improved reliability. The IPE first flew in an F-16C/D in August 1988, and a USAF field service evaluation programme was to begin in the latter half of 1990. Service entry is scheduled for 1991. The engine is also a contender to power Japan's FSX fighter.

The following refers to the F110-GE-129:

FAN: Three stages. Bypass ratio 0.76. Airflow 122 kg (270 lb)/s.

HP COMPRESSOR: Nine stages. Overall pressure ratio, 31 : 1 class.

COMBUSTOR: Annular scroll.

HP TURBINE: Single stage with aircooled blades.

LP TURBINE: Two stages, drives fan.

AUGMENTOR: Close coupled mixed-flow linear thrust afterburner.

EXHAUST NOZZLE: Convergent/divergent exhaust nozzle with hydraulic actuation.

DIMENSIONS:
Length	4,626 mm (182.3 in)
Diameter	1,180 mm (46.5 in)

PERFORMANCE RATINGS (S/L):
T-O	129 kN (29,000 lb st)
Max dry	75.7 kN (17,000 lb)

GENERAL ELECTRIC GE37
US military designation: F120

The F120-GE-100 is GE Aircraft Engines' propulsion candidate for the USAF's Advanced Tactical Fighter (ATF). The engine features advanced variable-cycle capability, counter-rotating turbine and a two-dimensional, vectoring exhaust nozzle. The variable-cycle technology enables the F120 to operate as a conventional turbojet at supersonic speeds, while maintaining the characteristics of a more fuel-efficient turbofan at subsonic speeds. The use of advanced materials and design technology enable the F120 to achieve a higher thrust-to-weight ratio than GEAE's

General Electric F110-GE-129 two-shaft augmented turbofan

current production aircraft fighter engines. The F120 prototype engines were undergoing factory test in preparation for flight test in 1990 in rival Lockheed YF-22A and Northrop YF-23A ATF prototype aircraft. The demonstrator engines completed testing in 1988.

GENERAL ELECTRIC F118

This unaugmented turbofan has been developed under USAF contract to meet the demanding propulsion requirements of the Northrop B-2A bomber. An 84.52 kN (19,000 lb st) thrust class derivative of the F101 and F110 engines, the non-afterburning **F118-GE-100** employs new long-chord fan technology with the compressor and turbine used on the F110. The F118 has a higher airflow capacity and higher air pressure ratio than the F110, resulting in higher thrust. The engine was fully qualified in 1987, has successfully powered the B-2A in the USAF flight test programme since July 1989, and has accumulated more than 6,000 test hours to date. A feature is the use of common F101/F110 production tooling for low cost.

The accompanying photograph shows the actuation ring for the trailing flaps of the inlet guide vanes, a large inlet bleed-air de-icing pipe, and the ribbed bypass duct. The cooled jets issue across what appear to be carbon areas above the B-2A wing.

In Autumn 1989 a Lockheed TR-1 began a flight test programme powered by a derivative of the F118, designated **F101-GE-F29**. This engine is lighter and shorter but delivers more dry thrust than the J75-P-13B normally fitted.

GENERAL ELECTRIC UDF

Using thin scimitar-like blades, the unducted fan (UDF) engine has a bypass ratio of 36. The proof of concept demonstrator used an F404 core and was rated in the 111.2 kN (25,000 lb st) class. Flight testing on a Boeing 727 started on 20 August 1986, and was completed in February 1987. Flight testing on an MD-80 began on 18 May 1987 and was completed in March 1988.

After accomplishing all flight objectives, GE started development of the product engine, which it considered suitable for use on the projected MD-91, MD-92 and 7J7. On 30 May 1985 GE and SNECMA signed an agreement assigning to the French company a 35 per cent share of the UDF programme. SNECMA participated in the proof of concept demonstration, and was to be involved in the design and development of major portions of the product engine.

The key to the light weight and low fuel consumption of the UDF lies in elimination of a drive gearbox. Instead, the gas from the core passes through large multi-stage contra-rotating turbines downstream. This substitutes rotor blades for what would normally be the turbine stators, and the visible propeller blades are mounted directly on the two rotors of the power turbine. Blade loading for the LP power turbines is normal, but speed is low and the resulting 'insignificant' stress levels allow the unique construction at low risk.

The external propulsor blades are designed using techniques established with fan blades, the hub radius ratio of more than 0.45 being more than twice that common for propellers. The composite blades change pitch from flight settings through feather to reverse, and the pitch is set to control speed and power output.

In June 1989 GE announced completion of UDF development, pending a time when a market might appear. Should work be resumed at a future date, about four years and $1.3 billion would be needed for certification.

GENERAL ELECTRIC T407

The T407 is a member of the T407/GLC38/CFE738 engine family, which includes turboprop, turboshaft, turbofan, and unducted fan (UDF) versions. Formerly called the GE38, the T407 is derived from the GE27, a highly successful turboshaft demonstrator engine that GE developed for the US Army's Modern Technology Demonstrator Engine (MTDE) programme.

The T407/GLC38 engine is being developed by the joint team of GE Aircraft Engines and Textron Lycoming, with Bendix Control, a division of Allied Signal; Ruston Gas Turbines Ltd of the UK, part of GEC Alsthom; and Steel Products Engineering Co (SPECO). Bendix is responsible for a FADEC for the whole T407/GLC38/CFE738 family; Ruston is manufacturing compressor blisks and power-turbine components; and SPECO is providing the T407 propeller reduction gears. GE and Textron will each assemble, test, and ship approximately 50 per cent of the T407 and GLC38 engines.

The first T407/GLC38 prototype engine (turboshaft configuration) was successfuly fired in December 1989 at Textron Lycoming's Stratford engine test facility. T407 certification is planned for early 1992, with initial production in 1993.

The first application for the **T407-GE-400** turboprop will be to power the Lockheed P-7A ASW aircraft. GE has responsibility for an integrated propulsion system complete with engine, propeller gearbox, advanced five-blade propeller and nacelle. The **GLC38** is the commercial turboprop engine. The following refers to the basic T407/GLC38 power plant (including the propeller gearbox):

TYPE: Two-shaft modular turbine engine.
COMPRESSOR: Five axial stages followed by one centrifugal stage.
COMBUSTION CHAMBER: Short annular type with 15 injectors.
TURBINES: Two-stage aircooled compressor turbine. Three-stage power turbine.
DIMENSIONS:
Max envelope length	2,972 mm (117 in)
Max envelope diameter	838 mm (33 in)
PERFORMANCE RATING (S/L, T-O):
T407	4,475 kW (6,000 shp) class
SPECIFIC FUEL CONSUMPTION:
"15-30 per cent better than engines in its class"

GENERAL ELECTRIC T64

The T64 was developed initially for the US Navy. It is available as a turboshaft or turboprop. Current versions are:

T64-GE-100. -7A with improved turbine. Powers CH-53C and MH-53J. Also being upgraded by kit from -7A.

Longitudinal section of General Electric F110 two-shaft augmented turbofan

General Electric F118-GE-100 two-shaft unaugmented turbofan

General Electric F120-GE-100 variable cycle fighter engine with vectoring nozzle

General Electric UDF engine installed on MD-80

T64-GE-413. Powers CH-53D.

T64-GE-415. Improved combustion liner and turbine cooling. Powers RH-53D.

T64-GE-416. As -415. Powers CH/MH-53E.

T64-GE-416A. As -416, improved turbine.

T64-GE-419. As -416A, with integral fuel/oil heat exchanger, and OEI emergency power on a 32.2°C day. To power CH/MH-53E from 1993.

CT64-820-4. Turboprop, powers DHC-5D.

T64/P4D. Turboprop, powers G222. Production by Fiat, supported by Alfa Romeo Avio from 1975.

TYPE: Free turbine turboshaft/turboprop.

COMPRESSOR: Fourteen-stage axial-flow, single-spool steel rotor for -820/-1/2/3, titanium and steel compressor for -100, -413, -415, -416, -416A, -419, -P4D and CT64-820-4. Inlet guide vanes and first four stages of stator vanes variable, air mass flow per second: -100, -413, -415, -416, -416A, -419, 13.3 kg (29.4 lb); -820-4, 11.9 kg (26.2 lb); P4D, 12.2 kg (27.0 lb). Pressure ratio: -820-4, 12.5; -100, -413, -415/-416/-416A, -419, 14.0; P4D, 13.0.

COMBUSTION CHAMBER: Annular type. Double fuel manifold feeds twelve duplex type fuel nozzles.

GAS GENERATOR TURBINE: Two-stage, coupled directly to compressor rotor by spline connection. Engines rated 3,228 kW (4,330 shp) or over have aircooled first-stage blades.

POWER TURBINE: Two-stage, independent of gas generator.

REDUCTION GEAR: Remotely mounted for turboprop, offset and accessible for inspection and replacement. Ratio 13.44.

STARTING: Mechanical, airframe supplied.

DIMENSIONS:

Length: T64-GE-100, -413, -415, -416, -416A, -419
2,006 mm (79 in)
T64/P4D, CT64-820-4   2,793 mm (110 in)
Width: T64-GE-100, -413, -415, -416, -416A, -419
660 mm (26.0 in)
T64/P4D, CT64-820-4   683 mm (26.9 in)
Height: T64-GE-100, -413, -415, -416, -416A, -419
825 mm (32.5 in)
T64/P4D, CT64-820-4   1,168 mm (46 in)

WEIGHT, DRY:

T64-GE-100, -413, -415, -416, -416A   327 kg (720 lb)
T64-GE-419   343 kg (755 lb)
CT64-820-4   520 kg (1,145 lb)
T64/P4D   538 kg (1,188 lb)

PERFORMANCE RATINGS (max rating (S/L)):

T64-GE-100   3,229 kW (4,330 shp) to 29.4°C
T64-GE-413   2,927 kW (3,925 shp)
T64-GE-415, -416, -416A   3,266 kW (4,380 shp)
T64-GE-419   3,542 kW (4,750 shp)
CT64-820-4   2,336 kW (3,133 shp)
T64/P4D   2,535 kW (3,400 shp)

SPECIFIC FUEL CONSUMPTION (max rating (S/L)):

T64-GE-100, -413, -415, -416, -416A, -419
79.4 µg/J (0.47 lb/h/shp)
CT64-820-4, T64/P4D   81 µg/J (0.48 lb/h/shp)

GENERAL ELECTRIC T700

The T700 was selected in 1971 to power the US Army's utility tactical transport aircraft system (UTTAS). The first

General Electric T407/GLC38 basic core

General Electric GLC38 turboprop mockup

T700 went to test in 1973, and in 1976 it was the first turboshaft to pass current US military qualification standards. The engine went into production in 1978. Of the following models, only the Step 2 growth derivatives are in production.

T700-GE-700. First production model delivered from early 1978. Following description refers to this version, except where otherwise noted. Powers UH-60A Black Hawk.

T700-GE-701. First-step growth derivative. Upgrade of 10 per cent. Powers AH-64 Apache.

T700-GE-401. Navalised and upgraded first-step derivative with over 95 per cent commonality. Powers SH-60B Seahawk, SH-2G Super Seasprite and AH-1W SuperCobra.

T700-GE-701C. Second-step growth derivative. Provides 20 per cent more power than -700. Went into production in 1988 for future Black Hawks and Apaches. Offered for future S-70/WS-70 Black Hawk derivatives for international sales.

T700-GE-401C. Navalised second-step growth derivative. Chosen by US Navy for future Seahawks and derivatives. First production engines delivered in 1988 to power HH-60H; Royal Australian Navy also a launch customer.

GE alliances on T700 engines include agreements with Ruston Gas Turbines of Great Britain that result in a UK-manufactured T700; a licence agreement with Alfa Romeo Avio (with additional participation of Fiat Avio) for manufacture and assembly of T700/CT7 engines in Italy; a licence agreement with Australia to assemble T700s; and another with Japan to build and test T700s for Black Hawks and Seahawks. Planning is under way for licensed production in South Korea.

TYPE: Ungeared free turbine turboshaft engine.

INTAKE: Annular, with anti-iced separator designed to remove 95 per cent of sand, dust and foreign object ingestion. Extracted matter discharged by blower driven from accessory gearbox.

COMPRESSOR: Combined axial/centrifugal. Five axial stages and single centrifugal stage mounted on same shaft. Each axial stage is one-piece 'blisk' (blades plus disc) in AM355 steel highly resistant to erosion. Inlet guide vanes and first two stator stages variable. Pressure ratio about 15. Mass flow about 4.5 kg (10 lb)/s at 44,720 rpm.

COMBUSTION CHAMBER: Fully annular. Central fuel injection to maximise acceptance of contaminated fuel and give minimal smoke generation. Ignition power from separate winding on engine mounted alternator serves dual plugs.

TURBINE: Two stage gas generator (HP) turbine operates at gas temperatures exceeding 1,100°C. First stage nozzle investment cast in X40. Second stage nozzle investment cast in two-vane segments in R80. Rated speed (S/L, ISA, max T-O), 44,720 rpm. Two stage free power turbine, with tip shrouded blades and segmented nozzles. Power turbine inlet temperature at intermediate power, 827°C. Output speed, 21,000 rpm.

General Electric T64-GE-415/416 turboshaft

CONTROLS: Hydromechanical control can be replaced in less than 12 minutes. Electrical control provides twin-engine speed and torque matching.

ACCESSORIES: Grouped at top of engine, together with engine control system. Integral oil tank, plus emergency mist lubrication. Torque sensor provides signal to electrical control.

DIMENSIONS:
Length overall	1,168 mm (46.0 in)
Width	635 mm (25 in)
Height overall	584 mm (23 in)

WEIGHT, DRY (with particle separator):
T700-700	198 kg (437 lb)
T700-401	197 kg (434 lb)
T700-701C	211 kg (465 lb)
T700-401C	213 kg (468 lb)

PERFORMANCE RATINGS (ISA, S/L, static):
T700-700:	
intermediate	1,210 kW (1,622 shp)
continuous	987 kW (1,324 shp)
T700-401:	
contingency	1,285 kW (1,723 shp)
intermediate	1,260 kW (1,690 shp)
continuous	1,072 kW (1,437 shp)
T700-701C:	
maximum	2,534 kW (1,890 shp)
intermediate	2,414 kW (1,800 shp)
continuous	2,229 kW (1,662 shp)
T700-401C:	
contingency	2,600 kW (1,940 shp)
intermediate	2,414 kW (1,800 shp)
continuous	2,229 kW (1,662 shp)

SPECIFIC FUEL CONSUMPTION (ISA, S/L, static):
T700-700:	
continuous	79.41 μg/J (0.470 lb/h/shp)
T700-401:	
intermediate	78.40 μg/J (0.464 lb/h/shp)
T700-701C:	
continuous	77.56 μg/J (0.459 lb/h/shp)
T700-401C:	
continuous	77.56 μg/J (0.459 lb/h/shp)

General Electric T700-401 free-turbine turboshaft

GENERAL ELECTRIC CT7

Commercial engine based on the T700. Certification in April 1977. The **CT7-2A** turboshaft powers the Bell 214ST. The **CT7-2D** and **-2D1** power S-70 Black Hawks. The CT7-2D is the commercial equivalent of the -701/-401. The CT7-2D1 is the commercial equivalent of the -701C/-401C and received FAA certification in June 1989.

The **CT7-6** is a Step 2 growth engine, co-developed by Alfa Romeo Avio, Fiat Avio and GE for the EH 101 and other helicopter applications, such as the NH 90. First delivery for the EH 101 took place in April 1988; first flight of a CT7-6 powered EH 101 took place in September 1988. The marinised **CT7-6A** powers the Italian Navy's EH 101 prototype. The CT7-6/-6A has received FAA certification, as well as RAI and BCAA validation.

The same core is used in the CT7 turboprop, which has a remote propeller gearbox. This engine received FAA certification in August 1983 and is in production as the **CT7-5A** for the Saab 340 and as the **CT7-7A** for the Airtech CN 235.

CT7 turboprop growth engines include the **CT7-9B** and **-9C** flat rated at 1,395 kW (1,870 shp). Increased power is obtained by improvements in aerodynamics, materials and turbine cooling. These engines power advanced versions of the CN 235 and Saab 340. The -9B has also been selected as the power plant for the Let L-610.

GE is also discussing a compact Dash-9 flat rated at 1,119 kW (1,500 shp). This **CT7-3** would have a Hamilton Standard gearbox located on the front of the engine, saving 660 mm (26 in) in length and 56.7 kg (125 lb) in weight.

Data below are for the current turboshaft versions:

DIMENSIONS:
Length	1,168 mm (46.0 in)
Diameter (max envelope)	635 mm (25.0 in)

WEIGHT, DRY:
CT7-2A	202 kg (444 lb)
CT7-2D/2B	201 kg (442 lb)
CT7-6	209 kg (460 lb)

Full scale model of General Electric CT7-6 turboshaft *(Brian M. Service)*

PERFORMANCE RATINGS (S/L, static, 15°C):
Contingency (2½ min OEI):	
CT7-2A, 2B, -2D	1,287 kW (1,725 shp)
CT7-6	1,491 kW (2,000 shp)
T-O (5 min) and en route contingency (30 min):	
CT7-2A, 2B, -2D	1,211 kW (1,623 shp)
CT7-2B	1,212 kW (1,625 shp)
CT7-6	1,491 kW (2,000 shp)

SPECIFIC FUEL CONSUMPTION:
Max continuous:	
CT7-2A, -2B	79.9 μg/J (0.473 lb/h/shp)
CT7-6 (15°C)	77.4 μg/J (0.458 lb/h/shp)
CT7-6 (35°C)	82.8 μg/J (0.490 lb/h/shp)

Data below are for the current turboprop versions:

General Electric CT7-9 free-turbine turboprop

CT7 turboprops	-5A	-7A	-9B	-9C
Length mm (in)	2,438 (96)	2,438 (96)	2,438 (96)	2,438 (96)
Max diameter mm (in)	737 (29)	737 (29)	737 (29)	737 (29)
Weight, dry kg (lb)	349.3 (770)	351.5 (775)	360.6 (795)	360.6 (795)
PERFORMANCE RATINGS:				
S/L T-O kW (shp)	1,294 (1,735)	1,268 (1,700)	1,305 (1,750)	1,305 (1,750)
APR auto power reserve kW (shp)	—	—	1,394 (1,870)	1,394 (1,870)
Max cruise at 4,575 m (15,000 ft) ekW (ehp)	978 (1,312)	978 (1,312)	1,052 (1,411)	1,118 (1,499)

IN-TECH

IN-TECH INTERNATIONAL INC

West 7510 Hall Avenue, Spokane, Washington 99204-5708
Telephone: 1 (509) 455 6116
Fax: 1 (509) 747 1701

In September 1985 In-Tech International acquired the Merlyn engine (see Machen in 1985-86 *Jane's*). Due to product liability exposure, the Merlyn will be available for aircraft only after experience shows that the risk can be minimised.

IN-TECH MERLYN

Research shows a need for a new piston engine in the 373-522 kW (500-700 hp) class, with liquid cooling. Design goals included a power: weight ratio better than 0.34 kg/kW (1 lb/hp); ability to use multifuels (Jet A, JP-4, JP-5, Nos. 1 and 2 diesel); an sfc 20 per cent lower than small turboprops; low frontal area and drag; and at least six accessory pads.
TYPE: Three-cylinder inline two-stroke diesel.
CYLINDERS: Bore 130 mm (5.125 in). Stroke 86 mm (3.388 in). Capacity 3.47 litres (210 cu in). Twin overhead camshaft and four exhaust valves per cylinder. Offset crankshaft.
DIMENSIONS:

Length	1,283 mm (50.5 in)
Width	457 mm (18.0 in)
Height	648 mm (25.5 in)
WEIGHT, DRY:	263 kg (580 lb)

In-Tech Merlyn three-cylinder two-stroke diesel

PERFORMANCE RATINGS:

T-O	485 kW (650 hp) at 4,800 rpm
Max continuous	448 kW (600 hp)

JAVELIN

JAVELIN AIRCRAFT COMPANY INC

Municipal Airport, Augusta, Kansas 67010
Telephone: 1 (316) 733 1011

Javelin has a long-term programme to produce liquid cooled aircraft engines. Extensive work has been done on the Javelin Ford 140 (cu in capacity). A completely engineered power plant with turbocharger was flight tested in a Cessna 172. The 140T continues in demand for replica fighters, but most homebuilders need the smaller Ford Escort/Lynx 98 of 1,607 cc (98 cu in). Six Ford 98s are on test, one being a 'hi-drive' for amphibians with the engine and radiator inside the hull and propeller above. The conventional installation weighs about 129 kg (285 lb) with toothed belt drive. By early 1982 one 98-size engine was flying in a Cessna 150, held to 93 kW (125 hp) and cruising at 44.8 kW (60 hp) with sfc of 62 µg/J (0.37 lb/h/hp). In 1983 intensive flight development was in progress on the Ford 230 (Windsor) V-6, with a continuous rating of 149 kW (200 hp) for a weight, with reduction gear and all accessories, of 176 kg (387 lb).

Javelin Ford 230 six-cylinder piston engine

LHTEC

LIGHT HELICOPTER TURBINE ENGINE COMPANY

The Paragon Building, Suite 400, 12400 Olive Boulevard, St Louis, Missouri 63141
MEMBER COMPANIES: **Allison Gas Turbine Division**
PO Box 420, Indianapolis, Indiana 46206
Garrett Engine Division
PO Box 5217, Phoenix, Arizona 85010

These two companies have combined their resources to develop the T800-LHT-800 975 kW (1,300 shp) class turboshaft engine for the multi-service LH (AH-66) programme. LHTEC was selected by the US Army over its competitor in October 1988.

LHTEC T800-LHT-800

This helicopter engine stems from programmes that the two partners started prior to 1983. The Garrett TSE109 used a core based on the F109 turbofan and did extensive running before leading to the T800 technology prototypes, incorporating Allison technology, which exceeded 940 kW (1,260 shp) in December 1984 with lower than the required fuel consumption. The initial flight evaluation of the adaptive fuel control was completed in January 1985. Chandler Evans and AiResearch Electronic Signal Division are teamed to develop the control system. Flight development of prototype engines began on 7 March 1985. By January 1990 prototype engines had run more than 7,300 h, including sand and ice ingestion and loss of oil demonstrations.

Twin T800s have been flying in an A 129 since October 1988. This programme has been followed by the Westland Lynx T800, USCG HH-65 T800 and Aerospatiale/LTV Dauphin T800 programmes. In 1989 LHTEC announced the civil **CTS 800**, to be FAA certificated in mid-1991 and available from production in 1992.

Cutaway drawing of LHTEC T800 free-turbine turboshaft

DIMENSIONS:

Length	800 mm (31.5 in)	T-O (5 min)	969 kW (1,300 shp)
Width	549 mm (21.6 in)	T-O (30 min)	895 kW (1,200 shp)
Height	658 mm (25.9 in)	Continuous	764 kW (1,025 shp)
WEIGHT, DRY: T800	143 kg (315 lb)	FUEL FLOW:	
CTS800 with gearbox	163 kg (360 lb)	Contingency	285 kg (630 lb)/h
PERFORMANCE RATINGS:		5 min	274 kg (603 lb)/h
Contingency (2 min)	1,007 kW (1,350 shp)	30 min	256 kg (565 lb)/h
		Continuous	219 kg (483 lb)/h

MARQUARDT

THE MARQUARDT COMPANY (subsidiary of International Signal and Control Group)

16555 Saticoy Street, Van Nuys, California 91409
Telephone: 1 (818) 989 6400
Telex: (910) 4951710
PRESIDENT: F. X. Marshall

Marquardt's main business continues to be advanced aerospace propulsion and the supply of ram air turbine power systems. Marquardt is developing composite rocket/air breathing propulsion systems for the US Air Force and Navy. Marquardt has developed bipropellant rockets for spacecraft since 1959, as described in the 1984-85 and earlier editions of *Jane's*.

MARQUARDT RAMJETS

Marquardt continues to be a principal developer of advanced ramjet systems. This activity has included the development of an integral rocket/ramjet for an advanced strategic air launched missile, the development of fixed and variable flow ducted rockets and small scale integral rocket/ramjets for air-launched missile applications.

MARQUARDT R-40A

This precision control rocket was developed and qualified for the Shuttle Orbiter and is being used as an orbit insertion engine for the US Navy's Shuttle Launch Dispenser.

TYPE: Liquid propellant reaction control rocket.

PROPELLANTS: Nitrogen tetroxide and monomethyl hydrazine.

THRUST CHAMBER ASSEMBLY: Single chamber. Area ratio 20. Made of silicide coated columbium, with welded-on orthogonal and scarfed nozzle extension in same material. Internal film cooling. Multiple doublet injector with hypergolic ignition.

PROPELLANT FEED SYSTEM: Pressurised tanks, with feed of 0.526 kg (1.16 lb)/s fuel and 0.838 kg (1.85 lb)/s oxidant at 16.4 bars (238 lb/sq in abs).

DIMENSIONS:
Length overall	472 mm (18.6 in)
Nozzle exit diameter	267 mm (10.5 in)

WEIGHT, DRY: 9.5 kg (21.0 lb)

PERFORMANCE RATINGS:
Max thrust (vacuum)	3.87 kN (870 lb)
Chamber pressure	10.5 bars (152 lb/sq in)
Specific impulse: area ratio 20	281
area ratio 120	306

Marquardt R-40A reaction control rocket

MARQUARDT R-1E

This small high performance rocket was qualified as the vernier for the Shuttle Orbiter.

TYPE: Liquid bipropellant rocket for use in space.

PROPELLANTS: Nitrogen tetroxide and monomethyl hydrazine.

THRUST CHAMBER: Single chamber. Minimum area ratio 26 with orthogonal and scarfed nozzles. Made of silicide coated columbium. Insulated for buried installation. Single doublet injector with hypergolic ignition.

PROPELLANT FEED SYSTEM: Pressurised tank. Flow rate 0.016 kg (0.0354 lb)/s fuel and 0.0256 kg (0.565 lb)/s oxidant.

Marquardt R-1E vernier long scarf thruster

DIMENSIONS:
Length overall	279 mm (11.0 in)
Width	147 mm (5.8 in)
Height (depth)	145 mm (5.7 in)

WEIGHT, DRY: 3.7 kg (8.2 lb)

PERFORMANCE RATINGS:
Max thrust (vacuum)	0.11 kN (25.0 lb)
Chamber pressure	7.45 bars (108 lb/sq in)
Specific impulse (area ratio 100)	290

MTI
MICROTURBO INC

2707 Forum Drive, Grand Prairie, Texas 75051-7027
Telephone: 1 (214) 660 5545
Telex: (510) 228 7320
Fax: 1 (214) 660 7181

PRESIDENT: Robert P. Schiller

This company was established in 1970 as the US subsidiary of Microturbo SA (see under France). It makes, overhauls and repairs Microturbo turbojets, APUs and other products.

NELSON
NELSON AIRCRAFT CORPORATION

PO Box 454, 8075 Pennsylvania Ave, Irwin, Pennsylvania 15642
Telephone: 1 (412) 863 5900
PRESIDENT: Charles R. Rhoades
DEVELOPMENT DEPARTMENT: 420 Harbor Drive, Naples, Florida 33940
Telephone: 1 (813) 261 1670

Nelson Aircraft Corporation, among its many industrial activities, produces to order the Nelson H-63 four-cylinder two-cycle aircooled engine, which is certificated by the FAA as a power unit for single-seat helicopters, and is also available as a power plant for propeller driven aircraft. These engines are capable of sustained inverted flight. Recommended overhaul period is 800 h.

The affiliated Sport Plane Power Inc in Naples, Florida, is the subject of a separate entry.

NELSON H-63
US military designation: YO-65

Developed originally as a power unit for single-seat helicopters, the H-63 is now available in two versions, as follows:

H-63C. Basic helicopter power unit for vertical installation. Battery/electronic ignition and direct drive. Certificated by FAA. Supplied as complete power package, including clutch, cooling fan and shroud.

H-63CP. Basically as H-63C, but without clutch, fan and shroud. Intended primarily for installation in horizontal position, with direct drive to propeller. FAA certificated.

Nelson has developed a 1.07 m (42 in) wooden propeller with glassfibre covering for use with the H-63. It is suitable for either tractor or pusher installation.

TYPE: Four-cylinder horizontally opposed aircooled, two-stroke.

CYLINDERS: Bore 68.3 mm (2¹¹⁄₁₆ in). Stroke 70 mm (2¾ in). Total capacity 1.03 litres (63 cu in). Compression ratio 8 : 1.

PISTONS: Aluminium alloy casting. Two piston rings. Two needle roller bearings pressed in boss.

CONNECTING RODS: Alloy steel forging. Caged roller bearing at big-end.

CRANKSHAFT: Four-throw. Nitralloy shaft on ball and roller bearings.

CRANKCASE: Two-piece magnesium alloy cast case divided on horizontal centreline.

INDUCTION: Nelson diaphragm type all-angle fuel control carburettor. Fuel/oil mixture valves from crankcase through rotary valve driven by crankshaft. Intake to and exhaust from cylinders through ports.

FUEL: 80/87 octane gasoline and SAE 30 ash-free-base oil in 16 : 1 mixture.

IGNITION: Battery/electronic dual ignition with two Champion D-9 or 5 COM spark plugs per cylinder.

LUBRICATION: See under 'Fuel'.

POWER TAKE-OFF (H-63C): Hollow shaft extension from Salisbury centrifugal clutch output drive.

STARTING: 12V DC Autolite electric motor and Bendix drive.

COOLING: (H-63C): Centrifugal aluminium fan and two-piece glassfibre shrouding for FAA hot day of 37.8°C. (H-63CP): by propeller slipstream.

DIMENSIONS (H-63C):
Length	508 mm (20.0 in)
Height	376 mm (14.8 in)
Width	605 mm (23.8 in)

WEIGHT, DRY (with accessories):
H-63C	34.5 kg (76 lb)
H-63CP	30.8 kg (68 lb)

POWER RATINGS:
T-O:
H-63C	32 kW (43 hp) at 4,000 rpm
H-63CP	35.8 kW (48 hp) at 4,400 rpm

Max continuous:
H-63C	32 kW (43 hp) at 4,000 rpm
H-63CP	33.6 kW (45 hp) at 4,000 rpm

Nelson H-63CP four-cylinder engine for fixed-wing aircraft

Nelson H-63C four-cylinder two-stroke engine

PRATT & WHITNEY
UNITED TECHNOLOGIES PRATT & WHITNEY

HEADQUARTERS: East Hartford, Connecticut 06108
Telephone: 1 (203) 565 4321
Fax: (PR) 1 (203) 565 8896

Government Engine Business
PO Box 109600, W Palm Beach, Florida 33410-9600
Telephone: (PR) 1 (407) 796 6796
Fax: (PR) 1 (407) 796 7258

PRESIDENT: Arthur E. Wegner

Pratt & Whitney Aircraft was formed in 1925. Today Pratt & Whitney is the world's largest producer of gas turbine engines. Excluding P & W Canada (which see) it had by 1989 delivered over 70,000 aircraft gas turbines, including more than 25,000 airline jet engines.

PRATT & WHITNEY JT8
US military designation: J52

The J52 is a two-spool turbojet, with 12 compressor stages, a can-annular combustion system fed by 36 dual orifice injectors and single-stage HP and LP turbines. The P-408 has two-position inlet guide vanes and aircooled first-stage turbine vanes and blades. P-8 and P-408 can be upgraded to P-409 by field retrofit.

J52-P-6A, 6B, 8A, 8B. Rated at 37.8 kN (8,500 lb st) (6A, 6B) or 41.4 kN (9,300 lb st) (8A, 8B). Powers A-4, and A-6.

J52-P-408. Rated at 49.8 kN (11,200 lb st). Powers A-4F, A-4M, some export A-4 versions, EA-6B.

J52-P-409. Rated at 53.4 kN (12,000 lb st).

Data below are for the P-408:

DIMENSIONS:
Diameter	814.3 mm (32.06 in)
Length	3,020 mm (118.9 in)

WEIGHT, DRY: 1,052 kg (2,318 lb)

PRATT & WHITNEY JT8D

This turbofan was developed to power the Boeing 727. Military versions have been developed in Sweden by Volvo Flygmotor (see RM8 in that company's entry).

The JT8D entered commercial service on 1 February 1964. It has since become the most widely used commercial jet engine, almost 12,000 having logged more than 400 million flight hours by January 1989.

The following are current versions:

JT8D-9, -9A. Develops 64.5 kN (14,500 lb st) to 28.9°C at S/L. Specified for 727-100, -100C and -200, 737-200, -200C and T-43A, DC-9-20, -30, -40, C-9A, C-9B and VC-9C, Caravelle 12 and Kawasaki C-1. Produced under licence in Japan (see Mitsubishi).

JT8D-11. Develops 66.7 kN (15,000 lb st) to 28.9°C at S/L. Specified for DC-9-20, -30 and -40.

JT8D-15. Develops 69 kN (15,500 lb st) to 28.9°C. Powers Mercure, Advanced 727 and 737, and DC-9.

JT8D-15A. In 1982 new components in the Dash-15 resulted in a 5.5 per cent reduction in cruise fuel consumption. The same parts in the Dash-17 produce the **JT8D-17A**, and when fitted to the Dash-17R the **JT8D-17AR**.

JT8D-17. Develops 71.2 kN (16,000 lb st) to 28.9°C. Powers Advanced Boeing 727 and 737, and DC-9.

JT8D-17R. Normal T-O rating 72.95 kN (16,400 lb st) but has capability of providing 4.448 kN (1,000 lb) additional thrust in the event of significant thrust loss on any other engine.

JT8D-200 Series. Described separately.

Since February 1970 all new JT8D engines have incorporated smoke reduction hardware, and conversion kits are available. Two noise reduction options are also available.

TYPE: Two-spool turbofan.

FAN: Two-stage front fan. Mass flow: -9, -9A, 145 kg (319 lb)/s; -11, -15, 146 kg (322 lb)/s; -17, 147 kg (324 lb)/s; -17R, 148 kg (326 lb)/s. Bypass ratio: -9, -9A, 1.04; -11, 1.05; -15, 1.03; -17, 1.02; -17R, 1.00.

LP COMPRESSOR: Six-stage, integral with fan.

HP COMPRESSOR: Seven-stage. Overall pressure ratio: -9, -9A, 15.9; -11, 16.2; -15, 16.5; -17, 16.9; -17R, 17.3.

COMBUSTION CHAMBER: Can-annular type with nine cylindrical flame tubes, each with a single Duplex burner.

HP TURBINE: Single-stage. Solid blades in -9, aircooled in -11 and later.

LP TURBINE: Three-stage.

DIMENSIONS:

Diameter	1,080 mm (42.5 in)
Length	3,137 mm (123.5 in)

WEIGHT, DRY:

JT8D-9, -9A	1,532 kg (3,377 lb)
JT8D-11	1,537 kg (3,389 lb)
JT8D-15	1,549 kg (3,414 lb)
-15A	1,576 kg (3,474 lb)
JT8D-17	1,556 kg (3,430 lb)
-17A	1,577 kg (3,475 lb)
JT8D-17R	1,585 kg (3,495 lb)
-17AR	1,588 kg (3,500 lb)

PERFORMANCE RATINGS:
T-O thrust (S/L, static)   see model descriptions
Max cruise thrust (10,670 m; 35,000 ft at Mach 0.8):

JT8D-9, -9A	18.2 kN (4,100 lb)
JT8D-11	17.6 kN (3,950 lb)
JT8D-15, -15A	18.2 kN (4,100 lb)
JT8D-17, -17R, -17A, -17AR	18.9 kN (4,240 lb)

SPECIFIC FUEL CONSUMPTION:
T-O rating:

JT8D-9, 9A	16.85 mg/Ns (0.595 lb/h/lb st)
JT8D-11	17.56 mg/Ns (0.620 lb/h/lb st)
JT8D-15	17.84 mg/Ns (0.630 lb/h/lb st)
-15A	16.63 mg/Ns (0.587 lb/h/lb st)
JT8D-17	18.27 mg/Ns (0.645 lb/h/lb st)
-17A	17.05 mg/Ns (0.602 lb/h/lb st)
JT8D-17R	18.55 mg/Ns (0.655 lb/h/lb st)
-17AR	17.31 mg/Ns (0.611 lb/h/lb st)

Max cruise rating, as above:

JT8D-9, -9A	22.86 mg/Ns (0.807 lb/h/lb)
JT8D-11	23.14 mg/Ns (0.817 lb/h/lb)
JT8D-15	22.97 mg/Ns (0.811 lb/h/lb)
JT8D-17, -17R	23.37 mg/Ns (0.825 lb/h/lb)

PRATT & WHITNEY JT8D-200 SERIES

This reduced noise derivative of the JT8D combines the HP compressor, HP turbine spool and combustion section of the JT8D-9 with advanced LP technology. It offers increased thrust with reduced noise and specific fuel consumption. The fan has increased diameter. The new six-stage LP compressor, integral with the fan, offers increased pressure ratio. The LP turbine has 20 per cent greater annular area and achieves a higher efficiency. Surrounding the engine is a new bypass duct. The exhaust system includes a 12 lobe mixer. FAA certification of the JT8D-209 was awarded in June 1979.

The following are current models:

JT8D-209. Rated at 82.2 kN (18,500 lb st) to 25°C, and 85.6 kN (19,250 lb st) following loss of thrust on any other engine. Entered service in October 1980, powering the MD-81.

JT8D-217. Rated at 88.96 kN (20,000 lb st), and 92.75 kN (20,850 lb st) following loss of thrust on any other engine. Powers MD-82.

JT8D-217A. T-O thrust available to 28.9°C or up to 1,525 m (5,000 ft). Powers MD-82.

JT8D-217C. Incorporates JT8D-219 performance improvements to reduce sfc. Powers MD-82 and -87.

JT8D-219. Rated at 93.4 kN (21,000 lb st), with a reserve power of 96.5 kN (21,700 lb st). Powers MD-83 and other MD-80 aircraft.

TYPE: Two-spool turbofan.

FAN: Single-stage front fan has 34 titanium blades, with part-span shrouds. Mass flow: -209, 213 kg (469 lb)/s; -217 (all), 219 kg (483 lb)/s; -219, 221 kg (488 lb)/s. Bypass ratio: -209, 1.78; -217 (all), 1.73; -219, 1.77.

LP COMPRESSOR: Six-stage axial, integral with fan.

HP COMPRESSOR: Seven-stage axial. Overall pressure ratio: -209, 17.1; -217 (all), 18.6; -219, 19.2.

COMBUSTION CHAMBER: Nine can-annular low-emissions burners with aerating fuel nozzles.

HP TURBINE: Single-stage. Aircooled blades in -217 and -219.

LP TURBINE: Three-stage.

DIMENSIONS:

Diameter	1,250 mm (49.2 in)
Length	3,911 mm (154 in)

WEIGHT, DRY:

JT8D-209	2,012 kg (4,435 lb)
JT8D-217, -217A	2,028 kg (4,470 lb)
JT8D-217C, -219	2,048 kg (4,515 lb)

PERFORMANCE RATINGS:
T-O (S/L static):   see model descriptions
Max cruise thrust (10,670 m; 35,000 ft at Mach 0.8):

JT8D-209	22.0 kN (4,945 lb)
JT8D-217, -217A, -217C	23.31 kN (5,240 lb)
JT8D-219	23.35 kN (5,250 lb)

SPECIFIC FUEL CONSUMPTION:
Max cruise rating, as above:

JT8D-209	20.50 mg/Ns (0.724 lb/h/lb)
JT8D-217, -217A	21.32 mg/Ns (0.753 lb/h/lb)
JT8D-217C	20.84 mg/Ns (0.736 lb/h/lb)
JT8D-219	20.87 mg/Ns (0.737 lb/h/lb)

PRATT & WHITNEY PW4000

The PW4000 is a third generation turbofan for wide-body transports. Ratings range from 213.5 kN (48,000 lb) to 302.5 kN (68,000 lb). The first engine achieved 275 kN (61,800 lb) thrust during initial testing in April 1984. First flight test on an A300B took place on 31 July 1985. Certificated July 1986 at 249 kN (56,000 lb st) and in 1988 at 266.9 kN (60,000 lb st). Entered service on Pan Am A310 on 20 June 1987. The last two numbers denote thrust (thus, the initially certificated 56,000 lb st engine is the PW4056). Programme sharing agreements have been signed with FN (Belgium), Fiat (Italy), Norske Jet Motors (Norway), Kawasaki (Japan), Samsung (South Korea), Eldim (Netherlands) and Singapore Aerospace.

Fuel consumption was initially reduced seven per cent compared with the JT9D-7R4. There are about half as many parts, promising reductions in maintenance cost exceeding 25 per cent. HP compressor pressure ratio is increased by 10 per cent and the HP rotor operates at 27 per cent higher speed.

The PW4000 incorporates single-crystal turbine blades, aerodynamically enhanced aerofoils, an efficiency improving Thermatic rotor, and a full-authority digital electronic engine control (FADEC). The PW4000 was the first FADEC engine approved for EROPS operations beyond 60 min from alternates. It fits into existing -7R4 nacelles with minimum changes.

Thrust beyond 289.1 kN (65,000 lb) is achieved by changing materials and modifying the HP turbine cooling airflow (the improved turbine is retrofittable). For the A330 the **PW4168** will have a fan diameter increased to 2,535 mm (99.8 in) and an extra stage on the LP compressor and LP turbine. Initial A330 deliveries will be at 284.7 kN (64,000 lb st).

The following data apply to the basic PW4000 except where indicated:

TYPE: Two-shaft turbofan.

FAN: Single-stage. Titanium alloy hub retains 38 titanium alloy blades with aft part-span shrouds. Diameter 2,373 mm (93.44 in). Data for 249 kN (56,000 lb st) rating: mass flow 773 kg (1,705 lb)/s. Fan pressure ratio 1.7. Bypass ratio 4.85.

LP COMPRESSOR: Four stages with controlled diffusion aerofoils.

HP COMPRESSOR: Eleven stages with first four vane rows variable. Clearance control accomplished via rotor

Pratt & Whitney J52-P-408 two-shaft turbojet

Pratt & Whitney JT8D-219 two-shaft turbofan

response to ventilation air temperature. Overall pressure ratio at 249 kN rating, 29.7.

COMBUSTOR: Annular, forged nickel alloy roll-ring with double-pass cooling. 24 air-blast anti-coking injectors.

HP TURBINE: Two stages with aircooled blades cast as single crystal (PWA 1480) in first row and directional crystal (PWA 1422) in second row, retained in double-hub nickel alloy rotor with active clearance control. Vane aerofoils thermal barrier coated.

LP TURBINE: Four stages with active clearance control.

CONTROL SYSTEM: Full authority digital electronic with dual channel computer.

DIMENSIONS:

Length: PW4000	3,371 mm (132.7 in)
PW4168	4,114 mm (162 in)
Fan case diameter: PW4000	2,463 mm (96.98 in)
PW4168	2,646 mm (104.2 in)
Exhaust case diameter: PW4000	1,467 mm (57.76 in)

WEIGHT, DRY:

Basic PW4000	4,173 kg (9,200 lb)
PW4168 (complete system)	6,350 kg (14,000 lb)

RATINGS: See table

SPECIFIC FUEL CONSUMPTION (ISA, ideal nozzle, Mach 0.8, 10,670 m/35,000 ft):

PW4000	15.21 mg/Ns (0.537 lb/h/lb)

PRATT & WHITNEY JT9D

This was the first of the new era of large, high bypass ratio turbofans on which the design of wide-body commercial transports rests. First run was in December 1966. The first flight of the Boeing 747 was on 9 February 1969.

Current versions include:

JT9D-3A. Water injection rating of 200.8 kN (45,150 lb) to 26.7°C. Powers 747-100 and -200B.

JT9D-7. Higher thrust version with aircooled DS HP turbine blades; powers 747-200B, C, F and SR.

JT9D-7A. Aerodynamic improvements; powers 747-200 and 747SP.

JT9D-7F, -7J. Improved DS blades, 7J with shower-head cooled first stage, giving -7F T-O rating without water injection.

JT9D-7Q, -7R. Described later.

JT9D-20, -20J. D-7A and D-7J with accessory gearbox under fan case.

JT9D-59A, -70A. Fan diameter approximately 25.4 mm (one inch) larger, with re-profiled blades; LP compressor has zero (fourth) stage and is redesigned; burners recontoured, HP turbine carbon seal added, HP blades directionally solidified, and HP annulus larger. Both configured for common nacelle for 747 (-70A) or DC-10 and A300B (-59A). The **-59D** and **-70D** are higher thrust versions.

JT9D-7Q Series. As -59A and -70A but configured like -7 for 747-200 nacelle. Thrust 236-249 kN (53,000-56,000 lb).

JT9D-7R4 Series. Seven models (7R4D to 7R4H), with larger fan with wide chord blades, zero stage on LP compressor, improved combustor, H has single crystal HP turbine blades, increased diameter LP turbine, supervisory electronic fuel control and many smaller changes. 7R4D, 7R4E and 7R4E4 for Boeing 767; 7R4D1 and 7R4E1 for A310; 7R4G2 for 747; 7R4H1 for the A300B-600.

Deliveries exceed 3,265 and flight time in early 1989 was in excess of 90 million h.

The following applies to early versions, with later models in parentheses.

TYPE: Two-shaft turbofan of high bypass ratio.

Pratt & Whitney PW4000 two-shaft turbofan

PW4000 MODELS

Model	Thrust (ideal nozzle)	Application
PW4152	231.3 kN (52,000 lb) to 42.2°C	A310-300
PW4156	249.1 kN (56,000 lb) to 30°C	A300-600
PW4158	258.0 kN (58,000 lb) to 30°C	A300-600R
PW4168	302.5 kN (68,000 lb) to 30°C	A330
PW4052	232.2 kN (52,200 lb) to 33.3°C	767-200/-200ER
PW4056	252.4 kN (56,750 lb) to 33.3°C	767-300/-300ER/747-400
PW4060	266.9 kN (60,000 lb) to 30°C	767-300ER/747-400
PW4460	266.9 kN (60,000 lb) to 30°C	MD-11

Ratings are S/L static, no bleed or power extraction

FAN: Single stage, with 46 titanium blades of 4.6 aspect ratio (-7R4, 40 blades of 4.0 a.r.) and two part-span shrouds (-7R4, one shroud) dovetailed in titanium LP rotor. Mass flow 684 kg (1,509 lb)/s at 3,650 rpm (-7, 698 kg; 1,540 lb/s at 3,750 rpm; -59A, -70A, -7Q, 744 kg; 1,640 lb/s at 3,430 rpm; -7R4G/H, 769 kg; 1,695 lb/s at 3,530 rpm). Pressure ratio typically 1.6 : 1. Bypass ratio: -3A, 5.17; -7, 5.15; -59A, -70A, 4.9; -7R4D, E, 5.0; -7R4G2, H1, 4.8.

LP COMPRESSOR: Three stages (JT9D-59A, -70A, -7Q, -7R4, four stages), rotating with fan. Rotor stages have 104, 132 and 130 (-7Q, -59A, -70, -7R4, 108, 120, 112, 100) dovetailed blades of titanium alloy. Core airflow typically 118 kg (260 lb)/s (all versions).

HP COMPRESSOR: Eleven stages. Rotor stages have 60, 84, 102, 100, 110, 108, 104, 94 and 100 dovetailed titanium blades and 102 and 90 nickel alloy blades. First three stator stages are variable, plus intermediate IGV stage.

Max HP speed: -3A, 7,850 rpm; -7, 8,000 rpm; -7R4E4/G/H, 8,080 rpm. Overall pressure ratio: -3A, 21.5; -7, 22.2; -7Q, -59A, -70, 24.5; -7R4D, D1, 23.4; -7R4E/E1/E4, 24.2; -7R4G2, 26.3; -7R4H1, 26.7.

COMBUSTION CHAMBER: Annular, nickel alloy. Ignition by dual AC 4-joule capacitor system serving two plugs.

FUEL SYSTEM: Hydraulic control operating at up to 76 bars (1,100 lb/sq in). (-7R4 except G2 has digital electronic system to control hydromechanical control; engine is operational with or without electronic system functioning.) Water injection adds 18.1 kg (40 lb) to weight (not fitted to -7R4).

FUEL GRADE: P&W specification PWA 522.

HP TURBINE: Two stages. First has 116 aircooled blades and second has 138 solid blades (aircooled in -D7 and subsequent; -7R4, DS to G2, single crystal first and second blades and two vanes for H). Turbine inlet temperature (-3A, max T-O), typically 1,243°C (-59A, -70A, 1,350-1,370°C, -7R4 1,200-1,300°C).

LP TURBINE: Four stages. Solid nickel alloy blades held in fir tree roots in discs of nickel alloy (fifth disc, iron alloy). In 1982 an improved LP turbine was introduced to -7R4 production.

REVERSER: Fan reverser comprises a translating sleeve which moves aft, causing links to close blocker doors and simultaneously pulling aft the cascade vanes. Primary (core) reverser, uses fixed cascades uncovered by aft movement of translating sleeves. No primary reverser on -59A, -70A, -7Q or -7R4.

ACCESSORY DRIVES: Main accessory gearbox driven from front of HP spool and mounted under central diffuser case (-20, -59A, -70A, under fan discharge case). Accessories include CSD (IDG on -7R4 except G2) fuel pump and control, starter, hydraulic pump, alternator and N_2 tachometer; Boeing 747 includes primary reverser motor and DC-10-40 a second hydraulic pump and fuel boost pump.

LUBRICATION SYSTEM: Pressure feed through fuel/oil cooler to four main bearings and return to 18.8-37.6 litre (5-10 US gallon; 4.16-8.32 Imp gallon) tank.

OIL GRADE: PWA 521C.

STARTING: Pneumatic, by HamStan PS 700 or AiResearch ATS100-384 (DC-10, PS 700 only).

DIMENSIONS:

JT9D-3A, -7, -7A, -7F, -7J, -20:

Diameter	2,427 mm (95.56 in)
Length (flange to flange)	3,255 mm (128.15 in)

JT9D-59A, -70A, -7Q:

Diameter	2,464 mm (97.0 in)
Length	3,358 mm (132.2 in)

Cutaway drawing of Pratt & Whitney JT9D-7R4 two-shaft turbofan

Pratt & Whitney PW2000 series two-shaft turbofan

service on 1 December. An uprated engine, the **PW2040**, was certificated in January 1987 and entered service in September 1987 powering the 757PF. The C-17 will be powered by four **F117-PW-100** engines similar to the PW2040. The F117 was certificated in December 1988.

The PW2000 engine family is expected to consist ultimately of a series of models which will span a take-off thrust range of 133.4 to 204.6 kN (30,000 to 46,000 lb).

TYPE: Two-shaft turbofan of high bypass ratio.

FAN: Single-stage. Titanium forged hub, with 36 inserted titanium alloy blades with part-span shrouds. Tip diameter 1,994 mm (78.5 in). Mass flow 608 kg (1,340 lb)/s. Pressure ratio 1.7. Bypass ratio 6.0.

LP COMPRESSOR: Four stages, with controlled diffusion aerofoils with thick leading- and trailing-edges.

HP COMPRESSOR: Twelve stages, with controlled diffusion aerofoils. Variable vanes on first five stages and active clearance control on last eight stages. Overall cruise pressure ratio 31.8.

COMBUSTION CHAMBER: Annular, with flame tube fabricated in nickel alloy. Single-pipe fuel nozzles.

HP TURBINE: Two stages with aircooled blades cast as single crystals in PW 1480 alloy. Rotors with active clearance control. Both discs of PW1100 nickel based powder.

LP TURBINE: Five stages, with active clearance control.

CONTROL SYSTEM: Full authority digital electronic with two redundant computers.

DIMENSIONS:
Length	3,591 mm (141.4 in)
Fan case diameter	2,154 mm (84.8 in)

WEIGHT, DRY: 3,311 kg (7,300 lb)

PERFORMANCE RATING (T-O, S/L):
PW2037	170.1 kN (38,250 lb st)
PW2040	185.5 kN (41,700 lb st)

SPECIFIC FUEL CONSUMPTION (ideal nozzle, cruise at Mach 0.8 at 10,670 m; 35,000 ft): 15.95 mg/Ns (0.563 lb/h/lb)

JT9D-7R4D to H:
Diameter	2,463 mm (96.98 in)
Length	3,371 mm (132.7 in)

WEIGHT, DRY:
Guaranteed, including standard equipment:
JT9D-3A	3,905 kg (8,608 lb)
JT9D-7, -7A, -7F, -7J	4,014 kg (8,850 lb)
JT9D-20	3,833 kg (8,450 lb)
JTRD-20J	3,883 kg (8,560 lb)
JT9D-59A	4,146 kg (9,140 lb)
JT9D-70A	4,153 kg (9,155 lb)
JT9D-7Q	4,216 kg (9,295 lb)
JT9D-7R4D, E, E4	4,039 kg (8,905 lb)
JT9D-7R4D1, E1	4,029 kg (8,885 lb)
JT9D-7R4G2	4,143 kg (9,135 lb)
JT9D-7R4H1	4,029 kg (8,885 lb)

PERFORMANCE RATINGS (ideal nozzle):
T-O, dry:
JT9D-3A	193.9 kN (43,600 lb st) to 26.7°C
JT9D-7	202.8 kN (45,600 lb st) to 26.7°C
JT9D-7A	205.7 kN (46,250 lb st) to 26.7°C
JT9D-7F	213.5 kN (48,000 lb st) to 26.7°C
JT9D-7J, -20J	222.4 kN (50,000 lb st) to 30°C
JT9D-20	206.0 kN (46,300 lb st) to 28.9°C
JT9D-59A, -70A, -7Q	236.0 kN (53,000 lb st) to 30°C
JT9D-7R4D, D1	213.5 kN (48,000 lb st) to 33°C
JT9D-7R4E, E1	222.4 kN (50,000 lb st) to 33°C
JT9D-7R4E4	222.4 kN (50,000 lb st) to 45.6°C
JT9D-7R4G2	243.4 kN (54,750 lb st) to 30°C
JT9D-7R4H1	249.0 kN (56,000 lb st) to 30°C

T-O, wet:
JT9D-3A	200.8 kN (45,150 lb st) to 26.7°C
JT9D-7	210.0 kN (47,200 lb st) to 30°C
JT9D-7A	212.4 kN (47,750 lb st) to 30°C
JT9D-7F	222.4 kN (50,000 lb st) to 30°C
JT9D-20	220.0 kN (49,400 lb st) to 30°C

Max cruise, 10,670 m (35,000 ft) at Mach 0.85:
JT9D-3A, -7	45.4 kN (10,200 lb)
JT9D-7A	48.2 kN (10,830 lb)

JT9D-7F, -7J	49.2 kN (11,050 lb)
JT9D-20, -20J	47.5 kN (10,680 lb)
JT9D-59A, -70A, -7Q	53.2 kN (11,950 lb)
JT9D-7R4D, D1	50.0 kN (11,250 lb)
JT9D-7R4E, E1	52.0 kN (11,700 lb)
JT9D-7R4G2, H1	54.5 kN (12,250 lb)

SPECIFIC FUEL CONSUMPTION (ideal nozzle):
Max cruise, ISA + 10°C, Mach 0.85 at 10,670 m (35,000 ft):
JT9D-3A	17.67 mg/Ns (0.624 lb/h/lb)
JT9D-7	17.55 mg/Ns (0.620 lb/h/lb)
JT9D-7A	17.69 mg/Ns (0.625 lb/h/lb)
JT9D-7F, -7Q, -59A, -70A	17.87 mg/Ns (0.631 lb/h/lb)
JT9D-20, -20J	17.67 mg/Ns (0.624 lb/h/lb)
JT9D-7R4D, D1	17.42 mg/Ns (0.615 lb/h/lb)
JT9D-7R4E, E1	17.55 mg/Ns (0.620 lb/h/lb)
JT9D-7R4G2	18.10 mg/Ns (0.639 lb/h/lb)
JT9D-7R4H1	17.79 mg/Ns (0.628 lb/h/lb)

PRATT & WHITNEY PW2000
US military designation: F117

The PW2000 is a third generation turbofan upon which major changes have been made since 1972. In mid-1980 it was scaled up to be compatible with the Boeing 757-200, at 170.1 kN (38,250 lb st). The first model was given the designation **PW2037**, the last two digits denoting thrust in thousands of pounds. The first engine test run took place in December 1981. FAA certification was achieved in December 1983, and the first flight was made on the prototype 757 on 14 March 1984.

Companies participating are MTU of Federal Germany and Fiat of Italy. Pratt & Whitney bears 80.8 per cent of the programme, MTU 11.2 per cent and Fiat and Volvo 4 per cent each. A collaboration agreement between these companies was signed in July 1977.

Current applications are in versions of the Boeing 757 and McDonnell Douglas C-17. The PW2037-powered 757 was certificated on 25 October 1984 and entered revenue

PRATT & WHITNEY JTF10A
US military designation: TF30

Development of this military engine began in 1958. It was chosen as the power plant for the F-111 and A-7A.

A third application is the F-14A Tomcat, powered by the **TF30-P-414**, since converted to **-414A** standard which significantly improves engine stability and extends overhaul interval to 2,400 h.

The following description refers to the P-414A:

TYPE: Two-shaft turbofan.

FAN: Three stages. Rotor and stator and casings all of titanium, except for steel containment case.

LP COMPRESSOR: Six stages integral with fan. Titanium, except steel stator blades.

HP COMPRESSOR: Seven stages, mainly nickel alloy.

COMBUSTION CHAMBER: Can-annular, with eight Hastelloy combustors, each with four dual-orifice burners.

FUEL SYSTEM: HP system (above 69 bars; 1,000 lb/sq in), with conventional hydromechanical control and electronic turbine temperature limiter.

FUEL GRADES: JP-4, JP-5, JP-8.

HP TURBINE: Single stage, with 40 aircooled nozzle guide vanes (stators) of single-crystal nickel based material and aircooled rotor blades of nickel-based alloy.

LP TURBINE: Three stages of nickel based alloys.

AFTERBURNER: Double wall outer duct and inner liner carrying five-zone combustion system. Ignition by auxiliary squirt, coupled with main squirt in No. 4 burner can which produces hot streak through turbine. Max gas temperature 1,677°C.

NOZZLE: Primary nozzle has six hinged segments actuated by fuel rams. Ejector nozzle has 18 iris segments.

ACCESSORY DRIVES: Main gearbox under compressor, driven by bevel shaft from HP spool.

LUBRICATION SYSTEM: Self contained dry sump system.

OIL GRADE: MIL-L-7808, MIL-L-23699.

STARTING: Air turbine starter on left forward drive pad.

DIMENSIONS:
Max diameter	1,293 mm (50.9 in)
Length overall	5,987 mm (235.7 in)

Longitudinal section of Pratt & Whitney PW2000 two-shaft turbofan

WEIGHT, DRY: 1,905 kg (4,201 lb)
PERFORMANCE RATING:
T-O, S/L 93 kN (20,900 lb st)
SPECIFIC FUEL CONSUMPTION (T-O):
78.75 mg/Ns (2.78 lb/h/lb st)

PRATT & WHITNEY JTF22
US military designation: F100

The JTF22 is a military turbofan with afterburner for supersonic applications. In February 1970 the decision was taken to use the JTF22 core engine as the basis for the **F100-PW-100** (JTF22A-25A) to power the F-15 Eagle. Subsequently, the F100 was adopted for the F-16, early versions of which are powered by the **F100-PW-200**, with a backup fuel control. By 1989 more than 5,100 engines had flown more than 5 million hours.

In mid-1985 the improved **F100-PW-220** was qualified for the F-15C and F-16C (see 'CONTROL SYSTEM' below). **F100-PW-220E** upgrade packages are available for PW-100 and -200 to give engines equivalent to the -220. Available from 1989 is the **F100-PW-229** (see PW1129).

TYPE: Two-shaft turbofan with afterburner.
FAN: Three stages. Fan blades have part-span shrouds. Entry diameter 884 mm (34.8 in). Bypass ratio 0.6.
COMPRESSOR: Ten-stage axial, on HP shaft. First three stages have variable stators. Pressure ratio 8. Overall pressure ratio 25.
COMBUSTION CHAMBER: Annular. Cobalt based alloy with film cooling. Air blast fuel nozzles. Capacitor-discharge ignition.
HP TURBINE: Two stages. Discs forged IN-100. Blades and

vanes directionally solidified Mar M200/Hf alloy with aluminide coating; first rotor transpiration convectively cooled, second with HP bleed only. Max gas temperature 1,399°C. Maximum speed 13,450 rpm.
LP TURBINE: Two stages. Discs forged IN-100. Blades, uncooled, cast in IN-100 with aluminide coating. Max speed 10,400 rpm.
AFTERBURNER: Five spray rings in flow from core and two downstream in bypass airflow. Flameholder downstream with high energy ignition to give modulated light-up.
NOZZLE: Multi-flap balanced beam articulated nozzle.
CONTROL SYSTEM: Unified hydromechanical fuel and nozzle area control, with electronic supervisory control. Dash-220 includes a digital electronic control, gear type main fuel pump, and ILC (increased life core) with a 4,000 cycle depot refurbishment interval.
DIMENSIONS:
Overall diameter 1,181 mm (46.5 in)
Length:
F100-PW-100, excl bullet 4,855 mm (191.2 in)
F100-PW-220 5,280 mm (208 in)
WEIGHT, DRY:
F100-PW-100 1,386 kg (3,055 lb)
F100-PW-200 1,410 kg (3,108 lb)
F100-PW-220 1,459 kg (3,218 lb)
PERFORMANCE RATINGS (S/L, ISA):
Max T-O, dry:
F100-PW-100 65.2 kN (14,670 lb st)
F100-PW-220 64.9 kN (14,590 lb st)
Max T-O, augmented:
F100-PW-100 106.0 kN (23,830 lb st)
F100-PW-220 105.7 kN (23,770 lb st)

PRATT & WHITNEY PW1120

The PW1120 is a turbojet derivative of the F100. Its development was initiated in June 1980. It retains the F100 core module, gearbox, fuel pump and forward ducts, as well as the F100 digital electronic control, with only minor modifications.

Unique PW1120 components include a wide chord LP compressor, single-stage uncooled LP turbine, simplified single stream augmentor, and a lightweight convergent/divergent nozzle. Mass flow is 80.9 kg (178 lb)/s and pressure ratio 26.8.

Full scale testing was initiated in June 1982, and the engine completed flight clearance testing in August 1984. The PW1120 was selected to power the Israeli Lavi, later cancelled. Flight demonstration in an F-4 began on 30 July 1986. The engine is a candidate for F-4 re-engining as well as for other fighter projects.

DIMENSIONS:
Max diameter 1,021 mm (40.2 in)
Length 4,110 mm (161.8 in)
WEIGHT, DRY: 1,292 kg (2,848 lb)
PERFORMANCE RATINGS (S/L, ISA):
Max T-O 91.7 kN (20,620 lb st)
Intermediate 60.3 kN (13,550 lb st)
SPECIFIC FUEL CONSUMPTION:
Maximum 52.65 mg/Ns (1.86 lb/h/lb)
Intermediate 22.7 mg/Ns (0.8 lb/h/lb)

PRATT & WHITNEY PW1129
US military designation: F100-PW-229

The PW1129 has been designed as an IPE (Increased Performance Engine) for F-15s and F-16s. Using com-

Cutaway drawing of Pratt & Whitney F100-PW-220 two-shaft augmented turbofan

Cutaway drawing of Pratt & Whitney TF30-P-414A two-shaft augmented turbofan

Cutaway drawing of Pratt & Whitney PW1120 two-shaft afterburning turbojet

Cutaway drawing of Pratt & Whitney PW1129 two-shaft augmented turbofan

Mockup of Pratt & Whitney F119, with 2D (two-dimensional) nozzle with limited thrust vectoring

PERFORMANCE RATINGS (S/L, ISA):
Max T-O	129 kN (29,000 lb st)
Intermediate	79.2 kN (17,800 lb st)

SPECIFIC FUEL CONSUMPTION:
Max T-O	58.07 mg/Ns (2.05 lb/h/lb)
Intermediate	20.96 mg/Ns (0.74 lb/h/lb)

ponents of the F100-PW-220 and PW1128 EMD (see 1984-85 *Jane's*), it has many new features including an improved compressor and Float-wall combustor. The first engine ran in late 1986, and the first flight was completed in April 1988. Production engines became available in 1989. The US Air Force is marginally favouring this engine over the rival F110, with 52 per cent of the USAF buy in the first two years going to the -229 for the F-15 and F-16. A USAF

F-15E began flight testing powered by two F100-PW-229 engines in May 1990. These are expected to become the standard engine from August 1991.

DIMENSIONS:
Length	5,280 mm (208 in)
Diameter	1,180 mm (46.5 in)

WEIGHT, DRY: 1,656 kg (3,650 lb)

PRATT & WHITNEY PW5000
US military designation: F119

This advanced augmented turbofan is competing against the General Electric GE37 as the ATF (advanced tactical fighter) engine for the period after 1995. The F119 will provide supersonic persistence, without afterburner. It has roughly 40 per cent fewer parts than predecessor fighter engines, and should have much greater durability. Initial development began in 1983. A demonstrator began sea-level testing in December 1988, and a prototype followed in 1989. Flight test of YF119 prototypes is planned for late 1990, with operational introduction due in the mid to late 1990s. Development is continuing on advanced exhaust nozzles that could incorporate reversing and limited vectoring features.

PW-ALLISON

MEMBER COMPANIES:
Allison Gas Turbine Division, GMC
Indianapolis, Indiana 46206
Pratt & Whitney, UTC
East Hartford, Connecticut 06108

United Technologies' Pratt & Whitney and General Motors' Allison Gas Turbine Division formed a joint partnership in 1986 to develop propfan propulsion technology.

PW-ALLISON MODEL 578-DX

PW-Allison developed the Model 578-DX geared counter-rotation propfan propulsion system for testing and technology demonstrations. The initial flight test demonstrator is rated at 88.97 kN (20,000 lb st). This incorporates a three-stage LP compressor, modified Allison 571 core engine, and an advanced technology 9,698 kW (13,000 shp) differential planetary gear system. The latter drives two 3.53 m (11 ft 7 in) six-blade Hamilton Standard propfans. A modified PW-HamStan full-authority digital electronic engine control regulates fuel flow, variable compressor stators and propfan blade angles. The 578-DX made its first flight on an MD-80 on 13 April 1989, and successfully completed the programme in the same quarter of 1989.

PW-Allison propfan installed on MD-80 aircraft

ROCKETDYNE
ROCKETDYNE DIVISION OF ROCKWELL INTERNATIONAL
6633 Canoga Avenue, Canoga Park, California 91303
Telephone: 1 (818) 710 6300
Telex: 698478
PRESIDENT: R. Schwartz

Rocketdyne is devoted primarily to rocket engines for the US Air Force and the National Aeronautics and Space Administration. It was established as a separate division in November 1955. Rocketdyne liquid propellant engines have powered more than three-quarters of all large US space vehicle stages.

ROCKETDYNE SSME

On 13 July 1971 Rocketdyne was selected by NASA to develop the main engine for the Shuttle Orbiter. Three of these engines provide a total of 6,523 kN (1,466,400 lb) vacuum thrust, and power the vehicle to near orbit.

The SSME (Space Shuttle Main Engine) was designed for high reliability, reusability, multiple re-start capability and low cost. It is designed for $7\frac{1}{2}$ h of burn time, or 55 flights.

The design combines the merits of high pressure operation, an optimum bell nozzle, and a regeneratively cooled thrust chamber, capable of 11° gimballing. The chamber wall is cooled to 567°C, although the combustion temperature is about 3,300°C. No propellants are wasted in

the cooling process. The combustion chamber wall is made of slotted metal, rather than tubes, using Rocketdyne developed NARloy-Z, copper alloy.

The SSME is controlled by a unique system incorporating dual redundant digital computers. This system monitors engine parameters such as pressure and flow rate, and the engine is adjusted automatically to operate at the required thrust and mixture ratio. The system also develops a record of engine operating history for maintenance purposes.

Flight certification was achieved in December 1980. Another cycle in the FPL (full power level) certification programme was completed in April 1983. Certification required four test series of 5,000 s each, involving engine power levels normally at 104 per cent. This testing provided flight readiness certification for engine sets for the *Challenger, Columbia, Discovery* and *Atlantis* orbiters.

The Shuttle programme began its operational phase with the STS-5 launch of the *Columbia* on 11 November 1982. On 4 April 1983 a second vehicle, *Challenger*, powered by SSMEs rated at 104 per cent thrust, was launched on STS-6. The third Orbiter, *Discovery*, was launched on 30 August 1984. A total of 24 launches, all successful, had been accomplished prior to the loss of *Challenger* on 28 January 1986. Excellent flight-to-flight performance repeatability had been achieved.

Testing is being continued to extend the life of the HP turbomachinery, increase performance margin by reducing flow losses, and investigate other modifications that could allow uprating or life extension.

COMBUSTION CHAMBER: Channel wall construction with regenerative cooling by the hydrogen fuel. Concentric element injector.

TURBOPUMPS: Two low pressure pumps boost the inlet pressures for two high pressure pumps. Dual pre-burners provide turbine drive gases to power the high-pressure pumps. Hydrogen pump discharge pressure is 485.4 bars

(6,445 lb/sq in) at 35,080 rpm; it develops 51,528 kW (69,100 hp).

CONTROLLER: Honeywell digital computer provides closed loop control, in addition to data processing and signal conditioning for control, checkout, monitoring engine status, and maintenance data acquisition.

CONTROLS: Hydraulic actuation. Dual redundant self-monitoring servo actuators respond to signals from the controller to position the ball valves. A pneumatic system provides backup for engine cut-off.

MAINTENANCE: Airline type maintenance procedure for on-the-vehicle servicing. Planned life between overhauls 55 flights.

DIMENSIONS:
Length	4,242 mm (167 in)
Diameter at nozzle exit	2,388 mm (94 in)

PERFORMANCE:
S/L thrust (one engine, 104%)	1,751.7 kN (393,800 lb)
Vacuum thrust	2,174.3 kN (488,800 lb)
Specific impulse	453 s
Chamber pressure	215.5 bars (3,126 lb/sq in)
Throttling ratio	1.67
Expansion ratio	77.5

SSME undergoing FPL test

ROTORWAY
ROTORWAY AIRCRAFT INC
300 South 25th Avenue, Phoenix, Arizona 85009
Telephone: 1 (602) 278 1199
Telex: 683 5059
Fax: 1 (602) 278 5887

RotorWay Aircraft has been producing its own liquid-cooled aircraft power plants since 1974, to power RotorWay helicopters.

ROTORWAY RW152
TYPE: Horizontally opposed, water-cooled, four-cylinder, four-stroke piston engine. Crankshaft vertical.

CYLINDERS: Offset left and right for plain connecting rods side by side. Capacity 2.66 litres (162 cu in). Compression ratio 9.6.

INDUCTION: Single two-barrel downdraught carburettor with integral manifold heating.

IGNITION: Dual direct-fire electronic, with redundant coils, sensors, timing processors and plugs.

FUEL GRADE: Autogas 92 octane or Avgas 100LL.

WEIGHT, DRY (with starter): 77.1 kg (170 lb)
PERFORMANCE RATING: 113 kW (152 hp) at 4,400 rpm

RotorWay RW152 four-cylinder helicopter engine

SOLOY
SOLOY CONVERSIONS LTD
450 Pat Kennedy Way SW, Olympia, Washington 98502
Telephone: 1 (206) 754 7000
Fax: 1 (206) 943 7659
PRESIDENT: Joe I. Soloy

Further details can be found in the US Aircraft section.

SOLOY TURBINE PAC
The Soloy Turbine Pac is an FAA Supplemental Type Certificate approved turboprop engine assembly, rated at 312 kW (418 shp) with a propeller rpm range of 1,450 to 1,810. Its Allison 250-C20S turboshaft engine is combined with Soloy's propeller gearbox and other components to produce a turboprop configured for single-engined aircraft. Its high thrust line and rear inlet suit it particularly to bush aircraft. The engine assembly includes propeller governing and overspeed systems, and a self-contained lubrication system. Customised models are available in pusher configuration and can utilise the 485 kW (650 shp) Allison 250-C30 engine for tractor or pusher configurations.

SOLOY DUAL PAC INC
Address as Soloy Conversions Ltd

SOLOY DUAL PAC
The first production model of the Soloy Dual Pac multi-engine system utilises two Allison 250-C30S turbo-shaft engines, each rated at 522 kW (700 shp). The Soloy combining gearbox is rated at 1,119 kW (1,500 shp) to accommodate possible future power increases for the Allison engine. The Dual Pac's redundancy, separation, and isolation of engine and drive train systems allows it to satisfy FAA requirements for designation as a twin engine, and Dual Pac powered aircraft to be defined as multi-engined. Patented free-wheeling units at the final stage drive train provide automatic disengagement in the event of an engine shutdown, with no adverse effect on aircraft drag or thrust symmetry.

The Dual Pac is designed for tractor or pusher configuration, and is planned for use in both single-propeller and multi-propeller aircraft.

Soloy 206 Turbine Pac free-turbine turboprop

SPP
SPORT PLANE POWER INC
3659 Arnold Avenue, Naples, Florida 33942
Telephone: 1 (813) 775 2214

This company is an associate of Nelson (see entry in this section). Its first product is the K-100A.

SPORT PLANE POWER K-100A
A four-cylinder four-stroke piston engine, the K-100A is an automotive derived high performance unit with liquid cooling, altitude compensation, overhead camshafts, electronic control and speed reducing drive, allowed for in the figure for weight.

WEIGHT, WET: 88.5 kg (195 lb)
PERFORMANCE RATING: 74.6 kW (100 hp)

Sport Plane Power K-100A four-cylinder engine

TCM
TELEDYNE CONTINENTAL MOTORS
(Aircraft Products)

PO Box 90, Mobile, Alabama 36601
Telephone: 1 (205) 438 3411
Telex: 505519
Fax: 1 (205) 432 2922
PRESIDENT: W. A. Boettger
DIRECTOR, PUBLIC RELATIONS: Susan Brane

TCM produces piston, rotary combustion and turboprop engines for general aviation.

CONTINENTAL O-200 SERIES

The O-200-A is a four-cylinder horizontally opposed aircooled engine. It is fitted with a single updraught carburettor, dual magnetos and starter and generator. The O-200-B is designed for pusher installation.

For other details see table.

TELEDYNE CONTINENTAL VOYAGER 200

This is the first of the company's liquid-cooled engines. Derived from the familiar O-200, it has a high-compression (11.4) cylinder with combustion chamber improvements aimed at minimising fuel consumption. The 60 per cent ethylene glycol coolant can operate at 121°C. The engine is more powerful than the aircooled predecessor (see table), and is claimed to offer improved cooling, reduced wear, reduced drag, longer life and TBO, and higher altitude capability. An sfc of 63.38 µg/J (0.375 lb/h/bhp) can be maintained across a broad operating range. A Voyager 200 powered the Voyager aircraft round the world.

TELEDYNE CONTINENTAL VOYAGER 300

This six-cylinder liquid-cooled engine uses the same high-turbulence high-compression cylinder as the 200. The turbocharged version has demonstrated sfc well below 62.5 µg/J (0.37 lb/h/bhp) at altitude. The weight given in the table includes magnetos, plugs, fuel injection system, coolant pump, alternator and starter.

CONTINENTAL O-360 SERIES

Newest member of this family of flat-six engines is the TSIO-360-MB, for the Mooney 252.

TELEDYNE CONTINENTAL VOYAGER 370

This liquid-cooled engine has four cylinders of the same size as the 550 series.

CONTINENTAL O-470 SERIES

Engines in the O-470 series (including the E-185 and E-225) are all basically similar. Engines prefixed 'IO' have direct injection.

CONTINENTAL O-520 SERIES

These engines are basically similar to the IO-470, but with cylinders of larger bore. They are fitted with an alternator driven either by a belt or by a face gear on the crankshaft. The TSIO-520 series are turbocharged. In 1981 TCM announced a lightweight series of engines with magnesium replacing aluminium in some areas, modified camshaft and cylinder heads (with parallel valves or inclined valves of larger diameter), and a range of turbocharging options. The first production models are the TSIO-520-AE and LTSIO-520-AE for the Cessna Crusader, with initial TBO of 2,000 h. The TSIO-520BE has a top intake, dual turbos and two aftercoolers. The GTSIO-520 series are geared.

TELEDYNE CONTINENTAL VOYAGER 550

Largest of the new range of liquid-cooled engines, the Voyager 550 offers the same advantages as its smaller predecessors. The T-550 was designed for Bonanza conversions and the geared GT-550 for the Chieftain.

CONTINENTAL O-550

In 1984 this series of fuel-injected engines was introduced, similar to the IO-520 but with greater stroke. Initial applications are the Beechcraft Baron and Bonanza.

TELEDYNE CONTINENTAL GR-18

This single-rotor engine is the first of the TCM rotaries (rotating-combustion, popularly called Wankel-type engines). Under development for several years, it is aimed at air and surface applications, chiefly in UAVs. Design features include a rotor cooled by the oil/air mixture entering the engine, liquid-cooled housings, reduction gear, rolling-element bearings, carburettor or direct fuel injection, dual capacitive-discharge electronic ignition, total loss metered oil-injection system, 12V starter and provision for alternator up to 2.5kW. Compression ratio is 9, and the carburettor type fuel system was in 1985 running on automotive or aviation petrol (gasoline) but in future will have multi-fuel capability, including JP-5 and DF-2. This engine was flown in a SkyEye R4E-50 UAV in November 1986 and is currently in production. It is readily adaptable to turbocharging.

ROTOR: Single multilobe with rolling element bearings.
Capacity 294 cc (17.9 cu in).
DIMENSIONS:
Length	536.2 mm (21.11 in)
Width	232.2 mm (9.14 in)
Height	254 mm (10 in)

WEIGHT, DRY (equipped): 22.7 kg (50 lb)
PERFORMANCE RATING (S/L): 33.5 kW (45 hp) at 7,500 rpm

TELEDYNE CONTINENTAL GR-36

This twin-rotor engine is virtually a double GR-18, and is available for UAV applications with or without reduction gear. It may be offered later for general aviation applications. It runs slightly slower than the single-rotor machine, at 6,900 rpm, giving a propeller speed of 2,300 rpm. Capacity is 588 cc (35.8 cu in). The GR-36 has the same features as the GR-18 but drives a 27A alternator. TCM claims for its rotary engines compactness, light weight, extremely low vibration and simple construction with few moving parts.

DIMENSIONS:
Length	678 mm (26.70 in)
Width (with coolant pipe)	298 mm (11.75 in)
Height	244 mm (9.60 in)

Teledyne Continental Voyager GT-550 six-cylinder liquid-cooled engine

Left: Teledyne Continental Voyager 370 four-cylinder liquid-cooled engine

Teledyne Continental TSIO-360-MB six-cylinder air-cooled engine

Teledyne Continental Voyager T-550 six-cylinder liquid-cooled engine

WEIGHT, DRY: 50 kg (110 lb)
PERFORMANCE RATINGS (S/L): 63.5 kW (85 hp) at 6,900 rpm
67 kW (90 hp) at 7,500 rpm

TELEDYNE CONTINENTAL TP-500

This simple turboprop was certificated in October 1988 and is now being marketed for general aviation. It first flew in a Cheyenne II on 29 September 1982. Though completely successful, the TP-500 is now awaiting a viable customer programme.

COMPRESSOR: Single centrifugal, stainless steel. Airflow 1.95 kg (4.3 lb)/s and pressure ratio 8 at 50,000 rpm.

COMBUSTION CHAMBER: Folded annular, reverse flow, ten burners.

TURBINE: Two-stage axial. Max inlet temperature 1,071°C. Stud/nut attachment.

FUEL SYSTEM: Hydromechanical with supervisory electronic control. Grade Jet A, A-1, B, JP-4.

PROPELLER DRIVE: Two-stage coupled planetary giving 2,014 rpm output. Modular design in cast casings with integral torquemeter.

ACCESSORY DRIVES: Two reduction gearcases drive fuel control, propeller governor, starter generator and tachometer generator. Optional belt drive for freon compressor or secondary alternator.

DIMENSIONS:
Length 1,325 mm (52.18 in)
Width 592 mm (23.31 in)
Height 541 mm (21.30 in)
WEIGHT, DRY: 152 kg (336 lb)
PERFORMANCE RATINGS (ISA):
T-O, S/L 358 kW (480 shp)
T-O, 3,050 m (10,000 ft) 261 kW (350 shp)
Cruise 97% at 4,575 m (15,000 ft) 216 kW (290 shp)
Cruise 97%, altitude limit 7,620 m (25,000 ft) 149 kW (200 shp)
FUEL FLOW (uninstalled, no power extraction):
T-O, S/L 147 kg (325 lb)/h
Cruise 7,620 m (25,000 ft) 64 kg (142 lb)/h

Teledyne Continental TP-500 turboprop (with cropped-blade display propeller)

**Teledyne Continental
GR-36 twin-rotor
engine**

REPRESENTATIVE TCM HORIZONTALLY OPPOSED ENGINES

Engine Model	No. of Cylinders	Bore and Stroke mm (in)	Capacity litres (cu in)	Power Ratings kW (hp) at rpm		Comp. Ratio	Dry Weight* kg (lb)	Dimensions			Octane Rating
				Take-off	M.E.T.O.			Length mm (in)	Width mm (in)	Height mm (in)	
O-200-A	4	103.2 × 98.4 (4¹/₁₆ × 3⁷/₈)	3.28 (201)	74.5 (100) at 2,750	74.5 (100) at 2,750	7.0	99.8 (220)	725 (28.53)	802 (31.56)	589 (23.18)	80/87
Voyager 200	4	103.2 × 98.4 (4¹/₁₆ × 3⁷/₈)	3.28 (201)	81.95 (110) at 2,750	81.95 (110) at 2,750	11.4	88.0 (194)	708 (27.86)	819 (32.25)	588 (23.16)	100/ 100LL
Voyager 300	6	103.2 × 98.4 (4¹/₁₆ × 3⁷/₈)	4.93 (301)	127 (170) at 2,700	127 (170) at 2,700	11.4	132 (291)	864 (34.0)	819 (32.25)	533 (21.0)	100/ 100LL
IO-360-D	6	112.7 × 98.4 (4⁷/₁₆ × 3⁷/₈)	5.9 (360)	157 (210) at 2,800	157 (210) at 2,800	8.5	148.3 (327)	877 (34.53)	798 (31.40)	618 (24.33)	100/130
IO-360-KB	6	112.7 × 98.4 (4⁷/₁₆ × 3⁷/₈)	5.9 (360)	145.5 (195) at 2,600	145.5 (195) at 2,600	8.5	148.3 (327)	864 (34.03)	841 (33.11)	781 (30.74)	100/130
TSIO-360-C, D	6	112.7 × 98.4 (4⁷/₁₆ × 3⁷/₈)	5.9 (360)	168 (225) at 2,800	168 (225) at 2,800	7.5	136 (300)	910† (35.84)	838 (33.03)	603 (23.75)	100/130
LTSIO-360-EB TSIO-360-FB	6	112.7 × 98.4 (4⁷/₁₆ × 3⁷/₈)	5.9 (360)	149 (200) at 2,575	149 (200) at 2,575	7.5	175 (385)	1,437 (56.58)	795 (31.30)	671 (26.44)	100/130
TSIO-360-LB	6	112.7 × 98.4 (4⁷/₁₆ × 3⁷/₈)	5.9 (360)	156.5 (210) at 2,700	156.5 (210) at 2,700	7.5	175 (386)	902 (35.52)	795 (31.30)	699 (27.53)	100/130
LTSIO-360-KB	6	112.7 × 98.4 (4⁷/₁₆ × 3⁷/₈)	5.9 (360)	164 (220) at 2,800	164 (220) at 2,800	7.5	178 (392)	1,437 (56.58)	795 (31.30)	672 (26.44)	100/130
TSIO-360-LB	6	112.7 × 98.4 (4⁷/₁₆ × 3⁷/₈)	5.9 (360)	156.5 (210) at 2,700	156.5 (210) at 2,700	7.5	180.5 (401)	1,087 (42.78)	860 (33.88)	822 (32.34)	100LL
TSIO-360-MB	6	112.7 × 98.4 (4⁷/₁₆ × 3⁷/₈)	5.9 (360)	156.5 (210) at 2,700	156.5 (210) at 2,700	7.5	186.9 (412)	1,087 (42.78)	873 (34.37)	834 (32.82)	100LL
Voyager IOL-370	4	133 × 108 (5¹/₄ × 4¹/₄)	6.06 (370)	142 (190) at 2,700	142 (190) at 2,700	9.0	127 (280)				100LL
Voyager TSIOL-370	4	133 × 108 (5¹/₄ × 4¹/₄)	6.06 (370)	168 (225) at 2,700	168 (225) at 2,700	7.5	142.4 (314)				100LL
IO-470-H	6	127 × 101.6 (5 × 4)	7.7 (471)	194 (260) at 2,625	194 (260) at 2,625	8.6	202.5 (446.5)	1,100 (43.31)	852 (33.56)	502 (19.75)	100/130
IO-470-L	6	127 × 101.6 (5 × 4)	7.7 (471)	194 (260) at 2,625	194 (260) at 2,625	8.6	215.4 (474.9)	1,100 (43.31)	852 (33.56)	678 (26.71)	100/130
O-470-R, S	6	127 × 101.6 (5 × 4)	7.7 (471)	172 (230) at 2,600	172 (230) at 2,600	7.0	193.2 (426)	915 (36.03)	852 (33.56)	723 (28.42)	80/87

*With accessories; †Not including turbocharger.

REPRESENTATIVE TCM HORIZONTALLY OPPOSED ENGINES (continued)

Engine Model	No. of Cylinders	Bore and Stroke mm (in)	Capacity litres (cu in)	Power Ratings kW (hp) at rpm		Comp. Ratio	Dry Weight* kg (lb)	Dimensions			Octane Rating
				Take-off	M.E.T.O.			Length mm (in)	Width mm (in)	Height mm (in)	
O-470-U	6	127 × 101.6 (5 × 4)	7.7 (471)	171.5 (230) at 2,400	171.5 (230) at 2,400	8.6	176.4 (388.9)	915 (36.03)	852 (33.56)	732 (28.42)	100LL
IO-520-A	6	133 × 101.6 (5¼ × 4)	8.5 (520)	212.5 (285) at 2,700	212.5 (285) at 2,700	8.5	215.9 (476)	1,053 (41.41)	852 (33.56)	502 (19.75)	100/130
IO-520-BA, -BB	6	133 × 101.6 (5¼ × 4)	8.5 (520)	212.5 (285) at 2,700	212.5 (285) at 2,700	8.5	207.3 (457)	1,009 (39.71)	853 (33.58)	678 (26.71)	100/130
IO-520-CB	6	133 × 101.6 (5¼ × 4)	8.5 (520)	212.5 (285) at 2,700	212.5 (285) at 2,700	8.5	204.7 (451.3)	1,087 (42.81)	852 (33.56)	502 (19.78)	100/130
IO-520-D	6	133 × 101.6 (5¼ × 4)	8.5 (520)	224 (300) at 2,850	212.5 (285) at 2,700	8.5	208.2 (459)	949 (37.36)	901 (35.46)	604 (23.79)	100/130
IO-520-L	6	133 × 101.6 (5¼ × 4)	8.5 (520)	224 (300) at 2,850	212.5 (285) at 2,700	8.5	211.7 (466.7)	1,039 (40.91)	852 (33.56)	591 (23.25)	100/130
IO-520-M, -MB	6	133 × 101.6 (5¼ × 4)	8.5 (520)	212.5 (285) at 2,700	212.5 (285) at 2,700	8.5	188 (415)	1,189 (46.80)	852 (33.56)	518 (20.41)	100/130
TSIO-520-C	6	133 × 101.6 (5¼ × 4)	8.5 (520)	212.5 (285) at 2,700	212.5 (285) at 2,700	7.5	208 (458)	1,040† (40.91)	852 (33.56)	509 (20.04)	100/130
TSIO-520-E, -EB	6	133 × 101.6 (5¼ × 4)	8.5 (520)	224 (300) at 2,700	224 (300) at 2,700	7.5	219 (483)	1,010† (39.75)	852 (33.56)	527 (20.74)	100/130
TSIO-520-J, N, -JB, -NB	6	133 × 101.6 (5¼ × 4)	8.5 (520)	231 (310) at 2,700	231 (310) at 2,700	7.5	221.3 (487.8)	997 (39.25)	852 (33.56)	516 (20.32)	100/130
TSIO-520-L, -LB	6	133 × 101.6 (5¼ × 4)	8.5 (520)	231 (310) at 2,700	231 (310) at 2,700	7.5	244.5 (539)	1,286 (50.62)	852 (33.56)	508 (20.02)	100/130
TSIO-520-M, R	6	133 × 101.6 (5¼ × 4)	8.5 (520)	231 (310) at 2,700	212.5 (285) at 2,600	7.5	198 (436)	1,040† (40.91)	852 (33.56)	598 (23.54)	100/130
TSIO-520-T	6	133 × 101.6 (5¼ × 4)	8.5 (520)	231 (310) at 2,700	231 (310) at 2,700	7.5	193.4 (426.3)	970 (38.2)	852 (33.56)	819 (32.26)	100/130
TSIO-520-VB	6	133 × 101.6 (5¼ × 4)	8.5 (520)	242.5 (325) at 2,700	242.5 (325) at 2,700	7.5	207.2 (456.7)	997 (39.25)	852 (33.56)	518 (20.41)	100/130
TSIO-520-UB	6	133 × 101.6 (5¼ × 4)	8.5 (520)	224 (300) at 2,700	224 (300) at 2,700	7.5	191.6 (422.5)	1,136 (44.5)	852 (33.56)	733 (28.86)	100/130
TSIO-520-WB	6	133 × 101.6 (5¼ × 4)	8.5 (520)	242.5 (325) at 2,700	242.5 (325) at 2,700	7.5	188.75 (416.1)	1,286 (50.62)	852 (33.56)	509 (20.02)	100/130
GTSIO-520-C	6	133 × 101.6 (5¼ × 4)	8.5 (520)	254 (340) at 3,200	254 (340) at 3,200	7.5	252.7 (557)	1,081 (42.56)	880 (34.04)	587 (23.1)	100/130
GTSIO-520-D, H	6	133 × 101.6 (5¼ × 4)	8.5 (520)	280 (375) at 3,400	280 (375) at 3,400	7.5	250 (550.4)	1,081 (42.56)	880 (34.04)	680 (26.78)	100/130
GTSIO-520-F, K	6	133 × 101.6 (5¼ × 4)	8.5 (520)	324 (435) at 3,400	324 (435) at 3,400	7.5	272.0 (600)	1,426 (56.12)	880 (34.04)	664 (26.15)	100/130
GTSIO-520-L, M, N	6	133 × 101.6 (5¼ × 4)	8.5 (520)	280 (375) at 3,350	280 (375) at 3,350	7.5	228 (502)‡	1,114 (43.87)	880 (34.04)	671 (26.41)	100/130
LTSIO-520-AE	6	133 × 101.6 (5¼ × 4)	8.5 (520)	186.5 (250) at 2,400	186.5 (250) at 2,400	8.5	172.2 (379.6)	967 (38.07)	846 (33.29)	543 (21.38)	100/130
TSIO-520-AF	6	133 × 101.6 (5¼ × 4)	8.5 (520)	231 (210) at 2,700	212.5 (285) at 2,600	7.5	197.8 (436.15)	1,039 (40.91)	852 (33.56)	598 (23.54)	100/130
TSIO-520-B, -BB	6	133 × 101.6 (5¼ × 4)	8.5 (520)	213 (285) at 2,700	213 (285) at 2,700	7.5	219 (483)	1,490 (58.67)	852 (33.56)	516 (20.32)	100/130
TSIO-520-BE	6	133 × 101.6 (5¼ × 4)	8.5 (520)	231 (310) at 2,600	231 (310) at 2,600	7.5	?	1,083 (42.64)	1,079 (42.5)	851 (33.5)	100LL
TSIO-520-CE	6	133 × 101.6 (5¼ × 4)	8.5 (520)	242.5 (325) at 2,700	242.5 (325) at 2,700	7.5	237 (527)	1,039 (40.91)	852 (33.56)	597 (23.54)	100LL
Voyager 550	6	133 × 108 (5¼ × 4¼)	9.0 (550)	261 (350) at 2,700	261 (350) at 2,700	7.5	228.6 (504)				100/100LL
Voyager T-550	6	133 × 108 (5¼ × 4¼)	9.0 (550)	224 (300) at 2,500	224 (300) at 2,500	7.5	204 (450)				100LL
Voyager GT-550	6	133 × 108 (5¼ × 4¼)	9.0 (550)	298 (400)	298 (400)	7.5	249.5 (550)				100LL
IO-550-B	6	133 × 108 (5¼ × 4¼)	9.0 (550)	224 (300) at 2,700	224 (300) at 2,700	8.5	207.9 (462)	964 (37.97)	852 (33.56)	694 (27.32)	100LL
IO-550-C	6	133 × 108 (5¼ × 4¼)	9.0 (550)	224 (300) at 2,700	224 (300) at 2,700	8.5	211.95 (471)	1,100.1 (43.31)	852 (33.56)	502 (19.78)	100LL

*With accessories; †Not including turbocharger;
‡N weight 220 kg (486 lb)

*With accessories; †Not including turbocharger.

TELEDYNE CAE
TELEDYNE CAE DIVISION OF TELEDYNE INC
1330 Laskey Road, Toledo, Ohio 43612-0971
Telephone: 1 (419) 470 3000
Telex: EASYLINK 6 288 4828
Fax: 1 (419) 470 3386
PRESIDENT: Robert R. Schwanhausser

Teledyne CAE produces small gas turbine engines for training aircraft, missiles and UAVs. See 1987-88 *Jane's* for further details.

TELEDYNE CAE 352 and 356
US military designation: J69

One version of this simple turbojet is used in manned aircraft:

J69-T-25 (Teledyne CAE Model 352-5A). Long life version; powers Cessna T-37B.

DIMENSIONS (nominal):

Length overall	899 mm (35.39 in)
Width	566 mm (22.30 in)

WEIGHT, DRY:	165 kg (364 lb)
PERFORMANCE RATINGS:	
Max T-O thrust	4.56 kN (1,025 lb) at 21,730 rpm
SPECIFIC FUEL CONSUMPTION (max T-O):	
	32.30 mg/Ns (1.14 lb/h/lb st)

TEXTRON LYCOMING
TEXTRON LYCOMING
550 Main Street, Stratford, Connecticut 06497
Telephone: 1 (203) 385 2000
PRESIDENT: J. R. Myers

Textron Lycoming produces several families of engines, including the T53, T55, ALF 502 and LT101, with turboshaft, turboprop, turbofan, vehicular and marine variants. In June 1987 Textron Lycoming and General Electric agreed joint development of gas turbines for aero and ground applications. The aero engine is the T407/GLC38, described under General Electric.

TEXTRON LYCOMING ALF 502
The ALF 502 was launched in 1969, primarily for commercial and executive aircraft. The core is the T55, and construction is modular.
Current versions are as follows:

ALF 502L. First commercial version, FAA certificated in February 1980. Powers Canadair Challenger 600 in ALF 502L-2 form. L-2A, L-2C and L-3 certificated 1982-3.

ALF 502R. Reduced rating, FAA certificated January 1981 as R-3 to power BAe 146. Improved R-3A, R-4 and R-5 certificated 1982-3. R-6 certificated 1984.

By 1990 a total of 184 engines had flown 350,000 h in the Challenger, while another 650 had flown 3,200,000 h in the BAe 146. TBO was 4,000 h, but the ALF 502 is usually operated on-condition.

TYPE: High bypass ratio, two-shaft geared turbofan.
FAN MODULE: Cast frame includes four engine mounts 90° apart, and may carry reverser. Fan rotor blades are base and part-span shrouded. Mounted directly behind rotor (6,700 lb st engines) is a single or (7,500 lb st engines) two stages of compression. Anti-icing of LP compressor inlet by bleed air. Accessory gearbox on fan frame takes HP shaft power. Reduction gear couples LP turbine to fan. Bypass ratio: 502R-3, 5.71; 502R-5, 5.6; 502L, 5.0.
COMPRESSOR: HP compressor has seven stages and single centrifugal. Acceleration bleed between stages 6 and 7 operated by main fuel control. Overall pressure ratio: R-3, 11.6; R-5, 12.0; L-2, 13.6.
TURBINE: HP has two aircooled stages. LP has two stages. All rotor blades base shrouded: LP tip shrouded.
COMBUSTION CHAMBER: One-piece annular combustor wraps around turbine. Atomising nozzles inserted through outer chamber at rear. Disconnecting permits removal of combustor/turbine module, providing access to HP turbine.
ACCESSORY DRIVES: Accessory gearbox carries main fuel control, oil pump and filter, tachometer (if required) and provisions for customer accessories.
DATA: See table.

TEXTRON LYCOMING LF500
In September 1988 Textron Lycoming announced plans for a family of commercial turbofans based on the ALF 502R, using the same core. The engines will range from 32.03 kN (7,200 lb st) to 44.48 kN (10,000 lb st), the most powerful version requiring a small increase in fan diameter. The basic model is expected to be certificated in 1991.

TEXTRON LYCOMING LTC1
US military designation: T53
The T53 was developed under a joint US Air Force/Army contract. More than 19,000 have logged over 41 million hours since 1956.

Cutaway drawing of Textron Lycoming ALF 502L geared turbofan

Cutaway drawing of Textron Lycoming T53-L-13B free-turbine turboshaft

TEXTRON LYCOMING ALF 502, LTC1/T53 and LTC4/T55 ENGINES

Manufacturer's and civil designation	Military designation	Type*	T-O Rating kN (lb st) or max kW (hp)	SFC μg/J; ‡ mg/Ns (lb/h/hp; ‡lb/h/lb st)	Weight, Dry less tailpipe kg (lb)	Max diameter mm(in)	Length overall mm (in)	Remarks
T5311A	—	ACFS	820 kW (1,100 shp)	115 (0.68)	225 (496)	584 (23)	1,209 (47.6)	Bell 204B
T5313B	—	ACFS	1,044 kW (1,400 shp)	98 (0.58)	245 (540)	584 (23)	1,209(47.6)	Bell 205A
T5317A	—	ACFS	1,119 kW (1,500 shp)	99.7 (0.59)	256 (564)	584 (23)	1,209(47.6)	Bell 205A-1
—	T53-L-13B	ACFS	1,044 kW (1,400 shp)	98 (0.58)	245 (540)	584 (23)	1,209 (47.6)	Advanced UH-1H, AH-1G
—	T53-L-703	ACFS	1,106 kW (1,485 shp)	101.4 (0.60)	247 (545)	584 (23)	1,209 (47.6)	Bell AH-1S TOW/Cobra
LTC1K-4K	—	ACFS	1,156 kW (1,550 shp)	98.7 (0.584)	234 (515)	584 (23)	1,209 (47.6)	Bell XV-15
—	T53-L-701	ACFP	1,082 ekW (1,451 ehp)	101.4 (0.60)	312 (688)	584 (23)	1,483 (58.4)	Grumman OV-1D, AIDC (Taiwan) T-CH-1
—	YT55-L-9	ACFP	1,887 ekW (2,529 ehp)	102.7 (0.608)	363 (799)	615 (24.2)	1,580 (62.2)	Piper Enforcer
—	T55-L-7C	ACFS	2,125 kW (2,850 shp)	101.4 (0.60)	267 (590)	615 (24.2)	1,118 (44)	
T5508D (LTC4B-8D)	—	ACFS	2,186 kW (2,930 shp) flat rated at 1,678 kW (2,250 shp)	100.1 (0.592) / 106.0 (0.628)	274 (605)	610 (24)	1,118 (44)	Bell 214A, 214B
—	T55-L-712†	ACFS	2,796 kW (3,750 shp)	89.6 (0.53)	340 (750)	615 (24.2)	1,181 (46.5)	Boeing CH-47D
AL5512	—	ACFS	3,039 kW (4,075 shp)	89.6 (0.53)	355 (780)	615 (24.2)	1,118 (44)	Boeing 234
—	T55-L-714	ACFS	3,629 kW (4,867 shp)	85.0 (0.503)	363 (800)	615 (24.2)	1,181 (46.5)	Boeing MH-47E
ALF 502R-3	—	ACFF	29.8 kN (6,700 lb)	‡11.64 (‡0.411)	576 (1,270)	1,059 (41.7)	1,443 (56.8)	BAe 146
ALF 502R-3A	—	ACFF	31.0 kN (6,968 lb)	‡11.55 (‡0.408)	576 (1,270)	1,059 (41.7)	1,443 (56.8)	BAe 146
ALF 502R-5	—	ACFF	31.0 kN (6,968 lb)	‡11.55 (‡0.408)	583 (1,283)	1,059 (41.7)	1,443 (56.8)	BAe 146
ALF 502R-6	—	ACFF	33.36 kN (7,500 lb)	‡11.73 (‡0.415)	589 (1,298)	1,059 (41.7)	1,487 (58.56)	BAe 146
ALF 502L/L-2	—	ACFF	33.36 kN (7,500 lb)	‡12.1 (‡0.428)	589 (1,298)	1,059 (41.7)	1,487 (58.56)	Canadair Challenger 600
ALF 502L-2A	—	ACFF	33.36 kN (7,500 lb)	‡11.70 (‡0.414)	589 (1,298)	1,059 (41.7)	1,487 (58.56)	
ALF 502L-3	—	ACFF	34.74 kN (7,800 lb)	‡11.73 (‡0.415)	589 (1,298)	1,059 (41.7)	1,487 (58.56)	

*ACFS = axial plus centrifugal, free-turbine shaft; ACFP = axial plus centrifugal, free-turbine propeller; ACFF = axial plus centrifugal, free-turbine fan
†Applies to T55-L-11A, C**, D, E** and 712**, those designated ** having 2½ min contingency rating of 3,357 kW (4,500 shp)

Cutaway drawing of Textron Lycoming T55-L-712 (military) or AL5512 (commercial) free-turbine turboshaft

Licences for manufacture of the T53 are held by Klöckner-Humboldt-Deutz in West Germany, Piaggio in Italy, Kawasaki in Japan, and in Taiwan.

Current versions are as follows:

T53-L-13. Uprated L-11. Redesigned 'hot end' and initial stages of compressor. Four turbine stages, compared with two in earlier models, and variable inlet guide vanes combined with redesigned first two compressor stages. Atomising combustor to facilitate operation on a wider range of fuels. Powers Bell UH-1M and UH-1H and AH-1G HueyCobra. The **T5313A** commercial version has been superseded by the **T5313B**.

T53-L-701. Turboprop incorporating 'split power' reduction gear.

T53-L-703. Improved durability L-13. Thermodynamic rating 1,343 kW (1,800 shp).

LTC1K-4K. Direct drive L-13 suitable for operation from 105° nose up to 90° nose down.

T5317A. Improvements over L-13 include improved cooling of first gas producer turbine nozzle plus aircooled blades in first turbine rotor.

The following details apply to the T53-L-13 and L-701:

TYPE: Free turbine turboshaft.

COMPRESSOR: Five axial stages followed by single centrifugal stage. Variable inlet guide vanes. Pressure ratio 7.2. Mass flow 5.53 kg (12.2 lb)/s at 25,150 gas producer rpm.

COMBUSTION CHAMBER: Annular reverse flow, with 22 atomising injectors.

FUEL CONTROL SYSTEM: Chandler Evans TA-2S system with one dual fuel pump, 41.4 bars (600 lb/sq in). Interstage air bleed control.

FUEL GRADE: ASTM A-1, MIL-J-5624, MIL-F-26005A, JP-1, JP-4, JP-5, CITE.

TURBINE: First two stages, driving compressor, use hollow aircooled stator vanes and cored-out cast steel rotor blades. Second two stages, driving reduction gearing, have solid steel blades.

ACCESSORIES: Electric starter or starter/generator. Bendix-Scintilla TGLN high energy ignition unit.

LUBRICATION: Recirculating system, with gear pump, 4.83 bars (70 lb/sq in).

OIL GRADE: MIL-L-7808, MIL-L-23699.

DATA: See table.

TEXTRON LYCOMING LTC4
US military designation: T55

This engine is based on the T53 with higher mass flow. Total operating time by early 1989 on more than 3,900 engines was over 5.0 million hours.

Current versions are as follows:

LTC4B-8D. Modified T55-L-7C.

T5508D. Commercial version of LTC4B-8D.

T55-L-11 (LTC4B-11B) series. Uprated L-7, with variable inlet guide vanes and two-stage compressor turbine.

T55-L-712. Improved L-11D. Wide chord compressor blades without inlet guide vanes, and one-piece rotor.

AL5512. Commercial L-712, with engine out contingency rating of 3,250 kW (4,355 shp).

T55-L-714. Growth version with cooled gas-generator turbine blades, FADEC and improved torquemeter. OEI rating (contingency) 3,780 kW (5,069 shp).

YT55-L-9A. Turboprop version of L-7C using split-power reduction gears.

The following description applies to the T55-L-11:

TYPE: Free turbine turboshaft.

COMPRESSOR: Seven axial stages followed by single centrifugal stage. Variable inlet guide vanes. Late models have wide chord blades in first two stages and no inlet guide vanes. Pressure ratio 8.2. Mass flow 12.25 kg (27 lb)/s.

COMBUSTION CHAMBER: Annular reverse flow. Twenty-eight downstream burners.

FUEL SYSTEM: Hamilton Standard JFC 31 fuel control. Gear type pump, with gas producer and power shaft governors.

FUEL GRADE: MIL-J-5624 grade JP-4, JP-5, MIL-F-46005A or CITE.

TURBINE: Gas generator turbine has two stages with cored-out cast steel blades. Two-stage power turbine has solid steel blades.

ACCESSORIES: Electric starter or starter/generator, or air or hydraulic starter. Bendix-Scintilla TGLN high energy ignition unit. Four igniter plugs.

LUBRICATION: Recirculating. Integral tank and cooler.
OIL GRADE: MIL-L-7808, MIL-L-23699.
DATA: See table.

TEXTRON LYCOMING LT 101
US military designation: YT702-LD-700

The LT 101 is designed for low life cycle costs. Each engine comprises an accessory reduction gearbox, gas generator and combustor/power turbine module. The engine has a single axial compressor stage followed by a single centrifugal stage, a reverse flow annular combustor, a single-stage gas generator turbine, and a single-stage power turbine. Front gearboxes provide output speeds of 1,925, 6,000 or 9,545 rpm. The 6,000 rpm gearbox has both forward and aft drives. The engine has either a scroll or radial inlet. Mass flow is 2.03 kg (4.8 lb)/s, and pressure ratio 8.5.

Current production versions include turboshaft (LTS) and turboprop (LTP) models, with max power in the 459 to 548 kW (615 to 735 shp) range. All are certificated under FAR Pt 33 for 2,400 h TBO or on-condition maintenance. LT 101 operating experience now totals more than 2 million h.

TEXTRON LYCOMING LTS 101

The **LTS 101-600A-2** is a 6,000 rpm power plant for the Aerospatiale AS 350D Astar. The **650C-2/C-3** is a 9,545 rpm power plant for the Bell 222. The **650B-1**, a 6,000 rpm engine with a radial inlet for the MBB/Kawasaki BK117A. The **750B-1** powers the BK117B. The **600A-3** powers the AS 350D Mk 3. A growth version, the **750C-1**, powers the Bell 222B and 222UT. The **750B-2**, with radial inlet, powers the AS 366 and HH-65A Dolphin.
DATA: See table.

TEXTRON LYCOMING LTP 101

The LTP 101 turboprop incorporates a free power turbine, provisions for tractor or pusher installation, hydraulic propeller governor, radial screened inlet and anti-icing protection. Output speed is 1,700-1,950 rpm. The **LTP 101-600A-1A** has been selected for the P.166-DL3, Air Tractor and Cresco agricultural aircraft, Riley Cessna 421 and Page Turbo Thrush and Ag-Cat. It has flown in Piper Brave, Turbine Islander and Dornier 128-6 prototypes. The **LTP 101-700A-1A** was certificated in July 1980.

DIMENSIONS:
Length	914 mm (36.0 in)
Diameter	533 mm (21.0 in)
WEIGHT, DRY:	152 kg (335 lb)

PERFORMANCE RATINGS (T-O, S/L):
LTP 101-600	462 ekW (620 ehp)
LTP 101-700	522 ekW (700 ehp)

SPECIFIC FUEL CONSUMPTION (T-O, S/L):
LTP 101-600, -700	93 µg/J (0.55 lb/h/ehp)

TEXTRON LYCOMING LTS 101 ENGINES

Engine Model	Performance Rating (T-O, S/L) kW (shp)	SFC µg/J (lb/h/shp)	Weight, Dry kg (lb)	Length mm (in)	Diameter mm (in)
LTS 101-600A-2	459 (615)	96.5 (0.571)	115 (253)	785 (30.9)	599 (23.6)
LTS 101-600A-3	459 (615)	98.4 (0.582)	120 (265)	785 (30.9)	599 (23.6)
LTS 101-650B-1	410 (550)	97.5 (0.577)	124 (273)	790 (31.1)	645 (25.4)
LTS 101-650C-2/C-3/C-3A	447 (600)	96.7 (0.572)	109.5 (241)	787 (31.0)	574 (22.6)
LTS 101-750B-2	461 (618)	96.3 (0.570)	123 (271)	822 (32.36)	627 (24.7)
LTS 101-750C-1	510 (684)	97.5 (0.577)	110.5 (244)	790 (31.1)	574 (22.6)

Left to right: Textron Lycoming LTS 101-650B-1 turboshaft, LTP 101-700A-1A turboprop and LTS 101-750C-1 turboshaft

WILLIAMSPORT

652 Oliver St, Williamsport, Pennsylvania 17701
Telephone: 1 (717) 327 7041
Fax: 1 (717) 327 7022

Williamsport is the world's largest producer of piston engines for general aviation.

TEXTRON LYCOMING O-235 SERIES

Four cylinders of 111 mm (4⅜ in) bore and 98.4 mm (3⅞ in) stroke. The high compression O-235-N is the most recent production version of the O-235, used in several trainers. It requires 100 octane fuel.

TEXTRON LYCOMING O-320 and IO-320 SERIES

Cylinder bore increased to 130 mm (5⅛ in). The O-320 is an engine in the 112-119 kW (150-160 hp) class. Both carburetted and fuel injected versions are produced in low and high compression models for use with 80/87 or 100 octane minimum grade fuels, respectively. Fully aerobatic models are available.

TEXTRON LYCOMING O-360 and IO-360 SERIES

The O-360 series is basically the same as the O-320 except for an increase in stroke to 111 mm (4⅜ in). Like the O-320, this engine is manufactured with low or high compression, with carburettor or fuel injection. The various models include aerobatic capability, a specific design for helicopters and a turbocharged version. The IO-360-A has fuel injection, tuned induction and high output cylinders, while the IO-360-B has continuous flow port injection and standard cylinders. In the TIO-360-C the turbocharger is pilot controlled.

TEXTRON LYCOMING O-540 and IO-540 SERIES

The O-540 is a direct drive, six-cylinder version of the four-cylinder O-360. It is available in low and high compression versions, and the VO-540 is a helicopter power plant with crankshaft vertical. Fuel injected IO-540 models are manufactured with ratings of 186-224 kW (250-300 hp). An aerobatic version is available.

TEXTRON LYCOMING TIO-540 SERIES

This is a turbocharged version of the fuel injected IO-540, some of which have tuned induction. It is manufactured for unpressurised and pressurised aircraft, and several models incorporate an intercooler.

TEXTRON LYCOMING TIO-541 SERIES

Although the displacement of this turbocharged, six-cylinder series is the same as that of the TIO-540, the TIO-541 and geared TIGO-541 are totally redesigned. The TIO-541-E is rated at 283 kW (380 hp) and the geared TIGO-541-E at 317 kW (425 hp). A double scroll blower is available to provide cabin pressurisation.

TEXTRON LYCOMING IO-720 SERIES

This eight-cylinder version of the IO-540 is used at ratings from 280 to 298 kW (375 to 400 hp).

Textron Lycoming IO-360 four-cylinder piston engine

Textron Lycoming TIO-540-AE2A turbocharged piston engine

Textron Lycoming IO-720 eight-cylinder piston engine

Textron Lycoming O-540 six-cylinder piston engine

TEXTRON LYCOMING HORIZONTALLY OPPOSED PISTON ENGINES

Engine Model*	No. of Cylinders	Rated output at Sea Level kW (hp) at rpm	Capacity litres (cu in)	Compression Ratio	Fuel grade Minimum	Weight, Dry kg (lb)	Length Overall mm (in)	Width Overall mm (in)	Height Overall mm (in)	Gear Ratio†
O-235-C	4	86 (115) at 2,800	3.85 (233)	6.75	80/87	97.5 (215)	751 (29.56)	812 (32.00)	569 (22.40)	D
O-235-L	4	86 (115) at 2,700 78 (105) at 2,400	3.85 (233)	8.5	100	98 (218)	738 (29.05)	812 (32.00)	569 (22.40)	D
O-235-N, P	4	87 (116) at 2,800	3.85 (233)	8.1	100	98 (218)	738 (29.05)	812 (32.00)	569 (22.40)	D
O-320-A	4	112 (150) at 2,700	5.2 (319.8)	7.0	80/87	110 (243)	751 (29.56)	819 (32.24)	584 (22.99)	D
O-320-D	4	119 (160) at 2,700	5.2 (319.8)	8.5	91/96	114 (253)	808 (31.82)	819 (32.24)	488 (19.22)	D
AEIO-320-D	4	119 (160) at 2,700	5.2 (319.8)	8.5	100	123 (271)	780 (30.70)	819 (32.24)	589 (23.18)	D
O-320-E	4	112 (150) at 2,700	5.2 (319.8)	7.0	80/87	113 (249)	738 (29.05)	819 (32.24)	584 (22.99)	D
O-320-H	4	119 (160) at 2,700	5.2 (319.8)	9.0	100	115 (253)	819 (32.26)	830 (32.68)	621 (24.46)	D
O-360-A	4	134 (180) at 2,700	5.92 (361)	8.5	91/96	118 (260)	808 (31.82)	848 (33.37)	488 (19.22)	D
LO-360-A	4	134 (180) at 2,700	5.92 (361)	8.5	91/96	120 (266)	808 (31.82)	848 (33.37)	488 (19.22)	D
O-360-F	4	134 (180) at 2,700	5.92 (361)	8.5	100	122 (269)	808 (31.81)	859 (33.38)	507 (19.96)	D
TO-360-C, F	4	157 (210) at 2,575 to 3,050 m (10,000 ft)	5.92 (361)	7.3	100	154 (343)	876 (34.50)	921 (36.25)	534 (21.02)	D

†Direct drive.

TEXTRON LYCOMING HORIZONTALLY OPPOSED PISTON ENGINES (continued)

Engine Model*	No. of Cylinders	Rated output at Sea Level kW (hp) at rpm	Capacity litres (cu in)	Compression Ratio	Fuel grade Minimum	Weight, Dry kg (lb)	Length Overall mm (in)	Width Overall mm (in)	Height Overall mm (in)	Gear Ratio†
IO-360-A	4	149 (200) at 2,700	5.92 (361)	8.7	100	133 (293)	757 (29.81)	870 (34.25)	491 (19.35)	D
IO-360-B	4	134 (180) at 2,700	5.92 (361)	8.5	100	122 (268)	757 (29.81)	848 (33.37)	631 (24.84)	D
IO-360-C	4	149 (200) at 2,700	5.92 (361)	8.7	100	134 (298)	855 (33.65)	870 (34.25)	495 (19.48)	D
TIO-360-C	4	210 (282) at 2,575 to 3,050 m (10,000 ft)	5.92 (361)	7.3	100	158 (348)	910 (35.82)	921 (36.25)	550 (21.65)	D
HIO-360-D	4	142 (190) at 3,200 to 1,280 m (4,200 ft)	5.92 (361)	10.0	100	132 (290)	894 (35.23)	904 (35.62)	495 (19.48)	D
HIO-360-E	4	142 (190) at 2,900	5.92 (361)	8.0	100	132 (290)	797 (31.36)	870 (34.25)	507 (19.97)	D
HIO-360-F	4	142 (190) at 3,050	5.92 (361)	8.0	100	133 (293)	797 (31.36)	870 (34.25)	507 (19.97)	D
AEIO-360-A	4	149 (200) at 2,700	5.92 (361)	8.7	100	139 (307)	780 (30.70)	870 (34.25)	492 (19.35)	D
AEIO-360-B	4	134 (180) at 2,700	5.92 (361)	8.5	91/96	125 (277)	738 (29.05)	848 (33.37)	631 (24.84)	D
O-540-B	6	175 (235) at 2,575	8.86 (541.5)	7.2	80/87	166 (366)	945 (37.22)	848 (33.37)	624 (24.56)	D
O-540-E	6	194 (260) at 2,700	8.86 (541.5)	8.5	91/96	167 (368)	976 (38.42)	848 (33.37)	624 (24.56)	D
O-540-G	6	194 (260) at 2,700	8.86 (541.5)	8.5	91/96	174 (386)	999 (39.34)	848 (33.37)	624 (24.56)	D
O-540-J	6	175 (235) at 2,400	8.86 (541.5)	8.5	100	162 (357)	989 (38.93)	848 (33.37)	519 (20.43)	D
VO-540-B	6	227 (305) at 3,200	8.86 (541.5)	7.3	80/87	202 (446)	882 (34.73)	880 (34.70)	617 (24.29)	D V
VO-540-C	6	227 (305) at 3,200 to 915 m (3,000 ft)	8.86 (541.5)	8.7	100	200 (441)	882 (34.73)	880 (34.70)	649 (25.57)	D V
IO-540-C	6	186 (250) at 2,575	8.86 (541.5)	8.5	91/96	170 (375)	976 (38.42)	848 (33.37)	622 (24.46)	D
IO-540-K	6	224 (300) at 2,700	8.86 (541.5)	8.7	100	201 (443)	999 (39.34)	870 (34.25)	498 (19.60)	D
IO-540-W	6	175 (235) at 2,400	8.86 (541.5)	8.5	100	166 (367)	989 (38.93)	848 (33.37)	492 (19.35)	D
AEIO-540-D	6	194 (260) at 2,700	8.86 (541.5)	8.5	91/96	174 (386)	999 (39.34)	848 (33.37)	621 (24.46)	D
AEIO-540-L	6	224 (300) at 2,700	8.86 (541.5)	8.7	100	202 (445)	989 (38.93)	870 (34.25)	622 (24.46)	D
TIO-540-A	6	231 (310) at 2,575 to 4,575 m (15,000 ft)	8.86 (541.5)	7.3	100	232 (511)	1,304 (51.34)	870 (34.25)	577 (22.71)	D
TIO-540-AE2A	6	261 (350) at 2,600	8.86 (541.5)	7.3	100	249 (549)				D
TIO-540-C	6	186 (250) at 2,575 to 4,575 m (15,000 ft)	8.86 (541.5)	7.2	100	205 (456)	1,026 (40.38)	848 (33.37)	770 (30.33)	D
TIO/LTIO-540-F	6	242 (325) at 2,575 to 4,575 m (15,000 ft)	8.86 (541.5)	7.3	100	233 (514)	1,304 (51.34)	870 (34.25)	570 (22.42)	D
TIO/LTIO-540-J	6	261 (350) at 2,575 to 4,575 m (15,000 ft)	8.86 (541.5)	7.3	100	235 (518)	1,308 (51.50)	870 (34.25)	573 (22.56)	D
TIO-540-S	6	224 (300) at 2,700 to 3,660 m (12,000 ft)	8.86 (541.5)	7.3	100	228 (502)	1,004 (39.56)	915 (36.02)	667 (26.28)	D
TIO/LTIO-540-U	6	261 (350) at 2,500 to 4,575 m (15,000 ft)	8.86 (541.5)	7.3	100	248 (547)	1,204 (47.40)	870 (34.25)	574 (22.59)	D
TIO/LTIO-540-V	6	269 (360) at 2,600 to 5,485 m (18,000 ft)	8.86 (541.5)	7.3	100	248 (547)	1,352 (53.21)	886 (34.88)	621 (24.44)	D
TIO-541-E	6	283 (380) at 2,900 to 4,575 m (15,000 ft)	8.86 (541.5)	7.3	100	270 (596)	1,282 (50.70)	905 (35.66)	640 (25.17)	D
TIGO-541-E	6	317 (425) at 3,200 to 4,575 m (15,000 ft)	8.86 (541.5)	7.3	100	319 (704)	1,462 (57.57)	885 (34.86)	575 (22.65)	0.667
IO-720-A	8	298 (400) at 2,650	11.84 (722)	8.7	100	257 (567)	1,179 (46.41)	870 (34.25)	573 (22.53)	D
IO-720-B	8	298 (400) at 2,650	11.84 (722)	8.7	100	252 (556)	1,218 (47.97)	870 (34.25)	530 (20.88)	D
IO-720-D	8	298 (400) at 2,650	11.84 (722)	8.7	100	259 (570)	1,189 (46.80)	870 (34.25)	562 (22.11)	D

*Model designation code: A, Aerobatic; AE, Aerobatic engine; G, Geared; H, Helicopter; I, Fuel injected; L, Left-hand rotation crankshaft; O, Opposed cylinders; S, Supercharged; T, Turbocharged; V, Vertical mounting. †D, Direct drive.

THERMO-JET
THERMO-JET STANDARD INC
PO Box 55976, Houston, Texas 77055
Telephone: 1 (713) 465 5735
MANAGER: John A. Melenric

This company specialises in valveless pulsejet units for UAVs and the homebuilt market. These engines are devoid of moving parts and are characterised by multiple reverse flow air inlets to a combustion chamber in which is burned propane, butane or compressed natural gas, fed under pressure from lightweight tanks. Intermittent combustion and expulsion takes place at a cycle frequency determined by the chamber size and geometry and combustion pressure.

Thermo-Jet offers six sizes of unit, the J3-200 (0.0179 kN, 4 lb st at S/L), J5-200 (0.045 kN, 10 lb st at S/L), J7-300 (0.09 kN, 21 lb st at S/L), J8-200 (0.045 kN, 10 lb st at S/L), J10-200 (0.244 kN, 55 lb st at S/L), and J13-202 (0.4 kN, 90 lb st at S/L). Further details were given in the 1979-80 *Jane's.*

Thermo-Jet J13-202 on test stand

THIOKOL
THIOKOL CORPORATION
2475 Washington Blvd, Ogden, Utah 84401
Telephone: 1 (801) 629 2000
Fax: 1 (801) 629 2420
SOLID PROPELLANT ROCKET MOTOR PLANTS: Elkton, Maryland; Huntsville, Alabama; Marshall, Texas; Brigham City, Utah
PRESIDENT: U. E. Garrison

In 1943, the discovery by Thiokol of liquid polymer, a new type of synthetic rubber, paved the way for the 'case-bonded' rocket. The company's polysulphide liquid polymer proved to be the catalyst for production of efficient solid motors.

THIOKOL SHUTTLE RSRM
Each Space Shuttle solid rocket motor **(SRM)** is cast in four segments, stacked vertically in pairs as part of the solid rocket booster system. Thrust vector control for each SRM is provided by a flexible bearing movable nozzle driven by two hydraulic actuators. After burnout, the two boosters are separated and fall back into the atmosphere, where parachutes control impact velocity into the ocean. The boosters are then towed back to a recovery site. In its original form, the SRM was the largest solid rocket propulsion system to reach operational status. It was also the first to be qualified for manned flight, and the first to demonstrate reusability of major components. A high performance motor (HPM) became standard from the eighth flight in August 1983. Development was also begun on a graphite epoxy case expected to increase into-orbit payload by 2,087 kg (4,600 lb).

As a result of the loss of STS-S.1 (Challenger) in January 1986, the SRM was redesigned, and the **RSRM** (redesigned SRM) has been used since flights resumed in 1988. The following data apply to the RSRM:

DIMENSIONS:
Length	38.47 m (126.2 ft)
Diameter	3,708 mm (146 in)

WEIGHTS:
Propellant	503,487 kg (1,110,000 lb)
Loaded motor	569,893 kg (1,256,400 lb)

THRUST:
Average vacuum	11,521 kN (2,590,000 lb)

BURN TIME: 123 s

UP

UP INC
PO Box 659, Temecula, California 92390
Telephone: 1 (714) 676 5652
Telex: 910 332 1306

WILLIAMS

WILLIAMS INTERNATIONAL
2280 West Maple Road, PO Box 200, Walled Lake, Michigan 48088
Telephone: 1 (313) 624 5200
PRESIDENT: Sam Williams
VICE-PRESIDENT, PUBLIC RELATIONS: David C. Jolivette

Details of the engines manufactured by Williams for unmanned applications can be found in the 1987-88 *Jane's*.

WILLIAMS FJ44
Development of this turbofan began in 1971. It was chosen at a rating of 3.78 kN (850 lb st) for the proposed Foxjet, but was subsequently redesigned to incorporate F107 technology, with bypass ratio of 3.24, resulting in increased thrust and reduced fuel consumption.

The first FJ44, built to meet FAR.33 requirements, achieved design thrust at "a very modest turbine inlet temperature" on its first build. Scaled Composites has built a proof of concept light business jet powered by twin FJ44 engines.

In October 1988 Gulfstream Aerospace announced a new low-cost business jet, now the Swearingen SJ-30 (see

Peter Brock of this company states that the Arrow P-4 (see Sport Aircraft section of 1987-88 edition) has not been put into production because UP is not satisfied with available engines. Accordingly the company has run the

Aircraft section). This will be powered by FJ44 engines, for which technical and marketing support, and some engine components, including the turbine rotors and LP shaft, will be provided by Rolls-Royce, the two companies having formed Williams-Rolls Inc for this purpose. A second application, announced in October 1989, is the Cessna CitationJet. In addition, Williams states that a number of airframe companies in Europe and Asia are studying the FJ44 for use in their proposed business aircraft, commuters and military trainers. FJ44 certification is expected in 1991.
FAN: Single piece titanium with 22 wide-chord snubberless blades. Bypass ratio 3.31.
COMPRESSOR: One axial, rotating with the fan, followed by one centrifugal stage.
COMBUSTION CHAMBER: Annular, folded reverse-flow.
TURBINES: Single-stage HP driving centrifugal compressor. Two-stage LP driving fan and axial compressor. All three rotors with inserted blades.
CONTROL SYSTEM: Hydromechanical, with FADEC to be offered as an option.
JETPIPE: Full-length fan duct but no mixer.
DIMENSIONS:
Length 1,356 mm (53.4 in)
Max diameter 602 mm (23.7 in)

prototype of a six-cylinder radial of 1,800 cc (110.9 cu in), weighing 18 kg (40 lb) and rated at 29.8 kW (40 hp), as well as a single cylinder of a proposed V-8 of 1,600 cc (98.5 cu in), to weigh 14.5 kg (32 lb) and be rated at 23.9 kW (32 hp).

Williams FJ44 two-shaft turbofan

WEIGHT, DRY: 202 kg (445 lb)
PERFORMANCE RATINGS:
T-O (S/L) to 24°C 8.44 kN (1,900 lb st)
Max cruise (11,000 m; 36,090 ft, Mach 0.6) 1.98 kN (445 lb)
SPECIFIC FUEL CONSUMPTION:
T-O (S/L) 12.69 mg/Ns (0.448 lb/h/lb st)
Max cruise (as above) 19.83 mg/Ns (0.70 lb/h/lb)

YUGOSLAVIA

ORAO
ORAO AIR FORCE DEPOT
Federal Directorate of Supply and Procurement
9 Nemanjina St, 11005 Belgrade 9
Telephone: 38 (11) 621522
Telex: 11360, 11541, 11591, 11821
Fax: 38 (11) 324981

The depot was established in 1944. Today its main task is licence manufacture of the Rolls-Royce Viper 632-41 and 632-46, and the latest afterburning 633-41, used in most of the Orao twin-engined combat aircraft at present flying.

The Orao works has built up a design and development team which, in collaboration with Turbomecanica of Romania, has been developing the afterburning Viper Mk

633-47 engine for production IAR-93s and Oraos. The first afterburning engines were overweight, but an Orao 2 flew with afterburning engines on 20 October 1983.

ADDENDA

AIRCRAFT

ARGENTINA

FMA (page 2)

FMA IA 63 PAMPA

Signature of a teaming agreement between FMA and the

Aircraft Products Group of The LTV Corporation (see US section), to develop a variant of the Pampa to meet the USAF/US Navy's JPATS requirement, was announced on 2 May 1990. RFPs for the JPATS (Joint Primary Aircaft

Training System) programme are expected to be issued in early 1994.

AUSTRALIA

AIRCORP (page 4)

AIRCORP PTY LTD

Suite 11, 261 Given Terrace (PO Box 21), Paddington, Queensland 4064
Telephone: 61 (7) 369 0188
Fax: 61 (7) 369 1120
MANAGING DIRECTOR: H. Anning
PROJECT DIRECTOR, BUSHMASTER: Brian P. Creer
Further information on this company's Bushmaster light aircraft (see page 4) was received just as this Addenda was closing for press.

AIRCORP BUSHMASTER

Aircorp was formed to develop and produce a range of light aircraft with STOL characteristics under the series name Bushmaster. The **B2-N** designation applies to the two-seat prototype (VH-BOI), which first flew on 28 October 1989 powered by a Norton Aerotor rotary engine. Wings of this aircraft were constructed with two metal spars, sheet alloy webs, extruded caps, metal ribs and fabric covering, and were braced by V struts. Fuel was carried in integral tanks within the metal D-nose of each wing leading-edge. The rear fuselage was fabric covered.

Difficulties during test flying, and the absence of expected certification of the Norton engine, obliged Aircorp to abandon its original plan to offer the Bushmaster with a choice of this or Textron Lycoming engines. Airframe changes have also been made to make the aircraft more suitable for series production. Principally, these involve

Aircorp B2-N Bushmaster two-seat prototype with Norton Aerotor rotary engine

using one-piece extruded spars with the fuel tanks between them, all-metal wing skins, adding three-stage trailing-edge flaps, and bracing each wing by a single I strut.

Production Bushmasters will be marketed in four basic versions, three of them powered by the 86.5 kW (116 hp) Textron Lycoming O-235-N2C flat-four engine and providing two, '2 + 2' and three seats respectively. The three-seat **B3-16** accommodates a single pilot on the centreline, with a bench seat behind for two persons. This rear seat can be removed for the carriage of cargo. The

fourth version, a full four-seater with a lengthened fuselage, is powered by a 119 or 134 kW (160 or 180 hp) engine (designations **B4-60** and **B4-80** respectively).

Data given on page 4 are correct for the B2 and B3 variants except for the following:

Cabin: Length	2.70 m (8 ft 10¼ in)
Fuel capacity (standard)	136.4 litres (36 US gallons; 30 Imp gallons)
Weight empty: Lycoming	410 kg (904 lb)

MAC (page 6)

MAC MAMBA

TYPE: Two-seat light aircraft.
WINGS: High-wing monoplane, with single bracing strut each side. NACA 4412 constant section; 1° 30′ dihedral from roots. Two tubular metal spars with aluminium alloy skin. Trailing-edges have split flaps and Frise type differentially operating ailerons, latter each fitted with servo tab.
FUSELAGE: 4130 steel tube frame with aluminium alloy skins.

TAIL UNIT: Slightly sweptback vertical and non-swept horizontal surfaces. Variable incidence tailplane (on prototype only). Trim tab in one elevator.
LANDING GEAR: Non-retractable tricycle type. MAC cantilever self-sprung mainwheel legs, each with Cleveland wheel and Dunlop 6.00-6 × 4 tyre. Cleveland tailwheel has 5.00-5 × 4 Dunlop tyre and is steerable ±30°. MAC mainwheel brakes. Provision to fit Edo floats.
POWER PLANT: As given on page 6. Hartzell or Hoffmann two-blade propeller. Oil capacity 9.1 litres (2.4 US gallons; 2 Imp gallons).

ACCOMMODATION: As given on page 6. Door on starboard side. Space for 20 kg (44 lb) of baggage aft of seats. Cabin heated and ventilated.
ELECTRICAL SYSTEM: 14V or 28V DC (50A alternator).
AVIONICS: Dual nav/com radios; glideslope, marker beacon receiver, ADF, PDR encoder and intercom.
ARMAMENT: External attachment under each outer wing (load limit 136 kg; 300 lb per station) for 3 in standard rockets or gun pods of up to 20 mm calibre.

BRAZIL

EMBRAER (page 10)

EMBRAER EMB-145

The following revised data were received too late for inclusion in page 14:

WEIGHTS AND LOADING (estimated):

Basic operating weight empty	10,940 kg (24,120 lb)
Max payload	4,580 kg (10,100 lb)
Max fuel weight (usable)	4,210 kg (9,280 lb)
Max T-O weight	18,000 kg (39,685 lb)

Max landing weight	17,500 kg (38,580 lb)
Max wing loading	360.0 kg/m² (73.77 lb/sq ft)

PERFORMANCE (estimated, at 95% of MTOGW, ISA):
Max operating speed:
at 7,925 m (26,000 ft)
310 knots (575 km/h; 357 mph) CAS
above 7,925 m (26,000 ft) Mach 0.75
Max cruising speed:
at 6,100 m (20,000 ft)
410 knots (760 km/h; 472 mph)

at 10,060 m (33,000 ft)
430 knots (797 km/h; 495 mph)
T-O and landing field length 1,550 m (5,085 ft)
Range at max cruising speed at 11,890 m (39,000 ft) with 45 passengers (4,082 kg; 9,000 lb payload)
899 nm (1,665 km; 1,035 miles)

IPE (page 16)

A late reply from IPE for this year's edition provides a photograph and brief details of the following recent design:

IPE 06 CURUCACA

Developed for the Brazilian market and first flown in January 1990, the Curucaca is a very lightweight tandem two-seat training or general purpose aircraft, powered by a 52.2 kW (70 hp) T2000 (modified VW) engine.

DIMENSIONS, EXTERNAL:

Wing span	9.90 m (32 ft 5¾ in)
Length overall (flying attitude)	6.30 m (20 ft 8 in)
Height overall (flying attitude)	2.30 m (7 ft 6½ in)
Elevator span	2.91 m (9 ft 6½ in)

AREA:

Wings, gross	13.00 m² (139.9 sq ft)

WEIGHTS:

Weight empty	224 kg (494 lb)
Max T-O weight	444 kg (979 lb)

Prototype IPE 06 Curucaca two-seat light aircraft

PERFORMANCE:

Cruising speed	65 knots (120 km/h; 74 mph)
Stalling speed	27 knots (50 km/h; 31 mph)

CANADA

CANADAIR (page 23)

CANADAIR CL-215 and CL-215T

Delivery of the last piston engined CL-215, completing the order for 17 placed by the Greek government, was made on 3 May 1990.

The auxiliary finlets, shown in the CL-215T drawing on page 26, have been introduced on the two prototypes to offset some lateral instability caused by tail area turbulence resulting from this version's slimline nacelles and new propellers. The two prototypes had completed about 250 hours' flying by 1 May 1990, and certification was expected before the end of the year.

COLOMBIA

AERO MERCANTIL (page 47)

AERO MERCANTIL EL1 GAVILÁN (SPARROWHAWK)

This utility aircraft first flew, as planned, on 27 April 1990, and is now being certificated by the Colombian Department of Civil Aviation. It was designed, with the consultancy of General Aviation Technical Services of Lock Haven, Pennsylvania, to meet US FAR Pt 23 standards, and will later be submitted for US certification.

Newly announced figures differing from those given in the main part of this edition are:

Useful load	771 kg (1,700 lb)
Fuel capacity	
	379 litres (100 US gallons; 83.3 Imp gallons)
Cruising speed, 75% power	
	138 knots (256 km/h; 159 mph)
Stalling speed, 40° flap	55 knots (102 km/h; 64 mph)
Range, 30 min reserves	800 nm (1,482 km; 921 miles)

Colombia's Aero Mercantil Gavilán, which first flew on 27 April 1990

CZECHOSLOVAKIA

AERO (page 49)

AERO L-270

In a complete departure from its previously all-military product line, Aero announced this multi-purpose utility aircraft in early 1990. Similar in concept to the Cessna Caravan (see US section), it is seen as a versatile passenger and/or cargo carrier with potentially wide military, police or civil uses. Power plant would be a 559 kW (750 shp) Walter M 601 E turboprop with an Avia V 510 five-blade constant-speed fully-feathering reversible-pitch propeller. Wheel, float, amphibian or ski landing gear could be fitted. Accommodation would provide for one or two pilots, with room in the main cabin for up to 12 passengers (four to seven in executive interior), six stretchers plus two other wounded or medical personnel, 13 parachutists, a 1,400 kg (3,086 lb) cargo payload, fire retardant or agricultural chemical tanks, or aerial survey equipment.

General appearance of the L-270 is shown in an accompanying three-view drawing. Aero expected a decision on go-ahead by the Autumn of 1990, which would lead to a first flight in 1992. Principal data are as follows:

DIMENSIONS, EXTERNAL:

Wing span	16.00 m (52 ft 6 in)
Length overall	11.80 m (38 ft 8½ in)
Height overall	4.70 m (15 ft 5 in)
Cargo door (rear, port): Height	1.80 m (5 ft 10¾ in)
Width	1.28 m (4 ft 2½ in)

DIMENSIONS, INTERNAL:

Cabin: Length	5.25 m (17 ft 2¾ in)
Max height	1.50 m (4 ft 11 in)
Max width	1.60 m (5 ft 3 in)

AREA:

Wings, gross	28.00 m² (301.4 sq ft)

WEIGHTS:

Weight empty, equipped	1,870 kg (4,122 lb)
Max internal fuel	800 kg (1,764 lb)
Max T-O weight	3,820 kg (8,421 lb)

PERFORMANCE (estimated):

Max cruising speed at 3,000 m (9,850 ft)	
	175 knots (325 km/h; 202 mph)
Stalling speed	61 knots (113 km/h; 71 mph)
Max rate of climb at S/L	360 m (1,181 ft)/min
T-O run: STOL	300 m (985 ft)
FAR 23	330 m (1,083 ft)
T-O to 15 m (50 ft): STOL	400 m (1,313 ft)
FAR 23	500 m (1,641 ft)
Landing from 15 m (50 ft): STOL	350 m (1,149 ft)
FAR 23	450 m (1,477 ft)
Landing run: STOL	250 m (821 ft)
FAR 23	300 m (985 ft)
Range at 3,000 m (9,850 ft), 30 min reserves	
	647-810 nm (1,200-1,500 km; 745-932 miles)

Aero L-39 MS prototype. It will be noted that the cockpits have a single canopy, not individual canopies as stated on page 50

Aero L-270 design for a multi-purpose utility aircraft *(Jane's/Mike Keep)*

ZLIN (page 53)

ZLIN AGRO TURBO

Current production models of the Agro Turbo (page 55) are designated **Z 137T**. In the absence of any information from Zlin for this year's edition, it is not possible to indicate how this may differ from the earlier Z 37T model.

FRANCE

DASSAULT AVIATION (page 68)

DASSAULT FALCON 2000

Dassault has selected the 26.7 kN (6,000 lb st) General Electric/Garrett CFE738 turbofan to power the Falcon 2000.

ROBIN (page 83)

ROBIN ATL

Robin has developed a new light aircraft known provisionally as the **Robin 2+2**, which is based on the ATL airframe and powered by an 88 kW (118 hp) Textron Lycoming O-235 engine. First flight was expected in Summer 1990.

GERMANY, WEST

DCA

DORNIER COMPOSITE AIRCRAFT GmbH & Co KG

This company (address/telephone/telex/fax details as for Claudius Dornier Seastar: see page 90) has assumed responsibility for the Seastar programme.

INDIA

CIVIL AVIATION DEPARTMENT
TECHNICAL CENTRE, CIVIL AVIATION DEPARTMENT

Opp. Safdarjung Airport, New Delhi 110006
Telephone: 91 (11) 611504
Telex: 31 66407 NAA
DIRECTOR GENERAL: P. C. Sen
DIRECTOR (R&D): Y. P. Bawa

LT-1

A prototype of this new two-seat aircraft (Light Trainer 1) was expected to fly by March 1990. It has been designed to meet FAR Pt 23 (Utility category) airworthiness requirements.

TYPE: Two-seat light trainer.

WINGS: Cantilever low-wing monoplane, of NASA GA(W)-1 constant section. Dihedral 4° from roots. Incidence 2°. Constant chord structure, comprising a box-type main spar of Himalayan spruce with laminated spruce flanges, plywood covered up to rear spar. Plain ailerons and trailing-edge flaps, all of single-spar spruce construction with ply covered nose cell and remainder fabric covered. Conventional controls (push/pull rods and cables). No aileron tabs.

FUSELAGE: Welded chromoly steel tube structure, fabric covered except for engine cowling and fairings, which are of glassfibre or aluminium alloy sheet.

TAIL UNIT: Fin and fixed incidence tailplane are two-spar all-metal structures; rudder and elevators similar but single-spar and fabric covered aft of nose cells. Metal trim tab in starboard elevator. Rudder and elevators actuated by push/pull rods and cables.

LANDING GEAR: Non-retractable bungee-sprung main-wheels, on side Vs and half-axles, with mechanical brakes. Non-retractable steerable tailwheel.

POWER PLANT: One 97 kW (130 hp) Rolls-Royce Continental O-240-A flat-four engine, driving a Hele Orient IA-135/BRM 7150 two-blade fixed-pitch metal propeller with spinner. Fuel capacity 90 litres (23.8 US gallons; 19.8 Imp gallons).

ACCOMMODATION: Two seats, with adjustable safety harnesses, side by side under one-piece cockpit canopy.

AVIONICS AND EQUIPMENT: VFR instrumentation standard. Provision for radio.

LT-1 two-seat light trainer designed by the Indian Civil Aviation Department's Technical Centre
(Jane's/Mike Keep)

DIMENSIONS, EXTERNAL:	
Wing span	9.20 m (30 ft 2¼ in)
Wing chord, constant	1.30 m (4 ft 3¼ in)
Wing aspect ratio	7.08
Length overall (flying attitude)	7.10 m (23 ft 3½ in)
Height overall (flying attitude)	1.78 m (5 ft 10 in)
Tailplane span	2.60 m (8 ft 6½ in)
Wheel track	2.00 m (6 ft 6¾ in)
Wheelbase	4.94 m (16 ft 2½ in)
Propeller diameter	1.83 m (6 ft 0 in)
AREAS:	
Wings, gross	11.96 m² (128.7 sq ft)
Ailerons (total)	1.10 m² (11.84 sq ft)
Trailing-edge flaps (total)	1.04 m² (11.19 sq ft)
Fin	0.81 m² (8.72 sq ft)
Rudder	0.65 m² (7.00 sq ft)
Tailplane	0.93 m² (10.01 sq ft)
Elevators (total, incl tab)	0.94 m² (10.12 sq ft)

WEIGHTS AND LOADINGS:	
Weight empty, equipped	475 kg (1,047 lb)
Max T-O weight	700 kg (1,543 lb)
Max wing loading	58.53 kg/m² (11.99 lb/sq ft)
Max power loading	7.23 kg/kW (11.87 lb/hp)
PERFORMANCE (estimated, at max T-O weight):	
Never-exceed speed	134 knots (250 km/h; 155 mph)
Max level speed	108 knots (200 km/h; 124 mph)
Econ cruising speed (75% power)	
	100 knots (185 km/h; 115 mph)
Stalling speed	45 knots (83 km/h; 52 mph)
Max rate of climb at S/L	180 m (590 ft)/min
Service ceiling	4,575 m (15,000 ft)
T-O run	225 m (739 ft)
Landing run	200 m (657 ft)
Range with max fuel	297 nm (550 km; 342 miles)
Max endurance	3 h 30 min
g limits	+4.4/-1.76

HAL (page 105)

HAL LIGHT ATTACK HELICOPTER

Hindustan Aeronautics has revealed its intention to develop a tandem two-seat gunship helicopter, based essentially upon the power plant and transmission system of its ALH (advanced light helicopter), described on pages 105-6. The LAH (light attack helicopter) variant, as the accompanying provisional drawing shows, will have stepped cockpits, an undernose gun turret, and stub wings for weapon carriage. According to HAL, no overseas assistance will be sought for the LAH programme.

Preliminary drawing of HAL's proposed light attack helicopter
(Jane's/Mike Keep)

INTERNATIONAL

US/EUROPEAN ADVANCED SST

On 9 May 1990, Aerospatiale and British Aerospace Commercial Aircraft Ltd agreed on a joint study of a second-generation supersonic airliner as a successor to Concorde during the next century. British Aerospace has investigated many aspects of such an aircraft under the project name Advanced Supersonic Transport (AST) and Aerospatiale has done the same with its Avion de Transport Supersonique Futur (ATSF). Work in Britain will be centred on the BAe Commercial Aircraft Airbus Division at Filton, Bristol, although the main Airbus Industrie company is not concerned in this programme.

The announcement gives the two companies the initiative in forming what they must hope will eventually be a single worldwide team to develop a new supersonic airliner. The number required is thought to be limited to between 300 and 500, and the market would hardly support two independent designs.

The first announcement was closely followed by another, on 23 May 1990, to the effect that a study group was being formed between Aerospatiale, British Aerospace, Deutsche Airbus (the airliner branch of Deutsche Aerospace), Boeing and McDonnell Douglas to explore the potential for next generation SSTs. Work would continue for about one year and look at the general issues of environmental implications, market potential, certification basis and the benefits of global co-operation. Eventual Japanese, Soviet and further European participation would have to be contemplated. Programme cost might be between $10 billion and $15 billion.

Principal justification for the new aircraft is the need for high-speed flights on the rapidly expanding long over-ocean routes across the Pacific and down to South America. A passenger capacity between 200 and 300 and a range of about 6,475 nm (12,000 km; 7,455 miles) are envisaged. Maximum speed is set at about Mach 2.4 in order to stay

with currently understood materials. There is no intention to fly supersonically overland. Variable cycle engines are probably the key to combining efficient supersonic performance with economic subsonic cruise and acceptable take-off and approach noise levels.

Aerospatiale and British Aerospace say they could start full-scale development in about 1995 and deliver the first aircraft in 2005.

Both Boeing and Douglas have done considerable work on new-generation SSTs, and the results of some detailed NASA technical studies are awaited.

Of the 16 original production **Concordes**, two prototypes and two pre-production aircraft built, 13 production Concordes remain in service, seven with British Airways and six with Air France. The first French production Concorde flew in December 1973, followed by the first British in February 1974. Full French and British certification was achieved late in 1975, followed by US certification in January 1979. The first commercial service was flown on 21 January 1976, and the first commercial Concorde arrival at New York Kennedy Airport, by Air France on 22 November 1977, was followed by British Airways in February 1978.

Braniff operated a joint extension with British Airways from Washington to Dallas Fort Worth, and Singapore Airlines operated a joint extension from Bahrain to Singapore. Iran Air and CAAC both signed preliminary purchase agreements, but did not eventually acquire the aircraft.

Concorde was last described in the 1980-81 *Jane's*.

Artist's impression of a possible future Anglo-French successor to the Concorde

ATR (page 121)

The ATR partnership was expected to announce, possibly by the time this edition of *Jane's* is published, plans to go ahead with a 100-seat version of its design, still aimed at regional carriers rather than major trunk operators. Other options being considered at the time of going to press included a re-engining programme for the ATR 72, and development of an 82-seat (ATR 82?) version of that aircraft. In the meantime, a wing demounting and modification programme was under way for all in-service ATR 42s.

EGRETT/D-500 (page 125)

EGRETT/D-500/PRISMA

The first two designations, covering the original prototype and first operational trials aircraft, have now been joined by the name PRISMA (PRimary Imaging Systems for Multiple Applications), a US/German programme to demonstrate an imaging radar in an **Egrett 2** variant of the platform aircraft in the second half of 1991.

EMBRAER/FAMA (page 128)

MBB/KAWASAKI (page 132)

Kawasaki has entered into an agreement to supply component kits of the BK 117 for local assembly in South Korea by Hyundai Precision Industry. The initial programme involves about 30 helicopters over a five-year period.

Turbomeca has flown a BK 117 powered by two Arriel 1E engines, to be offered as an alternative to the Lycoming LTS 101-750B1. MBB plans an updated BK 117 with new cockpit, five-blade main rotor and four-blade tail rotor.

MCDONNELL DOUGLAS/BAe (page 133)

HARRIER II PLUS

Italy, Spain and the US Navy were expected to sign in June an MoU confirming their intention to place orders for this upgraded variant of the Harrier II equipped with a Hughes AN/APG-65 multi-mode radar. Expected initial purchases are 12 each for the Italian and Spanish navies (the latter replacing existing EAV-8B/VA.2s) and 30-40 for the US Marine Corps. Meanwhile, first flight of an AV-8B with an F402-RR-408 (Pegasus 11-61) engine was expected to take place in July 1990.

T-45A GOSHAWK

First flight with the uprated F405-RR-401 (Adour 871) engine was expected to take place in April/May 1990.

The first Embraer/FAMA CBA-123 was completed in June and scheduled to fly in mid-July

MPC (page 136)

MPC 75

Deutsche Airbus and CATIC have again modified their pre-development specification for this twin-turbofan airliner. As announced in the Spring of 1990, two variants are now proposed, with single-class seating for 89 passengers in an **MPC 75-100** and 115 in an **MPC 75-200**. Candidate engines for both models are the Rolls-Royce Tay Mk 700 and Allison GMA 3014. The two versions will share a common wing (with an optional additional centre-section fuel tank for the -100), and the five-abreast seating layout is retained.

Planned programme dates for the MPC 75-100 are now as follows: first flight October 1994, certification December 1995 (October 1997 for longer-range version), and first deliveries January 1996. Certification and delivery dates for the -200 would then be November 1998 and early 1999 respectively.

The following amended data apply to these two variants:

DIMENSIONS, EXTERNAL:
Wing span: 100, 200	30.40 m (99 ft 9 in)
Length overall: 100	28.40 m (93 ft 2 in)
200	33.20 m (108 ft 11 in)

WEIGHTS:
Operating weight empty: 100	24,000 kg (52,910 lb)
200	26,400 kg (58,200 lb)
Max T-O weight: 100	39,000 kg (85,980 lb)
200	46,000 kg (101,410 lb)

PERFORMANCE (MPC 75-100, estimated):
Max operating speed	330 knots (611 km/h; 380 mph)
Max operating altitude	11,900 m (39,000 ft)

T-O field length at 600 m (1,970 ft) elevation, ISA +15°C
1,670 m (5,480 ft)

Nominal range:
standard fuel	1,700 nm (3,150 km; 1,957 miles)
with centre-section tank	2,700 nm (5,000 km; 3,110 miles)

NH 90 (page 137)

Revised national workshares are now 36 per cent each to France and Italy, 22 per cent to Germany and 6 per cent to the Netherlands. Estimated national requirements for the NH 90 are France 200, Italy 214, Germany 124 (Air Force 64, Navy 32, Army 28) and Netherlands 20. First flight is now forecast for mid-1993 and deliveries from mid-1997.

ITALY

AGUSTA (page 156)

AGUSTA A 139

The original A 129 Utility (Light Battlefield Helicopter) is evidently being replaced by the A 139, announced in June. The A 139 will be civil as well as military and draw on the technology of both the A 109 and A 129 Mangusta. Gross weight is expected to be about 5,000 kg (11,023 lb) and payload about 1,600 kg (3,527 lb) or 12 passengers. Most likely power plant at the moment is a pair of 895 kW (1,200 shp) LHTEC T800 turboshafts.

Co-operation with Argentina and Australia is still being discussed, and Agusta reports interest from Japanese manufacturers.

POLAND

PZL WARSZAWA-OKECIE (page 201)

PZL-140 GĄSIOR

It is understood that the PZL-140 project has been abandoned. Instead, a new agricultural aircraft, with a 1,200 kg (2,645 lb) payload, is being developed under the designation **PZL-107**.

PZL-126 MRÓWKA

The following data are now known:

DIMENSIONS, EXTERNAL:

Wing span: excl pods	6.00 m (19 ft 8¼ in)
incl pods	6.30 m (20 ft 8 in)
Wing chord, constant	0.75 m (2 ft 5½ in)
Length overall	4.66 m (15 ft 3½ in)
Height overall	2.53 m (8 ft 3½ in)
Tailplane span	2.00 m (6 ft 6¾ in)
Wheel track	1.94 m (6 ft 4½ in)
Wheelbase	0.92 m (3 ft 0¼ in)
Propeller diameter	1.40 m (4 ft 7 in)
Propeller ground clearance	0.18 m (7 in)

AREAS:

Wings, gross: excl pods	4.50 m² (48.44 sq ft)
incl pods	5.12 m² (55.11 sq ft)

Flaps (total)	0.572 m² (6.16 sq ft)
Flaperons (total)	0.414 m² (4.46 sq ft)
Vertical tail surfaces (total)	0.68 m² (7.32 sq ft)
Horizontal tail surfaces (total)	1.02 m² (10.98 sq ft)

PZL-110 KOLIBER 150 (HUMMING-BIRD)

Pezetel now reports that the Koliber 150 was certificated in Poland in January 1989 and that production aircraft have been delivered to Belgium, Denmark, West Germany, Norway and Sweden.

SOUTH AFRICA

ATLAS (page 213)

CELAIR

CELAIR (PTY) LTD

PO Box 77, Ermelo 2350
Telephone: 27 (1341) 4059
Fax: 27 (1341) 91925
MANAGING DIRECTOR: Dave Becker

Celair, whose GA-1 sailplane is described in the appropriate section of this edition, has also flown the prototype of a new lightplane known as the Eagle 300.

CELAIR EAGLE 300

Under development since August 1987, apart from a seven-month break in 1987 to concentrate on the GA-1 sailplane, the Eagle 300 is a light utility aircraft with good short-field and cruising performance. Construction uses the same LPET (low pressure/elevated temperature) technique as the GA-1, and the Eagle 300 is to be certificated by both the South African DCA and the US FAA. The prototype (ZS-WLD) made its first flight on 4 April 1990, and production is expected to start in early 1992.

TYPE: Single-engined light utility aircraft.

AIRFRAME: Cantilever high-wing monoplane, of mainly composites construction (pre-impregnated glassfibre). Wings have constant chord centre-section and tapered outer panels. Conventional tail unit and control surfaces. Non-retractable tailwheel type landing gear, with cantilever self-sprung mainwheel legs.

POWER PLANT: One 224 kW (300 hp) Textron Lycoming IO-540-K flat-six engine, driving an MT-9V three-blade constant-speed propeller with spinner.

ACCOMMODATION: Pairs of seats, in tandem, for four to six people including pilot, in fully enclosed cabin. Two large forward opening doors on each side.

DIMENSIONS, EXTERNAL:

Wing span	11.20 m (36 ft 9 in)
Wing aspect ratio	7.74
Length overall	9.04 m (29 ft 8 in)
Height over tail	2.30 m (7 ft 6½ in)

AREA:

Wings, gross	16.20 m² (174.4 sq ft)

WEIGHTS:

Weight empty, equipped	760 kg (1,675 lb)
Max T-O weight	1,520 kg (3,351 lb)

PERFORMANCE (estimated, at max T-O weight):

Max cruising speed (75% power) at S/L	
	153 knots (283 km/h; 176 mph)
Stalling speed, flaps down	57 knots (106 km/h; 66 mph)
Max rate of climb at S/L	405 m (1,330 ft)/min
T-O to 15 m (50 ft) at S/L	256 m (840 ft)
Range, 15% fuel reserves	588 nm (1,090 km; 677 miles)

South Africa's XH-2 Rooivalk armed helicopter began flight testing in February 1990. It is here armed with the old V3B Kukri air-to-air missile, 68 mm rockets, enclosed four-round anti-tank missile pods and a chin-mounted 20 mm gun *(H. Heitman)*

Prototype Celair Eagle 300 four/six-seat light utility aircraft

SWITZERLAND

GEPARD

GEPARD SENSOR TECHNOLOGIES SYSTEMS AG

Ludretikonerstrasse 44, CH-8800 Thalwil
Telephone: 41 (1) 721 1112
Fax: 41 (1) 720 3429
PRESIDENT: Andreas Reinhard
PROJECT MANAGER: Jürg Sommerauer

GEPARD S 10 gsm

Using the Stemme S 10 high performance motor glider (see German part of Sailplanes section) as the platform aircraft, this company has designed and developed the S 10 gsm (Gepard special mission) system enabling the aircraft to carry one or two interchangeable underwing pods which equip it for a wide variety of aerial sensor missions for both civil and military use. Virtual absence of platform vibration renders a complex stabilisation system unnecessary for most sensors. The S 10 has low thermal and radar signatures, and is given a state of the art (EFIS or FMS) instrument panel for the pilot, the right hand seat panel having a video monitor, observation equipment and associated avionics. An efficient data monitoring and recording system is installed for image, data and voice handling. The S 10 gsm is qualified for aerial reconnaissance, search and rescue, surveillance, and atmospheric or environmental research.

Types of underwing pod available include TV (high resolution CCD camera and Betacam SP); FLIR (high resolution IR scanner and Betacam SP); chemo (with air pollution monitoring equipment); radar (Doppler, low light camera and Betacam SP); photographic (various remotely controlled cameras); SAR (parachuting container); real-time (data transmission equipment); Nightsun (double-axis tracking searchlight and generator); meteorological (various atmospheric research sensors and DAT recorder); cargo; ferry (fuel tank); and an emergency engine pod with an 18.6 kW (25 hp) three-cylinder two-stroke autonomous power unit, three-blade folding propeller and other equipment.

The prototype S 10 gsm (D-KARD) was first displayed, with a FLIR pod and emergency engine pod attached, at the 1989 Paris Air Show. In January 1990 it made its first flight with two pods attached, at a T-O weight of 950 kg (2,094 lb). It is currently certificated under JAR 22; special certification under JAR 22 and FAR AC 21.23-1 is under consideration for later.

DIMENSIONS, EXTERNAL, AND AREAS: As for Stemme S 10, plus:

Pod: Length	2.26 m (7 ft 5 in)
Max diameter	0.345 m (1 ft 1½ in)

WEIGHTS AND LOADINGS:

Weight empty, no sensors	approx 640 kg (1,411 lb)
Cargo pod, empty	7 kg (15.4 lb)

Payload, each pod	60 kg (132 lb)
Max T-O weight: JAR 22	850 kg (1,874 lb)
JAR 22 & FAR AC 21.23-1:	
initially	908 kg (2,002 lb)
intended	980 kg (2,160 lb)
Wing loading at 850 kg (1,874 lb) AUW	
	45.36 kg/m² (9.29 lb/sq ft)
Power loading at 850 kg (1,874 lb) AUW	
	12.13 kg/kW (19.92 lb/hp)

PERFORMANCE, UNPOWERED: As for Stemme S 10
PERFORMANCE, POWERED: As for Stemme S 10, except:
Range with 120 litres (31.7 US gallons; 26.4 Imp gallons) of internal fuel

933 nm (1,730 km; 1,075 miles)
Range with two ferry pods (280 litres; 74 US gallons; 61.6 Imp gallons fuel)

2,158 nm (4,000 km; 2,485 miles)

PILATUS (page 224)

Pilatus announced on 17 May 1990 the signature of an MoU with Beech Aircraft Corporation of the USA under which the two companies will propose a modified version of the Pilatus PC-9 for the US Air Force/Navy Joint Primary Aircraft Training System (JPATS) requirement. Pilatus is to provide two PC-9s to Beech for development as Beech/Pilatus JPATS demonstrators; if selected, Pilatus would produce a major portion of the proposed aircraft, final assembly of which would take place at Beech's Kansas facilities.

S 10 motor glider with alternative Gepard pods for emergency engine (on wing pylon), photography (foreground) and cargo

UNION OF SOVIET SOCIALIST REPUBLICS

ILYUSHIN (page 242)

ILYUSHIN Il-108

The Il-108 business jet has been projected by the Ilyushin OKB in response to the *konversiya* directive, which requires the Soviet aerospace industry to increase design and manufacture of civilian aircraft. Similar to the BAe 1000 in configuration and size, it would be powered by two Lotarev DV-2 turbofans (each 21.58 kN; 4,852 lb st), pod-mounted on the rear fuselage, and is envisaged in two forms. The more luxurious of these would carry a crew of two and nine passengers, with facilities for work or relaxation on long flights. The alternative 15-passenger cabin, with three-abreast seating, is intended for either third-level airline or business transport use. Front and rear baggage compartments, and an aft toilet, would be standard.

DIMENSIONS, EXTERNAL:
Wing span	15.00 m (49 ft 2½ in)
Length overall	15.85 m (52 ft 0 in)
Height overall	5.50 m (18 ft 0½ in)
Fuselage diameter	2.35 m (7 ft 8½ in)
Tailplane span	5.29 m (17 ft 4¼ in)
Wheel track	3.00 m (9 ft 10¼ in)

WEIGHT:
Max T-O weight	14,300 kg (31,525 lb)

PERFORMANCE (estimated):
Econ cruising speed at 12,000 m (39,370 ft)
432 knots (800 km/h; 497 mph)
Range at econ cruising speed:
with 15 passengers and max fuel
2,615 nm (4,850 km; 3,010 miles)
with 9 passengers 3,235 nm (6,000 km; 3,725 miles)

Ilyushin Il-108 business aircraft (two Lotarev DV-2 turbofans) *(Pilot Press)*

ILYUSHIN Il-X

Similar in configuration to the Il-108, but slightly larger and turboprop powered, the Il-X is also projected in two forms. The executive transport version is equipped with five armchair seats, two of them in club layout with centre table, and a three-place settee. The commuter transport is intended to carry 19 passengers, basically three-abreast. Each version has front and rear baggage compartments, an aft toilet and buffet, with main passenger door at the front on the port side and a folding seat for an attendant at the rear of the cabin. Headroom in the main cabin is shown as 1.84 m (6 ft).

The power plant is specified as two Novikov TVD-1500 turboprops, each rated at 1,118 kW (1,500 shp) and driving two four-blade pusher contraprops.

DIMENSIONS, EXTERNAL:
Wing span	18.00 m (59 ft 0½ in)
Length overall	17.77 m (58 ft 3½ in)
Height overall	6.05 m (19 ft 10¼ in)
Fuselage diameter	2.40 m (7 ft 10½ in)
Tailplane span	6.00 m (19 ft 8¼ in)
Wheel track	3.60 m (11 ft 9¾ in)

WEIGHTS (A, with 19 passengers; B, with 7 passengers):
Max payload	2,100 kg (4,630 lb)
Max T-O weight: A	8,700 kg (19,180 lb)
B	9,180 kg (20,238 lb)
Max landing weight: A	7,900 kg (17,415 lb)
B	7,200 kg (15,870 lb)

Ilyushin Il-X executive/commuter transport (two Novikov TVD-1500 turboprops) *(Pilot Press)*

PERFORMANCE (estimated):
Max cruising speed at 7,000 m (22,965 ft)	Balanced field length	800 m (2,625 ft)
334 knots (620 km/h; 385 mph)	Max range:	
Econ cruising speed at 7,000 m (22,965 ft)	with 19 passengers	810 nm (1,500 km; 932 miles)
307 knots (570 km/h; 354 mph)	with 7 passengers	2,158 nm (4,000 km; 2,485 miles)

MiG *(page 254)*

MIKOYAN MiG-101

As an early contribution to *konversiya*, the Mikoyan OKB has projected two basic variants of a versatile twin-turboprop aircraft of twin-boom configuration, as follows:

MiG-101M. With 1,864 kW (2,500 shp) Isotov TV7-117 engines and constant chord outer wings. Accommodation for 12 passengers, 4,000 kg (8,818 lb) of freight, or equipment for casualty evacuation, police, firefighting, rescue and flying tanker roles. Clamshell rear loading doors on fuselage pod. Emphasis on short-field capability, with large trailing edge flaps.

MiG-101N. Generally similar to MiG-101M, but with tapered, longer-span outer wings and 1,118 kW (1,500 shp) Novikov TVD-1500 turboprops. Emphasis on longer range, with endurance of up to six hours. Seats for 14 passengers. Other roles as for MiG-101M. Paramilitary **MiG-101NP** could be equipped with a 360° radar, FLIR, IR linescan, camera, recording and data link systems for surveillance and maritime patrol missions.

DIMENSIONS, EXTERNAL:
Wing span: MiG-101M	13.50 m (44 ft 3½ in)
MiG-101N	17.10 m (56 ft 1¼ in)
Length overall	12.45 m (40 ft 10¼ in)
Height overall	4.40 m (14 ft 5¼ in)

AREA (MiG-101M):
Wings, gross	33.53 m² (360.9 sq ft)

WEIGHTS (MiG-101M):
Max payload	4,000 kg (8,818 lb)
Max fuel	2,000 kg (4,409 lb)
Max T-O weight	9,000 kg (19,840 lb)

PERFORMANCE (MiG-101M, estimated):
Max cruising speed at 7,000 m (22,965 ft)	
	361 knots (670 km/h; 416 mph)
Econ cruising speed at 11,500 m (37,730 ft)	
	286 knots (530 km/h; 329 mph)
T-O run	150 m (492 ft)
Landing run	200 m (656 ft)
Range with max fuel	1,457 nm (2,700 km; 1,677 miles)

Mikoyan MiG-101M multi-purpose aircraft, with additional side view (centre) and partial plan view of MiG-101N *(Pilot Press)*

MIKOYAN MiG 18-50

The MiG 18-50 is described as a projected long-range transport with a digital navigation system that provides automatic and manual all-weather, all-season, round-the-clock navigation and landing approach in accordance with ICAO Cat II regulations. Field performance is intended to permit operation from 1,800 m (5,906 ft) Soviet Class B airfields. Powered by two rear-mounted Lotarev D-36 turbofans (each 63.74 kN; 14,330 lb st), it is being promoted as both a 50-passenger airliner and a luxurious business jet for 18 persons. Both versions would have forward and rear baggage compartments and an aft toilet. Seating in the airliner would be four-abreast, in pairs, with centre aisle, at 75 cm (29.5 in) seat pitch.

DIMENSIONS, EXTERNAL:
Wing span	23.30 m (76 ft 5½ in)
Length overall	24.90 m (81 ft 8½ in)
Height overall	7.55 m (24 ft 9¼ in)
Fuselage diameter	2.80 m (9 ft 2¼ in)

DIMENSIONS, INTERNAL:
Passenger cabin: Length	10.66 m (34 ft 11½ in)
Width	2.60 m (8 ft 6¼ in)
Height	1.90 m (6 ft 3 in)

AREA:
Wings, gross	64.00 m² (689.0 sq ft)

WEIGHTS (A, 50 seats; B, 18 seats):
Weight empty, equipped: A, B	20,200 kg (44,530 lb)
Max payload: A	4,500 kg (9,920 lb)
B	1,620 kg (3,570 lb)
Max fuel: A, B	14,000 kg (30,865 lb)
Max T-O weight: A	39,000 kg (85,980 lb)
B	36,000 kg (79,365 lb)

PERFORMANCE (A, 50 seats; B, 18 seats; estimated):
Nominal cruising speed:	
A, B	458 knots (850 km/h; 528 mph)
Service ceiling: A	11,000 m (36,000 ft)
B	12,500 m (41,000 ft)
Balanced field length: A, B	1,800 m (5,906 ft)
Range, with 45 min reserves:	
A	4,530 nm (8,400 km; 5,220 miles)
B	5,395 nm (10,000 km; 6,215 miles)

Mikoyan MiG 18-50 long-range airliner/business aircraft *(Pilot Press)*

MIKOYAN MiG SVB

Very different from previous products of the Mikoyan OKB, the SVB has been projected as a fully pressurised twin-turboprop transport capable of operation into short fields in mountain areas. Intended primarily for civilian use, it has a rear loading ramp, integral ceiling hoist and cargo floor, but can be equipped to carry 50 passengers five-abreast. The flight crew of two can be supplemented by two cargo handlers or cabin attendants, as appropriate. Two 2,088 kW (2,800 shp) Isotov TV7-117 turboprops, driving six-blade low noise level propellers, are claimed to allow operation from airstrips up to 4,000 m (13,125 ft)

above sea level at ISA +25°C. Digital avionics will be standard.

DIMENSIONS, EXTERNAL:
Wing span	25.90 m (84 ft 11¾ in)
Length overall	22.20 m (72 ft 10 in)
Height overall	8.07 m (26 ft 5¾ in)

WEIGHTS:
Max freight payload	5,000 kg (11,023 lb)
Max fuel	3,100 kg (6,835 lb)
Max T-O weight	19,400 kg (42,770 lb)

PERFORMANCE (estimated):
Nominal cruising speed at 7,000 m (22,965 ft)	
	297 knots (550 km/h; 342 mph)
T-O run at 3,000 m (9,850 ft) at ISA +15°C	
	840 m (2,756 ft)
Landing run at 3,000 m (9,850 ft) at ISA +15°C, with propeller reversal	700 m (2,300 ft)
Range with max fuel, 45 min reserves	
	1,187 nm (2,200 km; 1,367 miles)

Mikoyan MiG SVB twin-turboprop pressurised passenger/freighter *(Pilot Press)*

MYASISHCHEV (page 272)

MYASISHCHEV M-17

On 28 and 30 March 1990, an M-17 set a number of records in the category for jet aircraft of 16,000 to 20,000 kg weight, subject to FAI confirmation. They included a height of 21,880 m (71,785 ft) and a speed of 301 knots (558 km/h; 347 mph) around a 100 km closed circuit. Its maximum speed is stated to be 405 knots (750 km/h; 466 mph).

TUPOLEV (page 280)

TUPOLEV Tu-204

In addition to the three variants of the Tu-204 to which reference is made on page 289, the Tupolev OKB is studying increased-range versions powered by engines such as the Lotarev D-18T and Pratt & Whitney PW4000. One of the projected versions, with a max T-O weight approaching 140,000 kg (308,650 lb), would be capable of carrying 180-200 passengers over distances of 5,935-7,550 nm (11,000-14,000 km; 6,835-8,700 miles). Another, designed for operation over 4,585-4,855 nm (8,500-9,000 km; 5,280-5,590 mile) routes, would use shrouded ultra-high bypass engines now being defined by the Trud engine bureau.

TUPOLEV GAS-FUELLED AIRLINERS

The Tupolev design bureau is working on the design of three airliners fuelled by liquid natural gas or liquid hydrogen.

The first would be a development of the Tu-154 airliner and experimental Tu-155 hydrogen-fuelled aircraft and be designated **Tu-156**. It would be powered by three NK-89 turbofans and carry 164 passengers. The second, designated **Tu-136OK**, would be powered by two D-30-IIs and carry 80 passengers. The third, designated **Tu-204SPG**, would be powered by two unspecified turbofans and carry 200 passengers.

In May 1990, Tupolev signed a co-operation agreement with Deutsche Airbus, which has proposed liquid-hydrogen fuelled versions of the Airbus A300/310 and the German-Chinese MPC 75.

YAKOVLEV (page 290)

YAKOVLEV Yak-46

At an initial design stage in 1990, the Yak-46 will be a derivative of the Yak-42M powered by two rear-mounted Lotarev D-27 pusher propfans, each driving an eight-blade forward propeller and a six-blade rear contra-rotating propeller, diameter 3.80 m (12 ft 5½ in). It will carry 150-162 passengers, six-abreast with centre aisle, and will dispense with the underfuselage airstair door in favour of conventional doors at the front and rear of the cabin. Nominal range with a 17,500 kg (38,580 lb) max payload is calculated at 1,535 nm (2,850 km; 1,770 miles), cruising at Mach 0.75.

YAKOVLEV Yak-48

Like other Soviet OKBs, in response to the *konversiya* directive, Yakovlev has projected an 8/12-passenger

business aircraft powered by two turbofans in the 29.5 kN (6,600 lb st) class. Manufacture would involve use of Western engines, as no suitable Soviet turbofan is available. Few other details are yet available, except that the wings would have a supercritical section, winglets, and an area of 35 m² (377 sq ft). Max T-O weight would be 12,000-15,000 kg (26,455-33,070 lb). Design range is at least 2,425 nm (4,500 km; 2,800 miles), cruising at 430 knots (800 km/h; 497 mph).

YAKOVLEV Yak-55M

The Soviet team that competed in the European Aerobatic Championships in Hungary, in August 1989, used as a reserve aircraft a new version of the Yak-55, last described in the 1989-90 *Jane's*. Known as the Yak-55M, it retained the usual 268 kW (360 hp) Vedeneyev M-14P radial engine, but had a modified wing section and flaperons (drooping ailerons) interconnected with the elevators. Another prototype has been evaluated with conventional ailerons. Two- and three-blade propellers are also undergoing comparative testing before a decision is taken on whether or not to put the Yak-55M into production.

YAKOVLEV Yak-56 and Yak-57

The **Yak-56** is a new single-seat aerobatic and sporting aircraft powered by an Ivchenko piston engine of what is described as "eight-cylinder double-cruciform" configuration. The prototype is expected to fly for the first time in 1992. The **Yak-57** will be a two-seat version of the same design.

UNITED STATES OF AMERICA

AASI

ADVANCED AERODYNAMICS AND STRUCTURES INC (page 343 under ASI)

10703 Vanowen Street, North Hollywood, California 91605
Telephone: 1 (818) 753 1888
Fax: 1 (818) 753 8554
CHAIRMAN: Song-gen Yeh
PRESIDENT: Dr Carl C. Chen
CHIEF EXECUTIVE OFFICER AND GENERAL MANAGER:
Darius Sharifzadeh
ENGINEERING MANAGER: Stan Fisher
MARKETING MANAGER: Bill Hubbard

AASI JET CRUZER 450

The production prototype should be completed in February 1991 and certification to FAR Pt 23 is expected in December 1991. Tooling and drawings are being completed, together with airframes for static and fatigue testing. Modifications include a 25 cm (10 in) fuselage stretch, addition of a fuel-carrying strake at the wingroot, a 43 cm (17 in) nose extension to allow the nosewheel to retract forwards, and canting the tipsails 15° inboard to improve aileron control.

Wings, foreplane and tipsails are metal, fuselage graphite epoxy/Nomex honeycomb sandwich. The power plant is a 335 kW (450 shp) Allison 250-B17F turning a Hartzell three-blade, constant-speed and reversing propeller of 2.03 m (6 ft 8 in) diameter at 2,030 rpm. Fuel capacity is 624 litres (165 US gallons; 137 Imp gallons).

New weight and performance details include:

WEIGHTS:
Weight empty	998 kg (2,200 lb)
Basic operating weight	1,102 kg (2,430 lb)
Max T-O weight	2,041 kg (4,500 lb)

PERFORMANCE:
Max operating speed (V_{MO})	200 knots (371 km/h; 230 mph)
Stalling speed, slats extended	59 knots (109 km/h; 68 mph)
Service ceiling	8,230 m (27,000 ft)
T-O distance to 15 m (50 ft)	735 m (2,410 ft)
Landing distance from 15 m (50 ft)	595 m (1,950 ft)
Range at 3,050 m (10,000 ft)	1,300 nm (2,409 km; 1,497 miles)

BOEING COMMERCIAL AIRPLANE GROUP (page 372)

BOEING 767-X

On 12 April 1990 Boeing signed a memorandum of understanding with three Japanese companies (Fuji, Kawasaki and Mitsubishi) that could lead to a co-operative effort to build the proposed Boeing 767-X later to be called 777. Under the terms of the memorandum the three Japanese companies would together share responsibility for providing Boeing with between 15 and 20 per cent of the airframe.

As envisaged in April 1990, the 767-X would be designed to carry 350-375 two-class passengers over a range of 4,600 nm (8,530 km; 5,300 miles). A heavier, longer-range derivative accommodating 300 passengers and with a maximum range of 6,600 nm (12,230 km; 7,600 miles) would follow. The 767-X would have a wing span of 60.05 m (197 ft), with no winglets, but the outboard portion of each wing, spanning approximately 6.10 m (20 ft), could be arranged to fold on the ground to enable the aircraft to use existing airport terminal gates. The aircraft is likely to feature a flight deck derived from that of the Boeing 747-400 rather than the Model 767.

BOEING HELICOPTERS (page 384)

Mockup of the Boeing/Sikorsky candidate for the US Army's LH (light helicopter) competition. Full scale LH development is due to begin in January 1991

CESSNA (page 400)

CESSNA CITATION IV

In early May 1990 Cessna announced that it had abandoned development of this proposed stretched version of the Citation III business jet, and would instead introduce two new models, the **Citation VI** and **Citation VII**. Each will be based on the Citation III's airframe. The Citation VI will also retain the Citation III's Garrett TFE731-3B-100 turbofans, but will be offered with a standard interior only and a Honeywell SPZ-650 analog autopilot in place of the Citation III's SPZ-8000 digital unit. An APU will be optional instead of standard. The Citation VI will share a common production line with the Citation III from c/n 200 onwards. First deliveries are scheduled for May 1991.

The Citation VII, which will be available in January 1992, will feature the Citation III's interior options, avionics and equipment, but will be powered by two 17.79 kN (4,000

lb st) Garrett TFE731-4 turbofans offering improved hot-and-high performance.

Cessna has also announced plans to develop a new medium-sized business jet, larger than the Citation III. No further details were known at the time of going to press.

GENERAL DYNAMICS (page 411)

GENERAL DYNAMICS FALCON 21

This designation represents continuing studies of F-16 follow-on aircraft and is being prepared by General Dynamics as a candidate for the US Air Force Advanced Multi-role Fighter, should that programme go ahead at the end of the century. Falcon 21 could conceivably also replace the Advanced Tactical Fighter if budget cuts force cancellation. The Agile Falcon, though still offered for export, is no longer considered suitable for the US Air Force.

The last production version of the USAF F-16 now firmly planned is the Block 50, purchase of which is to begin towards the end of FY 1990. A Block 60, with mainly avionic improvements, is another option for the future.

The current Falcon 21 design has a so-called clipped delta wing, with taper on both leading- and trailing-edges, designed to provide better manoeuvrability at both supersonic and subsonic airspeeds. Semi-recessed missile and weapon stowage under the wingroots is also planned.

GULFSTREAM AEROSPACE (page 421)

In March 1990 Gulfstream Aerospace announced that it was conducting market studies for a medium-sized twin-turbofan business jet aircraft. If launched, the aircraft would be known as the **Gulfstream V**.

LEARJET (page 428)

Learjet is reported to be developing two new aircraft, the **Model 45** and **Model 65**, which are believed to be larger and improved versions of the Learjet Model 35A and 55C respectively. No further details were known at the time of going to press.

MCDONNELL DOUGLAS (page 446)

The McDonnell Douglas MD-12X would be 10.36 m (34 ft) longer than the MD-11 and would carry 27 per cent more passengers and 40 per cent more freight

PIPER AIRCRAFT CORPORATION (page 475)

PIPER PROJECT PHOENIX

At the Hanover Air Show in May 1990 Piper announced preliminary details of 'Project Phoenix', a twin-turboprop private and business aircraft based on Piper Malibu and Malibu Mirage aerodynamics and manufacturing techniques, but powered by two 633.8 kW (850 shp) Pratt & Whitney Canada PT6B-35F turboshafts mounted side by side in the nose and driving a single propeller through a Soloy Dual Pac gearbox. The Dual Pac installation will enable the aircraft to be certificated and operated as a twin, meeting all FAR Pt 135 IFR requirements, and is claimed to offer substantial improvements in engine-out climb performance and controllability, cruising speed and fuel efficiency compared with conventional twin-engined aircraft of the same size and power ratings.

Preliminary design was proceeding in the Summer of 1990, with details of final configuration, specifications, projected performance and certification schedule anticipated later in the year. Piper is seeking international co-operation on development of the project.

THORP

THORP AERO INC

1156 Dogwood Ridge Road, Wheelersberg, Ohio 45694
Telephone: 1 (614) 574 4157
PRESIDENT: Clifford Rock

Thorp intends to put the Thorp T-211 back into production, for export only, after buying the assets and tooling from Adams Industries in 1988. The original plan was to manufacture in a foreign country, but no suitable partner was found. The 'export only' condition is because of US product liability laws.

Little has changed from the model first produced in the early 1960s, the T-211 now being powered by a 74.5 kW (100 hp) Continental in place of the 48.4 kW (65 hp) engine originally fitted. It is being produced to FAR Pt 23 for an export certificate of airworthiness only. Production rate is planned to reach 15 per month by July 1991, rising to 20-25 per month, dependent upon sales.

Distributors have been appointed in West Germany and the United Kingdom, where full public transport certification was expected by late 1990.

TYPE: Single-engined light trainer/club aircraft.
DIMENSIONS, EXTERNAL:

Wing span	7.62 m (25 ft 0 in)
Length overall	5.49 m (18 ft 0 in)
Height overall	1.92 m (6 ft 3½ in)

AREA:

Wings, gross	9.75 m² (105.0 sq ft)

WEIGHTS:

Weight empty	340 kg (750 lb)
Max T-O weight	576 kg (1,270 lb)

PERFORMANCE:

Cruising speed (75% power)	
	104 knots (193 km/h; 120 mph)
Stalling speed (flaps down)	39 knots (73 km/h; 45 mph)
Max rate of climb at S/L	228 m (750 ft)/min
Max range	412 nm (764 km; 475 miles)

USAF (page 523)

USAF ADVANCED TACTICAL FIGHTER

Rollout of the first prototype Northrop/McDonnell Douglas YF-23A (87-800) took place on 22 June 1990, and that of the Lockheed/Boeing/General Dynamics YF-22A was imminent at closing for press in early July. First flights were then expected in July and August respectively.

Engine testing began on 15 May 1990, when Pratt & Whitney YF119s in the YF-23A were run up to ground idling speed. The prototype YF-22A mounts General Electric YF120s, but the second example of each aircraft type will be fitted with the alternative power plant to its predecessor. After selecting a winning design by 1 May

SIKORSKY (page 505)

Sikorsky Fantail anti-torque tail for the proposed First Team LH being flown on an H-76 powered by P&WC PT6B-36 turboshafts

TRIDAIR (page 523)

Tridair Gemini st, a Bell LongRanger converted to twin Allison 250 engines with a Soloy Dual Pac combining transmission

BAe One-Eleven fitted with the Westinghouse/TRW advanced radar and Martin Marietta electro-optical sensor for the Northrop/McDonnell Douglas YF-23A Advanced Tactical Fighter

1991, USAF plans to issue a full-scale development contract by June 1991, leading to production start-up in 1994; initial flight of a development aircraft in the first quarter of 1995; and delivery of the first six service ATFs in 1996. Deliveries in 1997-2001 are planned to be 6, 12, 24, 36 and 48. First flight of a naval development aircraft is anticipated in 1998, with procurement delayed two years from 1998 to 2000. Naval requirements have been reduced from 618 to 546 ATFs, and some reduction in the USAF's target of 750 is also anticipated. Programme cost for 750 ATFs is estimated as $63.5 billion in 1990 values.

The YF-22A has wings more sharply swept on the leading-edge than the artist's impression implies; horizontal stabilisers which blend into the wing trailing-edge; and twin vertical tail fins (including conventional rudders) subtending an angle less than 90 degrees.

Advances in computer predictions of radar reflectivity have permitted stealthiness to be achieved without the angularity of the F-117A, although unavoidable reflecting angles are concentrated within a few narrow beams, as with the original stealth fighter. Compromises with low radar reflectivity include a more conventional, rounded wing leading-edge and lack of engine intake grids. However, intake ducts are S-shaped but not lined with radar-absorbent material. Intakes are of fixed geometry, consistent with moderate supersonic cruising speeds of Mach 1.4-1.5 — which, according to USAF, will be achieved without recourse to afterburning. Engines have two-dimensional variable nozzles for thrust vectoring in pitch.

Similar philosophies are followed by the YF-23A, which differs in having no horizontal tail surfaces; all-moving ruddervators enclosing an angle greater than 90 degrees; low-set air intakes; and engines slightly above the wing plane. Prominent chines on the forward fuselage recall the Lockheed SR-71. Both aircraft have an internal M61 20 mm Vulcan cannon in its long-barrel version and will be armed with AIM-9 Sidewinder and AIM-120 AMRAAM missiles.

The first Northrop/McDonnell Douglas YF-23A Advanced Tactical Fighter showed its sharply channelled fuselage contours when it was rolled out in June 1990. Approximate dimensions are: wing span 13.28 m (43 ft 7 in), length overall 20.55 m (67 ft 5 in and height overall 4.34 m (14 ft 3 in)

SPORT AIRCRAFT/MICROLIGHTS

CANADA

ZENAIR (page 538)

Zenair Super STOL CH-801 utility aircraft *(Jane's/Mike Keep)*

CHINA, PEOPLE'S REPUBLIC

CCMI

CENTRAL CHINA MECHANICAL INSTITUTE
Hubei
Telephone: 86/2525
Cables: 4282
Information on this new ultralight was sent by an aircraft engineering graduate from the above mechanical institute.

CCMI A-1 and A-1B
Developed by the Central China Mechanical Institute for a wide variety of missions from cropspraying to patrol to sport flying. First flight (A-1) May 1984. Flight testing and cropspraying trials have been completed. Production status not reported.
TYPE: Single- (A-1) or two-seat (A-1B) multi-purpose ultralight.
AIRFRAME: Three-axis control. Aviation aluminium and steel tube airframe covered with high strength synthetic and linen fabric. Semi-enclosed cockpit. Optional spray-tank occupies rear seat space.
POWER PLANT: One 38.8 kW (52 hp) Rotax 503 aircooled, two-stroke, two-cylinder engine. Fuel capacity 20 litres (5.3 US gallons; 4.4 Imp gallons).
DIMENSIONS, EXTERNAL:

Wing span	10.434 m (34 ft 2¾ in)
Length overall: A-1	5.917 m (19 ft 5 in)
A-1B	6.087 m (19 ft 11½ in)
Height overall	3.10 m (10 ft 2 in)
AREA:	
Wings, gross	18.289 m² (196.9 sq ft)

Central China Mechanical Institute A-1B *(Zhang Yi)*

WEIGHTS:				
Weight empty		160 kg (353 lb)	Stalling speed	28 knots (51 km/h; 32 mph)
Max T-O weight		320 kg (705 lb)	Max rate of climb at S/L	120 m (394 ft)/min
PERFORMANCE:			Min radius of turn	35 m (115 ft)
Max level speed	46 knots (85 km/h; 53 mph)		T-O run	50 m (164 ft)
Cruising speed			Landing run	76 m (249 ft)
	32-40 knots (60-75 km/h; 37-46 mph)		Max range	70 nm (130 km; 81 miles)

UNION OF SOVIET SOCIALIST REPUBLICS

ALGEZDAS

LOOKOSHAVITCHOUS ALGEZDAS
Vilnius, Lithuania

ALGEZDAS ATGEEMEEMAS

The Atgeemeemas (reconnaissance) is one of the smallest aircraft currently flying in the USSR. It first flew in 1989, powered by a 22.4 kW (30 hp) engine. As can be seen from the accompanying illustration, it is a conventional single-seat microlight with double surface wings, large ailerons hinged aft of the wing trailing-edge, and single-surface tailplane, elevators, fin and rudder.

Algezdas Atgeemeemas single-seat microlight *(Igor Krivoutsky)*

KENSGUYLA

V. KENSGUYLA
Panevezhees, Lithuania

KENSGUYLA AOUSHZA (THE DAWN)

This two-seat agricultural aircraft was built in 1989 and won the 5th national homebuilt convention at Riga-89. At that time it was also the largest homebuilt in the USSR. As can be seen from the accompanying illustration, it appears to be a conventional strut braced, low-wing cabin monoplane, with a faired non-retractable tailwheel landing gear. The wings incorporate leading-edge slats and the spraybooms are carried below the trailing-edge, ahead of the ailerons. The chemical tank capacity is 800 litres (211.3 US gallons; 176 Imp gallons). Power plant is provided by a 268 kW (360 hp) Vedeneyev M-14 radial piston engine.

Aoushza agricultural homebuilt, built by Mr V. Kensguyla *(Igor Krivoutsky)*

DIMENSIONS, EXTERNAL:

Wing span	14.85 m (48 ft 8½ in)
Length overall	9.57 m (31 ft 4¾ in)

AREA:

Wings, gross	28.40 m² (305.7 sq ft)

WEIGHT:

Max T-O weight	2,200 kg (4,850 lb)

PERFORMANCE:

Max level speed	119 knots (220 km/h; 137 mph)
Range	243 nm (450 km; 279 miles)

Mup-02M

Mup-02M single-seat microlight, built in Minsk. Wing span 9.04 m (29 ft 8 in); length 5.95 m (19 ft 6¼ in); wing area 12.46 m² (134.12 sq ft); take-off weight 320 kg (705 lb); and max level speed 57 knots (105 km/h; 65 mph)
(Igor Krivoutsky)

WEWYNE
Lithuania

WEWYNE

First flown in 1989, this is a conventional two-seat strut braced high-wing homebuilt. It was said to be the most comfortable aircraft at the Riga-89 convention.

DIMENSIONS, EXTERNAL:

Wing span	11.35 m (37 ft 3 in)
Length overall	7.00 m (22 ft 11½ in)

AREA:

Wings, gross	17.00 m² (182.98 sq ft)

WEIGHT:

Max T-O weight	767 kg (1,691 lb)

PERFORMANCE:

Max level speed	97 knots (180 km/h; 112 mph)
Range	323 nm (600 km; 373 miles)

Wewyne homebuilt monoplane *(Igor Krivoutsky)*

YAKOVLEV
Sazatov

YAKOVLEV KATTA
Little is known about this tiny strut braced cabin homebuilt, other than what can be gleaned from the accompanying illustration.

Yakovlev Katta single-seat homebuilt monoplane *(Igor Krivoutsky)*

AERO ENGINES

INTERNATIONAL

ROLLS-ROYCE TURBOMECA (page 703)

The British Ministry of Defence announced during June 1990 that the Royal Navy EH 101 Merlins are to be powered by Rolls-Royce Turbomeca RTM 322 turboshafts, each with max contingency and intermediate contingency ratings of 1,724 kW (2,312 shp) and 1,566 kW (2,100 shp) respectively.

TAIWAN

AIDC (page 228)

The two-seat version of the Taiwan AIDC Ching Kuo fighter (two International Turbo Engine Co TFE1042-70 reheated turbofans) was first exhibited in late June 1990

INDEXES

(Items in italics refer to the ten previous editions)

AIRCRAFT (including homebuilt aircraft)

X

Y

Z

SPORT AIRCRAFT

A

SAILPLANES

HANG GLIDERS

LIGHTER-THAN-AIR

AERO-ENGINES

Printed and bound in Great Britain by Butler & Tanner Ltd, Frome and London